Hoover's Handbook of

Private Companies

2022

HOOVERS™

A D&B COMPANY

Austin, Texas

Hoover's Handbook of Private Companies 2022 is intended to provide readers with accurate and authoritative information about the enterprises covered in it. Hoover's researched all companies and organizations profiled, and in many cases contacted them directly so that companies represented could provide information. The information contained herein is as accurate as we could reasonably make it. In many cases we have relied on third-party material that we believe to be trustworthy, but were unable to independently verify. We do not warrant that the book is absolutely accurate or without error. Readers should not rely on any information contained herein in instances where such reliance might cause financial loss. The publisher, the editors, and their data suppliers specifically disclaim all warranties, including the implied warranties of merchantability and fitness for a specific purpose. This book is sold with the understanding that neither the publisher, the editors, nor any content contributors are engaged in providing investment, financial, accounting, legal, or other professional advice.

The financial data (Historical Financials sections) in this book are from a variety of sources. Mergent Inc., provided selected data for the Historical Financials sections of publicly traded companies. For private companies and for historical information on public companies prior to their becoming public, we obtained information directly from the companies or from trade sources deemed to be reliable. Hoover's, Inc., is solely responsible for the presentation of all data.

Many of the names of products and services mentioned in this book are the trademarks or service marks of the companies manufacturing or selling them and are subject to protection under US law. Space has not permitted us to indicate which names are subject to such protection, and readers are advised to consult with the owners of such marks regarding their use. Hoover's is a trademark of Hoover's, Inc.

10 9 8 7 6 5 4 3 2 1

Publishers Cataloging-in-Publication Data

Hoover's Handbook of Private Companies 2022

    Includes indexes.

    ISBN: 978-1-64972-825-8

    ISSN 1073-6433

    1. Business enterprises — Directories. 2. Corporations — Directories.

HF3010 338.7

U.S. AND WORLD BOOK SALES

Mergent Inc.

580 Kingsley Park Drive
Fort Mill, SC
29715
Phone: 704-559-6961
e-mail: skardon@ftserussell.com
Web: www.mergentbusinesspress.com

Mergent Inc.

Executive Managing Director: John Pedernales

Publisher/Managing Director of Print Products: Thomas Wecera

Director of Print Products: Charlot Volny

Quality Assurance Editor: Wayne Arnold

Production Research Assistant: Davie Christna

Data Manager: Jason Horvat

MERGENT CUSTOMER SERVICE-PRINT
Support & Fulfillment: Stephanie Kardon
Phone: 704-559-6961
e-mail: skardon@ftserussell.com
Web: www.mergentbusinesspress.com

ABOUT MERGENT INC.

For over 100 years, Mergent, Inc. has been a leading provider of business and financial information on public and private companies globally. Mergent is known to be a trusted partner to corporate and financial institutions, as well as to academic and public libraries. Today we continue to build on a century of experience by transforming data into knowledge and combining our expertise with the latest technology to create new global data and analytical solutions for our clients. With advanced data collection services, cloud-based applications, desktop analytics and print products, Mergent and its subsidiaries provide solutions from top down economic and demographic information, to detailed equity and debt fundamental analysis. We incorporate value added tools such as quantitative Smart Beta equity research and tools for portfolio building and measurement. Based in the U.S., Mergent maintains a strong global presence, with offices in New York, Charlotte, San Diego, London, Tokyo, Kuching and Melbourne. Mergent, Inc. is a member of the London Stock Exchange plc group of companies. The Mergent business forms part of LSEG's Information Services Division, which includes FTSE Russell, a global leader in indexes.

Abbreviations

AFL-CIO – American Federation of Labor and Congress of Industrial Organizations
AMA – American Medical Association
AMEX – American Stock Exchange
ARM – adjustable-rate mortgage
ASP – application services provider
ATM – asynchronous transfer mode
ATM – automated teller machine
CAD/CAM – computer-aided design/computer-aided manufacturing
CD-ROM – compact disc – read-only memory
CD-R – CD-recordable
CEO – chief executive officer
CFO – chief financial officer
CMOS – complementary metal oxide silicon
COO – chief operating officer
DAT – digital audiotape
DOD – Department of Defense
DOE – Department of Energy
DOS – disk operating system
DOT – Department of Transportation
DRAM – dynamic random-access memory
DSL – digital subscriber line
DVD – digital versatile disc/digital video disc
DVD-R – DVD-recordable
EPA – Environmental Protection Agency
EPS – earnings per share
ESOP – employee stock ownership plan
EU – European Union
EVP – executive vice president
FCC – Federal Communications Commission
FDA – Food and Drug Administration
FDIC – Federal Deposit Insurance Corporation
FTC – Federal Trade Commission

GATT – General Agreement on Tariffs and Trade
GDP – gross domestic product
HMO – health maintenance organization
HR – human resources
HTML – hypertext markup language
ICC – Interstate Commerce Commission
IPO – initial public offering
IRS – Internal Revenue Service
ISP – Internet service provider
kWh – kilowatt-hour
LAN – local-area network
LBO – leveraged buyout
LCD – liquid crystal display
LNG – liquefied natural gas
LP – limited partnership
Ltd. – limited
mips – millions of instructions per second
MW – megawatt
NAFTA – North American Free Trade Agreement
NASA – National Aeronautics and Space Administration
NASDAQ – National Association of Securities Dealers Automated Quotations
NATO – North Atlantic Treaty Organization
NYSE – New York Stock Exchange
OCR – optical character recognition
OECD – Organization for Economic Cooperation and Development
OEM – original equipment manufacturer
OPEC – Organization of Petroleum Exporting Countries
OS – operating system
OSHA – Occupational Safety and Health Administration
OTC – over-the-counter

PBX – private branch exchange
PCMCIA – Personal Computer Memory Card International Association
P/E – price to earnings ratio
RAID – redundant array of independent disks
RAM – random-access memory
R&D – research and development
RBOC – regional Bell operating company
RISC – reduced instruction set computer
REIT – real estate investment trust
ROA – return on assets
ROE – return on equity
ROI – return on investment
ROM – read-only memory
S&L – savings and loan
SEC – Securities and Exchange Commission
SEVP – senior executive vice president
SIC – Standard Industrial Classification
SOC – system on a chip
SVP – senior vice president
USB – universal serial bus
VAR – value-added reseller
VAT – value-added tax
VC – venture capitalist
VoIP – Voice over Internet Protocol
VP – vice president
WAN – wide-area network

Contents

Companies Profiled

Companies Profiled (continued)

Companies Profiled (continued)

Companies Profiled (continued)

Companies Profiled (continued)

Companies Profiled (continued)

Companies Profiled (continued)

Companies Profiled (continued)

Companies Profiled (continued)

Companies Profiled (continued)

Companies Profiled (continued)

Companies Profiled (continued)

About Hoover's Handbook of Private Companies 2022

Finding current relevant information about non-public companies can be a challenge, as many of these organizations see secrecy as a competitive strategy. In this edition of Hoover's Handbook of Private Companies, we have done for you the tough work of compiling these hard-to-find facts.

We consider this volume to be one of the premier sources of business information on privately held enterprises in the US. It features the facts on 900 of the largest and most influential of those enterprises. Entries feature overviews of company operations, up to five years of financial information, product information, and lists of company executives as found in Hoover's huge database of company information. Some larger and more visable companies will feature an additional History section.

HOOVER'S ARCHIVES FOR BUSINESS NEEDS

In addition to the 2,550 companies featured in our handbooks, comprehensive coverage of more than 6 years of Hoovers Books are published in the Hoovers Archives.. Our goal is to provide one site that offers authoritative, updated intelligence on US and global companies, industries, and the people who shape them. Stay with the Hoovers famaily of products and History and package the books with the archives products.

We welcome the recognition we have received as a provider of high-quality company information — online, electronically, and in print — and continue to look for ways to make our products more available and more useful to you.

Hoover's Handbook of Private Companies is one of our four-title series of handbooks that covers, literally, the world of business. The series is available as an indexed set, and also includes Hoover's Handbook of American Business, Hoover's Handbook of World Business, and Hoover's Handbook of Emerging Companies. This series brings you information on the biggest, fast-growing, and most influential enterprises in the world.

We believe that anyone who buys from, sells to, invests in, lends to, competes with, interviews with, or works for a company should know all there is to know about that enterprise. Taken together, this book and the other Hoover's products and resources represent the most complete source of basic corporate information readily available to the general public.

HOW TO USE THIS BOOK

This book has four sections:

1. "Using Hoover's Handbooks" describes the contents of our profiles and explains the ways in which we gather and compile our data.

2. "A List-Lover's Compendium" contains lists of the largest and fastest-growing private companies. The lists are based on the information in our profiles, or compiled from well-known sources.

3. The company profiles section makes up the largest and most important part of the book — 900 profiles of major private enterprises, arranged alphabetically.

4. Three indexes complete the book. The first sorts companies by industry groups, the second by headquarters location. The third index is a list of all the executives found in the Executives section of each company profile.

Using Hoover's Handbooks

SELECTION OF THE COMPANIES PROFILED

The 900 enterprises profiled in this book include the largest and most influential companies in America. Among them are:

- private companies, from the giants (Cargill and Koch) to the colorful and prominent (Bad Boy Entertainment and L.L. Bean)
- mutuals and cooperative organizations owned by their customers (State Farm Insurance, Ace Hardware, Ocean Spray Cranberries)
- not-for-profits (Red Cross, Kaiser Permanente, Smithsonian Institution)
- joint ventures (Motiva Enterprises, Dow Corning)
- partnerships (PricewaterhouseCoopers, Baker & McKenzie)
- universities (Columbia, Harvard, University of California)
- government-owned corporations (US Postal Service and New York City's Metropolitan Transportation Authority)
- and a selection of other enterprises (National Basketball Association, AFL-CIO, Texas Lottery Commission).

ORGANIZATION

The profiles are presented in alphabetical order. You will find the commonly used name of the enterprise at the beginning of the profile; the full, legal name is found in the Locations section. If a company name is also a person's name, such as Henry Ford Health System or Mary Kay, it will be alphabetized under the first name; if the company name starts with initials, for example, L.L. Bean or S.C. Johnson, look for it under the combined initials (in the above examples, LL and SC, respectively).

Basic financial data are listed under the heading Historical Financials. The annual financial information contained in the profiles is current through fiscal year-ends occuring as late as January 2022. We have included certain nonfinancial developments , such as officer changes, through January 2022.

OVERVIEW

In the first section of the profile, we have tried to give a thumbnail description of the company and what it does. The description will usually include information on the company's strategy, reputation, and ownership. We recommend that you read this section first.

HISTORY

This extended section, which is available for some of the larger and more well-known companies, reflects our belief that every enterprise is the sum of its history and that you have to know where you came from in order to know where you are going. While some companies have limited historical awareness, we think the vast majority of the enterprises in this book have colorful backgrounds. We have tried to focus on the people who made the enterprises what they are today. We have found these histories to be full of twists and ironies; they make fascinating reading.

EXECUTIVES

Here we list the names of the people who run the company, insofar as space allows. In the few cases where available, we have shown the ages and pay of key officers. In some instances the published data is for the previous year, although the company has announced promotions or retirements since year-end. The pay represents cash compensation, including bonuses, but excludes stock option programs.

Although companies are free to structure their management titles any way they please, most modern corporations follow standard practices. The ultimate power in any corporation lies with the shareholders, who elect a board of directors, usually including officers or "insiders" as well as individuals from outside the company. The chief officer, the person on whose desk the buck stops, is usually called the chief executive officer (CEO). Often, he or she is also the chairman of the board.

As corporate management has become more complex, it is common for the CEO to have a "right-hand person" who oversees the day-to-day operations of the company, allowing the CEO plenty of time to focus on strategy and long-term issues. This right-hand person is usually designated the chief operating officer (COO) and is often the president of the company. In other cases one person is both chairman and president.

A multitude of other titles exists, including chief financial officer (CFO), chief administrative officer, and vice chairman. We have always tried to include the CFO, the chief legal officer, and the chief human resources or personnel officer.

The people named in the Executives section are indexed at the back of the book.

The Executives section also includes the name of the company's auditing (accounting) firm, where available.

LOCATIONS

Here we include the company's full legal name and its headquarters, street address, telephone and fax numbers, and Web site, as available. The back of the book includes an index of companies by headquarters locations.

In some cases we have also included information on the geographic distribution of the company's business, including sales and profit data. Note that these profit numbers, like those in the Products/Operations section below, are usually operating or pretax profits rather than net profits. Operating profits are generally those before financing costs (interest income and payments) and before taxes, which are considered costs attributable to the whole company rather than to one division or part of the world. For this reason the net income figures (in the Historical Financials section) are usually much lower, since they are after interest and taxes. Pretax profits are after interest but before taxes.

Headquarters for companies that are incorporated in Bermuda, but whose operational headquarters are in the US, are listed under their US address.

PRODUCTS/OPERATIONS

This section contains selected lists of products, services, brand names, divisions, subsidiaries, and joint ventures. We have tried to include a company's major lines and most familiar brand names.

The nature of this section varies by company and the amount of information contained in Hoover's storehouse of business information. If the company publishes sales and profit information by type of business, we have included it.

COMPETITORS

In this section we have listed companies that compete with the profiled company. This feature is included as a quick way to locate similar companies and compare them. The universe of competitors includes all public companies and all private companies with sales in excess of $500 million. In a few instances we have identified smaller private companies as key competitors.

HISTORICAL FINANCIALS

Here we have tried to present as much data about each enterprise's financial performance as we could compile in the allocated space. The information varies somewhat from industry to industry and is less complete in the case of private companies that do not release data.

(We have always tried to provide annual sales and employment, although in some instances those numbers are simply not available). There are a few industries, venture capital and investment banking, for example, for which revenue numbers are not reported as a rule. In the case of private companies that do not publicly disclose financial information, we have statistics when reliable sources are available.

The following information is generally present.

A five-year table, with relevant annualized compound growth rates, covers:

- Sales — fiscal year sales (year-end assets for most financial companies)
- Net income — fiscal year net income (before accounting changes)
- Net profit margin — fiscal year net income as a percent of sales (as a percent of assets for most financial firms)
- Employees — fiscal year-end or average number of employees

The information on the number of employees is intended to aid the reader interested in knowing whether a company has a long-term trend of increasing or decreasing employment. As far as we know, we are the only company that publishes this information in print format.

The numbers on the left in each row of the Historical Financials section give the month and the year in which the company's fiscal year actually ends. Thus, a company with a March 31, 2020, year-end is shown as 3/19. The last item in the Financials section is a graph, which for private companies shows net income, or, if that is unavailable, sales.

Key year-end statistics are included in this section for insurance companies and companies required to file reports with the SEC. They generally show the financial strength of the enterprise, including:

- Debt ratio (long-term debt as a percent of shareholders' equity)
- Return on equity (net income divided by the average of beginning and ending common shareholders' equity)
- Cash and cash equivalents
- Current ratio (ratio of current assets to current liabilities)
- Total long-term debt (including capital lease obligations)
- Fiscal year sales for financial institutions

Hoover's Handbook of

Private Companies

A List-Lover's Compendium

The 300 Largest Private Companies by Sales 2022

Rank	Company	Sales ($ mil.)
1	STATE OF CALIFORNIA	$255,725
2	CHINESE HOSPITAL ASSOCIATION	$226,958
3	STATE OF TEXAS	$115,336
4	CITY OF NEW YORK	$98,236
5	COMMONWEALTH OF PENNSYLVANIA	$82,404
6	ALBERTSONS COMPANIES, INC.	$62,455
7	STATE OF ILLINOIS	$62,452
8	STATE OF OHIO	$60,384
9	STATE OF MICHIGAN	$54,684
10	COMMONWEALTH OF MASSACHUSETTS	$53,391
11	COMMONWEALTH OF VIRGINIA	$53,086
12	STATE OF WASHINGTON	$50,993
13	NOVARTIS PHARMACEUTICALS CORPORATION	$49,436
14	STATE OF NORTH CAROLINA	$48,977
15	MCLANE COMPANY, INC.	$48,016
16	STATE OF GEORGIA	$45,109
17	STATE OF MINNESOTA	$41,930
18	STATE OF MARYLAND	$40,438
19	DHPC TECHNOLOGIES, INC.	$38,584
20	STATE OF INDIANA	$38,553
21	STATE OF ARIZONA	$37,221
22	JOHNSON CONTROLS, INC.	$37,179
23	STATE OF WISCONSIN	$33,422
24	COMMONSPIRIT HEALTH	$33,253
25	STATE OF TENNESSEE	$32,779
26	STATE OF LOUISIANA	$32,178
27	COUNTY OF WYOMING	$32,004
28	COMMONWEALTH OF KENTUCKY	$28,943
29	STATE OF OREGON	$28,755
30	STATE OF MISSOURI	$27,080
31	STATE OF ALABAMA	$26,308
32	COUNTY OF LOS ANGELES	$25,198
33	STATE OF SOUTH CAROLINA	$24,768
34	UPMC	$23,093
35	STATE OF COLORADO	$22,950
36	ASCENSION HEALTH ALLIANCE	$22,633
37	CANDID COLOR SYSTEMS, INC.	$21,742
38	BNSF RAILWAY COMPANY	$20,747
39	U.S. GENERAL SERVICES ADMINISTRATION	$20,457
40	STATE OF ARKANSAS	$19,761
41	STATE OF OKLAHOMA	$19,511
42	STATE OF IOWA	$19,439
43	TRINITY HEALTH CORPORATION	$18,833
44	STATE OF NEW MEXICO	$18,637
45	STATE OF MISSISSIPPI	$17,718
46	UNIVERSITY OF TEXAS SYSTEM	$16,360
47	WHOLE FOODS MARKET, INC.	$16,030
48	STATE OF KANSAS	$15,722
49	STATE OF UTAH	$15,502
50	KAISER FOUNDATION HOSPITALS INC	$14,795
51	PROVIDENCE HEALTH & SERVICES	$14,434
52	GENERAL ELECTRIC INTERNATIONAL, INC.	$14,100
53	DAIRY FARMERS OF AMERICA, INC.	$13,528
54	SUTTER HEALTH	$13,220
55	ADVENTIST HEALTH SYSTEM/SUNBELT, INC.	$12,623
56	STATE OF WEST VIRGINIA	$12,469
57	LELAND STANFORD JUNIOR UNIVERSITY	$12,455
58	STATE OF ALASKA	$12,422
59	ALLEGIS GROUP, INC.	$12,269
60	GOVERNMENT OF DISTRICT OF COLUMBIA	$12,096
61	STATE OF HAWAII	$12,091
62	STATE OF NEVADA	$11,924
63	WAKEFERN FOOD CORP.	$11,871
64	KIEWIT CORPORATION	$11,826
65	BAYLOR SCOTT & WHITE HEALTH	$11,704
66	BAYLOR SCOTT & WHITE HOLDINGS	$11,704
67	MASS GENERAL BRIGHAM INCORPORATED	$11,666
68	HY-VEE, INC.	$11,449
69	PETER KIEWIT SONS', INC.	$11,220
70	THE CLEVELAND CLINIC FOUNDATION	$10,628
71	THE TURNER CORPORATION	$10,524
72	TURNER CONSTRUCTION COMPANY INC	$10,516
73	ROBERT BOSCH LLC	$10,474
74	BANNER HEALTH	$10,397
75	CAMERON INTERNATIONAL CORPORATION	$10,381
76	SHI INTERNATIONAL CORP.	$10,372
77	TMV CORP.	$10,310
78	INTERMOUNTAIN HEALTH CARE INC	$10,082
79	LIMETREE BAY TERMINALS LLC	$10,048
80	STATE OF NEBRASKA	$10,006
81	BON SECOURS MERCY HEALTH, INC.	$9,970
82	EQUINOR MARKETING & TRADING (US) INC.	$9,959
83	BRISBANE SCHOOL DISTRICT	$9,941
84	DIGNITY HEALTH	$9,917
85	STATE OF MAINE	$9,869
86	ZEN-NOH GRAIN CORPORATION	$9,771
87	ASSOCIATED WHOLESALE GROCERS, INC.	$9,704
88	STATE OF IDAHO	$9,664
89	NEW YORK CITY HEALTH AND HOSPITALS CORP.	$9,551
90	ALTICOR INC.	$9,460
91	LOS ANGELES UNIFIED SCHOOL DISTRICT	$9,378
92	THE NEW YORK AND PRESBYTERIAN HOSPITAL	$9,115
93	ONEOK PARTNERS, L.P.	$8,918
94	SENTARA HEALTHCARE	$8,861
95	THE HERTZ CORPORATION	$8,803
96	THE PRIDDY FOUNDATION	$8,792
97	CHEVRON PHILLIPS CHEMICAL COMPANY LLC	$8,769
98	PERMANENT UNIVERSITY FUND	$8,725
99	JARDEN LLC	$8,604
100	STATE OF DELAWARE	$8,513
101	ALLIED UNIVERSAL HOLDCO LLC	$8,501
102	NEW YORK UNIVERSITY	$8,500
103	OCHSNER CLINIC FOUNDATION	$8,405
104	SPECTRUM HEALTH SYSTEM	$8,300
105	SOLSTICE HOLDINGS INC.	$8,235
106	U.S. VENTURE, INC.	$8,076
107	UPMC PRESBYTERIAN SHADYSIDE	$8,046
108	REGENTS OF THE UNIVERSITY OF MICHIGAN	$7,956
109	STATE OF NORTH DAKOTA	$7,861
110	THE JOHNS HOPKINS HEALTH SYSTEM CORP	$7,808
111	IHC HEALTH SERVICES, INC.	$7,742
112	CFJ PROPERTIES LLC	$7,672
113	R. DIRECTIONAL DRILLING & UNDERGR. TECH..	$7,668
114	COMPUTER SCIENCES CORPORATION	$7,607
115	STATE OF RHODE ISLAND AND PROVIDENCE	$7,547
116	GROWMARK, INC.	$7,541
117	FLORIDA DEPARTMENT OF LOTTERY	$7,512
118	FEDERAL-MOGUL HOLDINGS LLC	$7,434
119	MERCY HEALTH	$7,423
120	THE CHARLOTTE-MECKLENBURG HOSPITAL AUTH	$7,324
121	CITY OF LOS ANGELES	$7,196
122	CITY & COUNTY OF SAN FRANCISCO	$7,181
123	GEISINGER HEALTH	$7,122
124	CHEVRON PHILLIPS CHEMICAL COMPANY LIMITED	$7,106
125	CGB ENTERPRISES, INC.	$7,081
126	HEALTHPARTNERS, INC.	$7,033
127	PRECISION CASTPARTS CORP.	$7,002
128	EATON CORPORATION	$6,925
129	MEMORIAL HERMANN HEALTH SYSTEM	$6,925
130	THE PENNSYLVANIA STATE UNIVERSITY	$6,796
131	STATE OF MONTANA	$6,741
132	MEDSTAR HEALTH, INC.	$6,726
133	WORLD WIDE TECHNOLOGY HOLDING CO., LLC	$6,702
134	JOHNS HOPKINS UNIVERSITY	$6,659
135	CITY OF PHILADELPHIA	$6,647
136	SSM HEALTH CARE CORPORATION	$6,497
137	ALLY BANK	$6,427
138	STATE OF NEW HAMPSHIRE	$6,399
139	NIELSEN HOLDINGS PLC	$6,172
140	FAIRVIEW HEALTH SERVICES	$6,124
141	STATE OF VERMONT	$6,092
142	STATE UNIVERSITY OF NEW YORK	$5,961
143	AEROTEK, INC.	$5,859
144	HENRY FORD HEALTH SYSTEM	$5,854
145	UNIVERSITY OF WASHINGTON INC	$5,841
146	NOVANT HEALTH, INC.	$5,683
147	ADVOCATE HEALTH AND HOSPITALS CORP	$5,673
148	HILL FIRE PROTECTION, LLC	$5,669
149	CHALMETTE REFINING, L.L.C.	$5,648
150	CONSOLIDATED GRAIN & BARGE COMPANY	$5,640
151	LEVI STRAUSS & CO.	$5,575
152	STANFORD HEALTH CARE	$5,568
153	MEMORIAL SLOAN-KETTERING CANCER CENTER	$5,562
154	BOARD OF REGENTS OF THE UNIV. GEORGIA	$5,523
155	THE WHITING-TURNER CONTRACTING COMPANY	$5,522
156	ACE HARDWARE CORPORATION	$5,388
157	AURORA HEALTH CARE, INC.	$5,334
158	AIRGAS, INC.	$5,305
159	NEW YORK STATE CATHOLIC HEALTH PLAN, INC.	$5,305
160	HOUSTON METHODIST ST. JOHN HOSPITAL	$5,302
161	BOARD OF EDUCATION OF CITY OF CHICAGO	$5,273
162	THE MICHAELS COMPANIES INC	$5,271
163	THE METHODIST HOSPITAL	$5,226
164	FAIRFAX COUNTY VIRGINIA	$5,201
165	THE TRUSTEES OF COLUMBIA UNIVERSITY NY	$5,195
166	COUNTY OF SAN DIEGO	$5,148
167	NEW YORK CITY TRANSIT AUTHORITY	$5,061
168	UNIVERSITY OF COLORADO HEALTH	$5,055
169	UAW RETIREE MEDICAL BENEFITS TRUST	$5,051
170	ST. JOSEPH HEALTH SYSTEM	$4,956
171	VANDERBILT UNIVERSITY MEDICAL CENTER	$4,930
172	PLACID REFINING COMPANY LLC	$4,929
173	PLACID HOLDING COMPANY	$4,929
174	SPECTRA ENERGY, LLC	$4,916
175	GILBANE BUILDING COMPANY	$4,899
176	SCHWAB CHARITABLE FUND	$4,885
177	MERCY HEALTH	$4,860
178	TAUBER OIL COMPANY	$4,831
179	SANFORD HEALTH	$4,819
180	TEKSYSTEMS, INC.	$4,815
181	MARYLAND DEPARTMENT OF TRANSPORTATION	$4,792
182	MCCARTHY HOLDINGS, INC.	$4,784
183	BATTELLE MEMORIAL INSTITUTE	$4,775

SOURCE: MERGENT, INC., DATABASE, FEBRUARY 2022

The 300 Largest Private Companies by Sales 2022(continued)

Rank	Company	Sales ($ mil.)
184	UNIVERSITY OF MARYLAND MEDICAL SYS.	$4,770
185	LUKOIL PAN AMERICAS, LLC	$4,746
186	METROPOLITAN TRANSPORTATION AUTHORITY	$4,728
187	MCCARTHY BUILDING COMPANIES, INC.	$4,706
188	BALFOUR BEATTY, LLC	$4,690
189	TEXAS HEALTH RESOURCES	$4,689
190	SANFORD	$4,639
191	BIOURJA TRADING, LLC	$4,622
192	DUKE UNIVERSITY	$4,612
193	BEAUMONT HEALTH	$4,581
194	HOBBY LOBBY STORES, INC.	$4,544
195	NEW YORK PRESBYTERIAN HOSPITAL WEILL COR	$4,506
196	THE SCOULAR COMPANY	$4,486
197	MONTGOMERY COUNTY, MARYLAND	$4,465
198	THE SCHOOL BOARD OF MIAMI-DADE COUNTY	$4,458
199	ADVENTIST HEALTH SYSTEM/WEST, CORPOR	$4,434
200	THE PRESIDENT AND FELLOWS OF HARVARD	$4,409
201	COUNTY OF ORANGE	$4,388
202	STATE OF SOUTH DAKOTA	$4,349
203	KAISER FDN HEALTH PLAN OF COLORADO	$4,345
204	J.E. DUNN CONSTRUCTION GROUP, INC.	$4,329
205	COBANK, ACB	$4,321
206	SWINERTON INCORPORATED	$4,305
207	HARTFORD HEALTHCARE CORPORATION	$4,281
208	SWINERTON BUILDERS, INC.	$4,272
209	DUKE UNIVERSITY HEALTH SYSTEM, INC.	$4,269
210	YALE UNIVERSITY	$4,247
211	THE REGENTS OF THE UNIVERSITY OF COL.	$4,240
212	THE INCOME FUND OF AMERICA INC	$4,218
213	MONTEFIORE MEDICAL CENTER	$4,197
214	IOWA HEALTH SYSTEM	$4,157
215	CEDARS-SINAI MEDICAL CENTER	$4,142
216	WINCO HOLDINGS, INC.	$4,104
217	UNIVERSITY OF COLORADO	$4,098
218	CHS MCPHERSON REFINERY INC.	$4,081
219	AVAYA HOLDINGS CORP.	$4,081
220	XMED OXYGEN & MEDICAL EQUIPMENT, LP	$4,061
221	COUNTY OF RIVERSIDE	$4,044
222	NEW YORK UNIVERSITY	$4,017
223	CORNELL UNIVERSITY	$4,014

Rank	Company	Sales ($ mil.)
224	COUNTY OF SAN BERNARDINO	$4,008
225	HMH HOSPITALS CORPORATION	$4,000
226	BRASFIELD & GORRIE, L.L.C.	$3,970
227	CITY OF BOSTON	$3,953
228	THOMAS JEFFERSON UNIVERSITY	$3,952
229	MASSACHUSETTS INSTITUTE OF TECHNOLOGY	$3,945
230	CAPITAL INCOME BUILDER	$3,912
231	ALASKA PERMANENT FUND CORPORATION	$3,907
232	LONG ISLAND POWER AUTHORITY	$3,901
233	VCU HEALTH SYSTEM AUTHORITY	$3,896
234	SHAMROCK FOODS COMPANY	$3,895
235	DANONE US, INC.	$3,866
236	BALFOUR BEATTY CONSTRUCTION GROUP, INC.	$3,853
237	AMERICAN TIRE DISTRIBUTORS HOLDINGS, INC.	$3,839
238	THE WASHINGTON UNIVERSITY	$3,838
239	PROVIDENCE HEALTH & SERVICES - OREGON	$3,824
240	BALFOUR BEATTY CONSTRUCTION, LLC	$3,809
241	MERCY CARE	$3,797
242	SANFORD HEALTH	$3,741
243	SUTTER VALLEY HOSPITALS	$3,735
244	API GROUP, INC.	$3,730
245	TEMPLE UNIV.-OF THE COM.SYS.OF HIGH EDUC	$3,722
246	AMERICAN BALANCED FUND, INC.	$3,720
247	BARNES & NOBLE, INC.	$3,662
248	KWIK TRIP, INC.	$3,640
249	THE DELTA ACADEMY	$3,617
250	UNIVERSITY OF WISCONSIN SYSTEM	$3,614
251	UTI, (U.S.) HOLDINGS, INC.	$3,568
252	SCRIPPS NETWORKS INTERACTIVE, INC.	$3,562
253	THE PARSONS CORPORATION	$3,561
254	HCL AMERICA INC.	$3,559
255	ESTES EXPRESS LINES	$3,559
256	COUNTY OF SUFFOLK	$3,536
257	BLACK & VEATCH HOLDING COMPANY	$3,480
258	COUNTY OF HARRIS	$3,477
259	SALT RIVER PROJECT AGRICULTURAL IMPROVE	$3,476
260	KIEWIT INDUSTRIAL GROUP INC	$3,474
261	THE SCHOOL DISTRICT OF PHILADELPHIA	$3,474
262	THE WALSH GROUP LTD	$3,462
263	ADVANCED TECHNOLOGY INTERNATIONAL	$3,458

Rank	Company	Sales ($ mil.)
264	BEARINGPOINT, INC.	$3,456
265	THE UNIVERSITY OF IOWA	$3,451
266	LEHIGH VALLEY HEALTH NETWORK, INC.	$3,437
267	THE OHIO STATE UNIV. WEXNER MEDICAL CENT.	$3,433
268	THE GOLUB CORPORATION	$3,427
269	COUNTY OF NASSAU	$3,423
270	AG PROCESSING INC A COOPERATIVE	$3,411
271	COUNTY OF CLARK	$3,398
272	OHIOHEALTH CORPORATION	$3,388
273	MONSTER BEVERAGE 1990 CORPORATION	$3,369
274	MULTICARE HEALTH SYSTEM	$3,367
275	BVH, INC.	$3,364
276	CALIFORNIA INSTITUTE OF TECHNOLOGY	$3,354
277	NOBLE HOLDING (U.S.) CORPORATION	$3,352
278	CITY OF HOUSTON	$3,352
279	FRANCISCAN MISSIONARIES OF OUR LADY HEA.	$3,348
280	OREGON HEALTH & SCIENCE UNIVERSITY MED.	$3,313
281	FRANCISCAN ALLIANCE, INC.	$3,303
282	PRODUCTION TECHNOLOGIES, INC.	$3,289
283	DRIVETIME AUTOMOTIVE GROUP, INC.	$3,267
284	YALE NEW HAVEN HOSPITAL, INC.	$3,266
285	RAYMOND JAMES & ASSOCIATES INC	$3,256
286	VIRGINIA DEPARTMENT OF TRANSPORTATION	$3,240
287	PHILADELPHIA CONSOLIDATED HOLDING CORP.	$3,234
288	BARNABAS RWJ HEALTH INC	$3,211
289	USG CORPORATION	$3,204
290	ALEX LEE, INC.	$3,192
291	PROVIDENCE HEALTH & SERVICES-WASHINGTON	$3,178
292	UMASS MEMORIAL HEALTH CARE, INC.	$3,168
293	ATLANTIC HEALTH SYSTEM INC.	$3,163
294	REGAL ENTERTAINMENT GROUP	$3,163
295	RALEY'S	$3,162
296	SKF USA INC.	$3,139
297	WEST VIRGINIA UNITED HEALTH SYSTEM, INC.	$3,123
298	COUNTY OF SACRAMENTO	$3,115
299	MASSACHUSETTS DEPARTMENT OF TRANS	$3,115
300	PRATT CORRUGATED HOLDINGS, INC.	$3,114

The 300 Largest Private Companies by Employees 2022

Rank	Company	Employees
1	CITY OF NEW YORK	310,000
2	ALBERTSONS COMPANIES, INC.	210,000
3	STATE OF CALIFORNIA	208,580
4	ALLIED UNIVERSAL HOLDCO LLC	188,000
5	RYMAN HOSPITALITY PROPERTIES,	177,000
6	KAISER FOUNDATION HOSPITALS INC	175,668
7	ASCENSION HEALTH ALLIANCE	150,000
8	STATE OF TEXAS	144,175
9	ASCENSION HEALTH	109,000
10	JOHNSON CONTROLS, INC.	105,000
11	UNIVERSITY OF TEXAS SYSTEM	104,000
12	PROVIDENCE HEALTH & SER OREGON	103,036
13	COMMONWEALTH OF VIRGINIA	100,000
14	COUNTY OF LOS ANGELES	100,000
15	WHOLE FOODS MARKET, INC.	95,000
16	COMMONWEALTH OF PENNSYLVANIA	89,207
17	STATE UNIVERSITY OF NEW YORK	88,024
18	ALLEGIS GROUP, INC.	85,000
19	HY-VEE, INC.	83,000
20	STATE OF COLORADO	81,349
21	UPMC	80,000
22	COMMONSPIRIT HEALTH	72,500
23	STATE OF NORTH CAROLINA	69,869
24	STATE OF SOUTH CAROLINA	67,816
25	METROPOLITAN TRANSPORTATION Y	67,457
26	STATE OF GEORGIA	67,139
27	MASS GENERAL BRIGHAM INCORP	67,000
28	COMPUTER SCIENCES CORPORATION	66,000
29	LOS ANGELES UNIFIED SD	65,231
30	THE CHARLOTTE-MECKLENBURG HOS.	62,000
31	MAYO FOUNDATION FOR MEDICAL EDUCATION AND RESEARCH	60,000
32	STATE OF ILLINOIS	59,659
33	COMMONWEALTH OF MASSACHUSETTS	59,253
34	STATE OF MARYLAND	58,020
35	STATE OF WASHINGTON	57,659
36	STATE OF OHIO	57,631
37	ST. MARY'S MEDICAL CENTER, INC.	56,605
38	DIGNITY HEALTH	55,494
39	STATE OF MICHIGAN	55,416
40	THE UNIVERSITY OF NORTH CAROLINA	55,000
41	ALLIED SECURITY HOLDINGS LLC	53,760
42	FEDERAL-MOGUL HOLDINGS LLC	53,700
43	STATE OF MISSOURI	51,488
44	PILOT CORPORATION	51,337
45	TRINITY HEALTH CORPORATION	51,220
46	SANFORD	50,000
47	BAYLOR SCOTT & WHITE HEALTH	49,000
48	SUTTER HEALTH	48,000
49	NEW YORK CITY TRANSIT AUTHORITY	47,956
50	STATE OF LOUISIANA	47,937
51	ADVENTIST HEALTH SYSTEM/SUNBELT	46,960
52	THE MICHAELS COMPANIES INC	45,000
53	STATE OF HAWAII	44,201
54	THE CLEVELAND CLINIC FOUNDATION	44,000
55	THE PENNSYLVANIA STATE UNIVERSITY	44,000
56	MHM SUPPORT SERVICES	44,000
57	NIELSEN HOLDINGS PLC	43,061
58	BNSF RAILWAY COMPANY	41,000
59	CITY OF LOS ANGELES	41,000
60	COUNTY OF BROWARD	40,500
61	BOARD OF REGENTS OF THE UNIVERSITY SYSTEM OF GEORGIA	40,000
62	THE HERTZ CORPORATION	38,000
63	STATE OF TENNESSEE	37,737
64	STATE OF ALABAMA	37,659
65	STATE OF OKLAHOMA	37,613
66	JOHNS HOPKINS UNIVERSITY	37,600
67	THE DELTA ACADEMY	37,361
68	STEWARD HEALTH CARE SYSTEM LLC	37,000
69	STATE OF OREGON	36,176
70	NEW YORK CITY HEALTH AND HOSPITALS CORPORATION	35,700
71	STATE OF WISCONSIN	35,522
72	STATE OF MINNESOTA	35,217
73	BANNER HEALTH	35,000
74	INTERMOUNTAIN HEALTH CARE INC	35,000
75	BEAUMONT HEALTH	35,000
76	THE OHIO STATE UNIVERSITY WEXNER MEDICAL CENTER	35,000
77	MAXIM HEALTHCARE SERVICES, INC.	35,000
78	REGENTS OF THE UNIVERSITY OF MICH.	34,624
79	GOVERNMENT OF DISTRICT OF COL.	34,600
80	STATE OF ARIZONA	34,161
81	COMMONWEALTH OF KENTUCKY	34,000
82	BARNABAS RWJ HEALTH INC	34,000
83	STATE OF INDIANA	33,000
84	MEDSTAR HEALTH, INC.	33,000
85	MOSAIC HEALTH SYSTEM	32,000
86	BROWARD COUNTY PUBLIC SCHOOLS	31,174
87	UNIVERSITY OF MISSOURI SYSTEM	30,282
88	PRECISION CASTPARTS CORP.	30,116
89	UNIVERSITY HOSPITALS HEALTH SYS.	30,099
90	CITY & COUNTY OF SAN FRANCISCO	30,000
91	AURORA HEALTH CARE, INC.	30,000
92	CITY OF BROCKTON	30,000
93	CITY OF PHILADELPHIA	29,862
94	STATE OF UTAH	29,821
95	NPC RESTAURANT HOLDINGS, LLC	29,000
96	STATE OF ARKANSAS	28,272
97	SENTARA HEALTHCARE	28,000
98	STATE OF MISSISSIPPI	27,775
99	UNIVERSITY OF WASHINGTON INC	27,228
100	CITY OF BALTIMORE	26,400
101	OREGON UNIVERSITY SYSTEM	26,000
102	ROBINSON HEALTH SYSTEM, INC.	26,000
103	CHRISTUS HEALTH	25,700
104	REGAL ENTERTAINMENT GROUP	25,359
105	HILLSBOROUGH COUNTY SD	25,000
106	SCHOOL BOARD OF ORANGE CT FL.	25,000
107	CITY OF SCOTTSDALE	25,000
108	DALLAS INDEPENDENT SD	24,937
109	BARNABAS HEALTH, INC.	24,600
110	STATE OF IOWA	24,304
111	SSM HEALTH CARE CORPORATION	24,230
112	BARNES & NOBLE, INC.	24,000
113	THE ORANGE COUNTY PUBLIC SD	24,000
114	THE EVAN. LUTHERAN GOOD SAM.	24,000
115	THE TEXAS A&M UNIVERSITY SYSTEM	24,000
116	THE NEW YORK AND PRES. HOSPITAL	23,709
117	CITY OF HOUSTON	23,235
118	CAMERON INTERNATIONAL CORP.	23,000
119	HENRY FORD HEALTH SYSTEM	23,000
120	HOBBY LOBBY STORES, INC.	23,000
121	ORLANDO HEALTH, INC.	23,000
122	ACCENTCARE, INC.	23,000
123	ROCHESTER REGIONAL HEALTH	22,500
124	YALE NEW HAVEN HEALTH SERVICES	22,490
125	HOUSTON INDEPENDENT SCH. DIST.	22,440
126	STATE OF KANSAS	22,375
127	STATE OF NEW MEXICO	22,217
128	HEALTHPARTNERS, INC.	22,000
129	YALE NEW HAVEN HOSPITAL, INC.	22,000
130	PRINCE GEORGE'S COUNTY PUB SC	22,000
131	TEXAS HEALTH RESOURCES	21,277
132	THE SCHOOL DISTRICT OF PHIL.	21,065
133	DAIRY FARMERS OF AMERICA, INC.	21,000
134	NEW YORK UNIVERSITY	21,000
135	COUNTY OF ORANGE	21,000
136	SCHOOL BOARD OF PALM BEACH	21,000
137	THE VANDERBILT UNIVERSITY	21,000
138	MCLANE COMPANY, INC.	20,128
139	BATTELLE MEMORIAL INSTITUTE	20,000
140	COUNTY OF RIVERSIDE	20,000
141	BAYCARE HEALTH SYSTEM, INC.	20,000
142	LARSEN & TOUBRO INFOTECH LIMITED	20,000
143	NORTHWESTERN MEMORIAL HEALTH	20,000
144	AMC ENTERTAINMENT INC.	19,700
145	ADVENTIST HEALTH SYSTEM/WEST,	19,512
146	THE GOLUB CORPORATION	19,500
147	OREGON HEALTH & SCIENCE UNIVERSITY MEDICAL GROUP	19,500
148	STATE OF WEST VIRGINIA	19,357
149	BON SECOURS MERCY HEALTH, INC.	19,000
150	VANDERBILT UNIVERSITY MED CTR	19,000
151	FRANCISCAN ALLIANCE, INC.	19,000
152	OCHSNER HEALTH SYSTEM	19,000
153	IOWA HEALTH SYSTEM	18,923
154	PAREXEL INTERNATIONAL CORP	18,900
155	CITY OF BOSTON	18,760
156	STATE OF NEBRASKA	18,653
157	NATIONAL RAILROAD PASSENGER CORP	18,650
158	BLACK & VEATCH HOLDING COMPANY	18,568
159	BVH, INC.	18,568
160	STATE OF IDAHO	18,407
161	UNIVERSITY OF NEW MEXICO	18,362
162	WILLIAM BEAUMONT HOSPITAL	18,050
163	FAIRVIEW HEALTH SERVICES	18,000
164	THE UNIVERSITY OF UTAH	18,000
165	METROPOLITAN GOVERNMENT OF NASHVILLE & DAVIDSON COUNTY	18,000
166	WHEATON FRANCISCAN SERVICES, INC.	18,000
167	ST. JOHN PROVIDENCE	17,806
168	UNIVERSITY OF GEORGIA	17,800
169	UNIVERSITY OF CALIFORNIA, DAVIS	17,741
170	COMMONWEALTH OF PUERTO RICO	17,500
171	MAIN LINE HEALTH SYSTEM	17,485
172	CEC ENTERTAINMENT, INC.	17,200
173	JARDEN LLC	17,000

SOURCE: MERGENT, INC., DATABASE, FEBRUARY 2022

The 300 Largest Private Companies by Employees 2022 (continued)

Rank	Company	Employees
174	AIRGAS, INC.	17,000
175	COUNTY OF SAN DIEGO	17,000
176	THE UNIVERSITY OF IOWA	17,000
177	SAN DIEGO UNIFIED SCHOOL DISTRICT	17,000
178	WAKE COUNTY PUBLIC SCHOOL SYSTEM	17,000
179	SPECTRUM HEALTH SYSTEM	16,996
180	THE SALVATION ARMY	16,168
181	UNIVERSITY OF SOUTH FLORIDA	16,165
182	HOUCHENS INDUSTRIES, INC.	16,000
183	TRUSTEES OF INDIANA UNIVERSITY	16,000
184	BAPTIST HEALTH SOUTH FLORIDA, INC.	16,000
185	ALSCO INC.	16,000
186	INOVA HEALTH SYSTEM FOUNDATION	16,000
187	UNIVERSITY SYSTEM OF NEW HAMP.	16,000
188	SPECTRUM HEALTH PRIMARY CARE	16,000
189	MINNETONKA INDEP.SCHOOL DIST. 276	16,000
190	COUNTY OF MARICOPA	15,751
191	DST SYSTEMS, INC.	15,700
192	THE PARSONS CORPORATION	15,500
193	BEARINGPOINT, INC.	15,200
194	NEBRASKA MEDICINE	15,200
195	BOARD OF REG OF THE UNIV. NEB.	15,200
196	LELAND STANFORD JUNIOR UNIVERSITY	15,000
197	THE METHODIST HOSPITAL	15,000
198	OHIOHEALTH CORPORATION	15,000
199	PITT COUNTY MEMORIAL HOSPITAL	15,000
200	THE RESEARCH FOUNDATION FOR THE TATE UNIVERSITY OF NEW YORK	15,000
201	AKAL SECURITY, INC.	15,000
202	BUHLER INC.	15,000
203	MINNESOTA STATE COLLEGES	15,000
204	SCHOOL DISTRICT 1 IN THE CITY AND COUNTY OF DENVER COLORADO	14,965
205	LEVI STRAUSS & CO.	14,800
206	STATE OF NEVADA	14,790
207	PETER KIEWIT SONS', INC.	14,700
208	HOSPITAL SISTERS HEALTH SYSTEM	14,676
209	UNIVERSITY OF CINCINNATI	14,600
210	COUNTY OF NASSAU	14,500
211	COUNTY OF SANTA CLARA	14,500
212	WORLDWIDE MEDIA SERVICES GR	14,375
213	ALMOST FAMILY, INC.	14,200
214	ADVANCE SERVICES, INC.	14,200
215	MILWAUKEE PUBLIC SCHOOLS (INC)	14,154

Rank	Company	Employees
216	STANFORD HEALTH CARE	14,100
217	UNIVERSITY OF ARKANSAS SYSTEM	14,025
218	ALTICOR INC.	14,000
219	SOLSTICE HOLDINGS INC.	14,000
220	MEMORIAL HERMANN HEALTH SYSTEM	14,000
221	WINCO HOLDINGS, INC.	14,000
222	ESTES EXPRESS LINES	14,000
223	COUNTY OF HARRIS	14,000
224	RALEY'S	14,000
225	CITY OF PHOENIX	14,000
226	NAVY EXCHANGE SERVICE COMMAND	14,000
227	HONORHEALTH	14,000
228	THE HC AUTH.OF THE CITY OF HUNTSV	14,000
229	SHARP HEALTHCARE	14,000
230	JEFFERSON COUNTY BOARD OF ED.	14,000
231	MORTON HOSPITAL AND MEDICAL CENT	14,000
232	NOVANT HEALTH, INC.	13,800
233	NORTHSIDE INDEPENDENT SD	13,698
234	STATE OF RHODE ISLAND AND PROVID	13,535
235	THE CHILDREN'S HOSPITAL OF PHIL	13,519
236	THE FINISH LINE INC	13,500
237	FLORIDA STATE UNIVERSITY	13,497
238	COUNTY OF KING	13,300
239	RECTOR & VIS.OF THE UNIV. OF VA	13,300
240	MONTEFIORE HEALTH SYSTEM, INC.	13,295
241	THE TRUSTEES OF COLUMBIA UNIVERSITY IN THE CITY OF NEW YORK	13,200
242	UNIVERSITY OF MASSACHUSETTS	13,196
243	GEISINGER HEALTH	13,030
244	U.S. GENERAL SERVICES ADMIN.	13,000
245	THE JOHNS HOPKINS HEALTH SYSTEM	13,000
246	INOVA HEALTH CARE SERVICES	13,000
247	CITY OF DALLAS	13,000
248	CYPRESS-FAIRBANKS INDEPENDENT SC	13,000
249	DUVAL COUNTY PUBLIC SCHOOLS	13,000
250	TRIHEALTH, INC.	13,000
251	CITY OF TRENTON	13,000
252	THE PUBLIC HEALTH TRUST OF MIAMI	12,990
253	THE REGENTS OF THE UNIV. OF COL.	12,980
254	COUNTY OF SUFFOLK	12,814
255	UNIVERSITY OF HOUSTON SYSTEM	12,608
256	BAPTIST HEALTHCARE SYSTEM, INC.	12,601
257	THE FRESH MARKET INC	12,600
258	NORTH CAROLINA BAPTIST HOSPITAL	12,563

Rank	Company	Employees
259	HARTFORD HEALTHCARE CORPORATION	12,500
260	STATE OF NEW HAMPSHIRE	12,280
261	CORNELL UNIVERSITY	12,207
262	UNIVERSITY OF NC AT CHAPEL HILL	12,204
263	BOARD OF EDUCATION-MEM CITY SC.	12,015
264	STATE OF MAINE	12,000
265	FAIRFAX COUNTY VIRGINIA	12,000
266	UNIVERSITY OF MARYLAND MEDICAL	12,000
267	MASSACHUSETTS INSTITUTE OF TECH.	12,000
268	LEHIGH VALLEY HEALTH NETWORK	12,000
269	METALDYNE PERFORMANCE GROUP	12,000
270	JOHNS HOPKINS HOSPITAL	12,000
271	GEORGES PRINCE COUNTY GOVT	12,000
272	CITY OF SAN ANTONIO	12,000
273	ANC HEALTHCARE, INC.	12,000
274	THE GEISINGER CLINIC	12,000
275	WESTCHESTER COUNTY HEALTH CARE	12,000
276	UNIVERSITY OF TENNESSEE	12,000
277	JEFFERSON COUNTY SD NO. R-1	12,000
278	UNIVERSITY OF HAWAII SYSTEM	12,000
279	TESLA ENERGY OPERATIONS, INC.	12,000
280	BODDIE-NOELL ENTERPRISES, INC.	12,000
281	PORTLAND ADVENTIST MEDICAL CENT.	12,000
282	CHICAGO TRANSIT AUTHORITY (INC)	12,000
283	UNIVERSITY OF PUERTO RICO	12,000
284	HCL AMERICA INC.	11,993
285	RICH PRODUCTS CORPORATION	11,713
286	CALIFORNIA INSTITUTE OF TECH.	11,643
287	THE PRESIDENT AND FELLOWS OF HARVARD COLLEGE	11,500
288	METHODIST LE BONHEUR HEALTHCARE	11,459
289	CITY OF SAN DIEGO	11,200
290	LESTER E. COX MEDICAL CENTERS	11,170
291	UMASS MEMORIAL HEALTH CARE, INC.	11,103
292	MICHIGAN STATE UNIVERSITY	11,100
293	YALE UNIVERSITY	11,000
294	MONTEFIORE MEDICAL CENTER	11,000
295	SPECTRUM HEALTH HOSPITALS	11,000
296	DALLAS COUNTY HOSPITAL DISTRICT	11,000
297	MOHEGAN TRIBAL GAMING AUTHORITY	11,000
298	VIRGINIA COMMONWEALTH UNIVERSITY	11,000
299	COUNTY OF VOLUSIA	11,000
300	BEAUMONT UNIFIED SCHOOL DISTRICT PUBLIC FACILITIES CORPORATION	11,000

The 100 Largest Private Companies by Net Income 2022

Rank	Company Headquarters	Net Income ($mil)	Rank	Company Headquarters	Net Income ($mil)
1	AMERICAN BALANCED FUND, INC.	$25,217	51	ALASKA PERMANENT FUND CORPORATION	$1,406
2	FUNDAMENTAL INVESTORS, INC.	$24,162	52	IHC HEALTH SERVICES, INC.	$1,335
3	MASSACHUSETTS INSTITUTE OF TECHNOLOGY	$12,229	53	MERCY HEALTH	$1,330
4	BNSF RAILWAY COMPANY	$12,119	54	DHPC TECHNOLOGIES, INC.	$1,320
5	THE TRUSTEES OF PRINCETON UNIVERSITY	$10,984	55	CHEVRON PHILLIPS CHEMICAL COMPANY LIMITED PARTNER	$1,301
6	SMALLCAP WORLD FUND, INC.	$10,744	56	THE METHODIST HOSPITAL	$1,276
7	BRISBANE SCHOOL DISTRICT	$10,132	57	TRUSTEES OF BOSTON COLLEGE	$1,274
8	COMMONSPIRIT HEALTH	$8,303	58	ALLY BANK	$1,273
9	PERMANENT UNIVERSITY FUND	$7,589	59	STATE OF GEORGIA	$1,235
10	NOVARTIS PHARMACEUTICALS CORPORATION	$6,698	60	COBANK, ACB	$1,191
11	THE WASHINGTON UNIVERSITY	$5,982	61	UAW RETIREE MEDICAL BENEFITS TRUST	$1,176
12	CAPITAL INCOME BUILDER	$5,826	62	THE METROPOLITAN MUSEUM OF ART	$1,162
13	AMERICAN FUNDS PORTFOLIO SERIES	$5,755	63	STATE OF NEW MEXICO	$1,136
14	COMMONWEALTH OF VIRGINIA	$4,811	64	STATE OF UTAH	$1,117
15	STATE OF CALIFORNIA	$4,799	65	UPMC	$1,113
16	AMCAP FUND INC	$4,726	66	THE BOND FUND OF AMERICA INC	$1,099
17	THE PRESIDENT AND FELLOWS OF HARVARD COLLEGE	$4,608	67	AMERICAN MUTUAL FUND	$1,087
18	NEW WORLD FUND	$3,579	68	CEDARS-SINAI MEDICAL CENTER	$1,083
19	JOHNS HOPKINS UNIVERSITY	$3,427	69	ONEOK PARTNERS, L.P.	$1,072
20	THE TRUSTEES OF COLUMBIA UNIVERSITY IN NEW YORK	$3,332	70	CAPITAL WORLD BOND FUND, INC.	$1,051
21	TRUSTEES OF DARTMOUTH COLLEGE	$2,859	71	NEW YORK CITY TRANSIT AUTHORITY	$1,050
22	THE INCOME FUND OF AMERICA INC	$2,612	72	SPECTRA ENERGY, LLC	$1,020
23	CANDID COLOR SYSTEMS, INC.	$2,535	73	CORNELL UNIVERSITY	$986
24	STATE OF ALASKA	$2,276	74	WELLESLEY COLLEGE	$982
25	DUKE UNIVERSITY HEALTH SYSTEM, INC.	$2,195	75	UNIVERSITY OF RICHMOND	$966
26	AMERICAN FUNDS COLLEGE TARGET DATE SERIES	$2,157	76	STATE OF MISSOURI	$963
27	ST. JOSEPH HEALTH SYSTEM	$2,083	77	ADVENTIST HEALTH SYSTEM/SUNBELT, INC.	$951
28	HARVARD MANAGEMENT PRIVATE EQUITY CORPORATION	$2,025	78	PROVIDENCE HEALTH & SERVICES - OREGON	$946
29	UNIVERSITY OF WASHINGTON INC	$2,002	79	BOWDOIN COLLEGE	$937
30	LELAND STANFORD JUNIOR UNIVERSITY	$1,984	80	BARNABAS HEALTH, INC.	$926
31	STATE OF NORTH DAKOTA	$1,955	81	RECTOR & VISITORS OF THE UNIVERSITY OF VIRGINIA	$909
32	STATE OF TEXAS	$1,883	82	HOUSTON METHODIST ST. JOHN HOSPITAL	$870
33	BAYLOR SCOTT & WHITE HEALTH	$1,814	83	TEXAS HEALTH RESOURCES	$870
34	BAYLOR SCOTT & WHITE HOLDINGS	$1,814	84	CAMERON INTERNATIONAL CORPORATION	$848
35	STATE OF SOUTH CAROLINA	$1,775	85	STATE OF NORTH CAROLINA	$836
36	TEXAS COUNTY AND DISTRICT RETIREMENT SYSTEM	$1,761	86	STATE OF ALABAMA	$836
37	STATE OF OHIO	$1,717	87	FRANCISCAN MISSIONARIES OF OUR LADY HEALTH SYSTEM, INC.	$834
38	CHEVRON PHILLIPS CHEMICAL COMPANY LLC	$1,687	88	STATE OF MICHIGAN	$833
39	JOHNSON CONTROLS, INC.	$1,679	89	SANTA CLARA VALLEY TRANSPORTATION AUTHORITY	$830
40	ASCENSION HEALTH ALLIANCE	$1,639	90	EATON CORPORATION	$821
41	STATE OF ILLINOIS	$1,596	91	MONSTER BEVERAGE 1990 CORPORATION	$821
42	INTERMOUNTAIN HEALTH CARE INC	$1,571	92	CITY OF NEW YORK	$820
43	UNIVERSITY OF PITTSBURGH	$1,549	93	PRECISION CASTPARTS CORP.	$817
44	SCHWAB CHARITABLE FUND	$1,532	94	SCRIPPS NETWORKS INTERACTIVE, INC.	$814
45	CARNEGIE MELLON UNIVERSITY	$1,526	95	TRUSTEES OF TUFTS COLLEGE	$806
46	MEMORIAL HERMANN HEALTH SYSTEM	$1,512	96	KIEWIT CORPORATION	$796
47	THE CLEVELAND CLINIC FOUNDATION	$1,483	97	MILTON HERSHEY SCHOOL & SCHOOL TRUST	$785
48	THE JOHNS HOPKINS HEALTH SYSTEM CORPORATION	$1,434	98	PLAINS PIPELINE, L.P.	$783
49	THE SUNDERLAND FOUNDATION	$1,429	99	MEDSTAR HEALTH, INC.	$775
50	SUNOCO PIPELINE L.P.	$1,420	100	MEMORIAL HEALTH SERVICES	$770

SOURCE: MERGENT DATA FEBRUARY 2022

The 100 Largest Private Companies by Total Assets 2022

Rank	Company Headquarters	Net Income ($bil)	Rank	Company Headquarters	Net Income ($bil)
1	CHINESE HOSPITAL ASSOCIATION	$362,951	51	STATE OF COLORADO	$47,974
2	STATE OF CALIFORNIA	$333,689	52	COUNTY OF LOS ANGELES	$47,534
3	STATE OF TEXAS	$323,008	53	SIGNATURE FINANCIAL LLC	$47,365
4	CITY OF NEW YORK	$212,982	54	NEW WORLD FUND	$46,004
5	COBANK, ACB	$139,016	55	CITY & COUNTY OF SAN FRANCISCO	$45,963
6	COMMONWEALTH OF VIRGINIA	$132,606	56	DORMITORY AUTHORITY - STATE OF NEW YORK	$45,583
7	STATE OF OHIO	$130,570	57	YALE UNIVERSITY	$44,696
8	NOVARTIS PHARMACEUTICALS CORPORATION	$130,124	58	THE TRUSTEES OF PRINCETON UNIVERSITY	$44,460
9	STATE OF NORTH CAROLINA	$127,399	59	MASSACHUSETTS DEPARTMENT OF TRANSPORTATION	$43,040
10	ALLY BANK	$123,548	60	MASSACHUSETTS INSTITUTE OF TECHNOLOGY	$42,526
11	THE INCOME FUND OF AMERICA INC	$121,895	61	U.S. GENERAL SERVICES ADMINISTRATION	$40,338
12	COMMONWEALTH OF PENNSYLVANIA	$114,858	62	STATE OF IOWA	$37,662
13	FUNDAMENTAL INVESTORS, INC.	$108,900	63	STATE OF MISSISSIPPI	$37,222
14	STATE OF WASHINGTON	$108,197	64	SPECTRA ENERGY, LLC	$36,842
15	STATE OF ALASKA	$103,389	65	HARVARD MANAGEMENT PRIVATE EQUITY CORPORATION	$36,085
16	METROPOLITAN TRANSPORTATION AUTHORITY	$99,995	66	ASCENSION HEALTH ALLIANCE	$34,320
17	UNIVERSITY OF TEXAS SYSTEM	$89,495	67	STATE OF NORTH DAKOTA	$33,816
18	COMMONWEALTH OF MASSACHUSETTS	$87,795	68	STATE OF HAWAII	$33,391
19	STATE OF GEORGIA	$84,078	69	PERMANENT UNIVERSITY FUND	$32,857
20	BNSF RAILWAY COMPANY	$83,098	70	COUNTY OF WYOMING	$32,706
21	STATE OF MINNESOTA	$78,701	71	STATE OF ARKANSAS	$32,685
22	STATE OF MICHIGAN	$75,388	72	AGFIRST FARM CREDIT BANK	$32,487
23	STATE OF ILLINOIS	$74,914	73	STATE OF KANSAS	$31,971
24	STATE OF MARYLAND	$73,677	74	MISSOURI DEPARTMENT OF TRANSPORTATION	$31,573
25	STATE OF INDIANA	$73,173	75	TRINITY HEALTH CORPORATION	$30,457
26	STATE OF WISCONSIN	$72,263	76	STATE OF WEST VIRGINIA	$29,967
27	ALASKA PERMANENT FUND CORPORATION	$70,049	77	CITY OF HOUSTON	$29,869
28	AMERICAN HONDA FINANCE CORPORATION	$69,854	78	JOHNSON CONTROLS, INC.	$29,673
29	THE PRESIDENT AND FELLOWS OF HARVARD COLLEGE	$69,810	79	COUNTY OF CLARK	$29,583
30	STATE OF SOUTH CAROLINA	$67,044	80	CITY OF SAN ANTONIO	$28,661
31	STATE OF OREGON	$65,889	81	STATE OF NEBRASKA	$27,615
32	STATE OF TENNESSEE	$65,315	82	EATON CORPORATION	$27,466
33	AMCAP FUND INC	$65,300	83	GGP, INC.	$27,282
34	STATE OF ALABAMA	$64,751	84	STATE OF NEVADA	$26,820
35	CITY OF LOS ANGELES	$63,512	85	TEXAS COUNTY AND DISTRICT RETIREMENT SYSTEM	$26,387
36	LELAND STANFORD JUNIOR UNIVERSITY	$62,970	86	COUNTY OF HARRIS	$25,980
37	STATE OF MISSOURI	$62,083	87	BARCLAYS BANK DELAWARE	$25,013
38	COMMONWEALTH OF KENTUCKY	$61,984	88	FARM CREDIT SERVICES OF AMERICA	$24,773
39	STATE OF LOUISIANA	$61,852	89	ALBERTSONS COMPANIES, INC.	$24,735
40	AMERICAN MUTUAL FUND	$61,161	90	THE TRUSTEES OF COLUMBIA UNIVERSITY IN NEW YORK	$24,699
41	UAW RETIREE MEDICAL BENEFITS TRUST	$60,353	91	LOS ANGELES UNIFIED SCHOOL DISTRICT	$24,510
42	STATE OF ARIZONA	$58,251	92	REGENTS OF THE UNIVERSITY OF MICHIGAN	$24,233
43	SMALLCAP WORLD FUND, INC.	$55,418	93	MARYLAND DEPARTMENT OF TRANSPORTATION	$23,892
44	STATE OF UTAH	$55,374	94	STATE OF IDAHO	$23,349
45	THE BOND FUND OF AMERICA INC	$54,894	95	KAISER FOUNDATION HOSPITALS INC	$22,753
46	COMMONSPIRIT HEALTH	$54,876	96	BROOKFIELD PROPERTIES RETAIL INC.	$21,973
47	STATE OF NEW MEXICO	$53,842	97	THE CLEVELAND CLINIC FOUNDATION	$21,793
48	STATE OF OKLAHOMA	$51,159	98	UPMC	$21,586
49	NEW YORK CITY TRANSIT AUTHORITY	$49,670	99	ADVENTIST HEALTH SYSTEM/SUNBELT, INC.	$21,240
50	AMERICAN FUNDS PORTFOLIO SERIES	$48,215	100	FARM CREDIT BANK OF TEXAS	$21,222

SOURCE: MERGENT DATA FEBRUARY 2022

Hoover's Handbook of

Private Companies

The Companies

1199 SEIU NATIONAL BENEFIT FUND FOR HEALTH AND HUMAN SERVICE EMPLOYEES

Auditors: KPMG LLP NEW YORK NY

LOCATIONS

HQ: 1199 SEIU NATIONAL BENEFIT FUND FOR HEALTH AND HUMAN SERVICE EMPLOYEES , NEW YORK, NY 10108
Phone: 646 473-6020
Web: WWW.1199SEIU.ORG

HISTORICAL FINANCIALS

Company Type: Private

Income Statement				FYE: December 31
	REVENUE ($ mil.)	NET INCOME ($ mil.)	NET PROFIT MARGIN	EMPLOYEES
12/17	1,642	45	2.8%	7
12/09	1,167	(19)	—	—
Annual Growth	4.4%	—	—	—

2017 Year-End Financials

Return on assets: 5.3% Cash ($ mil.): 47
Return on equity: 8.2%
Current ratio: 8.70

21ST CENTURY ONCOLOGY HOLDINGS, INC

EXECUTIVES

Ceo, Kimberly Commins-Tzoumakas
Chb, Robert L Rosner
Pres-Ceo, William R Spalding
Cfo, Leanne M Stewart
Cmo, Constantine A Mantz
Sr V Pres-Cao-Contrl-asst Trea, Joseph Biscardi
Sr V Pres US Oprs, Gary Delanois
Coo, Charlie Powell
Manager, Kasha Holt
Auditors: DELOITTE & TOUCHE LLP MIAMI

LOCATIONS

HQ: 21ST CENTURY ONCOLOGY HOLDINGS, INC 2270 COLONIAL BLVD, FORT MYERS, FL 339071412
Phone: 239 931-7254
Web: WWW.RTSX.COM

HISTORICAL FINANCIALS

Company Type: Private

Income Statement				FYE: December 31
	REVENUE ($ mil.)	NET INCOME ($ mil.)	NET PROFIT MARGIN	EMPLOYEES
12/14	1,026	(343)	—	3,930
12/13	736	(78)	—	—
12/12	693	(151)	—	—
Annual Growth	21.6%	—	—	—

2014 Year-End Financials

Return on assets: (-29.9%) Cash ($ mil.): 99
Return on equity: —
Current ratio: 1.40

95 EXPRESS LANES LLC

EXECUTIVES

Mng MBR, Michael Kulper

LOCATIONS

HQ: 95 EXPRESS LANES LLC 6440 GENERAL GREEN WAY, ALEXANDRIA, VA 223122413
Phone: 571 419-6100
Web: WWW.EXPRESSLANES.COM

HISTORICAL FINANCIALS

Company Type: Private

Income Statement				FYE: June 30
	REVENUE ($ mil.)	NET INCOME ($ mil.)	NET PROFIT MARGIN	EMPLOYEES
06/20	975	722	74.1%	1
06/19	1,047	786	75.1%	—
06/18	92	32	35.6%	—
06/17	83	25	30.6%	—
Annual Growth	126.9%	204.7%	—	—

2020 Year-End Financials

Return on assets: 14.1% Cash ($ mil.): 332
Return on equity: 19.7%
Current ratio: 3.50

A-1 SPECIALIZED SERVICES & SUPPLIES, INC.

EXECUTIVES

Pres, Suresh Khosla
V Pres, Om Perkash
SEC, Ashok Kumar
SEC, Ashok K Khosla
Treas, Leena Khosla
Auditors: MEENA JERATH CPA MED MBA

LOCATIONS

HQ: A-1 SPECIALIZED SERVICES & SUPPLIES, INC. 347 MUNT PLSANT AVE STE 2, WEST ORANGE, NJ 07052
Phone: 215 788-9200
Web: WWW.NORTHAM.CO.ZA

HISTORICAL FINANCIALS

Company Type: Private

Income Statement				FYE: December 31
	REVENUE ($ mil.)	NET INCOME ($ mil.)	NET PROFIT MARGIN	EMPLOYEES
12/10	1,359	7	0.6%	25
12/09	1,205	2	0.2%	—
12/08	2,637	15	0.6%	—
Annual Growth	(28.2%)	(28.9%)	—	—

2010 Year-End Financials

Return on assets: 1.5% Cash ($ mil.): 8
Return on equity: 12.5%
Current ratio: 1.10

AAA COOPER TRANSPORTATION

AAA Cooper Transportation (ACT) is a trucking company offering freight hauling services primarily in the Southwest Southeast and Midwest along with carriers with coverage into Puerto Rico Canada and Mexico. ACT offers less-than-truckload (LTL) truck load international services freight brokerage services dedicated contract carriage and fleet maintenance services through 40 locations. The company's International Services division offers cross-border services to Canada and Mexico. ACT can also facilitate transportation in Puerto Rico. The company's fleet includes 3000 tractors and 6500 trailers.

Operations

The company's five primary service offerings are LTL Services dedicated services international services (including port services) managed services and fleet maintenance services.

Less than Truckload (LTL) services provides transportation to shipments typically falling between 50 and 10000 pounds. These shipments are commingled to ensure that these small sized shipments do not solely bear the full cost of transportation. Dedicated Services provides for the provisioning and dedication of transportation resources directly to a specific logistics need. International services offer cross border service to Canada and Mexico. Its system ensures seamless service complete control and single invoicing for shipments from origin to destination.

Managed services provides additional services which support and enhance shipping experience. These services are all offered through current sales associate. Some of fleet maintenance services include maintenance services to all type of diesel engines including CAT VOLVO INTERNATIONAL DETROIT CUMMINS among others and all types of trailing equipment PM flat rates are available based on requirements and engine part specifications and major repair work such as engine and transmission overhauls.

Geographic Reach

Headquartered in Alabama ACT offers less-than-truckload (LTL) all over the Southeast and Midwest. The company also facilitates transportation in Puerto Rico Canada Mexico and the US Virgin Islands as well as some 40 fleet maintenance locations.

Sales and Marketing

The company markets their products and services through websites such Less that Truckload Services (LTL) and Data Exchange. In additions the company provides dedicated services for the provisioning and dedication of transportation resources directly to a specific logistics need such as technology data exchange route planning asset tracking reporting & customized billing and customer portal.

Company Background

ACT was founded in 1955.

EXECUTIVES

Ceo, Reid Dove
Pres-Coo*, Charlie Prickett
V Pres-Cfo-Sec*, J Steven Roy
V Pres-Mkt-Pricing*, Brad Morris

V Pres Strategic Svcs*, Lee McMillan
V Chm, Pete Barkley
Executive of Information Techn, Phyllis Jordan
Human Resources Manager, Renee Lingo
Programmer, Gina Dittus
Vice President, Dan Christian
Project Lead, Jo A Weathers

LOCATIONS

HQ: AAA COOPER TRANSPORTATION
 1751 KINSEY RD, DOTHAN, AL 363035877
Phone: 334 793-2284
Web: WWW.AAACOOPER.COM

PRODUCTS/OPERATIONS

Selected Services

Dedicated
 Company branding
 Specialized equipment
International LTL
LTL
Port
 Consolidation
 Drayage
 Transloading

COMPETITORS

Arcbest	Saia
Averitt Express	Southeastern Freight
Estes Express	Lines
Fedex Freight	Ups Freight
Old Dominion Freight	Yrc Worldwide
R+l Carriers	

HISTORICAL FINANCIALS

Company Type: Private

Income Statement				FYE: January 1
	REVENUE ($ mil.)	NET INCOME ($ mil.)	NET PROFIT MARGIN	EMPLOYEES
01/17	592	17	3.0%	4,933
01/16*	595	14	2.4%	—
12/14	576	20	3.5%	—
Annual Growth	1.3%	(6.4%)	—	—

*Fiscal year change

2017 Year-End Financials

Return on assets: 4.9%   Cash ($ mil.): —
Return on equity: 9.9%
Current ratio: 1.40

AARP

AARP is a nonprofit nonpartisan organization with a membership of nearly 38 million current members. With staffed offices in all 50 states the District of Columbia Puerto Rico and the US Virgin Islands AARP works to strengthen communities and promote the issues that matter most to families such as healthcare security financial security and personal fulfillment. AARP also advocates for individuals in the marketplace by selecting products and services of high quality and value to carry the AARP name. It also produces the world's largest circulation magazine AARP The Magazine and AARP Bulletin. The company was founded in 1999.

Operations

AARP through its Foundation organization serves vulnerable people 50 and older by creating and advancing effective solutions that help them secure the essentials. To this end the organization operates Government Watch an interactive website

designed to allow older Americans to hold Congress and the President's administration accountable on key issues that affect them.

AARP oversees volunteer services as well. The AARP Experience Corps is for volunteers aged 50-plus who want to tutor and mentor youth in their communities primarily literacy for children in kindergarten through third grade.

Geographic Reach

Washington D.C-based AARP boasts staffed offices in all 50 US states Puerto Rico and the US Virgin Islands.

Financial Performance

Despite the novel coronavirus pandemic AARP's consolidated operating revenues grew by 2% increasing to $1.73 billion in 2020 as compared to $1.70 billion in 2019.

HISTORY

Ethel Andrus a retired Los Angeles high school principal who founded the National Retired Teachers Association (NRTA) in 1947 founded the American Association of Retired Persons (AARP) in 1958 with the assistance of Leonard Davis a New York insurance salesman who had helped her find an underwriter for the NRTA. The new organization's goal: to "enhance the quality of life" for older Americans and "improve the image of aging."

Andrus offered members the same low rates for health and accident insurance provided to NRTA members. She also started publishing AARP's bimonthly magazine Modern Maturity in 1958. The organization's first local chapter opened in Youngstown Arizona in 1960. Still an insurance man Davis formed Colonial Penn Insurance in 1963 to take over the AARP account. Andrus led the AARP and its increasingly powerful lobby for the elderly until her death in 1967.

With criticism of Colonial Penn mounting in the 1970s (critics charged the organization was little more than a front for the insurance company) Prudential won AARP's insurance business in 1979. The NRTA merged with AARP in 1982 and the following year it lowered the membership eligibility age from 55 to 50. The organization continued to expand its offerings adding an auto club and financial products such as mutual funds and expanded insurance policies. The organization also started a federal credit union for members in 1988 but despite rosy projections it ceased operations two years later.

AARP forked over $135 million to the IRS in 1993 as part of a settlement regarding the tax status of profits from some of its activities but the dispute remained unresolved. AARP switched insurance providers again in 1996 (New York Life) and started offering discounted legal services. Also that year AARP said it would let HMOs offer managed-care services to members. The plan drew objections over its potential violation of Medicare anti-kickback laws and AARP developed a revised payment plan in 1997.

AARP's image was bruised in 1998 when Dale Van Atta wrote a scathing account of the organization Trust Betrayed: Inside the AARP. The book accused the organization of operating out of lavish accommodations acting as a shill for businesses to hawk their wares and concealing a drop in membership. The next year recognizing that nearly a third of its members were working the organization dropped the American Association of Retired Persons moniker and began to refer to itself by the AARP abbreviation.

To end the long-running dispute with the IRS AARP reached a settlement over its alleged profit-making enterprises by creating a new taxable subsidiary called AARP Services in 1999. The following year AARP initiated a five-year plan to attract

aging baby boomers. AARP launched its My Generation magazine in 2001; two years later the organization combined My Generation with its Modern Maturity magazine to form a single publication: AARP The Magazine .

In 2005 the group's lobbying efforts focused on Social Security reform proposals and a new prescription drug benefit for Medicare recipients.

In 2008 the AARP celebrated its own 50th birthday.

In April 2009 A. Barry Rand a former head of Avis Group Holdings succeeded Bill Novelli as CEO of AARP. Novelli had held the position for eight years.

EXECUTIVES

Ceo, Jo Ann Jenkins
Evp & Coo*, Scott Frisch
Evp-Cdo*, Edna Kane-Williams
Reg Vp Community State, Rawle Andrews Jr
Contrl, John D Griffin
Cheif Bus Opers Offc, Nancy Zankowski
Director, Hubert H III
Director, Maeona M
Fin Mgr, Sharon V Roach
Evp and Gen Mgr, Cynthia L
Evp Member Value, Shereen R
Auditors: GRANT THORNTON LLP
 WASHINGTON

LOCATIONS

HQ: AARP
 601 E ST NW, WASHINGTON, DC 200490003
Phone: 202 434-2277
Web: WWW.AARP.ORG

PRODUCTS/OPERATIONS

2016 sales

	$ mil.	% of total
Royalties	880	55
Membership dues	299	19
Publications advertising	150	9
Contributions	96	6
Grant	97	6
Program income	73	5
Other	5	-
Total	**1,603**	**100**

Selected Operations & Programs

AARP Bulletin (monthly news update)
AARP Driver Safety (classroom refresher)
AARP Foundation Experience Corps
AARP Legal Services Network
AARP Services (taxable product management marketing and e-commerce subsidiary)
AARP The Magazine (bimonthly magazine)
Back to Work 50+
Financial Planning
Public Policy Institute
Research Information Center
Senior Community Service Employment Program (SCSEP)
Tax-Aide

HISTORICAL FINANCIALS

Company Type: Private

Income Statement				FYE: December 31
	REVENUE ($ mil.)	NET INCOME ($ mil.)	NET PROFIT MARGIN	EMPLOYEES
12/16	1,604	141	8.8%	1,800
12/14	1,399	84	6.0%	—
12/13	1,438	408	28.4%	—
Annual Growth	3.7%	(29.8%)	—	—

2016 Year-End Financials

Return on assets: 3.6%   Cash ($ mil.): 427
Return on equity: 9.8%
Current ratio: —

ABINGTON MEMORIAL HOSPITAL INC

Abington Hospital?Jefferson Health (formerly Abington Memorial Hospital) brings health care to residents of southeastern Pennsylvania. The not-for-profit community hospital has some 800 beds. In addition to general medical and surgical care the hospital offers specialized care centers for cancer and cardiovascular conditions operates high-tech orthopedic and neurological surgery units and serves as a regional trauma care facility. With approximately 126000 inpatient admissions 499000 Emergency Department visits and four million outpatient visits annually it also runs an inpatient pediatric unit in affiliation with The Children's Hospital of Philadelphia. Abington?Jefferson Health operates the neighboring 140-bed Lansdale Hospital?Jefferson Health and range of inpatient and outpatient facilities.

EXECUTIVES

Pres-Ceo, Laurence M Merlis
V Pres-Fin*, Thomas E Mallon
Radiology, Jeffrey C Pan
Vice President, Paul V O'Moore
Payroll Staff, Rose Manzo
Director of Case Management, Mary Theresa Mintz
Radiology, Linda B Griska
Executive Officer, Peg Below
Coordinator, John Erik
Associate Director, Rn M Whelan Cen
Chief Officer Medical, Richard Eisenstaedt

LOCATIONS

HQ: ABINGTON MEMORIAL HOSPITAL INC
1200 OLD YORK RD, ABINGTON, PA 190013788
Phone: 215 481-2000
Web: WWW.ABINGTONHEALTH.ORG

PRODUCTS/OPERATIONS

Selected Facilities
Abington Health Center ; Blue Bell Campus (Blue Bell PA)
Abington Health Center ; Schilling Campus (Willow Grove PA)
Abington Health Center ; Warminster Campus (Warminster PA)
Abington Memorial Hospital (Abington PA)
Abington Physicians at Montgomeryville (North Wales PA)
Lansdale Hospital (Lansdale PA)

COMPETITORS

Albert Einstein Healthcare Network
Aria Health
Crozer-keystone Health System
Doylestown Hospital
Grand View
Main Line Health System
Memorial Hospital (pa)
Mercy Health System
Moses Taylor Hospital
North Philadelphia Health System
Tuhs
Tenet Healthcare
University Of Pennsylvania Health System
Virtua Memorial

HISTORICAL FINANCIALS

Company Type: Private

Income Statement
FYE: June 30

	REVENUE ($ mil.)	NET INCOME ($ mil.)	NET PROFIT MARGIN	EMPLOYEES
06/16	740	35	4.8%	4,018
06/15	697	28	4.1%	—
06/14	697	0	0.1%	—
06/13	708	20	2.9%	—
Annual Growth	1.5%	19.2%	—	—

2016 Year-End Financials
Return on assets: 4.5%   Cash ($ mil.): 176
Return on equity: 87.7%
Current ratio: 2.00

ACCESS BUSINESS GROUP LLC

Somehow all those Amway products have to get from factories to the sales floor and that's where Access Business Group (ABG) comes in. The company manufactures and distributes cosmetics nutritional supplements home care and personal care products for its sister company Amway. (Both companies are units of Alticor.) It also offers contract manufacturing services for third-party consumer goods companies but to a lesser extent. Other offerings include product packaging services as well as catalog and direct mail printing services. In addition the company operates R&D labs that develop and test products for Amway. Alticor is the parent company of Access Business Group as well as Amway and is a holding company for Amway's non-direct selling companies.

EXECUTIVES

Chm, Steve Van Andel
Dir, Joey Edwards
Dir, Al McQueen
Bus Mgr, Jamie Francis
Dir, Stan Vander Roest
Scientist, Denise-Todd Skok-Vaughan
Scientist, Greg Evans
Scientist, David Byrne
Scientist, James J Koedam
Research and Staff, John V Scimeca
Scientist, Josh Taylor

LOCATIONS

HQ: ACCESS BUSINESS GROUP LLC
7575 FULTON ST E, ADA, MI 493550001
Phone: 616 787-6000
Web: WWW.ACCESSBUSINESSGROUP.COM

PRODUCTS/OPERATIONS

Selected Services and Products

Beauty
Blushes
Eye shadows
Lipsticks
Mascara
Skin care
Fulfillment
A-Frame
B2B & B2C
Customized order picking at the store level
High volume pick pack & ship
Pick-to-light
Tilt tray sorter
Home Care
Household cleaners
Plastic bottles
Powder and liquid dish washing detergents
Powder and liquid laundry detergents
Nutrition
Antioxidants/supplements/herbals
Food bars
Granulation
Multiminerals/multivitamins
OTC tableting
Powdered drinks
Personal Care
Bar soaps
Bath oils
Body mist
Conditioners
Lotions
Plastic bottles
Shampoos
Shower gels
Styling products
Print
Catalogs
Corrugated cases
Fine printing
Labels
L-Boards
Paperboard packaging

COMPETITORS

Apptech	Pfizer
Berry Global	Procter & Gamble
Botanical Laboratories	Strathmore
Essential Nutrition	Ups Supply Chain
Johnson & Johnson	Solutions

HISTORICAL FINANCIALS

Company Type: Private

Income Statement
FYE: December 31

	REVENUE ($ mil.)	NET INCOME ($ mil.)	NET PROFIT MARGIN	EMPLOYEES
12/15	1,009	0	—	3,000
12/14	1,068	0	—	—
12/13	1,135	0	—	—
Annual Growth	(5.7%)	—	—	—

ACE HARDWARE CORPORATION

In an age of big-box home improvement centers (Home Depot Lowes) wholesaler Ace makes the case for the local hardware store. By sales it is the leading hardware cooperative in the US. Ace Hardware is a retailer-owned hardware cooperative in the world with more than 5300 locally owned and operated hardware stores in approximately 70 countries. The overall home improvement industry is consists of a broad range of products and services including lawn and garden products paint and sundries certain building supplies and general merchandise. Ace also provides value-added services such as advertising market research merchandising assistance and store location and design services. Ace was founded in 1924 by a group of Chicago hardware store owners.

HISTORY

A group of Chicago-area hardware dealers — William Stauber Richard Hesse Gern Lindquist and Oscar Fisher — decided in 1924 to pool their hardware buying and promotional costs. In 1928 the group incorporated as Ace Stores named in honor of the superior WWI fliers dubbed aces. Hesse became president the following year retaining that position for the next 44 years. The company also opened its first warehouse in 1929 and by 1933 it had 38 dealers.

The organization had 133 dealers in seven states by 1949. In 1953 Ace began to allow dealers to buy stock in the company through the Ace Perpetuation Plan. During the 1960s Ace expanded into the South and West and by 1969 it had opened distribution centers in Georgia and California — its first such facilities outside Chicago. In 1968 it opened its first international store in Guam.

By the early 1970s the do-it-yourself market began to surge as inflation pushed up plumber and electrician fees. As the market grew large home center chains gobbled up market share from independent dealers such as those franchised through Ace. In response Ace and its dealers became a part of a growing trend in the hardware industry — cooperatives.

Hesse sold the company to its dealers in 1973 for $6 million (less than half its book value) and the following year Ace began operating as a cooperative. Hesse stepped down in 1973. In 1976 the dealers took full control when the company's first Board of Dealer-Directors was elected.

After signing up a number of dealers in the eastern US Ace had dealers in all 50 states by 1979. The co-op opened a plant to make paint in Matteson Illinois in 1984. By 1985 Ace had reached $1 billion in sales and had initiated its Store of the Future Program allowing dealers to borrow up to $200000 to upgrade their stores and conduct market analyses. Former head coach John Madden of the National Football League's Oakland Raiders signed on as Ace's mouthpiece in 1988.

A year later the co-op began to test ACENET a computer network that allowed Ace dealers to check inventory send and receive e-mail make special purchase requests and keep up with prices on commodity items such as lumber. In 1990 Ace established an International Division to handle its overseas stores. (It had been exporting products since 1975.) EVP and COO David Hodnik became president in 1995. That year the co-op added a net of 67 stores including a three-store chain in Russia. Expanding further internationally Ace signed a five-year joint-supply agreement in 1996 with Canadian lumber and hardware retailer Beaver Lumber. Hodnik added CEO to his title in 1996.

Ace fell further behind its old rival True Value in 1997 when ServiStar Coast to Coast and True Value merged to form TruServ (renamed True Value in 2005) a hardware giant that operated more than 10000 outlets at the completion of the merger.

Late in 1997 Ace launched an expansion program in Canada. (The co-op already operated distribution centers in Ontario and Calgary.) In 1999 Ace merged its lumber and building materials division with Builder Marts of America to form a dealer-owned buying group to supply about 2700 retailers. Ace gained 208 member outlet stores in 2000 but saw 279 member outlets terminated. The next year it gained 220 but lost 255.

Sodisco-Howden bought all the shares of Ace Hardware Canada in February 2003. To better serve international members Ace opened its first international buying office in Hong Kong in April 2004.

In all the company added 131 new stores in 2005. That year after 33 years with the company David F. Hodnik retired as president and CEO of Ace Hardware. He was succeeded by COO Ray A. Griffith.

In 2007 Griffith sent a letter to Ace's retailers saying the company was considering changing from a cooperative to a traditional corporation to become more competitive and to better fuel growth. Shortly after the company announced an accounting shortfall of about $150 million or nearly half of its equity which was uncovered while Ace prepared to convert formats. The error turned out to be an accident by a mid-level employee.

In 2009 Ace launched Aisle411 a free product-location service that can be accessed via phone similar to dialing for information. The company launched the service after learning that shoppers who were unable to find a product either left (about 20% of the time) or asked store associates for assistance (about 60%) which created a high demand for staff attention. Dedicated to pleasing its shoppers Ace was ranked "Highest in Customer Satisfaction among Home Improvement Stores" by J.D. Power and Associates in 2007 2008 and 2009.

In mid-2010 the hardware store chain became the first retailer — outside of Sears and Kmart stores — to sell Craftsman brand tools.

In January 2011 the company reorganized its international division into a stand-alone entity: Ace Hardware International Holdings. Ace Hardware owns about 78% of the newly-created entity.

In December 2012 Ace exited the paint manufacturing business with the sale of its paint manufacturing division including two paint manufacturing plants near Chicago to Valspar Corp. for about $45 million. Under the terms of the sale Valspar will continue to make and supply Ace-branded paint under a long-term supply agreement. Also it will supply a comprehensive line of Valspar-branded paints to Ace retail stores.

EXECUTIVES

Ceo-Pres, John Venhuizen
Chm*, Jim Ackroyd
Exec V Pres-Cfo*, William Guzik
Loss Prevention Supervisor, David Walton
Manager, James Jopson
Content Analyst Conten, Jennifer Plewa
Director, Retail Support Engin, Jonathan Harding
Facility Manager, Mike Conway
Office Manager, Omar Shaar
Agent, Deborah Ream
Vice President, Micheal Brennan
Auditors: ERNST & YOUNG LLP CHICAGO IL

LOCATIONS

HQ: ACE HARDWARE CORPORATION
  2200 KENSINGTON CT, OAK BROOK, IL 605232100
Phone: 630 990-6600
Web: WWW.ACEHARDWARE.COM

PRODUCTS/OPERATIONS

2014 Sales

	$ mil.	% of total
Wholesale Revenues	4,466	95
Retail Revenues	233	5
Total	**4,700**	**100**

Selected Services

Assembly
Automotive chip key cutting
Blade sharpening
Glass & Acrylic sheet cutting
Glass Repair
Hunting/Fishing licenseIn-store lock servicing
Selected Brands
ACCO BRANDS
ACE
ACME
ADANAC
BIG BEN
BILCO
EUREKA
EVEREADY

COMPETITORS

84 Lumber	Mccoy Corp.
Akzo Nobel	Menard
Bmc Stock	Northern Tool
Costco Wholesale	Orgill
Do It Best	Sutherland Lumber
Fastenal	True Value
Grossman's	United Hardware
Home Depot	Distributing
Kmart	Wal-mart
Lowe's	

HISTORICAL FINANCIALS
Company Type: Private

Income Statement				FYE: December 30
	REVENUE ($ mil.)	NET INCOME ($ mil.)	NET PROFIT MARGIN	EMPLOYEES
12/17	5,388	147	2.7%	4,500
12/16*	5,125	161	3.1%	—
01/16	5,045	156	3.1%	—
Annual Growth	3.3%	(2.9%)	—	—

*Fiscal year change

2017 Year-End Financials

Return on assets: 7.9% Cash ($ mil.): 23
Return on equity: 26.3%
Current ratio: 1.30

ADAMS 12 FIVE STAR SCHOOLS

EXECUTIVES

Supt, Christopher E Gdowski
Human Resources Manager, Sonia Velasquez
Teacher Coach, Matt Kroupa
Dean of Students, Bryan Davey
Head Custodian, Chris Bisgaard
Teacher, Angela Kent
1st Grade Teacher, Debbie Riley
Occupational Therapist, Jenifer Onge
Assistant, Kimberly Brady
Second Grade Teacher, Margaret Meier
Kindergarten Teacher, Marylou Keirns
Auditors: CLIFTONLARSONALLEN LLP BROOMF

LOCATIONS

HQ: ADAMS 12 FIVE STAR SCHOOLS
  1500 E 128TH AVE, THORNTON, CO 802412601
Phone: 720 972-4000
Web: WWW.ADAMS12.ORG

HISTORICAL FINANCIALS
Company Type: Private

Income Statement				FYE: June 30
	REVENUE ($ mil.)	NET INCOME ($ mil.)	NET PROFIT MARGIN	EMPLOYEES
06/20	555	(55)	—	5,040
06/19	512	22	4.4%	—
06/18	448	(55)	—	—
06/17	427	270	63.3%	—
Annual Growth	9.2%	—	—	—

ADVANCED TECHNOLOGY INTERNATIONAL

EXECUTIVES

Ceo, Chris Van Metre
Treas*, Julia Martin
Prin*, Caitlin Kunkle
Purchasing Administrator, Dee Green
Senior Project Manager, Jenny Swygert
Technical Director Advanced Te, Nick Melillo
Senior Program Manager, Jim Welborn
Program Administrator, Nikki Crosby
Nsrp Ase Program Administrator, Melissa Ingram
Senior Program Administrator, Amanda Newberry
Project Manager, Chelsea Anthony
Auditors: BDO USA LLP RALEIGH NC

LOCATIONS

HQ: ADVANCED TECHNOLOGY INTERNATIONAL
315 SIGMA DR, SUMMERVILLE, SC 294867790
Phone: 843 760-4500
Web: WWW.ATI.ORG

HISTORICAL FINANCIALS

Company Type: Private

Income Statement · FYE: September 30

	REVENUE ($ mil.)	NET INCOME ($ mil.)	NET PROFIT MARGIN	EMPLOYEES
09/20	3,457	24	0.7%	190
09/19	2,086	7	0.3%	—
09/18	1,190	0	0.1%	—
09/17	718	(11)	—	—
Annual Growth	68.8%	—	—	—

2020 Year-End Financials

Return on assets: 1.0%
Return on equity: 63.5%
Current ratio: 1.00
Cash ($ mil.): 716

ADVENTIST HEALTH SYSTEM/SUNBELT, INC.

Adventist Health System Sunbelt (AdventHealth) provides full system care from everyday wellness and preventive health care to life-saving diagnostic services and innovative medical treatments in cancer heart failure and more. It works with the world's brightest medical minds and innovators. Its integrated network of health care serves neighbors across more than 130 facilities nationwide including hospital campuses urgent-care centers home-health and hospice agencies and nursing homes across roughly 10 states. Extend the Healing Ministry of Christ its Christian mission shared vision common values and focus on whole-person health is its commitment to making communities healthier with a unified system with nearly 50 hospital campuses and hundreds of care sites in diverse markets.

Operations

AdventHealth offers a whole-person care from everyday wellness and preventive health care to life-saving diagnostic services and innovative medical treatments.

Its wide array of services include allergy care audiology care bariatric and weight care behavioral care and eye care to name a few.

Geographic Reach

Headquartered in Altamonte Springs Florida it has more than 130 facilities nationwide including hospital campuses urgent-care centers home-health and hospice agencies and nursing homes across around 10 states.

EXECUTIVES

Pres, Donald L Jernigan
V Pres, Robert Henerschedt
Vp-Treas, David Singleton
Cfo, Terry D Shaw
Chief Information Security Off, Wendell J Bobst
Client/Server Database Program, Tim Davis
Evp Coo, Florida, Lars D Houmann
Scientist, Roger Rosen
General Manager, Candy V Dyke
Information Specialist, David Smith
Database Administrator, James Jian
Auditors: ERNEST & YOUNG LLP ORLANDO

LOCATIONS

HQ: ADVENTIST HEALTH SYSTEM/SUNBELT, INC.
900 HOPE WAY, ALTAMONTE SPRINGS, FL 327141502
Phone: 407 357-1000
Web: WWW.ADVENTHEALTH.COM

Selected Facilities

Colorado
Avista Adventist Hospital (Louisville)
Littleton Adventist Hospital
Parker Adventist Hospital
Porter Adventist Hospital (Denver)
Florida
Florida Hospital Altamonte (Altamonte Springs)
Florida Hospital Apopka
Florida Hospital Carrollwood (Tampa)
Florida Hospital Celebration Health (Celebration)
Florida Hospital DeLand
Florida Hospital East Orlando
Florida Hospital Fish Memorial (Orange City)
Florida Hospital Flagler (Palm Coast)
Florida Hospital Heartland Medical Center (Sebring)
Florida Hospital Kissimmee
Florida Hospital Lake Placid
Florida Hospital Memorial Medical Center (Daytona Beach)
Florida Hospital North Pinellas (Tarpon Springs)
Florida Hospital Oceanside (Ormond Beach)
Florida Hospital Orlando
Florida Hospital Pepin Heart Institute (Tampa)
Florida Hospital Tampa
Florida Hospital Waterman (Tavares)
Florida Hospital Wauchula
Florida Hospital Winter Park Memorial Hospital
Florida Hospital Zephyrhills
Georgia
Gordon Hospital (Calhoun)
Emory-Adventist Hospital (Smyrna)
Illinois
Adventist Bolingbrook Hospital
Adventist GlenOaks Hospital (Glendale Heights)
Adventist Hinsdale Hospital
Adventist La Grange Memorial Hospital
Kansas
Shawnee Mission Medical Center
Kentucky
Manchester Memorial Hospital
North Carolina
Park Ridge Hospital (Fletcher)
Tennessee
Jellico Community Hospital
Takoma Regional Hospital (Greeneville)
Texas
Central Texas Medical Center (San Marcos)
Huguley Memorial Medical Center (Fort Worth)
Metroplex Adventist Hospital (Killeen)
Rollins Brook Community Hospital (Lampasas)
Wisconsin
Chippewa Valley Hospital (Durand)

PRODUCTS/OPERATIONS

Selected Products

Behavioral Health
Cardiovascular
Diabetes
Digestive Health
Emergency
Eye Care Center
Family Practice
Home Health/Home Care
Imaging Services
Mammography/Breast Center/Breast Care
Minimally Invasive/Robotic Surgery
Neurology
Neurosurgery
NICU
OB/Birth Care
Oncology/Cancer
Orthopedics
Outpatient Surgery
Pain Medicine
Pediatrics
Psychology
Rehab
Senior Care
Sleep Center
Stroke Care/Stroke Center
Surgery
Therapy Services
Urology
Wellness Center
Women's Services
Wound Care

COMPETITORS

Ascension Health	Hca
Baycare Health System	Kindred Healthcare
Christus Health	Mount Sinai Medical
Catholic Health	Center Of Florida
Initiatives	Orlando Health
Community Health	Tenet Healthcare
Systems	Universal Health
Encompass Health	Services

HISTORICAL FINANCIALS

Company Type: Private

Income Statement · FYE: December 31

	REVENUE ($ mil.)	NET INCOME ($ mil.)	NET PROFIT MARGIN	EMPLOYEES
12/20	12,623	951	7.5%	46,960
12/19	11,892	1,607	13.5%	—
12/09*	0	0	—	—
10/08	145	(8)	—	—
Annual Growth	45.1%	—	—	—

*Fiscal year change

2020 Year-End Financials

Return on assets: 4.5%
Return on equity: 7.5%
Current ratio: 2.70
Cash ($ mil.): 1,210

ADVENTIST HEALTH SYSTEM/WEST, CORPORATION

Not content to wait around for the advent of good health Adventist Health System/West o is a faith-based nonprofit integrated health system serving more than 80 communities on the West Coast and Hawaii as well as others across the US through its Blue Zones company a pioneer in taking a systemic and environmental approach to improving the health of entire cities and communities. Annually Adventist Health System/West has nearly 135000 admissions 757000 emergency department visits 208000 home health visits 2.2 million clinic visits and 1.5 million outpatient visits. Adventist Health maintains strong ties to the Seventh-day Adventist Church but is independently owned. A sister organization Adventist Health System operates in the central and southern parts of the country.

Operations

Adventist Health System/West offers additional services and partners with affiliates on various programs such as Clinical Engineering and TelepharmacyWest.

Adventist Health Clinical Engineering Services provides quality clinical technology services for Adventist Health and its healthcare community which include a variety of healthcare providers within California Oregon Washington and Hawaii.

TelepharmacyWest was established by a grant from Pacificare/UnitedHealthcare to help rural hospitals create sustainable pharmacy improvements. It is the only nonprofit telepharmacy service located on the campus of a hospital and backed by a team of pharmacists who are always available.

Adventist Health/West provides care in hospitals clinics and its innovative Adventist Health Hospital@Home program that provides virtual inpatient care at home home care agencies hospice agencies and joint-venture retirement centers in both rural and urban communities.

Geographic Reach

Adventist Health System/West serve patients throughout California Hawaii and Oregon.

EXECUTIVES

Ceo, Kerry Heinrich
Pres, Bill Wing
Cfo*, Todd Hofheins
Cco*, Joyce Newmyer
Cmo*, Alex Bryan
Ccio*, Jason Wells
Patient Representative, Janet Turner
Internal Auditor, Larry Mitchel
Clinical Quality Coordinator, Lisa Fowler
Director of Managed Care Physi, Mark Ashloc
Finance, Micah Smith
Auditors: ERNST & YOUNG LLP ROSEVILLE

LOCATIONS

HQ: ADVENTIST HEALTH SYSTEM/WEST, CORPORATION
1 ADVENTIST HEALTH WAY, ROSEVILLE, CA 956613266
Phone: 844 574-5686
Web: WWW.ADVENTISTHEALTH.ORG

COMPETITORS

Community Health Systems	Providence St. Joseph Health
Dignity Health	Queen's Medical Center
Hca	Shasta Regional
Hawai'i Pacific Health	Medical Center
John Muir Health	Sisters Of Charity Of
Kuakini Health System	Leavenworth
Legacy Health System	Stanford Health Care
Lifepoint Health	Sutter Health
Memorial Health Services	Tenet Healthcare
	Ucsf Medical

HISTORICAL FINANCIALS

Company Type: Private

Income Statement

FYE: December 31

	REVENUE ($ mil.)	NET INCOME ($ mil.)	NET PROFIT MARGIN	EMPLOYEES
12/18	4,434	544	12.3%	19,512
12/17	4,114	199	4.9%	—
12/16	3,945	185	4.7%	—
12/15	251	10	4.3%	—
Annual Growth	160.3%	267.8%	—	—

2018 Year-End Financials

Return on assets: 9.4%   Cash ($ mil.): 700
Return on equity: 19.3%
Current ratio: 2.90

ADVENTIST HEALTHCARE, INC.

Adventist HealthCare is the first and largest provider of healthcare in Montgomery County Maryland. The not-for-profit system with nearly 1950 physicians and medical providers is home to five acute care hospitals and more than 423540 outpatient visits. Its hospitals are Adventist Health-Care Shady Grove Medical Center (Rockville) White Oak Medical Center (Silver Spring) Fort Washington Medical Center (Fort Washington) Germantown Emergency Center and Adventist Rehabilitation (Rockville). Among its specialized medical services include heart and vascular car mental health care pregnancy care and birth and radiology and diagnostic imaging. Adventist HealthCare which is affiliated with the Seventh-day Adventist Church has been in operation since 1907.

Operations

Adventist HealthCare's Lourie Center for Children's Social & Emotional Wellness promotes the social and emotional health of parent-child relations through education training research early prevention and intervention. Its offerings include an early head start program to benefit low-income families parent-child programs and therapeutic nursery. The company operates three nationally accredited acute-care hospitals a nationally accredited rehabilitation hospital mental health services home health agencies physician networks urgent care centers and imaging centers. In addition to cancer care home care and orthopedic care the company's other specialized medical services also include rehabilitation and surgery.

Adventist HealthCare has more than 113575 emergency visits over 423540 outpatient visits approximately 107375 home health visits and delivers about 6035 babies a year. It also has approximately 6895 surgical admissions around 10685 outpatient surgeries nearly 22205 medical admissions and about 99755 health and wellness encounters.

Geographic Reach

Adventist HealthCare operates facilities in Maryland and Washington DC. Its headquarters is located in Gaithersburg Maryland.

Financial Performance

In 2013 Adventist HealthCare reported $731 million in revenue.

Strategy

Adventist HealthCare is dedicated to being the safest place to receive care and to deliver superior clinical outcomes. It recently unveiled plans to create a health destination in southern Prince George's County that will offer comprehensive specialty and preventative care services. The Harbor expansion aligns with Adventist's strategy to provide quality compassionate care throughout the metropolitan area. The health destination will serve as a link between nearby Adventist HealthCare Fort Washington Medical Center and its new primary care facility minutes away from the hospital. Together the facilities will provide critical services that are essential to meeting the healthcare needs of the community.

Adventist HealthCare also recently opened a new outpatient clinic in the White Oak Medical Pavilion in late 2020. Expanding its integrated multi-specialty rehabilitation services further fulfills the organization's commitment to providing innovative and compassionate care to help patients in the local community return to the life they want to live.

Company Background

In 1907 Washington Sanitarium opens in Takoma Park later to become Washington Adventist Hospital.

EXECUTIVES

Pres, Terry Forde
Cfo*, James Lee
Vice President General Counsel, Ken De Stefano
Chief of Medicine, Stephen Lakner
Sr. Vice President, Chief Huma, Marta P Rez
Coordinator, Nancy Moore
Coordinator, Sumesh Pandit
Human Resources Information MA, Patrise Prather
Vice President of Information, Faisal Farhan
Human Resources Manager, Gail Pasard
Assistant Vice President of Op, Jason Makaroff
Auditors: BAKER TILLY VIRCHOW KRAUSE L

LOCATIONS

HQ: ADVENTIST HEALTHCARE, INC.
820 W DIAMOND AVE STE 600, GAITHERSBURG, MD 208781469
Phone: 301 315-3030
Web: WWW.ADVENTISTHEALTHCARE.COM

PRODUCTS/OPERATIONS

Selected Home Health Services
Nursing and Home Health
  Adult nursing
  Diabetes management
  Maternal/child care
  Nutrition management
  Pediatric nursing
  Personal care
  Pre- and post-op care
  Rehabilitation
  Wound care
Home Assistance
  Laundry and linens
  Light housekeeping
  Meal preparation
  Medication reminders
  Personal care

COMPETITORS

Bon Secours Health	Johns Hopkins Health System
Calvert Memorial Hospital	Medstar Health
Dimensions Healthcare	Trinity Health (novi)
Frederick Memorial	University Of Maryland Medical System
Gbmc	

HISTORICAL FINANCIALS

Company Type: Private

Income Statement FYE: December 31

	REVENUE ($ mil.)	NET INCOME ($ mil.)	NET PROFIT MARGIN	EMPLOYEES
12/20	974	42	4.3%	5,236
12/19	862	32	3.8%	—
12/18	820	21	2.6%	—
12/17	723	31	4.4%	—
Annual Growth	10.5%	9.8%	—	—

2020 Year-End Financials

Return on assets: 2.6% Cash ($ mil.): 55
Return on equity: 8.1%
Current ratio: 1.80

ADVENTIST MIDWEST HEALTH

EXECUTIVES

V Pres-SEC, James R Garvell
V Pres-Nursing, Patricia A Sutton
V Pres-Marketing, Steve Davis
V Pres-Patients, Todd S Werner Jr
Executive Vice-President Marke, Susan King
Records Director, Barb Driscoll
Safety Director, Chris Harts
Physician Recruiter, Julie Farrell
Patient Education Dir, Katie Wiebel
Facilities Management Director, Kurt Martz
Chief of Pediatrics, Millen Peev

LOCATIONS

HQ: ADVENTIST MIDWEST HEALTH
120 N OAK ST, HINSDALE, IL 605213829
Phone: 630 856-9000
Web: WWW.AMITAHEALTH.ORG

HISTORICAL FINANCIALS

Company Type: Private

Income Statement FYE: December 31

	REVENUE ($ mil.)	NET INCOME ($ mil.)	NET PROFIT MARGIN	EMPLOYEES
12/19	561	(12)	—	2,470
12/16	305	10	3.4%	—
12/15	289	17	5.9%	—
12/14	287	0	0.3%	—
Annual Growth	14.3%	—	—	—

2019 Year-End Financials

Return on assets: (-1.9%) Cash ($ mil.): 84
Return on equity: (-5.0%)
Current ratio: 3.30

ADVOCATE HEALTH AND HOSPITALS CORPORATION

EXECUTIVES

Pres, James H Skogsbergh
Vp*, Patricia Smith-Calascibetta
Director of Professional Devel, Linda Plewniak
Social Worker, Alberto Godinez
Coordinator Perioperative Mate, Paul Cnor
Human Resource Coordinator Adv, Jessica Olague
Vice President of Human Resour, Francine Schaefer
Accounts Payable Supervisor, Janet Santos
Director of Human Resources, Jeremy Sadlier
Director of Finance, Beth Hickey
Coordinator Human Resources SE, Christy Huerta
Auditors: ERNST & YOUNG US LLP CHICAGO

LOCATIONS

HQ: ADVOCATE HEALTH AND HOSPITALS CORPORATION
3075 HIGHLAND PKWY FL 6, DOWNERS GROVE, IL 605155563
Phone: 630 929-6965
Web: WWW.ADVOCATEGIVING.ORG

HISTORICAL FINANCIALS

Company Type: Private

Income Statement FYE: December 31

	REVENUE ($ mil.)	NET INCOME ($ mil.)	NET PROFIT MARGIN	EMPLOYEES
12/19	5,672	(28)	—	4,110
12/17	5,310	243	4.6%	—
12/13	4,072	392	9.6%	—
12/12	3,645	419	11.5%	—
Annual Growth	6.5%	—	—	—

2019 Year-End Financials

Return on assets: (-0.2%) Cash ($ mil.): 129
Return on equity: (-0.5%)
Current ratio: 0.90

ADVOCATE HEALTH AND HOSPITALS CORPORATION

Advocate Lutheran General Hospital also known simply as Lutheran General provides acute and long-term medical and surgical care to the residents of Park Ridge Illinois and the surrounding northern suburban Chicago area. As one of the largest hospitals in the region Lutheran General boasts nearly 640 beds and a Level I trauma center. Its operations also include a complete children's hospital and pediatric critical care center. Lutheran General serves as a teaching hospital and its specialized programs include oncology cardiology women's health emergency medicine and hospice care. Lutheran General is part of the Advocate Health Care network.

Operations

Lutheran General the sixth largest hospital in the Chicago area is a not-for-profit faith-based organization related to the Evangelical Lutheran Church in America and the United Church of Christ. With some 1150 physicians representing more than 50 specialties and subspecialties Advocate Lutheran General saw 62500 patients in its emergency department in 2012.

That year the company reported more than 29000 admissions 19000 surgeries and more than 4000 births.

Geographic Reach

The hospital system is the primary academic referral hospital for northwest Chicago and north Greater Chicago.

Strategy

Increase its services to meet specific demographics in 2012 Lutheran General opened a new South Asian Cardiovascular Center in the Midwest; it also launched Expressions a program aimed at helping seniors in the early stages of Alzheimer's disease.

That year thee hospital introduced a new Pet Therapy program to the Adult Oncology unit. It also launched of its neuroendovascular program to expand Lutheran General's acute stroke care to provide advanced acute stroke care to patients throughout the northern Chicago area.

Company Background

Lutheran General serves those who live in the northern suburban Chicago area specifically Park Ridge Illinois.

The hospital was founded in 1897.

EXECUTIVES

Dir, Michael Wegel
Plastic Surgeon, Christopher V Pelletiere
Staff, Tenisha Matthews
Coordinator, Richard Schoemer
Chief Staff, Leo Kelly
Field Team Leader, Mari Partipilo
MD, Maureen A Quaid
Lab Technician, Julia Shumsky
Endocrinologist, Lawrence Domont
Physician Cardiology, Samuel Goldstein
MD, Susan Hann

LOCATIONS

HQ: ADVOCATE HEALTH AND HOSPITALS CORPORATION
1775 DEMPSTER ST, PARK RIDGE, IL 600681143
Phone: 847 723-6610
Web: WWW.CARE.ADVOCATEHEALTH.COM

Selected Hospitals

Advocate BroMenn Medical Center
Advocate Children's Hospital - Oak Lawn
Advocate Children's Hospital - Park Ridge
Advocate Christ Center for Breast Care
Advocate Christ Medical Center
Advocate Christ Medical Center - Physical Rehabilitation Center Center for Hearing and Sleep Center
Advocate Christ Outpatient Center
Advocate Condell Medical Center
Advocate Eureka Hospital
Advocate Good Samaritan Hospital
Advocate Good Shepherd Hospital
Advocate Illinois Masonic Medical Center
Advocate Lutheran General Hospital
Advocate South Suburban Hospital
Advocate Trinity Hospital

PRODUCTS/OPERATIONS

Selected Services

Adult Day Hospital
Adult Down Syndrome Center
Anticoagulation Center
Behavioral Health
Caldwell Breast Center

Cancer Care
Center for Fetal Care
Children's Services
The Comprehensive Continence Center
Emergency Services
Heart and Vascular
Hyperbaric Treatment
Interventional Radiology
Joint Reconstruction & Replacement
Nutrition Services Opthamology
Outpatient Testing Prep Instructions
Pain Management Center
Rehabilitation
Senior Services
Sleep Disorders
Surgical Services
The Center for Robotic Surgery
Women's Services
Wound Care

COMPETITORS

Children's Hopsital Of Chicago
Gottleib Memorial Hospital
Northshore University Healthsystem
Northwest Community Healthcare
Northwestern Lake Forest Hospital
Northwestern Memorial Healthcare
Rush System For Health University Of Chicago Medical Center

HISTORICAL FINANCIALS
Company Type: Private

Income Statement				FYE: December 31
	REVENUE ($ mil.)	NET INCOME ($ mil.)	NET PROFIT MARGIN	EMPLOYEES
12/17	790	79	10.0%	4,818
12/16	785	118	15.1%	—
12/15	752	104	13.9%	—
12/14	741	107	14.5%	—
Annual Growth	2.1%	(9.6%)	—	—

2017 Year-End Financials
Return on assets: 0.9%   Cash ($ mil.): 229
Return on equity: 1.6%
Current ratio: 1.00

AEROTEK, INC.

Aerotek a unit of staffing powerhouse Allegis Group offers commercial and technical staffing services throughout North America Europe and Asia Pacific. Through several divisions Aerotek staffs workers such as engineers mechanics scientists and technical professionals as well as administrative staff members general laborers and tradespeople. The company also provides training and support services. Along with aerospace auto and engineering companies Aerotek's clients include companies from the construction energy manufacturing health care and finance industries.

Operations
Aerotek solutions include staffing services workforce management engineering support and government services. Its staffing services provide short-term

Aerotek solutions include staffing services sciences support workforce management engineering support government services and managed resources. Its staffing services provide short-term seasonal high-volume and niche contract support. It also offers contract-to-hire talent for project-based positions with the option to hire contractors as permanent employees.

Workforce management services comprise customized support for complex projects and business

lines with specific timelines. Sciences support includes clinical and lab services across a range of industries through various delivery models. Aerotek also provides support and services to the government and government subcontractors with capabilities focused on contracts security compliance business development program management and finance.

seasonal high-volume and niche contract support. It also offers contract-to-hire talent for project-based positions with the option to hire contractors as permanent employees.

Workforce management services comprise customized support for complex projects and business lines with specific timelines. Sciences support includes clinical and lab services across a range of industries through various delivery models. Aerotek also provides support and services to the government and government subcontractors with capabilities focused on contracts security compliance business development program management and finance.

Geographic Reach
Aerotek is headquartered in Hanover MD. The company has office locations in Asia Pacific (Australia Hong Kong China and Japan) Europe (Belgium France Germany Netherlands Sweden Switzerland and UK) and North America (Canada and the US). Aerotek also operates a network of more than 250 non-franchised offices.

Sales and Marketing
Aerotek serves a wide variety of industries approximately 20000 clients and more than 300000 contract employees every year.

The company serves a wide variety of industries including accounting administrative & support services aerospace aviation & defense architecture & design automotive construction customer service energy & utilities engineering environmental financial services government & public administration healthcare manufacturing pharmaceutical sciences and warehouse & distribution.

Strategy
Aerotek realigned its business operations into three specialized business units. The business units reflect Aerotek's core areas of expertise ? Engineering & Sciences Industrial and Professional ? and led by dedicated leadership teams. Aerotek's business units also include its companies Aston Carter and EASi.

Company Background
Aerotek was founded in 1983 in Baltimore MD by entrepreneurs Steve Bisciotti and Jim Davis. It got its start by providing engineering staffing for the aerospace and defense industries and later for automotive manufacturers and suppliers. In 1990 the company formed Telecommunications Services now known as TEKsystems which has been recognized as the top information technology staffing firm in the US by the IT Services Business Report.

In 1993 Aerotek acquired Onsite Engineering & Management focused on environmental and energy services staffing. It later branched out to include staffing for other industries including biotechnology pharmaceuticals healthcare light industrial and light technical. It opened its first European office in 1993 and two years later expanded into Canada with an office in Mississauga Ontario.

In 1998 Allegis Group was formed as the parent entity of several operating companies including Aerotek TEKsystems and Onsite. In 2001 Aerotek and Onsite merged to become Onsite Companies and in 2004 Onsite Companies changed its name to Aerotek Inc. to leverage the reputation of the Aerotek name.

EXECUTIVES
Pres, Todd M Mohr
SEC, Randy Sones
Cfo*, Thomas B Kelly
Treas, Paul J Bowie
Sr V Pres*, John Flanigan
Sr V Pres*, Chad Koele
Aerotek Delivery Coordinator, Julian Martin
Business Operations Supervisor, Tracey Dorsey
Compliance Staff, Esther St James
Customer Staff, Katarina Biondic
Customer Staff, Leigh Coursey
Auditors: PRICEWATERHOUSECOOPERS LLP B

LOCATIONS
HQ: AEROTEK, INC.
7301 PARKWAY DR, HANOVER, MD 210761159
Phone: 410 694-5100
Web: WWW.AEROTEK.COM

PRODUCTS/OPERATIONS

INDUSTRIES SERVED

Accounting
Administrative & Support Services
Aerospace Aviation & Defense
Architecture & Design
Automotive
Construction
Customer Service
Energy & Utilities
Engineering
Environmental
Financial Services
Government & Public Administration
Healthcare
Manufacturing
Pharmaceutical
Sciences
Warehouse & Distribution

COMPETITORS

Amn Healthcare
Adecco
Bryant Bureau
Cdi
Comforce
Insight Global
Integrity Staffing
Kelly Services
Kforce
Msx International
Manpowergroup
On Assignment
Pinnacle Staffing
Randstad Holding
Robert Half
Roth Staffing

HISTORICAL FINANCIALS
Company Type: Private

Income Statement				FYE: December 31
	REVENUE ($ mil.)	NET INCOME ($ mil.)	NET PROFIT MARGIN	EMPLOYEES
12/20	5,859	0	—	4,200
12/19	6,662	0	—	—
12/18	6,586	0	—	—
12/17	6,070	0	—	—
Annual Growth	(1.2%)	—	—	—

2020 Year-End Financials
Return on assets: —   Cash ($ mil.): 26
Return on equity: —
Current ratio: 3.50

AFFILIATED FOODS MIDWEST COOPERATIVE, INC.

Affiliated Foods Midwest Cooperative is a wholesale food distribution cooperative that supplies more than 800 independent grocers in some 15 states in the Midwest. From its handful of distribution centers in Kansas Nebraska and Wisconsin the co-op distributes fresh produce meats deli items baked goods dairy products and frozen foods as well as general merchandise and equipment. It distributes goods under the Shurfine brand (from Topco Associates) and IGA labels. Additionally Affiliated Foods Midwest provides marketing merchandising and warehousing support services for its members. The cooperative was formed in 1931 to make wholesale purchases for a group of retailers in Nebraska.

Geographic Reach
Norfolk Nebraska-based Affiliated Foods Midwest Cooperative has distribution centers in Norfolk Elwood Kansas and Kenosha Wisconsin. It serves customers in 15 states across the Midwest.

Financial Performance
Affiliated Foods Midwest rang up an estimated $1.6 billion in sales in fiscal 2013 (ended June).

Auditors: BKD LLP LINCOLN NEBRASKA

LOCATIONS
HQ: AFFILIATED FOODS MIDWEST COOPERATIVE, INC.
1301 W OMAHA AVE, NORFOLK, NE 687015872
Phone: 402 371-0555
Web: WWW.AFMIDWEST.COM

PRODUCTS/OPERATIONS

Selected Private-Label Brands

CharKing
ChuckWagon (pet food)
Clear Value
Cow Belle Creamery (ice cream)
Domestix (household products)
Full Circle (organic natural products)
IGA
PAWS Premium (pet products)
Shurfine
TopCare (OTC drugs health and beauty)
Valu Time
Wide Awake Coffee Co. (coffee)
World Classics Trading Company

COMPETITORS

Associated Wholesale Grocers	Kroger
C&s Wholesale	Mclane
Central Grocers	Supervalu
Certco	Wal-mart
Dearborn Wholesale Grocers	

HISTORICAL FINANCIALS
Company Type: Private

Income Statement				FYE: June 26
	REVENUE ($ mil.)	NET INCOME ($ mil.)	NET PROFIT MARGIN	EMPLOYEES
06/15	1,527	1	0.1%	850
06/14	1,477	2	0.2%	—
06/13	1,391	2	0.2%	—
06/12	1,486	2	0.2%	—
Annual Growth	0.9%	(19.5%)	—	—

AFFILIATED FOODS, INC.

This company helps keep pantries stocked in the Texas Panhandle and elsewhere. Affiliated Foods is a leading wholesale distribution cooperative that supplies grocery stores and restaurants in about a half a dozen states including Texas New Mexico and Oklahoma. It distributes fresh produce meat and non-food products as well as dairy products and beverages through its Plains Dairy unit. Its Tri State Baking Company supplies bread and other baked goods. In addition Affiliated Foods owns a stake in private-label products supplier Western Family Foods. The company was founded in 1946 as Panhandle Associated Grocers which merged with South Plains Associated Grocers to form Affiliated Foods in 1968.

Geographic Reach
Based in Amarillo Texas Affiliated Foods supplies grocery stores and restaurants in Texas Oklahoma Kansas New Mexico Colorado Arizona and Arkansas.

Financial Performance
While privately-owned Affiliated Foods doesn't report its financial results the cooperative reported an estimated $1.5 billion in sales in fiscal 2012 (ends October).

EXECUTIVES

Ceo, Randy Arceneaux
Chb*, Roger Lowe
V Chb*, Dennis Porter Jr
SEC*, Jess Claiborne
Treas*, Lonnie Allsup
Coo*, Jeff Robinson
Cfo*, Noman Burr
Offc Mgr, Kim Clark
Senior Programmer, John Hawley
Administrative Assistant, Tana Bray
Administrative Assistant Accou, Paula Butler
Auditors: JOHNSON & SHELDON PLLC AMARI

LOCATIONS
HQ: AFFILIATED FOODS, INC.
1401 W FARMERS AVE, AMARILLO, TX 791186134
Phone: 806 372-3851
Web: WWW.AFIAMA.COM

PRODUCTS/OPERATIONS

Selected Subsidiaries
Affiliated Food Service (restaurant supply)
Plains Dairy (Amarillo Texas)
Tri-State Baking Co. (Amarillo Texas)

COMPETITORS

Affiliated Foods Midwest	Gsc Enterprises
	Iga
Associated Wholesale Grocers	Mclane
	Supervalu
C&s Wholesale	

HISTORICAL FINANCIALS
Company Type: Private

Income Statement				FYE: October 3
	REVENUE ($ mil.)	NET INCOME ($ mil.)	NET PROFIT MARGIN	EMPLOYEES
10/20*	1,556	1	0.1%	1,200
09/19	1,450	2	0.1%	—
09/17	1,421	1	0.1%	—
10/16	1,440	0	0.1%	—
Annual Growth	2.0%	21.2%	—	—
*Fiscal year change

2020 Year-End Financials
Return on assets: 0.7% Cash ($ mil.): 7
Return on equity: 2.2%
Current ratio: 1.10

AFJ, LLC

EXECUTIVES

Chairman, J Phillip Adams
Committee Member*, James A Baker
Committee Member*, Richard D Peterson
Commitee Member*, Andre Lortz
Contl, Robert Inkley

LOCATIONS
HQ: AFJ, LLC
1104 COUNTRY HILLS DR, OGDEN, UT 844032400
Phone: 801 624-1000
Web: WWW.FJMGT.COM

HISTORICAL FINANCIALS
Company Type: Private

Income Statement				FYE: January 31
	REVENUE ($ mil.)	NET INCOME ($ mil.)	NET PROFIT MARGIN	EMPLOYEES
01/07	661	(0)	—	57
01/06	574	(2)	—	—
01/05	401	3	0.8%	—
Annual Growth	28.4%	—	—	—

2007 Year-End Financials
Return on assets: (-0.3%) Cash ($ mil.): —
Return on equity: (-0.6%)
Current ratio: 0.40

AG PROCESSING INC A COOPERATIVE

Soy far soy good for Ag Processing (AGP) the largest farmer-owned soybean processor in the world and roughly the fourth-largest soybean processor in the US based on capacity. It purchases and processes more than 5.5 million acres of members' soybeans per year. The farmer-owned cooperative is also a leading supplier of refined vegetable oil in the US. It procures processes markets and transports grains and grain products ranging from human food ingredients to livestock feed to renewable fuels. AGP is owned by about 180 local and regional cooperatives and represents more than 250000 farmers in 15 states throughout the US.

Operations
In addition to its soybean processing and vegetable oil refining facilities AGP operates a merchandising and trading group called Ag Products subdivided into three areas of focus: Grain Protein and Export. Ag Products Grain focuses on marketing grain for members seeking to better compete in the global grain industry. Ag Products Protein markets soybean meal and soy hulls; it also manufactures AMINOPLUS a protein that improves milk production. Ag Products Export offers international marketing of soybean meal oilseeds

grains and other bulk agricultural commodities. Its main gateway to the fast growing Pacific Rim market is through a West Coast export shipping terminal in Washington state.

AGP also holds investment stakes in Masterfeeds a Canadian feed manufacturing business and in Protinal/Proagro Venezuela's largest poultry processor and one of country's largest animal feed producers.

Geographic Reach

AGP operates nine soybean processing plants including six located in Iowa. Other soybean processing plants are located in Minnesota Missouri and Nebraska. The company operates a growing ethanol plant in Nebraska to serve the renewable fuels market and soybean methyl ester plants in Iowa and Missouri. (Soy methyl ester an alternative to petroleum-based products is a byproduct that is used in everything from biodiesel to solvents.)

Financial Performance

AGP recorded its fourth best earnings year in the company's history in fiscal 2011. Its earnings from continuing operations (before income taxes) nearly doubled from 2010. Soybean processing rebounded from the previous year partly due to more aggressive export efforts. The company's vegetable oil business had its most profitable year yet as a result of improved demand from the soy biodiesel market improved oil quality and improved plant efficiency. Its renewable fuels business (ethanol and biodiesel) started slowly but finished 2011 strong posting improved earnings over 2010.

Strategy

With evolving EPA mandates the potential is still strong for integrated biodiesel producers like AGP which led it to acquire a 60-million gallon biodiesel plant in Algona Iowa in 2011. The acquisition doubled AGP's biodiesel production capacity now totaling about 120 million gallons.

Another major component of AGP's strategy is investing in expanding upgrading and modernizing various facilities for improved capacity and efficiency. In 2011 the company initiated major upgrade and modernization projects at soy processing plants in Sergeant Bluff Iowa and Dawson Minnesota. It also undertook a multi-million dollar expansion project at its Aberdeen Washington-based export terminal as overseas shipments to Pacific Rim countries increases.

In 2012 Ag Processing merged its Masterfeeds subsidiary with the Canadian commercial feed business (Feed-Rite) of Ridley to form the second-largest feed provider in Canada Masterfeeds LP. The new entity operates 22 manufacturing plants across the Quebec Ontario and Prairie provinces. Ridley and Ag Processing each own relative shares in Masterfeeds LP.

HISTORY

Seeking strength in numbers Ag Processing (AGP) was formed in 1983 when agricultural co-operatives Land O' Lakes and Farmland Industries merged their money-losing soybean operations into similarly struggling Boone Valley Cooperative.

Separately AGP's soybean mills had been unable to compete successfully against each other and larger corporations. The entire industry had been hampered by the Soviet grain embargoes imposed by the US in 1973 and 1979 and US government policies had contributed to increased competition from heavily subsidized soy producers in Argentina and Brazil. Soy exports from the US had fallen dramatically leading to a production capacity surplus.

Collectively AGP was able to attract a stronger management staff than its predecessors had; it hired 21-year Archer Daniels Midland (ADM) veteran James Lindsay as CEO and general manager.

With operations scattered over four states AGP placed its headquarters in Omaha Nebraska — chosen for its central location and close proximity to the co-op's main bank.

In its first two years AGP cut employee rolls by 20% and scaled back production thus trimming costs and squeezing higher prices for finished products. A turnaround came quickly and in 1985 members received a dividend from the co-op's $8 million pretax profit. That year AGP purchased two Iowa plants from AGRI Industries.

AGP dismantled two plants in 1987. By the next year the co-op witnessed an increase in domestic demand and had resumed selling to the Soviet Union. It generated additional sales by further processing soybean oil into food-grade products like hydrogenated oil and lecithin.

With an eye on diversification and value-added products by 1991 AGP had expanded to eight soybean plants and two vegetable oil refineries; it also acquired the feed and grain business of International Multifoods that year through an 80%-owned joint venture with ADM. The acquisition included 29 feed plants in the US and Canada 26 retail centers 18 grain elevators and the brands Supersweet and Masterfeeds. In 1994 AGP formed feed manufacturer Consolidated Nutrition a 50-50 joint venture with ADM.

Consolidated Nutrition introduced a Swine Operations program in 1996. The program quickly grew through the development of PORK PACT a partnership to serve pork producers. (The co-op has since exited the swine business.) The next year AGP's grain division sold nine grain elevators in Ohio and Indiana to Cargill. That year the co-op gained control of Venezuelan feed manufacturer Proagro.

By 1998 passage of the Freedom to Farm Act and growing demand had spurred soybean planting. The co-op in 1998 opened an additional processing plant in Emmetsburg Iowa followed by another in Eagle Grove Iowa. AGP sold off its pet food operations in 1998 to Windy Hill which was later acquired by Doane Pet Care Enterprises. Also that year Consolidated Nutrition combined its Master Mix and Supersweet feed brands into the Consolidated Nutrition label.

In 1999 the company added the Garner-Klemme-Meservey cooperative to its grain operations. It opened a new plant late that year in St. Joseph Missouri to make value-added products such as hardfat (used in emulsifiers).

In 2001 AGP sold its 50% share of Consolidated Nutrition to ADM. In 2002 the co-op's Masterfeeds business acquired four feed mills and a merchandising operation from Saskatchewan Wheat Pool (now Viterra). In 2003 AGP opened the Port of Grays Harbor vessel-loading terminal in Aberdeen Washington.

The company formed a subsidiary AgGrowth Products to market crop nutrients manufactured by Bio Tech Nutrients in 2005. Also that year the company announced facility expansions for its ethanol biodiesel and soybean processing operations.

In 2007 the co-op's board rejected a hostile takeover bid made by Ag Processors Alliance (APA). APA was formed exclusively to take over AGP and consisted of the leadership of Ag and Food Associates of Omaha an investment banking firm that manages the project on behalf of an investment group that has a specific interest and expertise in agricultural operations.

EXECUTIVES

Ceo, John Keith Spackler
V Pres-Coo*, Calvin Meyer
V Pres-Cfo*, Scott Simmelink
Manager, Mike Meyer

Information Specialist, Debbie Murray
Manager, Jerry Knapp
Programmer Analyst, Roja Peram
Vice President, Dennis Rademacher
Human Resource Manager, Jody Price
Plant Superintendent, John Dugger
Specialty Products, Logan Kuch

LOCATIONS

HQ: AG PROCESSING INC A COOPERATIVE
12700 W DODGE RD, OMAHA, NE 681546102
Phone: 402 496-7809
Web: WWW.AGP.COM

PRODUCTS/OPERATIONS

Selected Brands

Masterfeeds
AMINOPLUS (dairy cattle feed additive)
DIRECTOR (dairy cattle feed additive)
FUSION (horse feed additive)
Proagro/Protinal
Corral (Prepared chicken products Venezuela only)
SOYGOLD (bio-diesel fuel additives herbicides solvents surfacants fuel additives)

Selected Exported Products

Barley
Corn
Distillers dried grains (DDGS)
Feeding peas
High-protein soybean meal
Lecithin
Low-protein soybean meal
Oats
Soybean hulls
Soybean oil
Soybeans
Sunflowers
Wheat

Selected Operations and Products

Animal feed
Corn processing
Corn-based ethanol
Grain processing merchandising and sales
Industrial products (ethanol and methyl esters)
Soybean processing
Soybean oil
Soybean biodiesel
Prepared chicken products (Venezuela only)

COMPETITORS

Ach Food Companies	Liberty Vegetable Oil
Adm	Luckey Farmers
Bunge Limited	Marfrig
Cgb	Poet
Cgc	Smucker
Chs	South Dakota Soybean
Cargill	Processors
Conagra	Spectrum Foods
J-oil Mills	West Central Co-op
Land O'lakes Purina	Zeeland Farm
Feed	

HISTORICAL FINANCIALS

Company Type: Private

Income Statement   FYE: August 31

	REVENUE ($ mil.)	NET INCOME ($ mil.)	NET PROFIT MARGIN	EMPLOYEES
08/16*	3,410	134	3.9%	1,456
12/10	3	0	1.3%	—
08/06	2,360	62	2.7%	—
Annual Growth	3.7%	7.9%	—	—

*Fiscal year change

2016 Year-End Financials

Return on assets: 9.9%   Cash ($ mil.): 210
Return on equity: 15.3%
Current ratio: 2.80

AGFIRST FARM CREDIT BANK

AgFirst Farm Credit Bank is a member of the Farm Credit System the largest agricultural lending organization in the United States and one of the four banks in the Farm Credit Systems and provides funding to about 20 affiliated associations and provides services to 20 associations in 18 states and Puerto Rico. Boasting $30 billion in assets the bank provides financing to about 20 farmer-owned agricultural credit associations. The associations in turn offer mortgages and loans to some 80000 farmers agribusinesses and rural homeowners in 15 Eastern states and Puerto Rico. The company also offers credit and credit-related services to qualified borrowers. AgFirst raises money by selling bonds and notes on the capital markets. AgFirst Farm Credit Bank was founded in 1916.

EXECUTIVES

Ceo, Tim Amerson
Cfo*, Charl Butler
Staff, Christopher Bell
Vice-President, Felicia Morant
Coordinator, Gloria Brown
Benefits Supervisor, Beth Ward
Payroll Staff, Jackie Bennett
Financial Analyst, Robert Cummins
Gallery Director, Amanda Simpson
Investment Officer, Dick Wilkins
Senior Financial Officer, John W Weathers
Auditors: PRICEWATERHOUSECOOPERS LLP MI

LOCATIONS

HQ: AGFIRST FARM CREDIT BANK
1901 MAIN ST, COLUMBIA, SC 292012443
Phone: 803 799-5000
Web: WWW.AGFIRST.COM

PRODUCTS/OPERATIONS

2014 Sales

	$ mil.	% of total
Interest		
Loans	566	79
Investment securities & other	127	18
Non-interest		
Loan fees	8	2
Building lease income	3	-
Net other-than-temporary impairment losses	(1.4)	-
Gains (losses) on called debt	(7.7)	-
Gains (losses) on investments net	0	-
Gains (losses) on other transactions	0	-
Other	7	1
Total	**703**	**100**

COMPETITORS

Agribank	Farm Family Holdings
Bank Of America	First National Of
Country Financial	Nebraska
Cat Financial	Rabo Agrifinance

HISTORICAL FINANCIALS
Company Type: Private

Income Statement				FYE: December 31
	ASSETS ($ mil.)	NET INCOME ($ mil.)	INCOME AS % OF ASSETS	EMPLOYEES
12/17	32,487	344	1.1%	530
12/15	30,620	336	1.1%	—
Annual Growth	3.0%	1.2%	—	—

2017 Year-End Financials
Return on assets: 1.1%   Sales ($ mil): 883
Return on equity: 15.4%

AGTEGRA COOPERATIVE

Who loves you a bushel and a peck? South Dakota Wheat Growers may; it is an agricultural co-op comprising some 6800 member-farmers. It provides a grain warehouse along with grain marketing services intended to compete with big food and ag companies. In addition to storage and drying Wheat Growers offers agronomy spreading and spraying and transportation. It supplies feed fertilizer chemicals and other farm-related provisions for members in and around counties in North and South Dakota. Wheat Growers generates more than half of its revenues through marketing some 160 million bushels of grain (corn wheat and soybeans) each year. Remaining revenues are made through agronomy and retail sales and services.

EXECUTIVES

Pres, Hal Clemensen
V Pres*, Dave Thorson
Gen Mgr-Treas*, Dale Locken
SEC-Tres*, Todd Bushong
Cfo*, Robert Porter
Director, Bill Descamps
Information Technology Support, Charles Madsen
General Manager, David Clark
Svp-Agronomy, Daryl Molskness
Agronomy Controller, Kieth Hughes
Information Support Ex, Weylin Huber
Auditors: GARDINER THOMSEN PC DES MOIN

LOCATIONS

HQ: AGTEGRA COOPERATIVE
908 LAMONT ST S, ABERDEEN, SD 574015515
Phone: 605 225-5500
Web: WWW.AGTEGRA.COM

Selected Counties of Operation
North Dakota
Dickey
LaMoure
Stutsman
South Dakota
Aurora
Beadle
Brown
Brule
Clark
Corson
Day
Edmunds
Faulk
Hand
Hyde
Jerauld
Lyman
Marshall
Sanborn
Spink

COMPETITORS

Adm	North Central Farmers
Chs	Elevator
Cargill	Northern Growers

HISTORICAL FINANCIALS
Company Type: Private

Income Statement				FYE: July 31
	REVENUE ($ mil.)	NET INCOME ($ mil.)	NET PROFIT MARGIN	EMPLOYEES
07/19	1,509	(5)	—	638
07/18	1,544	32	2.1%	—
07/17	1,275	22	1.8%	—
07/16	1,209	6	0.6%	—
Annual Growth	7.7%	—	—	—

2019 Year-End Financials
Return on assets: (-0.6%)
Return on equity: (-1.7%)
Current ratio: 1.20
Cash ($ mil.): 6

AHS HOSPITAL CORP.

EXECUTIVES

Pres-Ceo, Joseph A Trunfio
V Pres*, Andrew L Kovach
V Pres*, Joseph A Dipaolo
Cfo*, Kevin Lenahan
Coordinator, Robert Swander
Executive Officer, Rubell Michael
Clinical Oncology Professional, Paul Heller
Rn, Alice Beadle
Vice President, Chief Diversit, Armond Kinsey
Assistant Nurse Manager, Conny Beam
Senior Manager, Danielle Melton
Auditors: PRICEWATERHOUSECOOPERS LLP F

LOCATIONS

HQ: AHS HOSPITAL CORP.
475 SOUTH ST, MORRISTOWN, NJ 079606459
Phone: 973 660-3100
Web: WWW.ATLANTICHEALTH.ORG

HISTORICAL FINANCIALS
Company Type: Private

Income Statement				FYE: December 31
	REVENUE ($ mil.)	NET INCOME ($ mil.)	NET PROFIT MARGIN	EMPLOYEES
12/20	3,069	324	10.6%	7,300
12/19	2,993	458	15.3%	—
12/18	2,776	30	1.1%	—
12/17	2,600	291	11.2%	—
Annual Growth	5.7%	3.7%	—	—

2020 Year-End Financials
Return on assets: 6.5%
Return on equity: 12.4%
Current ratio: 2.30
Cash ($ mil.): 1,003

AIDS HEALTHCARE FOUNDATION

EXECUTIVES

Ceo, Michael Arthur Weinstein

Chm, Rodney L Wright
Cfo, Lyle Honig
Sr V Pres, Peter Reis
Dir, Scott Carruthers
Coordinator, Santiago Leal
Senior Payroll Specialist, Johnny Nguyen
Director, Robert Heglar
Georgia Regional Director, Tiffany Roan
Director of Pharmacy, Anthony Dao
Pharmacy Director of Performan, Natalya
 Ormanzhy
Auditors: VASQUEZ & COMPANY LLP LOS ANG

LOCATIONS

HQ: AIDS HEALTHCARE FOUNDATION
 6255 W SUNSET BLVD FL 21, LOS ANGELES, CA
 900287422
Phone: 323 860-5200
Web: WWW.AIDSHEALTH.ORG

HISTORICAL FINANCIALS

Company Type: Private

Income Statement			FYE: December 31
	REVENUE ($ mil.)	NET INCOME ($ mil.)	NET PROFIT MARGIN	EMPLOYEES
12/19	1,366	98	7.2%	2,331
12/16	1,163	40	3.5%	—
12/15	1,039	56	5.4%	—
12/14	879	30	3.5%	—
Annual Growth	9.2%	26.5%	—	—

2019 Year-End Financials

Return on assets: 14.4%   Cash ($ mil.): 148
Return on equity: 20.2%
Current ratio: 3.30

AIR METHODS CORPORATION

With a fleet of more than 450 medically equipped aircraft mainly helicopters Air Methods is one of the largest providers of emergency medical air-transportation services in the US. The company operates through three divisions. A community-based operating company Air Methods also provides tourism operations around Hawaiian Islands through Blue Hawaiian Helicopters. The smallest division United Rotorcraft designs manufactures and installs aircraft medical-transport products. Air Methods was founded in 1980 by Roy Morgan.

Operations

The company's air medical services include three divisions such as Cypheron Healthcare Solutions Blue Hawaiian Helicopters and United Rotorcraft.

Cypheron is a Revenue Cycle Management Solutions provider with a unique patient advocacy approach. It has a historical track record of success in the Revenue Cycle Management space. It aligns with custmer's culture and continue the care it started-empathizing informing and collaborating with patients to avoid complaints and maximizing your recovery.

Blue Hawaiian is the only one that serves all four major Hawaiian islands: Oahu Maui Kauai and the Big Island.

United Rotorcraft is Air Methods' products division dedicated to being a leading provider of aircraft and land vehicle equipment and systems to meet its customer's unique mission requirements.

It designs integrates and installs medical equipment avionics and vehicle accessories for emergency medical services (EMS) medevac firefighting airborne law enforcement (ALE) and search and rescue (SAR) operators.

Geographic Reach

The company is headquartered in Greenwood Village Colorado.

EXECUTIVES

Ceo, Jaelynn Williams
Pres AMS*, Mike Allen
Cfo*, Peter Csapo
Exec V Pres Bus Development*, David M Doerr
Cao*, Sharon J Keck
Compliance Officer*, Crystal Gordon
Regional Vice President, Martin Delaney
Government Billing, Matrika Sonkur
Chief Accounting Officer, Sharon Keck
Supervisor, Shawna Shinault
Base Manager, Timothy Champion
Auditors: KPMG LLP DENVER COLORADO

LOCATIONS

HQ: AIR METHODS CORPORATION
 5500 S QUEBEC ST STE 300, GREENWOOD
 VILLAGE, CO 801111926
Phone: 303 792-7400
Web: WWW.AIRMETHODS.COM

PRODUCTS/OPERATIONS

2014 Sales

	$ mil.	% of total
AMS	863	85
Tourism	116	11
United Rotorcraft	36	4
Corporate Activities	86	0
Adjustments	(11.4)	-
Total	**1,004**	**100**

Fleets

Fleets
AS 350
EC 135
EC 130
Bell 407
EC 145
Bell 429
BK 117
A-109
SA 365
Bell 222
Bell 430
Bell 206
MD 902
King Air
PC 12
Agusta 119Kx

Services

AirCom
Complete Billing Solutions
DirectCall
TAMMA
United Rotorcraft
LifeShield Alliance

COMPETITORS

Acadian Ambulance Service Inc.	Chc Group
Bristow Group Inc	Evergreen Holdings
	Phi Inc.

HISTORICAL FINANCIALS

Company Type: Private

Income Statement			FYE: December 31
	REVENUE ($ mil.)	NET INCOME ($ mil.)	NET PROFIT MARGIN	EMPLOYEES
12/15	1,085	109	10.1%	5,133
12/14	1,004	95	9.5%	—
12/13	881	62	7.0%	—
Annual Growth	11.0%	32.7%	—	—

2015 Year-End Financials

Return on assets: 7.0%   Cash ($ mil.): 5
Return on equity: 19.0%
Current ratio: 3.20

AIRGAS, INC.

Airgas safely and reliably provides products services and expertise to industries through its more than 18500 associates in more than 1400 locations robust e-Business platform and Airgas Total Access telesales channel. Airgas distributes argon carbon dioxide hydrogen nitrogen oxygen and a variety of specialty gases as well as welding products tools and equipment dry ice and protective equipment (hard hats goggles). The company serves more than 1 million customers in various industries. The company is owned by Air Liquide SA.

Operations

Airgas operates through five product categories: Gases Gas equipment Safety products Tools and hardware and Welding products.

Its Gases include industrial application gases such as acetylene argon and helium; medical gases such as carbon dioxide nitrogen and oxygen; and specialty gases such as gas mixtures.

Gas equipment include balloon regulators; specialty gas equipment; welding gas equipment such as torches burning bars spark lighters and flints; and gas equipment accessories such as adapters and fittings cylinder carts hoses cable reels gas containers and valves.

Safety products include barricades clothing footwear gloves fire equipment first aid and head eye and face protection.

Tools and hardware products include abrasives cutting tools industrial brushes machine tools air compressors and plant maintenance equipment.

Welding products include fluxes and powders gas welding rods wires solders welders accessories such as plasma torches and cutters and welding support equipment such as blankets curtains pads and screens.

Geographic Reach

Headquartered in Radnor Pennsylvania the Airgas' US network covers more than 900 retail locations and is present in over 1400 locations in all 50 states.

Sales and Marketing

Airgas serves customers in a range of industries including manufacturing and metal fabrication power utilities and materials construction life sciences and healthcare food beverage and retail energy and chemical production and distribution basic materials and services. It also has government defense and aerospace clients. It interacts with customers through phone online and in physical stores.

Company Background

In the early 1980s Peter McCausland was a corporate attorney involved in mergers and acquisitions for Messer Griesheim a large German industrial gas producer. When the German firm declined McCausland's recommendation in 1982 to buy Connecticut Oxygen he raised money from private sources and bought it himself. He acquired other distributors and then left Messer Griesheim in 1987 to run Airgas full-time.

Since then the company made some 500 acquisitions becoming a nationwide company in the process.

HISTORY

In the early 1980s Peter McCausland was a corporate attorney involved in mergers and acquisitions for Messer Griesheim a large German industrial gas producer. When the German firm declined McCausland's recommendation in 1982 to buy Connecticut Oxygen he raised money from private sources and bought it himself. He acquired other distributors and then left Messer Griesheim in 1987 to run Airgas full-time.

Airgas began buying mostly small local and regional gas distributors in the US. By 1994 strategy shifted to purchasing larger "superregional" distributors such as Jimmie Jones Co. and Post Welding Supply of Alabama which added about $70 million combined to the company's revenues.

Airgas then began "rolling up" additional similar businesses. In 1995 it bought more than 25 companies and two years later it added more than 20 gas distributors. Also in 1997 Airgas expanded its manufacturing capabilities by building five plants that could fast-fill whole pallets of gas cylinders (the old manual system rolls cylinders two at a time). By 2000 the company had about 100 cylinder fill plants.

Struggling to integrate acquisitions while dealing with softening markets Airgas began a companywide realignment in 1998. To that end it sold its calcium carbide and carbon products operations to former partner Elkem ASA later that year; the company also consolidated 34 hubs into 16 regional companies and sold its operations in Poland and Thailand to Germany-based Linde in 1999.

In 2000 Airgas acquired distributor Mallinckrodt's Puritan-Bennett division (gas products for medical uses) with 36 locations in the US and Canada. The company also acquired the majority of Air Products' US packaged gas business excluding its electronic gases and magnetic resonance imaging-related helium operations in 2002.

In 2004 and 2005 it bought units from giants like Air Products and Chemicals BOC and LaRoche Industries. In 2006 Airgas continued to build with the purchase of 10 businesses including Union Industrial Gas which supplies Texas and much of the Southwest and then Linde's US bulk gas business for $495 million the next year. Linde in the process of integrating its 2006 acquisition of BOC then sold to Airgas a portion of its US packaged gas business for $310 million.

Rival Air Products had made a major bid to buy Airgas in 2010 but was rebuffed. Air Products extended its tender offer to Airgas stockholders several times and made a "best and final offer" of $70 a share (almost $6 billion) in December 2010. Airgas said it was holding out for $78 a share and rejected that offer too. In early 2011 a Delaware judge ruled for Airgas in a suit brought by Air Products to set aside a "poison pill" defense used by the Airgas board to fend off the takeover try. Following the verdict Air Products dropped its bid.

Airgas acquired six businesses in 2010 including Tri-Tech an independent distributor with 16 locations throughout Florida Georgia and South Carolina and annual sales of $31 million.

In 2011 Airgas reorganized its 12 regional segments into four new business support divisions — North South Central and West — to leverage a

new SAP information systems platform in 2011. Each of the units is headed by a division president. The new company structure is designed to accelerate sales growth and pricing management and create operating efficiencies.

In fiscal 2012 the company added eight businesses with total annual sales of about $106 million. The largest of the businesses acquired were ABCO Gases Welding and Industrial Supply Company (ABCO); Pain Enterprises; and Industrial Welding Supplies of Hattiesburg (doing business as Nordan Smith). Connecticut-based ABCO has 12 industrial and gas welding supply locations throughout New England. Indiana-based Pain operates 20 dry ice and liquid carbon dioxide production and distribution sites. Mississippi-based Nordan Smith has 17 locations that distribute industrial medical and specialty gases and supplies thoughout Alabama Arkansas and Mississippi.

In 2013 Airgas retained Chicago-based Acquity Group as a key partner in helping the company continue to provide new online digital customer platforms. As one of the leading digital marketing companies the Acquity Group will provide its e-channel expertise in leading the design and implementation of Airgas' new content-rich website.

In 2013 Airgas acquired two US-based industrial gas and welding supply distributors that complement the Airgas portfolio of products and services. Combined annual revenues for the two acquired businesses are more than $30 million.

In fiscal 2013 the company also acquired Illinois-based The Encompass Gas Group (one of the largest privately-owned suppliers of industrial medical and specialty gases and related hardgoods in the US) with about $55 million in annual revenues in 2012.

EXECUTIVES

Ceo, Marcelo Fioranelli
Coo*, Jay Worley
Coo*, Michael Molinini
Director Financial Management, Bob Bartos
Plant Manager, George Fox
Area Vice President, Jake Lucier
Branch Manager, John Emmerling
Account Manager, Mark Noblitt
Branch Manager, Randy Hanlon
Account Manager, Will Alleckson
Telecommunications Manager, Diane Puntel
Auditors: KPMG LLP PHILADELPHIA PENNSY

LOCATIONS

HQ: AIRGAS, INC.
259 N RADNOR CHESTER RD # 100, RADNOR, PA 190875240
Phone: 610 687-5253
Web: WWW.AIRGAS.COM

PRODUCTS/OPERATIONS

Selected Products and Services

Products
Carbon dioxide
Dry ice
Industrial gases
Argon
Helium
Hydrogen
Liquid oxygen
Nitrogen
Nitrous oxide
Oxygen
Safety equipment
Specialty gases
Services
Container rental
Welding equipment rental

Selected Subsidiaries
Airgas Canada

Airgas Carbonic
Airgas East
Airgas Great Lakes
Airgas Intermountain
Airgas Medical Services
Airgas Mid America
Airgas Mid South
Airgas Nitrous Oxide
Airgas Nor Pac
Airgas North Central
Airgas Northern California & Nevada
Airgas Refrigerant
Airgas Safety
Airgas South
Airgas Southwest
Airgas Specialty Gases
Airgas Specialty Products
Airgas West
National Welders Supply Company dba Airgas National Welders
Nitrous Oxide Corp.
Red-D-Arc
WorldWide Welding LLC

COMPETITORS

Air Products
Lincoln Electric
Matheson Tri-gas

Praxair Distribution
Valley National Gases
W.w. Grainger

HISTORICAL FINANCIALS

Company Type: Private

Income Statement				FYE: March 31
	REVENUE ($ mil.)	NET INCOME ($ mil.)	NET PROFIT MARGIN	EMPLOYEES
03/15	5,304	368	6.9%	17,000
03/13	4,957	340	6.9%	—
Annual Growth	3.4%	3.9%	—	—

2015 Year-End Financials

Return on assets: 6.2%   Cash ($ mil.): 50
Return on equity: 17.1%
Current ratio: 1.30

AKRON GENERAL MEDICAL CENTER INC

Akron General Medical Center the flagship hospital of Akron General Health System is a not-for-profit teaching hospital that boasts more than 530 acute care beds. The hospital serves the residents of Northeast Ohio as a regional referral center in a number of medical specialties including cardiovascular disease heart surgery cancer care women's health orthopedics sports medicine and trauma care. Akron General Medical also operates Edwin Shaw Rehab the area's only rehabilitation hospital. Edwin Shaw has 35 beds and treats patients who have experienced stroke head trauma and other critical injuries. Akron General Medical was founded in 1914 as Peoples Hospital.

Operations
Akron General is a level I trauma center and holds the county's first certified chest pain and primary stroke centers. It also offers a level III obstetric unit and it operates a freestanding outpatient surgery center. As a major teaching hospital with more than 1000 physicians as well as 3400 professional and support staff members Akron General Medical offers medical students about a dozen residency programs. It does so through its affiliations with Northeastern Ohio Medical University which serves as the medical college for University of Akron Youngstown State University and Kent

State University. Residencies include those in family medicine OB-GYN psychiatry and breast cancer.

Geographic Reach

Akron General Medical Center serves communities across the counties of Summit Medina Portage Stark and Wayne located in Northeast Ohio. In addition to facilities in Akron the hospital has satellite locations in Green Stow and Tallmadge. Edwin Shaw Rehab is located in the nearby town of Cuyahoga Falls. The center serves an area with a population of some 1.2 million people.

Strategy

The hospital conducts facility and equipment upgrades to meet the needs of a growing population in Northeast Ohio. Akron General enhanced its neurosurgical capabilities in 2012 as part of the establishment of its Neurosciences Institute. The center includes new Brainlab CT and MRI imaging systems for use during minimally invasive surgical procedures. The hospital is also upgrading its heart and vascular center which was certified as a heart failure clinic in 2013. In addition Akron General is working to upgrade IT systems to improve physician and patient resources.

EXECUTIVES

Chb, F William Steere
Director, Mary Beth Carroll
Director of Nursing, Phillip G Moser
Scientist, Barbara Klimonek
Scientist, Tookie Dunnie
Executive of Information Techn, Richard J Streck
Security Staff, Chris J Voller
Information Specialist, Paul Hayslip
Coordinator, Karen Orndorf
Emergency Medicine Specialist, David Peter
Family Practitioner, Kathie Greene
Auditors: LB BLUE & CO LLC COLUMBUS OH

LOCATIONS

HQ: AKRON GENERAL MEDICAL CENTER INC
   1 AKRON GENERAL AVE, AKRON, OH 443072432
Phone: 330 344-6000
Web: WWW.MY.CLEVELANDCLINIC.ORG

Selected Locations and Affiliates
Akron General Medical Center
Akron Health Center
Edwin Shaw Rehabilitation Institute
Green Health Center
Health and Wellness Centers (West North and Green)
Hospice Center
Lodi Community Hospital
Tallmadge Health Center

PRODUCTS/OPERATIONS

Selected Centers and Services
Anesthesiology
Audiology
Bariatric Surgery
Breast Health Center
Cancer Center
Community Health
Corporate Wellness
Critical Care Center
Diabetes Center
Diagnostic Services
Emergency Medicine/Level 1 Trauma Center
Endocrinology
Endoscopy
Executive Health Program
Family Medicine
Food and Nutrition Services
Gastroenterology
Health and Wellness
Heart and Vascular Center
Heartburn Center
Hyperbaric Medicine
Infectious Disease
Internal Medicine
Lab Services

Maternity Services
Nephrology
Neuroscience Institute
Nuclear Medicine
Occupational Therapy
Orthopedic Center
Osteoporosis Prevention
Pain Management
Physical Therapy
Primary Care
Psychiatry and Behavioral Sciences
Pulmonary Medicine
Radiology
Rehabilitation
Senior Services
Sleep Center
Speech and Language Pathology
Sports Medicine
Surgery
Urology
Women's Center
Wound Center

COMPETITORS

Akron Children's Hospital	Sharon Regional Health System
Community Health Systems	Summa Health System
Ohiohealth	Trinity Health System
Regency Hospital	University Hospitals Health System

HISTORICAL FINANCIALS
Company Type: Private

Income Statement				FYE: December 31
	REVENUE ($ mil.)	NET INCOME ($ mil.)	NET PROFIT MARGIN	EMPLOYEES
12/14	544	47	8.7%	875
12/13	507	22	4.4%	—
12/12	486	10	2.2%	—
12/04	0	0	—	—
Annual Growth	—	—	—	—

2014 Year-End Financials
Return on assets: 10.3%   Cash ($ mil.): 20
Return on equity: 35.3%
Current ratio: 0.40

ALASKA NATIVE TRIBAL HEALTH CONSORTIUM

The Alaska Native Tribal Health Consortium (ANTHC) brings good health to Alaska Natives. The company is a not-for-profit statewide health care organization managed by regional tribal governments and their respective regional health organizations. The organization connects disparate medical providers by providing a range of health programs and services including community health care public health advocacy and education initiatives health research (including water and sanitation) and medical supply distribution. The nearly 175-bed Alaska Native Medical Center (ANMC) a native-owned hospital is jointly managed by ANTHC and Southcentral Foundation a regional health corporation based in the Cook Inlet region.

EXECUTIVES

Pres, Teuber Andy
V Pres, Bean Lincoln
Board of Dir, Lincoln A Bean
Director, H Fally Smith
Directors, Charles Clements

Information Specialist, Ben Staheli
Information Specialist, Carol Greist
Information Specialist, Cherie Rains
Information Specialist, Edward Sullivan
Information Specialist, Gary Park
Information Specialist, Jennifer Arnold
Auditors: BDO USA LLP ANCHORAGE AK

LOCATIONS

HQ: ALASKA NATIVE TRIBAL HEALTH CONSORTIUM
   4000 AMBASSADOR DR, ANCHORAGE, AK 995085909
Phone: 907 729-1900
Web: WWW.ANTHC.ORG

PRODUCTS/OPERATIONS

2014 Sales

	$ mil.	% of total
Patient revenue	213	33
Compact revenue	161	25
Grant & project revenue	109	17
Warehouse revenue	22	3
Investment income	4	1
Other	133	21
Total	**643**	**100**

Selected Services
Ear Nose Throat
Emergency and Trauma
Family Medicine
Imaging and Laboratory Services
Internal Medicine Clinic
Maternal Fetal Medicine
OB/GYN Services
Oncology
Orthopedics Clinic
Pediatric ICU
Pediatrics
Pharmacy Services
Pregnancy and Childbirth
Primary Care Services
Respiratory Care

COMPETITORS

Hca	South Peninsula Hospital
Immediate Care	Tenet Healthcare
Peacehealth	
Providence St. Joseph Health	

HISTORICAL FINANCIALS
Company Type: Private

Income Statement				FYE: September 30
	REVENUE ($ mil.)	NET INCOME ($ mil.)	NET PROFIT MARGIN	EMPLOYEES
09/16	587	72	12.4%	1,850
09/15	511	3	0.7%	—
09/14	618	154	24.9%	—
Annual Growth	(2.6%)	(31.2%)	—	—

2016 Year-End Financials
Return on assets: 10.8%   Cash ($ mil.): 121
Return on equity: 13.8%
Current ratio: 1.60

ALASKA PERMANENT FUND CORPORATION

EXECUTIVES

Ceo, Angela Rodell
Coo*, Marcus Frampton
Chief Financial Officer*, Valerie Mertz

Information Specialist, Andrew Loney
Portfolio Manager, Timothy Andreyka
Human Resources Director, Chad Brown
Investment Officer Real Estate, Christi
 Grussendorf
Senior Associate Private Marke, Jared Brimberry
Senior Associate, Maria Skuratovskaya
Head of Private Equity, Stephen Moseley
Senior Portfolio Manager, Yup Kim
Auditors: KPMG LLP ANCHORAGE AK

LOCATIONS

HQ: ALASKA PERMANENT FUND CORPORATION
 801 W 10TH ST STE 302, JUNEAU, AK 998011878
Phone: 907 796-1500
Web: WWW.APFC.ORG

HISTORICAL FINANCIALS
Company Type: Private

Income Statement				FYE: June 30
	ASSETS ($ mil.)	NET INCOME ($ mil.)	INCOME AS % OF ASSETS	EMPLOYEES
06/19	70,049	1,405	2.0%	50
06/18	67,671	5,109	7.6%	—
06/17	61,824	6,675	10.8%	—
06/16	55,346	(30)	—	—
Annual Growth	8.2%	—	—	—

ALBANY MED HEALTH SYSTEM

Albany Medical Center (AMC) provides medical care in upstate New York. Serving residents of northeastern New York and western New England the health system has at its heart the 730-bed Albany Medical Center Hospital. The general medical-surgical facility also provides specialty care in such areas as oncology rehabilitation and organ transplantation. AMC also features a children's hospital an outpatient surgery center and a group medical practice. It employs some 400 full-time physicians. Its Albany Medical College is one of the nation's first private medical schools. It offers undergraduate and graduate medical degrees and residency programs as well as fellowships and continuing medical education.

Operations

AMC's assets includes a biomedical research enterprise and one of the region's largest physicians practices with more than 400 doctors. Its physicians have extensive training and experience in 34 subspecialties of pediatric medicine. The system's subsidiaries include the Albany Medical Center Kidskeller Corporation a not-for-profit day care facility and Madison Avenue Services Corporation a taxable corporation.

AMC is affiliated with several community physician groups including Albany Vascular Group Capital Cardiology Associates and Capital Region Orthopaedic Group.

In 2013 the system reported some 33000 admissions 581000 outpatient visits 28000 surgical cases and 68000 emergency department visits.

Geographic Reach

AMC offers services in 25 counties in northeastern New York and western New England. In addition to treating patients at the main site in Albany providers also treat patients at community-based locations throughout the region including Clifton Park Latham Malta North Greenbush Delmar and others.

Sales and Marketing

HMOs account for around a third of net patient revenue while Medicare and Medicaid represent about 20% and 15% respectively.

Financial Performance

The company's revenues grew by 3% to $752 million in 2013 (versus $728 million in 2012) due to an increase in net patient revenue; this was partially offset by declines in interest income dividends and other revenue. Net income grew 21% to $63 million in 2013 as net realized gains on sales of securities and impairment charges rose. Other gains were made in pension-related changes and net unrealized gains and losses in investments.

Cash flow from operations fell 55% that year to $37 million as more was used in receivables and other liabilities.

Strategy

AMC grows through organic expansion partnerships and product initiatives. The company is in the midst of a $360 million expansion including a new patient tower with more than 100 beds and increased intensive care resources. The project — expected to last several years — will also increase Albany Medical Center Hospital's bed count to more than 700.

In 2014 The Neurology Group and The Endocrine Group joined AMC's Albany Med Faculty Physician Group.

AMC and Union Graduate College joined forces in 2013 to offer a new joint degree combining medical school with an MBA.

That year AMC and Saratoga Hospital formed a joint venture and opened the $17.5 million Malta Med Emergent Care to provide area residents an alternative to hospital emergency rooms for all but the most serious medical circumstances.

On the product innovation side in 2013 AMC introduced advanced imaging technologies in a pair of its new Patient Pavilion operating rooms that provide for greater precision and patient safety during brain and spinal surgeries.

Also that year the company opened a Chronic Kidney Disease Clinic as the sole source for comprehensive care for 6000 people in its service area suffering from the slow loss of kidney function.

AMC also engages in research and development of new pharmaceuticals through partnerships with companies like Aegis Therapeutics with which it is developing an anti-obesity peptide to benefit patients with type 2 diabetes. The college's research department is also studying brain mapping techniques as well as Alzheimer's disease vascular disease and cancer and multiple sclerosis treatments.

Company Background

AMC which produced Nobel prize winners in both 2009 and 2011 annually awards its own $500000 prize the largest monetary award in medicine and biomedical research in the US. In 2010 combined federal-state entities awarded the center $10 million the center's largest grant since its founding which will be used to expand research labs at Albany Medical College.

AMC's status as the Capital Region's reigning health care giant was toppled by the 2011 merger of four locals hospitals to form St. Peter's Health Partners with nearly 12000 employees vs. 6000 at AMC. Post merger the newly-merged group has nearly 50% of the Capital Region market while AMC has 25%. While AMC is no longer the area's largest hospital as the region's trauma center and only medical school it continues to draw many patients from outside the four-county area.

Albany Medical College was formed in 1839; the hospital's predecessor was formed in 1849. The two combined under the AMC umbrella in 1982.

EXECUTIVES

Pres-Ceo, James J Barba
Sr V Pres-Cso, Courtney Burke
Ex V Pres, Arthur A Gross
Executive Administrative Coord, Jennifer
 Humphrey
Coo, Gary Kochem
Cfo, William C Hasselbarth
Svp-General Counsel, Matt Jones
V Pres-Fin, Frances Albert
Contrl, Patrick Kelly
Svp-Business Dev't & Strategic, Kevin M Leyden
Assistant Vice President For C, Tania Allard
Auditors: KPMG LLP ALBANY NEW YORK

LOCATIONS

HQ: ALBANY MED HEALTH SYSTEM
 43 NEW SCOTLAND AVE, ALBANY, NY 122083412
Phone: 518 262-3125
Web: WWW.AMC.EDU

PRODUCTS/OPERATIONS

2013 Sales

	$ mil.	% of total
Net patient service	720	96
Inter-institutional	8	1
Interest & dividends	2	.
Other	17	2
Net assets released from restrictions	3	1
Total	**752**	**100**

2013 Net Patient Service Revenue

	% of total
Health maintenance organizations	32
Medicare	19
Medicaid	15
Blue Cross and Blue Shield	14
Commercial carriers	9
No fault & worker's compensation	5
Private pay	2
Other third-party payors	4
Total	**100**

Selected Services

Cancer center
Children's Hospital
Center for Donation and Transplant
Diabetes service
Emergency medical services
Hearing center
HIV medicine
Pain management
Perinatal
Physical therapy
Radiology
Rheumatology
Surgical
Trauma center
Women's wellness center

COMPETITORS

Berkshire Health Systems	St. Joseph's Hospital Health Center
Ellis Hospital	St. Peter's Health Partners
Suny Upstate Medical University	United Health Services Hospitals
Southwestern Vermont Health Care	

HISTORICAL FINANCIALS
Company Type: Private

Income Statement				FYE: December 31
	REVENUE ($ mil.)	NET INCOME ($ mil.)	NET PROFIT MARGIN	EMPLOYEES
12/17	664	267	40.2%	8,760
12/16	317	77	24.5%	—
12/15	1,167	5	0.5%	—
12/13	980	115	11.7%	—
Annual Growth	(9.3%)	23.4%	—	—

2017 Year-End Financials

Return on assets: 36.5%   Cash ($ mil.): 113
Return on equity: 84.3%
Current ratio: 2.20

ALBANY MEDICAL CENTER HOSPITAL

EXECUTIVES

Pres, James J Barba
Coo*, Gary J Kochem
SEC*, Sabine Needham
Svp-Cno*, Lisa Massarweh
Patient Care Director, Diane Carey
Chief of Urology, Barry Kogan
Assistant, Audrey Piper
Employee, Begajeta Bektesevic
Anesthesiologist, Branko Furst
Doctor, Frederick Eames
Manager, Kathy Oconnor
Auditors: KPMG LLP ALBANY NEW YORK

LOCATIONS

HQ: ALBANY MEDICAL CENTER HOSPITAL
43 NEW SCOTLAND AVE, ALBANY, NY 122083478
Phone: 518 262-3125
Web: WWW.CDTNYVT.ORG

HISTORICAL FINANCIALS

Company Type: Private

Income Statement				FYE: December 31
	REVENUE ($ mil.)	NET INCOME ($ mil.)	NET PROFIT MARGIN	EMPLOYEES
12/19	1,133	86	7.6%	1,568
12/17	1,017	38	3.8%	—
12/16	960	46	4.8%	—
12/15	893	16	1.9%	—
Annual Growth	6.1%	50.3%	—	—

2019 Year-End Financials

Return on assets: 7.2%   Cash ($ mil.): 158
Return on equity: 16.2%
Current ratio: 3.10

ALBERICI CONSTRUCTORS, INC.

EXECUTIVES

Pres, Gregory J Kozicz
V Pres, John S Alberici
V Pres, Leroy Stromberg
Cfo, Gregory T Hesser
Sr Acct, Sherry Morrow
Chief Information Officer, Frank C Kropiunik
Quality Manager, Brian Miller
Subcontract Administration, Erin Yaeger
Executive Assistant, Gail Thompson
Chief Structural Engineer, Gary Broccard
Superintendent, Greg Forshee

LOCATIONS

HQ: ALBERICI CONSTRUCTORS, INC.
8800 PAGE AVE, SAINT LOUIS, MO 631146106
Phone: 314 733-2000
Web: WWW.ALBERICI.COM

HISTORICAL FINANCIALS

Company Type: Private

Income Statement				FYE: December 31
	REVENUE ($ mil.)	NET INCOME ($ mil.)	NET PROFIT MARGIN	EMPLOYEES
12/17	782	0	—	2,000
12/16	960	0	—	—
12/15	1,028	0	—	—
12/14	729	0	—	—
Annual Growth	2.4%	—	—	—

2017 Year-End Financials

Return on assets: —   Cash ($ mil.): 76
Return on equity: —
Current ratio: 1.20

ALBERICI CORPORATION

Alberici helped shape the St. Louis skyline; it now sets its sights — or its construction sites — across North America. As the parent company of Alberici Constructors the company encompasses a group of enterprises with a presence in North America Central America South America and Europe. Operations include construction services building materials and steel fabrication and erection units. Alberici offers general contracting design/build construction management demolition and specialty contracting services while also offering facilities management. Founded in 1918 the Alberici family still holds the largest share of the employee-owned firm.

Operations

The company boasts more than a dozen operating companies in the US Canada and Mexico that serve the automotive energy health care industrial manufacturing and wastewater treatment markets. Its Gunther-Nash subsidiary provides construction services to the mining industry. Another division Vertegy specializes in construction consulting for green and sustainable projects.

Geographic Reach

Alberici is active throughout North America and has offices in St. Louis Missouri; Detroit Michigan; Atlanta Georgia; Topeka Kansas; Burlington and Cambridge Ontario; Saskatoon Saskatchewan; and L©on Mexico.

Sales and Marketing

Alberici serves a range of different companies including those that are automotive building energy healthcare heavy industrial industrial process mining infrastructure or water-related.

Some of Alberici's completed projects include casinos for Ameristar modernization and new facilities for Anheuser-Busch and factories for Boeing. Nearly 80% of its revenue comes from repeat clients.

Financial Performance

While full financial information was not available for the privately held company Alberici reports that its annual revenue typically exceeds $1 billion. In 2013 the company took home $1.9 billion and was ranked the 46th largest contractor in the US by the Engineering News-Record .

In 2012 the company reported more than $530 million in industrial-related revenue thanks to a recovering economy supporting demand for major industrial projects in the US and Canada.

Strategy

In recent years the heavy construction firm has pursued acquisitions to better diversify its business both geographically and by entering new specialty markets. In 2013 for example Alberici purchased contractor Flintco LLC to broaden its reach into new markets in the southern and southwestern regions of the US. In early 2012 Alberici acquired a water treatment facility specialist to expand its service offerings in the water plant construction market.

Alberici has also become a recognized contractor in recent years which could help give the company a higher profile and thus more exposure to new potential clients. In 2013 the Associated General Contractors of St. Louis awarded Alberici with top prizes at its 16th Annual Keystone Awards for the company's work on the Seabrook Gates Complex and the Knights of Columbus Child Development Center. To date Alberici has won 14 Keystone Awards more than any other general contractor.

So far its high standing hasn't hurt business. In July 2014 Alberici was chosen to lead in the engineering procurement and construction of a major air quality improvement project — with the goal of installing environmental controls and reducing sulfur dioxide emissions by 90% — at one of the generating stations owned and operated by Alliant Energy's Wisconsin utility Wisconsin Power and Light Company.

Mergers and Acquisitions

Expanding it range of capabilities in January 2012 Alberici acquired water treatment facility specialist CAS Construction. The addition of CAS which has built facilities throughout the central and western US strengthens Alberici's capabilities in the water market. The company was renamed CAS Constructors.

In early 2013 Alberici closed on its acquisition of Flintco LLC a century-old Native American-owned contractor based in Tulsa Oklahoma. With offices in Oklahoma New Mexico Texas Arkansas and California Flintco presented an attractive geographic diversification opportunity for Alberici.

EXECUTIVES

Pres, Gregory J Kozicz
Chb*, John S Alberici
Accounting Staff, Amanda Dolan
Project Manager, Carl Miller
Accounting Staff Assistant, Genevieve Woodson
Shift Supervisor, Geoff Wick
Chief Technology Officer, Aaron Geiger
Executive Vice President, Chris Hermann
Project Engineer, Kendra Hibben
Executive Vice President, Kevin Williams
Project Administrator III, Jeannie Joyner

LOCATIONS

HQ: ALBERICI CORPORATION
8800 PAGE AVE, SAINT LOUIS, MO 631146106
Phone: 314 733-2000
Web: WWW.ALBERICI.COM

PRODUCTS/OPERATIONS

Selected Markets
Automotive
Building
Energy
Green building
Health care
Industrial
Manufacturing/Food and Beverage
Mining infrastructure
Steel fabrication
Water and Wastewater Treatment

Selected Subsidiaries and Brands

Alberici Global Group GmbH
  Alberici Constructors Ltd. (Canada)
  Alberici Construcciones S.A. de C.V. (Mexico)
Alberici Group Inc.
  Alberici Constructors Inc.
  Alberici Global Automotive Constructors (automotive construction)
  Alberici Healthcare Constructors
  Alberici Industrial LLC
  CAS Construction LLC (water wastewater)
  Flintco LLC (Native American-owned contractor)
  Gunther-Nash Inc. (shaft slope and tunnel construction for mining industry)
  Hillsdale Fabricators (steel fabrication)
  Kienlen Constructors (structural concrete structural steel)
  Vertegy (green building consulting)

COMPETITORS

Barton Malow	Jacobs Engineering
Bechtel	Mccarthy Building
Black & Veatch	Parsons Corporation
Dpr Construction	Peter Kiewit Sons'
Fluor	Tic Holdings
Hensel Phelps Construction	Tutor Perini
	Walbridge Aldinger
Hoffman Corporation	Walsh Group
Hunt Construction	Zachry Inc.

HISTORICAL FINANCIALS

Company Type: Private

Income Statement   FYE: December 31

	REVENUE ($ mil.)	NET INCOME ($ mil.)	NET PROFIT MARGIN	EMPLOYEES
12/17	1,531	0	—	2,080
12/16	1,742	0	—	—
12/15	1,885	0	—	—
12/14	1,532	0	—	—
Annual Growth	(0.0%)	—	—	—

2017 Year-End Financials

Return on assets: —   Cash ($ mil.): 182
Return on equity: —
Current ratio: 1.40

ALBERICI GROUP, INC.

EXECUTIVES

Ceo, Gregory J Kozicz
Chb*, John S Alberici
Coo*, Leroy J Stromberg Jr
Exe V Pres*, Michael W Burke
Executive Vice President Const, Joe Turner

LOCATIONS

HQ: ALBERICI GROUP, INC.
  8800 PAGE AVE, SAINT LOUIS, MO 631146106
Phone: 314 733-2000
Web: WWW.ALBERICI.COM

HISTORICAL FINANCIALS

Company Type: Private

Income Statement   FYE: December 31

	REVENUE ($ mil.)	NET INCOME ($ mil.)	NET PROFIT MARGIN	EMPLOYEES
12/17	838	0	—	2,000
12/16	1,036	0	—	—
12/15	1,124	0	—	—
12/14	729	0	—	—
Annual Growth	4.8%	—	—	—

2017 Year-End Financials

Return on assets: —   Cash ($ mil.): 105
Return on equity: —
Current ratio: 1.20

ALBERT EINSTEIN MEDICAL ASSOCIATES, INC.

EXECUTIVES

Pres, Barry Freedman
V Pres*, Penny Rezet
Treas*, Gerard McKee
Cfo*, Brian Derrick
Pres*, Herbert S Waxman
Treas*, John Murino
Coordinator, Monica Rollerson
Staff, John Skanse
Health Professional, Mel Hanick
Coordinator, Velma Maxwell
Coordinator, Laura Cook

LOCATIONS

HQ: ALBERT EINSTEIN MEDICAL ASSOCIATES, INC.
  5501 OLD YORK RD STE 1, PHILADELPHIA, PA
  191413018
Phone: 215 456-7890
Web: WWW.EINSTEIN.EDU

HISTORICAL FINANCIALS

Company Type: Private

Income Statement   FYE: June 30

	REVENUE ($ mil.)	NET INCOME ($ mil.)	NET PROFIT MARGIN	EMPLOYEES
06/09	670	0	—	5,251
06/08	693	33	4.9%	—
06/07	785	63	8.0%	—
06/06	718	29	4.1%	—
Annual Growth	(2.3%)	—	—	—

2009 Year-End Financials

Return on assets: —   Cash ($ mil.): 82
Return on equity: —
Current ratio: 0.40

ALBERTSONS COMPANIES, INC.

Albertsons Companies is one of the biggest supermarket retailers in the US with more than 2275 stores in about 35 states and the District of Columbia. In addition to traditional grocery items many of the stores offer pharmacies and coffee shops and over 400 include adjacent gas stations. The company operates under some 20 banners including Albertsons Vons Pavilions Randalls Tom Thumb Carrs Jewel-Osco Shaw's Star Market Safeway Market Street Haggen and United Supermarkets. It also owns meal kit company Plated. Albertsons which traces its roots to 1939 owned by Cerberus Capital Management went public in mid-2020.

HISTORY

J. A. "Joe" Albertson Leonard Skaggs (whose family ran Safeway) and Tom Cuthbert founded Albertson's Food Center in Boise Idaho in 1939. Albertson who left his position as district manager for Safeway to run the store thought big from the start. The 10000-sq.-ft. store was not only eight times the size of the average competitor it also offered an in-store butcher shop and bakery one of the country's first magazine racks and homemade "Big Joe" ice-cream cones. The men ended their partnership in 1945 the year Albertson's was incorporated and by 1947 it operated six stores in Idaho.

The company opened its first combination food store and drugstore a 60000-sq.-ft. superstore in 1951 and began locating stores in growing suburban areas. Albertson's went public to raise expansion capital in 1959 and by 1960 had 62 stores in Idaho Oregon Utah and Washington. The food retailer acquired Greater All American Markets (1964) a grocery chain based in Downey California and Semrau & Sons (1965) of Oakland which aided the company's thrust into the California market.

Albertson's and the Skaggs chain (by this time run by L. S. Skaggs Jr.) reunited temporarily in 1969 financing six Skaggs-Albertson's food-and-drug-combination stores. (The partnership dissolved in 1977 with each side taking half of the units.) By 1986 the company had reached $5 billion in sales a fivefold increase over 1975.

The company purchased 74 Jewel Osco combination food stores and drugstores (mostly in Arkansas Florida Oklahoma and Texas) from American Stores in 1992. Co-founder Albertson died in 1993 at age 86.

In 1997 the United Food and Commercial Workers union which represents supermarket employees sued Albertson's alleging the company forced employees to work overtime without pay. (It was settled in 1999 resulting in a $22 million charge.) Also in 1997 Albertson's began selling gasoline at a few stores. Acquisitions the next year (including Buttrey Food and Drug Stores) added stores and states. That year the company began serving online customers in the Dallas-Fort Worth area.

In 1999 the grocer revisited its roots when it acquired American Stores (Skaggs' successor) which operated more than 1550 stores in 26 states. To obtain regulatory approval for the $12 billion deal Albertson's sold 145 stores in overlapping markets in three states (most were in California).

In 2001 Larry Johnston former CEO of GE Appliances took over as chairman and CEO of Albertson's. Facing increasing competition (especially from Wal-Mart) Johnston announced in March 2002 aggressive restructuring plans that included job cuts and closing 95 stores in under-performing markets specifically Memphis and Nashville Tennessee and Houston and San Antonio Texas.

Already allowing customers to order drugs online (from its online drugstore Savon.com) and groceries in Seattle Albertson's expanded its online operations to San Diego in 2001 and in early 2002 to Los Angeles San Francisco and parts of Oregon and Washington. Albertson's exited the New England drugstore market in 2002 when it sold 80 New England Osco stores to Brooks Pharmacy.

In February 2004 Albertson's launched its "Blue Ribbon" brand of beef a private-label line of roasts and steaks. Also in February the company consolidated its Southwest Intermountain Northwest and Rocky Mountain divisions to form a new Intermountain West Division and combined the Acme and Florida divisions into a new Eastern Division.

A four-and-a-half month strike by grocery workers in Southern California ended in March 2004. The dispute pitted workers' demands for continued generous health care coverage vs. management's call for cost cuts to remain profitable in the face of Wal-Mart's entry into the Southern California grocery market. In April Albertson's completed the acquisition of JS USA Holdings which runs Shaw's and Star Markets stores in New England from UK grocer J Sainsbury. The deal to buy Shaw's was worth about $2.4 billion (cash and leases). In September Albertson's gained a toehold in the gourmet-food market with the purchase of Bristol Farms the operator of about a dozen upscale food markets in Southern California. In October Albertson's combined its Northern and Southern California food divisions into a single business unit the newly formed California Food Division. In an effort to improve efficiency Albertson's reorganized its supply chain food operations and Six Sigma Quality functions in May 2005.

In June 2006 Albertson's was sold to a consortium that included SUPERVALU CVS Cerberus Capital Management and Kimco for about $9.7 billion. Following the acquisition and the divvying up of Albertson's assets the surviving company went private and changed its name to Albertsons LLC. Concurrently Johnston left Albertsons and was succeeded by Robert Miller chairman of drugstore chain Rite Aid and the former head of Fred Meyer for eight years in the 1990s. Of the company's 27 price-impact Super Saver stores 25 closed their doors in mid-2006. Also in June the company put about 45 stores on the auction block. (It was announced in late 2006 that discount apparel retailer Ross Stores would acquire these stores.) In July the company shut down its online shopping service Albertsons.com.

In February 2007 Albertsons sold 132 grocery stores and two distribution centers in Northern California and Nevada to Save Mart Supermarkets for an undisclosed amount. Other recent closings include stores in Texas in the Dallas-Fort Worth Austin and Longview markets; Colorado; and Oklahoma.

Albertsons also sold eight of its stores in Wyoming to SUPERVALU in January 2008. The divestments continued in September with the sale of 49 supermarkets in Florida to Publix Super Markets for about $500 million. Also in 2008 Albertsons sold about 100 of its Express fuel centers in Arizona Colorado Florida Louisiana and Texas to Valero Energy and Reb Oil.

EXECUTIVES

Executive Vice President, Chief Information Officer, Anuj Dhanda, $634,615 total compensation
Director, Hersch Klaff
Independent Director, Kim Fennebresque
Director, Jay Schottenstein
Independent Director, Allen Gibson
Director, Scott Wille
Independent Director, Sharon Allen
Independent Director, Steven Davis
Independent Director, Alan Schumacher
Director, Shant Babikian
Executive Vice President, General Counsel, Secretary, Juliette Pryor, $515,865 total compensation
Executive Vice President, Chief Customer And Digital Officer, Christine Rupp, $750,000 total compensation
Independent Director, Mary West
Chief Human Resource Officer, Executive Vice President, Michael Theilmann, $323,077 total compensation
Co-chairman Of The Board, Chan Galbato

President, Chief Financial Officer, Sharon McCollam
Chief Operations Officer, Executive Vice President, Susan Morris, $900,000 total compensation
Executive Vice President, Chief Merchandising Officer, Geoff White
Vice Chairman Of The Board, Brian Turner
Co-chairman Of The Board, James Donald
Executive Vice President, Corporate Development And Real Estate, Justin Ewing
Auditors: DELOITTE & TOUCHE LLP BOISE

LOCATIONS

HQ: ALBERTSONS COMPANIES, INC.
250 E PARKCENTER BLVD, BOISE, ID 837063999
Phone: 208 395-6200
Web: WWW.ALBERTSONSCOMPANIES.COM

PRODUCTS/OPERATIONS

2018 Sales

	$ mil.	% of total
Non-perishables	26,372	44
Perishables	24,921	41
Pharmacy	4,987	8
Fuel	3,456	6
Other	799	1
Total	**60,535**	**100**

COMPETITORS

Aldi	Quality Food
Amazon.com	Roundy's
Costco Wholesale	Stater Bros.
Fry's Food	Target Corporation
H-e-b	Wal-mart
Kroger	Wegmans
Lidl	Winn-dixie
Publix	

HISTORICAL FINANCIALS

Company Type: Private

Income Statement				FYE: February 29
	REVENUE ($ mil.)	NET INCOME ($ mil.)	NET PROFIT MARGIN	EMPLOYEES
02/20	62,455	466	0.7%	210,000
02/19	60,534	131	0.2%	—
02/18	59,924	46	0.1%	—
Annual Growth	2.1%	217.4%	—	—

2020 Year-End Financials

Return on assets: 1.9%   Cash ($ mil.): 470
Return on equity: 20.5%
Current ratio: 1.00

ALBUQUERQUE MUNICIPAL SCHOOL DISTRICT NUMBER 12

EXECUTIVES

Supt, Jason Martinez
Superintendent, Raquel Martinez Reedy
Substitute Teacher, Alysa Louton
Voip Telecommunications Manage, Brian Thompson
Teacher, Cara Chavez
Teacher, Cicely Ryan

Truancy Social Worker, Danielle Burnett
Para Educator, Donna Huling
Teacher, Heather Worf
Claim Analyst, Janice Portillo
Special Education, Kiley Wiemeri
Auditors: MOSS ADAMS LLP ALBUQUERQUE N

LOCATIONS

HQ: ALBUQUERQUE MUNICIPAL SCHOOL DISTRICT NUMBER 12
6400 UPTOWN BLVD NE, ALBUQUERQUE, NM 871104202
Phone: 505 880-3700
Web: WWW.APS.EDU

HISTORICAL FINANCIALS

Company Type: Private

Income Statement				FYE: June 30
	REVENUE ($ mil.)	NET INCOME ($ mil.)	NET PROFIT MARGIN	EMPLOYEES
06/20	1,096	7	0.6%	134
06/19	1,006	(35)	—	—
06/18	954	50	5.3%	—
06/17	946	57	6.0%	—
Annual Growth	5.0%	(50.3%)	—	—

2020 Year-End Financials

Return on assets: 0.3%   Cash ($ mil.): 118
Return on equity: —
Current ratio: 2.30

ALDINE INDEPENDENT SCHOOL DISTRICT

EXECUTIVES

Supt, Dr Latonya Goffney
Principal, Ruth Dimmick
Principal, Jeannette Ross
Assistant, Akua Twumasi
Human Resources, Esther Hinojosa
Assistant Director of Public I, Debbie Willett
Teacher, Alicia Cerda
Registrar, Aurora Diaz
Executive Director of Student, Candice Moore
Special Education Teacher, David Broadhead
Mathematics Teacher, Isaac Valdez
Auditors: WHITLEY PENN LLP HOUSTON TX

LOCATIONS

HQ: ALDINE INDEPENDENT SCHOOL DISTRICT
2520 WW THORNE BLVD, HOUSTON, TX 770733406
Phone: 281 449-1011
Web: WWW.ALDINEISD.ORG

HISTORICAL FINANCIALS

Company Type: Private

Income Statement				FYE: June 30
	REVENUE ($ mil.)	NET INCOME ($ mil.)	NET PROFIT MARGIN	EMPLOYEES
06/20	814	(3)	—	7,000
06/19	791	106	13.5%	—
06/18	757	33	4.5%	—
06/17	743	(276)	—	—
Annual Growth	3.1%	—	—	—

2020 Year-End Financials

Return on assets: (-0.2%)   Cash ($ mil.): 48
Return on equity: —
Current ratio: —

ALEGENT HEALTH-BERGAN MERCY HEALTH SYSTEM

EXECUTIVES

Ceo, Cliff Robertson
Pres, Lawrence Beckman
Sr V Pres, Bonnie Burnett
Cfo, Jeanette Wojtalewicz
V Pres, Leigh Bertholf
Coo, Joan Neuhaus
Diagnostic Radiologist, Michael Schuster
Chief Officer, Devin Fox
Pacs Administrator, Lisa McCarty
Lead Rn, Anne Brennan
Administrator Clinical, Carol Henrichs

LOCATIONS

HQ: ALEGENT HEALTH- BERGAN MERCY HEALTH SYSTEM
7500 MERCY RD, OMAHA, NE 681242319
Phone: 402 398-6060
Web: WWW.CHIHEALTH.COM

HISTORICAL FINANCIALS

Company Type: Private

Income Statement				FYE: June 30
	REVENUE ($ mil.)	NET INCOME ($ mil.)	NET PROFIT MARGIN	EMPLOYEES
06/20	576	31	5.4%	1
06/18	695	60	8.7%	—
06/17	727	23	3.2%	—
06/14	543	88	16.3%	—
Annual Growth	1.0%	(16.0%)	—	—

2020 Year-End Financials

Return on assets: 2.8%
Return on equity: 3.5%
Current ratio: 0.90
Cash ($ mil.): 4

ALEX LEE, INC.

The Alex Lee family of companies includes Lowes Foods and Merchants Distributors (MDI). Alex Lee grew out of Merchants Produce Company which was founded in 1931 by Alex and Lee George. MDI supplies food and general merchandise to more than 600 retailers with food and non-food items in over 10 Eastern states. The company's Consolidation Services supplies an array of warehousing and logistics services. As part of its business Alex Lee also operates Lowes Food Stores a chain of approximately 75 grocery stores located in the Carolinas and Virginia. The George family continues to control Alex Lee.

Operations

Alex Lee named after Lebanese immigrant founder Moses George's two sons Alex and Lee boasts two operating companies: Merchants Distributors (MDI) and Lowes Foods.

MDI a privately-owned wholesale grocery store distributor offers cold storage to manufacturers provides digital services for retail has a large format print facility and exports to a wide range of stores in the US and internationally. Lowes Foods a homegrown grocery store offers convenient to-go meals and stellar guest services.

Geographic Reach

Alex Lee's Lowes Foods business operates some 75 stores while MDI supplies more than 600 retail food stores with food and non-food items in over 10 Eastern states.

Sales and Marketing

Alex Lee markets its products and services through its distribution companies such as Lowes Foods and MDI.

EXECUTIVES

Chb, Brian A George
Sr Vice President, Anita Harris
Sr V Pres-General Counsel-Sec, John B Orgain
Sr Vp Hr & Innovation, Robert Vipperman
Vp Communication & Corp Citize, Kimberly D George
Vice President, Robert H McTeir
Vice President, Shawn Beichler
Cfo, Andrew Almquist
Administrative Assistant, Toye Sigmon
Staff, Michael Martin
Staff, Tim Joyce
Auditors: RSM US LLP CHARLOTTE NORTH C

LOCATIONS

HQ: ALEX LEE, INC.
120 4TH ST SW, HICKORY, NC 286022947
Phone: 828 725-4424
Web: WWW.ALEXLEE.COM

PRODUCTS/OPERATIONS

Selected Operations

Lowe's Food Stores Inc.
Merchants Distributors Inc.
  Consolidation Services Inc.

COMPETITORS

Aldi	Kroger
Associated Wholesale Grocers	Maines
	Mclane
Ben E. Keith	Meadowbrook Meat Company
C&s Wholesale	
Food Lion	Supervalu
H. T. Hackney	Southeastern Grocers
Harris Teeter Supermarkets	Sysco
	Us Foods
Ingles Markets	Wal-mart
K-va-t Food Stores	Winn-dixie

HISTORICAL FINANCIALS

Company Type: Private

Income Statement				FYE: October 3
	REVENUE ($ mil.)	NET INCOME ($ mil.)	NET PROFIT MARGIN	EMPLOYEES
10/20*	3,192	56	1.8%	9,550
09/19	2,286	25	1.1%	—
09/18	2,238	14	0.7%	—
09/17	2,261	4	0.2%	—
Annual Growth	12.2%	130.8%	—	—

*Fiscal year change

2020 Year-End Financials

Return on assets: 5.3%
Return on equity: 10.9%
Current ratio: 1.20
Cash ($ mil.): 44

ALFRED I.DUPONT HOSPITAL FOR CHILDREN

EXECUTIVES

Ceo, Thomas Ferry
V Pres*, Stephen T Lawless
Cfo*, William Britton
Editor, Dustin Samples
Coordinator, Carol Eade-Viele
Coordinator, Julia Morrison
Faculty, Aaron Chidekel
Employee, Audrey Pope
Research Assistant, Petya Yorgova
Pediatrics, Samantha Mumford
Pediatrics, Stephen Shaffer

LOCATIONS

HQ: ALFRED I.DUPONT HOSPITAL FOR CHILDREN
1600 ROCKLAND RD, WILMINGTON, DE 198033607
Phone: 302 651-4000
Web: WWW.NEMOURS.ORG

HISTORICAL FINANCIALS

Company Type: Private

Income Statement				FYE: December 31
	REVENUE ($ mil.)	NET INCOME ($ mil.)	NET PROFIT MARGIN	EMPLOYEES
12/18	553	16	3.0%	3,068
12/17	525	34	6.6%	—
12/16	516	(31)	—	—
12/15	450	28	6.4%	—
Annual Growth	7.1%	(16.3%)	—	—

2018 Year-End Financials

Return on assets: 2.5%
Return on equity: 2.7%
Current ratio: 1.90
Cash ($ mil.): —

ALIEF INDEPENDENT SCHOOL DISTRICT

EXECUTIVES

Supt, H D Chambers
Cfo*, Deanna Wentz
Administrative Assistant, Brian Pilgreen
Management Info Dir, Doug Brown
Administration Manager, Jonell Keller
Coordinator, Laura Klubert
Assistant, Adan C Morales
Health Coordinator, Carleen Johnson
Teacher English, Easton Riley Massie
Administrative Support, Edith Williams
Education, Maria Diaz-Macha
Auditors: WHITLEY PENN LLP HOUSTON TE

LOCATIONS

HQ: ALIEF INDEPENDENT SCHOOL DISTRICT
4250 COOK RD, HOUSTON, TX 770721115
Phone: 281 498-8110
Web: WWW.ALIEFISD.NET

Income Statement				FYE: August 31
	REVENUE ($ mil.)	NET INCOME ($ mil.)	NET PROFIT MARGIN	EMPLOYEES
08/20	559	7	1.3%	6,000
08/19	553	35	6.3%	—
08/18	535	(25)	—	—
08/17	519	(5)	—	—
Annual Growth	2.5%	—	—	—

2020 Year-End Financials

Return on assets: 0.7%   Cash ($ mil.): 199
Return on equity: 15.4%
Current ratio: —

ALLAN MYERS, INC.

American Infrastructure provides heavy civil construction services for projects in the Mid-Atlantic. Operating as Allan A. Myers in Pennsylvania and Delaware and as American Infrastructure in Maryland and Virginia the family-run business builds and reconstructs highways water treatment plants medical facilities and shopping centers and offers site development for homebuilders. Its quarries and asphalt plants operate under the Independence Construction Materials (ICM) subsidiary which supplies aggregates asphalt and ready-mixed concrete to its construction companies. The company is ranked by Engineering News-Record as 25th on the country's Top 50 list of heavy civil contractors.

Operations

American Infrastructure builds projects ranging from $100000 to more than $100 million per project.

As a land developer interested in conservation American Infrastructure offers a unique all-terrain tree spade vehicle that is designed to carry large mature trees harvested from heavily wooded sites intended to be replanted on developed sites. The process allows mature trees to be saved and relocated on a developed site.

Geographic Reach

American Infrastructure and its subsidiaries operate in the Mid-Atlantic region through about 20 locations (including quarries and plants) in Pennsylvania Maryland Virginia Delaware and Washington DC as well as four satellite offices in the region. The company also has 15 materials mining and/or asphalt production facilities in four states.

Sales and Marketing

American Infrastructure serves private developers general contractors departments of transportation utilities local and state governments and federal military customers throughout the Mid-Atlantic region.

Customers include CRB Military Housing Frederick Winchester Service Authority O'Brien & Gere Delaware Department of Transportation The Goldenberg Group Morgan-Keller Construction Forest Park Water Uniwest Construction Divinity Trucking Nardi Construction Hunt Building Company the City of Wilmington and Maryland State Highway Administration.

Strategy

American Infrastructure's financial capacity is strengthened by a bonding capacity of $800 million which allows it to tackle major projects. Selected projects includes Richmond Airport Connector Route 715/40 Interchange Virginia SR 29 Bridge Jersey Shore Pump Station Aberdeen Test Track Argonne Drive Bridge MARC Wedge Railyard Nicodemus Bridge Route 52 Ballenger McKinney wastewater treatment plant and Mount Holly wastewater treatment plant.

Company Background

Some past projects include Eagle Heights at Dover Air Force Base ($13.3 million) Cool Springs Reservoir ($18.6 million) and MD 43 ($46.7 million) in Baltimore County Maryland.

The company was established in 1939 as Allan A. Myers and Son a local hauling company in the suburbs of Philadelphia.

EXECUTIVES

Ceo, A Ross Myers
Pres-Coo*, Richard W Dungan
Exec V Pres*, Robert A Herbein
SEC*, Teresa S Hasson
Treas*, Craig Little
Executive Assistant*, Joyce Harris
Internal Medicine Practitioner, Barrett Terrell
Manager, Chris Thomas
Director, Project Risk, John Schultz
Director of Project Cost, Russ Whiteman
Superintendent, Alan Brittingham
Auditors: PRICEWATERHOUSECOOPERS LLP PH

LOCATIONS

HQ: ALLAN MYERS, INC.
1805 BERKS RD, WORCESTER, PA 19490
Phone: 610 222-8800
Web: WWW.ALLANMYERS.COM

PRODUCTS/OPERATIONS

Selected Services
Site Development
   Concrete flatwork
   Excavation and grading
   Hauling
   Large-diameter tree relocation
   Milling and paving
   Rock drilling and blasting
   Soft dig capabilities
   Stone and curb
   Stormwater management
   Survey and stakeout
   Underground utilities
Transportation
   Asphalt paving
   Box culverts
   Bridges and structures
   Concrete paving
   Maintenance of traffic
Water Resources
   New water/wastewater treatment plants
   Reservoirs and dams
   Underground reservoirs
   Water and sewer transmission lines
   Wetland mitigation and reconstruction

Selected Subsidiaries
Allan A. Myers Inc.
American Infrastructure-Maryland
American Infrastructure-Virginia
Independence Construction Materials

COMPETITORS

Angelo Iafrate	English Construction
Balfour Beatty	Company
Infrastructure	Lane Construction
Barnhill Contracting	Peter Kiewit Sons'
Branch Group	Skanska Usa Civil
Cherry Hill	Traylor Bros.
Construction	Vecellio & Grogan

Income Statement				FYE: December 31
	REVENUE ($ mil.)	NET INCOME ($ mil.)	NET PROFIT MARGIN	EMPLOYEES
12/20	1,025	33	3.3%	2,000
12/19	989	48	5.0%	—
12/17	751	21	2.8%	—
12/16	756	15	2.0%	—
Annual Growth	7.9%	22.2%	—	—

2020 Year-End Financials

Return on assets: 5.3%   Cash ($ mil.): 127
Return on equity: 27.2%
Current ratio: 1.00

ALLEGHENY GENERAL HOSPITAL INC

If there is a critical trauma anywhere near Pittsburgh Allegheny General Hospital (AGH) is ready to take it on. The roughly 630-bed hospital is the Level I Shock Trauma Center for the five-state region surrounding Steel City. AGH offers traditional medical and surgical services as well as cardiology care and organ transplants. The hospital also is engaged in research in areas such as neuroscience oncology trauma and genetics. AGH which treats nearly 22000 patients each year has about 800 physicians on its staff. The hospital which is affiliated with Philadelphia's Drexel University College of Medicine is a subsidiary of Allegheny Health System which itself is owned by Highmark Inc.

Operations

AGH receives more than 50000 emergency visits each year as well as had 300000 outpatient visits and more than 21000 surgical procedures. In order to receive those emergencies in an expedient manner the hospital also operates a LifeFlight aero medical service.

The hospital's cancer center provides programs for a wide range of diseases such as lung breast colon prostate brain and liver cancer.

AGH also operates a smaller satellite facility in the northern Pittsburgh suburb of McCandless as well as an outpatient facility in suburban Pittsburgh.

Strategy

In 2014 AGH proposed investing part of $175 million from Highmark Inc. in renovations and technology upgrades at its AGH and West Penn hospitals anticipating that they will accommodate more patients when Highmark insurance subscribers lose in-network access to the University of Pittsburgh Medical Center in 2015.

Company Background

AGH first opened in 1885.

EXECUTIVES

Ceo, Gregory Burfitt
Cno*, Marcia Cook
Pres*, David Parda
Assistant To President, Diane Nugyen
Director of Pharmacy, Edward C Seidl
Chair Department of Pathology, Jan Silverman
Internal Medicine Practitioner, Christina M Sabeh
Internal Medicine Practitioner, Raman Khehra
Internal Medicine Practitioner, Brin Freund
Internal Medicine Practitioner, Siva K Soma
Anesthesiology, Qin Zhang

LOCATIONS

HQ: ALLEGHENY GENERAL HOSPITAL INC
320 E NORTH AVE, PITTSBURGH, PA 152124772
Phone: 412 359-3131
Web: WWW.AHN.ORG

COMPETITORS

Butler Health System
Excela Health
Heritage Valley Health
Jefferson Regional Medical Center Of Pennsylvania
Ohio Valley General
St. Clair Health
The Western Pennsylvania Hospital
Upmc
Upmc Mercy
Weirton Medical Center

HISTORICAL FINANCIALS

Company Type: Private

Income Statement				FYE: June 30
	REVENUE ($ mil.)	NET INCOME ($ mil.)	NET PROFIT MARGIN	EMPLOYEES
06/16	720	73	10.2%	5,064
06/15	700	107	15.4%	—
Annual Growth	2.8%	(31.7%)	—	—

2016 Year-End Financials

Return on assets: 19.5%   Cash ($ mil.): 1
Return on equity: —
Current ratio: 1.20

ALLEGIS GROUP, INC.

Allegis Group is one of the world's largest staffing and recruitment firms. Among its group of staffing companies are Aerotek (engineering automotive and scientific professionals) Aston Carter (recruitment for accounting finance and professional skills) and TEKsystems (information technology staffing and consulting). Other Allegis Group units include sales support outsourcer MarketSource. Allegis Group operates through more than 500 locations worldwide. Chairman Jim Davis helped found the company (originally known as Aerotek) in 1983 to provide contract engineering personnel to two clients in the aerospace industry.

Operations

Operating through a group of about 10 companies Allegis Group serves businesses and organizations from the engineering automotive finance IT life sciences and other industries. The company also serves government agencies and subcontractors. Aerotek and TEKsystems are among the group's largest and most established companies; other Allegis companies provide niche services including disability recruitment through its Getting Hired unit and legal recruitment though Major Lindsey & Africa.

Allegis Group's core services include staffing and recruitment (screening onboarding and retention) search (CEO and board member services) talent advisory (executive report data file and segment analysis) managed delivery and workforce management.

Geographic Reach

Hanover Maryland-based Allegis Group operates in more than 500 locations around the globe including offices throughout the US the UK and Europe as well as in the Middle East Asia and Asia Pacific region.

Sales and Marketing

Allegis Group has served approximately 20000 clients.

Strategy

Allegis Group has expanded its geographical footprint and improved its position in specialist staffing markets through the use of acquisitions. The company's specialized staffing firms cater to various industries.

Mergers and Acquisitions

In 2016 Allegis Group acquired Switzerland-based staffing recruiting and services organization The Stamford Group. The deal increased Allegis Group's global footprint and strengthened its European presence.

Company Background

In 1983 Stephen Bisciotti and Jim Davis founded the company (originally known as Aerotek) in Maryland. At the time the founders' firm matched job seekers with aeronautics engineering and light industrial positions. In the late 1980s the company expanded into the IT application markets.

Aerotek extended its reach into commercial environmental and energy industries through its 2001 acquisition of Onsite Companies. The company later changed its name to Allegis Group while the other divisions remained separate companies until eventually consolidating under the Allegis Group banner.

EXECUTIVES

Pres, Andy Hilger
Cfo, David Standeven
SEC, Randall D Sones
Coordinator, Francis Buckley
Payroll Staff, Laurie Stanzione
Executive Assistant, Casey Cruz
Program Manager, Dallas Knudson
Sales Manager, David Ruddy
Consultant, Frank Lange
Engineer, Joseph McBride
Manager, Julie McClure
Auditors: PRICEWATERHOUSECOOPERS LLP B

LOCATIONS

HQ: ALLEGIS GROUP, INC.
7301 PARKWAY DR, HANOVER, MD 210761159
Phone: 410 579-3000
Web: WWW.ALLEGISGROUP.COM

PRODUCTS/OPERATIONS

Selected Subsidiaries

Aerotek
  Aerotek Aviation LLC
  Aerotek Canada
  Aerotek Scientific LLC
Allegis Group Canada
Allegis Group India
Major Lindsey & Africa
MarketSource Inc
Stephen James Associates
TEKsystems
  TEKsystems Canada
  TEKsystems Netherlands
  TEKsystems United Kingdom

COMPETITORS

Asg Renaissance	Kelly Services
Adecco	Korn/ferry
Cdi	Manpowergroup
Curran Partners	Rdl Corporation
Execunet	Randstad Holding
Heidrick & Struggles	Robert Half
Horton International	Snelling Staffing
Innovative Management Solutions Group	Volt Information

HISTORICAL FINANCIALS

Company Type: Private

Income Statement				FYE: December 31
	REVENUE ($ mil.)	NET INCOME ($ mil.)	NET PROFIT MARGIN	EMPLOYEES
12/20	12,269	0	—	85,000
12/19	13,583	0	—	—
12/18	13,402	0	—	—
12/17	12,296	0	—	—
Annual Growth	(0.1%)	—	—	—

2020 Year-End Financials

Return on assets: —   Cash ($ mil.): 830
Return on equity: —
Current ratio: 3.00

ALLEGRO MICROSYSTEMS, LLC

Allegro MicroSystems is a leading global designer developer fabless manufacturer and marketer of sensor integrated circuits (ICs) and application-specific analog power ICs enabling critical technologies in the automotive and industrial markets. Its solutions are based on its monolithic Hall effect and xMR technology that allows customers to develop contactless sensor solutions that reduce mechanical wear and provide greater measurement accuracy and system control. The company went public after it closed its initial public offering in 2020.

IPO

In 2020 Allegro MicroSystems Inc. a global leader in sensing and power semiconductor technology announced the closing of its previously announced initial public offering of 28750000 shares of its common stock at a price to the public of $14.00 per share including the full exercise of the underwriters' option to purchase an additional 3750000 shares from certain existing stockholders. Allegro's common stock is listed on the Nasdaq Global Select Market under the ticker symbol "ALGM."

Operations

Allegro operates in one segment which involves the design development production and distribution of various integrated circuits in various markets worldwide. It is a leading supplier of power ICs and a market share leader in magnetic sensor ICs driven by its market leadership in the automotive market. Its products are foundational to automotive and industrial electronic systems. Its sensor ICs enable its customers to precisely measure motion speed position and current while its power ICs include high-temperature and high-voltage capable motor driver power management and light emitting diode (LED) driver ICs. Its recently acquired photonics portfolio provides eye-safe distance measurement and 3D imaging solutions.

Overall magnetic sensors integrated circuits (MS) account for some 5% of sales while the power integrated circuits (PIC) accounts for the rest.

Geographic Reach

Allegro is headquartered in Manchester New Hampshire. The company has design and applications centers located across the Americas Europe Asia and Japan.

Majority of the company's sales were generated in Asia with Japan accounting to about 20% of sales while the Americas and the EMEA region generated over 15% of sales each.

Sales and Marketing
Its products are sold primarily to major global OEMs and their key suppliers primarily in the automotive and industrial markets through a sales channel that includes a direct sales force independent sales representatives and distributors. It also sells its products to over 10000 end customers.

The company's advertising expense was $331 and $273 in fiscal years 2021 and 2020 respectively.

Financial Performance
Total net sales decreased by $58.9 million or 9% to $591.2 million in the fiscal year 2021 (ended March) from $650.1 million in the fiscal year 2020 (ended March). Of this decrease $107.8 million was attributable to the PSL Divestiture which was partially offset by increased net sales to our core end markets of $48.9 million due primarily to increased demand in industrial automation applications and data center applications and a COVID-related increase in demand for printers and other peripherals.

In fiscal year 2021 (ended March) the company had a net income of $18.1 million a 51% decrease compared to the previous year's net income of $37.1 million.

The company's cash at the end of the fiscal year 2021 (ended March) was $203.9 million. Operating activities generated $120.6 million while investing activities used $68.2 million mainly for capital expenditures. Financing activities used another $72.2 million primarily for dividends paid.

Strategy
In 2016 Allegro began a multi-year strategic transition to extend its market leadership in high-growth markets improve its operating model through a fabless and asset-lite manufacturing strategy increase its IC design footprint and capacity and accelerate growth through enhanced sales operations. To date Allegro believes that it has begun to successfully realize many of the key objectives of this transition and the company expects to continue to benefit from measures put in place to further enhance its competitiveness growth and profitability. As part of its strategic transformation Allegro began to streamline manufacturing to reduce fixed costs. This resulted in the recent divestiture of its wafer manufacturing facility Polar Semiconductor LLC (PSL) and the closure of its manufacturing facility in Thailand (the AMTC Facility) as of March 2021.

Mergers and Acquisitions
In 2020 Allegro acquired Oregon-based Voxtel Inc a privately held company specializing in advanced photonic and 3D imaging technology including long-range eye-safe Light Detection and Ranging (LiDAR). This acquisition brings together Voxtel's significant laser and imaging expertise with Allegro's automotive leadership and scale to enable the next generation of Advanced Driver Assistance Systems (ADAS). Terms were not disclosed.

EXECUTIVES

Ceo, Ravi Vig
Cfo*, Mark A Feragne
V Pres*, Andre G Labrecque
Exec V Pres*, Yoshihiro Suzuki
V Pres*, Steven Miles
Treas*, Diane Macaluso
Marketing Manager, Walter Sullivan Jr
Assistant Engineer, Nathan B Baribeau
Layout, Peter Van Hoesen
Assistant Engineer, Patricia Borglund
Tech, Edward Beaudoin

LOCATIONS

HQ: ALLEGRO MICROSYSTEMS, LLC
955 PERIMETER RD, MANCHESTER, NH 031033353
Phone: 603 626-2300
Web: WWW.ALLEGROMICRO.COM

PRODUCTS/OPERATIONS

Selected Products
Current sensor integrated circuits (ICs)
  Conductor sensor chips
  High-side hot-swap Hall-effect current monitor chips
Magnetic digital position sensor chips
  Bipolar switches
  Dual-element switches
  Hall-effect latches and bipolar switches
  Hall-effect unipolar switches
  Micropower switches and latches
Magnetic linear and angular position sensor chips
  Angular position sensor chips
  Linear position sensor chips
Magnetic speed sensor ICs (camshaft crankshaft transmission and wheel-speed sensor ICs)
Motor driver and interface ICs
  Bipolar stepper motor drivers
  Brushless DC motor drivers
  Photo and ion smoke detector ICs
Regulators and lighting
  LED drivers for backlighting and lighting
  Regulators (single-output multiple output low-noise block)
  Xenon photoflash drivers

COMPETITORS

Fairchild Semiconductor	Nxp Semiconductors
Honeywell	On Semiconductor
International	Optek Technology
Infineon Technologies	Power Integrations
Maxim Integrated Products	Stmicroelectronics
Micronas Semiconductor	Sypris Solutions
Micropac Industries	Texas Instruments
Nve	Toshiba Semiconductor & Storage Products
	Vishay Intertechnology

HISTORICAL FINANCIALS
Company Type: Private

Income Statement
FYE: March 30

	REVENUE ($ mil.)	NET INCOME ($ mil.)	NET PROFIT MARGIN	EMPLOYEES
03/18	654	72	11.1%	3,500
03/17	600	65	10.9%	—
03/16	526	43	8.3%	—
03/13	489	45	9.3%	—
Annual Growth	6.0%	9.7%	—	—

2018 Year-End Financials

Return on assets: 12.1%   Cash ($ mil.): 114
Return on equity: 14.8%
Current ratio: 3.40

ALLEN LUND COMPANY, LLC

The Allen Lund Company (ALC) knows loads; it matches shippers' loads with a network of truckload and less-than-truckload (LTL) carriers. (LTL carriers collect consolidate and haul freight from multiple shippers.) The brokerage firm arranges the transport of dry refrigerated (predominantly produce) and flatbed cargo. It operates from 30 offices throughout more than 20 US states. ALC Logistics ALC Perishable Logistics and ALC International (an international division) assist shippers in managing transportation costs tracking and tracing shipments managing appointments and executing freight forward management services overseas. The company was founded in 1976 by Allen Lund and his wife Kathie Lund.

Operations
ALC has a Logistics & Software division ALC Logistics.

Geographic Reach
The company's international division provides transportation services worldwide along with transportation to and from the US including Puerto Rico Hawaii Alaska and ground transportation for Canada and Mexico.

Strategy
In an effort to expand its operation in 2012 the company opened a new office in Joplin Missouri and another in McAllen Texas which mainly focuses on handling heavy haul flatbed particularly in and out of Mexico. In addition the company opened four additional offices in 2012.

Mergers and Acquisitions
In an effort to grow its business in early 2014 ALC acquired Wisconsin based Northern Freight Service Inc. a company provides truckload LTL and intermodal services to the customers ranging from small shippers to FORTUNE 500 shippers.

EXECUTIVES

Mng MBR, D Allen Lund
MBR*, David F Lund
MBR*, Kathleen M Lund
MBR*, Edward V Lund
MBR*, Steve Doerfler
Benefits Manager, Pam Stumbaugh
Customer Representativ, Margaret McHugh
Manager, Ashley Riddle
Sales Staff, Greg Babiarz
Broker, Aaron Field
Broker, Joshua Meyer

LOCATIONS

HQ: ALLEN LUND COMPANY, LLC
4529 ANGELES CREST HWY, LA CANADA FLINTRIDGE, CA 910113247
Phone: 818 790-8412
Web: WWW.ALLENLUND.COM

PRODUCTS/OPERATIONS

Selected Services
Software and Logistics
  LTL Freight
  Scheduling
  Spot Pricing and Bid Management
  Truck Load
Transportation Services
  Dry Van
  Flatbed Trucking
  International Freight Shipping
  LTL Freight
  Refrigerated Transportation

COMPETITORS

C.h. Robinson Worldwide	Ryder System
Ceva Logistics	Universal Logistics

HISTORICAL FINANCIALS
Company Type: Private

Income Statement
FYE: December 31

	REVENUE ($ mil.)	NET INCOME ($ mil.)	NET PROFIT MARGIN	EMPLOYEES
12/18	661	20	3.0%	310
12/17	515	10	2.0%	—
12/16	426	12	2.9%	—
12/15	457	13	2.9%	—
Annual Growth	13.1%	15.1%	—	—

2018 Year-End Financials
Return on assets: 19.6%   Cash ($ mil.): 32
Return on equity: 44.0%
Current ratio: 1.70

ALLIANCE LAUNDRY HOLDINGS LLC

Laundry day can't come often enough for Alliance Laundry Holdings (ALH). Through its wholly owned subsidiary Alliance Laundry Systems the company designs makes and markets commercial laundry equipment used in Laundromats multi-housing laundry facilities (such as apartments dormitories and military bases) and on-premise laundries (hotels hospitals and prisons). Its washers and dryers are sold under the brands Speed Queen UniMac Huebsch IPSO and Cissell. They're sold primarily in the US and Canada but also overseas. Investment firm BDT Capital Partners controls the company which was founded in 1908.

Operations
Commercial laundry equipment service and parts account for 98% of the firm's revenue. It also operates an equipment financing business which accounts for the rest.

Geographic Reach
North America is Wisconsin-based ALH's largest market accounting for about 70% of sales. Europe and Asia each represent about 10% of sales. The remainder comes from markets in Latin America the Middle East and Africa. The company's manufacturing facilities are located in Wisconsin and Wevelgem Belgium.

Sales and Marketing
ALH relies on an expansive distribution network to bring its goods to market. The company's more than 550 distributors in North America and 150-plus international distributors serve its Laundromat and on-premise laundry customers. Its multi-family housing laundry customers are served by ALH's roster of more than 100 route operators.

Financial Performance
The company's sales topped $505 million in 2012 a 10% increase compared with 2011. Net income fell 30% over the same period to $16.4 million as a result of a loss from early retirement of debt and higher expenses. The company attributed the gain in sales (its third in as many years) to increases across all of its markets with the exception of Europe. Increased sales volumes and price increases primarily in the US and Canada drove results. The strong performance over the past three years pushed sales to an all-time high following a drop-off during the recession.

Strategy
Despite difficult economic conditions globally ALH has seen its business strengthen driven by resilience in North America and international expansion. (The company is fortunate that consumers view clean clothes as an necessity with economic conditions historically having limited effect on frequency of use of commercial laundry equipment.) In the US and Canada the equipment financing business is posting higher earnings and demand for commercial laundry equipment is rising. Markets in Latin America including Colombia Peru and Venezuela are driving double-digit sales growth in the region. Expansion in Asia in such markets as Australia China the Philippines and Thailand is another growth driver.

In pursuit of future growth in 2013 the company completed a $23 million investment to increase production capacity for current and new products and to purchase tooling and equipment for its plant in Wisconsin. The expansion added more than 20000 square feet to the plant's existing assembly metal stampingand press shop facilities. The project increased ALH's production capacity for small chassis washers and dryers by more than 40% enabling the company to meet increasing consumer demand for its products.

EXECUTIVES
Chief Financial Officer, Vice President, Bruce Rounds
Vice Chairman Of The Board, Thomas L'Esperance, $397,512 total compensation
Senior Vice President, North America, Jeffrey Brothers
Vice President - Engineering, Robert Baudhuin
Vice President - International Sales, Richard Pyle
Director, J. Hugh MacDiarmid
Vice President, General Manager - Ripon Operations, R. Scott Gaster
Vice President - Operations Of Alliance International Bvba, Pascal Demarets
Chairman Of The Board, Lino Sienna
Director, Shael Dolman
Vice President, Chief Legal Officer And Secretary, Scott Spiller
Director, Charles Philippin
President, Chief Executive Officer, Michael Schoeb
Auditors: PRICEWATERHOUSECOOPERS MILWAU

LOCATIONS
HQ: ALLIANCE LAUNDRY HOLDINGS LLC
221 SHEPARD ST, RIPON, WI 549711390
Phone: 920 748-3121
Web: WWW.ALLIANCELAUNDRY.COM

COMPETITORS
Bsh Bosch Und Siemens Hausger ㅁte	Haier Group
Electrolux	Miele
Ge Appliances & Lighting	Whirlpool

HISTORICAL FINANCIALS
Company Type: Private

Income Statement   FYE: December 31

	REVENUE ($ mil.)	NET INCOME ($ mil.)	NET PROFIT MARGIN	EMPLOYEES
12/14	726	29	4.1%	2,100
12/12	505	16	3.2%	—
12/09	393	16	4.2%	—
Annual Growth	13.1%	12.3%	—	—

2014 Year-End Financials
Return on assets: 2.4%   Cash ($ mil.): 48
Return on equity: 31.0%
Current ratio: 1.40

ALLIED SECURITY HOLDINGS LLC

Better than a blanket Allied Security Holdings gives customers a sense of security. One of the largest private contract security firms in the US it does business as AlliedBarton Security Services. It recruits and employs trained security guards to serve thousands of customers (some of which are large FORTUNE 500 companies) and their facilities. They include government facilities hospitals offices ports residential communities shopping centers and universities. The firm also provides employment and background screening services through its HR Plus subsidiary. In mid-2016 AlliedBarton merged with Universal Services of America to create Allied Universal North America's largest security services group.

Geographic Reach
Allied Security Holdings operates through more than 120 regional and district offices nationwide.

Strategy
In the last few years the company has made strides to further build out its service offerings both organically and through acquisitions expand its geographic footprint across the US and increase the number of industries and types of facilities that it serves.

EXECUTIVES
Ceo-MBR, William C Whitmore Jr
Cfo-Svp*, William A Torzolini
Evp, David I Buckman
MBR-Treas*, James W Lennon
MBR*, Kim Gorman
Supervisor, Bruce Thompson
Customer Manager, Kathy Wicks
Network Operations Manager, Carlos Medina
Director, Contracts, Donald McAvoy
Program Manager, Leg Safety, Patricia Lee
Business Manager, Ryan Lacek

LOCATIONS
HQ: ALLIED SECURITY HOLDINGS LLC
161 WASHINGTON ST STE 600, CONSHOHOCKEN, PA 194282083
Phone: 484 351-1300
Web: WWW.AUS.COM

COMPETITORS
Afi International	Kroll
Asset Protection & Security Services	Securitas
Command Security	Transnational Security
G4s Secure Solutions	Walden Security
Guardsmark	Whelan Security

HISTORICAL FINANCIALS
Company Type: Private

Income Statement   FYE: December 31

	REVENUE ($ mil.)	NET INCOME ($ mil.)	NET PROFIT MARGIN	EMPLOYEES
12/14	2,149	24	1.1%	53,760
12/13	2,042	51	2.5%	—
12/12	1,923	43	2.3%	—
Annual Growth	5.7%	(25.0%)	—	—

2014 Year-End Financials
Return on assets: 2.6%   Cash ($ mil.): 51
Return on equity: —
Current ratio: 1.80

ALLIED UNIVERSAL HOLDCO LLC

EXECUTIVES

Ceo, Steve Jones
Global Cfo, Tim Brandt
Business Manager, Stephen Wright
General Manager, Greg Feldman
Client Manager, Dionta Moody
Branch Manager, Justin Vinyard
Account Manager, David Muse
Regional Vice President, Rafael Sorto
Director, Benefits, Vivian Maguire
Security Officer, William Stewart

LOCATIONS

HQ: ALLIED UNIVERSAL HOLDCO LLC
1551 N TUSTIN AVE STE 650, SANTA ANA, CA
927058664
Phone: 866 877-1965
Web: WWW.AUS.COM

HISTORICAL FINANCIALS

Company Type: Private

Income Statement				FYE: December 31
	ASSETS ($ mil.)	NET INCOME ($ mil.)	INCOME AS % OF ASSETS	EMPLOYEES
12/20	7,216	(84)	—	188,000
12/19	6,432	(381)	—	—
12/17	4,451	(69)	—	—
Annual Growth	17.5%	—	—	—

2020 Year-End Financials

Return on assets: (-1.2%)
Return on equity: (-19.5%)
Sales ($ mil): 8,501

ALLWAYS HEALTH PARTNERS, INC.

AllWays Health Partners previously known as Neighborhood Health Plan (NHP) packages and delivers innovative products and programs that improve the experience of accessing care and coverage and health outcomes. AllWays Health Partners offers health plans for small businesses large groups and families and individuals. The company offers Value HMO for Boston employees and retirees ensuring access to the highest quality care. The Value HMO networks include Massachusetts General Hospital Brigham and Women's Hospital Beth Israel Deaconess Medical Center Lahey Clinic Spaulding Rehab Mass Eye and Ear and more.

EXECUTIVES

Pres-Ceo, Deborah Enos
V Pres, Carla Bettano
Chief Customer Officer, Katie Catlender
V Pres, Jill D Arbeloff
Cfo, Garrett Parker
Controller, Charles Helstrom
Compliance, Doug Thompson
Vice President of Clinical Ope, Deb Bonin
Security Staff, Doug Demio
Manager of Pharmacy Operations, Kim Wong
Technology, Bill Nolan

LOCATIONS

HQ: ALLWAYS HEALTH PARTNERS, INC.
399 REVOLUTION DR, SOMERVILLE, MA 021451484
Phone: 617 772-5500
Web: WWW.NHP.ORG

COMPETITORS

Aetna
Blue Cross And Blue Shield Of Massachusetts
Cigna
Connecticare
Fallon Community Health Plan
Harvard Pilgrim
Health New England
Mvp Health Plan
Tufts Health Plan
Unitedhealth Group

HISTORICAL FINANCIALS

Company Type: Private

Income Statement				FYE: December 31
	REVENUE ($ mil.)	NET INCOME ($ mil.)	NET PROFIT MARGIN	EMPLOYEES
12/15	2,178	(22)	—	340
12/14	1,743	(108)	—	—
12/13	1,380	(68)	—	—
Annual Growth	25.6%	—	—	—

2015 Year-End Financials

Return on assets: (-4.9%)
Return on equity: (-11.6%)
Current ratio: 0.90
Cash ($ mil.): 120

ALLY BANK

Ally Bank is on your side when it comes to banking. Formerly known as GMAC Bank Ally Bank (which is a subsidiary of government-backed Ally Financial) offers savings and money market accounts as well as traditional and no-penalty CDs. The online bank also offers interest checking accounts. The bank offers its services online and over the phone; it operates no physical branch locations. Clients also can use any ATM in the US and Ally will reimburse any fees charged by other banks. Ally Bank was revamped and renamed in 2009 in the midst of GM's (very public) financial difficulties. Predecessor GMAC Bank had been in operation since 2001.

EXECUTIVES

Chb-Pres-Ceo, Diane E Morais
Exec V Pres, Jeffrey J Brown
Cfo, James N Young
SEC, Cathy L Quenneville
Director of Remarketing Sales, Mark Juday
Area Sales Manager, Anthony Stoothoff
CRA Officer, Jan Bergeson
Senior Credit Manager, Anthony Zimmer
Claims Operations Supervisor, Angelo Douvris
Assistant Controller, Brent Young
Underwriter, Christine McMahon

LOCATIONS

HQ: ALLY BANK
6985 S UNION PARK CTR # 435, MIDVALE, UT
840474177
Phone: 801 790-5005
Web: WWW.ALLY.COM

COMPETITORS

Bank Of America	Citibank
Bofi	E*trade Bank
Charles Schwab	State Farm

HISTORICAL FINANCIALS

Company Type: Private

Income Statement				FYE: December 31
	ASSETS ($ mil.)	NET INCOME ($ mil.)	INCOME AS % OF ASSETS	EMPLOYEES
12/16	123,547	1,273	1.0%	42
12/07*	28,472	291	1.0%	—
06/06	3,586	0	0.0%	—
Annual Growth	38.0%	114.3%	—	—

*Fiscal year change

2016 Year-End Financials

Return on assets: 1.0%
Return on equity: 7.2%
Sales ($ mil): 6,427

ALMOST FAMILY, INC.

Almost Family steps in when you're more than an arm's reach from family members with health needs. With its home health nursing services Almost Family offers senior citizens in 26 states (including Florida) an alternative to institutional care. Its Visiting Nurse unit provides skilled nursing care and therapy services at home under a variety of names including Apex Caretenders Community Home Health and Mederi-Caretenders. Its Personal Care Services segment operating under the Almost Family banner offers custodial care such as housekeeping meal preparation and medication management. Almost Family operates 175 Visiting Nurse agencies and about 65 Personal Care Services locations. The company is merging with LHC Group.

Operations

The company's services are carried out by nurses speech and occupational therapists medical social workers and home health aides. The services provided to a patient are determined by physician's prescribed plan of care — generally issued upon the patient's discharge from a hospital. Payments from Medicare account for 93% of revenue in the Visiting Nurse segment making Almost Family sensitive to any changes in Medicare reimbursement policies. The Personal Care segment receives 86% of its revenues from Medicare payments with the balance coming from private insurance private pay and Medicaid. This diversification of reimbursement risk is intentional but the company is also confident that its home-based services will always be lower in cost than institutional care.

Geographic Reach

As part of its business Kentucky-based Almost Family extends its reach to 16 states in the Northeast Southeast and Midwest. Florida Ohio and Tennessee are the company's three largest markets (in order of revenue significance).

Financial Performance

Almost Family posted a 4% rise in revenue in 2013 compared to 2012 to $357.8 million on a 4% increase in the Visiting Nurse segment primarily due to a pair of acquisitions (both in 2013) and an increase in service revenues. The company's Personal Care business which accounted for 23% of revenue in 2013 posted a 6% gain on incremental revenue from an acquisition as well as organic volume growth. Net income slid 52% year over year to $8.2 million in 2013 on higher expenses due to an increase in the provision for uncollectable commercial accounts and denials by Medicare. (Medicare is the company's single largest source of revenue accounting for about 71% of revenue in 2013.)

Strategy

As the health care industry grows and consolidates Almost Family is looking to grow through acquisitions and continue to open home health care agencies in existing and new markets. Its expansion is focused on the eastern US. In late 2013 the company made the largest acquisition in its history: SunCrest.

Mergers and Acquisitions

In 2015 the company had its most acquisitive year ever. It acquired Willcare Health Care adding to its operations in New York and elsewhere; it built up its operations in Ohio with the $40 million purchase of Black Stone Operations (which operates under the brand name Home Care by Black Stone). It also bought New Jersey-based Bayonne VNA Home Health Agency and Massachusetts-based Long Term Solutions (in-home nursing assessments for the insurance industry) both for undisclosed amounts.

In early 2017 Almost Family bought an 80% stake in Community Health Systems' (CHS') home health and hospice unit for $128 million. That business includes 74 home health locations and 15 hospice centers in 22 states. After that purchase Almost Family became the third-largest Medicare home health provider in the nation. Together with CHS the company provides services to some 50000 patients daily.

In 2017 Almost Family agreed to merge with LHC Group. After the merger LHC shareholders will own 58.5% of the combined entity while Almost Family shareholders will own the rest.

HISTORY

Almost Family was founded in 1976 as National Health Industries a Louisville Kentucky-based home health care company. After William Yarmuth became president in 1981 he expanded the company into such service areas as home infusion and home medical equipment.

The company became Caretenders Health in 1985 and in 1991 the company merged with Senior Service Corporation a small public adult day care services company. The company further expanded the range of services it offered to the elderly through its home health care operations. It established beachheads in new geographic markets by opening home health offices (or buying them) and then adding day care centers. It also bought some existing care centers.

The company grew energetically following its decision to specialize in elder care. It made three acquisitions in 1997 and surpassed that feat by closing on four acquisitions in little over a month in early 1998. The company lost one of its revenue streams that year: Two home health agencies in the Louisville area that had been managed by Caretenders were sold by their owner Columbia/HCA (now HCA). Caretenders sued Columbia/HCA for breach of contract and in 1999 won a $1.5 million settlement.

That year the company also sharpened its focus by selling its product operations (including infusion therapy respiratory and medical equipment) to Lincare Holdings but decided not to discontinue its visiting nurses services.

In 2000 the company changed its name to Almost Family to underscore its focus on adult day care. The following year it bought back the 23% stake that rehabilitation titan HEALTHSOUTH had maintained in the company.

EXECUTIVES

Pres, Steven Guenthner
Graphic Designer, Lisa Landers
Senior Living Coordinator, Jackie Alexander
Account Executive, Bob Magowan
Quality Director Clinical Serv, Carol Morley
Team Lead, Holly Pardo
Desktop Support Specialist, Jordan Logsdon
Corporate Marketing Manager, Marygen Boley
AP Specialist, Antonette Moore
Account Executive, Ashley Amundsen
Authorization, Betty Muller
Auditors: ERNST & YOUNG LLP LOUISVILLE

LOCATIONS

HQ: ALMOST FAMILY, INC.
  9510 ORMSBY STATION RD # 300, LOUISVILLE, KY 402235016
Phone: 502 891-1000
Web: WWW.ALMOSTFAMILY.COM

HISTORICAL FINANCIALS
Company Type: Private

Income Statement				FYE: December 29
	REVENUE ($ mil.)	NET INCOME ($ mil.)	NET PROFIT MARGIN	EMPLOYEES
12/17	796	20	2.6%	14,200
12/16*	623	18	2.9%	—
01/16	532	19	3.7%	—
12/14	495	13	2.7%	—
Annual Growth	17.1%	14.7%	—	—

*Fiscal year change

2017 Year-End Financials

Return on assets: 2.8%   Cash ($ mil.): 11
Return on equity: 4.0%
Current ratio: 2.00

ALPINE SCHOOL DISTRICT

EXECUTIVES

Supt, Vern Henshaw
Supt, Samuel Y Jarman
Coordinator, Alex Goold
Accounting Staff, Steven Reese
Public Information Director, David Stephenson
Coordinator, Barbara Langford
Director, Adam Dajany
Research/Development Director, David Mower
Director of Teacher Personnel, John Spencer
Administrative Vice President, Jim Melville
Transportation Director, DOT Dean
Auditors: SQUIRER & COMPANY PC OREM U

LOCATIONS

HQ: ALPINE SCHOOL DISTRICT
  575 N 100 E, AMERICAN FORK, UT 840031758
Phone: 801 610-8400

HISTORICAL FINANCIALS
Company Type: Private

Income Statement				FYE: June 30
	REVENUE ($ mil.)	NET INCOME ($ mil.)	NET PROFIT MARGIN	EMPLOYEES
06/21	821	(38)	—	8,000
06/20	757	(78)	—	—
06/19	726	(44)	—	—
06/18	680	77	11.4%	—
Annual Growth	6.5%			

ALRO STEEL CORPORATION

Alro Steel runs its service centers like a grocery store for metals keeping what customers need in easy reach. The service center operator which has a dozen facilities in the US Northeast Midwest and Southeast provides processing services such as aluminum circle cutting CNC flame cutting forming and machining. The company carries an extensive inventory of steel products along with industrial tools and supplies. It also offers plastic sheet rod tube and film through its Alro Plastics division and distributes industrial tools and materials through subsidiary Alro Industrial Supplies.

Operations

Led by its steel activities Alro Steel operates several other businesses: Alro Metals Service Center Alro Metals Plus (steel bars plates and sheet and brass copper aluminum and other products); Alro Plastics (fiberglass acrylics nylon urethanes and other); and Alro Industrial Supplies (threading milling boring holemaking reaming and other machinery and equipment).

Geographic Reach

Alro Steel has more than 50 facilities in 12 US states (Florida Illinois Indiana Kentucky Michigan Missouri New York North Carolina Ohio Oklahoma Pennsylvania and Wisconsin).

Sales and Marketing

The company distributes metals industrial supplies and plastics through its online store.

Strategy

Alro Steel is expanding its operations to meet demand.

In 2014 the company expanded its presence in Greensboro North Carolina by opening a 42000-sq.-ft. facility. It plans to potentially double the work force there within five years.

In 2013 it opened a new 70000 sq. ft. facility in St. Louis to provide regional manufacturers with Alro's broad range of metal products and extensive processing capabilities. That year the company also opened a new 98000 sq. ft. facility in Imperial Pennsylvania to serve manufacturers in western and central Pennsylvania and northern West Virginia.

Company Background

The company was established in 1948.

EXECUTIVES

Ceo, Alvin Glick
Pres, David Schmidt
E V Pres, Randy Glick
Cfo, Steve Laten
Treas, Jim Norman
V Chm, Barry Glick
V Pres-Admin, John Rumler
Administrative Assistant, Farrah Bertrand
Inside Sales, Melissa Jenkins
Sales, Mike Austin
Manager, David Ward
Auditors: DELOITTE & TOUCHE LLP DETRO

LOCATIONS

HQ: ALRO STEEL CORPORATION
  3100 E HIGH ST, JACKSON, MI 492036413
Phone: 517 787-5500
Web: WWW.ALROSTEEL.COM

COMPETITORS

Carlisle Companies	Mill Steel
Central Steel & Wire	Peerless Steel
Contractors Steel	
Flame Metals Processing	

Income Statement				FYE: May 31
	REVENUE ($ mil.)	NET INCOME ($ mil.)	NET PROFIT MARGIN	EMPLOYEES
05/20	1,941	149	7.7%	2,400
05/19	2,213	198	9.0%	—
05/18	1,989	165	8.3%	—
Annual Growth	(1.2%)	(5.1%)	—	—

ALSCO INC.

Alsco is a global leader in uniform and linen rental services. Operating from more than 180 branches in about 15 countries worldwide the company rents and sells uniforms linens towels napkins and soft blankets to more than 355000 customers worldwide. It also manages janitorial services provides washroom supplies and soap and sanitizer services. In addition Alsco provides professional textile rental services and offers First aid that is fresh and budget friendly. The company was founded in 1889 by George Steiner and is still owned and operated by the Steiner family. It is headquartered in Utah and has locations in Australia Brazil Canada China Germany Italy New Zealand Singapore Malaysia Thailand and the US.

Operations

Alsco provides products and services for linens uniforms floorcare washroom supplies and first-aid among others. In addition the company also offers isolation gowns face masks clean shield and disposable gloves.

Geographic Reach

Headquartered in Salt Lake City Utah Alsco operates in more than 180 locations around the world.

Sales and Marketing

Alsco serves customers in various industries including automotive building services food processing facilities food and beverage healthcare restaurant and industrial sectors. The company sell its products through its retail stores located across North America.

Strategy

In early 2022 Our Motorsports is proud to announce a partnership with Alsco Uniforms. The Utah-based company has signed a multi-race agreement with Jeb Burton and Our Motorsports. Alsco is the leader in providing rental services for uniforms linens floor mats first aid cabinets and restroom supplies to many businesses across North America including Our Motorsports.

In mid-2021 Alsco Uniforms the official uniform provider of race fans and a proud partner of Charlotte Motor Speedway (CMS) brings aboard long-time partner Darden Restaurants and its Long-Horn Steakhouse brand as presenting sponsor of the May NASCAR Xfinity Series (NXS) race.

EXECUTIVES

Pres, Robert Steiner
Dir*, Kevin Steiner
Treas*, James Kearns
Treas*, Shada Maple
Dir*, Victor Lund
Chief Engineer, Larry Galusha
Director Human Resources, Bettie Wicks
Direct Sales Manager, Cindy Janecek
Internal Audit Manager, Gary Hallman
Software Manager, Paul Charlson
Asst Office Mgr, Debra Harms

LOCATIONS

HQ: ALSCO INC.
505 E 200 S STE 101, SALT LAKE CITY, UT 841022053
Phone: 801 328-8831
Web: WWW.ALSCO.COM

PRODUCTS/OPERATIONS

Selected Products and Services
Clean room garments
Gown room management
Hospitality/restaurant apparel
Laundry services
Linens
Mats
Mops
Napkins
Restroom service
Towels
Uniform rental and sales
Vacuum filters
Washroom supplies

COMPETITORS

Aramark	Iss A/s
Angelica Corporation	Rentokil Initial
Berendsen	Servicemaster
Cintas	Sodexo Usa
Crothall Healthcare	Superior Uniform Group
Diversey	Swisher Hygiene
Ecolab	Tranzonic
G&k Services	Unifirst
Healthcare Services	

HISTORICAL FINANCIALS
Company Type: Private

Income Statement				FYE: December 31
	REVENUE ($ mil.)	NET INCOME ($ mil.)	NET PROFIT MARGIN	EMPLOYEES
12/17	892	64	7.2%	16,000
12/16	704	38	5.5%	—
12/15	683	30	4.5%	—
Annual Growth	14.3%	45.2%	—	—

2017 Year-End Financials

Return on assets: 5.2%   Cash ($ mil.): 22
Return on equity: 8.1%
Current ratio: 1.70

ALSTON CONSTRUCTION COMPANY, INC.

Alston Construction (formerly Panattoni Construction) offers a broad platform of general contracting construction management design-build services and virtual design management construction. The company serves a diverse array of industries including healthcare food and beverage industrial office athletic facilities and retail among others. Refurbishing and extending buildings from its network of offices throughout the US Alston Construction provides construction management services for such clients as Amazon.com Bridgestone Caterpillar Clorox FedEx Petco Helen of Troy Under Armour and Whirlpool. Completed approximately 6010 projects Alston Construction started in 1986.

Operations

Alston Construction has partnerships with designers subcontractors consultants local communities architects engineers and construction professionals. Its construction management offer is based on shared risk and as a result offers clients maximum flexibility. Alston offers Building Information Modeling (BIM) and Virtual Design & Construction (VDC) services in-house and it can forecasts conflicts minimize clashes and avoid inevitable delays. Its VDC Specialists use the latest technology in scanning modeling and virtual design.

Among its projects include Aggieland Fitness Artesian Spa Beal Bank Beltway 8 Interiors and Brooklyn Bedding HQ.

Geographic Reach

Based in the US Alston Construction operates from nearly 20 offices in Arizona California Florida Georgia Illinois Indiana and Washington among others.

Sales and Marketing

Alston Construction serves a wide array of industries that include government manufacturing education senior living interiors warehouse and distribution and commercial offices. Its clients include Bestbuy Big 5 Campbells J.Crew Kellogs Proctor & Gamble Volkswagon Disney and more.

EXECUTIVES

Ceo, Paul Little
Ceo*, Paul David Little
V Pres*, Evan Hamilton
Cfo*, Adam Nickerson
Regional Manager, Fat Peinado
Accounting Staff, Angel Kaminski
Executive Administrative Assis, Anna Logue
Senior Engineer, Randy Forgeur
Executive Assistant, Kelli Doyle
Preconstruction Manager, Kevin Daughtry
Regional Safety Coordinator, Dustin Gayton
Auditors: CAMPBELL TAYLOR WASHBURN ROSE

LOCATIONS

HQ: ALSTON CONSTRUCTION COMPANY, INC.
8775 FOLSOM BLVD STE 201, SACRAMENTO, CA 958263725
Phone: 916 340-2400
Web: WWW.ALSTONCO.COM

COMPETITORS

Alter Group	H And M Construction
Balfour Beatty Construction	Kprs Construction
	Skanska Usa Building
Bechtel	Turner Corporation
Fluor	

HISTORICAL FINANCIALS
Company Type: Private

Income Statement				FYE: December 31
	REVENUE ($ mil.)	NET INCOME ($ mil.)	NET PROFIT MARGIN	EMPLOYEES
12/19	1,271	18	1.5%	200
12/18	909	14	1.6%	—
12/17	865	13	1.6%	—
12/15	642	6	1.1%	—
Annual Growth	18.6%	28.4%	—	—

2019 Year-End Financials

Return on assets: 5.8%   Cash ($ mil.): 50
Return on equity: 54.2%
Current ratio: 1.10

ALTICOR INC.

Where there's a will (and an army of independent sales representatives) there's Amway. Operated through holding company Alticor Amway is the world's top direct-selling company with millions of individual ABOs (Amway Business Owners) pitching everything from air filters to vitamins. The company makes some 450 unique products across the categories of nutrition (which generates about half of sales) beauty and personal care and home. It is active in more than 100 countries across the globe with Asia (led by China) its largest market. Alticor is controlled by the families of Rich DeVos and Jay Van Andel who founded Amway in 1959.

Operations

Nutrition products (supplements skin care products weight management programs) account for about 50% of total Amway sales. Beauty and personal care items (makeup shampoo toothpaste) generate about a quarter of sales and home products (water and air filters cookware cleaners) contribute about 20%. The company's top products include Nutrilite supplements Artistry color cosmetics eSpring water treatment systems and XS energy drinks.

Geographic Reach

Based in Ada Michigan Amway operates in more than 100 countries. Its top markets by sales are China the US and South Korea; other leading markets include India Japan Malaysia Russia Taiwan and Thailand.

The company has manufacturing facilities farms and warehouses in Brazil China Hungary India Japan Mexico the Netherlands Poland Russia South Korea Taiwan Thailand Vietnam and the US.

Sales and Marketing

Amway's 450-plus products are marketing worldwide by more than 3 million independent distributors who purchase the products and resell them. The company provides a host of support services including personal mentors brand centers online learning tools and call centers.

Financial Performance

While privately-owned Alticor doesn't report full results Amway reported global sales of $8.6 billion in 2017 down from $8.8 billion in 2016. The company points to a challenging Chinese market for its revenue decline over the past few years

Strategy

Amway's strategy is pretty straight-forward: continue to enhance and expand its line of products to serve more markets and appeal to more customers and create tools that make selling those products easier for the 3+ million ABOs (Amway Business Owners).

In 2017 Amway introduced a new formula for its Nutrilife Double X product one of the best-selling supplements in the world that includes a phytonutrient blend designed to help the body fight free radicals. Other additions to the company's product portfolio that year include a reformulated Essentials by Artistry skincare line and its first in-car air filtration system Atmosphere Drive. Amway also pushed its XS brand of energy drinks into new countries in 2017 including China and India with more launches planned for 2018. The company has more than 800 patents worldwide and another 250 pending applications.

Direct selling of course looks a lot different in the age of Amazon than it did some 60 years ago when Amway was founded. The company has been making significant investment in tools and technologies in recent years to enable its ABOs to better compete. It has spent some $70 million in mobile apps for ABOs including the flagship Amway MyBiz app which provides back office data and analytics. In addition Amway has boosted its own customer service capabilities with instant messaging bots and other technologies to help it handle the more than 12 million annual customer requests. Other recent initiatives include a content sharing app for ABOs in the Philippines a beauty app for customers in South Korea and a one-stop product education and purchase portal in for ABOs in China.

Mergers and Acquisitions

EXECUTIVES

Chm, Steve Van Andel
Pres, Richard M Devos Sr
Pres, Doug Devos
V Pres, Robert P Hunter
Exec V Pres-Cfo, Michael Cazer
SEC, Michael A Mohr
Tres, Jeffery C Tuori
Scientist, Bob Faber
Other, Tanios Viviani
Manager, Heather Imbault
Manager, Jon Sprau

LOCATIONS

HQ: ALTICOR INC.
7575 FULTON ST E, ADA, MI 493550001
Phone: 616 787-1000
Web: WWW.AMWAY.COM

PRODUCTS/OPERATIONS

2017 Sales

	% of total
Nutrition	50
Beauty & personal care	26
Home	21
Other	3
Total	**100**

Selected Brands

Nutrition
  Nutrilite
Beauty & personal care
  Artistry
  G&H
  Glister
  Satinique
Home
  Amway Home
  Atmosphere Sky
  eSpring
  iCook
Other
  XS

COMPETITORS

Avon	Melaleuca
Bath & Body Works	New Avon
Bluestem Brands	Newell Brands
Colgate-palmolive	Nikken
Est ©e Lauder	Nu Skin
Forever Living	Procter & Gamble
Gnc	Revlon
Herbalife Ltd.	Shaklee
Johnson & Johnson	Tupperware Brands
L'or ©al	Unilever Plc
Mary Kay	

HISTORICAL FINANCIALS

Company Type: Private

Income Statement				FYE: December 31
	REVENUE ($ mil.)	NET INCOME ($ mil.)	NET PROFIT MARGIN	EMPLOYEES
12/15	9,459	0	—	14,000
12/14	10,804	0	—	—
12/13	11,754	0	—	—
Annual Growth	(10.3%)	—	—	—

2015 Year-End Financials
Return on assets: —   Cash ($ mil.): 1,300
Return on equity: —
Current ratio: 1.20

ALTISOURCE SOLUTIONS, INC.

EXECUTIVES

Ceo, William B Shepro
Cfo, Michelle Esterman
Coo, Marcello Mastioni
Facilities, CFM Herman
Recruiting Coordinator, Theresa Strenio
Regional Field Manage, Andrew Davis
Director Infrastructure, Eric Placencia
Chief Revenue Officer, John A Vella
Chief Administration, Kevin J Wilcox
Chief Legal and Compliance Off, Gregory J Ritts
Senior Vice President, Head, Kandy White
Auditors: DELOITTE & TOUCHE LLP ATLANT

LOCATIONS

HQ: ALTISOURCE SOLUTIONS, INC.
1000 ABERNATHY RD STE 200, ATLANTA, GA 303285604
Phone: 770 612-7007
Web: WWW.ALTISOURCE.COM

HISTORICAL FINANCIALS

Company Type: Private

Income Statement				FYE: December 31
	ASSETS ($ mil.)	NET INCOME ($ mil.)	INCOME AS % OF ASSETS	EMPLOYEES
12/13	724	133	18.5%	700
12/12	429	115	27.0%	—
Annual Growth	68.9%	15.4%	—	—

2013 Year-End Financials

Return on assets: 18.5%   Sales ($ mil.): 768
Return on equity: 84.8%

ALTRU HEALTH SYSTEM

Altru Health System provides medical care to over 200000 residents throughout northeastern North Dakota and northwestern Minnesota. The integrated health care network administers everything from primary care to inpatient medical and surgical care through its Altru Hospital (with more than 255 beds) and some 45 specialty centers. It also operates a cancer center a rehabilitation center dialysis facilities and home health providers. For area seniors Altru Health operates Parkwood Place a senior living facility that provides several levels of care to residents depending on need. A community of approximately 3800 health professionals and support staff the not-for-profit center was formed in 1997 by the integration of Grand Forks Clinic and United Health Services.

EXECUTIVES

Int Ceo, Dave Molmen
Pres*, Steven Weiser
Int Cfo*, Craig Faerber

Scientist, Tiffani Peterson
Coo, Brad Wehe
Cfo, Dwight Thompson
Chief Executive, Eric Lunn
Director Maintenance, Doug Twite
Supervisor, Jimmie Kennedy
Otolaryngologist Head, Alan Johnson
Chief Financial Officer, Sara Lusignan
Auditors: BRADY MARTZ & ASSOCIATES PC

LOCATIONS

HQ: ALTRU HEALTH SYSTEM
  1200 S COLUMBIA RD, GRAND FORKS, ND
  582014044
Phone: 701 780-5000
Web: WWW.ALTRU.ORG

PRODUCTS/OPERATIONS

2013 Sales

	$ mil.	% of total
Net patient service	426	93
Other operating revenue	31	7
Total	**457**	**100**

2013 Net Patient Revenue

	% of total
Medicare	41
Blue Cross	31
Medicaid	11
Other third party	14
Patients	3
Total	**100**

Selected Centers

Bariatric Center
Breast Center
Cancer Center
Diabetes Center
Family Birthing Center
Grief Center
Hand Therapy Center
Hearing Center
Heart and Vascular Center
Joint Replacement Center
Medical Fitness Center
Outpatient Procedure Center
Pre-Admission Center
Psychiatry Center
Truyu Aesthetic Center

COMPETITORS

Avera Health	St. Alexius Medical
Catholic Health	Center
Initiatives	St. Mary's Innovis
First Care	Health
Sanford	
Health-meritcare	

HISTORICAL FINANCIALS

Company Type: Private

Income Statement   FYE: December 31

	REVENUE ($ mil.)	NET INCOME ($ mil.)	NET PROFIT MARGIN	EMPLOYEES
12/20	595	45	7.7%	3,800
12/19	589	10	1.8%	—
12/18	566	(13)	—	—
12/17	549	20	3.7%	—
Annual Growth	2.7%	31.4%	—	—

2020 Year-End Financials

Return on assets: 6.4%   Cash ($ mil.): 146
Return on equity: 14.6%
Current ratio: 6.00

AMC ENTERTAINMENT INC.

EXECUTIVES

Executive Vice President - U.s. Operations, John Mcdonald, $422,384 total compensation
Director, Kathleen Pawlus
Senior Vice President, Corporate Strategy And Communications, Christina Sternberg
Senior Vice President, Treasurer Of The Company, Parent, American Multi-cinema, Inc., Terry Crawford
President - Programming Of The Company, Parent, American Multi-cinema, Inc., Robert Lenihan, $422,300 total compensation
Executive Vice President, Chief Financial Officer, Craig Ramsey, $428,505 total compensation
Senior Vice President - Finance Of The Company, Parent, American Multi-cinema, Inc., Michael Zwonitzer
Executive Vice President, Global Development, Mark McDonald, $283,808 total compensation
Director, Gary Locke
Senior Vice President, Human Resources, Carla Chavarria
Chairman, President & Chief Executive Officer, Adam Aron
Director, Jack Gao
President - Amc Film Programming Of The Company, Parent, American Multi-cinema, Inc., Samuel Gourley, $287,500 total compensation
Director, Maojun Zeng
Senior Vice President - Food And Beverage Of American Multi-cinema, Inc., George Patterson
Executive Vice President And Chief Content & Programming Officer, Elizabeth Frank
Executive Vice President, Chief Marketing Officer, Stephen Colanero, $374,920 total compensation
Senior Vice President, General Counsel, Secretary, Kevin Connor, $334,750 total compensation
Senior Vice President, Chief Accounting Officer, Chris Cox
Auditors: KPMG LLP KANSAS CITY MISSOUR

LOCATIONS

HQ: AMC ENTERTAINMENT INC.
  11500 ASH ST, LEAWOOD, KS 662117804
Phone: 913 213-2000
Web: WWW.AMCTHEATRES.COM

HISTORICAL FINANCIALS

Company Type: Private

Income Statement   FYE: December 31

	REVENUE ($ mil.)	NET INCOME ($ mil.)	NET PROFIT MARGIN	EMPLOYEES
12/15	2,946	103	3.5%	19,700
12/14	2,695	64	2.4%	—
12/13	2,749	364	13.3%	—
12/12	811	(37)	—	—
Annual Growth	53.7%	—	—	—

2015 Year-End Financials

Return on assets: 2.0%   Cash ($ mil.): 209
Return on equity: 6.7%
Current ratio: 0.60

AMCAP FUND INC

EXECUTIVES

President, Marry Clemeson
Treas, Mary C Hall
Sr V Pres, Gordon Crawford
Sr V Pres, Paul G Haaga Jr
SEC, Julie Williams
Principal, Walter Stern
Auditors: DELOITTE & TOUCHE LLP COSTA M

LOCATIONS

HQ: AMCAP FUND INC
  333 S HOPE ST STE LEVB, LOS ANGELES, CA
  900713003
Phone: 213 486-9200
Web: WWW.CAPITALGROUP.COM

HISTORICAL FINANCIALS

Company Type: Private

Income Statement   FYE: February 29

	ASSETS ($ mil.)	NET INCOME ($ mil.)	INCOME AS % OF ASSETS	EMPLOYEES
02/20	65,300	4,726	7.2%	15
02/19	65,322	1,248	1.9%	—
02/18	64,019	9,994	15.6%	—
02/16	44,148	(2)	—	—
Annual Growth	10.3%	—	—	—

AMERICA CHUNG NAM (GROUP) HOLDINGS LLC

America Chung Nam (ACN) sells recovered fiber sources to Chinese paper mills where it can be converted into fiberboard cardboard and packaging. It also collects and exports a number of grades of post-consumer plastics. The company sources its materials through exclusive relationships with recycling facilities. Founder Yan Cheung and Ming Chung Liu own the company. It was founded in 1990.

Operations

ACN makes and supplies recovered paper (Mixed ONP DLK Magazines OCC Office Paper and other paper grades) recyclable plastics (including PET HDPE LDPE PS ABS Commingled Plastic and other engineering plastics).

It annually exports more than seven million tons of paper annually. In terms of logistics services the company has strong relationships with ocean trucking and trans-loading partners to enable access to rails shipping routes and ports all over the world.

ACN is partnered with Nine Dragons. It is an environmentally-friendly recovered paper based paper manufacturer based on production capacity.

The company helps the environment every year by saving 153 million trees. It also saves barrels of oil gallons of water and acres of landfill.

Geographic Reach

The company has operations in North America Asia and Europe. It has offices in the US (Jersey City and California) Europe (the Netherlands and the UK) and Asia (China South Korea and Japan).

Sales and Marketing

The relationship between ACN and its major customer Nine Dragons Paper Group is a tremendous advantage for the company's suppliers enabling ACN to provide business continuity regardless of fluctuations in the global market.

Company Background

America Chung Nam was founded in 1990 by Yan Cheung and Ming Chung Liu. Recognizing the demand for packaging materials driven by China's product exports and having a ready source for fiber materials through America Chung Nam Cheung established Nine Dragons Paper in 1996.

EXECUTIVES

Ceo, Teresa Cheung
V Pres-Cntrl, John Wong
Cfo, Kevin Zhao
Vpres, Ken Liu
Coo, Sam Liu
Sap Project Manager, Alice Lin
It Manager, Anthony Chang
Executive Assistant To Vice Ch, Nicholas Ting
Chief Marketing Officer, Peter Wang
Director of National Accounts, Suzanne Whitney
Marketing Manager, Tom Doherty

LOCATIONS

HQ: AMERICA CHUNG NAM (GROUP) HOLDINGS LLC
1163 FAIRWAY DR, CITY OF INDUSTRY, CA
917892846
Phone: 909 839-8383
Web: WWW.ACNI.NET

COMPETITORS

Caraustar Recovered	International Paper
Fiber Group	Weyerhaeuser
Guanwei Recycling	

HISTORICAL FINANCIALS

Company Type: Private

Income Statement				FYE: December 31
	REVENUE ($ mil.)	NET INCOME ($ mil.)	NET PROFIT MARGIN	EMPLOYEES
12/19	664	83	12.6%	200
12/18	1,711	216	12.6%	—
12/09	1,125	16	1.5%	—
12/08	1,363	7	0.6%	—
Annual Growth	(6.3%)	23.9%	—	—

2019 Year-End Financials

Return on assets: 16.1%   Cash ($ mil.): 313
Return on equity: 19.7%
Current ratio: 5.20

AMERICAN BALANCED FUND, INC.

EXECUTIVES

Chb-Ceo, Robert G O'Donnell
Pres, Paul G Haaga Jr
V Pres, Hilda L Applbaum
Sr V Pres, Abner Goldstine
Sr V Pres, John H Smet
V Pres, J Dale Harvey
V Pres, Jeffrey T Lager
Asst Treas, R Marcia Gould
SEC, Patrick F Quan
Auditors: DELOITTE & TOUCHE LLP COSTA M

LOCATIONS

HQ: AMERICAN BALANCED FUND, INC.
1 MARKET, SAN FRANCISCO, CA 941051596
Phone: 707 864-3945
Web: WWW.CAPITALGROUP.COM

HISTORICAL FINANCIALS

Company Type: Private

Income Statement				FYE: December 31
	ASSETS ($ mil.)	NET INCOME ($ mil.)	INCOME AS % OF ASSETS	EMPLOYEES
12/19	164	25,217	15366.1%	9
12/18	129,090	2,254	1.7%	—
12/17	128,462	23,932	18.6%	—
12/15	87,394	4,903	5.6%	—
Annual Growth	(79.2%)	50.6%		

AMERICAN CHEMICAL SOCIETY

With more than 151000 members the American Chemical Society (ACS) is the world's largest scientific society. The not-for-profit organization provides information career services engagement programs and educational resources to members and scientists. The company also publishes magazines journals and books. Its Chemical Abstract Service provides the most comprehensive repository of research in chemistry and related sciences. ACS also serves as an advocate for its members on public policy issues. The ACS Member Insurance Program provides insurance plans to its members. The company was founded in 1876.

Operations

ACS has more than 65 journals more than 46 million Chemical Abstracts records; over 165 million CAS REGISTRY organic and inorganic substances; some 156 million ACS journal article downloads; and it has approximately 185 local sections. The society offers members the opportunity to participate in more than 30 specialty divisions ranging from food and agriculture to industrial and engineering chemistry.

Sales and Marketing

ACS serves client that include members and other chemistry-related practitioners corporations academic institutions and government agencies. It promotes its products and services through meetings reports papers and publications.

Company Background

ACS was founded in 1876 and chartered by the US Congress in 1937.

EXECUTIVES

Pres, Lorena Tribe
Treas*, Marina Ruths
Scientist, Dean Dunn
Mkt Staff, Jamie Liu
Mkt Staff, Jnai Baylor
Mkt Staff, Kevin Mills
Staff, Laura F Amster
Business Dir, Michael Spreher
Acting Director, Mary Kirchoff
Director, Mark Carpenter
Vice-President, Gary Calabrese
Auditors: IT KPMG LLP MC LEAN VA

LOCATIONS

HQ: AMERICAN CHEMICAL SOCIETY
1155 16TH ST NW, WASHINGTON, DC 200364892
Phone: 202 872-4600
Web: WWW.ACS.ORG

HISTORICAL FINANCIALS

Company Type: Private

Income Statement				FYE: December 31
	REVENUE ($ mil.)	NET INCOME ($ mil.)	NET PROFIT MARGIN	EMPLOYEES
12/13	568	62	11.0%	2,000
12/08	451	(38)	—	—
12/05	411	26	6.4%	—
Annual Growth	4.1%	11.3%	—	—

2013 Year-End Financials

Return on assets: 4.8%   Cash ($ mil.): 37
Return on equity: 7.0%
Current ratio: 0.60

AMERICAN CRYSTAL SUGAR COMPANY

Sugarbeet cooperative American Crystal Sugar is owned by some 2800 growers in the Red River Valley of North Dakota and Minnesota who farm approximately 425000 acres of cropland. The company has sugar packaging facilities located at the Moorhead Hillsboro Crookston East Grand Forks and Sidney factories. The cooperative's products are sold in the US and other markets to industrial users and retail and wholesale customers under the Crystal name as well as under private labels through marketing co-ops United Sugars and Midwest Agri-Commodities. American Crystal Sugar owns some 50% of a corn wet-milling plant leased to agriculture giant Cargill. It was founded by Henry Oxnard in 1890.

Operations

The company makes sugar products and agri-products from the highest quality sugar beets. Its beet sugar products are made for a variety of industries and uses. It offers its sugar in many forms ? from the fine granulated sugar powdered sugar and light brown sugar packages found in stores to customized sugar varieties used by commercial bakers and food manufacturers.

In addition American Crystal's sugar processing approach results in a variety of agri-products made from sugar beets. These agri-products include beet pulp pellets beet pulp shreds beet molasses and raffinate. These products are sold primarily for use in pet food manufacturing as a feed stock enhancer in dairy production for baker's yeast for manufacturing for beet pulp for cattle and for a variety of other feed-related applications.

Geographic Reach

The Moorhead Minnesota-based cooperative has cropland in the Red River Valley of North Dakota and Minnesota and five processing facilities in the same two states (Crookston East Grand Forks and Moorhead Minnesota and Drayton and Hillsboro North Dakota) as well as in Sidney Montana.

Sales and Marketing

American Crystal Sugar markets its sugar through United Sugars Corporation a marketing cooperative owned by the company and others; its agri-products are marketed by Midwest Agri-Commodities Company which the company also owns with others.

Financial Performance

From 2011 to 2012 American Crystal's revenues decreased by 4% and its net income plummeted by 32%. Revenues decreased mainly due to a decrease in volumes of sugar and pulp which reflect the impact of less product availability due to a smaller sugar beet crop in fiscal 2012 as compared to the previous year. The decrease in net income was attributed to an increase in operating costs which included additional costs associated with a union labor lockout.

Company Background

In 1973 sugarbeet growers organized to acquire the business and assets of the American Crystal Sugar Company which was a publicly held New Jersey corporation founded in 1899. It has been a cooperative ever since.

EXECUTIVES

Independent Director, Brian Erickson
Chief Operating Officer, Joseph Talley, $438,415 total compensation
Independent Chairman Of The Board, Robert Green
Independent Director, Curtis Knutson
Chief Financial Officer, Vice President - Finance, Thomas Astrup, $331,484 total compensation
Independent Director, John Brainard
Chief Accounting Officer, Corporate Controller, Assistant Treasurer, Assistant Secretary, Teresa Warne
President, Chief Executive Officer, David Berg, $653,775 total compensation
Independent Vice Chairman Of The Board, Steve Williams
Assistant Secretary, Treasury Operations Manager, Lisa Maloy
Assistant Treasurer, Assistant Secretary, Director - Economic Analysis, David Malmskog
Vice President - Administration, Brian Ingulsrud, $316,970 total compensation
Auditors: CLIFTONLARSONALLEN LLP STEVEN

LOCATIONS

HQ: AMERICAN CRYSTAL SUGAR COMPANY
101 3RD ST N, MOORHEAD, MN 565601990
Phone: 218 236-4400
Web: WWW.CRYSTALSUGAR.COM

COMPETITORS

Alexander & Baldwin
Amalgamated Sugar
American Sugar Refining
C&h Sugar
Cargill
Cumberland Packing
Florida Crystals
Imperial Sugar
M. A. Patout
Merisant
Michigan Sugar Company
Nippon Beet Sugar
Nutrasweet
Smbsc
Sterling Sugars
Sugar Cane Growers Cooperative Of Florida
Sugar Foods
S dzucker
Tate & Lyle
U.s. Sugar
Western Sugar Cooperative

HISTORICAL FINANCIALS

Company Type: Private

Income Statement   FYE: August 31

	REVENUE ($ mil.)	NET INCOME ($ mil.)	NET PROFIT MARGIN	EMPLOYEES
08/19	1,528	624	40.9%	1,365
08/18	1,515	650	43.0%	—
08/17	1,420	511	36.0%	—
08/16	1,290	561	43.5%	—
Annual Growth	5.8%	3.6%	—	—

2019 Year-End Financials

Return on assets: 61.6%   Cash ($ mil.): 1
Return on equity: 151.4%
Current ratio: 1.20

AMERICAN ELECTRIC POWER SERVICE CORPORATION

EXECUTIVES

Chb, Nicholas K Akins
Ex Vp Policy-Fin-Strat Plannin, Susan Tomasky
Deputy Gen Counsel, Jeffrey D Cross
Sr Vp Reg Svcs, J Craig Baker
Vp Corp Comm, Dale E Heydlauff
Exec V Pres- Cfo, Holly Koeppel
Svp Gen Counsel & SEC, John B Keane
Executive Vice President, Donald M Clements Jr
Dir Federal Agency Relations, Sabrina V Campbell
Vice-President, Van Der Walde
Information Specialist, Carole Root

LOCATIONS

HQ: AMERICAN ELECTRIC POWER SERVICE CORPORATION
1 RIVERSIDE PLZ FL 1 # 1, COLUMBUS, OH 432152373
Phone: 614 716-1000
Web: WWW.AEP.COM

HISTORICAL FINANCIALS

Company Type: Private

Income Statement   FYE: December 31

	REVENUE ($ mil.)	NET INCOME ($ mil.)	NET PROFIT MARGIN	EMPLOYEES
12/16	1,348	0	—	2,152
12/05	12,111	1,037	8.6%	—
12/02	1,391	0	—	—
Annual Growth	(0.2%)	—	—	—

2016 Year-End Financials

Return on assets: —   Cash ($ mil.): 16
Return on equity: —
Current ratio: 0.40

AMERICAN FUNDS PORTFOLIO SERIES

EXECUTIVES

Mgr, Alan N Berro
Auditors: DELOITTE & TOUCHE LLP COSTA

LOCATIONS

HQ: AMERICAN FUNDS PORTFOLIO SERIES
333 SUTH HOPE ST FL 55 FLR 55, LOS ANGELES, CA 90071
Phone: 213 486-9200
Web: WWW.CAPITALGROUP.COM

HISTORICAL FINANCIALS

Company Type: Private

Income Statement   FYE: October 31

	REVENUE ($ mil.)	NET INCOME ($ mil.)	NET PROFIT MARGIN	EMPLOYEES
10/20	894	5,755	643.2%	4
10/19	860	6,852	796.0%	—
10/18	684	(112)	—	—
Annual Growth	14.4%	—	—	—

AMERICAN FURNITURE WAREHOUSE CO INC

Tony the Tiger hawking home furnishings might give some marketers pause but the combination seems to work for American Furniture Warehouse. American Furniture's television commercials often spotlight white-haired president and CEO Jake Jabs (who has become a well-known personality in the state as well as in the home furnishings industry) accompanied by baby exotic animals mostly tigers. The company sells furniture electronics and decor at discounted prices. It boasts about a dozen retail locations in Colorado and Arizona and sells through its website which also features bridal and gift registries. The company has built a reputation as a home-spun local furniture retailer. Jabs bought the company in 1975.

Geographic Reach

American Furniture has locations in the Colorado cities of Aurora Englewood Centennial Lakewood Thornton Westminster Colorado Springs Firestone/Longmont Fort Collins Glenwood Springs Pueblo and Grand Junction. In Arizona it has locations in Phoenix Gilbert and Glendale. It serves customers in the neighboring states of Wyoming Utah Kansas Nevada and New Mexico.

Financial Performance

American Furniture's 2013 sales reached more than $390 million.

Strategy

In 2013 the company made its first move outside Colorado when it opened a 630000-sq.-ft. store in Gilbert Arizona (near Phoenix). It opens another store — in Glendale Arizona — in late 2014. American Furniture hopes to net $3.4 million in direct revenue from the Glendale store during its first year in operation. The furniture retailer also has an eye on expanding into north Scottsdale.

EXECUTIVES

Pres-Ceo, Jacob Jabs
SEC-Treas*, Lori Tielke
General Manager, Kevin Michalek
Convention Sales Information T, Rob Naish
Director of Communications, Charlie Shaulis
Information Technology/Interne, Daniel Jackson
Benefits Manager, Kendra Boyd
Information Technology, Chris Norman
Human Resources Assistant, Cathy Steffes
Buyer Assistant, Stella Gimpiliova
Truck Shop Manager, Wyatt Deines
Auditors: WIPFLI LLP DENVER COLORADO

LOCATIONS

HQ: AMERICAN FURNITURE WAREHOUSE CO INC
8820 AMERICAN WAY, ENGLEWOOD, CO 801127056
Phone: 303 799-9044
Web: WWW.AFW.COM

PRODUCTS/OPERATIONS

Selected Products
Decorative accessories
Electronics
Furniture
  Bedroom
  Chairs
  Dining room
  Home office
  Indoor/outdoor
  Living room
  Occasional tables
  Sectionals
  Sofas
  Youth bedroom
Lighting
Mattresses
Rugs

COMPETITORS

Ashley Furniture	Pier 1 Imports
Big Lots	Rooms To Go
Costco Wholesale	Target Corporation
Kmart	Wal-mart

HISTORICAL FINANCIALS

Company Type: Private

Income Statement				FYE: March 31
	REVENUE ($ mil.)	NET INCOME ($ mil.)	NET PROFIT MARGIN	EMPLOYEES
03/21	845	50	6.0%	3,500
03/20	740	21	2.9%	—
03/19	694	29	4.3%	—
03/18	673	28	4.2%	—
Annual Growth	7.9%	21.3%	—	—

2021 Year-End Financials
Return on assets: 9.7%   Cash ($ mil.): 113
Return on equity: 12.4%
Current ratio: 2.10

AMERICAN HIGH INCOME TRUST

EXECUTIVES

President, Larry Clemmenson
V Pres-Treas, Mary C Cremin
V Pres, Michael J Downer
SEC, Julie F Williams
Auditors: DELOITTE & TOUCHE LLP COSTA M

LOCATIONS

HQ: AMERICAN HIGH INCOME TRUST
333 S HOPE ST STE 5200, LOS ANGELES, CA
900713061
Phone: 949 766-6305
Web: WWW.CAPITALGROUP.COM

HISTORICAL FINANCIALS

Company Type: Private

Income Statement				FYE: September 30
	ASSETS ($ mil.)	NET INCOME ($ mil.)	INCOME AS % OF ASSETS	EMPLOYEES
09/20	17,028	276	1.6%	1
09/19	16,645	25	0.2%	—
09/18	16,817	577	3.4%	—
09/16	17,336	1,555	9.0%	—
Annual Growth	(0.4%)	(35.1%)	—	—

2020 Year-End Financials
Return on assets: 1.6%   Sales ($ mil): 1,103
Return on equity: 1.6%

AMERICAN HONDA FINANCE CORPORATION

If you're fonda the idea of driving a Honda you might want to call on American Honda Finance. Operating as Honda Financial Services the company provides retail financing in the US for Honda and Acura automobiles motorcycles all-terrain vehicles power equipment and outboard motors. Its American Honda Service division administers service contracts while Honda Lease Trust offers leases on new and used vehicles. Honda Financial Services also offers dealer financing and related dealer services. Ancillary services include servicing loans and securitizing and selling loans into the secondary market. A subsidiary of American Honda Motor the company began as a wholesale motorcycle finance provider in 1980.

Operations
American Honda Finance (AHF) acquires retail installment contracts and closed-end vehicle lease contracts from purchasers and lessees and authorized Honda and Acura dealers. It also provides these authorized dealers with wholesale flooring and commercial loans.

AHF also acquires used auto loans of non-Honda and non-Acura vehicles and provides these third-party dealers iwth wholesale loans. Additionally the company offers vehicle service contracts services underwriting and pricing of consumer financing services and incentive financing programs for Honda and Acura products.

Geographic Reach
The company is headquartered in Torrance California and operates nine regional offices that support all authorized Honda and Acura dealers across North America.

Financial Performance
While full financials of the subsidiary were not available American Honda Finance's (AHF) revenue has been on the uptrend as auto sales continue to strengthen along with the US economy. Revenue in fiscal 2014 (ended March 31 2014) grew by 22% to 5.97 trillion ($58.1 billion) thanks to larger revenues from its parent company's auto business and positive foreign currency exchange rates.

Despite higher selling general and administrative expenses and R&D expenses AHF's operating income also increased 39% to 290.9 billion ($2.83 billion) in 2014 after the company continued its cost reduction measures.

Strategy
American Honda Finance Corp. (AHFC) exists to provide stability to support sales of new and used Honda and Acura vehicles throughout North America Honda Motor's largest market. To that end AHFC seeks to preserve funding diversity balanced liquidity and maintain a prudent maturity profile. To spur growth of its US business in 2012 the company opened its ninth regional office a 25000-square-foot facility in Charlotte North Carolina to serve Honda buyers in the Carolinas Maryland Tennessee Virginia and West Virginia.

EXECUTIVES

Ceo, Hideo Tamaka
Sr V Pres*, Stephan Smith
V Pres-Cfo*, John Weisickle
Information Technology Directo, David Newallis
Information Technology Directo, John Thompson
Regional Manager, Dean Hardesty
General Manager, Glenn Yamamoto
Senior Customs Administrator, Jim Crane
Manager of Business Projects, Karen Hagman
Senior Engineer Develo, Lance Kudo
Regional Sales Manager, Martin Cervantes
Auditors: KPMG LLP LOS ANGELES CALIFOR

LOCATIONS

HQ: AMERICAN HONDA FINANCE CORPORATION
1919 TORRANCE BLVD, TORRANCE, CA 905012722
Phone: 310 972-2239
Web: WWW.HONDAFINANCIALSERVICES.COM

Selected Offices
Alpharetta GA
Charlotte NC
Cypress CA
Elgin IL
Holyoke MA
Irving TX
San Ramon CA
Torrance CA
Wilmington DE

COMPETITORS

Ally Financial
Automotive Finance Corporation
Bank Of America
Credit Acceptance
Ford Motor Credit
Mercedes-benz Financial Services Usa
Mitsubishi Motors Credit Of America
Toyota Motor Credit

HISTORICAL FINANCIALS

Company Type: Private

Income Statement				FYE: March 31
	ASSETS ($ mil.)	NET INCOME ($ mil.)	INCOME AS % OF ASSETS	EMPLOYEES
03/17	69,854	753	1.1%	1,000
03/16	66,653	910	1.4%	—
03/08	50,526	(45)	—	—
03/07	41,431	394	1.0%	—
Annual Growth	5.4%	6.7%	—	—

2017 Year-End Financials
Return on assets: 1.1%   Sales ($ mil): 2,066
Return on equity: 5.9%

AMERICAN INSTITUTES FOR RESEARCH IN THE BEHAVIORAL SCIENCES

The American Institutes for Research (AIR) lives and breathes to enhance human performance. The not-for-profit organization conducts behavioral and social science research on topics related to education and educational assessment health international development and work and training. Clients including several federal agencies use AIR's research in developing policies. As a major ongoing initiative the organization provides tools to improve education both in the US and internationally particularly in disadvantaged areas. John C. Flanagan who developed the Critical Incident Technique personnel-selection tool to identify human success indicators in the workplace founded the organization in 1946.

Operations

AIR has organized its group into six program areas: Analysis of Longitudinal Data in Education Research Assessment Education Healthand Social Development Workforce and International Development Evaluation and Research.

AIR's assessment program focuses on score reports and online reporting tools to translate large-scale testing data on student achievement into a benchmark for school performance. International human and social development programs aim to improve the quality of life and education in developing areas. It works to achieve this through teacher and school administrator training curriculum development and teaching materials coupled with mobilizing health communications HIV/AIDS education and raising awareness about such issues as child labor exploitation. Working with governments private health care providers and the general public AIR's health programs design implement and evaluate the impact of health care policies.

Geographic Reach

Begun as a small research group affiliated with the University of Pittsburgh AIR's corporate headquarters and business offices are located in Washington DC. The group maintains about a dozen offices in the US. Domestic offices are located in San Mateo and Sacramento California; Atlanta Georgia; Honolulu Hawaii; Chicago and Naperville Illinois; Indianapolis Indiana; Baltimore Frederick and Silver Spring Maryland; Portland Oregon; Columbus Ohio; Chapel Hill North Carolina; New York New York; and Waltham Massachusetts. AIR also operates nearly 10 international offices located in Egypt Honduras Kyrgyzstan Liberia Tajikistan Cote d'Ivoire and Zambia.

Strategy

The National Center for Education Statistics a key source for statistical data about education and AIR team up to develop large-scale databases for policymaking. Among various efforts AIR designs surveys and assessments develops questionnaires and tests items as well as informational materials. It also helps in producing The Condition of Education the agency's chief report. The organization's successes include campaigns that address public health emergencies such as the flu and H1N1 and the prevention of HIV/AIDS heart disease and birth defects.

Adding to its educational research capabilities AIR has pursued a number of strategic alliances and acquisitions. In 2015 SEDL joined forced with AIR. The combined organizations will have new and enhanced capabilities around for example disability research as well as an increased capacity to conduct large-scale randomized control trials and provide technical assistance to diverse populations across a broader geographic area.

In 2015 AIR awarded a $500000 grant to Impact Network a nonprofit seeking to make high-quality education in Zambia sustainable.

In 2014 AIR launched the Education Policy Center.

Company Background

In 2011 the National Center for Analysis of Longitudinal Data in Educational Research (CALDER) began operating as a joint project of AIR. CALDER examines how public policies and community conditions impact teacher-student results. A year earlier AIR acquired Learning Point Associates a Chicago-based firm that delivers research in the educational sector. Its clients include state education agencies single-school districts private foundations and for-profit organizations.

EXECUTIVES

Chm, Patricia B Gurin
Pres-Ceo*, David Myers
Cfo-Sr V Pres*, Marijo Ahlgrimm
SEC*, Dona Kilpatrick
Facilities Specialist, Derrick Lewis
Scientist, San Keller
Researcher, Leah Brown
Director, Sol H Pelavin
Managing Ta Consultant, Catherine Barbour
Senior Research Scientist, Jenifer Harr
Senior Researcher, Samantha Neiman
Auditors: RUBINO & COMPANY BETHESDA MA

LOCATIONS

HQ: AMERICAN INSTITUTES FOR RESEARCH IN THE BEHAVIORAL SCIENCES
1400 CRYSTAL DR FL 10, ARLINGTON, VA 222023289
Phone: 202 403-5000
Web: WWW.AIR.ORG

PRODUCTS/OPERATIONS

Selected Program Areas

Education
Education assessment
Health
Human development
International development
Work & training

HISTORICAL FINANCIALS
Company Type: Private

Income Statement				FYE: December 31
	REVENUE ($ mil.)	NET INCOME ($ mil.)	NET PROFIT MARGIN	EMPLOYEES
12/19	829	398	48.0%	1,500
12/17	497	55	11.1%	—
12/16	474	43	9.2%	—
12/15	488	45	9.2%	—
Annual Growth	14.2%	72.5%	—	—

2019 Year-End Financials

Return on assets: 45.8%   Cash ($ mil.): 81
Return on equity: 52.3%
Current ratio: 1.50

AMERICAN LEBANESE SYRIAN ASSOCIATED CHARITIES, INC.

EXECUTIVES

Pres-Ceo, Rick Shadyac Jr
Cmo, Emily Callahan
Chief Admin Ofcr, Emily S Greer
CIO, Robert Machen
Cfo, Jeffrey T Pearson
Svp-Ceo Ops, Betty Macdougall
Sharepoint Administrator, Justin Cooper
Senior Applications Analyst, Tina Currie
Strategic Partnerships, Tracy Nilles
Sr Regional Repres, Caitlin O'Brien-Rice
Director, Chase Carter
Auditors: DELOITTE & TOUCHE LLP MEMPHIS

LOCATIONS

HQ: AMERICAN LEBANESE SYRIAN ASSOCIATED CHARITIES, INC.
501 SAINT JUDE PL, MEMPHIS, TN 381051905
Phone: 901 578-2000
Web: WWW.STJUDE.ORG

HISTORICAL FINANCIALS
Company Type: Private

Income Statement				FYE: June 30
	REVENUE ($ mil.)	NET INCOME ($ mil.)	NET PROFIT MARGIN	EMPLOYEES
06/17	1,741	658	37.8%	1,300
06/16	1,161	(27)		—
06/15	1,182	251	21.2%	—
06/13	976	210	21.5%	—
Annual Growth	15.6%	33.0%	—	—

2017 Year-End Financials

Return on assets: 15.8%   Cash ($ mil.): 178
Return on equity: 16.1%
Current ratio: —

AMERICAN MITSUBA CORPORATION

EXECUTIVES

Pres-Ceo-Coo, Masayoshi Shirato
V Pres*, Hideaki Fujii
V Pres*, Takashi Ichinokawa
V Pres*, Hiroshi Naito
Sr V Pres*, David Stevens
Sr V Pres*, Mishel Ashtary
Acctng Mgr, Ken Garber
Auditors: PLANTE & MORAN PLLC AUBURN

LOCATIONS

HQ: AMERICAN MITSUBA CORPORATION
2945 THREE LEAVES DR, MOUNT PLEASANT, MI 488584596
Phone: 989 779-4962
Web: WWW.AMERICANMITSUBA.COM

Company Type: Private

Income Statement				FYE: December 31
	REVENUE ($ mil.)	**NET INCOME** ($ mil.)	**NET PROFIT MARGIN**	**EMPLOYEES**
12/16	697	(2)	—	765
12/15	687	9	1.4%	—
12/14	558	5	0.9%	—
12/13	557	17	3.1%	—
Annual Growth	7.7%			—

2016 Year-End Financials
Return on assets: (-0.9%)   Cash ($ mil.): 24
Return on equity: (-2.0%)
Current ratio: 1.70

AMERICAN MUNICIPAL POWER, INC.

Power to the Public is the motto of American Municipal Power (AMP). The non-profit membership organization supplies wholesale power to more than 80 community-owned distribution utilities in Ohio 30 in Pennsylvania 6 in Michigan 5 in Virginia 3 in Kentucky 2 in West Virginia 1 in Indiana and 1 in Delaware (a joint action agency). AMP and its members own and operate plants that generate more than 1500 MW of power. The company also handles projects on behalf of the Ohio Municipal Electric Generating Agency (OMEGA) Joint Ventures program (jointly owned generation and transmission projects). The power generation company is owned by its member municipalities. AMP member utilities serve some 635000 customers.

Operations
The company provides electric capacity and energy and furnishes other services to its members on a cooperative basis. As part of its joint venture responsibilities American Municipal Power also operates the Belleville Hydroelectric Plant a 42 MW plant located in Belleville West Virginia. AMP's wholly-owned subsidiary AMPO provides assistance in establishing electric and gas aggregation programs to benefit local consumers.

Geographic Reach
Ohio-based American Municipal Power serves 130 members - 129 member municipal electric communities in the states of Ohio Pennsylvania Michigan Indiana Virginia Kentucky and West Virginia as well as the Delaware Municipal Electric Corporation a joint action agency headquartered in Smyrna Delaware.

Financial Performance
American Municipal Power (AMP) reported $982.5 million in revenue in 2013 representing a 19% increase over 2012. Rising electric revenues and service fees up 19% and 44% respectively drove growth in 2013. AMP's net margin expanded to $5.3 million from $1.9 million over the same period.

Strategy
Expanding into Indiana in 2014 AMP gained its newest member the city of Cannelton.

Implementing a strategy to reduce carbon emissions the company is building six hydroelectric projects on the Ohio River. The Meldahl plant (with 105 MW of capacity) will be the largest hydroelectric plant on the Ohio River. American Municipal Power also has a deal to develop up to 300 MW of solar power with solar panel company Standard Energy. It also has wind power and landfill gas operations. Indeed AMP members' projected energy resource mix will be approximately 21% renewable by 2015.

In 2013 American Municipal Power and the Vermont Energy Investment Corporation agreed to extend the operation of Efficiency Smart beyond the end of the year. The program provides a broad range of energy efficiency services for the power coop's member utilities. Some 49 member communities in Ohio Pennsylvania and Michigan participated in Efficiency Smart in 2013.

Company Background
To replace lost capacity in 2011 it acquired the Fremont Energy Center in Fremont Ohio from FirstEnergy for $500 million. The 707-MW natural gas combined-cycle facility commenced commercial operation in early 2012. In 2010 American Municipal Power also secured a 368-MW ownership stake in the Prairie State Energy Campus in Illinois.

Expanding geographically American Municipal Power moved into a seventh state in 2011 when it made Delaware Municipal Electric its 129th member.

American Municipal Power was founded in 1971.

EXECUTIVES
Pres, Marc Gerken
Chb*, Jon Bisher
Sr V Pres-Cfo*, Robert W Trippe
Sr V Pres*, Jolene Thompson
Sr V Pres*, Pam Sullivan
Sr V Pres*, John Bentine
Sr V Pres*, Bobby Little
Assistant Vice President of FI, Chris Deeter
Operation, Tony Belcher
Sr Director of Communications, Kent Carson
Project Manager, Phillip Meier
Auditors: PRICEWATERHOUSECOOPERS LLP CO

LOCATIONS
HQ: AMERICAN MUNICIPAL POWER, INC.
1111 SCHROCK RD STE 100, COLUMBUS, OH 432291155
Phone: 614 540-1111
Web: WWW.AMPPARTNERS.ORG

PRODUCTS/OPERATIONS

2013 Sales
	% of total
Electric revenues	97
Service fees	1
Programs & other	2
Total	**100**

Selected Services
Aggregation
Business Development
Clean Energy & Conservation
Community Outreach
Financial
Legislative Regulatory & Legal
Power Supply / AMP Energy Control Center
Safety Programs
Scholarship Programs
Technical Services

COMPETITORS

Dominion Energy   Ohio Valley Electric
Duke Energy Ohio

Company Type: Private

Income Statement				FYE: December 31
	REVENUE ($ mil.)	**NET INCOME** ($ mil.)	**NET PROFIT MARGIN**	**EMPLOYEES**
12/20	1,091	2	0.2%	229
12/19	1,170	5	0.5%	—
12/15	1,127	5	0.5%	—
12/14	1,039	2	0.2%	—
Annual Growth	0.8%	(0.5%)	—	—

2020 Year-End Financials
Return on assets: —   Cash ($ mil.): 154
Return on equity: 2.7%
Current ratio: 1.90

AMERICAN MUTUAL FUND

EXECUTIVES

Chb, Jonathan B Lovelace Jr
Chb-Ceo*, James K Dunton
V Chb*, James W Ratzlaff
Pres*, Robert G O'Donnell
V Pres*, Joyce Gordon
V Pres*, Joanna F Jonsson
SEC*, Vince Carti
Treas*, Mary C Hall
Treasurer, Mary Hall
Associate Director, Thomas Onna
Auditors: DELOITTE & TOUCHE LLP COSTA M

LOCATIONS
HQ: AMERICAN MUTUAL FUND
333 S HOPE ST FL 51, LOS ANGELES, CA 900711420
Phone: 213 486-9200
Web: WWW.CAPITALGROUP.COM

HISTORICAL FINANCIALS
Company Type: Private

Income Statement				FYE: October 31
	ASSETS ($ mil.)	**NET INCOME** ($ mil.)	**INCOME AS % OF ASSETS**	**EMPLOYEES**
10/20	61,161	1,086	1.8%	200
10/19	60,172	9,524	15.8%	—
10/18	50,526	3,375	6.7%	—
Annual Growth	10.0%	(43.3%)	—	—

2020 Year-End Financials
Return on assets: 1.8%   Sales ($ mil.): 1,596
Return on equity: 1.8%

AMERICAN TIRE DISTRIBUTORS HOLDINGS, INC.

American Tire Distributors (ATD) is the largest independent tire and service distributor in North America. Its offerings include flagship brands Yokohama Hankook Continental Pirelli and Michelin as well as budget brands and private-label tires. ATD also markets custom wheels and tire service equipment. Its network of nearly 145 distribution centers and mixing warehouses serve independent tire dealers retail chains and auto service centers across the US and Canada and has approximately 1400 deliver vehicles on the road across the nation. In addition to some 40 million delivery miles annually the company provides access to over 4 million tires in every style and size from the top global brands in the industry.

Operations
Passenger and light truck tires contribute most of American Tire Distributors' sales; the company also supplies tires for medium trucks farm vehicles and specialty vehicles.

Beyond tires ATD distributes wheels and other automotive products. Its brands include Carlisle Drifz O.E. Performance Black Rock Dick Cepek Schrader and Advanti Racing.

Geographic Reach
North Carolina-based American Tire Distributors has a strong position in North America. It rings up most of its sales in the US where it has about 145 distribution centers. The company has nearly 25 distribution centers across Canada.

Sales and Marketing
American Tire Distributors sells tires to local regional and national independent tire retailers as well as mass merchandisers warehouse clubs tire-manufacturer-owned stores automotive dealerships and web-based markets. Its private fleet of approximately 1500 drivers hand-deliver tires wheels and supplies to approximately 80000 customers across the US and Canada.

Mergers and Acquisitions

EXECUTIVES

Ceo, Stuart Schuette
Exec V Pres-Cfo*, Jason Yaudes
Exec V Pres-General Counsel-SE*, J Michael Gaither
Sr V Pres*, J David Phillips
Sr V Pres*, Dan Seitler
Director, Purchasing, Steve Huffman
Brand Director, Tony Brown
Customer Team Member, Vanessa Lyles
Evp and Cfo, Jason T Yaudes
Customer Staff, Carl Young
Customer Staff, Troy Kidder
Auditors: PRICEWATERHOUSECOOPERS LLP CH

LOCATIONS

HQ: AMERICAN TIRE DISTRIBUTORS HOLDINGS, INC. 12200 HERBERT WAYNE CT # 150, HUNTERSVILLE, NC 280786335
Phone: 704 992-2000
Web: WWW.ATD-US.COM

PRODUCTS/OPERATIONS

Selected Brands

Tires
Alliance
BFGoodrich
Continental
Dunlop
Firestone
IronMan
Michelin
Toyo Tires
UniRoyal
Wheels
Center Line
ICW Racing
Konig
Motiv
Pacer
Ultra Motorsports

Supplies
Blaster
Chicago Pneumatic
Ingersoll-Rand
Ken-Tool
SuperSprings
Stoner
Western Pacific Storage Solutions

COMPETITORS

Amazon.com	Tci Tire Centers
Bridgestone	Tire Distribution
Dealer Tire	Systems
Goodyear Tire & Rubber	Tire Group
Sears Holdings	International Inc.
Sumitomo Corporation	Wal-mart
Of America	

HISTORICAL FINANCIALS
Company Type: Private

Income Statement   FYE: December 28

	REVENUE ($ mil.)	NET INCOME ($ mil.)	NET PROFIT MARGIN	EMPLOYEES
12/13	3,839	(6)	—	1,072
12/12	3,455	(14)	—	—
12/11	3,050	0	0.0%	—
Annual Growth	**12.2%**	—	—	—

2013 Year-End Financials

Return on assets: (-0.2%)   Cash ($ mil.): 35
Return on equity: (-0.9%)
Current ratio: 1.90

AMERICAN TRANSMISSION COMPANY, LLC

American Transmission Company is an entrepreneur in the US power grid business — a for-profit multi-state transmission-only utility. Connecting electricity producers to distributors American Transmission owns operates monitors and maintains 9480 miles of high-voltage electric transmission lines and 529 substations in portions of Illinois Michigan Minnesota and Wisconsin. The company a member of the Midwest Independent Transmission System Operator (MISO) regional transmission organization operates the former transmission assets of some of its shareholders. About 30 utilities municipalities electric companies and cooperatives in its service area have an ownership stake in American Transmission.

Operations
Unlike most other power utilities American Transmission is not engaged in the generation distribution or marketing of electricity. Its duties include reliable operation of the transmission system growing the system to meet current and future needs and upgrading and maintain the transmission equipment as needed.

American Transmission is a member of the MISO regional transmission organization and provides nondiscriminatory service to all customers supporting effective competition in energy markets without favoring any market participant.

Geographic Reach
American Transmission meets the power needs of about 5 million people in 72 counties in Illinois Michigan Minnesota and Wisconsin. It operates

North central Wisconsin Michigan's Upper Peninsula and Northern Wisconsin South Central/Southwest Wisconsin and North Central Illinois Northeast Wisconsin and Southeast Wisconsin.

Sales and Marketing
The company's customers include local electric distribution companies municipal utilities and cooperative utilities (that procure primary network transmission service and are interconnected or plan on interconnecting to its transmission system) local and national marketers generators and utilities (that procure primarily point-to-point transmission service generators and other transmission systems that want to interconnect with American Transmission's system).

Financial Performance
American Transmission reported revenues of about $603 million in 2012 a 6% increase over 2011 revenues.

Strategy
The company is trying to use its single focus on power transmission to win more customers. American Transmission has invested more than $2.8 billion on infrastructure upgrades (since 2001) including 2305 miles of power line. It has also built more 560 miles of new lines during this time period. By 2021 the company plans to spend a further $3.9-$4.8 billion on infrastructure improvement with a focus on adding new renewable sources to its expanded grid.

In 2014 American Transmission filed applications with the Public Service Commission of Wisconsin to rebuild a 12.5 mile 138000-volt transmission line in western Kenosha County at a cost $12.2 million and a 69000-volt transmission line between Dyckesville Wisconsin and Sturgeon Bay Wisconsin (for $23 million).

In 2013 American Transmission received authorizing to build two new 138-kilovolt transmission lines needed to improve electric system reliability in western Milwaukee County and began construction activities on a new 5.8-mile 345-kilovolt electric transmission line to strengthen the electric system in southeastern Wisconsin and northeastern Illinois. That year it energized the 32-mile 345-kilovolt Rockdale-West Middleton Transmission Line; and placed in service. In 2013 American Transmission

In 2012 it teamed up with ALLETE to study transmission options for transporting Midwestern wind energy as well as Canadian hydroelectric power into Minnesota Wisconsin and Michigan to help local utilities enhance reliability and meet renewable energy goals. To further enable movement of renewable energy that year the company and Minnesota Power agreed to develop a 50-mile double-circuit 345-kilovolt transmission line from the Mesabi Iron Range to the companies' jointly owned Arrowhead Substation in Duluth. The project is due to come into service in 2020.

Company Background
In 2010 it signed two agreements with the Department of Energy to access $12.7 million in investment grants for incorporating smart grid technologies into its transmission system.

In 2011 it announced a plan to build seven new transmission line projects (1800 miles of new line) aimed at filling gaps in the existing transmission grid improving grid reliability and enabling increased delivery of renewable power in Iowa Wisconsin Illinois Indiana and Ohio. The projects in total will cost about $4 billion. It also agreed to purchase of the Zephyr Power Transmission Project (950 miles of transmission line between Wyoming and southern Nevada) in another $4 billion deal.

Boosting its transmission assets in 2011 American Transmission formed a transmission utility joint venture with Duke Energy. Duke-American

Transmission Co. builds owns and operates new power transmission infrastructure across North America.

American Transmission is one of the first for-profit transmission companies formed (in 2001) when the US market deregulated in the early 2000s. It is 88% owned by investor-owned utilities and 12% owned by municipalities municipal electric companies and electric cooperatives.

EXECUTIVES

Chb-Pres-Ceo, Patricia Kampling
Pres-Ceo*, Michael Peters
Pres*, Allen Leverett
Chm-Pres-Ceo*, Gary Wolter
Mng Dir*, Stephen Yanisch
Prof*, Alan Schriber
Ceo*, John Jamar
Pres*, Gale Norton
Exec*, Lawrence Borgard
MBR-Exec V Pres*, Mike Rowe
Dir of Federal Affairs, Tonja L Wicks
Auditors: DELOITTE & TOUCHE LLP MILWAU

LOCATIONS

HQ: AMERICAN TRANSMISSION COMPANY, LLC
W234N2000 RDGVIEW PKY CT, WAUKESHA, WI 531881022
Phone: 262 506-6700
Web: WWW.ATCLLC.COM

PRODUCTS/OPERATIONS

Contributing Owners
Adams-Columbia Electric Cooperative
Alger Delta Cooperative Electric Association
Badger Power Marketing Authority
Central Wisconsin Electric Cooperative
City of Algoma
City of Columbus
City of Kaukauna
City of Menasha
City of Oconto Falls
City of Plymouth
City of Reedsburg
City of Sheboygan Falls
City of Sturgeon Bay
City of Sun Prairie
City of Wisconsin Rapids
Cloverland Electric Cooperative
Edison Sault Electric Company
Madison Gas & Electric Company
Manitowoc Public Utilities
Marshfield Electric and Water Department
Ontonagon County Rural Electrification Association
Rainy River Energy
Rock Energy Cooperative
Stoughton Utilities
Upper Peninsula Public Power Agency
Wisconsin Electric Power Company
Wisconsin Power & Light Company
Wisconsin Public Service Corporation
WPPI Energy

COMPETITORS

Aes	Exelon
Ameren	Firstenergy
Duke Energy	

HISTORICAL FINANCIALS

Company Type: Private

Income Statement				FYE: December 31
	REVENUE ($ mil.)	NET INCOME ($ mil.)	NET PROFIT MARGIN	EMPLOYEES
12/18	687	172	25.0%	547
12/17	714	172	24.2%	—
12/16	650	147	22.7%	—
12/15	615	200	32.5%	—
Annual Growth	3.7%	(5.0%)	—	—

2018 Year-End Financials

Return on assets: 3.5%   Cash ($ mil.): —
Return on equity: 14.2%
Current ratio: 0.20

AMERICAN TRANSMISSION SYSTEMS, INCORPORATED

EXECUTIVES

Pres, Richard R Grigg
Director, Richard A Ziegler

LOCATIONS

HQ: AMERICAN TRANSMISSION SYSTEMS, INCORPORATED
76 S MAIN ST, AKRON, OH 443081812
Phone: 330 761-4370
Web: WWW.FIRSTENERGYCORP.COM

HISTORICAL FINANCIALS

Company Type: Private

Income Statement				FYE: December 31
	REVENUE ($ mil.)	NET INCOME ($ mil.)	NET PROFIT MARGIN	EMPLOYEES
12/17	656	165	25.2%	1
12/16	540	133	24.7%	—
Annual Growth	21.6%	23.8%	—	—

AMERICARES FOUNDATION, INC.

AmeriCares Foundation provides emergency medical aid around the world. The not-for-profit charitable organization helps victims of natural disasters and supports long-term humanitarian programs by collecting medical supplies in the US and overseas and delivering them to places where they are needed. AmeriCares has provided aid in more than 90 countries worldwide. In the US the organization offers medical assistance runs a camp for kids with HIV/AIDS and conducts HomeFront a program that renovates housing for the needy in parts of Connecticut and New York. Robert C. Macauley founded AmeriCares in 1982.

Geographic Reach
The company has presence in US Latin America Caribbean Asia and Eurasia Africa and Middle East.

Financial Performance
AmeriCares' revenue decreased 9% to $572 million in 2014 due to a decline in public support and loss on investments.

EXECUTIVES

Ceo-Pres, Christine Squires
Svp-Operations*, Richard K Trowbridge Jr
Vp-US Programs & Partnership, Lindsay O'Brien
Senior Associate, Alexanne Neff
Multimedia Associate, Christopher Williams
Manager Institutional Relation, Jon Hillery
Senior Vice President, Human R, Kevin R Gilrain
Director of Logistics, Peter Tokarczyk
Manager, Social Media Strategy, Sam Kelly
Officer, Tess Gallegos
Associate Director Major Gifts, Vanessa Ball
Auditors: IT GRANT THORNTON LLP NEW YO

LOCATIONS

HQ: AMERICARES FOUNDATION, INC.
88 HAMILTON AVE STE 1, STAMFORD, CT 069023100
Phone: 203 658-9500
Web: WWW.AMERICARES.ORG

HISTORICAL FINANCIALS

Company Type: Private

Income Statement				FYE: June 30
	REVENUE ($ mil.)	NET INCOME ($ mil.)	NET PROFIT MARGIN	EMPLOYEES
06/20	1,440	192	13.4%	231
06/19	976	(101)	—	—
06/15	742	101	13.7%	—
06/14	560	(4)	—	—
Annual Growth	17.0%	—	—	—

2020 Year-End Financials

Return on assets: 45.7%   Cash ($ mil.): 23
Return on equity: 47.3%
Current ratio: —

AMES CONSTRUCTION, INC.

Ames Construction aims right for the heart of heavy construction. The company is a general contractor providing heavy civil and industrial construction services to the transportation mining and power industries mainly in the West and Midwest. The family-owned company works on highways airports bridges rail lines mining facilities power plants and other infrastructure projects. Ames also performs flood control environmental remediation reclamation and landfill work. Additionally the firm builds golf courses and undertakes commercial and residential site development projects. Ames typically partners with other companies to perform the engineering and design portion of construction jobs.

Operations
Some of Ames Construction's project include the Arlington Power Plant Dry Fork Station Unit 1 Site Work and Substructure Construction Rentech ClearFuels Cortez Hills Mine and Mills Site and Airport Extension Projects such as its MSP International Airport work.

Geographic Reach
Ames Construction has offices in the US in Minnesota Arizona California Colorado Nevada and Utah as well as in Canada.

Strategy
Through its subcontracting activities Ames Construction contributed to the construction of the Minnesota Twins ballpark and served as subcon-

tractor and partner in a joint venture with Fluor and Balfour Beatty Rail that that undertook a $1 billion design/build portion of a rail line project for the Denver Regional Transit District.

EXECUTIVES

President, Raymond G Ames
SEC-Cfo*, Michael J Kellen
Director of Communications, Ken Brandt
Manager, Brian Ruby
Director of Finance, Lawrence B Blakeborough
Regional Vice President of Eng, Robert Gillis
Citrix, Justin Hoveland
Vice President of Management S, Roger L McBride
Vice President Director Manage, Tony W Meyers
Vice President, Todd Goderstad
Manager, Chris Kemper
Auditors: CLIFTONLARSONALLEN LLP MINNE

LOCATIONS

HQ: AMES CONSTRUCTION, INC.
2500 COUNTY ROAD 42 W, BURNSVILLE, MN 553376911
Phone: 952 435-7106
Web: WWW.AMESCONSTRUCTION.COM

Selected Locations
Arizona
California
Canada
Colorado
Minnesota
Nevada
Utah

PRODUCTS/OPERATIONS

Selected Markets

Commercial
Commercial site development
Environmental remediation/ landfills
Residential site development
Mining
Contract mining
Leach pad construction
Mine development
Mine infrastructure
Mine reclamation/remediation
Mine tailings dam
Power
Coal fired
Combined-cycle/natural gas
Nuclear
Transmission
Wind
Transportation
Airports
Bridges
Highways
Railroads
Water resources
Dams reservoirs and flood control
Wastewater/water treatment
Water delivery
Water retention structures

COMPETITORS

American Civil Constructors Holdings
Balfour Beatty Construction
Clyde Companies
Granite Construction
Meadow Valley
Peter Kiewit Sons'
Sema Construction
Skanska Usa Civil
Sterling Construction
Tutor-saliba

HISTORICAL FINANCIALS
Company Type: Private

Income Statement				FYE: November 30
	REVENUE ($ mil.)	NET INCOME ($ mil.)	NET PROFIT MARGIN	EMPLOYEES
11/20	1,308	42	3.2%	2,500
11/19	1,248	61	4.9%	—
11/16	845	2	0.3%	—
11/15	1,068	5	0.5%	—
Annual Growth	4.1%	52.5%	—	—

2020 Year-End Financials

Return on assets: 8.2%   Cash ($ mil.): 96
Return on equity: 27.8%
Current ratio: 1.20

ANC HEALTHCARE, INC.

EXECUTIVES

Ceo-Pres, Ronald A Paulus
Cmo-Mission Hospital, William R Hathaway
Innovation, Marc B Westle
Operations, Sonya B Greck
Auditors: GRANT THORNTON LLP CHARLOTTE

LOCATIONS

HQ: ANC HEALTHCARE, INC.
425 W NEW ENG AVE STE 300, WINTER PARK, FL 327894228
Phone: 828 213-1111
Web: WWW.MISSIONHEALTH.ORG

HISTORICAL FINANCIALS
Company Type: Private

Income Statement				FYE: September 30
	REVENUE ($ mil.)	NET INCOME ($ mil.)	NET PROFIT MARGIN	EMPLOYEES
09/18	1,799	120	6.7%	12,000
09/17	1,753	161	9.2%	—
09/16	1,632	90	5.5%	—
09/08	17	7	42.3%	—
Annual Growth	59.1%	32.3%	—	—

2018 Year-End Financials

Return on assets: 4.5%   Cash ($ mil.): 149
Return on equity: 6.7%
Current ratio: 2.00

ANCHORAGE SCHOOL DISTRICT

EXECUTIVES

Supt, Ed Graff
Supt*, Carol Comeau
SEC Accounting*, Lois Hartsfield
Exe SEC*, Vanessa Blake
Doctor*, Deena Bishop
Substitute Teacher, Carla Goldberg
Business Analyst, Andria Johannes

Special Ed Teacher, Dawn Swensen
School Board Member, Elisa Snelling
Teacher Assistant, Jonnie Snell
Purchasing Agent, Katherine Williams
Auditors: BDO USA LLP ANCHORAGE ALASK

LOCATIONS

HQ: ANCHORAGE SCHOOL DISTRICT
5530 E NTHRN LIGHTS BLVD, ANCHORAGE, AK 99504
Phone: 907 742-4000
Web: WWW.ASDK12.ORG

HISTORICAL FINANCIALS
Company Type: Private

Income Statement				FYE: June 30
	REVENUE ($ mil.)	NET INCOME ($ mil.)	NET PROFIT MARGIN	EMPLOYEES
06/12	834	(8)	—	5,039
06/11	822	(2)	—	—
06/10	774	(19)	—	—
Annual Growth	3.8%	—	—	—

2012 Year-End Financials

Return on assets: (-0.6%)   Cash ($ mil.): 162
Return on equity: (-1.3%)
Current ratio: —

ANCHORAGE, MUNICIPALITY OF (INC)

Anchorage is Alaska's largest city in both size and population. The city encompasses almost 2000 sq. mi. of land — almost the size of Delaware. Anchorage had a 2010 population of about 290000 residents or about a quarter of the state's population. Anchorage is located in the south central part of the state and sits on the Gulf of Alaska.

EXECUTIVES

Mayor, Dave Bronson
General Manager, Mark Spafford
Library Assistant, Maureen Howard
Executive Director, Pamela Basler
Chief Fiscal Officer, Alexander Slivka
Administrative Officer, Alison Gutacker
Vice Chair, Austin Quinn-Davidson
Manager, Payroll Audit, Casey Boe
Manager, Public Finance, Chris Richardson
Director of Learning and Engag, Hollis Mickey
Supervisor, Finance, Jade Tsai
Auditors: BDO USA LLP ANCHORAGE ALASKA

LOCATIONS

HQ: ANCHORAGE, MUNICIPALITY OF (INC)
632 W 6TH AVE STE 810, ANCHORAGE, AK 995016312
Phone: 907 343-6610
Web: WWW.MUNI.ORG

HISTORICAL FINANCIALS

Company Type: Private

Income Statement				FYE: December 31
	REVENUE ($ mil.)	NET INCOME ($ mil.)	NET PROFIT MARGIN	EMPLOYEES
12/20	956	272	28.5%	3,680
12/19	800	21	2.7%	—
12/18	740	26	3.6%	—
12/17	816	(33)	—	—
Annual Growth	5.4%	—	—	—

2020 Year-End Financials

Return on assets: 3.4%
Return on equity: 6.4%
Current ratio: 3.30

Cash ($ mil.): 392

ANMED HEALTH

EXECUTIVES

Pres-Ceo, John Miller Jr
Dir, Jimmy Kimbell
Compliance Staff, Chandra Snyder
Telecommunications Technician, Freddy McGee
Pharmacy Director, George Reid
Hematologist Oncologist, Jay Nayak
Account Director, Sonya Gould
Anesthesiologist, Amy Weaver
Information Security, Cherry Kent
Rn House Supervisor (pcc), Greg Krakos
Physician, Jonathan Sappington
Auditors: DIXON HUGHES GOODMAN LLP GRE

LOCATIONS

HQ: ANMED HEALTH
800 N FANT ST, ANDERSON, SC 296215708
Phone: 864 512-1000
Web: WWW.ANMEDHEALTH.ORG

HISTORICAL FINANCIALS

Company Type: Private

Income Statement				FYE: December 31
	REVENUE ($ mil.)	NET INCOME ($ mil.)	NET PROFIT MARGIN	EMPLOYEES
12/20	546	77	14.1%	2,600
12/18	543	(15)	—	—
12/17	513	41	8.0%	—
12/16	504	40	8.0%	—
Annual Growth	2.0%	17.6%	—	—

2020 Year-End Financials

Return on assets: 6.8%
Return on equity: 10.4%
Current ratio: 2.00

Cash ($ mil.): 137

ANN & ROBERT H. LURIE CHILDREN'S HOSPITAL OF CHICAGO

When it comes to caring for kids Ann & Robert H. Lurie Children's Hospital of Chicago has the Windy City covered. Founded in 1882 the not-for-profit hospital provides a full range of pediatric services with acute and specialty care. Lurie Children's provides services through its main hospital campus with about 300 beds and outpatient centers in Chicago's Lincoln Park neighborhood and through more than a dozen suburban outpatient centers and outreach partner locations in the greater Chicago area. A leader in pediatric research the hospital operates the Children's Hospital of Chicago Research Center and is the pediatric teaching facility of Northwestern University's Feinberg School of Medicine.

Operations

Lurie Children's serves roughly 150000 patients each year and employs some 1350 pediatric specialists with expertise in 70 different specialties. The hospital is one of only about a dozen children's hospitals nationwide to perform more than 1000 liver transplants. The center performs on average 50 solid organ and 50 stem cell transplants annually.

A major research center Lurie Children's is one of nearly 30 interdisciplinary research centers and institutes belonging to the hospital's academic partner — Feinberg School of Medicine. Its research arm Stanley Manne Children's Research Institute employs some 200 physician-scientists and research investigators who in 2014 were awarded more than $40 million in external funding.

Geographic Reach

Based in Chicago Lurie Children's has cared for patients from throughout the US and about 50 countries around the globe.

Financial Performance

Lurie Children's saw revenues increase by 8% to $826 million in fiscal 2014 (ended August). That growth was attributed to a rise in patient care revenues and other earnings. Net income increased 198% to $128 million that year largely due to the higher revenue as well as strong investment returns.

Cash flow from operations rose 36% to $124.5 million in fiscal 2014.

Strategy

The hospital has all-private rooms even in the neonatal intensive care unit; private rooms are said to speed healing by reducing hospital-acquired infection and minimize noise. Lurie Children's is working to enhance its specialist services and has upgraded its information technology systems. In 2013 it implemented a Voalte system that allows nurses to communicate through rapid-response systems including text messages and high-definition voice calls. Also that year it opened the first pediatric gender identity clinic. In 2015 the hospital acquired the fourth-generation da Vinci Xi robotic system for use in minimally invasive surgery.

In 2014 Lurie Children's Health Partners (composed of Lurie Children's and two groups of pediatricians) launched the Clinically Integrated Network the first health care network in Chicago to focus exclusively on children and their families. Its areas of focus include care coordination obesity asthma immunizations and child development.

EXECUTIVES

Ceo-Pres, Thomas Shanley
Cfo*, Paula Noble
Lead Clinical Research Coordin, Heather Price
Registered Nurse, Claire O'Neil
Case Manager, Carol Millunchick
Professor Philosophy, J D Trout
Assistant Dean For Student Aff, James Mendez
Customer Manager, Janet Bergamo
Associate Professor School, Jasmine Tata
Officer, Jessica Brooks
Professor Emeritus Psychology, Joseph F Rychlak

LOCATIONS

HQ: ANN & ROBERT H. LURIE CHILDREN'S HOSPITAL OF CHICAGO
225 E CHICAGO AVE, CHICAGO, IL 606112991
Phone: 312 227-4000
Web: WWW.LURIECHILDRENS.ORG

Selected Illinois Locations

Lurie Children's at Cadence Health (Winfield)
Main Hospital (Chicago)
Outpatient Center in Arlington Heights (Arlington Heights)
Outpatient Center in Glenview (Glenview)
Outpatient Center in Lake Forest (Lake Forest)
Outpatient Center in Lincoln Park (Chicago)
Outpatient Center in New Lenox (New Lenox)
Outpatient Center in Westchester (Westchester)
Outpatient Services in Grayslake (Grayslake)
Outpatient Services in Gurnee (Gurnee)
Outpatient Services in Lincoln Square (Chicago)
Pediatrics - Uptown (Chicago)
Rehabilitation Services at Westbrook (Westchester)

PRODUCTS/OPERATIONS

2014 Sales

	$ mil.	% of total
Patient care revenues	706	85
Grants gifts & endowment income	62	8
Other revenues	57	7
Total	**825**	**100**

Selected Services

Adolescent Medicine
Allergy and Immunology
Anesthesiology
Audiology
Autonomic Medicine
Brain Tumor
Cancer and Blood Disorders
Cardiology (Heart Center)
Child Abuse Pediatrics
Child and Adolescent Psychiatry
Clinical Nutrition
Convenient Care
Critical Care
Cystic Fibrosis
Dentistry and Oral Surgery
Dermatology
Emergency Medicine
Endocrinology
Epilepsy
Fetal Health
Gastroenterology Hepatology and Nutrition (Digestive Disorders)
Gender and Sex Development
General Pediatric Surgery
General Pediatrics
Genetics Birth Defects and Metabolism
Heart Failure and Transplants
HIV/AIDS Prevention
Infectious Diseases
Intestinal Transplants
Kidney Diseases
Kidney Transplants
Liver Transplants
Medical Imaging (Radiology)
Neonatology
Neurology
Neurosurgery
Occupational Therapy
Ophthalmology

Orthopaedic Surgery
Orthotics/Prosthetics
Otolaryngology (ENT)
Palliative Care
Pathology and Laboratory Medicine
Physical Therapy
Plastic and Reconstructive Surgery
Pulmonary Medicine
Rehabilitative Services
Rheumatology
Speech-Language Pathology
Spina Bifida Center
Sports Medicine
Stem Cell Transplants
Transitioning to Adult Care
Transplantation
Urology

COMPETITORS

Advocate Health Care	Northshore University
Advocate Lutheran	Healthsystem
General Hospital	Northwestern Lake
Alexian Brothers	Forest Hospital
Health System	Northwestern Memorial
Covenant Ministries	Healthcare
Hca	Rush System For Health
Loyola University	Ssm Health Care
Health System	Sinai Health System
Mercy Hospital And	University Of Chicago
Medical Center	Medical Center

HISTORICAL FINANCIALS

Company Type: Private

Income Statement   FYE: August 31

	REVENUE ($ mil.)	NET INCOME ($ mil.)	NET PROFIT MARGIN	EMPLOYEES
08/13	694	28	4.2%	2,800
08/10	599	52	8.8%	—
08/09	533	(5)	—	—
Annual Growth	6.8%	—	—	—

2013 Year-End Financials

Return on assets: 1.4%   Cash ($ mil.): 92
Return on equity: 2.0%
Current ratio: 2.90

ANNE ARUNDEL COUNTY BOARD OF EDUCATION

EXECUTIVES

Pres, Stacy Korbelak
Teacher, Matt Heist
Auditors: CLIFTONLARSONALLEN LLP BALTIM

LOCATIONS

HQ: ANNE ARUNDEL COUNTY BOARD OF EDUCATION
2644 RIVA RD, ANNAPOLIS, MD 214017427
Phone: 410 222-5000
Web: WWW.AACPS.ORG

HISTORICAL FINANCIALS

Company Type: Private

Income Statement   FYE: June 30

	REVENUE ($ mil.)	NET INCOME ($ mil.)	NET PROFIT MARGIN	EMPLOYEES
06/13	1,147	3	0.3%	416
06/04	712	0	0.1%	—
06/03	701	50	7.1%	—
Annual Growth	5.1%	(23.0%)		

2013 Year-End Financials

Return on assets: 0.3%   Cash ($ mil.): 166
Return on equity: 0.6%
Current ratio: —

ANOKA-HENNEPIN SCHOOL DIST NO 11

EXECUTIVES

Supt, David Law
Accounting Mgr*, Renee Rodewald
Cfo*, Michelle Vargas
Coordinator, Dorothy Olsen
Coordinator, James Greer
Coordinator, Mark Hansen
Coordinator, Noella Fath
Coordinator, Tim Dahlheimer
Site Leader, Chrisanne Way
Site Leader, Donna Riley
Site Leader, Janet Sheils
Auditors: MALLOY MONTAGUE KARNOWSKI RA

LOCATIONS

HQ: ANOKA-HENNEPIN SCHOOL DIST NO 11
2727 N FERRY ST, ANOKA, MN 553031650
Phone: 763 506-1000
Web: WWW.AHSCHOOLS.US

HISTORICAL FINANCIALS

Company Type: Private

Income Statement   FYE: June 30

	REVENUE ($ mil.)	NET INCOME ($ mil.)	NET PROFIT MARGIN	EMPLOYEES
06/20	585	59	10.1%	6,100
06/19	574	(88)	—	—
06/18	550	151	27.5%	—
Annual Growth	3.1%	(37.5%)	—	—

2020 Year-End Financials

Return on assets: 4.8%   Cash ($ mil.): 354
Return on equity: —
Current ratio: —

ANR PIPELINE COMPANY

ANR Pipeline keeps natural gas in line a pipeline that is. The company operates one of the largest interstate natural gas pipeline systems in the US. A subsidiary of TransCanada Corp. ANR controls about 10350 miles of pipeline and delivers more than 1 trillion cu. ft. of natural gas per year. The company primarily serves customers in the Midwest but through its network is capable of connecting to all major gas basins in North America. In tandem with its ANR Storage and Blue Lake Gas Storage subsidiaries ANR Pipeline also provides natural gas storage services and has ownership interests in more than 250 billion cu. ft. of underground natural gas storage capacity.

Operations

The ANR System is part of TransCanada's network 37000 miles of wholly owned and 4900 miles of partially owned pipelines connecting major supply basins with major markets all across North America.

Geographic Reach

ANR transports natural gas from producing fields in Texas and Oklahoma from offshore and onshore regions of the Gulf of Mexico and from the US midcontinent for delivery mainly to Illinois Indiana Michigan Ohio and Wisconsin.

Strategy

To create greater operating efficiency in 2012 ANR Pipeline Company sold assets and certain related onshore facilities to its wholly owned subsidiary TC Offshore LLC.

To support the growing natural gas production in the Haynesville Shale play in Texas and Louisiana the company is developing the ANR Haynesville Lateral Project to transport up to 1.8 billion cu. ft. of natural gas a day. The Haynesville Lateral pipeline enables producers to transport shale gas to markets in the Southeast Midwest and Northeast.

Company Background

ANR Pipeline was founded as Michigan-Wisconsin Pipe Line Company in 1945 and adopted its current name in 1984.

El Paso Corp. sold ANR Pipeline to TransCanada in 2007. The deal gave TransCanada a regulated natural gas pipeline and storage assets that complemented its other North American gas transmission operations.

EXECUTIVES

Pres-Ceo, Lee Hobbs
Pres-Ceo, Lee G Hobbs
V Pres-Commercial Oprs, Gary C Charette
V Pres-Commercial Sls, Dean Patry
Land Administrator, Rocio Lozano
Board Member, Alan Resnick
Board Member, Angela Panzarella
Tax, Beth Carley
Vice President Gulf Coast Asse, Betsy McMahon
Executive Director, Dann Lindsay
Manager Project Manager, David Penning

LOCATIONS

HQ: ANR PIPELINE COMPANY
700 LOUISIANA ST STE 700 # 700, HOUSTON, TX 770022873
Phone: 832 320-2000
Web: WWW.ANRPL.COM

COMPETITORS

Alliance Pipeline	Transcontinental Gas
Buckeye Pipe Line	Pipe Line
Columbia Gulf	Vector Pipeline
Transmission	Williams Companies
Duke Energy	Williston Basin
Oge Energy	Interstate Pipeline
Oneok Partners	
Panhandle Eastern Pipe	
Line	

HISTORICAL FINANCIALS
Company Type: Private

Income Statement   FYE: December 31

	REVENUE ($ mil.)	NET INCOME ($ mil.)	NET PROFIT MARGIN	EMPLOYEES
12/17	758	139	18.5%	1,000
12/16	686	54	8.0%	—
12/06	540	152	28.1%	—
12/05	548	147	26.8%	—
Annual Growth	2.7%	(0.4%)	—	—

2017 Year-End Financials
Return on assets: 4.6%   Cash ($ mil.): —
Return on equity: 10.4%
Current ratio: 1.30

API GROUP, INC.

Holding company APi Group has a piece of the action in two main sectors: fire protection systems and industrial and specialty construction services. APi boasts about 40 subsidiaries which operate as independent companies across the US (nearly half of them in Minnesota) the UK and Canada. Services provided by the company's construction subsidiaries include HVAC and plumbing system installation; electrical industrial and mechanical contracting; industrial insulation; and garage door installation. Safety-focused units install a host of fire sprinkler detection security and alarm systems. The family-owned company was founded in 1926 by Reuben Anderson father of chairman Lee Anderson.

Operations
Through its various companies APi Group is involved in engineering designing constructing and installing LEED green-building certification program projects. Its divisions include Architectural Roofing and Mechanical Classic Industrial Services APi Construction APi Distribution and Industrial Fabricators among others.

Geographic Reach
Minnesota-based APi Group operates companies throughout North America and the UK.

Sales and Marketing
APi Group serves several sectors such as security and defense education commercial industrial medical oil and gas and residential.

Strategy
Although APi Group companies are independent they often pool resources and work together to service clients.

Mergers and Acquisitions
The highly acquisitive APi Group regularly acquires new companies to strengthen its growing group.

In 2013 the company's Western States Fire Protection (WSFP) acquired Advanced Fire an Oklahoma City-based fire-suppression company that specializes in military work. Buying Advanced Fire extends the company's reach in the fire protection industry and boosts its market share within Oklahoma City and the surrounding area. APi Group's Delta Fire Systems acquired Idaho's 3-D Fire which provides full-fire-system design fabrication installation testing and certification capabilities for commercial and private projects.

APi Group previous purchases include Dynamic Fire Protection LLC (DFP) Omlid & Swinney Fire Protection and Security Canada-based Fire Stop Enterprises Ohio-based 3S and Kansas-based mainline pipeline contractor Jomax Construction.

EXECUTIVES
Pres-Ceo, Russell A Becker
Co Chb*, Martin E Franklin
Co Chb*, James E Lillie
Cfo, Thomas A Lydon
Clo, Paul W Grunau
Sr V Pres-Gen Counsel-Sec, Andrea M Fike
V Pres- Controller, Andrew J Cebulla
Midwest Regional Manager, Aaron Price
Project Manager, Adam Tollefson
Client Manager, Ahmed Abdel-Kerim
Auditors: KPMG

LOCATIONS
HQ: API GROUP, INC.
1100 OLD HIGHWAY 8 NW, NEW BRIGHTON, MN 551126447
Phone: 651 636-4320
Web: WWW.APIGROUPINC.COM

PRODUCTS/OPERATIONS
Selected Subsidiaries
Fire Protection Systems
 Alliance Fire Protection Inc.
 APi National Service Group
 Davis-Ulmer Sprinkler Company
 Delta Fire Systems Inc.
 Grunau Company
 Halon Banking Systems
 International Fire Protection Inc.
 Island Fire Sprinkler Inc.
 Reliance Fire Protection
 Rich Fire Protection Co Inc.
 Security Fire Protection Company
 United States Fire Protection Company
 VFP Fire Systems Inc.
 Viking Automatic Sprinkler Company
 Vipond Fire Protection Inc. (Canada)
 Vipond Fire Protection Ltd. (UK)
 Western States Fire Protection Inc.
Industrial and Specialty Construction Services
   3S Incorporated
 Anco Products Inc.
 APi CAD Services
 APi Construction Company
 APi Distribution Inc.
 APi Electric
 APi Supply Inc.
 Classic Industrial Services Inc.
 Doody Mechanical Inc.
 Garage Door Store
 Grunau Company Inc.
 Industrial Contractors Inc.
 Industrial Fabricators Inc.
 Jamar Company
 Jomax Construction Co.
 LeJeune Steel Company
 NYCO Inc.
 Tessier's Inc.
 Twin City Garage Door Company
Low Voltage
 APi Systems Group Inc.
 APi Systems Integrators
 Vipond Systems Group

COMPETITORS

Comfort Systems Usa	Tdindustries
Emcor	Team
Ies Holdings	Turner Industries
Irex	Tyco Fire & Security
John E. Green	

HISTORICAL FINANCIALS
Company Type: Private

Income Statement   FYE: December 31

	REVENUE ($ mil.)	NET INCOME ($ mil.)	NET PROFIT MARGIN	EMPLOYEES
12/18	3,730	122	3.3%	4,237
12/17	3,046	112	3.7%	—
12/16	2,608	104	4.0%	—
12/15	2,448	106	4.3%	—
Annual Growth	15.1%	5.0%	—	—

2018 Year-End Financials
Return on assets: 6.2%   Cash ($ mil.): 54
Return on equity: 21.3%
Current ratio: 1.10

APPALACHIAN REGIONAL HEALTHCARE, INC.

Under-the-weather coal miners (and their daughters) can turn to Appalachian Regional Healthcare (ARH) for medical services. The not-for-profit health system serves residents of eastern Kentucky and southern West Virginia through a dozen hospitals with more than 1000 beds as well as dozens of clinics home health care agencies HomeCare Stores and retail pharmacies. Its largest hospital in Hazard Kentucky has 310 beds and features an inpatient psychiatric unit that serves as the state mental health facility. Several of the system's hospitals are Critical Access Hospitals a federal government designation for rural community hospitals that operate in medically underserved areas.

Operations
ARH's HomeCare Stores provide home medical equipment and oxygen delivery as well as 24-hour support through eight respiratory therapists. Its HomeCare Stores are supported by the ARH Home Health Agencies which provide access to nursing care occupational and physical therapy and social services.

Among the system's hospitals are Beckley ARH Hospital a not-for-profit 173-bed acute-care facility; Harlan ARH Hospital a state-licensed 150-bed acute-care facility; and Mary Breckinridge ARH Hospital a critical access facility.

ARH is the largest provider of care and single largest employer in southeastern Kentucky and the third-largest private employer in southern West Virginia. It employs almost 5000 people and has a network of more than 600 medical staff members. In 2013 the system had 153000 emergency department visits 482000 outpatient visits some 1500 births and about 12000 outpatient surgeries.

Geographic Reach
ARH serves residents of eastern Kentucky and southern West Virginia. It has hospitals in Harlan Hazard Hyden Martin McDowell Middlesboro Morgan County South Williamson and Whitesburg Kentucky; and in Beckley and Summers County West Virginia.

Strategy
As the primary provider of health care to medically underserved populations ARH doles out millions of dollars in uncompensated care each year to un- or underinsured residents of the Appalachian region.

Along with a larger population of uninsured patients and the resulting unpaid medical bills that come along with them rural health care providers face a number of hardships not encountered by their urban brethren. For example physician recruitment is more difficult at rural hospitals especially for some higher-risk specialties such as obstetrics. In order to attract and retain doctors ARH and other rural health care providers have to offer more competitive compensation packages pay for relocation and invest in technology and facility upgrades.

Also patients in rural areas are more likely to suffer from chronic health problems such as diabetes and obesity which can become a significant drain on a health system's resources. ARH is one of many health care providers looking to benefit from changes to the health care system outlined in Affordable Care Act especially the requirement that all US citizens carry health insurance.

To keep up with patient demand ARH also focuses on building and acquiring new facilities as well as investing in new technology and medical capacities.

Beckley ARH Hospital is undergoing a nearly $7 million renovation project that will add 19 more private rooms decrease utility costs and improve patient flow processes. In 2014 ARH completed a $47 million expansion project at the Hazard ARH Regional Medical Center that added an additional 100000 sq. ft. to the medical center including a new patient tower a new 24-bed emergency department on the first floor a dedicated 16-bed cardiac critical care unit and 34 private rooms. Hazard ARH is now the largest hospital in southeastern Kentucky.

Mergers and Acquisitions
In 2018 Appalachian Regional Healthcare acquired its twelfth hospital — the 25-bed Saint Joseph Martin Hospital — and its clinics. That facility now operates as ARH Our Lady of the Way.

Company Background
Appalachian Regional Healthcare was formed in 1956 by the United Mine Workers of America but became an independent not-for-profit entity in the early 1960s.

EXECUTIVES

Pres-Ceo, Jerry W Haynes
V Pres-Cfo, Christopher Ellington
V Pres, Joe Grossman
V Pres, Rick King
Pres, Joseph L Grossman
V Pres, Danny Harris
EC, Thomas Hyatt
Director of Centralized, Jill Scott
Materials Management, Joanna Napier
Nurse Manager, Kathi Searcy
Materials Manager, Kathy Bowling
Auditors: MCM CPA'S & ADVISORS LLP LOU

LOCATIONS

HQ: APPALACHIAN REGIONAL HEALTHCARE, INC.
2260 EXECUTIVE DR, LEXINGTON, KY 405054808
Phone: 859 226-2440
Web: WWW.ARH.ORG

PRODUCTS/OPERATIONS

Selected Facilities
Beckley ARH Hospital (Beckley West Virginia)
Hazard ARH Regional Medical Center (Hazard Kentucky)
Harlan ARH Hospital (Harlan Kentucky)
McDowell ARH Hospital (McDowell Kentucky)
Middlesboro ARH Hospital (Middlesboro Kentucky)
Morgan County ARH Hospital (West Liberty Kentucky)
Summers County ARH Hospital (Hinton West Virginia)
Tug Valley ARH Regional Medical Center (South Williamson Kentucky)
Whitesburg ARH Hospital (Whitesburg Kentucky)

Selected Services
Bariatrics
Behavioral Health
Cancer Care
Clinics
Emergency
Heart Care
Home Health
HomeCare Stores
Imaging
Laboratory
Medical Spa
Nephrology
Obstetrics and Gynecology
Pediatrics
Pharmacy
Rehabilitation Therapy
Respiratory Therapy
Rheumatology
Senior Care
Skilled Nursing
Sleep Lab
Surgery
Swing Beds

COMPETITORS

Baptist Health	Mercy Medical Center
Bon Secours Health	(ny)
Carilion Clinic	Montgomery Regional
Catholic Health	Hospital
Initiatives	Norton Healthcare
Community Health	Pikeville Medical
Systems	Center
Highlands Health	University Of Kentucky
Jewish Hospital & St.	Chandler Hospital
Mary's Healthcare	University Of Virginia
Kindred Healthcare	Health System

HISTORICAL FINANCIALS
Company Type: Private

Income Statement				FYE: June 30
	REVENUE ($ mil.)	NET INCOME ($ mil.)	NET PROFIT MARGIN	EMPLOYEES
06/20	868	23	2.7%	4,520
06/19	760	1	0.2%	—
06/18	689	65	9.4%	—
06/17	657	43	6.6%	—
Annual Growth	9.7%	(18.9%)	—	—

2020 Year-End Financials

Return on assets: 2.1%   Cash ($ mil.): 201
Return on equity: 7.7%
Current ratio: 0.90

APPLE HOSPITALITY REIT, INC.

EXECUTIVES

Ceo, Justin G Knight
Exec Chb*, Glade M Knight
Sr V Pres-Coo, Karen C Gallagher
Sr V Pres-Cao, Rachel S Labrecque
Sr V Pres-Cfo, Elizabeth S Perkins
Sr V Pres-Clo-Sec, Matthew P Rash
Pres, Real Estate & Investment, Nelson G Knight
Sr V Pres, Chief Capital Inves, Jeanette A Clarke
Senior Asset Manager, Chris Castellano
Manager Director, Debra Quin
Senior Asset Manager, Kelly Klocke
Auditors: ERNST & YOUNG LLP RICHMOND V

LOCATIONS

HQ: APPLE HOSPITALITY REIT, INC.
814 E MAIN ST, RICHMOND, VA 232193306
Phone: 804 344-8121
Web: WWW.HILTON.COM

HISTORICAL FINANCIALS
Company Type: Private

Income Statement				FYE: December 31
	REVENUE ($ mil.)	NET INCOME ($ mil.)	NET PROFIT MARGIN	EMPLOYEES
12/14	803	6	0.9%	66
12/13	387	115	29.7%	—
12/12	365	75	20.6%	—
12/11	320	69	21.8%	—
Annual Growth	35.9%	(54.0%)	—	—

APPLIED MEDICAL RESOURCES CORPORATION

EXECUTIVES

Pres-Ceo, Said S Hilal
Group Pres, Dist*, Stephen E Stanley
Group Pres, Tech*, Nabil Hilal
Cfo*, Samir Tall
Group Pres, Surgical*, Gary Johnson
Senior Vice President, Mary Jo Stegwell
Vice-President Legal, Michael Vaughn
Vice President, Matt Petrime
Engineering Manager, Tim Hopkins
Engineer, Alexander Sandstrom
Sales Associate, Cody Buck

LOCATIONS

HQ: APPLIED MEDICAL RESOURCES CORPORATION
22872 AVENIDA EMPRESA, RCHO STA MARG, CA
926882650
Phone: 949 713-8000
Web: WWW.APPLIEDMEDICAL.COM

HISTORICAL FINANCIALS
Company Type: Private

Income Statement				FYE: December 31
	REVENUE ($ mil.)	NET INCOME ($ mil.)	NET PROFIT MARGIN	EMPLOYEES
12/20	544	31	5.8%	4,319
12/19	585	47	8.1%	—
Annual Growth	(7.1%)	(33.6%)	—	—

ARCTIC SLOPE REGIONAL CORPORATION

The Inupiat-owned Arctic Slope Regional Corporation (ASRC) is a locally owned and operated business in Alaska. It gets the bulk of its sales from energy services (ASRC Energy Services) and petroleum refining and marketing unit (Petro Star). Other operations include construction (ASRC Construction Holding) governmental services (ASRC Federal Holding) economic development (Alaska Growth Capital BIDCO) local services (Eskimos Inc.) and tourism (Tundra Tours).

Operations
ASRC own titles to nearly 5 million acres of land on Alaska's North Slope which contain a high potential for oil gas coal and base metal sulfides.

It operates in six diverse major business segments: petroleum refining and marketing government contract services energy support services industrial services resource development and construction industries. Petro Star has two refineries (strategically positioned along the Trans-Alaska Pipeline) and serves Interior Alaska South Central Alaska Kodiak and Dutch Harbor. Its North Pole facility supplies the mining industry in the interior region of Alaska and provides home heating oil to several communities.

ASRC Federal Holding Company provides professional and technical services to the federal government (including defense and intelligence agencies engineering IT infrastructure support professional and technical services to civil).

ASRC Energy Services offers oilfield engineering operations maintenance construction fabrication regulation and permitting and other services to oil and gas companies. The company provides services to the energy industry throughout Alaska and the Gulf of Mexico.

ASRC Construction Holding Company provides construction services to commercial and government clients in Alaska the Lower 48 and in other countries.

ASRC Industrial Services (AIS) is a people-oriented organization of complementary yet diverse services focusing on the industrial end-use customers nationwide.

Geographic Reach
ASRC represents approximately 13000 I ±upiat shareholders in the villages of Point Hope Point Lay Wainwright Atqasuk Utqiagvik Nuiqsut Kaktovik and Anaktuvuk Pass. ASRC has its offices in Anchorage. It has other subsidiary offices in the Lower 48 states.

Company Background
ASRC was set up to own and manage 5 million acres on Alaska's North Slope after the Alaska Native Claims Settlement Act in 1971 cleared the way for oil development in the area.

In 2010 ASRC protested the US Fish and Wildlife Service's designation of Alaskan North Slope oil-producing areas as a critical habitat for endangered polar bears claiming it would cost ASRC millions of dollars in lost oil revenues. In 2011 it led a coalition of Native groups to sue the Department of the Interior over this issue.

In 2012 ASRC Construction Holding expanded into southeast Alaska with the acquisition of native-Alaskan owned McGraw's Custom Construction.

EXECUTIVES

Chm, Jacob Adams
Ceo*, Rex A Rock Sr
Vice Chairman*, George Sielak
Sr V Pres-Coo*, Mark Kroloff
Cfo*, Kristin Mellinger
Treasurer*, Crawford Patkotak
1st V-Pres*, Patsy Aamodt
2nd V-Pres*, George Kaleak Sr
3rd V-Pres*, Raymond Paneak
Sr Paralegal*, Melissa Ferreira
Procurement Manager, Diana Teel

LOCATIONS

HQ: ARCTIC SLOPE REGIONAL CORPORATION
3900 C ST STE 801, ANCHORAGE, AK 995035963
Phone: 907 339-6000
Web: WWW.ASRC.COM

PRODUCTS/OPERATIONS

Selected Businesses
Energy Services
  ASRC Energy Services Inc.
  Arctic Inupiat Offshore LLC.
Petroleum Refining and Marketing
  Petro Star Inc.
Government Services
  ASRC Federal Holding Company
Construction
  ASRC Construction Holding Company LLC
Resource Development
  Little Red Services
  Petrochem

COMPETITORS

Alaska Communications	Noble
Systems	Schlumberger
Baker Hughes	T-mobile Usa
Halliburton	Tesoro
Nabors Industries	

HISTORICAL FINANCIALS
Company Type: Private

Income Statement · FYE: December 31

	REVENUE ($ mil.)	NET INCOME ($ mil.)	NET PROFIT MARGIN	EMPLOYEES
12/08	2,297	151	6.6%	6,700
12/07	1,777	207	11.7%	—
12/06	1,700	206	12.1%	—
12/05	1,566	127	8.1%	—
Annual Growth	13.6%	5.8%	—	—

2008 Year-End Financials
Return on assets: 11.7%   Cash ($ mil.): 302
Return on equity: 19.0%
Current ratio: 1.70

ARIZONA STATE LOTTERY

EXECUTIVES

Dep Dir, Karen Emery
Director*, Gregory Edgar
Info Tech Specialist, Benita Martinez
Auditors: HENRY & HORNE LLP CASA GRAND

LOCATIONS

HQ: ARIZONA STATE LOTTERY
4740 E UNIVERSITY DR, PHOENIX, AZ 850347400
Phone: 480 921-4400
Web: WWW.ARIZONALOTTERY.COM

HISTORICAL FINANCIALS
Company Type: Private

Income Statement · FYE: June 30

	REVENUE ($ mil.)	NET INCOME ($ mil.)	NET PROFIT MARGIN	EMPLOYEES
06/20	1,097	5	0.5%	112
06/19	1,076	9	0.9%	—
06/17	853	0	0.0%	—
06/97	254	84	33.2%	—
Annual Growth	6.6%	(11.1%)	—	—

2020 Year-End Financials
Return on assets: 4.5%   Cash ($ mil.): 57
Return on equity: 26.8%
Current ratio: 0.90

ARIZONA STATE UNIVERSITY

Arizona State University (ASU) offers more than 800 degree programs for undergraduate and degree pursuing a master's degree or doctoral program. The university offers nearly 300 undergraduate and graduate degree programs and certificates are also offered 100% online. It has 54000 students enrolled. ASU was founded in 1885.

Operations
ASU offers more than 300 undergraduate and graduate degrees and certificates online through some of its colleges including the W. P. Carey School of Business Mary Lou Fulton Teachers College College of Nursing and Health Innovation and the Ira A. Fulton School of Engineering.

The university's extensive research programs cover a variety of fields in life science medicine and Physics and more.

Geographic Reach
ASU has an enrollment of students from more than 136 countries.

Sales and Marketing
Arizona State University offers academics with more than 400 undergraduate degrees and more than 450 graduate degree led by an expert faculty and highly ranked colleges and schools on the university websites.

Financial Performance
Operating revenues increased $132 million or 6% to over $2.1 billion in FY 2020 with the most significant increases occurring in net tuition and fees and research grants and contracts.

Cash held by the company at the end of fiscal 2020 increased to $546.4 million. Cash used for operations was $465.9 million while cash provided by investing and financing activities were $458.8 million and $34.1 million respectively.

Strategy
As part of the Arizona Board of Regents' strategic plan Impact Arizona key performance metrics are used to measure the success of ASU and the other state universities in achieving institutional and system-wide goals. Impact Arizona goals measure progress in delivering a high-quality university education; increasing the number of Arizonans with a college degree or certificate; creating new knowledge collaborations inventions and technology to solve critical problems; and engaging the communities through initiatives and partnerships to improve Arizona's economy and competitiveness. Key measures of progress toward achieving these goals are continually reviewed and monitored by ABOR and the universities. Overarching ASU goals as part of this strategic plan include demonstrating leadership in academic excellence and accessibility; achieving national standing in academic quality and impactful colleges and schools in every field; obtaining recognition as a global center for interdisciplinary research discovery and development; and enhancing local impact and social embeddedness.

Mergers and Acquisitions
Arizona State University has acquired Ashford University's 35000 students in a bid to create a new independent nonprofit entity dubbed UA

Global Campus to compete online education space. Ashford has a controversial history and its parent company will continue to operate the online university as a contractor. The UA acquired all of Ashford's assets for the symbolic value of one dollar. The new Global Campus is expected to generate over $225 million in revenue over 15 years according to the UA. Under the terms of the deal parent company Zovio will receive 19.5% of the tuition revenue from the campus in exchange for providing education technology services.

EXECUTIVES

Pres, Michael M Crow
Exec V Pres-Provost, Elizabeth Capaldi
Ex V Pres-Cfo, Carol Campbell
V Pres Fin-Treas, Gerald Snyder
CIO, Lev Gonick
Research Assistant, Erin Chiou
Mining Manager, Tom Billings
Desk Assistant, Cole Klosterman
Research Advancement Administr, Fernando Zacarias
Engineer, Zhenquan Liu
Marketing Communication, Aaron Pugh
Auditors: LINDSEY PERRY CPA CFE PHOEN

LOCATIONS

HQ: ARIZONA STATE UNIVERSITY
300 E UNIVERSITY DR # 410, TEMPE, AZ 852812061
Phone: 480 965-2100
Web: WWW.ASU.EDU

PRODUCTS/OPERATIONS

2014 Sales

	$ mil.	% of total
Tuition & fees	896	67
Research grants and contracts	244	18
Auxiliary enterprises	140	10
Other operating revenues	66	5
Total	**1,348**	**100**

Selected Colleges and Schools

Barrett Honors College
College of Health Solutions
College of Liberal Arts and Sciences
College of Nursing and Health Innovation
College of Public Programs
College of Technology and Innovation
Graduate College
Herberger Institute for Design and the Arts
Ira A. Fulton Schools of Engineering
Mary Lou Fulton Teachers College
New College of Interdisciplinary Arts and Sciences
Sandra Day O'Connor College of Law
School of Letters and Sciences
School of Sustainability
Thunderbird School of Global Management
University College
Walter Cronkite School of Journalism and Mass Communication
W.P. Carey School of Business

HISTORICAL FINANCIALS

Company Type: Private

Income Statement				FYE: June 30
	REVENUE ($ mil.)	NET INCOME ($ mil.)	NET PROFIT MARGIN	EMPLOYEES
06/20	2,180	6	0.3%	8,000
06/19	2,048	85	4.2%	—
06/18	1,915	63	3.3%	—
06/17	1,782	99	5.6%	—
Annual Growth	7.0%	(59.4%)	—	—

2020 Year-End Financials

Return on assets: 0.1%   Cash ($ mil.): 272
Return on equity: 0.5%
Current ratio: 1.00

ARIZONA STATE UNIVERSITY

EXECUTIVES

Prin, Nancy Scherer

LOCATIONS

HQ: ARIZONA STATE UNIVERSITY
951 S PALM WALK, TEMPE, AZ 852870001
Phone: 480 965-4385
Web: WWW.ASU.EDU

HISTORICAL FINANCIALS

Company Type: Private

Income Statement				FYE: June 30
	REVENUE ($ mil.)	NET INCOME ($ mil.)	NET PROFIT MARGIN	EMPLOYEES
06/15	1,482	92	6.2%	26
06/14	1,348	103	7.7%	—
Annual Growth	9.9%	(10.7%)	—	—

2015 Year-End Financials

Return on assets: 6.4%   Cash ($ mil.): 47
Return on equity: 6.2%
Current ratio: 0.60

ARKANSAS CHILDREN'S HOSPITAL

As the only pediatric medical center in the state Arkansas Children's Hospital (ACH) serves the youngest Razorbacks from birth to age 21. The not-for-profit hospital with its about 335 beds specializes in childhood cancer pediatric orthopedics and neonatology. Besides acute care services a staff of approximately 505 physicians and over 200 residents it operates more than 80 specialty clinics and outpatient centers. One of the US's largest pediatric hospitals ACH is also engaged in teaching and medical research through its affiliation with the University of Arkansas for Medical Sciences. Its Arkansas Children's Hospital Research Institute focuses on biological mechanisms underlying birth defects diabetes-related complications and childhood diseases.

EXECUTIVES

Exec V Pres, Chanda Chacon
Cfo*, Gena G Wingfield
Chm*, Tom Baxter
Sr V Pres*, Darrell Leonhardt
Coo*, Scott R Gordon
Svp-CIO*, Erin Parker
Chief of Staff and Director, Charles M Bower
Audiologist, Steve Upson
Doctor, Charlotte A Hobbs
Doctor, Charles N Glasier
Coordinator, Lisa Walker
Auditors: KPMG LLP MEMPHIS TN

LOCATIONS

HQ: ARKANSAS CHILDREN'S HOSPITAL
1 CHILDRENS WAY, LITTLE ROCK, AR 722023500
Phone: 501 364-1100
Web: WWW.ARCHILDRENS.ORG

PRODUCTS/OPERATIONS

Selected Services

Ambulatory Surgery
Audiology
Center for Good Mourning
Cleft Clinic
Dennis Developmental Center
Dental Clinic
ECMO
Gastroenterology Clinic
Genetic and Metabolic Clinic
Infectious Diseases
Neuroscience Unit
Physical Medicine & Rehab Outreach Clinics
Sleep Disorders Center
Volunteer Services
WHAM (Wellness Health Action & Motivation) Clinic

COMPETITORS

Arkansas Heart Hospital
Baptist Health (arkansas)
Children's Healthcare Of Atlanta
Children's Medical Center Of Dallas
Children's Mercy Hospital
Children's National Medical Center
Cook Children's Health Care System
Dell Children's Medical Center
East Tennessee Children's Hospital
Jefferson Regional Medical Center Of Arkansas
Methodist Healthcare
Shriners Hospitals For Children
St. Joseph's Mercy Health Center
St. Jude Children's Research Hospital
St. Vincent Health System
Texas Children's Hospital
Universal Health Services
White County Medical Center

HISTORICAL FINANCIALS

Company Type: Private

Income Statement				FYE: June 30
	REVENUE ($ mil.)	NET INCOME ($ mil.)	NET PROFIT MARGIN	EMPLOYEES
06/20	646	50	7.9%	3,700
06/19	703	93	13.3%	—
06/18	660	57	8.7%	—
06/17	615	59	9.7%	—
Annual Growth	1.7%	(5.2%)	—	—

2020 Year-End Financials

Return on assets: 5.3%   Cash ($ mil.): 92
Return on equity: 6.2%
Current ratio: 1.20

ARKANSAS ELECTRIC COOPERATIVE CORPORATION

Having access to power is the natural state in the Natural State thanks to Arkansas Electric Cooperative Corporation (AECC) the sole wholesale power provider for 17 Arkansas electric distribution cooperatives. The company operates power plants with 3418 MW of generating capacity owns transmission assets and buys wholesale power to meet its members' demands. Affiliate Arkansas Electric Cooperatives Inc. (AECI) provides administrative and maintenance services to the distribution companies. The distribution utilities serve about 500000 customers in more than 60% of

Arkansas. AECC and AECI along with the state's 17 electric distribution cooperatives are known as the Electric Cooperatives of Arkansas.

Operations

AECC's diverse generation assets include three hydropower plants three natural gas/oil-based plants and three natural gas-based-only plants. It also co-owns portions of four low-cost coal-based plants and has a long-term power purchase agreement for 51 MW wind energy. The coop also has four transmission lines.

Sales and Marketing

In fiscal 2013 co-op members Mississippi County Electric Cooperative First Electric Cooperative Carroll Electric Cooperative and Arkansas Valley Electric Corporation together accounted for 59% of AECC's total revenues.

Financial Performance

Thanks to a rebounding economy and growing demand for power the company saw its revenues grow by 13% in fiscal 2013.

Net income declined by 37% in fiscal 2013 due to higher operations maintenance generation and transmission expenses as well as an increase in administration and general expenses.

Strategy

AECC is ramping up its renewable energy resources in order to meet state and federal clean energy power requirements.

In 2013 the company signed a long-term deal to buy 150 MW of wind energy from RES America Developments Inc. a subsidiary of Renewable Energy Systems Americas Inc.

In 2012 it reached a long-term purchase power agreement for 51 MW of wind energy from the Flat Ridge 2 South Wind Farm in Kansas. AECC's 51 MW of capacity is part of 470 MW of potential generation provided by the farm's 294 GE wind turbines. BP and Sempra U.S. Gas & Power are equal joint venture partners for the facility which has a combined investment of more than $800 million. A wholly-owned affiliate of BP Wind Energy will monitor and maintain the farm

Mergers and Acquisitions

In another move to cut back on the use of coal-fired power plants in 2012 AECC bought a 746-MW combined cycle natural gas-fired power plant near Magnet Cove for $240 million.

Company Background

The first electric cooperative in Arkansas was formed in Jacksonville in 1938 as part of the Roosevelt Administration's national rural electrification drive.

EXECUTIVES

Exec Vp, Michael W Henderson
Controller*, Lisa Sigler
Pres*, Bill Conine
Attorney*, Lori Burrows
Payroll Staff, Denise Garrison
Vice President of Human Resour, Maria Smedley
Information Technology Directo, Barbara Harris
Tax Accountant, Jeff Roberts
Plant Manager, John Morgan
Senior Accountant Taxes, Justin Simpson
Human Resources Coordinator, Sarah Littleton
Auditors: BKD LLP LITTLE ROCK ARKANSA

LOCATIONS

HQ: ARKANSAS ELECTRIC COOPERATIVE CORPORATION
1 COOPERATIVE WAY, LITTLE ROCK, AR 722095493
Phone: 501 570-2200
Web: WWW.AECC.COM

HISTORICAL FINANCIALS

Company Type: Private

Income Statement				FYE: October 31
	REVENUE ($ mil.)	NET INCOME ($ mil.)	NET PROFIT MARGIN	EMPLOYEES
10/19	790	24	3.1%	220
10/18*	827	38	4.7%	—
12/15	462	35	7.7%	—
12/14	455	30	6.6%	—
Annual Growth	11.7%	(3.8%)		

*Fiscal year change

2019 Year-End Financials

Return on assets: 1.4% Cash ($ mil.): 154
Return on equity: 4.1%
Current ratio: 0.90

ARKANSAS ELECTRIC COOPERATIVES, INC.

EXECUTIVES

Chief Technology Officer, Vice President - Information Technology, Robert McClanahan
Vice President - Public Affairs And Member Services, Sandra Byrd
Vice President Of Human Resources And Corporate Strategy, Maria Smedley
President, Chief Executive Officer, Vernon Hasten
Chief Financial Officer, Vice President, David Frankenberg
Auditors: BKD LLP LITTLE ROCK ARKANSA

LOCATIONS

HQ: ARKANSAS ELECTRIC COOPERATIVES, INC.
1 COOPERATIVE WAY, LITTLE ROCK, AR 722095493
Phone: 501 570-2200
Web: WWW.AECC.COM

HISTORICAL FINANCIALS

Company Type: Private

Income Statement				FYE: December 31
	REVENUE ($ mil.)	NET INCOME ($ mil.)	NET PROFIT MARGIN	EMPLOYEES
12/18	679	50	7.4%	840
12/17	564	44	7.8%	—
12/15	462	35	7.7%	—
12/13	416	32	7.7%	—
Annual Growth	10.3%	9.4%	—	—

2018 Year-End Financials

Return on assets: 13.8% Cash ($ mil.): 101
Return on equity: 18.5%
Current ratio: 3.60

ARLINGTON INDEPENDENT SCHOOL DISTRICT (INC)

EXECUTIVES

Supt, Marcelo Bavazls
Principal, Webb Elementary, Michael Martin
Coordinator, Kathy Hitt
Tech Prep Coordinator, Ed Cannady
Sp Ed Teacher, Daisy Segovia
Chemistry Teacher, Israel Iyoke
Social Media Marketing, Becky Volk
Senior Project Manager Facilit, Michael Parkos
Teacher Elementary, Traci Underwood
Board of Trustees, Aaron Aisd
Administrative Assistant, America Mathias
Auditors: WHITLEY PENN FORT WORTH TX

LOCATIONS

HQ: ARLINGTON INDEPENDENT SCHOOL DISTRICT (INC)
690 E LAMAR BLVD STE 110, ARLINGTON, TX 760113869
Phone: 682 867-4611
Web: WWW.AISD.NET

HISTORICAL FINANCIALS

Company Type: Private

Income Statement				FYE: June 30
	REVENUE ($ mil.)	NET INCOME ($ mil.)	NET PROFIT MARGIN	EMPLOYEES
06/20	732	248	33.9%	8,000
06/19	688	(87)	—	—
06/18	680	(28)	—	—
06/17	641	(35)	—	—
Annual Growth	4.5%	—	—	—

2020 Year-End Financials

Return on assets: 16.0% Cash ($ mil.): 661
Return on equity: —
Current ratio: —

ASCENSION HEALTH ALLIANCE

EXECUTIVES

Pres-Ceo, Joseph Impicciche
Pres-Ceo*, Joseph R Impicciche
Sr Exec Advsr*, Sister Bernice Coreil DC
Evp*, John D Doyle
Evp*, Robert J Henkel
Evp*, Susan Nestor Levy
Evp*, Sister Maureen McGuire DC
Evp, David B Pryor
Executive Administrative Assis, Teresa Hatton
Regional Director, Andrew Gwin
Cco Clinical & Network Svs, Richard Fogel
Auditors: ERNST & YOUNG LLP ST LOUIS

LOCATIONS

HQ: ASCENSION HEALTH ALLIANCE
101 S HANLEY RD STE 450, SAINT LOUIS, MO
631053463
Phone: 314 733-8000
Web: WWW.HEALTHCARE.ASCENSION.ORG

HISTORICAL FINANCIALS

Company Type: Private

Income Statement				FYE: June 30
	ASSETS ($ mil.)	NET INCOME ($ mil.)	INCOME AS % OF ASSETS	EMPLOYEES
06/17	34,320	1,638	4.8%	150,000
06/16	32,469	(339)	—	—
06/15	30,963	(42)	—	—
Annual Growth	5.3%	—	—	—

2017 Year-End Financials

Return on assets: 4.8% Sales ($ mil): 22,633
Return on equity: 8.0%

ASCENSION PROVIDENCE HOSPITAL

Providence Hospital and Medical Centers provides health care in the Motor City and surrounding areas. The main Providence Hospital is a 408-bed teaching facility that has been recognized for its cardiology program and clinical expertise in behavioral medicine. It offers a variety of other services ranging from cancer treatment and neurosurgery to orthopedics and women's health. The network also includes dozens of affiliated general practice and specialty health clinics. The not-for-profit medical center founded in 1845 as St. Vincent's Hospital in Detroit by the Daughters of Charity is part of Catholic health ministry St. John Health (itself a subsidiary of Ascension Health).

Operations

As part of its health care system Providence Hospital and Medical Centers operates a host of hospitals and medical centers across the metropolitan Detroit area. They include Providence Southfield and four namesake Providence Medical Center locations in Farmington Hills Livonia Dearborn Heights and South Lyon. Across its system the medical facilities employ some 1500 physicians and enlist the help of about 300 active volunteers.

Carroll Manor is a skilled nursing center that provides short- and long-term medical care and rehabilitation services. The system's behavioral health division Seton House provides alcohol and addiction treatment in Washington DC.

Providence Hospital and Medical Centers had more than 41600 emergency department visits in 2013.

Strategy

In order to provide better services the hospital renovated and expanded its emergency department in 2014. Also that year its family medicine division opened a new office in the Glenn Dale/Bowie area.

EXECUTIVES

Pres-Ceo, Brant Russell
Prin, Diane Radloff
Internal Medicine Practitioner, Zaid Yaldo
Chief Operating Officer, Vijay Mittal
Internal Medicine Practitioner, Elias Zeine

Internal Medicine Practitioner, Michael J Di Loreto
Coordinator, Tiffany Tscherne
Internist, Gurbir Singh
Administrative Assistant, Leslie Tippett
Director, Lou Bischoff
Internist, Mousa Shukr
Auditors: DELOITTE TAX LP CINCINNATI O

LOCATIONS

HQ: ASCENSION PROVIDENCE HOSPITAL
16001 W 9 MILE RD, SOUTHFIELD, MI 480754818
Phone: 248 849-3000
Web: WWW.PROVIDENCEOBGYNRESIDENCY.COM

Selected Hospitals and Medical Centers

Providence Southfield-Southfield
Providence Medical Center-Farmington Hills
Providence Medical Center-Livonia
Providence Medical Center-Dearborn Heights
Providence Medical Center-South Lyon

PRODUCTS/OPERATIONS

Selected Primary Services

Cancer clinical trials
Cardiac rehabilitation
Childbirth
Congenital heart disease clinic
Emergency
Oncology
Orthopedics
Senior services
Surgery
Women's health

COMPETITORS

Beaumont Health System	Mclaren Health Care
Crittenton Hospital	Trinity Health (novi)
Detroit Medical Center	University Of Michigan
Henry Ford Health System	Health System

HISTORICAL FINANCIALS

Company Type: Private

Income Statement				FYE: June 30
	REVENUE ($ mil.)	NET INCOME ($ mil.)	NET PROFIT MARGIN	EMPLOYEES
06/16	703	21	3.1%	4,700
06/15	654	25	3.9%	—
06/14	659	53	8.1%	—
06/11	706	27	3.9%	—
Annual Growth	(0.1%)	(4.9%)	—	—

2016 Year-End Financials

Return on assets: 0.5% Cash ($ mil.): 3
Return on equity: 3.2%
Current ratio: 1.20

ASCENSION VIA CHRISTI HOSPITALS WICHITA, INC.

EXECUTIVES

President, Kevin Strecker
Ceo*, Michael Mullis
V Pres*, Michael McCullough
Aprn, Jamie K Gilstrap
Director of Nursing, Lori Campbell

MD, Nicholas Cahoj
Pharmacy Director, James Garrelts
Manager Pharmacy Operations, Charles Gerlach
Pharmacist, David Donelan
Senior Director Human Resource, Kristina Langrehr
Associate Manager Operations, Lesley Anderson

LOCATIONS

HQ: ASCENSION VIA CHRISTI HOSPITALS WICHITA, INC.
929 N ST FRANCIS ST, WICHITA, KS 672143821
Phone: 316 268-5880
Web: WWW.VIACHRISTI.ORG

HISTORICAL FINANCIALS

Company Type: Private

Income Statement				FYE: June 30
	REVENUE ($ mil.)	NET INCOME ($ mil.)	NET PROFIT MARGIN	EMPLOYEES
06/19*	597	64	10.7%	4,100
09/14	534	68	12.9%	—
09/13	534	24	4.5%	—
09/12	855	0	—	—
Annual Growth	—	515.2%	—	—

*Fiscal year change

2019 Year-End Financials

Return on assets: 17.1% Cash ($ mil.): —
Return on equity: 22.8%
Current ratio: —

ASI COMPUTER TECHNOLOGIES INC

ASI offers an extensive line of products components and services and also provides ISO-9001 compliant system integration and value add contract assembly. ASI Computer Technologies is a national distributor of IT software and hardware products. It offers more than 15000 products including PCs scanners security surveillance and data storage devices. The company has rapidly grown to become the partner of choice for over 20000 VARs throughout North America. Its vendor partners include companies the likes of AMD Intel Microsoft and Western Digital. ASI's services include custom systems integration. It also markets PCs and notebooks under its own brands: Pegatron and Nspire. Furthermore it caters to various industries such as retail and the SMB market The company was established in 1987 by president and owner Cristine Liang.

Operations

ASI offers an extensive line of products components and services and also provides ISO-9001 compliant system integration and value add contract assembly. More specifically it has other products including but not limited to cables drones desktops mount USBs software hard drives and printers. In addition it provides Converged Infrastructure Solutions and server solutions for different platforms.

The company has services such as hardware and software testing pre-sales system design and configuration assistance and bios and driver updates among others. The company has partnerships with Samsung ASUS AMD Intel Microsoft and Western Digital to name a few.

Geographic Reach

Based in California ASI operates nationwide as well as in Canada. To support its business the wholesaler operates regional offices in Atlanta Chicago Dallas Los Angeles Portland Kansas and New Jersey. Its Canadian offices are in Montreal Toronto and Vancouver. In Mexico ASI has offices in Monterrey and Nuevo Laredo.

Sales and Marketing
ASI's diverse portfolio of products and services allow it to service a broad customer base (it counts over 8000 customers) which includes VARs systems integrators OEMs and retailers.

EXECUTIVES

Ceo, Christine Liang
Prin*, Marcel Liang
Controller*, Mae Gauss
Distribution/Shipping/Transpor, Darrell Allen
Administrator, Kelvin Smith
Senior Credit Manager, Joseph Cox
Customer Representativ, John Boney
Manager, Alex Belman
Manager, Alice Zhao
Manager, Jason Yeh
Sales Manager, Laurie Svec
Auditors: MARCUM LLP SAN FRANCISCO CA

LOCATIONS

HQ: ASI COMPUTER TECHNOLOGIES INC
48289 FREMONT BLVD, FREMONT, CA 945386510
Phone: 510 226-8000
Web: WWW.ASIPARTNER.COM

PRODUCTS/OPERATIONS

Selected Products
Accessories
Cables
Cameras
Cases
CD-ROM drives
Central processing units
Controller cards
DVD drives
Fans
Floppy drives
Hard drives
Keyboards
Memory
Mice
Modems
Monitors
Motherboards
MP3 players
Multimedia products
Network connectivity products
Notebooks
Optical drives
PCs
Power supplies
Printers
Projectors
Removable drives and media
Scanners
Software
Sound cards
Speakers
Storage devices
Tape back-up products
Video cards
Zip drives

COMPETITORS

Ascii Group	Mtm Technologies
Agilysys	Merisel
Arrow Electronics	Microage
Avnet	New Age Electronics
Avnet Technology	Sed International
Compucom	Shi International
Continental Resources	Synnex
D & H Distributing	Softmart
En Pointe	Supercom
Flextronics	Tech Data
Ingram Micro	

HISTORICAL FINANCIALS
Company Type: Private

Income Statement   FYE: December 31

	REVENUE ($ mil.)	NET INCOME ($ mil.)	NET PROFIT MARGIN	EMPLOYEES
12/13	1,746	17	1.0%	76
12/04	1,057	12	1.2%	—
12/03	982	13	1.3%	—
12/02	865	10	1.2%	—
Annual Growth	6.6%	4.9%	—	—

2013 Year-End Financials

Return on assets: 5.4%   Cash ($ mil.): 28
Return on equity: 1.0%
Current ratio: 1.10

ASPIRUS WAUSAU HOSPITAL, INC.

EXECUTIVES

Ceo, Duane Erwin
Pres*, Darrell Lentz
Scientist, Cindy Geiss
Information Specialist, Mark Chickering
Chief of Medicine, Erik Anderson
Coordinator, Rhnea Cornils
Director, Bonnie M Samuelson
Registered Nurse Amb, Mary Stacker
Registered Nurse, Rachel Monday
Team Leader, Vicki Lepak
Manager of Graphic Design, Katie Szews
Auditors: WIPFLI LLP EAU CLAIRE WISCON

LOCATIONS

HQ: ASPIRUS WAUSAU HOSPITAL, INC.
425 PINE RIDGE BLVD # 1, WAUSAU, WI 544014122
Phone: 715 847-2019
Web: WWW.ASPIRUS.ORG

HISTORICAL FINANCIALS
Company Type: Private

Income Statement   FYE: June 30

	REVENUE ($ mil.)	NET INCOME ($ mil.)	NET PROFIT MARGIN	EMPLOYEES
06/20	565	7	1.3%	3,500
06/19	543	70	12.9%	—
06/18	497	8	1.7%	—
06/16	456	51	11.4%	—
Annual Growth	5.5%	(38.6%)	—	—

2020 Year-End Financials

Return on assets: 1.2%   Cash ($ mil.): 4
Return on equity: 2.0%
Current ratio: 1.80

ASPIRUS, INC.

Aspirus is a non-profit community-directed health system based in Wausau Wisconsin. The health system provides a comprehensive range of health and medical services to communities through four hospitals in Upper Michigan and about 15 hospitals in Wisconsin some 75 clinics home health and hospice care pharmacies critical care and air-medical transport medical goods nursing homes and a broad network of physicians. In addition to its four hospitals in Michigan Aspirus operates the Aspirus Wausau Hospital a 325-bed and staffed by 350 physicians in 35 specialties. With approximately 15000 admissions per year outpatient visits exceed 50000 and there are also more than 24000 annual emergency department visits.

Operations
Aspirus offers services that includes behavioral health & counseling hospice services sleep medicine and birthing services. It also offers inpatient rehabilitation spine and neurosciences breast care and mammography and NICU to name a few.

Its Aspirus Network is a Clinically Integrated Network of leading primary and specialty care physicians hospitals and allied health care professionals. Aspirus Network negotiates contracts on behalf of its members with employers and health plans. ANI works closely with Aspirus' health plan Aspirus Health Plan to help deliver direct access to high-value personalized health care that aims to improve the health and well-being through all health care needs.

Geographic Reach
Headquartered in Wausau Wisconcin it has operations in Amherst Antigo Hancock Athens and Stevens Point all in Wisconsin.

Sales and Marketing
Aspirus serves communities through four hospitals in Upper Michigan and thirteen hospitals in Wisconsin seventy-five clinics home health and hospice care pharmacies critical care and air-medical transport medical goods nursing homes and a broad network of physicians.

EXECUTIVES

Ceo, Matthew Heywood
Cfo*, Sidney Sczygelski
V Pres*, Jean Burgener
Chief of Medicine, Jeanne M Rowe
Purchasing Agent, Holly L Metz
Human Resources Information MA, Hannah Brabec
Coordinator, Julie Riemer
Administrative Assistant II, Deb Klocke
Timekeeping Coordinator, Amber Hoelter
Business Analyst, Jennifer Underwood
Registered Nurse, Lindsey Graff
Auditors: WIPFLI LLP EAU CLAIRE WISCO

LOCATIONS

HQ: ASPIRUS, INC.
2200 WESTWOOD DR, WAUSAU, WI 544017806
Phone: 715 847-2121
Web: WWW.ASPIRUS.ORG

Selected Facilities
U.P. of Michigan
Aspirus Grand View Aspirus Keweenaw Hospital
Aspirus Ontonagon Hospital
NORTHSTAR Health System Wisconsin
Aspirus Wausau Hospital
Aspirus Langlade Hospital
Aspirus Medford Hospital
Riverview Hospital

PRODUCTS/OPERATIONS

Selected Services
Alzheimer's & Memory Disorders
Anesthesia Services
Angioplasty
Anticoagulation Clinic
Cardiac Electrophysiology
Cardiac Rehab
Cardioversion

Dentistry
Oral & Maxillofacial Surgery
Prosthodontics
Psychiatry
Psychology
Pulmonary Medicine
Sleep Disorders

COMPETITORS

Dean Health Systems Inc.
Howard Young Health Care
Luther Midelfort
Thedacare Inc.
University Of Wisconsin Hospital And Clinics

HISTORICAL FINANCIALS

Company Type: Private

Income Statement				FYE: June 30
	REVENUE ($ mil.)	NET INCOME ($ mil.)	NET PROFIT MARGIN	EMPLOYEES
06/20	1,090	169	15.5%	7,100
06/19	996	102	10.3%	—
06/18	911	78	8.6%	—
06/13	536	47	8.9%	—
Annual Growth	10.7%	19.7%	—	—

2020 Year-End Financials

Return on assets: 9.3%   Cash ($ mil.): 328
Return on equity: 14.4%
Current ratio: 2.50

ASSOCIATED FOOD STORES, INC.

This business makes sure there's plenty of grub for the Wild West. Associated Food Stores (AFS) is a leading regional cooperative wholesale distributor that supplies groceries and other products to some 500 independent supermarkets in about eight Western states. It also offers support services for its member-owners including market research real estate analysis store design technology procurement and training. In addition AFS owns a stake in Western Family Foods a grocery wholesalers' partnership that produces Western Family private-label goods. The co-op formed in 1940 also operates 40-plus corporate stores in Utah under five different banners including Fresh Market.

Operations

In addition to its wholesale business AFS's retail arm — Associated Retail Operations — owns and operates corporate stores in Utah under five different formats and banners: Macey's; Fresh Market; Dan's Fresh Market in Salt Lake City; Lin's Fresh Market; and Dick's Fresh Market. The retail business accounts for about 35% of AFS's annual revenue.

The grocery distributor supplies independent supermarkets with over 3600 products. Products comprise a wide array including baking breakfast cereals frozen foods household supplies and even pet food and supplies. In early 2013 Associated closed its distribution centers in Helena and Billings Montana and consolidated warehouse operations for its nearly 100 Montana and Wyoming customers at its facility in Farr West Utah.

Geographic Reach

Salt Lake City-based Associated Food Stores has operations in Arizona Colorado Idaho Montana Nevada Oregon Utah and Wyoming. The

Financial Performance

While privately-owned Associated Food Stores doesn't report its financial results the company logged an estimated $2.2 billion in sales in fiscal 2013 (ended March) versus $2.1 billion in sales the previous year.

EXECUTIVES

Ceo, Neil Berube
V Pres*, Bill Price
V Pres*, Bob King
V Pres*, Brian T Duff
SEC*, Lezlie Sanders
V Pres*, David Rice
V Pres*, Wade Judd
Chief Administrative Officer*, Zulema Wiscovitch
Accounting Staff, Dayna Harrison
Director, Stephen Bitter
Director Retail Sales, April Rice
Auditors: DELOITTE & TOUCHE LLP SALT L

LOCATIONS

HQ: ASSOCIATED FOOD STORES, INC.
   1850 W 2100 S, SALT LAKE CITY, UT 841191304
Phone: 801 973-4400
Web: WWW.AFSTORES.COM

PRODUCTS/OPERATIONS

Selected Brands

Western Family
Full Circle
Shur Saving

Selected Retail Banners

Dan's Fresh Market
Dick's Fresh Market
Fresh Market
Lin's Fresh Market
Macey's

COMPETITORS

Amcon Distributing	Supervalu
C&s Wholesale	Safeway
Gsc Enterprises	Urm Stores
Kroger	Wal-mart
Mclane	

HISTORICAL FINANCIALS

Company Type: Private

Income Statement				FYE: March 31
	REVENUE ($ mil.)	NET INCOME ($ mil.)	NET PROFIT MARGIN	EMPLOYEES
03/12	2,011	5	0.3%	300
03/11	1,953	(6)	—	—
03/10	1,785	(2)	—	—
Annual Growth	6.1%	—	—	—

2012 Year-End Financials

Return on assets: 1.0%   Cash ($ mil.): 105
Return on equity: 5.4%
Current ratio: 0.90

ASSOCIATED WHOLESALE GROCERS, INC.

Associated Wholesale Grocers (AWG) knows its customers can't live on bread and milk alone. The one of -largest retailer-owned grocery cooperative in the US AWG supplies more than 3800 grocery

retail outlets in more than half of the US states from 10 distribution centers which collectively have some 7 million square feet of space. In addition to its wholesale grocery operation AWG offers a variety of business services to its members including print and digital marketing services and health beauty care general merchandise specialty/International foodsand pharmaceutical products. . AWG was founded by a group of independent grocers in 1924.

HISTORY

About 20 Kansas City Kansas-area grocers met in a local grocery in 1924 and organized the Associated Grocers Company to get better deals on purchases and advertising. They elected J. C. Harline president and each chipped in a few hundred dollars to make their first purchases. It took a while to find a manufacturer who would sell directly to them; a local soap maker was finally convinced and others gradually followed.

In 1926 the group was incorporated as Associated Wholesale Grocers (AWG). It outgrew two warehouses in four years finally moving to a 16000-sq.-ft. facility big enough to add new lines and more products. Membership doubled between 1930 and 1932 as grocers moved from ordering products a year ahead to the new wholesale concept and members took seriously the slogan: "Buy Sell Buy Some More." They met every week to plan how to sell their products and buyer and advertising manager Harry Small gave sales presentations and advertising ideas (his trade-in plan for old brooms sold more than two train-carloads of brooms in two weeks). Heavy newspaper advertising also paid off; AWG topped $1 million in sales in 1933.

The cooperative made its first acquisition in 1936 buying Progressive Grocers a warehouse in Joplin Missouri; a second warehouse named Associated Grocers was acquired the next year in Springfield Missouri. AWG continued building and expanding warehouses and annual sales were at $11 million by 1951.

Louis Fox became CEO in 1956. Fox maximized year-end rebates for members led several acquisitions and formed a new subsidiary for financing stores and small shopping centers where AWG members had a presence (Supermarket Developers). Sales increased nearly 15-fold to over $200 million in his first 15 years.

James Basha who succeeded Fox when he retired in 1984 saw sales reach $2.4 billion by the time of his own retirement in 1992.

Basha was followed by former COO Mike DeFabis once a deputy mayor of Indianapolis. DeFabis orchestrated several acquisitions including 41 Kansas City-area stores — most of which were quickly bought by members — from bankrupt Food Barn Stores in 1994 and 29 Oklahoma stores and a warehouse from Safeway spinoff Homeland Stores in 1995 (members bought all the stores).

AWG's non-food subsidiary Valu Merchandisers was established in 1995; its new Kansas warehouse began shipping health and beauty aids and housewares the following year to help members battle big discounters. Members narrowly defeated a proposal in late 1996 to convert the cooperative into a public company. Proponents promptly petitioned for a second vote which was defeated early the next year.

AWG veteran Doug Carolan succeeded DeFabis in 1998 becoming only the fifth CEO in the cooperative's history. The company bought five Falley's and 33 Food 4 Less stores in Kansas and Missouri from Fred Meyer in 1998 for $300 million. In a break with tradition AWG began operating the stores rather than selling them to members.

In 2000 after a months-long labor dispute with the Teamsters was resolved Carolan left AWG. The company's CFO Gary Phillips was named president and CEO later that year. In 2001 the company debuted a new format ALPS (Always Low Price Stores) — small stores that carry a limited selection of grocery top-sellers. Also that year AWG's Kansas City division began distributing to more than 10 new stores that had formerly been served by Fleming at the time the #1 US wholesale food distributor.

In 2002 supermarket operator Homeland Stores which operates stores in Oklahoma emerged from bankruptcy as a fully owned subsidiary of AWG. AWG formed a new subsidiary Associated Retail Grocers to oversee Homeland and its Falley's chain.

As a result of the 2003 sale of Fleming Companies' wholesale distribution business AWG picked up food distribution centers in Nebraska (two) Oklahoma (one) and Tennessee (two) and general-merchandise distribution centers in Tennessee and Kansas.

Introducing a "dollar" section in its stores in 2004 proved successful leading AWG to expand the category to more than 1000 food and nonfood items. The following year it merged the corporate offices of its Homeland and Food 4 Less chains.

AWG took steps to expand its capacity and its territory in 2007 when it acquired a distribution center in Fort Worth from Albertsons. The cooperative also took on supply operations for Albertsons locations in Arkansas Louisiana and Texas.

In 2009 AWG acquired the assets of Little Rock Arkansas-based Affiliated Foods Southwest in 2009 adding about a dozen new stores.

During 2010 the firm introduced a paperless coupon program.

In December 2011 AWG sold its corporate supermarkets to a group of employees. The corporate stores included 76 retail locations operating under the Homeland United of Oklahoma and Country mart banners in Oklahoma and the Super Saver banner in northern Texas.

In late 2012 AWG completed a 35000-square-foot addition to its corporate headquarters in Kansas City. The location is also home to AWG's Kansas City distribution centers and its Valu Merchandisers division.**EXECUTIVES**

Pres, David Smith
Auditors: GRANT THORTON LLP KANSAS CIT

LOCATIONS

HQ: ASSOCIATED WHOLESALE GROCERS, INC.
5000 KANSAS AVE, KANSAS CITY, KS 661061135
Phone: 913 288-1000
Web: WWW.AWGINC.COM

COMPETITORS

Affiliated Foods	Gsc Enterprises
Affiliated Foods	H. T. Hackney
Midwest	Mclane
Albertsons	Supervalu
Alex Lee	Spartannash
C&s Wholesale	Wakefern Food
Central Grocers	Wal-mart
Dearborn Wholesale	Winco Foods
Grocers	

HISTORICAL FINANCIALS
Company Type: Private

Income Statement   FYE: December 31

	REVENUE ($ mil.)	NET INCOME ($ mil.)	NET PROFIT MARGIN	EMPLOYEES
12/17	9,703	199	2.1%	2,997
12/15	8,935	198	2.2%	—
12/14	8,934	226	2.5%	—
12/13	8,380	192	2.3%	—
Annual Growth	3.7%	0.8%	—	—

2017 Year-End Financials

Return on assets: 12.3%   Cash ($ mil.): 166
Return on equity: 39.4%
Current ratio: 1.20

ATHENE ANNUITY & LIFE ASSURANCE COMPANY

EXECUTIVES

Ceo, James R Belardi
Pres, Chip Smith
V Pres Fin, Cfo, David Attaway
Evp, Matthew Easley
Pres, Guy H Smith
Exec V Pres, Christopher Grady
Sr V Pres, Rod Mims
Administrator, Ashley Buffamoyer
Director, Bob McNeely
Manager, Talent Acquisition, Joyce Whitcomb
Engineer, Kevin Schafer

LOCATIONS

HQ: ATHENE ANNUITY & LIFE ASSURANCE COMPANY
2000 WADE HAMPTON BLVD, GREENVILLE, SC 296151037
Phone: 864 609-1000
Web: WWW.ATHENE.COM

HISTORICAL FINANCIALS
Company Type: Private

Income Statement   FYE: December 31

	ASSETS ($ mil.)	NET INCOME ($ mil.)	INCOME AS % OF ASSETS	EMPLOYEES
12/13	11,775	49	0.4%	120
12/12	10,481	11	0.1%	—
Annual Growth	12.3%	330.4%		

2013 Year-End Financials

Return on assets: —   Sales ($ mil): 217
Return on equity: 22.8%

ATLANTIC DIVING SUPPLY, INC.

Atlantic Diving Supply (doing business as ADS) is geared toward gearing up the military. Serving agencies in the Federal Government the company specializes in helping customers procure tactical and operational military equipment. The Company is serving the local and military diving community and Defense Logistics Agency (DLA) as a prime vendor for marine and lifesaving diving and search and rescue equipment. The Company holds more than 50 Indefinite Delivery Indefinite Quantity (IDIQ) contracts and Blanket Purchase Agreement (BPAs) and has grown to be a top 5 DLA Supplier and Top 50 Federal Government Contractor.
Operations
ADS Inc. provides equipment procurement logistics and supply chain solutions. Products include apparel nylon equipment surveillance and sensors robotics and aviation equipment among others.
Geographic Reach
The company is headquartered in Virginia.
Sales and Marketing
ADS' customers are within the Department of Defense and the Federal Government other customers are Air Force Army and Army Reserves Coast Guard Marine Corps National Guardm Navy Space Force and U.S. Partner Nation.

EXECUTIVES

Ceo, Jason Wallace
V Chm*, Daniel J Clarkson
Chb*, Luke M Hillier
Cfo*, Kiran Rai
V Pres*, Charles M Salle
Chief Financial Officer*, John Dunn
Asst Contrl, Wendy Belisle
United States Coast Guard West, John Bailey
Inside Account Manager, Laura Amundson
Vice Chairman, Dan Clarkson
Business Manager, David Grotkin

LOCATIONS

HQ: ATLANTIC DIVING SUPPLY, INC.
621 LYNNHVEN PKWY STE 160, VIRGINIA BEACH, VA 23452
Phone: 757 481-7758
Web: WWW.ADSINC.COM

PRODUCTS/OPERATIONS

Selected Products
Apparel
Bags packs and cases
Eyewear
Footwear
Hydration systems
Knives
Lighting
Medical
Tools
Training aids

COMPETITORS

Amazon.com	Navy Exchange
Army And Air Force	Target Corporation
Exchange	Wal-mart
Kmart	

Income Statement				FYE: December 31
	REVENUE ($ mil.)	NET INCOME ($ mil.)	NET PROFIT MARGIN	EMPLOYEES
12/10	1,327	77	5.8%	360
12/09	938	54	5.8%	—
12/08	650	40	6.2%	—
Annual Growth	42.8%	38.7%	—	—

2010 Year-End Financials
Return on assets: 28.7% Cash ($ mil.): 1
Return on equity: 676.2%
Current ratio: 1.10

ATLANTIC HEALTH SYSTEM INC.

The not-for-profit Atlantic Health System (AHS) operates about dozen urgent care hospital providing general medical and surgical services to residents of northern New Jersey. Its flagship Morristown Medical Center is a nationally-recognized leader in cardiology orthopedics nursing critical care and geriatrics.. The system's Overlook Medical Center houses the Atlantic Neuroscience Institute; home to the Comprehensive Stroke Center. Its smaller Newton Medical Center serves patients in two New Jersey counties as well as counties in Pennsylvania and New York.

Operations
Atlantic Health System has a long-standing tradition of providing exceptional patient outcomes and experiences. It is home to seven award-winning hospitals including Morristown Medical Center the number one hospital in New Jersey. The system provides care for the full continuum of health needs across a wide array of settings including a dozen urgent care centers Atlantic Rehabilitation Institute Atlantic Visiting Nurse and Atlantic Anywhere's Virtual Visits. The hospital's top areas of acre have included HIV and AIDS cancer care brain tumors home care hospice stroke scoliosis and spine deformity and more.

Geographic Reach
Atlantic Health System hospitals provides services to New Jersey where it is headquartered and surrounding areas.

Sales and Marketing
Atlantic Health System serves more than half the state of New Jersey including about a dozen counties and about 4.9 million people.

EXECUTIVES

Pres-Ceo, Brian Gragnolati
Cdo*, Armond Kinsey
CIO*, Sylvia Romm
Vp-CIO*, Sunil Dadlani
Coordinator, Anne Berger
Coordinator, Nancy Markey
Coordinator, Angela Natale-Ryan
Coordinator, Dorothy Dungee
Assoc. Vice President, Susan Kuper
Coordinator, Adam Kieffer
Coordinator, Christine Tekula
Auditors: PRICEWATERHOUSECOOPERS LLP FL

LOCATIONS

HQ: ATLANTIC HEALTH SYSTEM INC.
475 SOUTH ST, MORRISTOWN, NJ 079606459
Phone: 973 660-3100
Web: WWW.ATLANTICHEALTH.ORG

PRODUCTS/OPERATIONS

Selected Operations
Atlantic Home Care
Atlantic Hospice
Atlantic Neuroscience Institute (Overlook Hospital)
Carol G. Simon Cancer Center (Morristown and Overlook hospitals)
Chilton Medical Center
Gagnon Cardiovascular Institute (Morristown Hospital)
Goryeb Children's Hospital
Morristown Medical Center
Newton Medical Center
Overlook Medical Center

COMPETITORS

Children's Specialized Hospital
Chilton Medical Center
Community Health Systems
East Orange General Hospital
Jfk Medical Center
Newark Beth Israel Medical Center
Raritan Bay Medical Center
Robert Wood Johnson University Hospital At Rahway
Saint Barnabas Medical
St. Joseph's Healthcare System
The Valley Hospital
Trinitas Regional Medical Center

HISTORICAL FINANCIALS
Company Type: Private

Income Statement				FYE: December 31
	REVENUE ($ mil.)	NET INCOME ($ mil.)	NET PROFIT MARGIN	EMPLOYEES
12/19	3,163	476	15.0%	3,100
12/17	0	(0)	—	
Annual Growth	8917.8%	—	—	—

2019 Year-End Financials
Return on assets: 11.0% Cash ($ mil.): 465
Return on equity: 19.8%
Current ratio: 2.10

ATLANTICARE REGIONAL MEDICAL CENTER

EXECUTIVES

Ceo, David Tilton
V Pres-Coo*, Lori Herndon
Senior Buyer, Nicole Hagan
Registered Nurse, Eunice Creamer
Anesthesiologist, Nicholas Incandela
Pharmacy Director, Charles Arrison
Cardiology Director, Sanjay Shetty
Anesthesiologist, Dipty Mangla
Chief of Neurosurgery, Fernando Delasotta
Security Director, John Hunt
Blood Bank Director, Kelly Vasquez

LOCATIONS

HQ: ATLANTICARE REGIONAL MEDICAL CENTER
65 W JIMMIE LEEDS RD, POMONA, NJ 082409102
Phone: 609 652-1000
Web: WWW.ATLANTICARE.ORG

HISTORICAL FINANCIALS
Company Type: Private

Income Statement				FYE: December 31
	REVENUE ($ mil.)	NET INCOME ($ mil.)	NET PROFIT MARGIN	EMPLOYEES
12/14	718	64	9.0%	249
12/08	560	(58)	—	
12/05	457	51	11.3%	—
Annual Growth	5.1%	2.5%	—	—

2014 Year-End Financials
Return on assets: 6.4% Cash ($ mil.): —
Return on equity: 14.0%
Current ratio: 0.50

ATLAS OIL COMPANY

EXECUTIVES

Ceo, Sam Simon
Pres*, Robert Kenyon
Cfo*, Joseph Rivera
Coo*, Michael Devoe
Vp-Wholesale & Real Estate, Jacob Leatherman
Pres of Truck & Rig Fueling, Michael Meredith
Vp of Business Development, Jeremiah Whiddon
Vp of Supply and Logistics, Clinton Werth
V Pres For Crude Hauling, Samuel Carmicheal
Director of Human Resources, Dawn Thomson
Coo, Michael Fahy
Auditors: ERNST & YOUNG LLP DETROIT M

LOCATIONS

HQ: ATLAS OIL COMPANY
24501 ECORSE RD, TAYLOR, MI 481801641
Phone: 313 292-5500
Web: WWW.ATLASOIL.COM

HISTORICAL FINANCIALS
Company Type: Private

Income Statement				FYE: December 31
	REVENUE ($ mil.)	NET INCOME ($ mil.)	NET PROFIT MARGIN	EMPLOYEES
12/08	1,153	1	0.1%	453
12/07	717	1	0.1%	—
12/06	617	0	0.1%	—
Annual Growth	36.7%	99.7%	—	—

2008 Year-End Financials
Return on assets: 1.6% Cash ($ mil.): 3
Return on equity: 8.6%
Current ratio: 1.00

ATLAS WORLD GROUP, INC.

Willing to carry the weight of a moving world agent-owned Atlas World Group is the holding company for Atlas Van Lines one of the largest moving companies in the US. Atlas Van Lines' more than 500 agents transport household goods domestically and between the US and Canada; it also offers specialized transportation of items such as trade show exhibits fine art and electronics. Atlas Van Lines International provides international corporate relocation and freight forwarding services. Its Atlas Canada unit moves household goods in that country while American Red Ball International specializes in military relocations and serves van lines outside Atlas' network.

Operations
Atlas World Group oversees a family of companies that deliver transportation and related services globally through a network agents and select service partners. Several of its key locations are concentrated in Evansville Indiana.

Strategy
The company continues to grow by adding offices and regional moving agents. In 2013 Atlantic Relocation Systems the second largest agency group within the Atlas Van Lines' US network expanded both its national footprint as well as its local service area in Colorado by opening a new office in Colorado Springs.

EXECUTIVES

Ceo, John P Griffin
Cfo*, Donald R Breivogel Jr
Sr Vp*, James K McMurray
Vp*, Nancy L Priebe
Corporate Counsel and Assistan*, Todd A Suter
Asst SEC*, Stacie L Banks
Asst SEC*, Jason Kempf
Coordinator, Desiree Shanks
Software Developer, Joe Harbert
Information Specialist, Sheila Lacey
Manager Pricing, Su Leach
Auditors: ERNST & YOUNG LLP INDIANAPOLI

LOCATIONS

HQ: ATLAS WORLD GROUP, INC.
1212 SAINT GEORGE RD, EVANSVILLE, IN 477112364
Phone: 812 424-2222
Web: WWW.ATLASVANLINES.COM

PRODUCTS/OPERATIONS

Selected Companies
American Red Ball International (international freight forwarding)
American Vanpac Carriers (international freight forwarding)
Atlas Terminal Company (relocation-related supplies and equipment)
Atlas Van Lines (transportation services)
Atlas Van Lines (Canada) (transportation services)
Atlas Van Lines International (transportation services)
Atlas World Class Travel (travel agency)
Avail Move Management (management programs)
AWG Logistics (transportation warehousing and distribution)
Cornerstone Relocation Group (relocation services)
Smart Move Transportation (containerized shipping)
Titan Global Distribution (logistics)

COMPETITORS

A-mrazek Moving	Graebel
Altair Global	Penske Truck Leasing
Relocation	Sirva
Amerco	Starving Students
Bekins	Unigroup
Budd Van Lines	
Business Products	
Group	

HISTORICAL FINANCIALS
Company Type: Private

Income Statement
FYE: December 31

	REVENUE ($ mil.)	NET INCOME ($ mil.)	NET PROFIT MARGIN	EMPLOYEES
12/20	805	8	1.0%	726
12/19	906	9	1.1%	—
12/18	900	10	1.1%	—
12/17	842	4	0.6%	—
Annual Growth	(1.5%)	19.0%	—	—

2020 Year-End Financials
Return on assets: 3.1%   Cash ($ mil.): 30
Return on equity: 5.5%
Current ratio: 2.20

ATMEL CORPORATION

Atmel is a leading maker of microcontrollers which are used in a wide range of products from computers and mobile devices (smartphones tablets e-readers) to automobile motor control systems television remote controls and solid-state lighting. In addition the company offers touchscreen controllers and sensors nonvolatile memory devices and radio frequency (RF) and wireless components. Its chips are used worldwide in consumer communications industrial military and networking applications. Most of Atmel's sales come from customers outside the US. In mid-2016 the company was bought by Microchip a chip maker for $3.6 billion.

Operations
In 2014 Atmel realigned its business segments for allocation of resources and focus on core its markets. The company created the Multi-Market and Other segment while eliminating the former Application Specific Integrated Circuit (ASIC) segment.

But it's the Microcontroller segment that leads the way for Atmel accounting for 70% of the company's sales. The segment includes Atmel's general purpose microcontroller and microprocessor families AVR 8-bit and 32-bit products SMART ARM-based products Atmel's 8051 8-bit products and designated commercial wireless products including low power radio and SOC products.

The Nonvolatile Memory segment 12% of sales includes electrically erasable programmable read-only erasable programmable read-only memory ('EPROM') devices and secure cryptographic products. The Automotive segment 11% makes devices for automotive electronics including products using radio frequency technology. The new segment Multi-Market and Other is 7% of sales and includes application specific and standard products for aerospace applications and legacy products.

Geographic Reach
The company generates about 60% of its sales from Asia including about a third from China and Hong Kong. After China and Hong Kong the US is Atmel's largest market accounting for 15% of sales with sales in Germany at 14%.

Sales and Marketing
Atmel markets its products to original equipment manufacturers (OEMs) via a direct sales force as well as through distribution partners; each method accounts for about half of revenue. Arrow Electronics and Samsung Electronics each account for more than 10% of sales.

End-market customers include some of the leading names in the fields of communications (Alcatel Lucent Cisco Ericsson) computer and consumer electronics (Acer Dell Motorola Nokia) automotive (Delphi Visteon) and military and aerospace (BAE Systems Airbus Honeywell Lockheed Martin).

Financial Performance
Revenue rose 2% to $1.4 billion in 2014 from $1.39 billion in 2013 boosted by a 4% increase in microcontroller sales. The unit experienced demand from industrial automotive and communications markets. The addition of Newport Media acquired in mid-2014 also abetted microcontroller revenue. Sales in the nonvolatile memory segment were up 9% for the year.

On the bottom line Atmel went from a $22 million loss in 2013 to a $32 million profit in 2014. Profit was pushed by revenue growth as well as a lack of charges the company contended with in 2013. Cash flow from operations jumped 41% higher in 2014 to about $180 billion from $127 million in 203.

Strategy
Looking to pursue a "fab-lite" strategy of streamlining existing facilities and relying more on silicon foundries (contract manufacturers of semiconductors) Atmel has sold most of its manufacturing plants and now operates only one fab located in Colorado. Wafer fabs are highly expensive to build and maintain mostly due to the cost of semiconductor production equipment and pushing some of those costs off on the foundries many of which have state-of-the-art plants is attractive.

Atmel has increased the release of new products in the past three years aiming to provide customers with high performing microcontrollers than use little power. The company has found a place for its products within the Internet of Things the conglomeration of devices that communicate through the Internet.

The company also has pushed its line of maX-Touch products for touchscreens in smartphones and tables. The products have found acceptance in automotive consumer and industrial markets. While that line thrives Atmel sold its XSense line of touch sensors to UniPixel in 2015. Atmel maintained possession of the XSense patent portfolio which it licensed to UniPixel.

With its sale to Dialog Atmel gets access to a range of new customers within Atmel's portfolio. Dialog expects to benefit from Atmel's products primed for the Internet of Things. The combined company would have about $2.7 billion sales annually. The deal is expected to close in the 2016 first quarter.

Mergers and Acquisitions
In agreeing to be bought by Microchip Atmel ended a deal to be purchased by Dialog. Atmel management said company shareholders would get a better return from the Microchip deal. Atmel was on the hook for a $137 million termination fee to be paid to Dialog. The Dialog offer had been valued at $4.6 billion when it was made but the value of Atmel stock has declined since then. The Atmel-Microchip deal enables the companies to gather competitive strength with complementary technologies and products.

In 2014 Atmel acquired Newport Media Inc. a provider of advanced Wi-Fi and Bluetooth products. This acquisition expands Atmel's wireless portfolio with the addition of 802.11n Wi-Fi and Bluetooth. Those product should speed up Atmel's introduction of low-energy Bluetooth products.

HISTORY
George Perlegos — a former Intel design engineer and co-founder of chip maker SEEQ Technology (later acquired by LSI Logic now LSI Corp.) — founded Atmel in 1984. (The name was short for Advanced Technology for Memory and Logic.) The enterprise started with a $30000 investment

and a $5.1 million design contract from General Instrument; it soon added military and corporate contracts. In 1991 the company went public and introduced the first three-volt flash memory.

Atmel built its business by developing fast power-efficient chips — perfect for portable electronics. It acquired Concurrent Logic a maker of field-programmable gate arrays (user-programmable chips) in 1993. One year later Atmel became the #1 producer of EEPROMs (electrically erasable programmable ROM chips) when it bought SEEQ's chip business.

To strengthen its product line in 1995 Atmel licensed SRAM (static random-access memory) technology in an alliance with Paradigm Technology (now part of IXYS) for use in creating multimedia chips. It purchased RISC chip technology (which uses shorter instruction sets for faster processing) from Norwegian chip maker Nordic VLSI in 1996.

LOCATIONS

HQ: ATMEL CORPORATION
1600 TECHNOLOGY DR, SAN JOSE, CA 951101382
Phone: 408 735-9110
Web: WWW.MICROCHIP.COM

2014 Sales

	$ mil.	% of total
Asia/Pacific		
China (including Hong Kong)	435	31
South Korea	119	9
Taiwan	60	4
Singapore	55	4
Japan	37	3
Other countries	102	7
Europe		
Germany	204	14
France	15	1
Other countries	139	10
US	211	15
Other regions	30	2
Total	**1,413**	**100**

PRODUCTS/OPERATIONS

2014 Sales

	$ mil.	% of total
Microcontrollers	994	70
Nonvolatile memory	166	12
Automotive	153	11
Multi-Market and others	99	7
Total	**1,413**	**100**

Selected Products and Applications

Application-Specific Integrated Circuits (ASICs)
  Cell-based ASICs
  Complex ASIC cores
  Gate arrays/embedded arrays
Application-Specific Standard Products (ASSPs)
  Aerospace and military
  Communications
  Cellular corded and cordless phones
  Internet appliances and voice over Internet Protocol (VoIP)
  Wireless datacom
  Industrial
  Industrial controls
  Power metering
  Multimedia
  Audio
  Video
  Power management
  Security and smart card
  Biometrics
  PC security
  Radio-frequency identification (RFID)
  Secure memories
  Secure microcontrollers
  USB controllers
Logic
  Field-programmable gate arrays (FPGAs)
  Programmable logic devices (PLDs)
Microcontrollers (MCUs)
  4- 8- 16- and 32-bit microcontrollers
  ARM microprocessor architecture-based MCUs
  Flash MCUs

Nonvolatile Memory
  EPROMs (erasable programmable read-only memories)
  Flash memory chips
  Parallel EEPROMs (electrically erasable PROMs)
  Serial EEPROMs

COMPETITORS

Cypress Semiconductor	Nxp Semiconductors
Fairchild	On Semiconductor
Semiconductor	Renesas Electronics
Fujitsu Semiconductor	Stmicroelectronics
Hitachi	Samsung Electronics
Infineon Technologies	Silicon Labs
Intel	Synaptics
Microchip Technology	Texas Instruments
Micron Technology	

HISTORICAL FINANCIALS

Company Type: Private

Income Statement

FYE: December 31

	REVENUE ($ mil.)	NET INCOME ($ mil.)	NET PROFIT MARGIN	EMPLOYEES
12/14	1,413	35	2.5%	5,200
12/13	1,386	(22)	—	
12/12	1,432	30	2.1%	
Annual Growth	(0.7%)	7.5%	—	—

2014 Year-End Financials

Return on assets: 2.6%
Return on equity: 4.0%
Current ratio: 2.70

Cash ($ mil.): 206

ATRIUS HEALTH, INC.

Atrius Health an innovative nonprofit healthcare leader delivers an effective system of connected care for adult and pediatric patients at some 30 medical practice locations in eastern Massachusetts. Atrius Health's physicians and primary care providers along with additional clinicians work in close collaboration with hospital partners community specialists and skilled nursing. Atrius Health provides high-quality patient-centered coordinated cost effective care to every patient it serves. Atrius Health was founded in 2004 by medical groups including Dedham Medical Associates and Harvard Vanguard Medical Associates; Granite Medical Group joined a short time later in 2005.

Operations

Atrius Health's network of doctors represent more than 50 medical specialties including primary care oncology cardiology and neurology. In addition to providing health care services the company operates the Center for Clinical Research which focuses on patient-centered models of care provider well-being and burnout prevention health technologies quality improvement and implementation science.

Atrius Health has primary/tertiary hospital affiliations with Emerson Hospital Lahey Hospital & Medical Center Lowell General Hospital Mount Auburn Hospital South Shore Hospital and Winchester Hospital. Specialty affiliations include Massachusetts Eye and Ear Infirmary an international center for treatment and home to the world's largest vision and hearing research centers and New England Baptist Hospital a premier regional provider for orthopedic surgery and the treatment of musculoskeletal diseases and disorders.

Atrius Health has an affiliation with Firefly Health a tech-enabled primary care and behavioral health provider which enables Firefly Health to contract through Atrius Health's value-based collaboration with Blue Cross Blue Shield of Massachusetts servicing HMO and PPO patients.

Geographic Reach

Atrius Health has four locations in the City of Boston about 30 locations in Greater Boston and two administrative offices in Newton and Needham.

Sales and Marketing

Atrius Health accepts insurance from most major health plans including Aetna Blue Cross and Blue Shield of Massachusetts CIGNA Coventry Health Care Harvard Pilgrim Health Care AllWays Health Partners and Tufts Health Plan among others.

Company Background

Atrius Health was founded in 2004 by medical groups including Dedham Medical Associates and Harvard Vanguard Medical Associates; Granite Medical Group joined a short time later in 2005.The companies work together to coordinate care in a number of ways including sharing an electronic medical records system. In 2015 the groups merged to create one not-for-profit group named Atrius Health. Reliant Medical Group Southboro Medical Group and South Shore Medical Center were no longer affiliated with the group after the transformation. In 2017 PMG Physician Associates joined Atrius Health adding seven new office locations to our practice.

EXECUTIVES

Pres-Ceo, Steven Strongwater
Treas-Cfo*, Leland J Stacy
Chief Officer, Jeffrey Levin-Scherz
Director, Noelle S Lawler
Chief Financial Officer, Carole N Martin
Chief Operating Officer, Glenn N Lewis
Chief of Medicine, Les N Schwab
Administrator, Null Y Null Yang
General Practice, Renee N Aucoin
Chief of Medicine, Matthew Shuster
Internal Medicine Practitioner, Steven Paskal
Auditors: PKF PC QUINCY MA

LOCATIONS

HQ: ATRIUS HEALTH, INC.
275 GROVE ST STE 3300, AUBURNDALE, MA 024662274
Phone: 617 559-8444
Web: WWW.ATRIUSHEALTH.ORG

PRODUCTS/OPERATIONS

Selected Specialty Affiliations
Massachusetts Eye and Ear Infirmary
New England Baptist Hospital

Selected OB/GYN Affiliations
Beth Israel Deaconess Medical Center
Beth Israel Deaconess Hospital - Milton
Emerson Hospital
Lowell General Hospital
Mount Auburn Hospital
Newton-Wellesley Hospital
South Shore Hospital

Selected Services
Allergy
Andrology
Audiology
Behavioral Health
Cardiology
Central Patient Registration
Complex Chronic Care Program
Cosmetic Dermatology
Dermatology
Developmental and Behavioral Pediatrics
Ear Nose & Throat
Endocrinology
Endoscopy
Eye Care
Family Medicine
Fertility & Reproductive Health

Gastroenterology
Genetics
Geriatrics
Hematology/Oncology
Imaging/Radiology
Infectious Disease
Internal Medicine
Interpreter Services
Laboratory
Medical Billing
Medical Records
Minimally-Invasive GYN Surgery
Nephrology
Neurology
Nutrition
Obstetrics/Gynecology
Occupational
Hand Therapy
Orthopedics & Sports Medicine
Pain Management
Palliative Care
Pediatrics
Pharmacy
Physical Therapy
Podiatry
Pulmonology
Rheumatology
Speech and Language Therapy
Surgery
Travel Medicine
Urgent Care
Urology
Weight Management/HMR®; Program

COMPETITORS

Boston Medical Center
Hallmark Health
Massachusetts General
  Hospital
St. Elizabeth's
  Medical Center
Winchester Healthcare

HISTORICAL FINANCIALS

Company Type: Private

Income Statement				FYE: December 31
	REVENUE ($ mil.)	NET INCOME ($ mil.)	NET PROFIT MARGIN	EMPLOYEES
12/19	2,167	5	0.3%	3,906
12/17	1,872	39	2.1%	—
12/15	1,577	(28)	—	—
12/14	28	(0)	—	—
Annual Growth	137.6%	—	—	—

2019 Year-End Financials

Return on assets: 0.6%
Return on equity: 2.1%
Current ratio: 0.80
Cash ($ mil.): 174

ATTORNEY GENERAL, TEXAS

The Office of the Attorney General of Texas defends the state Constitution represents the state in litigation and approves public bond issues. The office is legal counsel to state government boards and agencies and issues legal opinions when requested by the Governor and agency heads. The Attorney General also sits as an ex-officio member of state committees and commissions and defends state laws and suits against agencies and state employees. Other roles include enforcing health safety and consumer regulations; protecting elderly and disabled residents' rights; collecting court-ordered child support; and administering the Crime Victims' Compensation Fund. Greg Abbott was elected Attorney General in 2002.

EXECUTIVES

Exec Dir, Ken Paxton
Cfo*, Greg Herbert
Sergeant, Ingrid Retzer
Sergeant, Lamont Smith
Coordinator, Meghan Rainwater
Savin Administrator, Chris Gersbach
Director, Dwight Burns
Engineering Technician, Jorge Valle
Assistant General, Jose Almaraz
Assistant General, Meagan Conway
Programmer, Melissa Pau

LOCATIONS

HQ: ATTORNEY GENERAL, TEXAS
  300 W 15TH ST, AUSTIN, TX 787011649
Phone: 512 475-4375
Web: WWW.TEXASATTORNEYGENERAL.GOV

HISTORICAL FINANCIALS

Company Type: Private

Income Statement				FYE: August 31
	REVENUE ($ mil.)	NET INCOME ($ mil.)	NET PROFIT MARGIN	EMPLOYEES
08/16	659	45	6.8%	4,200
08/15	561	8	1.5%	—
08/14	571	(6)	—	—
08/06	0	0	—	—
Annual Growth	—	—	—	—

2016 Year-End Financials

Return on assets: 13.1%
Return on equity: 16.5%
Current ratio: 4.20
Cash ($ mil.): 87

AU HEALTH SYSTEM, INC.

EXECUTIVES

Ceo, Katrina Keefer
Pres*, Julie Thigpen
Coo*, Timothy Gaillard

LOCATIONS

HQ: AU HEALTH SYSTEM, INC.
  1120 15TH ST B8255, AUGUSTA, GA 309120004
Phone: 706 721-9439
Web: WWW.AUGUSTAHEALTH.ORG

HISTORICAL FINANCIALS

Company Type: Private

Income Statement				FYE: June 30
	REVENUE ($ mil.)	NET INCOME ($ mil.)	NET PROFIT MARGIN	EMPLOYEES
06/20	956	(4)	—	99
06/19	866	(36)	—	—
Annual Growth	10.3%	—	—	—

2020 Year-End Financials

Return on assets: (-0.6%)
Return on equity: (-1.6%)
Current ratio: 1.50
Cash ($ mil.): 154

AUGUSTANA HEALTH CARE CENTER OF APPLE VALLEY

EXECUTIVES

Pres, Timothy H Tucker
Coordinator, Alice Svihel
Quality Control Director, Diane Newman

LOCATIONS

HQ: AUGUSTANA HEALTH CARE CENTER OF APPLE VALLEY
  14650 GARRETT AVE, SAINT PAUL, MN 551247543
Phone: 952 431-7700
Web: WWW.APPLEVALLEYCAMPUS.ORG

HISTORICAL FINANCIALS

Company Type: Private

Income Statement				FYE: September 30
	REVENUE ($ mil.)	NET INCOME ($ mil.)	NET PROFIT MARGIN	EMPLOYEES
09/09	1,505	30	2.0%	280
09/05	6	(0)	—	—
Annual Growth	287.7%	—	—	—

2009 Year-End Financials

Return on assets: 162.5%
Return on equity: 784.9%
Current ratio: 3.10
Cash ($ mil.): 1

AURORA HEALTH CARE METRO, INC

EXECUTIVES

President, Marie Golanowski
Project Sys Dev, Shafei Fahim
Specialist, John Halverson
Chief of Medicine, Scott Hardin
Project Manager S, Alison Marianacci
Administrative Assistant, Annette Kachelmeyer
Supervisor Food, Jeffrey Gavitt
Administrative Assistant Senio, Jody Knoble
Diagnostic Radiologist, Joshua Lechusz
Diagnostic Radiologist, Mohammad Madani
Anesthesiologist, Palaniandy Sekaran

LOCATIONS

HQ: AURORA HEALTH CARE METRO, INC
  2900 W OKLAHOMA AVE, MILWAUKEE, WI 532154330
Phone: 414 649-6000
Web: WWW.AURORAHEALTHCARE.ORG

HISTORICAL FINANCIALS

Company Type: Private

Income Statement

FYE: December 31

	REVENUE ($ mil.)	NET INCOME ($ mil.)	NET PROFIT MARGIN	EMPLOYEES
12/17	1,428	141	9.9%	4,000
12/16	1,416	164	11.6%	—
Annual Growth	0.8%	(14.0%)	—	—

2017 Year-End Financials

Return on assets: 5.4% Cash ($ mil.): 1,804
Return on equity: 6.2%
Current ratio: 19.70

AURORA HEALTH CARE, INC.

EXECUTIVES

Chief Financial Officer, Dominic Nakis
President, Chief Executive Officer, Jim Skogsbergh
Chief Human Resource Officer, Kevin Brady
Chief Information Officer, Barbara Byrne
Auditors: DELOITTE & TOUCHE LLP MILWAUK

LOCATIONS

HQ: AURORA HEALTH CARE, INC.
750 W VIRGINIA ST, MILWAUKEE, WI 532041539
Phone: 800 326-2250
Web: WWW.AURORAHEALTHCARE.ORG

HISTORICAL FINANCIALS

Company Type: Private

Income Statement

FYE: December 31

	REVENUE ($ mil.)	NET INCOME ($ mil.)	NET PROFIT MARGIN	EMPLOYEES
12/17	5,334	437	8.2%	30,000
12/16	5,124	385	7.5%	—
12/15	4,930	428	8.7%	—
Annual Growth	4.0%	1.1%	—	—

2017 Year-End Financials

Return on assets: 7.7% Cash ($ mil.): 192
Return on equity: 14.4%
Current ratio: 3.50

AUSTIN INDEPENDENT SCHOOL DISTRICT (INC)

EXECUTIVES

Supt, Stephanie S Elizalde
Cfo*, Nicole Conley Johnson
Prin*, Teri Garcia
Coordinator, Artra Luckett
Executive Officer, Debbie Coco
Accounting Staff, Nancy Zuraitis
Occupational Specia, Gemma Cercone

Occupational Specia, Mary Coneway
Assistant Superintendent, Gilbert Hicks
Teacher, Joyce Brisco
Teacher, Lori Moon
Auditors: RSM US LLP AUSTIN TEXAS

LOCATIONS

HQ: AUSTIN INDEPENDENT SCHOOL DISTRICT (INC)
4000 S IH 35 FRONTAGE RD, AUSTIN, TX 78704
Phone: 512 414-1700
Web: WWW.AUSTINISD.ORG

HISTORICAL FINANCIALS

Company Type: Private

Income Statement

FYE: June 30

	REVENUE ($ mil.)	NET INCOME ($ mil.)	NET PROFIT MARGIN	EMPLOYEES
06/20	1,670	(343)	—	9,200
06/19	1,703	208	12.3%	—
06/18	1,534	(117)	—	—
06/16	1,231	110	9.0%	—
Annual Growth	7.9%	—	—	—

2020 Year-End Financials

Return on assets: (-12.1%) Cash ($ mil.): 38
Return on equity: (-239.5%)
Current ratio: —

AVAYA HOLDINGS CORP.

Avaya Holdings Corp. is the holding company that owns enterprise communications equipment and services provider Avaya Inc.. Spun off from Lucent Technologies in 2000 Avaya was a publicly traded company until 2007 when it was taken private by Silver Lake Partners and TPG Capital for more than $8 billion. After four years of unprofitable private ownership its investors are looking for an exit and Avaya Holdings Corp. was created to make a second bid for listing on a US stock exchange filing for an initial public offering in 2011. The IPO is on hold however and Avaya has been expanding its business and product line through acquisitions.

EXECUTIVES

President, Chief Executive Officer, Director, James Chirico, $1,250,000 total compensation
Chief Financial Officer, Executive Vice President, Kieran McGrath, $650,000 total compensation
Independent Director, Scott Vogel
Independent Director, Stephan Scholl
Independent Director, Stanley Sutula
Independent Director, Robert Theis
Executive Vice President, Chief Revenue Officer, Stephen Spears, $600,000 total compensation
Executive Vice President, Chief Administrative Officer, Shefali Shah, $600,000 total compensation
Independent Chairman Of The Board, William Watkins
Independent Director, Jacqueline Yeaney
Auditors: PRICEWATERHOUSECOOPERS LLP SA

LOCATIONS

HQ: AVAYA HOLDINGS CORP.
2605 MERIDIAN PKWY # 200, DURHAM, NC 277135253
Phone: 908 953-6000
Web: WWW.AVAYA.COM

COMPETITORS

Alcatel-lucent	Mitel Networks
Aspect Software	Nec
Cisco Systems	Nsn
Fujitsu	Shoretel
Hitachi	Tellabs
Huawei Technologies	Zte
Logitech	

HISTORICAL FINANCIALS

Company Type: Private

Income Statement

FYE: September 30

	REVENUE ($ mil.)	NET INCOME ($ mil.)	NET PROFIT MARGIN	EMPLOYEES
09/15	4,081	(168)	—	8,266
09/14	4,371	(253)	—	—
09/13	4,708	(376)	—	—
09/11	5,547	(863)	—	—
Annual Growth	(7.4%)	—	—	—

2015 Year-End Financials

Return on assets: (-2.5%) Cash ($ mil.): 323
Return on equity: —
Current ratio: 0.80

AVERITT EXPRESS, INC.

Small loads add up at Averitt Express. The company provides less-than-truckload (LTL) freight transportation service. (LTL carriers combine freight from multiple shippers into a single trailer.). Averitt Express directly serves the southern US and Mexico and it provides service elsewhere in North America through partnerships with other carriers such as Lakeville Motor Express and DATS. The company also offers truckload and expedited freight transportation along with logistics warehousing and international freight forwarding.
Geographic Reach
Averitt Express has a total of about 100 facilities that serve thousands of points throughout the Southern US (in around 20 states) Canada Mexico and the Caribbean.

EXECUTIVES

Pres-Ceo, Gary Sasser
SEC-Exec V Pres, Cfo, George Johnson
Appointment Specialist, Emily Fossey
Inside Sales, Justin Swingler
Customer Representativ, Ashley Vinson
Customer Team Member, Beth Hirner
Inside Sales Representative, Hannah Fox
Payroll Coordinator, Jayrah Humphrey
Customer Technology Support, Molly Morgan
Risk Management, Nancy Kelly
Senior Import Di, Nathan Stumpf
Auditors: CARR RIGGS & INGRAM LLC COOK

LOCATIONS

HQ: AVERITT EXPRESS, INC.
1415 NEAL ST, COOKEVILLE, TN 385014328
Phone: 931 526-3306
Web: WWW.AVERITTEXPRESS.COM

PRODUCTS/OPERATIONS

Selected Services

Cross-border/domestic offshore (Canada Mexico Puerto Rico/Virgin Islands)
Dedicated
Expedited
Intermodal
International ocean/air (ocean/air Asia-Memphis Express)
LTL (regional nationwide distribution/consolidation)
Portside
Retail specialized services
Transportation management
Truckload (dry van flatbed brokerage)
Warehousing

COMPETITORS

Aaa Cooper Transportation	Old Dominion Freight
Arcbest	R+l Carriers
C.h. Robinson Worldwide	Schneider National
	Southeastern Freight Lines
Estes Express	Swift Transportation
Fedex Freight	Ups Freight
J.b. Hunt	Yrc Worldwide

HISTORICAL FINANCIALS

Company Type: Private

Income Statement   FYE: December 31

	REVENUE ($ mil.)	NET INCOME ($ mil.)	NET PROFIT MARGIN	EMPLOYEES
12/20	1,204	77	6.4%	8,208
12/18	1,292	77	6.0%	—
12/16	1,088	45	4.1%	—
12/15	1,091	44	4.1%	—
Annual Growth	2.0%	11.5%	—	—

2020 Year-End Financials

Return on assets: 6.3%   Cash ($ mil.): 209
Return on equity: 7.9%
Current ratio: 6.40

AVERITT INCORPORATED

EXECUTIVES

Pres, Gary D Sasser
Exec V Pres, Phil Pierce
Exec V Pres, George Johnson
Site Operations Manager, Matthew Clark
Accounts Payable, Gwen Johnson
Senior Manager Supply Chain Di, Marilyn Jones
Compliance Specialist, Maria Wright
Customer Representativ, Ashley Dillard
Auditors: DUNCAN WHEELER & WILKERSON P

LOCATIONS

HQ: AVERITT INCORPORATED
1415 NEAL ST, COOKEVILLE, TN 385014328
Phone: 931 526-3306
Web: WWW.AVERITTEXPRESS.COM

HISTORICAL FINANCIALS

Company Type: Private

Income Statement   FYE: December 31

	REVENUE ($ mil.)	NET INCOME ($ mil.)	NET PROFIT MARGIN	EMPLOYEES
12/18	1,292	86	6.7%	8,210
12/17	1,157	93	8.1%	—
12/16	1,097	52	4.8%	—
12/15	1,104	52	4.8%	—
Annual Growth	5.4%	17.7%	—	—

2018 Year-End Financials

Return on assets: 7.6%   Cash ($ mil.): 96
Return on equity: 9.9%
Current ratio: 3.20

AVI-SPL HOLDINGS, INC.

EXECUTIVES

Ceo, John Zettel
Coo, John Murphy
Cfo, Steve Palmer
Technical Representat, Adam Beall
Financial Analyst I, Adil Akram
Lead Technician, Alex Irizarry
Account Manager Inside Sales, Ardis Warner
Internet Marketing Manager, Atina Hasty
Vice President, National Accou, Brad Weintraub
Sales Administrator, Brandi Rivera
Auditors: ERNST & YOUNG LLP TAMPA FL

LOCATIONS

HQ: AVI-SPL HOLDINGS, INC.
6301 BENJAMIN RD STE 101, TAMPA, FL 336345115
Phone: 866 708-5034
Web: WWW.AVISPL.COM

HISTORICAL FINANCIALS

Company Type: Private

Income Statement   FYE: December 31

	REVENUE ($ mil.)	NET INCOME ($ mil.)	NET PROFIT MARGIN	EMPLOYEES
12/11	555	5	1.1%	4,936
12/10	505	(0)	—	—
12/09	421	3	0.7%	—
Annual Growth	14.8%	38.5%	—	—

2011 Year-End Financials

Return on assets: 1.8%   Cash ($ mil.): 2
Return on equity: 4.2%
Current ratio: 1.50

AVIO INC.

EXECUTIVES

Pres-Ceo, Claudio Vinci
Controller, Theresa Gagliardi
Offc Mgr, Pat Alberti
Hr Mgr, Joseph Marcella
It Mgr, Michele Luca

LOCATIONS

HQ: AVIO INC.
270 SYLVAN AVE STE 130, ENGLEWOOD CLIFFS, NJ 076322545
Phone: 201 816-2720
Web: WWW.AVIOUSA.COM

HISTORICAL FINANCIALS

Company Type: Private

Income Statement   FYE: December 31

	REVENUE ($ mil.)	NET INCOME ($ mil.)	NET PROFIT MARGIN	EMPLOYEES
12/12	1,310	7	0.6%	34
12/05	293	0	0.2%	—
12/04	387	8	2.1%	—
12/03	1,817	0	—	—
Annual Growth	—	—	—	—

2012 Year-End Financials

Return on assets: 12.3%   Cash ($ mil.): 42
Return on equity: 0.6%
Current ratio: 0.60

AXEL JOHNSON INC.

The Johnson family of Stockholm Sweden has an investment arm that stretches across the ocean. Axel Johnson owns and operates North American businesses on behalf of the Johnson dynasty. The investment firm focuses on several industries such as energy medical device manufacturing and water treatment. Its portfolio includes Sprague Energy Parkson Corp. and Kinetico Incorporated. Axel Johnson's companies boast about $4 billion in annual revenues. Axel Johnson along with Axel Johnson AB and AXFast are all affiliated with Sweden-based Axel Johnson Group but are independent. Established in 1873 the Johnson family of companies is in its fourth generation of family ownership.

Operations

Axel Johnson which was formed in 1920 is a long-term investor that typically holds on to its companies for about 20 years. Some companies have been a part of Axel Johnson's portfolio for more than 40 years. Two of its holdings Parkson and Kinetico are part of Axel Johnson's AxWater Group which was formed in 2000.

Financial Performance

Following the economic downturn the company has seen sales increase for several years. Axel Johnson's revenue rose by 6% in 2012 to $4.2 billion as compared to 2011. Energy product sales generated the largest portion of the company's revenue. The results were powered by higher commodity prices and growth at Kinetico Cadence and Mountain Lumber; the first two along with ConforMis and Walk2Campus reported record sales in 2012.

Strategy

Through NewtrAX Axel Johnson makes minority investments in smaller businesses. NewtrAX has stakes in Cadence a manufacturer of cutting and piercing instruments used for the medical and industrial applications. It also owns portions of wood reclamation company Mountain Lumber Co. and Walk2Campus a real estate management and acquisition company. The company in late 2011 invested some $15 million in ConforMIS which develops and markets customized medical devices for the treatment of osteoarthritis and joint damage.

EXECUTIVES

Pres, Michael D Milligan
Chb, Antonia Axson Johnson
Exec V Pres, Ben J Hennelly
Exec V Pres, John Pascale
Vice President, Sally Sarsfield
V Pres, Clare Peeters
Chief Information Security Off, Janie Wintermyer
Administrative Assistant, Stephanie Moots
Director Benefits, Lawrence Haynes
Manager of Corporate Finance, Erika Cafarella
Manager Corporate, Morgan Kiss
Auditors: ERNST & YOUNG LLP NEW YORK N

LOCATIONS

HQ: AXEL JOHNSON INC.
155 SPRING ST FL 6, NEW YORK, NY 100125254
Phone: 646 291-2445
Web: WWW.AXELJOHNSON.COM

PRODUCTS/OPERATIONS

Selected Portfolio Companies
Cadence Incorporated
ConforMIS Inc.
Decisyon Inc.
Kinetico Incorporated
Mountain Lumber Company
Parkson Corporation
Sprague Energy Corp.
Walk2Campus Holdings LLC

COMPETITORS

Ccmp Capital
Court Square Capital
 Partners
Enterprise Partners

Kkr
Menlo Ventures
Sevin Rosen

HISTORICAL FINANCIALS

Company Type: Private

Income Statement				FYE: December 31
	REVENUE ($ mil.)	NET INCOME ($ mil.)	NET PROFIT MARGIN	EMPLOYEES
12/10	2,982	15	0.5%	1,200
12/09	2,598	11	0.5%	—
12/08	4,312	8	0.2%	—
Annual Growth	(16.8%)	35.5%	—	—

2010 Year-End Financials

Return on assets: 1.4%   Cash ($ mil.): 9
Return on equity: 5.2%
Current ratio: 1.70

AXOS BANK

EXECUTIVES

Ceo, Greg Garrabants
Sr V Pres-Cfo, Andrew Micheletti
Evp-Chief Credit Offr-Chief RE, Tom
 Constantine
Gen Counsel, Eshel Bar-Adon
Exec V Pres, Brian Swanson
Executive Vice-President, Adriaan Van Zyl
Assistant Vice-President, Joel Kodish
Underwriter, Jessica Montoya
Accounting Clerk, Jose Catalan
Financial Executive, Lior Assa
Loan Specialist Income, Aaron Shapiro

LOCATIONS

HQ: AXOS BANK
 4350 LA JOLLA VILLAGE DR # 100, SAN DIEGO, CA
 921221244
Phone: 858 350-6200
Web: WWW.AXOSBANK.COM

HISTORICAL FINANCIALS

Company Type: Private

Income Statement				FYE: December 31
	ASSETS ($ mil.)	NET INCOME ($ mil.)	INCOME AS % OF ASSETS	EMPLOYEES
12/17	8,908	150	1.7%	102
12/16	8,162	137	1.7%	—
12/15	6,656	104	1.6%	—
12/14	5,190	71	1.4%	—
Annual Growth	19.7%	28.1%	—	—

2017 Year-End Financials

Return on assets: 1.7%   Sales ($ mil): 483
Return on equity: 17.3%

B.L. HARBERT HOLDINGS, L.L.C.

EXECUTIVES

Ceo-Chm, Billy Harbert
Exe V Pres-Cfo-Sec, R Alan Hall
V Pres-Cao, James Stewart
V Pres-Risk MGT-Cco, William Lalor
Contrl-Treas-Asst SEC, John Rives
Office Manager, Andrea Jones
Commissioning Manager, Greg Jones
Project Superintendent, Hal Clements
Manager, Lakisha Williams
Project Manager, Matt Goldsworthy
Communications and Public Rela, Meg Sartain
Auditors: CROWE HORWATH LLP ATLANTA GE

LOCATIONS

HQ: B.L. HARBERT HOLDINGS, L.L.C.
 820 SHADES CREEK PKWY # 3000, BIRMINGHAM,
 AL 352094564
Phone: 205 802-2800
Web: WWW.BLHARBERT.COM

HISTORICAL FINANCIALS

Company Type: Private

Income Statement				FYE: December 31
	REVENUE ($ mil.)	NET INCOME ($ mil.)	NET PROFIT MARGIN	EMPLOYEES
12/14	807	53	6.7%	2,000
12/05	361	0	—	—
12/04	203	0	—	—
Annual Growth	14.8%	—	—	—

2014 Year-End Financials

Return on assets: 6.8%   Cash ($ mil.): 191
Return on equity: 6.7%
Current ratio: 0.60

BAKERSFIELD MEMORIAL HOSPITAL

EXECUTIVES

Ceo, Jon Van Boening
Chb*, Gordon K Foster
Chief Staff, Robert L Waguespack
Vp Affairs, R Mark R Root
Pharmacist, Brian Bickford
Chief of Radiology, David Schale
Operations Manager, Gary De Risio
Materials Management, Maria Salazar
Chief Officer, Mark Root
Marketing, Michelle Willow
Benefits Specialist, Shana Gonsman

LOCATIONS

HQ: BAKERSFIELD MEMORIAL HOSPITAL
 420 34TH ST, BAKERSFIELD, CA 933012237
Phone: 661 327-1792
Web: WWW.DIGNITYHEALTH.ORG

HISTORICAL FINANCIALS

Company Type: Private

Income Statement				FYE: June 30
	REVENUE ($ mil.)	NET INCOME ($ mil.)	NET PROFIT MARGIN	EMPLOYEES
06/20	540	16	3.0%	1,100
06/16	401	19	4.8%	—
06/15	423	71	16.9%	—
06/14	373	45	12.1%	—
Annual Growth	6.4%	(15.4%)	—	—

2020 Year-End Financials

Return on assets: 2.2%   Cash ($ mil.): 75
Return on equity: 2.8%
Current ratio: 1.70

BALFOUR BEATTY CONSTRUCTION GROUP, INC.

Balfour Beatty Construction is deep in the heart of Texas — and beyond. The company provides start-to-finish project management pre-construction and related services for commercial construction projects. Offerings include site evaluation and analysis general contracting cost consulting process equipment installation turnkey medical facility development capital equipment planning and closeout services. The company works on a range of facilities including hotels office buildings civic centers airports hospitals schools public buildings and retail locations. UK firm Balfour Beatty plc acquired the company then named Centex Construction from Centex Corp. in 2007.

Operations
Balfour Beatty Construction ranks as the fifth largest general builder in the US. The firm is also active in the construction services infrastructure investment and professionals and support services markets.

Geographic Reach
Dallas-based Balfour Beatty Construction has locations in the West Mid-Atlantic and Southeast.

Strategy
The US arm of the international infrastructure group Balfour Beatty Construction is poised to profit from the recovery of the US economy. Indeed the US market has seen a quicker return to growth that its UK counterpart with more private and complex construction projects coming to the market. To that end the construction service firm is expanding its Houston Division to capitalize on growing demand from the energy and multifamily housing markets in the Houston area. To build its Campus Solutions business which specializes in the construction of education facilities Balfour Beatty Construction absorbed Charter Builders a specialist in educational facilities in 2012. Recent student housing projects include a 1274-bed student housing project at Texas A&M University. Construction of the $104 million project began in mid-2014 with completion and occupancy set for August 2015.

Some of the company's more notable projects include NASA Mission Control (Houston) Texas Stadium (home of the Dallas Cowboys) the Mayo Clinic The James Madison Library of Congress

One America Plaza Miami International Airport and Cinderella's Castle at Walt Disney World.

EXECUTIVES

Chb-Ceo, Mark Layman
Exec V Pres*, Doug Jones
Exec V Pres*, John Tarpey
Sr V Pres*, John Parolisi
Exec V Pres*, Glenn Burns
Exec V Pres*, Eric Stenman
Exec V Pres*, John Woodcock
Cfo*, Richard Jaggers
V Pres*, Mark Crouser
Asst Contrl, Richard Howarth
Project Manager, Randy Bowden
Auditors: KPMG LLP DALLAS TX

LOCATIONS

HQ: BALFOUR BEATTY CONSTRUCTION GROUP, INC.
  3100 MCKINNON ST FL 10, DALLAS, TX 752017007
Phone: 214 451-1000
Web: WWW.BALFOURBEATTYUS.COM

PRODUCTS/OPERATIONS

Selected Key Markets

Airports
Defense housing
Education
Health care
Judicial & institutional
Rail
Roads

Selected Projects
Air Force Memorial (Arlington VA)
Army/Air Force Exchange Shopping Center (Fort Jackson SC)
Bank of America (Charlotte NC)
Broward County Convention Center (Fort Lauderdale FL)
Burger King corporate headquarters (Miami)
Cape Coral Parkway Expansion (Cape Coral FL)
Carnival Cruise Lines corporate headquarters (Miami)
Children's Hospital & Health Center (San Diego CA)
Cisco Systems corporate headquarters (Research Triangle Park NC)
Disney's Wilderness Lodge Resort (Lake Buena Vista FL)
Duke University Levine Science Research Center (Durham NC)
Harrah's Casino (New Orleans)
Harris Methodist Hospital (Fort Worth TX)
James Madison Memorial Building Library of Congress (Washington DC)
J.P. Morgan International Plaza (Dallas)
Lucayan Beach Resort (Grand Bahama Island Bahamas)
Mescalero Apache K-12 (Mescalero NM)
Music City Central MTA Bus Facility (Nashville TN)
NASA Space Station Control Center (Houston)
Osceoloa County Courthouse (Kissimmee FL)
Port of Miami (Miami)
Southwest Airlines corporate headquarters (Dallas)
United Spirit Arena (Lubbock TX)
Vanderbilt University Medical Center (Nashville TN)
Walter Reed Army Medical Center military housing (Silver Spring MD)
White Sands Missile Range military housing (White Sands NM)

COMPETITORS

American Constructors
Ames Construction
Axis Construction
Bechtel
Cutler Associates
Engelberth Construction
Falkenberg Construction
Fluor
G. A. Johnson & Son
Hardaway Construction
Lechase Construction
M & H Enterprises
Mw Builders
Mcgough Construction
Panattoni Construction
Rayco Construction
Satterfield & Pontikes
Skanska Usa Building
Turner Construction

HISTORICAL FINANCIALS
Company Type: Private

Income Statement   FYE: December 31

	REVENUE ($ mil.)	NET INCOME ($ mil.)	NET PROFIT MARGIN	EMPLOYEES
12/15	3,852	(14)	—	2,495
12/14	3,932	17	0.4%	—
12/13	3,816	24	0.6%	—
12/12	3,459	19	0.6%	—
Annual Growth	3.7%	—	—	—

2015 Year-End Financials

Return on assets: (-0.9%)   Cash ($ mil.): 69
Return on equity: (-3.0%)
Current ratio: 1.20

BALFOUR BEATTY CONSTRUCTION, LLC

EXECUTIVES

Ceo-Chb, Leon E Blondin
MBR-Pres, Eric Stenman
MBR-Div Pres, Pleas Mitchell
Clo, David Hodnett
MBR, Richard Jaggers
MBR, Glenn Burns
MBR, John Parolisi
MBR, John Tarpey
Cfo, Denise Hubley
Performance Awareness Cnsltnt, Patricia Laprade
Project Coordinator, Leonicio Alonzo
Auditors: KPMG LLP DALLAS TX

LOCATIONS

HQ: BALFOUR BEATTY CONSTRUCTION, LLC
  3100 MCKINNON ST FL 3, DALLAS, TX 752011081
Phone: 214 451-1000
Web: WWW.BALFOURBEATTYUS.COM

HISTORICAL FINANCIALS
Company Type: Private

Income Statement   FYE: December 31

	REVENUE ($ mil.)	NET INCOME ($ mil.)	NET PROFIT MARGIN	EMPLOYEES
12/16	3,809	13	0.3%	2,495
12/13	3,816	23	0.6%	—
12/12	3,365	8	0.3%	—
12/10	0	0	—	—
Annual Growth	—	—	—	—

2016 Year-End Financials

Return on assets: 0.8%   Cash ($ mil.): 53
Return on equity: 2.8%
Current ratio: 1.20

BALFOUR BEATTY, LLC

EXECUTIVES

V Pres, Peter Zinkin
V Pres, Leslie Cohn

V Pres-Asst SEC, Joanne Bonfiglio
Treas, Barry Crozier
SEC, Christine Schiltz
Asst Treas, Vicki Sizemore
Vp and Business Unit Leader Fo, Ed Prendergast
Superintendent, Chuck Howard
Senior Superintendent, Jack Fore
Project Engineer, Lexi Halperin
Project Manager, Matt Albright
Auditors: DELOITTE & TOUCHE LLP DALLAS

LOCATIONS

HQ: BALFOUR BEATTY, LLC
  1011 CENTRE RD STE 322, WILMINGTON, DE 198051266
Phone: 302 573-3873
Web: WWW.BALFOURBEATTY.COM

HISTORICAL FINANCIALS
Company Type: Private

Income Statement   FYE: December 31

	REVENUE ($ mil.)	NET INCOME ($ mil.)	NET PROFIT MARGIN	EMPLOYEES
12/15	4,690	(18)	—	2,495
12/12	4,378	43	1.0%	—
12/11	4,078	58	1.4%	—
Annual Growth	3.6%	—	—	—

2015 Year-End Financials

Return on assets: (-0.5%)   Cash ($ mil.): 391
Return on equity: (-1.0%)
Current ratio: 1.70

BALLAD HEALTH

EXECUTIVES

Chm-Pres-Ceo, Alan Levine
Cfo*, Lynn Krutak
Coo*, Marvin Eichorn
Svp-CIO*, Pam Austin
Cipo*, Jamie Swift
Cmo Northwest Division, Herb Ladley
Vp Oncology Services, Tony Dotson
Human Resources Generalist, Kasey Guy
Marketing Coordinator, Lori English
Operating Room Dir, Ruth Morelock
Marketing Coordinator, Amanda Hoyle
Auditors: PYA PC KNOXVILLE TENNESSE

LOCATIONS

HQ: BALLAD HEALTH
  400 N STATE OF FRNKLIN RD, JOHNSON CITY, TN 376046035
Phone: 423 431-6561
Web: WWW.BALLADHEALTH.ORG

HISTORICAL FINANCIALS
Company Type: Private

Income Statement   FYE: June 30

	REVENUE ($ mil.)	NET INCOME ($ mil.)	NET PROFIT MARGIN	EMPLOYEES
06/21	2,191	267	12.2%	6,114
06/20	2,077	(69)	—	—
06/19	2,106	99	4.7%	—
Annual Growth	2.0%	63.8%	—	—

Return on assets: 6.8%   Cash ($ mil.): 412
Return on equity: 14.0%
Current ratio: 1.50

BALTIMORE CITY PUBLIC SCHOOLS

EXECUTIVES

Ceo, Sonja B Santelises
Ceo, Bonnie S Copeland
Chief School Supports Officer, Karl E Perry
Chief Achievement and Accounta, Theresa Jones
Accounting Staff, Michele Hayes
Teacher, George Kessler
Elementary School Teacher, Jaime Clough
Esol Teacher, Laura Oxenreiter
Manager, Andrew Monger
Special Assistant (email), Julienne Vinson
Pre Kindergarten Teacher, Kathryn S Liberopoulos
Auditors: CLIFTONLARSONALLEN LLP
  BALTIM

LOCATIONS

HQ: BALTIMORE CITY PUBLIC SCHOOLS
  200 E NORTH AVE, BALTIMORE, MD 212025984
Phone: 443 984-2000
Web: WWW.BALTIMORECITYSCHOOLS.ORG

HISTORICAL FINANCIALS

Company Type: Private

Income Statement				FYE: June 30
	REVENUE ($ mil.)	NET INCOME ($ mil.)	NET PROFIT MARGIN	EMPLOYEES
06/12	1,480	(18)	—	10,800
06/02	988	(23)	—	—
Annual Growth	4.1%	—	—	—

2012 Year-End Financials

Return on assets: (-2.0%)   Cash ($ mil.): 183
Return on equity: (-3.6%)
Current ratio: —

BANNER HEALTH

EXECUTIVES

Pres-Ceo, Peter S Fine
Exe V Pres*, Kathy Bollinger
Cao*, Ron Bunnell
Cmo*, John Hensing
Exe V Pres-Comm Dev*, Rebecca Kuhn
Exe V Pres*, Chuck Lehn
Cfo*, Dennis Dahlen
CIO*, Deanna Wise
Director of Information Techno, Kay Smith
Director, Kevin Roche
Secretary, Laura Snow
Auditors: ERNST & YOUNG LLP PHOENIX AZ

LOCATIONS

HQ: BANNER HEALTH
  7251 W 4TH ST, GREELEY, CO 806349763
Phone: 602 747-4000
Web: WWW.BANNERHEALTH.COM

HISTORICAL FINANCIALS

Company Type: Private

Income Statement				FYE: December 31
	REVENUE ($ mil.)	NET INCOME ($ mil.)	NET PROFIT MARGIN	EMPLOYEES
12/20	10,397	711	6.8%	35,000
12/19	9,426	753	8.0%	—
Annual Growth	10.3%	(5.6%)	—	—

2020 Year-End Financials

Return on assets: 4.5%   Cash ($ mil.): 1,145
Return on equity: 9.7%
Current ratio: 1.30

BANNER-UNIVERSITY MEDICAL CENTER TUCSON CAMPUS LLC

Banner - University Medicine (formerly The University of Arizona Health Network) heals Arizonans and trains Wildcats. It operates three academic medical centers in Phoenix and Tucson serving as the primary teaching hospital for the University of Arizona (UA) and offering medical treatment research and education services. The not-for-profit center provides cancer cardiology geriatric respiratory transplant and dialysis care as well as general practice and home health services. Specialty services include burn care behavioral health integrative medicine sports medicine and level I trauma care. The network merged with Banner Healthcare in 2015.

Operations

The University of Arizona Health Network merged with Banner Health to create Banner - University Medicine. The division includes three hospitals: Banner - University Medical Center Tucson Banner - University Medical Center South and Banner - University Medical Center Phoenix. The network also includes Banner - University Medical Group (formerly named University of Arizona Physicians) a group of Tucson-based physicians.

Geographic Reach

Banner - University Medicine serves patients in and around Phoenix and Tucson Arizona.

Strategy

In 2015 Banner - University Medical Center Phoenix broke ground on a new $160 million emergency department that will have the capacity to serve an additional 20000 patients each year. Expected to open in mid-2017 the new facility will include 60 private exam rooms a new trauma unit and 40 observation beds.

Company Background

The University of Arizona Health Network was formed in 2010 when University Physicians Hospital merged with University Medical Center.

LOCATIONS

HQ: BANNER-UNIVERSITY MEDICAL CENTER
  TUCSON CAMPUS LLC
  1501 N CAMPBELL AVE, TUCSON, AZ 857240001
Phone:
Web: WWW.UAHEALTH.IXT.COM

COMPETITORS

John C. Lincoln Health
  Network
Northern Arizona
  Healthcare
Phoenix Children's
  Hospital
Scottsdale Healthcare
Sun Health
Yuma Regional Medical
  Center

HISTORICAL FINANCIALS

Company Type: Private

Income Statement				FYE: June 30
	REVENUE ($ mil.)	NET INCOME ($ mil.)	NET PROFIT MARGIN	EMPLOYEES
06/09	541	0	—	3,000
06/08	512	27	5.3%	—
06/05	708	0	0.0%	—
Annual Growth	(6.5%)	—	—	—

2009 Year-End Financials

Return on assets: 16.3%   Cash ($ mil.): 3
Return on equity: —
Current ratio: —

BAPTIST HEALTH

For those seeking medical salvation Baptist Health may be the answer to their prayers. The organization provides health services through about 175 points of care scattered throughout in Arkansas. Its facilities include seven hospitals and a number of rehabilitation facilities family clinics and therapy and wellness centers. Arkansas Health Group a division of Baptist Health runs more than 20 physician clinics across the state. Specialized services include cardiology women's health orthopedics rehabilitation and home and hospice care. Baptist Health's Parkway Village is a 90-acre retirement community for active seniors located close to Baptist Health Medical Center - Little Rock.

Operations

In addition to its hospitals the company has 47 physician clinics 20 therapy centers and 53 other centers and service locations. Its Baptist Health Mobile Health Unit travels the state to provide a temporary facility for health screenings health education and first-aid (emergent care) services.

Along with the standard roster of health care services Baptist Health also offers Little Rock residents nine programs of health care study through its Baptist Health Schools Little Rock division. The school coordinates with Arkansas Tech University to offer Baptist Health RN graduates an online option to complete their Bachelor of Science in Nursing degree. Its average enrollment is about 900 students each semester.

Geographic Reach

Baptist Health serves patients across Arkansas. Baptist Health's hospitals include Baptist Health Extended Care Hospital Baptist Health Medical Center - Arkadelphia Baptist Health Medical Center - Heber Springs Baptist Health Medical Center - Little Rock Baptist Health Medical Center - North Little Rock Baptist Health Medical Center - Stuttgart and Baptist Health Medical Center - Hot Spring County.

Sales and Marketing

Baptist Health works with a number of insurance policies and organizations including Aetna AMCO PPO Arkansas Blue Cross and Blue Shield Arkansas Municipal League Care Improvement Plus CIGNA Coventry/First Health PPO and GEHA.

Strategy

The hospital system has been growing to meet the needs of its customers. In 2013 it began leasing Hot Spring County Medical Center in Malvern. The 72-bed acute care hospital was renamed Baptist Health Medical Center Hot Spring County. Baptist Health also bought nearly 40 acres in Conway and began construction on a medical center to serve Faulkner county.

To improve operating efficiency in 2013 Baptist Health formed a new organization — Baptist Health Physician Partners a clinical integration program with more than 200 physician partners.

EXECUTIVES

Pres, Russ Harrington
Sr V Pres*, Allen Smith
Exec Vice Pres*, Missy Lewis
Prin*, Doug Weeks
Chief Dev Officer*, Lena Moore
Cco*, Marea Aspillaga
Svp-Cmo-Cqo*, David Rice
Real Estate Conultant, Carey Thompson
Coordinator, Daniel Davies
Vp-Admin Medical Center, Mike Perkins
Director, Debbie Green
Auditors: BKD LLP LITTLE ROCK ARKANSA

LOCATIONS

HQ: BAPTIST HEALTH
9601 BAPTIST HEALTH DR # 109, LITTLE ROCK, AR 722056323
Phone: 501 202-2000
Web: WWW.BAPTIST-HEALTH.COM

Selected Locations in Arkansas

Arkansas Health Group (statewide)
BH Extended Care (Little Rock)
BHMC Arkadelphia
BHMC Heber Springs
BHMC Hot Spring County
BHMC Little Rock
BHMC North Little Rock
BHMC Stuttgart
Baptist Health Rehabilitation Institute (Little Rock)
Parkway Village (Little Rock)

PRODUCTS/OPERATIONS

Selected Services

Behavioral Health
Cardiac Rehab
Diabetes Treatment & Management
Eye Center
Hospice & Home Health
Home Infusion Services
Imaging Services
Laboratory
MedFlight
Men's Health
Pastoral Care
Sleep Disorder
Transplant
Weight Loss Program
Wound Care Center

COMPETITORS

Arkansas Children's Hospital
Arkansas Heart Hospital
Baxter Regional Medical Center
Conway Regional Health System
Jefferson Regional Medical Center Of Arkansas
Saline Memorial
Sparks Health System
St. Joseph's Mercy Health Center
St. Vincent Health System
White County Medical Center

HISTORICAL FINANCIALS

Company Type: Private

Income Statement				FYE: December 31
	REVENUE ($ mil.)	NET INCOME ($ mil.)	NET PROFIT MARGIN	EMPLOYEES
12/20	1,650	155	9.4%	7,000
12/18	1,215	(45)	—	—
12/17	875	49	5.6%	—
12/09	924	64	7.0%	—
Annual Growth	5.4%	8.3%	—	—

2020 Year-End Financials

Return on assets: 7.5%   Cash ($ mil.): 193
Return on equity: 14.9%
Current ratio: 1.70

BAPTIST HEALTH SOUTH FLORIDA, INC.

Faith-based non-for-profit Baptist Health South Florida (BHSF) is the largest healthcare organization in the region With more than 1.5 million patient visits every year. Baptist Hospital is its flagship facility that offers a full range of medical and technological services and home to three Centers of Excellence ? Miami Cardiac & Vascular Institute Miami Neuroscience Institute and Miami Cancer Institute. Baptist Children's Hospital provides neonatal intensive care inpatient pediatric oncology services and pediatric care among other services.

Operations

BHSF's group of hospitals include Baptist Health Hospital Baptist Hospital Baptist Hospital of Miami Baptist Children's Hospital Bethesda Hospital East Bethesda Hospital West Boca Raton Regional Hospital Doctors Hospital Fishermen's Community Hospital Homestead Hospital Mariners Hospital West Kendall Baptist Hospital and South Miami Hospital.

BHSF offers an extensive range of medical surgical and technological services ? including cancer neuroscience cardiovascular sports medicine and orthopedics.

BHSF International offers a full range of services for international patients including access to multilingual patient coordinators who provide personalized concierge service outpatient diagnostics and procedures medical second opinions and special rates for hotel accommodations at the recently opened Hilton Miami Dadeland on the main campus of Baptist Hospital.

Geographic Reach

Headquartered in Coral Gables Florida BHSF operates a dozen of hospitals more than 100 outpatient facilities and physician practice locations.

Sales and Marketing

Baptist Health Care On Demand a telehealth app allows people to see its BHSF's urgent doctor from their phone or computer- any time day or night nationwide.

Company Background

Baptist Hospital opened in 1960 and the Baptist Health organization was formed in 1990.

The company added a number of hospitals through acquisitions and construction efforts over the years. It opened the West Kendall Baptist Hospital in 2011. In 2017 the system merged with the not-for-profit Bethesda Health adding two hospitals (Bethesda East and Bethesda West) in Boynton Beach. It also added the Fishermen's Community Hospital that year.

EXECUTIVES

Ceo, Alexandra Villoch
Pres*, Brian E Keeley
Chb*, George E Cadman III
Evp-Cfo*, Ralph E Lawson
Evp-Coo*, Fred M Messing
SEC*, David W Cleeland
Treas*, H Robert Berry
Evp-Chief Medical/Clinical Tra*, Jack A Ziffer
Exec Vp-Cfo*, Matthew Arsenault
Svp-Chief Digital Officer*, Tony Ambrozie
Orthopedic Surgeon, Keith Hechtman
Auditors: DELOITTE & TOUCHE LLP MIAMI

LOCATIONS

HQ: BAPTIST HEALTH SOUTH FLORIDA, INC.
6855 S RED RD, SOUTH MIAMI, FL 331433647
Phone: 305 596-1960
Web: WWW.BAPTISTHEALTH.NET

PRODUCTS/OPERATIONS

2013 Sales

	$ mil.	% of total
Managed Care	1,655	69
Medicare	278	12
Medicaid	122	5
Other	331	14
Total		100

Selected Florida Facilities

Baptist Hospital of Miami (Kendall)
  Baptist Cardiac & Vascular Institute
  Baptist Children's Hospital
Doctors Hospital (Coral Gables)
Homestead Hospital (Homestead)
Mariners Hospital (Tavernier)
South Miami Hospital (South Miami)
West Kendall Baptist Hospital (Kendall)

Selected Services

Addiction treatment
Behavorial medicine
Blood conservation program
Cancer services
Cardiovascular services
Care and counseling services
Children's health
Community wellness
Critical care center
Diabetes
eICU LifeGuard
Emergency
Endoscopy
Executive health
Gamma knife center
Heart surgery
Home care
Hyperbaric services
Imaging
Intensive care unit
International services
Interventional/surgical Services
Laboratory
Maritime medical services
Neonatal
Neuroscience
Nutrition counseling services
Occupational health
Online appointments
Orthopedics
Outpatient/diagnostic services
Pain center
Pastoral care
Pediatric
Pelvic health
Physical and speech therapy
Pregnancy and childbirth
Progressive care unit
Prostate cancer
Pulmonary services
Radiation oncology
Rehabilitation services
Robotic surgery
Senior services
Sleep diagnostic center

Sports medicine and orthopedic programs
Stroke services
Surgery
Weight-loss surgery
Wellness Center
Women's health
Wound care

COMPETITORS

Adventist Health System Sunbelt Healthcare
Boca Raton Regional Hospital
Broward Health
Hca
Holy Cross Hospital Fort Lauderdale
Jackson Health System
Lakeland Regional Medical Center
Miami Children's Hospital
Mount Sinai Medical Center Of Florida
South Broward Hospital District
Tenet Healthcare
The Cleveland Clinic
University Of Miami Hospital

HISTORICAL FINANCIALS
Company Type: Private

Income Statement				FYE: September 30
	REVENUE ($ mil.)	NET INCOME ($ mil.)	NET PROFIT MARGIN	EMPLOYEES
09/19	1,294	598	46.3%	16,000
09/17	608	244	40.2%	—
09/15	846	137	16.2%	—
09/09	616	121	19.7%	—
Annual Growth	7.7%	17.3%	—	—

2019 Year-End Financials
Return on assets: 8.8%   Cash ($ mil.): 132
Return on equity: 12.7%
Current ratio: 0.90

BAPTIST HEALTH SYSTEM, INC.

Founded in 1955 Baptist Health serves the Jacksonville Florida area through four acute care hospitals and a children's hospital with a combined total of more than 1200 physicians in about 90 specialties. Baptist MD Anderson Cancer Center is a regional destination for world-renowned cancer care which is clinically integrated with MD Anderson Cancer Center in Houston Across the street Wolfson Children's Hospital also cares for the city's youngest residents. The system's satellite acute-care facilities include Baptist Medical Center Beaches Baptist Medical Center Nassau and Baptist Medical Center South.

Operations
Baptist Health's flagship tertiary care hospital Baptist Medical Center is centrally located in Jacksonville and is a full-service medical center representing nearly all major health care specialties. Its Baptist Heart Hospital offers comprehensive cardiovascular care. Baptist Health has more than 200 primary care and specialty physician practices children's specialty clinics home health care behavioral health occupational health rehabilitation services and urgent care.

Its Health Care for Women provides a comprehensive health services for issues of concern to women such as breast health pregnancy childbirth gynecology and senior issues such as osteoporosis.

In addition Baptist Research Institute is currently overseeing more than 50 clinical research studies in a wide range of areas. Its primary areas of interest include endovascular neurology and cardiovascular and pediatrics.

Geographic Reach
Baptist Health is headquartered in Jacksonville Florida.

Company Background
A major construction project was completed in late 2012 with the opening of a new 11-story patient tower at Baptist Jacksonville. The new $200 million tower features all private patient rooms and high-tech surgical suites.

Baptist Health was founded in 1955.

EXECUTIVES

Int Pres-Ceo, Michael Mayo
Sr V Pres-Cfo*, Michael Lukaszewski
Exec V Pres-Coo*, John Willbanks
Chief of Medicine, Carol Wratten
Coordinator, Betsy Schifanella
Svp and Chief Nursing Officer, Diane S Raines
Evp and Coo, John F Wilbanks
Vice President, Chris Durkin
Transcription Manager, Sherry Martin
Purchasing, Angela Holden
Lpn, Bonnie Villarruel
Auditors: ERNEST & YOUNG LLP JACKSONVI

LOCATIONS

HQ: BAPTIST HEALTH SYSTEM, INC.
841 PRUDENTIAL DR # 1802, JACKSONVILLE, FL 322078329
Phone: 904 202-2000
Web: WWW.BAPTISTJAX.COM

PRODUCTS/OPERATIONS

Selected facilities
Baptist Medical Center Beaches (Jacksonville Beach Florida)
Baptist Medical Center Jacksonville (Jacksonville Florida)
Baptist Heart Hospital
Baptist Medical Center Nassau (Fernandina Beach Florida)
Baptist Medical Center South (Jacksonville Florida)
Wolfson Children's Hospital (Jacksonville Florida)

COMPETITORS

Bay Medical Center
Brooks Rehabilitation
Florida Hospital Tampa Bay Division
Florida Hospital Waterman
Hca
Mayo Clinic Jacksonville
Munroe Regional Health System
Nemours Foundation
Orlando Health
St. Vincent's Health System
Uf Health Jacksonville

HISTORICAL FINANCIALS
Company Type: Private

Income Statement				FYE: September 30
	REVENUE ($ mil.)	NET INCOME ($ mil.)	NET PROFIT MARGIN	EMPLOYEES
09/20	2,022	95	4.7%	7,000
09/19	1,923	176	9.2%	—
09/18	1,736	252	14.5%	—
09/17	1,630	304	18.7%	—
Annual Growth	7.4%	(32.0%)	—	—

2020 Year-End Financials
Return on assets: 2.1%   Cash ($ mil.): 294
Return on equity: 3.6%
Current ratio: 0.90

BAPTIST HEALTHCARE SYSTEM, INC.

Baptist Health owns eight acute-care hospitals in Kentucky with a total capacity of more than 2700 beds. The not-for-profit health system's largest facility is Baptist Health Louisville a 519-bed hospital in Louisville that provides a wide range of health services with special expertise in cardiology rehabilitation and women's health. In addition to its owned facilities Baptist Health manages Baptist Health Lexington a 434-bed tertiary care facility and Baptist Health Richmond with approximately 105 beds. The growing Baptist Health was founded as a single hospital in Louisville in 1924.

Operations
Along with inpatient acute care services Baptist Health offers home health care services more than 250 outpatient facilities and services including urgent care and retail-based clinics outpatient diagnostic and surgery centers occupational medicine physical therapy clinics and fitness centers. The Baptist Health Medical Group is a comprehensive network that includes more than 1100 physicians and advanced practice clinicians across Kentucky and southern Indiana and represents over 75 specialties including primary care and family medicine internal medicine osteopathic medicine emergency medicine general surgery and a wide range of surgical specialties offering advanced treatments and care.

In addition to its nine hospitals that include Baptist Health Hardin Baptist Health Floyd Baptist Health Richmond Baptist Health Madisonville Baptist Health Paducah Baptist Health Louisville Baptist Health La Grange Baptist Health Lexington and Baptist Health Corbin Baptist Health's clinicians are engaged in over 200 clinical studies throughout its network of hospitals working to advance treatments in oncology cardiology orthopedics neuroscience epidemiology diabetes and other areas.

Geographic Reach
Headquartered in Louisville the Baptist Health's home care is available in about 40 Kentucky counties four counties in Illinois and seven counties in Southern Indiana.

EXECUTIVES

Ceo, Gerard Colman
Pres, William Sisson
V Pres-Planning, Andy Sears
EC, Janet Norton
CIO, David J Bensema
Cmo, Timothy Jahn
Cfo, Stephen R Oglesby
Sr Admn, Pam Starnes
Security Staff, James Jester
Program Manager, Carey Ronan
Internist, Robert Sasser
Auditors: DELOITTE & TOUCHE LLP LOUISVI

LOCATIONS

HQ: BAPTIST HEALTHCARE SYSTEM, INC.
2701 EASTPOINT PKWY, LOUISVILLE, KY 402234166
Phone: 502 896-5000
Web: WWW.BAPTISTHEALTH.COM

PRODUCTS/OPERATIONS

Selected Facilities and Operations (Kentucky)
Hospitals
  Managed
  Baptist Health Corbin

Baptist Health La Grange
Baptist Health Lexington
Baptist Health Louisville
Baptist Health Richmond
Baptist Health Madisonville
Baptist Health Paducah
ContinueCARE Hospital (Corbin)
Owned
Hardin Memorial Hospital (Elizabethtown)
Russell County Hospital (Russell Springs)
Other operations
Baptist East Milestone Wellness Center (Louisville)
Baptist Express Care (various Walmarts in state)
Baptist Medical Associates (medical practice group Louisville area)
Baptist Urgent Care (Louisville)
Bluegrass Family Health (provider-sponsored insurance)

COMPETITORS

Appalachian Regional
  Healthcare
Catholic Health
  Initiatives
Jewish Hospital & St.
  Mary's Healthcare
Kindred Healthcare
Norton Healthcare
Pikeville Medical
  Center
University Health Care
University Of Kentucky
  Chandler Hospital

HISTORICAL FINANCIALS
Company Type: Private

Income Statement				FYE: August 31
	REVENUE ($ mil.)	NET INCOME ($ mil.)	NET PROFIT MARGIN	EMPLOYEES
08/20	2,994	199	6.7%	12,601
08/19	2,878	122	4.2%	—
08/18	2,725	149	5.5%	—
08/17	2,688	5	0.2%	—
Annual Growth	3.7%	224.5%	—	—

2020 Year-End Financials
Return on assets: 4.9%   Cash ($ mil.): 725
Return on equity: 9.2%
Current ratio: 2.00

BAPTIST HOSPITAL OF MIAMI, INC.

Baptist Hospital of Miami can treat many vices for Miami residents. The flagship facility of the Baptist Health South Florida health system provides residents of the city with a full range of health care services including pediatric cancer home health rehabilitation neurology and cardiovascular care. The hospital has more than 680 beds and includes the Baptist Children's Hospital which offers a pediatric emergency room and a neonatal intensive care unit. Baptist Hospital of Miami also includes the Baptist Cardiac & Vascular Institute a regional cancer program and a diabetes care center. Baptist Hospital of Miami was founded in 1960.

Operations
Baptist Children's Hospital offers 24-hour emergency care as well as two intensive care units and specialist services including pediatric cancer care. Baptist Hospital of Miami also contains the Baptist Cardiac and Vascular Institute which conducts treatment and research programs. The hospital's international care unit provides services to patients from the Caribbean Latin America and other regions. Other specialist divisions include a sleep diagnostic center and a spine care facility as well as a maternity ward. Baptist Hospital of Miami also operates several wellness centers.

As part of Baptist Health South Florida the Baptist Hospital of Miami is part of a network of six hospitals including South Miami Hospital Doctors Hospital and the West Kendall Baptist Hospital. In addition the health system includes outpatient care clinics including emergency surgery imaging and primary care centers.

Strategy
Controlling expenses through data management quality and wellness initiatives and other measures becomes increasingly important for the hospital and its affiliates as the cost of medical care in the US market continues to skyrocket. Maintaining an efficient organization is also imperative as the level of charity care provided by the system's facilities continues to rise in the face of economic difficulties.

As the largest hospital in the Baptist Health system Baptist Hospital of Miami takes a leading role in technology programs such as medical equipment and data management system upgrades. The Baptist Health network is in the process of installing an electronic health record (EHR) system to connect patient records across its facilities.

In 2012 Baptist Hospital of Miami launched a $90 million construction effort to expand the Cardiac and Vascular Institute. The new expanded institute facility will open in 2016 and will include centers for aneurysm treatment structural heart therapy and endovascular therapy. The project also includes expansion efforts on the hospital's surgery center which will have enhanced capabilities for neurological cardiac and robotic surgery procedures.

EXECUTIVES

Prin, William W White
Chm*, Calvin Babcock
Cfo*, Ralph Lawson
Treas*, Manuel Lasaga
Coordinator, Suzanne Balbosa
Pulmonary Disease Specialist, Mark J Hauser
Internal Medicine Practitioner, Ivette Acosta-Trant
Nuclear Medicine Specialist, Jason Samii
Information Specialist, Jorge Perez
Internist, Rania Albataineh
Manager Engineering, Richard Johenning

LOCATIONS

HQ: BAPTIST HOSPITAL OF MIAMI, INC.
  8900 N KENDALL DR, MIAMI, FL 331762197
Phone: 786 596-1960
Web: WWW.BAPTISTHEALTH.NET

PRODUCTS/OPERATIONS

Selected Centers and Services
Baptist Cardiac & Vascular Institute (Heart Care)
Baptist Children's Hospital (Pediatrics)
Breast Care
Cancer Services
Center for Spine Care
Children's Cancer Services
Children's Emergency Center
Clinical Research Trials
Community Wellness
Critical Care/eICU LifeGuard
Diabetes Care
Diagnostic Imaging
Emergency Services
Endoscopy
Gynecology
Home Care
Intensive Care
International Services
Interventional
Maternity
Neonatal Intensive Care Unit
Neuroscience Center
Neurosurgery
Orthopedic Services

Pain Management
Physical & Speech Therapy
Pulmonary Services
Rehabilitation Services
Robotic Surgery
Senior Services
Sleep Diagnostic Center
Spine Care
Stroke Services
Surgery
Women's Services

COMPETITORS

Broward Health
H. Lee Moffitt Cancer Center & Research Institute
Hca
Jackson Health System
Larkin Community Hospital
Miami Children's Hospital
Mount Sinai Medical Center Of Florida
South Broward Hospital District
University Of Miami Hospital

HISTORICAL FINANCIALS
Company Type: Private

Income Statement				FYE: September 30
	REVENUE ($ mil.)	NET INCOME ($ mil.)	NET PROFIT MARGIN	EMPLOYEES
09/19	1,717	282	16.4%	4,200
09/18*	1,169	143	12.3%	—
12/17	1,004	73	7.3%	—
09/16	867	39	4.6%	—
Annual Growth	25.6%	92.6%	—	—

*Fiscal year change

2019 Year-End Financials
Return on assets: 25.5%   Cash ($ mil.): —
Return on equity: 65.6%
Current ratio: 0.50

BAPTIST MEMORIAL HOSPITAL

When most of us think of Memphis we think of Elvis Presley. When doctors think of Memphis they think of Elvis and Baptist Memorial Hospital-Memphis. As the flagship facility of Baptist Memorial Health Care the 710-bed hospital often simply called Baptist Memphis offers patients the full spectrum of health care services including cancer treatment orthopedics surgical services and neurology. The campus also features the Baptist Heart Institute for cardiovascular care and research a pediatric emergency room a skilled nursing facility and the Plaza Diagnostic Pavilion for outpatient health care. Baptist Memphis established in 1979 is one of the state's highest volume hospitals.

Operations
Doctors at the hospital see more than 27000 admissions 54000 emergency department visits and nearly 116000 outpatient visits each year. The emergency department houses more than 30 treatment bays. In addition Baptist Memphis' skilled nursing center includes 30 beds. The hospital also operates a 30-bed rehabilitation hospital and a 165000 sq. ft. heart institute for diagnostic and surgical cardiac care. The facility boasts advanced surgical systems including the CyberKnife radiation system for cancerous and non-cancerous tumor removal.

EXECUTIVES

Exec V Pres, David Hogan
Sr Vice Pres-Cfo*, Don Pounds
Exec V Pres*, Robert Gordon
Ceo*, Jason Little
Information, Dick Escue
Human Resources Representative, Larry Braughton
Scientist, Denitrea Palmer
Scientist, Mary Robison
Chief of Medicine, Mike Abutineh
Food Director, Julie Craig
Housekeeping Director, Mike Perry

LOCATIONS

HQ: BAPTIST MEMORIAL HOSPITAL
  6019 WALNUT GROVE RD, MEMPHIS, TN 381202113
Phone: 901 226-5000
Web: WWW.BAPTISTONLINE.ORG

COMPETITORS

Methodist Healthcare
Parkwest Medical
  Center
Shelby County Health
  Care
St. Jude Children's
  Research Hospital
Tenet Healthcare

HISTORICAL FINANCIALS

Company Type: Private

Income Statement				FYE: September 30
	REVENUE ($ mil.)	NET INCOME ($ mil.)	NET PROFIT MARGIN	EMPLOYEES
09/15	691	(1)	—	6,000
09/14	663	(47)	—	—
09/13	504	17	3.4%	—
09/12	697	15	2.2%	—
Annual Growth	(0.3%)	—	—	—

2015 Year-End Financials
Return on assets: (-0.2%)   Cash ($ mil.): 28
Return on equity: (-0.5%)
Current ratio: 1.40

BARCLAYS BANK DELAWARE

Spending money is a rewarding experience for holders of Barclays Bank Delaware cards. With co-branded credit cards from Barclays Bank Delaware (aka Barclays US) customers accumulate points that can be redeemed for air travel hotel stays and other perks. The company a division of Barclays issues Visa and MasterCard credit cards in addition to co-branded credit cards through partnerships with over 25 top companies including Priceline Choice Privileges Carnival World and Jet-Blue. Founded as Juniper Financial in 2000; it became a part of Barclays in 2004.

Operations

The company creates customized co-branded credit card programs for some of the country's most successful travel entertainment retail cashback business expenses and financial institutions. Barclays also offer personal loans by invitation to some customers.

Geographic Reach

Barclays US is headquartered in Wilmington Delaware and has customers and clients across 40 countries.

Sales and Marketing

Barclays US collaborates with over 25 top companies to deliver an array of consumer and small business credit card programs uses partnerships to expand its business. Some of its major partners include Barnes & Noble Frontier Airlines Priceline.com Wyndham Holland America and Diamond Resorts World.

Strategy

Barclays US has been growing in recent years as the global economy improves and it continues to play a pivotal role in furthering innovation and shared growth for all as it evolves the future of banking.

Barclays US continues to focus on next-generation payment technology and digital safety for its customers. Its website and mobile app now utilize a new simplified log-in process to verify one's identity. It added a verification method a SecurPass code to help customers confirm their identity when they attempt to log in on an unknown device as well as Fraud Text Alerts that help protect customers' card in real time.

Company Background

In 1966 Barclays launches Barclaycard the first credit card in the UK. Following that year it introduces the world's first ATM. Barclays acquires Juniper Bank a credit card company formed in 2000 and creating Barclaycard US in 2004. In 2009 Barclaycard becomes a top-10 credit card issuer in the U.S. It launches the first mobile app for card members in 2011. In 2018 Barclaycard rebrands to Barclays in the U.S. offering a range of personal banking products to U.S. consumers.

EXECUTIVES

Ceo, Barry Rodrigues
Pres*, James Stewart
Vp Data Science, Vishal Morde
Accounts Payable, Diane Levin
Executive, Rich Harrington
Software Engineer In Test, Manish Singh
Vice-President, Stephanie Anelli

LOCATIONS

HQ: BARCLAYS BANK DELAWARE
  100 S WEST ST, WILMINGTON, DE 198015015
Phone: 302 255-8000
Web: WWW.CARDS.BARCLAYCARDUS.COM

PRODUCTS/OPERATIONS

Selected Card Partnerships
Ameriprise
Bank Atlantic
Barnes & Noble
BJ's
Frontier
L.L. Bean
US Airways
Best Western
Priceline.com
Payless
Travelocity
Virgin America

COMPETITORS

Alliance Data Systems
American Express
Bank Of America
Capital One
Citibank
Discover
Jpmorgan Chase

HISTORICAL FINANCIALS

Company Type: Private

Income Statement				FYE: December 31
	ASSETS ($ mil.)	NET INCOME ($ mil.)	INCOME AS % OF ASSETS	EMPLOYEES
12/14	25,012	239	1.0%	349
12/13	19,055	331	1.7%	—
12/08	12,418	20	0.2%	—
12/07	7,470	0	—	—
Annual Growth	18.8%	—	—	—

2014 Year-End Financials
Return on assets: 1.0%   Sales ($ mil): 2,245
Return on equity: 7.5%

BARNABAS HEALTH, INC.

EXECUTIVES

Ceo-Pres, Barry Ostrowsky
Cao*, Stephen Jones
Program Director, Anthony Carlino
Doctor, Isabel Roberti
Nurse, Lisa Depta
Administrative Assistant, Kelly Feteira
Director Neonatology, Shyan Sun
Purchasing Manager, Al Coleman
Diagnostic Radiologist, Alan Dembner
Internal Medicine, Alvin Bell
Director Information Technolog, Brian Keene
Auditors: KPMG LLP SHORT HILLS NJ

LOCATIONS

HQ: BARNABAS HEALTH, INC.
  95 OLD SHORT HILLS RD, WEST ORANGE, NJ
  070521008
Phone: 973 322-5000
Web: WWW.RWJBH.ORG

HISTORICAL FINANCIALS

Company Type: Private

Income Statement				FYE: December 31
	REVENUE ($ mil.)	NET INCOME ($ mil.)	NET PROFIT MARGIN	EMPLOYEES
12/19	793	926	116.6%	24,600
12/18	730	(131)	—	—
12/17	624	293	47.0%	—
12/02	2,159	(92)	—	—
Annual Growth	(5.7%)	—	—	—

2019 Year-End Financials
Return on assets: 16.8%   Cash ($ mil.): 777
Return on equity: 126.5%
Current ratio: 0.20

BARNABAS RWJ HEALTH INC

EXECUTIVES

Pres-Ceo, Barry Ostrowsky
Cfo- Vp Finance*, Peter Bihuniak
Svp-Cpo*, Indu Lew
Svp-Chief Transformation Offic*, Paul G Alexander
Cfao*, John Doll
Csbdo*, Mark Manigan
Cmco*, Michael Knecht
Svp-Chio*, Stephen O'Mahony
Svp-Csihes*, Deanna Minus-Vincent
Svp*, Nancy Holecek
It Manager, Virgil Agustin

LOCATIONS

HQ: BARNABAS RWJ HEALTH INC
95 OLD SHORT HILLS RD, WEST ORANGE, NJ 070521008
Phone: 973 322-4000
Web: WWW.RWJBH.ORG

HISTORICAL FINANCIALS

Company Type: Private

Income Statement   FYE: June 30

	REVENUE ($ mil.)	NET INCOME ($ mil.)	NET PROFIT MARGIN	EMPLOYEES
06/21*	3,210	324	10.1%	34,000
12/20	5,900	940	15.9%	—
12/19	5,624	602	10.7%	—
12/18	5,351	9	0.2%	—
Annual Growth	(22.5%)	475.5%	—	—

*Fiscal year change

2021 Year-End Financials

Return on assets: 3.0%   Cash ($ mil.): 256
Return on equity: 6.3%
Current ratio: 1.00

BARNES & NOBLE, INC.

Barnes & Noble is one of the largest bookstore chains in the US operating more than 600 Barnes & Noble superstores in all 50 states and Washington DC. Carrying about 5500 magazine titles and nearly 1000 newspaper titles the company sold approximately 190 million physical books between its retail stores and online operations annually. In addition Barnes & Noble has approximately 1 million unique physical book titles sold per year. The company's NOOK brand develops supports and creates digital content and products for the digital reading and digital education markets. Founded in 1971 by bookseller Leonard Riggio Barnes & Noble is now owned by Elliott Advisors (UK) Limited.

Operations

Barnes & Noble offers content digital media and educational products. Its Nook Digital business offers a lineup of NOOK tablets and e-Readers and an expansive collection of digital reading content through the NOOK Store. The company's offering categories include book annex books for teens kid's books toys and games and textbooks.

Geographic Reach

Headquartered in New York Barnes & Noble operates more than 600 retail bookstores in all 50 states.

Sales and Marketing

Barnes & Noble distributes its own books through retail bookstores in regional shopping malls major strip centers and freestanding locations as well as online. Barnes & Noble Members receive free express shipping on all BN.com orders and special offers and discounts throughout the year. In addition the Barnes & Noble Kids' Club Program is free for adult participants with kids age 12 and under while the Barnes & Noble Educator Program is free for K-12 educators.

Company Background

Barnes & Noble dates back to 1873 when Charles Barnes went into the used-book business in Wheaton Illinois.

After growing organically and through acquisitions and changing hands several times Barnes & Noble — by then a booming book superstore chain — went public in 1993.

In 2019 after years of struggle brought on by online book giant Amazon and other retail headwinds Barnes & Noble was purchased by private equity firm Elliott Management.

HISTORY

Barnes & Noble dates back to 1873 when Charles Barnes went into the used-book business in Wheaton Illinois. By the turn of the century he was operating a thriving bookselling operation in Chicago. His son William took over as president in 1902. William sold his share in the firm in 1917 (to C. W. Follett who built Follett Corp.) and moved to New York City where he bought an interest in established textbook wholesalers Noble & Noble. The company was soon renamed Barnes & Noble. It first sold mainly to colleges and libraries providing textbooks and opening a large Fifth Avenue shop. Over the next three decades Barnes & Noble became one of the leading booksellers in the New York region.

Enter Leonard Riggio who worked at a New York University bookstore to help pay for night school. He studied engineering but got the itch for bookselling. In 1965 at age 24 he borrowed $5000 and opened Student Book Exchange NYC a college bookstore. Beginning in the late 1960s he expanded by buying other college bookstores.

In 1971 Riggio paid $1.2 million for the Barnes & Noble store on Fifth Avenue. He soon expanded the store and in 1974 he began offering jaw-dropping competitor-maddening discounts of up to 40% for best-sellers. Acquiring Marlboro Books five years later the company entered the mail-order and publishing business.

By 1986 Barnes & Noble had grown to about 180 outlets (including 142 college bookstores). Along with Dutch retailer Vendex that year it bought Dayton Hudson's B. Dalton mall bookstore chain (about 800 stores) forming BDB Holding Corp. (Vendex had sold its shares by 1997.) In 1989 the company acquired the Scribner's Bookstores trade name and the Bookstop/Bookstar superstore chain. BDB began its shift to superstore format and streamlined its operations to integrate Bookstop and Doubleday (acquired in 1990) into its business.

BDB changed its name to Barnes & Noble in 1991. With superstore sales booming the retailer went public in 1993 (the college stores remained private). It bought 20% of Canadian bookseller Chapters (now Indigo Books) in 1996 (sold in 1999).

The bookseller went online in 1997 and in 1998 sold a 50% stake in its Web operation subsidiary to Bertelsmann (which it re-purchased in 2003) in an attempt to strengthen both companies in the battle against online rival Amazon.com.

Also in 1998 Barnes & Noble agreed to buy #1 US book distributor Ingram Book Group but the

deal was called off in 1999 because of antitrust concerns. Also in 1999 barnesandnoble.com went public and Barnes & Noble bought small book publisher J.B. Fairfax International USA which included coffee-table book publisher Michael Friedman Publishing Group. Later that year the company bought a 49% stake in book publishing portal iUniverse.com (later reduced to 22%). It also bought Riggio's financially struggling Babbage's Etc. a chain of about 500 Babbage's Software Etc. and GameStop stores for $215 million.

Subsidiary Babbage's Etc. (renamed GameStop Inc.) acquired video game retailer Funco for $161.5 million in 2000. In 2001 Barnes & Noble joined barnesandnoble.com in acquiring a majority stake in magazine subscription seller enews.com.

The company completed an IPO of its GameStop unit in 2003 reducing its ownership interest to about 63%. Leonard also handed over the CEO title to his brother Steve Riggio. Another development during that busy year included shutting down enews.com due to repeated quarterly losses.

In 2003 the company beefed up its self-publishing efforts with the purchase of Sterling Publishing a specialist in how-to and craft books. In addition Barnes & Noble's half-owned BOOK magazine shut down. The next year saw Barnes & Noble exit the video game retailing business when it spun off its remaining shares in GameStop.

In 2009 the firm sold its majority interest in Calendar Club for $7 million.

CEO Steve Riggio was replaced by William Lynch president of Barnes&Noble.com in 2010. Riggio remained chairman of the company. Barnes & Noble closed the last of its small-format B. Dalton bookstores in early 2010. (B. Dalton which once numbered more than 900 stores had been closing stores since 1989.) Later in the year hedge fund manager William Ackman offered to finance a $960 million merger of Barnes & Noble and its smaller rival Borders but nothing came of it.

CEO Lynch resigned in mid-2013 following an earnings report that underscored Barnes & Noble's failed attempt at building up its Nook division. CFO Michael Huseby was appointed chief executive of the Nook division and president of Barnes & Noble.

EXECUTIVES

Ceo, James Daunt
Exec V Pres-Cfo*, Allen W Lindstorm
Exec V Pres Oprs*, Joseph C Gorman
Exec V Pres*, William E Wood
V Pres-Cao-Corp Contrl*, Peter M Herpich
V Pres-General Counsel-Corp SE*, Bradley A Feuer
Prin*, Elliot Greenberg
Director, Ronald Altomare
Vice President Marketing, Julia Geffner
Director of Risk Management, Agnes Woros
Manager Community, Alex Garcia
Auditors: ERNST & YOUNG LLP NEW YORK N

LOCATIONS

HQ: BARNES & NOBLE, INC.
122 5TH AVE FL 2, NEW YORK, NY 100115634
Phone: 212 633-3300
Web: WWW.BARNESANDNOBLEINC.COM

2018 Stores

	No.
California	69
Texas	51
Florida	39
New York	38
Illinois	26
Pennsylvania	26
Virginia	25
New Jersey	22
North Carolina	21
Other states	310
Total	627

PRODUCTS/OPERATIONS

2019 Sales

	$ mil.	% of total
Retail	3,481	97
NOOK	92	3
Adjustments	(21.3)	-
Total	**3,552**	**100**

COMPETITORS

Amazon.com	Powell's Books
Apple Inc.	Target Corporation
Books-a-million	Wal-mart
Buy.com	Ebay
Costco Wholesale	

HISTORICAL FINANCIALS

Company Type: Private

Income Statement				FYE: April 28
	REVENUE ($ mil.)	NET INCOME ($ mil.)	NET PROFIT MARGIN	EMPLOYEES
04/18	3,662	(125)	—	24,000
04/17	3,894	22	0.6%	—
04/16	4,163	(24)	—	—
Annual Growth	(6.2%)	—	—	—

2018 Year-End Financials

Return on assets: (-7.2%) Cash ($ mil.): 10
Return on equity: (-30.5%)
Current ratio: 1.10

BARNES-JEWISH HOSPITAL

LOCATIONS

HQ: BARNES-JEWISH HOSPITAL
1 B J HOSPITAL PLAZA DR, SAINT LOUIS, MO 63110
Phone: 314 747-3000
Web: WWW.BARNESJEWISH.COM

HISTORICAL FINANCIALS

Company Type: Private

Income Statement				FYE: December 31
	REVENUE ($ mil.)	NET INCOME ($ mil.)	NET PROFIT MARGIN	EMPLOYEES
12/15	1,726	68	4.0%	30
12/14	1,664	83	5.0%	—
Annual Growth	3.7%	(18.2%)	—	—

2015 Year-End Financials

Return on assets: 5.1% Cash ($ mil.): —
Return on equity: 5.7%
Current ratio: 3.00

BARRICK ENTERPRISES, INC.

EXECUTIVES

President, Robert L Barrick
Auditors: CROSKEY LANNI PC ROCHESTER

LOCATIONS

HQ: BARRICK ENTERPRISES, INC.
4338 DELEMERE BLVD, ROYAL OAK, MI 480731876
Phone: 248 549-3737
Web: WWW.BARRICKENT.COM

HISTORICAL FINANCIALS

Company Type: Private

Income Statement				FYE: December 31
	REVENUE ($ mil.)	NET INCOME ($ mil.)	NET PROFIT MARGIN	EMPLOYEES
12/18	573	2	0.5%	35
12/17	534	0	0.1%	—
12/16	491	3	0.6%	—
12/15	552	3	0.7%	—
Annual Growth	1.2%	(8.8%)	—	—

2018 Year-End Financials

Return on assets: 8.5% Cash ($ mil.): 10
Return on equity: 11.4%
Current ratio: 2.00

BARRY-WEHMILLER GROUP, INC.

With Barry-Wehmiller you get the whole package. The company manufactures and supplies packaging corrugating paper converting filling and labeling automation equipment for a broad range of industries. It conducts business around the world through nine operating companies that together own more than 90 subsidiaries such as Accraply (labeling machinery) Design Group (automation and control systems) Winkler and Dunnebier (postage services and tissue and hygiene) and Synerlink (ultra-clean packaging for milk products and desserts). Other divisions manufacture paper converting machinery and offer engineering/IT consulting services. Berry-Wehmiller is privately owned by the Chapman family who took over from Fred Wehmiller in 1963.

Operations

Barry-Wehmiller's operations comprise four segments and nine divisions: BW Packaging Equipment (Accraply BW Flexible Systems BW Integrated systems Pneumatic Scale Angelus and Synerlink); BW Paper Processing Equipment (BW Papersystems); BW Converting Equipment (Paper Converting Machine Company and Winkler + D nnebier); and BW Engineering and IT Consulting (Design Group).

Geographic Reach

St. Louis-based Barry-Wehmiller operates in approximately 100 locations worldwide.

Sales and Marketing

Barry-Wehmiller's manufacturing technology and services serve a wide range of industries including packaging paper converting sheeting corrugating engineering and IT consulting.

Financial Performance

Through its aggressive acquisition strategy and the opening of new locations Barry-Wehmiller generated revenues of about $2 billion in 2014. The company has seen 18% compound revenue growth since 1987.

Strategy

Barry-Wehmiller has continued to grow its segments and divisions. BW Flexible Systems continues to create flexible packaging solutions by bringing together some of the industry's most trusted and innovative brands like Hayssen. In 2020 BW Flexible Systems introduced a new Hayssen ISB (intelligent sanitary bagger) aiming to provide best-in-class sanitary design modern industrial machine intelligence and intuitive operation for vertical form-fill-seal packaging.

Barry-Wehmiller's BW Flexible Systems also expanded in South Africa establishing a sales and support office in the region in early 2020. The new office aims to provide customers in the area the best service available by offering local support which BW Flexible Systems ensures to provide.

Mergers and Acquisitions

Barry-Wehmiller is highly acquisitive making several bolt-ons each year for a total of nearly 100.

Company Background

Originally a provider of conveying equipment to St. Louis malt houses Barry-Wehmiller was founded by Thomas Barry and Alfred Wehmiller in 1885. Ownership passed from the Wehmiller family to the Chapman family in 1963 and the Chapmans continue as the majority owners.

EXECUTIVES

Chm-Ceo, Robert H Chapman
V Pres-Cntrl-Asst SEC, Gregory L Coonrod
Vp Finance-Secretary, William Kuhn
Chief People Officer, Rhonda Spencer
Procurement Manager, Jeff Leavell
Corporate Information Technolo, Ken Hoff
Project Engineer, Patrick Dolan
Senior Vice President, Richard George
Controller, Roger Mound
Managing Partner Barry Wehmill, Sara Hannah
Treasury Analyst, Marilyn Whitney
Auditors: ERNST & YOUNG LLP ST LOUIS

LOCATIONS

HQ: BARRY-WEHMILLER GROUP, INC.
8020 FORSYTH BLVD, SAINT LOUIS, MO 631051707
Phone: 314 862-8000
Web: WWW.BARRYWEHMILLER.COM

PRODUCTS/OPERATIONS

Selected Operations

BW Engineering and IT Consulting
  Design Group
BW Converting Platform
  Paper Converting Machine Company (PCMC)
                    Winkler +
BW Packaging Systems
  Accraply Inc. (packaging label machinery)
  PneumaticScaleAngelus (fillers cappers seamers and labelers)
  BW Flexible Systems
  BW Integrated Systems
  Synerlink
BW Papersystems

COMPETITORS

Bradman Lake	Stt Enviro
Gilbreth	Sencorp Inc
Industria Macchine	Tetra Laval
Automatiche	Traco Manufacturing
Kl ¶ckner-werke	

HISTORICAL FINANCIALS

Company Type: Private

Income Statement				FYE: September 30
	REVENUE ($ mil.)	NET INCOME ($ mil.)	NET PROFIT MARGIN	EMPLOYEES
09/19	2,856	77	2.7%	4,500
09/18	3,037	85	2.8%	—
09/11	1,240	0	—	—
09/10	1,097	0	—	—
Annual Growth	11.2%	—	—	—

Return on assets: 4.0%   Cash ($ mil.): 199
Return on equity: 17.6%
Current ratio: 1.40

BARTON MALOW COMPANY

Barton Malow scores by building end zones and home plates. The construction management and general contracting firm which has built its share of sporting facilities also focuses on projects such as schools hospitals offices and plants. Across the eastern US and Mexico the company offers design/build and program management services ranging from the pre-planning stage to completion. Projects have included the Detroit Institute of Arts and Cultural Center and the Baltimore Orioles stadium. Affiliate Barton Malow Design provides architecture and engineering services while Barton Malow Rigging installs process equipment and machinery. Carl Osborn Barton founded the employee-owned firm as C.O. Barton Company in 1924.

Operations

Barton Malow is a general contractor and construction manager. It provides a variety of building services including building information modeling (BIM) planning & scheduling service conceptual and hard dollar estimating services. It specializes in several areas such as routine boiler installation & service foundation & architectural concrete forming machinery moving & equipment installation and procurement & erection of steel building framework.

The company addresses niche markets in its geography focusing on energy health industrial and sports industries along with K-12 education and government institutions.

Geographic Reach

Michigan-based Barton Malow operates about a dozen offices in the eastern third of the US. It also has an office in San Luis Potosi Mexico.

Financial Performance

A private company Barton Malow provides little financial information. However Forbes Magazine estimates its revenue to be $2.4 billion in 2016.

Strategy

Headquartered in a Detroit suburb Barton Malow has historically maintained a healthy relationship with the steel and auto industries. It is somewhat atypical in that it maintains a staff of workers to perform its trade-based services as with boiler servicing and steel erection; other firms commonly hire out such work.

In 2017 the company received a Best Projects award from trade magazine Engineering News-Record (ENR) for its work on a MATS (Mercury and Air Toxics Standards) compliance project with energy client DTE Energy. In that same year the company completed a complete redesign of Bloomfield Hills (Michigan) High School which involved a partial demolition and partial renovation of existing structures and the design and buildout of a new open-plan educational campus.

EXECUTIVES

Pres, Ryan Maibach
Chm*, Ben C Maibach III
Coo*, Chuck Binkowski
Cfo*, Lars Luedeman
Exec V Pres*, Tom Porter
Clo*, Maryann Kanary
Vpres*, Jonathon Feldotte
Vpres*, Brandon Leslie
Health Professional, Beth Yorke
Health Professional, Bruce Sondys
Corporate Analyst, Sherry Fellenz
Auditors: PRICEWATERHOUSECOOPERS LLP DE

LOCATIONS

HQ: BARTON MALOW COMPANY
26500 AMERICAN DR, SOUTHFIELD, MI 480342252
Phone: 248 436-5000
Web: WWW.BARTONMALOW.COM

Selected Locations
Atlanta
Baltimore
Charlottesville
Chicago
Columbus
Fairfax
Jacksonville
Oak Park
Orlando
Richmond
Southfield

PRODUCTS/OPERATIONS

Selcted Services
Architecture and planning
Building Information Management (BIM)
Concrete trade services
Construction management
Design/build
Facility audits
Facility services
   Administration
   Engineering
   Maintenance repair and operations
General contracting
Interior design
Interior trade services
Preconstruction
Program management
Rigging
Special projects
Technology consulting

COMPETITORS

Alberici	M. A. Mortenson
Clark Enterprises	Mccarthy Building
Gilbane	Miron Construction
H.j. Russell	Skanska Usa Building
Hensel Phelps	Turner Corporation
Construction	Walbridge Aldinger
Hunt Construction	Walsh Group
Kbr Building Group	Whiting-turner

HISTORICAL FINANCIALS

Company Type: Private

Income Statement   FYE: March 31

	REVENUE ($ mil.)	NET INCOME ($ mil.)	NET PROFIT MARGIN	EMPLOYEES
03/20	1,971	11	0.6%	1,600
03/19	1,634	8	0.5%	—
03/18	2,502	11	0.4%	—
03/17	2,361	0	0.0%	—
Annual Growth	(5.8%)	202.9%	—	—

2020 Year-End Financials

Return on assets: 1.7%   Cash ($ mil.): 94
Return on equity: 15.3%
Current ratio: 1.10

BARTON MALOW ENTERPRISES, INC.

EXECUTIVES

Pres, Benjamin C Maibach III
SEC-Exec V Pres, Douglas L Maibach
Treas-Cfo, Michael F Dishaw
V Pres, Ronald J Torbert
Dir, Sheryl B Maibach
Vice President, Lars Luedeman
Marketing Coordinator, Eliot Dolgin
Safety Manager, Anthony Allam
Software Developer, Brad Smith
Senior Project Manager, George Travis
Project Engineer, Eric Sifferman
Auditors: PRICEWATERHOUSECOOPERS LLP DE

LOCATIONS

HQ: BARTON MALOW ENTERPRISES, INC.
26500 AMERICAN DR, SOUTHFIELD, MI 480342252
Phone: 248 436-5000
Web: WWW.BARTONMALOW.COM

HISTORICAL FINANCIALS

Company Type: Private

Income Statement   FYE: March 31

	REVENUE ($ mil.)	NET INCOME ($ mil.)	NET PROFIT MARGIN	EMPLOYEES
03/20	1,972	19	1.0%	2,000
03/18	2,502	18	0.7%	—
03/17	2,361	14	0.6%	—
03/16	1,777	9	0.6%	—
Annual Growth	2.6%	17.6%	—	—

2020 Year-End Financials

Return on assets: 2.6%   Cash ($ mil.): 111
Return on equity: 17.1%
Current ratio: 1.10

BATTELLE MEMORIAL INSTITUTE

EXECUTIVES

BR Mgr, Jeffrey Wadsworth
Geologist, Joel Main
Researcher, Anthony Gutierrez
Research Scientist, Stephanie Eastwood
Program Manager, William Burke
Research Engineer, Charles Miele
Research In Public Health Lead, Marcia Nishioka
Research Scientist, Amy Thomas
Closeout Analyst, Olivia Bunders
Vice President of Marketing An, Patrick Jarvis
Auditors: DELOITTE & TOUCHE LLP COLUMBU

LOCATIONS

HQ: BATTELLE MEMORIAL INSTITUTE
2555 INTERNATIONAL ST, COLUMBUS, OH 432284604
Phone: 800 201-2011
Web: WWW.BATTELLE.ORG

HISTORICAL FINANCIALS
Company Type: Private

Income Statement
FYE: September 30

	REVENUE ($ mil.)	NET INCOME ($ mil.)	NET PROFIT MARGIN	EMPLOYEES
09/14	4,775	(95)	—	20,000
09/13	4,795	(7)	—	—
09/12	5,228	(20)	—	—
Annual Growth	(4.4%)	—	—	—

2014 Year-End Financials
Return on assets: 2.7%
Return on equity: (-2.0%)
Current ratio: 0.70

Cash ($ mil.): 117

BAYCARE HEALTH SYSTEM, INC.

BayCare Health System is the leading not-for-profit health care system that connects individuals and families to a wide range of services at hundreds of locations in the Tampa Bay and West Central Florida regions. The system's member hospitals boast approximately 4000 beds; the facilities offer a variety of specialty services ranging from orthopedics to cancer care to women's services. BayCare has about 6000 physicians and medical professionals. Established in 1997 the health system operates approximately 15 not-for-profit hospitals nearly 15 outpatient imaging facilities and about 20 urgent care centers.

Operations
BayCare's family of hospitals includes Morton Plant (about 600 beds) St. Joseph's (approximately 600 beds) Winter Haven (about 450) St. Anthony's (about 400 beds) Mease Countryside (about 310 beds) St. Joseph's Children's (nearly 220 beds) St. Joseph's Women's (about 125 beds) Winter Haven Women's Hospital (about 60 beds) Morton Plant North Bay (approximately 150 beds) South Florida Baptist (more than 145 beds) Mease Dunedin (approximately 120 beds) St. Joseph's Hospital-North (about 215 beds) St. Joseph's Hospital-South (over 210 beds) and Bartow Regional Medical Center (more than 70 beds).

Winter Haven Hospital serves as the major medical center for east Polk County.

BayCare has about 6000 physicians and medical professionals and reported about 80000 outpatient surgeries and about 600000 emergency room visits.

Geographic Reach
BayCare serves the residents of Florida's greater Tampa Bay area consisting of the Hillsborough Polk Pasco and Pinellas counties.

Financial Performance
Mergers and Acquisitions

EXECUTIVES

Ceo-Pres, Steve Mason
V Chm*, Jeff Lyash
SEC*, Trish Murdock
Prin*, Stewart Schaffer
Svp-Chief Transformation Offic*, Emily Allinder Scott
Corporate Communications Execu, Ronda Buffington
Executive Assistant, Tameral Torres
Customer Staff, Kathy J Meddings

Pulmonary Diseases, Himanshu V Chandarana
Chief of Medicine, Joseph Boulay
Anesthesiology, Vipul V Kabaria
Auditors: ERNST & YOUNG US LLP ATLANTA

LOCATIONS
HQ: BAYCARE HEALTH SYSTEM, INC.
2985 DREW ST, CLEARWATER, FL 337593012
Phone: 727 820-8200
Web: WWW.BAYCARE.ORG

Selected Locations
Baycare Alliant Hospital (Dunedin Florida)
Mease Countryside Hospital (Safety Harbor Florida)
Mease Dunedin Hospital (Mease Dunedin Florida)
Morton Plant Hospital (Clearwater Florida)
Morton Plant North Bay Hospital (New Port Richey Florida)
St. Anthony's Hospital (St. Petersburg Florida)
St. Joseph's Children's Hospital (Tampa Florida)
St. Joseph's Hospital (Tampa Florida)
St. Joseph's Hospital-North (Lutz Florida)
St. Joseph's Women's Hospital (Tampa Florida)
South Florida Baptist Hospital (Plant City Florida)
Winter Haven Hospital (Plok Florida)

PRODUCTS/OPERATIONS

Selected Services
Advance Care Planning
BayCare Behavioral Health
BayCare HomeCare
BayCare Outpatient Imaging
Breast Health
Behavioral Health Services
Patient Secure Identity
Pediatric Specialty Centers
Physician Office EMR
Robotic Surgery
Wellness Centers

COMPETITORS
Adventist Health System Sunbelt Healthcare
All Children's Hospital
Ascension Health
Bayfront Health
Desoto Memorial
Florida Hospital Tampa Bay Division
Hca
Lakeland Regional Medical Center
Lee Memorial
Manatee Memorial Hospital
Sarasota Memorial Health Care
Tampa General Hospital

HISTORICAL FINANCIALS
Company Type: Private

Income Statement
FYE: December 31

	REVENUE ($ mil.)	NET INCOME ($ mil.)	NET PROFIT MARGIN	EMPLOYEES
12/19	818	228	27.9%	20,000
12/14	463	163	35.3%	—
Annual Growth	12.0%	6.9%	—	—

2019 Year-End Financials
Return on assets: 3.7%
Return on equity: 21.2%
Current ratio: 0.10

Cash ($ mil.): 83

BAYHEALTH MEDICAL CENTER, INC.

EXECUTIVES

Pres, Terry Murphy
Warehouse Manager, David Webb
Physician, James Everette
Family Practice, Kenny Vu
Director of Orthopedic, Stephen Manifold
MD, Zi Xu
Public Relations, Leigh Coleman
Chief Information Officer, Lynn Gold
Chief Operations Officer, Mike Metzing
Clinical Instructor For Thomas, Laura Ryan
Purchasing Manager, Debbie B Betts
Auditors: GRANT THORNTON LLP PHILADELP

LOCATIONS
HQ: BAYHEALTH MEDICAL CENTER, INC.
640 S STATE ST, DOVER, DE 199013530
Phone: 302 674-4700
Web: WWW.BAYHEALTH.ORG

HISTORICAL FINANCIALS
Company Type: Private

Income Statement
FYE: June 30

	REVENUE ($ mil.)	NET INCOME ($ mil.)	NET PROFIT MARGIN	EMPLOYEES
06/21	782	218	28.0%	2,790
06/20	725	35	4.9%	—
06/19	677	58	8.7%	—
06/18	615	87	14.2%	—
Annual Growth	8.3%	35.8%	—	—

2021 Year-End Financials
Return on assets: 13.7%
Return on equity: 18.9%
Current ratio: 1.10

Cash ($ mil.): 130

BAYLOR SCOTT & WHITE HEALTH

EXECUTIVES

Ceo, Jim Hinton
Pres*, Pete McCanna
Cmo*, Alejandro Arroliga
Chief Strategy Officer*, Lavone Arthur
Chief Legal Offcr*, Jennifer Brown
Cfo*, Penny Cermak
CIO*, Matthew Chambers
Cmo*, Glen Couchman
Pres*, Pat Currie
Pres*, Clifford T Fullerton
Cmmo*, Mark Grace

LOCATIONS
HQ: BAYLOR SCOTT & WHITE HEALTH
301 N WASHINGTON AVE, DALLAS, TX 752461754
Phone: 214 820-3151
Web: WWW.BSWHEALTH.COM

HISTORICAL FINANCIALS

Company Type: Private

Income Statement				FYE: June 30
	REVENUE ($ mil.)	NET INCOME ($ mil.)	NET PROFIT MARGIN	EMPLOYEES
06/21	11,704	1,814	15.5%	49,000
06/20	416	51	12.5%	—
06/19	982	(17)	—	—
Annual Growth	245.1%	—	—	—

2021 Year-End Financials

Return on assets: 10.4%   Cash ($ mil.): 1,424
Return on equity: 20.9%
Current ratio: 1.30

BAYLOR SCOTT & WHITE HOLDINGS

EXECUTIVES

Ceo, Jim Hinton
ADM*, Jared Kastriner
Lmsw, Maggie Williams
Auditors: PRICEWATERHOUSECOOPERS LLP DA

LOCATIONS

HQ: BAYLOR SCOTT & WHITE HOLDINGS
301 N WASHINGTON AVE, DALLAS, TX 752461754
Phone: 214 820-3151
Web: WWW.BSWHEALTH.COM

HISTORICAL FINANCIALS

Company Type: Private

Income Statement				FYE: June 30
	REVENUE ($ mil.)	NET INCOME ($ mil.)	NET PROFIT MARGIN	EMPLOYEES
06/21	11,704	1,814	15.5%	310
06/20	72	(58)	—	—
06/19	62	(130)	—	—
06/17	9,084	630	6.9%	—
Annual Growth	6.5%	30.2%	—	—

2021 Year-End Financials

Return on assets: 10.4%   Cash ($ mil.): 1,424
Return on equity: 20.9%
Current ratio: 1.30

BAYLOR UNIVERSITY

Don't mess with Texas and don't mess around at Baylor University. The world's largest Baptist institution of higher learning requires its more than 15000 students to follow a strict code of conduct. The university has approximately 150 undergraduate degree programs as well as about 75 masters and more than 30 doctoral programs. With a student-to-faculty ratio of 15:1 the private co-educational university also offers degrees from its law school (juris doctor) and theological seminary (master of divinity and doctor of ministry) as well as extensive research programs. Founded in 1845 the college is affiliated with the Baptist General Convention of Texas.

Geographic Reach

Baylor University has a 1000-acre campus on the banks of the Brazos River in Waco Texas. Its students hail from across the US and some 90 international countries.

Financial Performance

Baylor University reported an 18% increase in revenues to $561 million in 2012 due to higher tuition fees and gifts. Net income fell by 101% (to a loss of some $2 million) due to higher program and support expenses.

The university's market endowment value was some $960 million as of mid-2012.

EXECUTIVES

Pres-Ceo, Robert Sloan PHD
Pres*, Ken Starr
V Pres*, John M Barry
V Pres*, Elizabeth Davis
V Pres*, Tommye Lou Davis
Coordinator, Stephen Rylander
Scientist, Diane Hartman
Assistant Professor, Brent Phillips
Assistant Professor, Lorin Matthews
Assistant Professor, Terry Hudson
Coordinator, Rebecca Derosa
Auditors: GRANT THORNTON LLP DALLAS TX

LOCATIONS

HQ: BAYLOR UNIVERSITY
700 S UNIV PKS DR STE 67, WACO, TX 767061003
Phone: 254 710-1561
Web: WWW.BAYLOR.EDU

PRODUCTS/OPERATIONS

Selected Colleges and Schools

College of Arts and Sciences
George W. Truett Theological Seminary
Graduate School
Hankamer School of Business
Honors College
Law School
Louise Herrington School of Nursing
School of Education
School of Engineering and Computer Science
School of Music
School of Social Work

Selected Institutes

Allbritton Art Institute
Institute for Air Science
Institute for Faith and Learning
Institute for Oral History
Institute of Biblical and Related Languages
Institute of Biomedical Studies
J. M. Dawson Institute of Church-State Studies

HISTORICAL FINANCIALS

Company Type: Private

Income Statement				FYE: May 31
	REVENUE ($ mil.)	NET INCOME ($ mil.)	NET PROFIT MARGIN	EMPLOYEES
05/21	920	524	56.9%	2,500
05/20	791	142	18.0%	—
05/19	710	19	2.8%	—
05/18	674	96	14.3%	—
Annual Growth	10.9%	76.0%	—	—

2021 Year-End Financials

Return on assets: 15.0%   Cash ($ mil.): 309
Return on equity: 19.9%
Current ratio: —

BAYLOR UNIVERSITY MEDICAL CENTER

Baylor University Medical Center at Dallas is the flagship institution of the Baylor Health Care System. The medical center (known as Baylor Dallas) serves more than 300000 patients annually with more than 1000 inpatient beds and some 1200 physicians. It offers general medical and surgical services to specialty care in a wide range of fields including oncology cardiovascular disease and neuroscience. The hospital also features a Level I trauma center neonatal ICU and organ transplantation center. Founded in 1903 the Baylor Dallas campus includes the Charles A. Sammons Cancer Center and the Baylor Research Institute which conducts basic and clinical research across numerous medical specialties.

Operations

The Baylor University Medical Center campus consists of 20 specialty centers for treating a range of medical conditions. Primary facilities include the Charles A. Sammons Cancer Center Neuroscience Center Annette C. and Harold C. Simmons Transplant Institute James M. and Dorothy D. Collins Womens and Children's Center and the George Truett James Orthopaedic Institute as well as a top trauma center digestive care program and heart and vascular unit. The Heart and Vascular Institute conducts more than 50 research studies a year.

Strategy

The hospital received a boost in 2011 when Texas A&M's Health Science Center struck an affiliation with Baylor Health Care System. The two parties agreed to make Baylor Dallas a primary teaching hospital for A&M's third and fourth-year medical students. No hospital in the Baylor Health Care System held such a designation after it became independent from Baylor University in 1997.

As one of only two adult Level 1 trauma centers in the region Baylor Dallas has worked to bolster its emergency services to keep up with increasing demand. To this end it has broadened its Level 1 trauma capabilities increased the size of its minor emergency care area and added more patient care areas. The Riggs Emergency Department treats some 67000 patients each year.

Baylor Dallas' transplant program is considered a national leader in solid organ transplantation and in partnership with the program at Baylor All Saints Medical Center is one of only three programs worldwide to have performed more than 3000 adult liver transplants. The program is also known for its kidney pancreas heart and lung small bowel and blood and marrow transplants.

EXECUTIVES

President, Jon Skinner
Pres*, John McWhorter
V Pres-Fin*, Fred Salvesbergh
President and Chief Nursing of*, Nancy Vish
President*, Michael Ramsay
President*, Chris York
President*, T Douglas Lawson
Techl Supt Mgr, M Vimolrat
Executive Assistant, E Pinckney
Information Specialist, Jon Wilburn
Doctor, Robert Goldstein

LOCATIONS

HQ: BAYLOR UNIVERSITY MEDICAL CENTER
2001 BRYAN ST STE 2200, DALLAS, TX 752013024
Phone: 214 820-3151
Web: WWW.BSWHEALTH.COM

Selected Locations
A. Webb Roberts Hospital
Baylor Charles A. Sammons Cancer Center
Baylor Jack and Jane Hamilton Heart and Vascular
  Hospital
Carr P. Collins Hospital
Erik and Margaret Jonsson Medical and Surgical
  Hospital
George W. Truett Memorial Hospital
Karl and Esther Hoblitzelle Memorial Hospital
Baylor Specialty Hospital
Our Children's House at Baylor

PRODUCTS/OPERATIONS

Selected Speciality Centers
Baylor Cancer Hospital
Baylor Center for Pain Management
Baylor Diagnostic Imaging Centers
Baylor George Truett James Orthopaedic Institute
Baylor Geriatric and Senior Center
Baylor Heart and Vascular Institute
Baylor Heart Failure Program
Baylor Motion and Sports Performance Center
Baylor Neuroscience Center
Baylor Radiosurgery Center
Baylor Ruth Collins Diabetes Center
Baylor Sammons Bone Tumor Center
Baylor Sammons Lung Cancer Center
Baylor Spine Center
Baylor SportsCare
Comprehensive Wound Center
Darlene G. Cass Women's Imaging Center
Digestive Care Services
Ernie's Appearance Center
Gastrointestinal and Endoscopy Laboratory
Hereditary Cancer Risk Program
Infectious Disease Center
James M. and Dorothy D. Collins Women and Children's
  Center
Kimberly H. Courtwright and Joseph W. Summers
  Institute of Metabolic Disease
Louise Gartner Center for Hyperbaric Medicine
Martha Foster Lung Care Center
Non-invasive Heart and Vascular Laboratory
Reuben H. Adams Family Health Center
Simply Mom's Mother and Baby Boutique
Sleep Center
TINY TOTS Clinic
Virginia R. Cvetko Cancer Patient Education Center
Visual Function Testing Center
W.H. and Peggy Smith Baylor Sammons Breast Center
Weight Loss Surgery Program

COMPETITORS

Christus Health	Presbyterian Hospital
Children's Medical	Of Dallas
Center Of Dallas	Southwestern Medical
Dynacq Healthcare	Center
Harris Methodist Fort	Texas Health Denton
Worth Hospital	Texas Health Resources
Parkland Health &	The Methodist Health
Hospital System	System

HISTORICAL FINANCIALS

Company Type: Private

Income Statement
FYE: June 30

	REVENUE ($ mil.)	NET INCOME ($ mil.)	NET PROFIT MARGIN	EMPLOYEES
06/15	1,394	378	27.2%	5,003
06/09	1,072	0	—	—
06/08	155	16	10.3%	—
06/06	937	114	12.2%	—
Annual Growth	4.5%	14.3%	—	—

2015 Year-End Financials
Return on assets: 18.8%   Cash ($ mil.): —
Return on equity: 19.5%
Current ratio: 3.10

BAYSTATE HEALTH SYSTEM HEALTH SERVICES, INC.

Patients in need of medical care can dock at this bay. Not-for-profit Baystate Health is the largest health care services provider in western Massachusetts. The system operates five acute-care and specialty hospitals with a total of approximately 1000 beds including the flagship Baystate Medical Center which operates a Level 1 Trauma Center and a specialized children's hospital. Baystate Health also offers ancillary medical services such as cancer care respiratory care infusion therapy visiting nurse and hospice services through its regional clinics and agencies. The system controls for-profit health plan provider Health New England as well as clinical pathology firm Baystate Reference Laboratories.

Operations
Baystate Medical Center accounts for more than 700 of the system's beds. Its other four acute care hospitals are Baystate Franklin Medical Center (89 beds) Baystate Wing Hospital (74 beds) Baystate Noble Hospital (97 beds) and Baystate Mary Lane Hospital (25 beds). The system also runs a physicians group Baystate Medical Practices which operates more than two dozen physician practices in several surrounding counties and towns. Other outpatient centers include surgery centers imaging and radiology clinics and neighborhood health centers. Altogether its facilities serve a population of 750000 western New England residents and admit more than 45000 inpatients perform some 34000 surgeries handle about 4500 births and conduct 1.4 million outpatient visits each year.

Baystate Health provides academic and community educational programs as well as conducting basic clinical and biomedical research. For instance the Baystate Medical Center is a teaching hospital that serves as the western campus of the Tufts University School of Medicine. Baystate Health also partners with a number of regional colleges to offer nursing programs.

In the research realm Tufts and Baystate Health work on biomedical studies through the Tufts Clinical and Translational Science Institute. Baystate Medical Center also has a partnership with the University of Massachusetts that forms the Pioneer Valley Life Sciences Institute. Areas of research include clinical care quality of care and diabetes and metabolism. The Baystate Health system receives about $10 million per year in research funding from the National Institutes of Health and other agencies.

Geographic Reach
Baystate Health has some 60 locations serving western Massachusetts including Berkshire Franklin Hampden Hampshire and Worcester counties.

Sales and Marketing
Patient service revenue accounts for a majority (about 60%) of the hospital system's sales; Medicare and Medicaid reimbursements make up 57% of patient service payments. Other sources

---

include commercial insurers and private-pay customers.

Financial Performance
In fiscal 2015 (ended September) Baystate Health revenues grew 17% to $1.2 billion; this was driven by a growth in premiums as well as net patient service revenue. However that year the system reported a net loss of $78 million due to higher medical claims and capitation as well as losses on investments and pension adjustments.

Following net income's suit cash flow from operations dropped 38% to $51 million in fiscal 2015.

Strategy
Baystate Health has been conducting expansion and renovation efforts at its facilities in recent years including medical technology and information system upgrades. The system's largest effort was the construction of a $300 million clinical building on the Baystate Medical Center Campus.

Other facilities and divisions are undergoing expansion as well: The system is adding new space to house a pharmacy and nearly 100 modern inpatient rooms at its flagship campus while a new surgical center is being added to Baystate Franklin Medical Center in Greenfield. Baystate Medical Practices continues to grow by adding new practices on a regular basis. Baystate Health is also upgrading its medical equipment and its information technology systems.

Mergers and Acquisitions
Baystate Health acquired Noble Hospital (now Baystate Noble Hospital) a 97-bed not-for-profit community hospital in 2015. The year before that it added another acute care facility when it bought the 74-bed Wind Memorial Hospital (now Baystate Wing Hospital) from UMass Memorial Healthcare.

Auditors: ERNST & YOUNG LLP BOSTON MAS

LOCATIONS

HQ: BAYSTATE HEALTH SYSTEM HEALTH SERVICES, INC.
280 CHESTNUT ST, SPRINGFIELD, MA 011991000
Phone: 413 794-9939

Selected Locations
Baystate Medical Center (Springfield)
  Baystate Children's Hospital (Springfield)
Baystate Franklin Medical Center (Greenfield)
Baystate Mary Lane Hospital (Ware)
Baystate Noble Hospital (Westfield)
Baystate Wing Hospital (Palmer)
Outpatient Centers
  Baystate Home Infusion & Respiratory Services
  Baystate Medical Practices
  Baystate Radiology and Imaging (BRI)
  Baystate Reference Laboratories (BRL)
  Baystate Visiting Nurse Association & Hospice
  Brightwood Health Center
  Chestnut Surgery Center
  D'Amour Center for Cancer Care
  High Street Center (adult and pediatrics)
  Mason Square Neighborhood Health Center
  Neurodiagnostics & Sleep Center
  Orthopedic Surgery Center
  Wesson Women & Infants Health Center

PRODUCTS/OPERATIONS

2015 Sales

	$ mil.	% of total
Net patient service revenue	1,222	57
Premiums	822	39
Other	94	4
Total	**2,138**	**100**

Selected Services
Ambulance
Anesthesiology
Behavioral health services
Birthing services
Cancer
Cardiovascular
Emergency medicine
Endoscopy

Home care and home medical supplies
Hospital medicine
Neurosciences
Obstetrics and gynecology
Pain management center
Pathology
Pediatrics
Radiology
Rehabilitation care
Reproductive medicine
Sleep program
Surgery
Weight management
Women's health

COMPETITORS

Berkshire Health Systems	Partners Healthcare
Cambridge Health Alliance	Shriners Hospitals For Children
Cape Cod Healthcare	Southcoast Hospitals Group
Caregroup	Steward Health Care
Harrington Memorial Hospital	Universal Health Services

HISTORICAL FINANCIALS

Company Type: Private

Income Statement   FYE: September 30

	REVENUE ($ mil.)	NET INCOME ($ mil.)	NET PROFIT MARGIN	EMPLOYEES
09/07	1,286	125	9.7%	5,000
09/06	1,209	83	6.9%	—
09/05	0	0	—	—
09/04	0	0	—	—
Annual Growth	—	—	—	—

2007 Year-End Financials

Return on assets: 5.4%
Return on equity: 9.7%
Current ratio: 0.70
Cash ($ mil.): 61

BCFS HEALTH AND HUMAN SERVICES

EXECUTIVES

Ceo, Kevin Dindin
Cfo-CPA*, Claudia Oliveira
Brd MBR*, Keisha Loftin-Gainer
Brd MBR*, David Sprouse
Brd MBR*, Scott Sharman
Brd MBR*, Robert Ownby Jr
Brd MBR*, Martha Morse
Brd MBR*, Garrett Vickrey
Brd MBR*, Lanny Hall
Brd MBR*, Janet Littlejohn
Iii., Brd V Chm-SEC*, George Cowden
Auditors: BKD LLP DALLAS TX

LOCATIONS

HQ: BCFS HEALTH AND HUMAN SERVICES
1506 BEXAR CROSSING ST, SAN ANTONIO, TX 782321587
Phone: 210 832-5000
Web: WWW.DISCOVERBCFS.NET

HISTORICAL FINANCIALS

Company Type: Private

Income Statement   FYE: August 31

	REVENUE ($ mil.)	NET INCOME ($ mil.)	NET PROFIT MARGIN	EMPLOYEES
08/20	873	23	2.7%	96
08/19	86	1	2.2%	—
08/13	70	(1)	—	—
08/12	72	3	4.8%	—
Annual Growth	36.6%	27.1%	—	—

2020 Year-End Financials

Return on assets: 11.1%
Return on equity: 79.9%
Current ratio: —
Cash ($ mil.): —

BEALL'S, INC.

Residents of the Sun Belt have been known to leave their homes with Beall's on. The retail holding company operates through subsidiaries Beall's Department Stores Beall's Outlet and Burke's Outlet Stores in a dozen states. The multi-brand retailer has more than 530 department and outlet stores (about 200 are in Florida) located throughout states in the southern and western US including Arizona California Georgia Louisiana and Texas. Products range from off-price clothing and footwear for men and women to cosmetics gifts and housewares. Each chain has its own online shopping destination. The family-owned company was founded in 1915 by the grandfather of chairman Robert Beall (pronounced "bell").

Operations

Beall's Inc. oversees operations of its three operating companies. Beall's Florida operates some 190 stores in the Sunshine State. Beall's Outlet operates about 300 stores in Arizona Florida Texas and Georgia while Burke's Outlet operates more than 190 stores in 16 states.

Geographic Reach

Beall's trio of chain's operate stores in Alabama Arkansas Arizona California Florida Georgia Kentucky Louisiana Mississippi Nevada New Mexico North Carolina South Carolina Tennessee Texas Virginia and West Virginia.

Financial Performance

Privately-owned Beall's rings ups more than $1 billion in sales annually.

Strategy

The company has aspirations to transform itself into a major discount retailer much like its larger rivals TJX and Ross Stores. To that end the company plans to add new stores outside its traditional markets with an eye on establishing a national retail presence. Targets include adding 30 to 50 stores a year for the next several years and raising brand awareness beyond Florida.

With many of its stores in Arizona Florida and California (three of the states hit hardest by the housing crisis and deep recession) Beall's Inc. should have been in a heap of retail trouble. However its largest chain — Beall's Outlet —proved to be quite popular during this recession. Indeed the budget-priced outlet chain outperformed its two sister chains as well as more moderately priced department stores. The retailer has also benefited from the demise of other retailers including Goody's Linens 'n Things and Mervyn's.

The three operating companies share resources provided by Beall's Inc. such as distribution finance loss prevention and information systems. Con-

versely each chain is responsible for its purchasing product development real estate and advertising activities.

Company Background

Stores operating under the Bealls name in Alabama New Mexico and Texas are owned by Stage Stores and are not affiliated with Beall's Inc.

EXECUTIVES

Ceo, Robert Beall III
Pres*, David Alves
Pres*, Dan Love
Art Director, Candice Anderson
Assistant Buyer Swimwear, Dana-Lise Acevedo
Senior Tax Accountant, Daniel Cordero
Divisional Vice President Gmm, Eric Kozlowski
Store Manager, Hillary Geiger
Operations Manager, Kathryn Boudreaux
Financial Analyst, Beth Flamini
Planning, Sarah Chase
Auditors: CHRISTOPHER SMITH LEONARD B

LOCATIONS

HQ: BEALL'S, INC.
E R BALL CTR 700 13TH AVE, BRADENTON, FL 34208
Phone: 941 747-2355
Web: WWW.BEALLSINC.COM

PRODUCTS/OPERATIONS

Selected Retail Operations
Bealls Department Stores (Florida)
Bealls Outlet (deep-discount outlet stores in Arizona Florida Georgia)
Burke's Outlet (11 southern states)

COMPETITORS

Bed Bath & Beyond	Ross Stores
Costco Wholesale	Stage Stores
Dillard's	Tjx Companies
J. C. Penney Company	Target Corporation
Kohl's	The Gap
Macy's	Wal-mart
Nordstrom	

HISTORICAL FINANCIALS

Company Type: Private

Income Statement   FYE: August 1

	REVENUE ($ mil.)	NET INCOME ($ mil.)	NET PROFIT MARGIN	EMPLOYEES
08/15*	1,321	25	1.9%	9,700
07/12	1,232	14	1.1%	—
07/11	1,166	15	1.3%	—
Annual Growth	3.2%	12.8%	—	—

*Fiscal year change

2015 Year-End Financials

Return on assets: 4.5%
Return on equity: 8.7%
Current ratio: 1.60
Cash ($ mil.): 107

BEARINGPOINT, INC.

Auditors: ERNST & YOUNG LLP MCLEAN VI

LOCATIONS

HQ: BEARINGPOINT, INC.
100 CRESCENT CT STE 700, DALLAS, TX 752012112
Phone: 214 459-2770

HISTORICAL FINANCIALS
Company Type: Private

Income Statement				FYE: December 31
	REVENUE ($ mil.)	NET INCOME ($ mil.)	NET PROFIT MARGIN	EMPLOYEES
12/07	3,455	(362)	—	15,200
12/06	3,444	(177)	—	
Annual Growth	0.3%	—	—	—

2007 Year-End Financials
Return on assets: (-18.3%)   Cash ($ mil.): 468
Return on equity: —
Current ratio: 1.40

BEAUMONT HEALTH

Beaumont Health is an eight-hospital regional health system in southeastern Michigan. The health system boasts about 3400 hospital beds 150 outpatient sites and 5000 affiliated physicians. Outpatient facilities include community medical centers nursing homes a home health agency a research institute and primary and specialty care clinics as well as rehabilitation cardiology and cancer centers. Beaumont is the exclusive clinical teaching site for the Oakland University William Beaumont School of Medicine; it also has affiliations with Michigan State University College of Osteopathic Medicine and Wayne State University School of Medicine. In 2019 it agreed to acquire Ohio hospital operator Summa Health.

OperationsBeaumont holds a Level I trauma designation in Oakland and Macomb counties. The system's Children's Hospital has more than 80 pediatric subspecialists. Its research institute has more than 1000 active clinical studies including interventional clinical research trials. A teaching hospital Beaumont has 40 residency and fellowship programs with more than 450 participants. The system is also the exclusive clinical partner of William Beaumont School of Medicine providing more than 1500 physicians to the school's faculty. The system handles about 180000 admissions some 18000 infant births more than 550000 emergency department visits annually.

Geographic Reach
Beaumont Health operates health care facilities throughout suburban Detroit (in Oakland Macomb and Wayne counties).

Strategy
Beaumont Health expands its care offerings by partnering with other service providers (such as insurance groups) adding new facilities to its network and by taking advantage of government initiatives to modernize its systems.

Mergers and Acquisitions
In 2019 Beaumont Health agreed to acquire Akron Ohio-based Summa Health which operates three acute care hospitals a rehab hospital a health plan and other health resources in northeastern Ohio. Summa with $1.4 billion in revenue will operate as a wholly owned subsidiary of Beaumont ($4.7 billion in revenue) and will retain its name and local leadership. In the face of reimbursement changes rising expenses and intensifying competition the deal aims to allow for continued expansion and growth while improving care for patients in the two states. No financial transaction will occur between Beaumont and Summa but the two companies will buy out Summa's minority shareholder Mercy Health (now part of Bon Secours Mercy Health).

Company Background

Beaumont Health system traces its roots to Dr. William Beaumont an army doctor who conducted groundbreaking research on the human digestive system on Mackinac Island Michigan in the 1820s. The first Beaumont Hospital was opened in Royal Oak in 1955; the Troy facility was opened in 1977; and its third hospital in Grosse Pointe was acquired in 2007 from Bon Secours Health System. In 2014 Beaumont merged with hospital operators Oakwood Healthcare and Botsford Hospital creating a $3.8 billion not-for-profit organization to provide improved care services across combined communities.

EXECUTIVES

Ceo, John Fox
Cfo*, John Keuten
Gen Counsel*, Gordon Walker
M.D., Chief Med*, David Wood
Chief Nursing Officer*, Brad Lukas
Infrastructure Analyst, Eleanor Dupuis
Senior Vice President, James Lynch
Application Analyst, Jay Cooper
Senior Vice President, Margaret Casey
Vice President, Maureen Bowman
Human Resources Director, Michael Woolsey
Auditors: ERNST & YOUNG LLP DETROIT MI

LOCATIONS

HQ: BEAUMONT HEALTH
3601 W 13 MILE RD, ROYAL OAK, MI 480736712
Phone: 248 898-5000
Web: WWW.BEAUMONT.ORG

Selected Michigan Locations
Lake Orion
Macomb
Rochester Hills
Royal Oak
St. Clair Shores
Sterling Heights
Warren
West Bloomfield

PRODUCTS/OPERATIONS

Selected Michigan Facilities
Health Wellness and Outpatient Care
  Beaumont Bon Brae Center (fitness; St. Clair Shores)
  Beaumont Health and Wellness Center (Rochester Hills)
  Beaumont Health Center (outpatient services; Royal Oak)
  Beaumont Medical Centers
Hospitals
  Beaumont Hospital Grosse Pointe
  Beaumont Hospital Royal Oak
  Beaumont Hospital Troy
Nursing and Rehabilitation
  Evergreen Health and Living Center (Southfield)
  Shelby Nursing Center (Shelby Township)
  ShorePointe Nursing Care (St. Clair Shores)
  ShorePointe Village Assisted Living (St. Clair Shores)
  West Bloomfield Nursing Center
  Woodward Hills Nursing Center (Bloomfield Hills)
Research and Education
  Oakland University William Beaumont School of Medicine (Royal Oak)

Selected Centers of Excellence
Cancer
Children's Hospital
Digestive health
Heart and vascular
Neuroscience
Orthopedics
Women's health

COMPETITORS

Children's Hospital Of Michigan	Providence Hospital And Medical Centers
Crittenton Hospital	Sinai-grace Hospital
Detroit Medical Center	St. John Health

Garden City Hospital
Henry Ford Health System
Kindred Healthcare
Mayo Clinic
Mclaren Health Care
Mount Clemens Regional Medical Center
St. John Hospital & Medical Center
Trinity Health (novi)
University Of Michigan Health System

HISTORICAL FINANCIALS
Company Type: Private

Income Statement				FYE: December 31
	REVENUE ($ mil.)	NET INCOME ($ mil.)	NET PROFIT MARGIN	EMPLOYEES
12/20	4,580	318	7.0%	35,000
12/19	4,703	401	8.5%	—
12/18	4,659	142	3.0%	—
12/17	4,438	392	8.8%	—
Annual Growth	1.1%	(6.7%)	—	—

2020 Year-End Financials
Return on assets: 4.6%   Cash ($ mil.): 1,585
Return on equity: 9.7%
Current ratio: 1.90

BEAVERTON SCHOOL DISTRICT

EXECUTIVES

Supt, Jerome Colonna
Asst Supt*, Sarah Boly
Asst Supt*, Bud Moore
Cfo*, Janice Essenberg
CIO*, Stephen Langford
Coordinator, Jill Bogle
Project Coordinator, Jay Dwyer
Information Technology/Interne, Sheila Bell
Teacher, Susan Rosenbaum
Information Technology Team ME, Judy Bride
2nd Grade Teacher, Stephanie Guy
Auditors: GROVE MUELLER & SWANK PC SA

LOCATIONS

HQ: BEAVERTON SCHOOL DISTRICT
16550 SW MERLO RD, BEAVERTON, OR 970035179
Phone: 503 591-8000
Web: WWW.BEAVERTON.K12.OR.US

HISTORICAL FINANCIALS
Company Type: Private

Income Statement				FYE: June 30
	REVENUE ($ mil.)	NET INCOME ($ mil.)	NET PROFIT MARGIN	EMPLOYEES
06/20	625	(54)	—	4,000
06/19	611	(93)	—	—
06/18	584	(97)	—	—
06/17	529	119	22.5%	—
Annual Growth	5.7%	—	—	—

BENCO DENTAL SUPPLY CO.

Benco Dental Supply is a one-stop shop for the tooth doc. Through regional showrooms and distribution centers Benco provides dental and dentistry supplies to more than 30000 dental professionals throughout the US. Its offerings include dental hand pieces furniture and disposable supplies. Its BencoNET division develops and distributes custom computers and proprietary programming and networking systems for dentists. Other services include dental office design practice consulting financing and real estate planning wealth management and equipment repairs.

Operations

Benco offerings range from large equipment to small supplies made by a broad range of manufacturers. The company supplies more than 80000 products including dental cement impression supplies and curing lights made by manufacturers such as 3M Dentsply Sirona Sybron (Kerr) Hu-Friedy and more. It also sells products under its own Benco Dental brand.

Support services include offers inventory management services and hand piece equipment and upholstery repair.

Benco Dental's practice management services include staff recruitment assistance product training programs for dentists peer-to-peer networking solutions and continuing medical education programs.

Geographic Reach

Benco Dental's main headquarters and showroom is located in Pittston Pennsylvania. It also operates another CenterPoint Experience (largescale) showroom in Costa Mesa California and it has a network of about 50 smaller regional showrooms and five distribution centers (in Pittston; Dallas; Fort Wayne Indiana; Jacksonville Florida; and Reno Nevada) across the US that serve customers in all 50 US states.

Although most of its operations are in the US the company also ships products to overseas customers.

Sales and Marketing

Benco markets its products and services directly to dental practices. It also increasing the number of orders placed through its online ordering system (Painless) and it promotes services to dentists through affiliations with dental organizations and associations (including the American Academy of Dental Group Practice and the American Association of Orthodontists). The company has more than 400 sales representatives. To support sales it also has about 300 factory-trained service technicians.

Financial Performance

Benco increased net sales by 9% in 2012 due to new product sales launches and increased sales of existing products in fields including 3D imaging equipment and digital sensors.

Strategy

Benco tends to expand its operations through organic growth initiatives including offering new products and services to a wider customer base. In addition the company grows through acquisitions in key growth regions. The company launched 14 Benco branded products during 2012 as well as 3800 new products made by its vendor partners. It also added about 50 new sales reps that year to meet rising customer demands. The company estimated that it grew market share to some 11% of the US market that year (placing itself among the top three dental supply distributors).

Benco increased sales to community health centers that year through its partnership with PSS. To expand its educational programs in 2012 the company also formed a partnership with the Kois Center which offers a nine-course program on topics including aesthetic and restorative dentistry.

To reach additional customers and expand its capacity the company opened its fifth distribution center — a 120000-sq. ft. facility in Reno Nevada — in 2011. It also opened a new sales branch office in Los Angeles to serve the Southern California market in 2012.

Benco Dental moved into its CenterPoint headquarters and showroom in Pittston Pennsylvania in early 2010. The facility is one of the largest dental equipment showrooms in the US with exhibits including more than two dozen dental rooms 14 digital X-ray units three sterilization centers and other oral surgery and orthodontic units as well as an office design concept suite and a training and education center. Following the success of that location the company opened a second CenterPoint Experience showroom in Costa Mesa California in 2012.

EXECUTIVES

Mng Dir, Charles F Cohen
Mng Dir, Richard S Cohen
Equipment Specialist, Equipmen, David Gardner
Long Island Equipment Coordina, Stephanie Varvaro
Distribution/Shipping/Transpor, Robert Foote
Coordinator, Cheryl Altemose
Coordinator, Eric Wright
Designer, Grngory Marinelli
Purchasing Manager, Melissa Bigelow
Senior Customer Soluti, Jamie Tosh
District Sales Assistant South, Jennifer Summerlin
Auditors: COHEN AND CO CLEVELAND OHIO

LOCATIONS

HQ: BENCO DENTAL SUPPLY CO.
  295 CENTERPOINT BLVD, PITTSTON, PA 186406136
Phone: 570 602-7781
Web: WWW.BENCO.COM

Selected Distribution Center Locations
Dallas Texas
Fort Wayne Indiana
Jacksonville Florida
Pittston Pennsylvania
Reno Nevada

PRODUCTS/OPERATIONS

Selected Brands
Large Equipment
  A-dec
  Belmont
  BIOLASE
  Cadent
  Gendex
  Instrumentarium
  Marus
  Midmark
  Pelton & Crane
  Sirona
  Soredex
  Vatech
Small Equipment
  Accutron
  Aceton
  Air Techniques
  Cadent
  KaVo
  Midmark
  Midwest
  Tuttnauer
  W&H
Supplies and technology (Benco brands)

BencoNET
BluChip rewards
BluPrint (dental impression material)
fas-TRACT
HD
Iris (dental pit and fissure sealant)
Natural Extensions (nitrile gloves)
Painless
ValuGrip (latex gloves)
Vision XR (oral x-ray film)
XLR8 (dental equipment)
Z3

COMPETITORS

Burkhart Dental	Henry Schein
Cardinal Health	Mckesson
Darby Dental	Owens & Minor
Dentsply Sirona	Patterson Companies
Discus Dental	Sybron Dental

HISTORICAL FINANCIALS
Company Type: Private

Income Statement · FYE: January 4

	REVENUE ($ mil.)	NET INCOME ($ mil.)	NET PROFIT MARGIN	EMPLOYEES
01/14*	620	8	1.4%	1,600
12/12	600	7	1.2%	—
12/07	389	5	1.3%	—
Annual Growth	8.1%	10.0%	—	—

*Fiscal year change

2014 Year-End Financials
Return on assets: 4.9%   Cash ($ mil.): —
Return on equity: —
Current ratio: 1.60

BENEFIS HOSPITALS, INC

EXECUTIVES

Ceo-Cfo, John Goodnow
Pres*, Laura Goldhahn
V Pres*, Steven Ballock
Dentist, Will Daniels DDS
Vice-President Information Ser, Alexander N Chung
Vice-President Information Ser, Mary Davis
General Practitioner, Justin Madill
Director, Patty Harris
Safety Director, Louis Dantuono
Internist, Jamina Charles
Records Director, Penny Crow
Auditors: MOSS ADAMS LLP PORTLAND OR

LOCATIONS

HQ: BENEFIS HOSPITALS, INC
  1101 26TH ST S, GREAT FALLS, MT 594055161
Phone: 406 455-5000
Web: WWW.BENEFIS.ORG

HISTORICAL FINANCIALS
Company Type: Private

Income Statement · FYE: December 31

	REVENUE ($ mil.)	NET INCOME ($ mil.)	NET PROFIT MARGIN	EMPLOYEES
12/19	1,147	49	4.3%	2,419
12/16	865	26	3.0%	—
12/15	860	20	2.4%	—
12/14	363	14	4.0%	—
Annual Growth	25.9%	27.7%	—	—

BERKSHIRE MEDICAL CENTER, INC.

EXECUTIVES

Pres- Ceo, David E Phelps
Treas*, Michael R Cullen
Dir*, Ann Trabulsi
Health Professional, Jessica Bridgmon
Health Professional, Azade Izadi
Internal Medicine Practitioner, Jansen Jones
Internal Medicine Practitioner, Katsiaryna
  Tsyrkunova
Internal Medicine Practitioner, Kipp Spencer
Internal Medicine Practitioner, Nidhi Aggarwal
Internal Medicine Practitioner, Shams Jubouri
Coordinator, Michelle Richard

LOCATIONS

HQ: BERKSHIRE MEDICAL CENTER, INC.
  725 NORTH ST, PITTSFIELD, MA 012014124
Phone: 413 447-2000
Web: WWW.BERKSHIREHEALTHSYSTEMS.ORG

HISTORICAL FINANCIALS
Company Type: Private

Income Statement				FYE: September 30
	REVENUE ($ mil.)	NET INCOME ($ mil.)	NET PROFIT MARGIN	EMPLOYEES
09/19	548	41	7.6%	1,375
09/18	472	49	10.5%	—
09/17	448	36	8.1%	—
09/16	437	34	7.9%	—
Annual Growth	7.8%	6.0%	—	—

2019 Year-End Financials

Return on assets: 6.7%   Cash ($ mil.): 28
Return on equity: 9.0%
Current ratio: 1.00

BERRY GLOBAL FILMS, LLC

Making plastic cling is this company's thing. AEP Industries manufactures plastic packaging films — more than 15000 types — including stretch wrap for industrial pallets packaging for foods and beverages and films for agricultural uses such as wrap for hay bales. AEP also makes dispenser-boxed plastic wraps which are sold to consumers as well as institutions ranging from schools to hospitals. Other industries courted by AEP are packaging transportation food autos chemicals textiles and electronics. The company operates in the US and in Canada. In the summer of 2016 AEP agreed to be acquired by rival Berry Plastics Group.

Geographic Reach
AEP conducts about 95% of its business in the US market. Remaining sales take place in Canada. It has about 15 manufacturing facilities in the US (about 11 states) and Canada. The company also exports its products to Latin America through its office in Waxahachie Texas.

Sales and Marketing
About two-thirds of AEP's sales are made to distributors and the remainder directly to end-users of its products. It serves about 3000 cus-tomers. The company works to maintain customer relationships and it provides technical training to its sales personal so that they are able to provide customer support and communicate customer needs to the company's product development team. Distribution functions are mostly contracted to third parties.

Financial Performance
AEP's revenues have fluctuated over the years. After peaking at $1.19 billion in 2014 revenues fell by 4% to $1.14 billion in 2015. The revenue decrease for 2015 was fueled by a 3% dip in average selling prices primarily due to the pass-through of lower resin costs negatively affecting net sales by $31 million.

The company in 2015 also experienced a 1% decrease in sales volumes attributed to volatility in the resin markets. This resulted in soft customer demand in certain stock product lines customer bankruptcies and the impact of exiting certain low-margin businesses during fiscal 2014.

After experiencing a net loss of $6 million in 2014 AEP posted positive net income of $29 million in 2015. This was the result of a decline in costs coupled with a larger amount of income tax benefits.

Strategy
With little product differentiation among plastic film producers AEP positions itself as the low-cost source with technological expertise to customize value-added flexible films to satisfy myriad manu-facturing and processing applications. The company aims to provide long-term value to share-holders by becoming the preferred provider of flexible packaging products in the North American market.

To strengthen its finances and increase manu-facturing output and productivity AEP is investing heavily in capital improvements. During the last decade it has purchased or leased new equipment and made equipment upgrades intended to opti-mize its manufacturing footprint in high-growth product categories.

The company looks for success in its sales and distribution model by establishing long-term rela-tionships with its customers. To mitigate the volatility of raw material prices the company pur-sues volume raw material rebates by making most of its purchases from three primary suppliers.

Company Background
Brendan Barba a former salesman for polyeth-ylene film maker PPD formed Flexible Plastics in 1967 in Lodi New Jersey. In 1970 his partner bought him out. That year Barba founded AEP In-dustries briefly called Automatically Extruded Products. In 1982 the company moved into the specialty and premium films market. It established a plant in Waxahachie Texas in 1985 and went public a year later.

EXECUTIVES

Ceo, Tom Salmon
Exec V Pres*, Jason K Greene
Cfo*, Mark W Miles
Benefits Manager, Tom Bradley
Vice President, James Rafferty
Director Printed Shrink Film, Jeff Melius
Human Resources Manager, Renee Porcile
Account Manager, Cynthia Clark
Facilities Manager, Ingrid Morea

LOCATIONS

HQ: BERRY GLOBAL FILMS, LLC
  95 CHESTNUT RIDGE RD, MONTVALE, NJ 076451801
Phone: 201 641-6600
Web: WWW.BERRYPLASTICS.COM

2015 Sales

	$ mil.	% of total
US	1,073	94
Canada	68	6
Total	**1,141**	**100**

PRODUCTS/OPERATIONS

2015 Sales

	$ mil.	% of total
Custom films	357	31
Stretch (pallet) wrap	332	29
Food contact	165	14
Canliners	144	13
PROformance films	63	6
Printed & converted films specialty films & other	77	7
Total	**1,141**	**100**

Selected Products
Canliners
Kitchen and standard garbage bags
Custom films (polyethylene co-extruded and monolayer
  custom designed film)
  Drum box carton pail liners
  Films to cover high value products
  Furniture and mattress bags
  Magazine overwrap
PROformance films (co-extruded and monolayer
  polyolefin films)
  Cereal box liners
  Fresh cut produce packaging
  Frozen foods
  Medical
Polyvinyl chloride wrap
  Food and freezer wrap
Printed and converted films (polyethylene)
  Printed laminated converted films for flexible
  packaging to consumer markets
  Printed shrink films
Stretch (pallet) wrap (polyethylene)
  Pallet wrap
Other products and specialty films (unplasticized
  polyvinyl chloride polyethylene)
  Agricultural films
  Battery labels
  Canliners
  Credit card laminate
  Retail and institutional films and products
  Table covers aprons bibs and gloves
  Twist wrap

COMPETITORS

Acme Packaging	Pactiv
Ampac	Plastic Suppliers
Bemis	Primex Plastics
Berry Global	Printpack
Dow Chemical	S.c. Johnson
Flexsol Packaging	Sealed Air Corp.
Griffon	Sigma Plastics
Inteplast	Tredegar
Intertape Polymer	

HISTORICAL FINANCIALS
Company Type: Private

Income Statement				FYE: October 31
	REVENUE ($ mil.)	NET INCOME ($ mil.)	NET PROFIT MARGIN	EMPLOYEES
10/15	1,141	28	2.5%	2,600
10/14	1,192	(5)	—	—
10/13	1,143	10	0.9%	—
Annual Growth	(0.1%)	63.8%	—	—

2015 Year-End Financials

Return on assets: 6.6%   Cash ($ mil.): 20
Return on equity: 32.2%
Current ratio: 2.10

BEST PETROLEUM CORPORATION

EXECUTIVES

Pres, Antonio De Jesus Nieves
Head of Business Development, Manuel F Rojas
Auditors: JESUS OYOLA CUADRADO BAYAMON

LOCATIONS

HQ: BEST PETROLEUM CORPORATION
KM 20 HM 5 RR 2, TOA BAJA, PR 00951
Phone: 787 251-6218
Web: WWW.BESTPETROLEUMCORP.COM

HISTORICAL FINANCIALS
Company Type: Private

Income Statement			FYE: December 31	
	REVENUE ($ mil.)	NET INCOME ($ mil.)	NET PROFIT MARGIN	EMPLOYEES
12/18	673	32	4.8%	130
12/17	547	26	4.8%	—
12/16	439	16	3.7%	—
12/15	479	11	2.4%	—
Annual Growth	12.0%	41.5%	—	—

2018 Year-End Financials
Return on assets: 18.8%   Cash ($ mil.): 110
Return on equity: 21.2%
Current ratio: 8.10

BETH ISRAEL DEACONESS MEDICAL CENTER, INC.

Beth Israel Deaconess Medical Center (BIDMC) is part of Beth Israel Lahey Health a new health care system that brings together academic medical centers and teaching hospitals community and specialty hospitals with more than 4000 physicians and 35000 employees. BIDMC has about 675 beds including around 495 medical/surgical beds more than 75 critical care beds and more than 60 OB/GYN beds. It also provides a full range of emergency services including a Level 1 Trauma Center and roof-top heliport. BIDMC a patient care teaching and research affiliate of Harvard Medical School. The health system traces its roots to Deaconess Hospital founded in 1896 and Beth Israel Hospital established in 1916.

Operations
BIDMC constantly rank as national leader among independent hospitals in National Institutes of health funding. The company research funding totally over $229.8 million annually 850 active sponsored projects 500 founded and non-founded clinical trials.

Beth Israel Deaconess Medical Center shares important clinical and research programs with institutions such as the Dana-Farber/Harvard Cancer Center Joslin Diabetes Center and Children's Hospital. It has some 1250 physicians on the active medical staff (including more than 800 full-time staff physicians). Most of these physicians hold faculty appointments at Harvard Medical School. In addition to its medical students Beth Israel Deaconess Medical Center provides clinical education to students in nursing; social work; radiologic technology ultrasound and nuclear medicine; and physical occupational speech and respiratory therapies.

The Carl J. Shapiro Institute for Education and Research provides medical students and physicians in training with an on-site centralized educational facility a state-of-the-art computer lab and a variety of educational resources that let students diagnose manage and learn technical skills on simulated patients.

Geographic Reach
BIDMC is located in Boston Massachusetts and has a growing presence in Eastern Massachusetts.

Sales and Marketing
BIDMC market its products and services through websites such as providing extraordinary care world-renowned experts provide care from patients call home from Newburyport to Plymouth from Lexington to Quincy.

EXECUTIVES

Ceo, Kevin Tabb
Pres, Eric Buehrens
Cfo, Steve Fischer
Treas, Allan Bufferd
Gastroenterologist, Rupa Mukherjee
Physician, Sharon Wright
Senior Director, Sherman Z Wu
Faculty, Tony Disalvatore
Scientist, Hava K Avraham
Assistant Professor, Alan Rigby
Assistant Professor, Dezheng Zhao

LOCATIONS

HQ: BETH ISRAEL DEACONESS MEDICAL CENTER, INC.
330 BROOKLINE AVE, BOSTON, MA 022155400
Phone: 617 667-7000
Web: WWW.BIDMC.ORG

PRODUCTS/OPERATIONS

Centers and Departments
Cancer Center
CardioVascular Institute
Digestive Disease Center
Spine Center
Transplant Institute
Clinical Departments
Anesthesia Critical Care and Pain Medicine
Dermatology
Emergency Medicine
Medicine
Neonatology
Neurology
Obstetrics and Gynecology
Orthopedic Surgery
Pathology
Psychiatry
Radiation Oncology
Radiology
Rehabilitation Services
Surgery

Selected Facilities
Beth Israel Deaconess HealthCare-Chelsea
Beth Israel Deaconess HealthCare-Chestnut Hill
Beth Israel Deaconess HealthCare-Lexington
Beth Israel Deaconess Hospital-Milton
Beth Israel Deaconess Hospital-Needham
Beth Israel Deaconess Hospital-Plymouth

COMPETITORS

Boston Medical Center
Brigham And Women's Hospital
Cambridge Health Alliance
Care New England
Children's Hospital Boston
Dana-farber
Massachusetts General Hospital
Newton-wellesley Hospital

Northeast Health System
Partners Healthcare
Southcoast Hospitals Group
Spaulding Rehabilitation Hospital
Steward Health Care

HISTORICAL FINANCIALS
Company Type: Private

Income Statement				FYE: September 30
	REVENUE ($ mil.)	NET INCOME ($ mil.)	NET PROFIT MARGIN	EMPLOYEES
09/19	1,945	68	3.5%	6,500
09/17	1,335	37	2.8%	—
09/16	1,279	28	2.3%	—
09/15	1,198	44	3.7%	—
Annual Growth	12.9%	11.1%	—	—

2019 Year-End Financials
Return on assets: 3.1%   Cash ($ mil.): 921
Return on equity: 6.4%
Current ratio: 1.40

BETH ISRAEL MEDICAL CENTER

Residents of New York City's Lower East Side look to Mount Sinai Beth Israel (formerly Beth Israel Medical Center) to keep them healthy. A member of Mount Sinai Health System the tertiary care medical facility has about 800 inpatient beds located in Manhattan. It emphasizes its services in heart disease cancer neurology orthopedics gastrointestinal disease chemical dependency psychiatric disorders pain management and palliative care and HIV/AIDS research and treatment. It is notable for its unique approach to combining medical excellence with clinical innovation. Its wide array of services have included addiction emergency department heart (cardiology) lung and pulmonology musictherapy neurology orthopedics pediatric emergency care psychiatry radiology surgery and urology. Headquartered in New York Mount Sinai Beth Israel has played an important role in providing health care to New Yorkers since the mid-20th century. The company traces its roots back in 1889.

EXECUTIVES

Ceo-Pres, Kenneth L Davis
Cfo*, Donald Scanlon
Staff, Donna Lewis
MD, Donna Mildvan
Gastroenterology, Dov Grant
Pediatrician, Emily Buchwald
Assistant Professor, Erica Grabscheid
Secretary, Esther Sanchez
Senior Chief Vascular Tech, Fernando Amador
Gastroenterology, Franklin Kasmin
Assistant Professor, Fukiat Ongseng
Auditors: PRICEWATERHOUSECOOPERS LLP NE

LOCATIONS

HQ: BETH ISRAEL MEDICAL CENTER
281 1ST AVE, NEW YORK, NY 100032925
Phone: 212 420-2000
Web: WWW.BETHISRAELNY.ORG

PRODUCTS/OPERATIONS

Selected Centers and Services

AIDS Services
Allergy and Immunology
Anesthesiology
Appel-Venet Comprehensive Breast Service
Asian Services
Beth Israel ALS Center
Beth Israel Hernia Center
Beth Israel Medical Group
Betty & Morton Yarmon Stroke Center
Brief Psychotherapy Research Program
Cancer Center (Oncology)
Center for Blood Management and Bloodless Medicine and Surgery
Center for Endovascular Surgery
Center for Health and Healing
Craniofacial and Cleft Palate Center
Cystic Fibrosis Center
Dermatology
Endocrinology and Metabolism
Epilepsy
Friedman Diabetes Institute
Genetics
Geriatrics
Heart Institute (Cardiology)
Hematology
Hospice
Hyman Newman Institute for Neurology and Neurosugery (INN)
The Chris and Morton P. Hyman Patient Care Unit
Hyperhidrosis Program
Incontinence
Integrative Medicine
Interventional Neuroradiology
Israeli Health Program
Karpas Health Information Center
Latino Health Institute
Live Well New York
Louis Armstrong Center for Music and Medicine:
Lung Nodule Center
Maternity Services
Methadone Maintenance Treatment Program
Midwifery
Nephrology
Neurology
Orthopedics
Ostomy Program
Pain Medicine and Palliative Care
Pediatrics
Phillips Beth Israel School of Nursing
Primary Care
Psychiatry
Pulmonary and Critical Care Medicine
Radiation Oncology
Radiology
Rheumatology
Senior Health
Sleep Health
Speech-Language and Learning Center
Spine Institute
Sports Medicine
Stroke Centers
Styuvesant Square Chemical Dependency Services
Surgery
Urology
Vascular and Birthmarks Institute of New York
Women's Health
Women's Heart NY
Wound Healing Center

COMPETITORS

Bronx-lebanon Hospital
Catholic Healthcare System
Kingsbrook Jewish Medical Center
Lutheran Healthcare
Maimonides Medical Center
Medisys Health Network
Memorial Sloan-kettering
Montefiore Medical
Nyu Hospital For Joint Diseases
New York City Health And Hospitals
Newyork-presbyterian Healthcare
Northwell Health
Suny Downstate

HISTORICAL FINANCIALS

Company Type: Private

Income Statement   FYE: December 31

	REVENUE ($ mil.)	NET INCOME ($ mil.)	NET PROFIT MARGIN	EMPLOYEES
12/09	1,256	15	1.2%	8,100
12/08	932	(59)	—	
Annual Growth 34.8%		—	—	—

2009 Year-End Financials

Return on assets: 1.6%
Return on equity: 5.6%
Current ratio: 0.50

Cash ($ mil.): 98

BETHESDA HOSPITAL, INC.

From modest beginnings as a informal cottage hospital Bethesda North Hospital has grown into the fourth largest medical center in Cincinnati Ohio. Bethesda North is a full-service acute care hospital with some 360 beds for adults and 60 for children. It provides comprehensive medical and surgical care including maternity and fertility services emergency care and diagnostic imaging. The hospital joined with fellow Cincinnati health care provider Good Samaritan Hospital in 1995 to form TriHealth. Together the two hospitals offer care at some 80 locations including primary care offices fitness centers and occupational health facilities.

Operations

The full-service 420-bed acute care hospital handles some 24000 inpatient admissions each year as well as 260000 outpatient visits 77000 emergency room visits and 4000 births. It employs 165 full-time doctors and dentists and provides more than $30 million in community outreach efforts (including charity care programs) each year.

Specialty units at Bethesda North Hospital include institutes for cancer heart surgical and digestive care as well as centers for outpatient imaging breast stroke obstetrics-gynecology orthopedics and emergency trauma care. As a regional teaching center the hospital offers residency programs in a number of specialties including family medicine internal medicine OB-GYN and surgery.

Geographic Reach

Bethesda North is located in northern Cincinnati Ohio and serves as a regional trauma center as well as a major teaching hospital in the area.

Strategy

Parent organization TriHealth has aligned skilled physicians specialists surgeons and its staff to create specialty institutes offering best-of-class medical assistance in fields including heart and cancer care. To further enhance its facilities in 2013 the organization renovated the labor and delivery wing at Bethesda North Hospital. Other recent projects include the addition of a seven-story patient tower and a new outpatient imaging center.

Additionally the company has invested in TriHealth Connect the electronic medical records system that will help access accurate patient information.

Company Background

In early 2012 TriHealth unveiled a new logo.

Bethesda North traces it roots to 1896 and a cottage occupied by seven German Methodist deaconesses ministering to the poor and sick.

EXECUTIVES

Pres, John Prout
Cfo*, Craig Rucker
Controller, Brian Krause
Logistics Management Lead Tech, Judy Booker-Westerfi
Physician, Ken Zwergel
Hr Director, Sharon Hancock
Benefits Consultant, Tracy Ford
Instructor, Meg McVaugh
MD, Danny Fischer
Client Administrator, Kim Hill
Senior Vice-President, Laura Cook
Auditors: ERNST & YOUNG LLP CINCINNATI

LOCATIONS

HQ: BETHESDA HOSPITAL, INC.
4750 WESLEY AVE, CINCINNATI, OH 452122244
Phone: 513 569-6100
Web: WWW.TRIHEALTH.COM

PRODUCTS/OPERATIONS

List of Selected Services

Breast health
Cancer care
Digestive diseases
Heart and vascular care
Maternity (OB-GYN childbirth)
Orthopedics
Outpatient imaging
Pallative Care
Pharmacy
Robotic-assisted surgery
Stroke care
Trauma/Emergency services

COMPETITORS

Cincinnati Children's Hospital
Deaconess Associations
Kettering Health Network
Miami Valley Hospital
Premier Health Partners
St. Elizabeth Healthcare
The Christ Hospital Corporation
Uc Health

HISTORICAL FINANCIALS

Company Type: Private

Income Statement   FYE: June 30

	REVENUE ($ mil.)	NET INCOME ($ mil.)	NET PROFIT MARGIN	EMPLOYEES
06/21	744	66	9.0%	3,000
06/20	643	(36)	—	—
06/19	624	32	5.2%	—
06/18	639	52	8.2%	—
Annual Growth	5.2%	8.5%	—	—

2021 Year-End Financials

Return on assets: 5.2%
Return on equity: 11.9%
Current ratio: 0.30

Cash ($ mil.): —

BETHESDA, INC.

EXECUTIVES

Pres, J James Pearce Jr
V Pres, Chip Crowther
SEC, Ellen Katz
Treas, William A Tsacalis

V Chm, Michael F Haverkamp
Officer, Lynn Meyer
Associate Director Divi, Steven Kleeman
MD, Phillip F Oblinger
Psychiatrist, Melvin Gale
Clinical Research Nurse Coordi, Angela Hein
Information Technology/Interne, Blair Riley
Auditors: ERNST & YOUNG LLP CINCINNATI

LOCATIONS

HQ: BETHESDA, INC.
 619 OAK ST 7N, CINCINNATI, OH 452061613
Phone: 513 569-6400
Web: WWW.BETHESDA-INC.ORG

HISTORICAL FINANCIALS
Company Type: Private

Income Statement				FYE: June 30
	REVENUE ($ mil.)	NET INCOME ($ mil.)	NET PROFIT MARGIN	EMPLOYEES
06/21	809	157	19.5%	5,543
06/20	667	(37)	—	—
06/19	651	28	4.4%	—
06/18	679	78	11.6%	—
Annual Growth	6.0%	26.2%	—	—

2021 Year-End Financials
Return on assets: 8.6%   Cash ($ mil.): —
Return on equity: 14.5%
Current ratio: 0.70

BI-MART ACQUISITION CORP.

EXECUTIVES

Pres-Coo, Richard Truett
SEC, David B Zientara
Cfo, Dan Chen
Exec Admin, Jodie Murchy
Auditors: DELOITTE & TOUCHE LLP PORTLAN

LOCATIONS

HQ: BI-MART ACQUISITION CORP.
 220 SENECA RD, EUGENE, OR 974022725
Phone: 541 344-0681
Web: WWW.BIMART.COM

HISTORICAL FINANCIALS
Company Type: Private

Income Statement				FYE: February 23
	REVENUE ($ mil.)	NET INCOME ($ mil.)	NET PROFIT MARGIN	EMPLOYEES
02/08	721	10	1.4%	3,300
02/07	694	11	1.7%	—
02/06	665	6	1.0%	—
02/05	648	7	1.1%	—
Annual Growth	3.6%	12.8%	—	—

2008 Year-End Financials
Return on assets: 5.6%   Cash ($ mil.): 3
Return on equity: 105.3%
Current ratio: 1.90

BIG RIVER RESOURCES, LLC.

EXECUTIVES

Ceo-Pres, Raymond E Defenbaugh
Coo, Jim Leiting
Cfo, Jim Hall
MBR-Treas, Les Allen
MBR-V Pres, Andy Brader
MBR, Gene Youngquist
Scientist, Jeannette Peterson
Operations Manager, Jim Gunter
Adminstrative Assistant, Sarah Huxley
Financial Controller, Tina McCulloch
Merchandiser Assistant, Tracey Damewood
Auditors: CHRISTIANSON PLLP WILLMAR M

LOCATIONS

HQ: BIG RIVER RESOURCES, LLC.
 211 N GEAR AVE STE 200, WEST BURLINGTON, IA 526551027
Phone: 319 753-1100
Web: WWW.BIGRIVERRESOURCES.COM

HISTORICAL FINANCIALS
Company Type: Private

Income Statement				FYE: December 31
	REVENUE ($ mil.)	NET INCOME ($ mil.)	NET PROFIT MARGIN	EMPLOYEES
12/19	823	17	2.2%	250
12/18	802	20	2.5%	—
12/17	817	33	4.2%	—
12/16	851	74	8.8%	—
Annual Growth	(1.1%)	(38.1%)	—	—

2019 Year-End Financials
Return on assets: 5.0%   Cash ($ mil.): 40
Return on equity: 5.9%
Current ratio: 2.70

BIG RIVERS ELECTRIC CORPORATION

EXECUTIVES

Ceo, Robert Berry
Chm*, Wayne Elliott
V Chm*, Larry Elder
SEC/Treas*, Paul Edd Butler
Dir*, James Sills
Dir/Acctg/Fin*, Donna Windhaus
Analyst, Tony Howard
Accounting Staff, Julia Book
Manager, Roger Hickman
Plant Manager, Keith Scott
Public Relations Manager, Nick Castlen

LOCATIONS

HQ: BIG RIVERS ELECTRIC CORPORATION
 201 3RD ST, HENDERSON, KY 424202979
Phone: 270 827-2561
Web: WWW.BIGRIVERS.COM

HISTORICAL FINANCIALS
Company Type: Private

Income Statement				FYE: December 31
	REVENUE ($ mil.)	NET INCOME ($ mil.)	NET PROFIT MARGIN	EMPLOYEES
12/12	568	11	2.0%	400
12/11	561	5	1.0%	—
12/10	527	6	1.3%	—
Annual Growth	3.8%	27.0%	—	—

2012 Year-End Financials
Return on assets: 0.7%   Cash ($ mil.): —
Return on equity: 2.8%
Current ratio: 1.70

BIG WEST OF CALIFORNIA, LLC

EXECUTIVES

Member, Fred Greener
Member, Eugene Cotten
Member, Robert Payne
Manager, Eric Byers

LOCATIONS

HQ: BIG WEST OF CALIFORNIA, LLC
 1104 COUNTRY HILLS DR, OGDEN, UT 844032400
Phone: 801 296-7890
Web: WWW.BIGWESTOIL.COM

HISTORICAL FINANCIALS
Company Type: Private

Income Statement				FYE: January 31
	REVENUE ($ mil.)	NET INCOME ($ mil.)	NET PROFIT MARGIN	EMPLOYEES
01/07	1,438	(32)	—	322
01/06	1,109	23	2.1%	—
Annual Growth	29.6%	—	—	—

BIG WEST OIL, LLC

 Big West Oil keeps the wagon trains rolling across the big West — at least the station wagons. The company is in the oil processing and products business centered around its 35000 barrels-a-day refinery in North Salt Lake Utah to its fleet of tanker trucks that gather crude oil from the refinery and other purchases and deliver to wholesale customers and gas station/convenience stores in seven Western states including Colorado Idaho Nevada Utah and Wyoming. The company's refinery processes crude oil produced in Utah Wyoming and Canada. Big West Oil is a subsidiary of FJ Management.

EXECUTIVES

Mng MBR, Fred Greener
Process Safety Management Coor, Laura Plummer
Compliance Manager, Stuart Smith

Unit Supervisor, John Stoops
Safety, Dusty Ott
Safety Manager, Nickolas Skabelund
Assistant Controller, Jonathan Dahlin
Manager of Crude Oil Supply, Ed Hatch

LOCATIONS

HQ: BIG WEST OIL, LLC
  333 W CENTER ST, NORTH SALT LAKE, UT
  840542805
Phone: 801 624-1000
Web: WWW.BIGWESTOIL.COM

COMPETITORS

Hollyfrontier   Sinclair Oil
Marathon Petroleum   Tesoro

HISTORICAL FINANCIALS

Company Type: Private

Income Statement				FYE: January 31
	REVENUE ($ mil.)	NET INCOME ($ mil.)	NET PROFIT MARGIN	EMPLOYEES
01/08	3,053	191	6.3%	460
01/07	2,399	89	3.7%	—
01/06	2,014	102	5.1%	—
01/05	735	50	6.9%	—
Annual Growth	60.7%	55.6%	—	—

2008 Year-End Financials

Return on assets: 19.9%   Cash ($ mil.): 6
Return on equity: 50.4%
Current ratio: 1.20

BIG-D CONSTRUCTION CORP.

Big-D builds big things. Founded in 1967 by Dee Livingood (who carried the nickname "Big-Dee") the family-run construction firm offers design/build services to customers in a dozen states from offices in Utah Arizona California and Wyoming. Known for its work on projects in the food and beverage sector Big-D also works on light commercial office and retail properties manufacturing health care and hospitality projects among others. Its clients have included Hampton and Marriott. Big-D's Signature Group division builds high-end luxury homes as well as condominiums spas and other special projects in resort communities. Its Self-Performed Services unit works on parking garage architectural and structural projects. Big-D ranked 2nd in Top Utah General Contractor by Utah Design & Construction Magazine (rankings are based on revenues).

Operations

Big-D generates around $1.5 billion in revenues per year and staffs about 1500 employees on average. The company has completed nearly 75 LEED projects and over 800 projects using construction management/general contractor and design-build services.

The contractor operates four main divisions. The Commercial division serves commercial and industrial customers that offers construction management and design-build services for projects exceeding $5 million in scope while the Light Commercial division offers more streamlined construction services for tenant improvement commercial and light industrial clients with smaller projects (less than $5 million in scope).

The Self-Performed Services division works on concrete (like parking garages) carpentry and specialty construction projects. The Signature division mostly works on higher-end housing and resort-related projects for private estate and resort property owners.

Geographic Reach

The Salt Lake City-based contractor serves clients with offices in a dozen of states. Its other offices are in Ogden Lindon and Park City in Utah; Pleasanton California; Tempe Arizona; Jackson Wyoming; Las Vegas Nevada; Bozeman Montana; Rexburg Idaho; and St. Paul Minnesota.

Sales and Marketing

Big-D serves industries from industrial/mining hospitality federal/state technology retail commercial education healthcare warehouse/distribution manufacturing and food/beverage.

Some of Big-D's clients Salt Lake City Public Library Crown Plaza Marriott University of Utah Kenco Freedman Hershey Dannon Yogurt and Malt-O-Meal among others.

Financial Performance

Big-D Construction reports an average yearly revenue of $1.5 billion.

Strategy

Big-D Construction applies management techniques that maintain a frictionless team environment at every stage of the building process.

The company also utilizes a "Design?Build" delivery system that enables clients to contract with a single entity to complete both the design and construction phases of the project. As all the elements of its clients' projects are facilitated through Big-D it is able to more readily control costs and schedules including offering a Guaranteed Maximum Price.

Big-D has taken on new projects in recent years. In mid-2020 it broke ground on a new Post House project. Big-D is working with Lowe Property Group Q Factor BCG Holdings and Bridge Investment Group to provide Construction Management and General Contracting services (CM/GC) for this monumental project.

Big-D also has a joint venture project with Holder Construction which is the new Salt Lake City Airport Redevelopment program. This major project has been in the works for the past six and a half years and is officially opening in late 2020. In early 2020 Big-D reported that this project was ahead of schedule due to the significant drop in the number of travelers. The enhanced construction opportunity saved hundreds of millions of dollars and has allowed the project to finish years ahead of schedule.

Company Background

Big-D courted more government projects as a way to weather the economic downturn which has put a halt on many commercial jobs. Among those public projects was the Utah Museum of Natural History at The University of Utah and the Wallace F. Bennett Federal Building in Salt Lake City. Big-D also is focusing on developing its eco-friendly construction business.

EXECUTIVES

Ceo, Rob Moore
Pres*, Robert Moore
Pres-Mountain West Grp*, Forrest McNabb
Evp*, Cory Moore
Evp*, Troy Thompson
Contrl, Blake Dan Roosandaal
Accounting Clerk, Karen Jensen
Project Assistant, Beverly Maxfield
Project Engineer, Mike Engstrom
Information Technology Special, Gary Bryson
Assistant Project Manager, Jeff Sabin
Auditors: GRANT THORNTON LLP SALT LAKE

LOCATIONS

HQ: BIG-D CONSTRUCTION CORP.
  404 W 400 S, SALT LAKE CITY, UT 841011108
Phone: 801 415-6000
Web: WWW.BIG-D.COM

Selected Markets
Arizona
Arkansas
California
Colorado
Georgia
Hawaii
Idaho
Montana
Nevada
New Mexico
North Carolina
North Dakota
Oklahoma
Oregon
South Dakota
Tennessee
Texas
Utah
Washington

PRODUCTS/OPERATIONS

Selected Services
Construction management
Design/build
Field services
  Architectural concrete
  Finish carpentry
  Rough framing
  Structural concrete
General contracting
Green and Leadership in Energy and Environmental Design

Selected Industry Specializations
Commercial/public spaces (governmental educational and office complexes; mixed-use projects)
Food processing and distribution
Health care
Hospitality and resort
Manufacturing
Retail

COMPETITORS

Bechtel   Jaynes Companies
Hensel Phelps   Layton
  Construction   Okland Construction
J.f. Shea   Swinerton
Jacobsen Construction

HISTORICAL FINANCIALS

Company Type: Private

Income Statement				FYE: December 31
	REVENUE ($ mil.)	NET INCOME ($ mil.)	NET PROFIT MARGIN	EMPLOYEES
12/12	541	0	—	1,384
12/11	554	0	—	—
12/10	259	0	—	—
Annual Growth	44.4%	—	—	—

2012 Year-End Financials

Return on assets: —   Cash ($ mil.): 38
Return on equity: —
Current ratio: 1.40

BILLINGS CLINIC

Billings Clinic is an integrated health care system that serves the residents of Big Sky Country. Through a group of more than 450 doctors and other providers the clinic caters a vast region covering much of Montana northern Wyoming and the western Dakotas. It offers 50-plus specialties such as emergency and trauma cancer orthopedics birthing cardiovascular neurosciences dialysis and pediatrics. Its operations include a more than 300-bed hospital and the organization's main clinic. Additionally Billings Clinic has nearly 15 regional partnerships including management agreements with more than 10 Critical Access Hospitals and a joint venture in Community Medical Center (Missoula MT) with RegionalCare Hospital Partners. The not-for-profit health care system is owned by the community.

Operations

With its vast service area the health care system provides a MedFlight advanced life support fixed-wing aircraft service that transports critically ill or injured patients from rural communities.

As part of its operations Billings Clinic runs a Level II emergency and trauma center 20-suite family birthing center Level III neonatal intensive care unit inpatient cancer care unit and surgery centers. The health care system's cancer center provides both inpatient and outpatient care in Billings.

Billings Clinic is led by a physician CEO Billings Clinic is governed by a board of community members nurses and physicians.

Billings Clinic's Community Benefit totalled more than $38 million including $9.9 million in financial assistance provided to nearly 11000 patients.

Geographic Reach

As the largest health care organization in the area Billings Clinic's service area extends 260000 miles to provide specialty care for residents of rural Montana (headquarters) Wyoming and North Dakota.

Strategy

Billings Clinic works with pharmaceutical sponsors on a variety of clinical research trials in various phases and indications.

In October 2019 Billings Clinic and Broadwater Health Center officially signed an affiliation agreement to partner together to provide essential health care services to the people of Townsend Montana. Earlier that month the Hospital District Board also voted in favor of the transaction for the hospital and ambulance service.

It also signed another affiliation agreement with Powell Valley Healthcare (PVHC) in early 2020 concluding a three-year long process of creating a new governance arrangement between the two organizations. In the new affiliation Billings Clinic will provide management services for PVHC.

Company Background

The Billings Clinic evolved from the general practice of Dr. Arthur J. Movius who founded his Billings practice in 1911.

It expanded its capacity for infusions in 2012 when its Billings Clinic Cody location opened an infusion center. In late 2012 the organization also opened a new Stillwater Billings Clinic medical facility which combines Stillwater Community Hospital and Billings Clinic Columbus and integrates the billing process for the two health care facilities.

EXECUTIVES

Ceo, Nicholas Wolter
Pres*, Michael Schaer
V Pres*, Lyle R Knight
SEC*, Linda Overstreet
Chair*, J Scott Millikan
Treas*, Joy Ott
SEC*, Liz Fulton
V Pres*, Maria Valandra
Cmo*, Toni Green-Cheatwood
Cfo*, Priscilla Needham
Manager of Business Office, Bonnie Conzelman

LOCATIONS

HQ: BILLINGS CLINIC
2800 10TH AVE N, BILLINGS, MT 591010703
Phone: 406 657-4000
Web: WWW.BILLINGSCLINIC.COM

PRODUCTS/OPERATIONS

Selected Services

Advance Medical Directives
Allergy Asthma Immunology
Aspen Meadows - Skilled Nursing and Assisted Living
Anticoagulation Clinic
Breast Center
Cancer Center
Cardiovascular Services
Cardiovascular Surgery
Children's Services
Continence Center
Community Training Center
Cosmetic Surgery
da Vinci Surgical System
Dermatology Center
Diabetes Management Center
Diagnostic Imaging
Diabetes
Dialysis Center
Eldercare Solutions
Emergency & Trauma Center
Emmi Educational Videos
Employer Services - Occupational Health
Endocrinology
Eye Center
Facial Plastic Surgery
Family Medicine
Family Birth Center
Gastroenterology
General Surgery
Genetic Counseling
Geriatric Assessment Program
Gynecologic Cancer
Heart Services
Heart Surgery
Home Oxygen & Medical Equipment
Hospitalist Program
Infectious Diseases
Insurance Finder
Internal Medicine
Laboratory Services
LifeFit
Maternal-Fetal Medicine
MedFlight Air Ambulance
Mental Health Services
Metabolism Center
Mohs Surgery
Nutrition Services
Neurosciences
Obstetrics & Gynecology
Occupational Health - Employer Services
Ophthalmology
Orthopedics & Sports Medicine
Palliative Care
Pediatrics
  Pediatric Center
  Pediatric Cancer
  Pediatric Diabetes
  Pediatric Gastroenterology
  Pediatric Pulmonology
  Rehabilitation (Therapy)
Pharmacy
Physical Medicine & Rehabilitation
Plastic Surgery
Primary Care for Adults
Pulmonary Rehabilitation Program
Radiology Services
Reproductive Medicine and Fertility Care
Robotic Surgery
SameDay Care
Senior Services
Sleep Disorders Center
Sports Medicine
Sports Specific Camps
Stroke Care
Surgery Center
Transitional Care Unit
Urology Services
Vascular Surgery
Vein Clinic
Women's Free Screenings
Women's and Children's Services

Selected Affiliate Hospitals and Clinics

Beartooth Billings Clinic - Red Lodge
Colstrip Medical Center - Colstrip
Daniels Memorial Healthcare - Scobey
Livingston HealthCare - Livingston
North Big Horn Hospital - Lovell
Pioneer Medical Center - Big Timber
Roundup Memorial Healthcare - Roundup
Sheridan Memorial Hospital Association
Stillwater Billings Clinic

COMPETITORS

Glendive Medical Center
St. Alexius Medical Center
St. James Healthcare
St. Patrick Hospital
Wyoming Medical Center

HISTORICAL FINANCIALS

Company Type: Private

Income Statement				FYE: June 30
	REVENUE ($ mil.)	NET INCOME ($ mil.)	NET PROFIT MARGIN	EMPLOYEES
06/16	586	(2)	—	3,300
06/15	565	30	5.4%	—
06/14	593	38	6.6%	—
06/13	560	14	2.6%	—
Annual Growth	1.6%	—	—	—

2016 Year-End Financials

Return on assets: (-0.3%)
Return on equity: (-0.6%)
Current ratio: 1.80
Cash ($ mil.): 13

BIOURJA TRADING, LLC

EXECUTIVES

Chm-Ceo, Amit Bhandari
Vp Hr*, Arpita Bhandari
Head of Ethanol Trading*, Jordan Fife
Law Specialist, Varinder Gill
Head of Human Resources, Steve Sfamenos
Manager, Paras Shah
Employee, Coco Richard
Auditors: CARR RIGGS & INGRAM LLC HOUST

LOCATIONS

HQ: BIOURJA TRADING, LLC
1080 ELDRIDGE PKWY # 1175, HOUSTON, TX 770772582
Phone: 832 775-9000
Web: WWW.BIOURJA.COM

HISTORICAL FINANCIALS

Company Type: Private

Income Statement				FYE: December 31
	REVENUE ($ mil.)	NET INCOME ($ mil.)	NET PROFIT MARGIN	EMPLOYEES
12/13	4,622	26	0.6%	72
12/12	2,992	11	0.4%	—
12/11	3,842	13	0.4%	—
Annual Growth	9.7%	38.6%	—	—

2013 Year-End Financials

Return on assets: 16.9%
Return on equity: 57.0%
Current ratio: 1.40
Cash ($ mil.): 15

BLACK & VEATCH HOLDING COMPANY

EXECUTIVES

Chb-Pres-Ceo, Steven L Edwards
Evp-Cfo, Kenneth L Williams
Svp-Treasurer, Michael Williams
Exec V Pres-SEC, Timothy W Triplett
Asst SEC, Andrea C Bernica
Employee, Benjamin Smith
Director Project Controls, David Walker
Project Accounting Associate, Kevin O'Connor
Telecommunications, Kevin Rucker
Business, Roxanne Powers
Lead Manager, Aldric Gomez
Auditors: KPMG LLP KANSAS CITY MISSOUR

LOCATIONS

HQ: BLACK & VEATCH HOLDING COMPANY
11401 LAMAR AVE, OVERLAND PARK, KS 662111598
Phone: 913 458-2000
Web: WWW.BV.COM

HISTORICAL FINANCIALS

Company Type: Private

Income Statement				FYE: December 28
	REVENUE ($ mil.)	NET INCOME ($ mil.)	NET PROFIT MARGIN	EMPLOYEES
12/18	3,479	80	2.3%	18,568
12/17	3,364	87	2.6%	—
12/16*	3,207	75	2.3%	—
01/16	2,955	109	3.7%	—
Annual Growth	5.6%	(9.7%)	—	—

*Fiscal year change

2018 Year-End Financials

Return on assets: 4.9%   Cash ($ mil.): 383
Return on equity: 54.7%
Current ratio: 1.10

BLACK & VEATCH INTERNATIONAL COMPANY

EXECUTIVES

Chb, Steve Edwards
President, Mario Azar
Evp-SEC, Timothy W Triplett
Evp-Cfo, Kenneth L Williams
Svp-Treasurer, Michael Williams
Svp-Assst SEC, Peter D Loftspring
Asst Secretary, Andrea C Bernica
Engineer, Jeff Coggins
Associate Vice President, Donnie Ginn
Auditors: KPMG LLP KANSAS CITY MO

LOCATIONS

HQ: BLACK & VEATCH INTERNATIONAL COMPANY
11401 LAMAR AVE, OVERLAND PARK, KS 662111598
Phone: 913 458-2000
Web: WWW.BV.COM

HISTORICAL FINANCIALS

Company Type: Private

Income Statement				FYE: December 31
	REVENUE ($ mil.)	NET INCOME ($ mil.)	NET PROFIT MARGIN	EMPLOYEES
12/09	711	43	6.1%	283
12/08	711	43	6.1%	—
12/07	1	(0)	—	—
12/06	1	(0)	—	—
Annual Growth	754.9%	—	—	—

2009 Year-End Financials

Return on assets: 8.5%   Cash ($ mil.): 39
Return on equity: 37.5%
Current ratio: 1.10

BLOUNT INTERNATIONAL, INC.

Formerly Blount International Oregon Tool produces cutting chain guide bars sprockets and accessories for chainsaws concrete-cutting equipment and lawnmower blades. Blount's lineup is sold under brands Oregon Carlton and KOX to dealers and consumers in key markets. End users are professionals and consumers engaged in forestry lawn and garden farming and construction activities. Blount was founded in 1947 as Oregon Saw Chain Company by Joe Cox. In 2021 Blount International Inc. is renamed to Oregon Tool Inc. to honor the company's legacy and unite all of its brands under one name moving forward.

Operations

The company produces saw chains bars and sprockets and outdoor equipment accessories and parts for the garden and landscape industry. Blount offers these products under the brand names OREGON Carlton and KOX.

Blount manufactures high-quality attachments and implements finish mowers seeders and other agriculture-related products. These products are marketed under the brand name Woods.

The company also manufactures and markets diamond-cutting chains assembles and markets concrete cutting chain saws and purchases other concrete cutting products that are marketed to the construction and utility industries.

Geographic Reach

Oregon-based Blount sells its products in more than 110 countries around the world.

Sales and Marketing

The company sells its products through dealers direct sales companies and mass merchants which sell to the global forestry lawn and garden; farm ranch and agriculture; and construction products end markets.

Company Background

Blount was founded in 1947 as Oregon Saw Chain Company by Joe Cox.

EXECUTIVES

Ceo, Paul Tonnesen
Chb*, Joshua L Collins
Pres-Coo*, David Willmott
Sr V Pres-Cfo*, Calvin Jenness
V Pres-General Counsel-Sec*, Chad Paulson
V Pres-Corp Contrl*, Mark Allred
Human Resources Representative, Barbara Wallis

National Account Manager, Chris Seeman
Director Customer Supply Chain, Margaret Kairis
Buyer, Mari-Len McHugh
Transportation Manager, Alfredo Camacho
Auditors: KPMG LLP PORTLAND OREGON

LOCATIONS

HQ: BLOUNT INTERNATIONAL, INC.
4909 SE INTERNATIONAL WAY, PORTLAND, OR 972224679
Phone: 503 653-8881
Web: WWW.OREGONTOOL.COM

PRODUCTS/OPERATIONS

Selected Products

Chain drive sprockets
Chainsaw guide bars
Concrete-cutting chainsaws and circular saws (gasoline and hydraulic powered)
Cutting chain (for chainsaws)
Diamond-segmented chain (for cutting concrete)
Farm accessories
Lawn and garden cutting attachments
Lawnmower and edger cutting blades
Log splitters
Maintenance tools (for chainsaws and mechanical timber harvesting equipment)
Tractor driven post-hole diggers
Tractor three-point linkage parts

COMPETITORS

Alamo Group	Great Plains
Ariens	Manufacturing
Briggs & Stratton	Husqvarna
Caterpillar	Kubota
Champion Cutting Tool	Mtd Products
Deere	Metso
Dover Corp.	Stihl Incorporated
Emak Group	Terex

HISTORICAL FINANCIALS

Company Type: Private

Income Statement				FYE: December 31
	REVENUE ($ mil.)	NET INCOME ($ mil.)	NET PROFIT MARGIN	EMPLOYEES
12/15	828	(49)	—	4,000
12/14	944	36	3.9%	—
12/13	900	4	0.5%	—
12/12	927	39	4.3%	—
Annual Growth	(3.7%)	—	—	—

2015 Year-End Financials

Return on assets: (-7.2%)   Cash ($ mil.): 25
Return on equity: (-45.1%)
Current ratio: 2.60

BLUE BUFFALO PET PRODUCTS, INC.

Blue Buffalo makes natural dog and cat food using whole meats fruits and vegetables with no by-products or artificial ingredients; some products are also grain-free. The company's products undergo a robust formulation manufacturing and testing process to ensure they are safe effective and compliant with all nutrient requirements outlined by AAFCO and the Global Nutrition Committee of the World Small Animal Veterinary Association (WSAVA). BLUE's exclusive LifeSource Bits are "cold-formed" to minimize heat exposure which can degrade the potency of many vitamins minerals antioxidants and enzymes. Blue Buffalo started in 2003.

IPO
Operations
Blue Buffalo operates its business in one reportable segment. It makes seven main lines of pet food covering different product types diet types breed sizes for dogs and life stages.

Geographic Reach
Blue Buffalo operates its business in one reportable segment. It makes seven main lines of pet food covering different product types diet types breed sizes for dogs and life stages.

Sales and Marketing
Blue Buffalo products are sold through its website and online retailers such as PetSmart Petco Chewy Target Walmart PetFlow and more.

EXECUTIVES

Pres, William Bishop Jr
Treas, Mike Nathenson
SEC, Larry Miller
V Pres, Kathryn K Garrison
V Pres, Gerald J Morris
Asst SEC, Robert B Polansky
Asst SEC, Benjamin A Backberg
Asst SEC, Christopher A Rauschl
Sr Director, Christian Setterlund
Board Member, Michael Eck
Board Member, Raymond Debbane
Auditors: KPMG LLP STAMFORD CONNECTICU

LOCATIONS

HQ: BLUE BUFFALO PET PRODUCTS, INC.
11 RIVER RD STE 103, WILTON, CT 068976011
Phone: 203 762-9751
Web: WWW.BLUEBUFFALO.COM

PRODUCTS/OPERATIONS

2017 Sales

	$ mil.	% of total
Dry foods	1,013	80
Wet foods treats and other	261	20
Total	**1,274**	**100**

Selected Product Lines
BLUE Life Protection Formula
BLUE Wilderness
BLUE Basics
BLUE Freedom
BLUE Natural Veterinary Diet

COMPETITORS

Big Heart Pet Brands	Ourpet's Co.
Breeder's Choice	Pet Supermarket
Hill's Pet Nutrition	Pet Valu
Iams	Procter & Gamble
Mars Incorporated	Royal Canin
Nestl © Purina Petcare	Simmons Foods
Nutro Products	Wellpet

HISTORICAL FINANCIALS

Company Type: Private

	REVENUE ($ mil.)	NET INCOME ($ mil.)	NET PROFIT MARGIN	EMPLOYEES
12/17	1,274	193	15.2%	1,800
12/16	1,149	130	11.3%	—
12/15	1,027	89	8.7%	—
Annual Growth	11.4%	47.1%	—	—

Income Statement — FYE: December 31

2017 Year-End Financials

Return on assets: 22.8%   Cash ($ mil.): 282
Return on equity: 64.7%
Current ratio: 3.70

BLUE CROSS & BLUE SHIELD ASSOCIATION

The Blue Cross and Blue Shield Association is a national federation of about 35 independent community-based and locally operated Blue Cross and Blue Shield companies that collectively provide health care coverage for one in three Americans across all 50 US states the District of Columbia and Puerto Rico. The association owns and manages the Blue Cross and Blue Shield trademarks and names in more than 170 countries. In addition the BCBS Federal Employee Program insures over 5.8 million federal employees retirees and their families. The company traces its roots back to 1929.

HISTORY

Blue Cross was born in 1929 when Baylor University official Justin Kimball offered schoolteachers 21 days of hospital care for $6 a year. A major plan feature was a community rating system that based premiums on the community claims experience rather than members' conditions.

The Blue Cross symbol was devised in 1933 by Minnesota plan executive E. A. van Steenwyck. By 1935 many of the 15 plans in 11 states used the symbol. Many states gave the plans not-for-profit status and in 1936 the American Hospital Association formed the Committee on Hospital Service (renamed the Blue Cross Association in 1948) to coordinate them.

As Blue Cross grew state medical societies sponsored prepaid plans to cover doctors' fees. In 1946 they united under the aegis of the American Medical Association (AMA) as the Associated Medical Care Plans (later the Association of Blue Shield Plans).

In 1948 the AMA thwarted a Blue Cross attempt to merge with Blue Shield. But the Blues increasingly cooperated on public policy matters while competing for members and each Blue formed a not-for-profit corporation to coordinate its plan's activities.

Blue Cross insured about a third of the US by 1960. Over the next decade the Blues started administering Medicare and other government health plans and by 1970 half of Blue Cross' premiums came from government entities.

In the 1970s the Blues adopted such cost-control measures as review of hospital admissions; many plans even abandoned the community rating system. Most began emphasizing preventive care in HMOs or PPOs. The two Blues finally merged in 1982 to form the Blue Cross and Blue Shield Association (BCBSA) but this had little effect on the associations' bottom lines as losses grew.

By the 1990s the Blues were big business. Some of the state associations offered officers high salaries and perks but still insisted on special regulatory treatment.

But as lower-cost plans attracted the hale and hearty the Blues' customers became older sicker and more expensive. With their quasi-charitable status and outdated rate structures many Blues plans lost market share.

The Blues fought back by updating their technology and rate structures merging among themselves creating for-profit subsidiaries forming alliances with for-profit enterprises or (in some cases) dropping their not-for-profit status and going public — while still using the Blue Cross Blue Shield name.

Blue Cross of California became the first chapter to give up its tax-free status when it was bought

---

by WellPoint Health Networks a managed care subsidiary it had founded in 1992. In a 1996 deal WellPoint became the chapter's parent and converted it to for-profit status assigning all of the stock to a public charitable foundation which received the proceeds of its subsequent IPO. WellPoint also bought the group life and health division of Massachusetts Mutual Life Insurance.

The for-profit switches picked up in 1997. Blue Cross of Connecticut merged with insurance provider Anthem and other mergers followed. Half the nation's Blues formed an alliance called BluesCONNECT (now BlueCard) competing with national health plans by offering employers one nationwide benefits organization. BCBSA also pursued overseas licensing agreements in Europe South America and Asia assembling a network of Blue Cross-friendly caregivers aiming for worldwide coverage.

In 1998 Blues in more than 35 states sued the nation's big cigarette companies to recoup costs of treating smoking-related illnesses. In a separate lawsuit Blue Cross and Blue Shield of Minnesota received nearly $300 million from the tobacco industry. In 1999 Anthem moved to acquire or affiliate with Blues in Colorado Maine Nevada and New Hampshire.

After years of discussions in 2000 the New York attorney general permitted Empire Blue Cross and Blue Shield to convert to for-profit status. The pace of for-profit conversions slowed down in following years however as state regulators became increasingly wary of signing off on the procedure. The improved financial situation of most of the not-for-profit Blues also took away a key incentive for for-profit conversion — access to capital markets.

In 2004 Anthem and WellPoint Health Networks merged and Anthem's name changed to Wellpoint (though it continued to use the Anthem brand name in certain markets) becoming the largest for-profit health insurer in the nation. WellPoint acquired Empire Blue Cross and its parent WellChoice as well as non-Blue consumer-driven plan provider Lumenos in 2005. In addition to snapping up Blues providers the for-profit WellPoint acquired a number of non-Blue subsidiaries such as American Imaging Management while meeting the requirement that it get two-thirds of its insurance revenue from Blue products to keep its BCBSA license. (Wellpoint changed its name back to Anthem in 2012.)

Consolidation among Blues plans continued when Health Care Service Corporation added its fourth not-for-profit Blues plan (Blue Cross and Blue Shield of Oklahoma) in 2005.

In 2007 BCBSA was approved under a Federal Savings Bank charter to provide health-related banking services through its Blue Healthcare Bank.

Two licensees Highmark and Independence Blue Cross had agreed to merge in 2008 but the deal was terminated in early 2009 after long delays and heavy regulatory concern that the merger would create an unfair advantage in the Pennsylvania market. Some consolidation continued however as Triple-S which operates under the Blue Shield brand in Puerto Rico acquired and absorbed Blue Cross licensee La Cruz Azul from Independence Blue Cross in 2009.

Highmark reached a formal affiliation agreement (including shared administrative and IT resources) with Blue Cross Blue Shield of Delaware in 2011.

Another regional Blues provider Cambia Health Solutions (formerly Regence Group) changed its name in 2011 to signify its diversification efforts though its BCBS subsidiaries continue to operate under the Regence name.

Three Blues companies — Anthem Health Care Service Corp. (HCSC) and BCBS of Michigan— joined together in 2011 to invest in a commercial insurance exchange (Bloom Health) designed to allow businesses to contribute to employees' selected health coverage. The venture was part of the Blues' efforts to meet the changing US insurance needs under health reform laws.

BCBSA launched a new wellness rewards program for FEP participants in 2012.

EXECUTIVES

Ceo, Kim A Keck
Chb*, Tim Vines
V Pres*, Catherine Peper
Chief Clinical Transformation*, Adam Myers
Vp Business Informatics and Bi, Shirley S Lady
Chief Officer, Nextgen, Sarah T Corley
Coordinator, Cordelia Henry
Executive Assistant, David Dupre
Administration Executive, Deanna Salazar
Manager, Diona Hughes
Manager, Elizabeth Hannigan
Auditors: PRICEWATERHOUSECOOPERS LLP PH

LOCATIONS

HQ: BLUE CROSS & BLUE SHIELD ASSOCIATION
225 N MICHIGAN AVE FL 5, CHICAGO, IL 606017658
Phone: 312 297-6000
Web: WWW.BCBS.COM

PRODUCTS/OPERATIONS

Selected Blue Cross and Blue Shield Licensees
Arkansas Blue Cross and Blue Shield
Blue Cross and Blue Shield of Alabama
Blue Cross and Blue Shield of Arizona
Blue Cross and Blue Shield of Delaware
Blue Cross and Blue Shield of Florida
Blue Cross and Blue Shield of Kansas
Blue Cross and Blue Shield of Kansas City
Blue Cross and Blue Shield of Louisiana
Blue Cross and Blue Shield of Massachusetts
Blue Cross and Blue Shield of Michigan
Blue Cross and Blue Shield of Minnesota
Blue Cross and Blue Shield of Mississippi
Blue Cross and Blue Shield of Montana
Blue Cross and Blue Shield of Nebraska
Blue Cross and Blue Shield of North Carolina
Blue Cross and Blue Shield of North Dakota
Blue Cross and Blue Shield of Rhode Island
Blue Cross and Blue Shield of South Carolina
Blue Cross and Blue Shield of Tennessee
Blue Cross and Blue Shield of Vermont
Blue Cross and Blue Shield of Wyoming
Blue Cross of Idaho Health Service
Blue Cross of Northeastern Pennsylvania
California Physicians' Service (dba Blue Shield of California)
Cambia Health Solutions Inc. (formerly The Regence Group)
  Regence BlueCross and BlueShield of Oregon
  Regence BlueCross BlueShield of Utah
  Regence BlueShield of Idaho
  Regence BlueShield (Washington)
Capital BlueCross (Pennsylvania)
CareFirst
  CareFirst Blue Cross and Blue Shield (District of Columbia)
  CareFirst Blue Cross and Blue Shield of Maryland
Excellus BlueCross BlueShield of New York
Hawaii Medical Service Association
Health Care Service Corporation
  Blue Cross and Blue Shield of Illinois
  Blue Cross and Blue Shield of New Mexico
  Blue Cross and Blue Shield of Oklahoma
  Blue Cross and Blue Shield of Texas
HealthNow New York
  BlueCross and BlueShield of Western New York
  BlueShield of Northeastern New York
Highmark Blue Cross Blue Shield (Pennsylvania)
  Mountain State Blue Cross and Blue Shield (West Virginia)
Horizon Healthcare Services (dba Horizon Blue Cross and Blue Shield of New Jersey)
Independence Blue Cross (Pennsylvania)
Premera Blue Cross (Alaska and Washington)

Triple-S (Puerto Rico)
Wellmark
  Wellmark Blue Cross and Blue Shield of Iowa
  Wellmark Blue Cross and Blue Shield of South Dakota
WellPoint
  Anthem Blue Cross and Blue Shield of Colorado
  Anthem Blue Cross and Blue Shield of Connecticut
  Anthem Blue Cross and Blue Shield of Indiana
  Anthem Blue Cross and Blue Shield of Kentucky
  Anthem Blue Cross and Blue Shield of Maine
  Anthem Blue Cross and Blue Shield of Nevada
  Anthem Blue Cross and Blue Shield of New Hampshire
  Anthem Blue Cross and Blue Shield of Ohio
  Anthem Blue Cross and Blue Shield of Virginia
  Blue Cross and Blue Shield of Georgia
  Blue Cross and Blue Shield of Missouri (dba Anthem Blue Cross and Blue Shield)
  BlueCross BlueShield of Wisconsin (dba Anthem Blue Cross and Blue Shield)
  California Blue Cross (Anthem Blue Cross)
  Empire Blue Cross and Blue Shield of New York
International plans
  Blue Cross & Blue Shield de Uruguay
  BlueCross BlueShield of Panama

COMPETITORS

Amerigroup	Kaiser Foundation
Aetna	Health Plan
Cigna	Molina Healthcare
Centene	Principal Financial
Health Net	Unitedhealth Group
Humana	Wellcare Health Plans

HISTORICAL FINANCIALS

Company Type: Private

Income Statement				FYE: December 31
	REVENUE ($ mil.)	**NET INCOME** ($ mil.)	**NET PROFIT MARGIN**	**EMPLOYEES**
12/17	591	(1)	—	1,880
12/06	320	14	4.5%	—
12/05	275	8	3.0%	—
12/04	270	11	4.3%	—
Annual Growth	6.2%	—	—	—

2017 Year-End Financials

Return on assets: (-0.2%)   Cash ($ mil.): 486
Return on equity: (-1.5%)
Current ratio: 1.00

BLUE CROSS AND BLUE SHIELD OF ARIZONA, INC.

Blue Cross Blue Shield of Arizona (BCBSAZ) provides health insurance products and services to more than 1.9 million Arizonans. The not-for-profit company offers a variety of managed care plans to small and large employer groups individuals and families including PPO HMO and high-deductible health plans. It also provides dental vision and prescription drug coverage as well as supplemental health plans for Medicare beneficiaries. Founded in 1933 the company is an independent licensee of the Blue Cross and Blue Shield Association.

Operations
Geographic Reach
BCBSAZ serves customers throughout the state of Arizona (headquarters) from its offices in Flagstaff Phoenix and Tucson.

Sales and Marketing
BCBSAZ offers insurance services to individuals and families seniors employers brokers and consultants and health care professionals through agents.
Strategy
In mid-2021 Blue Cross Blue Shield of Arizona (BCBSAZ) and Quartet Health (Quartet) joined forces to help increase access to mental health care in Arizona starting in Maricopa County. Quartet's technology platform will make it easier for patients with Blue Cross Blue Shield of Arizona health insurance to quickly connect with mental health care services including a therapist or psychiatrist.

This partnership extends Blue Cross Blue Shield of Arizona's commitment to improving the health and wellness of all Arizonans including an important focus on mental health. Through Quartet's secure virtual platform which proactively screens BCBSAZ members who may need care doctors in the network can seamlessly refer their adult patients to mental health care and offer access to timely appointments to in-network mental health providers. Working together BCBSAZ and Quartet aim to better address behavioral and mental health needs ? such as depression anxiety and substance use disorder ? many of which have increased during the COVID-19 pandemic.

EXECUTIVES

Chb, Gary L Trujillo
V Chb*, Bill Post
Pres-Ceo, Pam Kehaly
Sr V Pres-Cfo, Tony M Astorga CPA
Sr V Pres, H Jody Chandler
Sr V Pres, Richard M Hannon
V Pres-Treas, Kathryn Baker
Exec V Pres, Sandra Lee Gibson
Sr V Pres, Karen Abraham
Chief Medical Officer, Woodrow Myers Jr
Cgo, Paige Rothermel

LOCATIONS

HQ: BLUE CROSS AND BLUE SHIELD OF ARIZONA, INC.
2444 W LAS PALMARITAS DR, PHOENIX, AZ 850214860
Phone: 602 864-4100
Web: WWW.AZBLUE.COM

PRODUCTS/OPERATIONS

Selected Plans
Family and Individual Medical Plans
  BlueBasic Plus PPO
  BlueEssential Plus PPO
  BlueOptimum Plus PPO
  BluePortfolio Plus (high deductible PPO with HSA)
  BlueValue Plus PPO
  Medicare Part D
  Medicare Supplement
Group Medical Plans
  BlueAlliance benefit
  BluePreferred PPO
  BluePreferred HSA Plus (high deductable PPO with HSA)
  BlueSelect HMO
  Dental plans
  Eyewear plans
  GeoBlue Expat

COMPETITORS

Aetna	Southwest Catholic
Cigna Healthcare Of Arizona	Health Network
First Dental Health	Unitedhealth Group
Health Net	Western Dental
Humana	Services

Income Statement				FYE: December 31
	ASSETS ($ mil.)	NET INCOME ($ mil.)	INCOME AS % OF ASSETS	EMPLOYEES
12/09	1,059	64	6.1%	1,278
12/08	975	71	7.4%	—
Annual Growth	8.6%	(9.9%)	—	—

BLUE TEE CORP.

Handling a variety of steel products and scrap materials suits Blue Tee to a tee. The holding company which operates through two primary subsidiaries distributes steel building materials and scrap metal. Blue Tee's Brown-Strauss Steel subsidiary is one of the largest distributors of wide flange beam and structural steel products (beams pipe and tubing) in North America. The metal distributor's other primary business is Azcon a leading scrap processor broker and mill services management company which handles scrap metal sales rail cars and other steel parts.

Operations

Azcon is a major scrap processor broker and mill services management company. Brown-Strauss Steel distributes steel products.

Azcon buys collects warehouses and distributes a wide variety of rail and track accessories for the railroad industry across North America. Its core businesses include Processing Yard Mill Scrap Management and Brokerage. Other product lines include Relaying and Re-rolling Rail Railroad Equipment and Railroad Parts.

Brown-Strauss Steel's focus is on the distribution of new steel (wide flange beam and structural steel tubing) across the US.

Geographic Reach

The company has major offices in Denver Kansas City Longview (Washington) New York City Phoenix Salt Lake City and Stockton and Fontana (California). It has additional locations in Alton Chicago and Sterling (Illinois); Austin Texas; Duluth Minnesota; and Sharpsburg Pennsylvania.

In Canada Blue Tee has offices in Edmonton Calgary Grande Prairie Grimshaw Kamloops Prince George and Red Deer.

Sales and Marketing

Blue Tee serves a range of industries including construction forestry road building mining farming power oil and gas solid waste water waste management highway transportation environmental and groundwater monitoring.

Strategy

The company is focusing its resources developing Azcon and Brown-Strauss Steel. Brown-Strauss is looking to grow its product offerings to include structural tubing; it also plans to expand its facilities. In this regard in 2012 Blue Tee Corp (through Brown-Strauss) purchased a 69190 sq. ft. industrial building in Aurora Colorado from The Lowenberg Corp. for $6 million.

Company Background

Blue Tee is owned by its employees through an employee stock ownership plan.

In 2011 Blue Tee divested subsidiaries GEFCO (an OEM of portable drilling rigs and other industrial equipment) and STECO (transfer and dump-truck trailers) to Astec Industries for about $30.8 million.

The move to axe its GEFCO and STECO subsidiaries followed another sale. Blue Tee sold its pump parts subsidiary Texas-based Standard Alloys to German pump manufacturer KSB in mid-2010.

The Blue Tee holding company was founded in 1986. Azcon was formed in 1863 and Brown-Strauss Steel was established in 1905.

EXECUTIVES

Pres-Ceo, William M Kelly
Sr V Pres-Cfo-Chb, David P Alldian
Exec Dir, Annette Marino D'Arienzo
Real Estate Conultant, Cristina Hungria
Controller, Thomas Caruso
Auditors: DELOITTE & TOUCHE LLP NEW YO

LOCATIONS

HQ: BLUE TEE CORP.
387 PARK AVE S FL 5, NEW YORK, NY 100161495
Phone: 212 598-0880
Web: WWW.BLUETEE.COM

PRODUCTS/OPERATIONS

Selected Subsidiaries

Azcon Corporation (ferrous and nonferrous scrap; rail cars locomotives and parts; relay and reroll rail)
Brown-Strauss Steel (steel distribution including angles beams channels pipe and tubing)

Selected Azcon Services

Barge Services
Brokerage Services
Demolition Services
Foundries - Scrap Management
Industrial Plants - Scrap Management
Mill Service
Mine Services
Railroad Industry Services
Steel Mills - Scrap Management

Selected Brown-Strauss Steel Products and Services

Products:
Structural Angle
Structural Channels
Structural Pipe
Structural Tubing
Wide Flange Beams

Services:
Cambering
Inventory Stocking program
Length/cutting optimization program
Mill Brokerage
Saw Cutting
Track Torch Cutting

COMPETITORS

A. M. Castle	Reliance Steel
Api Group	Russel Metals
Dover Corp.	Ryerson
Metals Usa	Ttx
Omnisource	Wescast Industries
Pacesetter Steel	

HISTORICAL FINANCIALS

Company Type: Private

Income Statement				FYE: December 31
	REVENUE ($ mil.)	NET INCOME ($ mil.)	NET PROFIT MARGIN	EMPLOYEES
12/10	809	14	1.8%	900
12/09	564	(10)	—	—
12/08	1,549	33	2.1%	—
Annual Growth	(27.7%)	(34.4%)	—	—

2010 Year-End Financials

Return on assets: 3.7% Cash ($ mil.): 8
Return on equity: 8.2%
Current ratio: 2.10

BNSF RAILWAY COMPANY

BNSF Railway operates one of the largest railroad networks in North America. A wholly-owned subsidiary of Burlington Northern Santa Fe itself a unit of Berkshire Hathaway the company provides freight transportation over a network of about 32500 route miles of track across some 30 US states and three provinces in Canada. BNSF Railway owns or leases a fleet of about 8000 locomotives. It also has some 25 intermodal facilities that help to transport agricultural consumer and industrial products as well as coal. In addition to major cities and ports BNSF Railway serves smaller markets in alliance with short-line partners.

Operations

BNSF Railway transports a wide range of products and commodities through its four main product segments.

The Consumer Products segment generates about 35% of revenue and consists of the Domestic Intermodal International Intermodal and Automotive business units. The Industrial Products segment provides about 25% of revenue and comprises five business units: Construction Products Petroleum Products Building Products Chemicals and Plastics Products and Food and Beverages.

Agricultural Products represents 20% of revenue and includes the transportation of commodities like corn wheat ethanol soybeans fertilizer oil seeds flour and other grains. The Coal business (less than 20%) is primarily BNSF's operations that originate from the Powder River Basin of Wyoming and Montana.

The company also generates about 5% of revenue from its wholly-owned non-rail logistics subsidiary BSNF Logistics LLC through logistics and transportation services such as storage as well as demurrage (detention fees for delays in loading and unloading of freight).

Geographic Reach

Headquartered in Fort Worth TX BNSF Railway's network spreads across about 30 US states and three Canadian provinces.

Sales and Marketing

BNSF Railway serves smaller markets by working closely with 200 shortline partners. It also forms marketing agreements with other rail carriers expanding the marketing reach for each railroad and its customers.

Financial Performance

BNSF has seen steady growth in recent years with revenue reaching $23.9 billion in 2018 a 12% increase compared with $21.4 billion in 2017. The increase in 2018 was mainly due to increased volume and increased rates per car as well as tight truck capacity in the transportation sector which converted some business from highway to rail.

Net income however plummeted to $5.2 billion less than half that of the previous year. This was primarily due to an increased tax liability as a result of the Tax Cuts and Jobs Act.

Cash at the end of fiscal 2018 was $2.0 billion about the same as the prior year. Cash from operations contributed $7.9 billion to the coffers while investing activities used $3.2 billion mainly for capital expenditures related to equipment purchases. Financing activities used another $4.7 billion primarily for cash distributions to its parent company.

Strategy

BNSF plans capital spending of about $3.5 billion in 2019 for network maintenance and replacement of assets to ensure safe and reliable operations. These include expansion and efficiency projects focused on key growth areas along its Southern and Northern Trancon routes. The company faces challenges in its supply chain environment with competition from improving productivity in the trucking industry. Another hurdle is consumers' expectations for quicker and quicker delivery as online shopping continues to grow. In response BSNF is focusing on providing consistent reliable and efficient transportation services to its customers.

Company Background

BNSF's traces its roots to 1849 when the Aurora Branch Railroad was founded in Illinois with 12 miles of track. Over the years additional rail lines were built including Atchison Topeka & Santa Fe;Burlington Northern; Chicago Burlington & Quincy; Frisco; Great Northern; Northern Pacific; and Spokane Portland & Seattle.

BNSF was created in 1995 when Burlington Northern Inc. (the parent company of Burlington Northern Railroad) merged with Santa Fe Pacific Corporation (parent company of the Atchison Topeka & Santa Fe Railway). The company was acquired by Berkshire Hathaway in 2010 and BNSF now operates as a subsidiary of that company.

EXECUTIVES

Ceo, Kathryn Farmer
Pres*, Carl R Ice
Exec Chb*, Matthew K Rose
Exec V Pres-Cfo*, Julie A Piggott
V Pres-Cao-Contrl*, Jon I Stevens
Vp-Chief Sourcing Officer*, Andrew Ruiz
Director, Alan Boeckmann
Vice President, Dannis Johnson
Executive Vice President Law, Jeffrey Moreland
Executive Director, Peter Skosey
Director of Sales, Aaron Lakey
Auditors: DELOITTE & TOUCHE LLP FORT WO

LOCATIONS

HQ: BNSF RAILWAY COMPANY
2650 LOU MENK DR, FORT WORTH, TX 761312830
Phone: 800 795-2673
Web: WWW.BNSF.COM

PRODUCTS/OPERATIONS

2018 Sales

	$ mil.	% of total
Consumer Products	7,902	33
Industrial Products	5,967	25
Agricultural Products	4,697	20
Coal	4,012	17
Other revenues	1,277	5
Total	**23,855**	**100**

COMPETITORS

Csx	Kansas City Southern
Canadian National	Railway
Railway	Norfolk Southern
Canadian Pacific	Union Pacific Railroad
Railway	

HISTORICAL FINANCIALS
Company Type: Private

Income Statement				FYE: December 31
	REVENUE ($ mil.)	NET INCOME ($ mil.)	NET PROFIT MARGIN	EMPLOYEES
12/17	20,747	12,119	58.4%	41,000
12/16	19,278	4,260	22.1%	—
12/14	22,714	4,397	19.4%	—
12/13	21,552	4,271	19.8%	—
Annual Growth	(0.9%)	29.8%	—	—

2017 Year-End Financials

Return on assets: 14.6%   Cash ($ mil.): 516
Return on equity: 19.3%
Current ratio: 1.00

BOARD OF EDUCATION FOR THE CITY OF SAVANNAH AND THE COUNTY OF CHATHAM (INC)

EXECUTIVES

Pres, Jolene Byrne
Contrl, Beth Stanford
Auditors: KRT CPAS PC SAVANNAH GEORG

LOCATIONS

HQ: BOARD OF EDUCATION FOR THE CITY OF SAVANNAH AND THE COUNTY OF CHATHAM (INC)
208 BULL ST, SAVANNAH, GA 314013843
Phone: 912 395-1000
Web: WWW.SAVANNAH.COM

HISTORICAL FINANCIALS
Company Type: Private

Income Statement				FYE: June 30
	REVENUE ($ mil.)	NET INCOME ($ mil.)	NET PROFIT MARGIN	EMPLOYEES
06/20	587	41	7.1%	4,781
06/19	569	86	15.2%	—
06/18	525	41	7.8%	—
06/17	500	(30)	—	—
Annual Growth	5.5%	—	—	—

2020 Year-End Financials

Return on assets: 3.1%   Cash ($ mil.): 117
Return on equity: 9.0%
Current ratio: 2.30

BOARD OF EDUCATION OF CITY OF CHICAGO

EXECUTIVES

Pres, Frank Clark
Technology, James V Dispensa
Coordinator, Samantha Treworgy
Auditors: MCGLADREY LLP CHICAGO ILLINO

LOCATIONS

HQ: BOARD OF EDUCATION OF CITY OF CHICAGO
42 W MADISON ST FL 2, CHICAGO, IL 606024309
Phone: 773 553-1600
Web: WWW.CPSBOE.ORG

HISTORICAL FINANCIALS
Company Type: Private

Income Statement				FYE: June 30
	REVENUE ($ mil.)	NET INCOME ($ mil.)	NET PROFIT MARGIN	EMPLOYEES
06/16	5,272	(381)	—	852
06/12	5,760	324	5.6%	—
06/11	5,660	238	4.2%	—
06/08	17	(0)	—	—
Annual Growth	103.8%	—	—	—

BOARD OF EDUCATION- MEMPHIS CITY SCHOOLS

LOCATIONS

HQ: BOARD OF EDUCATION-MEMPHIS CITY SCHOOLS
160 S HOLLYWOOD ST, MEMPHIS, TN 381124801
Phone: 901 416-5300

HISTORICAL FINANCIALS
Company Type: Private

Income Statement				FYE: June 30
	REVENUE ($ mil.)	NET INCOME ($ mil.)	NET PROFIT MARGIN	EMPLOYEES
06/13	1,157	(12)	—	12,015
06/12	1,169	(2)	—	—
06/11*	1,173	(5)	—	—
12/09	449	(64)	—	—
Annual Growth	37.1%	—	—	—
*Fiscal year change				

2013 Year-End Financials

Return on assets: —   Cash ($ mil.): 177
Return on equity: (-1.1%)
Current ratio: —

BOARD OF PUBLIC EDUCATION SCHOOL DISTRICT OF PITTSBURGH (INC)

EXECUTIVES

Pres, Thomas Sumpter
SEC*, Cindy Polis
Coordinator, Susan Chersky
Budget Analyst, Leslie Payne
Chief Financial Officer, Ronald Joseph
Teacher, Alecia Adams
Special Education Supervisor, Allen Dealyn
Librarian, Amber Marchewka

School Secretary, Amy Jones
Computer Support Specialist, Andy Perhach
Teacher, Angela Morello
Auditors: MAHER DUESSEL PITTSBURGH PEN

LOCATIONS

HQ: BOARD OF PUBLIC EDUCATION SCHOOL
DISTRICT OF PITTSBURGH (INC)
341 S BELLEFIELD AVE, PITTSBURGH, PA
152133552
Phone: 412 622-3500
Web: WWW.PGHSCHOOLS.ORG

HISTORICAL FINANCIALS

Company Type: Private

Income Statement   FYE: December 31

	REVENUE ($ mil.)	NET INCOME ($ mil.)	NET PROFIT MARGIN	EMPLOYEES
12/14	631	13	2.1%	709
12/13	624	19	3.1%	—
12/12	613	3	0.6%	—
12/11	631	(14)	—	—
Annual Growth	(0.0%)	—	—	—

2014 Year-End Financials

Return on assets: 1.8%   Cash ($ mil.): 89
Return on equity: 4.9%
Current ratio: 2.70

BOARD OF REGENTS OF THE UNIVERSITY OF NEBRASKA

The University of Nebraska has sprouted four campuses out in the fields of the Cornhusker State. Founded in 1869 the university confers bachelor's master's and doctoral degrees in more than 200 majors including agriculture business education and engineering at its campuses in Kearney Lincoln and Omaha. The university's Medical Center in Omaha trains doctors performs research and is affiliated with a nearly 720-bed teaching hospital. The school also operates research and extension services across the state. More than 51420 students attend classes in the system that has a student-teacher ratio of about 17:1. It was founded as a land-grant university just two years after the Nebraska became a state.

Operations

Undergraduate and graduate students can find research opportunities in all six of colleges (arts and sciences business administration communication fine arts and media education information science & technology public affairs and community services). Its many research centers and labs provide a wealth of opportunity for students to work with faculty members who are known nationally for having expertise in their respective field. Agencies like the NIH US Department of Defense and NASA award millions of dollars to UNO annually.

Geographic Reach

The university campus size 856 acres and is located in Lincoln Nebraska.

Strategy

The resulting strategy is built around several key principles: the value of higher education is clear and growing; students come first; "our people are our greatest asset"; make the best use of every dollar; themes of equity and inclusion touch every-

thing the company does; and Nebraskans should know what to expect from their University.

EXECUTIVES

Chm, Timothy Clare
Pres*, James B Milliken
Prin*, Howard Hawks
SEC*, Carmen Maurer
Staff, Andrea L Chidress
Security Staff, Lynn M Doser
Project Coordinator, Sue E Ostrandr
Finance, Gordon V Karels
Security Staff, John R Folke
Vice Chancellor, Christine Jackson
Certified Public Accountant, David Lechner
Auditors: MARK AVERY CPA LINCOLN NEBR

LOCATIONS

HQ: BOARD OF REGENTS OF THE UNIVERSITY OF NEBRASKA
3835 HOLDREGE ST, LINCOLN, NE 685031435
Phone: 402 472-3906
Web: WWW.NEBRASKA.EDU

PRODUCTS/OPERATIONS

University Campuses

The University of Nebraska at Kearney
The University of Nebraska-Lincoln
The University of Nebraska Medical Center
The University of Nebraska at Omaha

HISTORICAL FINANCIALS

Company Type: Private

Income Statement   FYE: June 30

	REVENUE ($ mil.)	NET INCOME ($ mil.)	NET PROFIT MARGIN	EMPLOYEES
06/16	1,490	215	14.5%	15,200
06/15	1,405	221	15.8%	—
06/14	1,333	222	16.7%	—
06/13	1,313	254	19.4%	—
Annual Growth	4.3%	(5.4%)	—	—

2016 Year-End Financials

Return on assets: 4.3%   Cash ($ mil.): 613
Return on equity: 6.0%
Current ratio: 2.80

BOARD OF REGENTS OF THE UNIVERSITY SYSTEM OF GEORGIA

EXECUTIVES

Chancellor, Hank Huckaby
Director For Grants Accounting*, Jennifer Shaw
Coordinator, Taylor Smith
Coordinator, Charlotte Stauffer
Customer Representativ, Justina Washington
Administrative Coordinator, Blair Witte
Business Intelligence Technolo, Cherry Zhang
Ecampus Director, Christy Talley-Smith
Archival Manager, Kayla Barrett
Administrative Coordinator, Lameisha Estelle
Information Technology Client, Shay Brown
Auditors: GREG S GRIFFIN ATLANTA GEORG

LOCATIONS

HQ: BOARD OF REGENTS OF THE UNIVERSITY SYSTEM OF GEORGIA
270 WASHINGTON ST SW, ATLANTA, GA 303349056
Phone: 404 962-3050
Web: WWW.USG.EDU

HISTORICAL FINANCIALS

Company Type: Private

Income Statement   FYE: June 30

	REVENUE ($ mil.)	NET INCOME ($ mil.)	NET PROFIT MARGIN	EMPLOYEES
06/20	5,523	(116)	—	40,000
06/19	5,532	426	7.7%	—
06/18	5,210	221	4.3%	—
06/17	5,100	57	1.1%	—
Annual Growth	2.7%	—	—	—

2020 Year-End Financials

Return on assets: (-0.8%)   Cash ($ mil.): 1,628
Return on equity: (-6.0%)
Current ratio: 3.10

BOARD OF TRUSTEES OF STATE INSTITUTIONS OF HIGHER LEARNING

EXECUTIVES

Comm'r, Hank Bounds
Coordinator, Tonya Neely
Security Staff, Ivy Babb
Director, Jim Steil
Senior Designer, Pete Halverson
Marketing Team Member, Holly Johnson
Data, Kathy Burgess
Director, Pete Walley
Administrative Assistant, Sharon Scott
Assistant To Director, Carlton McGrone
Director, Caron Blanton
Auditors: CLIFTONLARSONALLEN LLP BALTI

LOCATIONS

HQ: BOARD OF TRUSTEES OF STATE INSTITUTIONS OF HIGHER LEARNING
3825 RIDGEWOOD RD, JACKSON, MS 392116453
Phone: 601 432-6198
Web: WWW.MISSISSIPPI.EDU

HISTORICAL FINANCIALS

Company Type: Private

Income Statement   FYE: June 30

	REVENUE ($ mil.)	NET INCOME ($ mil.)	NET PROFIT MARGIN	EMPLOYEES
06/20	2,752	41	1.5%	65
06/19	2,720	103	3.8%	—
06/18	2,588	(5)	—	—
06/17	2	0	1.1%	—
Annual Growth	929.1%	1044.4%	—	—

2020 Year-End Financials

Return on assets: 0.6%   Cash ($ mil.): 881
Return on equity: 1.9%
Current ratio: 2.50

BOARDRIDERS, INC.

Boardriders rides the wave of youth appeal. Formerly Quiksilver the company caters to the young and athletic with surfwear snowboardwear sportswear and swimwear sold under the Quiksilver Billabong Element VonZipper and Roxy names among others. It also owns the DC Shoes brand of footwear and apparel for young men and juniors. It sells its apparel footwear and accessories in specialty and department stores worldwide as well as through its own network of about 570 retail stores. It emerged from Chapter 11 bankruptcy protection in 2016 and is now owned by Oaktree Capital Management; in 2018 it bought rival Billabong.

Operations
Boardriders operate in over 55 countries with 15 flagship stores 570 retails stores over 7000 wholesale accounts and Ecom Platforms in 35 countries.

Geographic Reach
Boardriders has a presence in more than 55 countries; it has e-commerce capabilities in over 35 countries with around 570 retail stores. The company's global and Americas headquarters is located in Huntington Beach California.

Sales and Marketing
Financial Performance
Strategy
Boardriders owns a portfolio of the leading brands in surf and sportswear including Quiksilver DC Shoes Element and Billabong. The company is dedicated to preserving and promoting each of these distinctive historic brands.

The company is focused on maintaining its strong global retail footprint with its concept stores. These stores exist as a hub for the community with art entertainment food and drinks skateparks and barber shops. The company's concept stores are located near iconic surf spots around the world and offers good food cold drinks and all its well-loved products. Places where Boardriders has concept stores outside of the US include France Spain Russia and Portugal.

HISTORY

Australian surfers Alan Green and John Law started Quiksilver in 1969 to make "boardshorts" for surfers. In 1976 surfers Jeff Hakman and Bob McKnight bought the US rights to the Quiksilver name — Hakman displayed his enthusiasm for the line by eating a doily at a dinner with Green — and established Quiksilver USA. The firm went public in 1986.

The recession of the early 1990s and the dominance of grunge as the fashion du jour hurt Quiksilver and prompted it to restructure. It acquired French affiliate Na Pali in 1991 and began building its European operations. To gain surer footing in the fickle teen fashion market Quiksilver broadened its product offerings. It added the Roxy women's swimwear line in 1991 expanding it to clothing in 1993. It also launched the Boardriders Club concept — stores featuring Quiksilver merchandise but owned by independent retailers. In 1994 the company acquired swimwear maker The Raisin Company. In 1997 Quiksilver began advertising nationally and entered the snowboard market buying Mervin Manufacturing maker of Lib Technologies Gnu and Bent Metal snowboard products.

With its women's lines making waves and a strong current from European sales Quiksilver began opening its own Boardriders Club stores in 1998. In 1999 it launched the Quik Jeans and Roxy Jeans denim lines and the next year it added the Alex Goes line for women 25 to 40. Riding a tide of rising profits in 2000 the company acquired Fidra men's golf apparel; Freestyle the European licensee of rival youth wear label Gotcha; and pro-skateboarder Tony Hawk's apparel and accessories business. In a tail-that-wags-the-dog move the company bought its progenitor Quiksilver International the same year; in doing so Quiksilver gained sole possession of the Quiksilver name worldwide.

In June 2002 Quiksilver launched Quiksilver Entertainment a production company that creates actionsport-based programming for the entertainment industry. Later that year Quiksilver acquired Ug Manufacturing in Australia and Quiksilver Japan in an effort to gain control over nearly all its global business with the exception of a few licenses in small niche markets. At about the same time the company purchased and integrated Beach Street the owner and operator of 26 Quiksilver outlet stores.

The company formed a 50-50 joint venture in 2003 with Glorious Sun Enterprises to expand into China.

Quiksilver's entertainment unit in 2004 launched an actionsport film distribution company Union which is a supplier to more than 1000 retail locations in Australia China Europe Japan and the US. In 2004 Quiksilver completed its purchase of DC Shoes and bought the footwear firm's Canadian distributor Centre Skateboard Distribution in 2005. The footwear company's popularity in the skate and surf community serves to embed Quiksilver further in that market while ensuring its ability to compete with Nike and adidas in the footwear arena.

In 2005 Quiksilver flipped its board in a new direction however and broadened its reach into the mainstream. The company announced it has signed an exclusive licensing deal with Kohl's and Tony Hawk to give traction to its apparel outerwear and accessories. As part of the agreement Quiksilver will continue to design the Tony Hawk clothing brand and Kohl's will do the rest including sourcing distributing marketing and other functions.

Quiksilver exited the sports equipment manufacturing business in November 2008 when it sold its Rossignol unit.

It emerged from Chapter 11 bankruptcy protection in 2016 and changed its name to Boardriders.

EXECUTIVES

Ceo, Arne Arens
Pres, Greg Healy
Cfo-Int Pres Emea, Thomas Chambolle
Cro, Stephen Coulombe
Evp, Carol Scherman
Evp, Danny Kwock
SEC, Nicole Hall
Pres, American Region, Nate Smith
Pres Comm Strat & Growth, Shannan North
Assistant Sales Representative, Dalton Parker
Sales Associate, Nichole Ruiz
Auditors: DELOITTE & TOUCHE LLP COSTA M

LOCATIONS

HQ: BOARDRIDERS, INC.
5600 ARGOSY AVE STE 100, HUNTINGTON BEACH, CA 926491063
Phone: 714 889-5404
Web: WWW.BOARDRIDERS.COM

PRODUCTS/OPERATIONS

Selected Brands
Billabong
DC Shoes
Element
Kustom
Palmers
Quiksilver
Roxy
RVCA
VonZipper
Xcel

COMPETITORS

Abercrombie & Fitch	Nautica Apparel
Bleach Group	Oakley
Body Glove	Skullcandy
Burton	Sole Technology
Calvin Klein	St ssy
Columbia Sportswear	Tecnica
Fubu	Tommy Hilfiger
Fat Face	Under Armour
Foot Locker	Vf Corporation
Head N.v.	Volcom
Levi Strauss	Warnaco Swimwear
Nike	Adidas

HISTORICAL FINANCIALS

Company Type: Private

Income Statement   FYE: October 31

	REVENUE ($ mil.)	NET INCOME ($ mil.)	NET PROFIT MARGIN	EMPLOYEES
10/14	1,570	(320)	—	600
10/13	1,810	(233)	—	—
10/12	2,013	(9)	—	—
Annual Growth	(11.7%)	—	—	—

2014 Year-End Financials

Return on assets: (-25.5%)   Cash ($ mil.): 46
Return on equity: (-556.7%)
Current ratio: 2.10

BON SECOURS MERCY HEALTH, INC.

Bon Secours Mercy Health is one of the 20 largest health systems in the US and the fifth-largest Catholic health system in the country. The ministry's quality compassionate care is provided by more than 60000 associates serving communities in Florida Kentucky Maryland New York Ohio South Carolina Virginia and throughout Ireland.

Operations
Bon Secours Mercy Health operates in 50 hospitals with 60000 associates including some 3000 providers in the US and 450 consultants in Ireland.

Geographic Reach
Bon Secours Mercy Health has hospitals in Florida Kentucky Maryland New York Ohio South Carolina Virginia and Ireland.

Strategy
In mid-2021 Trilliant Health a health care analytics company that helps providers develop strategies for increasing market share growth and predicting consumer preferences to improve patient experience announced it has added Bon Secours Mercy Health as a strategic growth investor. The investment will help the company accelerate the development of its predictive analytics platform and joins previous investments made by Primus Capital Providence Ventures Martin Ventures Noro-Moseley Partners and Nashville Capital Network.

As part of the investment Deepesh Chandra chief analytics officer at Bon Secours Mercy Health will join Trilliant Health's Board of Directors as an observer.

EXECUTIVES

Pres-Ceo, John M Starcher Jr
Coo, Brian Smith
Chief Clinical Officer, Wael Haidar
Chief Strategy Officer, David Cannady
Cpho, Jean Haynes
Chief Digital Officer, Jason Szczuk
Chief Diversified Growth Offic, Andre Maksimow
Director Diagnostic, Mary Burleigh
Administrative Director of Cli, Michelle Hafner
Neurologist, Stacey Epps
Administrator, Stacy Guzik
Auditors: KPMG LLP CINCINNATI OHIO

LOCATIONS

HQ: BON SECOURS MERCY HEALTH, INC.
1701 MERCY HEALTH PL, CINCINNATI, OH
452376147
Phone: 513 952-5000
Web: WWW.BSMHEALTH.ORG

Selected Facilities

Florida
Bon Secours St. Petersburg Health System
Bon Secours - Maria Manor Nursing Care and
   Rehabilitation Center
Bon Secours Place at St. Petersburg
Bon Secours St. Petersburg Home Care Services
Kentucky
Bon Secours Kentucky Health System
Our Lady of Bellefonte Hospital (Ashland)
Maryland
Bon Secours Baltimore Health System
Bon Secours Hospital
Bon Secours Washington Village
Community Institute of Behavioral Sciences
Hollins Terrace/Benet House
New York
Bon Secours Charity Health System
Bon Secours Community Hospital (Port Jervis)
Good Samaritan Hospital (Suffern)
St. Anthony Community Hospital (Warwick)
Bon Secours New York Health System
Schervier Nursing Care Center (Riverdale)
Pennsylvania
Altoona Regional Health System (joint venture)
South Carolina
Bon Secours St. Francis Health System Inc.
St. Francis Hospital (Downtown and Eastside
   Campuses Greenville)
Roper St. Francis Healthcare (Charleston joint
   venture)
Virginia
Bon Secours Hampton Roads Health System
Bon Secours Maryview Nursing Care Center (Suffolk)
DePaul Medical Center (Norfolk)
Mary Immaculate Hospital (Newport News)
Maryview Medical Center (Portsmouth)
Province Place (Norfolk and Portsmouth)
St. Francis Nursing Care Center (Newport News)
Bon Secours Richmond Health System (joint venture)
Memorial Regional Medical Center (Mechanicsville)
Richmond Community Hospital
St. Francis Medical Center (Midlothian)
St. Mary's Hospital (Richmond)

Selected Affiliations

Cosponsoring Congregational Relationships
   Bernardine Sisters of the Third Order of St. Francis
   (Newport News Virginia)
   Sisters of Charity of Saint Elizabeth of Convent
   Station (New Jersey and New York)
Affiliated Organizations
   Health Corporation of Virginia (Richmond)
   Medical Society of South Carolina and Carolinas
   Health Care System (Charleston)
   Life Care Services (Florida and Virginia)

PRODUCTS/OPERATIONS

2014 Sales

	$ mil.	% of total
Net Patient Service Revenue	3,328	96
Other revenue	133	4
Total	**3,461**	**100**

COMPETITORS

Adventist Healthcare
Albany Medical Center
Albert Einstein
   Healthcare Network
Appalachian Regional
   Healthcare
Carilion Clinic
Catholic Health
   Initiatives
Centra Health Inc.
Christiana Care
Community Health
   Systems
Conemaugh Health
   System
Franklin Square
   Hospital Center
Gbmc
Hca

Highlands Health
Inova
Johns Hopkins Medicine
Medstar Health
Medisys Health Network
New York City Health
   And Hospitals
Novant Health
Riverside Health
   System (virginia)
Sentara Healthcare
St. Agnes Healthcare
University Of Maryland
   Medical System
University Of Miami
   Hospital
Upstate Affiliate
Virginia Hospital
   Center

HISTORICAL FINANCIALS

Company Type: Private

Income Statement   FYE: December 31

	REVENUE ($ mil.)	NET INCOME ($ mil.)	NET PROFIT MARGIN	EMPLOYEES
12/20	9,969	609	6.1%	19,000
12/19*	8,717	2,593	29.7%	—
08/10	3,084	(41)	—	—
08/09	2,895	(291)	—	—
Annual Growth 11.9%		—	—	—

*Fiscal year change

BONNEVILLE POWER ADMINISTRATION

Bonneville Power Administration (BPA) keeps the lights on in the Pacific Northwest. The US Department of Energy power marketing agency operates a transmission grid (with more than 15000 miles of high-voltage lines) that delivers about 30% of the electrical power consumed in the region. The electricity that BPA wholesales is generated primarily by around 30 federal hydroelectric dams (operated by the US Army Corp of Engineers) and one nonfederal nuclear facility and several small nonfederal power plants.

Operations

BPA operates and maintains about three-fourths of the high-voltage transmission in its service territory. It promotes energy efficiency renewable resources and new technologies. The agency also funds regional efforts to protect and rebuild fish and wildlife populations affected by hydroelectric power development in the Columbia River Basin.

Overall power accounts to about 70% of total sales transmission accounts for some 25% and US Treasury credits and others account for the rest.

Geographic Reach

Headquartered in Portland Oregon BPA's service territory includes Idaho Oregon Washington western Montana and small parts of eastern Montana California Nevada Utah and Wyoming.

Sales and Marketing

The company serves consumer-owned electric cooperatives municipalities public utility districts and tribal utilities.

It also sells wholesale power and transmission to entities that buy and sell non-federal power in the region in-region purchasers of federal power generators marketers and utilities that seek to transmit power into out of or through the region.

Financial Performance

BPA's 2019 revenue is similar to its 2018 revenue ($3.7 billion).

Cash and cash equivalents at the end of the year were $846.5 million 62% higher than in the previous year. Cash provided by operating activities was $972.3 million. Investing activities used $543.9 million primarily for Investment in utility plant including AFUDC while financing activities used $105.8 million primarily for repayment of borrowings from US Treasury.

Strategy

Technology and energy markets are changing rapidly impacting how BPA operates the transmission grid and hydropower plants it together with its federal partners are entrusted with managing. Its asset management program maximizes the value it derives from these and other assets including facilities and IT equipment. NIE is continually growing and updating its program to help maintain Bonneville's competitive edge in the marketplace enable industry change deliver on its public responsibilities and strengthen financial health by effectively managing asset lifecycle costs. This year NIE strengthened the tie between its strategic asset management plans and its financial planning process and it began implementing a common risk methodology to base all asset decisions on five dimensions of risk: financial reliability compliance safety and environmental.

It is also making significant headway in its effort to modernize BPA's systems and operations in response to new and changing markets. Out of a portfolio of 35 grid modernization projects six were completed this year three were completed in FY 2019 and all but one of the others are in flight. This work is essential for the agency to remain the region's wholesale power provider of choice by helping the company identify surplus capacity available on the power and transmission systems for additional sales manage grid congestion more efficiently and reliably and provide valuable insights into how best to invest in the system. Projects are already delivering significant value to BPA and our customers such as through a new program called One BPA Outage.

Company Background

In 2012 BPA bought electricity from a number of wind projects and had more than 4000 MW of wind power capacity tied in to its transmission grid. BPA harnessed and integrated about 6000 MW of wind power by the end of 2013.

BPA is also expanding its transmission grid building three new 500-kilovolt transmission lines to cater to expanding Columbia Gorge wind power. In this regard in 2011 the company began building a new high-voltage transmission line and substation (the Big Eddy-Knight Transmission Project) that would add more than 1150 MW of capacity to its transmission grid and accommodate new wind energy sources. In 2012 it completed a separate 79-mile $216-million line along the Columbia River east of the gorge.

BPA was founded in 1937.

EXECUTIVES

Ceo, John Hairston
Deputy ADM*, Steven G Hickok
Evp-Cfo*, Claudia Andrews
Coo*, Christine Hutchkin
Load Forecasting and Analysis,, Reed Davis
Dittmer Dispatch, Opera, Richard Ellison
Acting Vp Northwest Requiremen, Scott Coe
Transmission Scheduling, Trans, Sue Holden-Baker
Power Control Craftsman, Roger Peterson
Accounting/Auditing, Veronica Wittig
Auditors: PRICEWATERHOUSECOOPERS LLP PO

LOCATIONS

HQ: BONNEVILLE POWER ADMINISTRATION
905 NE 11TH AVE, PORTLAND, OR 972324169
Phone: 503 230-3000
Web: WWW.BPA.GOV

PRODUCTS/OPERATIONS

2014 Sales

	$ mil.	% of total
Power	2,572	71
Transmission	892	25
US Treasury credits for fish	104	3
Other	70	1
Adjustments	(38)	-
Total	**3,600**	**100**

COMPETITORS

Aep	Nw Natural
Aes	Pg&e Corporation
Avista	Pacificorp
Black Hills	Portland General
Centerpoint Energy	Electric
Duke Energy	Puget Energy
Idacorp	Sempra Energy

HISTORICAL FINANCIALS

Company Type: Private

Income Statement

FYE: September 30

	REVENUE ($ mil.)	NET INCOME ($ mil.)	NET PROFIT MARGIN	EMPLOYEES
09/10	3,055	(127)	—	3,100
09/09	2,870	(101)	—	—
09/08	3,036	264	8.7%	—
Annual Growth	0.3%	—	—	—

2010 Year-End Financials

Return on assets: (-0.6%)   Cash ($ mil.): 1,078
Return on equity: (-0.9%)
Current ratio: 1.20

BOSCOV'S, INC.

EXECUTIVES

Ceo, Albert Boscov
Evp Finance, Cao*, Russell C Diehm
Pres*, Sam Flamholz
Cfo*, Jason Curtis
Staff, Ronnie Eddinger
Sales Staff, Chantal Van Bauwel
Sales and Marketing Staff, Emile De Cordier
Director, Seppe De Roeck
Manager, Terry Moody
Director of Risk Management, Michael Conaway
Assistant Buyer, Megan Lambert
Auditors: KPMG LLP PHILADELPHIA PA

LOCATIONS

HQ: BOSCOV'S, INC.
4500 PERKIOMEN AVE, READING, PA 196063946
Phone: 610 779-2000
Web: WWW.BOSCOVS.COM

HISTORICAL FINANCIALS

Company Type: Private

Income Statement

FYE: January 30

	REVENUE ($ mil.)	NET INCOME ($ mil.)	NET PROFIT MARGIN	EMPLOYEES
01/21*	882	(1)	—	10,003
02/20	1,241	41	3.3%	—
02/19	1,215	47	3.9%	—
02/18	1,192	37	3.2%	—
Annual Growth	(9.5%)	—	—	—

*Fiscal year change

2021 Year-End Financials

Return on assets: (-0.3%)   Cash ($ mil.): 177
Return on equity: (-0.5%)
Current ratio: 2.60

BOSTON MEDICAL CENTER CORPORATION

Located in Boston's South End neighborhood Boston Medical Center (BMC) offers a full spectrum of health care services from prenatal care and obstetrics to surgery and rehabilitation. BMC is also the city's largest provider of indigent care spending millions of dollars annually on care for uninsured patients and offering free screenings and other community outreach programs. The not-for-profit hospital boasts more than nearly 500 licensed beds more than 700about 755 physicians and includes a Level 1 trauma center acute rehabilitation facilities and neonatal and pediatric intensive care units. The center is the primary teaching hospital of Boston University'sBoston University's School of Medicine.

Operations

BMC also operates Boston HealthNet a network affiliation of the medical center Boston University School of Medicine and more than a dozen community health centers. Boston HealthNet provides outreach prevention primary care and specialty care and dental services at sites located throughout the community.

Hand-in-hand with being a major teaching hospital is engaging in extensive medical research. BMC oversees more than 615 research and service projects and conducts both biomedical and clinical research programs exploring infectious disease cardiology vascular biology Parkinson's disease geriatrics and endocrinology among other areas.

BMC had more than 856000 outpatient clinic visits 139000 emergency department visits and 25800 admissions.

Sales and Marketing

In addition to its medical and research services BMC provides health insurance through its BMC HealthNet Plan a managed care plan that has more than 325000 Medicaid and low-cost health plan members. The center markets its services through social media.

Strategy

In mid-2020 Boston Medical Center's StreetCred program has been named to the second cohort of the Aspen Family Prosperity Innovation Community an Aspen Institute initiative for breakthrough innovations and collaborations that position families to reach educational success economic prosperity and health and well-being. The launch of this community Ascend could not come at a more crucial time as businesses and communities

reimagine how we support families as we navigate and respond to the coronavirus pandemic racial injustice and economic upheaval.

This new phase of Family Prosperity brings together 20 national and community-based organizations and 14 expert advisors from across the US including employers in the public and private sectors. Working beside families and guided by their expertise and experience this community will develop refine and amplify strategies and solutions that remove barriers and accelerate prosperity for families centering people of color and those with low incomes.

EXECUTIVES

Ceo, Kate Walsh
Treas*, Richard W Siveria
Assistant Professor, Babak Eliassi-Rad
Scientist, Elizabeth Pearce
Assistant Professor, Lisa Caruso
Assistant Professor, Jessica Kramer
Director of Research Safety, Ron L Morales
Research Assistant, Adriana Lopera
Information Technology Manager, Allison Bonner
Manager Business Sy, Brad Ridley
Social Worker, Dana Rous
Auditors: BMC HEALTH SYSTEM INC BOSTO

LOCATIONS

HQ: BOSTON MEDICAL CENTER CORPORATION
1 BOSTON MEDICAL CTR PL # 1, BOSTON, MA 021182999
Phone: 617 414-5000
Web: WWW.BMC.ORG

PRODUCTS/OPERATIONS

Selected Services and Programs
Alzheimer's Disease Center
Anesthesiology
Boston HealthNet
Boston University Affiliated Physicians
Boston University Cosmetic and Laser Center
Cardiovascular Center
Care Management
Dermatology
Diabetes
Elders Living at Home Program
Emergency Medicine
Facial Plastic and Reconstructive Surgery
General Internal Medicne / Primary Care
Geriatrics
Head and Neck Cancer Center of Excellence
Hematology & Medical Oncology
Immigrant & Refugee Health Program
Integrative Medicine
LocoMotor Training
Mattapan Community Health Center
Melanoma Program
Neurosurgery
Nursing
Ophthalmology
Oral and Maxillofacial Surgery
Pediatrics - bWell Center
Pediatrics
Rehabilitation Therapies
Renal Medicine
South End Community Health Center
Special Kids Special Help
Thoracic Surgery
Transplant Surgery
Uphams Corner Health Center
Urology
Vascular Center
Vascular and Endovascular Surgery
Weight Loss Surgery (Bariatric Surgery)
Whittier Street Health Center

COMPETITORS

Beth Israel Deaconess Medical Center
Brigham And Women's Hospital
Cambridge Health Alliance
Care New England
Caregroup

Children's Hospital Boston
Dana-farber
Massachusetts General Hospital
Newton-wellesley Hospital
Northeast Health System
Partners Healthcare
Shriners Hospitals For Children
Spaulding Rehabilitation Hospital
St. Elizabeth's Medical Center
Steward Health Care

HISTORICAL FINANCIALS

Company Type: Private

Income Statement				FYE: September 30
	REVENUE ($ mil.)	NET INCOME ($ mil.)	NET PROFIT MARGIN	EMPLOYEES
09/17	1,089	12	1.2%	4,200
09/15	1,004	7	0.8%	—
09/12	886	2	0.3%	—
Annual Growth	4.2%	38.0%	—	—

2017 Year-End Financials

Return on assets: 0.6% Cash ($ mil.): 125
Return on equity: 1.0%
Current ratio: 1.90

BOSTON UNIVERSITY

Auditors: KMPG LLP BOSTON MA

LOCATIONS

HQ: BOSTON UNIVERSITY
590 COMMONWEALTH AVE # 255, BOSTON, MA
022152521
Phone: 617 353-2600
Web: WWW.BU.EDU

HISTORICAL FINANCIALS

Company Type: Private

Income Statement				FYE: June 30
	REVENUE ($ mil.)	NET INCOME ($ mil.)	NET PROFIT MARGIN	EMPLOYEES
06/18	2,018	517	25.6%	70
06/17	1,895	507	26.8%	—
Annual Growth	6.5%	2.0%	—	—

2018 Year-End Financials

Return on assets: 8.1% Cash ($ mil.): 148
Return on equity: 13.2%
Current ratio: —

BOZZUTO'S, INC.

Bozzuto's is a leading wholesale grocery distribution company that supplies food and household products to retailers in New Jersey New York Pennsylvania and in New England. The company distributes a full line of grocery items including meat products produce and floral grocery dairy and frozen food bakery and deli fresh meat and seafood as well as seasonal and GM/HBC and specialty and organics. It carries goods sold under both the IGA and Hy-Top labels in addition to national brands. Bozzuto's also owns about five dis-

tribution centers in Connecticut and Pennsylvania. The company was founded in 1945.

Operations

Bozzuto's is a total service wholesale distributor of food and household products to retailers. It provides retail sales support grocery and perishable retail technology retail accounting and payroll creative custom design and store development merchandising and category management support and transportation ? logistics services.

In terms of brands the customers can choose from IGA brand products or Hy-Top brand products. The company also offers a growing line of store brand organics called Seven Farms.

Geographic Reach

Cheshire Connecticut-based Bozzuto's operates a pair of distribution centers in Cheshire as well as facilities in North Haven Connecticut and Allentown Pennsylvania. In terms of its clients it also has its presence in New England.

Sales and Marketing

Bozzuto's has sales associates and distributes its products to retailers.

Company Background

The company founded in 1945 is owned and operated by the Bozzuto family including chairman and CEO Michael Bozzuto.

EXECUTIVES

Pres-Chm-Ceo, Michael A Bozzuto
V Pres*, Jayne A Bozzuto
V Pres-Fin*, Robert H Wood
SEC-Asst Treas*, Patricia S Houle
Director, Craig Gagnier
Controller, Bert Condren
Hris Coordinator, Christine Infante
Training Manager, Dawn Brown
Chief Human Resource Officer, Don Anthony
Vice President Informationtech, Jhon Kelly
Warranty Manager, Russ McKusick
Auditors: FEDERMAN LALLY & REMIS LLC F

LOCATIONS

HQ: BOZZUTO'S, INC.
275 SCHOOLHOUSE RD, CHESHIRE, CT 064101257
Phone: 203 272-3511
Web: WWW.BOZZUTOS.COM

PRODUCTS/OPERATIONS

Selected Services

New store site and demographic analysis
Retail merchandising specialists and sales support
Retail financial services accounting and payroll
Operational analysis
Shelf management programs
Market/pricing strategies
Employee training seminars and workshops
Profit building ideas
Retail technology

COMPETITORS

Associated Grocers Of New England	Pine State Trading
C&s Wholesale	Supervalu
Krasdale Foods	Shaw's
Mclane	Stop & Shop
	Wakefern Food

HISTORICAL FINANCIALS

Company Type: Private

Income Statement				FYE: September 27
	REVENUE ($ mil.)	NET INCOME ($ mil.)	NET PROFIT MARGIN	EMPLOYEES
09/08	1,243	(5)	—	3,100
09/07	1,180	(0)	—	—
09/06	955,449	0	0.0%	—
Annual Growth	(96.4%)	—	—	—

2008 Year-End Financials

Return on assets: 7.0% Cash ($ mil.): 1
Return on equity: (-0.5%)
Current ratio: 0.60

BRANDSMART USA OF HENRY COUNTY, LLC

EXECUTIVES

Pres, Michael Pearlman
Exec V Pres, Larry Sinewgz
Cfo, Eric Beazley
Inside Sales Representative, Mendez Michael
Auditors: KAUFMAN ROSSIN AND CO

LOCATIONS

HQ: BRANDSMART USA OF HENRY COUNTY, LLC
3200 SW 42ND ST, FORT LAUDERDALE, FL
333126808
Phone: 954 797-4000
Web: WWW.BRANDSMARTUSA.COM

HISTORICAL FINANCIALS

Company Type: Private

Income Statement				FYE: September 25
	REVENUE ($ mil.)	NET INCOME ($ mil.)	NET PROFIT MARGIN	EMPLOYEES
09/10	800	7	0.9%	38
09/09	826	8	1.0%	—
Annual Growth	(3.2%)	(12.4%)	—	—

2010 Year-End Financials

Return on assets: 2.4% Cash ($ mil.): 2
Return on equity: 4.4%
Current ratio: 1.00

BRASFIELD & GORRIE, L.L.C.

EXECUTIVES

Mng MBR-Chm, M Miller Gorrie
MBR-Ceo*, M James Gorrie
MBR*, Jeffrey I Stone
MBR-Cfo*, Randall J Freeman
MBR-V Pres*, Tracey Renner Sibley
MBR-Supt*, Larry Helms
Executive Secretary, Kelli Nutting
Coordinator, Ryan Roberts
Coordinator, Contessa Smile
Assistant Project Manager, Chris Loft
Admin Assistant, Amanda Tolleson

LOCATIONS

HQ: BRASFIELD & GORRIE, L.L.C.
3021 7TH AVE S, BIRMINGHAM, AL 352333502
Phone: 205 328-4000
Web: WWW.BRASFIELDGORRIE.COM

Company Type: Private

Income Statement				FYE: December 31
	REVENUE ($ mil.)	NET INCOME ($ mil.)	NET PROFIT MARGIN	EMPLOYEES
12/20*	3,969	0	—	3,500
09/19	2,820	0	—	
/	0	0	—	—
Annual Growth	—	—	—	—

*Fiscal year change

2020 Year-End Financials

Return on assets: —
Return on equity: —
Current ratio: 1.30

Cash ($ mil.): 462

BRAZOS ELECTRIC POWER COOPERATIVE, INC.

Brazos means "arms" in Spanish and the generation and transmission arms of Brazos Electric Power Cooperative reach across 68 Texas counties. It serves 16 member/owner distribution cooperatives and one municipality in Northern and Central Texas. Brazos Electric Power annually generates (through its four power stations) and/or accesses from other power marketers some 3655 MW of electric power. The cooperative's members include Comanche Electric Cooperative Association Heart of Texas Electric Co-op (McGregor) Mid-South Synergy (Navasota) United Coop Services (Cleburne) and Wise Electric (Decatur).

EXECUTIVES

President, Dennis McWhorter
Chm*, Larry Corbett
V Pres*, Rick Haile
Exec V Pres*, Clifton D Karnei
Chief Financial Officer*, Khaki Bordovsky
V Pres*, Johnny York
V Pres*, Hugh Lenox
V Pres*, David Murphy
Pres*, John Hartgraves
V Pres*, Ronnie Robinson
Sr V Pres*, Loyd Jackson
Auditors: PRICEWATERHOUSECOOPERS LLP KA

LOCATIONS

HQ: BRAZOS ELECTRIC POWER COOPERATIVE, INC.
7616 BAGBY AVE, WACO, TX 767126924
Phone: 254 750-6500
Web: WWW.BRAZOSELECTRIC.COM

Brazos Electric Power Cooperative has operations in 68 counties in northern and Central Texas.

PRODUCTS/OPERATIONS

Member/Owners

Barlett Electric Cooperative
BEPC
Comanche Electric Cooperative
Cooke County Electric Cooperative
CoServ Electric
Fort Belknap Electric Cooperative
Hamilton County Electric Cooperative
Heart of Texas Electric Cooperative
HILCO Electric Cooperative
J-A-C Electric Cooperative
Mid-South Synergy
Navarro County Electric Cooperative
Navasota Valley Electric Cooperative
South Plains Electric Cooperative
Tri-County Electric Cooperative
United Cooperative Services
Wise Electric Cooperative

COMPETITORS

Aep	Entergy
Centerpoint Energy	Lcra
El Paso Electric	

HISTORICAL FINANCIALS

Company Type: Private

Income Statement				FYE: December 31
	REVENUE ($ mil.)	NET INCOME ($ mil.)	NET PROFIT MARGIN	EMPLOYEES
12/17	905	58	6.5%	366
12/09	963	56	5.9%	—
12/99	307	6	2.3%	—
Annual Growth	6.2%	12.6%	—	—

2017 Year-End Financials

Return on assets: 1.9%
Return on equity: 7.4%
Current ratio: 15.30

Cash ($ mil.): 353

BRG SPORTS, INC.

BRG Sports is a corporate holding company of leading brands that design develop and market innovative sports equipment smart helmet technology team apparel and accessories. The company's Riddell brand is a premier designer and developer of football helmets protective sports equipment head impact monitoring technologies apparel and related accessories. A recognized leader in helmet technology and innovation Riddell is the leading manufacturer of football helmets and shoulder pads and a top provider of reconditioning services (cleaning repairing repainting and recertifying existing equipment).

Operations

BRG offers innovative sports equipment smart helmet technology team apparel and accessories under Riddel brand.

Geographic Reach

BRG Sports is based in Illinois and has approximately 10 facilities worldwide.

Sales and Marketing

BRG serves youth sports equipment and apparel institutional/scholastic sports equipment and apparel professional football equipment industries.
Financial Performance

HISTORY

The company traces its roots to the Los Angeles suburb of Bell a hotbed of auto racing and Roy Richter a racer who operated Bell Auto Parts. Richter began making racing helmets in 1954 and became a leading maker of motorcycle and ski helmets during the 1960s. In 1975 Bell Helmets introduced the Bell Biker the first hard-shell bicycle helmet.

Phil Matthews a former executive with Wilson Sporting Goods and Terry Lee an executive with bankrupt motorcycle accessory maker Vetter Products purchased Bell Helmets with several partners in 1983 (the group merged Vetter and Bell). Motorcycle helmet sales slowed but sales of bicycle helmets (including lines for infants and children) propelled the company during the 1980s. Bell Helmets began selling products in Europe in 1988 and in 1991 it sold its motorcycle helmet business to Italian manufacturer Bieffe for $15 million.

The company went public in 1992 as Bell Sports and began benefiting from new state laws requiring children to wear helmets while bicycling. Also that year it acquired Blackburn a maker of pumps racks packs and accessories but by 1995 competition began cutting into sales and profits.

To protect its market share in 1995 the company acquired American Recreation the nation's #2 helmet maker. To reduce debt Bell sold its Mongoose bicycle unit in 1997 for $22 million. Investment firms Charlesbank Capital Partners and Brentwood Associates Buyout Fund II took the firm private the next year and installed Mary George as CEO.

In 1999 Bell narrowed its focus selling its auto-racing helmet business and closing or selling all but one of its factories. Investment firm Chartwell bought Bell in 2000 and moved Mary George to executive chairman. Bell moved its headquarters in 2001 to Irving Texas.

The company broadened its product offerings when it bought Bollinger Industries' fitness accessory product line in 2002; products range from yoga mats to jump ropes and weightlifting belts.

Fenway Partners acquired Bell Sports for $240 million in September 2004. Fenway combined the company with its Riddell Sports Group (football helmets) to form Riddell Bell Holdings. Under this umbrella Fenway created one of the top global suppliers of helmets. Bell Sports and Riddell were once a combined company when William Zimmerman (then president of Zimmerman Holdings) and James Marshall Galbraith purchased Bell Helmets and Riddell to form Bell-Riddell. The companies were sold separately in 1984.

In December 2004 Riddell Bell purchased Sports Instruments an athletic performance technology company. Sports Instruments' products which include heart rate monitors and sports watches were absorbed into Riddell Bell's specialty retail division. In January 2005 the company purchased auto racing helmets maker Bell Racing.

Easton-Bell Sports was formed in 2006 when Easton Sports and Riddell Bell Holdings merged their operations. Tony Palma Easton's former chief executive took over as CEO upon completion of the deal. He held that position until March 2008 when he departed the firm. Bill Fry Riddell Bell's top executive was named EBS's president. Fry left the company in early 2007 following the merger transition. Palma was replaced by former Reebok CEO Paul Harrington in April 2008.

EXECUTIVES

President And Ceo, Dan Arment
Auditors: ERNST & YOUNG LLP LOS ANGELE

LOCATIONS

HQ: BRG SPORTS, INC.
1700 E HIGGINS RD STE 500, DES PLAINES, IL 600183800
Phone: 224 585-5200
Web: WWW.BRGSPORTS.COM

2013 Sales

	$ mil.	% of total
North America	667	85
Europe	84	11
Other	28	4
Total	780	100

PRODUCTS/OPERATIONS

Selected Products

Riddell helmets
Riddell shoulder pads

Riddell padded shirts
Riddell game pants
Riddell compression shirts and pants

COMPETITORS

Amer Sports	Reebok-ccm Hockey
Bauer Hockey	Russell Brands
Merrithew	Under Armour
Nike	Wilson Sporting Goods
Rawlings Sporting Goods	Adidas

HISTORICAL FINANCIALS

Company Type: Private

Income Statement   FYE: December 29

	REVENUE ($ mil.)	NET INCOME ($ mil.)	NET PROFIT MARGIN	EMPLOYEES
12/12	827	(3)	—	2,370
12/11*	834	10	1.2%	—
01/11	772	8	1.1%	—
Annual Growth	3.5%	—	—	—

*Fiscal year change

2012 Year-End Financials

Return on assets: (-0.3%) Cash ($ mil.): 40
Return on equity: (-0.9%)
Current ratio: 2.50

BRIDGEPORT HOSPITAL

EXECUTIVES

Pres-Ceo, William M Jennings
Sr V Pres-Med Staff, Bruce Mc Donald
V Pres-Hr*, Joseph E Janell
SEC*, Norman Roth
Dir, David Bindelglass
Chief Medical Officer-Svp Med*, Victor Morris
Pediatrician, Mary Gaeta
Doctor, Armand J Wolff
Coordinator, Debra Miller
Nursing Director, Anita Schrum
Chief Financial Officer, Kishore Solanki

LOCATIONS

HQ: BRIDGEPORT HOSPITAL
267 GRANT ST, BRIDGEPORT, CT 066102870
Phone: 203 384-3000
Web: WWW.BRIDGEPORTHOSPITAL.ORG

HISTORICAL FINANCIALS

Company Type: Private

Income Statement   FYE: September 30

	REVENUE ($ mil.)	NET INCOME ($ mil.)	NET PROFIT MARGIN	EMPLOYEES
09/19	626	39	6.3%	200
09/18	550	72	13.2%	—
09/17	482	25	5.4%	—
09/16	470	46	9.9%	—
Annual Growth	10.0%	(5.5%)	—	—

2019 Year-End Financials

Return on assets: 5.3% Cash ($ mil.): 41
Return on equity: 11.8%
Current ratio: 1.50

BRISBANE SCHOOL DISTRICT

EXECUTIVES

Superintendent, Toni Presto
Administrative Assistant To Th, Aida Gamba
Superintendent, Ronan Collver
Teacher, Holly Rios
Bilingual Director, Jeannette Shereda
Information Director, Rafael Xolocotzi
Auditors: RT DENNIS ACCOUNTANCY RANCHO

LOCATIONS

HQ: BRISBANE SCHOOL DISTRICT
1 SOLANO ST, BRISBANE, CA 940051342
Phone: 415 467-0550
Web: WWW.BRISBANESD.ORG

HISTORICAL FINANCIALS

Company Type: Private

Income Statement   FYE: June 30

	REVENUE ($ mil.)	NET INCOME ($ mil.)	NET PROFIT MARGIN	EMPLOYEES
06/20	9,940	10,131	101.9%	82
06/19	9	0	9.8%	—
06/18	8	0	3.7%	—
06/17	8,244	(292)	—	—
Annual Growth	6.4%	—	—	—

2020 Year-End Financials

Return on assets: 999.9% Cash ($ mil.): 18
Return on equity: —
Current ratio: —

BRODER BROS., CO.

Selling clothes had been in the genes of sportswear distributor Broder Bros. for years. Begun as a haberdashery in 1919 the company evolved from making hats and gloves into a leading distributor of imprintable sportswear distributing 40000-plus SKUs across more than 40 retail brands including adidas Golf Champion Russell Athletic alternative Dickies and private labels. It operates under the Broder Alpha and NES divisions. Private labels include Devon & Jones Chestnut Hill and Harriton. Customers mostly small US retailers order merchandise through seasonal catalogs or online. Private investment firm Bain Capital has held a majority interest in the company since 2000 when the Broder family sold the company.

Operations

Broder Bros.' business comprises eight distribution facilities nationwide as well as 10 Express locations that offer pickup services to customers. Express facilities ship through ground parcel service to more than 80% of the continental US population within one business day and to more than 98% of the continental US population within two business days.

Its two primary markets are imprintable sportswear and accessories. Typically undecorated or blank items such as sweatshirts polo shirts fleece outerwear caps bags and other imprintable accessories are bought from Broder Bros. and decorated for the purposes of advertising and promotion. Decorator customers are offered value-added merchandising marketing and promotional support to help them grow their businesses.

Geographic Reach

Based in Pennsylvania Broder Bros. boasts the industry's largest distribution network. It provides its products to customers across the continental US.

Sales and Marketing

The company which caters to more than 70000 customers relies on a handful of suppliers such as Gildan Hanes and Fruit of the Loom.

In general Broder Bros. clients include advertising specialty companies screen printers embroiderers and specialty retailers that purchase Broder Bros. products (blank T-shirts sweatshirts polo shirts outerwear caps bags and more) to embellish for their own clients. Broder Bros. distributes popular brands such as Anvil Jerzees Hanes Fruit of the Loom and Gildan.

Strategy

Broder Bros. has seen its business pick up on the heels of a tough selling environment. One way it has turned its business around is by ensuring that it had in stock the most popular products while it rebuilt its inventory of proprietary brands. It also strengthened its commitment not to be undersold by rivals. To ensure that its dozen distribution centers were bustling with business Broder Bros. also recruited a senior sales and marketing executive to review and fine-tune how the company sells its products help to decide which product assortment is ideal going forward and figure out how to attract a wider customer base from the imprintable sportswear market.

Mergers and Acquisitions

Looking to post more than $900 million in sales and $50 million in pro forma EBITDA in 2013 Broder Bros. bought Denver-based Imprints Wholesale one of the top wholesale clothing distributors in the Rocky Mountain region. The deal is Broder Bros.' first acquisition since 2006 and first since private investment firm Littlejohn & Co. took over control of the board of directors in mid-2012.

EXECUTIVES

Ceo, Norman Hullinger
Pres*, Dan Pantano
SEC-Treas*, Martin J Matthews
Sr V Pres Mktg*, Girisha Chandraraj
V Pres Sls*, Christopher Blakeslee
V Pres*, Richard Emrich
Senior Modeler Marketing, Debby Krissinger
Regional Sales Manager, Denise Spencer
Director, Donough Deutsch
Sales Director, Doug Bonds
Sales Representative, Elysa Maryasis

LOCATIONS

HQ: BRODER BROS., CO.
6 NESHAMINY INTERPLEX DR 6T, TREVOSE, PA 190536964
Phone: 215 291-0300
Web: WWW.ALPHABRODER.COM

PRODUCTS/OPERATIONS

Selected Products

Accessories

Bags
Decoration supplies
Fleece
Headwear
Pants
Shorts
Sport shirts
T-shirts
Woven shirts

Selected Brands

Trade
Adams Cap
American Apparel
Anvil
Bella
Canvas
Cross Creek
Fruit of the Loom
Gildan
Hanes
Izod
Outer Banks
Van Heusen
Weatherproof
Yupoong

Retail
adidas Golf
Champion
Dickies Chef
Dickies Workwear
Rossignol Pure Mountain Company

Private-label
Chestnut Hill
Harriton
Devon & Jones
HYP
Harvard Square

COMPETITORS

Anvil Holdings	Hanesbrands
Concept One	M. J. Soffe
Accessories	Premiumwear
Delta Apparel	Russell Brands
Fruit Of The Loom	Vf Corporation
Gildan Activewear	

HISTORICAL FINANCIALS

Company Type: Private

Income Statement   FYE: December 26

	REVENUE ($ mil.)	NET INCOME ($ mil.)	NET PROFIT MARGIN	EMPLOYEES
12/09	705	(13)	—	1,826
12/08	926	(68)	—	
12/07	929	(124)	—	
Annual Growth	(12.9%)	—	—	—

2009 Year-End Financials

Return on assets: (-4.5%)   Cash ($ mil.): 3
Return on equity: —
Current ratio: 2.10

BRONSON METHODIST HOSPITAL INC

From your leg bone to your knee bone; your neck bone to your head bone Bronson Methodist Hospital has the specialists to cure what ails you. The 435-bed hospital is the flagship facility of the Bronson Healthcare Group a not-for-profit health care system. Bronson Methodist provides care in just about every specialty including orthopedics surgery and oncology. The hospital also contains specialist units for critical care (level I trauma center) neurology (primary stroke center) cardiology (Chest pain emergency center) women's health (BirthPlace) and pediatrics (children's hospital).

Operations

In addition to providing general emergency and specialty inpatient care to privately insured or self-paying customers the hospital serves a large percentage of Medicaid patients and provides charity care to uninsured patients. Altogether Bronson Methodist's charity and community outreach pro-

gram contributions total more than $55 million annually.

The hospital contains the Bronson Children's Hospital which offers burn and wound neonatal development and newborn pulmonary services among others.

Geographic Reach

Bronson Methodist serves patients throughout southwestern Michigan from its main facility in Kalamazoo.

Strategy

All of the hospital's inpatient rooms are private; this transition was made to reduce infection rates and increase privacy for Bronson Methodist patients.

Bronson Methodist began participation in the bundled payment program of the Centers for Medicare and Medicaid Services in 2013. The program is designed to improve the quality of care delivery for Medicare patients by changing the way that providers are reimbursed for services.

EXECUTIVES

Coo, Kenneth Taft
Cfo*, Mary Meitz
Exec Dir*, Terry K Morrow
Prin, Mark Atkinson
Prin, Donald Greydanus
Chief of Pediatric, Aaron Lane-Davies
Prin, Joshua Burnett
Payroll Specialist, Coral Zoll
Case Manager, Jill Beison
Case Manager, Joyce Anderson
Contractor, Katherine Stone
Auditors: PLANTE & MORAN PLLC CHICAGO

LOCATIONS

HQ: BRONSON METHODIST HOSPITAL INC
601 JOHN ST STE E-012, KALAMAZOO, MI
490075346
Phone: 269 341-7654
Web: WWW.BRONSONHEALTH.COM

PRODUCTS/OPERATIONS

Selected Services

Anticoagulation

Bereavement
Breast Health
Burn
Cancer Care
Critical Care
Diabetes
Flu
Heart and Vascular
Home Health
Hyperbaric Oxygen Therapy
Infusion
Laboratory
Medical and Surgical Weight Management
Neurosciences
Nutrition
Occupational Health
Orthopedics
Palliative Care
Pediatrics
Pharmacy
Pregnancy and Childbirth
Rehabilitation
Respiratory Care
Sleep
Surgery
Stomal Therapy
Testing and Imaging
Trauma and Emergency
Women's Health
Wound

COMPETITORS

Ascension Health	Holland Hospital
Borgess Health	Spectrum Health

Bronson Battle Creek
Community Hospital
Elkhart General
  Healthcare System
Hayes Green Beach
  Memorial Hospital

Trinity Health (novi)
Zeeland Community
  Hospital

HISTORICAL FINANCIALS

Company Type: Private

Income Statement   FYE: December 31

	REVENUE ($ mil.)	NET INCOME ($ mil.)	NET PROFIT MARGIN	EMPLOYEES
12/19	952	2	0.3%	2,861
12/18	864	26	3.1%	—
12/17	864	85	9.8%	—
12/15	726	69	9.5%	—
Annual Growth	7.0%	(55.6%)	—	—

2019 Year-End Financials

Return on assets: 0.2%   Cash ($ mil.): 552
Return on equity: 0.4%
Current ratio: 1.70

BRONXCARE HEALTH SYSTEM

Bronx-Lebanon Hospital Center cares for patients in the central and south Bronx no doubt while rooting for the Yankees a few blocks away. The health care provider maintains more than 970 beds across its two campuses as well as psychiatric and nursing home facilities. Hospital specialty units include chest pain orthopedic cancer and women's health centers. Bronx-Lebanon also manages a network of about 70 owned and affiliated medical practices (under the BronxCare brand). This network includes primary care doctors and specialty clinics as well as rehabilitation facilities. The hospital is also a primary teaching hospital for the Albert Einstein College of Medicine.

Operations

Aside from its two major hospitals Bronx-Lebanon operates a psychiatric facility a pair of specialized long-term care facilities and the Bronx-Care network of medical practices that include Dr. Martin Luther King Jr. Health Center and a 51-unit facility to house seniors and low-income residents. Bronx-Lebanon cares for those with mental or substance abuse problems through the Family Wellness Center. It also operates a 240-bed Special Care Center and the 90-bed Highbridge Woodycrest Center to provide long term health care to geriatric AIDS and disabled residents. Its ER Department responds to about 141000 patient visits a year.

Geographic Reach

The hospital system's 37 locations serve residents of central and south Bronx in New York.

Sales and Marketing

In 2013 the company spent about $144000 on advertising.

Financial Performance

The Hospital Center is supported primarily by patient service fees paid by Medicaid Medicare and commercial insurance carriers. In 2013 the Medicaid contributed 63% of the revenue whereas Medicare contributed 28% and the rest 9% was contributed other third-party insurance carriers.

In 2013 Bronx-Lebanon's net revenues increased by about 5% due to a rise in patient service revenues and grants partially offset by a decrease in auxiliary services.

The company's net income increased by more than 790% in 2013 as the result of an increase in revenues.

Bronx-Lebanon's operating cash flows increased by 53% thanks to higher income.

Strategy

Bronx-Lebanon emphasizes its role as a community health care provider not only through its BronxCare network but through a number of community outreach and service efforts including school-based programs mobile health units free health screening and even a weekly live television show that discusses health issues.

To accommodate the growing population in and around the Bronx the hospital system has expanded in recent years with a new children's wing for inpatient and outpatient services; a nine-story ambulatory care facility; and an extensive emergency room modernization. Bronx-Lebanon also maintains a short stay observation unit in the emergency room area to monitor and evaluate patients in cardiac distress prior to admission or discharge.

Bronx-Lebanon is one of many hospital organizations to have joined a regional health information organization (RHIO) to allow medical professionals to access a patient's medical records at any number of health care locations. Other members of the Bronx RHIO include Montefiore Medical Center Jacobi Medical Center St. Barnabas Hospital and Hebrew Home at Riverdale.

Bronx-Lebanon is also one of the few hospitals in New York that is fully computerized with a complete inpatient and outpatient electronic medical record.

The hospital center's expansion plans include a $42 million 60000 sq. ft ambulatory care facility and a $34 million 56000 sq. ft. life recovery center for chemical dependency services.

In 2014 the company completed the construction of its Health and Wellness Center a new state-of-the-art outpatient facility with general and specialty services and new treatment rooms and diagnostic equipment. It also completed the construction of its Life Recovery Center to combine inpatient outpatient and residential services for individuals suffering from chemical dependency.

The company also expanded its Emergency room adding a new 11-bay treatment area.

In the same year it also relocated and expanded its main Dentistry Practice adding 39 dental chairs (a 50% increase).

EXECUTIVES

Pres-Ceo, Miguel Fuentes
V Pres-Coo*, Steven Anderman
Chm*, Christopher Chang
Orthopedist, Randall V Ehrlich
Project Coordinator, Puneet Khullar
Assistant Professor, Jamilah Grant-Snyder
Coordinator, Juanita Fagello
Assistant Professor, Raghunandan S Loganathan
Chief of Medicine, Steven M Safyer
Assistant Professor, Jean M Tornatore
Psychiatry, Vicente Jose Liz Defillo
Auditors: LOEB & TROPER LLP NEW YORK N

LOCATIONS

HQ: BRONXCARE HEALTH SYSTEM
1276 FULTON AVE, BRONX, NY 104563402
Phone: 718 590-1800
Web: WWW.BRONXCARE.ORG

PRODUCTS/OPERATIONS

Selected Services
Anesthesiology
Asthma
  Adult
  Pediatric
Cardiology
Dentistry
Diabetes
  Adult
  Pediatric
Ear Nose & Throat
Gastroenterology
Hematology & Oncology
Neonatology
Neurology
Ophthalmology
Orthopaedics
Pediatrics
Physical Medicine
Psychiatry
Radiology
Special Care Center
Urology & Men's Health

Selected Academic Affiliations
Albert Einstein College of Medicine
Bronx Community College
Hostos Community College
Lehman College City University of New York
State University of New York at Stony Brook

COMPETITORS

Beth Israel Medical
  Center
Catholic Healthcare
  System
Continuum Health
  Partners
Lenox Hill Hospital
Maimonides Medical
  Center
Memorial
  Sloan-kettering

Montefiore Medical
New York City Health
  And Hospitals
Newyork-presbyterian
  Healthcare
Northwell Health
Winthrop-university
  Hospital

HISTORICAL FINANCIALS
Company Type: Private

Income Statement				FYE: December 31
	REVENUE ($ mil.)	NET INCOME ($ mil.)	NET PROFIT MARGIN	EMPLOYEES
12/17	750	12	1.6%	4,000
12/16	641	6	1.0%	—
12/15	631	18	3.0%	—
12/14	598	(34)	—	—
Annual Growth	7.9%	—	—	—

2017 Year-End Financials
Return on assets: 2.4%   Cash ($ mil.): 117
Return on equity: 19.6%
Current ratio: 0.70

BROOKFIELD PROPERTIES RETAIL INC.

EXECUTIVES

Director, Cheryl Casanova
Senior Director of Big Box Lea, Chris Milkie
Site Manager, Ken Hesse
Director, Credit, Dave Akash
Manager, Property Accounting, Howard Moel
Lease Accountant, Alex Legreid

Human Resources Coordinator, Ally Lubbers
Manager, Human Resour, Amy Friedman
Operations Administrative Assi, Annmarie Cronin
Director, Retail, Anthony Genovese
Senior Tenant Coordinator, Bibi Sukey
Auditors: DELOITTE & TOUCHE LLP CHICAGO

LOCATIONS

HQ: BROOKFIELD PROPERTIES RETAIL INC.
350 N ORLEANS ST STE 300, CHICAGO, IL 606541607
Phone: 312 960-5000
Web: WWW.BROOKFIELDPROPERTIES.COM

HISTORICAL FINANCIALS
Company Type: Private

Income Statement				FYE: December 31
	REVENUE ($ mil.)	NET INCOME ($ mil.)	NET PROFIT MARGIN	EMPLOYEES
12/19	1,563	480	30.7%	87
12/18	2,064	4,163	201.7%	—
Annual Growth	(24.2%)	(88.5%)	—	—

2019 Year-End Financials
Return on assets: 2.2%   Cash ($ mil.): 197
Return on equity: 14.6%
Current ratio: —

BROTHER INTERNATIONAL CORPORATION

Brother International is a leading supplier of innovative products for the home sewing and crafting enthusiast. A subsidiary of Japan-based Brother Industries Brother International sells a host of products ? including inkjet and laser printers fax machines scanners typewriters sewing machines gear motors and machine tools ? manufactured by its parent company. Its products are marketed to consumers and businesses in North America and across Latin America. Through its subsidiaries Brother International operates production and sales facilities in more than 30 countries worldwide and it serves customers in over 100 countries. The business was formed in 1954.

Operations
Brother International creates high-quality feature-rich printers scanners fax machines mobile solutions home sewing and embroidery machines and more.

Geographic Reach
Brother International is headquartered in Bridgewater New Jersey. In addition Brother has facilities in California Illinois and Tennessee as well as subsidiaries in Canada Brazil Chile Argentina Peru and Mexico.

Sales and Marketing
Brother International serves customers in agriculture education food/restaurant healthcare industrial manufacturing and retail industries.

Financial Performance
Thanks to exchange rate benefits and rising demand for both equipment and consumables Brother International's printing and solutions segment revenue rose some 23% in fiscal 2014 as compared to 2013.

EXECUTIVES

Pres, Kazufumi Ikeda
Chb, Tadashi Ishiguro
Sr V Pres-Prod Dev Prod Mgmt, Roger T Nakagawa
Senior Manufacturing Buyer, Nicole Harmon
Key Account Representative I, Matthew Palmer
Director of Marketing, Angela Swanson
Director Operations, Mark Murphy
Manager, William Slavoski
Senior Vp, Henry Sacco
Information Technology, Ryoichi Sumida
Manager, Tamara Bates

LOCATIONS

HQ: BROTHER INTERNATIONAL CORPORATION
200 CROSSING BLVD FL 1, BRIDGEWATER, NJ
088072861
Phone: 908 704-1700
Web: WWW.SUPPORT.BROTHER-USA.COM

PRODUCTS/OPERATIONS

Selected Services
Brother Business Solutions
Brother Cloud

Selected Products
Fax machines
Garment printers
Gear motors
Home sewing & embroidery
Industrial printing & sewing
Labeling systems
Machine tools
Mobile products (portable scanners printers industrial labelers)
Printers
Scanners
Sewing and embroidery machines
Stamp-making systems
Typewriters
Web conferencing

COMPETITORS

Canon Usa	Oki Data Americas
Epson	Oracle
Hp	Riso Inc.
Ibm	Retail Holdings
Kyocera Document Solutions America	Ricoh Americas
	Xerox
Microsoft	

HISTORICAL FINANCIALS

Company Type: Private

Income Statement — FYE: March 31

	REVENUE ($ mil.)	NET INCOME ($ mil.)	NET PROFIT MARGIN	EMPLOYEES
03/18	1,751	33	1.9%	2,000
03/15	1,852	3	0.2%	—
03/14	1,826	26	1.5%	—
Annual Growth	(1.0%)	6.1%	—	—

2018 Year-End Financials
Return on assets: 4.2%   Cash ($ mil.): 29
Return on equity: 6.0%
Current ratio: 3.30

BROWARD COUNTY PUBLIC SCHOOLS

EXECUTIVES

Supt, Robert W Runcie
Acct*, Paul Purrier
Executive of Information Techn, Sharon Simmons
Customer Staff, Kendra Demme
Director, Angela St Hubert
Teacher, Joann Hoy
Director, Judy Zinn
Office Manager, Kathryn McArthur
Administrative Assistant, Nicoletta Williams
Teacher, Adriana Cardoso
Management, Alden B Davis

LOCATIONS

HQ: BROWARD COUNTY PUBLIC SCHOOLS
600 SE 3RD AVE, FORT LAUDERDALE, FL 333013125
Phone: 754 321-0000
Web: WWW.BROWARDSCHOOLS.COM

HISTORICAL FINANCIALS

Company Type: Private

Income Statement — FYE: June 30

	REVENUE ($ mil.)	NET INCOME ($ mil.)	NET PROFIT MARGIN	EMPLOYEES
06/16	2,630	(37)	—	31,174
06/15	2,536	186	7.3%	—
06/11	2,515	(37)	—	—
Annual Growth	0.9%	—	—	—

2016 Year-End Financials
Return on assets: (-0.9%)   Cash ($ mil.): 671
Return on equity: (-6.4%)
Current ratio: 1.50

BROWN UNIVERSITY

Brown is a leading research university distinct for its student-centered learning and deep sense of purpose. The University's academic programs include: undergraduate graduate and professional schools and colleges academic departments centers and institutes libraries and collections global education as well as non-degree programs. The University founded in 1764 is located in Providence Rhode Island ? Brown's home for more than two and a half centuries.

EXECUTIVES

Ceo, Christina Paxson
Pres*, Shelia Blumstein
Exec V Pres*, Barbara Chernow
Sr V Pres*, Patricia A Watson
Exec V Pres*, Russell Carey
Director*, Patrice Carroll
Vice Chair, Douglas Anthony
Prin, Douglas R Nickel
Officer, Elizabeth Goldberg
Purchasing Operations Manager, Jane Bonacich
Clinical Instructor In Obstetr, A M Coppa
Auditors: KPMG LLP PROVIDENCCE RI

LOCATIONS

HQ: BROWN UNIVERSITY
1 PROSPECT ST, PROVIDENCE, RI 029129127
Phone: 401 369-0294
Web: WWW.IT.BROWN.EDU

PRODUCTS/OPERATIONS

2015 Revenues

	$ mil.	% of total
Net tuition & fees	289	36
Grants & contracts	151	18
Endowment income	142	18
Contributions	98	12
Auxiliary enterprises	90	11
Other	36	5
Total	**808**	**100**

Selected Programs
Africana Studies Department of
American Studies Department of
Anthropology Department of
Applied Mathematics Division of
Archaeology and the Ancient World Joukowsky Institute for
Behavioral and Social Sciences Department of
Biology & Medicine Division of
Biomedical Engineering Center for
Biostatistics Department of
Biotechnology Graduate Program
Brown-Pfizer MA Program in Biology
Chemistry Department of
Classics Department of
Cognitive Linguistic and Psychological Sciences Department of
Commerce Organizations & Entrepreneurship C.V. Starr Program in
Comparative Literature Department of
Computational Biology Center for
Computer Science Department of
Development Studies Program in

HISTORICAL FINANCIALS

Company Type: Private

Income Statement — FYE: June 30

	REVENUE ($ mil.)	NET INCOME ($ mil.)	NET PROFIT MARGIN	EMPLOYEES
06/13	732	289	39.6%	5,100
06/12	704	(69)	—	—
06/11	666	359	53.9%	—
Annual Growth	4.8%	(10.2%)	—	—

2013 Year-End Financials
Return on assets: 6.6%   Cash ($ mil.): 14
Return on equity: 8.4%
Current ratio: —

BRUCE OAKLEY, INC.

From little acorns mighty Oakleys grow. Bruce Oakley provides road and river (barge) transportation of dry bulk commodities as well as grain storage and bulk fertilizer sales. The company's trucking division which uses both end-dump and pneumatic tank trailers serves the continental US and Canada. Overall Bruce Oakley operates some 450 trailers. It maintains about half a dozen ports in Arkansas Louisiana and Missouri on the Arkansas Mississippi and Red rivers and the company's river barge transportation unit operates on those and other inland and intracoastal waterways. Grain storage services are available in five ports in Arkansas. Bruce Oakley was founded in 1968.

EXECUTIVES

Pres, Dennis B Oakley
V Pres*, Benny Weatherford
V Pres*, David Choate
V Pres*, Edward S Bubba Vance
Cfo*, Tim Cummins
SEC*, Sadie Ringgold
Vice President, Shane Smith
Recruiter, Dustin Eagle
Accounting, Katie Lowry
Manager, Raymond Mannis
Vice President, Edward Bubba Vance

LOCATIONS

HQ: BRUCE OAKLEY, INC.
3400 GRIBBLE ST, NORTH LITTLE ROCK, AR
721146406
Phone: 501 945-0875
Web: WWW.BRUCEOAKLEY.COM

PRODUCTS/OPERATIONS

Selected Products and Services
Bagging
Barges
Bulk fertilizer
Grain and grain storage
Oakley vessel freight
River ports and stevedoring
Trucking

COMPETITORS

American Commercial
Lines
Bulkmatic
Comcar
Graincorp

Groendyke Transport
Kansas City Southern
Superior Bulk
Logistics

HISTORICAL FINANCIALS

Company Type: Private

Income Statement				FYE: September 25
	REVENUE ($ mil.)	NET INCOME ($ mil.)	NET PROFIT MARGIN	EMPLOYEES
09/08	1,160	31	2.8%	639
09/07	526	11	2.2%	—
09/06	419	13	3.2%	—
Annual Growth	66.3%	53.6%	—	—

2008 Year-End Financials
Return on assets: 21.7%   Cash ($ mil.): 3
Return on equity: 34.6%
Current ratio: 2.50

BRUCKNER TRUCK SALES, INC.

EXECUTIVES

Pres, Brian M Bruckner
Exec V Pres, Chris B Bruckner
Sec-Treas-Cfo, Wesley L Lawhorn
V Pres, Keith Martin
V Pres, Brian Murphy
Outside Parts Sales Representa, Liz Anderson
General Manager, Jack Croy
Parts Sales, Tyler Ferrell
Gen Manager-Tulsa Operations, Dale Yommer
Manager,, Byron Hughes
Contractor, Chavela Thompson

Auditors: CLIFTON LARSON ALLEN LLP DALL

LOCATIONS

HQ: BRUCKNER TRUCK SALES, INC.
9471 E INTERSTATE 40, AMARILLO, TX 791186960
Phone: 806 376-6273
Web: WWW.BRUCKNERTRUCK.COM

HISTORICAL FINANCIALS

Company Type: Private

Income Statement				FYE: June 30
	REVENUE ($ mil.)	NET INCOME ($ mil.)	NET PROFIT MARGIN	EMPLOYEES
06/15	580	10	1.8%	900
06/14	490	10	2.1%	—
06/10	200	2	1.1%	—
Annual Growth	23.8%	37.9%	—	—

2015 Year-End Financials
Return on assets: 3.5%   Cash ($ mil.): 31
Return on equity: 12.9%
Current ratio: 1.20

BRYAN MEDICAL CENTER

Bryan Medical Center is the centerpiece of a not-for-profit health care system serving residents of Lincoln Nebraska and surrounding communities. The medical center which operates as part of Bryan Health features two acute-care hospitals (Bryan East and Bryan West) housing a combined 670 beds. In addition to providing general medical and surgical care it serves as a regional trauma center and provides specialty care in areas such as cancer orthopedics and cardiology. The Bryan Health organization also includes a rural hospital and several outpatient clinics and it provides medical training home health care services and wellness programs.

Operations
In addition to Bryan Medical Center the Bryan Health organization operates the Crete Area Medical Center a 25-bed community hospital. Outpatient facilities include the Bryan Heart Institute (cardiology and cardiothoracic surgery) the Bryan Physician Network (family practice urgent care and specialist locations) and Bryan LifePointe (wellness and fitness programs). In addition the network includes the Bryan College of Health Sciences which provides bachelor's and master's degrees in nursing and health professional fields and the Bryan Foundation. It also conducts community education activities.

In the latest year for which data is available the hospital had 5912 inpatient visits; 6650 outpatient surgeries; and 68352 emergency department visits.

Geographic ReachBryan Medical Center serves patients throughout Nebraska as well as portions of neighboring states including Kansas Iowa and Missouri with clinics in more than 30 communities including Lincoln Columbus and Hastings.

Sales and Marketing
Bryan Medical Center advertises through magazines and through the Internet.

Strategy
In 2015 the hospital became the first in Nebraska to utilize the CardioMEMS HF System a miniaturized and wireless monitoring device to manage heart failure and reduce hospital admissions. That year it also began using the Kiva VCF Treatment System for the treatment of patients with vertebral compression fractures.

Company Background
The BryanLGH system was formed through the 1997 combination of Bryan Memorial Hospital (named after populist firebrand William Jennings Bryan) and Lincoln General Hospital. Bryan Health is part of the Heartland Health Alliance a group of about 40 Nebraska hospitals that work together to improve rural health care services through shared services and best practices.

In 2012 the health organization rebranded itself to reflect its expanded position in the region's health care market. BryanLGH Medical Center was renamed Bryan Medical Center and the broader health organization changed its name from the BryanLGH Health System to simply Bryan Health.

EXECUTIVES

Ceo, Kim Russel
Ceo*, R Lynn Wilson
Pres*, Craig Ames
Exec Dir*, Keith Miller
Cfo*, Russell Gronewold
Chief of Pediatric, Robert Koch
Technical Manager, Philip Joy
Manager of Care Management, Suzan Mulligan
Laboratory Director, Christa Engel
Information Technology Site MA, Drew Kotil
Director, Ellen Beans
Auditors: CROWE HORWATH LLP SIMSBURY C

LOCATIONS

HQ: BRYAN MEDICAL CENTER
1600 S 48TH ST, LINCOLN, NE 685061283
Phone: 402 481-1111
Web: WWW.BRYANHEALTH.COM

PRODUCTS/OPERATIONS

Selected Services

Bariatrics
Cardiac Services
Cancer
Cardiothoracic Surgery
Childbirth/Family Birthplace
Corporate & Community Wellness
Diabetes Center
Early Detection
Emergency Department
Heart Valve Center of Excellence
Hospitalists
Independence Center
Inpatient Rehabilitation
Neuroscience
Mental Health
Orthopedics
Outpatient Specialty Clinic
Radiation Oncology
Radiology
Rehabilitation/Therapy
Robotic Surgery
Sleep Medicine
StarCare Air Ambulance
Substance Abuse
Trauma Center
Urgent Care
Vascular Services
Women's & Children's

COMPETITORS

Catholic Health
Initiatives
Children's Hospital &
Medical Center
Madonna Rehabilitation
Hospital

Methodist Health
System
Nebraska Medical
Center

HISTORICAL FINANCIALS
Company Type: Private

Income Statement				FYE: December 31
	REVENUE ($ mil.)	NET INCOME ($ mil.)	NET PROFIT MARGIN	EMPLOYEES
12/19	785	129	16.5%	3,970
12/17	606	74	12.3%	—
12/16	586	60	10.3%	—
12/15	558	43	7.8%	—
Annual Growth	8.9%	31.2%	—	—

2019 Year-End Financials
Return on assets: 9.9% Cash ($ mil.): 108
Return on equity: 13.0%
Current ratio: 2.20

BUFFALO CITY SCHOOL DISTRICT

EXECUTIVES

Supt, Kriner Cash
Coordinator, Shannon Standing
Coordinator, Jeanine Groll
Assistant Superintendent, Mary Jo Conrad
Associate Superintendent For T, Anne Botticelli
Assistant, Catherine Dulak
Central Cse Coordinator, Dawn Haring
General Counsel, Nathaniel Kuzma
Food Director, Brigitte O'Brien-Wood
Coordinator Team Lead, Jason Guzzetta
Community Marketing, Joann Steinmetz
Auditors: FREEDMAXICK CPAS PC BUFFALO

LOCATIONS

HQ: BUFFALO CITY SCHOOL DISTRICT
  712 CITY HALL, BUFFALO, NY 142027537
Phone: 716 816-3575
Web: WWW.BUFFALOSCHOOLS.ORG

HISTORICAL FINANCIALS
Company Type: Private

Income Statement				FYE: June 30
	REVENUE ($ mil.)	NET INCOME ($ mil.)	NET PROFIT MARGIN	EMPLOYEES
06/12	868	(194)	—	5,386
06/05	0	0	1.4%	—
Annual Growth	215.8%	—	—	—

2012 Year-End Financials
Return on assets: (-11.2%) Cash ($ mil.): 348
Return on equity: —
Current ratio: —

BVH, INC.

EXECUTIVES

Ceo-Chb-Pres, Steve L Edwards
Evp-SEC, Timothy W Triplett
Evp-Cfo, Kenneth L Williams
Svp-Treasurer, Michael Williams

Marketing Coordinator, Belinda Walk
Planning Manager Ener, Brent Burklund
Associate Vice President, Carl Petz
Recruitment Manager, Danielle David
Director of Mechanical, Ed Vogt
Manager Organization Effective, Glenda Friesen
Engineering Technician, James Beckord
Auditors: KPMG LLP KANSAS CITY MO

LOCATIONS

HQ: BVH, INC.
  11401 LAMAR AVE, OVERLAND PARK, KS 662111508
Phone: 913 458-2000
Web: WWW.BV.COM

HISTORICAL FINANCIALS
Company Type: Private

Income Statement				FYE: December 29
	REVENUE ($ mil.)	NET INCOME ($ mil.)	NET PROFIT MARGIN	EMPLOYEES
12/17	3,363	87	2.6%	18,568
12/16*	3,207	75	2.4%	—
01/16	2,955	108	3.7%	—
01/15	3,029	113	3.7%	—
Annual Growth	3.6%	(8.3%)	—	—

*Fiscal year change

2017 Year-End Financials
Return on assets: 5.6% Cash ($ mil.): 344
Return on equity: 73.5%
Current ratio: 1.10

C.R. ENGLAND, INC.

The world's top refrigerated trucking company and one of North America's largest transportation firms C.R. England hauls refrigerated and dry cargo throughout the US. The family-owned company also serves parts of Canada and through alliances points in Mexico. C.R. England's fleet includes more than 3500 Freightliner Peterbilt Volvo and International tractors and 8000 trailers. Besides for-hire freight hauling C.R. England offers dedicated contract carriage in which drivers and equipment are assigned to a customer long-term; logistics services including freight brokerage; and intermodal railroad service.

Operations
The company's operations include national US US regional and Mexican truckload service as well as dedicated (customized) truck contracts and intermodal service.

In addition to freight brokerage C.R. England's England Logistics unit offers intermodal service for refrigerated cargo in which customers' containerized freight is shuttled between truck and railroad facility. The logistics unit also arranges the transportation of less-than-truckload quantities of freight and provides ground transportation of ocean containers for shipping lines.

This unit also provides global logistics - international shipping and freight forwarding solutions); supply chain management (freight management) and carrier services (factoring solutions fuel discounts tire discounts and other services).

C.R. England's business also benefits from operating five truck driving schools in the US and a course on becoming a freight broker. The school helps improve driver safety as well as provides a pool of qualified truck drivers for hire.

Geographic Reach
The company operates primarily in California Illinois Texas and Utah.

Strategy
Greening its fleet C. R. England has announced a multi-year liquefied natural gas (LNG) bulk fueling agreement with Shell. C.R. England will replace existing diesel trucks with LNG-powered trucks servicing southern California the most mature US market for fueling LNG-powered trucks.

The company is focusing on innovation in its intermodal and dedicated operations. The intermodal division has more than 1000 TempStack 53 ft. temperature-controlled containers which can be double-stacked on the flatcars of its partner railroad reducing customer costs increasing shipping capacity and efficiency and lowering fuel costs.

C.R. England is also beefing up its trucking operations working to deliver faster more secure shipments for its customers in its national and regional divisions.

Company Background
C.R. England was founded in 1920 by Chester Rodney England and is run by his descendants.

EXECUTIVES

Chb, Daniel E England
Co-Chb*, Dean England
Ceo*, Chad England
Pres*, Josh England
Exec V Pres*, Todd England
Exec V Pres*, Corey England
V Pres*, Tj England
Coo*, Zach England
Cfo*, Tj McGeean
Cso*, Brandon Harrison
Exec V Pres, Corporate Sales, David A Kramer
Auditors: TANNER LLC SALT LAKE CITY UT

LOCATIONS

HQ: C.R. ENGLAND, INC.
  4701 W 2100 S, SALT LAKE CITY, UT 841201223
Phone: 800 421-9004
Web: WWW.CRENGLAND.COM

PRODUCTS/OPERATIONS

Selected Operations

Trucking
National - Long haul truckload service
Mexico - Shipments in and out of Mexico
Regional - Short haul truckload service positioned in the West Midwest and Texas and surrounding areas (AR LA OK)
Dedicated - Tailor-made services dedicating trucks and drivers to specific customer needs
Intermodal - Expedited priority rail service using TempStack 53' refrigerated containers
England Logistics

COMPETITORS

C.h. Robinson Worldwide	Kllm Transport Services
Central Refrigerated Service	Landstar System
Covenant Transportation	Marten Transport
Crete Carrier	Navajo Shippers
Frozen Food Express	Prime Inc.
J.b. Hunt	Stevens Transport
	Swift Transportation
	Willis Shaw Express

HISTORICAL FINANCIALS
Company Type: Private

Income Statement   FYE: December 31

	REVENUE ($ mil.)	NET INCOME ($ mil.)	NET PROFIT MARGIN	EMPLOYEES
12/12	1,579	56	3.6%	6,500
12/11	1,315	55	4.3%	—
12/07	829	41	5.0%	—
Annual Growth	13.7%	6.2%	—	—

2012 Year-End Financials
Return on assets: 7.4% Cash ($ mil.): 15
Return on equity: 24.7%
Current ratio: 1.40

CALGON CARBON CORPORATION

Calgon Carbon is a global leader in activated carbons and purification systems. It offers purification and a variety of industrial and commercial manufacturing processes. Services include ballast water treatment ultraviolet light disinfection and advanced ion-exchange technologies used in the treatment of drinking water wastewater odor control pollution abatement and a variety of industrial and commercial manufacturing processes. With more than 240 patents its products find usage in more than 700 discrete market applications including air drinking water foods and pharmaceuticals purification and the removal of mercury emissions from coal-powered electrical plants.

Operations
Calgon Carbon operates in three division ? Activated Carbon Applications and Products.

Activated Carbon makes granular and powdered activated carbon to remove organic compounds from liquids and gases.

Products include Granular Activated Carbon Reactivation Services UV Technologies ION Exchange Activated Carbon Pellets Activated Carbon Cloth and Equipment.

Applications services include Environmental Air Treatment Mercury Removal Industrial Processes Food and Beverage Personal Protection Equipment Metals Recovery Medical/Pharmaceutical and Energy Storage.

Geographic Reach
Pennsylvania-based Calgon Carbon operates in a geographically diverse array of markets. It operates approximately 25 global offices and more than 15 manufacturing and reactivation facilities.

Sales and Marketing
Calgon Carbon offer carbon technologies used in over 700 distinct market applications from purifying air and drinking water to purifying foods and pharmaceuticals to separating gas and removing mercury emissions from coal-fired power plants.

Strategy
In mid-2021 Calgon Carbon Corporation announced today that it has entered into a definitive Securities and Asset Purchase Agreement with De Nora Water Technologies LLC to sell its Ultraviolet Technologies (UVT) business to De Nora. This agreement which is expected to close at the end of June 2021 includes the products brands and assets of Hyde Marine a world-leader in UV ballast water treatment systems as well as municipal and industrial disinfection brands such as RAYOX SENTINEL and C3 SERIES UV.

Calgon Carbon decided to expand its Mississippi activated carbon plant in mid-2020. The expansion is expected to add 38 jobs at the plant when complete. The estimated investment in the additional production line will be $185 million. When completed Calgon Carbon's virgin granular activated carbon capacity will exceed 200 million pounds per year. the expansion enables its activated carbon products to be more broadly used to clean the world's air and water on an even larger scale.

Company Background
In 1942 the Company produced an activated carbon product using bituminous coal and that was the beginning of the firm now known as Calgon Carbon Corporation.

EXECUTIVES
Ceo-Pres, Stevan R Schott
Evp*, James A Coccagno
Cfo-Svp*, Robert Fortwangler
Coordinator, Ann Boyll
Director Business, Bill Aldridge
Transportation Manager, Fred Ferderber
Associate General Counsel, Jessica Underwood
Audit Supervisor, Matt Poljak
Engineer, Robert Gebhard
U S Planning, Cliff Meredith
Plant Coordinator, Joseph Dubois
Auditors: DELOITTE & TOUCHE LLP PITTSBU

LOCATIONS
HQ: CALGON CARBON CORPORATION
3000 GSK DR, MOON TOWNSHIP, PA 151081381
Phone: 412 787-6700
Web: WWW.CALGONCARBON.COM

2015 sales

	$ mil.	% of total
United States	288	53
United Kingdom	43	8
Japan	35	7
France	20	4
China	17	3
Germany	17	3
Canada	17	3
South Korea	12	2
Belgium	10	2
Singapore	9	2
Netherlands	5	1
Denmark	4	1
Switzerland	3	1
Spain	3	1
Thailand	3	1
Other	41	8
Total	**535**	**100**

PRODUCTS/OPERATIONS

2015 Sales

	$ mil.	% of total
Activated Carbon & Service	486	91
Equipment	39	7
Consumer	9	2
Total	**535**	**100**

Selected Products
Ballast Water Treatment
Energy Storage
Environmental Air Treatment
Environmental Water Treatment
Food and Beverage
Industrial Processes
Medical
Mercury Removal
Metals Recovery
Municipal Water Treatment
Personal Protection Equipment
Residential Point of Use/Entry

COMPETITORS
3m Purification
Itt Water & Wastewater
Herford
Met-pro
Norit
Siemens Water Technologies
Trojan Technologies

HISTORICAL FINANCIALS
Company Type: Private

Income Statement   FYE: December 31

	REVENUE ($ mil.)	NET INCOME ($ mil.)	NET PROFIT MARGIN	EMPLOYEES
12/17	619	21	3.4%	1,334
12/16	514	13	2.7%	—
12/15	535	43	8.1%	—
12/14	555	49	8.9%	—
Annual Growth	3.7%	(24.7%)	—	—

2017 Year-End Financials
Return on assets: 2.5% Cash ($ mil.): 42
Return on equity: 5.0%
Current ratio: 2.60

CALIFORNIA DEPARTMENT OF WATER RESOURCES

The California Department of Water Resources knows that water is gold. The agency is dedicated to managing the state's water resources in partnership with other agencies. Its core areas include designing the State Water Project (which supplies water to some 25 million farms businesses and residents) providing legislative guidance creating recreational opportunities educating the public and offering technical and financial support for local planning and regional water management. The department also provides flood control and dam safety services as well as plans for future water needs for the state.

Operations
The company has 3 branches of Government; Executive Legislative and Judicial.

The California government's executive branch is overseen by the Office of the Governor and includes elected officials and administrators.

The California Legislature has two branches the State Assembly and the Senate. The Legislature vote on state laws and draft legislation.

The judicial branch includes the California Supreme Court and all the lower courts in the state and it interprets and applies laws at state and local levels.

Geographic Reach
The company has 2640 Data sets in California Data.

EXECUTIVES
SEC, Karla Nemeth
Acting Director, Cindy Messer
Director, Mark Cowin
Program Manager II, Cassandra Enos
Auditors: EIDE BAILLY LP SACRAMENTO CA

LOCATIONS

HQ: CALIFORNIA DEPARTMENT OF WATER RESOURCES
1416 9TH ST, SACRAMENTO, CA 958145511
Phone: 916 653-9394
Web: WWW.CA.GOV

HISTORICAL FINANCIALS

Company Type: Private

Income Statement				FYE: June 30
	REVENUE ($ mil.)	NET INCOME ($ mil.)	NET PROFIT MARGIN	EMPLOYEES
06/19	1,149	(27)	—	3,000
06/18	1,206	0	—	—
06/17	1,223	0	—	—
06/05	0	0	—	—
Annual Growth	—	—	—	—

2019 Year-End Financials

Return on assets: (-0.3%)   Cash ($ mil.): 708
Return on equity: (-2.4%)
Current ratio: 1.50

CALIFORNIA INSTITUTE OF TECHNOLOGY

The California Institute of Technology (Caltech) is a world-renowned science and engineering Institute that marshals some of the world's brightest mind and most innovative tools to address fundamental scientific questions and pressing societal challenges. The institute has approximately 938 undergraduate students and 1299 graduate students. Caltech has a very low student-teacher ratio of 3:1. Caltech operates the Jet Propulsion Laboratory (JPL) which supervises robotic Mars exploration programs and other interplanetary missions under contract to NASA. The school was founded in 1891.

Operations

Caltech's academic divisions includes Biology & Biological Engineering Chemistry & Chemical Engineering & Applied Science Geological & Planetary Sciences Humanities & Social Sciences and Physics Mathematics & Astronomy. The school also owns and operates large-scale research facilities such as the Seismological Laboratory and a global network of astronomical observatories including the Palomar and W. M. Keck Observatories; and cofounded and co-manages LIGO.

The JPL lab has more than 100 research and mission collaborations with Caltech faculty.

Geographic Reach

Caltech's about 124-acre campus is located in Pasadena California. Among the institution's global facilities are the Jet Propulsion Laboratory Caltech Seismological Laboratory and International Observatory Network.

Sales and Marketing

California Institute of Technology offers online education programs aimed to improve and educate future generations of scientist and engineers in Caltech. In addition online learning opportunities will be available through Cousera and edx educational technology platforms that offer online university-level courses in a wide range of disciplines to a worldwide audience at no charge.

Company Background

Caltech's professors and graduates have snared more than 30 Nobel Prizes. Other alumni include

filmmaker Frank Capra and Apollo 17 astronaut Harrison Schmitt.

EXECUTIVES

Pres, Thomas Rosenbaum
SEC*, Mary L Webster
Chairman*, David Lee
Operations Manager, Sharon Brunett
Wind Tunnel Manager, Stephanie Rider
Vice-President Public Relation, Robert L O'Rourke
Trustee, Louis J Lavigne Jr
Trustee, Patrick H Nettles Jr
Senior Trustee, Stanley R Rawn Jr
Senior Trustee, Virginia V Weldon
Executive Officer, Erica O Howard
Auditors: PRICEWATERHOUSECOOPERS LLP L

LOCATIONS

HQ: CALIFORNIA INSTITUTE OF TECHNOLOGY
1200 E CALIFORNIA BLVD, PASADENA, CA 911250001
Phone: 626 395-6811
Web: WWW.CALTECH.EDU

PRODUCTS/OPERATIONS

Selected Academic Divisions

Academics
Biology
Chemistry and Chemical Engineering
Engineering and Applied Science
Geological and Planetary Sciences
Humanities and Social Sciences
Physics Mathematics and Astronomy
Jet Propulsion Laboratory (NASA partnership)
Galaxy Evolution Explorer Science Center
Infrared Processing and Analysis Center
NASA Exoplanet Science Institute
NASA Herschel Science Center
Spitzer Space Telescope Science Center

HISTORICAL FINANCIALS

Company Type: Private

Income Statement				FYE: September 30
	REVENUE ($ mil.)	NET INCOME ($ mil.)	NET PROFIT MARGIN	EMPLOYEES
09/20	3,354	82	2.5%	11,643
09/19	3,434	(11)	—	—
09/18	3,303	165	5.0%	—
09/17	2,894	412	14.3%	—
Annual Growth	5.0%	(41.5%)	—	—

2020 Year-End Financials

Return on assets: 1.3%   Cash ($ mil.): 46
Return on equity: 2.5%
Current ratio: —

CALIFORNIA STEEL INDUSTRIES, INC.

California Steel Industries (CSI) doesn't use forensic evidence but its work does involve a steel slab. The company uses steel slab produced by third parties to manufacture steel products such as hot-rolled and cold-rolled steel galvanized coils and sheets and electric resistance weld (ERW) pipe. Its customers include aftermarket automotive manufacturers oil and gas producers roofing makers tubing manufacturers and building suppliers.

CSI serves the western region of the US. The company operates slitting shearing coating and single-billing services for third parties. Japan's JFE Holdings and Brazilian iron ore miner Vale SA each own 50% of CSI.

Operations

CSI has an annual production capacity of 2.8 million metric tons of flat rolled steel and pipe. It is the leading producer of flat rolled steel in the Western US and the only West Coast steel supplier capable of producing more than 2 million tons of steel in five different product lines: hot rolled pickled and oiled galvanized and cold rolled sheet and electric resistance welded pipe.

Geographic Reach

At its California plant the company processes steel slab purchased from suppliers around the world including Brazil Mexico Australia Japan Europe and the US.

CSI buys more than two-thirds of its steel slab from ArcelorMittal subsidiary Lazaro Cardenas in Mexico; ArcelorMittal Tubar o in Brazil; and Australia's Bluescope Steel. The purchased slab is transported to the Port of Los Angeles and then sent by train to CSI's facilities.

Sales and Marketing

Most of CSI's product lines are also sold to service distribution centers throughout the Western and Midwestern US with some product also sold worldwide through the export market. Its steel framing studs roofing decking and metal lath products are used in the home and commercial building industries. Other uses include water gas and oil pipelines automotive pans tubing (used by construction and furniture makers) and heating and cooling parts.

Strategy

In 2014 CSI built a new pipe mill on its site near Fontana California. The mill produces high-strength electrical resistance welded pipe up to 24 inches in diameter and up to 80 feet in length. Its existing pipe mill was limited to 16-inch diameter and 60-foot lengths.

Since 1992 CSI has invested more than $1 billion on its facilities to maintain modernize and expand operations.

Company Background

The company was formed in 1983.

EXECUTIVES

Pres-Ceo, Marcelo Botelho
Chb*, Tadaaki Yamaguchi
Chb*, Hiroshi Adachi
Exec V Pres Commercial*, Ricardo Bernardes
Exec V Pres Fin & Admin-Corp S*, Brett Guge
Support Tech, Victor Subandhi
Controller, Ron Johnson
Research and Engin, Joe Castorena
Engineer, Paul Hawkins
Mechanical Engineer, Rey Huerta
Site Maintenance Manager, Richard Conti
Auditors: ERNST & YOUNG LLP LOS ANGELES

LOCATIONS

HQ: CALIFORNIA STEEL INDUSTRIES, INC.
14000 SAN BERNARDINO AVE, FONTANA, CA 923355259
Phone: 909 350-6300
Web: WWW.CALIFORNIASTEEL.COM

PRODUCTS/OPERATIONS

Selected Steel Products
Cold Rolled
ERW Pipe
Galvanized
Hot Rolled
Pickled and Oiled

COMPETITORS

Ak Steel Holding Corporation	Steel Dynamics
Evraz Inc. Na	Steelscape
Nucor	Ternium Mexico
O'neal Steel	Uss-posco Industries

HISTORICAL FINANCIALS

Company Type: Private

Income Statement				FYE: December 31
	REVENUE ($ mil.)	NET INCOME ($ mil.)	NET PROFIT MARGIN	EMPLOYEES
12/09	551	(13)	—	1,095
12/08	1,510	13	0.9%	
Annual Growth	(63.5%)	—	—	—

2009 Year-End Financials

Return on assets: (-2.2%)
Return on equity: (-4.4%)
Current ratio: 4.30

Cash ($ mil.): 61

CALIFORNIA'S VALUED TRUST

EXECUTIVES

Exec Dir, Valerie Cornuelle
Exec Dir, David Vaughn
Helpdesk Analyst, James Mason
Business Analyst, Nolan Clinard
Programmer Analyst, Chuck King
Member, Denise Boranian
Receptionist, Lois Casey
Director of Business Developme, Tierney Brien

LOCATIONS

HQ: CALIFORNIA'S VALUED TRUST
520 E HERNDON AVE, FRESNO, CA 937202907
Phone: 559 437-2960
Web: WWW.CVTRUST.ORG

HISTORICAL FINANCIALS

Company Type: Private

Income Statement				FYE: September 30
	ASSETS ($ mil.)	NET INCOME ($ mil.)	INCOME AS % OF ASSETS	EMPLOYEES
09/18	157	(3)	—	20
09/17	157	21	13.3%	—
09/15	136	(5)	—	—
Annual Growth	4.9%	—	—	—

CAMERON INTERNATIONAL CORPORATION

Cameron is a leading manufacturer provider and servicer of oil and gas industry equipment. The company makes products that control pressure at oil and gas wells including blowout preventers chokes controls wellheads measurement tools and valves. The company's products are used for offshore onshore and subsea applications. Cameron is a wholly owned subsidiary of oilfield product and services giant Schlumberger (a major provider of technology for reservoir characterization drilling production and processing services to the oil and gas industry).

Operations

The company provides oil and gas production support systems through separate business lines: Subsea Surface Drilling and Valves and Measurement (V&M).

Subsea delivers integrated solutions products systems and services to the subsea oil and gas market including integrated subsea production systems involving wellheads subsea trees manifolds and flowline connectors subsea processing systems for the enhanced recovery of hydrocarbons control systems connectors and services designed to maximize reservoir recovery and extend the life of each field. The Subsea segment includes the operations of OneSubsea.

Surface designs and manufactures complete wellhead and Christmas tree systems for onshore and offshore topside applications (from conventional to high-pressure high temperature systems to specialized systems for dry completions and heavy oil.

Drilling supplies integrated drilling systems for onshore and offshore applications to shipyards drilling contractors exploration and production companies and rental tool companies. Drilling equipment designed and manufactured includes ram and annular BOPs control systems drilling risers drilling valves choke and kill manifolds diverter systems topdrives drawworks mud pumps pipe handling equipment other rig products and parts and services.

V&M supplies valves and measurement systems primarily used to control direct and measure the flow of oil and gas as they are moved from wellheads to refineries petrochemical plants and industrial centers. Its products include gate valves ball valves butterfly valves plug valves globe valves check valves actuators chokes and measurement products such as totalizers turbine meters flow computers chart recorders and ultrasonic flow meters.

Geographic Reach

Cameron's 300 locations allow it serve most of the world's active major oil and gas basins. The bulk of its business comes from outside the US.

Sales and Marketing
Financial Performance

Cameron generates about 15% of Schlumberger's sales. The subsidiary's revenue declined 4% to $6.5 billion on lower sales for its OneSubsea and Valves & Measurements product segments. OneSubsea offers products and services for subsea oil and gas companies including wellheads subsea trees control systems and production system optimization. The company's Valves & Measurements products span valves and measurement systems for oil and gas flow for the upstream midstream and downstream sectors.

Strategy

To keep pace with rivals increasingly adopting automation technology Schlumbeger formed a joint venture in 2019 with Rockwell Automation to form Sensia. Sensia combines Cameron's sensor and measurement products with Rockwell's industrial automation technology and analytics capabilities. The new company's offerings will facilitate automated oilfield operations and connect equipment with software to gather data from sensors and devices. About two-fifths of the JV's revenue is expected to derive from North America.

Company Background

In 2013 Cameron and Schlumberger formed OneSubsea (60% owned by Cameron International) to manufacture and develop products systems and services for the subsea oil and gas market. The creation of OneSubsea allows the company to bring together Schlumberger's expertise in subsea processing and platform integration with its own capabilities in subsea equipment to allow customers to greatly increase their subsea reservoir recovery rates. (In 2014 OneSubsea Helix Energy Solutions and Schlumberger formed an alliance to develop technologies and deliver services to optimize the cost and efficiency of subsea well intervention systems.)

Cameron moved into the lucrative shale market in the US Northeast in 2011 through the acquisition of West Virginia-based Industrial Machine & Fabrication a leading aftermarket service provider for reciprocating engines and compressors.

That year it also expanded its drilling equipment portfolio buying LeTourneau Technologies Drillings Systems and Offshore Products divisions from Joy Global for $375 million.

In 2010 a BP rig in the Gulf of Mexico exploded and sank spewing oil into the Gulf. The blowout preventer on the system made by Cameron International failed to work properly. A board of inquiry was set up to find out the cause of the disaster and a separate government report found that the company's blowout preventer proved incapable of stopping the high-pressure flow from the doomed well. The company claimed that its equipment met industry standards and it was not found liable in any legal proceeding although it did pay $82.5 million to settle with BP. (BP accounted for 12% of the company's revenues in 2010).

Cameron traces its roots to the mid-1800s when it made steam engines to generate power for plants and textile and rolling mills.

EXECUTIVES

Ceo-Pres, Robert Scott Rowe
Cfo-Sr V Pres, Charles Sledge
Cao-V Pres-Controller, Dennis Baldwin
Chief ADM Officer-V Pres, Steven Geiger
Cto, Justin Rounce
Director, Mike Mills
Director Business, Nolan Roberts
Director, Robert Lopez
Administrative Assistant, Stephanie Lyons
Materials Manager, Alberto Garcia
Engineer, Craig Good
Auditors: ERNST & YOUNG LLP HOUSTON TE

LOCATIONS

HQ: CAMERON INTERNATIONAL CORPORATION
4646 W SAM HOUSTON PKWY N, HOUSTON, TX 770418214
Phone: 713 939-2282
Web: WWW.SLB.COM

PRODUCTS/OPERATIONS

COMPETITORS

Abb Inc.
Aker Solutions
Atlas Copco
Circor International
Dresser-rand
Dril-quip
Ebara
Fmc
Flotek
Ge Oil
Ingersoll-rand Industrial Technologies
Mcdermott
National Oilwell Varco
Weatherford International

HISTORICAL FINANCIALS
Company Type: Private

Income Statement				FYE: December 31
	REVENUE ($ mil.)	NET INCOME ($ mil.)	NET PROFIT MARGIN	EMPLOYEES
12/14	10,381	848	8.2%	23,000
12/13	9,838	724	7.4%	—
12/12	8,502	750	8.8%	—
Annual Growth	10.5%	6.3%	—	—

2014 Year-End Financials
Return on assets: 6.6%
Return on equity: 15.6%
Current ratio: 1.80
Cash ($ mil.): 1,513

CAMPUS CRUSADE FOR CHRIST INC

EXECUTIVES

Ceo-Pres, Stephen B Douglass
Dir*, Vonette Z Bright
Director, Marc Rutter
Coordinator, Matthew Anderson
Security Staff, Russ Licht
Audio Operations Manager, David Quiroz
Customer Manager, Anjelina Maldonado
National Director College Prep, Ben Burns
Executive, Irv Klaschus
Director, Brian Ellis
Regional Manager, Chris McQuirk

LOCATIONS

HQ: CAMPUS CRUSADE FOR CHRIST INC
100 LAKE HART DR, ORLANDO, FL 328320100
Phone: 407 826-2000
Web: WWW.CRU.ORG

HISTORICAL FINANCIALS
Company Type: Private

Income Statement				FYE: August 31
	REVENUE ($ mil.)	NET INCOME ($ mil.)	NET PROFIT MARGIN	EMPLOYEES
08/17	598	26	4.4%	7,688
08/08	7	1	25.1%	—
08/05	0	0	—	—
08/04	423	414	97.7%	—
Annual Growth	2.7%	(19.0%)	—	—

2017 Year-End Financials
Return on assets: 7.4%
Return on equity: 10.8%
Current ratio: 0.70
Cash ($ mil.): 45

CANDID COLOR SYSTEMS, INC.

EXECUTIVES

Pres-Ceo, Jack E Counts Jr
SEC-Treas, Beverly Ellis
Designer, David J Wall
Sales Business Analyst, Cristina Oconnor
Customer Support Manager, Cristina O'Connor
CIO, Demetri Barges
Manager, Jeremy Dabbs
Administrator, Sean Kendall

LOCATIONS

HQ: CANDID COLOR SYSTEMS, INC.
1300 METROPOLITAN AVE, OKLAHOMA CITY, OK 731082042
Phone: 405 947-8747
Web: WWW.CANDID.COM

HISTORICAL FINANCIALS
Company Type: Private

Income Statement				FYE: July 31
	REVENUE ($ mil.)	NET INCOME ($ mil.)	NET PROFIT MARGIN	EMPLOYEES
07/07	21,742	2,534	11.7%	300
07/05	22	1	8.3%	—
07/04	21	2	10.9%	—
07/03	21	1	9.4%	—
Annual Growth	467.2%	498.3%	—	—

2007 Year-End Financials
Return on assets: 999.9%
Return on equity: 999.9%
Current ratio: 2.30
Cash ($ mil.): 2

CAPE COD HEALTHCARE, INC.

Cape Cod Healthcare (CCHC) is a not-for-profit healthcare organization that operates two acute care hospitals (Cape Cod Hospital and Falmouth Hospital). Specializations include heart and vascular women's health bones and muscles cancer care and brain spine and nerves. CCHC also operates a home health services agency (Visiting Nurse Association of Cape Cod) more than 130-bed skilled nursing and rehabilitation facility (JML Care Center) and assisted living facility (Heritage at Falmouth). The health care system has affiliations with UMass Medical School Boston University University of New England and Cape Cod Community College. CCHC is the Cape's largest private employer with more than 5300 staff members 450 physicians and 790 volunteers.

EXECUTIVES

Ceo-Pres, Michael K Lauf
Cfo*, Michael Connors
Engineer, Mark Van Leeuwen
Director, Elizabeth L Acord
Svp and CIO, Jeanne M Fallon
Creative Manager, Deborah Woloski-Barnes
Administrative Assistant, Olga L Smith
Emergency Medicine Physician, Steven A Kohler

Information Analyst, Joan Bryant
Staff Pharmacist, Kate Garvey
Senior Vice President of Manag, Jack Lipomi
Auditors: PRICEWATERHOUSECOOPERS LLP BO

LOCATIONS

HQ: CAPE COD HEALTHCARE, INC.
27 PARK ST, HYANNIS, MA 026015230
Phone: 508 862-5030
Web: WWW.CAPECODHEALTH.ORG

PRODUCTS/OPERATIONS

Selected Massachusetts Facilities
Bourne Health Center
Cape Cod Hospital (Hyannis)
Davenport Mugar Cancer Center (Hyannis)
Falmouth Hospital
  Clark Cancer Center
Fontaine Medical Center (Harwich)
Heritage at Falmouth
JLM Care Center (Falmouth)
Mashpee Health Center
Sandwich Health Center
Wilkins Outpatient Medical Complex (Hyannis)

COMPETITORS

Baystate Health
Boston Medical Center
Cambridge Health Alliance
Care New England
Caregroup
Milford Regional Medical Center
Northeast Health System
Partners Healthcare
Southcoast Hospitals Group
Steward Health Care
Universal Health Services
Winchester Healthcare

HISTORICAL FINANCIALS
Company Type: Private

Income Statement				FYE: September 30
	REVENUE ($ mil.)	NET INCOME ($ mil.)	NET PROFIT MARGIN	EMPLOYEES
09/20	931	27	2.9%	1,850
09/19	978	29	3.0%	—
09/18	921	80	8.7%	—
09/17	872	74	8.5%	—
Annual Growth	2.2%	(28.4%)	—	—

2020 Year-End Financials
Return on assets: 2.0%
Return on equity: 3.2%
Current ratio: 1.20
Cash ($ mil.): 75

CAPE COD HOSPITAL

Get too much sun or eat too much lobster while visiting Cape Cod? Never fear Cape Cod Hospital can treat whatever ails you. Cape Cod Hospital a subsidiary of Cape Cod Healthcare is a 260-bed acute care hospital that serves the Cape Cod Massachusetts area. Its specialty services include pediatrics maternity care cancer treatment and infectious disease therapeutics. The not-for-profit Cape Cod Hospital also includes a specialty cardiovascular center a psychiatry unit a surgical pavilion and a diagnostic imaging facility as well as outpatient medical offices.

Operations

Cape Cod Hospital's emergency department treats about 85000 patients each year. The medical center also performs more than 12500 surgeries and 1000 birth procedures each year as well as about 2 million laboratory tests. Its 20-bed Cape

Psych Center provides inpatient and outpatient mental and behavioral services. The campus also includes more than a dozen medical offices buildings and a community health center. Cape Cod Hospital's staff includes about 300 physicians.

Geographic Reach

Cape Cod Hospital is located on a 40-acre campus on the shoreline of Hyannis Massachusetts.

Strategy

To keep its facilities modern and efficient in 2015 the company opened a new emergency center located adjacent to the existing emergency center. The 18-month $22 million project added 25000 sq. ft. of space and 72 patient treatment rooms.

In 2013 Cape Cod Hospital reopened the renovated and expanded Intensive Care Unit. That project cost $4.9 million and doubled the size of the original area.

To control the cost of providing hospital care parent Cape Cod Healthcare has also been expanding its outpatient and ambulatory care services. It is adding new urgent care centers and surgery centers both near the hospital and in surrounding communities.

Company Background

Cape Cod Hospital was established in Hyannis in 1920.

EXECUTIVES

Ceo, Michael K Lauf
Coo*, Arthur Mombourquette
Sr V Pres*, Michael L Connors
Sr V Pres*, Jeanne Fallon
Sr V Pres*, Theresa M Ahern
Off Shift Nursing Manager, Stephanie Ellis
MD, Ann M Trout
Cardiology, Bruce F Levy
Cardiology, Charles I Haffajee
Laboratory Director, Cheryl Connon
Officer, Courtney Bridge
Auditors: POWERHOUSECOOPERS LLP BOSTON

LOCATIONS

HQ: CAPE COD HOSPITAL
27 PARK ST, HYANNIS, MA 026015203
Phone: 508 771-1800
Web: WWW.CAPECODHEALTH.ORG

PRODUCTS/OPERATIONS

Selected Services
Allergy and Immunology
Behavioral Health
Blood Center
Dermatology
Foot Care & Surgery
Hand Surgery
Orthopedics
Pregnancy & Birth
Sports Medicine
Women's Health

COMPETITORS

Baystate Health
Boston Medical Center
Cambridge Health Alliance
Care New England
Caregroup
Children's Hospital Boston
Milford Regional Medical Center
Northeast Health System
Partners Healthcare
Southcoast Hospitals Group
Steward Health Care
Sturdy Memorial
Universal Health Services
Winchester Healthcare

HISTORICAL FINANCIALS

Company Type: Private

Income Statement — FYE: September 30

	REVENUE ($ mil.)	NET INCOME ($ mil.)	NET PROFIT MARGIN	EMPLOYEES
09/20	569	12	2.2%	1,700
09/19	599	25	4.3%	—
09/18	564	46	8.3%	—
09/17	526	47	9.0%	—
Annual Growth	2.7%	(36.3%)	—	—

2020 Year-End Financials

Return on assets: 1.6% Cash ($ mil.): 15
Return on equity: 2.5%
Current ratio: 1.40

CAPE FEAR VALLEY MEDICAL CENTER

LOCATIONS

HQ: CAPE FEAR VALLEY MEDICAL CENTER
1638 OWEN DR, FAYETTEVILLE, NC 283043424
Phone: 910 615-4000
Web: WWW.CAPEFEARVALLEY.COM

HISTORICAL FINANCIALS

Company Type: Private

Income Statement — FYE: September 30

	REVENUE ($ mil.)	NET INCOME ($ mil.)	NET PROFIT MARGIN	EMPLOYEES
09/15	630	23	3.8%	2,711
09/14	590	40	6.8%	—
09/13	823	398	48.4%	—
Annual Growth	(12.5%)	(75.5%)	—	—

2015 Year-End Financials

Return on assets: 2.6% Cash ($ mil.): 38
Return on equity: 5.1%
Current ratio: 2.80

CAPISTRANO UNIFIED SCHOOL DISTRICT

EXECUTIVES

Ceo, John M Alpay
SEC Brd*, Jane Boss
Supt*, Joseph M Farley
Dir of Fin*, Philippa Geiger
Mng MBR*, Joel Drew
Interm Dep Superintendent, Robyn Phillips
Executive Director, Michelle Hart
Executive Director, Matt Krause
Executive Director, Peggy Baerst
Assistant Superintendent, Philippa K Townsend
Executive Director, Stacy Yogi
Auditors: IT NIGRO & NIGRO PC MURRIETA

LOCATIONS

HQ: CAPISTRANO UNIFIED SCHOOL DISTRICT
33122 VALLE RD, SAN JUAN CAPISTRANO, CA 926754859
Phone: 949 234-9200
Web: WWW.CAPOUSD-CA.SCHOOLLOOP.COM

HISTORICAL FINANCIALS

Company Type: Private

Income Statement — FYE: June 30

	REVENUE ($ mil.)	NET INCOME ($ mil.)	NET PROFIT MARGIN	EMPLOYEES
06/20	549	(29)	—	4,500
06/19	2	0	9.2%	—
Annual Growth	20486.2%	—	—	—

CAPITAL DISTRICT PHYSICIANS' HEALTH PLAN, INC.

Capital District Physicians' Health Plan (CDPHP) is an independent not-for-profit health plan serving some 448000 members in two dozen New York counties. It offers employer-sponsored and individual managed care plans (including HMO PPO and consumer-directed plans) as well as a Medicare Advantage plan for seniors. The company's coverage include full coverage for some preventative medical services as well as options for covering prescription drugs dental work and vision services. CDPHP also provides wellness programs that help members with weight loss smoking cessation and chronic disease management.

Operations

In addition to its commercial and Medicare offerings CDPHP provides health plans under several state-subsidized insurance programs including Family Health Plus and Child Health Plus (intended for residents who don't qualify for Medicaid) and Healthy NY (intended for small businesses and sole proprietors). Altogether the CDPHP provider network includes more than 10000 physicians and facilities.

The company's classifies its products in three lines of business: Health Maintenance Organization (HMO) products (which includes Healthy New York Medicare Choices Medicaid Child Health Plus and Family Health Plus) provided by CDPHP; Preferred Provider Organization (PPO) products (which include PPO High Deductible PPO Medicare Choices Exclusive Provider Organization -EPO- and High Deductible EPO products) provided by CDPHP Universal Benefits Inc.; and the Administrative Services Organization (ASO) plans (which includes ASO and self-insured plans) provided by Capital District Physicians' Healthcare Network Inc.

In 2013 CDPHP's membership increased by about 38000.

Geographic Reach

CDPHP serves customers in 24 New York counties: Albany Broome Chenango Columbia Delaware Dutchess Essex Fulton Greene Hamilton Herkimer Madison Montgomery Oneida Orange Otsego Rensselaer Saratoga Schenectady Schoharie Tioga Ulster Warren and Washington.

Financial Performance

CDPHP reported a 13% increase in revenues in 2013 due to an increase in membership and in earned premiums.

The company suffered a loss of $43 million in 2013 (a decrease of more than 375%) due to an increase in claims and general expenses.

Strategy

CDPHP's self-proclaimed strategy is to use the majority of its premium income to pay out medical claims while maintaining necessary reserve levels to keep its solid financial performance and to comply with federal medical loss-ratio guidelines. It earmarks a small amount of income for operational expenses as well as to fund growth and wellness initiatives.

In mid-2014 the company teamed upewith Independent Health to build innovative products tools and services for providers employers and individuals across New York State. The partnership will focus on developing new tools technology and products along with recruiting new physicians.

In the early 2013 the company opened a new CDPHP Service Center location at Latham New York and a health and fitness center inside an Albany supermarket.

CDPHP also works to lower medical expenses by partnering with other regional care and plan providers.

Company Background

In 2011 CDPHP partnered with Trendshift in 2011 to provide a new group funding management system for employers.

An association of local Albany physicians founded CDPHP in 1984.

EXECUTIVES

Pres, John Bennett
Vpres*, William Cromie
Physical Therapy, Center Healt, Abigail Andrews
Information Technology Manager, Valerine Hines
Sales Manager, Alicia Kelleyfield
Information Specialist, Matthew Rickard
Information Specialist, Dominick Dipietro
Member Representative, Jordan Stewart
Director, Martin Symansky
Director, Reny Clifford
Executive Assistant, Ruth Potter

LOCATIONS

HQ: CAPITAL DISTRICT PHYSICIANS' HEALTH PLAN, INC.
500 PATROON CREEK BLVD, ALBANY, NY 122061057
Phone: 518 641-3700
Web: WWW.CDPHP.COM

PRODUCTS/OPERATIONS

Selected Products
Dental and Vision Health Plans
  CVS ExtraCare Health Card
  Delta Dental
Government Plans
  Child Health Plus
  Family Health Plus
  Medicaid Select Plan
  Medicare Choices (HMO)
Group Health Plans
  Embrace Health
  Exclusive Provider Organization (EPO)
  Group Medicare
  High Deductible Health Plans (HDHP)
  Health Maintenance Organization (HMO)
  Healthy Direction
  Lifestyle Riders
  Preferred Provider Organization (PPO)
  Transitional Health Plans
  Health Funding Arrangements
  Flexible Spending Accounts
  Health Reimbursement Arrangement
  Health Savings Account
Individual Health Plans

Healthy New York
Non-Group Health Plans

COMPETITORS

Aetna
Anthem
Cigna
Emblemhealth
Fidelis Care New York
Humana
Independent Health
Mvp Health Plan
Unitedhealth Group
Excellus Bluecross Blueshield Rochester Region
Healthnow New York Inc

HISTORICAL FINANCIALS

Company Type: Private

Income Statement — FYE: December 31

	REVENUE ($ mil.)	NET INCOME ($ mil.)	NET PROFIT MARGIN	EMPLOYEES
12/13	1,314	22	1.7%	700
12/09	1,037	33	3.2%	—
12/03	818	(1)	—	—
Annual Growth	4.9%	—	—	—

2013 Year-End Financials

Return on assets: 4.4% Cash ($ mil.): 61
Return on equity: 7.0%
Current ratio: 0.80

CAPITAL INCOME BUILDER

EXECUTIVES

Chm Ceo, Tim Armour
Vchm, Rob Lovelace
Pres, Phil De Toledo
Coo, Rob Klausner
Head Fixed Incm Glob Tradng, Mike Gitlin
Chm Ceo NA Distribution, Matt O'Connor
Auditors: PRICEWATERHOUSECOOPERS LLP LO

LOCATIONS

HQ: CAPITAL INCOME BUILDER
333 S HOPE ST FL 55, LOS ANGELES, CA 900713061
Phone: 213 486-9200
Web: WWW.CAPITALGROUP.COM

HISTORICAL FINANCIALS

Company Type: Private

Income Statement — FYE: October 31

	REVENUE ($ mil.)	NET INCOME ($ mil.)	NET PROFIT MARGIN	EMPLOYEES
10/19	3,912	5,826	148.9%	25
10/18	3,385	(7,919)	—	—
10/16	3,857	2,628	68.1%	—
Annual Growth	0.5%	30.4%	—	—

2019 Year-End Financials

Return on assets: 999.9% Cash ($ mil.): —
Return on equity: 999.9%
Current ratio: —

CARDINAL LOGISTICS HOLDINGS, LLC

EXECUTIVES

Ceo, Tom Hostetler
Exec Chm, Leo Suggs
Exec Chb, Tom White
Chm, Vin McLoughlin
Pres, Jerry Bowman
Exec V Pres-Treas, Robert C Larose
Sr V Pres-Gen Counsel-Sec, John Hove
V Pres-Chief Risk Offcr, Jeff Lester
V Pres-Contrl, Michael Skipworth
V Pres, Dan Curtis
Cfo, Michael Roberts
Auditors: KPMG LLP CHARLOTTE NORTH CA

LOCATIONS

HQ: CARDINAL LOGISTICS HOLDINGS, LLC
5333 DAVIDSON HWY, CONCORD, NC 280278478
Phone: 704 789-2000
Web: WWW.CARDLOG.COM

HISTORICAL FINANCIALS

Company Type: Private

Income Statement — FYE: December 31

	REVENUE ($ mil.)	NET INCOME ($ mil.)	NET PROFIT MARGIN	EMPLOYEES
12/18	804	(16)	—	3,040
12/17	791	(10)	—	—
Annual Growth	1.7%	—	—	—

2018 Year-End Financials

Return on assets: (-6.7%) Cash ($ mil.): 56
Return on equity: (-12.7%)
Current ratio: 1.60

CARE NEW ENGLAND HEALTH SYSTEM INC

Care New England Health System take pains to ease its patients' pain. The system operates four hospitals: Kent Hospital a general acute care facility with about 360 beds; the 290-bed Memorial Hospital of Rhode Island; psychiatric facility Butler Hospital; and Women & Infants Hospital of Rhode Island which specializes in obstetrics gynecology and newborn pediatrics. All told the system has more than 963 licensed beds. Care New England formed in 1996 by three member hospitals also operates a home health agency and outpatient care facilities. In late 2016 the system dropped its plans to merge with Southcoast Health. The following year it agreed to be acquired by Partners Health-Care which is expanding outside of Massachusetts.

Operations

Three of the Care New England hospitals — Memorial Hospital Women & Infants and Butler — are teaching hospitals for Brown University's Warren Alpert Medical School. Altogether the organization's facilities handle more than 40000 inpatient discharges each year as well as 129000 emergency room visits and 9800 births.

The organization's VNA of Care New England unit administers home health and hospice care as well as private duty nursing services for the elderly new mothers and terminally ill patients. The Care New England Wellness Center offers fitness and rehabilitation services. The health care network also includes physician practice locations and an adult day care center.

Geographic Reach
Based in Providence Rhode Island Care New England serves southeastern New England communities including Central Falls and Pawtucket Rhode Island and Plainville Massachusetts.

Financial Performance
In 2014 the system posted revenue of $1.1 billion.

Strategy
The Care New England system is focused on five key initiatives: system strength clinical excellence physician alignment strategic partnerships and academic excellence. It is working to strengthen operations in clinical fields including cardiology emergency medicine behavioral health pathology pediatrics and women's health. In 2013 the company enhanced its mental health services by forming an affiliation with The Providence Center. In addition Kent Hospital launched the construction of a new ambulatory surgery and primary care center.

Mergers and Acquisitions
The Care New England organization added its fourth hospital in 2013 through the acquisition of Memorial Hospital of Rhode Island. The purchase added acute care and primary care capacity and expanded the organization's regional presence.

In late 2015 Care New England and Southcoast Health signed a letter of intent to merge. The deal will create a new parent organization to oversee both health systems.

EXECUTIVES

Ceo, James Finale
Ceo, John Hynes
Pres, James Fanale
SEC, Paula Phelan
Chief Clinical Officer, Raymond Powrie
Chief of Medicine, Alfred Arcand
Scientist, Linda Lupo-Adams
Coordinator, Greg Spaziano
Programmer Analyst, Jim Manchester
Manager Payroll, Joseph Dalessandro
Vice President Human Resources, Dean Carlson
Auditors: PRICEWATERHOUSECOOPERS LLP BO

LOCATIONS

HQ: CARE NEW ENGLAND HEALTH SYSTEM INC
45 WILLARD AVE, PROVIDENCE, RI 029053218
Phone: 401 453-7900
Web: WWW.CARENEWENGLAND.ORG

COMPETITORS

Baystate Health
Community Health Systems
Lifespan Corporation
Partners Healthcare
Roger Williams Medical Center
Southcoast Hospitals Group
Tenet Healthcare
Universal Health Services
Yale New Haven Health System

HISTORICAL FINANCIALS
Company Type: Private

Income Statement				FYE: September 30
	REVENUE ($ mil.)	NET INCOME ($ mil.)	NET PROFIT MARGIN	EMPLOYEES
09/20	1,123	(26)	—	6,500
09/19	1,146	(30)	—	—
09/17	1,132	21	1.9%	—
09/16	1,154	(63)	—	—
Annual Growth	(0.7%)	—	—	—

2020 Year-End Financials
Return on assets: (-2.5%)   Cash ($ mil.): 133
Return on equity: (-11.7%)
Current ratio: 1.20

CAREOREGON, INC.

EXECUTIVES

Pres, Chris Krenk
Exec Dir*, Mylia Christensen
Coordinator, Crystal Page
Customer Representativ, Brian M McManus
Personnel Assistant, Vicki Greenwald
Claims Examiner Supervisor, Jeremy Brown
Human Resources Benefits Speci, Shannon Clesceri
Accounting Manager, Kinh Reynolds
Manager, Laura Doeckel
Employee, Mona Horne
Chief Officer, Scott Clement
Auditors: LB KPMG LLP SEATTLE WA

LOCATIONS

HQ: CAREOREGON, INC.
315 SW 5TH AVE STE 900, PORTLAND, OR 972041703
Phone: 503 416-4100
Web: WWW.CAREOREGON.ORG

HISTORICAL FINANCIALS
Company Type: Private

Income Statement				FYE: December 31
	REVENUE ($ mil.)	NET INCOME ($ mil.)	NET PROFIT MARGIN	EMPLOYEES
12/19	1,240	64	5.2%	140
12/16	886	(9)	—	—
12/14	851	87	10.3%	—
12/13	564	(0)	—	—
Annual Growth	14.0%	—	—	—

2019 Year-End Financials
Return on assets: 13.1%   Cash ($ mil.): 96
Return on equity: 19.6%
Current ratio: 4.20

CARILION MEDICAL CENTER

EXECUTIVES

Ceo, Nancy Howell Agee
Pres*, Steve Arner
SEC*, Briggs Andrews
V Pres-Treas*, Rob Vaughan
Treas*, George Robert Vaughan Jr
Cfo*, Donald E Lorton
Prin*, Edward Murphy
Department SEC, Donna Webb
Pathologist, Robert White
Internist, Bruce Johnson
Human Resources Coordinator, Carrie Boggess
Auditors: DELOITTE & TOUCHE LLP CHARLOT

LOCATIONS

HQ: CARILION MEDICAL CENTER
1906 BELLEVIEW AVE SE, ROANOKE, VA 240141838
Phone: 540 981-7000
Web: WWW.CARILIONCLINIC.ORG

HISTORICAL FINANCIALS
Company Type: Private

Income Statement				FYE: September 30
	REVENUE ($ mil.)	NET INCOME ($ mil.)	NET PROFIT MARGIN	EMPLOYEES
09/19	1,380	(137)	—	6,390
09/18	1,281	134	10.5%	—
09/17	1,232	134	10.9%	—
09/16	1,177	4	0.4%	—
Annual Growth	5.4%	—	—	—

2019 Year-End Financials
Return on assets: (-9.0%)   Cash ($ mil.): 2
Return on equity: (-26.4%)
Current ratio: 1.30

CARILION NEW RIVER VALLEY MEDICAL CENTER

EXECUTIVES

Pres, Donald Halliwill
Ceo*, John Piatkowski
Bus Anylst, Mike Bunker
Coordinator, Becky Garnett
Gis Technician, Maelynn Farmer

LOCATIONS

HQ: CARILION NEW RIVER VALLEY MEDICAL CENTER
2900 LAMB CIR STE 150, CHRISTIANSBURG, VA 240736341
Phone: 540 731-2000
Web: WWW.CARILIONCLINIC.ORG

HISTORICAL FINANCIALS
Company Type: Private

Income Statement				FYE: September 30
	REVENUE ($ mil.)	NET INCOME ($ mil.)	NET PROFIT MARGIN	EMPLOYEES
09/13	896	116	12.9%	45
09/05	30	2	6.5%	—
09/04	115	18	16.0%	—
09/03	88	11	13.5%	—
Annual Growth	26.1%	25.5%	—	—

Return on assets: 10.9%   Cash ($ mil.): —
Return on equity: 27.1%
Current ratio: 1.20

CARILION SERVICES, INC.

EXECUTIVES

Pres, Bill Flattery
SEC, Briggs Andrew
Prin, Carolyn Brown
Prin, Lawrence G Hincker
Prin, William J Flattery
Recruiter, Jill Lusher
Downtown Roanoke Site Manager, Aaron Washington
Sales Representative, Chris Deel
Aquatics Manager, Grace Milauskas
Aquatics Manager, Kayla Burnette
Assistant Director of Operatio, Lindsay Woods
Auditors: DELOITTE & TOUCHE LLP CHARLOT

LOCATIONS

HQ: CARILION SERVICES, INC.
213 S JEFFERSON ST # 633, ROANOKE, VA 240111700
Phone: 540-981-7000
Web: WWW.CARILIONCLINIC.ORG

HISTORICAL FINANCIALS

Company Type: Private

Income Statement			FYE: September 30
	REVENUE ($ mil.)	**NET INCOME** ($ mil.)	**NET PROFIT MARGIN**	**EMPLOYEES**
09/08	1,221	(147)	—	935
09/05	87	(2)	—	—
09/04	228	(23)	—	—
09/03	205	17	8.3%	—
Annual Growth 42.8%		—	—	—

2008 Year-End Financials

Return on assets: (-8.4%)   Cash ($ mil.): 1
Return on equity: (-18.4%)
Current ratio: 0.90

CARLE FOUNDATION HOSPITAL

Carle Foundation Hospital is a nearly 435-bed acute-care facility that serves the residents of east central Illinois. The hospital includes the region's only Level I trauma center as well as a Level III perinatal center a neonatal ICU and centers devoted to cardiac and cancer care. It also runs a handful of specialty centers in the region. Carle Foundation Hospital is the primary teaching hospital for the University of Illinois College of Medicine at Urbana-Champaign. With more than 20 primary care locations throughout the region it is controlled by the not-for-profit Carle Foundation;

sister company Carle Physician Group which boasts approximately 280 physicians representing early 75 specialties is one of the nation's largest private physician groups.

EXECUTIVES

Chm, Marty Smith
Director, Chuck Plotner
General Practitioner, Kourosh Moazemi
Director, Linda Glazier
Program Coordinator, Andrea Shaw
Professor, Christian Wagner
Surgery, Clifford Johnson
Executive Assistant, Diana Quigg
Director of Family Practice, Frances Kramer
Executive Assistant, Mary Nelson
Information Technology Directo, Steve Sexton

LOCATIONS

HQ: CARLE FOUNDATION HOSPITAL
611 W PARK ST, URBANA, IL 618012529
Phone: 217 326-2900
Web: WWW.CARLE.ORG

PRODUCTS/OPERATIONS

2014 Sales

	$ mil.	% of total
Net premium revenue-health insurance	1,296	63
Net patient service revenue	709	34
Rental income	15	1
Net assets released from restrictions	1	-
Other	34	2
Loss on the disposal of property & equipment	(2.8)	-
Total	**2,054**	**100**

Selected Medical Services

Bariatrics
Cancer
Cancer
Cardiology & Heart Surgery
Diabetes & Endocrinology
Ear Nose & Throat
Gastroenterology & GI Surgery
Geriatrics
Gynecology
Heart
Nephrology
Neurology & Neurosurgery
Sports Medicine
Stroke
Women's Health

COMPETITORS

Advocate Bromenn
Decatur Memorial Hospital
Hospital Sisters Health System
Iroquois Memorial Hospital
Memorial Health System
Morris Hospital
Osf Healthcare System

Sarah Bush Lincoln Health Center
Silver Cross Hospital
St. Elizabeth Regional Health
St. John's Hospital (illinois)
Union Hospital (indiana)

HISTORICAL FINANCIALS

Company Type: Private

Income Statement			FYE: December 31
	REVENUE ($ mil.)	**NET INCOME** ($ mil.)	**NET PROFIT MARGIN**	**EMPLOYEES**
12/18	937	216	23.1%	2,500
12/17	900	247	27.5%	—
12/16	812	185	22.8%	—
12/15	754	163	21.7%	—
Annual Growth	7.5%	9.8%	—	—

CARNEGIE MELLON UNIVERSITY

Carnegie Mellon University is a private global research university and one of the world's most renowned educational institutions. Drama is not all Carnegie Mellon teaches though ? the school has seven colleges and schools that offer academic programs in areas such as psychology computer science engineering biology and public policy. It has about 14190 students and more than 1470 faculty and it has a relatively small student-teacher ratio of 7:1. Carnegie Mellon was founded by philanthropist and industrialist Andrew Carnegie who established the Carnegie Technical Schools in 1900 for the sons and daughters of Pittsburgh's blue-collar workers.

Operations

In addition to the hundreds of programs offered by the schools and colleges Carnegie Mellon also offers dozens of interdisciplinary programs which are designed especially for students who want to work beyond just one discipline.

Carnegie Mellon has become a model for economic development in forming partnerships with companies such as Uber Google and Disney. Carnegie's CyLab is one of the largest university-based cybersecurity education and research centers in the country. Cylab consists of more than 30 core and 60 affiliated faculty who collaborate across 20 different departments across Carnegie Mellon and it is currently focusing on about 15 research areas related to security and privacy.

Tuition for residential undergraduates is approximately $57560.

The school's alumni network includes about 20 Nobel Prize laureates nearly 140 Emmy Award winners and about 11 Academy Award winners.

Geographic Reach

The school's main campus is located in Pittsburgh Pennsylvania. With more than a dozen degree-granting locations and more than 20 research partnerships Carnegie Mellon also has branch campuses in Africa Australia Qatar and Silicon Valley.

Company Background

Carnegie Tech merged with the Mellon Institute of Research to become Carnegie Mellon University in 1967.

EXECUTIVES

Pres, Subra Suresh
Pres*, Farnam Jahanian
Cfo*, Amir Rahnamay- Azar
Cto*, Tom Longstaff
Engineering Manager, Johnathan Huber
Professor, Kathleen Smith
Professor, Linda Babcock
Professor, Metin Sitti
Investigator, Yaron David
Assistant Professor, Jong S Lee
Emeritus Life Trustee, Alexander C Speyer Jr
Auditors: KPMG LLP PITTSBURGH PENNSYLV

LOCATIONS

HQ: CARNEGIE MELLON UNIVERSITY
5000 FORBES AVE, PITTSBURGH, PA 152133890
Phone: 412 268-2000
Web: WWW.CMU.EDU

Selected Locations

Adelaide Australia
Athens Greece
Aveiro and Coimbra Portugal
Doha Qatar

Kobe Japan
Lisbon Portugal
Los Angeles
Madeira Portugal
Minho and Porto Portugal
Mexico
Silicon Valley
Singapore

PRODUCTS/OPERATIONS

2015 Sales

	$ mil.	% of total
Tuition and other educational fees revenue net of financial aid	450	39
Sponsored projects revenue	376	32
Contributions revenue	136	12
Auxiliary services revenue	57	5
Investment income	37	3
Other sources	109	9
Total	**1,168**	**100**

Selected Departments

Chemical Engineering
Civil and Environmental Engineering
Energy Science Technology & Policy
Electrical and Computer Engineering
Engineering and Public Policy
Engineering & Technology Innovation Management
Information Networking Institute
Materials Science Engineering
Mechanical Engineering
Software Engineering and
Software Management
Architecture
Art
Design
Drama
Master of Arts Management
Master of Entertainment Industry Management
Music
English
History
Modern Languages
Philosophy
Psychology
Social and Decision Sciences
Statistics

Selected Schools

Carnegie Institute of Technology
School of Computer Science
College of Fine Arts
College of Humanities & Social Sciences
H. John Heinz III College
Mellon College of Science
Tepper School of Business

HISTORICAL FINANCIALS

Company Type: Private

Income Statement				FYE: June 30
	REVENUE ($ mil.)	NET INCOME ($ mil.)	NET PROFIT MARGIN	EMPLOYEES
06/21	1,672	1,525	91.2%	4,913
06/20	1,850	411	22.2%	—
06/19	1,363	207	15.2%	—
06/18	1,313	296	22.6%	—
Annual Growth	8.4%	72.6%	—	—

2021 Year-End Financials

Return on assets: 24.2%   Cash ($ mil.): 700
Return on equity: 29.8%
Current ratio: —

CAROLINA HEALTHCARE CENTER OF CUMBERLAND LP

EXECUTIVES

Endocrinologist, Anne La Rochelle
Human Resources Executive, Brenda Munn
Staff Physician, Davey Jim
Manager, Diane Allen
Family Practitioner, Jeffery Anderson
Director Corporate An, Joyce Hankins
Manager, Kathy Calhoun
Speech Pathologist, Kim Baumgartner
Family Practitioner, Mary Mason
Critical Care Nurse Practition, Melissa Gartner
Family Practitioner, Michael Kelley
Auditors: RSM MCGLADREY CHARLOTTE NC

LOCATIONS

HQ: CAROLINA HEALTHCARE CENTER OF
CUMBERLAND LP
4600 CUMBERLAND RD, FAYETTEVILLE, NC
283062412
Phone: 910 429-1690
Web: WWW.CAROLINA-HEALTH.COM

HISTORICAL FINANCIALS

Company Type: Private

Income Statement				FYE: September 30
	REVENUE ($ mil.)	NET INCOME ($ mil.)	NET PROFIT MARGIN	EMPLOYEES
09/09	1,019	62	6.2%	150
09/03	6	(0)	—	—
Annual Growth	132.0%	—	—	—

2009 Year-End Financials

Return on assets: 771.0%   Cash ($ mil.): —
Return on equity: 999.9%
Current ratio: 0.60

CAROLINAS MEDICAL CENTER NORTHEAST

LOCATIONS

HQ: CAROLINAS MEDICAL CENTER NORTHEAST
920 CHURCH ST N, CONCORD, NC 280252927
Phone: 704 783-3000
Web: WWW.ATRIUMHEALTH.ORG

HISTORICAL FINANCIALS

Company Type: Private

Income Statement				FYE: December 31
	REVENUE ($ mil.)	NET INCOME ($ mil.)	NET PROFIT MARGIN	EMPLOYEES
12/17	576	158	27.4%	4,500
12/16	552	130	23.6%	—
12/15	557	117	21.0%	—
Annual Growth	1.7%	16.3%	—	—

2017 Year-End Financials

Return on assets: 10.1%   Cash ($ mil.): —
Return on equity: 10.3%
Current ratio: 23.20

CARTER-JONES COMPANIES, INC.

EXECUTIVES

Ceo-Pres, Neil Sackett
Sr V Pres-Cfo*, Jeffrey Donley
SEC*, Judy Lee
Controller*, Brian Horning
Auditors: BDO USA LLP CLEVELAND OH

LOCATIONS

HQ: CARTER-JONES COMPANIES, INC.
601 TALLMADGE RD, KENT, OH 442407331
Phone: 330 673-6100
Web: WWW.DOITBEST.COM

HISTORICAL FINANCIALS

Company Type: Private

Income Statement				FYE: December 31
	REVENUE ($ mil.)	NET INCOME ($ mil.)	NET PROFIT MARGIN	EMPLOYEES
12/20	1,750	70	4.0%	3,225
12/19	1,504	45	3.0%	—
12/18	1,482	39	2.7%	—
12/17	1,365	29	2.1%	—
Annual Growth	8.6%	33.9%	—	—

2020 Year-End Financials

Return on assets: 7.3%   Cash ($ mil.): 18
Return on equity: 14.0%
Current ratio: 2.40

CARY OIL CO., INC.

EXECUTIVES

Pres-Ceo, Craig Stephenson
Chb*, Don Stephenson
V Pres*, Betty Phillips
V Pres*, Jim Bosworth
V Pres*, Mark Maddox
Asst SEC-Treas*, Rick Stephenson
V Pres-Chief Fin Officer*, Jason Holt
Director Operations Support, David Taylor
Senior Accountant, Samantha Haizel
It Manager, Buster Clark
Territory Sales Manager, Don Richardson
Auditors: BATCELOR TILLERY & ROBERTS L

LOCATIONS

HQ: CARY OIL CO., INC.
110 MACKENAN DR STE 300, CARY, NC 275117901
Phone: 919 462-1100
Web: WWW.CARYOIL.COM

HISTORICAL FINANCIALS
Company Type: Private

Income Statement				FYE: December 31
	REVENUE ($ mil.)	NET INCOME ($ mil.)	NET PROFIT MARGIN	EMPLOYEES
12/12	1,647	2	0.2%	100
12/11	1,608	2	0.1%	—
12/10	1,177	1	0.1%	—
Annual Growth	18.3%	28.2%	—	—

2012 Year-End Financials
Return on assets: 4.8%   Cash ($ mil.): 4
Return on equity: 25.1%
Current ratio: 1.00

CASE WESTERN RESERVE UNIVERSITY

Case Western Reserve University (CWRU) is an independent research school with an enrollment of about 12070 students from all US states and around 90 countries more than half of whom are graduate and professional students. CWRU offers approximately 230 undergraduate graduate and professional options and almost 140 dual-degree programs from its eight colleges and schools ? management engineering law arts and sciences dentistry social work nursing and medicine ? as well as a graduate school at its campus in Cleveland. The university has more than 3655 faculty members and a student-to-teacher ratio of 11:1.

Operations
CWRU receives approximately $462 million in external funding each year to pay for its various research enterprises. It is the only independent research-oriented university in a region bounded by Pittsburgh and Rochester on the east Nashville on the south and Chicago on the west. The school holds membership in the Association of American Universities and is fully accredited by the Higher Learning Commission and by several nationally recognized professional accrediting associations. With about $2.4 billion endowment funds the university's full-time undergraduate tuition is approximately $54020.

In addition to the university's approximately 95 undergraduate degree choices about 135 graduate and professional options and almost 140 dual-degree programs CWRU also has more than 100 interdisciplinary academic and research centers and institutes.

Geographic Reach
CWRU is located at more than 265-acre campus in Cleveland's University Circle; a 400-acre farm located in Hunting Valley Ohio; and houses approximately 40 educational medical cultural social and religious institutions. CWRU's students come from all 50 US states and around 90 countries.

Company Background
The university's origins date back to 1826 in the Ohio region then known as the Western Reserve of Connecticut; its current structure was formed in 1967 with the combination of neighboring Case Institute of Technology and Western Reserve College.

EXECUTIVES
Pres, Barbara R Snyder
Cfo*, Hossein Sadid
Gen Cnsl-SEC*, Jeanine Arden-Ornt

Pres*, Eric W Kaler
Executive Officer, Margaret Hewitt
Staff, Dusan Ignjatovic
Staff, Michael Tuason
Assistant Professor, Corey Smith
Assistant Professor, Erik D Andrulis
Assistant Professor, Karl Herrup
Assistant Professor, Kasturi Rangan
Auditors: PRICEWATERHOUSECOOPERS LLP CL

LOCATIONS
HQ: CASE WESTERN RESERVE UNIVERSITY
10900 EUCLID AVE, CLEVELAND, OH 441064901
Phone: 216 368-6062
Web: WWW.CASE.EDU

PRODUCTS/OPERATIONS

2014 Sales

	$ mil.	% of total
Grants and contracts	249	27
Student tuition and fees	218	24
Gifts and pledges	85	9
CCLCM grants and contracts	83	9
Facilities and administrative cost recovery	72	8
Others	217	23
Total	**926**	**100**

Selected Schools and Programs
Case School of Engineering
College of Arts and Sciences
Cleveland Clinic (part of the School of Medicine)
Frances Payne Bolton School of Nursing
Mandel Center for Nonprofit Organizations
Mandel School of Applied Social Sciences
School of Dental Medicine
School of Graduate Studies
School of Law
School of Medicine
Weatherhead School of Management

HISTORICAL FINANCIALS
Company Type: Private

Income Statement				FYE: June 30
	REVENUE ($ mil.)	NET INCOME ($ mil.)	NET PROFIT MARGIN	EMPLOYEES
06/21	1,101	679	61.7%	6,599
06/20	1,075	(49)	—	—
06/18	1,016	111	10.9%	—
06/17	1,022	208	20.4%	—
Annual Growth	1.9%	34.4%	—	—

2021 Year-End Financials
Return on assets: 17.5%   Cash ($ mil.): 145
Return on equity: 22.4%
Current ratio: —

CATHOLIC HEALTH INITIATIVES - IOWA, CORP.

EXECUTIVES
Ceo, David Vellinga
Coordinator, Kelli Cain
Coordinator, Valerie Diehl
Midwest Regional Sales Manager, Jeff Johnston
Buyer Purchaser, Debbie Soloman
Emergency Medicine Specialist, Benjamin Sweet

Family Practitioner, Butool Abdullah
Internist, Daniela Frankova
Registered Nurse, Elizabeth Hanson
Internist, Moanis Omar
Internist, Tagore Sunkara
Auditors: CATHOLIC HEALTH INITIATIVES E

LOCATIONS
HQ: CATHOLIC HEALTH INITIATIVES - IOWA, CORP.
1111 6TH AVE, DES MOINES, IA 503142613
Phone: 515 247-3121
Web: WWW.MERCYONE.ORG

HISTORICAL FINANCIALS
Company Type: Private

Income Statement				FYE: June 30
	REVENUE ($ mil.)	NET INCOME ($ mil.)	NET PROFIT MARGIN	EMPLOYEES
06/20	817	14	1.7%	6,100
06/16	804	58	7.3%	—
06/14	733	(14)	—	—
06/10	691	39	5.8%	—
Annual Growth	1.7%	(9.9%)	—	—

2020 Year-End Financials
Return on assets: 1.4%   Cash ($ mil.): 149
Return on equity: 2.2%
Current ratio: 2.00

CATHOLIC HEALTH INITIATIVES COLORADO

EXECUTIVES
Pres, Gregory H Burfitt
Corporate Revenue Integrity, Shelly Vendemo
Chief Officer, Terry Orourke
Orsos Reimbursement Coordinato, Terry Walb
Vice President of Operations, Geoffrey Lawton Pharmd
Chief Operating Officer, Jameson Smith Fache
Senior Vice President, Nick Barto
Knowledge Director, Jeff Sauvie
Vice President of Finance, Jerry Francis
Senior Vice President Strategy, Meta Dooley
Rn, Patricia Davidson
Auditors: LB CATHOLIC HEALTH INITIATIVES

LOCATIONS
HQ: CATHOLIC HEALTH INITIATIVES COLORADO
9100 E MINERAL CIR, CENTENNIAL, CO 801123401
Phone: 303 290-6500
Web: WWW.CATHOLICHEALTHINITIATIVES.ORG

HISTORICAL FINANCIALS
Company Type: Private

Income Statement				FYE: June 30
	REVENUE ($ mil.)	NET INCOME ($ mil.)	NET PROFIT MARGIN	EMPLOYEES
06/20	2,251	251	11.2%	8,000
06/19	2,190	203	9.3%	—
Annual Growth	2.8%	23.7%	—	—

2020 Year-End Financials
Return on assets: 8.8%   Cash ($ mil.): 349
Return on equity: 11.6%
Current ratio: 1.90

CATHOLIC MEDICAL MISSION BOARD INC

EXECUTIVES

Pres, John F Galbraith
Pres*, Bruce Wilkinson
Senior Vice-President, Marivette Cannon
Vice-Chairman, F W Smullen
Program Manager, Syndie Saint Hilaire
Country Director, Ariel Frisancho
Director, Jenny Paulk
Manager, Leanne Deshong
Warehouse Manager, Patrick Opembe
Finance Director, Alicia Defreitas
Senior Specialist Information, Isaac Roldan
Auditors: MARKS PANETH & SHRON LLP NEW

LOCATIONS

HQ: CATHOLIC MEDICAL MISSION BOARD INC
100 WALL ST FL 9, NEW YORK, NY 100055765
Phone: 212 242-7757
Web: WWW.CMMB.ORG

HISTORICAL FINANCIALS

Company Type: Private

Income Statement				FYE: September 30
	REVENUE ($ mil.)	NET INCOME ($ mil.)	NET PROFIT MARGIN	EMPLOYEES
09/18	740	105	14.2%	38
09/17	603	19	3.2%	—
09/16	371	(12)	—	—
09/15	290	(3)	—	—
Annual Growth	36.7%	—	—	—

2018 Year-End Financials

Return on assets: 48.2%   Cash ($ mil.): 5
Return on equity: 49.6%
Current ratio: —

CATHOLIC RELIEF SERVICES - UNITED STATES CONFERENCE OF CATHOLIC BISHOPS

EXECUTIVES

Ceo, Sean Callahan
Exec V Pres, Schuyler Thorup
Exec V Pres, Joan Rosenhauer
Exec V Pres, Annemarie Reilly
Exec V Pres-Dir, Mark Melia
Exec V Pres-Dir, Shawn Mood
Cfo-Dir, James Bond
Assistant I, Alexandra Charles
Associate II, Samantha Musson
Technical Associate II, Gabrielle Gueye
Talent Management Specialist, Scott Oconnor
Auditors: RSM US LLP GAITHERSBURG MARY

LOCATIONS

HQ: CATHOLIC RELIEF SERVICES - UNITED STATES CONFERENCE OF CATHOLIC BISHOPS
228 W LEXINGTON ST, BALTIMORE, MD 212013422
Phone: 410 625-2220
Web: WWW.CRS.ORG

HISTORICAL FINANCIALS

Company Type: Private

Income Statement				FYE: September 30
	REVENUE ($ mil.)	NET INCOME ($ mil.)	NET PROFIT MARGIN	EMPLOYEES
09/19	940	(21)	—	7,100
09/18	989	(3)	—	—
09/17	978	20	2.1%	—
09/16	917	(47)	—	—
Annual Growth	0.8%	—	—	—

2019 Year-End Financials

Return on assets: (-4.2%)   Cash ($ mil.): 64
Return on equity: (-13.2%)
Current ratio: 1.00

CCG SERVICES, INC.

EXECUTIVES

Pres, Mark A Steffen
Exec V Pres*, Dennis Barber
Treas*, Michael J Thomas
Dir of Fin*, John Verhoff
Vice President, Gary Aanenson
Vice President of Preconstruct, Grant Curtan
Senior Project Superintendent, Greg Horvath
Administrative Assistant, Jennifer West
Project Superintendent, Jim Jones
Project Manager, John Sanders
Superintendent, Rick Hansen

LOCATIONS

HQ: CCG SERVICES, INC.
6320 RESEARCH RD STE 200, FRISCO, TX 750333774
Phone: 309 263-0808
Web: WWW.CORECONSTRUCTION.COM

HISTORICAL FINANCIALS

Company Type: Private

Income Statement				FYE: December 31
	REVENUE ($ mil.)	NET INCOME ($ mil.)	NET PROFIT MARGIN	EMPLOYEES
12/15	782	0	—	450
12/12	624	0	—	—
12/06	620	0	—	—
Annual Growth	2.6%	—	—	—

2015 Year-End Financials

Return on assets: —   Cash ($ mil.): 34
Return on equity: —
Current ratio: 1.20

CEB INC.

Don't fear the competition; learn from it. So says CEB a provider of business research and analysis services to more than 10000 companies worldwide. Its program areas cover "best practices" in such topics as finance human resources information technology operations and sales and marketing. Unlike consulting firms which engage with one client at a time CEB operates on a membership-based business model. Members subscribe to one or more of the company's programs and participate in the research and analysis thus sharing expertise with others. Besides reports on best practices CEB offers seminars customized research briefs and decision-support tools.

Operations

The company operates through two segments: CEB (79% of net sales) and CEB Talent Assessment (21%). The CEB segment provides data analysis research and advisory services that align to executive leadership roles and key recurring decisions and enable members to focus efforts to address emerging and recurring business challenges. CEB Talent Assessment segment includes its SHL product and services of cloud-based products for talent assessment development strategy analytics decision support and professional services.

Geographic Reach

CED has offices in almost 20 locations through the US and almost 15 in Europe. The US accounts for 62% of its net sales; Europe generates 20% and other countries account for the remainder.

Financial Performance

CEB achieved unprecedented growth in 2015 with revenues peaking at a record-setting $928 million in 2015. The historic growth was fueled by a 4% bump in CEB segment sales and a 4% increase in the US. CEB was also helped by an increase in 2014 sales bookings and the positive impact of acquisitions.

Profits also skyrocketed by 80% to reach $93 million in 2015 another company milestone primarily due to the absence of an impairment loss which it incurred the previous year. After years of posting steadily increasing cash flow CEB saw its operating cash flow decrease by $34 million from 2014 to 2015 primarily due to unfavorable changes in deferred revenue and other liabilities.

Mergers and Acquisitions

One of the ways in which CEB posted milestone revenue growth for 2015 was through the use of acquisitions. In 2016 CEB agreed to acquire Evanta Ventures for $275 million. Portland Oregon-based Evanta offers best practices data for information technology human resources and finance executives through nearly 200 annual events online and offline learning platforms and subscription information offerings.

In 2015 CEB picked up Wanted Technologies Corporation a provider of real-time market intelligence and analytics for staffing and talent sourcing professionals. The same year CEB acquired Australia-based CEO Forum Group a provider of membership-based peer group briefing services serving senior executives of foreign-owned multinational organizations doing business in Australia.

EXECUTIVES

Ceo, Thomas L Monahan III
Cfo*, Richard S Lindahl
Cao*, J Barron Anschutz
Information Specialist, Gary Banks
Executive Officer, Christoffer Ellehuus
Head, Corporate Strategy and D, Jesse Levin
Chief Administrative Officer, Melody L Jones

LOCATIONS

HQ: CEB INC.
1201 WILSON BLVD STE 1800, ARLINGTON, VA
222092316
Phone: 571 303-3000
Web: WWW.CEBGLOBAL.COM

2015 Sales

	$ mil.	% of total
US	579	62
Europe	184	20
Other regions	164	18
Total	**928**	**100**

PRODUCTS/OPERATIONS

2015 Sales

	$ mil.	% of total
CEB	731	79
CEB Talent Assessment	196	21
Total	**928**	**100**

Selected Practice Areas

Communications
Financial services
General management
Human resources
Information technology
Legal and compliance
Operations and procurement
Sales and marketing
Strategy and research and development

HISTORICAL FINANCIALS

Company Type: Private

Income Statement   FYE: December 31

	REVENUE ($ mil.)	NET INCOME ($ mil.)	NET PROFIT MARGIN	EMPLOYEES
12/16	949	(34)	—	4,600
12/15	928	92	10.0%	—
12/14	908	51	5.6%	—
12/13	820	31	3.9%	—
Annual Growth	**5.0%**	—	—	—

2016 Year-End Financials

Return on assets: (-2.5%)   Cash ($ mil.): 134
Return on equity: —
Current ratio: 0.80

CEC ENTERTAINMENT, INC.

Don't let the mouse mascot fool you: This amusement kingdom is founded on the power of pizza. CEC Entertainment operates the Chuck E. Cheese's chain of pizza parlors with more than 610 locations in over 45 states and approximately 15 foreign countries and territories. The restaurants cater mostly to families with children and feature a broad array of entertainment offerings including arcade-style and skill-oriented games rides live entertainment shows. Entertainment and merchandise account for some 55% of sales. The menu features pizzas wings appetizers salads and desserts. CEC Entertainment owns and operates more than 550 of the pizza and fun joints while the rest are franchised.

Bankruptcy

CEC Entertainment Inc. a nationally recognized leader in family entertainment and dining announced that in order to overcome the financial strain resulting from prolonged COVID-19 related venue closures and position the company for long-term success CEC Entertainment and its domestic affiliates have filed for voluntary protection under Chapter 11 of the U.S. Bankruptcy Code. The company expects to use the time and legal protections made available through the Chapter 11 process to continue discussions with financial stakeholders as well as critical conversations with its landlords to achieve a comprehensive balance sheet restructuring that supports its re-opening and longer-term strategic plans.

Operations

Chuck E. Cheese is a highly recognized brand that appeals to primary guest base of families with children between below 5 and 12 years of age. Each venue includes approximately 75 games rides and attractions for kids of all ages including classic skill games such as arcade basketball skee-ball and Whack-a-Mole along with the Ticket Blaster machine. Chuck E. Cheese menu features fresh hand-made pizza boneless and bone-in chicken wings desserts and beverages including beer and wine at most locations.

Peter Piper Pizza serves fresh handcrafted food and beverages including craft beer and wine and offers state-of-the-art games for all ages. Venues feature a bold design and contemporary layout with open kitchens such as fresh mozzarella being shredded off the block vegetables being hand-chopped wings being hand-tossed and its Certified Dough Masters crafting pizzas with made-from-scratch dough. The company's open dining areas provide an enjoyable atmosphere for families and group events with attentive staff dedicated to providing an enjoyable and memorable experience to each guest.The company's entertainment and merchandise generate approximately 55% of sales food and beverage generate about 45% of sales and franchise fees and royalties generate the remaining.

Geographic Reach

The company and its franchisees operate a system of more than 600 Chuck E. Cheese and more than 120 Peter Piper Pizza venues with locations in over 45 states and more than 15 foreign countries and territories.

Peter Piper Pizza's office is located in Phoenix Arizona. The company also has a warehouse building in Topeka Kansas which primarily serves as a storage distribution and refurbishing facility for venue fixtures and game equipment. The company's headquarter is located in Irving Texas.

Sales and Marketing

The Chuck E. Cheese's concept has successfully cemented a place in the family dining market by focusing on the entertainment options available at its restaurants and marketing itself as a safe and convenient place for parents to take the kids. The company's advertising expenses were $45 million and $48.2 million for 2019 and 2018 respectively.

Financial Performance

After a dip in revenue in 2017 the company was back on its tracks and have increased revenue for three consecutive years. The net income for the last five years has been mostly in black. Only in 2017 did they reported a positive income.Net revenue in 2019 increased by 2% to $890 million. The increase in company venue sales was primarily attributable to a 2.7% increase in comparable venue sales partially offset by a $2.6 million decrease in company venue sales from its non-comparable venues primarily due to a net reduction of seven company-operated venues over the last two years. Net income loss incurred by the company in 2019 was $28.9 million. The decrease in income were due to higher operating costs and expenses and higher interest expense. Cash at the end of 2019 was $34.8 million. Cash generated by operations was $111.1 million. Investing and financing activities used $87.6 and $52.1 million respectively. Main cash uses for 2019 were for property and equipment purchases repayments of loans and re-purchases of senior notes.

Strategy

The company's strategic objectives are focused on becoming "the world's leading family - friendly entertainment restaurant brands" by entertaining and inspiring kids around the world and ensuring that every guest is happy. This strategic plan is centered on the following six growth pillars: Increasing traffic to its venues through marketing and sales promotions; Drive in-store guest spending; Pursuing a programmatic approach to our domestic remodel program; Expanding the global franchise network; Launching a division to focus on entertainment & licensing efforts; and Increasing efficiencies and lower operating costs with tight controls.

Also as part of its long-term growth strategy the company plans to upgrade the games rides and entertainment in most of its existing venues remodel certain of its existing venues and open additional new venues in selected markets. Over the years the company has made significant changes to its marketing and advertising strategy including the introduction of an updated Chuck E. Cheese character; change in the mix of its media expenditures increase in advertising directed to parents and promoting its brand and reasons to visit on television and online.

Company Background

The Chuck E. Cheese's concept was created by Nolan Bushnell founder of video game pioneer Atari Corporation in 1977. Showbiz Pizza acquired the chain in 1984 and changed its name to CEC Entertainment 1998.

EXECUTIVES

Chief Financial Officer, Executive Vice President, James Howell
Chief Executive Officer, Director, David McKillips
Chief Marketing Officer, Sherri Landry
Chief Human Resource Officer, Executive Vice President, General Counsel And Chief Legal Officer, Rudy Rodriguez
Chief Operating Officer, Executive Vice President, Randy Forsythe, $257,500 total compensation
Auditors: DELOITTE & TOUCHE LLP DALLAS

LOCATIONS

HQ: CEC ENTERTAINMENT, INC.
1707 MARKET PL STE 200, IRVING, TX 750638049
Phone: 972 258-8507
Web: WWW.CHUCKECHEESE.COM

2016

Stores	Company-Owned Total	Stores Franchised
Domestic		
Chuck E. Cheese's	12	
	29	541
Peter Piper Pizza	32	
	62	94
International		
Chuck E. Cheese's	12	
	39	51
Peter Piper Pizza	-	
	46	46
Total	**176**	**732**

2016 Sales

	$ mil.	% of total
Company store sales		
Entertainment and merchandise sales	497	54
Food and beverage sales	408	44
Franchise fees and royalties	17	2
Total	**922**	**100**

COMPETITORS

Brinker	Domino's
Buffets Inc	In-n-out Burgers
Burger King	Mcdonald's
California Pizza	Papa John's
Kitchen	Pizza Hut
Carlson Restaurants	Red Robin
Cheesecake Factory	Shakey's
Darden	Sonic Corp.
Dave & Buster's	Wendy's
Denny's	

HISTORICAL FINANCIALS
Company Type: Private

Income Statement   FYE: December 29

	REVENUE ($ mil.)	NET INCOME ($ mil.)	NET PROFIT MARGIN	EMPLOYEES
12/19	912	(28)	—	17,200
12/18	896	(20)	—	—
12/17*	886	53	6.0%	—
01/17	923	(3)	—	—
Annual Growth	(0.4%)	—	—	—

*Fiscal year change

2019 Year-End Financials

Return on assets: (-1.4%)   Cash ($ mil.): 34
Return on equity: (-13.5%)
Current ratio: 0.60

CEDARS-SINAI MEDICAL CARE FOUNDATION

EXECUTIVES

Exec Dir, Tom Gordeon
Exec Dir, Tom Gordon
Purchasing, Gary Young
Internist, Jon Rasak
Program Coordinator, Tattika Soreta
Auditors: ERNST & YOUNG LLP LOS
ANGELES

LOCATIONS

HQ: CEDARS-SINAI MEDICAL CARE FOUNDATION
200 N ROBERTSON BLVD # 101, BEVERLY HILLS, CA
902111769
Phone: 800 700-6424
Web: WWW.CEDARS-SINAI.ORG

HISTORICAL FINANCIALS
Company Type: Private

Income Statement   FYE: June 30

	REVENUE ($ mil.)	NET INCOME ($ mil.)	NET PROFIT MARGIN	EMPLOYEES
06/21	560	42	7.6%	4
06/20	447	(114)	—	—
06/19	441	127	28.9%	—
06/18	394	8	2.2%	—
Annual Growth	12.4%	70.6%	—	—

2021 Year-End Financials

Return on assets: 7.6%   Cash ($ mil.): 92
Return on equity: 13.7%
Current ratio: 1.80

CEDARS-SINAI MEDICAL CENTER

Cedars-Sinai is a nonprofit academic healthcare organization serving the diverse Los Angeles community and beyond. Cedars-Sinai is consistently listed as a top-ranked hospital by US News & World Report in such specialties as cancer cardiology endocrinology gastrointestinal disorders gynecology heart surgery kidney disease neurology orthopedics and respiratory disorders. Cedars-Sinai is a partner institution in the UCLA Clinical and Translational Science Institute (CTSI) an academic-clinical-community partnership and is engaged in hundreds of research programs in areas such as cancer neuroscience and genetics. It also partners with some 30 leading community service organizations advocacy groups health delivery networks churches and schools.

Operations

Cedars-Sinai ranks among the nation's top non-university hospitals for competitive research funding from the National Institutes of Health and currently has more than 1845 research projects many led by physician-scientists.

The hospital sees some 1.6 million outpatient visits and more than 111000 emergency department visits each year.

Geographic Reach

Cedars-Sinai serves more than one million people each year in over 40 locations.

EXECUTIVES

Chb, Lawrence B Platt
Pres - Ceo, Thomas M Priselac
Sr V Pres-Cfo, Edward M Pronchunas
Sr V Pres-Hr-Org Dev, Jeanne Flores
Chb, John C Law
V Chb, James A Nathan
Sr V Pres-Legal Affairs, Peter E Braveman
V Chb, Vera Guerin
Sr Vpres, David R Marshall
Chief Nursing Officer, Anita Girard
Assistant Vice President Plann, Richard Katzman
Auditors: ERNST & YOUNG LLP LOS
ANGELES

LOCATIONS

HQ: CEDARS-SINAI MEDICAL CENTER
8700 BEVERLY BLVD, WEST HOLLYWOOD, CA
900481804
Phone: 310 423-3277
Web: WWW.CEDARS-SINAI.ORG

PRODUCTS/OPERATIONS

Selected Centers and Services
Ambulatory Care Center
Cedars-Sinai Center for Chest Disease
Cedars-Sinai Center for Digestive Diseases
Cedars-Sinai Heart Institute
Cedars-Sinai Institute Spine Center
Cedars-Sinai Health Associates (affiliated independent physician association)
Cedars-Sinai Medical Group (multi-specialty physicians group)
Cedars-Sinai Orthopedic Center
Diagnostic imaging center
Emergency department and trauma center
Hospice services
Kidney and pancreas transplant center
Neuroscience services
Pediatric services
Psychiatry and mental health services
Samuel Oschin Comprehensive Cancer Institute
Surgical services
Organ and bone marrow transplantation
Radiation therapy
Radiology
Stroke program
Pain management services
Women's health services

COMPETITORS

Adventist Health System West
Brotman Medical Center
Childrens Hospital Los Angeles
City Of Hope
Community Health Systems
Dignity Health
Eisenhower Medical Center
Glendale Adventist Medical Center
Glendale Memorial Hospital
Golden State Health Centers
Good Samaritan Hospital (in)
Hca
Hollywood Presbyterian Medical Center
Newhall Memorial Hospital
Pasadena Hospital Association
Providence Health System Southern California
Scripps Health
Tenet Healthcare
Ucsf Medical
White Memorial Medical Center

HISTORICAL FINANCIALS
Company Type: Private

Income Statement   FYE: June 30

	REVENUE ($ mil.)	NET INCOME ($ mil.)	NET PROFIT MARGIN	EMPLOYEES
06/21	4,142	1,083	26.2%	8,000
06/20	3,647	443	12.2%	—
06/19	3,649	389	10.7%	—
06/18	3,470	418	12.0%	—
Annual Growth	6.1%	37.4%	—	—

2021 Year-End Financials

Return on assets: 12.8%   Cash ($ mil.): 1,077
Return on equity: 17.6%
Current ratio: 5.30

CENTERPOINT ENERGY SERVICES RETAIL LLC

EXECUTIVES

Pres-Ceo, David McClanahan
Auditors: GRANT THORNTON LLP TULSA OKL

LOCATIONS

HQ: CENTERPOINT ENERGY SERVICES RETAIL LLC
1111 LA ST FL 20 FLR 20, HOUSTON, TX 77002
Phone: 800 752-8036
Web: WWW.INFUSEENERGY.COM

HISTORICAL FINANCIALS

Company Type: Private

Income Statement   FYE: December 31

	REVENUE ($ mil.)	NET INCOME ($ mil.)	NET PROFIT MARGIN	EMPLOYEES
12/14	695	8	1.2%	35
12/13	549	9	1.7%	—
Annual Growth	26.6%	(11.9%)	—	—

CENTIMARK CORPORATION

Shout it from the rooftops Centimark is one of the commercial and industrial roofing contractors in the US Canada and Mexico. The company provides roof installation inspection repair and emergency leak service. Centimark typically works on flat roofs using EPDM rubber thermoplastic bitumen metal and coatings. Its QuestMark division offers commercial industrial and retail flooring do-it-yourself (DIY) products and floor maintenance and cleaning products. The company has more than 85 offices throughout US Canada and Mexico.

Operations

The company offers roof services roof replacement roof repairs roof cleaning preventative maintenance programs asset alert and asset management. Centimark also provides systems such as thermoplastic solutions sprayed polyurethane foams roof coatings modified bitumen and built-up roofing metal products and steep slope products.

QuestMark a division of Centimark offers materials for commercial retail and industrial floors. It specializes in DiamondQuest polished concrete flooring epoxy flooring floor repair materials floor maintenance and floor cleaning products.

Centimark's Asset Management service provides extensive roof surveys roof life expectancy models return-on-investment analysis for roof repairs and evaluations for roof repair or roof replacement.

Geographic Reach

Canonsburg Pennsylvania-based Centimark also does business in Canada through subsidiary Centimark Ltd. which has offices in Calgary Edmonton Toronto and Vancouver.

Sales and Marketing

The company serves customers in different segments including retail industrial general contractors and education.

Company Background

Chairman and CEO Edward Dunlap founded Centimark as an industrial cleaning business in 1967. Centimark is owned by its employees.

EXECUTIVES

Chb, Edward B Dunlap
Pres-Coo*, Timothy M Dunlap
Exec V Pres -Cand Grp Dir*, Robert Penney
Exec V Pres-Cfo*, John L Heisey
Exec V Pres-Grp Dir*, Steve M Ferencz
Exec V Pres-Reg Sales Dir*, John T Godwin Jr
Exec V Pres - Qm FL Grp Dir*, John Scanlon
Exec V Pres - Etn Grp Dir*, Mark Cooper
Exec V Pres - S Grp Dir*, Keith Battenfield
Vice President*, Thor Dicesare
Exec V Pres of Serv*, Kenneth Zmich
Auditors: SCHNEIDER DOWNS & CO INC P

LOCATIONS

HQ: CENTIMARK CORPORATION
12 GRANDVIEW CIR, CANONSBURG, PA 153178533
Phone: 724 514-8700
Web: WWW.CENTIMARK.COM

PRODUCTS/OPERATIONS

Selected Operations
CentiMark (roofing)
CentiMark ltd. (Canada roofing)
QuestMark (flooring)

Selected Systems
Roof Systems
EPDM
Green Roofing
Metal Roofs
Modified Bitumen and Built-Up Roofs
Roof Coatings
SPF
Steep Slope
TPO & PVC
Floor Systems
Chemical Resistant Systems
Decorative Broadcast
Decorative Concrete
Electric Static Dissipative
Heavy Duty Resurfacer
High Build Coating
Polished Concrete
Thin Mil

COMPETITORS

Armstrong World Industries	Duro-last Roofing
Cabral Roofing & Waterproofing	Garcia Roofing
	Holland Roofing
D. C. Taylor	Pickens Roofing
	Tecta America

HISTORICAL FINANCIALS

Company Type: Private

Income Statement   FYE: April 30

	REVENUE ($ mil.)	NET INCOME ($ mil.)	NET PROFIT MARGIN	EMPLOYEES
04/21	783	73	9.4%	3,500
04/18	670	54	8.1%	—
04/17	625	51	8.2%	—
04/15	817	0	—	—
Annual Growth	—	952.3%	—	—

2021 Year-End Financials

Return on assets: 10.7%   Cash ($ mil.): 309
Return on equity: 13.8%
Current ratio: 4.80

CENTRA HEALTH, INC.

Centra Health is a regional nonprofit healthcare system based in Lynchburg Virginia. Its entity's core are two acute care facilities in Lynchburg: The Lynchburg General which is the region's main emergency center and specializes in orthopedic pediatric and cardiac care; and Virginia Baptist facility focused on surgery women's health infant care mental health and rehabilitation. With nearly 800 physicians and medical staff Centra Health provides care to over 500000 people in some 50 locations throughout central and southern Virginia. It was founded on 1987.

Operations

Centra Lynchburg General Hospital is home to the Centra Stroobants Heart Center and Stroobants Cardiovascular Pavilion a national benchmark facility for cardiac care. Heart Center specialists perform more than 6000 major cardiac procedures each year. LGH is also a Level II Trauma Center providing emergency and critical care services to more than 85000 patients per year. LGH has a pediatric center outpatient surgery center and provides orthopaedic neurology neurosurgery diabetes and pulmonary services.

Centra Virginia Baptist Hospital is home to The Birth Center Women's and Children's Health and the region's neonatal intensive care unit. VBH also serves as the primary regional provider of children and adult mental health services. Virginia Baptist operates an outpatient surgery center and provides skilled care rehabilitation physical therapy and ambulatory surgery. VBH is home to a variety of specialty services including the Breast Imaging Center Heartburn Treatment Center Center for Wound Care and Hyperbaric Medicine Sleep Disorders Center and the Center for Pain Management.

Centra Southside Community Hospital in Farmville is an around 115-bed acute care facility. Its hospital inpatient services include obstetrics general medicine intensive care surgical services and general medicine. It serves as a medical hub for an eight-county region. Each year Southside has approximately 4000 admissions and sees more than 33000 patients through its emergency department.

Centra Bedford Memorial Hospital in Bedford is a full-service medical facility with special emphasis on women's health outpatient surgery emergency services cardiology care and rehabilitative services. The facility offers 24-hour emergency care to the local community of approximately 60000 residents. Centra Bedford Memorial Hospital has about 50 beds and a 111 bed long- term care facility.

The Centra Healthcare System includes the Centra Medical Group; a network of local family practices primary care physicians and medical and surgical specialists. Centra Medical Group provides the community with primary care physicians cardiologists cardiothoracic surgeons gerontologists neurosurgeons physiatrists psychiatrists therapists and urologists.

Geographic Reach

Centra Health serves Lynchburg and surrounding communities in central Virginia including Farmville (located in Prince Edward County) Bedford Burkeville Cumberland Forest Gretna Keysville and Moneta.

Company Background

Centra Health was founded in 1987 through the merger of Lynchburg General and Virginia Baptist. Southside Community Hospital joined the network in 2006.

EXECUTIVES

Pres-Ceo, Andrew Mueller
Pres*, Walker Sydnor
Tres*, Lewis C Addison
Director, A Lynchburg Pulmonologist
Chief Officer, Howard Podolsky
Chief of Medicine, Chalmers M Nunn
Vice-President, E W Tibbs
Physical Medicine Specialist, Joyce L Huerta
Coordinator, Carolyn Lepper
Senior Regulatory Analyst Fina, Demietre Payne
Manager Centra Sleep Disorders, George Morcom

LOCATIONS

HQ: CENTRA HEALTH, INC.
 1920 ATHERHOLT RD, LYNCHBURG, VA 245011120
Phone: 434 200-3204
Web: WWW.CENTRAHEALTH.COM

PRODUCTS/OPERATIONS

Selected Facilities
Bedford Memorial Hospital (Bedford Virginia;
 partnership with Carilion Health System)
Lynchburg General Hospital (Lynchburg Virginia)
Virginia Baptist Hospital (Lynchburg Virginia)
Southside Community Hospital (Farmville Virginia)
Physician Practices
 Altavista Medical Center (Altavista Virginia)
 Big Island Medical Center (North Big Island Virginia)
 Brookneal Family Medical Center (Brookneal Virginia)
 Gretna Medical Center (Gretna Virginia)
 Lynchburg Family Medicine Center (Lynchburg
 Virginia)
Other Facilities
 Bridges Treatment Center (Lynchburg Virginia)
 Fairmont Crossing Health and Rehabilitation Center
 (Amherst Virginia)
 Guggenheimer Health and Rehabilitation Center
 (Lynchburg Virginia)
 Piedmont Psychiatric Center (Lynchburg Virginia)
 Rivermont Schools (regional)
 The Summit (regional)

COMPETITORS

Alleghany Regional
 Hospital
Bon Secours Health
Carilion Clinic
Clinch Valley Medical
 Center
Danville Regional
 Medical Center
Encompass Health

Martha Jefferson
 Hospital
Mary Washington
 Healthcare
Montgomery Regional
 Hospital
Sentara Healthcare
University Of Virginia
 Health System

HISTORICAL FINANCIALS
Company Type: Private

Income Statement				FYE: December 31
	REVENUE ($ mil.)	NET INCOME ($ mil.)	NET PROFIT MARGIN	EMPLOYEES
12/19	1,078	8	0.8%	6,000
12/15	742	25	3.4%	—
12/14	553	63	11.5%	—
12/09	534	16	3.1%	—
Annual Growth	7.3%	(6.6%)	—	—

2019 Year-End Financials

Return on assets: 0.6%
Return on equity: 1.2%
Current ratio: 0.50

Cash ($ mil.): 37

CENTRACARE HEALTH SYSTEM

EXECUTIVES

Pres, Kenneth Holmen
Health Professional, Saul S Singh
Scientist, Christy Emerson
Physical Therapist Personal Tr, Audra Zastrow
Manager, David Covington
Administrative Assistant For G, Judy Haus
Endocrinologist, Mark Holm
Director, Paul Knutson
Compliance Specialist, Sue Stein
Womens Health Srv Director, Bryan Bauck
Vice President Erf Improement, Craig Dewer
Auditors: RSM US LLP MINNEAPOLIS MINN

LOCATIONS

HQ: CENTRACARE HEALTH SYSTEM
 1406 6TH AVE N, SAINT CLOUD, MN 563031900
Phone: 320 251-2700
Web: WWW.CENTRACARE.COM

HISTORICAL FINANCIALS
Company Type: Private

Income Statement				FYE: June 30
	REVENUE ($ mil.)	NET INCOME ($ mil.)	NET PROFIT MARGIN	EMPLOYEES
06/20	1,680	(37)	—	4,957
06/19	1,695	50	3.0%	—
06/15	176	(15)	—	—
06/13	115	27	23.8%	—
Annual Growth	46.5%			

2020 Year-End Financials

Return on assets: (-1.6%)
Return on equity: (-3.2%)
Current ratio: 1.30

Cash ($ mil.): 272

CENTRAL CRUDE, INC.

EXECUTIVES

Ceo, Steve Jordan
Pres*, George Jordan
V Pres*, Joe Milazzo
Health Professional, Lisa Gustas
Vice-President Business Develo, Kevin Hickey
Treasurer, Katy Bertrand
Auditors: MCELROY QUIRK & BURCH

LOCATIONS

HQ: CENTRAL CRUDE, INC.
 4187 HIGHWAY 3059, LAKE CHARLES, LA 706153310
Phone: 337 436-1000
Web: WWW.CENTRALCRUDE.COM

HISTORICAL FINANCIALS
Company Type: Private

Income Statement				FYE: March 31
	REVENUE ($ mil.)	NET INCOME ($ mil.)	NET PROFIT MARGIN	EMPLOYEES
03/09	637	1	0.2%	50
03/08	635	0	0.1%	—
03/06	280	0	0.1%	—
Annual Growth	31.5%	56.2%	—	—

2009 Year-End Financials

Return on assets: 2.4%
Return on equity: 40.0%
Current ratio: 1.00

Cash ($ mil.): —

CENTRAL ELECTRIC POWER COOPERATIVE, INC.

EXECUTIVES

Ceo, Robert Hochstetler
Ceo*, Ronald J Calcaterra
Sr V Pres*, Art Fusco
Sr V Pres*, Jim Lamb
Dir*, David Logeman
Cfo*, John Brantley
Prin*, John Tiencken
Director of Power Supply Opera, Gerald Fleming
Engineer, Kale Ford
Vice President of Engineer, John Boyt
Load Management Engineer, Mason Milligan
Auditors: BAUKNIGHT PIETRAS & STORMER
 PA

LOCATIONS

HQ: CENTRAL ELECTRIC POWER COOPERATIVE, INC.
 20 COOPERATIVE WAY, COLUMBIA, SC 292103112
Phone: 803 779-4975
Web: WWW.CEPCI.ORG

HISTORICAL FINANCIALS
Company Type: Private

Income Statement				FYE: December 31
	REVENUE ($ mil.)	NET INCOME ($ mil.)	NET PROFIT MARGIN	EMPLOYEES
12/15	1,220	0	0.0%	54
12/14	1,254	0	0.0%	—
12/13	1,198	0	0.0%	—
12/09	1,037	1	0.2%	—
Annual Growth	2.8%	(33.9%)	—	—

2015 Year-End Financials

Return on assets: —
Return on equity: 0.4%
Current ratio: —

Cash ($ mil.): 8

CENTRAL GROCERS, INC.

In a city of big stores Central Grocers helps keep neighborhood markets stocked. Founded in 1917 the cooperative wholesale food distributor is owned by some 225 members. It supplies 40000 food items and general merchandise to more than 400 independent grocery stores serving several states such as Illinois Indiana Iowa Michigan and Wisconsin. Central Grocers distributes products under both national brands and its own Centrella brand which is marketed exclusively to its member stores. The co-op also operates about 30 stores under a handful of banner names including Strack & Van Til Town & Country Key Market and the low-cost Ultra Foods chain.In 2017 the company filed for Chapter 11 bankruptcy protection.

Bankruptcy

In May 2017 Central Grocers filed for Chapter 11 bankruptcy protection. The company intends to sell its Strack & Van Tilstores and its Joliet Ill. distribution warehouse as its seeks to exit its wholesale distribution business.

Operations

As part of its business Central Grocers caters to its customers with the help of a fleet of 100 refrigerated trucks 300 dry trailers and about 70 Freightliner tractors.

Sales and Marketing

Central Grocers services a wide variety of store formats and ethnic groups including Hispanic Italian and African Americans. Besides older and smaller 5000-sq.-ft. stores its clients include large-scale warehouse discount stores that measure 75000 sq. ft. and large conventional stores that average 70000 sq. ft.

Financial Performance

While privately-owned Central Grocers doesn't report financial results. The co-op rings up an estimated $2 billion in sales and it returns (in the form of dividends) to its members about $243 million.

Strategy

Central Grocers the 7th largest grocery cooperative in the US boasts the second-largest market share in the Chicago area. It specializes in serving Chicago independent supermarkets. Central Grocers supplies them with a comprehensive menu of groceries produce fresh meat service deli items frozen foods ice cream and items from its own Centrella brand.

Central Grocers expanded its distribution center by 15000-sq.-ft. to 940000-sq.-ft. of storage capacity in 2011. The reason for expansion was due to demand for produce and fresh meats.

LOCATIONS

HQ: CENTRAL GROCERS, INC.
2600 HAVEN AVE, JOLIET, IL 604338467
Phone: 815 553-8800
Web: WWW.CENTRAL-GROCERS.COM

PRODUCTS/OPERATIONS

Selected Products
Fresh meat
Frozen foods
Groceries
Ice cream
Produce
Service deli items

COMPETITORS

Aldi	Kroger
Albertsons	Meijer
Alex Lee	Supervalu
Associated Wholesale	Safeway
Grocers	Schnuck Markets
C&s Wholesale	Wal-mart

Certco
Dearborn Wholesale
Grocers
Winkler

HISTORICAL FINANCIALS
Company Type: Private

Income Statement				FYE: July 28
	REVENUE ($ mil.)	NET INCOME ($ mil.)	NET PROFIT MARGIN	EMPLOYEES
07/07	1,197	(10)	—	2,300
07/06	1,108	5	0.5%	
07/05	1,103	4	0.4%	
07/04	1,047	3	0.3%	
Annual Growth	4.5%	—	—	—

2007 Year-End Financials

Return on assets: (-3.8%)   Cash ($ mil.): —
Return on equity: (-35.2%)
Current ratio: 1.00

CENTRAL HUDSON GAS & ELECTRIC CORPORATION

EXECUTIVES

Pres-Ceo, Charles A Freni
Chb, Margarita K Dilley
Evp-Cfo, Christopher M Capone
Chief Technology Officer, Donna Kladis
Asst V Pres, Eng'g & Envrnmntl, Paul E Haering
Human Resources Representative, Yvette Johnson
Project Engineer, Victor Pennes
Operating Supervisor Call Cent, Anthony Hannah
Engineer, Henry Wilson-Sowah
Plant Accounting, Barbara Giangaspro
Executive Vice President, James Laurito

LOCATIONS

HQ: CENTRAL HUDSON GAS & ELECTRIC CORPORATION
284 SOUTH AVE DEPT 100, POUGHKEEPSIE, NY 126014839
Phone: 845 452-2700
Web: WWW.CENHUD.COM

HISTORICAL FINANCIALS
Company Type: Private

Income Statement				FYE: December 31
	REVENUE ($ mil.)	NET INCOME ($ mil.)	NET PROFIT MARGIN	EMPLOYEES
12/17	671	55	8.2%	869
12/16	640	52	8.2%	
/	0	0	—	
Annual Growth	—	—	—	—

2017 Year-End Financials

Return on assets: 2.5%   Cash ($ mil.): 14
Return on equity: 8.8%
Current ratio: 1.80

CENTRAL IOWA HOSPITAL CORP

EXECUTIVES

Ceo, Eric Crowell
Executive Director-Finance*, Kara Dunham
Chief of Urology, Markham J J Anderson
Regional Vice-President, Jean Shelton

LOCATIONS

HQ: CENTRAL IOWA HOSPITAL CORP
1200 PLEASANT ST, DES MOINES, IA 503091406
Phone: 515 241-6212
Web: WWW.CENTRALIOWA.VA.GOV

HISTORICAL FINANCIALS
Company Type: Private

Income Statement				FYE: December 31
	REVENUE ($ mil.)	NET INCOME ($ mil.)	NET PROFIT MARGIN	EMPLOYEES
12/17	832	3	0.4%	3,495
12/16	573	153	26.8%	
12/15	548	152	27.9%	
12/14	534	145	27.2%	
Annual Growth	15.9%	(71.6%)	—	—

2017 Year-End Financials

Return on assets: 0.3%   Cash ($ mil.): 2
Return on equity: 0.4%
Current ratio: 3.20

CENTRAL STEEL AND WIRE COMPANY

When it comes to metal service center Central Steel & Wire Company (CS&W) can shape up and ship out. CS&W distributes ferrous and nonferrous metals in a variety of shapes and forms including bars coils plates sheets structurals tubing and wire. Among the company's processing services are annealing blanking computer numerical control (CNC) laser cutting galvanizing and structural fabrication. CS&W distributes its products throughout North America from five facilities that are located primarily in the Midwestern US. The company has metallurgical engineers on its staff to support customers with metal specifications and interpretation expertise.

Operations

The company distributes processed and unprocessed ferrous and nonferrous metals which are are generally obtained from rolling mills in many forms and distributed from CS&W's warehouses.

Geographic Reach

CS&W is based in Chicago. It has stocking facilities in Cincinnati Detroit Milwaukee Greensboro (North Carolina). Its Central Coil Processing unit is in Portage Indiana.

Financial Performance

In 2013 CS&W's revenues decreased by 10% due to lower prices caused by excess mill capacity and a 4% drop in tons shipped caused by lower net sales.

The company's net income decreased by 79% that year primarily due to a decline in revenues.

CS&W's operating cash inflow increased to $11 million (compared to $10 million in 2012) due to cash generated from inventories and receivables.

Strategy

In 2013 the company launched a new web based material test reporting feature increasing its ability to service customers more efficiently through an additional channel when material certifications are required.

Company Background

In 2011 CS&W added pre-painted steel and aluminum coil to its full-line inventory of metal products. The pre-paint program includes material stocked and processed to customer specific specifications for next day delivery. The main intent of this expansion is to develop inventory management programs to reduce total costs and support short-dated delivery requirements.

CS&W was founded in 1909. The company is majority-owned by a trust set up by a former chairman the late James Lowenstein.

EXECUTIVES

Ceo, Stephen E Fuhrman
Cfo*, Kevin G Powers
Assistant Manager Order Proces, Cindy Lambros
Customer Rep, Hilda Villalobos
Inside Sales, Jenna Romano
Inside Sales Representative, Jordan Alvarez
Territory Sales Manager, Kimberly Witkowski
Administrative Assistant, Laura Phipps
Transportation, Michael Hawkins
Coordinator, Steve Wilson
Payroll, Maria Liakopoulos

LOCATIONS

HQ: CENTRAL STEEL AND WIRE COMPANY
3000 W 51ST ST, CHICAGO, IL 606322198
Phone: 773 471-3800
Web: WWW.CENTRALSTEEL.COM

PRODUCTS/OPERATIONS

Selected Products
Alloy bars
Aluminum
Bar and structural shapes
Brass and copper
CF bars/flat wire
Grating/Morton products
HR bars
Steel plates
Steel sheets/strapping
Stainless steel
Steel tubing/pipe
Wire/drill rod/tool steel

Selected Processing Capabilities
Angle Rings
Annealing
Annodizing
Band Saw Cutting
Beam Splitting
Blanking
Burning - Oxyfuel
Centerless Grinding
Circle Shearing
CNC Laser Cutting
CNC Plasma Cutting
CNC Punching
CNC Waterjet Cutting
Coil Blanking
Coil Cut To Length
Cold Sawing Bar
Cold Sawing Plate
Contour Sawing
Deep Hole Drilling
Drilling & Tapping
F&D Heads
Facing & Centering
Forming
Galvanizing
Grinding
Heat Treating

Honing
Lathe Cut Tube/Pipe
Machining
Mech Descale and Oil
Miter Cutting
Normalizing
Painting
Perforating
Pickling & Oiling
Plate and Struct Rolling
Plating
Polishing
Precision Plasma
Precision Sawing
Protex Covering
Sand/Shot Blasting
SCS Finishing
Seam Planishing
Seam Welding
Shearing
Slitting
Straightening
Stress Relieving
Struct Fabrication
Threading
Tube/Pipe Fabrication
Tumble Deburring
Ultrasonic Testing
Welding
Wire Brush Deburr

COMPETITORS

Alro
Macsteel Service
  Centers Usa
Metals Usa
Olympic Steel

Precision Steel
Reliance Steel
Ryerson
Worthington Industries

HISTORICAL FINANCIALS
Company Type: Private

Income Statement   FYE: December 31

	REVENUE ($ mil.)	NET INCOME ($ mil.)	NET PROFIT MARGIN	EMPLOYEES
12/14	698	(2)	—	1,075
12/13	678	2	0.3%	—
12/12	750	10	1.4%	—
Annual Growth	(3.6%)	—	—	—

2014 Year-End Financials

Return on assets: (-1.3%)   Cash ($ mil.): 28
Return on equity: (-1.8%)
Current ratio: 7.10

CERTCO, INC.

Certco has built a business serving about 200 independent grocers in Minnesota Wisconsin Iowa and Illinois. The food distribution cooperative offers customers an inventory of more than 57000 items including bakery goods frozen foods meat products produce and general merchandise. It distributes products under the Shurfine Shurfresh and Top Care labels. Additionally Certco offers its member-operators such services as advertising accounting client data services warehousing merchandising store planning and design and other business support services. The cooperative was founded in 1930 as Central Wisconsin Cooperative Food Stores.

Operations

To support its business Certco operates a nearly 1 million-sq.-ft. distribution center. Its brands include Shurfine Shurfresh Value Time Full Circle Topco and Top Care.

Geographic Reach

Based in Madison Wisconsin Certco operates in Minnesota and Wisconsin with an extended reach into parts of Iowa and Illinois.

Sales and Marketing

Many of Certco's clients are Fortune 500 companies. It distributes the national brands of major companies such as Kraft General Mills Procter & Gamble and Johnson & Johnson. The company also distributes specialty items under the names Amy's Hodgson Mills Bob's Red Mill and Annie's that are only available through direct-store-delivery suppliers.

Company Background

Certco was established in 1930 when five Madison-area retailers formed an alliance to boost their combined purchasing muscle.

EXECUTIVES

Pres-Ceo, Randy Simon
Exe V Pres-Cfo*, Amy Niemetscheck
V Pres*, Dave Ryman
Dir*, Antonio Hernandez
Director of Information Techno*, Joe Dempich
Coordinator, Catheryn Miller
Business Manager, Diane Henschel
Merchandising, Mark Carney
Director of Procurement, Mike Baumgartner
Prod Manager Contact, Ron Prohaska
Safety Director, Tara Umanzor
Auditors: SATTELL JOHNSON APPEL & CO

LOCATIONS

HQ: CERTCO, INC.
5321 VERONA RD, FITCHBURG, WI 537116050
Phone: 608 271-4500
Web: WWW.CERTCOINC.COM

PRODUCTS/OPERATIONS

Selected Brands
Full Circle
Shurfine
Shurfresh
Top Care
Topco
Value Time

Selected Services
Advertising
Client data services
Retail accounting
Retail meetings/seminars
Retail support
Retail technology
Store planning & design
Trade shows
Value added services
Warehouses
Web architecture

COMPETITORS

Affiliated Foods
  Midwest
Associated Wholesale
  Grocers
C&s Wholesale
Central Grocers

Dearborn Wholesale
  Grocers
Kroger
Roundy's
Winkler

HISTORICAL FINANCIALS
Company Type: Private

Income Statement   FYE: April 26

	REVENUE ($ mil.)	NET INCOME ($ mil.)	NET PROFIT MARGIN	EMPLOYEES
04/14	640	5	0.9%	325
04/13	607	5	0.9%	—
04/12	569	5	0.9%	—
Annual Growth	6.0%	5.6%	—	—

2014 Year-End Financials
Return on assets: 5.0%   Cash ($ mil.): 11
Return on equity: 8.4%
Current ratio: 2.00

CFJ PROPERTIES LLC

EXECUTIVES

Chb, Crystal Call Maggelet
Exec Committee MBR*, Andre Lortz
Exec Committee MBR*, Richard D Peterson
Senior Corporate Counsel, Tom Schofield
Auditors: KPMG LLP SALT LAKE CITY UTAH

LOCATIONS

HQ: CFJ PROPERTIES LLC
5508 LONAS DR, KNOXVILLE, TN 379093221
Phone: 801 624-1000
Web: WWW.PILOTFLYINGJ.COM

HISTORICAL FINANCIALS

Company Type: Private

Income Statement				FYE: January 31
	REVENUE ($ mil.)	NET INCOME ($ mil.)	NET PROFIT MARGIN	EMPLOYEES
01/09	7,672	157	2.1%	6,250
01/07	6,769	50	0.7%	—
01/06	6,166	48	0.8%	—
Annual Growth	7.6%	47.7%	—	—

2009 Year-End Financials
Return on assets: 18.7%   Cash ($ mil.): 37
Return on equity: 47.1%
Current ratio: 0.60

CGB ENTERPRISES, INC.

CGB Enterprises is a leader in the grain and transportation industries. Located in Louisiana the agricultural company provides US farmers with a range of services including grain handling storage lending and merchandising. It offers inland grain transportation by barge rail and truck and also markets and sells seeds agricultural products and insurance. CGB's Consolidated Terminals and Logistics Co. (CTLC) subsidiary provides transportation logistics and bulk commodity services for both agricultural and non-agricultural customers. The company operates more than 125 locations across the US. Japanese trading conglomerates ITOCHU and ZEN-NOH own CGB.

Operations

CGB Enterprises provides an array of services for grain farmers from buying storing selling and shipping of agricultural products to global supply chain solutions.

The company operates an enterprise overseeing a diverse family of businesses that provide an array of services for producers and logistics services.

CGB's divisions include Consolidated Grain and Barge Co. AgriFinancial (services more than $2 billion in loans and leases for agricultural producers across the country) Diversified Services Soybean Processing CTLC CGB Marine (an operating business unit under the CTLC division directly involved in more than 10000 barge loads of cargo annually) Feed Ingredients (source Dried Distiller's Grains (DDGs) and other feed ingredients for export and domestic markets) and Container Shipping.

Geographic Reach

From its headquarters in the city of Covington Louisiana CGB operates its business through more than 125 locations nationwide including over 125 grain facilities. CGB Marine has facilities located on the Lower Mississippi River near the Gulf of Mexico the St. Louis Harbor Cairo and various other locations on the Mississippi the Ohio and the Illinois Rivers.

Sales and Marketing

Besides its core services of inland grain transportation via barge rail and truck CGB markets and sells its products beyond the agricultural industry. Its Soybean Processing provides high quality soybean products to a global base of meal and oil customers. Its Trucking business serves multiple industries such as wine beer and spirits agribusiness food and beverage and plastics and packaging among others.

Mergers and Acquisitions

In late 2021 Consolidated Grain and Barge Co. a wholly-owned subsidiary of CGB Enterprises acquired Agspring Logistics' business assets operated under the trade name Agforce Transport Services (Agforce). "The acquisition of Agforce business assets is a complement to our existing freight transportation company River Bend Brokerage and to our overall strategic business portfolio. We are excited to welcome new team members to CGB and to begin servicing a new customer base through expanded supply chain services" said Hector Orellana Senior Director of Inland Terminals and River Bend Brokerage at CGB. Terms of the agreement were not disclosed.

EXECUTIVES

Ceo-Pres, Kevin D Adams
Exec V Pres-Cfo-Sec, Richard S Pemberton
V Pres of Admin-Dir of Int Aud, Michael T Merkel
V Pres-Grain Div, Gregory A Beck
V Pres-Marine & Terminals, G Scott Leininger
Sr V Pres-Soybean Processing, Stephen B O'Nan
V Pres, Gen Counsel, Jonathan H Sandoz
Sr V Pres, Yuya Hashizawa
Sr V Pres, Kenji Tsukuda
Accounting Staff, Sherry Rowan
Vp, Ctlc and Marine Manager,, Scott Leininger
Auditors: KPMG LLP NEW ORLEANS LOUISI

LOCATIONS

HQ: CGB ENTERPRISES, INC.
1127 HWY 190 E SERVICE RD, COVINGTON, LA 704334929
Phone: 985 867-3500
Web: WWW.CGB.COM

PRODUCTS/OPERATIONS

Selected Business Units
Feed Ingredients
Fertilizer
Financial Services
Grain
Marine
Premium Grains
Risk Management
Soybean Processing
Terminals & Logistics

COMPETITORS

Adm	Crosby Tugs
Ag Processing Inc.	Jimmy Sanders

Alabama Farmers Cooperative	Kirby Corporation
Canal Barge Company	Southern States
Cargill	Tennessee Farmers Co-op

HISTORICAL FINANCIALS

Company Type: Private

Income Statement				FYE: May 31
	REVENUE ($ mil.)	NET INCOME ($ mil.)	NET PROFIT MARGIN	EMPLOYEES
05/21	7,081	116	1.6%	3,250
05/20	5,955	50	0.8%	—
05/19	6,498	67	1.0%	—
05/18	6,801	110	1.6%	—
Annual Growth	1.4%	1.8%	—	—

2021 Year-End Financials
Return on assets: 4.9%   Cash ($ mil.): 251
Return on equity: 20.0%
Current ratio: 1.00

CHALMETTE REFINING, L.L.C.

EXECUTIVES

Ceo, Thomas J Nimbley
Manager, Eric Beam

LOCATIONS

HQ: CHALMETTE REFINING, L.L.C.
500 W SAINT BERNARD HWY, CHALMETTE, LA 700434821
Phone: 504 281-1212
Web: WWW.CHALMETTEREFINING.COM

HISTORICAL FINANCIALS

Company Type: Private

Income Statement				FYE: December 31
	REVENUE ($ mil.)	NET INCOME ($ mil.)	NET PROFIT MARGIN	EMPLOYEES
12/07	5,647	364	6.4%	600
12/06	5,020	423	8.4%	—
12/05	3,462	264	7.6%	—
12/04	3,130	221	7.1%	—
Annual Growth	21.7%	18.1%	—	—

2007 Year-End Financials
Return on assets: —   Cash ($ mil.): 302
Return on equity: 6.4%
Current ratio: 0.50

CHARLESTON AREA MEDICAL CENTER, INC.

CAMC Health System is a catalyst for care in Charleston. The health network includes flagship facility Charleston Area Medical Center (CAMC) which is the largest hospital in West Virginia and consists of three campuses with some 840 beds total. The system also includes the CAMC Health Education and Research Institute which coordinates education programs for medical students from West Virginia University. In addition the health system operates smaller rural hospital CAMC Teays Valley and several urgent care and family practice clinics. CAMC Health System operates an online medical information system and physician services company Integrated Health Care Providers.

Operations

The three campuses of CAMC include CAMC General Hospital CAMC Memorial Hospital and CAMC Women and Children's Hospital all of which are located in Charleston. Specialty services at the hospitals include cardiology kidney transplants trauma and pediatrics. The CAMC Institute conducts graduate and continuing education courses; it also connects education and health care through clinical research projects in areas such as cancer and cardiovascular clinical science studies. The Teays Valley Hospital is a 70-bed facility located in nearby Hurricane West Virginia.

CAMC General Hospital is home to the highest level Trauma Center nationally-accredited Medical Rehabilitation and Stroke Centers The Center for Joint Replacement Neurosciences Center one of two Facial Surgery Centers Charleston's only accredited Sleep Center and West Virginia's only kidney transplant program affiliated with the Cleveland Clinic.

CAMC Memorial Hospital hosts one of highest volume heart programs in the US which performs 8000 procedures in the cardiac catheterization labs and more than 1600 open-heart bypass surgeries a year.

CAMC Women and Children's Hospital facilitates the birth of more than 3000 babies (including many high-risk births) per year.

Teays Valley Hospital is a not-for-profit 70-bed hospital. More than 100 doctors are authorized to practice at the hospital.

CAMC serves as a clinical training site for 700 additional learners per year through educational affiliations with regional colleges and universities.

Sales and Marketing

Commercial insurance providers and other third parties accounted for more than half of CAMC's net patient revenue in 2013; Medicare and Medicaid account for 30% and 13% respectively.

Financial Performance

The company's revenue grew by 4% to $969 million in 2013 due to higher net patient revenues and investment income. Net income fell 8% to $86 million though as expenses including salaries and employee benefits rose. Cash flow from operations dropped 48% to $33 million both as a result of the lower net income and an increase in cash used in short-term trading investments.

Strategy

In 2013 CAMC teamed up with The Ohio State University University of Michigan and West Virginia University to raise awareness and educate the community about cervical cancer. Community Awareness Resources and Education (CARE) is one of OSU Cancer Center's programs sponsored by the National Cancer Institute that focuses on an important health disparity among an underserved Appalachian population.

The following year CAMC teamed with Alliance Oncology a division of Alliance HealthCare Services to work on establishing a department of radiation therapy at CAMC Cancer Center.

Upgrading its infrastructure in 2013 Teays Valley Hospital completed a $3.7 million ICU expansion project.

EXECUTIVES

Pres, David L Ramsey
Jr M D, V Pres*, Glenn Crotty
SEC*, Angela Fenton Hill

Treas*, Larry Hudson
V Pres*, Elizabeth Keightley
Chief of Medicine, Mary Lou Lewis
Coordinator, Shirley Whitley
Corporate Counsel/Legal, Marshall McMullen
Director of Radiology, Jeffrey C Dameron
Clinical Research Fellow, Maher Kali
Information Specialist, Kathy Newsome
Auditors: DELOITTE TAX LLP CHICAGO IL

LOCATIONS

HQ: CHARLESTON AREA MEDICAL CENTER, INC.
501 MORRIS ST, CHARLESTON, WV 253011326
Phone: 304 348-5432
Web: WWW.CAMC.ORG

PRODUCTS/OPERATIONS

2013 Net Patient Revenue

	% of total
Commercial insurance & other third-party payment programs	51
Medicare	30
Medicaid	13
Self-pay	1
PEIA	5
Total	**100**

2013 Sales

	$ mil.	% of total
Net patient revenue less provision for bad debts	876	91
Investment income	49	5
Other revenue	41	4
Net assets released from restrictions	1	-
Total	**968**	**100**

Selected Service Areas

Behavioral health
Cancer
Cardiac
Children's medicine
Craniofacial surgery
Endoscopy
Fertility
Gynecology
Hemophilia
Kidney transplant
Orthopedics
Palliative care
Perinatal
Plastic surgery
Stroke
Trauma
Urology
Vascular

COMPETITORS

Charleston Hospital
Ohio Valley Medical Center
Princeton Community Hospital
St. Mary's Medical Center
Wvuhs
Weirton Medical Center
West Virginia University Hospitals

HISTORICAL FINANCIALS

Company Type: Private

Income Statement   FYE: December 31

	REVENUE ($ mil.)	NET INCOME ($ mil.)	NET PROFIT MARGIN	EMPLOYEES
12/19	1,273	40	3.2%	4,000
12/16	1,044	(17)	—	—
12/15	932	36	4.0%	—
12/14	877	42	4.9%	—
Annual Growth	7.7%	(1.0%)	—	—

2019 Year-End Financials

Return on assets: 3.8%   Cash ($ mil.): 113
Return on equity: 8.8%
Current ratio: 1.00

CHARTER MANUFACTURING COMPANY, INC.

Charter Manufacturing's magna carta calls for it to make steel products. The family-owned company manufactures such steel products as special bar quality (SBQ) bar rod wire and stainless steel rod. The company also supplies precision cold-rolled custom profiles and engineered components including driveline engine and transmission parts for the automotive industry. It operates primarily in the US but also in Europe and Asia through subsidiaries Charter Steel (general steel products) Charter Wire (precision cold-rolled custom profiles flat wire and standard shapes) Charter Dura-Bar (cast iron bar and bronze alloys) and Charter Automotive (engineered components for automotive applications).

Operations

The company manufactures special bar quality bar rod and wire as well as precision cold-rolled custom profiles flat wire and standard shapes and engineered components for use in engines transmissions and drivelines. Charter Steel is an integrated producer of special bar quality bar rod and wire products has an annual coil-making capacity of 1.2 million tons; Charter Dura-Bar is a leading producer of continuous cast iron bar stock and a distributor (through Dura-Bar Metal Services) of Dura-Bar products and bronze alloys; Charter Wire supplies precision cold-rolled custom profiles flat wire and standard shapes; while Charter Automotive supplies of engineered components for engine driveline and transmission applications.

Geographic Reach

Charter Manufacturing serves customers around the world and has plants in the US (Illinois North Carolina Ohio Pennsylvania and Wisconsin) China (one plant) and the UK (two plants).

Sales and Marketing

Charter Manufacturing sells its products through its operating subsidiaries and sales representatives.

Strategy

The company is looking to expand both geographically and in terms of product offerings. Growing its global footprint in 2012 the company expanded its European operations with the purchase of a 57000 sq.-ft. manufacturing plant in Burntwood UK. The expansion strengthens Charter Automotive's position as a global supplier to OEM automotive and powertrain industries and helps it meet the growing demands of customers in Europe and elsewhere.

Mergers and Acquisitions

In 2012 the company acquired Wells Manufacturing Company (owner of Dura-Bar and DuraBar Metal Services). The acquired assets (which added a fourth division to Charter Manufacturing's family of companies — Charter Dura-Bar) focus on producing specialty iron bar and distributing bronze alloy products.

Company Background

Facing tough market conditions Charter Automotive closed part of its steelmaking operations in Milwaukee Wisconsin in 2010. The company ceased making steel dipsticks and tubes for cars and trucks as part of a wider response to global market trends. The company which kept its engine components operations elsewhere in Milwaukee active sold the Heather Avenue plant idled by this move.

Charter Manufacturing was established in 1936 and is owned by the family of founder Alfred Mellowes.

EXECUTIVES

Pres, Thomas Glaister
Cfo, Todd Endres
Admn Assist, Anna M
Database Administrator, Jeff Richter
Engineering Program Manager, Donna Gibson
Information Technology Team ME, Bill Bumpus
Senior Programmer Analyst, Daniel Wierzbinski
Vice President, Sarah Urban
Assistant Controller, April Finger
Corporate Controller, Lisa Jauron
Global Head of Compensation, Sonya Vollmer
Auditors: DELOITTE & TOUCHE LLP MILWAU

LOCATIONS

HQ: CHARTER MANUFACTURING COMPANY, INC.
12121 CORPORATE PKWY, MEQUON, WI 530923332
Phone: 262 243-4700
Web: WWW.CHARTERMFG.COM

PRODUCTS/OPERATIONS

Selected Operating Units
Charter Automotive
Charter Dura-Bar
Charter Steel
Charter Wire

Selected Mergers and Acquisitions

COMPETITORS

Ak Steel Holding	Nucor
Corporation	Republic Steel
Federal-mogul	Timken
Gerdau Ameristeel	United States Steel

HISTORICAL FINANCIALS

Company Type: Private

Income Statement				FYE: December 31
	REVENUE ($ mil.)	NET INCOME ($ mil.)	NET PROFIT MARGIN	EMPLOYEES
12/10	903	74	8.3%	2,000
12/09	517	2	0.4%	—
12/08	996	26	2.7%	—
Annual Growth	(4.8%)	66.8%	—	—

2010 Year-End Financials
Return on assets: 14.4%   Cash ($ mil.): 85
Return on equity: 24.7%
Current ratio: 1.60

CHEMIUM INTERNATIONAL CORP.

EXECUTIVES

Pres, Ofer Levy
V-Pres*, Thomas Holzmann
Cfo*, Nicolas Folgado
Financial Analyst, Daniela Weir
Head of Crude, Ed More
Director of Global Business De, Jack Nicholas
Independent Representative, Cesar Calvo
Global Manager, Chad Johnson
Accounting, Jimena Ferrufino

Vice-President, Sanjeev Vora
Manager, Commercial, Steve Williams

LOCATIONS

HQ: CHEMIUM INTERNATIONAL CORP.
3773 RICHMOND AVE STE 600, HOUSTON, TX 770463725
Phone: 713 622-7766
Web: WWW.CHEMIUMCORP.COM

HISTORICAL FINANCIALS

Company Type: Private

Income Statement				FYE: December 31
	REVENUE ($ mil.)	NET INCOME ($ mil.)	NET PROFIT MARGIN	EMPLOYEES
12/15	2,015	3	0.2%	24
12/06	450	3	0.9%	—
12/03	103	0	—	—
Annual Growth	28.1%	—	—	—

2015 Year-End Financials
Return on assets: 2.9%   Cash ($ mil.): 5
Return on equity: 0.2%
Current ratio: 0.80

CHENEGA CORPORATION

An Alaska Native Corporation Chenega Corporation has gone from landowner to business titan. Representing the Chenega people residing in the central Alaskan Prince William Sound region it operates mostly through its subsidiaries. Chenega Integrated Systems and Chenega Technology Services offer information technology security training manufacturing research and development network engineering and military operation support services. Chenega Corporation's clients have included the Department of Defense Department of Homeland Security and EPA.

Geographic Reach
The company's headquarters are located in Anchorage Alaska. Chenega Corporation and its subsidiaries operate in 45 states and 11 countries.

Strategy
Government contracts are a source of revenue growth. Chenega Corporation began to participate in the Government Services marketplace in 1997. By 2012 it was performing on more than 158 prime contracts and 100 principal sub-contracts through a combination of competitive and negotiated best-value awards.

EXECUTIVES

Pres-Ceo, Charles Totemoff
Coo*, Jeff Hueners
SEC*, Paul Selanoff
Program Analyst, Dana Iraka
Profesional Rsume, Deborah Duren
Desktop Support Technician, George Akpakli
Senior Vice President, Hagen Renee
Hazwaste Technician, James Ray
Human Resources Analys, Jeff Doty
Full Stack Software Engineer, Joe Brock
Vice President, Kathy Ward

LOCATIONS

HQ: CHENEGA CORPORATION
3000 C ST STE 301, ANCHORAGE, AK 995033975
Phone: 907 277-5706
Web: WWW.CHENEGA.COM

PRODUCTS/OPERATIONS

Selected Services
Base operations and maintenance
Environmental management
Information technology
Intel and military operations
Light manufacturing
Logistics support
Telecommunications
Tourism and hospitality
Training services
Security services

COMPETITORS

Akal Security	Halliburton
Arctic Slope Regional	Ibm Global Services
Corporation	Parsons Corporation
Computer Sciences	Tkc Communications
Corp.	Chugach Alaska
Hp Enterprise Services	

HISTORICAL FINANCIALS

Company Type: Private

Income Statement				FYE: September 30
	REVENUE ($ mil.)	NET INCOME ($ mil.)	NET PROFIT MARGIN	EMPLOYEES
09/20	948	19	2.0%	4,500
09/19	871	19	2.3%	—
09/18	829	19	2.3%	—
09/17	875	12	1.4%	—
Annual Growth	2.7%	16.7%	—	—

2020 Year-End Financials
Return on assets: 4.5%   Cash ($ mil.): 48
Return on equity: 8.1%
Current ratio: 1.90

CHEROKEE NATION BUSINESSES LLC

EXECUTIVES

MBR-Ceo, Shawn Slaton
Chb*, Bill John Baker
MBR*, Gary Cooper
MBR-Cfo*, Doug Evans
MBR-Board MBR*, Bob Berry
Snr Dir Fin*, Kimberly Barnette
Information Specialist, Aaron Lowther
Information Specialist, Cody Hardy
Information Specialist, Curtis Starling
Information Specialist, Daniel Basden
Regional Vice-President, David Mullen
Auditors: BKD LLP TULSA OK

LOCATIONS

HQ: CHEROKEE NATION BUSINESSES LLC
777 W CHEROKEE ST, CATOOSA, OK 740153235
Phone: 918 384-7474
Web: WWW.CHEROKEENATIONBUSINESSES.COM

HISTORICAL FINANCIALS

Company Type: Private

Income Statement				FYE: September 30
	REVENUE ($ mil.)	NET INCOME ($ mil.)	NET PROFIT MARGIN	EMPLOYEES
09/19	1,183	48	4.1%	3,117
09/18	1,098	65	5.9%	—
09/17	1,018	40	4.0%	—
09/16	1,021	50	4.9%	—
Annual Growth	5.0%	(1.5%)	—	—

2019 Year-End Financials

Return on assets: 4.3%
Return on equity: 5.2%
Current ratio: 2.30

Cash ($ mil.): 237

CHEROKEE NATION ENTERTAINMENT, LLC

EXECUTIVES

Ceo, David Stewart
Prin*, Shawn Slaton
Coordinator, Amber Steele
Marketing Supervisor Cherokee, Kathryn Hemphill
Purchasing Manager, Stacyee Hall
Information Technology Support, Gene Garvin
Senior Director, Kimberly Barnett
DC Manager, Andy Pruitt
Cage Shift Manager, Becky James
Senior Manager, Brian Larson
Lead Security Officer, Caylen Ahtone
Auditors: BKD LLP TULSA OK

LOCATIONS

HQ: CHEROKEE NATION ENTERTAINMENT, LLC
777 W CHEROKEE ST, CATOOSA, OK 740153235
Phone: 918 384-7800
Web: WWW.CHEROKEECASINO.COM

HISTORICAL FINANCIALS

Company Type: Private

Income Statement				FYE: September 30
	REVENUE ($ mil.)	NET INCOME ($ mil.)	NET PROFIT MARGIN	EMPLOYEES
09/19	686	(14)	—	3,100
09/17	666	25	3.9%	—
Annual Growth	1.5%	—	—	—

2019 Year-End Financials

Return on assets: (-1.9%)
Return on equity: (-2.1%)
Current ratio: 2.30

Cash ($ mil.): 55

CHEVRON PHILLIPS CHEMICAL COMPANY LIMITED PARTNERSHIP

EXECUTIVES

Ceo, Peter Cella
Exec V Pres, Mark Lashier
Sr V Pres, Ron Corn
Sr V Pres, Tim Hill
V Pres, Mitch Eichelberger
Coordinator, Aprile Turner
Staff, Aaron Evitts
Coordinator, Tom Shomette
Safety Manager, Carolyn Rogers
Information Specialist, Marie Newhouse
Operations Manager, Art Orscheln
Auditors: ERNST & YOUNG LLP HOUSTON T

LOCATIONS

HQ: CHEVRON PHILLIPS CHEMICAL COMPANY LIMITED PARTNERSHIP
10001 SIX PINES DR, THE WOODLANDS, TX 773801498
Phone: 832 813-4100
Web: WWW.CPCHEM.COM

HISTORICAL FINANCIALS

Company Type: Private

Income Statement				FYE: December 31
	REVENUE ($ mil.)	NET INCOME ($ mil.)	NET PROFIT MARGIN	EMPLOYEES
12/16	7,106	1,301	18.3%	6,472
12/15	7,990	2,020	25.3%	—
12/14	11,758	2,444	20.8%	—
Annual Growth	(22.3%)	(27.0%)	—	—

2016 Year-End Financials

Return on assets: 11.1%
Return on equity: 13.5%
Current ratio: 1.30

Cash ($ mil.): 422

CHEVRON PHILLIPS CHEMICAL COMPANY LLC

Among the world's largest petrochemical firms Chevron Phillips Chemical (CPChem) produces ethylene propylene polyethylene and polypropylene — sometimes used as building blocks for the company's other products such as pipes and food containers. CPChem also produces aromatics such as benzene and styrene specialty chemicals such as acetylene black (a form of carbon black) and mining chemicals. Chevron Phillips Chemical Company LP is CPChem's wholly-owned primary US operating subsidiary. CPChem is 50% owned by Chevron U.S.A. Inc. an indirect wholly-owned subsidiary of Chevron Corporation and 50% by wholly-owned subsidiaries of Phillips 66.

Operations

CPChem divides its operations into two segments: Olefins & Polyolefins and Specialties Aromatics and Styrenics.

The Olefins & Polyolefins segment produces ethylene polyethylene normal alpha olefins polyalphaolefins propylene and high-density polyethylene pipe and conduit and pipe fittings.

The Specialties Aromatics and Styrenics segments makes cyclohexane styrene polystyrene benzene mining chemicals Soltex drilling mud additive scentinel mercaptans specialty organosulfur compounds racing fuels and E-Series acetylene hydrogenation catalysts.

CPChem generates some 55% of sales from petrochemicals products one-third form polymers and more than 10% from specialty products.

The company's chemical products are used in more than 70000 consumer and industrial products. Its brands include Marlex Aromax Scentinel Soltex and K-Resin.

Geographic Reach

CPChem operates about 30 factories across Belgium Colombia Qatar Saudi Arabia Singapore and the US. It has two R&D and quality control centers in Bartlesville Oklahoma and Kingwood Texas. CPChem is active in Qatar Saudia Arabia and Singapore through joint venture

Sales and Marketing

CPChem serves a range of markets including Adhesives and Sealants Agricultural Appliances Automotive Building and Construction Chemical Manufacturing Drycleaning Textiles Pharmaceuticals Paint and Coatings Imaging and Photography Packaging and Electronics.

It holds the leading market position in the US for polyethylne piping and is the world's largest marketer of cyclohexane. Subsidiary America Styrenics holds a nearly 30% market share in US polystyrene.

Financial Performance

CPChem has recorded growing sales over the past three years. In 2018 revenue climbed 25% to $11.3 billion. Profits dipped in 2017 but rebounded in 2018 growing 43% to $2.1 billion.

Strategy

External pressures on the petrochemicals industry including slowing growth the trade war between the US and China and a consumer backlash against plastic use have ushered in a period of consolidation. To diversify its output and geographic spread Chevron Phillips (CPChem) bid for Nova Chemicals in 2019 in a move that would make CPChem the third-largest producer of polyethylene in North America and the largest producer of high-density polyethylene.

Company Background

A coin toss determined whose name would go first when Chevron and Phillips Petroleum (now Phillips 66) formed 50-50 joint venture Chevron Phillips Chemical Company in 2000.

EXECUTIVES

Ceo, Mark Lashier
Pres*, Peter L Cella
Svp-Cfo*, Carolyn Burke
Sr V Pres-Ctrl*, Greg G Maxwell
Vp-Treas*, Joe M McKee
Sr V Pres-Gen Counsel-Sec*, Craig B Glidden
Exec V Pres*, Mark E Lashier
Sr V Pres*, Dan Coombs
Cfo*, Tim D Leveille
Sr V Pres*, Tim Hill
Sr V Pres*, Ron Corn
Auditors: ERNST & YOUNG LLP HOUSTON TX

LOCATIONS

HQ: CHEVRON PHILLIPS CHEMICAL COMPANY LLC
10001 SIX PINES DR, THE WOODLANDS, TX
773801498
Phone: 832 813-4100
Web: WWW.CPCHEM.COM

PRODUCTS/OPERATIONS

Selected Products
Olefins and polyolefins
  Ethylene
  Polyethylene
  Polyethylene pipe
  Polypropylene
  Propylene
Aromatics and styrenics
  Benzene
  Cumene
  Cyclohexane
  Paraxylene
  Styrene
Specialty products
  Acetylene black
  Alpha olefins
  Dimethyl sulfide
  Drilling specialty chemicals
  High-purity hydrocarbons and solvents
  Mining chemicals
  Neohexene
  Performance and reference fuels
  Polyalpha olefins
  Polystyrene

Selected Joint Ventures
Americas Styrenics (50%)
Chevron Phillips Singapore Chemicals (Private) Limited (50%)
KR Copolymer Co. Ltd. (60% South Korea)
Qatar Chemical Company Ltd. (Q-Chem 49%)
Saudi Chevron Phillips Company (50%)
Shanghai Golden Phillips Petrochemical Co. Ltd. (40%)

COMPETITORS

Dow Chemical	Sabic
Exxonmobil Chemical	Sasol
Lyondellbasell	Total Petrochemicals
Nova Chemicals	Westlake Chemical

HISTORICAL FINANCIALS

Company Type: Private

Income Statement   FYE: December 31

	REVENUE ($ mil.)	NET INCOME ($ mil.)	NET PROFIT MARGIN	EMPLOYEES
12/16	8,769	1,687	19.2%	6,472
12/15	9,859	2,651	26.9%	—
12/14	14,148	3,288	23.2%	—
Annual Growth	(21.3%)	(28.4%)	—	—

2016 Year-End Financials

Return on assets: 10.9%   Cash ($ mil.): 587
Return on equity: 14.7%
Current ratio: 1.90

CHG FOUNDATION

EXECUTIVES

Dir, Sheila Martz
High Risk Case Manager Supervi, Mark David
Auditors: MOSS ADAMS LLP LOS ANGELES C

LOCATIONS

HQ: CHG FOUNDATION
740 BAY BLVD, CHULA VISTA, CA 919105254
Phone: 619 422-0422
Web: WWW.CHGSD.COM

HISTORICAL FINANCIALS

Company Type: Private

Income Statement   FYE: December 31

	REVENUE ($ mil.)	NET INCOME ($ mil.)	NET PROFIT MARGIN	EMPLOYEES
12/19	943	(25)	—	372
12/16	1,098	206	18.8%	
12/14	622	34	5.5%	
12/13	323	(11)	—	
Annual Growth	19.5%	—	—	

2019 Year-End Financials

Return on assets: (-4.1%)   Cash ($ mil.): 460
Return on equity: (-5.7%)
Current ratio: 4.20

CHI ST. LUKE'S HEALTH BAYLOR COLLEGE OF MEDICINE MEDICAL CENTER CONDOMINIUM ASSOCIATION

EXECUTIVES

Pres, Debra Lee-Ebdie
Ceo*, David J Fine
Gastroenterology, Lynn R Copeland
Chief Staff, William A Redwine
Chief of Anesthesiology Svs, C David Collard
Gastroenterology, Frank V Meriano
Chief of Cardiology, James Michael Wilson
Assistant Professor, Michelle Barta
Chief Staff, Fredric L Hochman
Sr Vp of Quality Improvement, T Pinckney P
  McIlwain
Gastroenterologist, Lynn Copeland
Auditors: LB CATHOLIC HEALTH INIATNES E

LOCATIONS

HQ: CHI ST. LUKE'S HEALTH BAYLOR COLLEGE OF
MEDICINE MEDICAL CENTER CONDOMINIUM
ASSOCIATION
6720 BERTNER AVE, HOUSTON, TX 770302604
Phone: 832 355-1000
Web: WWW.STLUKESHEALTH.ORG

HISTORICAL FINANCIALS

Company Type: Private

Income Statement   FYE: June 30

	REVENUE ($ mil.)	NET INCOME ($ mil.)	NET PROFIT MARGIN	EMPLOYEES
06/20*	972	(29)	—	6,000
06/15*	15	(4)	—	—
12/08	1,078	1,155	107.2%	—
12/07	1,128	26	2.3%	—
Annual Growth	(1.2%)	—	—	—
*Fiscal year change

2020 Year-End Financials

Return on assets: (-3.0%)   Cash ($ mil.): 7
Return on equity: (-4.3%)
Current ratio: 1.40

CHICAGO COMMUNITY TRUST

You can trust this group to do the giving thing. The Chicago Community Trust gave more than $105 million in 2008 to not-for-profit organizations such as social services agencies schools health centers museums and theaters in the Chicago area. The grant program targets groups working in arts and culture basic human needs community development education and health. Past projects have included after-school programs for impoverished children funding a senior citizens center and health services for people with AIDS. Chicago Community Trust gets its funds from corporate and private donations. It was founded in 1915.

EXECUTIVES

Pres, Helene Gayle
Pres, Terry Mazany
V Pres Finance, Carol Crenshaw
Coordinator, Shari Pundrich
Senior Program Officer, Michael Davidson
Director of Marketing, Eva Penar
Consultant, Fabiola Ramirez
Chief Marketing Officer, Daniel Ash
Communications Specialist, Shannon Schmalz
Manager, External Communicatio, Stephen
  Schumacher
Manager, Policy and Advocacy, Aimee Ramirez
Auditors: O BDO USA LLP CHICAGO IL

LOCATIONS

HQ: CHICAGO COMMUNITY TRUST
225 N MICHIGAN AVE # 2200, CHICAGO, IL
606017672
Phone: 312 616-8000
Web: WWW.CCT.ORG

HISTORICAL FINANCIALS

Company Type: Private

Income Statement   FYE: September 30

	REVENUE ($ mil.)	NET INCOME ($ mil.)	NET PROFIT MARGIN	EMPLOYEES
09/19	564	194	34.4%	100
09/16	389	135	34.8%	—
09/15	363	136	37.5%	—
09/14	291	105	36.3%	—
Annual Growth	14.1%	12.9%	—	—

2019 Year-End Financials

Return on assets: 6.0%   Cash ($ mil.): 17
Return on equity: 6.1%
Current ratio: 1.00

CHILDREN'S HOSPITAL

EXECUTIVES

Pres, Kurt Newman
Chief Officer, Denice Cora-Bramble
Psychologist, Jesse Olague
Graduate Research Assistant, Sandra Kirsch
Pediatrician, Lily Chattopadhyay
Psychologist, Melissa Balderrama
Neonatologist, Rachel Chapman

Investigator, Kazue Hashimoto-Torii
Certified Anesthesiologist, Anya Gartner
Nurse Practitioner, Charlette Dampier
Physician Assistant, Michelle Sabol
Auditors: GRANT THORNTON LLP MC LEAN V

LOCATIONS

HQ: CHILDREN'S HOSPITAL
111 MICHIGAN AVE NW, WASHINGTON, DC
200102916
Phone: 202 232-0521
Web: WWW.CHILDRENSNATIONAL.ORG

HISTORICAL FINANCIALS
Company Type: Private

Income Statement				FYE: June 30
	REVENUE ($ mil.)	NET INCOME ($ mil.)	NET PROFIT MARGIN	EMPLOYEES
06/20	1,276	38	3.0%	6,000
06/15	1,076	118	11.0%	—
06/14	983	43	4.4%	—
Annual Growth	4.4%	(2.1%)	—	—

2020 Year-End Financials
Return on assets: 2.1%   Cash ($ mil.): 58
Return on equity: 5.0%
Current ratio: 0.60

CHILDREN'S HOSPITAL & RESEARCH CENTER AT OAKLAND

Children's Hospital & Research Center at Oakland (operating as Children's Hospital Oakland) does just what its name says provides medical care for children and performs research to advance the treatment of pediatric diseases. The freestanding hospital has about 190 beds and a staff of some more than 200 hospital-based physicians professionals with more than 30 medical specialties. Its services include orthopedics neurology oncology and cardiology as well as surgery trauma neonatal and intensive care. Additionally the hospital operates several satellite outpatient clinics providing general and specialized care. Children's Hospital Oakland also conducts teaching and community outreach programs.

Operations
The organization's research division Children's Hospital Oakland Research Institute conducts research programs on transmittable diseases vaccines cancer immune system diseases diabetes asthma and obesity. It receives funding from the National Institutes of Health. The research center has more than 300 scientists working on 150 clinical trials.

Children's Hospital Oakland is a teaching hospital and is one of only two solely designated California Level 1 pediatric trauma centers in the region (and has one of the largest pediatric intensive care units in Northern California).

In 2012 it had 236877 outpatient visits (of which 46142 were emergency visits); 10183 inpatient admissions; and 8640 surgical cases.

Financial Performance
The hospitals' revenues declined by 6% in 2012 due to a drop in net patient service fees fundraising investments and other revenue sources.

Some 47% of 2012 revenues came from Medi-Cal/California Children's Services and Medicare/Supplemental funds; 36% from other insurance private insurance (contract and commercial) and self-pay; and 12% from research programs.

Children's Hospital Oakland's net income decreased by 74% in 2012 due to lower revenues and an increase in expenses (including salaries benefits supplies and services).

In 2013 the hospital had an annual operating budget of more than $350 million.

Strategy
To boost coverage and resources in 2014 Children's Hospital Oakland and UCSF's Benioff Children's Hospital (also in the Bay area) formed an affiliation. Together the hospitals will be among the top ten largest children's health care providers in the US when the new UCSF Benioff Children's Hospital opens in 2015. In 2012 UCSF had 1230 physicians on staff including 150 clinicians at its current Benioff Children's Hospital location.

Previously the Oakland hospital held unsuccessful merger talks with Lucile Packard Children's Hospital at Stanford and Sutter Health network.

The hospital is also developing a master plan to maximize the use of existing property and buildings modernize facilities and provide individual rooms so that families can stay with their child during hospitalization.

In 2013 the Children's Hospital Oakland's Walnut Creek Campus completed a large-scale expansion and now include a Sports Medicine Center for Young Athletes and comprehensive Speech and Hearing Center.

Children's Hospital Oakland has had its share of financial troubles over the years. Along with a weak economy reduced reimbursement rates from both public and private payers and increasing health care costs added to the company's financial losses.

Company Background
In 2011 it received $532.8 million in research funding from the National Institutes of Health.

The hospital's research institute provided 85% of the DNA used for the Human Genome Project.

Children's Hospital Oakland was founded in 1942 and opened for business in 1914.

EXECUTIVES

Pres, Matthew Cook
Chb*, Harold Davis
Cfo*, Rina Smith
Sr V Pres*, Betsy Biern
Cfo*, Kathleen Cain
Project Coordinator, Colleen Gonzalez
Scientist, Damini Jawaheer
Scientist, Kristie Vetterli
Benefits Manager, Barbara Spindle
Oncologist, Mark Walters
Pediatrician, Jyothi N Marbin

LOCATIONS

HQ: CHILDREN'S HOSPITAL & RESEARCH CENTER AT OAKLAND
747 52ND ST, OAKLAND, CA 946091809
Phone: 510 428-3000
Web: WWW.CHILDRENSHOSPITALOAKLAND.ORG

PRODUCTS/OPERATIONS

Selected Services

Anesthesiology
Blood and Marrow Transplant (BMT) Program
Cardiology and Cardiothoracic Surgery
Center for Child Protection (CCP)
Center for the Vulnerable Child (CVC)
Clinical Laboratory Medicine & Pathology
Clinical Nutrition Department

Clinical Pathology Lab
Craniofacial Center
Cryopreservation Lab
Cytogenetics Laboratory
Developmental and Behavioral Pediatrics
Diagnostic Imaging/Radiology
Early Childhood Mental Health
Endocrinology/Diabetes
Family Outreach Clinic
Gastroenterology/Hepatology/Nutrition
Hematology/Oncology
Neonatology
Neuro-Oncology
Neurosurgery
Oncology/Hematology
Ophthalmology
Orthopedics
Otorhinolaryngology
Respiratory Care Services
Speech and Language Center
Sports Medicine Center
Urology

COMPETITORS

Alta Bates Summit Medical Center	John Muir Health
Children's Hospital Boston	Rady Children's Hospital
Children's Hospital Of Philadelphia	Shriners Hospitals For Children
Children's Hospital Of Pittsburgh	St. Jude Children's Research Hospital
Childrens Hospital Los Angeles	St. Luke's Hospital (ca)
Dignity Health	Sutter Health

HISTORICAL FINANCIALS
Company Type: Private

Income Statement				FYE: June 30
	REVENUE ($ mil.)	NET INCOME ($ mil.)	NET PROFIT MARGIN	EMPLOYEES
06/20	661	(8)	—	2,000
06/15*	178	34	19.5%	—
12/13	541	44	8.3%	—
12/05	313	15	5.0%	—
Annual Growth	5.5%	—	—	—

*Fiscal year change

2020 Year-End Financials
Return on assets: (-1.0%)   Cash ($ mil.): 180
Return on equity: (-2.3%)
Current ratio: 1.70

CHILDREN'S HOSPITAL COLORADO

Children's Hospital Colorado is a private nonprofit pediatric healthcare network dedicated to caring for kids at all ages and stages of growth. With more than 3000 pediatric specialists the company provides comprehensive pediatric care at its hospital on Anschutz Medical Campus and at several locations throughout the region. Children's Hospital Colorado also operates more than a dozen satellite locations in and around Denver that specialize in providing children with emergency and specialty care. Its affiliation with the University of Colorado School of Medicine means that its doctors are not only expert clinicians but also active researchers working toward better ways to care for kids.

Operations
Children's Hospital Colorado's hospital on Anschutz Medical Campus in Aurora was designed

and built to enhance its care for kids. Children's Colorado is the only dedicated Level 1 trauma center in its seven-state region handling the most challenging emergencies. It offers emergency and urgent care at multiple locations as well as numerous specialty care centers and clinics. In addition to these locations it brings its expertise to doctors and families throughout the Rocky Mountain region with more than 400 outreach clinics every year.

Children's Hospital Colorado also specializes in baby care bone and joint care brain and behavior endocrinology digestive issues cancer treatment fetal care heart health and respiratory issues.

The health care facility's research initiatives are conducted at the Children's Hospital Colorado Research Institute. Along with its affiliation with the university the Children's Hospital works with the Pediatric Clinical Translational Research Center to conduct research and clinical trials in a number of fields including cardiology gastroenterology oncology orthopedics pulmonology and psychiatry.

Geographic Reach

Based in Colorado Children's Hospital Colorado operates through some 20 locations.

EXECUTIVES

Ceo, Jena Hausemann
Svp-Cso*, Raphe Schwartz
Svp and CIO, Mary Anne Leach
Svp Patient Care and, Kelly M Johnson
Coordinator, Abbey Gesing
Coordinator, Alecia Wehr
Coordinator, Amanda Schafer
Staff, Amrita Shetty
Coordinator, Chantel Morgan
Internal Medicine Practitioner, Jeffrey A Bontrager
Staff, Jessica Gowey

LOCATIONS

HQ: CHILDREN'S HOSPITAL COLORADO
13123 E 16TH AVE, AURORA, CO 800457106
Phone: 720 777-1234
Web: WWW.CHILDRENSCOLORADO.ORG

Selected Locations
Children's Hospital Colorado Main Campus
Children's Hospital Colorado at Saint Joseph Hospital
Children's Hospital Colorado KidStreet
Children's Hospital Colorado Orthopedic Care Centennial
Children's Hospital Colorado Outpatient Specialty Care Centennial
Children's Hospital Colorado Outpatient Specialty Care Colorado Springs
Children's Hospital Colorado Outpatient Specialty Care Parker
Children's Hospital Colorado Therapy Care Parker
Children's Hospital Colorado Therapy Care Pueblo
Children's Hospital Colorado Urgent and Outpatient Specialty Care Wheat Ridge

PRODUCTS/OPERATIONS

Selected Departments
Adolescent Medicine Program
Adult Congenital Heart Disease Program
Aerodigestive Program
Allergy Program
Arrhythmia Center
Asthma Program
Audiology Speech and Learning Program
Bill Daniels Center for Children's Hearing
Bone Marrow Transplant Program
Breathing Institute
Burn program
Cardiac Anesthesia
Cardiac Catheterization
Cardiology Clinic
Cardiology Outreach Programs
Cardiomyopathy Program
Center for Cancer and Blood Disorders

Center for Celiac Disease
Child Abuse Services
Child Development Unit
Child Health Clinic
Colorado Fetal Care Center
Colorado Institute for Maternal and Fetal Health
Colorectal and Complex Pelvic Floor Disorders Program
Complex Congenital Heart Disease and Development Clinic
Craniofacial Center
Critical Care
Cystic Fibrosis Research and Care Center
Dental
Dermatology
Digestive Health Institute
Ear Nose and Throat
Eating Disorder Program
Emergency Department
Endocrinology
Endoscopy Clinic (ATECh)
Experimental Therapeutics Program
Extracorporeal Membrane Oxygenation (ECMO) Program
Eye
Fetal Cardiology Program
Fiberoptic Endoscopic Evaluation of Swallowing (FEES) Clinic
Flight for Life
Gastroenterology
Gastrointestinal Eosinophilic Diseases
Genetics Program
Gynecology
Healthy Expectations Perinatal Mental Health Program
Heart Institute
Heart Surgery
Heart Transplant Program
HOPE Clinic for Cancer Survivors
Hospitalist Services

COMPETITORS

Banner Health
Catholic Health Initiatives
Centura Health
Denver Health And Hospital Authority
Exempla Healthcare
Healthone
North Colorado Medical Center
Presbyterian/st. Luke's Medical Center
Rose Medical Center
Shriners Hospitals For Children
The Memorial Hospital

HISTORICAL FINANCIALS
Company Type: Private

Income Statement				FYE: December 31
	REVENUE ($ mil.)	NET INCOME ($ mil.)	NET PROFIT MARGIN	EMPLOYEES
12/19	1,327	63	4.8%	2,200
12/18	1,102	138	12.6%	—
12/17	960	76	8.0%	—
12/16	911	50	5.5%	—
Annual Growth	13.3%	8.0%	—	—

2019 Year-End Financials

Return on assets: 3.1%   Cash ($ mil.): 55
Return on equity: 6.5%
Current ratio: 0.40

CHILDREN'S HOSPITAL OF ORANGE COUNTY

EXECUTIVES

Ceo-Pres, Kimberly Cripe
Chb*, L Kenneth Heuler DDS
Pediatric Hematology Oncology, David K Buchbinder
Vice-President Engineering, Sally Gallagher
Patient Safety Officer, Cathy Mc Donnell
Nurse Practitioner, Jill D Stites
Manager, Dorit Ben Ezer
Senior Vice President and Acco, Susan Feidner
Senior Financial Analyst, Chris Rivanis
Human Resources Manager Busine, Hanna Ngo
Sys Dir, Hazel Villanueva
Auditors: KPMG LLP LOS ANGELES CA

LOCATIONS

HQ: CHILDREN'S HOSPITAL OF ORANGE COUNTY
1201 W LA VETA AVE, ORANGE, CA 928684203
Phone: 714 997-3000
Web: WWW.CHOC.ORG

HISTORICAL FINANCIALS
Company Type: Private

Income Statement				FYE: June 30
	REVENUE ($ mil.)	NET INCOME ($ mil.)	NET PROFIT MARGIN	EMPLOYEES
06/20	992	76	7.7%	3,200
06/16	523	10	2.0%	—
06/15	518	20	3.9%	—
06/14	517	(15)	—	—
Annual Growth	11.5%	—	—	—

2020 Year-End Financials

Return on assets: 5.6%   Cash ($ mil.): 497
Return on equity: 11.0%
Current ratio: 1.20

CHILDREN'S HOSPITAL OF WISCONSIN, INC

EXECUTIVES

Pres-Coo, Cindy Christensen
Treas*, Timothy L Birkenstock
V Pres-CIO*, Michael Jones
Corp V Pres of Hr*, Marge Nienen
Coordinator, Laurie Smrz
Cardiac Physician, Michele Frommelt
Acting Director, Rhonda Nowakowski
Hematologist, Mary K Hintermeyer
Talent Acquisition Manager, Julie Okoro
Director of Supply Chain, Lisa Fohey
Director, Karen Gralton

LOCATIONS

HQ: CHILDREN'S HOSPITAL OF WISCONSIN, INC
999 N 92ND ST STOP 1, MILWAUKEE, WI 532264876
Phone: 414 266-2000
Web: WWW.CHILDRENSWI.ORG

HISTORICAL FINANCIALS
Company Type: Private

Income Statement   FYE: December 31

	REVENUE ($ mil.)	NET INCOME ($ mil.)	NET PROFIT MARGIN	EMPLOYEES
12/13	600	57	9.6%	2,045
12/12	34	(0)	—	—
12/09	588	74	12.7%	—
Annual Growth	0.5%	(6.2%)	—	—

2013 Year-End Financials
Return on assets: 4.1%   Cash ($ mil.): 86
Return on equity: 5.8%
Current ratio: 3.20

CHILDREN'S MEDICAL CENTER OF DALLAS

Children's Medical Center of Dallas one of the largest and most prestigious pediatric health care providers and the leading pediatric health system in North Texas. Through the academic affiliation with UT Southwestern and leader in life changing treatments innovative technology and ground-breaking research. Among the campus Children's Health is licensed for around 600 beds including 490 beds at the main campus in the Southwestern Medical District and over 70 beds at Children's House facility in Dallas. Around 800 patients visits annually for 50 estates around the world. It was founded in 1913 when a group of nurses led by public health nurse May Forster Smith organized the Dallas Baby Camp.

Operations
Children's Medical Center of Dallas has licensed 490 beds for inpatient portion of the hospitals that provides all rooms a place for the family to spend for the night with the child. The hospital has critical care unites 47 bed level IV Neonatal Intensive Care Unit (NICU) Pediatric Intensive Care Unit (PICU) Cardiac Intensive Care Unit and the main campus home for pediatric level I trauma center.

Children's Health's specialty Dallas campus provides surgery center and includes eight operating rooms where outpatient surgical services are provided.

Children's Medical Center of Dallas provides pediatric sickle cell disease program that focus on the prevention of disease complications and management using newest treatment strategies. Children's Medical Center provides Level IV Neonatal Intensive Care Unit (NICU) specifically designed to meet the needs of premature and critically ill newborns. In additions providing respiratory support to surgical procedures renowned neonatologists surgeons and pediatric sub-specialist from UT Southwestern can care for all neonatal health issues.

Geographic Reach
Children's main hospital campuses are in Dallas (headquarters) and Plano Texas.

Sales and Marketing
Children's Medical Center of Dallas market its product and services through its website such as specialty care centers recognized pediatric care close to home families offering a wide array of outpatient pediatric specialties outpatient surgery lab services and rehabilitation Children's Health Specialty Centers have a wealth of resources under one roof.

Company Background
In the four-year period between 2001 and 2005 the center spent more than $250 million on new construction and expansion projects. It opened a 72-bed Children's Legacy Hospital in nearby Plano in 2008 and in 2009 Children's completed construction of a new $150 million tower on its main Dallas campus to house its heart center cancer center and neonatal intensive care unit.

The company was founded in 1913.

LOCATIONS
HQ: CHILDREN'S MEDICAL CENTER OF DALLAS
1935 MEDICAL DISTRICT DR, DALLAS, TX
752357701
Phone: 214 456-7000
Web: WWW.CHILDRENS.COM

Children's Medical Center Selected Locations
Chase Bank Building Specialty Center (Dallas)
Children's Medical Center and Ambulatory Care Pavilion at Legacy (Plano)
Children's Medical Center of Dallas Main Campus
Dallas Ambulatory Care Pavilion
Irving Specialty Center
Mesquite Specialty Center
MyChildren's Primary Care (about 16 locations)
Pediatric Urology Clinic at Rockwall
Southlake Specialty Care Center
Walnut Hill Urology Clinic

PRODUCTS/OPERATIONS

Children's Medical Center Selected Services

Allergy/Immunology/Asthma

Audiology
Cystic fibrosis
Day surgery
Dentistry
Dermatology
Diabetes
Ear/Nose/Throat
Endocrinology
Gastroenterology
General surgery
Genetics/Metabolism
International adoption medicine
Laboratory services
Neurology
Nutrition
Obesity program
Occupational therapy
Ophthalmology
Orthodontics
Orthopaedics
Physical therapy
Plastic Surgery
Pulmonary function lab
Pulmonology
Radiology
Rheumatology
Sickle cell treatment
Sleep disorders
Speech therapy
Trauma
Urology

COMPETITORS

Baylor University
 Medical Center
Cook Children's Health
 Care System
Dell Children's
 Medical Center

Hca
Parkland Health &
 Hospital System
Tenet Healthcare
Texas Children's
 Hospital

HISTORICAL FINANCIALS
Company Type: Private

Income Statement   FYE: December 31

	REVENUE ($ mil.)	NET INCOME ($ mil.)	NET PROFIT MARGIN	EMPLOYEES
12/15	712	(185)	—	5,318
12/14	1,120	135	12.1%	—
12/13	1,111	166	15.0%	—
12/08	744	(4)	—	—
Annual Growth	(0.6%)	—	—	—

2015 Year-End Financials
Return on assets: (-7.7%)   Cash ($ mil.): 9
Return on equity: (-6.6%)
Current ratio: 4.70

CHILDRENS HOSPITAL

EXECUTIVES
Prin, Kurt Newman
Doctor, Ashley D Hill
Dentist, Edwin Zechman DDS
Manager, David Thibodeau
Director of Mis/Is, Gary Manion
Quality Assurance Manager, Lorna Riach
Auditors: GRANT THORNTON LLP MC LEAN V

LOCATIONS
HQ: CHILDRENS HOSPITAL
1917 C ST NE, WASHINGTON, DC 200026753
Phone: 202 476-5000
Web: WWW.CHILDRENSNATIONAL.ORG

HISTORICAL FINANCIALS
Company Type: Private

Income Statement   FYE: June 30

	REVENUE ($ mil.)	NET INCOME ($ mil.)	NET PROFIT MARGIN	EMPLOYEES
06/13	970	24	2.5%	14
06/10	806	66	8.2%	—
Annual Growth	6.4%	(28.3%)	—	—

2013 Year-End Financials
Return on assets: 2.5%   Cash ($ mil.): 59
Return on equity: 6.0%
Current ratio: 0.50

CHILDRENS HOSPITAL INC

EXECUTIVES
President, Michael Warren
Ceo, Jim Dearth

LOCATIONS
HQ: CHILDRENS HOSPITAL INC
1513 4TH AVE S, BIRMINGHAM, AL 352331612
Phone: 205 251-3430
Web: WWW.AMELIACENTER.ORG

Income Statement				FYE: December 31
	REVENUE ($ mil.)	NET INCOME ($ mil.)	NET PROFIT MARGIN	EMPLOYEES
12/13	684	47	7.0%	5
12/12	576	34	5.9%	—
Annual Growth	18.7%	39.8%	—	—

2013 Year-End Financials
Return on assets: 5.9% Cash ($ mil.): 111
Return on equity: 12.3%
Current ratio: 0.60

CHILDRENS HOSPITAL MEDICAL CENTER OF AKRON

Akron Children's Hospital is the largest pediatric health care system in northeast Ohio. The health system operates through approximately 50 urgent primary and specialty care locations scattered around the state. Among Children's specialized services are cardiology orthopedics rehabilitation and home care. It added two new pediatric primary care locations: Akron Children's Hospital Pediatrics East Liverpool and Akron Children's Health Center Wooster The main hospital's emergency department treats nearly 70000 patients each year. With about 16445 urgent care visits the health system also has more than 337245 specialty visits per year. Akron Children's Hospital started as a nursery more than 100 years ago.

Operations
Each year Akron Children's Hospital sees more than 1 million outpatients performs about 15345 surgeries and admits more than 8045 inpatients.

Geographic Reach
Akron Children's Hospital is a major teaching facility affiliated with Northeastern Ohio Medical University and offering nearly a dozen subspecialty fellowship training programs. Children's also runs two children's hospitals approximately pediatrician offices and some 50 primary and specialty locations.

Sales and Marketing
Medicaid/Medicaid Managed Care payments account for about 55% of gross patient service revenue while commercial payments account for about 40%. Medicare/other governmental and other account for the remaining.

Strategy
Beyond the tremendous efforts devoted to COVID-19 the company made significant progress advancing its strategic goals in 2020. Akron's Children opened the Portage Health Center and new primary care offices in Lorain County and East Liverpool. The company started construction on a health center in Amherst and are looking forward to expanding access to pediatric care to families in this new region. The company added programs and specialty care services in many areas and set the stage to launch our Centers of Excellence in Spine Mitochondrial Disease and Vision which will offer the highest levels of quality care patient experience and research.

In 2020 there was also a focused spotlight on the inequities that exist within its society and health care systems bringing renewed urgency to its diversity and inclusion programs.

EXECUTIVES
Ceo, William Considine
V Pres*, Walt Schwoeble
Cfo*, Spencer A Kowal
Vice President*, Craig McGhee
Office Coordinator, Dotti Eitel
Chief Information Offi, Amy Maneker
Chief Officer, Robert McGregor
Director of Finance, Alicia Lamancusa
Executive of Information Techn, Jeff Hale
Director, Stefan Agamanolis
Nurse Manager, Theresa Borodkin
Auditors: ERNST & YOUNG LLP CLEVELAND

LOCATIONS
HQ: CHILDRENS HOSPITAL MEDICAL CENTER OF AKRON
1 PERKINS SQ, AKRON, OH 443081063
Phone: 330 543-1000
Web: WWW.AKRONCHILDRENS.ORG

COMPETITORS

Akron General Medical Center	Ohiohealth
Aultman Health Foundation	Parma Community General Hospital
Lake Health	Robinson Memorial Hospital
Mercy Medical Center (ny)	Summa Health System
Metrohealth System	The Cleveland Clinic
Nationwide Children's Hospital	University Hospitals Health System

HISTORICAL FINANCIALS
Company Type: Private

Income Statement				FYE: December 31
	REVENUE ($ mil.)	NET INCOME ($ mil.)	NET PROFIT MARGIN	EMPLOYEES
12/19	1,014	107	10.6%	4,763
12/14	701	93	13.3%	—
12/13	623	80	13.0%	—
Annual Growth	8.5%	4.8%	—	—

2019 Year-End Financials
Return on assets: 6.4% Cash ($ mil.): 52
Return on equity: 10.1%
Current ratio: 0.70

CHINESE HOSPITAL ASSOCIATION

EXECUTIVES
Ceo, Brenda Yee
Cfo*, Thomas Bolger
Coo*, Linda Schumacher
Lab Technician, Lisa Glaser
Training Manager, Josephine Lee
Executive Director, Angela Sun
Internal Medicine, Roderick Snow
Director, Scott Huang
Vice President, Chee Tong
Accountant, Christina Lam
MD, Edward Chan
Auditors: MOSS & ADAMS LLP SAN FRANCISC

LOCATIONS
HQ: CHINESE HOSPITAL ASSOCIATION
845 JACKSON ST, SAN FRANCISCO, CA 941334899
Phone: 415 982-2400
Web: WWW.CHINESEHOSPITAL.COM

HISTORICAL FINANCIALS
Company Type: Private

Income Statement				FYE: December 31
	REVENUE ($ mil.)	NET INCOME ($ mil.)	NET PROFIT MARGIN	EMPLOYEES
12/19	226,958	(10,648)	—	285
12/19	226,958	(10,648)	—	—
12/18	216	(28)	—	—
12/17	123	(11)	—	—
Annual Growth	4180.6%	—	—	—

2019 Year-End Financials
Return on assets: (-2.9%) Cash ($ mil.): 21,386
Return on equity: (-6.2%)
Current ratio: 1.10

CHRISTIAN HEALTHCARE MINISTRIES, INC.

EXECUTIVES
Exec Dir, Howard Russell
Cfo*, Roger Kittelson
Member Advocate, Sherry Noland
Consultant, Michael Jacobson
Data Entry, Elizabeth Cseplo-Adrian
Board Member, Jim Detwiler
Customer Advocate, Mayly Mancari
Executive Assistant and Human, Pamela Henneman
Member Assistance, Shannon Demarino
Director, Steven Chong
Member, Tim Chafins

LOCATIONS
HQ: CHRISTIAN HEALTHCARE MINISTRIES, INC.
127 HAZELWOOD AVE, BARBERTON, OH 442031316
Phone: 330 848-1511
Web: WWW.CHMINISTRIES.ORG

HISTORICAL FINANCIALS
Company Type: Private

Income Statement				FYE: December 31
	REVENUE ($ mil.)	NET INCOME ($ mil.)	NET PROFIT MARGIN	EMPLOYEES
12/20	633	(3)	—	40
12/16	220	27	12.7%	—
Annual Growth	30.2%	—	—	—

2020 Year-End Financials
Return on assets: (-2.4%) Cash ($ mil.): 54
Return on equity: (-2.5%)
Current ratio: 18.10

CHRISTUS NORTHEAST TEXAS HEALTH SYSTEM CORPORATION

EXECUTIVES

Pres, Chris Glenney
Cmo, Steve Keuer
Coo*, Jason Proctor
Cfo*, Elizabeth Tulliam
Chief Nursing Officer, Shelly Welch
Exec Asst, Susan Wilson
Physician, Donald Knarr
Office Manager III, Haley Clark
Registered Nurse, Jamie Slagle
Lactation Consultant, Jennifer Dean
Office Assistant, Jessica Hornsby
Auditors: ERNST & YOUNG LLP DALLAS TX

LOCATIONS

HQ: CHRISTUS NORTHEAST TEXAS HEALTH SYSTEM
CORPORATION
800 E DAWSON ST, TYLER, TX 757012036
Phone: 903 593-8441
Web: WWW.CHRISTUSHEALTH.ORG

HISTORICAL FINANCIALS

Company Type: Private

Income Statement				FYE: June 30
	REVENUE ($ mil.)	NET INCOME ($ mil.)	NET PROFIT MARGIN	EMPLOYEES
06/17	789	42	5.4%	4,000
06/15	752	48	6.4%	—
Annual Growth	2.5%	(5.6%)	—	—

CHRISTUS SANTA ROSA HEALTH CARE CORPORATION

EXECUTIVES

Pres, Don Beeler
Pres, Patrick B Carrier
Dir, Melissa Krause
Coo, Renato Baciarelli
Cfo, Kenneth Kolb
Coordinator, Carl Zepeda
Coordinator, Amy Lopez
Chief of Emergency Room, Greg Roth
Chief of Medicine, Hugo Castaneda
Executive of Information Techn, Ron Love
Coordinator, Bernice Avilez
Auditors: ERNST & YOUNG US LLP INDIANAP

LOCATIONS

HQ: CHRISTUS SANTA ROSA HEALTH CARE
CORPORATION
2827 BABCOCK RD, SAN ANTONIO, TX 782294813
Phone: 210 704-2011
Web: WWW.CHRISTUSHEALTH.ORG

HISTORICAL FINANCIALS

Company Type: Private

Income Statement				FYE: June 30
	REVENUE ($ mil.)	NET INCOME ($ mil.)	NET PROFIT MARGIN	EMPLOYEES
06/19	702	(13)	—	3,700
06/15	656	(14)	—	—
06/14	635	6	1.1%	—
06/13	612	2	0.4%	—
Annual Growth	2.3%	—	—	—

2019 Year-End Financials

Return on assets: (-2.1%)   Cash ($ mil.): —
Return on equity: (-16.2%)
Current ratio: 2.50

CHS MCPHERSON REFINERY INC.

Cooperation is a refined art and refining a cooperative art for the National Cooperative Refinery Association (NCRA) which provides its member owners farm supply cooperatives CHS GROWMARK and MFA Oil with gasoline and diesel fuel through its oil refinery in McPherson Kansas. The refinery's production rate is 85000 barrels per day. Fuel from the refinery is allocated to member/owners on the basis of ownership percentages. In addition to the refinery NCRA owns Jayhawk Pipeline stakes in two other pipeline companies and an underground oil storage facility.

Operations

NCRA's logistical system includes 76 trucks. (In 2012 almost 40000 barrels per day of crude was gathered from more than 6000 oil wells mainly in Kansas and transported to the McPherson refinery by truck.)

The system also includes more than 1000 miles of pipelines to move crude oil and finished products from its refinery to tanks and terminals. Its Conway Texas underground storage facility has 1.5 million barrels of refined products capacity. NCRA also has two refined products terminals (in McPherson Kansas and Council Bluffs Iowa).

Strategy

The cooperative's primary strategy is to gather oil and gas and make diesel and gasoline to serve it members (and the farms of rural America) while maintaining and upgrading its systems in order to stay competitive with better resourced private sector refining rivals.

In 2011 NCRA announced a $555 million investment to build a new Delayed Coking Unit at its McPherson refinery. The new facility will allow the refiner to process a larger variety of crude oils. It is scheduled to be completed in 2015 and will replace a unit that was built in 1952.

In 2012 the company agreed to pay $700000 in federal and state penalties to settle violations of environmental laws at its McPherson petroleum refinery and underground storage facility.

Company Background

The enterprise has its origins in 1943 when five regional farm supply cooperatives tired of wartime fuel shortages created the NCRA to buy the Globe oil refinery in McPherson Kansas.

EXECUTIVES

Exec V Pres-, Shirley Cunningham
Exec V Pres-Coo*, Jay Debertin
Exec V Pres-Cfo*, Timothy Skidmore
Exec V Pres*, Lisa Zell
Information Technology Manager, Jason Beckman
Admin, Jeanne Whitenack
Purchasing Agent, Andy Nelson
Yield Supervisor, Deann Guiot
Auditors: PRICEWATERHOUSECOOPERS LLP MI

LOCATIONS

HQ: CHS MCPHERSON REFINERY INC.
2000 S MAIN ST, MCPHERSON, KS 674609402
Phone: 620 241-2340
Web: WWW.CHSINC.COM

COMPETITORS

Bp	Hollyfrontier
Cvr Refining	Marathon Petroleum
Chevron	Tesoro
Exxon Mobil	Valero Energy

HISTORICAL FINANCIALS

Company Type: Private

Income Statement				FYE: August 31
	REVENUE ($ mil.)	NET INCOME ($ mil.)	NET PROFIT MARGIN	EMPLOYEES
08/13	4,081	686	16.8%	700
08/12	4,045	705	17.4%	—
08/11	3,405	378	11.1%	—
Annual Growth	9.5%	34.7%	—	—

2013 Year-End Financials

Return on assets: 32.8%   Cash ($ mil.): 386
Return on equity: 51.0%
Current ratio: 1.60

CHUGACH ALASKA CORPORATION

At the heart of Chugach Alaska Corporation is a vision of indigenous people running their own businesses on their own land. Chugach Alaska was formed following the activation of the Alaska Native Claims Settlement Act (which was passed by the US Congress in 1971) to provide land management services for the 928000-acre Chugach region of Alaska. The company derives the bulk of its sales from oil and gas production mining commercial timber and tourist activities that occur in the region and from its engagement in military base construction projects at more than 30 locations in Alaska the US Pacific Northwest and the Western Pacific. Chugach Alaska's shareholders consist of Aleut Eskimo and Indian natives.

Operations

In 2011 the company's Chugach World Services unit secured a $32 million contract (with the option for an additional $33 million) for housing and maintenance operations at Naval Base Guam and Andersen Air Force Base Guam.

In late 2010 the Chugach Alaska Services unit won a renewal of its existing oil spill prevention and response contract with Alyeska Pipeline Service Company. The new contract to service the Alaska Pipeline runs from 2011 to 2016.

Geographic Reach

With operations in Alaska the Pacific Northwest and the Western Pacific the company has major offices in Alabama Alaska Hawaii and Nevada.

Financial Performance

To raise cash in 2013 Chugach Alaska sold its three-story former headquarters building in downtown Anchorage.

Strategy

Developing and sustaining multiple revenues streams has been a key to the company's growth. Chugach Alaska is looking to continue to grow its Alaskan gas natural gas projects while diversifying into markets that are not traditional for the company such as the niche market of environmentally responsible guided tourism.

Expanding its global engineering footprint in 2012 the company acquired bankrupt Hawaii-based engineering firm Heide & Cook LLC.

Company Background

Chugach Alaska was founded in 1972 as an Alaska Native Claims Settlement Act Corporation. A nine-person board of directors elected from the corporation's more than 2300 shareholders oversees Chugach Alaska's management and operations. The company has gone from filing bankruptcy protection in 1990 (in the wake of the Exxon Valdez oil spill and a major cannery fire) to generating about $1 billion in annual revenues.

EXECUTIVES

Chb-Int Ceo, Sheri Buretta
Exec V Pres*, Angela Astle
Pres-Coo*, Daniel Fenza
Information Specialist, Curtin Schafer
Accounting Staff, Wojwa Loeak
Law Specialist, Elizabeth Difuntorum
Information Specialist, Ivan Vasquez
Senior Vice President of Opera, Scott Davis
Education Capture Manager, Korey Adams
Accounts Payable Staff Account, Meg Benson
Land, David Phillips

LOCATIONS

HQ: CHUGACH ALASKA CORPORATION
3800 CNTRPINT DR STE 1200, ANCHORAGE, AK 99503
Phone: 907 563-8866
Web: WWW.CHUGACH.COM

PRODUCTS/OPERATIONS

Selected Services
Base Operating Services
Construction Services
Educational Services
Engineering Services
IT/Telecommunications
Manufacturing Services
Oil and Gas Services

Selected Subsidiaries
Chugach Alaska Services Inc. (CASI)
Chugach Education Services Inc. (CESI)
Chugach Federal Solutions Inc. (CFSI)
Chugach Government Services Inc. (CGSI)
Chugach Industries Inc. (CII)
Chugach Information Technology Inc. (CITI)
Chugach Management Services Inc. (CMSI)
Chugach McKinley Inc. (CMI)
Chugach Support Services Inc. (CSSI)
Chugach Systems Integration Llc (CSI)
Chugach World Services Inc. (CWSI)
Heide & Cook LLC. (H&C)
Wolf Creek Federal Services Inc. (WCFS)

COMPETITORS

Conocophillips Alaska
Doyon
Fluor
Freegold Ventures
Jacobs Engineering
Sealaska

HISTORICAL FINANCIALS

Company Type: Private

Income Statement | | | | FYE: December 31

	REVENUE ($ mil.)	NET INCOME ($ mil.)	NET PROFIT MARGIN	EMPLOYEES
12/17	919	20	2.3%	4,822
12/16	842	35	4.2%	—
12/15	758	22	3.0%	—
12/14	7	(12)	—	—
Annual Growth	387.6%	—	—	—

2017 Year-End Financials

Return on assets: 4.5%   Cash ($ mil.): 66
Return on equity: 6.5%
Current ratio: 2.60

CIC GROUP, INC.

CIC Group can see clearly that its future (like its present) is in heavy manufacturing and construction. Its group of commercial and industrial subsidiaries specialize in the manufacture maintenance and repair of equipment for the crude oil natural gas coal and other energy industries. Its largest subsidiary is Nooter/Eriksen which supplies heat recovery steam generators for combustion gas turbines worldwide. CIC's Nooter Construction is a construction contractor serving the refining petrochemical pulp and paper and power industries among others. The employee-owned holding company was formed in 2002.

Operations

CIC through its 20 subsidiaries is engaged in the heavy industrial construction of refineries and petrochemical and power plants. It also designs and builds heat recovery systems for power plants.

Sales and Marketing

Some of the company's largest customers include Ameren Calpine Chevron ConocoPhillips Exxon Mobil Florida Power & Light and Royal Dutch Shell.

Financial Performance

Although privately held the company reported 2012 revenue of $1.2 billion up 30% from 2011. CIC anticipates revenue of $2 billion by 2017 or 2018.

Strategy

The company is taking advantage of the low price and abundance of natural gas in the US which has encouraged companies to shift the manufacture of petrochemical plants to the US from the Middle East and Asia.

However CIC is also strengthening its position in the growth markets of Eastern Europe and Asia. In 2012 the company announced plans to work on photovoltaic projects for Chinese solar manufacturer LDK Solar and to act as a distributor for the company.

EXECUTIVES

Pres-Ceo, Donald H Lange
V Pres Finance-Treas, Derek J Falb
Benefits Manager, Kayla Cabrera
Director Corporate Risk Manage, Michael Murphy
Vice President of Operations, Don Majchrowski
Office Manager, Jennifer Rossomanno
Project Coordinator, Melissa Vasel
Director of Information Techno, Van M Rick
Field Coordinator, Tom Hance

LOCATIONS

HQ: CIC GROUP, INC.
1509 OCELLO DR, FENTON, MO 630262406
Phone: 314 682-2900
Web: WWW.CICGROUP.COM

PRODUCTS/OPERATIONS

Selected Subsidiaries

ArcMelt
Delta Nooter
Megamet Sold Metals Co.
Nooter Construction
Nooter/Eriksen s.r.l.
Pressline Services
RMF Nooter
Schoeller Bleckmann Nooter GmbH
St. Louis Metallizing
Superior Corporate Travel
Wyatt Field Service Co.
Wyatt Virgin Islands

COMPETITORS

Bwx Technologies
Clarkson Construction
Fluor
Fred Weber
Jacobs Engineering
Mitsubishi Heavy Industries
Phillips-medisize
U.s. Pipe

HISTORICAL FINANCIALS

Company Type: Private

Income Statement | | | | FYE: November 30

	REVENUE ($ mil.)	NET INCOME ($ mil.)	NET PROFIT MARGIN	EMPLOYEES
11/11	838	0	—	1,500
11/10	758	0	—	—
11/08	1,120	0	—	—
Annual Growth	(9.2%)	—	—	—

2011 Year-End Financials

Return on assets: —   Cash ($ mil.): 136
Return on equity: —
Current ratio: 1.70

CIMA ENERGY, LP

EXECUTIVES

Pres, Thomas K Edwards
Cfo, Michael D Rupe
Accounting Staff, Audrey Blum
Business, Kyoichi Miyazaki
Accounting, Emily Smith
Vice President Western Divisio, Bryan Hassler
Manager, Operations, Jefferson Trujillo
Manager, Accounting, Leslie Christensen
Marketing Operations Analyst, Chris Tucker
Manager, Clinton Davis
Vice President of Sales, Coley Gaynor
Auditors: DELOITTE & TOUCHE LLP HOUSTON

LOCATIONS

HQ: CIMA ENERGY, LP
1221 MCKINNEY ST STE 3700, HOUSTON, TX 770102046
Phone: 713 209-1112
Web: WWW.CIMA-ENERGY.COM

HISTORICAL FINANCIALS
Company Type: Private

Income Statement				FYE: December 31
	REVENUE ($ mil.)	NET INCOME ($ mil.)	NET PROFIT MARGIN	EMPLOYEES
12/07	1,195	8	0.7%	140
12/06	902	11	1.3%	—
12/05	872	0	—	—
12/04	569	4	0.8%	—
Annual Growth	28.0%	19.1%	—	—

2007 Year-End Financials
Return on assets: 5.6%   Cash ($ mil.): 16
Return on equity: 26.2%
Current ratio: 1.20

CINCINNATI PUBLIC SCHOOLS

EXECUTIVES

Supt, Laura Mitchell
SEC*, Denae Coco
Cfo-Treas*, Jonathan Boid
Facilities, Michael L Burson
Coordinator, Melvina Stokes
Network Administrator, Christine Shields
Teacher, Lisa Shelly
Teacher, Monique Wallace
Superintendent, C Laura Mitchell
Teacher, Elizabeth Ventre
Science Teacher, William Schnure
Auditors: PLATTENBURG & ASSOCIATES INC

LOCATIONS

HQ: CINCINNATI PUBLIC SCHOOLS
  2651 BURNET AVE, CINCINNATI, OH 452192551
Phone: 513 363-0000
Web: WWW.CPS-K12.ORG

HISTORICAL FINANCIALS
Company Type: Private

Income Statement				FYE: June 30
	REVENUE ($ mil.)	NET INCOME ($ mil.)	NET PROFIT MARGIN	EMPLOYEES
06/17	703	17	2.5%	7,070
06/16	650	13	2.1%	—
06/15	654	(0)	—	—
06/05	402	0	—	—
Annual Growth	4.8%	—	—	—

CITIZENS ENERGY GROUP

Hoosiers are happy to have their homes provided with gas and water services by Public Utilities of the City of Indianapolis (dba Citizens Energy and CWA Authority public charitable trusts). Its Citizens Water unit provides water and wastewater services to 300000 customers in Indianapolis; Citizens Gas serves more than 266000 gas customers. Citizens Energy also provides steam heating and chilled water cooling services to about 250 customers through Citizens Thermal Energy. The regional utility also has a small oil production unit (Citizens Oil Division). Its Citizens Resources unit has joint venture stakes in some companies not regulated by the Indiana Utility Regulatory Commission such as ProLiance Energy.

Operations
Citizens Energy operates six business segments: Citizens Gas Water Steam Chilled Water Oil and Citizens Resources Steam and Chilled Water. Citizen Resources holds affiliate joint venture interests including ProLiance Energy and a number of subsidiaries including Westfield Gas a regulated natural gas distribution utility. Citizens Oil has produced more than 6 million barrels of oil since 1969 from Greene County Indiana. CWA Authority provides wastewater services.

Financial Performance
The company's revenues increased by 50% in 2012 due to an increase in water and wastewater revenues. (The water and wastewater segments which were acquired in August 2011). This growth was offset by a decrease in Westfield Gas and Citizens Gas revenues due to lower usage driven by a warmer winter lower gas cost recovery revenues.

Strategy
In 2012 Citizens Energy filed a plan with the Indiana Utility Regulatory Commission to create a multistate transportation and industrial fueling business Using liquefied natural gas (LNG) the new Citizens Energy subsidiary will market and sell LNG as a competitive alternative to diesel fuel for use by heavy-duty vehicles and by drilling rigs marine vessels and railway locomotives.

Mergers and Acquisitions
Expanding its water and wastewater coverage in 2013 Citizens Energy (with the cooperation of The Indiana Office of Utility Consumer Counselor and the City of Westfield agreed to transfer Westfield Utilities to Citizens Energy for $91 million.

Responding to the company's efficient operation of its gas utility in 2011 the Indianapolis City/County Council sold its debt-laden water and wastewater utility (CWA Authority) to Citizens Energy in a $1.9 billion deal. The transaction reshaped the utility's business organization and transformed Citizens Energy into a multiutility.

Company Background
The company was first organized as a public charitable trust in 1887. In a 2008 rebranding Citizens Gas & Coke Utility changed its operating name to Citizens Energy Group to reflect the company's closing of its old smokestack industry (coke manufacturing operations for steelmakers and smelter) and its new strategic emphasis on energy conservation.

EXECUTIVES

Pres, Pres-Ceo, Jeffrey Harrison
Prin*, David N Griffiths
Sr V Pres*, Martin C Dusel
Sr V Pres ADM*, M Jean Richcreek
SEC*, Kyndall Weber
Citizens Gas, Public Charitabl, Jeanette Easley
Citizens Gas, Public Charitabl, Mary Simms
Purchasing Director, Jeff Ford
Human Resources Information MA, Robyn Nelson
Coordinator, Arish Rountree
Applications Archite, Marco Cutchin

LOCATIONS

HQ: CITIZENS ENERGY GROUP
  2020 N MERIDIAN ST, INDIANAPOLIS, IN 462021306
Phone: 317 924-3341
Web: WWW.CITIZENSENERGYGROUP.COM

PRODUCTS/OPERATIONS

2012 Sales
	$ mil.	% of total
Utility	650	93
Non-utility	45	7
Total	696	100

2012 Sales
	% of total
Citizens Gas	37
Water	24
Wastewater	22
Steam	9
Chilled Water	6
Oil	1
Resources	1
Total	100

COMPETITORS

American States Water	Nipsco
Duke Energy	Vectren
Indiana Municipal Power Agency	Veolia Environnement

HISTORICAL FINANCIALS
Company Type: Private

Income Statement				FYE: September 30
	REVENUE ($ mil.)	NET INCOME ($ mil.)	NET PROFIT MARGIN	EMPLOYEES
09/12	696	(11)	—	1,100
09/11	463	32	7.0%	—
09/10	440	(1)	—	—
Annual Growth	25.7%	—	—	—

2012 Year-End Financials
Return on assets: (-0.3%)   Cash ($ mil.): 393
Return on equity: (-10.5%)
Current ratio: 1.50

CITY & COUNTY OF HONOLULU

With a population of almost 1 million people Honolulu County located on the island of Oahu is the largest city and county in Hawaii. The city and county are governed by a mayor and a nine-member legislative council. Honolulu's largest industry is tourism but the city is also the financial center of Hawaii.

EXECUTIVES

Mayor, Rick Blangiardi
Mng Dir*, Michael D Formby
Dir of Community Services, Pamela Witty Oakland
Dir of Emergency Services, Mark Knapp Rigg
Corporation Counsel, David Z Arakawa
Mis Manager, Jian WEI Huang
Vice-Chairman, Ikaika Anderson
Private Secretary To, Aileen Nagamine
Dep Project Manager, Alvina Lutu
Police Officer, Art Takamiya
Administrative Assistant, Carol Fukunaga
Auditors: ACCUITY LLP HONOLULU HAWAII

LOCATIONS

HQ: CITY & COUNTY OF HONOLULU
  530 S KING ST RM 300, HONOLULU, HI 968133019
Phone: 808 768-4141
Web: WWW.HONOLULU.GOV

HISTORICAL FINANCIALS
Company Type: Private

Income Statement				FYE: June 30
	REVENUE ($ mil.)	NET INCOME ($ mil.)	NET PROFIT MARGIN	EMPLOYEES
06/20	2,211	336	15.2%	8,000
06/19	2,013	315	15.6%	—
06/18	1,848	482	26.1%	—
06/17	1,728	(89)	—	—
Annual Growth	8.6%	—	—	—

2020 Year-End Financials
Return on assets: 1.7%   Cash ($ mil.): 648
Return on equity: 6.8%
Current ratio: —

CITY & COUNTY OF SAN FRANCISCO

The City of San Francisco is the 14th largest in the US and its dense population geographic detachment and cultural diversity have made San Francisco a favorite with both tourists and residents. San Francisco's government is a consolidated city-county bureaucracy with both entities led by an elected mayor. The government includes an executive branch led by the mayor and consisting of other elected officials and city departments and a legislative branch consisting of an 11-member Board of Supervisors. The city is also home to several federal institutions including the Federal Reserve Bank and the US Mint.

EXECUTIVES

Mayor, London Breed
Assessor*, Doris M Ward
City Attorney*, Louise Renne
District Attorney*, Terence Hallian
Public Defender*, Jeff Brown
Sheriff*, Michael Hennessey
Treas*, Susan Leal
City ADM*, William Lee
Purchaser*, Edwin Lee
City Attorney*, Dennis Herrera
Prin*, Tomio Takeshita
Auditors: MACIAS GINI & O'CONNELL LLP

LOCATIONS

HQ: CITY & COUNTY OF SAN FRANCISCO
   1 DR CARLTON B GOODLETT P, SAN FRANCISCO, CA 941024604
Phone: 415 554-7500
Web: WWW.SF.GOV

HISTORICAL FINANCIALS
Company Type: Private

Income Statement				FYE: June 30
	REVENUE ($ mil.)	NET INCOME ($ mil.)	NET PROFIT MARGIN	EMPLOYEES
06/20	7,181	(100)	—	30,000
06/19	7,561	563	7.4%	—
06/18	6,411	1,172	18.3%	—
06/17	5,971	569	9.5%	—
Annual Growth	6.3%	—	—	—

CITY CENTER HOLDINGS, LLC

Auditors: DELOITTE & TOUCHE LLP LAS VE

LOCATIONS

HQ: CITY CENTER HOLDINGS, LLC
   3950 LAS VEGAS BLVD S, LAS VEGAS, NV 891191005
Phone: 702 632-9800
Web: WWW.CITIZENSLASVEGAS.COM

HISTORICAL FINANCIALS
Company Type: Private

Income Statement				FYE: December 31
	REVENUE ($ mil.)	NET INCOME ($ mil.)	NET PROFIT MARGIN	EMPLOYEES
12/12	1,189	(510)	—	—
12/11	1,081	(502)	—	—
Annual Growth	10.0%	—	—	—

2012 Year-End Financials
Return on assets: (-5.6%)   Cash ($ mil.): 252
Return on equity: (-8.3%)
Current ratio: 1.20

CITY OF ALBUQUERQUE

Albuquerque is by far New Mexico's largest city with a 2015 estimated population of 561380 (about 970680 in the greater metropolitan area). Albuquerque is located in the central part of the state and is home to The University of New Mexico. While Pueblo Indians lived in the general area for several centuries Spanish explorers arrived in the 16th century. The city of Albuquerque was founded in 1706 and named after the Spanish town of Albuquerque (with an extra "r"). The City of Albuquerque is administered by a Mayor and a nine-person City Council.

EXECUTIVES

Mayor, Timothy M Keller
Project Coordinator, Lancing Adams
Coordinator, Steve Herrera
Acting Dir, Economic Dev, Fred Mondragon
Director of Senior Affairs, Anna V Sanchez
City Treasurer, Cilia Aglialoro
Head Information Technology, Chike Nwagbo
Cfo, Sanjay Bhakta
Chief Administrative Officer, Sarita Nair
Executive Assistant, Laurel Hager
Project Engineer, Lisa Manwill
Auditors: MOSS ADAMS LLP ALBUQUERQUE N

LOCATIONS

HQ: CITY OF ALBUQUERQUE
   400 MARQUETTE AVE NW, ALBUQUERQUE, NM 871022117
Phone: 505 768-3000
Web: WWW.CABQ.GOV

HISTORICAL FINANCIALS
Company Type: Private

Income Statement				FYE: June 30
	REVENUE ($ mil.)	NET INCOME ($ mil.)	NET PROFIT MARGIN	EMPLOYEES
06/20	913	209	23.0%	6,500
06/19	825	20	2.5%	—
06/18	722	45	6.2%	—
06/17	709	(5)	—	—
Annual Growth	8.8%	—	—	—

2020 Year-End Financials
Return on assets: 3.6%   Cash ($ mil.): —
Return on equity: 6.3%
Current ratio: 2.30

CITY OF ALEXANDRIA

Historically a wartime victim of occupying forces modern Alexandria is home to many Defense Department contractors and employees. It uses a council-manager form of government wherein the mayor is part of the six-member city council (all elected at large) which determines city policy. The city manager works to carry out the policy and run the day-to-day operations of Alexandria. In addition to the city manager the council also appoints the city attorney city clerk and members of various commissions and boards. Alexandria's more than 30 departments operate on an annual budget of about $400 million and serve about 130000 citizens. The city was founded in 1749.

EXECUTIVES

Mayor, Allison Silberberg
City Mgr*, Mark Jinks
Deputy Cty Mgr*, Emily A Baker
U.S. Attorney, Tyler McGaughey
Coordinator Is To Build On Tha, Azuree Bowman
Management, Steven F Bloomfield
Program Manager, Helen Lee
Police Sergeant, Nick Ruggiero
Manager, Sylvie Kaboy
Manager, Grant Rogers
Team Leader, Phil Caldwell
Auditors: CLIFTONLARSONALLEN LLP ARLING

LOCATIONS

HQ: CITY OF ALEXANDRIA
   301 KING ST, ALEXANDRIA, VA 223143211
Phone: 703 746-4000
Web: WWW.ALEXANDRIAVA.GOV

HISTORICAL FINANCIALS
Company Type: Private

Income Statement				FYE: June 30
	REVENUE ($ mil.)	NET INCOME ($ mil.)	NET PROFIT MARGIN	EMPLOYEES
06/21	924	(75)	—	2,375
06/20	910	167	18.4%	—
06/19	880	(8)	—	—
06/18	842	108	12.9%	—
Annual Growth	3.2%	—	—	—

2021 Year-End Financials
Return on assets: (-3.2%)   Cash ($ mil.): 551
Return on equity: (-19.4%)
Current ratio: —

CITY OF ANAHEIM

Anaheim is a city in sunny southern Orange County California. The state's 10th largest city is home to Disneyland Resort one of Walt Disney Parks and Resorts' theme parks. The city also features a number of professional sports franchises such as the Anaheim Ducks hockey team and the Angels baseball team. Anaheim was founded in 1857.

EXECUTIVES

Mayor, Harry Sidhu
Secretary, Karen Harrell
Administrative Assistant, Indhira Gagnon
Operations, Sean Saxton
Public Works Crew Supervisor, Ted Robles
Assistant City, Alison Kott
City Librarian, Audrey Lujan
Technology Manager, Bruce Fruchter
Prin, Carole Kanegae
Associate Power Engineer, Chamreoun Keo
Parts Supervisor, Craig Rasco
Auditors: KPMG LLP LOS ANGELES CALIFOR

LOCATIONS

HQ: CITY OF ANAHEIM
  200 S ANAHEIM BLVD, ANAHEIM, CA 928053820
Phone: 714 765-5162
Web: WWW.ANAHEIM.NET

HISTORICAL FINANCIALS

Company Type: Private

Income Statement				FYE: June 30
	REVENUE ($ mil.)	NET INCOME ($ mil.)	NET PROFIT MARGIN	EMPLOYEES
06/20	574	(100)	—	3,100
06/19	592	12	2.2%	—
06/18	566	27	4.9%	—
06/17	602	92	15.4%	—
Annual Growth	(1.6%)	—	—	—

2020 Year-End Financials

Return on assets: (-1.9%)
Return on equity: (-5.3%)
Current ratio: 3.40

Cash ($ mil.): 104

CITY OF ATLANTA

City of Atlanta leaders have a dream to improve Atlantans' quality of life. The birthplace of civil rights activist Martin Luther King Jr. Atlanta is run by a mayor and a 16-member council. With a metropolitan population of more than 5 million Atlanta is the most populous city in Georgia. It's also the state capital and home to such major companies as The Coca-Cola Company The Home Depot and UPS. In addition Atlanta has a number of professional sports franchises namely the Atlanta Braves Hawks and Falcons.

EXECUTIVES

Mayor, Keisha Lance Bottoms
City Attorney*, Linda Disantis
President*, Lisa Borders
Cfo*, J Anthony Beard
Controller*, Ray Zies
Chief Resilience Officer*, Stephanie Stuckey Benfield
Acting Chief Procurement Offic*, Angela Hinton
Public Works, Norman Koplon
Manager, Anthony Stanley
Finance Manager, Robin Sanford
Director of Sustainability, John R Seydel III
Auditors: KPMG LLP ATLANTA GA

LOCATIONS

HQ: CITY OF ATLANTA
  55 TRINITY AVE SW # 3900, ATLANTA, GA 303033543
Phone: 404 330-6100
Web: WWW.ATLANTAGA.GOV

HISTORICAL FINANCIALS

Company Type: Private

Income Statement				FYE: June 30
	REVENUE ($ mil.)	NET INCOME ($ mil.)	NET PROFIT MARGIN	EMPLOYEES
06/17	1,044	146	14.0%	8,885
06/15	920	274	29.8%	—
06/14	883	9	1.0%	—
06/13	850	14	1.7%	—
Annual Growth	5.3%	79.0%	—	—

2017 Year-End Financials

Return on assets: 0.8%
Return on equity: 2.0%
Current ratio: 3.20

Cash ($ mil.): 48

CITY OF AUSTIN

Deep in the heart of Texas you'll find Austin the capital of the state and self-proclaimed Live Music Capital of the World. The city covering more than 300 square miles follows the council/manager model where the mayor and six city council members all elected to three-year terms enact policy and the city manager carries it out. The manager's office oversees about 30 departments/offices the municipal court system city utilities and the city's airport. Austin has a city population of more than 820000 and a greater metro population of more than 1.8 million. Stephen F. Austin brought the first Anglo settlers to the area in 1821.

EXECUTIVES

Mayor, Steve Adler
Mayor Pro Tem, Mike Martinez
Executive Assistant, Jason Garza
Risk Manager, Leslie Milvo
Manager, Marcia Brooks
Deputy Director, Rodney Gonzales
Coordinator, Rex Gressett
Assistant Chief, Chris McIlvain
Coordinator, Jorge Rousselin
Asst City Mgr, Christopher J Shorter
Detective, Andy Westbrook
Auditors: DELOITTE & TOUCHE LLP AUSTIN

LOCATIONS

HQ: CITY OF AUSTIN
  301 W 2ND ST, AUSTIN, TX 787014652
Phone: 512 974-2000
Web: WWW.AUSTINTEXAS.GOV

Selected Departments and Offices

Austin Resource Recovery
Animal Services Office
Austin Convention Center Department
Austin Water Utility
Aviation Department
Capital Planning Office
Code Compliance Department

Communications and Public Information Office
Contract Management Department
Economic Growth and Redevelopment Services Office
Emergency Medical Services Department
Fire Department
Health and Human Services Department/Medical Director
Human Resources
Labor Relations Office
Law Department
Library Department
Neighborhood Housing and Community Development
Office of Homeland Security and Emergency Management
Office of Police Monitor
Office of Real Estate Services
Parks and Recreation Department
Planning and Development Review Department
Police Department
Public Works Department
Small and Minority Business Resources Department
Sustainability Office
Transportation Department
Watershed Protection Department

HISTORICAL FINANCIALS

Company Type: Private

Income Statement				FYE: September 30
	REVENUE ($ mil.)	NET INCOME ($ mil.)	NET PROFIT MARGIN	EMPLOYEES
09/20	1,449	(34)	—	10,922
09/19	1,352	33	2.5%	—
09/18	1,279	67	5.2%	—
09/17	1,186	28	2.4%	—
Annual Growth	6.9%	—	—	—

2020 Year-End Financials

Return on assets: (-0.2%)
Return on equity: (-1.0%)
Current ratio: 2.40

Cash ($ mil.): 10

CITY OF BALTIMORE

Although it is the birthplace of the National Anthem home to the first commercial ice cream factory in the US and among the nation's oldest cities Baltimore is more than an asterisk to history. With a population of about 620000 the city — Maryland's largest — supports a major seaport and is part of the Baltimore-Washington metropolis. The city's economy is founded on shipping transportation auto manufacturing and steel processing. It is however shifting to a diverse service base attractive to tourists. Baltimore is home to two professional sports teams the Baltimore Orioles and the Baltimore Ravens.

EXECUTIVES

Mayor, Brandon Scott
Dep Coo*, Khalil Zaied
CIO-Cdo*, Frank Johnson
Architect, Joseph L Henley
Mayor, Catherine E Pugh
Crime Fighting Strategist, Pol, Baltimore City of
Licensed Clinical Social Worke, Patricia Pencil
Chief of Staff, Bruce H Williams
Acting Police Commissioner, Michael S Harrison
Human Resources Business Partn, Catherine B Phr
Scheduling Coordinator, Durre Smith
Auditors: SB & COMPANY LLC OWING MILLS

LOCATIONS

HQ: CITY OF BALTIMORE
  100 HOLLIDAY ST STE 250, BALTIMORE, MD
  212023459
Phone: 410 396-3835
Web: WWW.BALTIMORECITY.GOV

HISTORICAL FINANCIALS

Company Type: Private

Income Statement				FYE: June 30
	REVENUE ($ mil.)	NET INCOME ($ mil.)	NET PROFIT MARGIN	EMPLOYEES
06/20	2,391	(5)	—	26,400
06/19	2,413	133	5.5%	—
06/18	2,147	126	5.9%	—
06/17	2,167	63	2.9%	—
Annual Growth	3.3%	—	—	—

2020 Year-End Financials

Return on assets: —
Return on equity: (-0.1%)
Current ratio: —

Cash ($ mil.): 1,418

CITY OF BOSTON

Boston's legacy includes a famous Tea Party Paul Revere's Ride and clam chowder. With about 625000 residents Boston has been called the economic and cultural hub of New England. The Greater Boston metro area is home to about 4.6 million people making it the 10th largest city in the US. Boston also boasts world class educational institutions (Harvard Massachusetts Institute of Technology) champion sports teams (Red Sox Celtics Patriots) and a rich cultural and historical identity. Boston is also the capital of Massachusetts.

EXECUTIVES

Mayor, Michelle Wu
Controller, Lisa Obrien
Budget Director Public Works D, Ann Carbone
Executive Director Bcdc Senior, David Carlson
Regional Operations Manager, Cherie Cope
Staff Support Specialist, Chris Morawski
Assistant Commissioner, Elaine Vieira
Branch Manager, Emily Haber
Talent Acquisition Manager, Frank Woods
Network Engineer, Jasper Melton
Director of Intergovernmental, Miriam Carr
Auditors: KPMG LLP BOSTON MA

LOCATIONS

HQ: CITY OF BOSTON
  1 CITY HALL SQ STE 242, BOSTON, MA 022011020
Phone: 617 635-4545
Web: WWW.BOSTON.GOV

HISTORICAL FINANCIALS

Company Type: Private

Income Statement				FYE: June 30
	REVENUE ($ mil.)	NET INCOME ($ mil.)	NET PROFIT MARGIN	EMPLOYEES
06/19	3,953	213	5.4%	18,760
06/17	3,542	93	2.7%	—
06/16	3,393	138	4.1%	—
06/15	3,278	79	2.4%	—
Annual Growth	4.8%	28.1%	—	—

CITY OF BUFFALO

Buffalo New York is the second-largest city in the state (behind New York City of course). Located in the western part of the state of the state by Lake Erie Buffalo is home to more than 260000 people. The greater metropolitan area including the famed Niagara Falls is home to more 1.2 million people. It also has two professional sports franchises the Buffalo Bills football team and the Sabres hockey team.

EXECUTIVES

Mayor, Byron Brown
Dep Mayor*, Ellen Grant
City Clerk*, Charles Michaux
Comptroller, Mark J F Schroeder
Coordinator, Dave Krug
Engineer, Dan Connors
Coordinator, Daniel Bonner
Information Technology Manager, Ann Forti-Sciarrino
Engineer, Brian Shea
Mayor, Byron Bron
Engineering Assistant, Eric Schmarder
Auditors: DRESCHER & MALECKI LLP BUFFAL

LOCATIONS

HQ: CITY OF BUFFALO
  65 NIAGARA SQ RM 201, BUFFALO, NY 142023392
Phone: 716 851-4200
Web: WWW.BUFFALONY.GOV

HISTORICAL FINANCIALS

Company Type: Private

Income Statement				FYE: June 30
	REVENUE ($ mil.)	NET INCOME ($ mil.)	NET PROFIT MARGIN	EMPLOYEES
06/21	587	59	10.1%	3,426
06/20	504	(18)	—	—
06/19	525	(19)	—	—
06/18	516	(25)	—	—
Annual Growth	4.4%	—	—	—

2021 Year-End Financials

Return on assets: 1.5%
Return on equity: —
Current ratio: —

Cash ($ mil.): 371

CITY OF CAMBRIDGE

The City of Cambridge houses an abundance of prominent minds. Part of the Greater Boston area it is home to prestigious universities Harvard and the Massachusetts Institute of Technology (MIT). With a population of more than 100000 the city covers just seven square miles. Most of its commercial districts are major street intersections (which act as neighborhood centers) which has given rise to its nickname "City of Squares." They include: Central Harvard Inman Kendall Lechmere and Porter Squares. Cambridge's city government is a bit unusual. The city manager (appointed by its nine city council members) rather than the mayor (also elected by the council) serves as the chief executive of the city.

EXECUTIVES

City Mgr, Robert W Healy
Budget Analyst, David Holland
Administrator, Elizabeth Lewis
Executive Director, Nancy Tauber
Project Manager, Daniel Vallee
Hmis Project Manager, Marianne Colangelo
Assistant Director, Michelle Farnum
Director of Adult Employment, Susan Mintz
Director of Equity and Inclusi, Betsy Allen
Manager of Web Communications, David Kale
Gis Specialist, George Stylianopoulos
Auditors: KPMG LLP BOSTON MA

LOCATIONS

HQ: CITY OF CAMBRIDGE
  795 MASSACHUSETTS AVE, CAMBRIDGE, MA
  021393219
Phone: 617 349-4260
Web: WWW.CAMBRIDGEMA.GOV

HISTORICAL FINANCIALS

Company Type: Private

Income Statement				FYE: June 30
	REVENUE ($ mil.)	NET INCOME ($ mil.)	NET PROFIT MARGIN	EMPLOYEES
06/20	782	25	3.3%	2,000
06/19	754	38	5.1%	—
06/18	726	65	9.0%	—
06/17	667	55	8.3%	—
Annual Growth	5.4%	(22.6%)	—	—

CITY OF CHARLOTTE

You can bank on Charlotte ... the nation's second-largest banking center (behind New York City). The City of Charlotte delivers public services and promotes safety and health among residents. Policies are set by a mayor and 11 council members elected for two-year terms. The day-to-day operations are handled by a city manager. Charlotte has a population of more than 750000 and covers about 280 square miles. It's home to a handful of Fortune 500 companies including Bank of America Family Dollar and Duke Energy as well as the Carolina Panthers and Charlotte Motor Speedway. It also boasts some 700 places of worship earning it the nickname "The City of Churches."

EXECUTIVES

Mayor, Vl Lyles
Manager Mecklenburg County Gov, Frances Davis
Information Technology Manager, Harold Gaines
Technology, Olaf Kinard
Assistant Fire Marshal, Randy Frazier
Claims, Tammy Wrobleski
Developer Advocate, Nan Peterson
Administrative Officer III, Pamela Alexander
Cppo, Philip Keller
Director, Rob Phocus
Budget, Sylvia Boland
Auditors: CHERRY BEKAERT LLP CHARLOTTE

LOCATIONS

HQ: CITY OF CHARLOTTE
  600 E 4TH ST, CHARLOTTE, NC 282022816
Phone: 704 336-7600
Web: WWW.CHARLOTTENC.GOV

HISTORICAL FINANCIALS
Company Type: Private

Income Statement				FYE: June 30
	REVENUE ($ mil.)	NET INCOME ($ mil.)	NET PROFIT MARGIN	EMPLOYEES
06/20	1,102	(83)	—	5,011
06/19	1,065	148	13.9%	
06/18	997	(10)	—	
06/17	945	(36)	—	
Annual Growth	5.2%	—	—	—

CITY OF CHESAPEAKE

The City of Chesapeake attracts both beach-combers and history buffs. Located about 20 miles from Virginia Beach Chesapeake was established in 1963 through the merging of the city of South Norfolk and Norfolk County which was created in 1691. The first English settlement in the area began around 1620 along the banks of the Elizabeth River. The mayor vice mayor and seven city council members (elected for four-year terms) govern the city which has a population of more than 233370. The third-largest city in Virginia Chesapeake is home to the College of William and Mary and Hampton University.

EXECUTIVES

Mayor, Alan P Krasnoff
City Treas*, Barbara O Carraway
City Mgr*, Clarence V Cuffee
Prin*, John De Triquet
Council MBR*, Lonnie E Craig
Temp, Michelle Bell
City, Ronald S Hallman
Coordinator, Gigie Button
Biology Teacher, Lee Susie
City Manager, James Baker
Central Fleet Management, Denise Smith
Auditors: CHERRY BEKAERT LLP VIRGINIA B

LOCATIONS

HQ: CITY OF CHESAPEAKE
 306 CEDAR RD, CHESAPEAKE, VA 233225597
Phone: 757 382-6586
Web: WWW.CITYOFCHESAPEAKE.NET

HISTORICAL FINANCIALS
Company Type: Private

Income Statement				FYE: June 30
	REVENUE ($ mil.)	NET INCOME ($ mil.)	NET PROFIT MARGIN	EMPLOYEES
06/20	703	54	7.7%	2,893
06/16	621	14	2.4%	
06/15	595	4	0.8%	
06/14	0	4	—	
Annual Growth	—	53.3%		

2020 Year-End Financials
Return on assets: 1.4%   Cash ($ mil.): 599
Return on equity: 3.0%
Current ratio: —

CITY OF CINCINNATI

Founded in 1788 Cincinnati is home to almost 300000 people and covers roughly 80 square miles. It is the third-largest city in Ohio trailing behind Columbus and Cleveland. The city's government consists of the mayor and nine city council members (elected at large). Council committees deal with a wide range of issues including public education health economic concerns and community development. The city is also home to two major-league sports franchises — baseball's Cincinnati Reds and football's Cincinnati Bengals.

EXECUTIVES

Mayor, John Cranley
Prin*, Roxanne Qualls
Pres*, Wendell Young
Vice Mayor*, Christopher Smitherman
Coordinator, Chris Eilerman
Real Estate Conultant, Andrea Yang
Coordinator, Lynn Melzer
Council President Pro Tem, Tamaya Dennard
Acting City Manager, Patrick Duhaney
Recycling Coordinator, Sue Magness
Deputy Chief of Staff, Bobbi Dillon
Auditors: DAVE YOST COLUMBUS OHIO

LOCATIONS

HQ: CITY OF CINCINNATI
 801 PLUM ST RM 246, CINCINNATI, OH 452025704
Phone: 513 352-3221
Web: WWW.CINCINNATI-OH.GOV

HISTORICAL FINANCIALS
Company Type: Private

Income Statement				FYE: June 30
	REVENUE ($ mil.)	NET INCOME ($ mil.)	NET PROFIT MARGIN	EMPLOYEES
06/19	769	25	3.3%	5,964
06/18	728	(22)	—	
06/17	708	10	1.5%	
Annual Growth	4.2%	52.5%	—	—

2019 Year-End Financials
Return on assets: 0.6%   Cash ($ mil.): 93
Return on equity: 2.0%
Current ratio: 2.40

CITY OF CLEVELAND

It's only rock and roll but Cleveland residents like it. The City of Cleveland Ohio (C-Town) is home to the Rock and Roll Hall of Fame and is the nation's 45th largest city and Ohio's second largest (behind Columbus). C-Town with more than 390000 residents is run by a mayor-council form of government. The legislative branch consists of a 21-member council and the executive branch comprises the mayor his adjunct offices advisors and the city's administrative departments. The mayor is the city's CEO and is elected to enforce its charter ordinances and state laws. The Village of Cleveland was incorporated in 1814.

EXECUTIVES

Mayor, Frank G Jackson
City Treas*, Algernon Walker
Law Director*, Subodh Chandra
Clerk of Council*, Valerie Mc Call
City Council, Michael D Polensek
Associate Engineer, Alketa Panozaqi
Officer, Dan Wyman
Instructor Police Academy, George Kwan
Administrative, Jennifer Rosich
Officer, Stephanie Ashford
Grant Administrator, Shawn Sherrod
Auditors: CLARK SCHAEFER HACKETT & CO

LOCATIONS

HQ: CITY OF CLEVELAND
 601 LAKESIDE AVE E RM 210, CLEVELAND, OH 441141015
Phone: 216 664-2000
Web: WWW.CLEVELANDOHIO.GOV

HISTORICAL FINANCIALS
Company Type: Private

Income Statement				FYE: December 31
	REVENUE ($ mil.)	NET INCOME ($ mil.)	NET PROFIT MARGIN	EMPLOYEES
12/20	816	8	1.1%	8,073
12/19	839	31	3.7%	
12/17	801	75	9.5%	
12/15	706	20	3.0%	
Annual Growth	2.9%	(15.8%)	—	—

2020 Year-End Financials
Return on assets: 0.1%   Cash ($ mil.): 1,411
Return on equity: 0.3%
Current ratio: —

CITY OF COLUMBUS

So what if European explorer Christopher Columbus didn't sail the Scioto River? Columbus the capital of Ohio is located smack dab in the middle of the state. With a population of almost 836000 people Columbus is the largest city in the Buckeye State. (Cleveland and Cincinnati however have larger populations in their greater metropolitan areas.) Columbus is home to a handful of Fortune 500 companies including Nationwide Insurance and retailer L Brands. While the area had been home to European fur trappers since the 1700s and Native Americans for centuries Columbus became a city in 1812.

EXECUTIVES

Mayor, Andrew Ginther
Coordinator, Abdikhayr Soofe
Program Manager, Jo St Clair
Information Specialist, Mark Gist
Coordinator, Tony Barnett
Health Professional, Toya Johnson
Media Relations Director, Robin Davis
Plant Manager, William Eitel
Program Coordinato, Tonya Barnett
Management Analyst, Brent Angel
Contracting Supervisor, Jeff Duffield
Auditors: PLANTE & MORAN PLLC COLUMBUS

LOCATIONS

HQ: CITY OF COLUMBUS
 90 W BROAD ST RM B33, COLUMBUS, OH 432159061
Phone: 614 645-7671
Web: WWW.COLUMBUS.GOV

HISTORICAL FINANCIALS
Company Type: Private

Income Statement				FYE: December 31
	REVENUE ($ mil.)	NET INCOME ($ mil.)	NET PROFIT MARGIN	EMPLOYEES
12/20	1,805	(72)	—	8,385
12/19	1,630	29	1.8%	—
12/18	1,478	94	6.4%	—
12/17	1,442	(1)	—	—
Annual Growth	7.8%			

2020 Year-End Financials
Return on assets: (-0.7%)   Cash ($ mil.): 1,460
Return on equity: (-2.6%)
Current ratio: —

CITY OF DALLAS

EXECUTIVES

Mayor, Eric Johnson
City Manager, Mary Suhm
Controller, Edward Scott
Controller, Regina Horne Givens
Sr Accountant, Mr Mushtaq Ali
Coordinator, Richard Carrizales
Dallas Police Chief, Ulysha R Hall
Senior Airport Operations Offi, Andrew Edgar
Assistant Director, Avis Chaisson
Hr Mgr, Carrie Prysock
Assistant City, Chloe Corbett
Auditors: GRANT THORNTON DALLAS TEXAS

LOCATIONS

HQ: CITY OF DALLAS
 1500 MARILLA ST, DALLAS, TX 752016390
Phone: 214 670-3146
Web: WWW.DALLASCITYHALL.COM

HISTORICAL FINANCIALS
Company Type: Private

Income Statement				FYE: September 30
	REVENUE ($ mil.)	NET INCOME ($ mil.)	NET PROFIT MARGIN	EMPLOYEES
09/20	2,067	45	2.2%	13,000
09/19	1,898	147	7.7%	—
09/18	1,802	258	14.3%	—
09/17	1,678	(58)	—	—
Annual Growth	7.2%			

2020 Year-End Financials
Return on assets: 0.3%   Cash ($ mil.): 1,524
Return on equity: 3.8%
Current ratio: —

CITY OF HARTFORD

EXECUTIVES

Mayor, Luke Bronin
City Treas*, Kathleen Plam
City Manager*, Sandra Kee Borges
Spokesperson, Lily Richardson
Public Relations Executive, Maribel La Luz

Police Officer, Chris Van Wey
Senior Project Manager, Claude Trapp
CPA, Joseph Caruso
Mayors Scheduling Assistant, Latoya Aitcheson
Registrar of Voters, Sheila Hall
Grants Administration, Steve Biancardi
Auditors: BLUM SHAPIRO & COMPANY PC W

LOCATIONS

HQ: CITY OF HARTFORD
 550 MAIN ST STE 1, HARTFORD, CT 061032913
Phone: 860 757-9311

HISTORICAL FINANCIALS
Company Type: Private

Income Statement				FYE: June 30
	REVENUE ($ mil.)	NET INCOME ($ mil.)	NET PROFIT MARGIN	EMPLOYEES
06/20	1,013	(10)	—	10,000
06/19	948	5	0.6%	—
06/18	940	(11)	—	—
06/17	885	(75)	—	—
Annual Growth	4.6%			

2020 Year-End Financials
Return on assets: (-0.4%)   Cash ($ mil.): 161
Return on equity: (-1.9%)
Current ratio: —

CITY OF HOPE NATIONAL MEDICAL CENTER

EXECUTIVES

Ceo, Michael A Friedman
Ceo*, Robert Stone
Information Technology/Interne, Adrian Aguila
Coordinator, Lori Stancer
Assistant Professor, Xueli Liu
Scientist, Jun Wu
Scientist, Helen Lin
Senior Specialist, Layla Rouse
Study Coordinator, Rosa Mejia
Compliance Program Manager, Merle S Smith
Project Administrator, Janice Sowinski

LOCATIONS

HQ: CITY OF HOPE NATIONAL MEDICAL CENTER
 1500 DUARTE RD, DUARTE, CA 910103012
Phone: 626 256-4673
Web: WWW.CITYOFHOPE.ORG

HISTORICAL FINANCIALS
Company Type: Private

Income Statement				FYE: September 30
	REVENUE ($ mil.)	NET INCOME ($ mil.)	NET PROFIT MARGIN	EMPLOYEES
09/19	1,357	41	3.1%	1,900
09/15	860	107	12.5%	—
09/14	0	0	—	—
09/13	696	59	8.5%	—
Annual Growth	11.8%	(5.7%)		

2019 Year-End Financials
Return on assets: 1.8%   Cash ($ mil.): 107
Return on equity: 5.7%
Current ratio: 1.00

CITY OF HOUSTON

It is bigger in Texas when you consider the City of Houston. As the largest city in the state and one of the largest cities nationwide Houston is more than an oil town. Founded in 1836 and home to Rice University and the Astros it also has a noteworthy museum district and operates the Texas Medical Center one of the world's largest health care facilities. While a mayor oversees Houston's management 14 council members (elected for two-year terms) have the power to enact and enforce city ordinances. With a population of more than 2 million Houston operates through some 20 departments including health and human services police and parks and recreation. It has an annual budget of about $2 billion.

Geographic Reach

Houston reaches more than 656 square miles and comprises Harris Fort Bend and Montgomery counties. The larger area of Houston Sugar Land and Baytown with some 6.5 million residents makes up the fifth-largest metropolitan area in the US.

Strategy

Looking to provide staff with flexible transportation options the City of Houston partnered with car-sharing network Zipcar in 2012 to launch Houston Fleet Share. As part of the program the city maintains an owned fleet of 50 plug-in electric and hybrid vehicles that are outfitted with Zipcar's car-sharing technology. Houston Fleet Share is funded by the State Energy Conservation Office American Recovery and Reinvestment Act (SECO-ARRA) transportation program.

Company Background

Houston's operations were battered when Hurricane Ike — called the worst storm to hit Texas in nearly 50 years — rolled through the city in 2008. Water and electricity services were interrupted for days and municipal services were severely limited in the aftermath of the storm.

Houston gained national attention soon after by electing the first openly gay mayor of a major US city Annise Parker. She is Houston's second female mayor and served as an at-large member of the Houston City Council from 1997-2003 and City Controller from 2004-2009.

EXECUTIVES

Mayor, Sylvester Turner
Dir*, Tina Paez
Acting Cfo*, Tantri Emo
Chief of Staff*, Marvalette Hunter
Senior Assistant City, Cell Price
Assistant City, Charles Miers
Program Coordinator, Jason Jeffries
Assistant City, Mayura Ramanna
Assistant To Jill Jewett, Mayo, Veronica Juarez
Theater Event Coordinator, Anna Cardona
Council Member, District B, Carol Mims Galloway
Auditors: MCCONNELL & JONES LLP

LOCATIONS

HQ: CITY OF HOUSTON
 901 BAGBY ST, HOUSTON, TX 770022049
Phone: 832 393-1000
Web: WWW.HOUSTONTX.GOV

PRODUCTS/OPERATIONS

Selected City Sites
Art Car Parade
Baylor College of Medicine
Houston Auto Show
Houston Greek Festival
Houston Livestock Show and Rodeo
Houston Theater District
Lyndon B. Johnson Space Center
MD Anderson Cancer Center
Memorial Hermann Hospital
Museum District
Rice University
Theater District
University of Houston
Uptown District
UT Health Science Center

HISTORICAL FINANCIALS

Company Type: Private

Income Statement — FYE: June 30

	REVENUE ($ mil.)	NET INCOME ($ mil.)	NET PROFIT MARGIN	EMPLOYEES
06/20	3,351	22	0.7%	23,235
06/19	3,253	98	3.0%	—
06/18	3,110	52	1.7%	—
06/17	494	128	25.9%	—
Annual Growth	89.3%	(44.0%)	—	—

2020 Year-End Financials
Return on assets: 0.1%   Cash ($ mil.): 1,902
Return on equity: 1.1%
Current ratio: —

CITY OF JACKSONVILLE

In Jacksonville residents and visitors can enjoy the Florida wilderness. The city which offers some 57000 acres of parks provides more land for recreation than any other city in the US. Its 19 city council members (five at-large members and 14 representing geographic districts) enact the legislation for the Jacksonville. Elected for four-year terms the mayor oversees the administration of the central government and appoints directors for its 10 departments. The 14th-largest city in the US Jacksonville has a population of more than 850000 residents.

EXECUTIVES

Mayor, Lenny Curry
General Legal Practice, Deborah D Walters
Payroll Staff, Tina Rehmel
Customer Staff, Ken Roper
Internal Auditor, Mitchell Perin
Customer Representativ, Amy Maddox
Director of Intra Governmental, Craig Thompson
Animal Placement Supervisor, Daniel Clavel
Teen Court Program Case Manage, Danielle Felton
Legislative Superviso, Jessica Matthews
Executive Assistant To CHI, Julie Rivera
Auditors: CARR RIGGS & INGRAM JACKSONVI

LOCATIONS

HQ: CITY OF JACKSONVILLE
117 W DUVAL ST, JACKSONVILLE, FL 322023700
Phone: 904 630-1776
Web: WWW.COJ.NET

HISTORICAL FINANCIALS

Company Type: Private

Income Statement — FYE: September 30

	REVENUE ($ mil.)	NET INCOME ($ mil.)	NET PROFIT MARGIN	EMPLOYEES
09/18	1,599	64	4.0%	7,908
09/17	1,560	12	0.8%	—
09/16	1,493	33	2.3%	—
09/15	1,414	50	3.6%	—
Annual Growth	4.2%	8.7%		—

2018 Year-End Financials
Return on assets: 0.4%   Cash ($ mil.): 187
Return on equity: 2.5%
Current ratio: —

CITY OF LAS VEGAS

Some 585000 people call Sin City home. Las Vegas Nevada's largest city is the gaming capital of the US. The city is overseen by a mayor an appointed city manager and six elected city council members. Its largest industry is tourism; the casino resorts attract visitors seeking business and pleasure — Las Vegas hosts almost 20000 conventions every year.

EXECUTIVES

Mayor, Carolyn G Goodman
City Mgr*, Douglas A Selby
Dep City Mgr*, Steve Houchens
Dep City Mgr*, Betsy Fretwell
Director of Finance*, Mark Vincent
Customer Staff, Roshanda Potter
Payroll Staff, Jessica Lindelow
Designer, Marti Siska
Designer, Erik Singman
Information Technologies Direc, Michael Sherwood
Information Specialist, David Barnett
Auditors: BDO LLP LAS VEGAS NEVADA

LOCATIONS

HQ: CITY OF LAS VEGAS
495 S MAIN ST, LAS VEGAS, NV 891012986
Phone: 702 229-6321
Web: WWW.LASVEGASNEVADA.GOV

HISTORICAL FINANCIALS

Company Type: Private

Income Statement — FYE: June 30

	REVENUE ($ mil.)	NET INCOME ($ mil.)	NET PROFIT MARGIN	EMPLOYEES
06/20	999	(95)	—	2,500
06/19	857	58	6.9%	—
06/18	782	69	8.9%	—
06/17	688	10	1.6%	—
Annual Growth	13.2%	—	—	—

CITY OF LONG BEACH

It's a city it's a port it's Long Beach. The City of Long Beach boasts the Port of Long Beach one of the busiest ports in the nation. With a population of more than 460000 Long Beach is part of the greater Los Angeles metropolitan area. The city uses a charter form of government with an elected mayor and city council as well as an appointed city manager. It's also known for its large oil reserves managed by the Long Beach Gas & Oil Department.

EXECUTIVES

Mayor, Robert Garcia
Mayor*, Bob Foster
City Treas*, David Nakamoto
Mayor*, Robert G Foster
City, Robert E Shannon
Director Financial Management, Lori Ann Farrell
Document Specialist, Frederick Wagner
Information Department, Sergeant Bell
City Manager, Patrick H West
Coordinator, Baldev Gill
Coordinator, Carlos Carrion
Auditors: KPMG LLP LOS ANGELES CALIFOR

LOCATIONS

HQ: CITY OF LONG BEACH
411 W OCEAN BLVD, LONG BEACH, CA 908024664
Phone: 562 570-6450
Web: WWW.LONGBEACH.GOV

HISTORICAL FINANCIALS

Company Type: Private

Income Statement — FYE: September 30

	REVENUE ($ mil.)	NET INCOME ($ mil.)	NET PROFIT MARGIN	EMPLOYEES
09/20	889	19	2.2%	5,028
09/19	864	36	4.3%	—
09/18	779	26	3.4%	—
09/17	716	9	1.3%	—
Annual Growth	7.5%	29.0%	—	—

2020 Year-End Financials
Return on assets: 0.2%   Cash ($ mil.): 717
Return on equity: 0.4%
Current ratio: 1.60

CITY OF LOS ANGELES

Los Angeles may be a Mecca for the rich and famous but there is little glamour in running a city of more than 4 million people. Governing responsibilities are shared among the city's mayor and city council while various commissions departments and bureaus see to the daily operations that keep the wheels spinning. Elected every four years the mayor appoints most commission members (subject to approval by the city council) and serves as the city's executive officer. The City of Los Angeles is located in the County of Los Angeles.

EXECUTIVES

Mayor, Eric Garcetti
Architect, Michael Munsch
Attorney, Jeanne Di Conti
City, Rocky Delgadillo
Administrative Assistant, Gustavo Plascencia
Staff, Neil Shieh
Civic Center Facilities L A MA, Joi Oubre
Assistant Director of Building, Loretta Quenon
Administrative Section, Raquel Jarel
Professor Department of Radiol, Michael Siegel
Public Relations Rep, Paul Gomez

LOCATIONS

HQ: CITY OF LOS ANGELES
   200 N SPRING ST STE 303, LOS ANGELES, CA
   900123239
Phone: 213 978-0600
Web: WWW.LACITY.ORG

HISTORICAL FINANCIALS

Company Type: Private

Income Statement

FYE: June 30

	REVENUE ($ mil.)	NET INCOME ($ mil.)	NET PROFIT MARGIN	EMPLOYEES
06/16	7,196	231	3.2%	41,000
06/09*	6,281	(285)	—	—
12/08	0	0	—	—
Annual Growth	274.6%	—	—	—

*Fiscal year change

2016 Year-End Financials

Return on assets: 0.4%   Cash ($ mil.): 7,446
Return on equity: 1.2%
Current ratio: —

CITY OF MEMPHIS

Home to Graceland and Beale Street Memphis has both feet entrenched in the world of music. With a population of more than 670000 it is located in the southwestern corner of the state and stretches over 300 square miles. Serving the largest urban population in Tennessee it is run by a mayor and 13 city council members (elected from nine districts). City government is responsible for economic development public education housing public utilities homeland security and landmark preservation. Set atop the eastern bank of the Mississippi River and named after the ancient capital of Egypt Memphis was founded in 1820.

EXECUTIVES

Mayor, Jim Strickland
Coo*, Doug McGowen
Cfo*, Shirley Ford
Special Assistant, Gale Jones - Carson
City, Elbert Jefferson
Vice Chair, Amber Floyd
Chief Investigator, Arthur Robinson
It Project Manager, Sylvia Thomas
Communications Director, Ursula Madden
Grants Coordinator, Notimba Brooks
City, Herman Morris
Auditors: BANKS FINLEY WHITE & CO ME

LOCATIONS

HQ: CITY OF MEMPHIS
   125 N MAIN ST STE 628, MEMPHIS, TN 381032032
Phone: 901 676-6657
Web: WWW.MEMPHISTN.GOV

HISTORICAL FINANCIALS

Company Type: Private

Income Statement

FYE: June 30

	REVENUE ($ mil.)	NET INCOME ($ mil.)	NET PROFIT MARGIN	EMPLOYEES
06/16	906	8	0.9%	6,000
06/15	863	1	0.2%	—
06/14	840	26	3.2%	—
06/13	845	(25)	—	—
Annual Growth	2.3%	—	—	—

2016 Year-End Financials

Return on assets: 0.1%   Cash ($ mil.): 285
Return on equity: 0.3%
Current ratio: —

CITY OF MESA

This city which literally covers a "mesa" or plateau stands roughly 100 feet higher than Phoenix and spreads across 130 square miles. With a population of more than 468000 the City of Mesa is the third-largest city in Arizona behind Phoenix and Tucson. Its city government consists of the mayor six city council members (elected to four-year terms) and a city manager. Mesa is also home to the Chicago Cubs baseball team during spring training. The city was founded in 1878 by Mormon (Latter-day Saint or LDS) pioneers who gave it its name; Mesa still has a large Mormon population. It was incorporated in 1883.

EXECUTIVES

Mayor, John Giles
City Mgr*, Chris Braidi
Dir*, Sharon Seekins
Dir*, Don Ayers
Deputy Director*, Aric H Bopp
Attorney, Neal Beets
Prin, John Vega
Prin, Randy Booze
City, Debbie Spinner
Staff, Donna Salemi
Staff, Lisha Garcia
Auditors: CLIFTON LARSON ALLEN LLP PHOE

LOCATIONS

HQ: CITY OF MESA
   20 E MAIN ST, MESA, AZ 852017425
Phone: 480 644-2011
Web: WWW.MESAAZ.GOV

HISTORICAL FINANCIALS

Company Type: Private

Income Statement

FYE: June 30

	REVENUE ($ mil.)	NET INCOME ($ mil.)	NET PROFIT MARGIN	EMPLOYEES
06/20	646	89	13.9%	4,068
06/19	539	50	9.3%	—
06/18	515	47	9.1%	—
06/17	476	38	8.1%	—
Annual Growth	10.7%	32.6%	—	—

CITY OF MIAMI

Thankfully the City of Miami is much more than Dolphins sound-machines and vice cops. With a population of more than 400000 the city has little trouble attracting tourists and residents alike to the bustling international hub of business entertainment and culture. Thanks to its status as a transportation hub and the businesses that make the city home to international operations the city is also known as the Gateway to Latin America. The city government consists of its elected mayor five commissioners a city manager and the heads of Miami's various public services departments.

EXECUTIVES

Mayor, Francis X Suarez
Commissioner*, Mark Sarnoff
Manager, Rasha Cameau
Mayor, Tomas Regalado
Director of Architecture and D, Brian Zeltsman
Budget Director, Chris Rose
Park Manager II, Patrice Jackson
Finance Manager, Eugene Codner
Property, Frank Gomez
Veteran Coordinator, Juan Duenas
Public Affairs Manager, Natalia Vanegas
Auditors: RSM US LLP MIAMI FLORIDA

LOCATIONS

HQ: CITY OF MIAMI
   3500 PAN AMERICAN DR FL 2, MIAMI, FL 331335595
Phone: 305 250-5300
Web: WWW.MIAMIGOV.COM

HISTORICAL FINANCIALS

Company Type: Private

Income Statement

FYE: September 30

	REVENUE ($ mil.)	NET INCOME ($ mil.)	NET PROFIT MARGIN	EMPLOYEES
09/16	837	15	1.8%	3,000
09/15	792	(1)	—	—
09/12	675	(18)	—	—
09/09	691	(30)	—	—
Annual Growth	2.8%	—	—	—

CITY OF MINNEAPOLIS

One half of Minnesota's famed Twin Cities Minneapolis is a combination of the Sioux word for water with the Greek word for city. With 20 lakes and wetlands plus the Mississippi River waterfront and many creeks and streams the City of Minneapolis is known as the City of Lakes. It is governed by a mayor and city council with 13 members representing the city's wards. The mayor appoints the chief of police but has little other power. Independent boards oversee public housing the tax office and public parks and libraries. The city's more than 80 parks serve as a model for city park systems nationwide. Formed in 1856 Minneapolis is now home to a population of almost 400000.

EXECUTIVES

Mayor, Jacob Frey
City Clerk*, Steve Ristuben
Councilman*, Andrea Jenkins
Program Inspector, Michael Kjos
Deputy Controller, Dawn Koenig
Executive Committee Member, Jeff Sands
Transportation Planning Intern, Katie Page
Internal Auditor, Travis Kamm
Employee, Ann Kjos
Assistant City, Burt Osborne
Network Administrator, Dan Comfort
Auditors: JULIE BLAHA ST PAUL MN

LOCATIONS

HQ: CITY OF MINNEAPOLIS
   350 S 5TH ST STE 325M, MINNEAPOLIS, MN
   554151315
Phone: 612 673-3000
Web: WWW.MINNEAPOLISMN.GOV

HISTORICAL FINANCIALS
Company Type: Private

Income Statement				FYE: December 31
	REVENUE ($ mil.)	NET INCOME ($ mil.)	NET PROFIT MARGIN	EMPLOYEES
12/20	903	(21)	—	5,000
12/19	916	85	9.3%	—
12/18	858	84	9.8%	—
12/17	846	36	4.3%	—
Annual Growth	2.2%	—	—	—

CITY OF NEW HAVEN

EXECUTIVES

Mayor, John Destefano Jr
Coordinator, Bill Macmullen
Coordinator, Tomi Veale
Education, Typhanie Jackson
Alderman, Alberta Witherspoon
Executive Administrative Asst, Dawn Lewis
Executive Director, Douglas Hausladen
Education, Jose Romero
Director of Communications, Laurence Grotheer
Information Technology Directo, Richard Tsou
Chief of Staff, Tomas Reyes
Auditors: MCGLADREY LLP NEW HAVEN CONN

LOCATIONS

HQ: CITY OF NEW HAVEN
165 CHURCH ST FL 2, NEW HAVEN, CT 065102010
Phone: 203 946-8200
Web: WWW.NEWHAVENCT.GOV

HISTORICAL FINANCIALS
Company Type: Private

Income Statement				FYE: June 30
	REVENUE ($ mil.)	NET INCOME ($ mil.)	NET PROFIT MARGIN	EMPLOYEES
06/18	776	10	1.3%	4,500
06/17	819	5	0.7%	—
06/16	811	10	1.3%	—
06/15	738	3	0.5%	—
Annual Growth	1.7%	45.2%	—	—

2018 Year-End Financials

Return on assets: 0.5%   Cash ($ mil.): 96
Return on equity: —
Current ratio: —

CITY OF NEW ORLEANS

New Orleans is a city with a story. The city was founded in 1718 and became famous for its architecture music food and parties. The city is home to a major port the New Orleans Saints the French Quarter and is the regarded as the birthplace of jazz. Devastated by Hurricane Katrina and the flooding which ensued in 2005 the city has undertaken a massive rebuilding and recovery effort utilizing state and federal assistance. The city of New Orleans is governed by a city council consisting of seven members and an elected mayor.

EXECUTIVES

Mayor, Latoya Cantrell
Administrator, Charles Rice
Principal, Mosanda Mvula
Chief of Staff, Troy P Savage
Vice President, Tyra Brown
Coordinator, Chris Mark
Mayor, Mitchell J Landrieu
Assistant To Cao, Joyce Christopher
Program Director, Angela Cryer
Fuse Executive Advisor For Cli, Siobhan Foley
Office Assistant, Angel Jones
Auditors: POSTLETHWAITE & NETTERVILLE N

LOCATIONS

HQ: CITY OF NEW ORLEANS
1300 PERDIDO ST BSMT FL2, NEW ORLEANS, LA 701122128
Phone: 504 658-4900
Web: WWW.NOLA.GOV

HISTORICAL FINANCIALS
Company Type: Private

Income Statement				FYE: December 31
	REVENUE ($ mil.)	NET INCOME ($ mil.)	NET PROFIT MARGIN	EMPLOYEES
12/18	1,056	1	0.1%	6,658
12/17	901	(74)	—	—
12/16	881	39	4.5%	—
12/15	905	65	7.2%	—
Annual Growth	5.2%	(71.4%)	—	—

2018 Year-End Financials

Return on assets: —   Cash ($ mil.): 318
Return on equity: 0.1%
Current ratio: —

CITY OF NEW YORK

EXECUTIVES

Mayor, Bill De Blasio
Contrl*, William C Thompson Jr
Deputy Mayor*, Dennis Walcott
Deputy Dir*, George Davis III
Mbr-Cmptrlr*, Scott Stringer
MBR-City Council*, Melissa Mark Viverito
MBR-Public Advocate*, Letitia James
Chief of Staff*, Thomas G Snyder
Commissioner*, Lorraine A Cortes-Vazquez
Executive Director, Mayor's Ad, Desir E Kim
Deputy Director and General Co, Rebecca K Sternhell
Auditors: GRANT THORTON LLP NEW YORK N

LOCATIONS

HQ: CITY OF NEW YORK
CITY HALL PARK, NEW YORK, NY 10007
Phone: 212 788-3000
Web: WWW.NYC.GOV

HISTORICAL FINANCIALS
Company Type: Private

Income Statement				FYE: June 30
	REVENUE ($ mil.)	NET INCOME ($ mil.)	NET PROFIT MARGIN	EMPLOYEES
06/20	98,235	819	0.8%	310,000
06/18	90,568	1,348	1.5%	—
Annual Growth	4.1%	(22.0%)	—	—

2020 Year-End Financials

Return on assets: 0.4%   Cash ($ mil.): 11,219
Return on equity: —
Current ratio: —

CITY OF NEWPORT NEWS

There are nearly as many theories on where the unusual city name came from as there are citizens of Newport News Virginia. Whether it was founded on land chosen by Sir William Newce or the point where Captain Newport delivered good news to early settlers Newport News today boasts a population of some 193000. The mayor and six-member city council (representing three districts) work together to serve residents and visitors backed by an annual budget of about $750 million. The council sets up city policies and controls funding while the city manager attorney and clerk carry out the day-to-day administration of Newport News. The city which was settled around 1621 is well known as a military shipbuilding hub.

EXECUTIVES

Mayor, McKinley Price
City Mgr*, Edgar Maroney
City Mgr*, Hilde Brandt
Prin*, James M Bourey
Project Coordinator, Aaron Shivers
Project Coordinator, Wendy Ledford
Sergeant, Xavier O Falero
Chief Television Engineer, Ishrat Mohammad
Production Specialist, Wade Harrington
Sr Production Specialist, John Corriere
Administrative Assistant II, Maria Tisdale
Auditors: CHERRY BEKAERT CCP RICHMOND

LOCATIONS

HQ: CITY OF NEWPORT NEWS
2400 WASHINGTON AVE MAIN, NEWPORT NEWS, VA 236074300
Phone: 757 926-8411
Web: WWW.NEWPORTNEWSHISTORY.ORG

HISTORICAL FINANCIALS
Company Type: Private

Income Statement				FYE: June 30
	REVENUE ($ mil.)	NET INCOME ($ mil.)	NET PROFIT MARGIN	EMPLOYEES
06/20	598	(30)	—	5,000
06/19	602	50	8.4%	—
06/17	563	33	5.9%	—
06/16	544	10	1.9%	—
Annual Growth	2.4%	—	—	—

2020 Year-End Financials

Return on assets: (-1.3%)   Cash ($ mil.): 332
Return on equity: (-4.9%)
Current ratio: —

CITY OF NORFOLK

You could say that the City of Norfolk Virginia is at home on the water. The second-largest city in Virginia with a population of more than 245400 Norfolk sports miles of lake river and bay front as well as a bustling international port and the world's largest naval base. The city was founded in 1682 and offers such attractions as the battleship USS Wisconsin the National Maritime Center and Old Dominion University. Norfolk Southern Railway's corporate headquarters are also located in the city. Norfolk city government consists of its seven-member city council and mayor. The city manager serves as the city's COO and is appointed by the city council.

EXECUTIVES

Mayor, Kenneth Cooper Alexander
City Mgr*, Regina V K Williams
Cmo*, Michael G Brown
Attorney, Charles Prentace
Attorney, Bernard A Pishko
Public Information Officer, Jo Hughes
Design Engineer, Tammy Halstead
Fire Captain, Wayne Watson
Budget and Strategic Planning, Gregory Patrick
Box Office Manager, Heather Mitchell
Special Assistant To City, Jared Chalk
Auditors: CLIFTONLARSONALLEN LLP ARLING

LOCATIONS

HQ: CITY OF NORFOLK
 810 UNION ST STE 508, NORFOLK, VA 235108048
Phone: 757 664-7300
Web: WWW.NORFOLK.GOV

HISTORICAL FINANCIALS

Company Type: Private

Income Statement				FYE: June 30
	REVENUE ($ mil.)	NET INCOME ($ mil.)	NET PROFIT MARGIN	EMPLOYEES
06/20	749	(15)	—	4,364
06/19	751	162	21.6%	—
06/18	730	73	10.0%	—
06/17	702	22	3.3%	—
Annual Growth	2.2%	—	—	—

CITY OF OAKLAND

Joining San Francisco and San Jose Oakland makes up one-third of Northern California's Golden Triangle . Founded in 1852 Oakland boasts of a diverse population numbering more than 390000 residents a Mediterranean climate and thriving hip arts scene. The city is a hub for the port of San Francisco Bay as well as for the business elite and the higher educated. Environmental policies have helped propel Oakland to stand among the top green economies in the US. The city is served by a mayor and eight council members who oversee a budget of almost $1 billion. It is home to the NBA's Golden State Warriors NFL's Oakland Raiders and national landmark Lake Merritt.

EXECUTIVES

Mayor, Libby Schaaf
City Mgr*, Deborah Edgerly
Film Coordinator, AMI Zins
Staff, Joseph Feiccabrino
Captain, Brian Oftedal
Sergeant, Bryan Hubbard
Captain, Drennon Lindsey
Captain, Leronne Armstrong
Human Resources Analyst, Lisette Del Pino
Coordinator, Mary Costello
Sergeant, Mary Guttormson
Auditors: MACIAS GINI & O'CONNELL LLP W

LOCATIONS

HQ: CITY OF OAKLAND
 1 FRANK H OGAWA PLZ 2ND, OAKLAND, CA 946121904
Phone: 510 238-3280
Web: WWW.OAKLANDCA.GOV

HISTORICAL FINANCIALS

Company Type: Private

Income Statement				FYE: June 30
	REVENUE ($ mil.)	NET INCOME ($ mil.)	NET PROFIT MARGIN	EMPLOYEES
06/20	1,239	163	13.2%	4,000
06/19	1,211	28	2.3%	—
06/18	1,164	184	15.8%	—
06/17	1,071	100	9.4%	—
Annual Growth	5.0%	17.6%	—	—

CITY OF OKLAHOMA CITY

Oklahoma City was born overnight as a boomtown named Oklahoma Station in 1889 during the celebrated land rush in Oklahoma Territory. It became in time the state capital and largest city (with a population approaching 600000) and is headquarters of oil and gas companies Chesapeake Energy and Devon Energy as well as electric utility OGE Energy and service station operator Love's Truck Stops. City government is headed by a mayor and council members representing eight wards. The city captured its first top-rank sports franchise when the Oklahoma City Thunder NBA team began play in 2008.

EXECUTIVES

Mayor, David Holt
City Manager*, James D Couch
City Clerk*, Frances Kersey
Asst Fin Dir*, Kenton Tsoodle
Mayor, Mick Cornett
Coordinator, Yolinda Washington
Master Sergeant, Rob High
Property Technician, Heather Lung-Close
Administrative Support Technic, Angelita Duran
Network Engineer, Chad King
Police Sergeant, Darrin Guthrie
Auditors: ALLEN GIBBS & HOULIK LC W

LOCATIONS

HQ: CITY OF OKLAHOMA CITY
 100 N WALKER AVE, OKLAHOMA CITY, OK 731022230
Phone: 405 297-2506
Web: WWW.OKC.GOV

HISTORICAL FINANCIALS

Company Type: Private

Income Statement				FYE: June 30
	REVENUE ($ mil.)	NET INCOME ($ mil.)	NET PROFIT MARGIN	EMPLOYEES
06/18	865	112	13.0%	4,500
06/17	806	(21)	—	—
06/16	800	26	3.3%	—
06/15	803	65	8.2%	—
Annual Growth	2.5%	19.5%	—	—

2018 Year-End Financials

Return on assets: 1.6%   Cash ($ mil.): 76
Return on equity: 3.1%
Current ratio: 4.40

CITY OF OMAHA

Owing it name to one the tribes living in the area the City Omaha was once bypassed by the Lewis and Clark expedition. Founded in 1854 Omaha has become the 42nd largest city in the U.S. with a population of almost 409.000 in an area measuring little more than 130 square miles. The city is ruled by a mayor-council consisting of of an "at-large" mayor and 7 district councilmembers. The City of Omaha is home for megacompanies Berkshire Hathaway ConAgra Peter Kiewit Sons Mutual of Omaha TD Ameritrade Union Pacific West Corporation Valmont Industries and Werner Enterprises.

EXECUTIVES

Mayor, Jean Stothert
Manager, Harry Owen
Coordinator, Brenda Paul
Captain, Michael McGee
Mechanical Chief, Tom Phipps
Captain, Melanie Bates
Engineering, Richard Wilkinson
Swat Team Leader, Eric White
Executive Secretary, Jenna Garcia
Buyer, John Stolinski
Buyer, Mark Biodrowski
Auditors: BKD LLP OMAHA NEBRASKA

LOCATIONS

HQ: CITY OF OMAHA
 1819 FARNAM ST RM 300, OMAHA, NE 681831000
Phone: 402 444-5000
Web: WWW.CITYOFOMAHA.ORG

HISTORICAL FINANCIALS

Company Type: Private

Income Statement				FYE: December 31
	REVENUE ($ mil.)	NET INCOME ($ mil.)	NET PROFIT MARGIN	EMPLOYEES
12/20	707	4	0.7%	2,800
12/19	636	1	0.2%	—
12/18	593	(29)	—	—
12/17	589	24	4.2%	—
Annual Growth	6.3%	(41.8%)	—	—

CITY OF PHILADELPHIA

Known as the City of Brotherly Love Philadelphia is the fifth largest city in the nation with a population of more than 1.5 million. The city which covers 135 square miles operates through some 50 departments boards offices and other units that include emergency medical services sanitation services and street maintenance. Founded in 1682 by William Penn Philadelphia has a mayor 10 districts and 17 council members. The city which hosts millions of tourists each year is home to the Phillies the Eagles the Flyers the 76ers Bryn Mawr College the Liberty Bell and the National Constitution Center. The City of Philadelphia has an annual budget of more than $3.5 billion.

EXECUTIVES

Mayor, Jim Kenney
Staff, Frank Galioto
Coordinator, Francesco Cerrai
Scientist, Anne Harvey
Law Specialist, Rita Cairy
Solicitor, Marcel S Pratt
Procurement Manager, Anita Sharpe
Information Technology Trainin, Nick Demarco
Senior Appeals, Elise Bruhl
Judge, Anne Lazarus
Paralegal, Debbie Decolli
Auditors: CHRISTY BRADY CPA PHILADELPH

LOCATIONS

HQ: CITY OF PHILADELPHIA
    215 CITY HALL, PHILADELPHIA, PA 191073214
Phone: 215 686-2181
Web: WWW.PHILA.GOV

PRODUCTS/OPERATIONS

Selected Units
Behavioral Health
Board of Pensions and Retirement
Board of Revision of Taxes
City Controllers Office
City Planning Commission
City Treasurer
Civil Service Commission
Commerce
Department of Human Services
Ethics Board
Finance
Fire
Fleet Management
Health Department
Historical Commission
Human Relations
Inspector General
Labor Relations
Law
Library
Licenses and Inspections
Parking Authority
Philadelphia International Airport
Police
Procurement
Recreation
Records Department
Redevelopment Authority
Water Revenue Bureau

HISTORICAL FINANCIALS
Company Type: Private

Income Statement				FYE: June 30
	REVENUE ($ mil.)	NET INCOME ($ mil.)	NET PROFIT MARGIN	EMPLOYEES
06/17	6,646	20	0.3%	29,862
06/16	6,264	(64)	—	—
06/15	6,070	(92)	—	—
06/14	5,947	(10)	—	—
Annual Growth	3.8%	—	—	—

2017 Year-End Financials

Return on assets: 0.1%   Cash ($ mil.): 1,744
Return on equity: —
Current ratio: —

CITY OF PHOENIX

Phoenix the capital of Arizona has a population of about 1.4 million and is the sixth largest city in the US. Located in the south-central portion of the state Phoenix covers a sprawling 500 square miles and is geographically larger than Los Angeles. The City of Phoenix operates through some 30 departments including street transportation water services human services and public transit. Eight city council members (representing eight districts) and the mayor make up the city council which develop laws and policy for governing the city. Phoenix was incorporated in 1881.

EXECUTIVES

Mayor, Kate Gallego
Sales and Marketing Executive, Lexie Van Haren
Sergeant, Dale Skjerping
Sergeant, Tom Osborne
Information Specialist, James Baran
Counsel, Diego Leal
Management Assistant II, Amy Hartle
Career Advisor, Angela Boozer
Officer, Mark Aker
Staff, Alberto N Mejia
Aviation Program Manager, Anne Kurtenbach
Auditors: BKD LLP DALLAS TEXAS

LOCATIONS

HQ: CITY OF PHOENIX
    200 W WASHINGTON ST FL 11, PHOENIX, AZ 850031611
Phone: 602 262-7111
Web: WWW.PHOENIX.GOV

HISTORICAL FINANCIALS
Company Type: Private

Income Statement				FYE: June 30
	REVENUE ($ mil.)	NET INCOME ($ mil.)	NET PROFIT MARGIN	EMPLOYEES
06/20	2,786	27	1.0%	14,000
06/19	2,588	54	2.1%	—
06/18	2,521	(34)	—	—
06/17	2,318	198	8.6%	—
Annual Growth	6.3%	(48.1%)	—	—

2020 Year-End Financials

Return on assets: 0.1%   Cash ($ mil.): 681
Return on equity: 0.5%
Current ratio: —

CITY OF PITTSBURGH

Take one look at the skyline and it's no wonder Pittsburgh's been nicknamed "The City of Bridges." With more than 440 bridges 150 skyscrapers and a countless number of steel behemoths Pittsburgh is Pennsylvania's second largest city (behind Philadelphia) with a population of more than 305700. The city is composed of nine districts each represented by a council member while the mayor rounds out the executive side. Its annual budget goes toward enhancements to health care and retirement as well as hiring police and fire prevention personnel; most of its revenue comes from real estate taxes. Pittsburgh was founded in 1758.

EXECUTIVES

Mayor, William Peduto
Prin*, Sara Deroy
Sr Bdgtg Anlst, Kathleen Butter
Program Inspector, Alan Asbury
Chief of Staff, Dan Gilman
Executive Manager and Ethics O, Leanne Davis
Police Officer, Steve Mescan
Information Technology Manager, Thomas Vennero
Assistant City Solicitor, Kelly Mistick
Commissioner, Amanda Neatrour
Clerk II, Angela Grieser
Auditors: MAHER DUESSEL PITTSBURGH PEN

LOCATIONS

HQ: CITY OF PITTSBURGH
    414 GRANT ST, PITTSBURGH, PA 152192409
Phone: 412 255-2640
Web: WWW.PITTSBURGHPA.GOV

HISTORICAL FINANCIALS
Company Type: Private

Income Statement				FYE: December 31
	REVENUE ($ mil.)	NET INCOME ($ mil.)	NET PROFIT MARGIN	EMPLOYEES
12/19	651	48	7.4%	3,500
12/18	635	2	0.3%	—
12/14	537	22	4.2%	—
12/13	542	(30)	—	—
Annual Growth	3.1%	—	—	—

2019 Year-End Financials

Return on assets: 2.1%   Cash ($ mil.): 432
Return on equity: —
Current ratio: 2.70

CITY OF PORTLAND

A rose by any other name would smell as sweet may be only way to tell this city from 18 other Portlands in the US. Portland has been known as the City of Roses since 1888 and has hosted an annual rose festival since 1905.

EXECUTIVES

Mayor, Ted Wheeler
City Commissioner*, Steve Novick
Commissioner*, Nick Fish
Commissioner*, Amanda Fritz
Commissioner*, Dan Saltzman
Chief of Staff*, Tera Pierce

Deputy Chief of Staff*, Diana Nunez
Attorney, Jeffrey L Rogers
Coordinator, David Galat
Manager, Alisa Kane
Coordinator, Beth Baisch
Auditors: MOSS ADAMS PORTLAND OREGON

LOCATIONS

HQ: CITY OF PORTLAND
1221 SW 4TH AVE RM 340, PORTLAND, OR
972041900
Phone: 503 823-4120
Web: WWW.PROSPERPORTLAND.US

HISTORICAL FINANCIALS

Company Type: Private

Income Statement				FYE: June 30
	REVENUE ($ mil.)	NET INCOME ($ mil.)	NET PROFIT MARGIN	EMPLOYEES
06/21	1,768	(9)	—	5,684
06/20	1,648	269	16.3%	—
06/19	1,604	138	8.6%	—
06/18	1,483	110	7.5%	—
Annual Growth	6.0%	—	—	—

CITY OF PROVIDENCE

EXECUTIVES

Mayor, Jorge O Elorza
Coordinator, Rita Murphy
Deputy Chief of Staff, Marisa O'Gara
City Council, David Salvatore
Chief of Staff, Emily Martineau
Human Resources Director, Emmanuel Echevarria
City, Jeffrey Padwa
Emergency Director, Kevin Kugel
Court Clerk, Paul Jabour
Detective, Shawn Maxwell
Security Coordinator, Tony Feola
Auditors: MARCUM LLP PROVIDENCE RI

LOCATIONS

HQ: CITY OF PROVIDENCE
25 DORRANCE ST UNIT 1, PROVIDENCE, RI
029031738
Phone: 401 421-7740
Web: WWW.PROVIDENCERI.GOV

HISTORICAL FINANCIALS

Company Type: Private

Income Statement				FYE: June 30
	REVENUE ($ mil.)	NET INCOME ($ mil.)	NET PROFIT MARGIN	EMPLOYEES
06/20	849	(4)	—	2,800
06/19	853	7	0.8%	—
06/18	836	15	1.9%	—
06/17	821	5	0.6%	—
Annual Growth	1.1%	—	—	—

2020 Year-End Financials

Return on assets: (-0.2%)   Cash ($ mil.): 268
Return on equity: —
Current ratio: 2.30

CITY OF RICHMOND

Music legends Joan Baez and Jerry Garcia both sang about seeing Richmond fall but these days Richmond is rising. The city which made its living on tobacco and slave trading early in its history now thrives on business law and the research center at the Virginia Biotechnology Research Park. Richmond is home to several major corporations including CarMax Dominion Resources Genworth Financial and MeadWestvaco. It's also home to more than 200000 people who are governed by a city council representing nine districts along with an at-large mayor. The city follows a council-manager system and the mayor is not part of the council. Richmond which was founded in 1737 has an annual budget of about $1.4 billion.

EXECUTIVES

Mayor, Levar M Stoney
Chief Administrative Officer, Selena Cuffee-Glenn
Vice-President Legal, Ketisha Bullard
Information Specialist, Robert Sturdevant
Coordinator, Christopher Johnston
Senior Policy Adviser For Inno, Jon Baliles
Senior Policy Adviser For Enga, Lisa S Davis
Senior Policy Adviser For Oppo, Thad Williamson
Executive Assistant, Steven Hammond Jr
Coordinator, Anedra Bourne
Sergeant, Gary Borges
Auditors: CLIFTONLARSONALLEN LLP ARLING

LOCATIONS

HQ: CITY OF RICHMOND
900 E BROAD ST STE 201, RICHMOND, VA
232191907
Phone: 804 646-7970
Web: WWW.RVA.GOV

HISTORICAL FINANCIALS

Company Type: Private

Income Statement				FYE: June 30
	REVENUE ($ mil.)	NET INCOME ($ mil.)	NET PROFIT MARGIN	EMPLOYEES
06/20	824	(6)	—	5,315
06/19	800	72	9.0%	—
06/18	757	(41)	·	—
06/17	786	51	6.6%	—
Annual Growth	1.6%	—	—	—

2020 Year-End Financials

Return on assets: (-0.1%)   Cash ($ mil.): 599
Return on equity: (-0.6%)
Current ratio: 2.10

CITY OF ROCHESTER

Known as "The World's Image Center" the City of Rochester situated on the south of Lake Ontario encompasses some 37 sq. mi. The city incorporated in 1703 was one of the first "boomtowns" in the US due to a large number of flour mills. Rochester is now a center of higher education medical and technological research with University of Rochester Rochester Institute of Technology Bausch & Lomb and Kodak calling it home. Xerox still has a large presence in the city. A population of over 200000 makes the city the third largest in the state. The government is a "strong mayor" style with 4 district and 5 at-large council members. Previously known as "The Flower City" it hosts an annual lilac festival.

EXECUTIVES

Mayor, Lovely A Warren
Sergeant, Michael Lesniak
Director of Financial Audits, Jacqueline Farabell
Architectural Drafting Technic, Luigi Ianniello
Purchasing, Ella Harbison
Asar Release Administrators, John Rowe
Commander, Fabian Rivera
Recreation Leader, Maria Suarez
Director, Preston Sanders
Office Manager, Suzanne McSain
Manager, William Curran
Auditors: FREED MAXICK CPA PC ROCHESTE

LOCATIONS

HQ: CITY OF ROCHESTER
30 CHURCH ST, ROCHESTER, NY 146141206
Phone: 585 428-6755
Web: WWW.CITYOFROCHESTER.GOV

HISTORICAL FINANCIALS

Company Type: Private

Income Statement				FYE: June 30
	REVENUE ($ mil.)	NET INCOME ($ mil.)	NET PROFIT MARGIN	EMPLOYEES
06/20	559	(44)	—	3,200
06/19	577	(3)	—	—
06/18	584	17	2.9%	—
06/17	581	(19)	—	—
Annual Growth	(1.3%)	—	—	—

2020 Year-End Financials

Return on assets: (-1.4%)   Cash ($ mil.): 335
Return on equity: —
Current ratio: —

CITY OF SACRAMENTO

With its Mediterranean climate and location at the foot of the Sierra Nevadas living in the city of Sacramento is no sacrifice. Founded in 1849 Sacramento is the oldest incorporated city in the state and its seventh most populated comprising about 470000 residents. California's capital city uses a council-manager form of government with council members from eight districts elected to four-year terms. The council sets up city policies approves contracts and a budget of nearly $800 million as well as hears appeals of city decisions. The four council-appointed officers that carry out the city's business are the city manager attorney treasurer and clerk. A Legislative Affairs Unit supports the council.

EXECUTIVES

Mayor, Darrell Steinberg
Chief Innovation Officer*, Louis Stewart
Customer Staff, Thompson Raquel
Assistant City Manager For Pub, Chris Conlin
Typist Clerk, Cynthia Laurenzi
Chief of Staff, Dennis Rogers
City Manager, Howard Chan
Director, Khaalid Muttaqi
Account Manager, Leslie Wisniewski

Community Center Director, Monica Blanco
Riverfront Project Manager, Richard Rich
Auditors: VAVRINEK TRINE DAY & CO LL

LOCATIONS

HQ: CITY OF SACRAMENTO
915 I ST FL 5, SACRAMENTO, CA 958142622
Phone: 916 808-5300
Web: WWW.CITYOFSACRAMENTO.ORG

HISTORICAL FINANCIALS
Company Type: Private

Income Statement   FYE: June 30

	REVENUE ($ mil.)	NET INCOME ($ mil.)	NET PROFIT MARGIN	EMPLOYEES
06/19	838	86	10.3%	4,500
06/18	723	2	0.3%	—
06/17	694	46	6.7%	—
06/16	709	91	12.9%	—
Annual Growth	5.7%	(1.9%)	—	—

CITY OF SAN ANTONIO

When you "Remember the Alamo" don't forget San Antonio! The second-largest Texas city (behind Houston) with a population of about 1.5 million San Antonio was the site of the Battle of the Alamo. Today it's home to major tourist attractions like the River Walk SeaWorld and Six Flags Fiesta Texas as well as the San Antonio Spurs NBA franchise and more than 50 golf courses. It has a huge military presence with three major Army and Air Force bases. San Antonio is run by a mayor and 10 district representatives who pass laws and establish policies for the city. Its city manager oversees day-to-day operations including nearly 40 departments. San Antonio has an annual budget of more than $2 billion.

EXECUTIVES

Mayor, Ron Nirenberg
City Mgr*, Sheryl Sculley
Senior Customer Rep, Michael Arriaga
Coordinator, Angelica Mata
Coordinator, Arthur Pena
Coordinator, Grace Solis
Mayor, Ivy R Taylor
Real Estate Conultant, Marcia Orlandi
Real Estate Conultant, Steven Hodges
Police Officer, Michael Johnson
Education Coordinator, Susan Campbell
Auditors: GRANT THORNTON LLP HOUSTON T

LOCATIONS

HQ: CITY OF SAN ANTONIO
100 W HOUSTON ST STE 1800, SAN ANTONIO, TX 782051404
Phone: 210 207-6000
Web: WWW.SANANTONIO.GOV

HISTORICAL FINANCIALS
Company Type: Private

Income Statement   FYE: September 30

	REVENUE ($ mil.)	NET INCOME ($ mil.)	NET PROFIT MARGIN	EMPLOYEES
09/20	2,167	(15)	—	12,000
09/19	2,150	192	9.0%	—
09/18	2,056	284	13.8%	—
09/16	0	0	—	—
Annual Growth	—	—	—	—

2020 Year-End Financials
Return on assets: (-0.1%)   Cash ($ mil.): 591
Return on equity: (-0.2%)
Current ratio: 3.30

CITY OF SAN DIEGO

The City of San Diego offers more than just warm weather and beautiful beaches. The second-largest city in California (with a population of more than 1.3 million) known as Telecom Valley is also one of the centers in the US for technological manufacturing. Its council members each represent one of its nine districts. Founded in 1769 San Diego is the home to 3 universities as well as professional sports teams Padres of MLB and Chargers of the NFL. The city operates through some 50 programs and departments including environmental services homeland security parks and recreation and the commission for arts and culture. The City of San Diego has an annual budget of approximately $3 billion.

EXECUTIVES

Mayor, Todd Gloria
City Mgr*, Michael Uberuaga
Information Specialist, Carl Marquez
Physician, Michael Ott
Purchasing Agent, Ray Falcon
Program Manager, David Steinmetz
Revenue Audit Manager, Douglas Enger
Associate Engineer Traffic, Esmerelda White
Accountant III, Norman Reyes
Associate Civil Engineer, Paul Jacob
Assistant Engineer Civil, Tamara Miller
Auditors: MACIAS GINI & O'CONNELL LLP S

LOCATIONS

HQ: CITY OF SAN DIEGO
202 C ST, SAN DIEGO, CA 921013860
Phone: 619 236-6330
Web: WWW.SANDIEGO.GOV

HISTORICAL FINANCIALS
Company Type: Private

Income Statement   FYE: June 30

	REVENUE ($ mil.)	NET INCOME ($ mil.)	NET PROFIT MARGIN	EMPLOYEES
06/20	2,237	(103)	—	11,200
06/19	2,283	62	2.7%	—
06/18	2,021	(82)	—	—
06/16	1,978	263	13.3%	—
Annual Growth	3.1%	—	—	—

CITY OF SAN JOSE

Do you know the way to San Jos ©? If so you're probably a high tech worker and hopefully one with a salary to match its real estate prices. The city is known for its Silicon Valley location and technology-driven economy. More than 500 tech firms are the major employers in the area which is also known for its premium home prices (median $495000). San Jos © was founded in 1777 and incorporates some 180 square miles. 950000 residents make San Jos © the third largest city in the state. The city government uses the council/manager model wherein the council made up of the mayor (elected at large) and the 10 council members (one from each district) sets policy and the council-appointed city manager carries it out.

EXECUTIVES

Mayor, Sam Liccardo
Fin Dir*, Scott P Johnson
City Clerk*, Patricia O'Hearn
Deputy City Mgr, Norberto Due As
Asst Dir, David Sykes
I T Manager, Arturo Cervantes
Management, Anita M Flores
Investment Officer, Christina Wang
Associate Landscape, Yoshifumi Yano
Senior Analyst, Amy Morton
Associate Environmental Servic, Ariel Carpenter
Auditors: MACIAS GINI & O'CONNELL LLP W

LOCATIONS

HQ: CITY OF SAN JOSE
200 E SANTA CLARA ST 13TH, SAN JOSE, CA 951131905
Phone: 408 535-3500
Web: WWW.SANJOSECA.GOV

HISTORICAL FINANCIALS
Company Type: Private

Income Statement   FYE: June 30

	REVENUE ($ mil.)	NET INCOME ($ mil.)	NET PROFIT MARGIN	EMPLOYEES
06/20	1,868	309	16.6%	7,500
06/19	1,731	134	7.8%	—
06/18	1,629	9	0.6%	—
06/17	1,526	48	3.1%	—
Annual Growth	7.0%	86.2%	—	—

CITY OF SPRINGFIELD

EXECUTIVES

Mayor, Domenic J Sarno
Treasurer*, Ehsanul Bhuiya
Tresauer*, Stephen Lonergan
Coordinator, Judy Dziobek
Coordinator, Ramon Planas
Small Business Pro, Shayvonne Plummer
Director of Member, Teresa D'Agostino
Financial Analyst, Christina Rooney
Clerk and Typist, Christine Barnes
Account Clerk, Diane Jendrysik
Computer Programmer Analyst, Dianne Woods
Auditors: POWERS & SULLIVAN LLC WAKEFI

LOCATIONS

HQ: CITY OF SPRINGFIELD
36 COURT ST, SPRINGFIELD, MA 011031687
Phone: 413 736-3111
Web: WWW.SPRINGFIELD-MA.GOV

HISTORICAL FINANCIALS

Company Type: Private

Income Statement   FYE: June 30

	REVENUE ($ mil.)	NET INCOME ($ mil.)	NET PROFIT MARGIN	EMPLOYEES
06/17	813	40	5.0%	6,107
06/14	765	(10)	—	—
06/13	751	(19)	—	—
06/12	0	0	—	—
Annual Growth	—	—	—	—

2017 Year-End Financials

Return on assets: 3.6%   Cash ($ mil.): 207
Return on equity: —
Current ratio: 2.50

CITY OF ST. LOUIS

The Gateway to the West is bordered by the Mississippi River on the east and occupies approximately 62 square miles with a population of more than 300000. The government of the City of St. Louis is comprised of the city's mayor and a Board of Aldermen (made up of 28 elected members in addition to the board president). Unlike most city governments the mayor shares executive authority with other independent citywide elected officials such as the treasurer and comptroller. During the 21st century St. Louis has transitioned from a manufacturing and industrial economy to one heavily dependent on medicine biotechnology and other sciences. It is home to MLB's St. Louis Cardinals and NFL's St. Louis Rams.

EXECUTIVES

Mayor, Lyda Krewson
Chief of Staff, Tim O'Connell
Security Staff, Charles Pratt
Senior Policy Adviser, Nicole Hudson
City Counselor, Julian Bsh
Register, Dionne Flowers
Comptroller, Darlene Green
Coordinator, Erin Thiemann
Customer Representativ, Lisa Burton
Information Manager, Fred Zeller
Circuit Manager, Donald Williams
Auditors: KPMG LLP ST LOUIS MO

LOCATIONS

HQ: CITY OF ST. LOUIS
1200 MARKET ST RM 212, SAINT LOUIS, MO 631032805
Phone: 314 622-3201
Web: WWW.STLOUIS-MO.GOV

HISTORICAL FINANCIALS

Company Type: Private

Income Statement   FYE: June 30

	REVENUE ($ mil.)	NET INCOME ($ mil.)	NET PROFIT MARGIN	EMPLOYEES
06/20	863	8	1.0%	4,500
06/19	870	111	12.8%	—
06/18	848	50	5.9%	—
06/17	796	14	1.8%	—
Annual Growth	2.7%	(14.9%)	—	—

2020 Year-End Financials

Return on assets: 0.2%   Cash ($ mil.): 270
Return on equity: 1.7%
Current ratio: —

CITY OF STAMFORD

EXECUTIVES

Mayor, David Martin
Sergeant, Diedrich Hohn
Project Coordinator, Laura Labosky
Coordinator, Sharon Wade
Risk Manager, Ann Mones
Gis Coordinator, Cindy Barber
Assistant Corporation Counsel, Burt Rosenberg
Associate Planner, Erin McKenna
Desk Top Technician, Esther Librandi
Clerk, Jeannie Laughlin
Police Sergeant, Jennifer Pinto
Auditors: BLUM SHAPIRO & COMPANY PC W

LOCATIONS

HQ: CITY OF STAMFORD
888 WASHINGTON BLVD, STAMFORD, CT 069012924
Phone: 203 977-4150
Web: WWW.CI.STAMFORD.CT.US

HISTORICAL FINANCIALS

Company Type: Private

Income Statement   FYE: June 30

	REVENUE ($ mil.)	NET INCOME ($ mil.)	NET PROFIT MARGIN	EMPLOYEES
06/18	709	(6)	—	2,878
06/17	678	5	0.8%	—
06/16	648	29	4.5%	—
06/15	627	19	3.0%	—
Annual Growth	4.2%	—	—	—

2018 Year-End Financials

Return on assets: (-0.5%)   Cash ($ mil.): 67
Return on equity: (-3.9%)
Current ratio: —

CITY OF SYRACUSE

Syracuse New York is located in the center of the state but it is a world apart from the " Big Apple". Named after the Sicilian city of Syracuse the city owes much of its growth and history to two things— salt and the Erie Canal. Although neither is as important as it once was to the city Syracuse is still a regional transportation hub and the city has managed to weather the economic trends supplanting a salt-centric economy with industrial manufacturing before evolving to a service industry centered economy. The city has a population of about 150000 and is governed by its mayor and a ten-person Common Council.

EXECUTIVES

Mayor, Stephanie Miner
Information Manager, Randy Scott
Project Records Manager, Emma Patterson
Director, Janet Burke
City Manager, William Ryan
Assistant To Deputy Commission, Debbie Ramsey-Burns
Executive Assistant To May, Elizabeth Dejoseph
Sustainability Coordinator, Rebecca Klossner
Chief Data Officer, Sam Edelstein
District Chief, Steve McLaughlin
Communications, Dee Klees
Auditors: BONADIO & CO LLP SYRACUSE

LOCATIONS

HQ: CITY OF SYRACUSE
233 E WSHNGTN ST STE 231, SYRACUSE, NY 132021423
Phone: 315 448-8005
Web: WWW.SYRGOV.NET

HISTORICAL FINANCIALS

Company Type: Private

Income Statement   FYE: June 30

	REVENUE ($ mil.)	NET INCOME ($ mil.)	NET PROFIT MARGIN	EMPLOYEES
06/20	779	21	2.7%	6,456
06/19	775	16	2.1%	—
06/18	758	122	16.2%	—
06/17	741	6	0.8%	—
Annual Growth	1.7%	51.2%	—	—

2020 Year-End Financials

Return on assets: 1.1%   Cash ($ mil.): 172
Return on equity: —
Current ratio: —

CITY OF TAMPA

Disregarded by its first owners the Spanish in 1517 and the British in 1763 Tampa is now a thriving city on the Gulf Coast of Florida. It joins Clearwater and St. Petersburg in forming the Tampa Bay Area. The city uses a mayor-council form of government with seven council members one from each of four districts and three at-large. The mayor and council members are elected to four year terms. They set policy and the chief of staff carries it out by running the day-to-day operations of the city. In addition to tourism and the port of Tampa major area industry includes agriculture construction health care and military operations. Tampa which has a population of about 350000 was incorporated in 1855.

EXECUTIVES

Mayor, Jane Castor
Procurement Staff, Celeste Gibbons-Peoples
Project, Kevin Henika
Senior Programmer Analyst, Karen Romo
Wastewater Department Operatio, Ocea Lattimore
Captain, Mike Stout

Teacher, Lloyd Zweben
Human Resources Executive, Carrie Ortolano
Assistant City, Ursula Richardson
City Bicycle, Calvin Thornton
Senior Network Analyst, Carl Martin
Auditors: RSM US LLP TAMPA FLORIDA

LOCATIONS

HQ: CITY OF TAMPA
306 E JACKSON ST, TAMPA, FL 336025223
Phone: 813 274-8211
Web: WWW.TAMPA.GOV

HISTORICAL FINANCIALS

Company Type: Private

Income Statement				FYE: September 30
	REVENUE ($ mil.)	NET INCOME ($ mil.)	NET PROFIT MARGIN	EMPLOYEES
09/20	652	43	6.7%	4,500
09/19	610	33	5.5%	—
09/18	558	64	11.5%	—
09/17	491	(8)	—	—
Annual Growth	9.9%	—	—	—

CITY OF TUCSON

There's no such thing as too much sun in Tucson. The City of Tucson Arizona enjoys 360 sunny days a year is divided into six wards each represented by a council member. Together with the mayor the members form the Tucson City Council which sets city policies; a city manager leads all departments in implementing these policies. Tucson has about half a million residents and a culture that blends Native American and Mexican influences. It's home to The University of Arizona Davis-Monthan Air Force Base and The National Optical Astronomy Observatories. The Arizona Diamondbacks are based in Tucson and the Chicago White Sox hold spring training here. The city has an annual budget of greater than $2 billion.

EXECUTIVES

Mayor, Jonathan Rothschild
Executive Officer, Carl Dresher
Coordinator, Bruce Plenk
Sergeant, Dominic Flores
Sergeant, Gary Downard
Sergeant, Jack Woolridge
Sergeant, Jim Schneden
Coordinator, Joe Loranger
Staff, Lucy Bravo
Sergeant, Mandy Abrams
Sergeant, Marc Weiler
Auditors: CLIFTON LARSON ALLEN LLP TUCS

LOCATIONS

HQ: CITY OF TUCSON
255 W ALAMEDA ST, TUCSON, AZ 857011362
Phone: 520 791-4561
Web: WWW.TUCSONAZ.GOV

HISTORICAL FINANCIALS

Company Type: Private

Income Statement				FYE: June 30
	REVENUE ($ mil.)	NET INCOME ($ mil.)	NET PROFIT MARGIN	EMPLOYEES
06/19	903	58	6.4%	5,900
06/16	763	19	2.5%	—
06/15	723	(16)	—	—
06/14	728	31	4.4%	—
Annual Growth	4.4%	12.8%	—	—

2019 Year-End Financials

Return on assets: 1.2%   Cash ($ mil.): 392
Return on equity: 3.2%
Current ratio: 2.40

CITY OF VIRGINIA BEACH

Whether you're looking for seaside peace and seclusion or bustling boardwalk adventure Virginia Beach is the spot. With nearly 40 miles of Chesapeake Bay and Atlantic Ocean coastline the city's economy thrives largely on travel and tourism and supports a population of more than 435000 people. Virginia Beach's city council consists of 11 elected members (including its mayor) and is responsible for legislative duties including levying taxes adopting an annual budget and appointing a city manager. The city manager carries out executive and administrative tasks in this city's Council-Manager government.

EXECUTIVES

Mayor, Robert M Dyer
City Manager*, David L Hansen
Law, Kalfus Nachman
Real Estate Conultant, Charlie Mills
Coordinator, Christina Uperti
Prin, Allison Bouillon
Prin, Amanda Bryan
Prin, Amanda Kidder
Prin, Angel Fogle
Public Safety Portfolio Projec, Anthony Fox
Prin, Brandi Ohmer
Auditors: CLIFTONLARSONALLEN LLP ARLING

LOCATIONS

HQ: CITY OF VIRGINIA BEACH
2401 COURTHOUSE DR 13R, VIRGINIA BEACH, VA 234569120
Phone: 757 385-3111
Web: WWW.MALIBUES.VBSCHOOLS.COM

HISTORICAL FINANCIALS

Company Type: Private

Income Statement				FYE: June 30
	REVENUE ($ mil.)	NET INCOME ($ mil.)	NET PROFIT MARGIN	EMPLOYEES
06/21	1,463	(12)	—	7,500
06/20	1,412	156	11.1%	—
06/19	1,379	(70)	—	—
06/18	1,356	61	4.5%	—
Annual Growth	2.6%	—	—	—

CITY OF WATERBURY

EXECUTIVES

Mayor, Neil M O'Leary
Executive Secretary, Laina Dibona
Payroll Staff, Alyce Cass
Information Specialist, Andrea Nixon
Project Coordinator, Samuel Bowens
and Board of Alderma, Joe Begnal
Hris Analyst, Laura Webb-Beers
Alderman, Sandra Martinez-Mccart
Staff, Angela Juliani
Maintenance Manager, Art Daigle
Executive Director, Bill Quinn
Auditors: BLUM SHAPIRO & COMPANY PC

LOCATIONS

HQ: CITY OF WATERBURY
235 GRAND ST, WATERBURY, CT 067021915
Phone: 203 574-6712
Web: WWW.WATERBURYCT.ORG

HISTORICAL FINANCIALS

Company Type: Private

Income Statement				FYE: June 30
	REVENUE ($ mil.)	NET INCOME ($ mil.)	NET PROFIT MARGIN	EMPLOYEES
06/17	558	(16)	—	3,200
06/16	536	22	4.1%	—
06/15	530	(20)	—	—
06/08	505	(15)	—	—
Annual Growth	1.1%	—	—	—

2017 Year-End Financials

Return on assets: (-1.7%)   Cash ($ mil.): 25
Return on equity: —
Current ratio: 3.90

CITY OF WORCESTER

EXECUTIVES

Mayor, Joseph M Petty
City Mgr*, Edward Augustus Jr
Asst Treas*, Kathy Johnson
Coordinator, Sharon Arnold
Coordinator, Nancy E Moses
Mayor, Joseph Petty
Mayor, Konstantina Lukes
Assistant City Clerk, Aj Pottle
Youth Opportunities Coordinato, Raquel Castro-Corazzin
Senior Crime Analyst, Annemarie Bagley
Civil Engineer, Andre Louzado
Auditors: CLIFTONLARSONALLEN LLP BOSTON

LOCATIONS

HQ: CITY OF WORCESTER
455 MAIN ST RM 112, WORCESTER, MA 016081805
Phone: 508 799-1049

Income Statement				FYE: June 30
	REVENUE ($ mil.)	NET INCOME ($ mil.)	NET PROFIT MARGIN	EMPLOYEES
06/13	726	9	1.3%	5,637
06/12	703	(15)		—
06/11	720	21	3.0%	—
Annual Growth	0.4%	(33.2%)	—	—

2013 Year-End Financials

Return on assets: 0.7%   Cash ($ mil.): 145
Return on equity: 4.0%
Current ratio: —

CITY PUBLIC SERVICES OF SAN ANTONIO

CPS Energy (formerly City Public Service of San Antonio) is owned by the City of San Antonio. It is the largest municipally-owned gas and electric utility in the US. About 15% of its gross revenues support over one-fourth of the general operating budget of San Antonio's municipal government providing financial resources for the delivery of basic services such as streets and infrastructure public safety parks and youth programs and libraries. It serves about 840750 electricity customers and some 352585 natural gas customers in the greater San Antonio Texas area.

Operations
CPS Energy's plant-in-service includes four power stations that are solely owned and operated by the company. In total there are more than 15 generating units at these four power stations two of which are coal-fired and 15 of which are gas-fired. CPS Energy also has two solar generating units one which also includes battery storage.

Nearly 95% of sales were generated from electric sales while gas and nonoperating sales account for the rest.

Geographic Reach
CPS Energy serves customers in the greater San Antonio Texas area where it is headquartered including Bexar County.

Sales and Marketing
Throughout its service territory CPS Energy provides electric and natural gas services for residential and commercial customers. It serves more than 840750 electric customers and 352585 natural gas customers.

Financial Performance
Representing 99% of total revenues and nonoperating income electric and gas revenues of $2.5 billion decreased by $59.4 million or 2% compared to FY2020.

In 2021 the company had a net income of $12.4 million which was $149.2 million lower than last year's net income of $161.6 million a decrease of 92% primarily due to lower retail revenues as a result of greater bad debt attributable to the impact of COVID-19 and lower wholesale revenues from fewer market opportunities as well as lower nonoperating income due to the impact from the lower interest rate environment in the current year.

The company's cash at the end of FY2021 was $538.4 million. Operating activities generated $1 billion while financing activities used $661.3 million mainly for cash paid for additions to utility plant and net removal costs. Investing activities provided another $118.1 million.

Strategy
In support of CPS Energy's commitment to provide world-class energy solutions to meet the diverse and unique needs of its customers CPS Energy is now focused on its Flexible PathSM Strategy. The Flexible Path is the company's strategic approach to prudently leverage its existing community-owned generation assets to bridge to a future that enables more low and non-emitting resources such as wind solar energy storage and new technology. CPS Energy will use its Guiding Pillars of Reliability Customer Affordability Security Safety Environmental Responsibility and Resiliency as key priorities to drive this strategy. These Guiding Pillars are all grounded in financial responsibility.

CPS Energy's goals include integrating new and emerging technologies like battery storage and electric vehicles renewable energy resources and adding more programs and services like energy efficiency and demand response. Strategic and operational flexibility will allow the company to remain successful with a diverse generation portfolio that focuses on the environment as well as traditional generation assets that continue to be an important bridge to the future while ensuring value and reliability to customers. This Flexible Path strategy ultimately positions CPS Energy to embrace the changing utility landscape while serving its customers.

Company Background
A venerable company CPS Energy traces its roots to the 1860s when its predecessor opened a manufactured gas plant on Houston Street.

EXECUTIVES

Pres-Ceo, Paula Gold-Williams
Cfo-Treas*, Delores Lenzy-Jones
Coo*, Dr Cris Eugster
Chief Admin & Bus Dev Offc*, Frank Almaraz
Chief Customer Engagement Offc*, Felicia Etheridge
Chief Security Safety & Gas So*, Fred Bonewell
CIO*, Vivan Bouet
Int Chief Legal & Ethics Offic*, Shanna Ramirez
Program Manager, Shon Essman
Coordinator, Sylvia Garza
Staff, Phillip Scheel
Auditors: GARZA PREIS & CO LLC/BAKER

LOCATIONS

HQ: CITY PUBLIC SERVICES OF SAN ANTONIO
500 MCCULLOUGH AVE, SAN ANTONIO, TX
782152104
Phone: 210 353-2222
Web: WWW.CPSENERGY.COM

PRODUCTS/OPERATIONS

2015 Sales

	$ mil.	% of total
Electric	2,320	92
Gas	175	7
Other	36	1
Total	**2,531**	**100**

COMPETITORS

Aep	Nextera Energy
Aes	Oneok
Duke Energy	

Income Statement				FYE: January 31
	REVENUE ($ mil.)	NET INCOME ($ mil.)	NET PROFIT MARGIN	EMPLOYEES
01/12	2,258	21	0.9%	3,100
01/11	2,068	78	3.8%	—
01/10	1,930	107	5.6%	—
Annual Growth	8.1%	(55.5%)	—	—

2012 Year-End Financials

Return on assets: 0.2%   Cash ($ mil.): 148
Return on equity: 0.6%
Current ratio: 1.30

CITYSERVICEVALCON, LLC

You don't have to live in the city to get the services of CityServiceValcon which markets and distributes petroleum products throughout the Inland Northwest and Rocky Mountain regions of the US as well as in the adjacent Plains states. Its products include gasoline diesel aviation fuels lubricants propane and heating oil. The company has diesel gasoline and heating oils for delivery through its network of bulk plants. CityServiceValcon also operates cardlock fueling facilities under the Pacific Pride brand name. Regional independent petroleum marketers City Service and Valcon merged their operations in 2003 to form CityServiceValcon.

EXECUTIVES

Ng MBR, Dallas Herron
Mng MBR*, Clifford F Kunnary
Mng MBR*, Lary P Johnson
Prin*, Benjamen M Binger
Prin*, James M Binger
Marketing Sales Manager, Bonnie Grande
Administrator, Eric Wyman
Sales, Bethany R
Marketing Sales, Drew Pike
Vice President Finance, Kurt Tonjum
Employee, Scott Effinger

LOCATIONS

HQ: CITYSERVICEVALCON, LLC
640 W MONTANA ST, KALISPELL, MT 599013834
Phone: 406 755-4321
Web: WWW.CITYSERVICEVALCON.COM

COMPETITORS

Farstad Oil	Spf Energy
Redwood Coast Petroleum	Wilson Oil

HISTORICAL FINANCIALS
Company Type: Private

Income Statement				FYE: September 30
	REVENUE ($ mil.)	NET INCOME ($ mil.)	NET PROFIT MARGIN	EMPLOYEES
09/08	625	4	0.6%	150
09/07	490	3	0.6%	—
09/06	459	4	1.0%	—
Annual Growth	16.6%	(8.0%)	—	—

2008 Year-End Financials

Return on assets: 9.3% Cash ($ mil.): 1
Return on equity: 19.2%
Current ratio: 1.30

CLARCOR INC.

CLARCOR cleans up with filters. The company's industrial and environmental filtration unit makes air and antimicrobial filters for commercial industrial and residential buildings along with filters used in industrial processes. Brands include Airguard Facet ATI Transweb UAS Keddeg MKI TF-Sand Purolator. Companies in CLARCOR's engine and mobile filtration business make products under brands such as Baldwin Hastings Filters and Clark that filter the air oil fuel coolant and hydraulic fluids. In 2017 in order to expand its filtration portfolio Parker-Hannifin acquired CLARCOR for about $4.3 billion.

Operations

CLARCOR operates in two industry segments: Engine/Mobile Filtration and Industrial/Environmental Filtration.

The Engine/Mobile Filtration segment (about 60% of total revenue) makes and sells filtration products for engines used in stationary power generation and for engines in mobile equipment applications including trucks automobiles buses and locomotives and marine construction industrial mining and agricultural equipment. The company manufactures and sells both 'First-fit' filtration systems and replacement products such as oil air fuel coolant transmission and hydraulic filters.

The company's Industrial/Environmental Filtration segment (about 40%) centers around the manufacturing and marketing of filtration products used in industrial and commercial processes and in buildings and infrastructures of various types. Its liquid process filtration products include specialty industrial process liquid filters; filters for pharmaceutical processes and beverages; and filtration systems and filters for the oil and natural gas industry sewage treatment and water recycling and other industrial uses.

Its air filtration products represent air filters and systems including advanced medias and treatments and high efficiency first-fit systems used in gas turbine power generation systems heavy industrial manufacturing processes thermal power plants commercial buildings hospitals general factories residential buildings paint spray booths medical devices and facilities motor vehicle systems aircraft cabins clean rooms compressors and compressor stations.

Geographic Reach

CLARCOR makes and sells its products worldwide and more than 30% of the company's sales come from outside the US. The company has manufacturing distribution and service facilities in US Brazil China France Germany India Italy Malaysia Netherlands the UAE the UK Japan and Mexico.

Sales and Marketing

The company's filtration products are sold through independent distributors and dealers for OEMs as well as directly to end users.

The 10 largest customers of the Engine/Mobile Filtration segment accounted for 35% of 2016 fiscal year (November year end) segment sales.

The 10 largest customers of the Industrial/Environmental Filtration segment accounted for more than 15% of that segment's revenue.

Financial Performance

In fiscal 2016 CLARCOR's revenue declined by 6% ($91 million) due to a number of factors in-

cluding the 2015 divestiture of J.L. Clark (the former Packaging Segment) which accounted for $40.9 million; decreased net sales volume (due to lower industrial demand) of $26.3 million in the Industrial/Environmental Filtration segment; and $25.1 from a negative currency exchange rate impact due to the strong dollar.

CLARCOR's net income grew by 3.4% to $139.3 million primarily due to Other net income of $20.7 million (flat in 2015) which primarily reflected $27.3 million from 3M to settle a patent litigation case.

Net cash provided by operating activities increased by $131.7 million in 2016 to $285.4 million. Some $18.1 million of this increase came from the 3M patent litigation award and the remainder primarily from cost cutting activities including lowering inventory levels by $36.4 million (resulting in a $58.5 million improvement in cash from operations). The company also reported a $26 million impact from lower cash taxes paid driven by the timing of tax payments in 2016 and 2015.

Strategy

Following the closing of its acquisition by Parker Hannifin in 2017 CLARCOR will be combined with Parker's Filtration Group to form a diverse global filtration business.

Restructuring to focus on two core business lines in 2015 CLARCOR sold its J.L. Clark business (the former Packaging Segment) to CC Industries.

Mergers and Acquisitions

In addition to organic growth CLARCOR has pursued a strategy of expanding its portfolio through acquisitions.

To support its global growth and innovation activities in 2016 the company acquired certain assets of US-based FibeRio Technology (a technology company focused on the research development and commercialization of performance fabric and filtration media) for $11.9 million. That year its CLARCOR Industrial Air division acquired TDC Filter Manufacturing a top US manufacturer and supplier of pleated filter bags dust collection cartridges and gas turbine air filters for $11 million.

In 2014 the company acquired Stanadyne's diesel fuel filtration business for $327.7 million and changed its name to CLARCOR Engine Mobile Solutions. That year it also bought Filter Resources Inc. Filtration Inc. and Fabrication Specialties Inc. for $21.9 million.

Company Background

In 2013 CLARCOR purchased the air filtration business of General Electric's power and water division for $260.3 million.

In 2013 CLARCOR announced plans to invest $40 million for subsidiary Baldwin Filters Inc. to build a new 400000 sq. ft. warehouse and distribution center adjacent to Baldwin's manufacturing facility in Kearney Nebraska.

In 2012 the company acquired Modular Engineering Pty Ltd. an Australian manufacturer of natural gas filtration products as well as a distributor of aftermarket elements. Modular a longtime supplier to CLARCOR's PECOFacet division became part of the division. PECOFacet is included in the company's Industrial/Environmental Filtration segment. Modular produces skid-mounted equipment for the natural gas industry in the Asia/Pacific region and expands CLARCOR's presence in that region in both manufacturing and aftermarket sales.

In 2011 the company purchased one of its suppliers of filtration media Transweb LLC. New Jersey-based Transweb manufactures and supplies media used in end-market applications including respirators and HVAC filters.

CLARCOR was founded in 1904 and reincorporated in 1969.

Auditors: PRICEWATERHOUSECOOPERS LLP NA

LOCATIONS

HQ: CLARCOR INC.
840 CRESCENT CENTRE DR # 600, FRANKLIN, TN 370674687
Phone: 615 771-3100
Web: WWW.PARKER.COM

Sales 2016

	$ mil.	% of total
United States	944	68
Europe	152	11
Asia	144	10
Other International	148	11
Total	**1,389**	**100**

PRODUCTS/OPERATIONS

sales 2016

	$ mil.	% of total
Industrial/Environmental Filtration	803	58
Engine/Mobile Filtration	586	42
Total	**1,389**	**100**

COMPETITORS

Crown Holdings	Emd Millipore
Cummins	Esco Technologies
Dana	Pall Corporation
Delphi Automotive	Parker-hannifin
Systems	W rth Group
Donaldson Company	

HISTORICAL FINANCIALS

Company Type: Private

Income Statement   FYE: November 30

	REVENUE ($ mil.)	NET INCOME ($ mil.)	NET PROFIT MARGIN	EMPLOYEES
11/16	1,389	139	10.0%	5,773
11/15	1,481	134	9.1%	—
11/14	1,512	144	9.5%	—
11/13	1,130	118	10.5%	—
Annual Growth	7.1%	5.6%	—	—

2016 Year-End Financials

Return on assets: 8.0% Cash ($ mil.): 134
Return on equity: 12.2%
Current ratio: 3.10

CLARK EQUIPMENT COMPANY

EXECUTIVES

Ceo, Jong Min Kim
Vice-President, Joel Honeyman
Utility Vehicle Manage, Brad Claus
Training Manager, Ellie Nickel
Talent Management Specialist, Caren Loebs
Manager, Curt Kasper
Network Administrator, David Landsiedel
Engineer, Gerald Duppong
Vice President, James Flynn
General Accounting, Jasmine Rambousek
Information Technology Coordin, Juan Vargas
Auditors: DELOITTE & TOUCHE LLP MINNEA

LOCATIONS

HQ: CLARK EQUIPMENT COMPANY
250 E BEATON DR, WEST FARGO, ND 580782656
Phone: 701 241-8700
Web: WWW.BOBCAT.COM

HISTORICAL FINANCIALS

Company Type: Private

Income Statement				FYE: December 31
	REVENUE ($ mil.)	NET INCOME ($ mil.)	NET PROFIT MARGIN	EMPLOYEES
12/17	2,543	174	6.9%	5,822
12/16	2,415	166	6.9%	—
12/15	0	0	—	—
12/14	2,539	492	19.4%	—
Annual Growth	0.1%	(29.3%)	—	—

2017 Year-End Financials

Return on assets: 6.1%   Cash ($ mil.): 127
Return on equity: 24.8%
Current ratio: 1.40

CLEVELAND MUNICIPAL SCHOOL DISTRICT

EXECUTIVES

Ceo, Eric Gordon
Coo*, Patrick Zohn
Chb*, Denise W Link
Cfo*, John Scanlan
Exec Dir*, Megan Obryan
Teacher, Paul Wesley
Technology Manager, Andretta Montgomry
Hr Absence Management Expert, Irene Scherzer
Supervisor, Katrina Myers
Teacher, Lena Pogrebinsky
Custodian, Michael Romine
Auditors: KEITH FABER COLUMBUS OH

LOCATIONS

HQ: CLEVELAND MUNICIPAL SCHOOL DISTRICT
1111 SUPERIOR AVE E # 1800, CLEVELAND, OH
441142500
Phone: 216 838-0000
Web: WWW.MC2STEMHIGHSCHOOL.ORG

HISTORICAL FINANCIALS

Company Type: Private

Income Statement				FYE: June 30
	REVENUE ($ mil.)	NET INCOME ($ mil.)	NET PROFIT MARGIN	EMPLOYEES
06/20	896	(35)	—	9,500
06/19	941	(119)	—	—
06/18	957	(49)	—	—
06/17	854	(71)	—	—
Annual Growth	1.6%	—	—	—

2020 Year-End Financials

Return on assets: (-1.9%)   Cash ($ mil.): 203
Return on equity: (-20.9%)
Current ratio: —

CLIFTONLARSONALLEN LLP

CliftonLarsonAllen (CLA) is all about the CPAs. Boasting more than $7.5 billion in client assets under management CLA is on the list of top 10 largest accounting firm that serves privately-owned firms and the firm's principals along with not-for-profits and government agencies. Also serving as a financial advisory and business consultancy CLA is organized as a holding company with three main business segments: wealth advisory outsourcing and audit tax and consulting. It mostly serves clients in the agribusiness financial employee benefit plan healthcare manufacturing and government sectors. With more than 6200 professionals in approximately 120 US locations and a global affiliation the firm's annual revenues was about $955 million.

Operations

The company's service include audit accounting tax consulting outsourcing and wealth advisory. Its investment advisory services are conducted through CliftonLarsonAllen Wealth Advisors LLC.

Other services include cybersecurity and risk management data analytics employee benefits plans M&A advisory and investment banking talent solutions and tax educations for CPAs.

Geographic Reach

Minnesota-based CLA boasts with more than 120 locations across the US.

Sales and Marketing

CLA which counts more than 183450 clients serves privately-held businesses individuals not-for-profits and governmental entities. Its major client groups include agribusiness and cooperatives dealerships employee benefit plans federal government financial institutions healthcare manufacturing and distribution companies as well as state and local governments. CLA serves clients outside the US through its affiliations with Nexia International.

Financial Performance

In 2019 CLA eclipsed the $1 billion revenue milestone. CLA reported approximately $1.2 billion in revenues in 2019 a vast improvement from $954 million the year prior.

Strategy

CLA continues to expand into new geographic markets while bolstering its service offerings and client list. In early 2020 CLA opened a new office in Irvine California. The newest addition to the Southern California region will serve several industries including real estate construction private equity financial institutions and manufacturing and distribution.

CLA also welcomed Seattle CPA firm Watson McDonell in early 2019 expanding CLA's nonprofit and low-income housing industries ? two key industries that it has been focused on and looking to expand throughout Puget Sound.

In addition CLA launched an innovative tracking tool to help health care organizations record COVID-19 economic relief spending. Now organizations can arrange spending in accordance with the compliance and reporting initiatives coming soon.

Company Background

CLA was formed in 2011 by the merger of Clifton Gunderson and LarsonAllen. Prior to the pairing both companies had been active in expanding across the country by purchasing smaller firms and parts of other firms.

EXECUTIVES

Ceo, Jen Leary
Coo, Scott Engelbrecht
Cso, John Richter
Cfo, Heidi Hillman
Cpo, Larry Taylor
Ceo Emeritus, Denny Schleper
Mng Dir, Todd Benson
Senior Marketing Associate, Amanda Jeffers
Senior Accountant, Amanda Sykora
Accountant, Bradley Orth
Tax Manager, Brandt Self

LOCATIONS

HQ: CLIFTONLARSONALLEN LLP
220 S 6TH ST STE 300, MINNEAPOLIS, MN
554021418
Phone: 612 376-4500
Web: WWW.BLOGS.CLACONNECT.COM

Selected Locations
Arizona
California
Colorado
Florida
Idaho
Illinois
Indiana
Iowa
Maryland
Massachusetts
Michigan
Minnesota
Mississippi
Missouri
New Jersey
New Mexico
New York
North Carolina
Ohio
Pennsylvania
Texas
Virginia
Washington
Wisconsin

PRODUCTS/OPERATIONS

Selected Services: Audit and assuranceConsultingCLA Intuition financial modelingEmployee benefit plansExecutive searchForensicInformation securityIntacct softwareLitigation supportRisk managementTechnologyTransaction supportValuationInternationalOutsourci

COMPETITORS

Bdo	Grant Thornton
Bkd Llp	Kpmg L.l.p.
Baker Tilly Virchow Krause	Moore Stephens International
Crowe Horwath	Pricewaterhousecoopers
Deloitte & Touche	Uk
Eide Bailly	Rsm Us
Ernst & Young Llp	Sva

HISTORICAL FINANCIALS

Company Type: Private

Income Statement				FYE: December 4
	REVENUE ($ mil.)	NET INCOME ($ mil.)	NET PROFIT MARGIN	EMPLOYEES
12/15	650	170	26.3%	4,786
12/14	598	163	27.3%	—
12/13	563	154	27.5%	—
Annual Growth	7.5%	5.1%	—	—

2015 Year-End Financials

Return on assets: 68.4%   Cash ($ mil.): 12
Return on equity: 95.9%
Current ratio: 3.50

CLOUD PEAK ENERGY RESOURCES LLC

EXECUTIVES

Ceo, Colin Marshall
Treas*, Oscar Martinez
Exec V Pres*, Michael Barrett
Exec V Pres*, Gary Rivenes
Sr V Pres*, Bruce Jones
Sr V Pres*, Cary W Martin
Executive Assistant, Karen Nelson
Electrical Engineer Asset Mana, Craig Russell
Manager, Project Management, David Hamlin
Account Receivable Accountant, Dominick Villarreal
Accounts Payable Analyst, Leslee Richardson
Auditors: PRICEWATERHOUSECOOPERS LLP DE

LOCATIONS

HQ: CLOUD PEAK ENERGY RESOURCES LLC
  505 S GILLETTE AVE, GILLETTE, WY 827164203
Phone: 303 956-7596
Web: WWW.CLOUDPEAKENERGY.COM

HISTORICAL FINANCIALS
Company Type: Private

Income Statement				FYE: December 31
	REVENUE ($ mil.)	NET INCOME ($ mil.)	NET PROFIT MARGIN	EMPLOYEES
12/13	1,396	58	4.2%	1,200
12/12	1,516	155	10.3%	—
12/11	1,553	201	13.0%	—
12/10	1,370	170	12.4%	—
Annual Growth	0.6%	(29.8%)	—	—

2013 Year-End Financials
Return on assets: 2.5%　　Cash ($ mil.): 231
Return on equity: 5.5%
Current ratio: 1.80

COASTAL CHEMICAL CO., L.L.C.

EXECUTIVES

MBR-Pres, Randy King
Pres*, Jim Doyle
Controller, Bonnie Broussard
Network Administrator, Bryant Angelle
Facility Manager, Dane Hutchings
Territory Manager, Kyle Frese

LOCATIONS

HQ: COASTAL CHEMICAL CO., L.L.C.
  3520 VETERANS MEMORIAL DR, ABBEVILLE, LA 705105708
Phone: 337 898-0001
Web: WWW.COASTALCHEM.COM

HISTORICAL FINANCIALS
Company Type: Private

Income Statement				FYE: December 31
	REVENUE ($ mil.)	NET INCOME ($ mil.)	NET PROFIT MARGIN	EMPLOYEES
12/14	736	33	4.6%	750
12/09	386	10	2.6%	—
12/08	635	16	2.6%	—
Annual Growth	2.5%	12.9%	—	—

2014 Year-End Financials
Return on assets: 10.3%　　Cash ($ mil.): 3
Return on equity: 88.0%
Current ratio: 0.90

COASTAL PACIFIC FOOD DISTRIBUTORS, INC.

Coastal Pacific Food Distributors (CPF) fuels the military forces from facility to fork. The company is one of the top wholesale food distributors that primarily serves the US armed forces across the Western US and in the Far East. As part of its business CPF provides a full line of groceries to military bases run by the US Army Navy Air Force and Marines. It delivers a variety of products from distribution centers located in California Washington and Hawaii. CPF also offers information system programming services for its customers to track sales and shipping as well as procurement and logistics through partnerships in Iraq Kuwait and Saudi Arabia. The company was founded in 1986.

Operations

CPF has grown to become the second-largest worldwide military distributor of food and related products.

As part of its business CPF operates distribution centers in California Washington Hawaii and Canada. In California its largest Stockton facility spans more than 500000 sq. ft. while its Ontario center boasts 429000 sq. ft. Its distribution center in Fife Washington is 153000 sq. ft. A 45000-sq.-ft. facility in Hawaii delivers food to four military commissaries.

Geographic Reach

California-based CPF caters to the Western US as well as Alaska Hawaii Guam Japan Okinawa Korea Singapore Kwajalein Diego Garcia and the Philippines. Its business extends to the Middle East through partnerships for procurement and logistics with other companies. These additional areas include Iraq Kuwait and Saudi Arabia.

Sales and Marketing

Industry partners that keep CPF busy include the Defense Logistics Agency the Defense Commissary Agency Air Force NAF Purchasing Office Navy Exchange (NEXCOM) Army and Air Force Exchange Service (AAFES) and the American Logistics Association to name a few.

The company counts on food manufacturers to keep its customers happy. They include Kraft Foods Tyson Foods Procter & Gamble General Mills Nestle ConAgra Unilever Frito-Lay Campbell J.M. Smucker Global Military Marketing Mars S&K Sales Del Monte Corp. Georgia-Pacific Johnson & Johnson and Alder Foods.

Strategy

The company works to support its existing markets. In 2013 CPF opened a new prime vendor platform in Calamba Luguna Philippines as it looks to serve future growth there. The platform supports Naval ships with dry chill and frozen items.

EXECUTIVES

Eo, Terrence Wood
V Chm, David Jared
SEC, Wayne Duncan
Treas, John Payne
V Pres, Edmond Jared
Oo, Jeff King
Fo, Matthew Payne
Accounts Payable, Allison Crutcher
Manager, Joy Sawyer
Administrator, Donna Baker
Night Operations Manager, George Ashwood
Auditors: DIXON HUGHES GOODMAN LLP NORF

LOCATIONS

HQ: COASTAL PACIFIC FOOD DISTRIBUTORS, INC.
  1015 PERFORMANCE DR, STOCKTON, CA 952064925
Phone: 909 947-2066
Web: WWW.CPFD.COM

PRODUCTS/OPERATIONS

Selected Products
Bakery
Candy
Deli
Fresh & frozen meats
Frozen foods
Pet foods
Refrigerated items
Sushi

Selected Brokers
Acosta Sales & Marketing
Alder Foods Inc.
Bisek & Co. Inc.
Dixon Marketing Inc.
Dunham & Smith Agencies
Elite Brands
Finnegan International Sales
First Wave Sales
Gateway Military LLC
Global Office Building
HI-PAC Ltd
Mid Valley
Overseas Service Corporation
Otis McAllister
Parra Sales Inc
Reese Group
S&K
S. Schwartz Sales Inc.
Turnkey Management
WEBCO General Partnership

COMPETITORS

Advancepierre	Richmond Wholesale
Jtm Provisions	Meat

HISTORICAL FINANCIALS
Company Type: Private

Income Statement				FYE: December 29
	REVENUE ($ mil.)	NET INCOME ($ mil.)	NET PROFIT MARGIN	EMPLOYEES
12/12	1,212	15	1.2%	459
12/11*	1,162	25	2.2%	—
01/11	1,113	17	1.6%	—
Annual Growth	4.4%	(7.6%)	—	—

*Fiscal year change

2012 Year-End Financials
Return on assets: 6.7%　　Cash ($ mil.): 5
Return on equity: 50.6%
Current ratio: 2.60

COBANK, ACB

CoBank is a national cooperative bank serving vital industries across rural of America. The bank provides loans; leases export financing and other financial services to agribusiness and rural power water and communication providers in all 50 estates and a member of Farm Credit System a nationwide network of banks and retail lending associations. The bank farm credit leasing offers flexible leasing options vehicles such as equipment and facilities that can deliver significant benefits to agriculture and utility business. Its core agribusiness customers range from local and single facility grain cooperatives to national global food beverage and agribusiness companies. Formed in 1989 CoBank merged with US AgBank in early 2012.

Operations

CoBank operates three main business segments: Farm Credit Banking Agribusiness and Rural Infrastructure.

Farm Credit banking provides loans and financial services to more than 75 000 farmers ranchers and other rural borrowers in about 25 states. It serves a diverse array of industries from fruits nuts and vegetables to grains and other row crops to dairy beef poultry and forest products.

Agribusiness provides lending to regional and corporate business customers export finance customers and leasing customers. Its serves cooperatives and other customers involve in a wide variety of industries including grain handling and marketing farm supply food processing dairy livestock fruits nuts vegetables cotton biofuels and forest products.

Rural Infrastructure provides lending to rural infrastructure borrowers across in the US and its serves rural utilities and other customers across a wide variety of industries including electric generation transmission and distribution cooperatives midstream energy and gas pipeline providers water and wastewater companies broadband and more.

Geographic Reach

Based in Colorado the bank operates nearly 15 regional offices throughout the US including locations in Iowa Georgia Texas Connecticut Kansas Missouri and Kentucky. It also has an international office in Singapore.

Sales and Marketing

CoBank mainly serves clients in rural America in the agribusiness water communications and power sectors.

Financial Performance

CoBank in 2020 had a net interest income of $1.6 billion a 12% growth from the previous year.

For the full year 2020 net income rose 16% to $1.3 billion up from $1.1 billion in 2019.

EXECUTIVES

Pres-Ceo, Robert B Engel
Pres*, Mary E McBride
Sr V Pres*, James R Bernsten
Cfo*, David P Burlage
Cbo*, Eric Itambo
Executive Vice President, Robert F West
Senior Manager Collateral, James Rogers
Credit Supervisor, Justin Merkowitz
Senior Relationship Manager, Keith Schieler
Senior Credit Officer, Nigel Pretty
Vice President Digital Busines, Noelle Daghe
Auditors: PRICEWATERHOUSECOOPERS LLP
D

LOCATIONS

HQ: COBANK, ACB
6340 S FIDDLERS GREEN CIR, GREENWOOD VILLAGE, CO 801114951
Phone: 303 740-6527
Web: WWW.COBANK.COM

Selected Regional Offices

Ames IA
Atlanta GA
Austin TX
Enfield CT
Fargo ND
Louisville KY
Lubbock TX
Minneapolis MN
Omaha NE
Roseville CA
Spokane WA
St. Louis MO
Washington D.C.
Wichita KS

COMPETITORS

Agfirst	Northwest Farm Credit
Agstar	Rabo Agrifinance
Agribank	Wells Fargo
Bank Of America	
Farm Credit Services Of Mid-america	

HISTORICAL FINANCIALS

Company Type: Private

Income Statement   FYE: December 31

	ASSETS ($ mil.)	NET INCOME ($ mil.)	INCOME AS % OF ASSETS	EMPLOYEES
12/18	139,015	1,190	0.9%	500
12/17	129,210	1,125	0.9%	—
12/16	126	945	749.8%	—
12/15	117,470	936	0.8%	—
Annual Growth	5.8%	8.3%	—	—

2018 Year-End Financials

Return on assets: 0.9%   Sales ($ mil): 4,320
Return on equity: 12.5%

COBB COUNTY BOARD OF EDUCATION

EXECUTIVES

Chair, Randy Scamihorn
Cfo*, Cathy Adams
Staff, Cherry Herron
Staff, Danielle Jesko
Auditors: MAULDIN & JENKINS LLC ATLANT

LOCATIONS

HQ: COBB COUNTY BOARD OF EDUCATION
514 GLOVER ST SE, MARIETTA, GA 300602750
Phone: 770 426-3300
Web: WWW.COBBK12.ORG

HISTORICAL FINANCIALS

Company Type: Private

Income Statement   FYE: June 30

	REVENUE ($ mil.)	NET INCOME ($ mil.)	NET PROFIT MARGIN	EMPLOYEES
06/17	1,299	(13)	—	601
06/16	1,238	(1)	—	
06/15	1,166	(29)	—	
06/14	532	67	12.6%	
Annual Growth	34.7%	—	—	—

2017 Year-End Financials

Return on assets: (-0.6%)   Cash ($ mil.): 247
Return on equity: (-1.6%)
Current ratio: —

COBB COUNTY MEDICAL EXAMINER'S OFFICE

EXECUTIVES

Chb, Tim Lee
Commissioner*, George Woody Thompson Jr
Commissioner*, Joe L Thompson
Commissioner*, Helen Goron
County Mgr*, David Hanerkson
Dir of Fin-Comptroller*, Brad Bowser
Dir*, Tony Hagler
General Manager, Ryan Hardage
Server Administrator, Sonal Siddiqui
Public Services Dir, J Virgil Moon
Coordinator, Daryl Sawyer
Auditors: MOORE & CUBBEDGE LLP MARIETT

LOCATIONS

HQ: COBB COUNTY MEDICAL EXAMINER'S OFFICE
1497 COUNTY SERVICES PKWY, MARIETTA, GA 300084030
Phone: 770 528-3300
Web: WWW.COBBCOUNTY.ORG

HISTORICAL FINANCIALS

Company Type: Private

Income Statement   FYE: September 30

	REVENUE ($ mil.)	NET INCOME ($ mil.)	NET PROFIT MARGIN	EMPLOYEES
09/20	924	68	7.5%	5,000
09/19	834	57	6.9%	
09/18	793	4	0.6%	
09/17	823	11	1.4%	
Annual Growth	3.9%	81.0%	—	—

2020 Year-End Financials

Return on assets: 1.0%   Cash ($ mil.): 132
Return on equity: 1.4%
Current ratio: 3.70

COBB COUNTY PUBLIC SCHOOLS

EXECUTIVES

Principal, Dr Ashley Hosey
Treasurer, An Goh
Assistant Dean For Finance, Anthony Roberts
Region Director, Chris Corzine
Department Coordinator, Denise Reeves
Professor, Jeff Qin
Board Member, Charisse Davis
Auditors: MAULDIN & JENKINS ATLANTA GE

LOCATIONS

HQ: COBB COUNTY PUBLIC SCHOOLS
4575 WADE GREEN RD NW, ACWORTH, GA
301023407
Phone: 678 594-8320
Web: WWW.COBBK12.ORG

HISTORICAL FINANCIALS
Company Type: Private

Income Statement   FYE: June 30

	REVENUE ($ mil.)	NET INCOME ($ mil.)	NET PROFIT MARGIN	EMPLOYEES
06/20	1,503	(21)	—	3,607
06/17	1,299	(13)	—	—
06/16	1,238	(1)	—	—
06/15	1,166	(29)	—	—
Annual Growth	5.2%	—	—	—

2020 Year-End Financials
Return on assets: (-0.8%)   Cash ($ mil.): 458
Return on equity: (-12.1%)
Current ratio: —

COBB COUNTY SCHOOL DISTRICT

EXECUTIVES

Spdt, Chris Ragsdale
Vice President, Jenifer Farmer
Risk Manager, Adolphus Drain
Deputy Superintendent of Leade, Alice Stouder
Attendance Clerk, Cori Pedraza
Math Coach, Diane Rice
Bookkeeper, Donna Graves
Esol Mentoring Specialist, Eddie Bennett
Assessment Secretary, Kris Freshour
Local School Accounting Suppor, Nancy Breu
Graduation Coach, Necole McGhee
Auditors: MAULDIN & JENKINS LLC ATLANT

LOCATIONS

HQ: COBB COUNTY SCHOOL DISTRICT
514 GLOVER ST SE, MARIETTA, GA 300602706
Phone: 770 426-3300
Web: WWW.COBBK12.ORG

HISTORICAL FINANCIALS
Company Type: Private

Income Statement   FYE: June 30

	REVENUE ($ mil.)	NET INCOME ($ mil.)	NET PROFIT MARGIN	EMPLOYEES
06/20	1,503	(21)	—	42
06/19	1,407	24	1.7%	—
06/17	0	0	—	—
06/16	0	(0)	—	—
Annual Growth	1310.5%	—	—	—

2020 Year-End Financials
Return on assets: (-0.8%)   Cash ($ mil.): 458
Return on equity: (-12.1%)
Current ratio: —

COBB ELECTRIC MEMBERSHIP CORPORATION

Cobb Electric Membership Corporation (Cobb EMC) makes sure that Cobb County Georgia residents can cook corn on the cob (and anything else) using either electric power or natural gas. The utility distributes electricity to more than 200000 meters (more than 177000 residential commercial and industrial members) in Cobb County and four other north metro Atlanta counties. Cobb EMC operates about 10000 miles of power lines. The company's Gas South unit markets natural gas to customers who receive their service on Atlanta Gas & Light's natural gas distribution pipelines in Georgia.

Operations

Its Cobb Energy Management provides administrative and labor support to Cobb EMC and offers phone and Internet services to Cobb EMC's customers primarily through subsidiaries. Cobb Energy Management provides call center training tree trimming and billing software services and other ancillary support to EMC's core activities.

Geographic Reach

One of the largest of Georgia's 41 EMCs Cobb EMC's distribution system covers approximately 1434 square miles (Cobb Bartow Cherokee Fulton and Paulding counties in the north metro Atlanta area and Randolph Calhoun Quitman and Clay counties in Southwest Georgia).

Financial Performance

In 2012 the company reported a 46% increase in revenues thanks to a 10% rise in natural gas sales which outpaced a 2% decline in electric revenues. Net income grew by 194% in 2012 as a result of higher net sales and lower operating costs.

Strategy

Cobb EMC is a partner in Power4Georgians a consortium of six Georgia EMCs that collectively is developing a comprehensive strategy to provide reliable and affordable energy to the EMC members.

In 2013 as part of its ongoing transition out of non-energy businesses Cobb EMC announced today plans to cut its workforce by up to 20% percent through a company-wide offer of voluntary separation packages.

In 2012 Smart Energy Capital LLC and Jacoby Development Inc. signed a power purchase deal with Cobb EMC to provide power from the Azalea Solar Facility the largest solar power plant (10MW) in Georgia and one of the largest in the Southeast.

Company Background

The cooperative has been embroiled in litigation in recent years and in 2011 a Cobb County grand jury indicted Cobb EMC Dwight Brown on 31 counts of theft and racketeering. Brown was replaced as CEO by W.T. "Chip" Nelson.

The gas and support companies were merged into EMC as wholly owned units in 2009 as a way to streamline EMC's overall operations. The company has also sold a number of former assets to raise cash including Cooperative Business Ventures in 2009 for $2 million and the health and welfare brokerage business of Cooperative Benefits and Financial Services for a gain of $470000 in 2010.

Formed in 1938 Cobb EMC began life as an electric utility with 489 residential members and 14 commercial customers.

EXECUTIVES

Ceo, W T Chip Nelson III
Cfo*, Robert Steele
V Pres*, Kevan Espy
SEC-Treas*, Cheryl G Meadows
Vp*, Kristen Delaney
Vp*, Tim Harshbarger
Engineer, Nathan Sutton
Associate Vice President, Jim Gantt
Corporate Communications, Angela Croce
Director, Cliff Reisig
Director, Esther Prieto
Auditors: MCNAIR MCLEMORE MIDDLEBROOKS

LOCATIONS

HQ: COBB ELECTRIC MEMBERSHIP CORPORATION
1000 EMC PKWY NE, MARIETTA, GA 300607908
Phone: 770 429-2100
Web: WWW.COBBEMC.COM

HISTORICAL FINANCIALS
Company Type: Private

Income Statement   FYE: December 31

	REVENUE ($ mil.)	NET INCOME ($ mil.)	NET PROFIT MARGIN	EMPLOYEES
12/20*	802	49	6.1%	548
04/18	849	25	3.0%	—
12/13	416	(8)	—	—
04/09	641	3	0.6%	—
Annual Growth	1.9%	24.4%	—	—

*Fiscal year change

2020 Year-End Financials
Return on assets: 3.7%   Cash ($ mil.): 2
Return on equity: 11.1%
Current ratio: 1.00

COBORN'S, INCORPORATED

Coborn's operates more than 120 stores across Midwest of the US under the Coborn's Cash Wise Captain Jack's Marketplace Foods and Hornbacher's. Coborn's operates its own central bakery fuel and convenience division pharmacy division in-house grocery warehouse and distribution center and tops cleaners. Along with its grocery stores the firm owns and operates pharmacies and convenience and liquor stations. The company manages the delivery logistics of hundreds of grocery products for its entire family of stores throughout the upper Midwest. Founded in 1921 Coborn's is a fourth generation business managed by its CEO Chris Coborn.

Operations

As part of its business Coborn's operates under several banner names including Cash Wise Marketplace Foods Hornbacher's and namesake Coborn's. These supermarkets are supported by their own central bakery fuel and convenience division pharmacy division in-house grocery warehouse and distribution center and tops cleaners. The company also runs convenience pharmacy and liquor stores under the brands Coborn's Liquor Cash Wise Liquor and Captain Jack's.

Geographic Reach

Based in Minnesota Coborn's operates two support center offices in North Dakota and Wisconsin.

Sales and Marketing

Coborn's distribution channel includes grocery convenience liquor retail stores and online.

Strategy

In mid-2021 Associated Wholesale Grocers Inc. (AWG) and Coborn's Inc. (Coborn's) announced they have reached an agreement for AWG to serve as the primary wholesale supplier to Coborn's. AWG will commence supply of grocery products to the Coborn's stores in January 2022 from AWG's new Upper Midwest Division in St Cloud Minnesota situated in the former Creative Memories warehouse facility located in St. Cloud's I-94 Business Park at Opportunity Drive and I-94. Fresh and frozen products will temporarily ship from AWG's Nebraska and Great Lakes Divisions.

Later in 2022 AWG will complete a new fresh and frozen warehouse at a location still to be determined. Once completed these warehouses will provide more than 650000 square feet of warehouse space and accommodate the full-line distribution of products to Coborn's and other AWG member stores in the region. Additionally once a site is selected for the new fresh and frozen warehouse and completed AWG plans a future expansion into a single state-of-the-art facility with automated high-tech operations and with up to one million square feet of space based on retail demand. In total AWG expects this project to create over 400 new jobs.

Company Background

Founded in 1921 when Chester Coborn started a single produce market the company opened its first Cash Wise Foods store in 1979 and its first convenience store in 1986.

EXECUTIVES

Ceo, Christopher Coborn
V Pres of Org Dev*, Rebecca Estby
V Pres*, Emily Coborn
V Pres*, Andy Knowblauch
V Pres*, David Meyer
V Pres*, Bruce Miller
V Pres*, Dennis Host
Cfo*, James Shaw
Real Estate Conultant, Christie Schulte
Administrative Assistant, Beth Mineart
Produce Supervisor, Mike Pfannenstein
Auditors: RSM US LLP MINNEAPOLIS MINNE

LOCATIONS

HQ: COBORN'S, INCORPORATED
  1921 COBORN BLVD, SAINT CLOUD, MN 563012100
Phone: 320 252-4222
Web: WWW.COBORNSINC.COM

PRODUCTS/OPERATIONS

Selected Store Formats

Convenience stores (Little Dukes Holiday)
Hardware stores (Ace)
Liquor stores
Pharmacies
Restaurants (Subway)
Supermarkets (Coborn's Cash Wise Foods JK Markets Save-A-Lot)
Video stores

COMPETITORS

7-eleven	Kroger
Aldi	Lunds
Couche-tard	Target Corporation
Cub Foods	Wal-mart
Kowalski's Markets	

HISTORICAL FINANCIALS

Company Type: Private

Income Statement				FYE: December 28
	REVENUE ($ mil.)	NET INCOME ($ mil.)	NET PROFIT MARGIN	EMPLOYEES
12/13	1,246	30	2.5%	7,200
12/12	1,220	32	2.7%	—
Annual Growth	2.1%	(5.0%)	—	—

2013 Year-End Financials

Return on assets: 8.8%   Cash ($ mil.): 21
Return on equity: 17.7%
Current ratio: 1.10

COC PROPERTIES, INC.

EXECUTIVES

Chb, Harry D Stephenson
Pres, Don Stephenson
V Pres, Betty Phillips
V Pres, Mark Maddox
V Pres, Jim Bosworth
Vice President, Craig Stephenson
Territory Sales Manager, Don Richardson
Auditors: BATCHELOR TILLERY & ROBERTS

LOCATIONS

HQ: COC PROPERTIES, INC.
  110 MACKENAN DR STE 300, CARY, NC 275117901
Phone: 919 462-1100

HISTORICAL FINANCIALS

Company Type: Private

Income Statement				FYE: December 31
	ASSETS ($ mil.)	NET INCOME ($ mil.)	INCOME AS % OF ASSETS	EMPLOYEES
12/20	117	13	11.4%	230
12/19	110	13	12.5%	—
12/18	102	8	8.8%	—
12/16	90	9	10.3%	—
Annual Growth	6.7%	9.4%	—	—

2020 Year-End Financials

Return on assets: 11.4%   Sales ($ mil): 1,028
Return on equity: 22.4%

COLORADO STATE UNIVERSITY

Colorado State University (CSU) got its start as an agricultural college in 1870 six years before Colorado was even a state. The school still has agricultural and forestry programs as well as a veterinary medicine school but it also offers degrees in liberal arts business engineering and the sciences. True to its roots as a land-grant college CSU engages the larger community in research and outreach through statewide Cooperative Extension programs and centers like the Colorado Agricultural Experiment Station. More than 30000 students are enrolled at CSU about 80% of whom are Colorado residents. It employs about 1500 faculty members and has a student-to-teacher ratio of 19:1.

Operations

The school's student body is largely composed of undergraduate students (more than 80%) but also includes some graduate and professional veterinary medicine students. CSU's most popular undergraduate majors are business health and exercise science psychology biological science construction management and human development and family studies. Overall the university offers about 150 undergraduate graduate and professional degree programs through eight colleges.

CSU has extensive research programs in fields including atmospheric science clean energy the environment biomedicine and infectious diseases. The university's research programs attract some $300 million in external funding each year.

Geographic Reach

CSU's main campus and its nearby foothills agricultural and mountain campuses are located on about 5000 acres in Fort Collins Colorado. The university has more than 1200 international students and scholars from about 90 countries on its campus. Additionally about 900 CSU students travel abroad every year to participate in educational programs.

Financial Performance

CSU's revenues increased 8% in 2012 to $827 million from higher earnings on student tuition and fees grants and contracts auxiliary enterprises and other education activity sales and service income. Net income increased by 63% to $67 million that year as a result of the university's revenue growth.

CSU has primarily experienced an increase in revenues over the last five years with the exception a slight dip during 2010 caused by decreased state capital contributions and grants and contracts.

Student tuition and fees run at about $9000 per year for Colorado residents and $24000 for out-of-state students.

EXECUTIVES

Pres, Joyce E McConnell
President-Global Campus, Becky Takeda
Assistant Professor, Marlis Douglas
Scientist, Grace Borlee
Coordinator, Cassidy Kurtz
Assistant Professor, J H Burton
Assistant Professor, Jangyul R Kim
Assistant Professor, Lori Ziegelmeier
Coordinator, Aaron Darnell
Information Specialist, Phil Chambers
Coordinator, Doug Sink

LOCATIONS

HQ: COLORADO STATE UNIVERSITY
6003 CAMPUS DELIVERY, FORT COLLINS, CO
805236003
Phone: 970 491-1372
Web: WWW.LIB.COLOSTATE.EDU

PRODUCTS/OPERATIONS

Selected Colleges Schools and Programs

Colleges
College of Agricultural Sciences
College of Applied Human Sciences
College of Business
College of Engineering
College of Liberal Arts
College of Natural Sciences
College of Veterinary Medicine and Biomedical
Sciences
Warner College of Natural Resources
Schools and Programs
Graduate School
International Programs
Online Degrees and Courses (Online Plus)
School of the Arts
School of Biomedical Engineering
School of Education
School of Global Environmental Sustainability
School of Social Work

HISTORICAL FINANCIALS

Company Type: Private

Income Statement   FYE: June 30

	REVENUE ($ mil.)	NET INCOME ($ mil.)	NET PROFIT MARGIN	EMPLOYEES
06/08	740	(44)	—	6,701
06/06	562	26	4.7%	—
Annual Growth	14.7%	—	—	—

2008 Year-End Financials

Return on assets: (-3.6%)   Cash ($ mil.): 249
Return on equity: (-6.6%)
Current ratio: 4.20

COLORADO STATE UNIVERSITY SYSTEM FOUNDATION, DELINQUENT FEBRUARY 1, 2020

EXECUTIVES

Chancellor, Joe Blake
Chancellor, Michael Martin
Cfo, Henry Sobanet
Pres-Colorado State Univ.-Glob, Becky Takeda
Assistant Professor, Deborah Fidler
Director, Guadalupe Salazar
Director of Graduate Programs, Sharon Anderson
Information Technology Profess, Tom Harmon
Audit Manager, Candice Bridgers
CIS Manager, Dipen Patel
Senior Auditor, Robb Hartman
Auditors: BKD LLP DENVER COLORADO

LOCATIONS

HQ: COLORADO STATE UNIVERSITY SYSTEM
FOUNDATION, DELINQUENT FEBRUARY 1, 2020
555 17TH ST STE 1000, DENVER, CO 802023910
Phone: 303 534-6290
Web: WWW.CSUSYSTEM.EDU

HISTORICAL FINANCIALS

Company Type: Private

Income Statement   FYE: June 30

	REVENUE ($ mil.)	NET INCOME ($ mil.)	NET PROFIT MARGIN	EMPLOYEES
06/15	1,011	33	3.3%	6,701
06/14	938	(5)	—	—
06/13	884	22	2.6%	—
Annual Growth	6.9%	21.7%	—	—

2015 Year-End Financials

Return on assets: 1.5%   Cash ($ mil.): 352
Return on equity: 7.5%
Current ratio: 2.40

COLUMBIA GAS OF OHIO, INC.

Columbia Gas of Ohio takes pride in the fact that it can deliver gas first class en masse without impasse to the working class the middle class and the upper class. The utility is the largest natural gas utility in the state serving 1.4 million customers (including about 1.3 million residential 112000 commercial and 2600 industrial customers in more than 1030 communities in more than 60 of Ohio's 88 counties). The NiSource subsidiary offers a customer choice program which allows customers to choose their energy suppliers while Columbia Gas of Ohio continues to deliver the gas.

Operations

In addition to operating more than 19160 miles of distribution mains the company also provides other gas products services and programs across its 25400-sq.-mi. service area. Columbia Gas of Ohio is part of the NiSource's Gas Distribution segment which contributed about 54% of the total sales in fiscal 2013.

Geographic Reach

Columbia Gas of Ohio distributes natural gas to residential commercial and industrial customers in Columbus Mansfield Parma Springfield and Toledo. It is one of a handful of NiSource's distribution companies which collectively serve about 3.4 million gas and electric customers in seven states and operates about 58000 miles of pipeline.

Financial Performance

Columbia Gas of Ohio is part of the NiSource's Gas Distribution segment which reported an increase of 9% in 2013 due primarily to an increase for regulatory and service programs (including the impact from the rate cases at Columbia of Pennsylvania and Columbia of Massachusetts and the implementation of rates under Columbia of Ohio's approved infrastructure replacement program); the effects of colder weather which increased residential commercial and industrial usage; and an increase in the numbers of residential and commercial customers.

Strategy

The company's strategy includes spending about $2 billion over 25 years to improve its underground pipeline system.

In 2014 it asked state regulators for permission to replace a mile-long 12-inch diameter pipeline that crosses the Maumee River between Maumee and Perrysburg with a new 20-inch pipeline.

Upgrading its main offices in order to be more efficient in 2013 Columbia Gas of Ohio announced plans to relocated to the Arena District of Columbus taking about 208000 sq. ft. of a planned 288000-sq.-ft. office complex.

In 2012 Columbia Gas of Ohio has finished work on its $14 million Ackerman Road natural gas pipeline replacement project in Columbus.

That year it moved more than 722000 customers to independent suppliers as part of a decade-long deregulation plan by the state.

Company Background

In 2011 Columbia Gas of Ohio announced plans to secure permission from the Public Utilities Commission of Ohio for a five year extension of its energy efficiency programs (home energy audits weatherization and other initiatives) aimed at bringing down energy costs for individual customers.

In 2010 Columbia Gas of Ohio commenced a $1.3 million gas mains upgrade in two neighborhoods in Toledo.

EXECUTIVES

Pres, Jack Partridge
V Pres Trea Cro, Devit Vajda
Acct Dept, Ms Jaime Hartenback
Executive Officer, Trudy Zielinski
Vice-President Information Ser, Dick James
Director, Shana Eiselstein
Area Director Southeast, Anthony Iachini
Area Director Northwest, Jamie Beier-Grant
Area Director Southwest, Jennifer Ekey
Ex Officio Director, Karen Conrad
Area Director Southwest, Martin Russell

LOCATIONS

HQ: COLUMBIA GAS OF OHIO, INC.
290 W NATIONWIDE BLVD # 1, COLUMBUS, OH
432151082
Phone: 614 460-6000
Web: WWW.NISOURCE.COM

COMPETITORS

Dominion East Ohio	The Illuminating
Duke Energy Ohio	Company
Ohio Edison	Toledo Edison
Ohio Power	Vectren Energy
Stand Energy	Delivery Of Ohio

HISTORICAL FINANCIALS

Company Type: Private

Income Statement   FYE: December 31

	REVENUE ($ mil.)	NET INCOME ($ mil.)	NET PROFIT MARGIN	EMPLOYEES
12/17	908	96	10.7%	2,500
12/16	854	114	13.4%	—
12/15	872	113	13.0%	—
12/14	993	102	10.3%	—
Annual Growth	(3.0%)	(1.9%)	—	—

2017 Year-End Financials

Return on assets: 2.3%   Cash ($ mil.): 7
Return on equity: 7.9%
Current ratio: 0.40

COLUMBUS CITY SCHOOL DISTRICT

EXECUTIVES

Supt, Gene T Harris
Dpty Supt*, Marvenia Bosley
Treas*, Mike Kinneer
V Pres*, Terry Boyd
Executive Officer, Blain Waldron
Executive Officer, Carol Rood
Executive Officer, Craig Bickley
Executive Officer, David Nelson
Executive Officer, Lean Katterheinrich
Executive Officer, Roxanne Moses
Coordinator, Jeri Griffith
Auditors: DAVE YOST COLUMBUS OHIO

LOCATIONS

HQ: COLUMBUS CITY SCHOOL DISTRICT
    270 E STATE ST FL 3, COLUMBUS, OH 432154312
Phone: 614 365-5000
Web: WWW.CCSOH.US

HISTORICAL FINANCIALS
Company Type: Private

Income Statement				FYE: June 30
	REVENUE ($ mil.)	NET INCOME ($ mil.)	NET PROFIT MARGIN	EMPLOYEES
06/20	966	(90)		10,000
06/18	1,087	66	6.2%	—
06/17	1,038	106	10.3%	—
06/16	972	(13)		—
Annual Growth	(0.1%)	—	—	—

2020 Year-End Financials
Return on assets: (-4.3%)   Cash ($ mil.): 608
Return on equity: —
Current ratio: —

COMENITY BANK

World Financial Network National Bank (WFNNB) will take credit for the credit it extends. The company is the private-label and co-branded credit card banking subsidiary of Alliance Data Systems. Along with affiliate World Financial Capital Bank the company underwrites cards on behalf of more than 85 businesses. The company's largest clients include apparel retailers L Brands and Redcats USA. WFNNB oversees about 120 million cardholder accounts and roughly $4 billion in receivables. Private equity giant Blackstone planned to acquire parent Alliance Data Systems for more than $6 billion but that deal was terminated in 2008.

EXECUTIVES

Pres, Timothy King
Computer Operations, Mike Schick
Project Manager, Connie Murphy
Information Technology, Paul Wroten
Client Sales Manager, Stacey Siak
Director Financial Planning, Don Borowy
Client Sales Manager, Jennifer Staten
Marketing Staff, Jeffrey Fasino
Administrative Assistant, Kurt Fraczkowski

Senior Vice President Chief Co, Michael F Swallow

LOCATIONS

HQ: COMENITY BANK
    12921 S VISTA STATION BLV, DRAPER, UT 840202377
Phone: 614 729-4000
Web: WWW.COMENITY.COM

COMPETITORS

American Express	Citigroup
Bank Of America	Target Receivables
Barclays Bank Delaware	

HISTORICAL FINANCIALS
Company Type: Private

Income Statement				FYE: December 31
	ASSETS ($ mil.)	NET INCOME ($ mil.)	INCOME AS % OF ASSETS	EMPLOYEES
12/14	9,149	389	4.3%	200
12/13	7,453	350	4.7%	—
12/05	332	10	3.2%	—
12/03	672	88	13.2%	—
Annual Growth	26.8%	14.4%	—	—

2014 Year-End Financials
Return on assets: 4.3%   Sales ($ mil): 1,976
Return on equity: 30.8%

COMFORT SYSTEMS USA (ARKANSAS), INC.

EXECUTIVES

Pres, Clyde A Jester
V Pres*, Trent McKenna
SEC*, Dawn McElyea
Auditors: ERNST & YOUNG LLP HOUSTON TE

LOCATIONS

HQ: COMFORT SYSTEMS USA (ARKANSAS), INC.
    9924 LANDERS RD, NORTH LITTLE ROCK, AR 721171588
Phone: 501 834-3320
Web: WWW.COMFORTAR.COM

HISTORICAL FINANCIALS
Company Type: Private

Income Statement				FYE: December 31
	REVENUE ($ mil.)	NET INCOME ($ mil.)	NET PROFIT MARGIN	EMPLOYEES
12/15	1,580	49	3.1%	102
12/14	1,410	28	2.0%	—
12/13	1,357	28	2.1%	—
Annual Growth	7.9%	31.5%	—	—

2015 Year-End Financials
Return on assets: 7.1%   Cash ($ mil.): 56
Return on equity: 13.5%
Current ratio: 1.40

COMMONSPIRIT HEALTH

Formed in 2019 through the merger of Catholic hospital systems Catholic Health Initiatives and Dignity Health CommonSpirit Health is a not-for-profit organization with more than 140 hospitals in about 20 states. Its hospitals range from large urban medical centers (many with educational and research programs) to small hospitals in rural areas. The company also operates clinics long-term care assisted-living and senior residential facilities (totaling more than 1500 care sites) and provides home-based care services.

Geographic Reach

CommonSpirit operates in Arizona Arkansas California Colorado Georgia Indiana Iowa Kansas Kentucky Minnesota Nebraska Nevada New Mexico North Dakota Ohio Oregon Pennsylvania Tennessee Texas and Wisconsin.

CommonSpirit national office is located in Illinois.

Sales and Marketing

Managed care accounted for about half of patient revenue and Medicare accounted for about 40%.

Financial Performance

The company's revenue for fiscal 2021 increased to $33.3 billion compared with $29.6 billion.

Cash held by the company at the end of fiscal 2021 increased to $3.3 billion. Cash used for operations investing and financing activities were $2.1 billion $267 million and $194 million respectively. Main cash uses were purchases of property and equipment repayments and investment in health-relates activities.

Strategy

CommonSpirit's strategic vision encompasses five transformative strategies: advocate for health populations; coordinate and customize care; address unique needs of the communities it serves; enhance consumer engagement; and inspire the CommonSpirit workforce.

HISTORY

In 1860 the Sisters of St. Francis established a hospital in Philadelphia laying the foundation for a larger health care organization. In 1981 Franciscan Health System was formally established to be a national holding company for Catholic hospitals and related organizations. By the mid-1990s the system consisted of 12 member and two affiliate hospitals and 11 long-term-care facilities located in the mid-Atlantic states and the Pacific Northwest.

Sisters of Charity of Cincinnati and the Sisters of St. Francis Perpetual Adoration of Colorado Springs co-sponsored The Sisters of Charity Health Care Systems incorporated in 1979 as a multi-institutional health care network. By the mid-1990s the system included 20 hospitals in Colorado Kentucky Nebraska New Mexico and Ohio.

Three congregations collaborated to form Catholic Health Corporation in 1980 one of the first such health care partnerships between religious communities within the Roman Catholic Church in the US. By 1996 this coalition operated 100 health care facilities in 12 states.

The development of modern managed care health care systems put pressure on the smaller Catholic hospital operations so the three systems established Catholic Health Initiatives (CHI) in 1996 as a national entity serving five geographic regions. Patricia Cahill a lay health care veteran who previously served the Archdiocese of New York was appointed president and CEO of CHI. The following year CHI absorbed the 10-hospital Sisters of Charity of Nazareth Health Care System based in Bardstown Kentucky (founded in a log cabin in 1812).

That year CHI continued to seek new partnerships to improve efficiency. With Alegent Health it formed provider network Midwest Select with nearly 200 hospitals marketing discounted rates to businesses. CHI allied with the Daughters of Charity to form for-profit joint venture Catholic Healthcare Audit Network to provide operational financial compliance and information systems audits as well as due diligence reviews. CHI also joined insurance joint venture NewCap Insurance with the Daughters of Charity and Catholic Health East; the firm allowed CHI to operate independently of commercial insurers.

CHI made a secular tie-in with the University of Pennsylvania Health System in 1998 whereby the university's system would offer care through five Catholic hospitals (CHI made plans to transfer these hospitals to Catholic Health East in 2001). The next year CHI announced its first loss due to lackluster performance in the Midwest. During 2000 the company responded by streamlining operations and changing management resulting in a positive bottom line. In 2001 it sold three hospitals in Pennsylvania one in Delaware and one in New Jersey to Catholic Health East.

EXECUTIVES

Chief Human Resource Officer, Darryl Robinson
Chief Operating Officer, Marvin O'Quinn
Senior Executive Vice President, Chief Information Officer And Chief Digital Officer, Suja Chandrasekaran
Chief Executive Officer, Lloyd Dean
Cfo, Dan Morissette
Auditors: ERNST & YOUNG LLP IRVINE CA

LOCATIONS

HQ: COMMONSPIRIT HEALTH
444 W LAKE ST STE 2500, CHICAGO, IL 606060097
Phone: 312 741-7000
Web: WWW.COMMONSPIRIT.ORG

COMPETITORS

Adventist Health System Sunbelt Healthcare
Allina Hospitals
Ascension Health
Baptist Health
Baptist Health (arkansas)
Bryanlgh Medical Center
Denver Health And Hospital Authority
Exempla Healthcare
Hca
Life Care Centers
Memorial Health System (colorado)
Methodist Health System
Ohiohealth
Tenet Healthcare
Universal Health Services

HISTORICAL FINANCIALS

Company Type: Private

Income Statement				FYE: June 30
	REVENUE ($ mil.)	NET INCOME ($ mil.)	NET PROFIT MARGIN	EMPLOYEES
06/21	33,253	8,303	25.0%	72,500
06/19	7,170	9,008	125.6%	—
06/18	14,982	222	1.5%	—
06/17	15,547	128	0.8%	—
Annual Growth	20.9%	183.6%	—	—

2021 Year-End Financials

Return on assets: 15.1%   Cash ($ mil.): 3,329
Return on equity: 37.9%
Current ratio: 1.30

COMMONWEALTH CARE ALLIANCE, INC.

EXECUTIVES

Ceo, Christopher D Palmieri
Pres, Lola Simon
Treas, Eugene Wallace
Ccdo, Don Stiffler
Coordinator, Carolyn Montilla
Coordinator, Jeannette Lopez
Coordinator, Jillian Parsons
Director Talent, Cathy Bates
Financial Analyst, Nicholas Rodrigues
Senior Care Options Program Di, Judy Sklare
Chief Information Officer, Miriam Manning
Auditors: GRANT THORNTON LLP HARTFORD

LOCATIONS

HQ: COMMONWEALTH CARE ALLIANCE, INC.
30 WINTER ST, BOSTON, MA 021084720
Phone: 617 426-0600
Web: WWW.COMMONWEALTHCAREALLIANCE.ORG

HISTORICAL FINANCIALS

Company Type: Private

Income Statement				FYE: December 31
	REVENUE ($ mil.)	NET INCOME ($ mil.)	NET PROFIT MARGIN	EMPLOYEES
12/19	1,544	21	1.4%	30
12/18	1,259	14	1.1%	—
Annual Growth	22.6%	52.4%	—	—

2019 Year-End Financials

Return on assets: 5.3%   Cash ($ mil.): 17
Return on equity: 16.6%
Current ratio: 6.60

COMMONWEALTH HEALTH CORPORATION, INC.

EXECUTIVES

President and Ceo, Connie Smith
Executive Vice President*, Jean Cherry
Executive Vice President and C*, Ron Sowell
Executive Vice President*, Sarah Moore
Executive Vice President*, Betsy Kullman
Executive Vice President*, Wade Stone
Chief Development Officer*, Cornelio Catena
Vp Marketing and, Doris C Thomas
Accounting Staff, Beth Wooldridge
Director, Brent Ballard
Vice President Marketing and D, Doris Thomas
Auditors: BLUE & CO LLC INDIANAPOLIS I

LOCATIONS

HQ: COMMONWEALTH HEALTH CORPORATION, INC.
800 PARK ST, BOWLING GREEN, KY 421012347
Phone: 270 745-1500
Web: WWW.CHC.NET

HISTORICAL FINANCIALS

Company Type: Private

Income Statement				FYE: March 31
	REVENUE ($ mil.)	NET INCOME ($ mil.)	NET PROFIT MARGIN	EMPLOYEES
03/21	598	150	25.2%	2,700
03/20	531	18	3.5%	—
/ 0	0	—	—	
Annual Growth	—	—	—	—

2021 Year-End Financials

Return on assets: 15.7%   Cash ($ mil.): 54
Return on equity: 21.7%
Current ratio: 1.60

COMMONWEALTH OF KENTUCKY

EXECUTIVES

Governor, Andy Beshear
Lt Govenor, Jenean Hampton
Chief Information Security Off, Joe Manley
Staff, Donna Cordier
Coordinator, Joe Wolford
Coordinator, Laronda Davis
Project Coordinator, Teresa Bailey
First Supreme Court Judge, David C Buckingham
Government Affairs Manager, Amy Mefford
Aging Program Case Manager, Dorris Phillips
Resource Management Advisor, Jerry Kilby
Auditors: MIKE HARMON FRANKFORT KY

LOCATIONS

HQ: COMMONWEALTH OF KENTUCKY
700 CAPITAL AVE STE 100, FRANKFORT, KY 406013410
Phone: 502 564-2611
Web: WWW.KENTUCKY.GOV

HISTORICAL FINANCIALS

Company Type: Private

Income Statement				FYE: June 30
	REVENUE ($ mil.)	NET INCOME ($ mil.)	NET PROFIT MARGIN	EMPLOYEES
06/20	28,942	578	2.0%	34,000
06/19	27,091	3	0.0%	—
06/18	25,692	338	1.3%	—
Annual Growth	6.1%	30.8%	—	—

2020 Year-End Financials

Return on assets: 0.9%   Cash ($ mil.): 5,634
Return on equity: —
Current ratio: —

COMMONWEALTH OF MASSACHUSETTS

EXECUTIVES

Governor, Charlie Baker
Lt Gov*, Karyn Polito
State Superior Court Judges, Kenneth V Desmond
State Superior Court Judges, James R Lemire
State Solicitor, Peter Sacks
Assistant Attorney General, Sookyoung Shin
MA Orange District Court Clerk, Joella E Fortier
Engagement Director, Deidre Travis-Brown
Deputy Director Office of Empl, John Langan
Superior Court Judge, Valerie A Yarashus
District Court Judge, Shelby M Smith
Auditors: KPMG LLP BOSTON MA

LOCATIONS

HQ: COMMONWEALTH OF MASSACHUSETTS
  1 ASHBURTON PL FL 9, BOSTON, MA 021081518
Phone: 617 727-5000
Web: WWW.MASS.GOV

HISTORICAL FINANCIALS

Company Type: Private

Income Statement				FYE: June 30
	REVENUE ($ mil.)	NET INCOME ($ mil.)	NET PROFIT MARGIN	EMPLOYEES
06/17	53,391	323	0.6%	59,253
06/16	52,992	(31)	—	—
06/15	50,609	685	1.4%	—
06/14	47,709	(250)	—	—
Annual Growth	3.8%	—	—	—

2017 Year-End Financials

Return on assets: 0.4%   Cash ($ mil.): 7,580
Return on equity: —
Current ratio: 1.40

COMMONWEALTH OF PENNSYLVANIA

EXECUTIVES

Governor, Tom Wolf
Lt Governor*, John Fetterman
General*, Linda Kelly
Chief of Staff*, Stephen Aichele
Acting Attorney General*, Bruce L Castor Jr
Mail Inspector Supervisor, Barbara McCabe
Certified Purchasing Agent, Basima Shunnara
Chemist 1, Davis Ly
Division Director, Eve Lickers
Director, James O'Donnell
Ucc Administrator, Joseph Marchioni
Auditors: CLIFTONLARSONALLEN LLP BALTIM

LOCATIONS

HQ: COMMONWEALTH OF PENNSYLVANIA
  238 MAIN CAPITOL BUILDING, HARRISBURG, PA 171200022
Phone: 717 787-5962
Web: WWW.PA.GOV

HISTORICAL FINANCIALS

Company Type: Private

Income Statement				FYE: June 30
	REVENUE ($ mil.)	NET INCOME ($ mil.)	NET PROFIT MARGIN	EMPLOYEES
06/20	82,404	(3,299)	—	89,207
06/19	78,418	(338)	—	—
06/18	73,689	2,198	3.0%	—
06/17	72,373	187	0.3%	—
Annual Growth	4.4%	—	—	—

2020 Year-End Financials

Return on assets: (-2.9%)   Cash ($ mil.): 5,191
Return on equity: —
Current ratio: 1.30

COMMONWEALTH OF VIRGINIA

EXECUTIVES

Gov, Ralph Northam
Lt Gov, Justin E Fairfax
Atty Gen, Ronald F McDonnell
Press SEC, Crystal Carson
SEC of Fin, Jody Wagner
Exec Dir, Diana Cantor
Treas, Lee Andes
Treas, Manju Ganeriwala
Director, Tod Massa
Policy Director, Jennie O'Holleran
Special Asst For Constituent S, Rickee Jones
Auditors: MARTHA S MAVREDES RICHMOND

LOCATIONS

HQ: COMMONWEALTH OF VIRGINIA
  101 N 14ST JAMES MONROE ST, RICHMOND, VA 23219
Phone: 804 225-3131
Web: WWW.VIRGINIA.GOV

HISTORICAL FINANCIALS

Company Type: Private

Income Statement				FYE: June 30
	REVENUE ($ mil.)	NET INCOME ($ mil.)	NET PROFIT MARGIN	EMPLOYEES
06/20	53,086	4,811	9.1%	100,000
06/19	40,939	1,480	3.6%	—
06/18	38,725	1,353	3.5%	—
06/17	36,395	18	0.1%	—
Annual Growth	13.4%	541.4%	—	—

2020 Year-End Financials

Return on assets: 3.6%   Cash ($ mil.): 14,484
Return on equity: 7.7%
Current ratio: —

COMMUNITY BEHAVIORAL HEALTH

EXECUTIVES

Director, Arthur C Evans Jr
Director*, Estelle Richmond
Director*, Nancy Luckas
Clinical Care Manager, Dana Carlomagno
Benefits Director, Leslie Edwards
Member Representative, Aadam Muhammad
Mental Health Professional, Abby Concino
Compliance Analyst, Alva Robinson
Complaints and Grievances Spec, Alyssa Bowers
Clinical Care Manager, Amra Handline
Supervisor, Amy Swett
Auditors: MITCHELL & TITUS LLP PHILADEL

LOCATIONS

HQ: COMMUNITY BEHAVIORAL HEALTH
  801 MARKET ST STE 7000, PHILADELPHIA, PA 191073158
Phone: 215 413-3100
Web: WWW.CBHPHILLY.ORG

HISTORICAL FINANCIALS

Company Type: Private

Income Statement				FYE: December 31
	REVENUE ($ mil.)	NET INCOME ($ mil.)	NET PROFIT MARGIN	EMPLOYEES
12/17	935	0	—	270
12/16	919	0	—	—
12/15	811	0	—	—
12/02	453	(0)	—	—
Annual Growth	4.9%	—	—	—

2017 Year-End Financials

Return on assets: —   Cash ($ mil.): 42
Return on equity: —
Current ratio: —

COMMUNITY FOUNDATION OF NORTHWEST INDIANA, INC.

EXECUTIVES

Pres, Frankie Fesko
SEC*, James J Richards
Treas*, David E Wickland
Cfo*, Gregg Ferlin
Security Staff, Derek Gilliam
Phlebotomy Supervisor, Dorothy Grisham
Security Officer Armed, Jeffery Malachowski
Physician Physical Therapy, Kevin Gahan
Director, Alicia Stanley
Erp Developer, Jonathan Joyce
Regional Director, Karen Schneider

LOCATIONS

HQ: COMMUNITY FOUNDATION OF NORTHWEST INDIANA, INC.
905 RIDGE RD, MUNSTER, IN 463211773
Phone: 219 836-0130

HISTORICAL FINANCIALS

Company Type: Private

| Income Statement | | | | FYE: June 30 |
	REVENUE ($ mil.)	NET INCOME ($ mil.)	NET PROFIT MARGIN	EMPLOYEES
06/21	1,248	350	28.1%	2,000
06/20	1,133	87	7.7%	—
06/19	1,125	104	9.3%	—
06/18	1,150	137	12.0%	—
Annual Growth	2.7%	36.4%	—	—

2021 Year-End Financials

Return on assets: 16.0%
Return on equity: 24.4%
Current ratio: 0.70

Cash ($ mil.): 28

COMMUNITY HEALTH CHOICE TEXAS, INC.

EXECUTIVES

Dir, Jose Garcia Jr
Dir, Vivian Ho
Dir, Vicki Keiser
Dir, Raymond Khoury
Dir, Elena Marks
Dir, Daisy Stiner
Dir, Stephen L McKernan
Director, Lucretia Butler
Auditors: BKD LLP DALLAS TEXAS

LOCATIONS

HQ: COMMUNITY HEALTH CHOICE TEXAS, INC.
2636 S LOOP W STE 125, HOUSTON, TX 770542696
Phone: 713 295-6704
Web: WWW.COMMUNITYHEALTHCHOICE.ORG

HISTORICAL FINANCIALS

Company Type: Private

| Income Statement | | | | FYE: February 28 |
	REVENUE ($ mil.)	NET INCOME ($ mil.)	NET PROFIT MARGIN	EMPLOYEES
02/21	1,232	139	11.3%	7
02/20	976	(17)	—	—
02/19	959	2	0.2%	—
Annual Growth	13.3%	723.3%	—	—

2021 Year-End Financials

Return on assets: 36.5%
Return on equity: 64.9%
Current ratio: 2.20

Cash ($ mil.): 310

COMMUNITY HEALTH CHOICE, INC.

EXECUTIVES

Coo, Karen Love
Cfo, Brian Maude
Coordinator, Richard Hobbs
Director, John Coakley
Vice-President, John Petrosino
Sales Staff, Leticia Neri
Administrative Assistant, Delwin Beene
Vice President, Jeff Allen
Director of Claims, Mychelle Scott
Controller, Peter Grant
Marketing Manager, Amber Buchanan
Auditors: I KPMG LLP OKLAHOMA CITY OK

LOCATIONS

HQ: COMMUNITY HEALTH CHOICE, INC.
2636 S LOOP W STE 700, HOUSTON, TX 770545630
Phone: 713 295-2200
Web: WWW.COMMUNITYHEALTHCHOICE.ORG

HISTORICAL FINANCIALS

Company Type: Private

| Income Statement | | | | FYE: December 31 |
	ASSETS ($ mil.)	NET INCOME ($ mil.)	INCOME AS % OF ASSETS	EMPLOYEES
12/15	239	1	0.5%	700
12/14	192	16	8.6%	—
12/13	166	(3)	—	—
12/12	172	(17)	—	—
Annual Growth	11.6%	—	—	—

2015 Year-End Financials

Return on assets: 0.5%
Return on equity: 1.2%

Sales ($ mil): 851

COMMUNITY HEALTH NETWORK, INC.

As a non-profit health system with more than 200 sites of care and affiliates throughout Central Indiana Community's full continuum of care integrates hundreds of physicians specialty and acute care hospitals surgery centers home care services MedChecks behavioral health and employer health services. Its state-of-the-art emergency departments are open 24/7 to treat emergency medical conditions including stroke head trauma heart attack chest pain broken bones wounds and more. Community Health has partnership with Marian University's College of Osteopathic Medicine. Community Health has been deeply committed to the communities it serves since opening its first hospital Community Hospital East in 1956.

Operations

Community Health provide health services including breast care cancer care children's health heart and vascular genetic testing and counseling medical imaging post-acute care plastic and reconstructive surgery primary care and sleep wake services among others.

Community Health hospitals are Community Heart Vascular Hospital Community Fairbanks Recovery Centers Community Hospital Anderson Community Hospital East Community Hospital North Community Hospital South Community Howard Regional Health Community Rehabilitation Hospital North and Community Rehabilitation Hospital South.

Geographic Reach

Community Health is based in Indianapolis Indiana.

EXECUTIVES

Pres, Bryan Mills
Cfo*, Kyle Fisher
Respiratory Site Manager, Richard Hooper
Director Regional Clinical RES, Robert Clutter
Clinical Resource Nurse, Sara Haycock
Social Worker, Sarah Minges
Administrative Assistant, Shawny Gaither
Licensed Practical Nurse, Stacy Scarlett
Clinical Consultant, Vinod Pallekonda
Staff Coordinator, Becky Prigg
Executive Officer, Daniel Rench
Auditors: KSM BUSINESS SERVICES INC IND

LOCATIONS

HQ: COMMUNITY HEALTH NETWORK, INC.
1500 N RITTER AVE, INDIANAPOLIS, IN 462193027
Phone: 317 355-1411
Web: WWW.ECOMMUNITY.COM

PRODUCTS/OPERATIONS

2014 Sales

	$ mil.	% of total
Net patient service revenue less provision for bad debts	1,815	94
Service fee revenue	25	1
Other revenue	100	5
Total	**1,942**	**100**

Selected Services

Advanced Wound Center
Assisted Fertility Services
Bariatric Services
Behavioral Health
Breast Care Services
Cancer Care Services
Children's Health
Clinical Research Trials
Community Home Health
Diet and Nutrition Services
Digestive Health Services
Emergency Services
Heart and Vascular
Inpatient Rehabilitation
Interventional Radiology
Maternity Services
Mid America Clinical Labs
Neuroscience Services
Orthopedic Services
Physical Therapy and Rehab
Radiology/Imaging Services
Sleep Wake Services
Sports Medicine
Surgical Services
Symptom Management Group
Weight Loss and Wellness
Women's Services

Selected Facilities and Affiliates

Community Health Pavilions
Community Heart and Vascular Hospital
Community Hospital Anderson
Community Hospital East
Community Hospital North
Community Hospital South
Community Imaging Centers
Community Physicians of Indiana network
Community Spine Center
Community Westview Hospital
Hook Rehabilitation Center
Indiana Surgery Centers
Indianapolis Endoscopy Center
MedCheck walk-in clinics
MedCheck Express clinics
Wellspring Pharmacy chain

COMPETITORS

Ball Memorial Hospital	Riverview Hospital
Henry County Memorial Hospital	St. Elizabeth Regional Health
Iu Health	St. Vincent Health
Iu Health Bloomington Hospital	Wabash County Hospital
Memorial Hospital (logansport)	

HISTORICAL FINANCIALS

Company Type: Private

Income Statement   FYE: December 31

	REVENUE ($ mil.)	NET INCOME ($ mil.)	NET PROFIT MARGIN	EMPLOYEES
12/19	1,645	413	25.1%	5,000
12/14	1,942	(0)	—	—
12/13	1,763	179	10.2%	—
Annual Growth	(1.1%)	15.0%	—	—

2019 Year-End Financials

Return on assets: 10.4%   Cash ($ mil.): 191
Return on equity: 15.5%
Current ratio: 0.60

COMMUNITY HOSPITAL OF THE MONTEREY PENINSULA

Community Hospital of the Monterey Peninsula has a sunny disposition when it comes to medical care. The not-for-profit health care facility provides general medical and surgical services to residents of Monterey California. It has about 235 acute care and skilled nursing beds and offers specialty services including cardiac and cancer care obstetrics orthopedics and rehabilitation. In addition to its main facility the hospital operates several ancillary centers including a mental health clinic an inpatient hospice medical laboratory branches and several outpatient centers offering diagnostic imaging diabetes care and other services.

Operations

Community Hospital offers a broad range of healthcare services at 15 locations including the main hospital outpatient facilities satellite laboratories a mental health clinic a short-term skilled nursing facility Hospice of the Central Coast and business offices.

In 2012 the hospital systems served 12130 inpatients in 2012. It also had 49565 emergency visits 283181 outpatient visits and assisted in 1193 births.

Geographic Reach

The company has facilities in Carmel Marina Monterey and Seaside counties in California.

Financial Performance

Medicare accounted for 53% of Community Hospital of the Monterey Peninsula's revenues in 2012; commercial insurance 23% and Medi-Cal 10%.

Strategy

To improve care in its service territory the hospital is working to increase best-practice sharing among physicians. It is also supporting information sharing by coordinating electronic health records (EHRs).

In 2014 the hospital received a $200000 contribution from the Auxiliary of Community Hospital of the Monterey Peninsula completing a five-year $1 million pledge by the service organization to support the hospital.

Company Background

As health care costs skyrocket in the US Community Hospital of the Monterey Peninsula has worked to lower its expenses. Between 2008 and 2011 the organization lowered annual costs by about $44 million.

Community Hospital of the Monterey Peninsula was founded in 1934.

EXECUTIVES

Pres-Ceo, Steven J Packer
V Pres*, Terrill Lowe
Cfo*, Laura Zehm
V Pres*, Cynthia Peck
V Pres*, Tim Nylen
SEC*, Shelley Post
Vp*, Steven X Cabrales
Chief of Medicine, Berry Gendelman
Health Professional, Christian Le
Security Staff, Garry Glaser
General Surgery, Jeffrey Hyde
Auditors: MOSS ADAMS LLP SAN FRANCISCO

LOCATIONS

HQ: COMMUNITY HOSPITAL OF THE MONTEREY PENINSULA
23625 HOLMAN HWY, MONTEREY, CA 939405902
Phone: 831 624-5311
Web: WWW.MONTAGEHEALTH.ORG

PRODUCTS/OPERATIONS

Selected Community Hospital Service Locations

Community Hospital of the Monterey Peninsula: Monterey
Carol Hatton Breast Care Center: Monterey
Development/Patient Business Services: Monterey
Hartnell Professional Center: Monterey Peninsula
  Primary Care/Satellite Laboratory: Carmel
Peninsula Wellness Center: Marina
Ryan Ranch Outpatient Campus: Monterey
Seaside Satellite Laboratory: Seaside
Westland House: Monterey

Selected Services

Bariatric Surgery
Behavioral Health Services
Carol Hatton Breast Care Center
Comprehensive Cancer Center
Diabetes
Diagnostic and Interventional Radiology
Emergency
Family Birth Center
Hospice of the Central Coast
Intermediate Intensive Care Nursery
Laboratory Services
Nutrition Therapy Program
Orthopedics
Outpatient Immunology Services
Outpatient Surgery Center
Pulmonary Wellness Services
Radiation Oncology
Rehabilitation Services
Sleep disorders
Social Services
Stroke Program
Tyler Heart Institute (Cardiac Care)
Westland House Skilled Nursing Facility
Wound Care and Hyperbaric Healing

COMPETITORS

Dignity Health	Stanford Health Care
John Muir Health	Sutter Health
Queen Of The Valley Medical Center	The Palo Alto Medical Foundation
Salinas Valley Memorial	Ucsf Medical
Sequoia Healthcare District	

HISTORICAL FINANCIALS

Company Type: Private

Income Statement   FYE: December 31

	REVENUE ($ mil.)	NET INCOME ($ mil.)	NET PROFIT MARGIN	EMPLOYEES
12/19	693	77	11.2%	1,947
12/16	526	71	13.7%	—
12/15	560	66	11.9%	—
12/12	442	81	18.4%	—
Annual Growth	6.6%	(0.7%)	—	—

2019 Year-End Financials

Return on assets: 11.7%   Cash ($ mil.): 57
Return on equity: 41.0%
Current ratio: 1.70

COMMUNITY HOSPITALS OF CENTRAL CALIFORNIA

Community Medical Centers helps California's San Joaquin Valley stay healthy. The not-for-profit system operates four hospitals ? along with nursing homes and freestanding outpatient facilities ? in the greater Fresno area. Its Community Regional Medical Center is a roughly 685-bed academic hospital that provides advanced care in areas such as trauma cardiac care neuroscience and orthopedics. Clovis Community Medical Center (nearly 210 beds) provides general medical-surgical care with expertise in women's health and bariatric surgery. Specialty hospitals Fresno Heart & Surgical Hospital and Community Behavioral Health Center (the largest psychiatric care facility in the area) each have about 60 beds.

EXECUTIVES

Ceo, Tim A Joslin
Evp-Cfo, Joseph Nowicki
Sr V Pres-Coo, Craig S Castro
Sr V Pres-Clo, Robin Van Patton
Svp Human Resources, Ginny R Burdick
Scientist, Rex Hiatt
Princ, Charles Anderson
Pharmacy Information, Janie Hatai
Microwave, Rich Beeber
Vice Chairman, Gordon Webster Jr
Manager, Norlina Dela Vega
Auditors: MOSS ADAMS LLP SAN FRANCISCO

LOCATIONS

HQ: COMMUNITY HOSPITALS OF CENTRAL CALIFORNIA
2823 FRESNO ST, FRESNO, CA 937211324
Phone: 559 459-6000
Web: WWW.COMMUNITYMEDICAL.ORG

PRODUCTS/OPERATIONS

Selected Locations

Hospitals
  Clovis Community Medical Center (Fresno)
  Community Regional Medical Center (Fresno)
  Community behavioral Health Center (Fresno)
  Fresno Heart & Surgical Care (Fresno)
Outpatient centers
  Advanced Medical Imaging
  California Cancer Center

Community Medical Center-SierraDeran Koligian
Ambulatory Care Center

COMPETITORS

Adventist Health
  System West
Catholic Health
  Initiatives
Dignity Health
Good Samaritan
  Hospital (san Jose)
Hca
Saint Agnes Medical
  Center

Sierra View District
  Hospital
Stanford Health Care
Sutter Health
Tenet Healthcare
Ucsf Medical
Valleycare Health
  System

HISTORICAL FINANCIALS

Company Type: Private

Income Statement — FYE: August 31

	REVENUE ($ mil.)	NET INCOME ($ mil.)	NET PROFIT MARGIN	EMPLOYEES
08/20	1,857	100	5.4%	6,200
08/19	1,813	117	6.5%	—
08/18*	1,667	108	6.5%	—
06/10	33	0	2.1%	—
Annual Growth	49.4%	64.0%	—	—

*Fiscal year change

2020 Year-End Financials

Return on assets: 3.8%
Return on equity: 7.0%
Current ratio: 1.40

Cash ($ mil.): 144

COMMUNITY HOSPITALS OF CENTRAL CALIFORNIA

EXECUTIVES

Pres, Tim Joslin
Nurse Coordinator, Kathy Norkunas
Pharmacy Residency Program Dir, Alice Ung-Robbins
Materials Manager, Don Moyer
Chief Information Officer, Craig Castro
Registered Nurse, Lee Vang
Vice President, Matt Joslin
General Surgeon, Amy Kwok
Anesthesiologist, Christopher Young
Chief of Neurology, Jeffrey Rosenfeld
Clinical Coordinator, Jennifer Trytten
Auditors: MOSS ADAMS LLP STOCKTON CA

LOCATIONS

HQ: COMMUNITY HOSPITALS OF CENTRAL CALIFORNIA
  2823 FRESNO ST, FRESNO, CA 937211324
Phone: 559 459-6000
Web: WWW.COMMUNITYMEDICAL.ORG

HISTORICAL FINANCIALS

Company Type: Private

Income Statement — FYE: August 31

	REVENUE ($ mil.)	NET INCOME ($ mil.)	NET PROFIT MARGIN	EMPLOYEES
08/17	1,529	48	3.1%	1,000
08/14	127	0	0.5%	
Annual Growth	128.9%	320.6%	—	—

2017 Year-End Financials

Return on assets: 2.4%
Return on equity: 4.3%
Current ratio: 1.60

Cash ($ mil.): 64

COMPASSION INTERNATIONAL INC

EXECUTIVES

Pres-Ceo, Santiago Mellado
Gen Dir*, Ronald Mathieu
V Chm*, Laurent Mbanda
Chm*, Karen Wesolowski
Gen Dir*, Jean-Franois Bussy
Svp-Gen Coun*, Robert Hawkins
Gen Dir*, Mike Jeffs
Gen Dir*, Francisco Batres
SEC*, Judy Briscoe Golz
Gen Mgr*, Kenneth Morgan
Gen Dir*, Chris Knepper
Auditors: CAPIN CROUSE LP COLORADO SPRI

LOCATIONS

HQ: COMPASSION INTERNATIONAL INC
  12290 VOYAGER PKWY, COLORADO SPRINGS, CO 809213694
Phone: 719 487-7000
Web: WWW.COMPASSION.COM

HISTORICAL FINANCIALS

Company Type: Private

Income Statement — FYE: June 30

	REVENUE ($ mil.)	NET INCOME ($ mil.)	NET PROFIT MARGIN	EMPLOYEES
06/16	800	13	1.6%	2,002
06/15	768	(8)	—	—
06/14	719	8	1.2%	—
06/13	659	15	2.3%	—
Annual Growth	6.6%	(4.4%)	—	—

2016 Year-End Financials

Return on assets: 4.4%
Return on equity: 6.2%
Current ratio: 1.30

Cash ($ mil.): 95

COMPUTER AID, INC.

EXECUTIVES

Ceo, Anthony J Salvaggio
Pres-Dir*, Thomas Salvaggio
Cfo*, Andrew McIntyre

Division Manager, Tom Gibson
Project Manager and Business, Sara Rusniak
Vendor Network Coordinator, Amy Ebersole
Team Leader, Andrew Haak
Delivery Manager, Brian Kapp
Senior Project Manager, Brian Keefer
Managing Director, Chris Roth
Human Resources Intern, Cydney Comfort

LOCATIONS

HQ: COMPUTER AID, INC.
  1390 RIDGEVIEW DR STE 300, ALLENTOWN, PA 181049065
Phone: 610 530-5000
Web: WWW.CAI.IO

HISTORICAL FINANCIALS

Company Type: Private

Income Statement — FYE: December 31

	REVENUE ($ mil.)	NET INCOME ($ mil.)	NET PROFIT MARGIN	EMPLOYEES
12/20	874	0	—	1,411
12/19	733	0	—	—
12/18	603	0	—	—
Annual Growth	20.4%	—	—	—

COMPUTER SCIENCES CORPORATION

Computer Sciences Corporation (CSC) has been one of the world's leading providers of systems integration and other information technology services. It offers application development data center management communications and networking development IT systems management and business consulting. It also provides business process outsourcing (BPO) services in such areas as billing and payment processing customer relationship management (CRM) and human resources. CSC boasts 2500 clients in more than 70 countries. In 2017 CSC merged with the Enterprise Services segment of Hewlett-Packard Enterprise to form DXC Technology Co. This report is based on CSC's last year as an independent company.

Operations

Prior to the creation of DXC CSC conducted business in through Global Business Services (GBS) and Global Infrastructure Services (GIS). GBS (55% of revenue) addresses key business challenges such as consulting applications services and software. GIS (45% of revenue) provides IT infrastructure services such as managed and virtual desktop solutions unified communications and collaboration services data center management cyber security and cloud-based offerings.

Geographic Reach

CSC has major operations throughout North America Europe Asia and Australia. The company has clients in more than 70 countries. About 40% of sales are made in the US and about 20% are in the UK the second biggest market.

Sales and Marketing

CSC's clients have included AboveNet Communications Deutsche Telekom DirecTV Vodafone and Ryman Hospitality Properties (formerly Gaylord Entertainment).

Financial Performance

After seven straight years of revenue declines CSC's sales rebounded in 2017 (ended March) to $7.6 billion a 7% increase from 2016. The increase was driven by the Global Business Services unit's business processing services offerings and contributions from recent acquisitions in the Digital Applications business. The Global Infrastructure Services unit posted a small revenue increase from new business and sales from acquisitions.

CSC lost about $123 million in 2017 down from a $251 million profit in 2016 mainly due to large restructuring charges.

Cash flow from operating activities rose to $978 million in 2017 from $802 million in 2016. The increase flowed from an increase in trade payables and a decrease in net account receivables.

Strategy

After going through corporate breakups DXC Technology bets that bigger will be better and stronger in competing in the worldwide market for IT services. The companies have a wide footprint and with some $26 billion in annual revenue and will have some weight to throw around. A question will be if the company can effectively compete with companies that provide similar services such as Cognizant WiPro Accenture IBM Global Service and Dell Technologies.

DXC has bulked up to ride the wave of digital transformation that its customers and potential customers are going through. The company's range of services could lead customers from legacy systems to private or public or hybrid cloud systems.

Mergers and Acquisitions

In 2016 CSC acquired Xchanging plc provider of technology-enabled business services for $633 million. Xchanging brings its Xuber software which is used by commercial insurance companies around the world.

Also in 2016 CSC acquired Aspediens a European provider in the service-management sector and a preferred partner of ServiceNow. The deal extended CSC's reach in software-as-a-service in Europe.

HISTORY

Computer Sciences Corporation (CSC) was founded in Los Angeles in 1959 by Fletcher Jones and Roy Nutt to write software for manufacturers such as Honeywell. In 1963 CSC became the first software company to go public. Three years later it signed a $5.5 million contract to support NASA's computation laboratory. Annual sales had climbed to just over $53 million by 1968.

In 1969 CSC agreed to merge with Western Union but the deal ultimately fell through. When Jones died in a plane crash in 1972 William Hoover a former NASA executive who had come aboard eight years earlier became chairman and CEO. Under Hoover CSC began transforming itself into a systems integrator. In 1986 when federal contracts still accounted for 70% of sales the company started diversifying into the commercial sector.

CSC signed a 10-year $3 billion contract in 1991 with defense supplier General Dynamics. In 1995 Hoover after more than three decades with CSC stepped down as CEO (remaining chairman until 1997); he was succeeded by president and COO Van Honeycutt. Also that year CSC bought Germany's largest independent computer services company Ploenzke. In 1996 CSC acquired insurance services provider Continuum Company for $1.5 billion.

EXECUTIVES

Ceo-Pres, J Michael Lawrie
Exec V Pres-Cfo, Paul N Saleh
Exec V Pres-Gen Counsel-Sec, William L Deckelman Jr
Exec V Pres, Stephen Hilton
Exec V Pres, James R Smith

Evp-Operations and Integration, Eric Harmon
Cto-Svp, Dan Hushon
Evp-Chro, Jo Mason
Evp, Mike Nefkens
Cmco-Svp, Gary Stockman
Chief Information Officer-Vp, Erich Windmuller
Auditors: DELOITTE & TOUCHE LLP MCLEAN

LOCATIONS

HQ: COMPUTER SCIENCES CORPORATION
1775 TYSONS BLVD FL 8, TYSONS, VA 221024251
Phone: 855 716-0853
Web: WWW.DXC.COM

2017 Sales

	$ mil.	% of total
United States	2,986	40
United Kingdom	1,482	19
Australia	921	12
Other Europe	1,594	21
Other International	624	8
Total	**7,607**	**100**

PRODUCTS/OPERATIONS

2017 Sales

	$ mil.	% of total
Global Business Services	4,173	55
Global Infrastructure Services	3,434	45
Total	**7,607**	**100**

Selected Service Areas

Application outsourcing
Business process outsourcing
Customer relationship management
Data hosting
Enterprise application integration
Knowledge management
Management consulting
Risk management
Security
Supply chain management

Selected Solutions

Application Services
Big Data & Analytics
Business & Technology Consulting
Cloud Solutions & Services
Cybersecurity
Industry Software & Solutions
Infrastructure Services
Managed Services & Outsourcing
Mobility Solutions

COMPETITORS

Adp
Accenture
Atos
Booz Allen
Caci International
Ciber
Capgemini
Cognizant Tech Solutions
Computacenter
Convergys
Dell
Deloitte Consulting
Dimension Data
General Dynamics Information Technology
Getronics
Hcl Technologies
Honeywell International
Ibm Global Services
Infosys
Leidos
Mantech
Ntt Data
Northrop Grumman
Siemens Ag
Tata Consultancy
Tech Mahindra
Unisys
Wipro
Wipro Technologies

HISTORICAL FINANCIALS

Company Type: Private

Income Statement				FYE: March 31
	REVENUE ($ mil.)	NET INCOME ($ mil.)	NET PROFIT MARGIN	EMPLOYEES
03/17*	7,607	(100)	—	66,000
04/16	7,106	263	3.7%	—
04/15	12,173	7	0.1%	—
03/14	12,998	690	5.3%	—
Annual Growth	(16.4%)	—	—	—

*Fiscal year change

2017 Year-End Financials

Return on assets: (-1.2%)   Cash ($ mil.): 1,263
Return on equity: (-4.6%)
Current ratio: 1.10

CONROE INDEPENDENT SCHOOL DISTRICT

EXECUTIVES

Supt, Don Stockton
Asst Supt For Elementary Schl, Cathy Gibson
Special Education Assistant, Marla Mong
Teacher Jhstudent Success Teac, Vonelle Clark
Teacher, Wendy Ward
Office Administrator Worship, Calah Smith
Teacher, Ariel Aymond
Teacher, Christine Broyles
Assistant, Dawn Poole
Teacher, Deanna Meekins
Teacher, Dennis Bouchillon

LOCATIONS

HQ: CONROE INDEPENDENT SCHOOL DISTRICT
3205 W DAVIS ST, CONROE, TX 773042039
Phone: 936 709-7751
Web: WWW.CONROEISD.NET

HISTORICAL FINANCIALS

Company Type: Private

Income Statement				FYE: August 31
	REVENUE ($ mil.)	NET INCOME ($ mil.)	NET PROFIT MARGIN	EMPLOYEES
08/20	719	70	9.8%	6,223
08/19	683	(80)	—	—
08/18	637	57	9.0%	—
08/17	609	7	1.2%	—
Annual Growth	5.7%	115.2%	—	—

2020 Year-End Financials

Return on assets: 3.6%   Cash ($ mil.): 14
Return on equity: —
Current ratio: 5.40

CONSIGLI CONSTRUCTION CO INC.

EXECUTIVES

Ceo, Anthony Consigli
Pres-Ceo*, Anthony M Consigli
V Pres*, Matthew D Consigli
V Pres-Cfo*, J Scott Lerner
Internal Medicine Practitioner, Harrison Bond
Coordinator, Morgan Buckley
Accounting Staff, Patrick McNamara
Internal Medicine Practitioner, Zach Pearce
Mep Manager, Janice Narowski
Superintendent, Kyle Shea
Project Superintendent, Mark Placek

LOCATIONS

HQ: CONSIGLI CONSTRUCTION CO INC.
72 SUMNER ST, MILFORD, MA 017571663
Phone: 508 473-2580
Web: WWW.CONSIGLI.COM

HISTORICAL FINANCIALS
Company Type: Private

Income Statement				FYE: December 31
	REVENUE ($ mil.)	NET INCOME ($ mil.)	NET PROFIT MARGIN	EMPLOYEES
12/12	616	34	5.6%	500
12/11	297	12	4.3%	—
12/10	0	0	—	—
12/09	297	12	4.3%	—
Annual Growth	27.5%	39.6%	—	—

2012 Year-End Financials
Return on assets: 21.7%
Return on equity: 120.7%
Current ratio: 1.20
Cash ($ mil.): 29

CONSOLIDATED GRAIN & BARGE COMPANY

EXECUTIVES

Ceo, Kevin D Adams
V Pres, Gregory Beck
Treasurer, Connie Brubaker
CGB Fertilizer Accounting Mana, Keith Brown
Regional Supervisor, Darin Cole
Loan Underwriter, John Graves
Corporate Controller, Joseph Barnett
Accounting Manager, Larry Bauman
Supervisor, Megan Barklow
Scale Operations, Tom Smith
Director of Business Strategie, Bill Lankswert
Auditors: KPMG LLP NEW ORLEANS LOUISI

LOCATIONS

HQ: CONSOLIDATED GRAIN & BARGE COMPANY
1127 HWY 190 E SERVICE RD, COVINGTON, LA
704334929
Phone: 985 867-3500
Web: WWW.CGBGRAIN.COM

HISTORICAL FINANCIALS
Company Type: Private

Income Statement				FYE: May 31
	REVENUE ($ mil.)	NET INCOME ($ mil.)	NET PROFIT MARGIN	EMPLOYEES
05/20	5,640	54	1.0%	2,000
05/19	6,160	57	0.9%	—
05/17	6,430	16	0.3%	—
05/16	5,759	21	0.4%	—
Annual Growth	(0.5%)	27.2%	—	—

2020 Year-End Financials
Return on assets: 3.9%
Return on equity: 11.2%
Current ratio: 1.10
Cash ($ mil.): —

CONSOLIDATED PIPE & SUPPLY COMPANY, INC.

Consolidated Pipe and Supply lives up to its name: Its nine divisions supply pipe and pipeline materials to a swath of industries from energy to water and waste treatment chemical mining nuclear oil and gas and pulp and paper. Its industrial unit specializes in carbon and stainless alloy pipe valves and fittings. Vulcan makes all types of PVC. Corrosion resistant coatings are offered by a Line Pipe and Tubular unit and liquid applied coatings by Specialty Coatings. Its Consolidated Power Supply is the largest in the business of safety related metallic materials for commercial nuclear generation. Another unit caters to utilities. Consolidated also provides engineering services and inventory systems.

Operations

Consolidated Pipe and Supply is one of nearly 20 US Steel distributors authorized to sell seamless and electric resistance welded products in North America. Not limited to its branch and sales centers Consolidated Pipe and Supply's fitted semi-trailers complete with area row and bin and bar coded shelving serve as mobile warehouses for construction customers requiring on-site materials management.

The company operates through nine divisions: Industrial Line Pipe Structural Pipeline Coatings Utility Products Specialty Coatings Consolidated Power Vulcan Plastics and Consolidated Controls.

Geographic Reach

The company's reach extends to 19 US states including Alabama Arkansas Florida Georgia Illinois Indiana Kentucky Missouri Mississippi North Carolina Pennsylvania South Carolina Tennessee Texas and Virginia. It has nearly 50 sales offices in 15 states.

EXECUTIVES

Pres, Howard J Kerr
Exec V Pres*, Robert W Kerr
SEC-Treas*, Barry Howton
Accounting Staff, Dana Grimes
Staff, Jeff Hallmark
Sales Team Member, Kevin Wessler
Utility Sales, Bert Wilkison
Estimator Representative, Clinton Jones
Marketing Executive, Daryl Fleming
Outside Sales, Dustin Hallmark
Gas Sales Represent, Eric Rudolph
Auditors: WARREN AVERETT CPAS AND ADVISO

LOCATIONS

HQ: CONSOLIDATED PIPE & SUPPLY COMPANY, INC.
1205 HILLTOP PKWY, BIRMINGHAM, AL 352045002
Phone: 205 323-7261
Web: WWW.CONSOLIDATEDPIPE.COM

PRODUCTS/OPERATIONS

Selected Industries Served
Chemical
Energy
Mining
Nuclear Generation
Oil and Gas
Petro-Chemical
Pulp and Paper
Water and Waste Treatment

Selected Divisions
Consolidated Controls (valves)
Consolidated Power (provides materials to energy industries)
Industrial (provides materials construction commercial energy pulp and paper chemical petro-chemical mining and fabrication industries)
Line Pipe (line pipe and tubular products)
Pipeline Coatings
Specialty Coatings (specialty linings for use in jet fuel and military applications)
Structural (1/8" through 48" structural and prime grades of carbon steel pipe)
Utility Products (provides utilities with products such as steel ductile iron PVC polyethylene and brass fittings and valves and steel PVC and polyethylene pipe)
Vulcan Plastics (water and sewer pipe)

COMPETITORS

American Cast Iron Pipe	Phoenix Tube
Bristol Metals	Seymour Tubing
Bull Moose Tube	Southland Tube
Chicago Tube & Iron	Steel Ventures
Kelly Pipe Co. Llc	U.s. Pipe

HISTORICAL FINANCIALS
Company Type: Private

Income Statement				FYE: December 31
	REVENUE ($ mil.)	NET INCOME ($ mil.)	NET PROFIT MARGIN	EMPLOYEES
12/19	808	25	3.2%	900
12/18	810	44	5.4%	—
12/16	550	17	3.3%	—
12/15	575	7	1.3%	—
Annual Growth	8.9%	36.9%	—	—

2019 Year-End Financials
Return on assets: 7.7%
Return on equity: 12.4%
Current ratio: 2.70
Cash ($ mil.): 7

CONSUMER PRODUCT DISTRIBUTORS, LLC

Consumer Product Distributors helps convenience stores provide convenient services to their customers. The company which operates as J. Polep Distribution Services is a leading wholesale supplier serving more than 4000 convenience retailers in New York Pennsylvania and the New England states. J. Polep distributes a variety of products including cigarettes and other tobacco items candy dairy products frozen foods snack items and general merchandise as well as alcohol and other beverages. As part of its business J.

Polep provides merchandising sales and marketing and technology services. The family-owned company was founded as Polep Tobacco in 1898 by Charles Polep.

Operations
Consumer Product Distributors ranks as one of the nation's top 12 convenience store distributors. To support its operations the company supplies customers with products through distribution centers located in Massachusetts (in Chicopee and Woburn) in Rhode Island (in Providence) and in Connecticut (in West Haven).

Geographic Reach
The distribution company serves chain and independent retailers in six New England states as well as New York and Pennsylvania. Its distribution centers are located in Massachusetts Rhode Island and Connecticut.

Mergers and Acquisitions
Company subsidiary Rachael's Food Corporation based in Chicopee Massachusetts entered the meat manufacturing business in late 2012 when the company acquired 122-year-old family-owned Grote and Weigel a hot dog and meat processor based in Bloomfield Connecticut. Soon after Rachael's Food Corporation also purchased family-owned meat processor Mucke's and transferred its operations to the Grote and Weigel unit. The 2012 purchases followed the company's acquisition of Springfield Smoked Fish. The food corporation's facilities are USDA-inspected and HACCP-certified.

EXECUTIVES

Pres-Ceo, Jeff Polep
V Pres*, Stephen J Martin
Exec V Pres*, Kenneth Morris
V Pres-Data Proc*, Lori Polep Saffer
Sr V Pres-Cfo*, Bill Fitzsimmons
SEC*, David A Shrair
Whse Transportation Manager PR, Alan Ritchotte
Plant Manager, Craig Kearney
Accounts Receivable, Lynn Carson
Director of Sales, Eric Polep
Network Administrator, Brendan Duffy
Auditors: MEYERS BROTHERS KALICKA PC

LOCATIONS

HQ: CONSUMER PRODUCT DISTRIBUTORS, LLC
705 MEADOW ST, CHICOPEE, MA 010134820
Phone: 413 592-4141
Web: WWW.JPOLEP.COM

PRODUCTS/OPERATIONS

Selected Products

Alcohol
  Spirits
  Wine
Automotive
  Branded Motor Oils
    Mag 1
  Additives
  Cleaning Supplies
Bakery/Pastry
  Rachael's Gourmet
  Mrs. Freshley's
  Dolly Madison
  Bon Appetite
  Bellow's House
  Diana's
  Table Talk
Beverages
  Poland Springs (Nestle Waters)
  Adirondack Soda
  Arizona
  Florida's Natural
  Simply Juices
  Sweet Leaf Tea
  Trade Winds
  Daily Juice

Selected Services
Credit & Return Policy
Management Information Systems
Merchandising Support
Sales and Marketing Support

COMPETITORS

Atlantic Dominion	Harold Levinson
C&s Wholesale	Mclane
Core-mark	Supervalu
Eby-brown	Tripifoods
H. T. Hackney	

HISTORICAL FINANCIALS
Company Type: Private

Income Statement   FYE: September 29

	REVENUE ($ mil.)	NET INCOME ($ mil.)	NET PROFIT MARGIN	EMPLOYEES
09/18	1,248	1	0.1%	400
09/17*	1,101	5	0.5%	—
10/16	1,005	5	0.6%	—
10/15	968	2	0.3%	—
Annual Growth	8.8%	(14.4%)	—	—

*Fiscal year change

2018 Year-End Financials
Return on assets: 0.9%
Return on equity: 5.0%
Current ratio: 3.20
Cash ($ mil.): 6

CONTINUUM ENERGY SERVICES, L.L.C.

EXECUTIVES

MBR-Exec V Pres-Cfo, Dan Hawk
MBR*, Robert Rosene Jr
MBR*, John Greene
Program Director, Rick Pemberton
Auditors: GRANT THORNTON LLP TULSA OKL

LOCATIONS

HQ: CONTINUUM ENERGY SERVICES, L.L.C.
1323 E 71ST ST STE 100, TULSA, OK 741365036
Phone: 918 492-2840
Web: WWW.CONTINUUMENERGYSERVICES.COM

HISTORICAL FINANCIALS
Company Type: Private

Income Statement   FYE: December 31

	REVENUE ($ mil.)	NET INCOME ($ mil.)	NET PROFIT MARGIN	EMPLOYEES
12/13	2,092	5	0.2%	159
12/12	1,558	16	1.0%	—
12/11	2,021	26	1.3%	—
Annual Growth	1.7%	(56.3%)	—	—

2013 Year-End Financials
Return on assets: 1.0%
Return on equity: 3.3%
Current ratio: 1.10
Cash ($ mil.): 11

CONTINUUM MIDSTREAM, L.L.C.

EXECUTIVES

Member, Kent Dunbar
Member*, Robert B Rosene Jr
Member*, Daniel Frey
Member*, John Greene
Member*, Bob Malapkowski
Vice-President Business Develo, Brian Cutter
Auditors: GRANT THORNTON LLP TULSA OKL

LOCATIONS

HQ: CONTINUUM MIDSTREAM, L.L.C.
1323 E 71ST ST STE 100, TULSA, OK 741365036
Phone: 918 492-2840
Web: WWW.SEMINOLEENERGY.COM

HISTORICAL FINANCIALS
Company Type: Private

Income Statement   FYE: December 31

	REVENUE ($ mil.)	NET INCOME ($ mil.)	NET PROFIT MARGIN	EMPLOYEES
12/14	1,153	(2)	—	75
12/13	296	0	0.2%	—
12/02	17	0	5.3%	—
12/01	13	1	11.9%	—
Annual Growth	40.8%	—	—	—

2014 Year-End Financials
Return on assets: (-1.7%)
Return on equity: (-2.2%)
Current ratio: 0.70
Cash ($ mil.): 3

COOK CHILDREN'S HEALTH PLAN

EXECUTIVES

Pres, Doris Hunt
Coordinator, Chase Robinson
Coordinator, Allyson Tate
Manager of Fleet Operations, Robert Hailey
Procurement Coordinator, Willy Rensing
Deputy Chief Investment Office, Apurva Mehta
Librarian, Dena Hanson
Interim Chief Investment Offic, Eli Bloshtein
Senior Network Engineer, Lud Pendery
Director, Andrea Keane
Pediatric Hematologist Oncolog, Anish Ray
Auditors: BKD LLP HOUSTON TX

LOCATIONS

HQ: COOK CHILDREN'S HEALTH PLAN
801 7TH AVE, FORT WORTH, TX 761042733
Phone: 817 334-2247
Web: WWW.COOKCHILDRENS.ORG

HISTORICAL FINANCIALS

Income Statement				FYE: September 30
	REVENUE ($ mil.)	NET INCOME ($ mil.)	NET PROFIT MARGIN	EMPLOYEES
09/19	567	1	0.3%	27
09/18	547	5	0.9%	—
09/17	484	(8)	—	—
09/15	307	17	5.8%	—
Annual Growth	16.6%	(44.5%)	—	—

2019 Year-End Financials

Return on assets: 1.0%   Cash ($ mil.): 100
Return on equity: 2.0%
Current ratio: 11.60

COOPERATIVE ENERGY, A MISSISSIPPI ELECTRIC COOPERATIVE

EXECUTIVES

Pres-Ceo, Jeff Bowman
V Pres*, Harlan Rogers
V Pres*, Billy Harden
SEC*, W T Shows
Gen Mgr*, James M Compton
Senior Vice President, Brad Wolfe
Senior Vice President, Chris Rhodes
Vice President, Don Hinton
Senior Vice President, Mark Smith
Economic Manager, Mitch Stringer
Senior Vice President, Nathan Brown

LOCATIONS

HQ: COOPERATIVE ENERGY, A MISSISSIPPI ELECTRIC COOPERATIVE
7037 U S HIGHWAY 49, HATTIESBURG, MS 394029128
Phone: 601 268-2083
Web: WWW.COOPERATIVEENERGY.COM

HISTORICAL FINANCIALS

Income Statement				FYE: December 31
	REVENUE ($ mil.)	NET INCOME ($ mil.)	NET PROFIT MARGIN	EMPLOYEES
12/16	822	0	—	238
12/13	811	0	—	—
12/12	771	0	—	—
12/11	766	0	—	—
Annual Growth	1.4%	—	—	—

2016 Year-End Financials

Return on assets: —   Cash ($ mil.): 41
Return on equity: —
Current ratio: 1.50

COOPERATIVE FOR ASSISTANCE AND RELIEF EVERYWHERE, INC. (CARE)

The Cooperative for Assistance and Relief Everywhere (CARE) strives to be the beginning of the end of poverty. The organization works to reduce poverty in about 85 countries by helping communities in areas such as health education economic development emergency relief and agriculture. CARE supports more than 1100 projects to combat poverty. It also operates a small economic activity development (SEAD) unit that supports moneymaking activities. Through SEAD CARE provides technical training and savings and loans programs to help people — particularly women — open or expand small businesses. CARE was founded in 1945 to give aid to WWII survivors.

Operations

In addition to its home office in Georgia CARE maintains field offices in about 10 US cities including Boston Chicago Miami New York and Washington DC. The group's international field offices are located in more than 55 countries.

CARE's 1100 projects reach 122 million people more than half of which are women. About 90% of the funds that CARE receives go toward its aid efforts. The organization helps people in the poorest communities of developing nations. (It does not provide assistance in the US.)

Geographic Reach

From its headquarters in Atlanta CARE serves poor communities in nearly 85 countries. It does not provide assistance in the US.

Financial Performance

CARE's revenue increased a modest 1% to $590 million in fiscal 2011 as compared to 2010. While it logged a drop in revenues from the US government the organization saw a boost in private contributions — totaling $310 million — from CARE international members.

Strategy

CARE is supported by donations from thousands of individuals and dozens of corporations foundations and other charitable organizations in the US. Some of the participating organizations include World Wildlife Fund Covance Merck Meredith Corporation and the Wal-Mart Foundation. The group also receives funding and supplies from government agencies including the United Nations and European Union. As a result of the economic downturn CARE has been working to raise contribution levels as governments businesses and individuals cut back their spending including charitable donations.

EXECUTIVES

Ceo, Michelle Nunn
Cfo*, Vickie J Barrow-Klien
SEC*, Carol Hudson
Coo*, Tjada Doyen McKenna
Executive Officer, Louise Hough
Coordinator, Amanda Person
Manager, Astor Chirinos
Technical Specialist, Carolyn Grant
Executive Officer, David Ray

Education Specialist, Eugene Da
Director, Jeff Yaschik
Auditors: ERNST & YOUNG LLP ATLANTA GA

LOCATIONS

HQ: COOPERATIVE FOR ASSISTANCE AND RELIEF EVERYWHERE, INC. (CARE)
151 ELLIS ST NE, ATLANTA, GA 303032420
Phone: 404 681-2552
Web: WWW.CARE.ORG

PRODUCTS/OPERATIONS

Selected International Partner Organizations
Covance Inc.
Merck Foundation
Meredith Corporation
The Wal-mart Foundation
WWF

HISTORICAL FINANCIALS

Income Statement				FYE: June 30
	REVENUE ($ mil.)	NET INCOME ($ mil.)	NET PROFIT MARGIN	EMPLOYEES
06/20	609	(37)	—	10,000
06/19	620	16	2.7%	—
06/18	604	15	2.6%	—
06/16	530	(21)	—	—
Annual Growth	3.5%	—	—	—

2020 Year-End Financials

Return on assets: (-7.5%)   Cash ($ mil.): 95
Return on equity: (-11.4%)
Current ratio: 1.60

COOPERATIVE REGIONS OF ORGANIC PRODUCER POOLS

Cooperative Regions of Organic Producers Pool (CROPP) is the largest organic farming cooperative in North America. The group's 1840-plus farmer/members produce the co-op's Organic Valley Family of Farms and Organic Prairie brands of fluid and shelf-stable milk along with cheese butter and soy milk. Beyond the dairy barn the cooperative also offers organic citrus juices produce eggs meats and poultry. Its Organic Valley products are sold by food retailers and its ingredients are marketed to other organic food processors. Wisconsin-headquartered CROPP's farmer/members are located throughout North America and Australia. The co-op was founded in 1988.

Geographic Reach

The Wisconsin-based cooperative's farmer members are located in 35 US states including California and Florida and three Canadian provinces. It also has members in Australia.

Financial Performance

The co-op's sales grew 8% in 2013 versus 2012 to $928 million after increasing by 20% in the previous annual comparison. Sales have risen sharply along with increasing demand for organic milk and other dairy foods. CROPP added 10 new members in 2013. The co-op struggled in 2013 as a result of a fire that burned down part of its headquarters building. The blaze occurred about a year after the co-op completed a $6.7 million addition to the structure.

Strategy

CROPP seeks to quench consumers' growing thirst for organic milk with new products including the 2012 launch of Organic Valley Grassmilk an organic specialty milk produced from cows that are 100% grass fed. Organic Valley Grassmilk attained nationwide distribution in mid-2013.

The co-op operates under a regional business model by which milk is produced bottled and distributed in the region where it's farmed to ensure fewer miles from farm to table and to support local economies. About 75% of the co-ops 1800-plus farmers are located in the "Heartland" region of the US which includes Iowa Illinois Kansas Minnesota North Dakota Nebraska South Dakota Wisconsin Indiana Ohio and Michigan.

EXECUTIVES

Int Ceo, Bob Kirchoff
Cfo, Michael Bedessem
Coo, Louise Hemstead
Coordinator, Carrie-Ann Morey
Director of Dairy, Jeff Kragt
Quality Assurance Manager, Gloria Joseph
Chief Financial Officer, Mike Bedessem
Marketing Team Member, Hellen Gudgeon
Northeast Dairy Pool Coordinat, John Cleary
Associate Manager, Eric Snowdeal
Staff Veterinarian, Guy Jodarski

LOCATIONS

HQ: COOPERATIVE REGIONS OF ORGANIC
PRODUCER POOLS
1 ORGANIC WAY, LA FARGE, WI 546396604
Phone: 608 625-2602
Web: WWW.ORGANICVALLEY.COOP

PRODUCTS/OPERATIONS

Selected Products
Butter
Cheese
Cottage cheese
Cream
Cream cheese
Eggs
Healthy snacks
Juice
Meat
Milk
Sour cream
Soy
Yogurt

COMPETITORS

Albert's Organics	Keller's Creamery
Aurora Organic Dairy	Land O'lakes
Berkeley Farms	Laura's Lean Beef Co.
Chiquita Brands	Lifeway Foods
Crowley Foods	Niman Ranch
Dairy Crest	Oberweis Dairy
Dairy Farmers Of	Odwalla
America	Organically Grown
Dakota Beef	Company
Dannon	Rachel's Organic Dairy
Dean Foods	Rockview Dairies
Dole Food	Sargento
Egg Innovations	Springfield Creamery
Foster Dairy Farms	Stonyfield Farm
Fresh Del Monte	Straus Family Creamery
Produce	Stremicks Heritage
Friendship Dairies	Foods
Galaxy Nutritional	Tyson Foods
Foods	Tyson Fresh Meats
Garelick Farms	United Natural
Great Lakes Cheese	Willow Wind Organic
Jonathan Sprouts	Farms

HISTORICAL FINANCIALS
Company Type: Private

Income Statement   FYE: December 31

	REVENUE ($ mil.)	NET INCOME ($ mil.)	NET PROFIT MARGIN	EMPLOYEES
12/10	619	12	2.0%	764
12/08	527	3	0.7%	—
12/07	432	6	1.4%	—
Annual Growth	12.7%	24.6%	—	—

2010 Year-End Financials

Return on assets: 7.5%   Cash ($ mil.): 29
Return on equity: 12.8%
Current ratio: 2.20

CORNELL UNIVERSITY

Cornell is the federal land-grant institution of New York State a private endowed university a member of the ivy League/Ancient Eight and a partner of the State University of New York. The Ivy League school's some 23620 students can select undergraduate graduate and professional courses from around 16 colleges and schools. In addition to its Ithaca New York campus the university has medical and professional programs in New York City and Doha Qatar. Cornell's faculty includes some 1695 of regular and part time employee. It was founded 1865 by Ezra Cornell and Andrew Dickson White.

Operations

Cornell awarded the nation's first university degree in veterinary medicine and first doctorates in electrical engineering and industrial engineering. It awarded the world's first degree in journalism and established the first four-year schools of hotel administration and industrial and labor relations.

Cornell is deeply involved in research with more than 100 interdisciplinary research organizations 18 Cornell research centers and national research centers. Cornell offers nearly 80 formal major fields including agricultural sciences astronomy biological engineering chemistry civil engineering computer literature earth and atmospheric science and more. Cornell has dozens of research centers such as the Cornell High Energy Synchrotron Source (CHESS) the Cornell Electroacoustic Music Center (CEMC) the Cornell Wildlife Health Center (CWHC) the National Biomedical Center for Advanced ESR Technology (ACERT) and the Laboratory of Elementary-Particle Physics (LEPP).

Geographic Reach

Cornell's main campus in Ithaca New York is composed of endowed colleges and contract colleges (operated on behalf of the state) spanning a 2300-acre campus in New York State's Finger Lakes region. In New York City Cornell operates Weill Medical College which has an extension campus in Doha Qatar and the Graduate School of Medical Sciences. Also in New York City is Cornell Tech is a diverse environment of academics and practitioners who excel at imagining researching and building digitally-enabled products and services to directly address societal and commercial needs. It is operated with Israel's Technion University.

Sales and Marketing

Cornell University is a private research university providing an exceptional education for undergraduates and graduate and professional students. Cornell's colleges and schools includes four contract colleges (operated by Cornell under contract with

New York state) encompassing 100-field study. It has locations in Ithaca New York New York City and Doha Qatar.

Company Background

The Ivy League university was founded in 1865 as a land grant university as set out in the Morrill Act passed by the US Congress in 1862.

EXECUTIVES

Pres, Martha E Pollack
Int Pres, Hunter R Rawlings III
Sales Manager, Phil Shapiro
Manager, Ameen Moheed
Horticultural Lab Technician, Amy Albam
Research Assistant, Andrea Sherwood
Executive Education Program Co, Anita Vogel
Theatrical Technician, Astrid Jacobson
Lab Assistant, Berta Gutierrez
Temp Serv Tech Biomedical Engi, Bethsabe Romero
Field Manager For Organic Crop, Brian Caldwell
Auditors: PRICEWATERHOUSECOOPERS LLP R

LOCATIONS

HQ: CORNELL UNIVERSITY
308 DUFFIELD HALL, ITHACA, NY 148532700
Phone: 607 254-4636
Web: WWW.CORNELL.EDU

HISTORICAL FINANCIALS
Company Type: Private

Income Statement   FYE: June 30

	REVENUE ($ mil.)	NET INCOME ($ mil.)	NET PROFIT MARGIN	EMPLOYEES
06/17	4,013	985	24.6%	12,207
06/16	3,809	(442)	—	—
06/12	2,956	(341)	—	—
06/11	2,955	814	27.5%	—
Annual Growth	5.2%	3.2%	—	—

2017 Year-End Financials

Return on assets: 7.5%   Cash ($ mil.): 181
Return on equity: 9.8%
Current ratio: —

CORONA-NORCO UNIFIED SCHOOL DISTRICT

EXECUTIVES

Ceo, Cathy L Sciortino
Supt*, Kent Bechler
Prin*, Ted Rozzi
Pres*, John Z Zickefoose
Trustee Area*, Jose W Lalas
SEC*, Linda Hawkins
Clerk, Mary Abeyta
High School Teacher, Kelly Bustany
Director, Gina Boster
Assistant Superintendent, Glen Gonsalves
Secretary, Marlena Reyes
Auditors: EIDE BAILLY LLP RANCHO CUCAMO

HQ: CORONA-NORCO UNIFIED SCHOOL DISTRICT
2820 CLARK AVE, NORCO, CA 928601903
Phone: 951 736-5000
Web: WWW.CNUSD.K12.CA.US

HISTORICAL FINANCIALS
Company Type: Private

Income Statement				FYE: June 30
	REVENUE ($ mil.)	NET INCOME ($ mil.)	NET PROFIT MARGIN	EMPLOYEES
06/20	696	20	3.0%	614
06/19	717	(47)	—	—
06/18	658	42	6.5%	—
06/17	637	(8)	—	—
Annual Growth	3.0%	—	—	—

COUNTRYMARK COOPERATIVE HOLDING CORPORATION

EXECUTIVES
Ceo, Matt Smorch
Cfo, Jo Biggers
Director, Belinda Puetz
Lubricant Sales Specialist, David Bates
Director, Glenn Keller
Analyzer Technician, Matt Norrick
Programmer Analyst, William Walker
Fleet Manager, Charles Smith
Utility Technician, Chuck Stapleton
Production, Brian Pope
Manager of Financial Planning, Chris Coffman

LOCATIONS
HQ: COUNTRYMARK COOPERATIVE HOLDING CORPORATION
225 S EAST ST STE 144, INDIANAPOLIS, IN 462024059
Phone: 800 808-3170
Web: WWW.COUNTRYMARK.COM

HISTORICAL FINANCIALS
Company Type: Private

Income Statement				FYE: December 31
	REVENUE ($ mil.)	NET INCOME ($ mil.)	NET PROFIT MARGIN	EMPLOYEES
12/08	1,325	26	2.0%	425
12/07	964	56	5.9%	—
12/05	774	40	5.2%	—
Annual Growth	19.6%	(12.7%)	—	—

2008 Year-End Financials
Return on assets: 7.7%   Cash ($ mil.): 8
Return on equity: 13.5%
Current ratio: 1.60

COUNTY OF ADAMS

EXECUTIVES
Admin, Terry L Funderburk
Director of Finance*, Rich Lemkey
Director*, Jim Robinson
Coordinator, Roxanne Sherrill
Executive Director, Joel Estes
Administrative Assistant of Vs, Veronica Cortez
Specialist, Cathi Smith
Mis Coordinator, Jennifer McDaniel
Assistant County, Kerri Booth
Performance Analyst, Max Cercone
Business Outreach Coordinator, Noelle Glasser
Auditors: CLIFTONLARSONALLEN LLP BROOMF

LOCATIONS
HQ: COUNTY OF ADAMS
4430 S ADAMS, BRIGHTON, CO 80601
Phone: 720 523-6100
Web: WWW.ADCOGOV.ORG

HISTORICAL FINANCIALS
Company Type: Private

Income Statement				FYE: December 31
	REVENUE ($ mil.)	NET INCOME ($ mil.)	NET PROFIT MARGIN	EMPLOYEES
12/20	589	24	4.2%	1,740
12/18	427	46	10.9%	—
12/16	0	(29)	—	—
12/15	342	77	22.5%	—
Annual Growth	11.5%	(20.2%)	—	—

COUNTY OF ALAMEDA

Just east of San Francisco Bay lies Alameda County. Governed by a five-member board of supervisors it includes 14 cities among them Hayward Oakland and San Leandro. Nearly 60 departments handle services like behavioral health care emergency medical and human resources along with law enforcement property tax assessment and collection and community development for a population of more than 1.5 million. The county also serves as the keeper of birth death and marriage certificates and other public records. Its budget is more than $2.7 billion; most of it goes to public assistance public protection and health care. Alameda was incorporated in 1853 from parts of neighboring Contra Costa and Santa Clara counties.

EXECUTIVES
County Admin, Susan Moranishi
Supervisor Dist 1*, Scott Haggerty
Supervisor Dist 2*, Gail Steele
Supervisor Dist 4*, Nate Miley
Supervisor Dist 5, Chb*, Keith Carson
Supervisor District 3*, Ellis Lai-Bitker
Deputy Dir*, David Anderson
Human Resources Information MA, Sharen Stanek
Program Inspector, Jeff Israel
Administrator, Lidice La Fuente
Customer Representativ, Claudio Lane
Auditors: MACIAS GINI & O'CONNELL LLP O

LOCATIONS
HQ: COUNTY OF ALAMEDA
1221 OAK ST STE 555, OAKLAND, CA 946124224
Phone: 510 272-6691
Web: WWW.ACGOV.ORG

HISTORICAL FINANCIALS
Company Type: Private

Income Statement				FYE: June 30
	REVENUE ($ mil.)	NET INCOME ($ mil.)	NET PROFIT MARGIN	EMPLOYEES
06/15	2,714	(26)	—	8,000
06/14	2,579	203	7.9%	—
06/13	2,622	65	2.5%	—
06/12	2,403	(155)	—	—
Annual Growth	4.1%	—	—	—

COUNTY OF ALBANY

EXECUTIVES
County Exec, Daniel P McCoy
Director of Finance, Jeff Neal
Executive Deputy Comptroller, John Curran
Chief Information Officer Chie, Joseph Paratore
Chief Deputy, Kerry Thompson
Database Administrator, Qun Lu
Marketing Executive, Edward Dott
Director, John Marsolais
Director, Mark Horan
Director of Communications, Mary Rozak
Stormwater Program Coordinator, Nancy Heinzen
Auditors: BST & CO CPAS LLP ALBANY

LOCATIONS
HQ: COUNTY OF ALBANY
112 STATE ST RM 1200, ALBANY, NY 122072023
Phone: 518 447-7040
Web: WWW.ALBANYCOUNTY.COM

HISTORICAL FINANCIALS
Company Type: Private

Income Statement				FYE: December 31
	REVENUE ($ mil.)	NET INCOME ($ mil.)	NET PROFIT MARGIN	EMPLOYEES
12/20	552	(21)	—	2,567
12/19	588	14	2.4%	—
12/18	582	63	10.9%	—
12/17	563	(9)	—	—
Annual Growth	(0.7%)	—	—	—

2020 Year-End Financials
Return on assets: (-1.6%)   Cash ($ mil.): 144
Return on equity: —
Current ratio: 1.90

COUNTY OF ALLEGHENY

EXECUTIVES

County Mgr, William McKey
Cheif Deputy, Dennis Skosnik
Dpty Prothonota, Michael Lamb
Fiscal Offc, Joseph Gurcak
Staff, Dave Hamrock
Law Specialist, Celeste McGraw
Coordinator, Carol Veal
Purchasing Agent, Matthew Breitenbach
Lan Tech, Bill Snyder
Environmental Health Superviso, Donna Scharding
Microbiologist, Gim Yee
Auditors: ZELENKOFSKE AXELORD LLC PITT

LOCATIONS

HQ: COUNTY OF ALLEGHENY
 436 GRANT ST STE 104, PITTSBURGH, PA 152195403
Phone: 412 350-5300

HISTORICAL FINANCIALS

Company Type: Private

| Income Statement | | | FYE: December 31 |
	REVENUE ($ mil.)	NET INCOME ($ mil.)	NET PROFIT MARGIN	EMPLOYEES
12/20	2,004	111	5.6%	7,013
12/19	1,768	(51)	—	—
12/18	1,722	53	3.1%	—
12/17	1,640	(40)	—	—
Annual Growth	6.9%	—	—	—

COUNTY OF ANNE ARUNDEL

EXECUTIVES

County Exec, Steuart Pittman
Budget Offcr, John Hammond
Executive Officer, Janet Owens
Coordinator, Tyjuan Thompson
Coordinator, Anne Shawkey
Deputy States Atty, Attorney's, David P Ash
Maryland Circuit Court Judge, Pamela K Alban
Maryland Circuit Court Judge, Elizabeth S Morris
Maryland Circuit Court Judge, Robert Jeffrey
Environmental Policy Specialis, Matt Johnston
Risk Manager, Amy Lanham
Auditors: CLIFTONLARSONALLEN LLP BALTIM

LOCATIONS

HQ: COUNTY OF ANNE ARUNDEL
 44 CALVERT ST STE 1, ANNAPOLIS, MD 214011930
Phone: 410 222-1166
Web: WWW.AACOUNTY.ORG

COUNTY OF ARLINGTON

EXECUTIVES

Gen Mgr, Barbara Donnellan
County Clerk*, Hope Halleck
Liet*, Chuck Kramaric
Deputy County Manager*, James Schwartz
Auditor*, Chris Horton
HB*, Jay Fisette
Human Resources Information MA, Alycia Pippen
Acting Fire Chief, Joseph Reshetar
Fire Chief, David Povlitz
Communications Manager, Kurt Larrick
Benefits Specialist, Sheryl Lan
Auditors: CLIFTONLARSONALLEN LLP ARLIN

LOCATIONS

HQ: COUNTY OF ARLINGTON
 2100 CLARENDON BLVD # 500, ARLINGTON, VA 222015447
Phone: 703 228-3130
Web: WWW.ARLINGTONECONOMICDEVELOPMENT.COM

HISTORICAL FINANCIALS

Company Type: Private

| Income Statement | | | FYE: June 30 |
	REVENUE ($ mil.)	NET INCOME ($ mil.)	NET PROFIT MARGIN	EMPLOYEES
06/19	1,409	71	5.1%	4,000
06/18	1,349	(14)	—	—
06/17	1,321	99	7.5%	—
06/16	1,261	(10)	—	—
Annual Growth	3.8%	—	—	—

2019 Year-End Financials

Return on assets: 1.3%   Cash ($ mil.): —
Return on equity: 3.2%
Current ratio: —

COUNTY OF BERGEN

EXECUTIVES

County Exec, James Tedesco
Payroll Staff, Donna Pallatta
Coordinator, Linda Cross
Administrative Assistant, Bernadette Losito
Case Manager, Crystal Gong
Clerical Assistant, Mary Raftery

HISTORICAL FINANCIALS

Company Type: Private

| Income Statement | | | FYE: June 30 |
	REVENUE ($ mil.)	NET INCOME ($ mil.)	NET PROFIT MARGIN	EMPLOYEES
06/20	1,858	58	3.2%	4,600
06/19	1,700	(20)	—	—
06/18	1,635	3	0.2%	—
06/17	1,573	40	2.6%	—
Annual Growth	5.7%	13.0%	—	—

Public Works Director, Raymond Dressler
Health Care Center Administrat, Harvey Silberstein
Advisory Board Member, Julie Obrien
Clerk To Board, Lara Rodriguez
Director, Richard Daul

LOCATIONS

HQ: COUNTY OF BERGEN
 1 BERGEN COUNTY PLZ RM 1 # 1, HACKENSACK, NJ 076017075
Phone: 201 336-6000
Web: WWW.CO.BERGEN.NJ.US

HISTORICAL FINANCIALS

Company Type: Private

| Income Statement | | | FYE: December 31 |
	REVENUE ($ mil.)	NET INCOME ($ mil.)	NET PROFIT MARGIN	EMPLOYEES
12/17	565	26	4.7%	2,347
12/16	604	22	3.8%	—
12/02	369	19	5.1%	—
12/01	18	0	—	—
Annual Growth	23.9%	—	—	—

2017 Year-End Financials

Return on assets: 1.0%   Cash ($ mil.): 248
Return on equity: 1.8%
Current ratio: —

COUNTY OF BEXAR

EXECUTIVES

County Judge, Nelson W Wolff
County Clerk*, Gerry Rickhoff
District Attorney*, Susan Reed
Auditor*, Susan Yeatts
Clerk*, Donna Kay McKinney
Assistant Auditor*, Leo Caldera
Sergeant, Al Damiani
Coordinator, Art Herrera
Sergeant, Augustin Pruneda
Coordinator, Marisa Nunez
Coordinator, Marlena Kelly
Auditors: GARZA/GONZALEZ & ASSOCIATES S

LOCATIONS

HQ: COUNTY OF BEXAR
 101 W NUEVA STE 1019, SAN ANTONIO, TX 782053482
Phone: 210 335-2626

HISTORICAL FINANCIALS

Company Type: Private

| Income Statement | | | FYE: September 30 |
	REVENUE ($ mil.)	NET INCOME ($ mil.)	NET PROFIT MARGIN	EMPLOYEES
09/20	776	96	12.5%	4,200
09/19	703	131	18.7%	—
09/18	672	(103)	—	—
09/16	619	(43)	—	—
Annual Growth	5.8%	—	—	—

2020 Year-End Financials

Return on assets: 1.4%   Cash ($ mil.): 1,226
Return on equity: 6.5%
Current ratio: 4.20

COUNTY OF BROWARD

EXECUTIVES

ADM, Bertha Henry
Asst Cnty ADM, Monica Cepero
Assistant County Administrator, Alphonso
Jefferson Jr
Property Appraiser, Sheriff Lori Parrish
Coordinator, Efrem Crenshaw
Information Specialist, Lina Kulikowski
Sheriff, Gregory Tony
Librarian, Frank Pennetti
Facilities Management Division, Alexander Bass
Maintenance Manager, Ash Morgan
Director, David Kahn
Auditors: CROWE HORWATH LLP FORT
LAUDER

LOCATIONS

HQ: COUNTY OF BROWARD
115 S ANDREWS AVE STE 409, FORT LAUDERDALE,
FL 333011817
Phone: 954 357-7050
Web: WWW.BROWARD.ORG

HISTORICAL FINANCIALS
Company Type: Private

Income Statement				FYE: September 30
	REVENUE ($ mil.)	NET INCOME ($ mil.)	NET PROFIT MARGIN	EMPLOYEES
09/11	1,525	(76)	—	40,500
09/09	1,693	(28)	—	—
09/06	1,799	116	6.5%	—
Annual Growth	(3.3%)	—	—	—

2011 Year-End Financials
Return on assets: (-1.0%)   Cash ($ mil.): 593
Return on equity: (-1.6%)
Current ratio: 3.60

COUNTY OF BUTTE

EXECUTIVES

Cao, Paul Hahn
County Treas*, C Linda Barnes
Board Member*, Jane Dolan
Chief Administrative Officer, Paul J Hahn
Director, Joana Brooks
Director Servic, Tim Snellings
Supervisor Buildings, Dean Olson
Civil Engineering Technician, Rick Furmanski
Dispatch Supervisor, Trina Wehle
Assistant Treasurer, Lisa Lam
Benefits Coordinator, Raeshell Forrester
Auditors: CLIFTONLARSONALLEN LLP ROSEV

LOCATIONS

HQ: COUNTY OF BUTTE
25 COUNTY CENTER DR # 125, OROVILLE, CA
959653316
Phone: 530 538-7701
Web: WWW.BUTTECOUNTY.NET

HISTORICAL FINANCIALS
Company Type: Private

Income Statement				FYE: June 30
	REVENUE ($ mil.)	NET INCOME ($ mil.)	NET PROFIT MARGIN	EMPLOYEES
06/20	673	241	35.8%	2,000
06/19	424	(2)	—	—
06/18	399	3	1.0%	—
06/17	388	3	0.8%	—
Annual Growth	20.2%	324.8%	—	—

2020 Year-End Financials
Return on assets: 36.7%   Cash ($ mil.): —
Return on equity: 127.1%
Current ratio: —

COUNTY OF CHESTERFIELD

EXECUTIVES

Admin, James J L Stegmaier
Prin*, Steve Elswick
Acting Deputy Administrator*, Rebecca T
Dickson
Human Resources Information MA, Carla Shust
Accounting Staff, Donna Loehr
Coordinator, Lorne Field
Officer, Stephanie Brown MBA
Customer Staff, Bonita China
Detective, Chris Rizzuti
Librarian, Donna Siebold
Manager Human Resources, Karyn Carpenter
Auditors: KPMG LLP RICHMOND VA

LOCATIONS

HQ: COUNTY OF CHESTERFIELD
9901 LORI RD, CHESTERFIELD, VA 238326626
Phone: 804 748-1000
Web: WWW.CHESTERFIELD.GOV

HISTORICAL FINANCIALS
Company Type: Private

Income Statement				FYE: June 30
	REVENUE ($ mil.)	NET INCOME ($ mil.)	NET PROFIT MARGIN	EMPLOYEES
06/21	1,022	186	18.2%	4,618
06/20	894	75	8.5%	—
06/19	841	80	9.6%	—
06/18	857	(30)	—	—
Annual Growth	6.1%	—	—	—

2021 Year-End Financials
Return on assets: 4.0%   Cash ($ mil.): 571
Return on equity: 9.0%
Current ratio: —

COUNTY OF CLARK

EXECUTIVES

County Mgr, Don Burnette
County Manager*, Don Burnett
Cfo*, Yolanda King
Staff, Hanks Jeffrey
Information Specialist, Bill Bonner
Family Supervisor, Angela Ranck
Manager, Jim Nance
Rec, Kelly Salyer
Administrator, Maureen Buen
Management Assistant, Michael Shields
Program Assistant, Natalie Swanson
Auditors: CROWE LLP COSTA MESA CALIFOR

LOCATIONS

HQ: COUNTY OF CLARK
500 S GRAND CENTRAL PKWY # 6, LAS VEGAS, NV
891554502
Phone: 702 455-3530
Web: WWW.CO.CLARK.NV.US

HISTORICAL FINANCIALS
Company Type: Private

Income Statement				FYE: June 30
	REVENUE ($ mil.)	NET INCOME ($ mil.)	NET PROFIT MARGIN	EMPLOYEES
06/20	3,398	107	3.2%	8,528
06/19	3,301	625	18.9%	—
06/18	3,021	89	3.0%	—
06/17	2,873	96	3.4%	—
Annual Growth	5.7%	3.6%	—	—

COUNTY OF CONTRA COSTA

EXECUTIVES

Prin, David Twa
Cfo*, Robert Campbell
Treas, Russell V Watts
Database Admin, Barry Schamach
Admin Asst, Cindy Ray
Educ Specialist, Clayton Johnson
Health Dir, William Walker
Teacher, Adeola Lashore
Mgr, Alexandra Madsen
Offc, Cheree Morgan
Teller, Gen Pierce
Auditors: MACIAS GINI & O'CONNELL LLP W

LOCATIONS

HQ: COUNTY OF CONTRA COSTA
625 COURT ST STE 100, MARTINEZ, CA 945531231
Phone: 925 957-5280
Web: WWW.CC-COURTS.ORG

HISTORICAL FINANCIALS

Company Type: Private

Income Statement

FYE: June 30

	REVENUE ($ mil.)	NET INCOME ($ mil.)	NET PROFIT MARGIN	EMPLOYEES
06/20	2,514	47	1.9%	7,193
06/19	2,438	98	4.0%	—
06/18	2,259	84	3.7%	—
06/17	2,182	215	9.9%	—
Annual Growth	4.8%	(39.7%)	—	—

COUNTY OF CUYAHOGA

EXECUTIVES

Commissioner, Timothy F Hagan
Ceo*, Bob Reid
Executive Officer, Sandra Bizzell
Purchasing Agent, Kristen Kaspar
Managing, Farah Emeka
Gis Analyst, Jordan Abbott
Fiscal Officer, Diane Kirchendorfer
Ehs Manager, Jay Medlock
Assistant Law, Kelly Spring
Payroll Officer, Thelma Gantt
Scheduler, Victoria Baskovic
Auditors: KEITH FABER AUDITOR OF STATE

LOCATIONS

HQ: COUNTY OF CUYAHOGA
1215 W 3RD ST, CLEVELAND, OH 441131532
Phone: 216 443-7022
Web: WWW.CUYAHOGABDD.ORG

HISTORICAL FINANCIALS

Company Type: Private

Income Statement

FYE: December 31

	REVENUE ($ mil.)	NET INCOME ($ mil.)	NET PROFIT MARGIN	EMPLOYEES
12/19	1,428	64	4.5%	9,800
12/18	1,371	(118)	—	—
12/17	1,325	64	4.9%	—
12/16	1,324	(78)	—	—
Annual Growth	2.5%	—	—	—

2019 Year-End Financials

Return on assets: 1.1%   Cash ($ mil.): 1,591
Return on equity: 73.1%
Current ratio: —

COUNTY OF DALLAS

EXECUTIVES

County Judge, Clay Jenkins
Commissioner Prec 1*, Jimmy L Jackson
Commissioner Prec 2*, Mike Cantrell
Commissioner Prec 3*, John Wiley Price
Auditor*, Virginia Porter
Senior Analyst, Karl Warren
Hr Analyst, Kelvin Alexander
Office Manager, Chad Cook
Grants Manager, Joe Thekkekara

Office Manager, Martha Rodriguez
Administrative Assistant, Shelia Graham
Auditors: DELOITTE & TOUCHE LLP DALLAS

LOCATIONS

HQ: COUNTY OF DALLAS
900 JACKSON ST STE 680, DALLAS, TX 752024425
Phone: 214 653-7099
Web: WWW.DALLASCOUNTY.ORG

HISTORICAL FINANCIALS

Company Type: Private

Income Statement

FYE: September 30

	REVENUE ($ mil.)	NET INCOME ($ mil.)	NET PROFIT MARGIN	EMPLOYEES
09/20	1,081	(34)	—	6,600
09/19	931	(34)	—	—
09/18	871	4	0.5%	—
09/17	821	(7)	—	—
Annual Growth	9.6%	—	—	—

COUNTY OF DANE

EXECUTIVES

Cty Exec, Kathleen Falk
Auditors: BAKER TILLY VIRCHOW KRAUSE LL

LOCATIONS

HQ: COUNTY OF DANE
210 M LTHR KNG JR BLV 425, MADISON, WI 53703
Phone: 608 266-4114
Web: WWW.COUNTYOFDANE.COM

HISTORICAL FINANCIALS

Company Type: Private

Income Statement

FYE: December 31

	REVENUE ($ mil.)	NET INCOME ($ mil.)	NET PROFIT MARGIN	EMPLOYEES
12/20	544	6	1.2%	1,568
12/19	456	27	6.1%	—
12/18	463	22	4.9%	—
12/17	509	18	3.6%	—
Annual Growth	2.2%	(29.5%)	—	—

COUNTY OF DEKALB

EXECUTIVES

Ceo, Vernon Jones
Interim Ceo*, Lee May
Cpo*, Talisa R Clark
Attorney, Jonathan Weintraub
Gis Specialist, Tony Hall
Acting Sheriff, Ruth M Stringer
Communications, Yvette Jones
Director, Raymond R White
Employee, Patrick Kelly
Director of Facilities and SEC, Raymond Clunie Sr
Auditors: KPMG LLP ATLANTA GA

HQ: COUNTY OF DEKALB
1300 COMMERCE DR, DECATUR, GA 300303222
Phone: 404 371-2881
Web: WWW.DEKALBCOUNTYGA.GOV

HISTORICAL FINANCIALS

Company Type: Private

Income Statement

FYE: December 31

	REVENUE ($ mil.)	NET INCOME ($ mil.)	NET PROFIT MARGIN	EMPLOYEES
12/19	749	34	4.6%	7,300
12/18	698	49	7.1%	—
12/17	628	20	3.2%	—
12/16	577	15	2.7%	—
Annual Growth	9.1%	30.2%	—	—

2019 Year-End Financials

Return on assets: 0.8%   Cash ($ mil.): 561
Return on equity: 2.7%
Current ratio: —

COUNTY OF DELAWARE

EXECUTIVES

Chm, Tom McGarrigle
Exec Dir*, Marianne Grace
Manager, Dennis De Rosa
Health, Ellen Williams
Regional Safety Manager, Michael Fluck
Director, Linda F Hill
Vp Operations, Tom Bockius
Coordinator, Brittany Fiorito
Manager, Charles Burr
General Manager, Charlie Tustin
Sys Dir, Edward Coleman
Auditors: BAKER TILLY VIRCHOW KRAUSE LL

LOCATIONS

HQ: COUNTY OF DELAWARE
201 W FRONT ST FRNT, MEDIA, PA 190632700
Phone: 610 891-4000
Web: WWW.DELAWARECOUNTYPA.COM

HISTORICAL FINANCIALS

Company Type: Private

Income Statement

FYE: December 31

	REVENUE ($ mil.)	NET INCOME ($ mil.)	NET PROFIT MARGIN	EMPLOYEES
12/20	651	45	7.0%	3,100
12/19	583	(16)	—	—
12/18	584	40	7.0%	—
12/17	562	(8)	—	—
Annual Growth	5.0%	—	—	—

2020 Year-End Financials

Return on assets: 4.9%   Cash ($ mil.): 181
Return on equity: —
Current ratio: —

COUNTY OF ERIE

EXECUTIVES

County Exec, Mark Poloncarz
County Clerk*, Michael Kearns
Cashier, Sara Hart
Assoc Depty, Peggy A Lagree
Coordinator, Kelly Asher
Coordinator, Jack O'Connor
Assistant, Jacques Desjardins
Coordinator, James McCullough
Coordinator, John Ryan
Coordinator, Thomas Hersey
Majority Leader, Maria Whyte
Auditors: DRESCHER & MALECKI LLP BUFFAL

LOCATIONS

HQ: COUNTY OF ERIE
95 FRANKLIN ST RM 1603, BUFFALO, NY 142023914
Phone: 716 858-8500
Web: WWW.ERIE.GOV

HISTORICAL FINANCIALS
Company Type: Private

Income Statement				FYE: December 31
	REVENUE ($ mil.)	NET INCOME ($ mil.)	NET PROFIT MARGIN	EMPLOYEES
12/20	1,767	(6)	—	10,200
12/19	1,693	23	1.4%	—
12/18	1,646	34	2.1%	—
12/17	1,630	48	3.0%	—
Annual Growth	2.7%	—	—	—

2020 Year-End Financials
Return on assets: (-0.2%) Cash ($ mil.): 303
Return on equity: —
Current ratio: —

COUNTY OF ESSEX

EXECUTIVES

Prin, Joseph N Divincenzo
Acting Cty Treas*, Ron Weitz
Cty Admin*, Vincent A Dimauro
Chief of Staff, Alan Steinberg
Deputy, William Narvaez
Registrar, Carole Graves
Districtwide Parent Coordinato, Delores Wallace
Guidance Counselor, Patricia Parisi
Accounting Personnel, Zoe Lopez
Director, David Berkowitz
Captain, John Napolitano
Auditors: SAMUEL KLEIN AND COMPANY-JOSEP

LOCATIONS

HQ: COUNTY OF ESSEX
465 MARTIN LUTHER KING, NEWARK, NJ 071021735
Phone: 973 621-4454
Web: WWW.ECDPW.ORG

HISTORICAL FINANCIALS
Company Type: Private

Income Statement				FYE: December 31
	REVENUE ($ mil.)	NET INCOME ($ mil.)	NET PROFIT MARGIN	EMPLOYEES
12/16	862	31	3.6%	5,300
12/09	784	25	3.2%	—
12/97	478	7	1.6%	—
12/95	1,107	0	—	—
Annual Growth	(1.2%)	—	—	—

2016 Year-End Financials
Return on assets: 1.2% Cash ($ mil.): 182
Return on equity: 1.7%
Current ratio: —

COUNTY OF FREDERICK

EXECUTIVES

Commissioner, Jan H Gardener
County Mgr, Lori Depies
Council Pres-Vp, Bud Otis
Director, Wayne Howard
Chief Administrative Officer, Rick Harcum
Dir, Erin White
Occupational Specia, Heidi Ach
Coordinator, Sandy Turner
Sergeant, Mark Landahl
Foreman Supervisor, Jason Jenkins
Marketing Manager, Shawn Dennison

LOCATIONS

HQ: COUNTY OF FREDERICK
12 E CHURCH ST, FREDERICK, MD 217015402
Phone: 301 600-9000
Web: WWW.DISCOVERFREDERICKMD.COM

HISTORICAL FINANCIALS
Company Type: Private

Income Statement				FYE: June 30
	REVENUE ($ mil.)	NET INCOME ($ mil.)	NET PROFIT MARGIN	EMPLOYEES
06/20	744	1	0.2%	1,800
06/19	723	22	3.1%	—
06/18	662	21	3.2%	—
06/17	625	8	1.4%	—
Annual Growth	6.0%	(44.7%)	—	—

2020 Year-End Financials
Return on assets: — Cash ($ mil.): 524
Return on equity: 0.1%
Current ratio: —

COUNTY OF FRESNO

EXECUTIVES

Chb, Bob Waterston
Exec Dir, Brad Maggy
Dir, David Pomaville
Prin, David Luchini
Architect, Richard Wood
Attorney, Don Penner
Attorney, Robert Freed
Engineer, Bao Xiong
Program Technician, Crystal Ybarra
Financial Analyst, Letha Hood
Finance Director, Emilia Reyes
Auditors: BROWN ARMSTRONG ACCOUNTANCY CO

LOCATIONS

HQ: COUNTY OF FRESNO
2420 MARIPOSA ST, FRESNO, CA 937212204
Phone: 559 600-1710
Web: WWW.CO.FRESNO.CA.US

HISTORICAL FINANCIALS
Company Type: Private

Income Statement				FYE: June 30
	REVENUE ($ mil.)	NET INCOME ($ mil.)	NET PROFIT MARGIN	EMPLOYEES
06/20	1,781	19	1.1%	971
06/19	1,649	30	1.9%	—
06/18	1,538	5	0.3%	—
Annual Growth	7.6%	98.0%		

COUNTY OF FULTON

EXECUTIVES

Dty Cty Mgr, Richard Anderson
Admin Coordinator, Ronda Sanchez
Coordinator, Melba Blount
Coordinator, Michelle Broussard
Coordinator, Sandra Johnson
Coordinator, Juree Hall
Procurement Specialist, Lisa McKine
Contracting Officer, Jacqueline Davis
Assistant Commander, Mike Hughes
Financial Supervisor, Kevies McBride
Projects Manager, Michelle Cox
Auditors: PJC GROUP LLC ATLANTA GEORG

LOCATIONS

HQ: COUNTY OF FULTON
141 PRYOR ST SW STE 7001, ATLANTA, GA 303033468
Phone: 404 612-4000
Web: WWW.FULTONCOUNTYGA.GOV

HISTORICAL FINANCIALS
Company Type: Private

Income Statement				FYE: December 31
	REVENUE ($ mil.)	NET INCOME ($ mil.)	NET PROFIT MARGIN	EMPLOYEES
12/20	947	(11)	—	5,000
12/19	816	3	0.5%	—
12/18	843	70	8.3%	—
12/15	760	1	0.3%	—
Annual Growth	4.5%	—	—	—

2020 Year-End Financials
Return on assets: (-0.2%) Cash ($ mil.): 952
Return on equity: (-1.0%)
Current ratio: —

COUNTY OF GUILFORD

EXECUTIVES

Administrator, Marty Lawing
Superior Court Judge, Judicial, Lora Cubbage
Environmental Enforcement Offi, Lorelei Elkins
Member, Stephen Dew
Deputy County, Dean Hollandsworth
Legal Administrator, Donna Riner
Executive Director, Dibrelle Tourret
Teacher, Andrea Heilborn
Teacher, Angela Doty
Revenue Agent, An 'dino Thomas
Registered Nurse, Betsy Wilcox
Auditors: CHERRY BEKAERT & HOLLAND LLP

LOCATIONS

HQ: COUNTY OF GUILFORD
  301 W MARKET ST, GREENSBORO, NC 274012514
Phone: 336 641-3836
Web: WWW.COUNTYWEB.CO.GUILFORD.NC.US

HISTORICAL FINANCIALS
Company Type: Private

Income Statement				FYE: June 30
	REVENUE ($ mil.)	NET INCOME ($ mil.)	NET PROFIT MARGIN	EMPLOYEES
06/16	596	3	0.6%	2,700
06/15	584	(21)	—	—
06/08	577	(70)	—	—
06/07	548	67	12.3%	—
Annual Growth	0.9%	(28.4%)	—	—

COUNTY OF HAMILTON

EXECUTIVES

Administrator, Jeff Aluotto
Administrator*, David Krings
Commissioner*, Tom Neyer
Treasurer*, Robert A Goering
Commissioner*, John Dowlin
C-Level Human Resources, Kim Pennekamp
C-Level Human Resources, Marcie McDonald
District Chief, Cedric Robinson
Building Manager, Darnell Edwards
Program Manager, David Spatholt
Information Technology Manager, Mike Fossett
Auditors: DAVE YOST COLUMBUS OHIO

LOCATIONS

HQ: COUNTY OF HAMILTON
  138 E COURT ST RM 607, CINCINNATI, OH
  452021226
Phone: 513 946-4400
Web: WWW.HAMILTON-CO.ORG

HISTORICAL FINANCIALS
Company Type: Private

Income Statement				FYE: December 31
	REVENUE ($ mil.)	NET INCOME ($ mil.)	NET PROFIT MARGIN	EMPLOYEES
12/20	1,058	82	7.8%	6,000
12/19	853	44	5.2%	—
12/18	770	(10)	—	—
12/17	741	69	9.4%	—
Annual Growth	12.6%	5.8%	—	—

2020 Year-End Financials

Return on assets: 1.7%   Cash ($ mil.): 71
Return on equity: 5.4%
Current ratio: —

COUNTY OF HARFORD

EXECUTIVES

County Exec, David Craig
Council Pres*, William Boniface
Treas*, Kathryn Hewitt
Procurement Staff, James P Barker
Procurement Staff, Stacy R Appold
Procurement Staff, Peter D Wakefiel
Procurement Staff, Stephanie L Si
Procurement Staff, Walter Ballesteros
Information Specialist, Constance Hirsch
Deputy Treasurer, Rick Pernas
Senior Internal Auditor, Brad Delauder
Auditors: SB & COMPANY LLC HUNT VALLEY

LOCATIONS

HQ: COUNTY OF HARFORD
  220 S MAIN ST, BEL AIR, MD 210143820
Phone: 410 638-3000
Web: WWW.HARFORDCOUNTYMD.GOV

HISTORICAL FINANCIALS
Company Type: Private

Income Statement				FYE: June 30
	REVENUE ($ mil.)	NET INCOME ($ mil.)	NET PROFIT MARGIN	EMPLOYEES
06/21	790	40	5.1%	1,400
06/20	692	(5)	—	—
06/18	630	22	3.5%	—
06/17	603	47	7.9%	—
Annual Growth	7.0%	(4.1%)	—	—

COUNTY OF HARRIS

EXECUTIVES

County Clerk, Teneshia Hudspeth
Coordinator, Fred King
Project Coordinator, Sgt Butler
Network Security Specialist, Marco Bayarena
Network Administrator, Raymond Miranda
Communication Officer, Brittney Powell
Administrat, David Jackson
Director of Communications, Hector De
Captain, John Shannon

Accountant, Nancy Baggett
Chief Clerk, Sylvia Ybarbo
Auditors: DELOITTE & TOUCHE LLP
  HOUSTON

LOCATIONS

HQ: COUNTY OF HARRIS
  201 CAROLINE ST FL 4, HOUSTON, TX 770021901
Phone: 713 274-8600
Web: WWW.CO.HARRIS.TX.US

HISTORICAL FINANCIALS
Company Type: Private

Income Statement				FYE: February 28
	REVENUE ($ mil.)	NET INCOME ($ mil.)	NET PROFIT MARGIN	EMPLOYEES
02/21	3,477	319	9.2%	14,000
02/20	3,076	176	5.7%	—
Annual Growth	13.0%	81.2%	—	—

2021 Year-End Financials

Return on assets: 1.2%   Cash ($ mil.): 2,983
Return on equity: 2.4%
Current ratio: —

COUNTY OF HAWAII

EXECUTIVES

Mayor, William P Kenoi
Human Resources, Lee Botelho
Civil Defense Administrator, Quince Mento
Civil Defense Administrator, Troy Kindred
Human Resources, Jennifer Sakamoto
Band Director, Paul Arceo
Manager, Reid Sewake
Human Resources, William Brilhante
Planner, Bethany Morrison
Tax Maps and Records Superviso, Mary Aken
Division Chief, Neil Azevedo
Auditors: N&K CPAS INC HONOLULU HAWAI

LOCATIONS

HQ: COUNTY OF HAWAII
  25 AUPUNI ST STE 107, HILO, HI 967204245
Phone: 808 961-8211
Web: WWW.HAWAIICOUNTY.GOV

HISTORICAL FINANCIALS
Company Type: Private

Income Statement				FYE: June 30
	REVENUE ($ mil.)	NET INCOME ($ mil.)	NET PROFIT MARGIN	EMPLOYEES
06/20	578	25	4.4%	2,000
06/19	524	10	2.0%	—
06/18	475	50	10.6%	—
06/17	427	(30)	—	—
Annual Growth	10.6%	—	—	—

2020 Year-End Financials

Return on assets: 1.1%   Cash ($ mil.): 139
Return on equity: 6.9%
Current ratio: 1.90

COUNTY OF HENRICO

EXECUTIVES

County Mgr, John A Vithoulkas
Superintendent*, Amy Cashwell
Recreation Coordinator, Elbert Grinnell
Human Resources Analyst Depart, Bettyann Moriarty
Battalion Chief 1a, John Shaffer
Assistant Director, Rebecca Simulcik
Administerative Assistant, Regina Windsor
Wastewater Collection Engineer, Ricky Blunt
Deputy Chief Community Risk RE, Tom Labelle
Human Resources Analyst, Karen Isaac
Information Technology Senior, Rebecca Cottle
Auditors: KPMG LLP RICHMOND VA

LOCATIONS

HQ: COUNTY OF HENRICO
4301 E PARHAM RD, HENRICO, VA 232282745
Phone: 804 501-4000
Web: WWW.HENRICO.US

HISTORICAL FINANCIALS

Company Type: Private

Income Statement				FYE: June 30
	REVENUE ($ mil.)	NET INCOME ($ mil.)	NET PROFIT MARGIN	EMPLOYEES
06/21	979	112	11.5%	9,178
06/20	935	74	8.0%	—
06/19	906	72	8.0%	—
06/18	853	(13)	—	—
Annual Growth	4.7%	—	—	—

COUNTY OF HILLSBOROUGH

EXECUTIVES

County Admin, Mike Merrill
Dep County Admin*, Gregory Horwedel
Chief Fin Admin*, Bonnie Wise
Chief Development Svs*, Lucia Garsys
Chief of Human Svs*, Carl Harness
Grants Admin*, Wayne Finley
Executive of Information Techn, Hammond R Powes
Program Inspector, Wayne New
Admin Splst, Catherine Achat
Information Specialist, Douglas Blythe
Sergeant, Rick Roebuck
Auditors: RSM US LLP TAMPA FLORIDA

LOCATIONS

HQ: COUNTY OF HILLSBOROUGH
601 E KENNEDY BLVD, TAMPA, FL 336024156
Phone: 813 276-2720
Web: WWW.HILLSBOROUGHCOUNTY.ORG

HISTORICAL FINANCIALS

Company Type: Private

Income Statement				FYE: September 30
	REVENUE ($ mil.)	NET INCOME ($ mil.)	NET PROFIT MARGIN	EMPLOYEES
09/20	2,072	129	6.2%	10,000
09/19	1,933	421	21.8%	—
09/18	1,737	66	3.9%	—
09/17	1,613	83	5.2%	—
Annual Growth	8.7%	15.5%	—	—

2020 Year-End Financials

Return on assets: 1.0% Cash ($ mil.): 413
Return on equity: 1.3%
Current ratio: 4.40

COUNTY OF JOHNSON

EXECUTIVES

Prin, Michael B Press
Information Specialist, Michael Chamberlin
Coordinator, Lory Rodak
Coordinator, Anthony Oropeza
Coordinator, Brian Greever
Executive Officer, Jim Bill
Vice Chair, Chris Evans-Hands
Special Events Coordinator, Katy Renner
Chief Surveyor Project Manager, Wes Root
Assistant Lab Director, David Wright
Vice President, Brenda Cameron
Auditors: ALLEN GIBBS & HOULIK LC WIC

LOCATIONS

HQ: COUNTY OF JOHNSON
111 S CHERRY ST STE 1200, OLATHE, KS 660613451
Phone: 913 715-0435
Web: WWW.JOCOGOV.ORG

HISTORICAL FINANCIALS

Company Type: Private

Income Statement				FYE: December 31
	REVENUE ($ mil.)	NET INCOME ($ mil.)	NET PROFIT MARGIN	EMPLOYEES
12/20	658	97	14.8%	2,242
12/18	487	13	2.7%	—
12/17	464	19	4.1%	—
12/16	451	13	3.1%	—
Annual Growth	9.9%	62.7%	—	—

COUNTY OF KERN

EXECUTIVES

Admin, John Nilon
Dir*, Robert Lerude
Staff, Eric Arias
Sergeant, Ed Komin
Probation Supervisor, Ahmed Baameur
Vice President, Carol Cox
Mental Health Nurse, Sara Bell
Auditors: BROWN ARMSTRONG ACCOUNTANCY CO

LOCATIONS

HQ: COUNTY OF KERN
1115 TRUXTUN AVE RM 505, BAKERSFIELD, CA 933014630
Phone: 661 868-3690
Web: WWW.KERNCOUNTY.COM

HISTORICAL FINANCIALS

Company Type: Private

Income Statement				FYE: June 30
	REVENUE ($ mil.)	NET INCOME ($ mil.)	NET PROFIT MARGIN	EMPLOYEES
06/16	1,561	1	0.1%	8,000
06/15	1,546	94	6.1%	—
06/11	1,365	21	1.6%	—
06/06	1,141	13	1.2%	—
Annual Growth	3.2%	(21.8%)	—	—

2016 Year-End Financials

Return on assets: — Cash ($ mil.): 1
Return on equity: 0.6%
Current ratio: —

COUNTY OF KING

EXECUTIVES

County Exec, Dow Constantine
Mgr-Treas Div, Garry Holmes
Captain, Douglas Justus
Captain, Michael Woodbury
Legislative Relations Manager, April Putney
Education Specialist, Claudia Sierra
Manager, Matthew Sykora
Communications Specialist, Annie Kolb-Nelson
Preservation Program Manager, Brandi Link
Capital Project Manager, Joe Hicker
Administrator, Richard Meeks
Auditors: PAT MCCARTHY OLYMPIA WA

LOCATIONS

HQ: COUNTY OF KING
201 S JACKSON ST, SEATTLE, WA 981043854
Phone: 206 296-4040
Web: WWW.KINGCOUNTY.GOV

HISTORICAL FINANCIALS

Company Type: Private

Income Statement				FYE: December 31
	REVENUE ($ mil.)	NET INCOME ($ mil.)	NET PROFIT MARGIN	EMPLOYEES
12/20	2,765	(25)	—	13,300
12/19	2,367	61	2.6%	—
12/18	2,295	16	0.7%	—
12/17	2,191	121	5.5%	—
Annual Growth	8.1%	—	—	—

2020 Year-End Financials

Return on assets: (-0.2%) Cash ($ mil.): 4,080
Return on equity: (-0.3%)
Current ratio: —

COUNTY OF LEE

EXECUTIVES

Dir, Roger Desjarlais
Exec Dir*, Jeff Mulder
Staff, Beth Moff
Director Digital Marketing, Allison Paula
Engineer, Ryerson John
Supervisor, Shawn Fournier
Lead Operator, Cadd Balogh
Implementation Analyst, Castro Enrique
Administrative Specialist, Leslie Erschen
Administrative Specialist, Debbie West
Tradesworker III Facilities Co, John Kelso
Auditors: CLIFTONLARSONALLEN LLP FORT M

LOCATIONS

HQ: COUNTY OF LEE
2115 SECOND ST, FORT MYERS, FL 339013012
Phone: 239 533-2236
Web: WWW.LEEGOV.COM

HISTORICAL FINANCIALS
Company Type: Private

Income Statement				FYE: September 30
	REVENUE ($ mil.)	NET INCOME ($ mil.)	NET PROFIT MARGIN	EMPLOYEES
09/20	804	76	9.5%	3,000
09/19	726	(4)	—	—
09/18	693	0	0.1%	—
09/17	638	17	2.7%	—
Annual Growth	8.0%	64.3%	—	—

COUNTY OF LOS ANGELES

The County of Los Angeles could easily be its own country; all it really needs is just an "r." It encompasses more than 4000 square miles 88 cities two islands and has a population of more than 10 million. The regional level of state government provides such services as law enforcement property assessment tax collection public health protection and other social services within its boundaries (sometimes sharing and often providing municipal services for unincorporated cities). The county's elected Board of Supervisors provide political direction filling executive legislative and judicial roles while the various departments manage daily operations. LA County has an annual budget of nearly $30 billion.

Financial Performance
The county's 2014 budget proposal of $24.7 billion was the first in five years to not include major cuts or include a deficit as the economy improves. It has weathered the economic recession better than many but most departments were trimmed an average of 15% over the last five years. In addition the county dipped into its reserves and froze pay for most of its employees.

EXECUTIVES

Ceo, Fesia Davenport
Exec Offc*, Violet Varona-Lukens
Supvr-First Dist*, Gloria Molina
Supvr-Second Dist*, Yvonne Brathwaite Burke
Supvr-Third Dist*, Zev Yaroslavsky
Supvr-Fourth Dist*, Don Knabe
Supvr-Fifth Dist*, Michael D Antonovich
Exec Asst*, Aileen Gerald
Executive Officer, Debbie Lizzari
Staff, Ed Castorena
Information Specialist, Ed Lamas
Auditors: MACIAS GINI & O'CONNELL LLP L

LOCATIONS

HQ: COUNTY OF LOS ANGELES
500 W TEMPLE ST STE 437, LOS ANGELES, CA 900122724
Phone: 213 974-1101
Web: WWW.LACOUNTY.GOV

HISTORICAL FINANCIALS
Company Type: Private

Income Statement				FYE: June 30
	REVENUE ($ mil.)	NET INCOME ($ mil.)	NET PROFIT MARGIN	EMPLOYEES
06/20	25,198	323	1.3%	100,000
06/19	23,510	915	3.9%	—
06/18	21,191	403	1.9%	—
06/17	20,064	393	2.0%	—
Annual Growth	7.9%	(6.3%)	—	—

COUNTY OF LOUDOUN, VIRGINIA

EXECUTIVES

County Admin, Kirby M Bowers
Treas*, H Roger Zurn Jr
Cntrl, Janet Romancyk
Payroll Staff, Michelle McTier
Coordinator, Fred Firestone
Coordinator, Tim Dudek
Coordinator, Marcus Gill
Coordinator, Kevin Johnson
Executive Officer, Indira Dholakia
Sergeant, Andrew Apollony
Captain, Chuck Wyant
Auditors: CHERRY BEKAERT LLP TYSONS COR

LOCATIONS

HQ: COUNTY OF LOUDOUN, VIRGINIA
1 HARRISON ST SE FL 1 # 1, LEESBURG, VA 201753102
Phone: 703 777-0100
Web: WWW.LOUDOUN.GOV

HISTORICAL FINANCIALS
Company Type: Private

Income Statement				FYE: June 30
	REVENUE ($ mil.)	NET INCOME ($ mil.)	NET PROFIT MARGIN	EMPLOYEES
06/19	1,797	133	7.4%	6,999
06/18	1,716	71	4.2%	—
06/17	1,638	126	7.7%	—
06/16	1,470	59	4.1%	—
Annual Growth	6.9%	30.8%	—	—

2019 Year-End Financials

Return on assets: 2.1%   Cash ($ mil.): 1,321
Return on equity: 7.3%
Current ratio: —

COUNTY OF MACOMB

EXECUTIVES

County Exec, Mark Hackel
Network Specialist, David F King
Commissioner District 9, Elizabeth Ann Lucido
Senior Secretary, Joann Priester
Commissioner District 4, Joseph Romano
Commissioner District 8, Phil Kraft
Commissioner District 10, Robert Leonetti
Police Officer, Nancy Lepage
Senior Secretary, Michelle Johnson
Auditors: PLANTE & MORAN PLLC CLINTON

LOCATIONS

HQ: COUNTY OF MACOMB
1 S MAIN ST FL 8, MOUNT CLEMENS, MI 480432306
Phone: 586 469-7001
Web: WWW.MACOMBGOV.ORG

HISTORICAL FINANCIALS
Company Type: Private

Income Statement				FYE: December 31
	REVENUE ($ mil.)	NET INCOME ($ mil.)	NET PROFIT MARGIN	EMPLOYEES
12/20	558	56	10.0%	3,000
12/19	425	15	3.6%	—
12/18	392	16	4.3%	—
12/17	373	(9)	—	—
Annual Growth	14.3%	—	—	—

COUNTY OF MARICOPA

EXECUTIVES

Cfo, Shelby Scharbach
Coordinator, Michele Hamm
Manager, Jeannie Taylor
Analyst, David Bross
Procurement Specialist, Michael Cora
Infrastructure Technology Cent, Roseann Osborn-Perez
Lawyer, Art Merchant
Director of Business Strategie, Christopher Bradley
Public Information Officer, Melissa Gable
Deputy Chief of Staff, Nicole Bendle
Community Dietitian Supervisor, Tina Wegner
Auditors: LINDSEY PERRY CPA CFE AUDIT

LOCATIONS

HQ: COUNTY OF MARICOPA
301 W JEFFERSON ST # 960, PHOENIX, AZ 850032143
Phone: 602 506-3011
Web: WWW.MARICOPA.GOV

HISTORICAL FINANCIALS
Company Type: Private

Income Statement				FYE: June 30
	REVENUE ($ mil.)	NET INCOME ($ mil.)	NET PROFIT MARGIN	EMPLOYEES
06/20	2,444	278	11.4%	15,751
06/19	2,266	21	1.0%	—
06/18	2,136	25	1.2%	—
06/17	2,063	(34)	—	—
Annual Growth	5.8%	—	—	—

2020 Year-End Financials
Return on assets: 4.1%   Cash ($ mil.): 67
Return on equity: 7.4%
Current ratio: —

COUNTY OF MARIN

EXECUTIVES
ADM, Matthew Hymel
Supervisor*, Susan Adams
Supervisor*, Katie Rice
Supervisor*, Kathrin Sears
Supervisor*, Stephen Kinsey
Supervisor*, Judy Arnold
Accounting Specialist, Wendy Collins
Assistant Clerk, Diane Patterson
Probation Officer, Fred Blum
Management, Howard Grimes
Management, James Parivash
Auditors: CLIFTONLARSONALLEN LLP ROSEVI

LOCATIONS
HQ: COUNTY OF MARIN
3501 CIVIC CENTER DR # 225, SAN RAFAEL, CA 949034112
Phone: 415 473-6358

HISTORICAL FINANCIALS
Company Type: Private

Income Statement				FYE: June 30
	REVENUE ($ mil.)	NET INCOME ($ mil.)	NET PROFIT MARGIN	EMPLOYEES
06/20	656	41	6.2%	2,122
06/19	651	69	10.7%	—
06/18	608	32	5.4%	—
06/17	567	28	5.0%	—
Annual Growth	5.0%	12.9%	—	—

COUNTY OF MAUI

EXECUTIVES
Mayor, Alan Arakawa
Executive Assistant, John Buck
Assistant, Lois Whitney
Program Inspector, Ryan Otsubo
Assistant Communications Direc, Ryan Piros
Software Engineer, Ty Takeno
Software Engineer, Wendy Kobashigawa
Deputy Director, Brianne Savage
Administrative Assistant, Dena To
Clerk III, Jo-Anne Tanaka
Program Assistant, Lillian Lechler
Auditors: N&K CPAS INC HONOLULU HAWA

LOCATIONS
HQ: COUNTY OF MAUI
200 S HIGH ST, WAILUKU, HI 967932155
Phone: 808 270-7855
Web: WWW.MAUICOUNTY.GOV

HISTORICAL FINANCIALS
Company Type: Private

Income Statement				FYE: June 30
	REVENUE ($ mil.)	NET INCOME ($ mil.)	NET PROFIT MARGIN	EMPLOYEES
06/20	621	14	2.3%	2,000
06/16	463	3	0.8%	—
06/15	445	4	1.0%	—
06/14	429	(117)	—	—
Annual Growth	6.4%	—	—	—

COUNTY OF MECKLENBURG

EXECUTIVES
Dir, Dena Diorio
Grant Admin, Anna Marie Cutijar
Information Specialist, Stefahn Orr
Employee Relations Analyst, Teresa Curlin
His Supervisor, Angie Craig
Administrative Assistant, Latonya Brewer
Captain, Mark McLaughlin
Director, Nha Yang
Senior It Business Analyst, Sandy Goodwin
Human Resources Manager, Andrea Grier
Senior Social Worker III, Anissa Rhyne
Auditors: CHERRY BEKAERT LLP RALEIGH N

LOCATIONS
HQ: COUNTY OF MECKLENBURG
600 E 4TH ST, CHARLOTTE, NC 282022816
Phone: 704 336-2108
Web: WWW.MECKNC.GOV

HISTORICAL FINANCIALS
Company Type: Private

Income Statement				FYE: June 30
	REVENUE ($ mil.)	NET INCOME ($ mil.)	NET PROFIT MARGIN	EMPLOYEES
06/16	1,603	(46)	—	4,800
06/15	1,469	17	1.2%	—
06/14	1,485	41	2.8%	—
06/13	1,433	109	7.7%	—
Annual Growth	3.8%	—	—	—

COUNTY OF MERCED

EXECUTIVES
Cnty ADM, Demitrios Tatum
Supervisor Programmer Analyst, Richard Harp
Programmer Analyst II, Ryan Wilson
Finance Executive, Jeri Allgood
Programmer Analyst III, Arnie Carvajal
Chief Auditor Appraiser, Patricia Houbein
Paralegal, Rhonda Amezcua
Sergeant, Rick Blodgett
Prin, Anne McCarthy
Human Resources Office Supervi, Annette Giacalone
Supervising Programmer Analyst, Brian Liebelt
Auditors: BROWN ARMSTRONG BAKERSFIELD

LOCATIONS
HQ: COUNTY OF MERCED
2222 M ST, MERCED, CA 953403729
Phone: 209 385-7511
Web: WWW.COUNTYOFMERCED.COM

HISTORICAL FINANCIALS
Company Type: Private

Income Statement				FYE: June 30
	REVENUE ($ mil.)	NET INCOME ($ mil.)	NET PROFIT MARGIN	EMPLOYEES
06/20	551	12	2.3%	2,700
06/19	518	16	3.1%	—
06/18	477	(3)	—	—
06/17	452	14	3.1%	—
Annual Growth	6.8%	(3.4%)	—	—

COUNTY OF MONMOUTH

EXECUTIVES
Dir, John Curley
Admin*, Teri O'Connor
Fin Dir*, Craig Marshall
Chief Acct, Joseph M Morris
Dir, Charles Brown III
Vice-Chairman, William Potter
Assistant Engineer, Daniel Olivares
Public Information Assistant, Tricia Ring
Human, Charlie Brown
DDS, Frank Ortolano
Gis Coordinator, Meghan Leavey
Auditors: HOLMAN FRENIA ALLISON PC F

LOCATIONS
HQ: COUNTY OF MONMOUTH
1 E MAIN ST, FREEHOLD, NJ 077282273
Phone: 732 431-7000
Web: WWW.CO.MONMOUTH.NJ.US

HISTORICAL FINANCIALS
Company Type: Private

Income Statement				FYE: December 31
	REVENUE ($ mil.)	NET INCOME ($ mil.)	NET PROFIT MARGIN	EMPLOYEES
12/20	670	33	4.9%	3,800
12/19	589	38	6.6%	—
12/18	563	38	6.9%	—
12/17	563	41	7.3%	—
Annual Growth	6.0%	(7.2%)	—	—

2020 Year-End Financials
Return on assets: 1.2%   Cash ($ mil.): 314
Return on equity: 2.0%
Current ratio: —

COUNTY OF MONROE

EXECUTIVES

Exec Dir, Maggie Brooks
Controller, Toni Feransi
Controller, Anthony Feroce
Director, Hilary Tantillo
Information Technology Interne, Mike Burke
Senior Manager, Trish Vantucci
Community Coordinator, Amy Mills
Vice President For Release, Charlene Leistman
Information Technology Interne, Elizabeth Prescod
Probation Officer, Jennifer Oliphant
Purchasing Representative, Meagan Brennan
Auditors: KPMG LLP ROCHESTER NY

LOCATIONS

HQ: COUNTY OF MONROE
 39 W MAIN ST STE 110, ROCHESTER, NY 146141408
Phone: 585 753-1700
Web: WWW.MONROECOUNTY.GOV

HISTORICAL FINANCIALS
Company Type: Private

Income Statement				FYE: December 31
	REVENUE ($ mil.)	NET INCOME ($ mil.)	NET PROFIT MARGIN	EMPLOYEES
12/18	1,353	21	1.6%	4,800
12/15	1,299	39	3.0%	—
Annual Growth	1.4%	(18.2%)	—	—

2018 Year-End Financials
Return on assets: 0.8%   Cash ($ mil.): 248
Return on equity: 10.6%
Current ratio: 1.30

COUNTY OF MONTGOMERY

EXECUTIVES

Chb-Chm, Josh Shapiro
Comm*, Bruce L Castor Jr
Cfo*, Uri Z Monson

Coo*, Lauren M Lambrugo
Prin*, Leslie Richards
Dep Contrl, Kevin Hoke
Asst Contrl, Diane Morgan
Information Specialist, William Pergine
Information Specialist, Carolyn Mayinja
Coordinator, Claudine Schull
Information Specialist, Mark Houseal
Auditors: MAILLIE LLP OAKS PENNSYLVAN

LOCATIONS

HQ: COUNTY OF MONTGOMERY
 530 PORT INDIAN RD, NORRISTOWN, PA 194033502
Phone: 610 630-2252
Web: WWW.MONTCOPA.ORG

HISTORICAL FINANCIALS
Company Type: Private

Income Statement				FYE: December 31
	REVENUE ($ mil.)	NET INCOME ($ mil.)	NET PROFIT MARGIN	EMPLOYEES
12/19	661	17	2.6%	3,278
12/17	635	5	0.8%	—
12/15	525	(27)	—	—
12/12	542	(16)	—	—
Annual Growth	2.9%	—	—	—

2019 Year-End Financials
Return on assets: 1.7%   Cash ($ mil.): 167
Return on equity: 52.2%
Current ratio: —

COUNTY OF MONTGOMERY

EXECUTIVES

Cnty Admin, Michael Colbert
Coms*, Deborah Lieberman
Coms*, Judy Dodge
Coms*, Dan Foley
Coordinator, Jim Lewis
Director, Timothy S Nolan
Coordinator, Lenza Smith
Senior Buyer, Jacqueline Bailey
Director, Tyler Small
Information Technology Manager, Janet Holman
Treasurer, Jenny Hunley
Auditors: PLATTENBURG & ASSOCIATES INC

LOCATIONS

HQ: COUNTY OF MONTGOMERY
 451 W 3RD ST, DAYTON, OH 454220001
Phone: 937 225-4000
Web: WWW.MCOHIO.ORG

HISTORICAL FINANCIALS
Company Type: Private

Income Statement				FYE: December 31
	REVENUE ($ mil.)	NET INCOME ($ mil.)	NET PROFIT MARGIN	EMPLOYEES
12/20	654	13	2.0%	5,000
12/19	559	25	4.5%	—
12/18	528	12	2.3%	—
12/17	495	(5)	—	—
Annual Growth	9.7%	—	—	—

2020 Year-End Financials
Return on assets: 0.6%   Cash ($ mil.): 610
Return on equity: 1.2%
Current ratio: —

COUNTY OF MULTNOMAH

EXECUTIVES

Superintendent, Robert Dunton
Education, Dorthy Hayden
Teacher Gs Assistant, Desiree Chiu
Culinary Art Teacher, Jenny Radulesk
Charter School Teacher, Rhiannon Young
Teacher, Kristin Wold
Middle School, Randy Trani
Board Member, Katey Kinnear
Software Manager, Anthony Young
Health Nurse Director, Debbie Baker
Business Manager, Doana Anderson
Auditors: WILCOX ARREDONDO & CO CANBY

LOCATIONS

HQ: COUNTY OF MULTNOMAH
 35800 E HISTRC COLMB RIV, CORBETT, OR 970199687
Phone: 503 261-4200
Web: WWW.CORBETT.K12.OR.US

HISTORICAL FINANCIALS
Company Type: Private

Income Statement				FYE: June 30
	REVENUE ($ mil.)	NET INCOME ($ mil.)	NET PROFIT MARGIN	EMPLOYEES
06/21	1,687	530	31.5%	297
06/20	14	2	17.9%	—
06/18	13	0	1.4%	—
06/16	10	(1)	—	—
Annual Growth	174.5%	—	—	—

COUNTY OF MULTNOMAH

EXECUTIVES

County Chair, Jeff Cogen
Accounting Spelialist, Leslie Ryan
Coordinator, Tameka Brazile
Staff, Tara Bowen-Biggs
Project Coordinator, Kappes Courtney
Acting Director, John Wasiutynski
Information Technology Manager, Rodney Chin
Director of Data Processing, Anita Whynot
Senior Business Analys, Jason Heilbrun
Senior Human Resources Analyst, James Opoka
Human Resources Manager, Karin T Lamberton
Auditors: MOSS ADAMS LLP EUGENE OREGON

LOCATIONS

HQ: COUNTY OF MULTNOMAH
501 SE HAWTHORNE BLVD # 5, PORTLAND, OR
972143587
Phone: 503 988-3511
Web: WWW.MULTCO.US

HISTORICAL FINANCIALS

Company Type: Private

Income Statement				FYE: June 30
	REVENUE ($ mil.)	NET INCOME ($ mil.)	NET PROFIT MARGIN	EMPLOYEES
06/20	1,319	(38)	—	5,000
06/19	1,469	(56)	—	—
06/18	1,273	93	7.3%	—
06/17	1,238	(19)	—	—
Annual Growth	2.1%	—	—	—

COUNTY OF NASSAU

EXECUTIVES

County Exec, Laura Curran
County Comptrl*, Jack Schnirman
Art Director, Fat C Paperie
Clerk Typist, Eileen Venditto
Human Resources, Howard Marisa
Deputy Director, Irina Sedighi
Director, Kim Collins
Deputy Counsel, Martin Meaney
Intelligence Analyst, Megan Dollery
Associate Director Athletic Co, Tim Hahn
Senior Deputy Director, Christopher Nolan
Auditors: MARKS PANETH LLP NEW YORK N

LOCATIONS

HQ: COUNTY OF NASSAU
1 WEST ST, MINEOLA, NY 115014813
Phone: 516 571-3131
Web: WWW.NASSAUCOUNTYNY.GOV

HISTORICAL FINANCIALS

Company Type: Private

Income Statement				FYE: December 31
	REVENUE ($ mil.)	NET INCOME ($ mil.)	NET PROFIT MARGIN	EMPLOYEES
12/20	3,422	15	0.5%	14,500
12/19	3,522	150	4.3%	—
12/18	3,442	111	3.2%	—
12/17	3,401	(115)	—	—
Annual Growth	0.2%	—	—	—

2020 Year-End Financials

Return on assets: 0.2%
Return on equity: —
Current ratio: 1.10
Cash ($ mil.): 1,055

COUNTY OF OAKLAND

EXECUTIVES

County Exec, L Brooks Patterson
Treasurer*, Patrick M Dohany
Management, Laurie Van Pelt

Information Specialist, Tina Labeau
Coordinator, Bradley Hansen
Coordinator, Andrea Bayer
Sergeant, Richard Cummins
Project Coordinator, Robert Burch
Assistant Prosecuting, Micah Wallace
Information Technology Directo, David Wurtz
Senior Business Consultant, Erick Phillips
Auditors: PLANTE & MORAN PLC SOUTHFIELD

LOCATIONS

HQ: COUNTY OF OAKLAND
1200 N TELEGRAPH RD STE 1, PONTIAC, MI
483411043
Phone: 248 858-1000
Web: WWW.OAKGOV.COM

HISTORICAL FINANCIALS

Company Type: Private

Income Statement				FYE: September 30
	REVENUE ($ mil.)	NET INCOME ($ mil.)	NET PROFIT MARGIN	EMPLOYEES
09/20	620	(6)	—	4,229
09/18	500	(11)	—	—
09/17	483	(8)	—	—
09/16	468	26	5.6%	—
Annual Growth	7.3%	—	—	—

2020 Year-End Financials

Return on assets: (-0.2%)
Return on equity: (-0.2%)
Current ratio: 2.80
Cash ($ mil.): 71

COUNTY OF ONEIDA

EXECUTIVES

Exec Dir, Anthony Pecente
Cfo-Cmptrl*, Joseph Timpano
Chief of Staff, Alfred Candido
Executive Director, Joseph Griffo
Director, Thomas Keeler
Program Director, John Kent
Director, Annemarie Ambrose
Commissioner, Dennis Davis
Sergeant, Arthur Broccoli
Director of Traffic Safety, Bob Engels
Director, Diana Noviasky
Auditors: DRESCHER & MALECKI LLP BUFFAL

LOCATIONS

HQ: COUNTY OF ONEIDA
800 PARK AVE STE 5, UTICA, NY 135012939
Phone: 315 798-5780
Web: WWW.OCGOV.NET

HISTORICAL FINANCIALS

Company Type: Private

Income Statement				FYE: December 31
	REVENUE ($ mil.)	NET INCOME ($ mil.)	NET PROFIT MARGIN	EMPLOYEES
12/20	554	3	0.6%	1,700
12/19	423	6	1.5%	—
12/18	412	17	4.2%	—
12/17	388	(3)	—	—
Annual Growth	12.5%	—	—	—

2020 Year-End Financials

Return on assets: 0.3%
Return on equity: 4.4%
Current ratio: —
Cash ($ mil.): 51

COUNTY OF ONONDAGA

EXECUTIVES

Prin, Joanne M Mahoney
County Exec*, Nicholas J Pirro
Coordinator, Madison Quinn
Account Clerk II, April Warrick
Deputy County Executive, Bill Fisher
Intergovernmental Affairs, Bob Andrews
Special Education Transportati, Jason Laroche
Financial Analyst, Lori Pietruniak
Commissioner, Michele Sardo
Director, Travis Glazier
Administrator, William Blanchard
Auditors: BONADIO & CO LLP SYRACUSE

LOCATIONS

HQ: COUNTY OF ONONDAGA
1000 ERIE BLVD W, SYRACUSE, NY 132042748
Phone: 315 435-8683
Web: WWW.ONGOV.NET

HISTORICAL FINANCIALS

Company Type: Private

Income Statement				FYE: December 31
	REVENUE ($ mil.)	NET INCOME ($ mil.)	NET PROFIT MARGIN	EMPLOYEES
12/20	947	34	3.7%	508
12/19	981	26	2.7%	—
12/18	964	(0)	—	—
12/17	906	(42)	—	—
Annual Growth	1.5%	—	—	—

COUNTY OF ORANGE

EXECUTIVES

Ceo, Frank Kim
Ceo*, Michael Gincola
Cfo*, Bob Franz
Prin*, Mary Chin
Information Technology Manager, Luis Najera
Accounting Specialist, Cynthia Vela
Director, Martha Campbell
Program Manager, Quazi Hashmi
It Analyst, Carrie Dooling
Community Outreach Director, Francis Hur
Clerk, Francisco Mora
Auditors: EIDE BAILLY LLP LAGUNA HILLS

LOCATIONS

HQ: COUNTY OF ORANGE
333 W SANTA ANA BLVD, SANTA ANA, CA 927014084
Phone: 714 834-6200
Web: WWW.OCGOV.COM

HISTORICAL FINANCIALS
Company Type: Private

Income Statement				FYE: June 30
	REVENUE ($ mil.)	NET INCOME ($ mil.)	NET PROFIT MARGIN	EMPLOYEES
06/20	4,387	40	0.9%	21,000
06/19	4,105	152	3.7%	—
06/18	4,045	(78)	—	—
06/17	3,884	220	5.7%	—
Annual Growth	4.1%	(43.4%)	—	—

2020 Year-End Financials
Return on assets: 0.3% Cash ($ mil.): 4,386
Return on equity: 1.0%
Current ratio: —

COUNTY OF ORANGE
EXECUTIVES

Mayor, Teresa Jacobs
County Administrator*, Ajit Lalchandani
Clerk*, Lydia Gardner
Comptroller*, Andy Diloreto
Commissioner Dist 1*, Betsy Vanderley
Commissioner Dist 2*, Rod A Love
Commissioner Dist 3*, Pete Clarke
Commissioner Dist 4*, Jennifer Thompson
Commissioner Dist 5*, Emily Bonilla
Commissioner Dist 6*, Victoria P Siplin
Customer Representativ, Deja Wallace
Auditors: CHERRY BEKAERT LLP ORLANDO F

LOCATIONS

HQ: COUNTY OF ORANGE
201 S ROSALIND AVE FL 5, ORLANDO, FL 328013527
Phone: 407 836-7350
Web: WWW.OCCOMPT.COM

HISTORICAL FINANCIALS
Company Type: Private

Income Statement				FYE: September 30
	REVENUE ($ mil.)	NET INCOME ($ mil.)	NET PROFIT MARGIN	EMPLOYEES
09/20	1,970	113	5.7%	7,315
09/19	1,822	205	11.3%	—
09/18	1,694	126	7.5%	—
09/17	1,564	91	5.9%	—
Annual Growth	8.0%	7.3%	—	—

COUNTY OF ORANGE
EXECUTIVES

Cnty Exec, Edward A Diana
Comm-Fin*, Joel Kleiman
MBR*, Steven M Neuhaus
Cntrl, Joel Kileman
Accounting Assistant, Brenda Christie
Commissioner, Brendan Casey
Director of Account Strategy, Kelly Bradley
DBA, Mary Mirabella
Director Integratio, Ray Jagos

Information Technician, Luke Ercoline
Executive Secretary, Christine Rudy

LOCATIONS

HQ: COUNTY OF ORANGE
255 MAIN ST STE 1055, GOSHEN, NY 109241641
Phone: 845 291-2480
Web: WWW.ORANGECOUNTYGOV.COM

HISTORICAL FINANCIALS
Company Type: Private

Income Statement				FYE: December 31
	REVENUE ($ mil.)	NET INCOME ($ mil.)	NET PROFIT MARGIN	EMPLOYEES
12/20	680	10	1.6%	2,700
12/19	724	12	1.7%	—
12/18	699	(33)	—	—
12/17	674	5	0.8%	—
Annual Growth	0.3%	27.7%	—	—

2020 Year-End Financials
Return on assets: 0.9% Cash ($ mil.): 113
Return on equity: —
Current ratio: —

COUNTY OF PALM BEACH
EXECUTIVES

Mayor, Dave Kerner
Clerk*, Sharon R Bock
Cfo*, Darlene Malaney
MBR*, Elena Madonna
Grants Coordinator, Claudia Salazar
Accounting Staff, Nancy Welling
Captain, Wendy Wise
Coordinator, Lauren Kurth
Coordinator, Tyrell Hall
Elections Supervisor, Wendy Link
Palm Beach County Supervisor O, Susan Bucher
Auditors: RSM US LLP WEST PALM BEACH F

LOCATIONS

HQ: COUNTY OF PALM BEACH
301 N OLIVE AVE FRNT, WEST PALM BEACH, FL
334014703
Phone: 561 355-4950
Web: WWW.DISCOVER.PBCGOV.ORG

HISTORICAL FINANCIALS
Company Type: Private

Income Statement				FYE: September 30
	REVENUE ($ mil.)	NET INCOME ($ mil.)	NET PROFIT MARGIN	EMPLOYEES
09/20	2,366	153	6.5%	5,500
09/18	2,081	134	6.5%	—
09/17	1,960	28	1.5%	—
09/16	1,821	68	3.8%	—
Annual Growth	6.8%	22.5%	—	—

COUNTY OF PASCO
EXECUTIVES

Dmin, Michele Baker
Admin*, John J Gallagher
Budget Anaylst, Linda Bullard
Sr. Clerk, Debra Cleveland
Project Coordinator, Chris Dewey
Customer Staff, Lisa Stinnett
Engineering Director, Margaret Smith
Human Resources Director, Barbara Hitzemann
Laboratory Manager, Candia Mulhern
Teacher, Frank Nichols
Teacher, James Drury
Auditors: KPMG LLP TAMPA FL

LOCATIONS

HQ: COUNTY OF PASCO
8731 CITIZENS DR, NEW PORT RICHEY, FL
346545572
Phone: 727 847-2411
Web: WWW.PASCOCOUNTYFL.NET

HISTORICAL FINANCIALS
Company Type: Private

Income Statement				FYE: September 30
	REVENUE ($ mil.)	NET INCOME ($ mil.)	NET PROFIT MARGIN	EMPLOYEES
09/18	577	41	7.1%	1,540
09/17	520	58	11.3%	—
09/16	475	48	10.2%	—
09/15	447	28	6.3%	—
Annual Growth	8.9%	13.7%	—	—

2018 Year-End Financials
Return on assets: 1.3% Cash ($ mil.): 501
Return on equity: 2.0%
Current ratio: 7.30

COUNTY OF PIERCE
EXECUTIVES

Ceo, Patricia McCarthy
Software Engineer Developer, Chuck Buzzard
Prevention Specialist, Gregory Tanbara
Assessor Treasurer, Mike Lonergan
Executive Assisstant, Alice McDaniel
Chief of Staff, Brian Hardtke
Executive Administrative Servi, Briana Fagan
Division Manager, Celia Taylor
Public Information Specialist, Mike Halliday
Executive Office Assistant, Tamara Svec
Auditors: PAT MCCARTHY STATE AUDITOR O

LOCATIONS

HQ: COUNTY OF PIERCE
950 FAWCETT AVE STE 100, TACOMA, WA 984025603
Phone: 253 798-7285
Web: WWW.PIERCECOUNTYWA.GOV

HISTORICAL FINANCIALS
Company Type: Private

Income Statement   FYE: December 31

	REVENUE ($ mil.)	NET INCOME ($ mil.)	NET PROFIT MARGIN	EMPLOYEES
12/20	839	35	4.2%	2,270
12/19	647	107	16.6%	—
12/18	606	34	5.7%	—
12/17	582	27	4.7%	—
Annual Growth	13.0%	8.5%	—	—

2020 Year-End Financials
Return on assets: 1.2%   Cash ($ mil.): 251
Return on equity: 1.7%
Current ratio: —

COUNTY OF PLACER

EXECUTIVES

Ceo*, Andrew Health
Administrative Direct, Darlene King
Program Supervisor, Gina Geisler
Librarian, Sheri Callow
Executive Director, Tiffany Johnson
Educational Audiologist, Christina Barbao
Assistant Risk Manager, Joe Ney
Vice Chair, John Allard
Assistant Planner, Kathleen Hanley
Administrative Technician, Lynn Gullion
Cte Instructor, Marcella Cruz
Auditors: VAVRINEK TRINE DAY & CO LL

LOCATIONS

HQ: COUNTY OF PLACER
 2986 RICHARDSON DR, AUBURN, CA 956032640
Phone: 530 889-4200
Web: WWW.PLACER.CA.GOV

HISTORICAL FINANCIALS
Company Type: Private

Income Statement   FYE: June 30

	REVENUE ($ mil.)	NET INCOME ($ mil.)	NET PROFIT MARGIN	EMPLOYEES
06/20	700	(11)	—	3,024
06/19	638	18	3.0%	—
06/18	596	7	1.2%	—
06/17	557	(19)	—	—
Annual Growth	7.9%	—	—	—

COUNTY OF PRINCE WILLIAM

EXECUTIVES

County Exec, Melissa S Peacor
Dir*, Chris Martino
Admin Coordinator, Deborah R Eaton
Assistant Count, Melissa Peacor
Cite Inspector, Alan Roberts
Cite Inspector, Keith Harper
Cite Inspector, Greg Compton
Cite Inspector, Todd Sheppard
Specialist II, Eduardo Londres
Specialist III, Carolyn Garrity
District Supervisor, John Jenkins
Auditors: CHERRY BEKAERT LLP TYSONS CO

LOCATIONS

HQ: COUNTY OF PRINCE WILLIAM
 1 COUNTY COMPLEX CT, WOODBRIDGE, VA
 221929202
Phone: 703 792-4640
Web: WWW.PWCVA.GOV

HISTORICAL FINANCIALS
Company Type: Private

Income Statement   FYE: June 30

	REVENUE ($ mil.)	NET INCOME ($ mil.)	NET PROFIT MARGIN	EMPLOYEES
06/20	1,417	33	2.3%	2,700
06/19	1,366	10	0.7%	—
06/18	1,261	(42)	—	—
06/17	1,217	(43)	—	—
Annual Growth	5.2%	—	—	—

2020 Year-End Financials
Return on assets: 0.8%   Cash ($ mil.): 1,318
Return on equity: 3.4%
Current ratio: —

COUNTY OF RAMSEY

EXECUTIVES

Ceo, Julie Kleinschmidt
Hr*, Gail Blackstone
Cfo*, Lee Mehrkens
Attorney*, John Choi
Officer*, Matt Bostrom
Asst Mgr, Heather Worthington
Administrator, Dawn Siegling
Sergeant, Fred Gray
Assistant Chief, Todd Axtell
Dpty County Manager, Informati, Karen Francois
Senior Vice President Human RE, Susan Gaertner
Auditors: REBECCA OTTO SAINT PAUL MN

LOCATIONS

HQ: COUNTY OF RAMSEY
 121 7TH PL E STE 4000, SAINT PAUL, MN 551012419
Phone: 651 266-8044
Web: WWW.RAMSEYCOUNTY.US

HISTORICAL FINANCIALS
Company Type: Private

Income Statement   FYE: December 31

	REVENUE ($ mil.)	NET INCOME ($ mil.)	NET PROFIT MARGIN	EMPLOYEES
12/20	1,087	129	12.0%	4,000
12/19	934	39	4.2%	—
12/18	725	91	12.5%	—
12/17	638	(5)	—	—
Annual Growth	19.4%	—	—	—

2020 Year-End Financials
Return on assets: 7.4%   Cash ($ mil.): —
Return on equity: 13.5%
Current ratio: 5.50

COUNTY OF RIVERSIDE

EXECUTIVES

First Dist Sup, Bob Buster
2nd Dist Sup*, John Tavaglinoe
3rd Dist Sup*, Jeff Stone
Sup*, Cynthia R
Sup*, Marion Ashley
SEC*, Judy Green
Dir*, Jean Strey
Dir*, John Mooney
Dir*, Lucas Robert
Acct Mngr, Susan Porte
Human Resources Analyst III, Anabel Mulhern
Auditors: BROWN ARMSTRONG
 ACCOUNTANCY CO

LOCATIONS

HQ: COUNTY OF RIVERSIDE
 4080 LEMON ST FL 11, RIVERSIDE, CA 925013609
Phone: 951 955-1110
Web: WWW.RIVCO.ORG

HISTORICAL FINANCIALS
Company Type: Private

Income Statement   FYE: June 30

	REVENUE ($ mil.)	NET INCOME ($ mil.)	NET PROFIT MARGIN	EMPLOYEES
06/20	4,044	76	1.9%	20,000
06/19	3,727	26	0.7%	—
Annual Growth	8.5%	190.0%	—	—

COUNTY OF ROCKLAND

EXECUTIVES

County Exec, Edwin Day
SEC*, Melanie Smith
Assistant To Sheriff, Robert Winzinger
Vice President of Habitat, Alden Wolfe
Board Member, Aron Wieder
Majority Leader, Michael Grant
County Commissioner, Christopher Carey
Transit Marketing Coordinator, Michael Prendergast
Office Clerk, Brenda Mone
Technician, Bryan Schaub
Fleet Manager, Cesar Perez
Auditors: MARKS PANETH LLP NEW YORK NY

LOCATIONS

HQ: COUNTY OF ROCKLAND
 11 NEW HEMPSTEAD RD # 10, NEW CITY, NY
 109563664
Phone: 845 638-5122
Web: WWW.ROCKLANDGOV.COM

HISTORICAL FINANCIALS

Company Type: Private

Income Statement				FYE: December 31
	REVENUE ($ mil.)	NET INCOME ($ mil.)	NET PROFIT MARGIN	EMPLOYEES
12/20	612	30	5.0%	3,100
12/19	624	34	5.6%	—
12/18	616	61	10.0%	—
12/17	703	(5)	—	—
Annual Growth	(4.5%)	—	—	—

2020 Year-End Financials

Return on assets: 1.8%   Cash ($ mil.): 329
Return on equity: —
Current ratio: 1.80

COUNTY OF SACRAMENTO

EXECUTIVES

Ced, David Villanueva
Sup*, Patrick Kennedy
Sup*, Susan Peters
Sup*, Sue Frost
Sup*, Don Nottoli
Inspector General, Rick Braziel
Information Specialist, Luyen Le
Public Defender, Steven M Garrett
Director, Dept of Health Servi, Peter Beilenson
Registrar of Voters, Courtney Bailey-Kanelos
Court Manager, Brenda Allen
Auditors: VAVRINEK TRINE DAY & CO LL

LOCATIONS

HQ: COUNTY OF SACRAMENTO
  700 H ST STE 7650, SACRAMENTO, CA 958141280
Phone: 916 874-8515
Web: WWW.SACCOUNTY.NET

HISTORICAL FINANCIALS

Company Type: Private

Income Statement				FYE: June 30
	REVENUE ($ mil.)	NET INCOME ($ mil.)	NET PROFIT MARGIN	EMPLOYEES
06/20	3,114	98	3.2%	10,968
06/19	2,857	(17)	—	—
06/18	2,801	62	2.2%	—
06/17	2,700	77	2.9%	—
Annual Growth	4.9%	8.3%	—	—

COUNTY OF SALT LAKE

EXECUTIVES

Mayor, Ben McAdams
C-Level Human Resources, Gaylyn Larson
Coordinator, Ashlee Yoder
Vice-President Legal, Janyce Syndergaard
Project Coordinator, Richard Poulsen
Project Coordinator, Raegan Scharman

Assistant, Anna Borres
Real Estate Conultant, Bonnie Thomson
Project Coordinator, Angel Kent
Information Security Analyst, Christensen Mark
Program Coordinator, Angela Smith
Auditors: SQUIRE & COMPANY PC OREM UT

LOCATIONS

HQ: COUNTY OF SALT LAKE
  2001 S STATE ST STE 2-200, SALT LAKE CITY, UT 841900001
Phone: 801 468-3225
Web: WWW.SLCO.ORG

HISTORICAL FINANCIALS

Company Type: Private

Income Statement				FYE: December 31
	REVENUE ($ mil.)	NET INCOME ($ mil.)	NET PROFIT MARGIN	EMPLOYEES
12/20	1,284	29	2.3%	4,200
12/15	972	35	3.7%	—
12/10	564	79	14.1%	—
12/09	504	27	5.5%	—
Annual Growth	8.9%	0.4%	—	—

2020 Year-End Financials

Return on assets: 1.5%   Cash ($ mil.): —
Return on equity: 3.1%
Current ratio: —

COUNTY OF SAN BERNARDINO

EXECUTIVES

Chm, Janice Rutherford
Aud-Ctrl-Treas*, Ensen Mason
Aud-Ctrl-Rec*, Errol J Mackzum
Chf Dep Aud*, Howard Ochi
Aud-Ctrl-Rec*, Larry Walker
Staff, Allen Simmons
Buyer, Bob Page
Assistant, Gary McBride
Coordinator, Maggie Latimer
Assistant Chief, Mary O'Toole
Assistant Chief, Mischelle Scray
Auditors: VAVRINEK TRINE DAY & CO LL

LOCATIONS

HQ: COUNTY OF SAN BERNARDINO
  385 N ARROWHEAD AVE, SAN BERNARDINO, CA 924150103
Phone: 909 387-3841
Web: WWW.SANBAG.CA.GOV

HISTORICAL FINANCIALS

Company Type: Private

Income Statement				FYE: June 30
	REVENUE ($ mil.)	NET INCOME ($ mil.)	NET PROFIT MARGIN	EMPLOYEES
06/20	4,008	223	5.6%	6,094
06/19	3,806	228	6.0%	—
06/16	3,186	165	5.2%	—
06/15	3,077	176	5.8%	—
Annual Growth	5.4%	4.8%	—	—

2020 Year-End Financials

Return on assets: 2.6%   Cash ($ mil.): 3,950
Return on equity: 6.0%
Current ratio: —

COUNTY OF SAN DIEGO

EXECUTIVES

Chief Admin, H Robbins-Meyer
Sup 1st Dist*, Greg Cox
Sup 2nd Dist*, Dianne Jacob
Sup 3rd Dist*, Pam Slater
Sup 4th Dist*, Ron Roberts
Sup 5th Dist*, Bill Horn
Assistant Professor of Public, Getachew Redae
Director, Phillip Smith
Senior Departmental Personnel, Mark Mandel
Admin Assistant, Carol Wallace
Financial Policy, Dianson Wong
Auditors: VAVRINEK TRINE DAY & CO LL

LOCATIONS

HQ: COUNTY OF SAN DIEGO
  1600 PACIFIC HWY STE 209, SAN DIEGO, CA 921012422
Phone: 619 531-5880
Web: WWW.SANDIEGOCOUNTY.GOV

HISTORICAL FINANCIALS

Company Type: Private

Income Statement				FYE: June 30
	REVENUE ($ mil.)	NET INCOME ($ mil.)	NET PROFIT MARGIN	EMPLOYEES
06/20	5,148	100	2.0%	17,000
06/19	4,657	172	3.7%	—
06/18	4,480	169	3.8%	—
06/17	4,163	138	3.3%	—
Annual Growth	7.3%	(10.2%)	—	—

2020 Year-End Financials

Return on assets: 1.0%   Cash ($ mil.): —
Return on equity: 3.0%
Current ratio: —

COUNTY OF SAN JOAQUIN

EXECUTIVES

County ADM, Monica Nino
Chief Information Officer*, Chris Cruz
Facilities Specialist, Tom Bugarin
Assistant Planner San Joaquin, Alisa Goulart
San Joaquin County Capital Pro, Eduardo Ramirez
Information Analyst SA, Jeff Marcelo
Employee, Maria Montalvo
Solid Waste Site Manager, Bill Baier
City Manager, Cruz Ramos
Information Analyst, Gregory Moore
Administrator, Kris Hamilton
Auditors: EIDE BAILLY SACRAMENTO CALIF

LOCATIONS

HQ: COUNTY OF SAN JOAQUIN
44 N SAN JOAQUIN ST # 640, STOCKTON, CA
952022924
Phone: 209 468-3203
Web: WWW.SJGOV.ORG

HISTORICAL FINANCIALS

Company Type: Private

Income Statement				FYE: June 30
	REVENUE ($ mil.)	NET INCOME ($ mil.)	NET PROFIT MARGIN	EMPLOYEES
06/20	1,290	106	8.3%	6,498
06/19	1,169	64	5.5%	—
06/18	1,154	97	8.4%	—
06/17	1,081	54	5.0%	—
Annual Growth	6.1%	25.3%	—	—

COUNTY OF SAN MATEO

EXECUTIVES

Manager*, John L Maltbie
Payroll Manager, Juan Raigoza
Human Resources Information MA, Austine Quien
Human Resources Information MA, Conny TSE
Human Resources Information MA, Danna Bandoma
Human Resources Information MA, Kate Singleton
Information Specialist, Alex Buencamino
Human Resources Information MA, Eliza Rodriguez
Coordinator, Filomena Viveiros
Information Technology Manager, Andrew Sedik
Associate Civil Engineer, Anthony Lum
Auditors: MACIAS GINI & O'CONNELL LLP W

LOCATIONS

HQ: COUNTY OF SAN MATEO
555 COUNTY CTR FL 4, REDWOOD CITY, CA
940631665
Phone: 650 363-4123
Web: WWW.SMCGOV.ORG

HISTORICAL FINANCIALS

Company Type: Private

Income Statement				FYE: June 30
	REVENUE ($ mil.)	NET INCOME ($ mil.)	NET PROFIT MARGIN	EMPLOYEES
06/20	1,731	190	11.0%	5,800
06/19	1,721	443	25.7%	—
06/18	1,475	84	5.7%	—
06/16	1,325	62	4.7%	—
Annual Growth	6.9%	32.0%	—	—

COUNTY OF SANTA BARBARA

EXECUTIVES

Chb, Brooks Firestone
Cty ADM*, Michael Brown
Supervisor*, Joni Gray
Chairperson*, Joseph Centeno
Supervisor*, Salud Carbajal
Supervisor*, Janet Wolf
Principal, Ken Masuda
Principal, Shirley Moore
Director, Polly Baldwin
Deputy District, Christopher Dalbey
Technical Support Manager, Virginia Butterfield
Auditors: BROWN ARMSTRONG BAKERSFIELD

LOCATIONS

HQ: COUNTY OF SANTA BARBARA
105 E ANAPAMU ST RM 406, SANTA BARBARA, CA
931012065
Phone: 805 568-3400
Web: WWW.JJDPC.ORG

HISTORICAL FINANCIALS

Company Type: Private

Income Statement				FYE: June 30
	REVENUE ($ mil.)	NET INCOME ($ mil.)	NET PROFIT MARGIN	EMPLOYEES
06/20	1,007	44	4.4%	4,582
06/19	987	53	5.4%	—
06/18	930	15	1.7%	—
06/17	889	21	2.4%	—
Annual Growth	4.3%	27.5%	—	—

COUNTY OF SANTA CLARA

EXECUTIVES

County Exec, Jeffrey V Smith
Prin, Alan Minato
Health Professional, Bea Herrick
Information Specialist, Judith McWilliams
Executive Officer, Neelima Palacherla
Assistant District, Brian Welch
Assistant District, David Angel
Chief of Staff, Derrick Seaver
Controller Treasurer Departmen, Lynette Feliciano
Assistant District, Stacey Capps
Assistant District, Terry Harman
Auditors: MACIAS GINI & O'CONNELL LLP W

LOCATIONS

HQ: COUNTY OF SANTA CLARA
70 W HEDDING ST 2WING, SAN JOSE, CA 951101768
Phone: 408 299-5200
Web: WWW.SCCGOV.ORG

HISTORICAL FINANCIALS

Company Type: Private

Income Statement				FYE: June 30
	REVENUE ($ mil.)	NET INCOME ($ mil.)	NET PROFIT MARGIN	EMPLOYEES
06/15	2,866	183	6.4%	14,500
06/14	2,660	12	0.5%	—
06/13	2,395	147	6.2%	—
06/11	2,408	54	2.2%	—
Annual Growth	4.5%	35.7%	—	—

COUNTY OF SANTA CRUZ

EXECUTIVES

Coord, Susan Mauriello
District 1*, Janet K Beautz
District 2*, Ellen Pirie
District 3, Chb*, Mardi Wormoudt
District 4*, Tony Campos
District 5*, Jeff Almquist
Prop Tax Acct, Marianne Ellis
Acct Tech, Mary Lou Cross
Facility Management, Mary Chavez
Tribal Administrator, Melinda Meek
Dental Assistant, Felipe Fuentes
Auditors: BROWN ARMSTRONG ACCOUNTANCY CO

LOCATIONS

HQ: COUNTY OF SANTA CRUZ
701 OCEAN ST RM 520, SANTA CRUZ, CA 950604015
Phone: 831 454-2100
Web: WWW.CO.SANTA-CRUZ.CA.US

HISTORICAL FINANCIALS

Company Type: Private

Income Statement				FYE: June 30
	REVENUE ($ mil.)	NET INCOME ($ mil.)	NET PROFIT MARGIN	EMPLOYEES
06/20	602	(2)	—	1,654
06/19	583	18	3.2%	—
06/18	544	0	0.0%	—
06/17	508	(4)	—	—
Annual Growth	5.8%	—	—	—

COUNTY OF SARASOTA

EXECUTIVES

Ctny Admin, James Ley
Dir of Fin*, Peter Ramsden
Attorney, Steven Demarsh
Project Coordinator, Andrea King
Program Inspector, Bob Levan
Coordinator, Gigi Bates
Assistant Chief, Rodney Vanorsdol
Media Relations, Jason Bartolone
Information Technology Profess, Quentin Beach

Board Member, Rod Myers
Scat Facilities Project Coordi, Darreil McElwee
Auditors: CLIFTONLARSONALLEN LLP TAMPA

LOCATIONS

HQ: COUNTY OF SARASOTA
1660 RINGLING BLVD, SARASOTA, FL 342366808
Phone: 941 861-5165
Web: WWW.SCGOV.NET

HISTORICAL FINANCIALS

Company Type: Private

Income Statement				FYE: September 30
	REVENUE ($ mil.)	NET INCOME ($ mil.)	NET PROFIT MARGIN	EMPLOYEES
09/19	586	56	9.6%	3,600
09/18	547	12	2.3%	—
09/16	482	(43)	—	—
09/15	482	(23)	—	—
Annual Growth	5.0%	—	—	—

COUNTY OF SHELBY

EXECUTIVES

Mayor, Mark H Luttrell Jr
Dir of ADM & Fin*, James Huntzicker
ADM of Fin*, Micheal A Swift
Mobile Security Officer, Charlie Brown
Mobile Security Officer, Keno Belford
Senior Manager, Caleb Tinkle
Officer, Lasundra Price
Secretary Counselor, Diane Morrow
Public Safety Talent Manager, Fonda Fouche
Police Officer, Gary Meador
Paramedic Firefighter, Germaine Pringle
Auditors: BANKS FINLEY WHITE & CO ME

LOCATIONS

HQ: COUNTY OF SHELBY
160 N MAIN ST FL 4, MEMPHIS, TN 381031866
Phone: 901 222-2050
Web: WWW.SHELBYCOUNTYTN.GOV

HISTORICAL FINANCIALS

Company Type: Private

Income Statement				FYE: June 30
	REVENUE ($ mil.)	NET INCOME ($ mil.)	NET PROFIT MARGIN	EMPLOYEES
06/20	1,125	(83)	—	7,990
06/19	1,125	39	3.5%	—
06/18	1,113	(10)	—	—
Annual Growth	0.5%	—	—	—

2020 Year-End Financials

Return on assets: (-2.0%)   Cash ($ mil.): 428
Return on equity: (-90.1%)
Current ratio: —

COUNTY OF SNOHOMISH

EXECUTIVES

Prin, Tam T Bui
County Executive*, Aaron Reardon
Councilman*, Gary Nelson
Councilman*, Kirke Sievers
Councilman*, John Koster
Councilman*, Dave Gossett
Councilman*, Jeff Sax
Prin*, Gompf Robert
Coordinator, Janet Gant
Senior Program Coordinator, Kristine Morse
Environmental Supervi, Clarissa Barrett
Auditors: PAT MCCARTHY OLYMPIA WA

LOCATIONS

HQ: COUNTY OF SNOHOMISH
3000 ROCKEFELLER AVE MS508, EVERETT, WA
982014071
Phone: 425 388-3460
Web: WWW.SNOHOMISHCOUNTYWA.GOV

HISTORICAL FINANCIALS

Company Type: Private

Income Statement				FYE: December 31
	REVENUE ($ mil.)	NET INCOME ($ mil.)	NET PROFIT MARGIN	EMPLOYEES
12/20	699	(2)	—	2,500
12/18	532	(4)	—	—
12/17	502	25	5.1%	—
12/16	486	5	1.0%	—
Annual Growth	9.5%	—	—	—

2020 Year-End Financials

Return on assets: (-0.1%)   Cash ($ mil.): 314
Return on equity: (-0.2%)
Current ratio: 3.30

COUNTY OF SONOMA

EXECUTIVES

Admin, Sheryl Bratton
Chm*, Margaret Killian
Treas-Collector*, Rodney Dole
Information Specialist, Robert S Lee
Health Professional, Reid Harper
Programmer, Vinh Gruenhagen
Administrative Analyst, Peter Bruland
Accountant Auditor, Vanessa Thomas
Analyst, Troy Anderson
Management Director, Dagny Thomas
Cad Manager, Greg Walsh
Auditors: VAVRINEK TRINE DAY & CO LL

LOCATIONS

HQ: COUNTY OF SONOMA
585 FISCAL DR 100, SANTA ROSA, CA 954032824
Phone: 707 565-2431
Web: WWW.SONOMACOUNTY.CA.GOV

HISTORICAL FINANCIALS

Company Type: Private

Income Statement				FYE: June 30
	REVENUE ($ mil.)	NET INCOME ($ mil.)	NET PROFIT MARGIN	EMPLOYEES
06/20	1,017	7	0.8%	5,260
06/19	1,019	77	7.6%	—
06/18	984	26	2.7%	—
06/17	905	(6)	—	—
Annual Growth	3.9%	—	—	—

COUNTY OF ST LOUIS

EXECUTIVES

Cnty Exec, Charles Dooley
Dir of Admin*, Glen Powers
Dir of Admin*, Pamela Reitz
Director of Personnel*, Kirk McCarley
Supervisor, Sergeant Wendling
Supervisor, Sergeant R Rizzuti
Sergeant, Craig Molden
Security Staff, Joe Strehl
Associate County Counselor, Carl Becker
Assistant Treasurer, Cindy Williams
Sergeant, Jim Molden
Auditors: HOCHCHILD BLOOM & COMPANY
LL

LOCATIONS

HQ: COUNTY OF ST LOUIS
41 S CENTRAL AVE, SAINT LOUIS, MO 631051719
Phone: 314 615-7016
Web: WWW.STLOUISCOUNTYMO.GOV

HISTORICAL FINANCIALS

Company Type: Private

Income Statement				FYE: December 31
	REVENUE ($ mil.)	NET INCOME ($ mil.)	NET PROFIT MARGIN	EMPLOYEES
12/20	856	(5)	—	4,100
12/19	810	49	6.1%	—
12/18	804	49	6.2%	—
12/17	715	27	3.8%	—
Annual Growth	6.2%	—	—	—

2020 Year-End Financials

Return on assets: (-0.2%)   Cash ($ mil.): 470
Return on equity: (-0.5%)
Current ratio: 2.70

COUNTY OF STANISLAUS

EXECUTIVES

Dir, Monica Nino Reid
Chief*, Stan Risen
Planner, Aicp Wall
Recreation Coordinator, Azia Ingram
Assistant City Clerk, Cathi Erbe

Chief Information Officer, Charlie Haase
Purchasing Manager, Cynthia Kline
Administrative Office Assist I, Dana Sanchez
Operations Supervisor, David Arroyo
Administrative Analyst I, David Paladini
Senior Buyer, Dianne Love
Auditors: BROWN ARMSTRONG
  ACCOUNTANCY CO

LOCATIONS

HQ: COUNTY OF STANISLAUS
  1010 10TH ST STE 5100, MODESTO, CA 953540872
Phone: 209 525-6398
Web: WWW.STANCOUNTY.COM

HISTORICAL FINANCIALS

Company Type: Private

Income Statement				FYE: June 30
	REVENUE ($ mil.)	NET INCOME ($ mil.)	NET PROFIT MARGIN	EMPLOYEES
06/20	1,234	21	1.8%	4,972
06/18	940	18	2.0%	—
06/17	0	0	—	—
06/16	882	18	2.1%	—
Annual Growth	8.7%	4.1%	—	—

COUNTY OF SUFFOLK

EXECUTIVES

County Exec, Steven Bellone
Comptroller*, John Kennedy Jr
Commanding Officer Lieutenant, Thomas
  Zagajeski
Acting Chief Engineer, Walter Dawydiak
Manager, Cliff Mitchell
Chief Environmental Analyst, Tom Iwanejko
Laboratory Technician, Amiann Forino
Chief Planner, Andrew Freleng
Executive Assistant, Angela Glaser
Purchasing Technician, Ann Bravico
Executive Director, Anthonyj Catapano
Auditors: DELOITTE & TOUCHE LLP JERICHO

LOCATIONS

HQ: COUNTY OF SUFFOLK
  100 VETERANS HWY, HAUPPAUGE, NY 117885402
Phone: 631 853-4000
Web: WWW.SUFFOLKCOUNTYNY.GOV

HISTORICAL FINANCIALS

Company Type: Private

Income Statement				FYE: December 31
	REVENUE ($ mil.)	NET INCOME ($ mil.)	NET PROFIT MARGIN	EMPLOYEES
12/20	3,535	254	7.2%	12,814
12/19	3,378	36	1.1%	—
12/18	3,257	(69)	—	—
12/17	3,174	(9)	—	—
Annual Growth	3.7%	—	—	—

2020 Year-End Financials

Return on assets: 3.0%   Cash ($ mil.): 1,152
Return on equity: —
Current ratio: 1.30

COUNTY OF TARRANT

Auditors: KPMG LLP DALLAS TX

LOCATIONS

HQ: COUNTY OF TARRANT
  100 E WEATHERFORD ST, FORT WORTH, TX
  761960206
Phone: 817 884-1205
Web: WWW.ACCESS.TARRANTCOUNTY.COM

HISTORICAL FINANCIALS

Company Type: Private

Income Statement				FYE: September 30
	REVENUE ($ mil.)	NET INCOME ($ mil.)	NET PROFIT MARGIN	EMPLOYEES
09/16	597	5	1.0%	139
09/15	580	52	9.1%	—
09/14	0	0	—	—
09/13	537	20	3.8%	—
Annual Growth	3.6%	(33.8%)	—	—

COUNTY OF TRAVIS

EXECUTIVES

Clerk, Dana Debeauvoir
Treasurer*, Dolores Ortega-Carter
District Attorney, Margaret Moore
Information Specialist, Don Castiglioni
Information Technology Directo, Judy Pittsford
Commissioner Precinct 1, Jeff Travillion
Facility Manager, Mark Buchanan
Director, Tina Morton
Program Manager, Tonya Watson
Gis Coordinator, David Shore
Business Analyst II, David Lee
Auditors: ATCHLEY & ASSOCIATES LLP AUST

LOCATIONS

HQ: COUNTY OF TRAVIS
  700 LAVACA ST FL 11, AUSTIN, TX 787013101
Phone: 512 854-9125
Web: WWW.TRAVISCOUNTYTX.GOV

HISTORICAL FINANCIALS

Company Type: Private

Income Statement				FYE: September 30
	REVENUE ($ mil.)	NET INCOME ($ mil.)	NET PROFIT MARGIN	EMPLOYEES
09/20	940	41	4.4%	3,900
09/19	846	384	45.4%	—
09/17	758	(41)	—	—
09/16	726	58	8.0%	—
Annual Growth	6.7%	(8.4%)	—	—

2020 Year-End Financials

Return on assets: 1.2%   Cash ($ mil.): 1,166
Return on equity: 7.9%
Current ratio: —

COUNTY OF TULARE

EXECUTIVES

Assistant, Jean M Rousseau
Auditor-Contrl, Rita Woodard
Staff, Dennis Haines
Captain, Mike Boudreaux
Network Administrator, Daniel Ruiz
Director, Jim Sullins
Grants, Darlene Tyndal
Chief Deputy County Administra, Jean Rousseau
Director, John Kindle
Management, Yvette Botello
Manager, Manuel O Avila
Auditors: BROWN ARMSTRONG AC
  BAKERSFIEL

LOCATIONS

HQ: COUNTY OF TULARE
  2800 W BURREL AVE, VISALIA, CA 932914517
Phone: 559 636-5005
Web: WWW.TULARECOUNTYLIBRARY.ORG

HISTORICAL FINANCIALS

Company Type: Private

Income Statement				FYE: June 30
	REVENUE ($ mil.)	NET INCOME ($ mil.)	NET PROFIT MARGIN	EMPLOYEES
06/20	882	45	5.2%	4,485
06/19	882	80	9.1%	—
06/18	814	30	3.7%	—
06/17	739	16	2.2%	—
Annual Growth	6.1%	41.4%	—	—

2020 Year-End Financials

Return on assets: 1.7%   Cash ($ mil.): 2
Return on equity: 2.6%
Current ratio: —

COUNTY OF UNION

EXECUTIVES

Exec Dir, George W Devanney
Prin*, Deborah P Scanlon
Prin*, Angel G Estrada
Prin*, Carolyn Sullivan
Exec Dir*, Alfred Faella
Sergeant, George Valladares
Acting Prosecutor, Thomas K Isenhour
Special Asst To The Pres, Dir, Steven Cheung
County Commissioner, Alexander Mirabella
County Commissioner, Bruce Bergen
Purchasing Agent, Laura Scutari

LOCATIONS

HQ: COUNTY OF UNION
  10 ELIZABETH AVE, ELIZABETH, NJ 07206
Phone: 908 659-7407
Web: WWW.UCNJ.ORG

HISTORICAL FINANCIALS
Company Type: Private

Income Statement				FYE: December 31
	REVENUE ($ mil.)	NET INCOME ($ mil.)	NET PROFIT MARGIN	EMPLOYEES
12/20	685	58	8.6%	2,700
12/18	561	36	6.5%	—
12/17	550	47	8.6%	—
12/16	577	32	5.6%	—
Annual Growth	4.4%	16.2%	—	—

2020 Year-End Financials
Return on assets: 2.6%
Return on equity: 5.3%
Current ratio: —

Cash ($ mil.): 573

COUNTY OF VENTURA

EXECUTIVES

County Exec Offc, Michael Powers
Health Professional, Simone Mongiello
Supervisor, Karen Barstow
Program Inspector, Bruce Tanner
Law Specialist, Dean Kiser
Coordinator, Matt Savard
Officer, Christy Madden
Coordinator, Katy Hadduck
Coordinator, Marcy Snider
Information, David Stuart
Child Welfare Supervisor, Elizabeth Watson

LOCATIONS

HQ: COUNTY OF VENTURA
  800 S VICTORIA AVE, VENTURA, CA 930090003
Phone: 805 654-2644
Web: WWW.VENTURA.ORG

HISTORICAL FINANCIALS
Company Type: Private

Income Statement				FYE: June 30
	REVENUE ($ mil.)	NET INCOME ($ mil.)	NET PROFIT MARGIN	EMPLOYEES
06/20	1,561	52	3.3%	7,433
06/19	1,482	66	4.5%	—
06/18	1,463	64	4.4%	—
06/17	1,388	41	3.0%	—
Annual Growth	4.0%	8.2%	—	—

COUNTY OF VOLUSIA

EXECUTIVES

Admn, Thomas C Kelly
Comm, James Dineen
Building Andamp, Mike Nelson
Office Assistant, Joy Meyer
Operations Manager, Tara Boujoulian
Fire Chief, Joseph E Pozzo
County Commissioner, Billie Wheeler
Information Technology Special, Brian Whiting
Manatee Protection Program Man, Debbie
  Wingfield

County Commissioner, Fred Lowry
County Commissioner, Heather Post
Auditors: JAMES MOORE & CO PL DAYTON

LOCATIONS

HQ: COUNTY OF VOLUSIA
  123 W INDIANA AVE STE A, DELAND, FL 327204615
Phone: 386 736-2700
Web: WWW.VOLUSIA.ORG

HISTORICAL FINANCIALS
Company Type: Private

Income Statement				FYE: September 30
	REVENUE ($ mil.)	NET INCOME ($ mil.)	NET PROFIT MARGIN	EMPLOYEES
09/20	573	77	13.5%	11,000
09/18	497	18	3.6%	—
09/17	462	12	2.7%	—
09/16	428	19	4.7%	—
Annual Growth	7.6%	40.3%	—	—

COUNTY OF WASHINGTON

EXECUTIVES

Administrator, Robert Davis
Human Resources Manager, Stephanie Reitmajer
Senior Info Analyst, Don Hunt
Chief Information Officer, Christopher Gensler
Benefits Supervisor, Cynthia Kodachi
Department of Assessment, Jennifer Ramstad
Public Affairs, Lisa Dupre
Analyst, Ana Noyola
Manager, Bob Davis
Senior Accountant, Deanna Henkel
Operations Manager, Judy Brennan
Auditors: TALBOT KORVOLA & WARWICK LLP

LOCATIONS

HQ: COUNTY OF WASHINGTON
  155 N 1ST AVE STE 300, HILLSBORO, OR 971243001
Phone: 503 846-8685
Web: WWW.CO.WASHINGTON.OR.US

HISTORICAL FINANCIALS
Company Type: Private

Income Statement				FYE: June 30
	REVENUE ($ mil.)	NET INCOME ($ mil.)	NET PROFIT MARGIN	EMPLOYEES
06/20	624	(50)	—	1,800
06/19	577	(7)	—	—
06/18	522	(35)	—	—
06/17	499	220	44.2%	—
Annual Growth	7.7%	—	—	—

COUNTY OF WASHOE

EXECUTIVES

Chm, Marsha Berkbigler

Commissioner*, Bob Lucey
Sheriff, Scott Thomas
Msw Lcsw Mental Health Counsel, Al Hearn
MPH Program Coordinator Educat, Keri Pruitt
Mental Health Counselor Superv, Marynne Lcsw
Administrative Secretary, Stephanie Zoncki
Administrative Secretary Super, Kelly Martinez
Assistant County Manager, Christine Vuletich
Director Technology, Craig Betts
Facility Maintenance Superviso, Patricc
  McDonald
Auditors: EIDE BAILLY LLP RENO NEVADA

LOCATIONS

HQ: COUNTY OF WASHOE
  1001 E 9TH ST, RENO, NV 895122845
Phone: 775 328-2552
Web: WWW.WASHOECOUNTY.GOV

HISTORICAL FINANCIALS
Company Type: Private

Income Statement				FYE: June 30
	REVENUE ($ mil.)	NET INCOME ($ mil.)	NET PROFIT MARGIN	EMPLOYEES
06/20	542	18	3.5%	2,800
06/19	518	30	5.9%	—
06/18	500	7	1.6%	—
06/17	463	(10)	—	—
Annual Growth	5.4%	—	—	—

COUNTY OF WYOMING

EXECUTIVES

Chairman, Anthony Latwin
Commissioner, Judy Mead
Commissioner, Ronald Williams
Member, Dennis Montross
Director, Lynnelle Bennett
Court Clerk, Karen Bishop
Assistant Director, Bernie Scalzo
Chief Deputy Assessor, Kelley Cosner
Auditor, Ashley Darby
Gis Coordinator, Charles Mead
Director of Operations, Florence Ball
Auditors: HALLOCKSHANNON PC
  TUNKHANNOC

LOCATIONS

HQ: COUNTY OF WYOMING
  1 COURT HOUSE SQ OFC, TUNKHANNOCK, PA
  18657
Phone: 570 836-3200
Web: WWW.WYCOPA.ORG

HISTORICAL FINANCIALS
Company Type: Private

Income Statement				FYE: December 31
	REVENUE ($ mil.)	NET INCOME ($ mil.)	NET PROFIT MARGIN	EMPLOYEES
12/19	32,004	(675)	—	167
12/17	25	1	6.6%	—
12/15*	25	3	12.5%	—
06/05	0	0	—	—
Annual Growth	—	—	—	—

*Fiscal year change

Return on assets: (-2.1%)　　Cash ($ mil.): 9,610
Return on equity: (-5.3%)
Current ratio: —

COUNTY OF YORK

EXECUTIVES

Pres-Comm, Steven Chronister
V Pres-Comm*, Doug Hoke
Commissioner*, Christorpher B Reilly
Executive Director, Richard Farr
Director Center For Traffic SA, Barbara Zortman
Judicial Assistant To Hono, Jane Dentler
Executive Director, Joseph Sassano
Technical Support Analyst, Kurtis Sterner
Director of Divorce Master Ser, Megan Dietz
Judicial Administrative Assist, Melissa Taylor
Judicial Administrative Assist, Melissa Urey
Auditors: ZELENKOFSKE AXELROD LLC HARRI

LOCATIONS

HQ: COUNTY OF YORK
　28 E MARKET ST RM 216, YORK, PA 174011587
Phone: 717 771-9964
Web: WWW.YORKDA.COM

HISTORICAL FINANCIALS

Company Type: Private

Income Statement				FYE: December 31
	REVENUE ($ mil.)	NET INCOME ($ mil.)	NET PROFIT MARGIN	EMPLOYEES
12/20	541	35	6.6%	2,600
12/19	481	(3)	—	—
12/18	475	32	6.9%	—
12/17	445	7	1.7%	—
Annual Growth	6.7%	68.1%	—	—

2020 Year-End Financials
Return on assets: 4.5%　　Cash ($ mil.): 114
Return on equity: 12.1%
Current ratio: —

COUNTY SANITATION DISTRICT NO. 2 OF LOS ANGELES COUNTY

EXECUTIVES

Gen Mgr, Stephen Maguin
Acctg, Sherry Rachman
Director, Debra Bogdanoff
Scientist, Jennipher CU
Project Engineer, Ryan Hall
Chemist, Jorge Garcia
Senior Engineer, Roya Phillips
Engineer, Scott Partridge
Secretary Financial Management, Brenda Wilcox
Training Manager, Robert Condra
Senior Engineer, Ajaymalik Malik
Auditors: MOSS LEVY & HARTZHEIM LLP CU

LOCATIONS

HQ: COUNTY SANITATION DISTRICT NO. 2 OF LOS ANGELES COUNTY
　1955 WORKMAN MILL RD, WHITTIER, CA 906011415
Phone: 562 699-7411

HISTORICAL FINANCIALS

Company Type: Private

Income Statement				FYE: June 30
	REVENUE ($ mil.)	NET INCOME ($ mil.)	NET PROFIT MARGIN	EMPLOYEES
06/19	627	211	33.8%	1,700
06/16	545	144	26.4%	—
06/15	555	92	16.7%	—
06/12	550	74	13.6%	—
Annual Growth	1.9%	16.0%	—	—

2019 Year-End Financials
Return on assets: 3.5%　　Cash ($ mil.): 519
Return on equity: 5.0%
Current ratio: 14.10

COVENANT HEALTH

Covenant Health has made a pact to provide good health to the good people of Tennessee. The not-for-profit health care system established in 1996 provides a variety of medical services through seven acute care hospitals a psychiatric hospital and a number of specialty outpatient centers offering geriatrics pediatric care cancer services weight management and diagnostics. Covenant Health also operates home health and hospice agencies and a physician practice management company. Covenant Health provides staffing and medical management services to its affiliated facilities and to make itself a really well-rounded health care provider it operates the Covenant Health Federal Credit Union.

EXECUTIVES

Pres-Ceo, Jim Vandersteeg
Exec V Pres-Cfo, John Geppi
Exec V Pres, Mike Belbeck
Exec V Pres, Luke Johnson
Purchasing, Matt Ogle
Procurement Specialist, Eileen Kozsan
Case Manager, George Tolbert
Senior Analyst, Ken Boyd
Internist, Kimberly Russell
Internal Medicine, Rebecca Jackson
Director, Richard Bremer

LOCATIONS

HQ: COVENANT HEALTH
　100 FORT SANDERS W BLVD, KNOXVILLE, TN 379223353
Phone: 865 531-5555
Web: WWW.COVENANTHEALTH.COM

PRODUCTS/OPERATIONS

Selected Tennessee Facilities
Fort Loudon Medical Center (Lenoir City TN)
Fort Sanders Regional Medical Center (Knoxville TN)
LeConte Medical Center (formerly Fort Sanders Sevier Medical Center; Sevierville TN)
Methodist Medical Center of Oak Ridge (Oak Ridge TN)
Parkwest Medical Center (Knoxville TN)
　Peninsula Hospital (behavioral health care Louisville TN)
Roane Medical Center (Harriman TN)

COMPETITORS

Blount Memorial Hospital	Saint Thomas Rutherford Hospital
East Tennessee Children's Hospital	Tennova Healthcare
Kindred Healthcare	University Health System Inc.
Lifepoint Health	Vanderbilt University Medical Center
Parkridge Medical Center	
Saint Thomas Midtown Hospital	

HISTORICAL FINANCIALS

Company Type: Private

Income Statement				FYE: December 31
	REVENUE ($ mil.)	NET INCOME ($ mil.)	NET PROFIT MARGIN	EMPLOYEES
12/20	1,470	158	10.8%	2,469
12/19	1,407	183	13.1%	—
12/18	1,296	(49)	—	—
12/17	1,268	144	11.4%	—
Annual Growth	5.0%	3.1%	—	—

2020 Year-End Financials
Return on assets: 5.3%　　Cash ($ mil.): 213
Return on equity: 9.3%
Current ratio: 1.60

COVENANT HEALTH SYSTEM

Covenant Health System ties West Texas and Eastern New Mexico together with quality health care. The health services provider offers some 1100 beds in its five primary acute-care and specialty hospitals; it also manages about a dozen affiliated community hospitals. Covenant Health System part of Providence St. Joseph Health also maintains a network of family health care and medical clinics. Covenant Health System's major facilities are Covenant Medical Center Covenant Specialty Hospital and Covenant Women's and Children's Hospital. The health system also includes some 20 clinics and 50 physician practices and its extensive outreach programs target isolated rural communities with mobile services.

Operations
The system's five hospitals include Covenant Medical Center Covenant Medical Center-Lakeside Covenant Specialty Hospital and Covenant Children's Hospital. It also operates three schools for healthcare careers in nursing radiography and surgical technology respectively.

Strategy
The Christian-based system which calls itself a ministry focuses on providing benefits to the community. Its key priorities include mental health dentistry diabetes home health management and childhood obesity.

Company Background
Covenant Health System was founded when two Lubbock hospitals St. Mary of the Plains Hospital (now known as Covenant Medical Center-Lakeside) and the Lubbock Methodist Hospital System (including the flagship Methodist Hospital which is now known as Covenant Medical Center) merged in 1998.

EXECUTIVES

Ceo, Richard Parks

Coo*, Troy Thibodeaux
Exec Asst of Cfo*, Denise Saenz
SEC*, Linda Robins
Cfo*, John Grigson
Sr Accountant, Russell Owens
Chief of Pediatric, Joel T Brodbeck
Coordinator, Teresa Clifford
Coordinator, Tiji Falcon
Coordinator, Sylvia Brito
Emergency Medicine Specialist, Barry Thomas
Auditors: ERNST & YOUNG US LLP IRVINE

LOCATIONS

HQ: COVENANT HEALTH SYSTEM
   3615 19TH ST, LUBBOCK, TX 794101209
Phone: 806 725-1011
Web: WWW.COVENANTHEALTH.ORG

COMPETITORS

Baptist St. Anthony's Health System	Tenet Healthcare
Del Sol Medical Center	Texas Health Resources
Encompass Health	The Methodist Health System
Hunt Memorial	University Medical Center Of El Paso
Nw Texas Healthcare	
Parkland Health & Hospital System	

HISTORICAL FINANCIALS

Company Type: Private

Income Statement   FYE: June 30

	REVENUE ($ mil.)	NET INCOME ($ mil.)	NET PROFIT MARGIN	EMPLOYEES
06/15	703	76	10.9%	5,000
06/13	552	35	6.5%	
06/09	1,185	(38)	—	
Annual Growth	(8.3%)	—	—	

2015 Year-End Financials

Return on assets: 10.5%   Cash ($ mil.): 39
Return on equity: 14.7%
Current ratio: 3.20

COVENANT HEALTH, INC.

EXECUTIVES

Pres-Ceo, David R Lincoln
SEC*, Patricia Karl
Treas*, Harold R Acres
Chm*, Dorothy Cooper
V Chb*, Richard J Hanley
Dir*, Margaret Mary Modde
Svp-Cfo*, Stephen Forney
Controller*, Donald Clark
Asst Cfo, Laural Haug
Assistant Controller, Becky Lehoux
Admin Associate, Linda Gorgone
Auditors: BAKER NEWMAN & NOYES LLC BOST

LOCATIONS

HQ: COVENANT HEALTH, INC.
   100 AMES POND DR STE 102, TEWKSBURY, MA 018761240
Phone: 978 654-6363
Web: WWW.COVENANTHEALTH.NET

HISTORICAL FINANCIALS

Company Type: Private

Income Statement   FYE: December 31

	REVENUE ($ mil.)	NET INCOME ($ mil.)	NET PROFIT MARGIN	EMPLOYEES
12/20	718	10	1.4%	6,500
12/18	666	(74)	—	
12/17	670	38	5.8%	
12/16	645	18	2.9%	
Annual Growth	2.7%	(13.8%)	—	

2020 Year-End Financials

Return on assets: 1.1%   Cash ($ mil.): 66
Return on equity: 1.9%
Current ratio: 1.50

COVENANT MEDICAL CENTER, INC.

Covenant Medical Center (operating as Covenant HealthCare) has made a pact with Wolverine Staters to try to keep them in good health. The not-for-profit health care provider operates more than 20 inpatient and outpatient care facilities including its two main Covenant Medical Center campuses. It serves residents in a 20-county area of east-central Michigan with additional facilities in Bay City Frankenmuth and Midland. Specialized care services include cardiovascular health cancer treatment and obstetrics. The regional health care system has more about 650 beds.

Operations

Covenant HealthCare programs and services range from high-risk obstetrics and neonatal/pediatric intensive care to acute care. Its assets include cardiology oncology orthopedics robotic surgery and Level II Adult and Pediatric Trauma Center.

The health system has more than 20 inpatient and outpatient facilities and a trauma/emergency department that provides 85000 visits per year. The system employs more than 500 physicians from 52 medical specialties.

Sales and Marketing

Covenant HealthCare markets its services via social media.

Financial Performance

In 2014 the company's revenue increased 4% to $528 million as patient service revenue rose; this gain was partially offset by a decline in realized gain and other revenues. An increase in salaries and wages as well as higher supplies expenses led to a 12% decline in net income (to $57 million).

Cash flow from operations also fell slipping 20% to $48 million as accounts receivable increased.

Strategy

Expanding its infrastructure to keep up with demand in 2014 Covenant HealthCare added 11456 sq. ft. to its Emergency Department. The addition allows for more efficient triage enhanced patient waiting areas and additional space for current technology. It added 18 treatment bays to the existing 47 and also brought a dedicated CT scanner and mini-laboratory within the department.

Also that year it opened the assisted living community of Covenant Glen in Frankenmuth. The 35000 sq. ft. structure has 45 rooms (15 dedicated to memory care and 30 with assisted living beds).

Company Background

Covenant HealthCare was formed in 1998 through the merger of Saginaw General and St. Luke's Hospitals.

EXECUTIVES

Ceo, Edward Bruff
Pres*, Spencer T Maidlow
Cfo*, Mark Gronda
Dir of Info Tech, Keith Grantham
Director, John Germain
Supply Chain Management, Christa Marcoux
Purchasing Agent, Darlene Rose
Adminstrator, Gary Gasta
Director of Pharmacy, Terry Wernette
Manager Gift Shops, Tim Schultz
Administrator, Brenda Spiker

LOCATIONS

HQ: COVENANT MEDICAL CENTER, INC.
   1447 N HARRISON ST, SAGINAW, MI 486024727
Phone: 989 583-0000
Web: WWW.COVENANTHEALTHCARE.COM

PRODUCTS/OPERATIONS

2014 Revenues

	% of total
Net patient service revenues	95
Other revenues	5
Total	**100**

Selected services

Bariatrics
Birth Center
Cancer Care
Cardiology - Center for the Heart
Childbirth Classes
da Vinci Robotic Surgery
Diabetes Self-Management Program
Emergency Care Center
Imaging and Diagnostics
Neonatal Intensive Care
Neurology
Osteoporosis
Orthopaedics
Pediatrics
Physical Medicine and Rehab.
Pulmonary/Respiratory Care
Sleep Center
Surgical Services
Trauma
Urologic Surgery
Women's Health
Wound Healing Center

COMPETITORS

Genesys Health System	Mclaren Health Care
Genesys Regional Medical Center	Munson Healthcare
Hurley Medical Center	Sparrow Health System
Mclaren Bay	University Of Michigan Health System

HISTORICAL FINANCIALS

Company Type: Private

Income Statement   FYE: June 30

	REVENUE ($ mil.)	NET INCOME ($ mil.)	NET PROFIT MARGIN	EMPLOYEES
06/16	579	40	7.0%	4,000
06/15	535	31	5.8%	
06/14	566	34	6.1%	
06/10	508	28	5.5%	
Annual Growth	2.2%	6.2%	—	

2016 Year-End Financials

Return on assets: 6.4%   Cash ($ mil.): 21
Return on equity: 12.9%
Current ratio: 1.80

CREIGHTON ALEGENT HEALTH

EXECUTIVES

Ceo-Pres, Jeanette Wojtalewicz
Svp-Coo*, Kathy Bressler
Cfo*, Nick O'Toole
Pres-Ceo, Alegent Cr Clinic, Richard Rolston
Purchasing, Kris McDonald
Physician Assistant, Chris Jankovich
Division Vice President Qualit, Cathy Jesus
Supervisor Human Resources Ser, Donna
 Cloonan
Rn, Hattie Jackson
Department Secretary, Laurie Dilocker
Surgical Business Coo, Rosalie Weber
Auditors: LB CATHOLIC HEALTH INITIATIVES

LOCATIONS

HQ: CREIGHTON ALEGENT HEALTH
 12809 W DODGE RD, OMAHA, NE 681542155
Phone: 402 343-4300
Web: WWW.CHIHEALTH.COM

HISTORICAL FINANCIALS

Company Type: Private

Income Statement				FYE: June 30
	REVENUE ($ mil.)	NET INCOME ($ mil.)	NET PROFIT MARGIN	EMPLOYEES
06/20	636	12	2.0%	10,000
06/19	599	27	4.6%	—
06/13	525	63	12.2%	—
Annual Growth	2.8%	(20.5%)	—	—

2020 Year-End Financials

Return on assets: 1.4%   Cash ($ mil.): 1
Return on equity: 3.0%
Current ratio: 0.40

CREIGHTON UNIVERSITY

EXECUTIVES

Pres, Timothy R Lannon
Assistant Professor, Andrea Zardetto-Smith
Assistant Professor, Cortni Krusemark
Assistant Professor, Cynthia Hadenfeldt
Assistant Professor, Howard Bachman
Assistant Professor, Jon M Schrage
Assistant Professor, Kristoffer Boyle
Assistant Professor, Littleton Alston
Assistant Professor, Toni Laguzza
Assistant Professor, Helen Chapple
Assistant Professor, Joseph A Allen

LOCATIONS

HQ: CREIGHTON UNIVERSITY
 2500 CALIFORNIA PLZ, OMAHA, NE 681780002
Phone: 402 280-2900
Web: WWW.CREIGHTON.EDU

HISTORICAL FINANCIALS

Company Type: Private

Income Statement				FYE: June 30
	REVENUE ($ mil.)	NET INCOME ($ mil.)	NET PROFIT MARGIN	EMPLOYEES
06/20	563	61	10.9%	5,000
06/19	567	62	11.0%	—
06/17	394	107	27.4%	—
Annual Growth	12.6%	(17.2%)	—	—

2020 Year-End Financials

Return on assets: 4.4%   Cash ($ mil.): 95
Return on equity: 6.2%
Current ratio: 0.50

CRETE CARRIER CORPORATION

Holding company Crete Carrier Corporation's flagship business Crete Carrier provides dry van truckload freight transportation services in the 48 contiguous states. It operates from some two dozen terminals mainly in the mid-western and southeastern US. The company's Shaffer Trucking unit transports temperature-controlled cargo and Hunt Transportation (no relation to J.B. Hunt Transport Services) hauls heavy equipment and other cargo on flatbed trailers. Overall the companies operate more than 5400 tractors and 13000 trailers. Family-owned Crete Carrier was founded in 1966 by chairman Duane Acklie; president and CEO Tonn Ostergard is his son-in-law.

EXECUTIVES

Ceo, Tonn Ostergard
Pres-Coo*, Timothy Aschoff
Administrative Assistant, Laurie Edwards
Sales Manager, Patty Bideaux
Accounts Payable, Kim Wacha
Management, Michael Fiedler
Management, Pat Derickson
Management, Thomas Baker
Traier Control Coordinator, Bill Tichota
Asset Manager Team Leader, Darin Sherman
Driver Manager, Issac Phillips

LOCATIONS

HQ: CRETE CARRIER CORPORATION
 400 NW 56TH ST, LINCOLN, NE 685288843
Phone: 800 998-4095
Web: WWW.CRETECARRIER.COM

COMPETITORS

Boyd Bros.
 Transportation
C.r. England
Celadon
Comcar
Covenant
 Transportation
Heartland Express

J.b. Hunt
Landstar System
Prime Inc.
Schneider National
Swift Transportation
U.s. Xpress
Werner Enterprises

CROWE LLP

EXECUTIVES

Ceo, Mark Baer
Cdso, Justin Bass
Coo, Brenda Torres
Cro, Steve Strammello
Cfo, Raymond Calvey
Senior Manager, Adriane Counts
Marketing Manager Engi, Betty Morris
Tax Partner, Joseph Quinn
Director, Martin Joseph
Director, Rick L Childs
National Tax Office Partner, Shelby Ford
Auditors: CROWE LLP

LOCATIONS

HQ: CROWE LLP
 225 W WACKER DR STE 2600, CHICAGO, IL
 606061228
Phone: 312 899-7000
Web: WWW.CROWE.COM

HISTORICAL FINANCIALS

Company Type: Private

Income Statement				FYE: March 31
	REVENUE ($ mil.)	NET INCOME ($ mil.)	NET PROFIT MARGIN	EMPLOYEES
03/15	700	204	29.2%	3,130
03/14	670	163	24.4%	—
03/13	0	0	—	—
Annual Growth	—	—	—	—

2015 Year-End Financials

Return on assets: 71.1%   Cash ($ mil.): 6
Return on equity: 260.7%
Current ratio: 2.00

CROWLEY MARITIME CORPORATION

Crowley founded in 1892 is a privately-held US-owned and operated logistics government marine and energy solutions company headquartered in Jacksonville Florida. Crowley owns operates

---

HISTORICAL FINANCIALS

Company Type: Private

Income Statement				FYE: September 30
	REVENUE ($ mil.)	NET INCOME ($ mil.)	NET PROFIT MARGIN	EMPLOYEES
09/18	1,150	139	12.1%	6,000
09/16	984	95	9.7%	—
09/15	0	0	—	—
09/14	1,034	127	12.3%	—
Annual Growth	2.7%	2.3%	—	—

2018 Year-End Financials

Return on assets: 13.3%   Cash ($ mil.): 128
Return on equity: 15.8%
Current ratio: 2.20

and/or manages a fleet of more than 200 vessels consisting of RO/RO (roll-on-roll-off) vessels LO/LO (lift-on-lift-off) vessels articulated tug-barges (ATBs) LNG-powered container/roll-on roll-off ships (ConRos) and multipurpose tugboats and barges. Land-based facilities and equipment include port terminals warehouses tank farms gas stations office buildings trucks trailers containers chassis cranes and other specialized vehicles.

Operations

Crowley owns operates and/or manages a fleet of more than 200 vessels consisting of RO/RO (roll-on-roll-off) vessels LO/LO (lift-on-lift-off) vessels articulated tug-barges (ATBs) LNG-powered container/roll-on roll-off ships (ConRos) and multipurpose tugboats and barges. Land-based facilities and equipment include port terminals warehouses tank farms gas stations office buildings trucks trailers containers chassis cranes and other specialized vehicles.

Services are provided worldwide by four primary business units ? Crowley Logistics Crowley (Government) Solutions Crowley Shipping and Crowley Fuels.

Crowley Logistics a singular supply chain division serves more than 12000 customers and manages more than one million shipments annually on a global scale. The group blends company-owned assets and services with its worldwide network of service providers to reduce complexity and add velocity to customers' supply chains.

Crowley Shipping owns operates and manages conventional and dual fuel (LNG) vessels for Crowley and other customers. These vessels include tankers articulated tug barges (ATBs) container ships LNG-powered container/roll-on roll-off ships (ConRos) and multipurpose tugboats and barges.

Crowley Solutions is a key partner for the Department of Defense (DoD) Department of Homeland Security (DHS) and other government agencies.

Crowley Fuels is a leader in Alaska's fuel industry providing safe dependable transportation distribution and sales of petroleum products to more than 280 communities across the state.

Company Background

Crowley traces its historical roots back to 1892.

EXECUTIVES

Chb-Ceo-Pres, Thomas Crowley Jr
V Chb-Exec V Pres*, William Pennella
Sr V Pres*, Arthur Mead III
Sr V Pres-Contrl*, John Calvin
Sr V Pres-Treas*, Daniel Warner
Sr V Pres Admin*, Susan Rodgers
Sr V Pres*, Michael Roberts
Vp-Deputy Gen Counsel*, Tim Bush
Svp-General Manager*, Brett Bennett
Cfo*, Dan Warner
Chief Marketing Officer*, John Claybrooks

LOCATIONS

HQ: CROWLEY MARITIME CORPORATION
9487 REGENCY SQUARE BLVD # 101,
JACKSONVILLE, FL 322257800
Phone: 904 727-2200
Web: WWW.CROWLEY.COM

PRODUCTS/OPERATIONS

Selected Services
Energy industry support services

Fuel sales and distribution
Liner services
Logistics
Ocean towing and transportation
Petroleum and chemical transportation
Project management
Salvage and emergency response

Ship assist and escort
Ship management
Vessel construction and naval architecture
Alaska fuel sales and distribution
Arctic all-terrain transportation
Harbor ship assist and tanker escort
Marine salvage wreck removal and emergency response
Ocean towing and barge transportation
OPA 90 compliance
Petroleum and chemical transportation
Ship management
Shipping And Logistics
Vessel design and construction management

COMPETITORS

A.p. M ̧ller - M ̧rsk	Sea Star Line
Apl	Tidewater Inc.
Foss Maritime	Trailer Bridge
Horizon Lines	U.s. Shipping
Hornbeck Offshore	Ups Supply Chain
K-sea Transportation	Solutions
Lynden Incorporated	Washington Companies
Seacor	

HISTORICAL FINANCIALS

Company Type: Private

Income Statement   FYE: December 31

	REVENUE ($ mil.)	NET INCOME ($ mil.)	NET PROFIT MARGIN	EMPLOYEES
12/08	1,955	86	4.4%	4,329
12/07	1,622	122	7.5%	—
12/06	1,467	38	2.6%	—
12/05	1,190	38	3.3%	—
Annual Growth	18.0%	30.3%	—	—

2008 Year-End Financials

Return on assets: 6.2%   Cash ($ mil.): 64
Return on equity: 18.2%
Current ratio: 1.40

CRST INTERNATIONAL, INC.

CRST International promises f-a-s-t freight transportation through its operating units. CRST Expedited provides standard dry van truckload transportation primarily on long-haul routes along with dedicated and expedited transportation services. CRST Malone hauls steel and other freight requiring flatbed trailers or trailers with removable sides and CRST Logistics arranges freight transportation and provides other third-party logistics services. The family-owned business' other operations include CRST Dedicated Services and Specialized Transportation. Overall the companies operate a fleet of about 4500 tractors and 7300 van trailers.

Operations

CRST operates through seven distinct operations. CRST Expedited is a long-haul truckload carrier and CRST Malone is a flatbed carrier serving customers in North America. The company's CRST Dedicated Services unit offers tailor-made specialized transportation services while CRST Logistics helps customers reduce costs and optimize their performance.

CRST Specialized Transportation provides multi-modal logistics supported by distribution centers located throughout the US and Canada. Other operations include Temperature Controlled Team Service (TCTS) (expedited transcontinental transportation of perishable products) and BESL

Transfer Company (provider of short haul flatbed services).

Geographic Reach

Based in Cedar Rapids Iowa CRST operates more than 50 distribution centers terminals and offices across North America.

Sales and Marketing

The company targets the business and retail industrial metals building products technology telecommunications automotive government tradeshows and events health care transportation and residential markets.

Strategy

In 2015 CRST broke ground on its new $37 million world headquarters in downtown Cedar Rapids Iowa.

In 2013 CRST Expedited opened a training and repair facility in Riverside California.

Mergers and Acquisitions

CRST also continues to grow through the use of acquisitions.

In 2015 the company bought privately-held Pegasus Transportation based in Louisville Kentucky. The acquisition allows CRST to expand its temperature controlled operations nationwide footprint through its expanded customer base.

In early 2014 CRST obtained a privately held short haul and flatbed services provider BESL Transfer Co. based in Cincinnati Ohio in a transaction that fortified its CRST Malone operations. The acquisition of BESL allowed CRST to expand its flatbed operations nationwide footprint through its short haul regional services and expanded agent base.

In 2013 it picked up the Allied Special Products Division of Allied Van Lines based in Fort Wayne Indiana. The deal enabled its Specialized Transportation operations to further develop its distribution center network and provide better service and faster transit to its customers. That year subsidiary CRST Logistics added Top Shelf Logistics LLC to its rapidly growing agency network.

Company Background

CRST was founded in 1955 by Herald Smith father of chairman John Smith.

EXECUTIVES

Ceo, Hugh Ekberg
V Pres-Cfo-Treas*, Wesley Brackey
V Pres*, Steve Hannah
Pres, Dry-Van Truckload Group, John Labrie
Coordinator, Scot Korte
Customer Staff, Danielle Williams
Recruiter, Javon Rocke
Driver Manager, Robert Blevins
Supervisor Recruiting, Templin Rolen
Safety Manager, Brian Brown
IBM Administrator, Joseph Hronek
Auditors: DELOITTE & TOUCHE LLP CEDAR R

LOCATIONS

HQ: CRST INTERNATIONAL, INC.
201 1ST ST SE STE 400, CEDAR RAPIDS, IA 524011423
Phone: 319 396-4400
Web: WWW.CRST.COM

PRODUCTS/OPERATIONS

Selected Services
Expedited Team Service
Dry Van
Flatbed
Dedicated
High Value/White Glove
Temperature Controlled
Transportation Management
Brokerage
Home Delivery/First & Final Mile
Warehousing/Inventory Solutions

LTL
Intermodal
Equipment Sales

COMPETITORS

Anderson Trucking	J.b. Hunt
Service	Ruan Transportation
Boyd Bros.	Management Systems
Transportation	Schneider National
C.h. Robinson	Swift Transportation
Worldwide	Ups Supply Chain
Comcar	Solutions
Crete Carrier	Werner Enterprises
Forward Air	

HISTORICAL FINANCIALS

Company Type: Private

Income Statement				FYE: December 31
	REVENUE ($ mil.)	NET INCOME ($ mil.)	NET PROFIT MARGIN	EMPLOYEES
12/12	1,258	75	6.0%	5,960
12/11	1,143	81	7.1%	—
Annual Growth	10.1%	(7.8%)	—	—

2012 Year-End Financials

Return on assets: 13.7%   Cash ($ mil.): 71
Return on equity: 45.2%
Current ratio: 2.70

CSC SUGAR, LLC

EXECUTIVES

MBR-Pres, Paul J Farmer
Cfo-Treas, Francis X Claps
Assistant Plant Manager, Eric Metcalf
Business Manager,, Russ Lapier
Auditors: GRANT THORNTON LLP
MINNEAPOLI

LOCATIONS

HQ: CSC SUGAR, LLC
36 GROVE ST STE 2, NEW CANAAN, CT 068405329
Phone: 203 846-5610
Web: WWW.CSCSUGAR.COM

HISTORICAL FINANCIALS

Company Type: Private

Income Statement				FYE: December 31
	REVENUE ($ mil.)	NET INCOME ($ mil.)	NET PROFIT MARGIN	EMPLOYEES
12/09	574	18	3.2%	300
12/08	790	5	0.7%	—
12/07	515	6	1.2%	—
Annual Growth	5.6%	74.5%	—	—

2009 Year-End Financials

Return on assets: 24.8%   Cash ($ mil.): 4
Return on equity: 104.6%
Current ratio: 1.20

CURRENT LIGHTING SOLUTIONS, LLC

EXECUTIVES

MBR, Manish Bhandari
Cfo, John Irvine
Commercial Operations-Prin, Daniel Phalen
Gen Counsel, Inger Eckert
Project Manager, Anthony Rando
Manager, Accounts Payable, Bernard Womack
Project Finance Analyst, Jonathan Leissler
Manager, Sourcing, Joseph Moreno
Tax Director, Lori Bohm
Project Management Leader, Matthew Kniskern
Operational Controller, Sophia Koukouvitakis
Auditors: RSM US LLP BOSTON MASSACHUSE

LOCATIONS

HQ: CURRENT LIGHTING SOLUTIONS, LLC
1975 NOBLE RD STE 328, CLEVELAND, OH
441121719
Phone: 216 462-4700
Web: WWW.GECURRENT.COM

HISTORICAL FINANCIALS

Company Type: Private

Income Statement				FYE: December 31
	REVENUE ($ mil.)	NET INCOME ($ mil.)	NET PROFIT MARGIN	EMPLOYEES
12/20	669	(18)	—	1,300
12/19	621	(48)	—	—
Annual Growth	7.8%	—	—	—

2020 Year-End Financials

Return on assets: (-4.3%)   Cash ($ mil.): 7
Return on equity: (-24.5%)
Current ratio: 1.60

CYPRESS-FAIRBANKS INDEPENDENT SCHOOL DISTRICT

EXECUTIVES

Supt, Mark Henry
Supt*, Richard E Berry
General, Mary Jadlowski
Maintenance Buyer, Greg Segura
Information Technology Project, Andrew Bailey
Secretary Assistant Director H, Debora McNair
Information Technology Project, Leonard Chance
Athletic Secretary, Renee Mullen
Special Education Paraprofessi, Selena Tristan
Assistant High Schoo, Nicole Chandler
Head Custodian, Andres Gonzalez
Auditors: WEAVER AND TIDWELL LLP
CONROE

LOCATIONS

HQ: CYPRESS-FAIRBANKS INDEPENDENT SCHOOL
DISTRICT
10300 JONES RD, HOUSTON, TX 770654208
Phone: 281 897-4000
Web: WWW.CFISD.NET

HISTORICAL FINANCIALS

Company Type: Private

Income Statement				FYE: June 30
	REVENUE ($ mil.)	NET INCOME ($ mil.)	NET PROFIT MARGIN	EMPLOYEES
06/21	1,410	161	11.5%	13,000
06/20	1,331	208	15.7%	—
06/19	1,342	32	2.4%	—
06/18	1,259	20	1.6%	—
Annual Growth	3.8%	99.5%	—	—

2021 Year-End Financials

Return on assets: 3.8%   Cash ($ mil.): 1
Return on equity: —
Current ratio: —

D. H. PACE COMPANY, INC.

EXECUTIVES

Ceo, Rex E Newcomer
Pres, Overhead Door Division*, Steve Pascuzzi
Sr Exec-V Pres*, Thomas S Palmer
V Pres-Cfo*, Brian Gillespie
Exec V Pres-CIO*, Chris Mann
Exec V Pres*, N Nelson Newcomer
Exec V Pres, Gen Counsel*, Emily J Bailey
Sr V Pres-Dir of Human Resourc*, Rhonda
Johnson
Project Coordinator, Kecia Williams
Manager, Zach Treacy
Administration, Jennifer Harris

LOCATIONS

HQ: D. H. PACE COMPANY, INC.
1901 E 119TH ST, OLATHE, KS 660619502
Phone: 816 221-0543
Web: WWW.DHPACE.COM

HISTORICAL FINANCIALS

Company Type: Private

Income Statement				FYE: December 31
	REVENUE ($ mil.)	NET INCOME ($ mil.)	NET PROFIT MARGIN	EMPLOYEES
12/20	711	26	3.7%	2,800
12/19	677	28	4.1%	—
12/07	0	0	—	—
12/06	140	0	—	—
Annual Growth	12.3%	—	—	—

D/L COOPERATIVE INC.

Yes the farmer takes a wife then hi-ho the dairy-o the farmer takes membership in milk-marketing organizations such as Dairylea Cooperative. Owned by some 2000 dairy farmers in the northeastern US Dairylea processes and markets 6.3 billion pounds of milk for its farmers annually to dairy-product customers including food manufacturers. Its Agri-Services holding company provides members with a full range of financial and farm-management services as well as insurance. Its Empire Livestock Marketing unit operates regional livestock auction locations. Dairylea which was established in 1907 by New York dairy farmers merged with the US's largest milk marketing coop Dairy Farmers of America in 2014.

Operations
Through its DMS partnership with Dairy Farmers of America Dairylea sells and distributes raw milk. DMS serves both organizations as well as independent producers and cooperatives that produce 16 billion pounds of milk each year.

Geographic Reach
Dairylea sells 6 billion pounds of raw milk annually through a milk-marketing network that stretches from Maine to Ohio to Maryland.

Services provided by holding company Agri-Services LLC include insurance coverage information management livestock marketing loan programs milk price risk management services business planning and consulting services purchasing programs and investment and retirement planning advice.

Financial Performance
Dairylea has annual sales of about $1 billion.

Auditors: HERBEIN COMPANY INC READING

LOCATIONS

HQ: D/L COOPERATIVE INC.
5001 BRITTONFIELD PKWY, EAST SYRACUSE, NY 130579201
Phone: 315 233-1000
Web: WWW.DAIRYLEA.COM

PRODUCTS/OPERATIONS

Selected Affiliates & Subsidiaries
Agri-Edge Development
Agri-Max Financial Services
Agri-Services Agency
Dairy Risk Management Services
Eagle Dairy Direct
Empire Livestock Marketing Services

COMPETITORS

Agri-mark	Keller's Creamery
Associated Milk	Land O'lakes
Producers	Maryland & Virginia
Dean Foods	Milk Producers
Foremost Farms	Quality Chekd
Garelick Farms	

HISTORICAL FINANCIALS
Company Type: Private

Income Statement   FYE: March 31

	REVENUE ($ mil.)	NET INCOME ($ mil.)	NET PROFIT MARGIN	EMPLOYEES
03/11	1,333	1	0.1%	107
03/10	1,066	1	0.1%	—
Annual Growth	25.1%	7.6%	—	—

2011 Year-End Financials
Return on assets: 9.2%   Cash ($ mil.): 14
Return on equity: 0.1%
Current ratio: 0.60

DAIRY FARMERS OF AMERICA, INC.

Dairy Farmers of America (DFA) is one of the world's largest dairy cooperatives with more than 12500 member farmers across the US. Along with fresh and shelf-stable fluid milk the co-op produces cheese butter powders and sweetened condensed milk for industrial wholesale and retail customers. It also offers contract manufacturing services. The company's brands include Borden and Cache Valley for consumer cheese; Keller's Creamery Plugr Breakstone's Falfurrias and Oakhurst Dairy; and other dairy products under Sport Shake (sports beverage) La Vaquita (queso) Kemps Guida's and Cass Clay. The company owns around 85 production plants nationwide.

Operations
In addition to DFA's fresh and wholesome dairy products that include butter cheese ice cream milk and yogurt the company also offers services such as DFA Risk Management DFA Grazing DFA Insurance DFA Farm Supplies DFA Energy DFA Financing Empire Livestock Dairy One and Member Savings Network.

Geographic Reach
DFA is based in Kansas City Missouri and divides the US into seven areas: Central (which shares the main headquarters) Mideast (Medina Ohio) Mountain (Salt Lake City Utah) Northeast (East Syracuse New York) Southeast (Knoxville Tennessee) Southwest (Grapevine Texas) and Western (Ripon California).

Sales and Marketing
DFA's customers include food manufacturers school cafeterias large restaurants and retailers among others.

Company Background
DFA was established in 1998 by leaders of four of the nation's leading milk cooperatives: Associated Milk Producers Mid-America Dairymen Milk Marketing and Western Dairymen Cooperative.

HISTORY

Mid-America Dairymen (Mid-Am) the largest of the cooperatives that merged to form Dairy Farmers of America (DFA) was born in 1968. At that time several Midwestern dairy co-ops banded together to attack common economic problems such as reduced government subsidies price drops resulting from a rising milk surplus dealer consolidation and improvements in production processing and packaging. The merging organizations — representing 15000 dairy farmers — were Producers Creamery Company (Springfield Missouri) Sanitary Milk Producers (St. Louis) Square Deal Milk Producers (Highland Illinois) Mid-Am (Kansas City Missouri) and Producers Creamery Company of Chillicothe (north central Missouri).

During the early 1970s Mid-Am struggled with internal restructuring. Most dairy farmers and co-ops were hit hard by the energy crisis and the government's decision to allow increased dairy imports in 1973 the same year the US Justice Department filed an antitrust suit against Mid-Am. (A judge cleared the co-op 12 years later.)

In 1974 Mid-Am lost almost $8 million on revenues of $625 million chalked up to record-high feed prices a weakened economy a milk surplus and a massive inventory loss. Co-op veteran Gary Hanman was named CEO that year. Over the next two years Mid-Am cut costs sold corporate frills downsized management and began marketing more of its own products under the Mid-America

Farms label thus reducing dependency on commodity sales.

Mid-Am expanded its research and development efforts throughout the 1980s. The co-op opened its services to farmers in California and New Mexico in 1993 and a series of mergers in 1994 and 1995 nearly doubled its size. In 1997 it purchased some of Borden's dairy operations including rights to the valuable Elsie the Cow and Borden's trademarks.

Wary of falling milk prices Mid-Am merged with Western Dairymen Cooperative Milk Marketing and the Southern Region of Associated Milk Producers at the end of 1997 to form DFA. Hanman moved into the seat of CEO at the new co-op. DFA began a series of joint ventures with the #1 US dairy processor Suiza Foods (now Dean Foods).

DFA added California Gold (more than 330 farmers 1998) and Independent Cooperative Milk Producers Association (730 dairy farmer members in Michigan and parts of Ohio and Indiana 1999). In another joint venture with Suiza in early 2000 DFA sold its 50% stake in the US's #3 fluid milk processor Southern Foods in exchange for 34% of a new company named Suiza Dairy Group.

After mollifying the government's antitrust fears DFA acquired the butter operations of Sodiaal North America in 2000. It then molded all its butter businesses into a new entity Keller's Creamery. However another acquisition did not fare as well. The same year DFA acquired controlling interest in Southern Belle Dairy only to have the merger challenged three years later by the Department of Justice. Arguing that the merger formed a monopoly in school milk sales in several states the Department of Justice filed suit which a federal judge later dismissed.

During 2001 the cooperative went in with Land O'Lakes 50/50 to purchase a cheese plant from Kraft. Later in the year as Suiza Foods acquired Dean Foods (and took on its name) DFA sold back its stake in Suiza Dairy Group to the new Dean Foods. DFA then teamed up with a group of dairy investors to form a new 50/50 joint venture National Dairy Holdings which received 11 processing plants from Dean Foods as part of the exchange for Suiza Dairy.

EXECUTIVES

Pres-Ceo, Rick Smith
Sr V Pres, Alex Bachelor
Cfo, Kevin Strathman
V Pres, Kevin Cody
Member Payroll, Kami Poole
Staff Accountant, Katelynn Misciasci
Quality Specialist, Kathleen Hutsell
Team Leader, Kelly Stensland
Internal Auditor, Kelsey McConnell
Laboratory Director, Linda Farnham
Manager, Lindsey Burks
Auditors: KPMG LLP KANSAS CITY MISSOU

LOCATIONS

HQ: DAIRY FARMERS OF AMERICA, INC.
1405 N 98TH ST, KANSAS CITY, KS 661111865
Phone: 816 801-6455
Web: WWW.DFAMILK.COM

PRODUCTS/OPERATIONS

Selected Products and Brands
Consumer brands
  Borden cheese
  Breakstone's butter
  Cache Valley cheese
  Keller's Creamery butter
  Plugrá butter
  Sport Shake energy milk shake
Contract manufacturing
  Cheese dips

Cheese powders & flavors
Coffee-based flavored drinks
Instant formula
Sour cream
Sports drinks
Dairy ingredients
Cheeses (American & Italian)
Nonfat dry milk powder
Skim milk powder
Sweetened condensed milk

COMPETITORS

Arla Foods	Glanbia Plc
Associated Milk	Great Lakes Cheese
Producers	Hp Hood
Berkeley Farms	Humboldt Creamery
California Dairies	Lactalis
Inc.	Land O'lakes
Conagra	Marathon Cheese
Darigold Inc.	Mayfield Dairy Farms
Dean Foods	Northwest Dairy
Farmland Dairies	Prairie Farms Dairy
Foremost Farms	Quality Chekd
Friendship Dairies	Sargento
Garelick Farms	

HISTORICAL FINANCIALS
Company Type: Private

Income Statement				FYE: December 31
	REVENUE ($ mil.)	NET INCOME ($ mil.)	NET PROFIT MARGIN	EMPLOYEES
12/16	13,528	136	1.0%	21,000
12/15	13,803	98	0.7%	—
12/14	17,856	48	0.3%	—
Annual Growth	(13.0%)	67.6%	—	—

2016 Year-End Financials
Return on assets: 3.8%   Cash ($ mil.): 85
Return on equity: 14.1%
Current ratio: 1.10

DAIRYAMERICA, INC.

EXECUTIVES

Pres-Ceo, Patricia Smith
SEC, Bill Schreiber
Treas, Craig Alexander
Customer Rep, Diane Calaman
It Manager, Tim Berryhill
Director of Sales, Aj Cecconi
Office Manager, Annette Smith
Executive Director of Supply C, Derik Toy
Director, Portfolio Management, Grant Gondell
Export Documentation Superviso, Teri Covacevich
Regional Sales Manager, Todd Wittlinger
Auditors: DELOITTE & TOUCHE LLP FRESNO

LOCATIONS

HQ: DAIRYAMERICA, INC.
7815 N PALM AVE STE 250, FRESNO, CA 937115528
Phone: 559 251-0992
Web: WWW.DAIRYAMERICA.COM

HISTORICAL FINANCIALS
Company Type: Private

Income Statement				FYE: December 31
	REVENUE ($ mil.)	NET INCOME ($ mil.)	NET PROFIT MARGIN	EMPLOYEES
12/12	1,222	21	1.8%	51
12/11	1,319	19	1.5%	—
12/10	1,514	19	1.3%	—
Annual Growth	(10.2%)	5.5%	—	—

2012 Year-End Financials
Return on assets: 12.8%   Cash ($ mil.): 1
Return on equity: 108.5%
Current ratio: 1.80

DALLAS COUNTY HOSPITAL DISTRICT

Parkland Health & Hospital System (PHHS) is one of the largest public hospital systems and a level I Trauma Center and second largest civilian burn center in the U.S. and Level III Neonatal Intensive Care Unit. Parkland Memorial sits at the heart of the health system and is Dallas' only public hospital. PHHS also manages a network of about 20community clinics as well as Parkland Community Health Plan a regional HMO for Medicaid and CHIP (Children's Health Insurance Program) members. Additionally the system offers Parkland Financial Assistance a program to help residents of Dallas County pay for health care services. Founded in 1894.

Operations
PHHS is one of the largest public hospital systems in the US. In addition to its community-based clinics it offers a number of outreach and education programs to improve wellness in its service area.
Parkland Memorial Hospital has 878 single-patient rooms and is a Level I trauma center. Each year the hospital has some 33388 inpatient discharges and some 204506 emergency department visits. Its Specialty community and women's clinic outpatient visits total more than 1 million.
The system also manages the health system for Lew Sterrett — Dallas County Jail one of the nation's largest jails.

Geographic Reach
PHHS is based in Dallas Texas.

Sales and Marketing
PHHS markets its products and services through its websites.

Financial Performance

EXECUTIVES

Ceo, Frederick Cerise
Sr V Pres*, James R Johnson
Evp-Gen. Counsel*, Steven J Roth
V Pres*, Paul S Leslie
Cfo*, John Moore
Coo*, Ron Laxton
Coordinator, Sharletta Simpson
Staff, Jeff Hulstein
Ancillary Cardiology Manager I, Greggory Ervin
Director Government Reimbursem, Keri Disney
Director of Homeless O, Susan Spalding
Auditors: BKD LLP DALLAS TEXAS

LOCATIONS

HQ: DALLAS COUNTY HOSPITAL DISTRICT
5200 HARRY HINES BLVD, DALLAS, TX 752357709
Phone: 214 590-8000
Web: WWW.PARKLANDHOSPITAL.COM

PRODUCTS/OPERATIONS

Selected Facilities
Bluitt Flowers Health Center
de Haro-Saldivar Health Center
East Dallas Health Center
Garland Health Center
Oak West Health Center
Pediatric Primary Care Center
Simmons Ambulatory Surgery Center
Southeast Dallas Health Center
Vickery Health Center

COMPETITORS

Baylor University	Jps Health Network
Medical Center	Presbyterian Hospital
Christus Health	Of Dallas
Children's Medical	Tenet Healthcare
Center Of Dallas	Texas Health Resources
Community Health	The Methodist Health
Systems	System
Hca	
Harris Methodist Fort	
Worth Hospital	

HISTORICAL FINANCIALS
Company Type: Private

Income Statement				FYE: September 30
	REVENUE ($ mil.)	NET INCOME ($ mil.)	NET PROFIT MARGIN	EMPLOYEES
09/20	1,850	297	16.1%	11,000
09/19	1,600	208	13.0%	—
09/18	1,456	17	1.2%	—
09/17	1,734	(17)	—	—
Annual Growth	2.2%	—	—	—

2020 Year-End Financials
Return on assets: 9.4%   Cash ($ mil.): 595
Return on equity: 21.1%
Current ratio: 2.40

DALLAS INDEPENDENT SCHOOL DISTRICT

EXECUTIVES

Supt, Michael Hinojosa
Treas*, Darlene Williams
Cfo*, Larry Throm
Principal, Bill Quinones
Ronald E. McNair E, Cheryl Williams
Alternative Programs Assistant, Joseph Brew
Human Resources Information MA, Eric Shu
Coordinator, Lawana Porter
Designer, Jeff Houle
Teacher, Ashton Martin
Dcp Coordinator, Gary Rees
Auditors: WEAVER AND TIDWELL LLP DALLA

LOCATIONS

HQ: DALLAS INDEPENDENT SCHOOL DISTRICT
9400 N CNTL EXPY STE 1510, DALLAS, TX 75231
Phone: 972 925-3700
Web: WWW.DALLASISD.ORG

HISTORICAL FINANCIALS

Company Type: Private

Income Statement   FYE: June 30

	REVENUE ($ mil.)	NET INCOME ($ mil.)	NET PROFIT MARGIN	EMPLOYEES
06/21	2,324	321	13.8%	24,937
06/20	2,248	240	10.7%	
06/19	2,241	(17)	—	—
Annual Growth	1.8%	—	—	—

2021 Year-End Financials

Return on assets: 5.5%
Return on equity: 117.5%
Current ratio: —

Cash ($ mil.): 1,442

DALLAS-FORT WORTH INTERNATIONAL AIRPORT FACILITY IMPROVEMENT CORPORATION

Many things are bigger in Texas and Dallas/Fort Worth International Airport (DFW) is no exception. Covering some 30 square miles DFW is one of the world's largest airports by land mass. The facility includes seven runways two active control towers five terminals and 165 gates. Some 65 million passengers pass through DFW annually to destinations domestic and international. Aside from airport fare DFW provides private warehouse and distribution centers to tenants and features Grand Hyatt and Hyatt Regency hotels. Opened in 1974 DFW is owned by the cities of Dallas and Fort Worth; it is situated halfway between them and within about a four-hour flight time of most US destinations.

Operations

DFW's primary operating goal is the facilitation of movement of people cargo and airplanes. Beyond that it leases land to travel-related businesses (car rental agencies) provide parking coordinates concessions and permits hotels to operate within its confines. About 45% of revenue comes from airlines (landing fees terminal usage fees) and 55% comes from non-airline activities.

With about 1800 flights per day serving 65 million customers a year DFW is the world's fourth busiest airport. Airlines flying out of DFW provide nonstop service to 163 domestic and 55 international non-stop destinations through about 25 passenger carriers and nearly 20 cargo carriers.

DFW is the home airport for the world's largest carrier American Airlines (AA) which operates 745 flights per day to nearly 200 domestic destinations and some 50 international destinations. AA is constructing a new headquarters on a 300-acre campus on DFW property.

Financial Performance

In FY2016 (ended September 30 2016) Dallas Fort Worth International Airport generated revenue of $745 million a 10% increase from the prior year.

The airport's earnings in FY2016 had a hard landing losing almost $94 million. Although its operations incurred a relatively small $4.6 million loss the big contributor was massive interest expense on its revenue bonds. The interest is a recurring annual charge and the airport has recently been running at an annual loss.

Strategy

DFW is in the midst of a $2.34 billion terminal improvement project that's expected to be completed in late 2018. Improvements include new gates and a new concourse light rail connections to downtown Dallas and renovations to existing terminals. Improvements to Terminals A B and E completed in 2017 and work on Terminal C is on hold due to financing decisions. The physical airfield is also on tap to receive capital funding: runway 17C to get $250 million and end-around taxiways to get $430 million.

The airport has excellent connectivity to Latin & South America and to Asia and believes it is well positions to serve as a gateway between the two world regions. It is geographically situated in an advantageous place and already has an extensive network of destinations into Mexico and Latin & South America.

EXECUTIVES

Ceo, Jeff P Fegan
Information Specialist, Julie Pagenkopf
Law Specialist, Maria Mountford
Coordinator, Jasmine Brazile
Evp Administration, Linda V Thompson
Law Specialist, Matina Garrett
Information Technology Manager, Guadalupe Roman
DBA, Debra Mitcham
Civilian Security Officer, Domingo Fuentes
Software Developer, Huilu Wang
Cad Designer, John Gordon
Auditors: DELOITTE & TOUCHE LLP DALLAS

LOCATIONS

HQ: DALLAS-FORT WORTH INTERNATIONAL AIRPORT FACILITY IMPROVEMENT CORPORATION
2400 AVIATION DR, DFW AIRPORT, TX 75261
Phone: 972 973-5400
Web: WWW.DFWAIRPORT.COM

HISTORICAL FINANCIALS

Company Type: Private

Income Statement   FYE: September 30

	REVENUE ($ mil.)	NET INCOME ($ mil.)	NET PROFIT MARGIN	EMPLOYEES
09/18	929	54	5.9%	1,700
09/16	745	(88)	—	
09/07	567	28	5.0%	—
09/06	388	140	36.2%	—
Annual Growth	7.5%	(7.6%)	—	—

2018 Year-End Financials

Return on assets: 0.7%
Return on equity: 16.1%
Current ratio: 1.70

Cash ($ mil.): 154

DANA-FARBER CANCER INSTITUTE, INC.

The Dana-Farber Cancer Institute fights cancer on two fronts: It provides treatment to cancer patients young and old and researches new cancer diagnostics treatments and preventions. The organization's scientists also research AIDS treatments and cures for a host of other deadly diseases. Patients receive treatment from Dana-Farber through its cancer centers operated in conjunction with Brigham and Women's Hospital Boston Children's Hospital and Massachusetts General Hospital. The institute is also a principal teaching affiliate of Harvard Medical School. Dana-Farber is funded by the National Cancer Institute the National Institute of Allergy and Infectious Diseases and private contributions.

Operations

Dana-Farber reports more than 640000 annual outpatient visits more than 1000 hospital discharges per year and is involved in over 1100 clinical trials.

Dana-Farber provides care to children and adults with cancer while advancing the understanding diagnosis treatment cure and prevention of cancer and related diseases. As an affiliate of Harvard Medical School and a Comprehensive Cancer Center designated by the National Cancer Institute the institute also provides training for new generations of physicians and scientists designs programs that promote public health particularly among high-risk and underserved populations and disseminates innovative patient therapies and scientific discoveries to target community across the US and around the world.

Dana-Farber researchers have contributed to the development of 35 of 75 cancer drugs recently approved by the FDA for use in cancer patients.

Patients services generates about 65% of total sales research accounts for nearly 30% while unrestricted contributions and bequests and other revenue account for the remaining.

Geographic Reach

The institute primarily serves patients in New England. Dana-Farber's main campus is in Boston's Longwood Medical Area and it also has facilities in Brighton Milford South Weymouth and Methuen (all in Massachussets); Londonderry New Hampshire; and Waterford Connecticut.

Dana-Farber Community Cancer Care physician practices are in communities throughout eastern Massachusetts.

Company Background

In 2013 the institute and Lawrence + Memorial Cancer Center opened a $34.5 million 47000 sq.-ft. cancer facility in Waterford Connecticut.

The Yawkey Center for Cancer Care named in honor of long-time contributor The Yawkey Foundation opened in 2011 to serve a growing number of patients. The 275000-sq.-ft center's 14-stories house most of Dana-Farber's adult outpatient care. The building has more than 100 exam rooms about 140 infusion chairs and a number of consultation rooms for family and patients. It also connected Dana-Farber to other campus buildings and to its clinical partners Brigham and Women's Hospital and Children's Hospital Boston.

Dana-Farber Cancer Institute was founded as a children's cancer research foundation in 1947 by Dr. Sidney Farber. The institute later expanded its services to provide programs for adults as well as children.

EXECUTIVES

Chb, Gary L Countryman
Ceo*, Edward J Benz Jr
Pres*, David G Nathan
V Pres*, Dorothy E Puhy
V Pres*, Richard S Boskey
Treas*, Richard K Lubin
CIO-Svp, Innovation*, Lesley Solomon
Cro*, Kevin Haigis
Svp-Gen Counsel-Cgo*, John Ryan
Cca&eo*, Christopher Lathan
Scientist, Adam Bass

LOCATIONS

HQ: DANA-FARBER CANCER INSTITUTE, INC.
450 BROOKLINE AVE, BOSTON, MA 022155450
Phone: 617 632-3000
Web: WWW.DANA-FARBER.ORG

PRODUCTS/OPERATIONS

2014 Sales

	% of total
Patients Services	62
Research	30
Unrestricted Contributions and Bequests	6
Other revenue	2
Total	**100**

Selected Clinical Affiliations

Dana-Farber/Brigham and Women's Cancer Center (outpatient services for adult cancer patients provided by Dana-Farber; and inpatient care provided by Brigham and Women's Hospital)

Dana-Farber/Children's Hospital Cancer Center (Dana-Farber Cancer Institute and Children's Hospital Boston outpatient care for children provided at Dana-Farber's Jimmy Fund Clinic)

Dana-Farber/Harvard Cancer Center (Beth Israel Deaconess Medical Center Brigham and Women's Hospital Children's Hospital Boston and Massachusetts General Hospital collaborate on research cancer prevention and treatments and therapies for cancer patients)

Dana-Farber/Lawrence + Memorial Cancer Center (cancer facility Waterford Connecticut)

Dana-Farber/Partners Cancer Care (consolidated adult oncology programs and clinical research of Dana-Farber Cancer Institute Brigham and Women's Hospital and Massachusetts General Hospital)

Selected Satellite Centers

Dana-Farber/Brigham and Women's Cancer Center at Faulkner Hospital in Jamaica Plain (southwest Boston area)

Dana-Farber/Brigham and Women's Cancer Center at Milford Regional Medical Center (Massachusetts)

Dana-Farber/Brigham and Women's Cancer Center in clinical affiliation with South Shore Hospital (South Weymouth Massachusetts)

Dana-Farber/New Hampshire Oncology-Hematology (Londonderry)

Adult Treatment Centers and Clinical Services

Blood Cancers

Breast Cancer

Cancer Genetics and Prevention

Cutaneous (Skin) Cancer

Gastrointestinal Cancer

Genitourinary Cancer

Gynecologic Cancer

Head and Neck Cancer

Hematology

Melanoma

Neuro-Oncology

Sarcoma

Thoracic (Lung) Cancer

Pediatric Treatment Centers and Clinical Services

Blood Disorders Center

Brain Tumor Center

Hematologic Malignancies Center

Solid Tumors Center

Stem Cell Transplant Center

COMPETITORS

Baystate Health	Johns Hopkins Medicine
Beth Israel Deaconess Medical Center	Md Anderson Cancer Center
Boston Medical Center	Mayo Clinic
Brigham And Women's Hospital	Memorial Sloan-kettering
Care New England	Partners Healthcare
Caregroup	Roswell Park Cancer Institute
Children's National Medical Center	St. Elizabeth's Medical Center
Emory Healthcare	St. Jude Children's Research Hospital
Fox Chase Cancer Center	

HISTORICAL FINANCIALS

Company Type: Private

Income Statement

FYE: September 30

	REVENUE ($ mil.)	NET INCOME ($ mil.)	NET PROFIT MARGIN	EMPLOYEES
09/19	1,985	102	5.1%	3,000
09/14	672	34	5.1%	—
09/13	635	56	8.8%	—
09/10	894	16	1.9%	—
Annual Growth	**9.3%**	**22.2%**	—	—

2019 Year-End Financials

Return on assets: 3.3%   Cash ($ mil.): 142
Return on equity: 5.3%
Current ratio: 3.10

DANFOSS POWER SOLUTIONS INC.

Danfoss Power Solutions (formerly Sauer-Danfoss) is one of the largest companies in the mobile hydraulics industry which designs manufactures and sells a complete range of engineered hydraulic electronic and electric components and solutions. The mobile equipment manufacturers rely on its expertise for the most innovative propel control work function and steering solutions around the world. Its solutions have included motors pumps valves and software among others. Danfoss Power Solutions is a wholly-owned subsidiary of Denmark-based industrial company Danfoss A/S. The company traces its roots back to 1946.

Operations

The company offers a complete range of engineered hydraulic electronic and electric components and solutions including motors (hydrostatic gear orbital and electric) pumps (hydrostatic gear and digital displacement) valves (PVG proportional valve DCV directional control valves and ICS cartridge valves and HICs) and steering components and systems (hydraulic and electrohydraulic) as well as electronic controls electrical systems and software. Under its separate brand Hydro-Gear it supplies hydrostatic drive systems to a number of markets.

Geographic Reach

Danfoss Power Solutions operates about 30 manufacturing facilities in the Americas Asia/Pacific and Europe.

Strategy

The company has adopted a strategy aimed at investing in the BRIC (Brazil Russia India and China) countries where its major customers — John Deere and Caterpillar included — are expecting to grow. Danfoss Power Solutions has its eye focused especially on China where it plans to invest in the construction of several new factories in that country. It is also taking steps to reduce the number of subcontractors to 1380 (a 70% decrease).

EXECUTIVES

Pres-Ceo, Eric Alstrom
Exec V Pres-Cfo-Treas, Jesper V Christensen
V Pres-Cao-Sec, Kenneth D McCuskey
Exec V Pres-Cmo, Marc A Weston
Exec V Pres Hr, Anne Wilkinson
Chb*, Jorgen M Clausen
Vp-Pres Work Function Division, Helge Jorgensen

Coordinator, Lisa Williams
Customer Representativ, Kristen Behling
Procurement Staff, Richard Wang
Research, Aleksander Gust
Auditors: KPMG LLP DES MOINES IOWA

LOCATIONS

HQ: DANFOSS POWER SOLUTIONS INC.
2800 E 13TH ST, AMES, IA 500108600
Phone: 515 239-6000
Web: WWW.DANFOSS.COM

PRODUCTS/OPERATIONS

Selected Products

Controls
  Control valves
  Mobile electronics
Propel
  Hydrostatic transmissions
  Open circuit piston pumps
Stand-Alone
  Cartridge valves and HICs
  Directional control valves
  Investors
  Light duty hydrostatic transmissions
  Open circuit gear pumps and motors
Work Function
  Low speed high torque motors
  Open circuit gear pumps and motors
  Steering units

Selected Markets

Agriculture and turf care
Construction and road building
Material handling
Specialty vehicles

COMPETITORS

Bosch Rexroth	Shimadzu
Eaton Hydraulics	Sun Hydraulics
Husco International	Tb Wood's
Haldex	The Linde Group
Parker-hannifin	Twin Disc

HISTORICAL FINANCIALS

Company Type: Private

Income Statement

FYE: December 31

	REVENUE ($ mil.)	NET INCOME ($ mil.)	NET PROFIT MARGIN	EMPLOYEES
12/11	2,057	259	12.6%	6,400
12/10	1,640	246	15.0%	—
12/09	1,159	(332)	—	—
Annual Growth	**33.2%**	—	—	—

2011 Year-End Financials

Return on assets: 20.3%   Cash ($ mil.): 251
Return on equity: 45.0%
Current ratio: 2.30

DANONE US, INC.

WhiteWave Foods rides a wave of dietary changes as consumers seek alternatives to conventional foods. The company is best known for its refrigerated Silk soymilk in the US and Alpro brand soy products in Europe. WhiteWave also produces organic dairy products under the Horizon Organic label and dairy related foods including International Delight coffee creamers and LAND O'LAKES-branded creamers and dairy dessert toppings (licensed from dairy co-op Land O'Lakes). WhiteWave products are sold through natural food and grocery stores as well as mass merchandisers and restaurants and food service businesses in the

US and Canada and parts of Europe. WhiteWave has been part of French dairy giant Danone since 2017.

Operations

WhiteWave's plant-based food and drinks include Silk (milk from soy almonds cashews and coconuts as well as dairy-free yogurt); So Delicious Dairy Free (drinks creamers ice-cream shredded cheese); Alpro (dairy alternatives); and Vega (plant-based sports nutrition).

Other brands include Horizon (organic milk-based products); International Delight (sweet drinks and iced coffee); Half & Half (creamer); Earthbound Farm (salads frozen and dried fruit and fresh fruit and vegetables).

Geographic Reach

WhiteWave is headquartered in Denver Colorado.

Sales and Marketing

WhiteWave Foods' largest customer is Wal-Mart Stores which accounts for about 15% of sales. The company's 10 biggest customers account for about 50% of sales.

Financial Performance

WhiteWave has maintained healthy if not entirely organic revenue gains for the past ten years.

Strategy

In becoming part of Danone WhiteWave gets access to the bigger company's resources and to the European market which has produced about 15% of revenue. Danone plans to use WhiteWave's plant-based products to supplement its dairy-based offerings as consumers in the Americas and Europe turn to healthier foods. WhiteWave conducts research on new products and packing at facilities in Colorado California and Belgium.

Mergers and Acquisitions

In 2016 WhiteWave acquired Mexico based Innovation Packaging and Process (IPP) for about $18 million. IPP manufactures products for White-Wave and third parties and the addition on in-house manufacturing could propel growth in Latin American markets.

In 2015 WhiteWave acquired Sequel Naturals which owns the Vega brand and has been a pioneer in developing plant-based nutrition products for some $550 million. This acquisition extended the company's plant-based foods and beverages platform into nutritional powders and bars.

In another 2015 deal WhiteWave bought EIEIO Inc. which owned the Magicow brand and other brands for $40 million. The acquisition expanded WhiteWave's portfolio of bulk coffee creamer and flavor dispensing products and provided new product capabilities to support growth in away-from-home channel.

EXECUTIVES

Ceo, Gregg L Engles
Senior Developer, David Allen
Operations Manager, John Strong
Director of Procurement, Lynne Urbina
Vice President Engineering, Rick Wietharn
Supervisor Quality Assurance, Shivani Gupta
Ecommerce Manager, Tammy Bieber
Vice President, Kelly Shea
Nutrition Research Scientist, Mona Rosene
Environment Health and Safety, Paul Robbertz
Sr Manager Supply Chain Strate, Flavia Oliveira
Auditors: DELOITTE & TOUCHE LLP DENVER

LOCATIONS

HQ: DANONE US, INC.
12002 AIRPORT WAY, BROOMFIELD, CO 800212546
Phone: 303 635-4000
Web: WWW.DANONENORTHAMERICA.COM

2016 Sales

	% of total
North America	86
Europe	14
Total	**100**

PRODUCTS/OPERATIONS

Selected Products and Brands

Europe
  Plant-based foods and beverages (Alpro Provamel)
  Almond
  Hazelnut
  Oat
  Rice
  Soy
North America
  Coffee creamers and beverages (Land O Lakes International Delight)
  Flavored coffee creamers
  Half & Half
  Iced coffee
  Unflavored coffee creamers
  Plant-based foods and beverages (Silk)
  Almond
  Coconut
  Soy
  Premium dairy (Horizon Organic)
  Organic milk
  Other organic dairy
  Other premium milk

COMPETITORS

Aurora Organic Dairy	Lifeway Foods
Eden Foods	Nestl ©
Galaxy Nutritional Foods	Odwalla
	Old Home Foods
Hp Hood	Organic Valley
Hain Celestial	Rockview Dairies
Kraft Heinz	Springfield Creamery

HISTORICAL FINANCIALS

Company Type: Private

Income Statement				FYE: December 31
	REVENUE ($ mil.)	NET INCOME ($ mil.)	NET PROFIT MARGIN	EMPLOYEES
12/15	3,866	168	4.4%	500
12/14	3,436	140	4.1%	—
12/13	2,542	99	3.9%	—
Annual Growth	23.3%	30.4%	—	—

2015 Year-End Financials

Return on assets: 4.0%
Return on equity: 13.9%
Current ratio: 1.00
Cash ($ mil.): 38

DARTMOUTH COLLEGE

EXECUTIVES

Mgr, James Fries
Assistant Professor, Ethan M Berke
Assistant Professor, WEI Wang
Coordinator, Ben Myers
Associate Professor, Sean Smith
Project Director, Carole Meyers
Director of Advancement Servic, Dominic Albanese
Database Administrator, Jonathan Crossett
Associate Director of Informat, Kathleen Martin
Research Translation Coordinat, Laurie Rardin
Acquisitions Assistant, Marianne Densmore
Auditors: PRICEWATERHOUSECOOPERS LLP BO

LOCATIONS

HQ: DARTMOUTH COLLEGE
6193 HINMAN, HANOVER, NH 037554007
Phone: 603 646-2191
Web: WWW.DARTMOUTHCOOP.COM

HISTORICAL FINANCIALS

Company Type: Private

Income Statement				FYE: June 30
	REVENUE ($ mil.)	NET INCOME ($ mil.)	NET PROFIT MARGIN	EMPLOYEES
06/19	927	314	34.0%	10
06/18	893	739	82.8%	—
06/17	887	691	77.9%	—
06/16	859	(301)	—	—
Annual Growth	2.6%	—	—	—

2019 Year-End Financials

Return on assets: 3.7%
Return on equity: 4.7%
Current ratio: 1.50
Cash ($ mil.): 293

DARTMOUTH-HITCHCOCK CLINIC

The New England Alliance for Health (NEAH) brings together health care facilities and professionals looking to improve health in the New England region. Members of the alliance include about 20 community hospitals home health care agencies and mental health centers in New Hampshire Vermont and Massachusetts. While the members collaborate on wellness quality and communication initiatives each member of the alliance is an independently owned and operated not-for-profit organization with its own board of directors. Collaborative services provided by NEAH include procurement staff training information technology quality control and finance as well as the coordination of facility policies and planning.

Operations

NEAH's core services are provided to and funded by all of its member organizations. In addition the alliance provides some voluntary services (such as licensing and insurance services) that are funded only by the participating members.

An affiliated organization the New England Pharmacy Collaborative (NEPC) handles drug purchases for the health care members.

Geographic Reach

New Hampshire holds the largest number of NEAH members (11) while the organization has seven participants in Vermont and one in Massachusetts.

Company Background

NEAH was formerly known as Dartmouth-Hitchcock Alliance; it changed its name in 2009.

EXECUTIVES

Ceo, James N Weinstein
Pres-Ceo*, Nancy Sormella
Coo*, Dan Jantzen
Cfo*, Robin Mackey
Dentist, Rocco R Addante DDS
Doctor, Thomas Colacchio
Physician, Amogh Karnik
Pathologist, Bing Ren

Physician, Ivan Chik
Physician, Kedong Wang
Diagnostic Radiologist, Kyle Winking
Auditors: PRICEWATERHOUSE LLP BOSTON

LOCATIONS

HQ: DARTMOUTH-HITCHCOCK CLINIC
1 MEDICAL CENTER DR, LEBANON, NH 037560001
Phone: 603 650-5000
Web: WWW.DARTMOUTH-HITCHCOCK.ORG

PRODUCTS/OPERATIONS

Selected Services
Core Services
  Financial Planning and Benchmarking
  Information Services
  Materials Management and Pharmacy Services
  Professional Staff Education and Development
  Program Administration
  Quality Improvement/Loss Prevention
Other Services
  Licenses
  Property/Casualty Insurance Program

Selected Alliance Members
Massachusetts
  Cooley Dickinson Health Care (Northampton)
New Hampshire
  Alice Peck Day Memorial Hospital (Lebanon)
  Cheshire Medical Center (Keene)
  Cottage Hospital (Woodsville)
  Dartmouth-Hitchcock Medical Center (Lebanon
  includes Mary Hitchcock Memorial Hospital)
  Monadnock Community Hospital
  New London Hospital
  Upper Connecticut Valley Hospital (Colebrook)
  Valley Regional Hospital (Claremont)
  Weeks Medical Center (Lancaster)
  West Central Behavioral Health (Lebanon)
Vermont
  Brattleboro Memorial Hospital
  Grace Cottage Hospital (Townshend)
  Mt. Ascutney Hospital (Windsor)
  Northeastern Vermont Regional Hospital (St. Johnsbury)
  Southwestern Vermont Medical Center (Bennington)
  Springfield Hospital
  VNA and Hospice of VT and NH

COMPETITORS

Amn Healthcare	Premier Inc.
Healthtrust	Vizient Inc.
Medassets	Winchester Healthcare

HISTORICAL FINANCIALS

Company Type: Private

Income Statement				FYE: June 30
	REVENUE ($ mil.)	NET INCOME ($ mil.)	NET PROFIT MARGIN	EMPLOYEES
06/19	1,888	22	1.2%	7,999
06/15	6	0	—	—
Annual Growth	313.1%	—	—	—

2019 Year-End Financials
Return on assets: 1.3%   Cash ($ mil.): 47
Return on equity: 4.9%
Current ratio: 1.50

DARTMOUTH-HITCHCOCK HEALTH

EXECUTIVES

Ceo, James Weinstein
Cfo, Daniel Jantzen
General Counsel, John Kacavas
Cao, Stephen Leblanc
Cqvo, Carol Barsky
Coo, Patrick Jordan III
Electrical Supervisor, Will Moore
Administrative Assistant, Bridget Connolly
Director of Clinical Microbiol, Isabella Martin
Associate Director, Database M, Moira Clark
Auditors: PRICEWATERHOUSECOOPERS LLP

LOCATIONS

HQ: DARTMOUTH-HITCHCOCK HEALTH
1 MEDICAL CENTER DR, LEBANON, NH 037560001
Phone: 603 653-1118
Web: WWW.DARTMOUTH-HITCHCOCK.ORG

HISTORICAL FINANCIALS

Company Type: Private

Income Statement				FYE: June 30
	REVENUE ($ mil.)	NET INCOME ($ mil.)	NET PROFIT MARGIN	EMPLOYEES
06/21	2,663	359	13.5%	8,000
06/20	2,344	(119)	—	—
06/19	2,299	40	1.8%	—
06/18	2,069	87	4.2%	—
Annual Growth	8.8%	59.9%	—	—

2021 Year-End Financials
Return on assets: 11.1%   Cash ($ mil.): 374
Return on equity: 38.1%
Current ratio: 1.30

DATASITE GLOBAL CORPORATION

Datasite formerly known as Merrill Corporation is a leading SaaS provider for the M&A industry empowering dealmakers around the world with the tools they need to succeed across the entire deal lifecycle. As the premiere virtual data room for M&A due diligence globally Datasite is consistently recognized for breakthrough technologies like its AI/ML-enabled capabilities and automated redaction tools. Beyond due diligence Datasite provides transaction and document management solutions for investment banks corporate development private equity and law firms across industries. In late 2020 Datasite agreed to be acquire by funds managed by CapVest Partners LLP an international private equity firm.

Operations
Datasite provides secure software solutions for managing the full spectrum of financial transactions ? including M&A restructuring & administration and capital raising. Its intuitive platform offers ironclad security enabling file sharing and collaboration within and across organizations. More than a virtual data room (VDR) Datasite supports advisors and their clients across the entire deal lifecycle with secure collaborative software

that shortens timelines for buy-side and sell-side teams from deal sourcing and deal preparation to post-merger integration (PMI) while meeting regulatory compliance ? including GDPR and CCPA requirements.

Geographic Reach
Headquartered in the Minneapolis Minnesota Datasite has operates throughout North and South America Europe and Asia Pacific.

Sales and Marketing
Datasite serves investment banking corporate development private equity and law firms.

Strategy
Datasite has ballooned in revenue and headcount since changing its name from Merrill Corp. in March 2020.

The software-as-a-service provider for mergers and acquisitions has increased its headcount at its Minneapolis headquarters by 37%. And its revenue has increased nearly 40% between fiscal 2019 and 2021.

Over the past year the company which was acquired by London-based private equity firm CapVest Partners last year has hosted half of the top 10 largest M&A deals in the US. And it's now on pace to facilitate 12000 deals per year in 170 countries and 14 languages.

The company's success can largely be attributed to a growing product line that leverages artificial intelligence. In the past 18 months Datasite has launched three new products: Prepare which organizes documents; Acquire which supports workflow on the buyer side of a deal; and Share which allows companies to trade highly confidential documents with outside parties.

Mergers and Acquisitions
In 2021 Datasite announced the strategic acquisition of Firmex a leading virtual data room and subscription file-sharing provider based in Toronto Canada. The acquisition of Firmex supports our aggressive growth strategy into new markets including supporting a wider range of use cases. The financial terms of the acquisition are not being disclosed.

HISTORY

Kenneth Merrill founded K. F. Merrill with his wife Lorraine in 1968 and grew the company into a major regional printer. He turned over the reins in 1984 to John Castro who had worked his way up from production manager. The company went public two years later.

EXECUTIVES

Chief Executive Officer, Rusty Wiley
Auditors: PRICE WATER HOUSE COOPER LLP

LOCATIONS

HQ: DATASITE GLOBAL CORPORATION
733 MARQUETTE AVE STE 600, MINNEAPOLIS, MN 554022357
Phone: 651 632-4000
Web: WWW.DATASITE.COM

PRODUCTS/OPERATIONS

SERVICES
Capital Transactions
Contract Management
Data Warehousing
Elections
Financial Services Marketing & Communications
Healthcare Member Communications
Intellectual Property Management
M&A Reorganizations & Exchange Offers
Merrill IFN
Portfolio Management
Regulatory Disclosure

COMPETITORS

Applied Discovery	Pitney Bowes
Diebold	R.r. Donnelley
Harte-hanks	Ricoh Usa
Intralinks	St Ives
Kroll Ontrack	Williams Lea
Lionbridge	Xerox

HISTORICAL FINANCIALS
Company Type: Private

Income Statement
FYE: January 31

	REVENUE ($ mil.)	NET INCOME ($ mil.)	NET PROFIT MARGIN	EMPLOYEES
01/17	609	53	8.9%	6,010
01/16	579	78	13.5%	—
01/15	691	64	9.3%	—
Annual Growth	(6.1%)	(8.5%)	—	—

2017 Year-End Financials
Return on assets: 17.4%   Cash ($ mil.): 62
Return on equity: —
Current ratio: 2.30

DATS TRUCKING, INC.

DATS Trucking specializes in less-than-truck-load (LTL) freight transportation in the western US but that's not all there is to the company's operations. In addition to its LTL operations in which freight from multiple shippers is combined into a single trailer DATS Trucking provides truckload transportation. The company's tanker division Overland Petroleum transports gasoline diesel fuel and other petroleum products. Overall DATS Trucking operates a fleet of about 500 tractors and 2500 trailers. It offers LTL service outside its home territory via The Reliance Network a group of regional carriers that covers the US and Canada. President and CEO Don Ipson founded DATS Trucking in 1988.

LOCATIONS
HQ: DATS TRUCKING, INC.
321 N OLD HIGHWAY 91, HURRICANE, UT 847373194
Phone: 435 673-1886
Web: WWW.DATSTRUCKING.COM

COMPETITORS

Bulkmatic	Schneider National
Central Freight Lines	Swift Transportation
Fedex Freight	Ups Freight
J.b. Hunt	Werner Enterprises
Kenan Advantage Group	Yrc Worldwide
Penn Tank Lines	

HISTORICAL FINANCIALS
Company Type: Private

Income Statement
FYE: December 31

	REVENUE ($ mil.)	NET INCOME ($ mil.)	NET PROFIT MARGIN	EMPLOYEES
12/07	717	1	0.3%	475
12/06	658	7	1.2%	—
12/05	600	1	0.2%	—
12/04	391	1	0.4%	—
Annual Growth	22.3%	4.6%	—	—

DAVIS SCHOOL DISTRICT

EXECUTIVES

Pres, John Robinson
V Pres*, Burke Larsen
Supt*, W Bryan Bowles
Asst Supt*, Lynn V Trenbeath
Asst Supt*, Nancy Fleming
MBR*, Barbara A Smith
MBR*, Larry Smith
MBR*, Peter Cannon
Facilities Director, John Swain
Before/After School Coordinato, Susy Jenson
Business Administrator, Craig Carter
Auditors: SQUIRE & COMPANY PC OREM UT

LOCATIONS
HQ: DAVIS SCHOOL DISTRICT
45 E STATE ST, FARMINGTON, UT 840252344
Phone: 801 402-5261
Web: WWW.DAVIS.K12.UT.US

HISTORICAL FINANCIALS
Company Type: Private

Income Statement
FYE: June 30

	REVENUE ($ mil.)	NET INCOME ($ mil.)	NET PROFIT MARGIN	EMPLOYEES
06/18	645	(15)	—	6,310
06/14	509	12	2.5%	—
06/13	500	(6)	—	—
06/11	482	1	0.4%	—
Annual Growth	4.2%	—	—	—

DB US HOLDING CORPORATION

EXECUTIVES

Pres-Ceo, Dr Josef Blank
Ex V Pres-Cfo, Joseph L Groneman
V Pres-SEC, Brian P Lynch
Vice President, Brian Lynch
Assistant General Counsel, Dennis St George
Executive Secretary, Rosemary Humphries
Office Manager, Andrea Hollandt
General Counsel, Labor and Emp, Vicki Hassman
Auditors: PRICEWATERHOUSECOOPERS LLP N

LOCATIONS
HQ: DB US HOLDING CORPORATION
120 WHITE PLAINS RD, TARRYTOWN, NY 105915526
Phone: 914 366-7200
Web: WWW.DBUSHOLDING.COM

HISTORICAL FINANCIALS
Company Type: Private

Income Statement
FYE: December 31

	REVENUE ($ mil.)	NET INCOME ($ mil.)	NET PROFIT MARGIN	EMPLOYEES
12/16	914	(2)	—	6,300
12/15	1,766	(10)	—	—
/	0	0	—	—
Annual Growth	—	—	—	—

2016 Year-End Financials
Return on assets: (-2.2%)   Cash ($ mil.): 122
Return on equity: (-2.3%)
Current ratio: 102.70

DBSI INC

EXECUTIVES

Pres, Douglas Swenson
V Pres-Sec-Treas*, Charles Hassard
V Pres*, John Mayeron
Contrl, Paris Cole
Representative, Bonni L White
Administration Manager, Jeremy Evans
Human Resources Manager, Richard Stonhill

LOCATIONS
HQ: DBSI INC
12426 W EXPLORER DR # 100, BOISE, ID 837131560
Phone: 208 955-9800
Web: WWW.DBSI-INC.COM

HISTORICAL FINANCIALS
Company Type: Private

Income Statement
FYE: December 31

	ASSETS ($ mil.)	NET INCOME ($ mil.)	INCOME AS % OF ASSETS	EMPLOYEES
12/07	244	15	6.4%	42
12/06	168	2	1.6%	—
12/05	150	25	17.0%	—
12/04	70	49	69.9%	—
Annual Growth	51.2%	(31.7%)	—	—

2007 Year-End Financials
Return on assets: 6.4%   Sales ($ mil): 625
Return on equity: 14.9%

DC WATER AND SEWER AUTHORITY

EXECUTIVES

Ceo-Gen Mngr, David L Gadis
Cfo, Olo Adebo
Treas, Robert Hunt
CIO, Omer Siddiqui
Acting Manager, Maxine Buchanan
Designer, Walter Burnett
Coordinator, Nicole Kaiser
Emergency Planning Coordinator, Dusti Lowndes
Manager, Craig Fricke
Facilities Director, Johnnie Walker
Human Resources, Mitsopoulos Stella
Auditors: KPMG LLP WASHINGTON DC

LOCATIONS
HQ: DC WATER AND SEWER AUTHORITY
5000 OVERLOOK AVE SW, WASHINGTON, DC 200325212
Phone: 202 787-2000
Web: WWW.DCWATER.COM

HISTORICAL FINANCIALS

Company Type: Private

Income Statement				FYE: September 30
	REVENUE ($ mil.)	NET INCOME ($ mil.)	NET PROFIT MARGIN	EMPLOYEES
09/18	684	187	27.4%	1,000
09/06	0	0	18.4%	—
09/05	272	48	17.6%	—
Annual Growth	7.3%	11.0%	—	—

2018 Year-End Financials

Return on assets: 2.4%
Return on equity: 9.0%
Current ratio: 1.40

Cash ($ mil.): 123

DCR WORKFORCE, INC.

EXECUTIVES

Prin, Naveen Dua
Pres*, Ammu Warrier
Cgo*, Daniel Weinfurter
Human Resources Lead, Allen Alexander
Supervisor, Kathleen Belotto
On Site Program Manager, Chris Stevens
Customer Engagement Consultant, Neal Johnson
Client Engagement Consultant, Paul Williams
Director of Business Developme, Scott Wade
Software Engineer, Umut Celik
Director of Professional Servi, Bradley Slivinski
Auditors: JOHN KAMMERER BOCA RATON FLO

LOCATIONS

HQ: DCR WORKFORCE, INC.
7795 NW BCN SQ BLVD # 201, BOCA RATON, FL 334871394
Phone: 561 998-3737
Web: WWW.WORKSPEND.COM

HISTORICAL FINANCIALS

Company Type: Private

Income Statement				FYE: December 31
	REVENUE ($ mil.)	NET INCOME ($ mil.)	NET PROFIT MARGIN	EMPLOYEES
12/12	548	2	0.5%	82
12/11	464	2	0.6%	—
12/01	12	0	6.3%	—
Annual Growth	41.0%	11.9%	—	—

2012 Year-End Financials

Return on assets: 16.9%
Return on equity: 21.1%
Current ratio: 3.80

Cash ($ mil.): —

DE PAUL UNIVERSITY

In the land of da Bulls and da Bears there's DePaul. One of the largest private not-for-profit universities in the US DePaul has more than 21920 students attending classes at its Chicago-area campuses and its increasing offerings of online learning courses. The university offers more than 300 undergraduate and graduate programs through 10 colleges and schools including the Driehaus College of Business and the College of Communication. It has a student teacher ratio of 16 to 1. One of the country's largest Catholic institutions of higher learning DePaul was founded in 1898 by the Vincentian religious community and is named after 17th century French priest St. Vincent de Paul.

Operations

The university's more than 130 undergraduate majors include accountancy acting animation chemistry criminology data science history journalism and marketing. Its more than 175 graduate programs include Counseling: Clinical Mental Health Counseling (MEd) Creative Producing (MFA) Early Childhood Education (EdD) Healthcare Markets & Analytics (MBA) Information Systems (MS) and Marketing Strategy and Planning (MBA) among its graduate programs. These programs are offered in School and Colleges of Business Communication Education Law Liberal Arts and Social Sciences Science and Health Music Continuing and Professional Studies as well as in Driehaus College of Business and The Theatre School.

Geographic Reach

DePaul's Chicago-area campuses are located in Lincoln Park (which is home to five colleges/schools) the Loop (for another five DePaul colleges and schools). DePaul's student body hosts learners from about 50 US states and more than 135 countries. In addition it study abroad programs are offered in more than 30 countries.

EXECUTIVES

President, A Gabriel Esteban
V Pres Fin- Cfo*, Bonnie Frankel
Exec V Pres*, Robert Kozoman
Trea*, Brian Sulivan
V Pres*, Sherri Sidler
MBR*, Douglas Stanford
Vp and General Counsel, Jos D Padilla
Accounting Staff, Carol Caridine
Assistant Professor, Elizabeth Hardman
Assistant Professor, Shiro Akiyoshi
Payroll Staff, Wenqin Zhang
Auditors: KPMG LLP CHICAGO ILLINOIS

LOCATIONS

HQ: DE PAUL UNIVERSITY
1 E JACKSON BLVD, CHICAGO, IL 606042287
Phone: 312 362-6714
Web: WWW.DEPAUL.EDU

HISTORICAL FINANCIALS

Company Type: Private

Income Statement				FYE: June 30
	REVENUE ($ mil.)	NET INCOME ($ mil.)	NET PROFIT MARGIN	EMPLOYEES
06/21	568	254	44.7%	3,895
06/20	595	67	11.3%	—
06/19	580	45	7.9%	—
06/18	575	67	11.7%	—
Annual Growth	(0.4%)	56.0%	—	—

2021 Year-End Financials

Return on assets: 13.0%
Return on equity: 17.4%
Current ratio: —

Cash ($ mil.): 34

DEACONESS HOSPITAL INC

Deaconess Hospital provides benevolent medical assistance to residents of southern Indiana western Kentucky and southeastern Illinois. The not-for-profit hospital is a 365-bed acute care medical facility that is the flagship hospital of the Deaconess Health System. Specialized services include cardiovascular surgery cancer treatment orthopedics neurological and trauma care. The hospital also offers home health care hospice services and medical equipment rental and it operates outpatient family practice surgery wellness and community outreach centers. Founded in 1892 Deaconess Hospital is a teaching and research facility affiliated with the Indiana University School of Medicine.

Operations

Deaconess handles about 18000 inpatient visits per year. It also sees about 350000 outpatients and 65000 emergency room visitors and it handles about 7500 annual surgery procedures.

Geographic Reach

Deaconess Hospital is located in Evansville Indiana and provides services to about 26 surrounding counties.

Strategy

To improve services to area residents Deaconess Hospital is expanding its outpatient care facilities and enhancing its IT resources. For instance in 2013 it moved its urgent care center to a larger more efficient facility. The hospital is also pursuing recognition for specialist programs such as its stroke center which was certified as a level one facility in 2013.

EXECUTIVES

Pres-Ceo, Linda E White
Chb, John Lipert
Cfo-Asst SEC, Richard Stivers
Program Director, Kim Volz
Pharmacist, Mark Bauer
Pharmacist, Tracy Herr
Business Coordinat, Catherine Perkins
Hospitalist, John Meunier
Creative Coordinator, Michael Hart
Anesthesiology, Nirmal Joshi
Integration Analyst, Betty Schmitt
Auditors: IT BLUE & CO LLC INDIANAPOLI

LOCATIONS

HQ: DEACONESS HOSPITAL INC
600 MARY ST, EVANSVILLE, IN 477101674
Phone: 812 450-5000
Web: WWW.DEACONESS.COM

Selected Services

24-hour Emergency Center
Cancer Services
Corporate Wellness
Family Medicine Clinic
Heart Services
Home Medical Equipment
Home-based Medical Care
Hospice Care
Inpatient and Outpatient Surgery
Mental Health Services
Neuro Services
Orthopedics
Pediatrics
Physician Referral Service
Radiology Services
Residency Program
Support Groups and Programs
Women's Hospital

COMPETITORS

Ball Memorial Hospital
Baptist Health
Baptist Health
  Madisonville
Commonwealth Health
  Corporation
Community Health
  Network
Daviess Community
  Hospital
Good Samaritan
  Hospital (in)

Henry County Memorial
  Hospital
Jewish Hospital & St.
  Mary's Healthcare
Kosciusko Community
  Hospital
Memorial Hospital
  (logansport)
Norton Healthcare
St. Mary's Medical
  Center Of Evansville

HISTORICAL FINANCIALS

Company Type: Private

Income Statement				FYE: September 30
	REVENUE ($ mil.)	NET INCOME ($ mil.)	NET PROFIT MARGIN	EMPLOYEES
09/19	1,047	159	15.2%	5,300
09/18	823	153	18.6%	—
09/17	725	94	13.0%	—
09/16	698	108	15.5%	—
Annual Growth	14.5%	13.6%	—	—

2019 Year-End Financials

Return on assets: 9.6%
Return on equity: 14.4%
Current ratio: 0.60

Cash ($ mil.): 83

DEER PARK REFINING LIMITED PARTNERSHIP

Auditors: ERNST & YOUNG LLP HOUSTON TE

LOCATIONS

HQ: DEER PARK REFINING LIMITED PARTNERSHIP
  5900 HIGHWAY 225, DEER PARK, TX 775362434
Phone: 713 246-7280
Web: WWW.DEERPARKTX.GOV

HISTORICAL FINANCIALS

Company Type: Private

Income Statement				FYE: December 31
	REVENUE ($ mil.)	NET INCOME ($ mil.)	NET PROFIT MARGIN	EMPLOYEES
12/17	867	97	11.2%	3
12/16	897	154	17.2%	—
Annual Growth	(3.3%)	(36.9%)	—	—

2017 Year-End Financials

Return on assets: 4.7%
Return on equity: 6.7%
Current ratio: 1.90

Cash ($ mil.): 77

DEKALB COUNTY BOARD OF EDUCATION

EXECUTIVES

Chm, Michael A Erwin
Vice Chm*, Marshall D Orson
Executive of Information Techn, Will Thomas
Auditors: RUSSELL W HINTON CPA CGFM

LOCATIONS

HQ: DEKALB COUNTY BOARD OF EDUCATION
  1701 MOUNTAIN INDUS BLVD, STONE MOUNTAIN,
  GA 300831027
Phone: 678 676-1200
Web: WWW.DEKALB.K12.GA.US

HISTORICAL FINANCIALS

Company Type: Private

Income Statement				FYE: June 30
	REVENUE ($ mil.)	NET INCOME ($ mil.)	NET PROFIT MARGIN	EMPLOYEES
06/07	1,128	350	31.1%	270
06/06	1,055	10	0.9%	—
Annual Growth	7.0%	3405.8%	—	—

2007 Year-End Financials

Return on assets: 22.9%
Return on equity: 33.3%
Current ratio: 3.60

Cash ($ mil.): 116

DEKALB COUNTY PUBLIC LIBRARY

EXECUTIVES

Exec Dir, Darro Willey
Asst Dir*, Mag Dasossa
Information Technology Manager, Chris Lee
Director, Allison Weissinger
Assistant Director, Nancy Wright
Librarian Senior, Candace Ushery
Continuing Education, Heather Salters
Special Education Teacher, Karen Gregory
Branch Operations Coordinator, George Ford
Facilities Administrative Coor, Ray Hill
Library Specialist, DEA Martin
Auditors: KPMG LLP ATLANTA GA

LOCATIONS

HQ: DEKALB COUNTY PUBLIC LIBRARY
  215 SYCAMORE ST FL 4, DECATUR, GA 300303413
Phone: 404 370-3070
Web: WWW.FOUNDATION.DEKALBLIBRARY.ORG

HISTORICAL FINANCIALS

Company Type: Private

Income Statement				FYE: December 31
	REVENUE ($ mil.)	NET INCOME ($ mil.)	NET PROFIT MARGIN	EMPLOYEES
12/07	622	(124)	—	228
12/06	622	186	30.0%	—
12/05	564	56	10.0%	—
Annual Growth	5.1%	—	—	—

2007 Year-End Financials

Return on assets: (-3.8%)
Return on equity: (-6.5%)
Current ratio: —

Cash ($ mil.): 536

DENNIS K. BURKE INC.

EXECUTIVES

Ceo, Edmund F Burke
Cfo*, Joe Cote
Customer, Jenifer Miller
Manager, Shawn Barboza
Commercial Sales Manager SE MA, Mark Collins
Engineer, Daniel Klimoski
Financial and Process, Erin Leale
Human Resources Manager, Heidi Cabral
Credit Manager, Nancy Brown
Senior Staff Accountant, Susan Boncariewski
Auditors: TONNESON & COMPANY INC WAKE

LOCATIONS

HQ: DENNIS K. BURKE INC.
  555 CONSTITUTION DR, TAUNTON, MA 027807365
Phone: 617 884-7800
Web: WWW.BURKEOIL.COM

HISTORICAL FINANCIALS

Company Type: Private

Income Statement				FYE: April 30
	REVENUE ($ mil.)	NET INCOME ($ mil.)	NET PROFIT MARGIN	EMPLOYEES
04/12	929	3	0.3%	110
04/11	807	0	0.1%	—
04/10	2,050	0	—	—
Annual Growth	—25724.5%	—	—	—

2012 Year-End Financials

Return on assets: 5.3%
Return on equity: 21.3%
Current ratio: 1.20

Cash ($ mil.): 1

DENVER HEALTH AND HOSPITALS AUTHORITY INC

When you live a mile high you sometimes need a safety net; that's where Denver Health and Hospital Authority comes in. Though it serves all the people of Colorado's capital annually attending to a fourth of the city's population and a third of its children Denver Health is also the "safety net" care provider for the city's indigent uninsured mentally ill and other high-risk patients. The medical system's primary facility is the Denver Health Medical Center a 525-bed hospital offering care in more than 50 medical specialties that also houses a regional trauma center. It also includes a network of family health and dental clinics; a poison and drug center; and a 911 response system for Denver County.

Operations

Denver Health's principal facility Denver Health Medical Center is a teaching hospital affiliated with the University of Colorado at Denver and is one of the busiest medical centers in the state. The trauma center (known as Rocky Mountain Regional Trauma Center) has Level I status and is known for having one of the highest survival rates in the nation. In addition the hospital operates an ambulance service a pediatric emergency center and a terrorism and catastrophe response center. Denver Health operates Denver's 911 medical emergency response system. Annually Denver Health paramedics respond to about 90000 calls for emergency medical assistance and transport more than 61000 patients to 11 area hospitals.

The health system provides medical care at 16 K-12 school-based health centers as well as eight family health centers located throughout the city. It also runs a number of public health clinics that offer immunizations infectious disease treatment detoxification and behavioral health consultation.

Denver Health cares for some 66000 children each year. In 2013 the system delivered 3175 babies and reported 55511 emergency department visits.

Financial Performance

Denver Health's revenue increased 7% to $793 million in 2013 due to an increase in net patient service revenue as well as safety net reimbursements and government grants. The number of uninsured patients has fallen dramatically under the Affordable Care Act which has helped the system improve its earnings. However the company reported a net loss of $15 million as non-operating revenue declined and fair value of investments fell.

Strategy

Denver Health integrates acute hospital and emergency care with public and community health offerings to deliver preventive primary and acute care services.

The health system's health plan covers 17000 city and hospital employees members of Medicaid's child plan and Medicare and another 53000 Medicaid patients. It expects to serve 40000 new Medicaid customers over the next few years as a result of the 2014 Affordable Care Act including about 15000 the hospital already sees without any payment.

In 2014 the company opened the Lowry Family Health Center adding new exam rooms to its operations. It also opened a new dental clinic and Women Infants and Children (WIC) office location.

Company Background

Denver Health traces its beginnings back to territorial days in 1860. As Denver General Hospital it operated as an agency of Denver's city and county governments until 1997 when it became a freestanding authority.

Denver Health's flagship medical center joined forces with Children's Hospital Colorado in late 2010 to share best practices and resources to expand and improve pediatric care throughout the region. Through the collaboration the two have increased access to pediatric mental health services; they also coordinate recruitment and sharing of highly specialized pediatric providers.

EXECUTIVES

Ceo, Arthur Gonzalez
Pres*, Patricia Gabow
Coo*, Stephanie Thomas
Asst To The Cfo, Lorraine Montoya
Chief Officer, Phillip S Mehler
Doctor, Judith Shlay
Information Specialist, Andrew Nill
Information Specialist, Camille Marthaler

Psychiatrist, Christian Thurstone
Clinical Social Worker, Robin List
Assistant Professor, Jennifer Kiser

LOCATIONS

HQ: DENVER HEALTH AND HOSPITALS AUTHORITY INC
777 BANNOCK ST, DENVER, CO 802044597
Phone: 720 956-2580
Web: WWW.DENVERHEALTH.ORG

PRODUCTS/OPERATIONS

2013 Sales

	$ mil.	% of total
Net patient service	368	46
Captation earned net of reinsurance expense	129	16
Medicaid disproportionate share & other safety net reimbursements	125	16
Federal state & other grants	71	9
Others	98	13
Total	**793**	**100**

Selected Medical Centers Clinics and Affiliates

Denver Emergency Center for Children
Denver Health Dental Care Clinics
Denver Health Medical Center
Denver Health Medical Plan (for Denver Health employees)
Denver Health Primary Care Clinics
Denver Paramedics
Denver Public Health
Rocky Mountain Center for Medical Response to Terrorism Mass Casualties and Epidemics
Rocky Mountain Poison & Drug Center
Rocky Mountain Regional Trauma Center

COMPETITORS

Banner Health	Healthone
Catholic Health Initiatives	Porter Adventist Hospital
Centura Health	Rose Medical Center
Children's Hospital Colorado	University Of Colorado Hospital
Exempla Healthcare	

HISTORICAL FINANCIALS

Company Type: Private

Income Statement				FYE: December 31
	REVENUE ($ mil.)	NET INCOME ($ mil.)	NET PROFIT MARGIN	EMPLOYEES
12/19	1,111	127	11.4%	3,541
12/18	1,119	62	5.6%	—
12/17	1,056	14	1.3%	—
12/16	505	(6)	—	—
Annual Growth	**30.0%**	—	—	—

2019 Year-End Financials

Return on assets: 10.1%   Cash ($ mil.): 63
Return on equity: 23.2%
Current ratio: 1.30

DESAROLLADORA DEL NORTE S E

EXECUTIVES

Pres, Gabriel Escarrer
V Pres of Devel, Edgar Motta
Buyer, Luis Molina

LOCATIONS

HQ: DESAROLLADORA DEL NORTE S E
200 COCO BCH BLVD HWY 955, RIO GRANDE, PR 00745
Phone: 787 657-1026

HISTORICAL FINANCIALS

Company Type: Private

Income Statement				FYE: December 31
	REVENUE ($ mil.)	NET INCOME ($ mil.)	NET PROFIT MARGIN	EMPLOYEES
12/16	1,801	102	5.7%	500
12/15	1,738	0	—	—
Annual Growth	**3.7%**	—	—	—

2016 Year-End Financials

Return on assets: 3.1%   Cash ($ mil.): 366
Return on equity: 6.6%
Current ratio: 0.90

DETROIT WAYNE MENTAL HEALTH AUTHORITY

EXECUTIVES

Ceo, Thomas Watkins
MA Ba Customer Member, Michael Shaw
Assistant To Chief Operati, Sonya Davis
Business Analyst, Steve Jamison
Department Manager Quality Man, April Siebert
Children's Initiatives Coordin, Monica Hampton
Manager of Quality, Brad Klemm
Deputy Chief Financial Officer, Dhannetta Brown
Supervisor, Toni Jones
Director, Andrea Smith
Finance Manager, Keisha Burnett

LOCATIONS

HQ: DETROIT WAYNE MENTAL HEALTH AUTHORITY
707 W MILWAUKEE ST, DETROIT, MI 482022943
Phone: 313 833-2500
Web: WWW.DWMHA.COM

HISTORICAL FINANCIALS

Company Type: Private

Income Statement				FYE: September 30
	REVENUE ($ mil.)	NET INCOME ($ mil.)	NET PROFIT MARGIN	EMPLOYEES
09/16	736	4	0.6%	99
09/15	701	19	2.8%	—
Annual Growth	**5.0%**	**(77.0%)**	—	—

2016 Year-End Financials

Return on assets: 2.1%   Cash ($ mil.): 176
Return on equity: 4.7%
Current ratio: 1.70

DEVCON CONSTRUCTION INCORPORATED

Devcon Construction has built a sturdy business from building in the Bay Area. One of the area's top general building contractors Devcon has constructed more than 30 million sq. ft. of office industrial and commercial space. Its focus is on Northern California mainly in the San Francisco Bay Area and Silicon Valley. The company provides engineering design/build and interior design services. It specializes in high-tech projects including data centers and industrial research and development facilities. In addition to building company facilities and offices Devcon works on such projects as hotels restaurants parking structures retail stores sports facilities and schools.

Geographic Reach

Based in Milpitas California Devcon maintains several satellite offices in California in Petaluma Stockton and Santa Cruz as well as an office in Reno Nevada.

Strategy

Although most of Devcon's work is in California the company also has completed projects in Nevada Oregon Idaho Texas Massachusetts and Florida. Recent projects in the San Francisco Forty Niners Stadium in Santa Clara San Jose Sharks Ice Center in Pleasanton and the Stanford Research Computing Facility.

The company partnered with US-based Central Concrete in 2012 to supply its high-performing low-CO2 concrete for the new San Francisco 49er Stadium. The move showcases Devcon's focus on sustainability as part of its projects.

EXECUTIVES

Pres-Ceo, Gary Filizetti
SEC*, Justine Pereira
Cfo*, Brett Sisney
Superintendent, Rich Van Kirk
Accounting Staff, Jennifer Chavez
Senior Project Manager, Rick Buellesbach
Senior Project Manager, Garret Tomforde
Project Manager, S Bridges
Superintendent, Kim Kizer
Project Superintendent, Bob Stroberg
Superintendent, Clint Magill
Auditors: JOHANSON & YAU ACCOUNTANCY COR

LOCATIONS

HQ: DEVCON CONSTRUCTION INCORPORATED
690 GIBRALTAR DR, MILPITAS, CA 950356317
Phone: 408 942-8200
Web: WWW.DEVCON-CONST.COM

PRODUCTS/OPERATIONS

Selected Projects

1880 Mission Street San Francisco

3333 Scott Blvd. Buildings A B & C Santa Clara
Anderson Collection At Stanford University Stanford
Barnes & Nobles Palo Alto
Cisco Parking Structure 1 San Jose
Cisco Parking Structure 2 San Jose
Downtown Sunnyvale Town Center Sunnyvale
El Camino Family Housing South San Francisco
Fresno Hyatt Place Hotel Fresno
Friedenrich Center For Translational Research At 800 Welch Road
Lawson Lane East - Buildings A & B Santa Clara
Oakland Air Traffic Control Tower (ATCT) Oakland
San Francisco 49ers Stadium Santa Clara
San Jose Earthquakes - MLS Soccer Stadium San Jose
SanDisk Milpitas
Santa Clara University Admissions & Enrollment Services Building Santa Clara
Sharks Ice Center Pleasanton
Stanford Research Computing Facility Stanford
The Plaza At Triton Park Foster City
University Plaza Palo Alto
Villa Siena Nursing Care Units Mountain View

COMPETITORS

Charles Pankow   Kprs Construction

Builders   Obayashi
Dpr Construction   Rudolph & Sletten
Hathaway Dinwiddie   Structure Tone
Construction   Swinerton
Hensel Phelps   Turner Corporation
Construction   Webcor Builders

HISTORICAL FINANCIALS
Company Type: Private

Income Statement   FYE: December 31

	REVENUE ($ mil.)	NET INCOME ($ mil.)	NET PROFIT MARGIN	EMPLOYEES
12/14	1,181	20	1.7%	550
12/13	1,012	12	1.2%	—
12/12	779	3	0.5%	—
Annual Growth	23.1%	138.8%		

2014 Year-End Financials
Return on assets: 6.0%   Cash ($ mil.): 64
Return on equity: 54.9%
Current ratio: 1.10

DHPC TECHNOLOGIES, INC.

EXECUTIVES

Ceo-Pres, John M Curtis
Director, Robert Lake
Senior Consultant, Dan Glasel
Engineer, Kevin Sullivan
Chief Scientist, Frank Barone
Contracts Manager, Natalya Gnyp
Training Manager, Susan Missenheim
Electrical Engineer, Jenny Maung
Software Engineer, John Morgan
Director Human Resources, Iris Simpson
Electrical Engineer, Joseph Diaz

LOCATIONS

HQ: DHPC TECHNOLOGIES, INC.
10 WODBRDGE CTR DR STE 65, WOODBRIDGE, NJ 07095
Phone: 732 791-5400
Web: WWW.DHPCTECH.COM

HISTORICAL FINANCIALS
Company Type: Private

Income Statement   FYE: May 11

	REVENUE ($ mil.)	NET INCOME ($ mil.)	NET PROFIT MARGIN	EMPLOYEES
05/17*	38,584	1,320	3.4%	150
12/09	11	1	9.0%	—
12/07	6	1	29.2%	—
06/06	1,726	0	0.0%	—
Annual Growth	32.6%	179.9%	—	—

*Fiscal year change

2017 Year-End Financials
Return on assets: 14.5%   Cash ($ mil.): 2,039
Return on equity: 21.9%
Current ratio: 2.80

DIALYSIS CLINIC, INC.

Dialysis Clinic Inc. or DCI is dedicated to caring for patients with end-stage renal disease (ESRD). The not-for-profit company which operates a network of more than 210 dialysis centers serving more than 14000 patients in 27 states also provides kidney transplant assistance services. Affiliate DCI Donor Services is an organ and tissue procurement agency. DCI also funds kidney-related research and educational programs and is affiliated with various universities and teaching hospitals throughout the US including Tufts University the University of Arizona and Tulane University.

Geographic Reach

The company has its locations in Alabama Arizona Arkansas California Colorado Connecticut Florida Georgia Indiana Iowa Kentucky Louisiana Maine Massachusetts Missouri Montana Nebraska Nevada New Jersey New Mexico New York North Carolina Ohio Pennsylvania South Carolina Tennessee and Texas.

Strategy

DCI grows its network of facilities by forming partnerships with health care providers and other organizations. The company provides funding for construction and operation of the facility and it provides clinic support services including supply procurement and central laboratory services (through its DCI Lab subsidiary).

In 2012 the company opened a dialysis clinic in Albuquerque its first dialysis clinic in the South Valley region of New Mexico.

Company Background

DCI was established in 1971 by nephrologist Keith Johnson.

EXECUTIVES

Chb, H Keith Johnson
Dir*, James Perry
Pres*, Ed Attrill
SEC-Treas*, William Wood
Attorney, Karin A Barrett
Nurse Manage, Debra Breault
Nurse Manage, Kimberly Kale
Director of Corporate, Hal Whetstone
Accounts Receivable Specialist, Allison Discello
Controller, Andy Parker
Care Coordinator, Angela Tillotson
Auditors: DELOITTE & TOUCHE LLP NASHVIL

LOCATIONS

HQ: DIALYSIS CLINIC, INC.
1633 CHURCH ST STE 500, NASHVILLE, TN 372032948
Phone: 615 327-3061
Web: WWW.DCIINC.ORG

COMPETITORS

Davita   Renal Advantage
Fmcna   U.s. Renal Care
Fresenius

HISTORICAL FINANCIALS
Company Type: Private

Income Statement   FYE: September 30

	REVENUE ($ mil.)	NET INCOME ($ mil.)	NET PROFIT MARGIN	EMPLOYEES
09/19	739	7	1.1%	5,000
09/18	760	5	0.7%	—
09/17	736	23	3.3%	—
09/16	719	22	3.2%	—
Annual Growth	0.9%	(30.0%)	—	—

Return on assets: 1.1%   Cash ($ mil.): 127
Return on equity: 1.3%
Current ratio: 26.90

DIGNITY HEALTH

Dignity Health is the largest hospital provider in California and the fifth largest health system in the US. The not-for-profit health care provider operates a network of more than 400 care centers including nearly 40 hospitals urgent and occupational care imaging and surgery centers home health and primary care clinics in more than 20 states. Dignity Health is the official health care provider of the San Francisco Giants. With more than 60000 caregivers and staff who deliver excellent care to diverse communities the company has more than 10000 active physicians.

Operations

Dignity Health offers inpatient outpatient subacute and home health care services as well as physician services through affiliates including Dignity Health Medical Foundation a not-for-profit organization providing award-winning patient-centered health care in a variety of areas including primary and specialty care diagnostic imaging vision occupational health urgent care and behavioral health.

Geographic Reach

Headquartered in San Francisco Dignity Health operates some 40 hospitals urgent care centers clinics emergency rooms and specialty care centers in California Nevada and Arizona.

Sales and Marketing

Dignity Health serves all communities with physical mental and spiritual needs.

Financial Performance

Dignity Health's revenue increased 3% to $10.7 billion in 2014 due to increases in premiums health-related activities and other operating earnings (including a gain on sale of certain assets related to outreach lab services). Net income fell 21% to $281 million as a result of higher salaries and benefits as well as income tax expenses.

Cash flow from operations grew 33% in 2014 to $422 million mostly due to cash generated from accounts payable and a decline in cash used in estimated receivables and payables.

Company Background

Dignity Health traces its roots to 1857. The Sisters of Mercy Catholic order was established in Dublin in 1831. In the 1850s eight Sisters arrived in San Francisco and began caring for residents with cholera typhoid and influenza. They established St. Mary's Hospital now that city's oldest continuously operating hospital. The order merged operations with another community of Sisters of Mercy in 1986 to create Catholic Healthcare West. The combined system had one retirement home and 10 hospitals throughout California.

The system changed its name to Dignity Health in early 2012 as part of a governance restructuring program. While the firm remained a not-for-profit organization with Catholic roots and its Catholic hospitals continued to be sponsored by their founding congregations (and governed by the Catholic health care directives) the parent organization itself was no longer an official ministry of the Catholic church. In 2019 Dignity Health joined forces with Catholic Health Initiatives to create CommonSpirit Health the nation's largest not-for-profit health system.

HISTORY

Dignity Health formerly Catholic Healthcare West (CHW) traces its roots to 1857 when the Sisters of Mercy founded St. Mary's Hospital in San Francisco. The order expanded in that area and in 1986 two different communities of the Sisters of Mercy merged their hospitals into an organization with one retirement home and 10 hospitals from the Bay Area to San Diego. Declining membership in Roman Catholic religious orders combined with consolidation in the field led the orders to see merger as their only route to survival.

CHW continued to add facilities including AMI Community Hospital in Santa Cruz California in 1990. Since CHW already owned the area's only other acute care hospital Dominican Santa Cruz Hospital CHW in 1993 was ordered not to acquire any more acute care hospitals in Santa Cruz County without FTC approval.

As the trend to managed care became a stampede in the 1990s CHW moved more into preventive care and began reigning in costs through productivity improvement plans. It continued to add hospitals including tax-supported institutions trying to compete with national for-profit systems.

The network increased its medical clout in 1994 by allying with San Diego-based Scripps one of the state's largest HMO systems. In 1995 the Daughters of Charity Province of the West realigned its six-hospital operation with CHW. The next year the Dominican Sisters (California) the Dominican Sisters of St. Catherine of Siena (Wisconsin) and the Sisters of Charity of the Incarnate Word allied their California hospitals with CHW. New community hospitals included Bakersfield Memorial Sierra Nevada Memorial (Grass Valley) Sequoia Hospital (Redwood City) and Woodland Healthcare.

Charity and cost-consciousness clashed in 1996 when union members staged a walkout to protest nonunion outsourcing of vocational nursing housekeeping and kitchen jobs. This dispute was settled but CHW continued to be a target for union organizers with a bitter battle against the Service Employees International Union (SEIU) starting in 1998.

The year 2000 brought CHW more problems with labor relations: SEIU argued that the organization was resistant to unionization. Continued losses led the organization to implement major restructuring the following year as its 10 regional divisions were consolidated into four.

The company parted ways with one of its sponsoring organizations the Franciscan Sisters of the Sacred Heart of Frankfort Illinois in 2003. The sponsorship ended when CHW closed St. Francis Medical Center of Santa Barbara. However the hospital operator that fiscal year posted its first operating profit in seven years.

The company changed its name from Catholic Healthcare West (CHW) to Dignity Health in early 2012 as part of a governance restructuring program. While the firm remained a not-for-profit organization with Catholic roots and its Catholic hospitals continued to be sponsored by their founding congregations (and governed by the Catholic health care directives) the parent organization itself was no longer an official ministry of the Catholic church.

The company's rebranding and restructuring aimed to give it more flexibility to pursue its growth strategy of widening its presence into additional regions of the US while lowering the overall cost of care (a desire of most large hospital operators as the US government works to reform its ailing health system). At the time of the governance shift Dignity Health operated 25 Catholic hospitals and 15 non-Catholic hospitals.

EXECUTIVES

Pres-Ceo, Lloyd Dean
Co-Ceo*, Kevin E Lofton
V Pres-Coo*, Marvin O'Quinn
V Pres-Cfo*, Michael Blaszyk
Treas*, Lisa Zuckerman
Chief Admin Ofcr*, Elizabeth Shih
Coordinator, Jill Babowal
Principal, Ronald Reece
It Mgr, Zoe Mc Nevin
Manager, Rachel Toro
Dir of Hr, Marc De Zordo
Auditors: IT KPMG LLP SAN FRANCISCO C

LOCATIONS

HQ: DIGNITY HEALTH
185 BERRY ST STE 200, SAN FRANCISCO, CA 941071777
Phone: 415 438-5500
Web: WWW.DIGNITYHEALTH.ORG

Selected Facilities

Arizona
Barrow Neurological Institute (Phoenix)
Chandler Regional Medical Center
Mercy Gilbert Medical Center
St. Joseph's Hospital and Medical Center (Phoenix)
California
Arroyo Grande Community Hospital
Bakersfield Memorial Hospital
California Hospital Medical Center (Los Angeles)
Community Hospital of San Bernardino
Dominican Hospital (Santa Cruz)
French Hospital Medical Center (San Luis Obispo)
Glendale Memorial Hospital and Health Center
Marian Medical Center (Santa Maria)
Mark Twain St. Joseph's Hospital (San Andreas)
Mercy General Hospital (Sacramento)
Mercy Hospital of Bakersfield
Mercy Hospital of Folsom
Mercy Medical Center Merced Community Campus
Mercy Medical Center Merced Dominican Campus
Mercy Medical Center Mt. Shasta
Mercy Medical Center Redding
Mercy San Juan Medical Center (Carmichael)
Mercy Southwest Hospital (Bakersfield)
Methodist Hospital of Sacramento
Northridge Hospital Medical Center
Oak Valley Hospital (Oakdale)
Saint Francis Memorial Hospital (San Francisco)
Sequoia Hospital (Redwood City)
Sierra Nevada Memorial Hospital (Grass Valley)
St. Bernardine Medical Center (San Bernardino)
St. Elizabeth Community Hospital (Red Bluff)
St. John's Pleasant Valley Hospital (Camarillo)
St. John's Regional Medical Center (Oxnard)
St. Joseph's Behavioral Health Center (Stockton)
St. Joseph's Medical Center (Stockton)
St. Mary Medical Center (Long Beach)
St. Mary's Medical Center (San Francisco)
Woodland Healthcare
Nevada
St. Rose Dominican Hospital Rose de Lima Campus (Henderson)
St. Rose Dominican Hospital San Martí;n Campus (Las Vegas)
St. Rose Dominican Hospital Siena Campus (Henderson)

PRODUCTS/OPERATIONS

Sponsoring Organizations

Congregation of the Dominican Sisters of St. Catherine of Siena of Kenosha (Kenosha Wisconsin)
Congregation of the Sisters of Charity of the Incarnate Word (Houston Texas)
Sisters of Mercy of the Americas West Midwest Community (Omaha Nebraska; formerly Auburn Regional Community of the Sisters of Mercy and Burlingame Regional Community of the Sisters of Mercy in California)
Sisters of St. Dominic Congregation of the Most Holy Rosary (Adrian Michigan)
Sisters of St. Francis of Penance and Christian Charity St. Francis Province (Redwood City California)

Sisters of the Third Order of St. Dominic Congregation
of the Most Holy Name (San Rafael California)

COMPETITORS

Adventist Health System West
Banner Health
Community Health Systems
Community Hospital Of The Monterey Peninsula
Ensign Group
Hca
John C. Lincoln Health Network
John Muir Health
Loma Linda University Medical Center
Memorial Health Services
Prospect Medical
Providence St. Joseph Health
Salinas Valley Memorial
Shasta Regional Medical Center
Stanford Health Care
Sutter Health
Tenet Healthcare
Ucsf Medical
Universal Health Services
Vitas Healthcare

HISTORICAL FINANCIALS

Company Type: Private

Income Statement				FYE: June 30
	REVENUE ($ mil.)	NET INCOME ($ mil.)	NET PROFIT MARGIN	EMPLOYEES
06/19	9,916	119	1.2%	55,494
06/09	8,957	(799)	—	—
Annual Growth	1.0%	—	—	—

2019 Year-End Financials

Return on assets: 0.8%
Return on equity: 2.3%
Current ratio: 1.00

Cash ($ mil.): 1,845

DIGNITY HEALTH MEDICAL FOUNDATION

EXECUTIVES

Pres, Laurie Schwarctz
Cfo*, Theresa Hylen
Coordinator, Leticia Mendoza
Clinic Manager, Isabel Reyes
Financial Analyst, Sonja Greene
Director, Steve Scharmann
Telehealth Coordinator, Harinder Buttar
Senior Counsel, Kelley Evans
Manager, Janet Duffy
AP Customer, Paula Villa
Administrative Assistant, Sherry Penlesky
Auditors: KPMG LLP SAN FRANCISCO CA

LOCATIONS

HQ: DIGNITY HEALTH MEDICAL FOUNDATION
3400 DATA DR, RANCHO CORDOVA, CA 956707956
Phone: 916 851-2000
Web: WWW.DIGNITYHEALTH.ORG

HISTORICAL FINANCIALS

Company Type: Private

Income Statement				FYE: June 30
	REVENUE ($ mil.)	NET INCOME ($ mil.)	NET PROFIT MARGIN	EMPLOYEES
06/14	570	17	3.1%	1,000
06/09	297	0	0.1%	—
Annual Growth	13.9%	120.7%	—	—

2014 Year-End Financials

Return on assets: 9.4%
Return on equity: 19.7%
Current ratio: 1.40

Cash ($ mil.): 31

DISTRICT OF COLUMBIA WATER & SEWER AUTHORITY

EXECUTIVES

Ceo, George Hawkins
Customer Manager, Donna Lewis
Senior Network Administrator, Joe Edwards
Counsel, Meena Gowda
Executive Assistant, Deborah Cole
Assistant Facilities Manager, Quintin Wilkinson
Senior Vice President, CIP Pro, Leonard Benson
Computer Specialist, Rhonda Green
Green Infrastructure Assistant, Seth Charde
Assistant General Manager, Charles Kiely
Compliance Officer, Deborah Cook
Auditors: KPMG LLP WASHINGTON DC

LOCATIONS

HQ: DISTRICT OF COLUMBIA WATER & SEWER
AUTHORITY
5000 OVERLOOK AVE SW, WASHINGTON, DC
200325212
Phone: 202 787-2000
Web: WWW.DCWATER.COM

HISTORICAL FINANCIALS

Company Type: Private

Income Statement				FYE: September 30
	REVENUE ($ mil.)	NET INCOME ($ mil.)	NET PROFIT MARGIN	EMPLOYEES
09/20	736	222	30.3%	1,100
09/19	705	165	23.4%	—
09/17	643	194	30.2%	—
Annual Growth	4.6%	4.7%	—	—

2020 Year-End Financials

Return on assets: 2.6%
Return on equity: 9.0%
Current ratio: 1.50

Cash ($ mil.): 186

DITECH HOLDING CORPORATION

Walter Investment Management does its best to collect from the credit-challenged. The firm owns and services residential mortgages (particularly those of the subprime and nonconforming variety) for itself as well as for government sponsored entities government agencies third-party securitization trusts and other credit owners. Operating through subsidiaries Walter Mortgage Company; Hanover Capital; Marix Servicing; Ditech; and third-party credit servicer Green Tree Walter Investment Management services 2 million residential loan accounts with unpaid balances of $256 billion making it one of the 10 largest mortgage servicers in the US. The firm also originates residential loans including reverse loans. The firm filed for Chapter 11 bankruptcy in 2017 and is expected to emerged from it less $800 million in debt overhang in early 2018.

Operations

Walter Investment Management operates three main business segments. Its Servicing segment which generates more than 50% of Walter's revenue mostly services mortgage loans for third-party creditors and its own mortgage loan portfolio on a fee-for-service basis. Following the simplification of its business in 2015 the segment also consists of an insurance agency serving residential loan borrowers and credit owners and a collections agency that performs collections of post charge-off deficiency balances for third parties and Walter's own portfolio. It also holds the assets and mortgage-backed debt of the Residual Trusts.

As one of the US' top 20 largest mortgage loan originators Walter's Origination segment (32% of revenue) purchases and originates mortgage loans that are sold to third parties with servicing rights generally retained. The Reverse Mortgage segment (10% of revenue) purchases and originates securitized loans backed by secured borrowings services loans for third-party credit owners and its portfolio and also provides complementary reverse mortgage services like property management and dispositions.

Geographic Reach

The Tampa-based firm has offices across the US.

Sales and Marketing

Walter's origination business sells nearly all of its mortgage loans into the secondary market for securitization or private investors as whole loans. It sells conventional conforming and government-backed mortgage loans through agency-sponsored securitizations where mortgage-backed securities are made and sold to third-party investors. Its nonconforming mortgage loans are sold to private investors.

The firm's consumer direct retail channel originates reverse loans through call centers and purchases leads from lead purveyors or through advertising campaigns. The wholesale channel sources reverse loans from a broker network. The correspondent channel buys reverse loans from a correspondents network in the marketplace.

Financial Performance

Walter Investment Management's revenues and profits have mostly trended higher over the past few years thanks to regular loan portfolio acquisitions as well as acquisitions of other servicing companies and financial firms.

The firm's revenue reversed course in 2014 however diving 18% to $1.49 billion for the year. Most of the decline came from the Servicing division which suffered from a $278 million decrease in fair value of servicing rights due to market-driven changes. The Origination segment's income fell by 24% on lower loan sales due to a shift in volume from the higher-margin consumer retention channel to the lower-margin correspondent lending channel.

Revenue declines coupled with an $82.3 million- impairment charge caused Walter to suffer a net loss of $110.33 million in 2014. The impairment charge came after an evaluation found its reverse mortgage's goodwill was less than its carrying value. Walter's operations continued to use more cash than it produced — operations used $204 million — though its cash levels improved greatly from the year before as it sold a higher volume of loans in relation to originated loans given the ramp up of its mortgage loan originations business in 2013.

Strategy

Walter Investment hopes to tap into growing demand from big lenders looking to shift their debt servicing functions to outside firms. A rise in borrower delinquencies and foreclosures following the recession has forced traditional loan servicers and owners such as banks to look for third-party assistance. Accordingly part of Walters' growth strategy focuses on acquiring and servicing large loan portfolios that other banks and other financial companies haven't been able to successfully collect on.

The firm also hopes to grow its consumer-facing origination business seeking more cross-sell opportunities as well as opportunities to grow its consumer direct and consumer retail channels to meet demand for low-cost mortgage loans in the market. To this end in 2015 it planned to leverage its well known Ditech brand (while saving $75 million in annual costs) by consolidating its Ditech and Green Tree Servicing into a single company: Ditech a Walter company.

In early 2017 the company agreed to sell Green Tree Insurance Agency to Assurant for $125 million thereby focusing further on its core operations.

Mergers and Acquisitions

In early 2013 in taking advantage of the opportunity to further expand its servicing portfolio Walter closed on two separate purchases (from Bank of America and Residential Capital LLC) of Fannie Mae mortgage serving rights for loans totaling $132 billion in unpaid principal balance.

Also in 2013 Walter Investment Management acquired a $12 billion reverse mortgage servicing portfolio from Wells Fargo. The portfolio with $12.2 billion in unpaid balance houses more than 76000 loans. The portfolio transferred to Walter's wholly-owned subsidiary Reverse Mortgage Solutions and doubled the size of its serviced book.

Company Background

The company entered the reverse mortgage business in late 2012 with the purchase of Reverse Mortgage Solutions (RMS) for some $120 million. RMS provided servicing origination asset management and technology services to the fast-growing reverse mortgage industry.

In 2011 Walter Investment Management increased its loan portfolio and transformed into a fee-based service provider when it paid $1 billion for GTCS Holdings the parent of Green Tree Servicing. As a result Walter Investment Management no longer qualified as a real estate investment trust (REIT). The Green Tree acquisition represented a dramatic increase the size and scope of Walter Investment Management's business. The company's servicing portfolio grew by 50% and nearly 2000 employees were added. Green Tree also increased Walter Investment Management's geographic footprint by adding 27 offices in the US.

Walter Investment Management was created in 2009 when Hanover Capital Mortgage merged with the home financing business of Walter Industries (now Walter Energy). Walter Energy was spun off after the closure of troubled homebuilder Jim Walter Homes.

EXECUTIVES

Chb-Pres-Ceo, Thomas F Marano
Exec V Pres-Cfo*, Gerald A Lombardo
Exec V Pres-Chief Risk & Compl*, Alfred W Young Jr
Sr V Pres-Chief Hr Officer*, Elizabeth F Monahan
General Counsel-Clo-Sec*, John J Haas
Chief Operating Officer, Ritesh Chaturbedi
Director, Daniel Beltzman
Investor Relations Officer, Jason Harbes
Director, John Brecker
Director, Neal Goldman
Auditors: ERNST & YOUNG LLP PHILADELPHI

LOCATIONS

HQ: DITECH HOLDING CORPORATION
  500 OFFICE CENTER DR # 400, FORT WASHINGTON, PA 190343219
Phone: 844 714-8603
Web: WWW.DITECHHOLDING.COM

PRODUCTS/OPERATIONS

2014 Sales

	$ mil.	% of total
Servicing	563	37
Originations	481	32
Reverse Mortage	157	10
ARM	58	4
Insurance	71	5
Loans & Residuals	134	9
Other	41	3
Elliminations	(20.2)	-
Total	**1,487**	**100**

COMPETITORS

Annaly Capital Management	Firstcity Financial
Cifc	Nationstar Mortgage
Capstead Mortgage	Ocwen Financial
Dvl	Redwood Trust
Drive Shack	Resource Capital

HISTORICAL FINANCIALS

Company Type: Private

Income Statement   FYE: December 31

	REVENUE ($ mil.)	NET INCOME ($ mil.)	NET PROFIT MARGIN	EMPLOYEES
12/18	658	(205)	—	3,800
12/17	831	(426)	—	—
12/16	995	(529)	—	—
12/15	1,274	(263)	—	—
Annual Growth	**(19.7%)**	—	—	—

2018 Year-End Financials

Return on assets: (-1.8%)   Cash ($ mil.): 187
Return on equity: —
Current ratio: —

DO IT BEST CORP.

Founded in 1945 Do it Best Corp. is a member-owned wholesaler of hardware lumber builder supplies and related products operating as a wholesaler cooperative. Besides the usual tools and building materials merchandise includes automotive items bicycles camping gear housewares office supplies and small appliances. Customers also can have products specially shipped to their local stores through Do it Best's e-commerce site. The co-op's buying power enables members to offer items at competitive prices.

Operations

The company offers a wide array of products including hardware outdoor living farm and ranch holiday decoration and supplies building materials sporting goods cleaning supplies clothing and apparel electronics food and snacks and more. In addition its popular product categories include Grills & Accessories Paint Applicators & Accessories Lawn & Leaf Bag Paint Cordless Power Tools Power Equipment Parts & Accessories Lawn & Garden Tools and Fire Protection & Accessories.

Geographic Reach

Based in Fort Wayne Indiana Do it Best operates warehouses in Illinois South Carolina Ohio Nevada New York Missouri Texas and Oregon as well as regional lumber center in Minnesota Indiana South Carolina New York and Oregon.

Sales and Marketing

Nearly all of the Do it Best's sales are to dealer-members. Members are required to buy 20 voting common shares at $50 per share on becoming a member.

Advertising and promotion costs net charged to operation in 2021 2020 and 2019 were $10081 $11886 and $14027 respectively.

Financial Performance

In 2021 the company's revenue increase by 45% to $5.2 billion from $3.6 billion in 2020.

The company's net income for the year was $4.1 million a $2.3 million increase from the previous year's $1.5 million.

Cash and cash equivalents at the end of the year were $4.1 million a $82.5 million decrease from 2019. Operating investing and financing activities used $37.4 million 15.1 million and $30.0 million respectively.

Company Background

Formerly named Hardware Wholesalers Do it Best was founded in 1945 in Fort Wayne Indiana by Arnold Gerberding. The company launched its doitbest.com e-commerce site in 1996.

EXECUTIVES

Ceo-Pres, Dan Starr
V Pres Sls & Bus Dev't*, Nick Talarico
V Pres Fin*, David W Dietz
V Pres Merchandising*, Steve Markley
V Pres*, Tim Miller
Store Dev't Mgr, Brian Kimball
Coordinator, Lisa Ellert
Merchandise Mgr, Jenna Myers
Coordinator, Chris Hill
Accounting Supervisor, Verna Doehrman
Public Relations Director, Christian Parra
Auditors: CLIFTONLARSONALLEN LLP INDIAN

LOCATIONS

HQ: DO IT BEST CORP.
  6502 NELSON RD, FORT WAYNE, IN 468031947
Phone: 260 748-5300
Web: WWW.DOITBESTONLINE.COM

COMPETITORS

84 Lumber	Northern Tool
Ace Hardware	Orgill
Home Depot	Sutherland Lumber
Lowe's	True Value
Menard	Wal-mart

Income Statement				FYE: June 25
	REVENUE ($ mil.)	NET INCOME ($ mil.)	NET PROFIT MARGIN	EMPLOYEES
06/16	2,925	0	0.0%	1,519
06/11	2,328	0	0.0%	—
06/10	2,296	0	0.0%	—
Annual Growth	4.1%	(5.7%)	—	—

2016 Year-End Financials

Return on assets: 0.1%   Cash ($ mil.): 20
Return on equity: 0.2%
Current ratio: 1.40

DOCTOR'S ASSOCIATES INC.

Doctor's Associates owns the Subway chain of sandwich shops the world's largest quick-service restaurant chain by number of locations surpassing burger giant McDonald's. The company boasts more than 44000 restaurants in greater than 110 countries. Virtually all Subway restaurants are franchised and offer such fare as hot and cold sub sandwiches turkey wraps and salads. The widely recognized eateries are in freestanding buildings as well as in airports convenience stores sports facilities and other locations.

Operations

With the ability to fit one of its restaurants almost anywhere Subway can offer franchisees lower startup costs as compared to other concepts that require large areas for food preparation or dining space. Many of Subway's franchisees operate just a single location but a few oversee a large estate.

Local operators who own the individual restaurants use the Subway name in exchange for royalties and other fees. This allows Doctor's Associates to expand its sandwich business without the cost of construction and operation. (Domiciled in Florida the company operates its franchising business largely through Connecticut-based affiliate World Franchise Headquarters.)

Geographic Reach

The company's network of eateries stretching from Afghanistan to Zambia is a testament to how effectively the franchising model can be used to expand a dining concept. Part of the reason for Subway's success is the portability and adaptability of the dining concept. The sandwich restaurants can be found in a vast array of locations including shopping center food courts suburban strip malls and even military bases. The company is particularly focused on expanding its international presence in Asia and Central Europe.

Sales and Marketing

Like its fast-food brethren Subway relies heavily on continuous television advertising and sponsorships to promote itself. It has marketing partnerships with dozens of companies and celebrity spokespeople.

Strategy

The Subway chain has tapped into the health food and weight loss zeitgeist in the US prominently featuring in its advertising Jared Fogle a man who famously lost nearly 250 lbs. by switching to a Subway sandwich diet. The chain continues to tout the health benefits of its sandwiches over traditional burgers and fries by introducing new low-fat menu items.

Subway has been developing an upscale concept called Subway Caf ©. The new format conceived for office buildings and other high-end locations is larger than the average Subway restaurant and features coffee espresso lattes and hot chocolate along with an expanded breakfast menu.

The company also seeks partnerships with other food brands to generate buzz around its products. In 2019 the company partnered with Halo Top Creamery to introduce Halo Top milkshakes at almost 1000 Subway restaurants. That year it also collaborated with Hubert's Lemonade to offer the company's drinks at its locations. The company also began testing a Kings Hawaiian-branded bread offering at three cities.

The company is investing in improving the look of its operations. It has remodeled nearly 1400 franchise locations and has around 900 remodels underway. In 2019 Subway announced a grant program that will cover 25% of remodeling costs for more than 10500 restaurants.

Company Background

Co-founders DeLuca and Buck opened the first Subway in 1965.

HISTORY

In 1965 17-year-old Fred DeLuca dreamed of becoming a doctor while working as a stock boy in a Bridgeport Connecticut hardware store to earn college tuition. It wasn't enough so he cornered family friend Peter Buck at a backyard barbecue and asked for advice. Buck a nuclear physicist suggested DeLuca open a submarine sandwich shop and put up $1000 to get him started.

As the summer of 1965 was coming to an end DeLuca rented a small location in a remote area of Bridgeport opened Pete's Super Submarines and there he sold foot-long sandwiches. On the first day the sandwiches were so popular that DeLuca hired his own customers to work behind the counter; by the end of the day he had sold out of all his supplies. The sandwiches continued to be popular for a while but within a few months the shop started losing money and DeLuca and Buck found that selling submarine sandwiches was a seasonal business. They decided they could create an illusion of success by opening a second location and then a third. The third store was finally successful partly because of its more visible location and increased marketing and partly because of a new name — Subway.

DeLuca and Buck had set a goal of 32 shops opened by 1975 but they had only 16 by 1974. They realized that the only way they could reach their goal in one year was to license the Subway name. The first franchise opened that year in Wallingford Connecticut and they opened 32 by the end of 1975. The partners hit 100 by 1978 then 200 by 1983 and DeLuca set a new goal: 5000 Subway shops by 1994. The first international Subway opened in Bahrain in 1984 and DeLuca achieved his goal of 5000 shops by 1990.

During the 1990s DeLuca experimented with several other franchise concepts including We Care Hair (budget styling salons) Cajun Joe's (spicy fried chicken) and Q Burgers. But none of these ventures fared as well as his sandwich empire. As Subway grew however controversy surrounding its treatment of franchisees began to surface. A Federal Trade Commission investigation of the company was dropped in 1993 but Subway continued to battle franchisees complaining about broken contracts market over-saturation (and therefore too much competition and self-cannibalization) and what the franchisees viewed as unreasonably high royalty fees.

In spite of its franchising troubles Subway kept growing. It expanded into Russia and China in the mid-1990s and opened its 11000th restaurant in 1995. In 1997 Subway inked deals with the Army Navy and Air Force exchange services to bring Subway units to military bases. Two years later the company opened its 14000th restaurant in Mount Gambier Australia an event that coincided with Subway's renewed push to expand internationally.

The company got some unexpected publicity in 1999 when 22-year-old Jared Fogle claimed that he dropped 245 pounds from his 425-pound frame by subsisting on a diet of Subway turkey sandwiches. Subway helped Fogle extend his 15 minutes of fame by featuring him and his oversized pants in a TV commercial. (The company has since built an entire campaign around Fogle that features other weight watchers attributing their success to Jared and Subway.) Subway introduced its largest menu initiative ever in 2000 when it unveiled its Subway Selects Gourmet Sandwiches adding 13 items to the menu. In April 2001 the company opened its 15000th store.

Also that year Buck retired as chairman but stayed on as a member of the board of directors. Becoming one of the fastest-growing franchises in the world Subway expanded from 16000 locations in 2002 to more than 22000 stores by the end of 2004.

All US Subway outlets switched from Pepsi to Coke products in 2005. Two years later the chain surpassed 21000 locations in the US.

EXECUTIVES

Pres, Frederick A Deluca
V Pres*, Mildred M Shinn
Prin, Julie McCoy
Vice-President Information Ser, Alim Meoon
Prin, Jon Goldwasser
Customer Staff, Giuseppe Brancatella
Internal Medicine Practitioner, Katherine Elmer
Coordinator, Zeinab Baghdadi
Quality Assurance Director, Julia Linn
Supervisor, Maria Goings
Manager, Richard Gold

LOCATIONS

HQ: DOCTOR'S ASSOCIATES INC.
325 SUB WAY, MILFORD, CT 064613081
Phone: 203 877-4281
Web: WWW.SUBWAY.COM

COMPETITORS

Burger King	Panera Bread
Cke Restaurants	Papa John's
Chick-fil-a	Popeyes
Chipotle	Potbelly Sandwich Shop
Church's Chicken	Quiznos
Dairy Queen	Sonic Corp.
Domino's	Starbucks
Jack In The Box	Tim Hortons
Mcdonald's	Wendy's
Panda Restaurant Group	Yum!

HISTORICAL FINANCIALS
Company Type: Private

Income Statement				FYE: December 31
	REVENUE ($ mil.)	NET INCOME ($ mil.)	NET PROFIT MARGIN	EMPLOYEES
12/10	1,049	7	0.7%	650
12/08	926	6	0.7%	—
12/07	780	5	0.7%	—
Annual Growth	10.4%	9.8%	—	—

Return on assets: 6.5%   Cash ($ mil.): 43
Return on equity: 49.4%
Current ratio: 1.00

DOCTORS HOSPITAL AT RENAISSANCE, LTD.

EXECUTIVES

Ceo, Lawrence Gelman
Pres*, Susan Turley
Accounting Staff, Joyce Lustgarten
Clinical Coordinator For Pedia, Andrew Kosko
Director, Shahbaz Salehi
Rn Bed Board Coordinator, Jan Trevino
Senior Vice President, Bhatt Vadlamani
Director of Security, Frank Nunez
Graphic Designer, Jose Ruiz
Human Resources Business Partn, Lily Alvarado
Financial Analyst, Andrea Cardenas

LOCATIONS

HQ: DOCTORS HOSPITAL AT RENAISSANCE, LTD.
5501 S MCCOLL RD, EDINBURG, TX 785395503
Phone: 956 362-8677
Web: WWW.DHR-RGV.COM

HISTORICAL FINANCIALS
Company Type: Private

Income Statement				FYE: December 31
	REVENUE ($ mil.)	NET INCOME ($ mil.)	NET PROFIT MARGIN	EMPLOYEES
12/16	580	80	13.9%	176
12/14	436	63	14.4%	—
Annual Growth	15.3%	13.1%	—	—

2016 Year-End Financials
Return on assets: 17.7%   Cash ($ mil.): 49
Return on equity: 44.6%
Current ratio: 2.00

DOCTORS MEDICAL CENTER OF MODESTO, INC.

EXECUTIVES

Ceo, Warren J Kirk
Cfo*, Greg Berry
Prin*, Dharati Trivedi
Manager, Cindy Vingerhoets
Internist, Veronica Ortiz
Clinical Operationws Manager P, Joseph Garcia
Nurse, Linda Hawkins
Chemistry Supervisor, Amandip Mahil
SPD Manager, Anthony Vasquez
Hospitalist, Arun Manoharan
Staff Pharmacist, Berna Hilgers

LOCATIONS

HQ: DOCTORS MEDICAL CENTER OF MODESTO, INC.
1441 FLORIDA AVE, MODESTO, CA 953504404
Phone: 209 578-1211
Web: WWW.DMC-MODESTO.COM

HISTORICAL FINANCIALS
Company Type: Private

Income Statement				FYE: May 31
	REVENUE ($ mil.)	NET INCOME ($ mil.)	NET PROFIT MARGIN	EMPLOYEES
05/16	587	86	14.6%	2,000
05/09	306	4	1.4%	—
Annual Growth	9.8%	52.8%	—	—

2016 Year-End Financials
Return on assets: 28.1%   Cash ($ mil.): —
Return on equity: 41.1%
Current ratio: 2.30

DON FORD SANDERSON INC

EXECUTIVES

Pres, David Kimmerle
Chb*, La Verne Sanderson
SEC-Treas*, Stephen C Wendt
Prin*, Sandra Sue Kimmerle
Parts Manager, Dave Beard
Sales Manager, John Pratt
Sales Staff, Steve Haines
Used Vehicle Sales Manager, Mario Fernandez
Administrator, Mike Gilbert
Outside Sales, Wade Kaczmarek
Human Resources, Leslie Brock

LOCATIONS

HQ: DON FORD SANDERSON INC
6400 N 51ST AVE, GLENDALE, AZ 853014600
Phone: 623 842-8600
Web: WWW.SANDERSONFORD.COM

HISTORICAL FINANCIALS
Company Type: Private

Income Statement				FYE: December 31
	REVENUE ($ mil.)	NET INCOME ($ mil.)	NET PROFIT MARGIN	EMPLOYEES
12/14	671	4	0.7%	416
12/13	692	5	0.8%	—
12/12	590	3	0.6%	—
Annual Growth	6.6%	11.2%	—	—

2014 Year-End Financials
Return on assets: 4.1%   Cash ($ mil.): 6
Return on equity: 14.1%
Current ratio: 1.50

DORMITORY AUTHORITY - STATE OF NEW YORK

EXECUTIVES

Pres-Ceo, Reuben McDaniel III
Exec V Pres-Cheif ADM*, Maryanne Gridley
Gen Counsel*, Jeffery Pohl
Cfo*, John G Pasicznyk
Mng Dir Public Fin*, Cheryl Ishmael
Mng Dir Construction*, Douglas Vanvleck
Mng Dir Policy & Prog Dev*, Thomas E Guiley
Deputy Exec Dir*, Micheal Coorigan
Chief of Staff*, Caroline Griffin
Cfo-Treasurer*, Kim Nadeau
and Design Manager, Eric Gerken
Auditors: KPMG LLP ALBANY NY

LOCATIONS

HQ: DORMITORY AUTHORITY - STATE OF NEW YORK
515 BROADWAY STE 100, ALBANY, NY 122072964
Phone: 518 257-3000
Web: WWW.DASNY.ORG

HISTORICAL FINANCIALS
Company Type: Private

Income Statement				FYE: March 31
	REVENUE ($ mil.)	NET INCOME ($ mil.)	NET PROFIT MARGIN	EMPLOYEES
03/11	2,075	(115)	—	625
03/06	1,693	(40)	—	—
03/05	0	0	—	—
Annual Growth	—	—	—	—

2011 Year-End Financials
Return on assets: (-0.3%)   Cash ($ mil.): 452
Return on equity: (-27.6%)
Current ratio: 1.10

DOUGLAS COUNTY SCHOOL DISTRICT

EXECUTIVES

Pres, David Ray
Supt*, Thomas Tucker
Teacher, Jason Dunkle
Teacher, Jim Dollaghan
Teacher of Cougar Run Elementa, Julie Davidson
Principals Secretary, Liz Thompson
Teacher, Peg Collins
Accounting Specialist, Denise Ruthenbeck
Teacher, Inga McAllen
Teacher Mathematics, Janet Jackson
Art Teacher, Jill Caven
Auditors: CLIFTONLARSONALLEN LLP GREENW

LOCATIONS

HQ: DOUGLAS COUNTY SCHOOL DISTRICT
620 WILCOX ST, CASTLE ROCK, CO 801041730
Phone: 303 387-0100
Web: WWW.DCSDK12.ORG

HISTORICAL FINANCIALS

Company Type: Private

Income Statement				FYE: June 30
	REVENUE ($ mil.)	NET INCOME ($ mil.)	NET PROFIT MARGIN	EMPLOYEES
06/13	562	(0)	—	8,000
06/10	551	(11)	—	—
06/08	480	(48)	—	—
06/07	0	0	—	—
Annual Growth	—	—	—	—

DPR CONSTRUCTION, INC.

From bio labs to wafer fabs DPR Construction runs the gamut for its high-tech and health care clients. The employee-owned firm provides general contracting and construction management services for the advanced technology/mission-critical life sciences health care higher education and corporate office markets. The construction firm specializes in developing retail stores hospitals data centers clean rooms laboratories manufacturing facilities and green buildings. Altogether DPR Construction boasts more than 25 regional offices nationwide. Company head Doug Woods former CEO Peter Nosler and secretary/treasurer Ron Davidowski (the D P and R in DPR Construction) founded the firm in 1990.

Operations
Since its founding the company has completed more than 12000 projects. DPR Construction has expertise in collaborative virtual building and Building Information Modeling (BIM) Integrating Project Delivery (IPD) sustainability preconstruction prefabrication and other niche areas. DPR also has Special Services Group where it focuses on small- to mid-size projects including building core upgrades hospital renovations office reconfigurations roof replacements and site improvements among others.

Geographic Reach
To maintain a presence near customers DPR boasts more than 25 regional offices. Its operations span around 15 states including Arizona California Colorado North Carolina Florida Georgia Maryland Texas Virginia and Washington DC. DPR also includes three international offices located in Netherlands South Korea and Singapore.

Sales and Marketing
DPR serves several core markets including advanced technology corporate offices healthcare higher education and life sciences. Customers have includes Adobe Systems AT&T EVA Airways Baptist Health Medical Center CHRISTUS Health Clif Bar & Company Intuit Facebook and Kaiser Permanente.

Strategy
DPR Construction pushed the envelope of sustainable design in the construction of its new office in Sacramento California in late 2019. DPR transformed an existing building with a material never used in Sacramento for a building's structure. The new DPR office space will house approximately 48 full-time employees with the intention to grow.

Earlier in 2019 DPR also finished the move to a new space of its Austin Texas office. The new office which occupies the third floor of the Foundry at 310 Canal Street was built by DPR employees. Aside from East Austin's growth the thriving entertainment district the eclectic local business and diverse community the Foundry's location offers new proximity to many of its clients partners and projects.

Company Background
Company head Doug Woods former CEO Peter Nosler and secretary/treasurer Ron Davidowski (the D P and R in DPR Construction) founded the firm in 1990 with offices in Redwood City CA and Sacramento CA. In 1993 DPR ranks #1 on both San Francisco Business Times' and San Jose/Silicon Valley Business Journal's Fastest-Growing Private Companies in the bay Area lists.

EXECUTIVES

Pres, George Pfeffer
Exec V Pres, Eric Lamb
Exec V Pres, Peter Salvati
Exec V Pres, James Dolen
Exec V Pres, Michael Ford
Cfo, Michele Leiva
SEC & Treas, Ron J Davidowski
Division Vice-President, Alison Lyons
Coordinator, Erin S Moss
Accounting Staff, Anna Bickford
Coordinator, Sara Steele
Auditors: PRICEWATERHOUSECOOPERS LLP LO

LOCATIONS

HQ: DPR CONSTRUCTION, INC.
1450 VETERANS BLVD, REDWOOD CITY, CA 940632617
Phone: 650 474-1450
Web: WWW.DPR.COM

Selected Offices

Atlanta
Austin TX
Baltimore
Denver
Houston
Newport Beach CA
Orlando Florida
Pasadena CA
Phoenix
Raleigh-Durham NC
Redwood City CA
Richmond VA
Sacramento CA
San Diego CA
San Francisco CA
San Jose CA
Tampa Florida
Washington DC
West Palm Beach FL

COMPETITORS

Austin Industries	Jacobs Engineering
Bechtel	M. A. Mortenson
Devcon Construction	Pc Construction
Fluor	Skanska Usa Building
Hensel Phelps Construction	Swinerton
Hoffman Corporation	Turner Corporation
	Whiting-turner

HISTORICAL FINANCIALS

Company Type: Private

Income Statement				FYE: December 31
	REVENUE ($ mil.)	NET INCOME ($ mil.)	NET PROFIT MARGIN	EMPLOYEES
12/08	1,836	68	3.7%	8,002
12/00	1,958	25	1.3%	—
Annual Growth	(0.8%)	13.0%	—	—

2008 Year-End Financials

Return on assets: 13.0%   Cash ($ mil.): 162
Return on equity: 37.9%
Current ratio: 1.50

DRISCOLL CHILDRENS HEALTH PLAN

EXECUTIVES

Pres, Mary D Peterson
Dir*, William J Sterett
Dir*, Samuel L Neal Jr
SEC*, David E Hamon
Secretary Treasurer, David Hamon
Auditors: BKD LLP HOUSTON TX

LOCATIONS

HQ: DRISCOLL CHILDRENS HEALTH PLAN
4525 AYERS ST, CORPUS CHRISTI, TX 784151401
Phone: 361 694-6432
Web: WWW.DRISCOLLHEALTHPLAN.COM

HISTORICAL FINANCIALS

Company Type: Private

Income Statement				FYE: December 31
	REVENUE ($ mil.)	NET INCOME ($ mil.)	NET PROFIT MARGIN	EMPLOYEES
12/19	711	(59)	—	49
12/14	385	(9)	—	—
12/13	317	1	0.4%	—
12/09	135	(0)	—	—
Annual Growth	18.0%	—	—	—

2019 Year-End Financials

Return on assets: (-32.3%)   Cash ($ mil.): 71
Return on equity: (-69.2%)
Current ratio: —

DRIVETIME AUTOMOTIVE GROUP, INC.

In this story the ugly duckling changes into DriveTime Automotive Group. Formerly known as Ugly Duckling the company is a used-car dealership chain that primarily targets low-income customers and those with less-than-stellar credit. To cater to subprime clients it's a "buy here-pay here" dealer meaning it finances and services car loans rather than using outside lenders. DriveTime operates more than 125 dealerships in 50 US metropolitan areas in 24 mostly southern and western states. The company provides customers with a comprehensive end-to-end solution for their automotive needs including the sale financing and maintenance of their vehicle.

Operations
The company's activities includes vehicle acquisition vehicle reconditioning and distribution vehicle sales underwriting and finance loan servicing and after sale support. DriveTime has sold more than 750000 used cars to consumers of all credit types and services a $2 billion loan portfolio.

DriveTime's financing business operates under the name DT Acceptance Corporation. The unit generates about a quarter of the company's total revenues

The company also offers DriveCare a 36-month/36000 miled (5-Year/50000 miled in some states) vehicle protection plan and extended powertrain coverage.

Geographic Reach

Phoenix-based DriveTime operates dealerships in 47 US metro areas throughout 24 states. More than a third of the dealerships are located in Florida and Texas.

Sales and Marketing

DriveTime markets its automotive products and services through TV commercials.

Strategy

DriveTime's long-term strategic goal is to expand its network of dealerships throughout the US targeting metropolitan areas with populations of 500000 to 3 million residents. In 2015 the company opened its first New Jersey location in Williamstown. In 2014 it established its presence in the Chicago area with the opening of the Lombard location; it also opened first location in the Washington DC area.

The used car dealer is also expanding in Texas opening a dealership in Corpus Christi in late 2013 its 20th in the Lone Star State.

As part of its business model DriveTime acquires used vehicles at auction. In 2013 the company purchased more than 96000 vehicles nationwide primarily from used vehicle auctions.

That year DriveTime teamed up with fellow car dealer Manheim to form Go Auto Exchange a new separate and independent wholesale auction company focused on independent dealers and the low-end vehicle segment.

Company venture Carvana (launched in early 2013) allows customers to buy its used cars online. Carvana expands the company's customer base by targeting customers outside its traditional credit-impaired low-income cohort.

Company Background

Chairman Ernest Garcia III owns the company through his Verde Investments firm. In 2012 the company abandoned plans to split its finance and used vehicle retail operations by selling the financing arm to Santander Consumer USA and the used car dealerships to a group of third-party investors. Prior to that DriveTime in early 2010 filed to go public but withdrew the proposed offering seven months later. It with drew a second IPO attempt in 2014.

EXECUTIVES

Prin, Ernest C Garcia II
Exec V Pres*, Jon D Ehlinger
Cfo*, Kurt Wood
Cfo*, Matthew Peel
Dir*, Gregg Tryhuss
Director, William N Plamondon
Corp Liaison, Kimberly Moon
General Manager, Matthew Bergantzel
CIO Cto, Paul Kaplan
Sales Manager, Gary Fuller
Information Technology, Steve Hansman

LOCATIONS

HQ: DRIVETIME AUTOMOTIVE GROUP, INC.
1720 W RIO SALADO PKWY, TEMPE, AZ 852816590
Phone: 602 852-6600
Web: WWW.DRIVETIME.COM

2014 Stores

	No.
Alabama	5
Arkansas	1
Arizona	6
California	5
Colorado	2
Delware	1
Florida	21
Georgia	9
Illinois	2
Indiana	2
Kentucky	2
Maryland	2
Missouri	4

Mississippi	1
North Carolina	9
New Jersey	1
New Mexico	3
Nevada	2
Ohio	7
Oklahoma	3
South Carolina	4
Tennessee	6
Texas	22
Virginia	7
Total	**127**

COMPETITORS

Autonation	Gunn Automotive
Carmax	Mccombs Enterprises
Gillman Auto	Sonic Automotive

HISTORICAL FINANCIALS

Company Type: Private

Income Statement   FYE: December 31

	REVENUE ($ mil.)	NET INCOME ($ mil.)	NET PROFIT MARGIN	EMPLOYEES
12/17	3,267	(16)	—	991
12/15	2,372	32	1.4%	—
/ 0	0	0	—	—
Annual Growth	—	—	—	—

2017 Year-End Financials

Return on assets: (-0.3%)
Return on equity: (-3.0%)
Current ratio: 1.20
Cash ($ mil.): 32

DST SYSTEMS, INC.

Financial firms and health institutions focus on making clients wealthy and healthy respectively. So they might be wise to turn to DST Systems to handle their information processing tasks. The company provides information processing software and services to the mutual fund insurance retirement and healthcare industries. The company's financial services segment offers software and systems used to handle a wide range of tasks including shareowner recordkeeping investment management and business process management. Among the healthcare offerings are claims adjudication and benefit and care management. DST makes most of its sales to customers in the US. The company was acquired by SS&C Technologies Holdings in 2018.

Operations

DST Systems' Domestic Financial Services business produces about 55% of revenue. The segment supports direct and intermediary sales of mutual funds alternative investments securities brokerage accounts and retirement plans. Its software also handles reports to investors for confirmations statements and tax forms web access and electronic delivery of documents. Systems include TA 2000 and TRAC. The company offers its AWD workflow software to clients and licenses it to third parties.

The International Financial Services segment which accounts for almost a quarter of its revenue offers investor and policyholder administration and technology services on a Remote and BPO basis in the UK and in Canada Ireland and Luxembourg through the IFDS joint venture.

The Healthcare Services segment which provides medical and pharmacy claims administration generates about a fifth of sales. The segment provides healthcare organizations with pharmacy and healthcare administration software and health out-

comes optimization services. Specific tasks handled by DST software include claims adjudication benefit management care management and business intelligence.

DST sold its North American Customer Communications business in 2016 for about $410 million followed by the sale of its UK counterpart in 2017 for about $45 million.

DST operates its own data centers that provide secure infrastructure for its products and services.

Geographic Reach

The US is DST Systems' largest market accounting for about 75% of sales. The UK is its largest international market with about 25% of sales. The Kansas City Missouri-based company also has customers in Australia Canada and several other geographic markets.

Sales and Marketing

DST Systems markets its products directly and through subsidiaries joint venture affiliates and strategic alliances. The Domestic Financial Services business works in some areas through joint ventures with State Street Corp. In the US the companies work through Boston Financial Data Services and through International Financial Data Services overseas.

DST's five largest customers overall account for about 25% of its revenue. The healthcare business is the more heavily concentrated with its five largest customers generating almost half of revenue including nearly 20% from one customer. International Financial Services' five largest customers supply almost 55% of the segment's revenue with the largest customer generating nearly 25%.

Primary customers for Financial Services are mutual fund managers insurers and platform providers. The main healthcare customers are managed care organizations preferred provider organizations third-party administrators dental vision and behavioral health organizations. The company also works with government sponsored programs such as the Health Insurance Exchanges that operate under the Patient Protection and Affordable Care Act Medicare Advantage Medicare Part D and Medicaid.

Financial Performance

Charting DST Systems' five-year revenue record shows a dip to about $1.4 billion in 2015 before rebounding in 2015 and 2016 following a series of divestments and acquisitions.

In 2017 revenue jumped about 42% to $2.2 billion which include reimbursements for out-of-pocket expenses (about 6% of total revenue). A good chunk of the increase came from BFDS and IFDS UK in which DST took controlling interest in 2017.

Net income increased about 6% to $451 million in 2017 from 2016 due to the acquired interests in BFDS and IFDS UK. The company also recorded a gain on the sale of securities in 2017.

DST's cash fell to about $80 million in 2017 from $199 million in 2016. A difference was that the company had about $248 million from discontinued operations that it didn't have in 2017.

Strategy

The acquisition by DST Systems by SS&C Technologies unites two major players in financial software. The combined product portfolios cover a wide range of financial services and it provides SS&C with DST's healthcare component. The deal doesn't do much however to expand their geographic reach other than to deepen their UK business. The companies are not strangers. SS&C bought DST's Global Solutions subsidiary in 2014.

Mergers and Acquisitions

DST Systems has been active on the acquisition front to complement its product line and expand into new geographic areas. DST has balanced its acquisition strategy by purchasing technology providers and service providers with an emphasis on business process outsourcing concerns and consulting firms.

In 2017 DST acquired the remaining interests in IFDS UK and BFDS that it didn't own for about $330 million. The businesses have been strategically important to DST which intends to make enhancements as full owner.

In 2016 DST bought Kaufman Rossin Fund Services a provider of administration services to the investment community for $95 million. This acquisition provides DST with products for the alternative investment market.

HISTORY

After expanding into mutual funds during the early 1960s Kansas City Southern Industries (KCSI) formed an electronic computer data processing unit to handle its mutual fund transactions using technology designed originally for tracking railroad cars and their revenues.

In 1968 KCSI incorporated its data processing unit as DST Systems and began offering its services to the financial industry. To establish itself on the East Coast in 1974 DST formed Boston Financial Data Services a joint venture with State Street. Also during the 1970s DST entered the insurance market with a system for variable annuity policyholders.

In 1983 KCSI bought a majority stake in Janus Capital a Denver-based mutual funds company. DST went public later that year; KCSI kept an 86% stake. Thomas McDonnell president since the early 1970s was named CEO in 1984.

EXECUTIVES

Ceo, William C Stone
Pres-Coo, Normand A Boulanger
Sr V Pres-Cfo, Patrick J Pedonti
Sr V Pres-Gencounsel-Sec, Paul G Igoe
SEC, Cristine Johnson
Director, Roger Stanley
Administrator Lan Administrato, Anthony Lombardo
Information Technology Manager, Debbie Brunk
Facilities Manager, Brenda Finn
Unit Manager, Eric Davis
Director of Corporate Tax, Gennie Harold
Auditors: PRICEWATERHOUSECOOPERS LLP K

LOCATIONS

HQ: DST SYSTEMS, INC.
333 W 11TH ST FL 5, KANSAS CITY, MO 641051628
Phone: 816 654-6067
Web: WWW.SSCTECH.COM

HISTORICAL FINANCIALS

Company Type: Private

Income Statement				FYE: December 31
	REVENUE ($ mil.)	NET INCOME ($ mil.)	NET PROFIT MARGIN	EMPLOYEES
12/17	2,218	452	20.4%	15,700
12/16	1,556	426	27.4%	—
12/15	2,825	358	12.7%	—
12/14	2,749	593	21.6%	—
Annual Growth	(6.9%)	(8.7%)	—	—

2017 Year-End Financials

Return on assets: 15.4%   Cash ($ mil.): 80
Return on equity: 36.4%
Current ratio: 1.10

DUKE HEALTH RALEIGH HOSPITAL GUILD

EXECUTIVES

Pres, David Zaas
Coo*, Rick Gannotta
Cfo*, Terri Newsom
Ceo*, Doug Dinsel
Internal Medicine Practitioner, Asghar Yamadi
Pulmonologist, Jerry B Hung
Chief Human Resources Officer, Alyson Gordon
Lpn, Patricia Daniel
Director, Ted Kunstling
Specialties Otolaryngology, David Jang
Specialties Otolaryngology, John McElveen

LOCATIONS

HQ: DUKE HEALTH RALEIGH HOSPITAL GUILD
3400 WAKE FOREST RD, RALEIGH, NC 276097317
Phone: 919 954-3000
Web: WWW.DUKEHEALTH.ORG

HISTORICAL FINANCIALS

Company Type: Private

Income Statement				FYE: June 30
	REVENUE ($ mil.)	NET INCOME ($ mil.)	NET PROFIT MARGIN	EMPLOYEES
06/21	609	84	13.9%	600
06/19	528	19	3.6%	—
06/18	478	22	4.6%	—
06/16	384	58	15.3%	—
Annual Growth	9.7%	7.6%	—	—

DUKE UNIVERSITY

Duke University has 15 551 undergraduate and graduate students. Duke School and Colleges includes Trinity College of Art and Sciences the Fuqua School of Business and the Pratt School of Engineering and more. The private institution which boasts some 3956 faculty members also operates the Duke University Health System (DUHS). Duke was founded in 1924 but traces its roots to 1838.

Operations

Undergraduates at Duke enter either the Trinity College of Arts and Sciences or the Pratt School of Engineering. Top majors for Duke undergraduates include computer science economics public policy biology and biomedical engineering. The university's eight graduate schools cover law divinity medicine nursing business public policy the environment and other fields. Academic sources of revenue include government and private grants and contracts investment returns tuition and fees auxiliary enterprises and contributions.

Duke's operating revenue come from Grants and Contracts (27%) Investment return designated for current operations (22%) Tuition and fees (16%) Private grants contracts (12%) support from clinical operation (6%) auxiliary enterprises (6%) and other income (4%). Duke University Health System consists of Duke University Hospital Duke Regional Hospital Duke Raleigh Hospital Duke University Affiliated Physicians Inc. and Durham Casualty Company Ltd.

Other Duke programs include student athletics (27 NCAA Division I teams) about a dozen research institutes Duke Libraries (one of the top US private library systems) the Duke Marine Laboratory and Duke University Press (publishes some 120 new books annually).

Like most universities Duke is governed by a board of trustees which serves as the institution's fiduciary. The board manages and oversees long-term financial health strategic direction educational policy finances and operations.

Geographic Reach

Most of Duke's operations occur in the heart of Durham North Carolina. Its facilities include iconic architecture and classic landscape design. It covers 1300 acres which includes West Campus East Campus and Central Campus. Another 7000 acres are designated as Duke Forest. At the heart of Duke Quest Campus lies Abele Quad and includes a Marine Lab campus located in Beaufort NC.

The Duke Kunshan University is a partnership campus between Duke and China's Wuhan University. Duke also partners with the National University of Singapore to operate the Duke-NUS Medical School in Singapore.

Sales and Marketing

Duke University provide campus tours for student applicants and its academic offerings are found in the school website.

Financial Performance

Total operating revenues for the University declined $18 million to $3 billion in fiscal 2021.

Duke's consolidated net asset base increased $7.9 billion in fiscal 2021 to $22.2 billion as of June 30 2021. The increase is driven by strong investment performance.

Cash held by the University at the end of 2021 was $445.6 million. Cash provided by operations and financing activities were $174.7 million and $134.8 million respectively. Cash used for investing activities was $445.4 billion mainly for purchases of investments.

Strategy

Investment strategies employed by DUMAC and investment managers retained by DUMAC incorporate the use of various derivative financial instruments. DUMAC uses these instruments for a number of investment purposes including hedging or altering exposure to certain asset classes and cost-effectively adding exposures to portions of the portfolio.

During fiscal 2021 and 2020 Duke or external investment managers on Duke's behalf entered into swap agreements futures contracts or forward contracts and acquired warrants or rights to increase reduce or otherwise modify investment exposures.

Company Background

Duke traces its roots to the founding of Union Institute in Randolph County North Carolina in 1838. Union Institute later became Trinity College which in 1892 moved to Durham where the Duke family became a primary benefactor. In 1924 American Tobacco Co. magnate James B. Duke established the Duke Endowment which allowed Trinity College to expand into Duke University.

The original Durham campus became known as the East Campus and a new West Campus opened in 1930. The East Campus served as a women's college until 1972 when the undergraduate colleges merged. The East Campus was transformed into a home for first-year students in 1995.

EXECUTIVES

Pres, Richard Brodhead
Exec V Pres, Tallman Trask III
Univ Counsel, David B Adcock
Cfo, Kenneth Morris
V Pres, Pamela J Bernard

V Pres, Kyle Cavanaugh
Professorfaculty Faculty Biome, Gregg Trahey
Associate Professor, John Sundy
Professor, Patrick Casey
Assistant Professor, Purnima Valdez
Physician Recruiter, Stacy Connoley
Auditors: KPMG LLP GREENSBORO NC

LOCATIONS

HQ: DUKE UNIVERSITY
   2200 W MAIN ST STE 710, DURHAM, NC 277054677
Phone: 919 684-8111
Web: WWW.DUKE.EDU

PRODUCTS/OPERATIONS

Selected Institutes
Center for the Study of Aging and Human Development
Duke Cancer Institute
Duke Global Health Institute
Duke Institute for Brain Sciences
Duke Science & Society Initiative
Duke University Energy Initiative
Institute for Genomic & Computational Biology
Interdisciplinary Studies
John Hope Franklin Humanities Institute
Kenan Institute for Ethics
Nicholas Institute for Environmental Policy Solutions
Trent Center for Bioethics Humanities and History of
   Medicine
Social Science Research Institute

Selected Schools and Colleges
Divinity School (Since 1926)
Duke Kunshan University (Since 2014; China)
Duke-NUS Medical School (Since 2005)
Fuqua School of Business (Since 1969)
Graduate School (Since 1926)
Nicholas School of the Environment (Since 1938)
Pratt School of Engineering (Since 1939)
Sanford School of Public Policy (Since 1971)
School of Law (Since 1904)
School of Medicine (Since 1930)
School of Nursing (Since 1931)
Trinity College of Arts & Sciences (Since 1859)

HISTORICAL FINANCIALS
Company Type: Private

Income Statement   FYE: June 30

	REVENUE ($ mil.)	NET INCOME ($ mil.)	NET PROFIT MARGIN	EMPLOYEES
06/12	4,611	(507)	—	8,852
06/05	1,832	246	13.5%	—
06/04	2,806	679	24.2%	—
Annual Growth	6.4%	—	—	—

2012 Year-End Financials
Return on assets: (-3.6%)   Cash ($ mil.): 526
Return on equity: (-5.2%)
Current ratio: —

DUKE UNIVERSITY HEALTH SYSTEM, INC.

Duke University Health System is a world-class hospital and health care network supported by outstanding and renowned clinical faculty nurses and care teams. In addition to its hospitals Duke Health has an extensive geographically dispersed network of outpatient facilities that include primary care offices urgent care centers multi-specialty clinics and outpatient surgery centers. Its Duke Health & Well-Being includes a medically-based weight loss program medically-based fitness wellness and rehabilitation programs at the Duke Health & Fitness Center and Duke Integrative Medicine which combines evidence-based treatment with proven complementary therapies.

Operations
The health system operates through three hospitals: Duke University Hospital (DUH); Duke Regional Hospital (DRH); and Duke Raleigh Hospital (DRaH).

DUH is a quarternary care teaching hospital located on the campus of University in Durham North Carolina licensed for about 1050 acute and specialty care beds leased from Duke University operated by the health system and providing patient care and serving as a site for medical education and clinical research provided by the Duke University School of Medicine. DUH generates more than 65% health system's total revenue.

DRaH (about 15% of revenue) is a community hospital located Raleigh North Carolina licensed for about 185 acute care beds leased from the university operated by health system and providing patient care.

DRH (around 10% of revenue) is a full-service community hospital located in Durham North Carolina licensed for about 390 acute and specialty care beds and providing patient care; DRH is owned by Durham County North Carolina and leased to the Durham County Corporation in which has in turn subleased DRH to the health system.

Duke HomeCare & Hospice offers hospice home health and infusion services. Hospice care is offered to terminally ill patients in their home skilled-nursing facilities assisted-living facilities and at our two inpatient facilities located in Hillsborough and Durham North Carolina. Home health services are available to patients who are homebound and in need of nursing services physical therapy speech therapy or occupational therapy. Infusion services are provided at home or at work for individuals who need intravenous therapy.

Geographic Reach
The Private Diagnostic Clinic owns and operates more than 140 primary and specialty care clinics in 10 counties in central and eastern North Carolina.

Financial Performance
The company's revenue increased by 8% from $4 billion in 2020 to $4.3 billion in 2021. This was primarily due to a higher sales volume across all of the patient revenue services' components.

In 2021 the company had net assets of $5.7 billion a 63% increase from the previous year's net assets of $3.5 billion. This was mainly due to a higher sales volume for the year.

The company's cash at the end of 2021 was $98.5 million. Operating activities generated $285.2 million while investing activities used $174.3 million primarily for purchases of investments. Financing activities used another $170.2 million mainly for transfers to the university.

EXECUTIVES

MD, Victor Dzau
Cntrl, Robert Willis Jr
Purchasing, Paul Brummett
Chief Officer, Thomas A Owens
Vp Patient Care and and, Mary Ann Fuchs
Information Specialist, Kathy Pettiford
Staff, Olga Richmond
Research and Staff, Zhuowei LI
Information Specialist, Amanda Schwing
Coordinator, Carmella Bianca
Assistant Professor, Deirdre Thornlow
Auditors: KPMG LLP GREENSBORO NC

LOCATIONS

HQ: DUKE UNIVERSITY HEALTH SYSTEM, INC.
   2301 ERWIN RD, DURHAM, NC 277054699
Phone: 919 684-8111
Web: WWW.DUKEHEALTH.ORG

Selected Facilities
Duke Clinic (Durham North Carolina)
Duke Raleigh Hospital (Raleigh North Carolina)
Duke University Hospital (Durham North Carolina)
   Duke Children's Hospital & Health Center
Durham Regional Hospital (Durham North Carolina)

PRODUCTS/OPERATIONS

2014 Sales

	$ mil.	% of total
Patient service	2,437	50
Grants & contracts	1,097	22
Tuition & fees	408	8
Investment return	384	8
Auxiliary enterprises	186	5
Contributions	92	4
Net assets released from restrictions	46	2
Other	228	1
Total	**4,882**	**100**

Selected Services
AIDS Research and Treatment Center (DART)
Anesthesiology
Aortic Disease
Asthma and Allergies
Attention Deficit Hyperactivity Disorder
Breast Cancer
Cardiac Rehabilitation
Children's Health
Coronary Artery Disease
Dermatology
Developmental and Behavioral Pediatrics
Diabetes
Diet & Fitness Center
Duke Heart Center
Duke Medicine
Ear Nose Throat Head & Neck Surgery
Eating Disorders
Endocrinology
Esophageal Cancer
Executive Health
Eye Center
Foot and Ankle
Gastroenterology
Gastrointestinal Cancer
General Orthopaedics
General and Consultative Heart Care
Geriatrics
Gynecologic Cancer
Gynecology
Health & Fitness Center
Health and Wellness
Healthy Lifestyles for Children
Heart Rhythm Services
Hematology
Hereditary Cancer
Hyperbaric Diving and Altitude Medicine
Infectious Diseases
Integrative Medicine
Knee Treatments
Leukemias Lymphomas and Myelomas
Lung Cancer
Men's Health
Neurological Disorders
Neuroscience
Obstetrics and Gynecology
Pain Disorders
Peripheral Vascular Disease
Prostate Cancer
Psychiatry
Pulmonology and Respiratory Medicine
Radiology
Research
Rheumatology and Immunology
Skin Cancer
Sleep Disorders
Smoking/Smoking Cessation
Speech and Audiology
Sports Medicine
Stroke Center
Transplants
Urologic Cancer

Valvular Heart Disease
Vascular Diseases
Women's Health
Women's Heart Care

COMPETITORS

Carolinas Healthcare System
Cone Health
Cumberland County Hospital System
Danville Regional Medical Center
Firsthealth Of The Carolinas
Morehead Memorial Hospital
Novant Health
Rex Healthcare
Rowan Regional Medical Center
Unc Hospitals
Vidant Health
Wakemed
Wesley Long Community Hospital

HISTORICAL FINANCIALS
Company Type: Private

Income Statement				FYE: June 30
	REVENUE ($ mil.)	NET INCOME ($ mil.)	NET PROFIT MARGIN	EMPLOYEES
06/21	4,269	2,194	51.4%	2,400
06/20	3,951	(296)	—	—
06/19	3,836	160	4.2%	—
06/18	3,597	688	19.1%	—
Annual Growth	5.9%	47.2%	—	—

2021 Year-End Financials
Return on assets: 24.2%
Return on equity: 38.7%
Current ratio: 1.90
Cash ($ mil.): 98

DUKE UNIVERSITY HOSPITAL

LOCATIONS
HQ: DUKE UNIVERSITY HOSPITAL
1 DUKE MEDICAL CTR, DURHAM, NC 277100007
Phone: 919 684-8111
Web: WWW.DUKEHEALTH.ORG

HISTORICAL FINANCIALS
Company Type: Private

Income Statement				FYE: June 30
	REVENUE ($ mil.)	NET INCOME ($ mil.)	NET PROFIT MARGIN	EMPLOYEES
06/19	2,597	25	1.0%	25
06/18	2,467	(0)	—	—
Annual Growth	5.3%	—	—	—

DUTCHESS, COUNTY OF (INC)

EXECUTIVES
Cnty Exec, Marcus J Molinaro
Deputy Commissioner*, Corinna Wu
Exec SEC*, Sandra Strippoli

Cntrl, Diane Jablonsky
Accounting Staff, Diane E Brangan
Personnel Assistant, Deirdre Caamano
Instructor of Film, Stephen Lawson
Network Support Specialist, Andrew Marallo
Fire Coordinator, David Alfonso
Senior Human Resources Associa, Karl Menuau
Technical Manager Office of He, Patricia Mensler
Auditors: DRESCHER & MALECKI LLP BUFFAL

LOCATIONS
HQ: DUTCHESS, COUNTY OF (INC)
626 DUTCHESS TPKE, POUGHKEEPSIE, NY 126031906
Phone: 845 486-2000
Web: WWW.CO.DUTCHESS.NY.US

HISTORICAL FINANCIALS
Company Type: Private

Income Statement				FYE: December 31
	REVENUE ($ mil.)	NET INCOME ($ mil.)	NET PROFIT MARGIN	EMPLOYEES
12/20	564	4	0.8%	1,852
12/19	511	6	1.3%	—
12/18	549	9	1.8%	—
12/17	467	(16)	—	—
Annual Growth	6.5%	—	—	—

2020 Year-End Financials
Return on assets: 0.3%
Return on equity: 1.0%
Current ratio: —
Cash ($ mil.): 109

DUVAL COUNTY PUBLIC SCHOOLS

EXECUTIVES
Supt, John C Fryer Jr
Payroll Staff, Bobbie Johns
Instructor, Amy Guth
Cashier, Anastasia Dixon
Supervisor, Beth Tramel
Teacher, Denisha Jordan
Assistant, Jonathan Brown
Education Specialist, Megan McCumber
Teacher, Rusty Mathews
Teacher, Steven Shields
Technology/Computer Coord, Alexandra Vlachakis
Auditors: MSL PA ORLANDO FLORIDA

LOCATIONS
HQ: DUVAL COUNTY PUBLIC SCHOOLS
1701 PRUDENTIAL DR, JACKSONVILLE, FL 322078152
Phone: 904 390-2000
Web: WWW.DCPS.DUVALSCHOOLS.ORG

HISTORICAL FINANCIALS
Company Type: Private

Income Statement				FYE: June 30
	REVENUE ($ mil.)	NET INCOME ($ mil.)	NET PROFIT MARGIN	EMPLOYEES
06/20	1,310	45	3.5%	13,000
06/19	1,279	22	1.8%	—
06/18	1,231	(7)	—	—
06/17	1,207	(25)	—	—
Annual Growth	2.8%	—	—	—

2020 Year-End Financials
Return on assets: 2.6%
Return on equity: 12.2%
Current ratio: —
Cash ($ mil.): 223

DYNCORP INTERNATIONAL LLC

EXECUTIVES
Ceo, George Krivo
Coordinator, Jeff Angus
Director, Kathryn Van Vleck
Accounting Staff, Arthur Jordan
Management Vice-President, Richard Minor
Information Specialist, Jason Granger
Manager, Bradley Salls
Fuels Manager, Claude Poole
Logistics Advisor, Eric Ogborn
Senior Director, James Sagen
Financial Analyst, Kristen Kosla
Auditors: FRYE & COMPANY CPAS MANASSAS

LOCATIONS
HQ: DYNCORP INTERNATIONAL LLC
1700 OLD MEADOW RD, MC LEAN, VA 221024302
Phone: 571 722-0210
Web: WWW.AMENTUM.COM

HISTORICAL FINANCIALS
Company Type: Private

Income Statement				FYE: April 3
	REVENUE ($ mil.)	NET INCOME ($ mil.)	NET PROFIT MARGIN	EMPLOYEES
04/09*	3,101	69	2.2%	100
03/08	2,139	47	2.2%	—
Annual Growth	44.9%	45.5%	—	—
*Fiscal year change

2009 Year-End Financials
Return on assets: 4.5%
Return on equity: 14.0%
Current ratio: 2.00
Cash ($ mil.): 200

EAST TEXAS MEDICAL CENTER REGIONAL HEALTHCARE SYSTEM

East Texas Medical Center (ETMC) Regional Healthcare System works to meet the health care needs of residents of the Piney Woods. The not-for-profit health system operates more than a dozen hospitals across eastern Texas along with behavioral rehabilitation and home health care businesses. Its flagship 450-bed Tyler location serves as the hub and referral center for satellite medical centers located in more rural locations. The system also runs numerous primary care and outpatient clinics throughout the region. Serving more than 300000 patients each year ETMC operates an emergency ambulance service subsidiary and a clinical laboratory which provide services to the ETMC Regional Healthcare System.

Operations

The flagship ETMC Tyler facility offers specialized care for cancer and cardiovascular and neurological conditions. It is a Level I regional trauma center and provides diagnostic and outpatient surgery services.

The system is organized so that primary care is provided in the rural health clinics. Secondary care is also provided locally in the ETMC affiliate hospitals. High-level secondary and tertiary care is provided at ETMC Tyler.

Geographic Reach

ETMC serves the more than 1 million people who reside in East Texas communities. It caters to nearly 20 Texas counties including Anderson Camp Cherokee Ellis Franklin Freestone Henderson Hopkins Houston Panola Red River Rusk Shelby Smith Trinity Upshur Van Zandt and Wood. These communities range in size from fewer than 500 residents to more than 50000.

Sales and Marketing

The Medicare program accounted for 50% of net patient revenues in 2012; Medicaid contributed 12% of the same. Some 16% of total net patient service revenue came from commercial insurance carriers and preferred provider organizations.

Financial Performance

Due to an increase in patient service revenue ETMC's revenue rose by 6% to $942 million in 2012 from $888 million in 2011. Net income for the same reporting period dropped some 92% to $1.1 million from $16 million due to rising salaries and wages and employee benefits expenses as well as from an increase in loss from defined benefit pension adjustment.

Strategy

To keep up with the needs of its residents the ETMC Regional Healthcare System works to expand its operations.

In 2013 ETMC Pittsburg broke ground on a 5000-sq.-ft. expansion of the hospital's surgery department. Its East Texas Medical Center Regional Healthcare System also added a pair of emergency transport helicopters valued at more than $9 million.

In 2012 the company completed $30-million expansion and renovation project at East Texas Medical Center Henderson including a new emergency department grand lobby and clinic space. It also wrapped up the second phase of an expansion project at ETMC Fairfield that involved adding a new entrance lobby clinic space cardiopulmonary rehabilitation facility and administrative suite.

Its 100-bed Henderson Memorial Hospital joined the network in 2009 as ETMC Henderson. Soon after becoming part of the network ETMC assisted its new affiliate with facility upgrades that included building new emergency department facilities renovating old rooms and installing new electrical and HVAC systems all completed in 2011. ETMC also expanded its Trinity facility with a 15-bed patient wing at the cost of $7.4 million and expanded its mammography services at ETMC Cedar Creek Lake. A $35 million ETMC Quitman facility is expected to be completed in 2013.

ETMC also concentrates on upgrading its information systems. The healthcare system's data exchange organization FirstNet Exchange received a grant from the state of Texas in 2011 to develop and operate a secure health information network to support hospitals and clinicians.

EXECUTIVES

Pres-Ceo, Elmer G Ellis
V Pres*, Cherie Martin
Sr V Pres*, Robert E Evans
Sr V Pres*, Jerry L Massey
Branch Manager, Susan Mc Clendon
Training and Direc, Vicky Pehl
Information Technology Manager, Evelyn Williams
Chief of Medicine, Lucia Williams
Pediatrician, Bevan Steadman
Chief of Anesthesiology, Kevin King
Registered Nurse, Monique Witty

LOCATIONS

HQ: EAST TEXAS MEDICAL CENTER REGIONAL HEALTHCARE SYSTEM
1000 S BECKHAM AVE, TYLER, TX 757011908
Phone: 903 596-3267
Web: WWW.UTHEALTHEASTTEXAS.COM

PRODUCTS/OPERATIONS

Selected Health and Medical Services
Bariatric Surgery Center
Behavioral Health Center
Cancer Institute
Cardiovascular Institute
Digestive Disease Center
Emergency Services
Fitness Centers
Home Health
Neurological Institute
Orthopedic Institute
Plastic Surgery
Podiatry Care
Radiology and Imaging
Rehabilitation Center
Sleep Disorders Center
Specialty Hospital
Transplant Center
Urology Institute
Women's Health
Wound Healing Center

Selected East Texas Medical Center Hospitals
ETMC Athens
ETMC Carthage
ETMC Clarksville
ETMC Crockett
ETMC Fairfield
ETMC Gilmer
ETMC Henderson
ETMC Jacksonville
ETMC Lake Palestine
ETMC Mount Vernon
ETMC Pittsburg
ETMC Quitman
ETMC Rehabilitation Hospital (Tyler)
ETMC Specialty Hospital (Tyler)
ETMC Trinity
ETMC Tyler

COMPETITORS

Community Health Systems
Good Shepherd Health System
Hca
Hunt Memorial Memorial Health System Of East Texas
Tenet Healthcare
Trinity Mother Frances Hospital And Clinics
Wadley Regional Medical Center
Woodland Heights Medical Center

HISTORICAL FINANCIALS
Company Type: Private

Income Statement
FYE: October 31

	REVENUE ($ mil.)	NET INCOME ($ mil.)	NET PROFIT MARGIN	EMPLOYEES
10/08	876	30	3.4%	7,600
10/07	827	40	4.8%	—
10/06	837	0	—	—
10/05	837	17	2.1%	—
Annual Growth	1.5%	20.4%	—	—

2008 Year-End Financials
Return on assets: 4.0%
Return on equity: 11.1%
Current ratio: 3.20
Cash ($ mil.): 175

EASTERN MAINE HEALTHCARE SYSTEMS

Eastern Maine Healthcare Systems (EMHS) keeps the folks in the Pine Tree State feeling fine. With more than a dozen member hospitals and multiple medical practices and clinics the organization offers patients emergency primary mental-health laboratory and other specialty services. It primarily serves eastern central and northern portions of rural Maine. Some hospitals include Eastern Maine Medical Center (410 beds) Acadia Hospital (100 beds) Aroostook Medical Center (75 beds) and Inland Hospital (50 beds). The system also operates long-term care hospice and home health facilities as well as emergency transportation and administrative services businesses.

Operations

Besides its Acadia Hospital Aroostook Medical Center Eastern Maine Medical Center and Inland Hospital EMHS operates three smaller community hospitals with 15 to 30 beds each: Blue Hill Memorial Hospital Charles A. Dean Memorial Hospital and Sebasticook Valley Hospital. The system has affiliations with the Houlton Regional Hospital and Millinocket Regional Hospital.

Subsidiaries of EMHS include Affiliated Healthcare Systems (medical communications and retirement ventures) Affiliated Laboratory (pathology services) Affiliated Material Services (medical supplies distribution and pharmacies) and Affiliated Healthcare Management (transcription and employee services).

As part of its operations EMHS also runs the Eastern Maine Medical Center Clinical Research Center which performs clinical studies in several medical disciplines and diseases including cancer hospital-acquired infections heart disease and physician best practices.

In fiscal 2014 EMHS had 105629 emergency room visits; 32964 inpatient and outpatient surgeries; 3017 births; and 388920 primary care visits.

The company's total Community Benefit that year was about $200 million and its philanthropy giving was nearly $3 million.

Geographic Reach

Despite its name Eastern Maine Healthcare System serves those in eastern central and northern portions of rural Maine.

Strategy

EMHS continues to work collaboratively at the national level looking at not only making a difference in healthcare in Maine but to be a change leader throughout the country. The Northern New England Accountable Care Collaborative is creating resources necessary to propel the reinvention of care model. In addition their work in the High Value Healthcare Collaborative (co-owned with Dartmouth MaineHealth and the University of Vermont Medical Center) this past year has been focused on sepsis care and prevention patient engagement and shared decision-making pilot projects.

In fiscal 2015 Maine's largest health insurer teamed up with Eastern Maine Healthcare Systems under a new venture aimed at keeping patients healthier while reducing costs. The deal involves Anthem Blue Cross and Blue Shield in Maine EMHS and an EMHS-led coalition of hospitals and physician practices across the state. EMHS and its partners have agreed to avoid any cost increase for services they deliver to 40000 Anthem policyholders.

In mid-2014 EMHS completed a community health needs assessment of the northern two-thirds of Maine including the counties of Aroostook Cumberland Hancock Kennebec Penobscot Piscataquis Somerset and Washington. This report was seen as foundational to the company achieving its mission of improving the health and well-being of the communities it serves.

Company Background

The system was established in 1982.

EXECUTIVES

Pres, Michelle Hood
Sr V Pres, John Dalton
Information Process Sp, Greta Dube
Information and Teleco, Wayne Burke
Coordinator, Ambie Hayes-Crosby
Physical Therapist, Pierre Rougny
Manager, Brooke M Turner
Sam Poc, Malisa Blessington
Security Staff, Jay Rankin
Trustee, Iyad Sabbagh
Human Resources Customer Servi, Diane Simpson
Auditors: BERRY DUNN MCNEIL & PARKER LL

LOCATIONS

HQ: EASTERN MAINE HEALTHCARE SYSTEMS
43 WHITING HILL RD # 500, BREWER, ME 044121005
Phone: 207 973-7000
Web: WWW.NORTHERNLIGHTHEALTH.ORG

PRODUCTS/OPERATIONS

Selected Strategic Affiliates
Houlton Regional Hospital
Millinocket Regional Hospital
Member Hospitals
Acadia Hospital
Affiliated Healthcare Systems
Aroostook Medical Center
Beacon Health
Blue Hill Memorial Hospital
Charles A. Dean Memorial Hospital and Nursing Home
Dirigo Pines Retirement Community
Eastern Maine HomeCare
Eastern Maine Medical Center
Healthcare Charities

Inland Hospital
Rosscare
Sebasticook Valley Hospital

COMPETITORS

Franklin Community Health Network
Maine Coast Memorial Hospital
Mainegeneral Health
Mainehealth
Mercy Health System Of Maine
Miles Health Care
Millinocket Regional Hospital
St. Joseph Healthcare

HISTORICAL FINANCIALS

Company Type: Private

Income Statement   FYE: September 30

	REVENUE ($ mil.)	NET INCOME ($ mil.)	NET PROFIT MARGIN	EMPLOYEES
09/20	1,753	(77)	—	8,175
09/19	1,744	16	0.9%	—
09/18	1,672	8	0.5%	—
09/17	1,654	43	2.6%	—
Annual Growth	2.0%	—	—	—

2020 Year-End Financials

Return on assets: (-3.8%)   Cash ($ mil.): 151
Return on equity: (-10.9%)
Current ratio: 2.00

EASTERN MAINE MEDICAL CENTER

EXECUTIVES

Ceo, Deborah C Johnson
V Pres-Cfo*, Elmer Doucette
V Pres*, John Doyle
Vice President, Mer Doucette
Security Staff, Michael Parsons
Anesthesiologist, Sara Barwise
Pain Management Specialist, Shubha Raju
Director, Susan Dow
Coor, Melissa Cadieux
Manager, Michelle Mayo
Health Professional, Resmi Rajan
Auditors: BERRY DUNN MCNEIL & PARKER LL

LOCATIONS

HQ: EASTERN MAINE MEDICAL CENTER
489 STATE ST, BANGOR, ME 044016674
Phone: 207 973-7000
Web: WWW.NORTHERNLIGHTHEALTH.ORG

HISTORICAL FINANCIALS

Company Type: Private

Income Statement   FYE: September 30

	REVENUE ($ mil.)	NET INCOME ($ mil.)	NET PROFIT MARGIN	EMPLOYEES
09/19	932	53	5.7%	1,119
09/16	776	23	3.0%	—
09/15	720	41	5.8%	—
09/13	646	56	8.8%	—
Annual Growth	6.3%	(1.1%)	—	—

2019 Year-End Financials

Return on assets: 5.9%   Cash ($ mil.): 151
Return on equity: 16.5%
Current ratio: 1.20

EATON CORPORATION

EXECUTIVES

Chair-Ceo, Craig Arnold
Cfo, Richard Fearon
Exec V Pres, Mark McGuire
Sr V Pres-SEC, Thomas Moran
Sr V Pres-Contrl, Billie Rawot
Sr V Pres Corp Devt & Treas, David Foster
Gen Counsel, April Boise
Scp-CIO, Katrina R Redmond
Sales Manager, Sam Digiacomo
Technical Program Manager, Steven Solloway
Technical Support Coordinator, Mike PEC
Auditors: ERNST & YOUNG LLP CLEVELAND

LOCATIONS

HQ: EATON CORPORATION
1000 EATON BLVD, CLEVELAND, OH 441226058
Phone: 440 523-5000
Web: WWW.EATONELECTRICAL.COM

HISTORICAL FINANCIALS

Company Type: Private

Income Statement   FYE: December 31

	REVENUE ($ mil.)	NET INCOME ($ mil.)	NET PROFIT MARGIN	EMPLOYEES
12/15	6,925	821	11.9%	736
12/14	6,990	170	2.4%	—
Annual Growth	(0.9%)	382.9%	—	—

EDUCATIONAL TESTING SERVICE

Please completely fill in each circle on the answer sheet as prepared by Educational Testing Service (ETS). ETS develops and administers the Graduate Record Examinations (GRE) and Test of English as a Foreign Language (TOEFL). The nonprofit group develops and administers more than 50 million achievement admissions academic and professional tests a year at more than 9000 locations in more than 180 countries. It also develops assessment programs for corporations professional associations and state entities. ETS' research unit conducts advancing educational measurement and policy studies; test-development firm Prometric is a for-profit subsidiary.

Operations

ETS' K-12 products include Criterion an online writing evaluation service that helps students plan write and revise essays. Teachers are not forgotten — the company also develops and administers the Praxis Series assessments for teacher licensing and certifications. For college-bound scholars ETS supports The College Board's Scholastic Assessment Test (SAT) and National Assessment of Educational Progress (NAEP) test.

ETS Global the international arm of ETS has more than 3200 employees work at ETS's offices worldwide. Of these more than 2300 of its professional staff have training and expertise in education psychology statistics psychometrics computer sciences sociology and the humanities. Almost 1000 have advanced degrees and 390 hold doctorates. Some 1150 employees support ETS's wholly owned subsidiary Prometric.

Its EdAgree subsidiary offers a free platform and services to help students identify universities for international students. Edusoft Ltd. a foreign subsidiary is a global leader in technology-based comprehensive English Language Learning solutions serving a range of educational government and corporate sectors worldwide.

Prometric a global leader in technology-enabled testing and assessment services provides test development test delivery and data management capabilities to clients in the academic professional and government markets via the web or by utilizing a robust test center network in more than 160 countries.

Geographic Reach
ETS serves US customers from offices in (San Antonio & Austin) Texas (Concord Sacramento and San Francisco) California Florida Kansas New Jersey (headquarters) and Washington DC. In addition ETS has direct operating subsidiaries in Canada China Korea and other countries in South America Asia Europe the Middle East and Africa; these offices provide services to customers in about 80 countries.

Sales and Marketing
The company serves students educators schools businesses and governments.

Company Background
In 2011 the company opened several new customer support centers to support international customers seeking to take the TOEFL test.

The company bulked up its testing technology in early 2011 with the acquisition of Computerized Assessments and Learning (CAL). Operating as a subsidiary of ETS CAL offers assessment products for K-12 education systems.

To move beyond assessment and into actual education ETS acquired Edusoft an English language learning firm in 2011. The 2011 acquisition brought in Edusoft's English Discoveries Online product used around the world. The online product is designed to accompany and support classroom instruction with courses for general and technical English language instruction. Edusoft operates as a for-profit subsidiary.

ETS was founded in 1947.

EXECUTIVES

Pres, Walt Macdonald
Cfo, Jack Hayon
Treas, John Basehore
Corp SEC, David Hobson
Gen Counsel, Glenn Schroeder
Executive Director, Informatio, Ann Willard
Team Lead Program Coordinator, Annette Argust
Process Coordinator, Iridious Jones
Financial Analyst, John Kokinda
Test Administration C, Veronica Robinson
Senior Accountant, Maryjean Hancock
Auditors: DELOITTE & TOUCHE LLP

LOCATIONS

HQ: EDUCATIONAL TESTING SERVICE
  660 ROSEDALE RD, PRINCETON, NJ 085402218
Phone: 609 921-9000
Web: WWW.ETS.ORG

PRODUCTS/OPERATIONS

Selected Testing Programs
Advanced Placement (AP)
Algebra end of course assessment (EOC)
California High School Exit Examination (CAHSEE)
California State University Placement Test (EPT/ELM)
College-Level Examination Program (CLEP)
ETS Literacy
ETS Proficiency Profile
EXADEP
Graduate Record Examinations (GRE)
High Schools That Work Assessment

iSkills Assessment
Major Field Tests (MFT)
Middle Grades Assessment (MGA)
National Assessment of Educational Progress (NAEP)
ParaPro Assessment
The Praxis Series: Professional Assessments for Beginning Teachers
Preliminary SAT/National Merit Scholarship Qualifying Test (PSAT/NMSQT)
Scholastic Aptitude Test (SAT)
School Leaders Licensure Assessment (SLLA)
School Leadership Series (SLS)
School Superintendent Assessment (SSA)
Secondary Level English Proficiency Test (SLEP)
Test Link Test Collection
TFI Test
Test of English as a Foreign Language (TOEFL)
Test of English for International Communication (TOEIC)

Selected Acquisitions

COMPETITORS

Act Inc.	S&p Global
Houghton Mifflin Harcourt	Scantron
	The Princeton Review
Kaplan	University Of Iowa
Questar Assessment	

HISTORICAL FINANCIALS
Company Type: Private

Income Statement				FYE: September 30
	REVENUE ($ mil.)	NET INCOME ($ mil.)	NET PROFIT MARGIN	EMPLOYEES
09/20	1,050	(85)	—	2,756
09/19	1,358	(22)	—	—
09/18	1,392	686	49.3%	—
09/17	1,398	53	3.8%	—
Annual Growth	(9.1%)	—	—	—

2020 Year-End Financials
Return on assets: (-4.5%)   Cash ($ mil.): 144
Return on equity: (-6.0%)
Current ratio: 1.00

EDWARD HOSPITAL

EXECUTIVES

System Ceo, Pamela Davis
System Evp-Cfo*, William Devoney
System Vp-Physician Ambulatory*, Bill Kottman
Vice Pres-Facilities*, Gary Mielak
System Evp-Gen Counsel*, Chris Mollet
Exec V Pres*, Vince Pryor
V Pres*, Barbara Byrne
V Pres*, Patti Ludwig-Beymer
System Evp-Hr*, Susan Mitchell
System Vp-CIO*, Bobbie Byrne
System Vp-Cmo*, Brian Davis

LOCATIONS

HQ: EDWARD HOSPITAL
  801 S WASHINGTON ST, NAPERVILLE, IL 605407499
Phone: 630 355-0450
Web: WWW.EEHEALTH.ORG

HISTORICAL FINANCIALS
Company Type: Private

Income Statement				FYE: June 30
	REVENUE ($ mil.)	NET INCOME ($ mil.)	NET PROFIT MARGIN	EMPLOYEES
06/20	665	21	3.2%	4,700
06/16	592	2	0.5%	—
06/15	567	39	7.0%	—
06/14	615	106	17.2%	—
Annual Growth	1.3%	(23.5%)	—	—

EDWARD-ELMHURST HEALTHCARE

EXECUTIVES

Ceo, Lou Mastro
Pres, Pamela Meyer-Davis
Exec V Pres, Chris Mollet
Exec V Pres, Susan Mitchell
V Pres, Bobbie Byrne
Cfo, Vince Pryor
Vice President-Facilities, Gary Mielak
Neurology, Henry C Echiverri
Director, Glenn Nelson
BSN, Donna Preisler
Director Care Coordinat, Marcie Cns
Auditors: KPMG LLP CHICAGO IL

LOCATIONS

HQ: EDWARD-ELMHURST HEALTHCARE
  4201 WINFIELD RD, WARRENVILLE, IL 605554025
Phone: 630 355-0450
Web: WWW.EEHEALTH.ORG

HISTORICAL FINANCIALS
Company Type: Private

Income Statement				FYE: June 30
	REVENUE ($ mil.)	NET INCOME ($ mil.)	NET PROFIT MARGIN	EMPLOYEES
06/21	1,650	358	21.7%	6,500
06/20	1,487	(107)	—	—
06/19	1,514	76	5.1%	—
06/18	1,474	119	8.1%	—
Annual Growth	3.8%	44.1%	—	—

2021 Year-End Financials
Return on assets: 11.9%   Cash ($ mil.): 167
Return on equity: 25.0%
Current ratio: 1.10

EL CAMINO HEALTHCARE DISTRICT

EXECUTIVES

Cfo, Carlos Bohorquez
Auditors: MOSS ADAMS LLP SAN FRANCISCO

HQ: EL CAMINO HEALTHCARE DISTRICT
  2500 GRANT RD, MOUNTAIN VIEW, CA 940404302
Phone: 650 940-7000
Web: WWW.ELCAMINOHEALTHCAREDISTRICT.ORG

HISTORICAL FINANCIALS
Company Type: Private

Income Statement				FYE: June 30
	REVENUE ($ mil.)	NET INCOME ($ mil.)	NET PROFIT MARGIN	EMPLOYEES
06/21	1,150	354	30.8%	13
06/20	1,031	129	12.6%	—
Annual Growth	11.5%	173.3%	—	—

2021 Year-End Financials
Return on assets: 10.9%   Cash ($ mil.): 161
Return on equity: 15.4%
Current ratio: 2.70

EL PASO COUNTY HOSPITAL DISTRICT

University Medical Center is a community not-for-profit health care system serving West Texas and southern New Mexico. The network includes the 330-bed University Medical Center of El Paso (formerly also known as Thomason General Hospital) several neighborhood primary care clinics and the El Paso First Health Plans HMO. The hospital is an acute-care teaching hospital affiliated with Texas Tech. It specializes in emergency/trauma care obstetrics pediatric medicine and orthopedics. The hospital district through its affiliates provides a range of outpatient services including physical rehabilitation speech therapy family planning dental care cancer treatment diagnostics and pharmacy services.

Company Background
University Medical Center of El Paso opened in 1915. The hospital was rebranded under the University Medical Center name in 2009 when Texas Tech opened a full four-year medical school on the Thomason General campus.

EXECUTIVES

Ceo, James N Valenti
Cfo*, Michael Nunez
Coo*, Maria Zampini
Chief Nursing Officer*, Amyra Daher
Chief Financial Officer, Leticia Flores
Records Director, Monica Blancas
Director of Laboratory, David Stevens
Security Manager, Victor Barreda
Manager, Terry Sanchez
Executive Chief of Staff, Lorena Navedo
Internal Medicine Practitioner, Rodrigo S
 Alvarado
Auditors: BKD LLP DALLAS TEXAS

LOCATIONS

HQ: EL PASO COUNTY HOSPITAL DISTRICT
  4815 ALAMEDA AVE, EL PASO, TX 799052705
Phone: 915 544-1200
Web: WWW.UMCELPASO.ORG

PRODUCTS/OPERATIONS

Selected Services
After Hours Pediatrics

Aquatic Therapy
Cardiac Cath
CAT Scan
Case Management
Dental Clinic
Diabetes Management
Diagnostic Radiology
Echocardiograms
Electrocardiograms
Emergency Department
Endoscopy/Special Procedures
Family Planning
Infusion Center
Interventional Radiology
Laboratory Services
Labor and Delivery
Laparoscopic Surgery
Lithotripsy
Mammography
Medical Unit
Mother/Baby Unit
MRI
Neonatal Intensive Care
Neonatal Intermediate Care
Neonatal Continuing Care
Newborn Nursery
Neurosurgery
Nuclear Medicine
Nutritional Care
Occupational Health
Occupational Therapy
Patient Financial Services
Pediatric Unit
Pediatric Rehabilitation
Pharmacy
Physical Therapy
Poison Control Center
Prenatal Services
Primary Care Clinics
Public Affairs
Rehabilitative Services
Respiratory Services
Special Care Nurseries
Speech Therapy
Surgical Services
Surgical Unit
Telemetry Unit
Trauma - Level 1
Ultrasound
West Texas Regional Poison Control Center
Wound Care

COMPETITORS

Covenant Health System   Tenet Healthcare
Del Sol Medical Center   Texas Health Resources
Encompass Health

HISTORICAL FINANCIALS
Company Type: Private

Income Statement				FYE: September 30
	REVENUE ($ mil.)	NET INCOME ($ mil.)	NET PROFIT MARGIN	EMPLOYEES
09/20	769	30	4.0%	1,898
09/19	679	(10)	—	—
09/18	599	(31)	—	—
09/16	578	0	0.1%	—
Annual Growth	7.4%	187.2%	—	—

2020 Year-End Financials
Return on assets: 4.0%   Cash ($ mil.): 181
Return on equity: 24.7%
Current ratio: 1.30

EL PASO INDEPENDENT SCHOOL DISTRICT EDUCATION FOUNDATION

EXECUTIVES

Spdt, Juan Cabrera
Network Infrastructure Manager, Stephen Crye
Auditors: GIBSON RUDDOCK PATTERSON LLC

LOCATIONS

HQ: EL PASO INDEPENDENT SCHOOL DISTRICT
  EDUCATION FOUNDATION
  1014 N STANTON ST, EL PASO, TX 799024109
Phone: 915 230-2000
Web: WWW.EPISD.ORG

HISTORICAL FINANCIALS
Company Type: Private

Income Statement				FYE: June 30
	REVENUE ($ mil.)	NET INCOME ($ mil.)	NET PROFIT MARGIN	EMPLOYEES
06/21	685	(213)	—	9,000
06/20	688	44	6.4%	—
06/19	648	196	30.3%	—
06/18	625	(34)	—	—
Annual Growth	3.1%	—	—	—

2021 Year-End Financials
Return on assets: (-12.3%)   Cash ($ mil.): 283
Return on equity: —
Current ratio: —

EL PASO NATURAL GAS COMPANY, L.L.C.

EXECUTIVES

Pres-Ceo, James J Cleary
Exec V Pres-Cfo, John R Sult
V Pres-Controller-Cao, Rosa P Jackson
Tech, Jesse Watkins
Project Manager, Rene Camarillo

LOCATIONS

HQ: EL PASO NATURAL GAS COMPANY, L.L.C.
  1001 LOUISIANA ST, HOUSTON, TX 770025089
Phone: 713 420-2600
Web: WWW.KINDERMORGAN.COM

HISTORICAL FINANCIALS
Company Type: Private

Income Statement				FYE: December 31
	REVENUE ($ mil.)	NET INCOME ($ mil.)	NET PROFIT MARGIN	EMPLOYEES
12/17	648	141	21.8%	525
12/16	627	128	20.5%	—
/	0	0	—	—
Annual Growth	—	—	—	—

ELECTRIC POWER BOARD OF CHATTANOOGA

Pardon me .... is that the Electric Power Board (EPB) of Chattanooga? EPB keeps on choo-chooin' along by providing electricity to more than 167410 residents and businesses. The utility (a non-profit agency of the City of Chattanooga) distributes energy in a 600 sq.-ml. area that includes greater Chattanooga as well as parts of surrounding counties in Georgia and Tennessee. It gets its wholesale power supply from the Tennessee Valley Authority. EPB also provides telecommunications (telephone and Internet) services to area homes and businesses through its EPB Fiber Optics unit.

Operations

In addition to its electric distribution business the company's all-fiber Internet product gives 50000 businesses and residences access to up to 500 Mbps of bandwidth a capacity 300 times faster than standard DSL cable or T1 connections. This service gives all EFB customers internet bandwidth capacity and service on a par with or superior to that offered in Atlanta Chicago and Los Angeles.

Geographic Reach

EPB serves greater Chattanooga and parts of surrounding counties (Bledsoe Bradley Marion Rhea and Sequatchie) and North Georgia (parts of Catoosa Dade and Walker counties).

Financial Performance

The company saw its operating revenues rise by 1% in 2013 thanks to an increase of $12.4 million in Fiber Optics residential services sales.

Strategy

EFB is pushing technological innovation and the modernization of its systems as a way to increase value and efficiency.

To help reduce power outages in 2013 the company added 200 smart switches to its 46 Kv system (in addition to its 1200 smart swtiches on the 12kV system already in place.

Company Background

During 2009 the company received a $111 million federal stimulus grant to build and operate a Smart Grid (an automated electric system with communication capabilities to help improve response time reduce outages cut down on theft and help clients take charge of their own power use). In 2012 EFB completed the installation of the 1170 IntelliRupter® PulseCloser (smart switches) making EPB's Smart Grid the most automated system of its size in the US.

The utility was established in 1935 to provide electric power to the people of the greater Chattanooga area.

EXECUTIVES

Pres-Ceo, Harold De Priest
Sr V Pres, Steve Clark
V Pres, Diana Bullock
Cfo, Greg Eaves
Coo, David Wade
Corporate Communications Staff, Pam Baker
Manager of Management Informat, Blair Brown
Manager, Hal Dickey
Customer Representativ, Mandy Clements
Credit and Collections Supervi, Tina Long
Materials Management Superviso, Erik Teichroew
Auditors: MAULDIN & JENKINS LLC CHATTA

LOCATIONS

HQ: ELECTRIC POWER BOARD OF CHATTANOOGA
10 W MRTIN LTHER KING BLV, CHATTANOOGA, TN 374021832
Phone: 423 756-2706
Web: WWW.EPB.COM

PRODUCTS/OPERATIONS

2013 Sales

	% of total
Electric	86
Fiber Optics	12
Other	2
Total	**100**

COMPETITORS

At&t	Southern Company Gas
Constellation Energy Group	

HISTORICAL FINANCIALS

Company Type: Private

Income Statement   FYE: June 30

	REVENUE ($ mil.)	NET INCOME ($ mil.)	NET PROFIT MARGIN	EMPLOYEES
06/19	741	36	5.0%	400
06/18	729	43	6.0%	—
06/17	716	35	4.9%	—
06/16	683	32	4.7%	—
Annual Growth	2.7%	4.8%	—	—

2019 Year-End Financials

Return on assets: 4.0%   Cash ($ mil.): 104
Return on equity: 8.1%
Current ratio: 1.20

ELECTRIC POWER BOARD OF THE METROPOLITAN GOVERNMENT OF NASHVILLE & DAVIDSON COUNTY

The Electric Power Board of the Metropolitan Government of Nashville and Davidson County is a mouthful. Its operating name Nashville Electric Service (NES) sounds much better. And talking of sound the legendary "Nashville Sound" would be hard to hear without the resources of this power distributor which serves more than 360000 customers in central Tennessee. NES is one of the largest government-owned utilities in the US. The company is required to purchase all its power from another government-owned operator the Tennessee Valley Authority (TVA).

EXECUTIVES

Pres, Decosta Jenkins
Jr.vice Chair Partner*, Robert Campbell
Vp and Cfo, Teresa Broyles Aplin
Accounting Staff, Melissa Stenberg
Meter Maintenance Supervisor, Billy Deaderick
Senior Engineer, Carla Nelson
Manager Human Resources, Cheryl Cole
Associate Engineer, Donnie Hunter
Senior Engineer, Frederick Friton
Manager Management Director, Pat Greer
Supervisor Underground, Ty Jones
Auditors: PRICEWATERHOUSECOOPERS LLP NA

LOCATIONS

HQ: ELECTRIC POWER BOARD OF THE METROPOLITAN GOVERNMENT OF NASHVILLE & DAVIDSON COUNTY
1214 CHURCH ST, NASHVILLE, TN 372460001
Phone: 615 747-3831
Web: WWW.NESPOWER.COM

COMPETITORS

Aep	Public Service
Constellation Energy Group	Enterprise Group
	Scana
Mlgw	Southern Company
Piedmont Natural Gas	Southern Company Gas

HISTORICAL FINANCIALS

Company Type: Private

Income Statement   FYE: June 30

	REVENUE ($ mil.)	NET INCOME ($ mil.)	NET PROFIT MARGIN	EMPLOYEES
06/19	1,342	90	6.7%	950
06/18	380	94	24.7%	—
06/16	1,203	28	2.4%	—
06/15	1,246	55	4.5%	—
Annual Growth	1.9%	12.7%	—	—

2019 Year-End Financials

Return on assets: 4.8%   Cash ($ mil.): 387
Return on equity: 14.7%
Current ratio: 2.50

ELEMENT14 US HOLDINGS INC

EXECUTIVES

Pres, Ralf Buehler
Vp, Gen Counsel and Secretary, Joseph R Daprile
Treasurer and Assistant Secret, Paul M Barlak
Vice President Value Added Ser, Neil Davies
Director Echannel Sales, Renee Mack
Director Western Sales, Rodney Sellers
Director of Assets, Roy Hoffman
Director of Operations, Scott McNeill
Continuous Improvement Analyst, Mark Ellis
Senior Sales Associate, Vicky Villicana

LOCATIONS

HQ: ELEMENT14 US HOLDINGS INC
4180 HIGHLANDER PKWY, RICHFIELD, OH 442869352
Phone: 330 523-4280
Web: WWW.AVNET.COM

HISTORICAL FINANCIALS

Company Type: Private

Income Statement				FYE: February 1
	REVENUE ($ mil.)	NET INCOME ($ mil.)	NET PROFIT MARGIN	EMPLOYEES
02/16	598	9	1.6%	1,043
02/15	717	48	6.7%	—
02/14	698	35	5.1%	—
Annual Growth	(7.5%)	(48.4%)	—	—

2016 Year-End Financials

Return on assets: 3.0%   Cash ($ mil.): 70
Return on equity: 4.2%
Current ratio: 6.40

ELLIOT HEALTH SYSTEM

EXECUTIVES

Ceo, Doug Dean
Coo*, Joseph Tate Curti
Human Resources Department, Paul Carter
Physical Medicine Specialist, Jill Mack
Analyst, Bob Blanchette
Benefits Administrator, Joanna Block
Assistant Business Manager, Mary Guarino
Accounts Receivable Coordinato, Jenny Kane
Aers Partner, Robert Dow
Accounts Payable Supervisor, Irene Fairfield
Trauma Program Manager, Adam Rembisz
Auditors: BAKER NEWMAN & NOYES LLC MANC

LOCATIONS

HQ: ELLIOT HEALTH SYSTEM
1 ELLIOT WAY, MANCHESTER, NH 031033502
Phone: 603 663-1600
Web: WWW.ELLIOTHOSPITAL.ORG

HISTORICAL FINANCIALS

Company Type: Private

Income Statement				FYE: June 30
	REVENUE ($ mil.)	NET INCOME ($ mil.)	NET PROFIT MARGIN	EMPLOYEES
06/21	657	153	23.3%	3,400
06/20	582	6	1.0%	—
06/19	592	0	0.1%	—
06/18	556	9	1.6%	—
Annual Growth	5.7%	156.2%	—	—

2021 Year-End Financials

Return on assets: 19.2%   Cash ($ mil.): 178
Return on equity: 42.9%
Current ratio: 1.50

ELLIOT HOSPITAL OF THE CITY OF MANCHESTER

Elliot Health System provides medical care to southern New Hampshire. The health care organization operates Elliot Hospital an acute care hospital with nearly 300 beds that is home to a regional cancer center a designated regional trauma center and a level III neonatal intensive care unit (NICU). In addition to general and surgical care the hospital offers rehabilitation behavioral health obstetrics cardiology and lab services. The system also operates the Elliot Physician Network which operates primary care centers specialty clinics and surgery centers in various regional communities. Elliot Hospital was founded in 1890.

Operations

Elliot Hospital is Manchester's designated Regional Trauma Center. Additional facilities include the Elliot Breast Health Center Elliot Urgent Care Elliot Senior Health Center and New Hampshire's Hospital for Children.

Strategy

Elliot Health System has expanded throughout the region by constructing new outpatient care centers in nearby towns. Most recently Elliot Health completed construction of satellite facilities including an ambulatory care center and a senior health center. In 2015 it partnered with Northeast Rehabilitation Hospital to create a new rehabilitation floor within its Elliot Hospital.

EXECUTIVES

Pres-Ceo, Douglas Dean
Cfo*, Richard Elwell
Internal Medicine Practitioner, Allison A Hutson
Internal Medicine Practitioner, Jennifer L Steichen
Vice President, Carla Braveman
Oncologist, Stephen Harris
Staff Rn, Luz Fernandez
Internist, Chung-Mok Yoo
Emergency Medicine Specialist, Joey Scollan
Hospitalist, Luigi Lim
Case Management Director, Rebecca Rully
Auditors: BAKER NEWMAN & NOYES LLC MANC

LOCATIONS

HQ: ELLIOT HOSPITAL OF THE CITY OF MANCHESTER
1 ELLIOT WAY, MANCHESTER, NH 031033502
Phone: 603 669-5300
Web: WWW.ELLIOTHOSPITAL.ORG

PRODUCTS/OPERATIONS

Selected Centers and Services

Aeronautics Medicine
Adult Day Programs
Bariatric Surgery
Behavioral Health
Breast Health Center
Cardiology Services
Center for Sleep Evaluation
Center for Wound Care & Hyberbaric Medicine
Childbirth And Family Education
Community Health and Wellness
Critical Care at The Elliot
Diabetes and Outpatient Nutrition Services
Diagnostic Imaging
Elliot 1-Day Surgery Center
The Elliot at Hooksett

Elliot Behavioral Health Services
Elliot Endocrinology Associates
Elliot Gastroenterology
Elliot General Surgical Specialists
Elliot Maternal Fetal Medicine
Elliot Medical Center at Londonderry
Elliot Neurology Associates
Elliot Obstetrics and Gynecology
Elliot Orthopaedic Surgical Specialists
Elliot Physician Network
Elliot Regional Cancer Center
Elliot Sports Medicine
Elliot Trauma Center
Elliot Wellness Center
Endoscopy Center
Health Education Library
Home Medical Equipment
Hospitalist Program
Infection Control Department
Inpatient Care/Nursing Units
Laboratory Services
Max K. Willscher Urology Center
Neurophysiology
New England EMS Institute
New Hampshire Arthritis Center
Nursing Units/Inpatient Care
Nutrition Services
Occupational Health & Wellness
Oral Maxillofacial Surgery Center
Oxygen Therapy
Pain Management Center
Pediatric Surgery
Pharmacy Services
Pulmonary Medicine
Pulmonary Rehabilitation
Physical Therapy
Rehabilitation
Respiratory Care
Senior Health Center
Sports Medicine
Surgery
Speech Therapy
Urgent Car
Urgent Car
Visiting Nurse Association of Manchester & So. NH Inc.
Weight Management
Wellness Center
Women's & Children's Services
Wound Center

COMPETITORS

Caritas Holy Family Hospital
Catholic Medical Center
Concord Hospital
Exeter Health Resources
Frisbie Memorial Hospital
Hca
Southern New Hampshire Medical Center

HISTORICAL FINANCIALS

Company Type: Private

Income Statement				FYE: June 30
	REVENUE ($ mil.)	NET INCOME ($ mil.)	NET PROFIT MARGIN	EMPLOYEES
06/21	621	139	22.5%	2,000
06/20	549	(27)	—	—
06/19	560	(4)	—	—
06/16	394	49	12.5%	—
Annual Growth	9.5%	23.1%	—	—

2021 Year-End Financials

Return on assets: 20.4%   Cash ($ mil.): 146
Return on equity: 54.5%
Current ratio: 1.40

EMJ CORPORATION

EMJ does it all for the mall. Founded in 1968 by namesake Edgar M. Jolley the company specializes in building and renovating retail outlets and shopping centers throughout the US. It is also known for other building projects such as offices warehouses churches hotels multifamily residences hospitals and wind farms. Working from five offices nationwide EMJ provides general construction and construction management. The company's pre-construction services include creating detailed budgets and construction schedules and coordinating permitting utility companies and municipal requirements. To track a project's progress and monitor costs EMJ offers quality control and safety and warranty management.

Operations

EMJ owns several operating divisions including Signal Energy which engineers and builds renewable energy projects such as wind farms and solar and biomass energy projects. Another division Accent Construction Management provides site selection budgeting scheduling and other services. Its RedStone Construction Services builds commercial retail hospitality healthcare government facilities and others. It is focused on fostering economic growth in Native American communities.

Geographic Reach

From its base in Chattanooga Tennessee EMJ serves clients through a handful of US offices in Massachusetts Tennessee Texas and California.

Sales and Marketing

EMJ has built more than 500 million sq. ft. of construction projects. Its client roster includes Academy Barnes & Noble Bed Bath & Beyond Blue Cross and Blue Shield Home Depot PetSmart and Winn-Dixie.

The company serves several sectors such as airports education entertainment government and civic grocery healthcare hospitality industrial and warehouse and Native American tribal communities office buildings parking lifestyle and mixed use development retail renewable energy renovations and worship centers.

Strategy

The company is working on projects for Whole Foods Market TownPlace Suites Silverdale Baptist student center and Dick's Sporting Goods. Inked in 2013 EMJ's $250-million deal with Native American Chris Samples operating under the name RedStone Construction Services is building a 500-room hotel and expanding a casino in Tulsa Oklahoma.

EXECUTIVES

Ceo, James Jolley
Pres*, Burt Odom
Coo*, Doug Martin
Cfo*, Chuck McGlothlen
Cfo*, Steve Coughran
Clo*, Colby Cox
Vp Management, Ed Jolley Jr
Vice President Southwest Offic, Drew Halsey
Payroll Staff, Kyla Castleberry
Director, Michelle Bernard
It Support Manager, Sarah Kirby

LOCATIONS

HQ: EMJ CORPORATION
2034 HAMILTON PLACE BLVD # 400,
CHATTANOOGA, TN 374216102
Phone: 423 855-1550
Web: WWW.EMJCORP.COM

PRODUCTS/OPERATIONS

Selected Projects
Airports
Education
Entertainment
Government/civic
Grocery
Healthcare

Hospitality
Industrial/warehouse
Lifestyle/mixed use development and retail
Native American tribal communities
Office buildings
Parking
Renewable energy
Renovations
Worship centers

Selected Services
Construction
Construction management
General contracting
Pre-construction services
Quality control
Safety consultation
Site evaluation
Warranty

COMPETITORS

Case Contracting
Embree Construction
Fisher Development
Graycor
Hardaway Construction
Hardin Construction
Hayward Baker

Hoar Construction
Jesco
Rodgers Builders
S.d. Deacon
Skanska Usa Building
Weis Builders
Workman Commercial

HISTORICAL FINANCIALS
Company Type: Private

Income Statement				FYE: March 7
	REVENUE ($ mil.)	NET INCOME ($ mil.)	NET PROFIT MARGIN	EMPLOYEES
03/17*	960	4	0.5%	210
12/11	437	0	0.1%	—
12/08	821	7	1.0%	—
12/07	959	10	1.1%	—
Annual Growth	0.0%	(7.9%)	—	—

*Fiscal year change

2017 Year-End Financials
Return on assets: 2.3%   Cash ($ mil.): 29
Return on equity: 18.5%
Current ratio: 1.10

EMORY UNIVERSITY HOSPITAL MIDTOWN

EXECUTIVES

Ceo, Robert J Bachman
Dir*, Rosalind K Lett
Pres*, John T Fox
Exec V Pres*, S Wright Caughman
Attorney, Lorraine Spencer
Chief of Medicine, Harold Ramos
Director, Jakob V Johansen
Assistant Professor, James Weisberg
Coordinator, Crystal Evans
Otolaryngologist, Sarah Wise
Cardiovascular Disease, Alexis G Cutchins

LOCATIONS

HQ: EMORY UNIVERSITY HOSPITAL MIDTOWN
550 PEACHTREE ST NE, ATLANTA, GA 303082212
Phone: 404 686-4411
Web: WWW.EMORYHEALTHCARE.ORG

HISTORICAL FINANCIALS
Company Type: Private

Income Statement				FYE: August 31
	REVENUE ($ mil.)	NET INCOME ($ mil.)	NET PROFIT MARGIN	EMPLOYEES
08/16	735	64	8.7%	2,500
08/15	641	(21)	—	—
Annual Growth	14.8%	—	—	—

2016 Year-End Financials
Return on assets: 9.9%   Cash ($ mil.): 269
Return on equity: 38.5%
Current ratio: 2.50

EMPIRE SOUTHWEST, LLC

Empire Southwest is a third-generation family-owned Cat Dealer that sells rents and services heavy equipment tractors and power generation equipment to clients throughout Arizona and Southeastern California. One of the largest Caterpillar dealerships in the US Empire Southwest operates through four divisions: hydraulic service fluid labs precision machining and rebuilds. The company's equipment includes backhoe loaders compactors dozers electric rope shovels track loaders pipelayers telehandlers and tractors. It also handles equipment used for mining and forestry projects. The company was founded by Jack Whiteman in 1950 as Empire Machinery an Eastern Oregon Caterpillar dealer.

Operations

Empire Southwest consists of four operating divisions. Empire Machinery sells rents and provides product support for Caterpillar equipment and other brands.

Its Empire Fluids Lab can detect potential problems long before they materialize. Its Scheduled Oil Sampling (SOS) is a regular maintenance program designed to monitor the overall condition of all equipment brands and machine types. Empire Precision Machining is fully equipped to work on small to large components used in today's top industries including mining construction and agriculture. Empire Hydraulic Service specializes in repairing and rebuilding of hydraulic cylinders pumps and motors.

Geographic Reach

Headquartered in Mesa Arizona Empire has carved out a territory that includes about 30 communities in Arizona southeastern California and portions of northern Mexico.

Sales and Marketing

The company targets the agriculture mining demo and scrap forestry and logging on-highway truck general construction heavy construction electric power and waste management industries.

Company Background

The company was founded in 1950 when Jack Whiteman acquired Empire Machinery (which held the Caterpillar and John Deere dealerships in eastern Oregon). In 1959 he relocated to Arizona and took over a Caterpillar dealership there.

EXECUTIVES

MBR-Ceo, Jeffrey S Whiteman
Executive Vice President*, Chris Zaharis
Manager Production Management, James Kell

Transport Operations Manager, Harold Merkel
Director of Credit Six Sigma, Rob Wahlin
Marketing Analytics Manager, Ron Wilson
Programmer Analyst, Darlene Miller
Condition Monitoring Manager, Dolan Hall
Sales Manager, Jay Eller
Vice President, Jim Smith
Equipment Manager, John Overton

LOCATIONS

HQ: EMPIRE SOUTHWEST, LLC
  1725 S COUNTRY CLUB DR, MESA, AZ 852106099
Phone: 480 633-4000
Web: WWW.CATERPILLAR.COM

PRODUCTS/OPERATIONS

Selected Industries Served

Agriculture
Demo and Scrap
Forestry
General Construction
Governmental
Heavy Construction
Landscaping
Marine
Mining
Oil and Gas
On-Highway Truck
Paving
Pipeline
Quarry and Aggregates
Waste

COMPETITORS

Arnold Machinery	Multiquip
Cashman Equipment	Nes Rentals
Cummins	Sunbelt Rentals
Komatsu	United Rentals
Komatsu America	

HISTORICAL FINANCIALS

Company Type: Private

Income Statement			FYE: October 31	
	REVENUE ($ mil.)	NET INCOME ($ mil.)	NET PROFIT MARGIN	EMPLOYEES
10/11	683	38	5.6%	1,450
10/10	528	22	4.3%	—
10/09	448	7	1.6%	—
Annual Growth	23.5%	127.0%	—	—

ENERGY RESEARCH AND DEVELOPMENT AUTHORITY, NEW YORK STATE

The New York State Energy Research and Development Authority (NYSERDA) uses technological innovation to solve the state's energy and environmental problems. The public benefit corporation funds energy supply and conservation research and energy-related environmental issues. It also conducts research projects that help state and city groups solve their energy problems. Its Energy Efficiency Services group works helps more than 450 schools businesses and municipalities find ways to reduce their energy costs. In-

vestor-owned electric and gas utilities grants and contributions from the New York Power Authority and the Long Island Power Authority fund NY-SERDA which was created in 1975.

EXECUTIVES

Chb, Richard Kauffman
Pres-Ceo*, John B Rhodes
Coo*, David L Margalit
Tres*, Jeff Pitkin
V Pres*, Janet Joseph
V Pres-Prgm*, Robert G Callender
Governor*, Andrew M Cuomo
Project Coordinator, Steven Lebel
Project Coordinator, Harith Saam
Auditors: KPMG LLP ALBANY NEW YORK

LOCATIONS

HQ: ENERGY RESEARCH AND DEVELOPMENT
  AUTHORITY, NEW YORK STATE
  17 COLUMBIA CIR, ALBANY, NY 122035156
Phone: 518 862-1090
Web: WWW.ENERGYPLAN.NY.GOV

HISTORICAL FINANCIALS

Company Type: Private

Income Statement			FYE: March 31	
	REVENUE ($ mil.)	NET INCOME ($ mil.)	NET PROFIT MARGIN	EMPLOYEES
03/19	1,091	51	4.7%	345
03/17	0	(0)	—	—
Annual Growth	7215.0%	—	—	—

ENGLEWOOD HOSPITAL AND MEDICAL CENTER FOUNDATION INC.

EXECUTIVES

V Pres, Anthony T Orlando
Chb*, Richard Lerner
SEC*, Warren Geller
Vp Info Tech-CIO*, Dimitri J Cruz
Principal, Phil Maneri
Training and Direc, Barbara Wilkinski
Scientist, Mazyar Javidroozi
Anesthesiology, Lorraine V Volpe
Health Professional, Mercedes Delgado
Anesthesiology, Payyanadan V Chithran
Health Professional, Silvia Daici

LOCATIONS

HQ: ENGLEWOOD HOSPITAL AND MEDICAL CENTER
  FOUNDATION INC.
  350 ENGLE ST, ENGLEWOOD, NJ 076311808
Phone: 201 894-3725
Web: WWW.ENGLEWOODHEALTH.ORG

HISTORICAL FINANCIALS

Company Type: Private

Income Statement			FYE: December 31	
	REVENUE ($ mil.)	NET INCOME ($ mil.)	NET PROFIT MARGIN	EMPLOYEES
12/19	770	45	5.8%	38
12/17	11	7	66.8%	—
12/16	552	19	3.5%	—
12/15	480	12	2.5%	—
Annual Growth	12.5%	38.6%		

2019 Year-End Financials

Return on assets: 7.2%   Cash ($ mil.): 21
Return on equity: 14.2%
Current ratio: 0.40

ENTERGY SERVICES, LLC

EXECUTIVES

Ceo, Leo P Denault
Cfo*, Andrew Marsh
Coo*, Mark T Savoff
Pres*, Theo Bunting Jr
Exec Pres*, Marcus V Brown
V Pres*, Kimberly H Despeaux
V Pres*, Jere M Ahrens
V Pres*, Kay K Arnold
V Pres*, Michael A Balduzzi
V Pres*, Kelle J Barfield
Director, Cory Gruntz

LOCATIONS

HQ: ENTERGY SERVICES, LLC
  639 LOYOLA AVE STE 300, NEW ORLEANS, LA
  701137106
Phone: 504 576-4000
Web: WWW.ENTERGY.COM

HISTORICAL FINANCIALS

Company Type: Private

Income Statement			FYE: December 31	
	REVENUE ($ mil.)	NET INCOME ($ mil.)	NET PROFIT MARGIN	EMPLOYEES
12/16	1,112	10	0.9%	1,325
12/04	10,123	933	9.2%	—
Annual Growth	(16.8%)	(31.2%)	—	—

2016 Year-End Financials

Return on assets: 0.8%   Cash ($ mil.): 51
Return on equity: —
Current ratio: 0.70

ENTERPRISE CRUDE PIPELINE LLC

EXECUTIVES

Pres, W Randall Fowler
Technician Mechanical, Willie Stubbs

LOCATIONS

HQ: ENTERPRISE CRUDE PIPELINE LLC
1100 LOUISIANA ST # 1000, HOUSTON, TX
770025227
Phone: 713 381-6500
Web: WWW.ENTERPRISEPRODUCTS.COM

HISTORICAL FINANCIALS

Company Type: Private

Income Statement				FYE: December 31
	REVENUE ($ mil.)	NET INCOME ($ mil.)	NET PROFIT MARGIN	EMPLOYEES
12/17	596	378	63.5%	300
12/16	472	284	60.2%	—
Annual Growth	26.2%	33.1%	—	—

ENTERPRISE TE PRODUCTS PIPELINE COMPANY LLC

EXECUTIVES

Ceo-MBR, Jerry E Thompson
Cfo-MBR*, William G Manias
Technician Pipeline, Kenneston Hale
Operations, Tim Kistner
Operations, Juan Contreras
Technician Pipeline, Paul Deken
Operations, Ross Corbett
Maintenance Specialist, Randy Robison
Technician, Pipeline, Richard Ames

LOCATIONS

HQ: ENTERPRISE TE PRODUCTS PIPELINE COMPANY LLC
1100 LOUISIANA ST # 1600, HOUSTON, TX
770025221
Phone: 713 381-6500
Web: WWW.ENTERPRISEPRODUCTS.COM

HISTORICAL FINANCIALS

Company Type: Private

Income Statement				FYE: December 31
	REVENUE ($ mil.)	NET INCOME ($ mil.)	NET PROFIT MARGIN	EMPLOYEES
12/17	659	337	51.1%	1
12/16	628	275	43.9%	—
Annual Growth	5.0%	22.3%	—	—

EP ENERGY CORPORATION

EP Energy is into the (E)xploration and (P)roduction of oil and gas. The company's primary operations are at the Eagle Ford Shale in South Texas Northeastern Utah (NEU) in the Uinta basin and the Permian basin in West Texas. It owns proved reserves of around 190 million barrels of oil equivalent about 75% of which is oil and NGLs (natural gas liquids). In early 2020 EP Energy emerged from Chapter 11 bankruptcy protection. EP Energy was formed in 2012 when the former El Paso Corporation sold its exploration and production assets to an investment group for $7.2 billion.

Bankruptcy

The company and certain of its direct and indirect subsidiaries (collectively with the company the debtors) filed voluntary petitions (the "Chapter 11 Cases") in the United States Bankruptcy Court for the Southern District of Texas (the "Bankruptcy Court") seeking relief under Chapter 11 of title 11 of the United States Code (the "Bankruptcy Code"). To ensure ordinary course operations the debtors obtained approval from the Bankruptcy Court for a variety of "first day" motions including motions to obtain customary relief intended to assure the company's ability to continue its ordinary course operations after the filing date. In addition to this the debtors received authority to use cash collateral of the lenders under the RBL Facility.

The company will reduce its debt by approximately $3.3 billion will receive approximately $629 million in senior secured exit financing from the company's existing revolving loan lenders and approximately $325 million of new-money equity financing from certain of its existing noteholders upon emergence.

Operations

Of EP Energy's 190MMboe (millions of barrels of oil equivalent) of proved reserves around 90% are oil reserves more than 5% of sales from natural gas liquids and approximately 5% of sales from natural gas.

It produces around 70850 boe each day via nearly 1560 producing wells.

Geographic Reach

Headquartered in Houston Texas the company operates in three areas: the Eagle Ford Shale (in South Texas) Northeastern Utah (NEU) (in the Uinta basin) and the Permian (basin in West Texas).

Sales and Marketing

EP Energy sells oil and natural gas to third parties in the US at spot market prices. NGLs are sold at market prices under monthly or long-term contracts.

Nine purchasers account for about 90% of the company's oil revenues. The top two purchasers are: Shell Trading U.S. Co. (an affiliate of Shell Oil Company) and Flint Hills Resources LP (an affiliate of Koch Industries) which together accounted for approximately 45% of our oil revenues.

The majority of its produced gas flows are on the Camino Real gas gathering system via pipelines. The gas is then redelivered into interconnects with ETC Texas Pipeline LTD Enterprise Hydrocarbons LP Regency Energy Partners LP and Eagle Ford Gathering LLC. Wax crude is sold to Salt Lake City refineries under long-term sales agreements.

Financial Performance

EP Energy's revenue has been fluctuating in the last five years with an overall decline of 57% between 2015 and 2019. The company's revenue declined 38% from $1.3 billion in 2018 to $820 million in 2019.

EP Energy suffered a $943 million net loss in 2019 due to decrease in revenue.

The company's cash at the end of 2019 was $33 million 6$ million more than the previous year. Operating activities generated $227 million while investing activities used $518 million. Financing activities provided another $297 million mainly from proceeds from issuance of long-term debt.

Strategy

EP Energy's strategy is to invest in opportunities that provide the highest return across our asset base continually seek out operating and capital efficiencies effectively manage costs and identify accretive acquisition opportunities and divestitures all with the objective of enhancing our portfolio growing asset value improving cash flow and increasing financial flexibility.

Mergers and Acquisitions

EXECUTIVES

Pres-Ceo, Russell E Parker
Non Exec Chb, Alan R Crain Jr
Sr V Pres-Cfo-Treas, Kyle A McCuen
Sr V Pres Oprs, Chad D England
V Pres-Gen Counsel-Corp SEC, Jace D Locke
Vice President, Eric Kleinhenz
Human Resources Executive, James Cleary
Director, John Hannan
Production Supervisor, Ron Theener
Engineer, Victor Salazar
Compliance Staff, Alan Bishop
Auditors: ERNST & YOUNG LLP HOUSTON TE

LOCATIONS

HQ: EP ENERGY CORPORATION
601 TRAVIS ST STE 1400, HOUSTON, TX 770023253
Phone: 713 997-1000
Web: WWW.EPENERGY.COM

PRODUCTS/OPERATIONS

2016 sales

	$ mil.	% of total
Oil	653	78
Natural gas	122	14
NGLs	65	8
Financial derivatives	(73)	-
Total	**767**	**100**

HISTORICAL FINANCIALS

Company Type: Private

Income Statement				FYE: December 31
	REVENUE ($ mil.)	NET INCOME ($ mil.)	NET PROFIT MARGIN	EMPLOYEES
12/19	820	(943)	—	372
12/18	1,324	(1,003)	—	—
12/17	1,066	(194)	—	—
12/16	767	(27)	—	—
Annual Growth	2.3%	—	—	—

2019 Year-End Financials

Return on assets: (-25.4%) Cash ($ mil.): 32
Return on equity: —
Current ratio: 0.10

EP ENERGY LLC

EXECUTIVES

Sr V Pres-Cfo, Kyle A McCuen
Land Advisor, Michael Walcher
Senior Instrument Tech Analyst, Robert Love
Supervisor, Carol Tillman
Information Technology Senior, Christopher Smoke
Business Area Manager, Daniel Rohling
Petroleum Engineer, David Stilson
Senior Vice President Central, Frank Falleri
Production Engineering Manager, Iva Tomova
Senior Counsel, Patricia Francis
Information Technolo, Chengdi Bao
Auditors: ERNST & YOUNG LLP HOUSTON T

LOCATIONS

HQ: EP ENERGY LLC
  601 TRAVIS ST STE 1400, HOUSTON, TX 770023253
Phone: 713 997-1200
Web: WWW.EPENERGY.COM

HISTORICAL FINANCIALS
Company Type: Private

Income Statement   FYE: December 31

	REVENUE ($ mil.)	NET INCOME ($ mil.)	NET PROFIT MARGIN	EMPLOYEES
12/19	820	(943)	—	372
12/18	1,324	(1,003)	—	—
12/17	1,066	(203)	—	—
12/16	767	(21)	—	—
Annual Growth	2.3%	—	—	—

2019 Year-End Financials
Return on assets: (-25.4%)   Cash ($ mil.): 32
Return on equity: —
Current ratio: 0.10

EQUINOR MARKETING & TRADING (US) INC.

Check the stats. Oil. Hundreds of thousands of barrels of oil gasoline and more. Statoil Marketing & Trading is a wholesaler of oil and petroleum products. The company is the US trading arm of Statoil the leading Scandinavian oil and gas enterprise. Statoil Marketing & Trading delivers about 600000 barrels a day in the form of crude oil gasoline liquefied petroleum gas (LPG) propane and butane to the North American market. In addition to supplying Norwegian crude the company trades crude oil from Africa South America and North America. Statoil Marketing & Trading sells it oil products primarily to customers in Northeastern Canada the US East Coast and Gulf Coast.

EXECUTIVES

Pres, Kjetil Johnsen
General Counsel-Secretary, Charles O'Brien
Controller, Todd Walls
Mgr Energy Trading, Stein-Erling Brekke
Mgr Crude Oil Trading, Oddgeir Wskeland
Manager, Daniel Ward
Information Specialist, Steffan Sorenes
Senior Manager, Kimberly Soika
Vice President Middle East, Kjetil Tonstad
Executive Vice President, Lars Bacher
Vice President Operations, Lars Hier
Auditors: KPMG LLP STAMFORD
  CONNECTICU

LOCATIONS

HQ: EQUINOR MARKETING & TRADING (US) INC.
  120 LONG RIDGE RD 3EO1, STAMFORD, CT
  069021839
Phone: 203 978-6900
Web: WWW.EQUINOR.COM

COMPETITORS

Global Partners	Irving Oil Limited
Gulf Oil	Shell Oil
Hess Corporation	Tauber Oil

HISTORICAL FINANCIALS
Company Type: Private

Income Statement   FYE: December 31

	REVENUE ($ mil.)	NET INCOME ($ mil.)	NET PROFIT MARGIN	EMPLOYEES
12/20	9,959	209	2.1%	5
12/19	13,594	88	0.7%	—
12/18	14,852	140	0.9%	—
12/17	9,874	(28)	—	—
Annual Growth	0.3%	—	—	—

2020 Year-End Financials
Return on assets: 9.6%   Cash ($ mil.): 97
Return on equity: 28.4%
Current ratio: 1.60

EQUINOR NATURAL GAS LLC

EXECUTIVES

Pres, Asbjrn Skretting
Sec-General Counsel, Charles T O'Brien
Controller, Neil Tarling
Leader Tax, Kathleen Parchinski
Assistant Secretary, Josh Kaplan
Cfo, Gary A Turiano
V Pres of Tax, Martin J Pastore
Operator, Paula Ahern
Researcher, Yaping Zhu
Executive Vice President, Geir Tungesvik
Originator, Hugh Gleason
Auditors: ERNST & YOUNG LLP NEW YORK N

LOCATIONS

HQ: EQUINOR NATURAL GAS LLC
  120 LONG RIDGE RD, STAMFORD, CT 069021839
Phone: 203 978-6900
Web: WWW.EQUINOR.COM

HISTORICAL FINANCIALS
Company Type: Private

Income Statement   FYE: December 31

	REVENUE ($ mil.)	NET INCOME ($ mil.)	NET PROFIT MARGIN	EMPLOYEES
12/19	1,964	32	1.6%	15
12/15	1,967	722	36.7%	—
12/13	3,507	(127)	—	—
12/10	1,614	149	9.3%	—
Annual Growth	2.2%	(15.7%)	—	—

2019 Year-End Financials
Return on assets: 3.1%   Cash ($ mil.): 23
Return on equity: 7.9%
Current ratio: 2.60

ERIE COUNTY MEDICAL CENTER CORP.

EXECUTIVES

Ceo, Jody L Lomeo
Cfo*, Jonathan T Swiatkowski
Coo*, Richard C Cleland
R V Pres*, Ronald Krawiec
R V Pres*, Karen Ziemianski
Cfo*, Steven Gary
Chro-General Counsel*, Joseph T Giglia II
Evp*, Anthony J Colucci III
Asst Ceo, Kathleen Gellart
Infectious Diseases, Chiu Bin Hsiao
Internal Medicine Practitioner, Nelda Lawler
Auditors: RSM US LLP

LOCATIONS

HQ: ERIE COUNTY MEDICAL CENTER CORP.
  462 GRIDER ST, BUFFALO, NY 142153098
Phone: 716 898-3000
Web: WWW.ECMC.EDU

HISTORICAL FINANCIALS
Company Type: Private

Income Statement   FYE: December 31

	REVENUE ($ mil.)	NET INCOME ($ mil.)	NET PROFIT MARGIN	EMPLOYEES
12/20	638	(64)	—	3,300
12/19	750	12	1.7%	—
12/18	661	1	0.2%	—
12/16	616	1	0.3%	—
Annual Growth	0.9%	—	—	—

2020 Year-End Financials
Return on assets: (-5.9%)   Cash ($ mil.): 120
Return on equity: —
Current ratio: 1.30

ESTES EXPRESS LINES

Estes Express is the largest privately-owned freight shipping company in North America. Its fleet of over 7000 tractors and some 30000 trailers operates via a network of more than 260 terminals dotting the US. The company provides reliable Less Than Truckload (LTL) freight solutions to and from all 50 states Canada Mexico and the Caribbean as well as asset-based and brokered Volume LTL and Truckload shipping to regional national international and offshore destinations. The company was founded in 1931 when W.W. Estes bought a used Chevrolet truck to haul livestock to market for his neighbors in rural Virginia.

Operations

The company operates through several divisions and companies. Divisions include Estes Time-Critical (offering guaranteed and time-sensitive service for maximum shipping flexibility) Estes Logistics (helps create B2B and B2C shipping solutions) Estes Specialized Truckload and Delivery Services and Estes SureMove (customers load shipments themselves and Estes provides transportation). Companies include Estes Forwarding Worldwide Estes Leasing and Big E Transportation.

Geographic Reach

Headquartered in Richmond Virginia Estes Express offers regional service to all 50 US states. It also offers direct service to Canada Mexico and the Caribbean.

Company Background

The company was formed in 1931.

EXECUTIVES

Pres-Ceo, Robey W Estes Jr
Exec V Pres*, William T Hupp
Treas*, Gary D Okes
SEC*, Stephen E Hupp
V Pres*, Patricia A Garland
Director, Betty Reed
Regional Safety Manager, David Ondik
Manager, Janice Chalkley
Hardware Support Leader, Michael Wimbush
Account Manager, Mike Pierce
Vice President Sales, Patricia Robinson

LOCATIONS

HQ: ESTES EXPRESS LINES
3901 W BROAD ST, RICHMOND, VA 232303962
Phone: 804 353-1900
Web: WWW.ESTES-EXPRESS.COM

PRODUCTS/OPERATIONS

Selected Services

Global (airfreight ocean international consolidation/deconsolidation customs brokerage international freight forwarding)
Less-than-truckload (regional national international/offshore)
Time critical (expedited guaranteed time/date definite)
Volume & truckload (LTL full loads backhaul services truckload brokerage dedicated truckload)

COMPETITORS

Aaa Cooper Transportation	R+l Carriers
Arcbest	Ryder System
Averitt Express	Saia
Fedex Freight	Ups Freight
Old Dominion Freight	Vitran
Penske Truck Leasing	Yrc Worldwide

HISTORICAL FINANCIALS

Company Type: Private

Income Statement				FYE: December 31
	REVENUE ($ mil.)	NET INCOME ($ mil.)	NET PROFIT MARGIN	EMPLOYEES
12/20	3,559	494	13.9%	14,000
12/19	3,259	251	7.7%	—
12/18	3,159	252	8.0%	—
12/17	2,731	231	8.5%	—
Annual Growth	9.2%	28.9%	—	—

2020 Year-End Financials

Return on assets: 26.0%
Return on equity: 56.0%
Current ratio: 1.70
Cash ($ mil.): 99

EVANS GENERAL CONTRACTORS, LLC

EXECUTIVES

President, Richard T Evans
Sr V Pres*, Christian Hersacher
Exec V Pres*, Jeff Jepson
V Pres*, Chris Hilgeman
Sr V Pres of Legal*, Jared W Heald
Cfo*, Walter Puckett

LOCATIONS

HQ: EVANS GENERAL CONTRACTORS, LLC
2710 OLD MILTON PKWY # 2, ALPHARETTA, GA 300092208
Phone: 678 713-7616
Web: WWW.EVANSGENERALCONTRACTORS.COM

HISTORICAL FINANCIALS

Company Type: Private

Income Statement				FYE: December 31
	REVENUE ($ mil.)	NET INCOME ($ mil.)	NET PROFIT MARGIN	EMPLOYEES
12/20	650	14	2.2%	145
12/10	55	1	2.2%	—
12/08	89	2	2.4%	—
12/07	55	1	2.2%	—
Annual Growth	20.9%	20.7%	—	—

2020 Year-End Financials

Return on assets: 5.5%
Return on equity: 53.5%
Current ratio: 1.10
Cash ($ mil.): 85

EVERGY MISSOURI WEST, INC.

EXECUTIVES

Ceo, Terry D Bassham
Sr V Pres*, Paul Perkins
V Pres*, Maria Jenks
V Pres*, Marvin L Rollison
V Pres*, Chuck Tickles
V Pres*, Stephen T Easley
V Pres*, Scott Heidtbrink
V Pres*, Lori A Wright
V Pres*, Jim Alberts
V Pres*, Kevin E Bryant
V Pres*, Lora C Cheatman

LOCATIONS

HQ: EVERGY MISSOURI WEST, INC.
1200 MAIN ST FL 30, KANSAS CITY, MO 641052122
Phone: 816 556-2200
Web: WWW.EVERGY.COM

HISTORICAL FINANCIALS

Company Type: Private

Income Statement				FYE: December 31
	REVENUE ($ mil.)	NET INCOME ($ mil.)	NET PROFIT MARGIN	EMPLOYEES
12/18	833	27	3.3%	1,088
12/17	818	(40)	—	—
12/16	801	60	7.6%	—
Annual Growth	2.0%	(32.8%)	—	—

2018 Year-End Financials

Return on assets: 0.8%
Return on equity: 2.3%
Current ratio: 2.50
Cash ($ mil.): 1

EVERSOURCE ENERGY SERVICE COMPANY

Northeast Utilities Service Company (NUSCO) provides support and reports for its cohorts. The company was created in 1966 to centralize corporate activities for Northeast Utilities (renamed Eversource Energy). NUSCO acts as an agent and offers centralized administrative services not only for its parent company Northeast Utilities but all of its subsidiaries (Connecticut Light and Power Public Service Company of New Hampshire Western Massachusetts Electric and Yankee Gas Services Company) as well. NUSCO duties include accounting financial legal operational information technology engineering planning and purchasing services.

EXECUTIVES

Ceo, James Judge
Exec V Pres*, Gregory B Butler
Cfo*, Philip Lembo
SEC*, Richard J Morrison
Data, Charles Barriere
Vice President Finance, Michael J Ausere
Information Technology Directo, Allen Pollock
Director Applications, Joseph Aivano
Director Community Relations, Bill Dam
Supervisor Field Sales, Joseph Heller
Senior Information Technology, Lori Talman

LOCATIONS

HQ: EVERSOURCE ENERGY SERVICE COMPANY
56 PROSPECT ST, HARTFORD, CT 061032818
Phone: 800 286-5000
Web: WWW.EVERSOURCE.COM

COMPETITORS

Connecticut Water Service	Pseg Fossil

HISTORICAL FINANCIALS

Company Type: Private

Income Statement				FYE: December 31
	REVENUE ($ mil.)	NET INCOME ($ mil.)	NET PROFIT MARGIN	EMPLOYEES
12/16	831	11	1.4%	4,550
12/08	5,800	260	4.5%	—
12/07	5,822	246	4.2%	—
12/05	0	0	—	—
Annual Growth	—	—	—	—

2016 Year-End Financials

Return on assets: 0.8%
Return on equity: 8.2%
Current ratio: 0.60
Cash ($ mil.): 11

EXCELA HEALTH

EXECUTIVES

Ceo, Jonnie Anderson
Assistant, Amy Gramlich
Registered Nurse, Julianne Lenzi
Director, Matt Rubin
Clinical Staff Pharmacist, Robbie Letterio

Auditors: BAKER TILLY US LLP PITTSBURG

LOCATIONS

HQ: EXCELA HEALTH
56 CLUB LN STE 101, BLAIRSVILLE, PA 157177957
Phone: 724 459-0595
Web: WWW.EXCELAHEALTH.ORG

HISTORICAL FINANCIALS

Company Type: Private

Income Statement				FYE: June 30
	REVENUE ($ mil.)	NET INCOME ($ mil.)	NET PROFIT MARGIN	EMPLOYEES
06/21	662	127	19.3%	18
06/20	575	(38)	—	
Annual Growth	15.1%	—	—	—

2021 Year-End Financials

Return on assets: 15.7%   Cash ($ mil.): 65
Return on equity: 29.6%
Current ratio: 1.30

EXTENDED STAY AMERICA, INC.

EXECUTIVES

Pres-Ceo, Bruce Haase
Chb*, Douglas G Geoga
Cfo, David Clarkson
Gen Counsel-Corp SEC, Christopher Dekle
Manager, Jessica Rodriguez
Manager, Karen Rivera
District Manager, Kenneth Witcher
Member, Lewis Weins
Regional Sales Director, Marie Wimberly
Regional Director of Operation, Michael Daddona
Branch Manager, Sarah Davis
Auditors: DELOITTE & TOUCHE LLP CHARLOT

LOCATIONS

HQ: EXTENDED STAY AMERICA, INC.
11525 N CMNITY HSE RD, CHARLOTTE, NC 282773609
Phone: 980 345-1600
Web: WWW.EXTENDEDSTAYAMERICA.COM

COMPETITORS

Capital Hotel Management	Island Hospitality Sage Hospitality
Dow Hotel Company	Travelodge
Hostmark Hospitality	Westmont Hospitality
Interstate Hotels	Group

HISTORICAL FINANCIALS

Company Type: Private

Income Statement				FYE: December 31
	REVENUE ($ mil.)	NET INCOME ($ mil.)	NET PROFIT MARGIN	EMPLOYEES
12/20	1,042	96	9.2%	8,400
12/19	1,218	165	13.6%	—
12/18	1,275	211	16.6%	—
12/17	1,282	172	13.4%	—
Annual Growth	(6.7%)	(17.6%)	—	—

2020 Year-End Financials

Return on assets: 2.4%   Cash ($ mil.): 396
Return on equity: 8.5%
Current ratio: —

FAIRFAX COUNTY VIRGINIA

EXECUTIVES

City Exec, Anthony H Griffin
Business Dir, Angela Shaw
Telecommunications Staff, Alton Drew
Information, Tanya Quinonez
Captain, Roger Arnn
Coordinator, Kelly Bachand
Assistant Chief, Daryl Louder
Information Specialist, Joseph Sorrentino
Information Specialist, Michael Liddle
Battalion Chief Fire, Andrew Duke
Director, Catherine Spage
Auditors: KPMG LLP WASHINGTON DC

LOCATIONS

HQ: FAIRFAX COUNTY VIRGINIA
12000 GVRNMENT CTR PKWY S, FAIRFAX, VA 220350002
Phone: 703 324-3126
Web: WWW.FAIRFAXCOUNTY.GOV

HISTORICAL FINANCIALS

Company Type: Private

Income Statement				FYE: June 30
	REVENUE ($ mil.)	NET INCOME ($ mil.)	NET PROFIT MARGIN	EMPLOYEES
06/20	5,201	(75)	—	12,000
06/18	4,806	71	1.5%	—
06/17	4,695	171	3.6%	—
06/16	4,469	49	1.1%	—
Annual Growth	3.9%	—	—	—

2020 Year-End Financials

Return on assets: (-0.4%)   Cash ($ mil.): 38
Return on equity: (-9.1%)
Current ratio: —

FAIRVIEW HEALTH SERVICES

It's fair to say that when it comes to health care Fairview Health Services takes the long view. The not-for-profit system serves Minnesota's Twin Cities and nearby communities. Fairview Health is affiliated with the medical school of the University of Minnesota and counts among its 10 hospitals the University of Minnesota Medical Center. The hospitals house more than 2500 beds and provide comprehensive medical and surgical services. The system also operates primary and specialty care clinics that provide preventive and wellness care. Additionally it operates retail pharmacies and nursing homes and provides home health care and re-habilitation. Merger talks with University of Minnesota Physicians have stalled.

Operations

Fairview operates more than 40 primary care clinics seven urgent care clinics more than 55 specialty service centers some 50 senior housing locations and 30-plus retail pharmacies scattered across the state. It employs more than 2300 physicians. The health system was one of the first in the nation to initiate a pay scheme for clinic doctors that rewards them for the manner in which they treat patients favorable satisfaction surveys and their ability to keep patients healthy and out of the hospital rather than simply for the number of tests run.

Fairview provides a host of senior care options through its Ebenezer unit that include assisted and independent living adult day care and health services designed specifically for the elderly and administered by specialists that include geriatricians.

The company's affiliated physician organizations include Behavioral Healthcare Providers University of Minnesota Physicians and Fairview Physician Associates.

Sales and Marketing

Negotiated contracts and commercial channels account for about two-thirds of the company's revenues while Medicare accounts for about a quarter of revenues. Medicaid and self-pay channels round out the sales.

Financial Performance

Fairview's revenues grew by 5% to $3.4 billion in 2013 due to an increase in revenues from net patient services and other operating revenues; this was slightly offset by a decrease in revenue from net assets released from restriction. Net income grew 51% that year to $244.3 million led by the increase in revenues and investment returns. Also contributing to the improvement was the absence of disaffiliation loss of subsidiaries which had occurred the prior year.

Cash flow from operations grew by $8 million to $79.3 million in 2013; the rise in net income and changes in current liabilities and other assets led to the inflow.

Strategy

Fairview has grown through organic initiatives and via acquisitions. It has recently made several improvements to its new specialty center including adding a physical therapy gym refurbishing its pediatric floor renovating the neonatal intensive care unit and adding a larger laboratory.

In 2013 the University of Minnesota proposed taking over Fairview which would have then been combined with South Dakota's Sanford Health. That deal ultimately fell through but in 2015 Fairview announced plans to instead merge with the school's private physician network University of Minnesota Physicians. The combined company is to be named University of Minnesota Health. (That brand was launched in early 2014 prior to organizations' announced intention to combine forces.)

Company Background

Fairview was founded in 1906.

EXECUTIVES

Ceo, Rulon F Stacey
Sr V Pres-Cfo*, James M Fox
Sr V Pres*, Daniel Fromm
V Pres*, Bob Beacher
Exec V Pres*, Carolyn Wilson
CIO*, Sameer Badlani
Manager of Lan, D Ick Neubaur
Director, Roby Thompson Jr
Chief of Emergency Room, Kevin S Meyer
Scientist, Gerald August

Scientist, Scott Crow
Auditors: ERNST & YOUNG LLP
  MINNEAPOLIS

LOCATIONS

HQ: FAIRVIEW HEALTH SERVICES
  1700 UNIVERSITY AVE W, SAINT PAUL, MN
  551043727
Phone: 612 672-6300
Web: WWW.FAIRVIEW.ORG

COMPETITORS

Abbott Northwestern	Mayo Clinic
Hospital	North Memorial Health
Allina Hospitals	Care
Bethesda Hospital	Park Nicollet Health
Catholic Health	Services
Initiatives	Regions Hospital
Centracare Health	St. John's Hospital
Healtheast Care System	(minnesota)

HISTORICAL FINANCIALS

Company Type: Private

Income Statement				FYE: December 31
	REVENUE ($ mil.)	NET INCOME ($ mil.)	NET PROFIT MARGIN	EMPLOYEES
12/20	6,123	(18)	—	18,000
12/19	6,049	13	0.2%	—
12/18	5,709	5	0.1%	—
12/17	5,275	511	9.7%	—
Annual Growth	5.1%	—	—	—

2020 Year-End Financials

Return on assets: (-0.3%)   Cash ($ mil.): 94
Return on equity: (-0.7%)
Current ratio: 1.50

FAMILY HEALTH INTERNATIONAL INC

Known as FHI 360 Family Health International believes that health is wealth. From a handful of offices located in the US Asia-Pacific and South Africa FHI 360 funds and manages public health programs research education and other resources in more than 60 countries. Founded in 1971 as the International Fertility Research Program of the University of North Carolina at Chapel Hill FHI 360 primarily focuses on and supports HIV/AIDS prevention research reproductive health services and maternal and neonatal health programs. The organization works with governments private agencies and non-governmental organizations to develop the most appropriate programs for different areas.

EXECUTIVES

Ceo, Patrick C Fine
Ceo*, Albert J Siemens
Dir*, R Peyton Woodson III
Cfo*, Hubert C Graves
Exec Vpres*, Robert R Price
Coo*, Marjorie N Williams
Sr V Pres*, Sheila Mitchell
Dir*, Torrey C Brown
Dir*, Luella V Klein
Dir*, Peter W McClean
Treas*, Martin M Lenkheym
Auditors: ERNST & YOUNG US LLP TAMPA F

LOCATIONS

HQ: FAMILY HEALTH INTERNATIONAL INC
  359 BLACKWELL ST STE 200, DURHAM, NC
  277012477
Phone: 919 544-7040
Web: WWW.FHI360.ORG

PRODUCTS/OPERATIONS

Selected Services

Behavior-change communication
Capacity-building
Clinical trials services
Creative services
Data analysis
Quality assurance
Research services
Social marketing
Training and technical assistance

HISTORICAL FINANCIALS

Company Type: Private

Income Statement				FYE: September 30
	REVENUE ($ mil.)	NET INCOME ($ mil.)	NET PROFIT MARGIN	EMPLOYEES
09/19	781	0	0.1%	4,000
09/14	653	(3)	—	—
09/13	664	10	1.5%	—
09/09	327	2	0.9%	—
Annual Growth	9.1%	(10.2%)	—	—

2019 Year-End Financials

Return on assets: 0.4%   Cash ($ mil.): 123
Return on equity: 1.1%
Current ratio: 1.60

FAMILY HEALTH NETWORK, INC.

EXECUTIVES

Ceo, Keith Kudla
Pres*, Philip C Bradley
Cfo*, Tom Tennison
Information Specialist, Shawn Cull
Senior Financial Analyst, Elisa Chiu
Intake Coordinator, Karin Fields
Compliance Director, Camille Trunkett
Claims Supervisor, James Segatto
Training and Manag, Teterina Winfrey
Web Developer, Alton Kusch
Business Analyst, Belinda Williams

LOCATIONS

HQ: FAMILY HEALTH NETWORK, INC.
  222 MERCHANDISE MART PLZ # 960, CHICAGO, IL
  606541236
Phone: 312 243-5235
Web: WWW.FHNCHICAGO.COM

HISTORICAL FINANCIALS

Company Type: Private

Income Statement				FYE: December 31
	REVENUE ($ mil.)	NET INCOME ($ mil.)	NET PROFIT MARGIN	EMPLOYEES
12/17	549	(23)	—	30
12/09	60	2	4.9%	—
12/08	56	0	—	—
Annual Growth	28.7%	—	—	—

2017 Year-End Financials

Return on assets: (-15.2%)   Cash ($ mil.): 59
Return on equity: (-341.2%)
Current ratio: —

FARM CREDIT BANK OF TEXAS

The largest member of the federal Farm Credit System the Farm Credit Bank of Texas provides loans and financial services to about 20 lending cooperatives and financial institutions in Alabama Louisiana Mississippi New Mexico and Texas. These include agricultural credit associations which provide agricultural production loans agribusiness financing and rural mortgage financing; and federal land credit associations which offer real estate loans on farms ranches and other rural property. Farm Credit Bank of Texas is owned by the lending cooperatives it serves.

EXECUTIVES

Chief Audit Executive, Nisha Rocap
Chief Financial Officer, Brandon Blaut
General Counsel And Leads Corporate Affairs, Nanci Tucker
Chief Executive Officer, Amie Pala
Chief Credit Officer, Isaac Bennett
Auditors: PRICEWATERHOUSECOOPERS LLP A

LOCATIONS

HQ: FARM CREDIT BANK OF TEXAS
  4801 PLZ ON THE LK # 1200, AUSTIN, TX 787461081
Phone: 512 465-0400
Web: WWW.FARMCREDITBANK.COM

HISTORICAL FINANCIALS

Company Type: Private

Income Statement				FYE: December 31
	ASSETS ($ mil.)	NET INCOME ($ mil.)	INCOME AS % OF ASSETS	EMPLOYEES
12/16	21,222	192	0.9%	200
12/13	16,212	179	1.1%	—
/	0	0	—	—
Annual Growth	—	—	—	—

2016 Year-End Financials

Return on assets: 0.9%   Sales ($ mil): 530
Return on equity: 11.9%

FARM CREDIT SERVICES OF AMERICA

EXECUTIVES

Pres-Ceo, Doug Stark
Exec V Pres*, Neil Olsen
Sr V Pres-Cfo*, Eugene College
Sr V Pres*, Michelle Mapes
Sr V Pres*, David Martin
Turner Youth Initiative Direct, Twila Phillips

Engineer, Dave Cook
Senior Vice President Agribusi, Marshall Hansen
Vp-Agribusiness Lending, Marvin Kokes
Employee, David Binerer
Auditors: PRICEWATERHOUSECOOPERS LLP
M

LOCATIONS

HQ: FARM CREDIT SERVICES OF AMERICA
5015 S 118TH ST, OMAHA, NE 681372210
Phone: 800 884-3276
Web: WWW.FCSAMERICA.COM

HISTORICAL FINANCIALS

Company Type: Private

Income Statement				FYE: December 31
	ASSETS ($ mil.)	NET INCOME ($ mil.)	INCOME AS % OF ASSETS	EMPLOYEES
12/15	24,772	514	2.1%	10,000
12/04	8,475	294	3.5%	—
12/03	7,633	114	1.5%	—
12/02	0	132	—	—
Annual Growth	—	11.0%	—	—

2015 Year-End Financials

Return on assets: 2.1%   Sales ($ mil): 1,099
Return on equity: 11.9%

FARM CREDIT WEST

EXECUTIVES

Ceo-Pres, Mark D Littlefield
Sr V Pres, Chris N Brumfield
Exec V Pres, John C Boyes
Exe V Pres, William M Noland
Cfo, Chris Doherty
Exec V Pres-Fiscal ADM, Ernest M Hodges
Prin, K E Graff
Senior Vice President Chief, Denise Warkomski
Executive Vice President Chief, Dan Clawson
Regional Vice President Credit, Marc Ehlers
Assistant Vice President, Ross Tenhaeff
Auditors: PRICEWATERHOUSECOOPERS LLP
SA

LOCATIONS

HQ: FARM CREDIT WEST
3755 ATHERTON RD, ROCKLIN, CA 957653701
Phone: 916 724-4800
Web: WWW.FARMCREDITWEST.COM

HISTORICAL FINANCIALS

Company Type: Private

Income Statement				FYE: December 31
	ASSETS ($ mil.)	NET INCOME ($ mil.)	INCOME AS % OF ASSETS	EMPLOYEES
12/12	6,668	151	2.3%	165
12/11	6,282	176	2.8%	—
12/10	6,129	0	—	—
Annual Growth	4.3%	—	—	—

2012 Year-End Financials

Return on assets: 2.3%   Sales ($ mil): 295
Return on equity: 12.5%

FARMERS COOPERATIVE

EXECUTIVES

Pres, Ron Velver
SEC-Treas*, Glen Capek
Branch Manager, Terry King
General Manager, Desten Segrest
Operations Manager, Randi Webb
Agronomy Sales, Angie Baker
Manager, Doug Brandt
Accounting Specialist, Jamie Sand
Beef Specialist, Linda McKay
Human Resources Director, Micaela Rahe
Regional, Odell-Jeff Humphreys
Auditors: GARDINER THOMSEN LINCOLN NE

LOCATIONS

HQ: FARMERS COOPERATIVE
208 W DEPOT ST, DORCHESTER, NE 683432375
Phone: 402 946-4631
Web: WWW.FARMERSRESP3.AGRICHARTS.COM

HISTORICAL FINANCIALS

Company Type: Private

Income Statement				FYE: August 31
	REVENUE ($ mil.)	NET INCOME ($ mil.)	NET PROFIT MARGIN	EMPLOYEES
08/14	830	19	2.3%	470
08/12	918	22	2.5%	—
08/11	695	21	3.1%	—
08/10	636	0	0.0%	—
Annual Growth	6.9%	1803.9%	—	—

2014 Year-End Financials

Return on assets: 7.6%   Cash ($ mil.): 28
Return on equity: 11.5%
Current ratio: 1.80

FARMERS COOPERATIVE COMPANY

The importance of cooperation — it's one of life's most important lessons. Dating back to the early 1900s the Farmers Cooperative Company (FCC) learned that lesson early on. The 5500-member-plus co-op offers agronomy and grain marketing services to its members who oversee some 3 million acres of farmland in central and north central Iowa. The largest of its kind in Iowa FCC operates 40 grain elevators and provides soil testing and mapping services. It sells supplies including seed feed and fertilizer to its members. The coop merged with another Iowa coop West Central Cooperative in 2016 to form Landus Cooperative.

Operations

Farmers Cooperative (FCC) operates four departments: Agronomy Feed Grain and Seed. Agronomy serves customers at some 40 locations across central Iowa and is one of largest agronomy divisions in the state. The Feed department has six manufacturing locations across central north central and northwest Iowa. FCC's feed mills produce more than 900000 tons of complete feed annually. FCC has 40 grain elevators across its membership area. More than 118 million bushels of grain are handled annually. FCC also has grain storage capacity of 75 million bushels. The coop-

erative's Seed department works closely with the Agronomy division since both serve the same customers.

EXECUTIVES

Ceo, James Chism
Pres*, Rick Brand
V Pres*, Chuck Lindberg
Information Analyst, Bernard Cockerham
Regional Operations Manager, Brett Fc
Business Analyst, Janie Hertel
Vp Sales, John Malin
Auditors: MERIWETHER WILSON & COMPANY

LOCATIONS

HQ: FARMERS COOPERATIVE COMPANY
105 GARFIELD AVE, FARNHAMVILLE, IA 505386712
Phone: 515 817-2100
Web: WWW.LANDUSCOOPERATIVE.COM

PRODUCTS/OPERATIONS

Selected Departments

Agronomy

Feed

Grain

Seed

COMPETITORS

Adm	Five Star Co-op
Ag Processing Inc.	Gold-eagle Cooperative
Chs	Heartland Co-op
Cargill	Ingredion
Debruce Grain	Scoular
Farm Service Cooperative	Swiss Valley Farms
Farmers Cooperative Society	West Central Co-op

HISTORICAL FINANCIALS

Company Type: Private

Income Statement				FYE: August 31
	REVENUE ($ mil.)	NET INCOME ($ mil.)	NET PROFIT MARGIN	EMPLOYEES
08/10	779	10	1.3%	450
08/09	894	13	1.5%	—
Annual Growth	(12.8%)	(19.9%)	—	—

2010 Year-End Financials

Return on assets: 5.6%   Cash ($ mil.): —
Return on equity: 1.3%
Current ratio: —

FARMERS GRAIN TERMINAL, INC.

EXECUTIVES

Pres-Ceo, Steve Nail
Exec V Pres*, Harvey Parrish
V Pres*, C C Craig
V Pres*, John Oakes
Director, Herbert H Huddleston Jr
Assistant Elevator Manager, Gary Ballard
Staff Accountant, Brian Strazi
Manager, Nash Knighton
Manager, Ronnie Ferrell

Office Manager, and Barge Acco, Stacy Walker
Auditors: HUDSON CISNE & CO LLP LITT

LOCATIONS

HQ: FARMERS GRAIN TERMINAL, INC.
  1977 HARBOR FRONT RD, GREENVILLE, MS
  387019588
Phone: 662 332-0987
Web: WWW.FGTCOOP.COM

HISTORICAL FINANCIALS
Company Type: Private

Income Statement				FYE: July 31
	REVENUE ($ mil.)	**NET INCOME** ($ mil.)	**NET PROFIT MARGIN**	**EMPLOYEES**
07/13	929	19	2.1%	102
07/12	615	12	2.1%	—
07/11	471	8	1.8%	—
Annual Growth	40.4%	53.0%	—	—

2013 Year-End Financials
Return on assets: 15.6%   Cash ($ mil.): 64
Return on equity: 30.0%
Current ratio: 2.20

FCTG HOLDINGS, INC.

EXECUTIVES

Pres, Craig Johnston
Cfo*, Derrick Coder
SEC*, Carl Neil
Sales Specialty Wood Products, Jared Bjur
Information Technology Directo, Kris Breuing
General Manager, Troy Bailey

LOCATIONS

HQ: FCTG HOLDINGS, INC.
  10250 SW GREENBURG RD # 200, PORTLAND, OR
  972235461
Phone: 503 246-8500
Web: WWW.FCTG.COM

HISTORICAL FINANCIALS
Company Type: Private

Income Statement				FYE: January 31
	REVENUE ($ mil.)	**NET INCOME** ($ mil.)	**NET PROFIT MARGIN**	**EMPLOYEES**
01/09	1,535	2	0.2%	406
01/08	2,055	1	0.1%	—
01/07	2,798	(0)	—	—
Annual Growth	(25.9%)	—	—	—

2009 Year-End Financials
Return on assets: 2.7%   Cash ($ mil.): 3
Return on equity: 11.0%
Current ratio: 1.20

FEDERAL-MOGUL HOLDINGS LLC

Auditors: GRANT THORNTON LLP
SOUTHFIELD

LOCATIONS

HQ: FEDERAL-MOGUL HOLDINGS LLC
  27300 W 11 MILE RD # 101, SOUTHFIELD, MI
  480346193
Phone: 248 354-7700
Web: WWW.FEDERALMOGUL.COM

HISTORICAL FINANCIALS
Company Type: Private

Income Statement				FYE: December 31
	REVENUE ($ mil.)	**NET INCOME** ($ mil.)	**NET PROFIT MARGIN**	**EMPLOYEES**
12/16	7,434	90	1.2%	53,700
12/15	7,419	(104)	—	—
12/14	7,317	(161)	—	—
Annual Growth	0.8%	—	—	—

2016 Year-End Financials
Return on assets: 1.3%   Cash ($ mil.): 300
Return on equity: 10.2%
Current ratio: 1.70

FIDELITY INV CHARITABLE GIFT FUND

EXECUTIVES

Planning Staff, Colin Roth

LOCATIONS

HQ: FIDELITY INV CHARITABLE GIFT FUND
  200 SEAPORT BLVD STE 1, BOSTON, MA 022102000
Phone: 617 392-8679
Web: WWW.FIDELITYCHARITABLE.ORG

HISTORICAL FINANCIALS
Company Type: Private

Income Statement				FYE: June 30
	REVENUE ($ mil.)	**NET INCOME** ($ mil.)	**NET PROFIT MARGIN**	**EMPLOYEES**
06/11	1,874	599	32.0%	1
06/10	1,274	147	11.6%	—
Annual Growth	47.1%	306.7%	—	—

2011 Year-End Financials
Return on assets: 10.7%   Cash ($ mil.): 77
Return on equity: 10.8%
Current ratio: 1.90

FINANCIAL INDUSTRY REGULATORY AUTHORITY, INC.

FINRA is dedicated to protecting investors and safeguarding market integrity in a manner that facilitates vibrant capital markets. It is a not-for-profit organization that ? working under the supervision of the SEC ? actively engages with and provides essential tools for investors member firms and policymakers. In addition it is authorized by the congress to protect America's investors by making sure the broker-dealer industry operates fairly and honestly. FINRA oversee more than 624000 brokers across the country and analyze billion dollars of market events. FINRA was formed in 2007 from the consolidation of the National Association of Securities Dealers and certain regulatory and enforcement elements of the NYSE.

Operations

FINRA regulates the Broker-Dealers Capital Acquisition Brokers and Funding Portals. In additions Broker Dealer is in the business of buying or selling securities on behalf of its customers or its own account or both. A Capital Acquisition Broker is a Broker Dealer subject to a narrower rule book. A Funding Portal is a crowd-funding intermediary. FINRA plays a critical role in ensuring the integrity of America's financial system. It writes and enforces rules governing the ethical activities of all registered broker-dealer firms and registered brokers in the U.S. examines firms for compliance with rules fosters market transparency and educates investors.

Its operating revenues include regulatory revenues (approximately 55% of sales) user revenue (nearly 30%) and contract services revenue (over 15%).

Geographic Reach

FINRA operates from Washington DC where it is headquartered and New York with about 20 regional offices around the US.

Sales and Marketing

FINRA markets its services through conference and events virtual conference Panels and Webinars.

Financial Performance

In 2020 the company's revenue increased to $1.2 billion compared to $938.5 million in 2019.

FINRA reported net income of $19.8 million in 2020 versus a net loss of $45.9 million in 2019 an increase of $65.7 million year over year. The company's 2020 net income was driven by operating income of $30.9 million offset by other expenses net of investment gains of $11.1 million.

Cash held by the company at the end of fiscal 2020 increased to $597.3 million. Cash provided by operations and investing activities were $147.7 million and $63.2 million respectively. Financing activities used $1.2 million mainly for debt principal payments.

Strategy

FINRA's Enterprise Risk Management (ERM) program is designed to provide a consolidated organization-wide view of the risks that FINRA faces in the execution of its mission strategic goals and key business objectives. The program covers a broad spectrum of risks in various risk categories such as strategic operational legal and compliance and financial and provides transparency for senior management and the Board regarding FINRA's enterprise-level risks and how they are being managed. The chart below shows the governance structure FINRA has in place to oversee and manage enterprise risk.

In determining a benchmarking strategy for key executives the Committee and its advisor (see next section) engaged in substantial research and consideration of the functions and operations of several potential comparisons as well as general competitive conditions. Ultimately the Committee approved a benchmarking process for key executives that focused on the following sources: Public comparison group composed of a blend of public financial services organizations engaged in brokerage or other related banking activities; Public exchanges and regulators; Financial services industry survey data; Legal industry survey data; and Other not-for-profit sector data.

Company Background

FINRA was founded in 2007 by NASD and NYSE.

EXECUTIVES

Pres-Ceo, Robert Cook
Cfo-Exec V Pres-Cao*, Todd Diganci
V Pres*, Rob Renner
Exec V Pres*, J Bradley Bennett
Sr V Pres Hr*, Tracy Johnson
Exec V Pres-Gen Counsel*, Marc Menchel
Exec V Pres*, Howard Schloss
Exec V Pres*, Thomas Selman
Exec V Pres*, Marcia Asquith
Exec V Pres*, Stephanie Dumont
Exec V Pres*, Bari Havlik
Auditors: ERNST & YOUNG LLP MCLEAN VIR

LOCATIONS

HQ: FINANCIAL INDUSTRY REGULATORY AUTHORITY, INC.
 1735 K ST NW, WASHINGTON, DC 200061506
Phone: 301 590-6500
Web: WWW.FINRA.ORG

PRODUCTS/OPERATIONS

2015 Sales

	$ mil.	% of total
Regulatory revenue	444	45
User revenue	218	22
Contract services revenue	125	13
Fines	93	6
Transparency services revenue	63	4
Dispute resolution revenue	41	1
Other revenue	5	9
Total	**992**	**100**

HISTORICAL FINANCIALS

Company Type: Private

Income Statement				FYE: December 31
	REVENUE ($ mil.)	NET INCOME ($ mil.)	NET PROFIT MARGIN	EMPLOYEES
12/20	1,162	19	1.7%	3,400
12/19	938	(45)	—	—
12/12	878	10	1.2%	—
12/11	880	(84)	—	—
Annual Growth	3.1%	—	—	—

2020 Year-End Financials

Return on assets: 0.8% Cash ($ mil.): 597
Return on equity: 1.4%
Current ratio: 2.40

FINANCIAL TRADER CORPORATION

LOCATIONS

HQ: FINANCIAL TRADER CORPORATION
 5743 LONGMONT LN, HOUSTON, TX 770572510
Phone: 713 206-4600

HISTORICAL FINANCIALS

Company Type: Private

Income Statement				FYE: December 31
	ASSETS ($ mil.)	NET INCOME ($ mil.)	INCOME AS % OF ASSETS	EMPLOYEES
12/13	398	6	1.7%	1
12/11	10	0	5.6%	—
Annual Growth	525.1%	243.5%	—	—

2013 Year-End Financials

Return on assets: — Sales ($ mil.): 992
Return on equity: 0.7%

FLATIRON CONSTRUCTORS, INC.

EXECUTIVES

Ceo, John Diciurcio
Exec V-Pres-Coo*, Robert W French
Cfo*, Paul Driscoll
Coo*, Dale Swanberg
Exec Asst*, Judy Schek
Coo*, Javier Sevilla
Cfo*, Lars Leitner
Accounting Staff, Donna Clardy
Vice President, Brian Stieritz
Project Engineer, Abraham Aceves
Operations, Allen Carnesecca
Auditors: DELOITTE & TOUCHE LLP DENVER

LOCATIONS

HQ: FLATIRON CONSTRUCTORS, INC.
 385 INTERLOCKEN, BROOMFIELD, CO 80021
Phone: 303 485-4050
Web: WWW.FLATIRONCORP.COM

HISTORICAL FINANCIALS

Company Type: Private

Income Statement				FYE: December 31
	REVENUE ($ mil.)	NET INCOME ($ mil.)	NET PROFIT MARGIN	EMPLOYEES
12/12	941	(96)	—	611
12/11	1,017	39	3.9%	—
Annual Growth	(7.5%)	—	—	—

2012 Year-End Financials

Return on assets: (-18.5%) Cash ($ mil.): 123
Return on equity: (-55.9%)
Current ratio: 1.60

FLORIDA CLINICAL PRACTICE ASSOCIATION, INC.

EXECUTIVES

Pres, Anthony Mancuso
Exec V Pres, William W Tharp
Auditors: PYA PC TAMPA FL

LOCATIONS

HQ: FLORIDA CLINICAL PRACTICE ASSOCIATION, INC.
 1329 SW 16TH ST STE 4250, GAINESVILLE, FL 326081128
Phone: 352 265-8017
Web: WWW.COMFS.UFL.EDU

HISTORICAL FINANCIALS

Company Type: Private

Income Statement				FYE: June 30
	REVENUE ($ mil.)	NET INCOME ($ mil.)	NET PROFIT MARGIN	EMPLOYEES
06/20	741	(10)	—	2
06/18	667	11	1.8%	—
06/17	642	(1)	—	—
06/15	598	19	3.3%	—
Annual Growth	4.4%	—	—	—

2020 Year-End Financials

Return on assets: (-3.8%) Cash ($ mil.): 104
Return on equity: (-7.2%)
Current ratio: 4.70

FLORIDA DEPARTMENT OF LOTTERY

The State of Florida Department of the Lottery runs instant-play scratch tickets and lotto games including Florida Lotto Mega Money Fantasy 5 and Cash 3. In addition to its own games Florida is part of the Multi-State Lottery Association which operates the popular Powerball drawing. Proceeds from the games are contributed to Florida's Educational Enhancement Trust Fund which provides funding for a variety of education programs from pre-kindergarten up to the state university level. The lottery has returned more than $19 billion to the state since starting in 1988.

EXECUTIVES

Secretary, Cynthia O'Connell
SEC*, Jim Poppell
Senior Manager, Darlene Green
Administrator, Elizabeth Miles
Lottery Marketing Specialist, Jessica Booker
Auditors: SHERRILL F NORMAN CPA TALLA

LOCATIONS

HQ: FLORIDA DEPARTMENT OF LOTTERY
 250 MARRIOTT DR, TALLAHASSEE, FL 323012983
Phone: 850 487-7777
Web: WWW.FLALOTTERY.COM

COMPETITORS

Georgia Lottery
Seminole Tribe Of
 Florida

HISTORICAL FINANCIALS
Company Type: Private

Income Statement   FYE: June 30

	REVENUE ($ mil.)	NET INCOME ($ mil.)	NET PROFIT MARGIN	EMPLOYEES
06/20	7,511	4	0.1%	400
06/19	7,157	36	0.5%	—
06/03	2,872	117	4.1%	—
06/02	2	0	2.0%	—
Annual Growth	56.6%	28.3%	—	—

2020 Year-End Financials

Return on assets: 0.5%   Cash ($ mil.): 355
Return on equity: 4.6%
Current ratio: 1.00

FLORIDA HEALTH SCIENCES CENTER, INC.

Florida Health Sciences Center which does business as Tampa General Hospital (TGH) provides health care services in west-central Florida serving a dozen counties. The medical center offers general medical and surgical care as well as tertiary offerings including a Level 1 trauma center a burn unit a pediatric ward women's and cardiovascular centers and an organ transplant unit. The not-for-profit hospital has more than 1005 acute-care beds as well as nearly 60 beds in its rehabilitation unit which specializes in helping patients recover from stroke head or spine trauma and other neuromuscular conditions. TGH is the primary teaching hospital for USF Health Morsani College of Medicine.

EXECUTIVES

Ceo, John Couris
Exec V Pres-Cfo*, Steve Short
V Pres*, Janet Davis
V Chm*, Jim Warren
Exec V Pres*, Deana L Nelson
V Pres*, Jean M Mayer
V Pres*, Judith M Ploszek
V Pres*, Joseph D Resnick
V Pres*, Marcos F Lorenzo
Direc, Margarita Cancio
Direc*, Phillip S Dingle

LOCATIONS

HQ: FLORIDA HEALTH SCIENCES CENTER, INC.
 1 TAMPA GENERAL CIR, TAMPA, FL 336063571
Phone: 813 844-7000
Web: WWW.TGH.ORG

COMPETITORS

All Children's
 Hospital
Baycare Health System
Bayfront Health
Desoto Memorial
Florida Hospital Tampa
 Bay Division
Hca

Lakeland Regional
 Medical Center
Lee Memorial
Manatee Memorial
 Hospital
Sarasota Memorial
 Health Care
Winter Haven Hospital

HISTORICAL FINANCIALS
Company Type: Private

Income Statement   FYE: September 30

	REVENUE ($ mil.)	NET INCOME ($ mil.)	NET PROFIT MARGIN	EMPLOYEES
09/20	1,590	146	9.2%	8,000
09/19	1,447	57	4.0%	—
09/18	1,325	79	6.0%	—
09/17	1,257	98	7.8%	—
Annual Growth	8.2%	14.2%	—	—

2020 Year-End Financials

Return on assets: 6.7%   Cash ($ mil.): 311
Return on equity: 12.3%
Current ratio: 1.20

FLORIDA HOSPITAL MEDICAL GROUP, INC.

EXECUTIVES

Pres, James Moffett
Chief Operating Officer, Warren Wylie II
Dir, Michael Thompson
Treas, Amy Zbaraschuk
Diagnostic Radiologist, Antonio Gonzalez
Diagnostic Radiologist, Henry Chou
Training Consultant, A Sharpe
Receptionist, Alex Hall
Interventional Cardiologist, Andrew Taussig
Rn, BSN, Brittany Johnson
Data Entry, Christine Proto

LOCATIONS

HQ: FLORIDA HOSPITAL MEDICAL GROUP, INC.
 2600 WESTHALL LN STE 400, MAITLAND, FL
 327517107
Phone: 407 200-2700
Web: WWW.ADVENTHEALTHMEDICALGROUP.COM

HISTORICAL FINANCIALS
Company Type: Private

Income Statement   FYE: December 31

	REVENUE ($ mil.)	NET INCOME ($ mil.)	NET PROFIT MARGIN	EMPLOYEES
12/19	595	(4)	—	350
12/18	562	2	0.4%	—
12/15	421	0	0.2%	—
12/14	363	(17)	—	—
Annual Growth	10.4%	—	—	—

2019 Year-End Financials

Return on assets: (-2.3%)   Cash ($ mil.): 57
Return on equity: (-5.6%)
Current ratio: 1.80

FLORIDA HOUSING FINANCE CORP

Owning a home in Florida is just a bit easier thanks to Florida Housing Finance Corporation. Established in 1997 by the Florida Legislature as a public corporation Florida Housing's mission is to help Floridians obtain safe decent housing that might otherwise be unavailable to them. Florida Housing pursues its mission through a number of programs that provide financial assistance for first time homebuyers and for developers of multifamily dwellings that serve elderly and low income Floridians. Florida Housing partners with various local state and federal agencies as well as developers and not-for-profit organizations to achieve its goals.

EXECUTIVES

Exec Dir, Stephen Auger
Exec Dir*, Harold Price
Executive Officer, Vicki Robinson
Director of Asset Management, Laura J Cox
Senior Financial Administrator, Melanie
 Weathers
Homeownership Programs Adminis, Charles
 White
CIO, David Hearn
Human Resources Administrator, Jessica Cherry
Compliance Manager, Domingo Tuckler
Homeownership Programs Adminis, Nicole
 Gibson
Finance Manager, Robin Fowler
Auditors: ERNST & YOUNG LLP ORLANDO F

LOCATIONS

HQ: FLORIDA HOUSING FINANCE CORP
 227 N BRONOUGH ST # 5000, TALLAHASSEE, FL
 323011367
Phone: 850 488-4197
Web: WWW.FLORIDAHOUSING.ORG

PRODUCTS/OPERATIONS

Selected Programs
First Time Homebuyer Program
Down Payment Assistance
Homeownership Loan Program
Mortgage Credit Certificate
Multifamily Development Programs
Multifamily Mortgage Revenue Bonds
Florida Affordable Housing Guarantee Program
HOME Investment Partnerships
Elderly Housing Community Loan Program
Low Income Housing Tax Credits
State Apartment Incentive Loan
Predevelopment Loan Program
State Housing Initiative Partnerships
Demonstration Loans
Affordable Housing Catalyst Program

HISTORICAL FINANCIALS
Company Type: Private

Income Statement   FYE: December 31

	ASSETS ($ mil.)	NET INCOME ($ mil.)	INCOME AS % OF ASSETS	EMPLOYEES
12/20	5,701	332	5.8%	130
12/19	5,373	224	4.2%	—
12/18	4,974	125	2.5%	—
12/17	4,764	206	4.3%	—
Annual Growth	6.2%	17.1%	—	—

Return on assets: 5.8%   Sales ($ mil): 214
Return on equity: 10.5%

FLORIDA MUNICIPAL POWER AGENCY

Unlike some politicians Florida Municipal Power Agency (FMPA) doesn't believe in holding on to power. The non-profit public agency generates and supplies electric power to 31 county or municipally owned distribution utilities which in turn serve 2 million Florida residents and businesses. Each of the distribution utilities appoints one representative to FMPA's board of directors which governs the Agency's activities. The Agency is authorized to undertake joint power supply projects for its members and to issue tax-exempt bonds to finance the costs of such projects. It is also empowered to implement a pooled financing program for utility-related projects.

Operations

FMPA has five distinct power supply projects and has stakes in 15 operating power plants. Each of its members have the option of whether or not to participate in a power supply project. Some members receive all their power from FMPA some receive part of their power and others receive no power. Agency members may participate in more than one project although each project is independent from the others.

FMPA supplies all of the power needs for 13 of its members and some of the power supply needs of seven others. All together FMPA supplies more than 40% of its members' total power needs.

Strategy

The Agency is looking to diversify its fuel mix in the long term adding nuclear and renewable energy powered plants to reduce the carbon emission output from its generation activities.

Company Background

FMPA has also been modernizing its power plant fleet since 2003 and in 2011 it opened a new low-emission high efficiency generator known as Cane Island Unit 4. Plant modernization has led to lower power costs enabling Florida Municipal Power Agency to reduce its wholesale rates to a number of members' cities in 2011 by 20% over 2009 levels.

The Agency was formed in 1978 to support the activities of Florida's locally owned and operated municipal utilities in projects requiring joint action such as the development of large power plants to serve a number of municipalities.

EXECUTIVES

Ceo, Jacob Williams
Chm*, Howard McKinnon
Manager, Richard Montgomery
Asst Treas, Edwin Nunez
Paralegal, Karen Culpepper
Compliance Audit Mana, Liyuan Woerner
Public Relations Specialist, Ryan Dumas
Cash Manager, Victoria Bidwell
Security, Carol Chinn
Director Information Technolog, Carter Manucy
Director, Chris Gowder
Auditors: PURVIS GRAY & COMPANY LLP OC

LOCATIONS

HQ: FLORIDA MUNICIPAL POWER AGENCY
8553 COMMODITY CIR, ORLANDO, FL 328199002
Phone: 407 355-7767
Web: WWW.FMPA.COM

HISTORICAL FINANCIALS

Company Type: Private

Income Statement   FYE: September 30

	REVENUE ($ mil.)	NET INCOME ($ mil.)	NET PROFIT MARGIN	EMPLOYEES
09/20	582	(0)	—	67
09/19	620	0	0.1%	—
09/18	604	32	5.3%	—
Annual Growth	(1.8%)	—	—	—

2020 Year-End Financials

Return on assets: —   Cash ($ mil.): 61
Return on equity: (-3.2%)
Current ratio: 2.20

FLORIDA STATE UNIVERSITY

Home to the Florida State Seminoles Florida State University offers more than 300 undergraduate graduate and professional programs including M.D. (medicine) and J.D. (law) programs. The educational institution has 16 colleges dedicated to academic fields ranging from liberal arts music visual arts and education to criminology engineering social work and information. A major research institution the university is home to the National High Magnetic Field Laboratory or "Mag Lab" the only national lab in Florida and the only such high-magnetic facility in the US. Florida State was founded in 1851 and is part of the 11-school State University System of Florida.

Operations

Florida State boasts more than 41000 students and has a student/faculty ratio of 26:1. The school's reputation as a top-notch research school stems from its extensive network of research facilities that cover areas such as biological medicine social sciences and energy. Its facilities also include the Center for Advanced Power Systems which is supported by the US Department of Defense and the Department of Energy. The Mag Lab is funded by the National Science Foundation. Florida State also operates the John and Mable Ringling Museum of Art in Sarasota Florida.

Geographic Reach

The main Florida State University campus in Tallahassee covers about 450 acres. The university also offers degree programs in Sarasota Florida and in the Republic of Panama. It boasts instructional programs in London Florence and Valencia as well as programs in research development and/or services in Costa Rica Croatia and Italy.

Sales and Marketing

The Florida university enrolls students from more than 120 foreign countries.

EXECUTIVES

Pres, Eric Barron
Prov Ex Vice President Academi, Lawrence Abele
Sr V Pres, John R Carnaghi
Head of Post Production, Charles Allen
Director of Communications, Christi Morgan
Administrator, John Dingus

Administrative Specialist, John Metz
Information Technology Helpdes, Nicholas Voran
Program Director, Scott Maynard
Int Dean College of Nursing, Laurie Grubbs
Business Officer Clerical Etc, Edward Young
Auditors: SHERRILL F NORMAN CPA TALLA

LOCATIONS

HQ: FLORIDA STATE UNIVERSITY
600 W COLLEGE AVE, TALLAHASSEE, FL 323061096
Phone: 850 644-5482
Web: WWW.FSU.EDU

PRODUCTS/OPERATIONS

Selected Colleges
College of Applied Studies
College of Arts and Sciences
College of Business
College of Communication and Information
College of Criminology and Criminal Justice
College of Education
College of Engineering
College of Human Sciences
College of Law
College of Medicine
College of Motion Picture Arts
College of Music
College of Nursing
College of Social Sciences and Public Policy
College of Social Work
College of Visual Arts Theatre and Dance

HISTORICAL FINANCIALS

Company Type: Private

Income Statement   FYE: June 30

	REVENUE ($ mil.)	NET INCOME ($ mil.)	NET PROFIT MARGIN	EMPLOYEES
06/12	654	40	6.1%	13,497
06/11	607	188	31.0%	—
06/10	567	121	21.4%	—
Annual Growth	7.4%	(42.4%)	—	—

2012 Year-End Financials

Return on assets: 1.2%   Cash ($ mil.): 48
Return on equity: 1.4%
Current ratio: 6.00

FLOWORKS INTERNATIONAL LLC

EXECUTIVES

Ceo, Scott Jackson
Cfo, Gary Haire
Pres, Fabrication & Distributi, John Higgins
Pres, Ipvf, Michael Stanwood
Evp, Corp Strategy & Bus Dev, Rob Broyles
Vp & Treas, Rick Hawthorne
SEC, Suzanne Mailes-Dineff
Sr Vp & Chro, Herbert Allen
Vp, Corp Contrl & Acctng Offic, Michael Goldberg
Evp, Ipvf, Jeff Legrand
Pres,valves & Automation, Keith Barnard
Auditors: PRICEWATERHOUSECOOPERS LLP HO

LOCATIONS

HQ: FLOWORKS INTERNATIONAL LLC
3750 HWY 225, PASADENA, TX 77503
Phone: 713 943-3544
Web: WWW.GOFLOWORKS.COM

HISTORICAL FINANCIALS

Company Type: Private

Income Statement — FYE: February 2

	REVENUE ($ mil.)	NET INCOME ($ mil.)	NET PROFIT MARGIN	EMPLOYEES
02/14*	805	(30)	—	785
06/12	222	(5)	—	
Annual Growth	90.5%	—	—	

*Fiscal year change

2014 Year-End Financials

Return on assets: (-5.2%) Cash ($ mil.): 12
Return on equity: (-12.6%)
Current ratio: 4.70

FONTANA UNIFIED SCHOOL DISTRICT

EXECUTIVES

Supt, Leslie Boozer
Sergeant, Doug Imhof
Strategic Transportation Engin, Kevin Ryan
Network Analyst, Dawn Ziegler
Library Media, Debbie Ellis
Assistant, Renee Gullixson
Coordinator of Library, Claudia Mason
Counselor, Delia Ramos
Selpa Director, Amy Foody
Community Coordinator, Bianca Gutierrez
Secretary To, Bonnie Prybycien
Auditors: NIGRO NIGRO & WHITE PC TEMEC

LOCATIONS

HQ: FONTANA UNIFIED SCHOOL DISTRICT
9680 CITRUS AVE, FONTANA, CA 923355571
Phone: 909 357-7600
Web: WWW.FUSD.NET

HISTORICAL FINANCIALS

Company Type: Private

Income Statement — FYE: June 30

	REVENUE ($ mil.)	NET INCOME ($ mil.)	NET PROFIT MARGIN	EMPLOYEES
06/20	574	7	1.3%	3,627
06/19	589	(0)	—	
06/18	543	31	5.7%	
06/17	531	27	5.1%	
Annual Growth	2.6%	(35.3%)	—	

FOOD FOR THE POOR, INC.

Food For The Poor feeds spiritual and physical hunger. The Christian charity provides health social economic and religious services for impoverished people in 17 countries in Latin America and the Caribbean. Food For The Poor believes its organization serves God by helping those most in need distributing requested goods through local churches and charities. The group works through Caritas the American-Nicaraguan Foundation and others to provide vocational training clinic and school construction educational materials feeding programs and medical supplies. Food For The Poor has distributed more than $3 billion in goods since its 1982 inception; the group uses 96% of its funds on programs.

EXECUTIVES

Pres-Ceo, Ed Raine
Cfo*, Dennis North
Evp-Cmo*, Angel Aloma
Evp Special Proj*, Frederick Khouri
Evp-Coo*, Mark Khouri
SEC-Gen Counsel*, Gail Hamaty-Bird
Director, Carlton Lewis
Marketing Staff, Kathy Skipper
Coordinator, Bambi Ziadie
Coordinator, Kelley Gentry
Digital & Social Media Special, Linda Lynch
Auditors: MAYER HOFFMAN MCCANN PC BOCA

LOCATIONS

HQ: FOOD FOR THE POOR, INC.
6401 LYONS RD, COCONUT CREEK, FL 330733602
Phone: 954 427-2222
Web: WWW.FOODFORTHEPOOR.ORG

HISTORICAL FINANCIALS

Company Type: Private

Income Statement — FYE: December 31

	REVENUE ($ mil.)	NET INCOME ($ mil.)	NET PROFIT MARGIN	EMPLOYEES
12/19	914	13	1.5%	418
12/18	942	(10)	—	
12/17	948	(1)	—	
12/16	994	14	1.5%	
Annual Growth	(2.8%)	(1.7%)	—	

2019 Year-End Financials

Return on assets: 31.2% Cash ($ mil.): 23
Return on equity: 35.9%
Current ratio: 5.00

FOOD GIANT SUPERMARKETS, INC.

EXECUTIVES

Pres, Kevin Ladd
V Pres-Oprs*, Gary Duncan
Asst SEC-Treas*, Steve Malone
SEC*, Spencer Coates

Site Manager, Kenny Counts
Regional Auditor, Deb Scott
Information Technology Interne, Tom Walker
Merchandiser, Bill Cook
Office Manager, Marsha Strobel
Vice President, Sean Schulke
Produce Supervisor, Jeff Turner

LOCATIONS

HQ: FOOD GIANT SUPERMARKETS, INC.
120 INDUSTRIAL DR, SIKESTON, MO 638015216
Phone: 573 471-3500
Web: WWW.FOODGIANT.COM

HISTORICAL FINANCIALS

Company Type: Private

Income Statement — FYE: October 1

	REVENUE ($ mil.)	NET INCOME ($ mil.)	NET PROFIT MARGIN	EMPLOYEES
10/16	725	22	3.1%	4,500
10/15	757	25	3.4%	
10/10*	616	22	3.6%	
09/06	468	108	23.1%	
Annual Growth	4.5%	(14.6%)	—	—

*Fiscal year change

2016 Year-End Financials

Return on assets: 12.8% Cash ($ mil.): 18
Return on equity: 14.0%
Current ratio: 1.70

FORDHAM UNIVERSITY

A private Catholic university Fordham offers its nearly 16365 students numerous degree programs through nine graduate and undergraduate schools. Called the Jesuit University of New York Fordham has multiple locations including the original Rose Hill campus in the Bronx (often the scene of location shooting for movies TV shows and commercials) the Westchester campus and the Lincoln Center campus in Manhattan. It also operates a biological field station in Armonk New York and an international center in the UK. With about 755 full-time instructors the university has a 13:1 undergraduate student-to-faculty ratio. Fordham was founded in 1841.

EXECUTIVES

Pres, Rev Joseph M McShane Sj
Sr V Pres*, Martha Hirst
Sr V Pres*, Stephen Freedman
V Pres Fin*, Nicholas B Milowski
Assistant Professor, Katherine Little
Assistant Professor, Berthold Ringeisen
Assistant Professor, Hongwu Ouyang
Dean, Elaine Congress
Vice President For Lincoln Cen, Ines V Garcia
Specialist, Jim Castillo
Senior Vice President, Chief F, John J Lordan
Auditors: KPMG LLP NEW YORK NY

LOCATIONS

HQ: FORDHAM UNIVERSITY
441 E FORDHAM RD, BRONX, NY 104589993
Phone: 718 817-1000
Web: WWW.FORDHAM.EDU

PRODUCTS/OPERATIONS

2017 Sales

	$ mil.	% of total
Net tuition & fees	424	71
Net auxiliary enterprises	78	13
Investments	27	5
Contributions & private grants	27	4
Government grants	17	3
Net assets released from restrictions	4	1
Other	16	3
Total	**596**	**100**

Selected Colleges

Graduate and Professional
  Graduate School of Arts and Sciences
  Graduate School of Business
  Graduate School of Education
  Graduate School of Religion and Religious Education
  Graduate School of Social Services
  School of Law
Undergraduate
  Fordham College at Lincoln Center
  Fordham College at Rose Hill
  Gabelli School of Business
  School of Professional and Continuing Studies

HISTORICAL FINANCIALS

Company Type: Private

Income Statement
FYE: June 30

	REVENUE ($ mil.)	NET INCOME ($ mil.)	NET PROFIT MARGIN	EMPLOYEES
06/20	665	(20)	—	4,070
06/19	933	59	6.4%	—
06/18	631	41	6.6%	—
06/16	588	(52)	—	—
Annual Growth	3.1%	—	—	—

2020 Year-End Financials

Return on assets: (-1.0%) Cash ($ mil.): 25
Return on equity: (-1.5%)
Current ratio: —

FORREST COUNTY GENERAL HOSPITAL (INC)

EXECUTIVES

Pres, Thane Forthman
Cfo*, Andy Woodard
Chief Officer, Steven Farrell
Coordinator, Susan Graham
Supervisor, Carissa Bryant
It Executive, Richard Golladay
Doctor, Todd Williamson
Rn, Arvie Fenner
Nurse Assistant, Carrie Huff
Physician, Constantine Charoglu
DDS, Dean Miller
Auditors: BKD CPAS & ADVISORS JACKSON

LOCATIONS

HQ: FORREST COUNTY GENERAL HOSPITAL (INC)
6051 U S HIGHWAY 49, HATTIESBURG, MS 394017200
Phone: 601 288-7000
Web: WWW.FORRESTHEALTH.ORG

HISTORICAL FINANCIALS

Company Type: Private

Income Statement
FYE: September 30

	REVENUE ($ mil.)	NET INCOME ($ mil.)	NET PROFIT MARGIN	EMPLOYEES
09/21	595	43	7.2%	4,030
09/20	556	18	3.4%	—
09/19	546	9	1.7%	—
09/18	0	0	—	—
Annual Growth	—	—	—	—

2021 Year-End Financials

Return on assets: 5.6% Cash ($ mil.): 139
Return on equity: 8.1%
Current ratio: 3.20

FORSYTH COUNTY BOARD OF EDUCATION

EXECUTIVES

Chairperson, Darla Light
Cfo*, Dan Jones
Executive, Amanda Studt
Media Specialist, Jean Lipscomb
Teacher, Karen Pierce
Auditors: MAULDIN & JENKINS LLC ATLANT

LOCATIONS

HQ: FORSYTH COUNTY BOARD OF EDUCATION
1120 DAHLONEGA HWY, CUMMING, GA 300404536
Phone: 770 887-2461
Web: WWW.FORSYTH.K12.GA.US

HISTORICAL FINANCIALS

Company Type: Private

Income Statement
FYE: June 30

	REVENUE ($ mil.)	NET INCOME ($ mil.)	NET PROFIT MARGIN	EMPLOYEES
06/20	622	80	13.0%	4,160
06/19	582	127	21.9%	—
06/17	526	(16)	—	—
06/16	472	21	4.5%	—
Annual Growth	7.1%	39.5%	—	—

2020 Year-End Financials

Return on assets: 5.0% Cash ($ mil.): 359
Return on equity: 128.1%
Current ratio: —

FORT WORTH INDEPENDENT SCHOOL DISTRICT

EXECUTIVES

Sup, Kent Scribner
Executive Officer, Martin Yarobough
Executive Officer, Camille Rodriguez

Executive Officer, Judy Needham
Executive Officer, Blaine Buchenau
Executive Officer, Diana Vargas
Staff, Micheal Lee
Executive Officer, Steven Senevy
Accounting Staff, Deborah Cooper-Boone
Technology, Carter Cook
Nurse, Allison Bradford
Auditors: WEAVER AND TIDWELL LLP FO

LOCATIONS

HQ: FORT WORTH INDEPENDENT SCHOOL DISTRICT
100 N UNIVERSITY DR, FORT WORTH, TX 761071360
Phone: 817 871-2000
Web: WWW.FWISD.ORG

HISTORICAL FINANCIALS

Company Type: Private

Income Statement
FYE: June 30

	REVENUE ($ mil.)	NET INCOME ($ mil.)	NET PROFIT MARGIN	EMPLOYEES
06/17	924	133	14.4%	10,360
06/16	909	(101)	—	—
06/15	843	64	7.7%	—
06/12	777	(98)	—	—
Annual Growth	3.5%	—	—	—

FORTIS CONSTRUCTION, INC.

Fortis Construction isn't afraid to get its hands dirty. The fast-growing US construction company offers general contracting preconstruction construction management and environmentally-friendly green building services to customers primarily in Portland Oregon and others in the Pacific Northwest. It specializes in remodeling and upgrading corporate offices health care facilities retail complexes and schools; it also conducts seismic and structural upgrades. Customers have included Oregon State University Portland State University PPG Industries and StanCorp.

EXECUTIVES

President, James T Kilpatrick
Executive Vice President*, David Aaroe
Secretary*, Rene G Gonzalez
Project Engineer, Mike Frede
Foreman, Barry Shephard
Project Manager, Brian Gruenemay
Safety Manager, Johnny Sandoval
Project Engineer, Kellen Nicol
Project Accountant, Michelle L Brown
Project Engineer, Nicklaus Abdou
Project Accountant, Angelica Martinez
Auditors: ALDRICH CPAS AND ADVISORS LLP

LOCATIONS

HQ: FORTIS CONSTRUCTION, INC.
1705 SW TAYLOR ST STE 200, PORTLAND, OR 972051922
Phone: 503 459-4477
Web: WWW.FORTISCONSTRUCTION.COM

PRODUCTS/OPERATIONS

Selected Services
Construction management
General contracting
Green building

Preconstruction
Web-based collaboration and electronic document management

COMPETITORS

Andersen Construction R&h Construction
Hoffman Corporation   S.d. Deacon
Jacobsen Construction Swinerton Builders
Panattoni Construction

HISTORICAL FINANCIALS

Company Type: Private

Income Statement				FYE: December 31
	REVENUE ($ mil.)	NET INCOME ($ mil.)	NET PROFIT MARGIN	EMPLOYEES
12/16	782	30	3.9%	175
12/15	468	18	3.9%	—
12/14	282	14	5.0%	—
Annual Growth	66.6%	48.0%	—	—

2016 Year-End Financials

Return on assets: 20.5%   Cash ($ mil.): 41
Return on equity: 75.8%
Current ratio: 1.40

FRANCISCAN ALLIANCE, INC.

Franciscan Alliance is a not-for-profit organization operating more than a dozen hospitals in Indiana and south suburban Chicago. The hospitals include specialist centers for cancer care heart and vascular care weight loss pediatrics and women's health. In addition to inpatient acute care services they operate numerous outpatient facilities and medical practices within their local service areas. Other subsidiaries and affiliates perform clinical laboratory tests offer home health services and provide support services to the system. Franciscan Alliance was founded and is sponsored by the Sisters of St. Francis of Perpetual Adoration.

Operations

Along with providing a wide range of health care services Franciscan Alliance educates future health care providers through affiliations with area universities. The schools offer a variety of degree programs in fields including nursing medical technician and pharmacy residency.

Geographic Reach

Franciscan Alliance's hospitals are located in more than ten communities in Indiana as well as in southern Chicago suburbs. The facilities serve patients in parts of Michigan as well. The organization also operates outpatient clinics and physician offices in the area as well as a data center in Beech Grove Indiana.

EXECUTIVES

Pres-Ceo, Kevin D Leahy
Chb- Chm, Jane Marie Klein
V Pres, Corita Last
SEC, Vincetta Traffas
Treas, Ann Kathleen Magiera
Svp-System Chief Nursing Offic, Agnes Therady
Director, Robert E McBride
Director, Anna Marie Hofmeyer
Director, Kathleen Goeppinger
Director, Rose Agnes Pfautsch
Director, James D Rogge
Auditors: I PNCEWATERHOUSECOOPERS LLP

LOCATIONS

HQ: FRANCISCAN ALLIANCE, INC.
  1515 W DRAGOON TRL, MISHAWAKA, IN 465444710
Phone: 574 273-3867
Web: WWW.FRANCISCANHEALTH.ORG

PRODUCTS/OPERATIONS

Selected Operations

St. Anthony Health (Crown Point and Michigan City Indiana)
St. Elizabeth Health (Crawfordsville Lafayette Central Lafayette East Indiana)
St. Francis Health (Carmel Indianapolis and Mooresville Indiana)
St. James Health (Chicago Heights and Olympia Fields Illinois)
St. Margaret Health (Hammond and Dyer Indiana)
Franciscan Healthcare Munster (formerly Physicians Hospital; Munster Indiana)

Selected Services

Anticoagulation Clinics
Behavioral Health
Cancer Care
Colon and Rectal Surgery
Diabetes Care
Ear Nose and Throat
Emergency Medicine
Heart & Vascular
Home Health Care
Hospice
Imaging
Joint & Spine Care
Laboratory Services
Neurology
Neurosurgery
Occupational Health
Ophthalmology
Pain Management
Palliative Medicine
Pediatrics
Plastic Surgery
Primary Care Physicians
Pulmonary Medicine
Registered Dietitians
Rehabilitation Services
Robotic Surgery
Senior Services
Sleep Disorders
Sports Medicine
Surgical Services
Urgent Care
Weight Loss/Bariatrics
Women's Health/OBGYN
Wound Care

Selected Hospitals

Franciscan St. Anthony - Crown Point
Franciscan St. Anthony - Michigan City
Franciscan St. Elizabeth - Lafayette Central
Franciscan St. Elizabeth - Lafayette East
Franciscan St. Elizabeth - Crawfordsville
Franciscan St. Francis - Carmel
Franciscan St. Francis - Indianapolis
Franciscan St. Francis - Mooresville
Franciscan St. James - Chicago Heights
Franciscan St. James - Olympia Fields
Franciscan St. Margaret - Dyer
Franciscan St. Margaret - Hammond
Franciscan Healthcare - Munster

COMPETITORS

Advocate Health Care
Ascension Health
Community Health Network
Covenant Ministries
Iu Health
Memorial Hospital & Health System
Northshore University Healthsystem
Northwestern Memorial Healthcare
Porter Health Care System
Riverview Hospital
Rush System For Health
Sinai Health System
St. Bernard Hospital And Health Care Center
Union Hospital (indiana)
University Of Chicago Medical Center

HISTORICAL FINANCIALS

Company Type: Private

Income Statement				FYE: December 31
	REVENUE ($ mil.)	NET INCOME ($ mil.)	NET PROFIT MARGIN	EMPLOYEES
12/19	3,302	409	12.4%	19,000
12/18	3,144	14	0.5%	—
12/15	2,731	250	9.2%	—
12/14	2,661	274	10.3%	—
Annual Growth	4.4%	8.3%	—	—

2019 Year-End Financials

Return on assets: 7.0%   Cash ($ mil.): 28
Return on equity: 11.6%
Current ratio: 1.40

FRANCISCAN HEALTH SYSTEM

St. Francis himself may have hailed from Italy but his followers look after the health of the residents of the South Puget Sound area through the Franciscan Health System. The not-for-profit system includes five full-service hospitals. The oldest and largest hospital is St. Joseph Medical Center in Tacoma Washington a 320-bed facility. Its facilities include community hospitals St. Clare Hospital (in Lakewood) and St. Francis Hospital (in Federal Way) as well as a hospice program and numerous primary and specialty care clinics. Its St. Anthony Hospital is an 80-bed full service pharmacy and home medical equipment retail location at Gig Harbor.

Geographic Reach

Franciscan Health System serves patients in Tacoma Washington and surrounding areas.

Financial Performance

The company gets most of its revenues from patient services. Other sources of income includes foundation gifts and investment community benefit charity care and uncompensated care (unreimbursed costs of serving patients enrolled in Medicaid and other state-subsidized programs).

Strategy

Franciscan Health System and Harrison Medical Center are looking to join forces while Franciscan's parent continues in talks to combine its Northwest operations with PeaceHealth of Vancouver Washington. If both plans are approved by regulators Harrison will become part of the largest community hospital system in the Northwest with facilities in Alaska Washington and Oregon. Both the Harrison-Franciscan affiliation and that of Franciscan's parent Catholic Health Initiatives with PeaceHealth is slated to be approved in 2013.

In addition Franciscan Health System is collaborating with the MultiCare Health System and TRA Medical Imaging to build a women's imaging and breast cancer care center.

St. Elizabeth Hospital opened its doors in 2011 in Enumclaw replacing Enumclaw Regional Hospital as that community's acute-care facility.

Company Background

St. Joseph Medical Center in Tacoma (the health system's oldest facility) was founded by the Sisters of St. Francis in 1891.

EXECUTIVES

Pres-Ceo, Joseph W Wilczek
V Pres-Cfo, Mike Fitzgerald

Pres, Jennifer Schomburg
Vp and Chief Nursing Officer, Laurie B Rn
Occupational Specia, Julie Milasich
Training and Direc, Jeffery Olson
Coordinator, Candy Mansfield
Health Professional, Angela Brown
Security Staff, Carissa Carnahan
Internal Medicine Practitioner, Joseph Barthelemy
Coordinator, Tracy Gregg

LOCATIONS

HQ: FRANCISCAN HEALTH SYSTEM
1717 S J ST, TACOMA, WA 984054933
Phone: 253 426-4101
Web: WWW.CHIFRANCISCAN.ORG

PRODUCTS/OPERATIONS

Key Facilities and Services

Carol Milgard Breast Center Tacoma
Franciscan Center for Weight Management Federal Way
Franciscan Dialysis Center Eastside Tacoma
Franciscan Medical Group primary-care and specialty-
    care clinics
Franciscan Hospice House University Place
Franciscan Port Clinic Tacoma
Gig Harbor Medical Pavilion Gig Harbor
Gig Harbor Ambulatory Surgery Clinic Gig Harbor
St. Anthony Hospital Gig Harbor
St. Clare Hospital Lakewood
St. Clare Specialty Center Lakewood
St. Clare Medical Pavilion Lakewood
St. Elizabeth Hospital Enumclaw
St. Francis Hospital Federal Way
St. Francis Outpatient Center Federal Way
St. Joseph Medical Center Tacoma
St. Joseph Outpatient Center Tacoma
St. Joseph Heart & Vascular Center Tacoma
St. Joseph Dialysis Center Tacoma
St. Joseph Dialysis Center Gig Harbor
St. Joseph Dialysis Center Puyallup
St. Joseph Medical Clinic Tacoma
St. Joseph Medical Pavilion Tacoma
Milgard Medical Pavilion at St. Anthony Gig Harbor
Women's Health & Breast Center Federal Way

COMPETITORS

Harrison Medical
    Center
Multicare Health
    System
Overlake Hospital
Peacehealth
Providence St. Joseph
    Health

Seattle Children's
    Hospital
Swedish Health
    Services
Yakima Valley Memorial

HISTORICAL FINANCIALS
Company Type: Private

Income Statement				FYE: June 30
	REVENUE ($ mil.)	NET INCOME ($ mil.)	NET PROFIT MARGIN	EMPLOYEES
06/16	637	51	8.0%	3,183
06/15	610	56	9.2%	—
06/14	1,190	(106)	—	—
06/10	1,093	71	6.5%	—
Annual Growth	(8.6%)	(5.4%)	—	—

2016 Year-End Financials
Return on assets: 11.2%   Cash ($ mil.): 113
Return on equity: 13.8%
Current ratio: 3.10

FRANCISCAN MISSIONARIES OF OUR LADY HEALTH SYSTEM, INC.

EXECUTIVES

Pres-Ceo, Richard R Vath
V Pres, Pete Guarisco
SEC-Treas, Sr Helen Cahill
Cfo, Howard Harvill
Information Specialist, Chris Jones
Information Specialist, Trisha A Tunis
It Security, Becky Davis
Member, Denicca Dorsey
Coordinator, Denise Broussard
Law Specialist, Diane Allen
Information Specialist, Elizabeth McCurdy
Auditors: KMG LLP BATON ROUGE LOUISIA

LOCATIONS

HQ: FRANCISCAN MISSIONARIES OF OUR LADY
    HEALTH SYSTEM, INC.
    4200 ESSEN LN, BATON ROUGE, LA 708092158
Phone: 225 923-2701
Web: WWW.FMOLSISTERS.COM

HISTORICAL FINANCIALS
Company Type: Private

Income Statement				FYE: June 30
	REVENUE ($ mil.)	NET INCOME ($ mil.)	NET PROFIT MARGIN	EMPLOYEES
06/21	3,347	833	24.9%	9,000
06/20	3,007	44	1.5%	—
06/19	2,296	27	1.2%	—
06/18	2,029	106	5.3%	—
Annual Growth	18.1%	98.3%	—	—

2021 Year-End Financials
Return on assets: 16.4%   Cash ($ mil.): 1,105
Return on equity: 32.5%
Current ratio: 2.20

FRANKLIN COUNTY BOARD OF COMMISSIONERS

EXECUTIVES

Commissioner, Marilyn Brown
Staff, Jenell Williams
Coordinator, Cecilia Weirick
Coordinator, Kris McDaniel
Coordinator, Kysten Palmore
Coordinator, Patti Froehlich
Coordinator, Phyllis Roberts
Contractor, Catherine Richards
Admin SEC, Victoria C
Network Administrator, Sharon Evrard
Licensed Social Worker, Carolyn Pierce-Jones
Auditors: KEITH FABER COLUMBUS OHIO

LOCATIONS

HQ: FRANKLIN COUNTY BOARD OF COMMISSIONERS
    373 S HIGH ST FL 26, COLUMBUS, OH 432154591
Phone: 614 525-3322
Web: WWW.FCBDD.ORG

HISTORICAL FINANCIALS
Company Type: Private

Income Statement				FYE: December 31
	REVENUE ($ mil.)	NET INCOME ($ mil.)	NET PROFIT MARGIN	EMPLOYEES
12/20	1,403	12	0.9%	6,000
12/19	1,348	(48)	—	—
12/17	1,281	85	6.7%	—
12/16	1,226	48	3.9%	—
Annual Growth	3.4%	(28.5%)	—	—

2020 Year-End Financials
Return on assets: 0.4%   Cash ($ mil.): 1,332
Return on equity: 1.2%
Current ratio: 17.20

FRANKLIN SQUARE HOSPITAL CENTER, INC.

Franklin Square Hospital Center has made a declaration to care for the residents of eastern Baltimore County Maryland. The facility offers a wide range of specialties through some 700 doctors and about 380 beds. Since 1998 the hospital has been part of MedStar Health the region's largest integrated health system. As a teaching hospital Franklin Square offers a number of residency programs including internal and family medicine OB-GYN and surgery. The not-for-profit hospital offers its medical services through half a dozen primary service lines: Medicine Surgery Women's and Children's Care Oncology Behavioral Health and Community Health and Wellness.

Operations
Franklin Square Hospital boasts more than 3000 skilled professions including 1000-plus nurses and 400 staff physicians and more than 750 independently practicing physicians.

Geographic Reach
The only one of its kind in the region Franklin Square's Cancer Institute serves oncology patients by offering education and prevention services research and diagnostic treatment.

Strategy
The hospital which logs one of the highest numbers of cancer admissions in Maryland is working to expand its cancer services as it anticipates admissions to grow.

In fact the company is expanding other services as well also in anticipation of future patient demand. The hospital built a 300-bed patient tower on the campus that includes an expanded emergency department dedicated pediatric and inpatient suites and an expanded 50-bed critical care unit.

EXECUTIVES

Pres, Samuel E Moskowitz
Cfo*, Robert P Lally Jr
V Pres*, Anthony Sclama
V Pres*, Larry Strassner
V Pres*, Karen Robertson-Keck
Occupational Specia, Stacy A Goldstein
Assistant Professor, Katie McPeak
Education Specialist, Regina Straw

Director Clinical Informatics, Sharon Bonner
Assistant To Director of C, Sandi Smith
Neonatologist, Sarah Harper

LOCATIONS

HQ: FRANKLIN SQUARE HOSPITAL CENTER, INC.
9000 FRANKLIN SQUARE DR, BALTIMORE, MD
212373901
Phone: 410 933-2777
Web: WWW.MEDSTARFRANKLINSQUARE.ORG

PRODUCTS/OPERATIONS

Selected Services
Ambulatory & Minimally Invasive Surgery
Cancer Services
Cyberknife
da Vinci Robotic Surgery
Diagnostic Imaging and Radiology
Obstetrics & Neonatology
Orthopedics & Joint Replacement Therapies
Sleep Disorders
Women's Services

COMPETITORS

Anne Arundel Medical
  Center
Bon Secours Health
Gbmc
Good Samaritan
  Hospital Of Maryland
Harbor Hospital
Johns Hopkins Bayview
  Medical Center
Johns Hopkins Health
  System
Johns Hopkins Medicine

Lifebridge Health
Medstar Union Memorial
  Hospital
Sinai Hospital Of
  Baltimore
St. Agnes Healthcare
St. Joseph Medical
  Center
University Of Maryland
  Medical System
Upper Chesapeake
  Health

HISTORICAL FINANCIALS

Company Type: Private

Income Statement   FYE: June 30

	REVENUE ($ mil.)	NET INCOME ($ mil.)	NET PROFIT MARGIN	EMPLOYEES
06/20	605	56	9.2%	3,019
06/16	506	10	2.1%	—
06/15	492	17	3.5%	—
06/11	452	18	4.0%	—
Annual Growth	3.3%	13.4%	—	—

2020 Year-End Financials
Return on assets: 15.9%   Cash ($ mil.): 4
Return on equity: 30.4%
Current ratio: 2.40

FREEMAN HEALTH SYSTEM

Freeman Health System (FHS) offers comprehensive health and behavioral health services to the residents of Arkansas Kansas Missouri and Oklahoma through three hospitals with a total of more than 500 beds. Specialty facilities include a full-service cardiothoracic and vascular program at the Freeman Heart Institute and behavioral health services through its Ozark Health Center. Community-owned not-for-profit FHS also operates two urgent care centers a separate sleep center several doctors' office buildings and serves as a teaching hospital with three residency programs (ear nose and throat; emergency medicine; and internal medicine). FHS employs more than 300 physicians in 60 specialties.

Operations

FHS operates three Missouri hospitals - Freeman Hospital West and Freeman Hospital East in Joplin and Freeman Neosho in Neosho. Its Ozark Center provides behavioral health services to patients from Missouri Arkansas Oklahoma and Kansas.

Strategy

Like most health care providers FHS has been working to update it facilities and expand it offerings. To that end in 2013 it opened a transitional living and life skills assistance center for homeless teens and teamed with an autism support group to design an autism treatment program for its Ozark Center. The prior year it christened Will's Place behavioral health center for children and opened a $2 million sports and rehabilitation center.

Company Background

Located in Joplin Missouri — the site of the deadly E5 tornado that killed 161 people in May 2011— Freeman Health System was the only fully functional hospital in the aftermath of the disaster. Rival St. John's Regional Medical Center just two miles away was destroyed. However Ozark Health Center FHS's behavioral health division lost nine buildings in the disaster.

EXECUTIVES

Pres- Ceo, Paula Baker
Cfo*, Steven Graddy
Cro*, Kevin Gaudette
Cco*, Jeff Thompson
Specialist, Thomas Coy
Controller, Michael Sanders
Director, Mike Leone
Director, Sue Annesser
Auditors: BKD LLP SPRINGFIELD MISSOUR

LOCATIONS

HQ: FREEMAN HEALTH SYSTEM
1102 W 32ND ST, JOPLIN, MO 648043503
Phone: 417 347-1111
Web: WWW.FREEMANHEALTH.COM

PRODUCTS/OPERATIONS

Selected Services
Autism Services
Behavioral/mental health
Bladder care
Cancer care
Children's Miracle Network Hospitals
Clinical trials
Cosmetic/reconstructive surgery
Critical Care (ICU)
Diabetes education
Digestive care
Emergency medicine
Family care
Family counseling
Geriatric medicine
Health screenings
Hearing services
Home care
Internal medicine
Internet Addiction Services
Kidney Care
Lung care
Maternity
Neonatal intensive care
Nephrology & dialysis
Neurology & neurosurgery
Occupational medicine
Orthopedics
Pain management
Palliative care
QuickMeds Pharmacy;
Radiology
Rehabilitation
Senior Services
Skilled nursing
Sleep disorders

Sports medicine
Substance abuse services
Surgery
Tobacco cessation
Transitional Care Unit (TCU)
Urgent care
Women's Services
Wound care

Selected Facilities
Freeman Hospital West - Joplin MO
Freeman Hospital East - Joplin MO
Freeman Neosho Hospital - Neosho MO
Freeman Business Center - Joplin MO
Ozark Center - Joplin Missouri

COMPETITORS

Catholic Health
  Initiatives
Children's Mercy
  Hospital

Heartland Regional
  Medical
Mercy Health

HISTORICAL FINANCIALS

Company Type: Private

Income Statement   FYE: March 31

	REVENUE ($ mil.)	NET INCOME ($ mil.)	NET PROFIT MARGIN	EMPLOYEES
03/21	676	164	24.3%	4,500
03/20	562	16	3.0%	—
03/19	624	57	9.2%	—
03/18	588	51	8.7%	—
Annual Growth	4.8%	47.6%	—	—

2021 Year-End Financials
Return on assets: 17.4%   Cash ($ mil.): 136
Return on equity: 24.8%
Current ratio: 1.80

FRESH MARK, INC.

Fresh Mark is a leading producer of smoked and processed pork products for the domestic and international retail and foodservice industries. From its four plants in Ohio the company makes and markets such products as bacon (raw par-cooked and cooked) dry sausage ham (natural and smoked) hot dogs and lunch meats under the Sugardale and Superior's brands. Sugardale label is available in all 50 states and over 20 countries. The company also produces private-label processed meat products for others and supplies the foodservice industry through its Sugardale Food Service business. Founded in 1920 Ohio-based Fresh Mark is owned and operated by the Genshaft family.

Operations

Fresh Mark makes and supplies smoked and processed meats for the US retail and foodservice industries. Products include bacon ham wieners dry sausages specialty meat items and deli and luncheon meats. All of its products are gluten-free and free of the Big-8 allergenic foods including milk eggs fish crustacean shellfish tree nuts peanuts wheat and soybeans.

Some of its brands include Superior's Brand and Sugardale.

Geographic Reach

Headquartered in Ohio Fresh Mark has facilities in Canton Massillon and Salem.

Sales and Marketing

The company markets its products through restaurants delis grocers retailers and food service operators.

Strategy

One of the largest privately owned companies in its industry Fresh Mark has grown from a regional supplier of smoked and processed meats to a leading supplier nationwide. It's ranked among the top 40 of the nation's leading 150 meat and poultry companies as measured by National Provisioner magazine.

EXECUTIVES

Chmn-Ceo, Neil Genshaft
Pres-Coo*, Tim Cranor
SEC*, Tom Cicarella
Cfo, Exec V-Pres*, David Cochenour
Superintendent, Bob Goode
Quality Assurance Supervisor, Greg Davis
Director, Tim Calvin
Marketing Manager, Alicia Pucky
National Account Retail Sales, Bill Gryszkiewicz
Corporate Director of Engineer, Bill Yeager
Purchasing Manager, Lee Poludniak
Auditors: ERNST & YOUNG LLP AKRON OH

LOCATIONS

HQ: FRESH MARK, INC.
1888 SOUTHWAY ST SW, MASSILLON, OH 446469429
Phone: 330 832-7491
Web: WWW.FRESHMARK.COM

PRODUCTS/OPERATIONS

Selected Products

Bacon
Deli meats
Dry sausage
Ham
Luncheon meats
Specialty meat items
Weiners

COMPETITORS

Birchwood Meat & Provision	Farmland Foods
Boar's Head	Hormel
Cargill Meat Solutions	Indiana Packers
Carl Buddig	Jbs Usa
Coleman Natural Foods	Johnsonville Sausage
Conagra	Smithfield Foods
	Tyson Foods

HISTORICAL FINANCIALS

Company Type: Private

Income Statement				FYE: January 1
	REVENUE ($ mil.)	NET INCOME ($ mil.)	NET PROFIT MARGIN	EMPLOYEES
01/11*	795	59	7.5%	2,300
12/07	534	31	5.8%	—
12/06	481	21	4.5%	—
12/05	481	23	4.9%	—
Annual Growth	10.6%	20.4%	—	—

*Fiscal year change

2011 Year-End Financials

Return on assets: 3.9%
Return on equity: 7.5%
Current ratio: 0.90
Cash ($ mil.): 4

FRESNO COMMUNITY HOSPITAL AND MEDICAL CENTER

EXECUTIVES

Pres-Ceo, Phillip Hinton
Ceo*, Tim A Joslin
Cfo*, William Grigg
Treas*, Roger Fretwell
Sr V Pres*, Mike Kingbury
Sr V Pres*, Stephen Walter
V Pres*, Les Abercrombie
Network Administrator, Ian Reith
Pacs Administrator, Jason Hulsey
Vice President Cancer, John Strubert
Senior Network Engineer, Lyndon Apostol
Auditors: MOSS ADAMS LLP STOCKTON CA

LOCATIONS

HQ: FRESNO COMMUNITY HOSPITAL AND MEDICAL CENTER
2823 FRESNO ST, FRESNO, CA 937211324
Phone: 559 459-3948
Web: WWW.COMMUNITYMEDICAL.ORG

HISTORICAL FINANCIALS

Company Type: Private

Income Statement				FYE: August 31
	REVENUE ($ mil.)	NET INCOME ($ mil.)	NET PROFIT MARGIN	EMPLOYEES
08/15	1,571	139	8.9%	5,045
08/10	1,027	9	0.9%	—
08/09	1,010	65	6.5%	—
Annual Growth	7.6%	13.3%	—	—

2015 Year-End Financials

Return on assets: 7.8%
Return on equity: 13.3%
Current ratio: 0.50
Cash ($ mil.): 62

FRESNO UNIFIED SCHOOL DISTRICT EDUCATIONAL FACILITIES CORPORATION

EXECUTIVES

Supt, Michael Hanson
Asst Supt-Oprs, Rick Hausman
Magnet School Coordinator, Tammy Townsend
Manager III, David Jansen
Chief Technology Officer, Kurt Madden
Office Manager, Grace Ornelas
Athletic Director, Addison Lyons
Chief Information Officer, Anthony Aboularage
Superintendent, Bob Nelson
Athletic Manager, Brett Mar
Auditors: PERRY SMITH SACRAMENTO CALIF

LOCATIONS

HQ: FRESNO UNIFIED SCHOOL DISTRICT EDUCATIONAL FACILITIES CORPORATION
2309 TULARE ST, FRESNO, CA 937212266
Phone: 559 457-3000
Web: WWW.FRESNOUNIFIED.ORG

HISTORICAL FINANCIALS

Company Type: Private

Income Statement				FYE: June 30
	REVENUE ($ mil.)	NET INCOME ($ mil.)	NET PROFIT MARGIN	EMPLOYEES
06/10	692	(13)	—	8,400
06/09	757	0	0.1%	—
06/08	771	(40)	—	—
06/07	781	74	9.5%	—
Annual Growth	(3.9%)	—	—	—

2010 Year-End Financials

Return on assets: (-1.5%)
Return on equity: (-4.6%)
Current ratio: —
Cash ($ mil.): 221

FROEDTERT HEALTH, INC.

EXECUTIVES

Ceo, Cathy Jacobson
SEC, Douglas H Stadelmann
Treas, Thomas Knoll
Coo, Dennis Pollard
Cfo, Scott Hawig
Exec Vpres, Eric Conley
Pediatrician, Lara C Totzke
Vice President Marketing, Kathy Perlewitz
Vice President, Robert Degrand
Director, Douglas Stadelmann
Coordinator, Ron Heimann
Auditors: KPMG LLP COLUMBUS OH

LOCATIONS

HQ: FROEDTERT HEALTH, INC.
9200 W WISCONSIN AVE, MILWAUKEE, WI 532263522
Phone: 414 805-3666
Web: WWW.FROEDTERT.COM

HISTORICAL FINANCIALS

Company Type: Private

Income Statement				FYE: June 30
	REVENUE ($ mil.)	NET INCOME ($ mil.)	NET PROFIT MARGIN	EMPLOYEES
06/20	675	55	8.2%	3,458
06/14	362	66	18.4%	—
06/13	269	13	5.2%	—
Annual Growth	14.0%	21.8%	—	—

2020 Year-End Financials

Return on assets: 1.9%
Return on equity: 3.8%
Current ratio: 0.40
Cash ($ mil.): 250

FROEDTERT MEMORIAL LUTHERAN HOSPITAL, INC.

Patients in southeastern Wisconsin count on Froedtert Memorial Lutheran Hospital for a full range of health services including trauma transplant sports medicine and senior care. The 500-bed hospital also known as Froedtert & The Medical College of Wisconsin is part of the Froedtert (pronounced "fray-dert") Health system. Specialty units include cancer dermatology neuroscience birthing fertility urology and vein clinics. The hospital also serves as a teaching facility for the Medical College of Wisconsin and it partners with the Children's Hospital of Wisconsin to provide pediatric services. Froedtert Hospital which was founded in 1980 operates the only adult Level I trauma center in the region.

Operations

Froedtert Health offers medical practice care in roughly 25 specialties and sub-specialties. Beyond the hospital's walls it operates four diagnostic imaging centers as well as rehabilitation facilities and a handful of primary care clinics in the community. The Froedtert Health system also includes Community Memorial Hospital in Menomonee Falls Wisconsin; St. Joseph's Hospital in West Bend Wisconsin; and Froedtert Health Medical Group.

Altogether the system's hospitals have 781 beds and see nearly 40000 admissions annually. They also manage more than 900000 outpatient visits each year. In 2014 Froedtert Hospital alone had about 65000 emergency department visits more than 736000 outpatient visits and delivered more than 2000 babies.

Strategy

To help advance the health of its service communities Froedtert Health is investing some $12 million to establish a new 22000-sq.-ft. health clinic in Milwaukee. It is partnering with clinic operator Sixteenth Street Community Health Centers on the project which is intended to address the needs of medically underserved neighborhoods. The facility will provide specialty care cancer prevention and access to cancer clinical trials.

EXECUTIVES

Ceo, William Petasnick
Chm*, P Michael Mahoney
Treas*, Roger Pierce
SEC*, Phillip R Smith
Infection Control Coordinator, Patti Wilson
Occupational Specia, James Ninomiya
Occupational Specia, Paula G Galaviz
Edi, Jeff Vandekreeke
Compliance Staff, Rhonda Joseph
Chief Officer, Froedte, Lee Biblo
Occupational Specia, Paula Galaviz
Auditors: KPMG LLP COLUMBUS OH

LOCATIONS

HQ: FROEDTERT MEMORIAL LUTHERAN HOSPITAL, INC.
  9200 W WISCONSIN AVE, MILWAUKEE, WI 532263522
Phone: 414 805-3000
Web: WWW.FROEDTERT.COM

PRODUCTS/OPERATIONS

Selected Departments Centers and Programs
Clinical Cancer Center
  Blood and Lymph Node Cancer Program
  Blood and Marrow Transplant Program
  Bone and Connective Tissue Cancer Program
  Brain and Spine Tumor Program
  Breast Cancer Program
  Cancer Genetics Screening Program
  Colorectal Cancer Program
  Endocrine Cancer Program
  Eye/Orbital Cancer Program
  Geriatric Oncology
  Gynecologic Cancer Program
  Head and Neck Cancer Program
  Liver Pancreas and Bile Duct Cancer Program
  Neuro-oncology Cognitive Clinic
  Palliative Care Program
  Plastic Surgery Center
  Prostate and Urologic Cancer Program
  Skin Cancer Center
  Thoracic Cancer Program (Lung and Esophageal Cancers)
Heart and Vascular Center
  Adult Congenital Heart Disease
  Advanced Heart Failure and Cardiac Transplantation
  Aortic Disease
  Arrhythmia and Atrial Fibrillation
  Coronary Artery Disease (CAD)
  Hereditary Hemorrhagic Telangiectasia (HHT)
  Hypertrophic Cardiomyopathy (HCM)
  Preventive Cardiology and Lipid Therapy
  Peripheral Arterial Disease (PAD)
  Pulmonary Hypertension
  Valvular Disease
  Venous Thrombotic Disease
  Venous and Vein Disease
  Women and Heart Disease
Neurosciences Center
  Brain Injury Program
  Brain and Spine Tumor Program
  Comprehensive Epilepsy Program
  Comprehensive Spasticity Management Program
  Memory Disorders Program
  Neuro-Oncology Cognitive Clinic
  Normal Pressure Hydrocephalus
  Parkinson's and Movement Disorders Program
  Sleep Disorders Program
  SpineCare Program
  Spinal Cord Injury Center
  Stroke and Neurovascular Program

COMPETITORS

Children's Hospital And Health System	Rockford Health System
Columbia St. Mary's	Waukesha Memorial
Ministry Health Care	Wheaton Franciscan Services
Prohealth Care	

HISTORICAL FINANCIALS

Company Type: Private

Income Statement				FYE: June 30
	REVENUE ($ mil.)	NET INCOME ($ mil.)	NET PROFIT MARGIN	EMPLOYEES
06/20	1,958	143	7.3%	3,400
06/14	1,164	92	7.9%	—
06/11	980	79	8.1%	—
06/10	894	59	6.7%	—
Annual Growth	8.2%	9.2%	—	—

2020 Year-End Financials

Return on assets: 11.6%
Return on equity: 15.2%
Current ratio: 3.20
Cash ($ mil.): 2

FRONTROW CALYPSO LLC

EXECUTIVES

Ceo-Pres, Jens Holstebro
V Pres*, John Merline
V Pres*, Leo Stearns
SEC*, Per Lund
Manager, Kris Hutchins
Vice President, Mark Jones
Regional Sales Manager, Eddie Navarro

LOCATIONS

HQ: FRONTROW CALYPSO LLC
  1690 CORPORATE CIR, PETALUMA, CA 949546912
Phone: 707 769-1110
Web: WWW.GOFRONTROW.COM

HISTORICAL FINANCIALS

Company Type: Private

Income Statement				FYE: December 31
	REVENUE ($ mil.)	NET INCOME ($ mil.)	NET PROFIT MARGIN	EMPLOYEES
12/08	1,009	128	12.7%	40
12/07	1,083	214	19.8%	—
12/04	21	(1)	—	—
Annual Growth	162.1%	—	—	—

2008 Year-End Financials

Return on assets: 17.4%
Return on equity: 126.6%
Current ratio: 0.80
Cash ($ mil.): 26

FS KKR CAPITAL CORP. II

Auditors: DELOITTE & TOUCHE LLP SAN FRA

LOCATIONS

HQ: FS KKR CAPITAL CORP. II
  201 ROUSE BLVD, PHILADELPHIA, PA 191121902
Phone: 215 495-1150
Web: WWW.FSKKRCAPITALCORP.COM

HISTORICAL FINANCIALS

Company Type: Private

Income Statement				FYE: December 31
	ASSETS ($ mil.)	NET INCOME ($ mil.)	INCOME AS % OF ASSETS	EMPLOYEES
12/20	8,522	(376)	—	9
12/19	8,970	238	2.7%	—
12/18	4,554	(37)	—	—
12/17	5,110	189	3.7%	—
Annual Growth	18.6%	—	—	—

2020 Year-End Financials

Return on assets: (-4.4%)
Return on equity: (-8.8%)
Sales ($ mil): 731

FTD COMPANIES, INC.

Mercury the Roman god of speed and commerce with winged feet comes bearing flowers. FTD is a leader in the floral industry for over a century supported by the iconic Mercury Man logo displayed in more than 30000 floral shops in over 125 countries. The company works with local florists to hand-craft floral arrangements available for same-day delivery on FTD.com and ProFlowers.com. In addition the company provides technology marketing and digital services to members of its florist network. The company was founded by John A. Valentine in 1910.

Operations

Product revenue for FTD comes from selling floral gift and related items to consumers through its web sites and by phone as well as through its floral network members.

Geographic Reach

Based in Downers Grove Illinois FTD serves consumers across the US Canada and India through its floral network members web sites and by phone.

Sales and Marketing

FTD markets its products through FTD.com ProFlowers.com and ProPlants.com and also in social media including Facebook and Instagram.

Auditors: DELOITTE & TOUCHE LLP CHICAGO

LOCATIONS

HQ: FTD COMPANIES, INC.
3113 WOODCREEK DR, DOWNERS GROVE, IL 605155420
Phone: 630 719-7800
Web: WWW.FTDCOMPANIES.COM

2014 Sales

	% of total
US	72
International	28
Total	**100**

2014 Sales

Revenue by Segments (in million)	% Contribu	
Product Revenues:		
Consumer	318	48
International	155	24
Florist	46	7
Service Revenues:		
Florist	116	18
International	22	3
Intersegment Elimination	(18)	
Total	**640**	**100**

PRODUCTS/OPERATIONS

Selected Businesses

Consumer
US
    1-800-SEND-FTD
www.ftd.com
Canada
www.ftd.ca
Ireland
www.interflora.ie
UK
www.drakealgar.com
www.interflora.uk
www.flyingflowers.co.uk
www.flowersdirect.co.uk
Floral Network
US
Canada
Ireland
UK

COMPETITORS

1-800-flowers	Marks & Spencer
Costco Wholesale	Next Plc

Harry & David Holdings	Organic Bouquet
John Lewis	Provide Commerce
Kabloom	Safeway
Kroger	Teleflora

HISTORICAL FINANCIALS
Company Type: Private

Income Statement
FYE: December 31

	REVENUE ($ mil.)	NET INCOME ($ mil.)	NET PROFIT MARGIN	EMPLOYEES
12/18	1,014	(224)	—	1,501
12/17	1,084	(234)	—	—
12/16	1,122	(83)	—	—
12/15	1,219	(78)	—	—
Annual Growth	**(6.0%)**	—	—	—

2018 Year-End Financials

Return on assets: (-58.1%)   Cash ($ mil.): 16
Return on equity: —
Current ratio: 0.20

FULTON COUNTY BOARD OF EDUCATION

EXECUTIVES

Pres, Linda McCain
Cfo*, Michael Russell
Contrl, W Harold Grindle
Coordinator, Ashley Garrison
Auditors: MAULDIN & JENKINS LLC ATLANT

LOCATIONS

HQ: FULTON COUNTY BOARD OF EDUCATION
6201 POWERS FERRY RD, ATLANTA, GA 303392926
Phone: 404 768-3600
Web: WWW.FULTONSCHOOLS.ORG

HISTORICAL FINANCIALS
Company Type: Private

Income Statement
FYE: June 30

	REVENUE ($ mil.)	NET INCOME ($ mil.)	NET PROFIT MARGIN	EMPLOYEES
06/20	1,392	18	1.3%	10,000
06/19	1,351	32	2.4%	—
06/18	1,268	40	3.2%	—
06/17	1,252	14	1.2%	—
Annual Growth	**3.6%**	**7.5%**	—	—

2020 Year-End Financials

Return on assets: 0.6%   Cash ($ mil.): 509
Return on equity: 2.0%
Current ratio: 3.10

FUNDAMENTAL INVESTORS, INC.

EXECUTIVES

Prin, Franklin Gowdy
Co-Founder & President & Manag, R D Andrews
Auditors: DELOITTE & TOUCHE LLP COSTA M

LOCATIONS

HQ: FUNDAMENTAL INVESTORS, INC.
1 MARKET, SAN FRANCISCO, CA 941051596
Phone: 800 421-0180

HISTORICAL FINANCIALS
Company Type: Private

Income Statement
FYE: December 31

	REVENUE ($ mil.)	NET INCOME ($ mil.)	NET PROFIT MARGIN	EMPLOYEES
12/19	2,262	24,161	1068.1%	5
12/18	2,151	(8,234)	—	—
Annual Growth	**5.2%**	—	—	—

2019 Year-End Financials

Return on assets: 22.2%   Cash ($ mil.): 11
Return on equity: 22.3%
Current ratio: —

GARDEN GROVE UNIFIED SCHOOL DISTRICT

EXECUTIVES

Supt, Gabriela Mafi
Supt*, Laura Schwalm
Prin*, Coleen Cross
SEC*, Joyan Spraus
Pres*, George West
V Pres*, Lan Quoc Nguyen
Accounting Staff, Cathy Joseph
Accounting Staff, Roxanne Linss
Teacher, Anna Lopez
Superintendent, Darrell Sy
Teacher, Judy Edwards

LOCATIONS

HQ: GARDEN GROVE UNIFIED SCHOOL DISTRICT
10331 STANFORD AVE, GARDEN GROVE, CA 928406351
Phone: 714 663-6000
Web: WWW.GGUSD.US

HISTORICAL FINANCIALS
Company Type: Private

Income Statement
FYE: June 30

	REVENUE ($ mil.)	NET INCOME ($ mil.)	NET PROFIT MARGIN	EMPLOYEES
06/20	658	(38)	—	5,000
06/19	655	2	0.4%	—
06/18	613	(90)	—	—
06/17	602	7	1.2%	—
Annual Growth	**3.0%**	—	—	—

GARFF ENTERPRISES, INC.

EXECUTIVES

Chm, Robert Garff
Pres*, John Garff
SEC*, Matthew Garff
V Pres*, Rick Fulkerson
Vice-President Business Develo, Sam Bracken
Marketing Team Member, Kirk Koenen
Finance, Colton Maxwell
Director of Brand Advocacy, Dana Geddes
Manager, Denim Simkins
Fleet Sales Representative CHR, Jake Robertson
General Sales Manager, Joey Burns
Auditors: MAYER HOFFMAN MC CANN PC SAL

LOCATIONS

HQ: GARFF ENTERPRISES, INC.
111 E BROADWAY STE 900, SALT LAKE CITY, UT 841115235
Phone: 801 257-3400
Web: WWW.KENGARFF.COM

HISTORICAL FINANCIALS
Company Type: Private

Income Statement				FYE: December 31
	REVENUE ($ mil.)	NET INCOME ($ mil.)	NET PROFIT MARGIN	EMPLOYEES
12/13	576	14	2.5%	855
12/03	481	10	2.1%	—
12/02	270	4	1.5%	—
12/01	189	0	—	—
Annual Growth	9.7%	—	—	—

2013 Year-End Financials
Return on assets: 1.4%
Return on equity: 2.5%
Current ratio: 0.20
Cash ($ mil.): 26

GBMC HEALTHCARE, INC.

EXECUTIVES

Pres-Ceo, John B Chessare
V Pres, Richard Borschuk
Cfo, Eric L Melchior
Sr V Pres, John W Ellis
Sr V Pres, Jody Porter
Coo, Keith Poisson
V Pres, Michael A Forthman
V Pres, Deloris Simpson Tuggle
V Pres, Cathy Hamel
V Pres, Jenny Coldiron
V Pres, George Bayless
Auditors: KMPG LLP BALTIMORE MD

LOCATIONS

HQ: GBMC HEALTHCARE, INC.
6701 N CHARLES ST, BALTIMORE, MD 212046808
Phone: 443 849-2000
Web: WWW.GBMC.ORG

HISTORICAL FINANCIALS
Company Type: Private

Income Statement				FYE: June 30
	REVENUE ($ mil.)	NET INCOME ($ mil.)	NET PROFIT MARGIN	EMPLOYEES
06/21	666	160	24.1%	3,900
06/20	605	26	4.4%	—
06/19	602	40	6.7%	—
06/18	573	30	5.3%	—
Annual Growth	5.1%	73.8%	—	—

2021 Year-End Financials
Return on assets: 13.4%
Return on equity: 21.2%
Current ratio: 1.10
Cash ($ mil.): 44

GCI, LLC

EXECUTIVES

Ceo, Ronald Duncan
Pres, David Morris
Vpres, Wilson Hughes
Vpres, Bruce L Broquet
Exec V Pres, Gregory F Chapados
SEC-Treas, John M Lowber
Sales Staff, Carl St George
Chief Operating Officer, Greg Chapados
Senior Mananger, Carmen Shearer
Chief Operating Officer, Gregory Chapados
Manager, John Gaydos
Auditors: KPMG LLP DENVER COLORADO

LOCATIONS

HQ: GCI, LLC
2550 DENALI ST STE 1000, ANCHORAGE, AK 995032751
Phone: 907 868-5400
Web: WWW.GCI.COM

HISTORICAL FINANCIALS
Company Type: Private

Income Statement				FYE: December 31
	REVENUE ($ mil.)	NET INCOME ($ mil.)	NET PROFIT MARGIN	EMPLOYEES
12/18	739	(917)	—	7
12/17	919	31	3.4%	—
12/16	933	(1)	—	—
12/15	978	(10)	—	—
Annual Growth	(8.9%)	—	—	—

2018 Year-End Financials
Return on assets: (-11.2%)
Return on equity: (-20.5%)
Current ratio: 0.40
Cash ($ mil.): 170

GEISINGER HEALTH

Geisinger Health System serves more than 1 million residents. Founded more than 100 years ago by Abigail Geisinger the system includes ten hospital campuses a health plan with more than half a million members a research institute and the Geisinger Commonwealth School of Medicine. With nearly 24000 employees and more than 1600 employed physicians Geisinger offers women's health sleep services surgery senior health dental medicine and addiction treatment among others. Its Geisinger Health Plan is an integrated health system that provides its member and patients with exceptional healthcare.

Operations

Geisinger Commonwealth School of Medicine offers a community-based model of undergraduate medical education as well as doctor of medicine program master of Biomedical Sciences and a portfolio of graduate programs. Geisinger Commonwealth School of Medicine is also home to around 585 residents and fellows comprising more than 35 accredited residency programs and about 30 subspecialty fellowships which encompass Accreditation Council for Graduate Medical Education physician programs as well as dental podiatry pharmacy and more.

Geographic Reach

Geisinger Health is based in Danville Pennsylvania. Its Geisinger Commonwealth School of Medicine has regional campuses in Atlantic City Danville Lewistown Sayre Scranton and Wilkes-Barre.

Sales and Marketing

Its health plan serves more than 500000 residents throughout central south-central and northeast Pennsylvania and works with affiliates in Delaware and Maine.

EXECUTIVES

Int Pres-Ceo, Jaewon Ryu
Exec V Pres, Joanne E Wade
Chief Quality Officer Evp CHI, Albert Bothe Jr
Coo, Frank J Trembulak
Evp-Coo, Matthew Walsh
Chb, Frank M Henry
Evp, and Managing Partner, Gei, Bruce H Hamory
Chitvo, Ronald A Paulus
Evp-Cso, Dominic Moffa
Exec V Pres-CIO, David Tilton
Cdio, David K Vawdrey
Auditors: KPMG LLP PHILADELPHIA PA

LOCATIONS

HQ: GEISINGER HEALTH
100 N ACADEMY AVE, DANVILLE, PA 178229800
Phone: 800 275-6401
Web: WWW.GEISINGER.ORG

PRODUCTS/OPERATIONS

Selected Services
Adolescent & Young Adult Medicine
Allergy
Anesthesia
Audiology
Bariatric Surgery
Cancer Institute
Cardiology
Colorectal Surgery
Cosmetics Program
Critical Care
Dental Medicine
Dermatology
Ear Nose & Throat
Emergency Medicine
Endocrinology & Metabolism
Fertility Center
Gastroenterology
Gynecology
Gynecologic Oncology
Heart Services
Hip & Knee Center
Imaging Services
Infectious Disease
Internal Medicine
Joint Replacement
Laboratory Medicine
LASIK Surgery

Mammography
Maternal Fetal Medicine
Mental Health
Minimally Invasive Surgery
Mohs Surgery
Neonatology
Nephrology
Neurodevelopmental Pediatrics
Neuroscience Institute
Neurology
Neurosurgery
Obstetrics
Ophthalmology
Orthopaedics
Osteoporosis
Pain Management
Palliative Medicine
Pediatrics (General)
Pediatric Allergy & Immunology
Pediatric Anesthesia & Sedation
Pediatric Cardiology
Pediatric Dental Surgery
Pediatric Dentistry
Pediatric Dermatology
Pediatric Endocrinology
Pediatric Gastroenterology
Pediatric General Surgery
Pediatric Genetics
Pediatric Hematology/Oncology
Pediatric Hospitalists
Pediatric Infectious Disease
Pediatric Intensive Care
Pediatric Interventional Radiology
Pediatric Nephrology
Pediatric Neurology
Pediatric Neuropsychology
Pediatric Neurosurgery
Pediatric Ophthalmology
Pediatric Orthopaedics
Pediatric Otolaryngology
Pediatric Plastic Surgery
Pediatric Psychology & Psychiatry
Pediatric Pulmonology
Pediatric Rehabilitation
Pediatric Rheumatology
Pediatric Transplant Surgery
Pediatric Trauma
Pediatric Urology
Pediatric Weight Management & Nutrition
Plastic & Reconstructive Surgery
Podiatry
Psychiatry
Pulmonary Medicine
Radiology
Rehabilitation
Rheumatology
Sleep Services
Spine Medicine
Sports Medicine
Surgery
Thoracic Surgery
Transplant Surgery
Trauma Center
Urogynecology
Urology
Vascular Surgery
Weight Management Clinic
Women's Health

Selected Facilities

Geisinger HealthSouth Rehabilitation Hospital
(Danville)
Geisinger Medical Center (Danville)
 The Janet Weis Children's Hospital
Geisinger Wyoming Valley Medical Center (Wilkes-Barre)
 Pearsall Heart Hospital
Geisinger South Wilkes-Barre Outpatient Center
Shamokin Area Community Hospital

COMPETITORS

Ascension Health
Blue Cross Of Northeastern Pennsylvania
Capital Bluecross
Community Health Systems
Healthamerica
Highmark
Pinnaclehealth System
Upmc
Universal Health Services
Wyoming Valley Health Care System

HISTORICAL FINANCIALS
Company Type: Private

Income Statement				FYE: June 30
	REVENUE ($ mil.)	NET INCOME ($ mil.)	NET PROFIT MARGIN	EMPLOYEES
06/20	7,121	(190)	—	13,030
06/19	7,145	174	2.4%	—
06/18	6,536	359	5.5%	—
06/17	6,337	552	8.7%	—
Annual Growth	4.0%	—	—	—

2020 Year-End Financials

Return on assets: (-2.1%)   Cash ($ mil.): 1,125
Return on equity: (-4.5%)
Current ratio: 1.60

GEISINGER HEALTH PLAN

EXECUTIVES

Pres, Kurt Wrobel
V Pres*, Frank J Trembulak
Cfo-Coo*, Mark McCullough
Coordinator, Kevin Boyles
Senior Analyst, Kim Hackenberg
Nurse Underwriter, Patrice Molesevich
Customer Team Member, Christine Jaegers
Quality Assurance Manager, Dave Evans
Customer Operations, Becky Hess
Quality Assurance Manager, Jean Fetterman
Sales Operations Analyst, Andrew Hergan
Auditors: GEISINGER SYSTEM SERVICES INC

LOCATIONS

HQ: GEISINGER HEALTH PLAN
 100 N ACADEMY AVE, DANVILLE, PA 178229800
Phone: 570 271-8778
Web: WWW.HEALTHPLAN.GEISINGER.ORG

HISTORICAL FINANCIALS
Company Type: Private

Income Statement				FYE: June 30
	REVENUE ($ mil.)	NET INCOME ($ mil.)	NET PROFIT MARGIN	EMPLOYEES
06/19	2,704	107	4.0%	900
06/18	2,638	55	2.1%	—
06/17	2,337	79	3.4%	—
06/10	875	35	4.0%	—
Annual Growth	13.4%	13.2%	—	—

2019 Year-End Financials

Return on assets: 16.9%   Cash ($ mil.): 15
Return on equity: 25.1%
Current ratio: —

GEISINGER MEDICAL CENTER

EXECUTIVES

Ceo, Glenn D Steele Jr
Exec V Pres*, Frank J Trembulak
Exec V Pres*, Joanne E Wade
Exec V Pres*, Albert Bothe Jr
Exec V Pres*, Lynn Miller
SEC*, Jessica Robertson
Chief Medical Officer*, Rosemary Leeming
Evp-CIO*, Karen Murphy
Evp-Cfo*, Kevin V Roberts
Director, Michael Komar
Director, Michael Progar

LOCATIONS

HQ: GEISINGER MEDICAL CENTER
 100 N ACADEMY AVE, DANVILLE, PA 178220001
Phone: 570 271-6211
Web: WWW.GEISINGER.ORG

HISTORICAL FINANCIALS
Company Type: Private

Income Statement				FYE: June 30
	REVENUE ($ mil.)	NET INCOME ($ mil.)	NET PROFIT MARGIN	EMPLOYEES
06/20	1,356	98	7.3%	8,000
06/16	1,095	108	9.9%	—
06/15	1,058	120	11.4%	—
06/10	815	79	9.7%	—
Annual Growth	5.2%	2.3%	—	—

2020 Year-End Financials

Return on assets: 8.5%   Cash ($ mil.): 174
Return on equity: 67.9%
Current ratio: —

GENERAL ELECTRIC INTERNATIONAL OPERATIONS COMPANY, INC.

EXECUTIVES

Pres, Robert Smits
Manager, Scott Sandlin
Auditors: KPMG LLP CINCINNATI OHIO

LOCATIONS

HQ: GENERAL ELECTRIC INTERNATIONAL
 OPERATIONS COMPANY, INC.
 191 ROSA PARKS ST, CINCINNATI, OH 452022573
Phone: 513 813-9133
Web: WWW.GE.COM

HISTORICAL FINANCIALS
Company Type: Private

Income Statement				FYE: December 31
	REVENUE ($ mil.)	NET INCOME ($ mil.)	NET PROFIT MARGIN	EMPLOYEES
12/17	966	192	19.9%	1,504
12/16	925	(55)	—	—
12/15	925	(22)	—	—
12/14	760	(8)	—	—
Annual Growth	8.3%	—	—	—

2017 Year-End Financials
Return on assets: 1.9% Cash ($ mil.): 101
Return on equity: 2.1%
Current ratio: 0.60

GENERAL ELECTRIC INTERNATIONAL, INC.

EXECUTIVES
Pres, Giuseppe Recchi
V Pres, Candace Carson
V Pres, Daniel Janki
SEC, Pierrot Christophe
SEC, Kristen Urso-Rio
Treas, Michael Geary
Senior Specialist, A Carbone
Power Performance Mana, Jerry King
Fbw Integrator, Joseph Desormeaux
Manufacturing Engineer, Mark Leeds
Accountant, Brianna Heyne
Auditors: KPMG LLP CINCINNATI OHIO

LOCATIONS
HQ: GENERAL ELECTRIC INTERNATIONAL, INC.
  1 RIVER RD, SCHENECTADY, NY 123456000
Phone: 617 443-3000
Web: WWW.GE.COM

HISTORICAL FINANCIALS
Company Type: Private

Income Statement				FYE: December 31
	REVENUE ($ mil.)	NET INCOME ($ mil.)	NET PROFIT MARGIN	EMPLOYEES
12/17	14,100	685	4.9%	125
12/16	13,364	1,339	10.0%	—
12/15	13,288	82	0.6%	—
12/14	12,884	(304)	—	—
Annual Growth	3.1%	—	—	—

2017 Year-End Financials
Return on assets: 3.5% Cash ($ mil.): 961
Return on equity: 10.5%
Current ratio: 1.50

GENESIS HEALTH SYSTEM

Genesis Health System operates three acute care hospitals in Iowa and Illinois that have more than 660 beds total and employ some 700 doctors. Genesis Medical Center in Davenport Iowa with more than 500 beds is the system's flagship facility; the hospital offers a range of general surgical and specialist health services. The system's Illini Campus in Silvis Illinois features an assisted-living center. The Genesis Medical Center Dewitt Campus serves that Iowa town and the surrounding area with its 13-bed hospital nursing home and related care facilities. Genesis Health System also operates physician practices outpatient centers and a home health agency.

Operations
Altogether Genesis Health System has more than 100 locations including hospitals convenient care locations Genesis Health Group sites physical rehabilitation clinics and outpatient service centers.

Strategy
In 2014 the system invested $15 million in the new Genesis HealthPlex in Bettendorf.

The following year Genesis Health System entered into a partnership with technology vendor Cerner Corporation to improve its patient care enterprise management systems.

Company Background
Genesis Health System had its genesis in 1869 with the establishment of Mercy Hospital (one of the first hospitals west of the Mississippi) and in the 1895 founding of St. Luke's Hospital. The two hospitals merged in 1994 to form the health system.

EXECUTIVES
Ceo, Doug Cropper
Pres*, Leo A Bressanelli
Sr V Pres*, Flo Spyrow
V Pres*, Robert Frieden
V Pres*, Kenneth Croken
V Pres*, Jackie Anhalt
V Pres*, Peter Metcalf
Coo*, Wayne Diewald
Cfo*, Mark Rogers
SEC*, Roger Hill
Treas*, Greg Bush
Auditors: RSM US LLP DAVENPORT IOWA

LOCATIONS
HQ: GENESIS HEALTH SYSTEM
  1227 E RUSHOLME ST, DAVENPORT, IA 528032459
Phone: 563 421-1000
Web: WWW.GENESISHEALTH.COM

PRODUCTS/OPERATIONS

Selected Services
Bariatric Surgery
Behavioral Health
Birthing Services
Cancer
Cardiology
Home Health/Hospice
Neuroscience
Nursing Homes
Physical Medicine & Rehab
Senior Services

COMPETITORS
Blessing Hospital
Catholic Health Initiatives
Mcdonough District Hospital
Mercy Health Network
Osf Healthcare System
Unitypoint Health

HISTORICAL FINANCIALS
Company Type: Private

Income Statement				FYE: June 30
	REVENUE ($ mil.)	NET INCOME ($ mil.)	NET PROFIT MARGIN	EMPLOYEES
06/21	706	73	10.5%	5,000
06/20	648	4	0.7%	—
06/19	646	13	2.1%	—
06/18	511	20	4.1%	—
Annual Growth	11.4%	52.3%	—	—

2021 Year-End Financials
Return on assets: 6.2% Cash ($ mil.): 170
Return on equity: 9.3%
Current ratio: 1.90

GENPACT LIMITED

LOCATIONS
HQ: GENPACT LIMITED
  1155 AVENUE OF THE AMERIC, NEW YORK, NY 100362711
Phone: 212 896-6600
Web: WWW.GENPACT.COM

HISTORICAL FINANCIALS
Company Type: Private

Income Statement				FYE: December 31
	REVENUE ($ mil.)	NET INCOME ($ mil.)	NET PROFIT MARGIN	EMPLOYEES
12/11	1,600	191	11.9%	325
12/10	1,258	149	11.8%	—
12/09	1,120	134	12.0%	—
Annual Growth	19.5%	19.0%	—	—

2011 Year-End Financials
Return on assets: 1.3% Cash ($ mil.): 408
Return on equity: 11.9%
Current ratio: 1.20

GEOKINETICS INC.

Using kinetic energy to assess the Earth's hydrocarbon sources Geokinetics is a global provider of geophysical services to the oil and gas industry. It acquires seismic data in North America and internationally and processes and interprets that data at processing centers in the US and the UK. The company's seismic crews work in a range of terrains including land marsh swamp shallow water and difficult transition zones (between land and water). Not dependent on any one customer its client base consists of international and national oil companies as well as smaller independent oil and gas exploration and production companies.

Bankruptcy
Hurt by project delays and a 2011 incident in which three employers were killed on a mapping

expedition in 2013 the company filed for Chapter 11 bankruptcy protection citing assets of $12 million and liabilities of $351 million.

Operations
The company is an industry leader in land transition zone and shallow water environments with more than 30 seismic crews with 200000 channels of seismic data acquisition equipment and five data processing centers around the world and 10443 square miles of multi-client data. Geokinetics offers two types of contracts: proprietary (individual contracts controlled by the client) and multi-client (prefunded contracts managed by Geokinetics). It has a multi-client data library with data covering areas in the Brazil Canada and the US.

Geographic Reach
Geokinetics has offices in 29 major countries and operations in Angola Brazil Canada Colombia Libya Mexico Singapore Suriname Tunisia the UAE the UK and the US. The company focuses on seismic acquisition activities in the US (Gulf Coast Mid-Continent and Rocky Mountain regions) and in Canada.

Sales and Marketing
The company's customers include independent international and state-owned national oil companies.

Financial Performance
In 2012 Geokinetic's revenue declined by 22% primarily due to lower activity in North America Africa and Asia Pacific offset by higher activity in Latin America. North America proprietary revenue decreased by 30% due to decreased crew activity in the US because of postponed projects. Multi-Client revenues dropped by 31% as the result of permit delays in certain areas of the US and a drop in new projects due to lower gas prices.

The company reported a net loss $82.9 million (compared to a net loss of $222 million in 2011). In 2011 Geokinetic's net loss increased dramatically led by costs related to a suspended contract a lost liftboat vessel and related fatalities in the Gulf of Mexico and subsequent litigation and a credit rating downgrade.

Strategy
A key part of Geokinetics' growth strategy is to offer a broad range of seismic services. To this end it plans to pursue strategic acquisitions to complement its existing acquisition processing and interpretation products and services and to expand its geographic footprint. It also hopes to partner with oil and gas exploration and production companies on multi-client library projects. Together these integrated set of services can help customers better evaluate known oil and gas deposits and improve the amount of recoverable hydrocarbons.

Company Background
In 2010 Geokinetics purchased the onshore seismic data acquisition and multi-client library business of Petroleum Geo-Services (PGS). The acquisition of PGS Onshore made Geokinetics the second largest provider of onshore seismic data acquisition services in the world in terms of crew count and the largest based in the West. The $183 million acquisition built on Geokinetics' expertise in transition zone and ocean bottom cable (OBC) environments two areas that the company believes are underserved but growing within the overall seismic services market. The acquisition also added new operating areas such as Alaska Mexico and certain countries in the Middle East and North Africa.

EXECUTIVES

Pres-Ceo, David J Crowley
Exec V Pres-Cfo*, Michael Muse
Exec V Pres of Operations*, Richard M Cieslewicz
Evp of Processing, Reservoir &*, James W Bogardus
Gen Counsel & Corp SEC*, Jessica Palomino
Chief Human Resource Officer-S*, James Tastard
Scientist, Zhihong Lin
Human Resources Administrator, Lina Colon
Operations Staff, Parker Lee
Manager, Christina Buchanan
Human Resources Analyst, Anita Piat

LOCATIONS

HQ: GEOKINETICS INC.
1500 CITYWEST BLVD # 800, HOUSTON, TX 770422300
Phone: 713 850-7600
Web: WWW.GEOKINETICSINC.COM

HISTORICAL FINANCIALS
Company Type: Private

Income Statement				FYE: December 31
	REVENUE ($ mil.)	NET INCOME ($ mil.)	NET PROFIT MARGIN	EMPLOYEES
12/11	763	(222)	—	5,695
12/10	558	(138)	—	—
12/09	510	(5)	—	—
Annual Growth	22.3%	—	—	—

2011 Year-End Financials
Return on assets: (-43.2%)   Cash ($ mil.): 44
Return on equity: —
Current ratio: 1.10

GEORGES PRINCE COUNTY GOVERNMENT

EXECUTIVES

Executive, Jack Johnson
County Executive*, Angela Alsobrooks
Budget Administratvie Speciali, Cynthia Moore
Assistant Chief, Kevin Foster
Training Section Chief, Alecia Creighton
Policy, Alison Flores
Chief Human Resources Officer, Audra Russell
Administrative Aide, Betty Nealy-Carter
Career Consultant Workforce SE, Candra Jalloh
Programmer Analyst, Charles Warner
County Auditor, David V Dyke
Auditors: CLIFTONLARSONALLEN LLP BALTIM

LOCATIONS

HQ: GEORGES PRINCE COUNTY GOVERNMENT
1301 MCCORMICK DR # 4200, LARGO, MD 207745416
Phone: 301 952-3300
Web: WWW.PRINCEGEORGESCOUNTYMD.GOV

HISTORICAL FINANCIALS
Company Type: Private

Income Statement				FYE: June 30
	REVENUE ($ mil.)	NET INCOME ($ mil.)	NET PROFIT MARGIN	EMPLOYEES
06/20	2,251	(17)	—	12,000
06/18	2,109	550	26.1%	—
Annual Growth	3.3%	—	—	—

2020 Year-End Financials
Return on assets: (-0.2%)   Cash ($ mil.): 1,274
Return on equity: —
Current ratio: —

GEORGIA CARESOURCE CO

EXECUTIVES

Ceo, Pamela Morris
Manager, Pascale Cadet-Dantes
Regulatory Manager, Candice Green

LOCATIONS

HQ: GEORGIA CARESOURCE CO
600 GALLERIA PKWY SE # 400, ATLANTA, GA 303398146
Phone: 678 214-7500
Web: WWW.CARESOURCE.COM

HISTORICAL FINANCIALS
Company Type: Private

Income Statement				FYE: December 31
	REVENUE ($ mil.)	NET INCOME ($ mil.)	NET PROFIT MARGIN	EMPLOYEES
12/18	669	(20)	—	1
12/17	307	15	5.0%	—
Annual Growth	117.6%	—	—	—

2018 Year-End Financials
Return on assets: (-15.7%)   Cash ($ mil.): 42
Return on equity: (-81.1%)
Current ratio: —

GEORGIA TECH APPLIED RESEARCH CORPORATION

EXECUTIVES

Ceo-Cfo, Stephen Cross
Chm, Leslie R Sibert
Pres, G Wayne Clough
SEC, Robert McGrath
Vice Pres, Chaouki Abdallah
Director of Sponsored Programs, G Duane Hutchison
Controller, Barbara J Alexander
Assistant SEC Treasurer, Barbara Alexander
Facilities, Nicolas F Perez
Associate, Eric Sadler
Director, Kevin Wozniak
Auditors: CHERRY BEKAERT LLP ATLANTA G

LOCATIONS

HQ: GEORGIA TECH APPLIED RESEARCH
CORPORATION
926 DALNEY ST NW, ATLANTA, GA 303186395
Phone: 404 894-6934
Web: WWW.GTRC.GATECH.EDU

HISTORICAL FINANCIALS
Company Type: Private

Income Statement				FYE: June 30
	REVENUE ($ mil.)	NET INCOME ($ mil.)	NET PROFIT MARGIN	EMPLOYEES
06/20	567	8	1.4%	1,100
06/19	491	7	1.5%	—
06/16	358	(0)	—	—
06/15	340	0	0.1%	—
Annual Growth	10.7%	87.0%	—	—

2020 Year-End Financials
Return on assets: 5.0%   Cash ($ mil.): 57
Return on equity: 19.6%
Current ratio: 2.40

GERBER SCIENTIFIC PRODUCTS INC

LOCATIONS

HQ: GERBER SCIENTIFIC PRODUCTS INC
83 GERBER RD W, SOUTH WINDSOR, CT 060743230
Phone: 860 648-8300

HISTORICAL FINANCIALS
Company Type: Private

Income Statement				FYE: April 30
	REVENUE ($ mil.)	NET INCOME ($ mil.)	NET PROFIT MARGIN	EMPLOYEES
04/07	574	13	2.4%	300
04/06	530	0	—	—
Annual Growth	8.4%	—	—	—

2007 Year-End Financials
Return on assets: 4.0%   Cash ($ mil.): 8
Return on equity: 9.3%
Current ratio: 1.70

GGP, INC.

Auditors: DELOITTE & TOUCHE LLP
CHICAGO

LOCATIONS

HQ: GGP, INC.
350 N ORLEANS ST STE 300, CHICAGO, IL
606541607
Phone: 312 960-5000
Web: WWW.GGP.COM

HISTORICAL FINANCIALS
Company Type: Private

Income Statement			FYE: December 31
	ASSETS ($ mil.)	NET INCOME ($ mil.)	INCOME AS % OF ASSETS	EMPLOYEES
12/12	27,282	(471)	—	1,500
12/11	29,518	(306)	—	—
12/10	32,367	(256)	—	—
12/09	28,149	(1,304)	—	—
Annual Growth	(1.0%)	—	—	—

2012 Year-End Financials
Return on assets: (-1.7%)   Sales ($ mil): 2,511
Return on equity: (-6.1%)

GILBANE BUILDING COMPANY

Gilbane Building Company has built a big business constructing for equally large customers. The firm provides construction services consulting subcontracting and facilities management to commercial institutional and governmental markets. Operating as the construction arm of Gilbane the company builds schools hospitals laboratories and prisons serving both the public and private sectors. Its completed projects include the Stroh Center at Bowling Green State University and the National WWII Memorial in Washington DC. Founded in 1870 as a carpentry and general contracting shop the family-owned Gilbane Building Company operates from more than 45 offices around the world.

Operations

The company offers Building Information Modeling (BIM) and Virtual Design and Construction (VDC) construction design-build disaster recovery & reconstruction environmental services facilities management fueling facilities construction & repair interdisciplinary document coordination multimedia studio multi-site project delivery systems preconstruction schedule risk analysis and transition planning & management. Its delivery methods include construction management; Integrated Project Delivery (IPD) a delivery model based on lean construction that collaborates and involve the owner A/E builders trade contractors facility managers end users; lump sum contracting and program/project management.

Geographic Reach

Rhode Island-based the company has more than 45 offices and 1000 projects underway around the world some of its domestic location are in Arizona California Colorado Florida Georgia New York and South Carolina. Gilbane Building Company enjoys a geographic footprint that extends from the US to Japan the United Arab Emirates Guam Ireland Saudi Arabia South Korea and Afghanistan.

Sales and Marketing

Gilbane Building Company serves several sectors such as healthcare higher education K-12 schools federal and public entities mission critical corporate and sports and recreation. The company reported over 75% of its work comes from repeat clients.

Some of its clients have included: Cleveland Museum Discovery World Science & Technology Center Dunkin' Donuts Marathon Petroleum Corp Phillips 66 PricewaterhouseCoopers LLP Arizona State University and Duke University.

Strategy

Gilbane Building Company has been appointing leadership for different segments and locations of the company in order to expand client relationships as well as expand business development strategies.

Company Background

In 1870 William Gilbane founded a carpentry firm and in 1871 Thomas Gilbane apprenticed with his brother William. Together the brothers worked tirelessly to found Gilbane Building Company in 1870.

EXECUTIVES

Chairman Of The Board, Thomas Gilbane
Chief Financial Officer, Senior Vice President,, John Ruggieri
Executive Vice President Of Global Sales And Marketing, Karen Medeiros
Chief Human Resource Officer, Senior Vice President, Katherine Johnson
President, Chief Executive Officer, Michael McKelvy
Auditors: RSM US LLP BOSTON MASSACHUSE

LOCATIONS

HQ: GILBANE BUILDING COMPANY
7 JACKSON WALKWAY STE 2, PROVIDENCE, RI
029033694
Phone: 401 456-5800
Web: WWW.GILBANECO.COM

PRODUCTS/OPERATIONS

Selected Markets
Convention/cultural
Corporate
Criminal justice
Federal/public
Health care
  Children's hospitals
  Women's centers
  Cardiac-care centers
  Cancer centers
  Clinical and research facilities
Higher education
  Research laboratories
  Academic facilities
  Admissions buildings
  Residence halls
  Performing arts centers
  Sports and recreational centers
  Libraries and technology centers
  Student unions
K-12 schools
Life sciences
Mission critical
Sports/recreation
Transportation
Water/wastewater

Selected Services
Pre-construction
  Transition planning and management
  Building information modeling
  Conceptual cost modeling
  High-performance building & energy modeling
  Interdisciplinary document coordination
Consulting
  CAT-response
  Facilities management services
  Schedule & risk analysis
  Transition planning & management
Construction
  Construction management at risk
  Construction management as agent
  Lump sum general contracting
  Integrated project delivery

COMPETITORS

Barton Malow	Mccarthy Building
Batson-cook	Peter Kiewit Sons'
Bechtel	Skanska Usa Building
Bernards Brothers	Swinerton

Clark Construction	The Pike Company
Group	Thos. S. Byrne
Dimeo Construction	Turner Construction
Fluor	Turner Corporation
Kbr	Tutor Perini
L.f. Driscoll	Walbridge Aldinger
Medco Construction	Whiting-turner

HISTORICAL FINANCIALS
Company Type: Private

Income Statement				FYE: December 31
	REVENUE ($ mil.)	NET INCOME ($ mil.)	NET PROFIT MARGIN	EMPLOYEES
12/17	4,899	63	1.3%	2,500
12/14	3,840	0	—	—
12/13	4,100	0	—	—
Annual Growth	4.5%	—	—	—

2017 Year-End Financials
Return on assets: 3.9%   Cash ($ mil.): 252
Return on equity: 22.6%
Current ratio: 1.20

GLOBAL HEALTH SOLUTIONS INC

EXECUTIVES
Vice President, T Rosenberger
V Pres, Thomas Rosenberger

LOCATIONS
HQ: GLOBAL HEALTH SOLUTIONS INC
325 SWANTON WAY, DECATUR, GA 300303001
Phone: 404 592-1430
Web: WWW.TASKFORCE.ORG

HISTORICAL FINANCIALS
Company Type: Private

Income Statement				FYE: August 31
	REVENUE ($ mil.)	NET INCOME ($ mil.)	NET PROFIT MARGIN	EMPLOYEES
08/15	1,609	0	—	2
08/14	1,790	0	—	—
08/13	1,574	0	—	—
08/10	1,120	0	0.0%	—
Annual Growth	7.5%	—	—	—

GLU MOBILE INC.

EXECUTIVES
Pres-Ceo, Nick Earl
Exec Chb*, Niccolo De Masi
Exec V Pres-Coo-Cfo, Eric R Ludwig
Cro, Chris Akhavan
V Pres-Gen Counsel-Corp SEC, Scott J Leichtner
Vp-Gen Mgr, Jon David
Software Engineer, Brooke Jackson
Production Artist, Caitlin Ono
Marketing Associate, Daphne Nguyen
Associate Producer, Dashel Thompson

Associate Engineer, David Nishball
Auditors: PRICEWATERHOUSECOOPERS LLP SA

LOCATIONS
HQ: GLU MOBILE INC.
875 HOWARD ST STE 100, SAN FRANCISCO, CA 941033032
Phone: 415 800-6100
Web: WWW.GLU.COM

COMPETITORS
Atlus U.s.a.	Hands-on Mobile
Dena	Konami
Digital Chocolate	Namco Limited
Digital Turbine	Rovio Entertainment
Electronic Arts	Zynga
Gameloft	

HISTORICAL FINANCIALS
Company Type: Private

Income Statement				FYE: December 31
	REVENUE ($ mil.)	NET INCOME ($ mil.)	NET PROFIT MARGIN	EMPLOYEES
12/20	540	20	3.8%	546
12/19	411	8	2.2%	—
12/18	366	(13)	—	—
12/17	286	(97)	—	—
Annual Growth	23.5%	—	—	—

2020 Year-End Financials
Return on assets: 3.1%   Cash ($ mil.): 364
Return on equity: 4.9%
Current ratio: 2.60

GOOD SAMARITAN HOSPITAL MEDICAL CENTER

The folks at Good Samaritan Hospital Medical Center have plenty of reasons to feel good about their efforts. The hospital is part of Catholic Health Services of Long Island (CHS) and serves the south shore community of West Islip New York. The full-service medical center boasts 900 physicians and 440 acute care beds offering a complete range of health care counseling and rehabilitation services. Good Samaritan provides emergency medicine and trauma care in addition to oncology cardiology pediatric woman's health diagnostic and surgical care. It also operates the Good Samaritan Nursing Home a 100-bed skilled nursing facility as well as satellite clinics and a home health care agency.

Operations
Good Samaritan which contributes about 28% of its parent's revenue logged more than 95000 emergency department visits in 2012. Its ambulatory surgery department treats an average of nearly 300 patients weekly as part of its focus on same-day procedures. Additionally the medical facility in 2012 admitted 27615 patients and logged 2820 births 66000 rehabilitation inpatient visits and 49640 dialysis treatments.

The hospital's outpatient services include same day surgeries pulmonary rehabilitation pediatric specialty visits and physical occupational and speech therapy sessions; it also has satellite locations that provide dialysis treatment. Good Samar-

itan's palliative care program offers an 11-bed dedicated acute palliative care inpatient unit.

Geographic Reach
Good Samaritan Hospital Medical Center serves those in and around West Islip New York.

Financial Performance
Net patient revenue dragged down Good Samaritan's revenue increases in fiscal 2012 vs. 2011. During the reporting period the medical center posted $579 million in revenue representing a marginal $260000 rise. Net income dropped some 77% to $8.3 million in 2012 vs. 2011 thanks to rising operating expenses from increases in CHS Services.

Strategy
Good Samaritan is recognized for its cancer care and radiology programs as well as its cardiac pediatric and women's health services all of which it has been expanding and enhancing in recent years. For instance the hospital added a nephrology unit in 2011 within its pediatric division to evaluate and treat children with kidney disease. It expanded its pediatric nephrology unit in 2012 by opening a new 16-bed surgical intensive care unit (SICU). Good Samaritan also added a new diagnostic imaging center in 2012 that provides radiology services including breast imaging.

In addition Good Samaritan is working to add an open-heart surgery program to its cardiology division through a partnership with St. Francis Hospital another member of the CHS organization also known as The Heart Center. In 2013 Good Samaritan became the first facility in the New York metropolitan region to install and offer the GE Innova IGS 530 digital cardiovascular and interventional imaging system in its cardiac catheterization laboratory.

The not-for-profit facility's growth measures are supported in part by its charitable organization The Guilds of Good Samaritan Hospital Medical Center. The Good Samaritan hospital provides some $50 million in community service and charity care each year.

Company Background
Founded in 1959 Good Samaritan became part of the CHS organization in 1997.

EXECUTIVES
Evp & Cao, Thomas Ockers
Vp Quality MGT*, Vincent Angeloro
Avp Plant Engg*, Richard Bie
Avp Imaging*, Ralph Corbino
Vp of Risk MGT*, Gail Donheiser
Avp Medical Affairs*, Michele Dykstra
Svp of Patient Serv*, Gara Edelstein
Medical Dir*, Gino Giorgini
Coo*, Joseph Loiacono
Vp Hr*, Lori Spina
Avp Finance*, Christine Stehlik

LOCATIONS
HQ: GOOD SAMARITAN HOSPITAL MEDICAL CENTER
1000 MONTAUK HWY, WEST ISLIP, NY 117954927
Phone: 631 376-3000
Web: WWW.GOODSAMARITAN.CHSLI.ORG

PRODUCTS/OPERATIONS

Selected Premier Services
Cancer Care
Cardiac Care
Children's Care
Emergency Services
Satellites
Surgery
Women's Care

Selected Services
Ambulatory Surgery Unit
Audiology/Hearing Aids

BirthPlace
Breast Health Center
Cancer Care
Cancer Surgery
Cardiac Rehabilitation
Cardiology Services
Center for Pediatric Specialty Care
Care Management and Social Work
Child Life Services
da Vinci Surgery
Dentistry
Dermatology
Dialysis Services
Ear Nose and Throat
Emergency Department
Endocrinology
Family Practice
Gastroenterology
Good Samaritan Hospital Foundation
Good Samaritan Nursing Home
Hematology and Oncology
Imaging Services
Infectious Diseases
Inpatient Dialysis
Internal Medicine
Laboratory
Long Term Home Health Care
Managed Care
Martin Luther King Jr. Community Health Center
Maternal Fetal Medicine
Medical Education
Neonatology
Nephrology
Neurosurgery
Nursing at Good Sam
Nutrition and Food Services
Obstetrics and Gynecology
Oncology
Ophthalmology
Oral Surgery
Orthopaedics
Osteoporosis
Palliative Care
Pain Management
Pastoral/Spiritual Care Department
Pathology
Pediatric Services
Perinatal Education
Plastic and Reconstructive Services
Podiatry
Pre-Surgical Testing
Psychiatry
Pulmonary Rehabilitation
Radiation Oncology Center
Rehabilitation Services
Respiratory Care
Safe Haven Program
Sleep Apnea Center
Special Care
Support Groups
Surgery
Thoracic Surgery
Trauma Services
Urology
Vascular Suite
Vascular Surgery
Weight Loss Surgery/Bariatric Surgery
Women's Imaging Center

COMPETITORS

Brookhaven Memorial Hospital Medical Center
Csh
Catholic Healthcare System
Continuum Health Partners
Mather Memorial Hospital
Memorial Sloan-kettering
New York City Health And Hospitals
Newyork-presbyterian Healthcare
Northwell Health
Winthrop-university Hospital

HISTORICAL FINANCIALS

Company Type: Private

Income Statement   FYE: December 31

	REVENUE ($ mil.)	NET INCOME ($ mil.)	NET PROFIT MARGIN	EMPLOYEES
12/19	725	20	2.8%	3,774
12/15	505	28	5.7%	—
12/14	488	36	7.5%	—
12/13	534	(28)	—	—
Annual Growth	5.2%	—	—	—

2019 Year-End Financials

Return on assets: 3.6%   Cash ($ mil.): 96
Return on equity: 7.4%
Current ratio: 2.10

GOOD SAMARITAN HOSPITAL OF CINCINNATI

EXECUTIVES

Ceo, Mark Clement
Pres*, John S Prout
Chm*, Robert L Walker
Sr V Pres*, John R Robinson
Cfo*, Craig Rucker
Coo*, Gerald Oliphant
Internal Medicine Practitioner, Aleksandr Yultyev
Internal Medicine Practitioner, Ashirf Al-Ghanoudi
Internal Medicine Practitioner, Hiro Kawata
Internal Medicine Practitioner, Irina Gagua
Health Professional, Jiang Wu
Auditors: ERNST & YOUNG LLP CINCINNATI

LOCATIONS

HQ: GOOD SAMARITAN HOSPITAL OF CINCINNATI
   375 DIXMYTH AVE, CINCINNATI, OH 452202489
Phone: 513 569-6251
Web: WWW.TRIHEALTH.COM

HISTORICAL FINANCIALS

Company Type: Private

Income Statement   FYE: June 30

	REVENUE ($ mil.)	NET INCOME ($ mil.)	NET PROFIT MARGIN	EMPLOYEES
06/21	743	157	21.1%	3,452
06/20	563	(60)	—	—
06/19	563	33	5.9%	—
06/18	579	48	8.3%	—
Annual Growth	8.7%	48.3%	—	—

2021 Year-End Financials

Return on assets: 13.3%   Cash ($ mil.): —
Return on equity: 16.6%
Current ratio: 1.10

GOOD SAMARITAN HOSPITAL, L.P.

Good Samaritan Hospital lends a hand to help Silicon Valley's techies and their neighbors stay healthy. The facility part of the HCA family of for-profit hospitals administers care through campuses in San Jose (the main campus) and Los Gatos California. Good Samaritan Hospital provides general acute care as well as a host of tertiary services that include cardiology and cardiovascular surgery; oncology; obstetrics and gynecology; and psychiatry (both inpatient and outpatient care). The main campus hospital has some 408 patient beds and 600 physicians and the Los Gatos outpatient and short-stay facility houses approximately 100 beds.

Operations
Each year Good Samaritan admits 17000 patients (excluding newborns) and handles more than 93500 outpatient visits. More than 4000 deliveries and 8000 surgeries are performed annually in 18 surgical suites.

Strategy
In addition to being a community hospital Good Samaritan is a world-class academic medical center affiliated with both USC and UCLA Schools of Medicine. To cater to the diverse urban population the hospital system serves Good Samaritan's medical staff and employees speak more than 54 languages/dialects.

Company Background
Good Samaritan Hospital opened its doors in 1965 as an acute care hospital with a staff of about 400.

EXECUTIVES

V Pres, Frank Hirano
Cfo, Darrel Neuenschwander
Coo-Chief Medical Officer, Paul Deaupre
Cfo, Lana Arad
Coo, Jordan Herget
Chief Operating Officer, Paul Beaupre
Internal Medicine Practitioner, Darryl Neuenschwander
Director of Human Resources, Stacey Lawson
Vice President of Operations, Jim Lamar
Clinical Coord of Er, Abby Valbuena
Chemical Substance Abuse Dir, Amy Gerberry

LOCATIONS

HQ: GOOD SAMARITAN HOSPITAL, L.P.
   2425 SAMARITAN DR, SAN JOSE, CA 951243985
Phone: 408 559-2011
Web: WWW.GOODSAMSANJOSE.COM

PRODUCTS/OPERATIONS

Selected Services and Departments

Cardiology
Cardiac Surgery
Comprehensive Sleep Center
Diagnostic Imaging (Radiology)
ENT (Ear Nose & Throat)
Emergency Services
Gamma Knife
Gastroenterology
Laboratory
Neurosciences
Oncology (Cancer)
Opthalmology & Retinal Medicine
Orthopedics
Podiatry
Physical Medicine
Pulmonary Medicine & Respiratory Care
Radiation Oncology

Surgery
Women's Health & Newborn Services
Urology

COMPETITORS

Dignity Health
Mills-peninsula Health
  Services
Sequoia Healthcare
  District

Stanford Health Care
The Palo Alto Medical
  Foundation
Valleycare Health
  System

HISTORICAL FINANCIALS

Company Type: Private

Income Statement   FYE: January 31

	REVENUE ($ mil.)	NET INCOME ($ mil.)	NET PROFIT MARGIN	EMPLOYEES
01/17	618	141	22.8%	1,800
01/09*	413	30	7.3%	—
05/05	170	0	—	—
12/03	0	0	—	—
Annual Growth	—	—	—	—

*Fiscal year change

2017 Year-End Financials

Return on assets: 53.2%   Cash ($ mil.): —
Return on equity: 37.7%
Current ratio: 2.10

GOVERNMENT OF DISTRICT OF COLUMBIA

Government of the District of Columbia manages ticket and tax payments housing and property issues children and youth services and motor vehicles registration among other duties for Washington DC. More than 689000 people live in Washington DC and many more commute to the city every day to work for the federal government. Washington DC is overseen by a mayor and a 13-member city council. It acquires contracts with more than 30 local government agencies. The Government of the District of Columbia was created in 1790 with donated land from Maryland and Virginia as part of the Residence Act.

EXECUTIVES

Mayor, Muriel Bowser
Cfo*, Natawar Gandhi
Chief Procurement Officer*, George Schutter
Attorney, Wilma A Lewis
Sr Analyst, Gary Muren
Procurement Staff, Leon Borroum
Sergeant, Robert Panizari
Dep Chief of Staff, Sheila Bunn
Dir Homeland SEC/Emer Mgmt, Christopher T Geldart
Customer Representativ, Alicia James
Staff, Frances Nugent
Auditors: SB & COMPANY LLC WASHINGTON

LOCATIONS

HQ: GOVERNMENT OF DISTRICT OF COLUMBIA
441 4TH ST NW, WASHINGTON, DC 200012714
Phone: 202 727-0252
Web: WWW.DC.GOV

PRODUCTS/OPERATIONS

Selected Services

311 Service Request Online
Children and Youth Services
District Neighborhoods
Emergency Preparedness
Health and Human Services
Housing and Property
Pay a Ticket
Public Safety
Public Works Sanitation and Utilities
Taxpayer Service Center
Transportation and Motor Vehicles

HISTORICAL FINANCIALS

Company Type: Private

Income Statement   FYE: September 30

	REVENUE ($ mil.)	NET INCOME ($ mil.)	NET PROFIT MARGIN	EMPLOYEES
09/16	12,095	(78)	—	34,600
09/15	11,637	583	5.0%	—
09/11	9,822	102	1.0%	—
09/05	0	0	—	—
Annual Growth	—	—	—	—

2016 Year-End Financials

Return on assets: (-0.4%)   Cash ($ mil.): 1,687
Return on equity: (-1.4%)
Current ratio: —

GPM INVESTMENTS, LLC

Convenience is key for GPM Investments which operates or supplies fuel to more than 1100 convenience stores in about 20 US states. The stores sell BP Exxon Marathon and Valero brand gas among others as well as the usual beer smokes and snacks. Some locations also offer fresh made-to-order salads sandwiches and other items or offer branded food from Subway Taco Bell and others. The company which primarily serves the Midwest and eastern US operates or supplies stores under a host of names including Fas Mart Shore Stop Jiffi Stop Young's and Roadrunner Markets.

Operations

In addition to convenience stores GPM also operates 15 Subway franchises one Taco Bell franchise and 50 restaurants that serve Southern fried chicken.

Geographic Reach

Richmond Virginia-based GPM operates more than 600 convenience stores in Virginia North Carolina Delaware Maryland Pennsylvania New Jersey Connecticut Rhode Island South Carolina and Tennessee.

Strategy

To help fund investments in new capital improvement projects and in acquisitions GPM entered into a $35 million credit facility with PNC Bank N.A. in 2012. Maturing in November 2016 the credit facility allows GPM to open new stores and improve existing locations. To this end the convenience store operator has offered to buy a 50% stake in EZ Energy Ltd. based in Ramat Gan Israel for $15 million. The company typically uses funding received through credit facilities to improve its locations with brighter interior and exterior lighting wider aisles and cleaner stores. It is also increasing its marketing efforts through social media to target younger shoppers.

Fast-growing GPM Investments in growing through acquisitions. Indeed in 2013 the company made its largest acquisition to date propelling its

store count to more than 600 locations in 10 states.

Mergers and Acquisitions

In August 2013 GPM acquired the Southeastern division of VPS Convenience Store Group from Sun Capital Partners. The regional division operates more than 260 stores and 33 dealer sites and was cobbled together from acquisitions that included the Scotchman Young's Li'l Cricket Everyday Shop and Cigarette City banners. Most of the newly-acquired stores are in the Carolinas where GPM's retail presence is thin. Earlier in August GPM purchased five stores operating under the Get & Zip banner in Virginia. Most of the

EXECUTIVES

MBR, Dave McComas
MBR*, Mark King
MBR*, Chris Giacobone
Sr V Pres For Mrktg, Bill Reilly
Controller, Mark Koschmeder
Corporate Communications Manag, Michael Yates
Public Relations Manager, Caroline Ward
Controller, Denise Johnson
Accounting Manager, Jim Pearce
Regional Food Beverage Manager, Joe Brickey
Cash Accountant, Katie Lewis
Auditors: GRANT THORNTON LLP RALEIGH

LOCATIONS

HQ: GPM INVESTMENTS, LLC
8565 MAGELLAN PKWY # 400, RICHMOND, VA
232271167
Phone: 276 328-3669
Web: WWW.GPMINVESTMENTS.COM

Selected Locations

Connecticut
Delaware
Maryland
New Jersey
North Carolina
Pennsylvania
Rhode Island
South Carolina
Tennessee
Virginia

COMPETITORS

7-eleven
Cumberland Farms
Exxon Mobil
Gate Petroleum

Racetrac Petroleum
Sheetz
Wawa Inc.

HISTORICAL FINANCIALS

Company Type: Private

Income Statement   FYE: December 31

	REVENUE ($ mil.)	NET INCOME ($ mil.)	NET PROFIT MARGIN	EMPLOYEES
12/08	1,249	(1)	—	2,150
12/07	891	3	0.4%	—
Annual Growth	40.2%	—	—	—

2008 Year-End Financials

Return on assets: 1.7%   Cash ($ mil.): 12
Return on equity: (-0.1%)
Current ratio: 0.40

GRADY MEMORIAL HOSPITAL CORPORATION

EXECUTIVES

Pres-Ceo, John M Haupert
Prin, Timothy Jefferson
Pres, Joselyn Butler Baker
Cfo, Richard Rhine
Prin, Kelley Carroll
Prin, Lindsay Caulfield
Prin, Matthew Hicks
Executive Vice President Chief, Robert Jansen
Vp of Fin, Ozzie Gilbert
Senior Vice-President, Calvin Thomas IV
Grants Manager, David Noble
Auditors: KPMG LLP ATLANTA GA

LOCATIONS

HQ: GRADY MEMORIAL HOSPITAL CORPORATION
  80 JESSE HILL JR DR SE, ATLANTA, GA 303033050
Phone: 404 616-4360
Web: WWW.GRADYHEALTH.ORG

HISTORICAL FINANCIALS
Company Type: Private

Income Statement				FYE: December 31
	REVENUE ($ mil.)	NET INCOME ($ mil.)	NET PROFIT MARGIN	EMPLOYEES
12/19	2,032	29	1.5%	7
12/17	1,494	42	2.9%	—
12/16	1,444	47	3.3%	—
12/15	1,230	47	3.9%	—
Annual Growth	13.4%	(11.1%)	—	—

2019 Year-End Financials
Return on assets: 3.0%   Cash ($ mil.): 216
Return on equity: 4.2%
Current ratio: 2.40

GRAEBEL HOLDINGS, INC.

EXECUTIVES

Chb-Ceo-Pres, David W Graebel
Ceo, Bill Graebel
Pres, Craig Broback
Cfo, Brad Siler
Coo-SEC, William Graebel
Assignment Consu, Wendy Harrison
Customer Care, Lisa Bement
Operations Manag, Jana Karaskova
Relocation Consultant, Alysia Shoemaker
On Site Manager, Amy Wagner
Consultant, Andrea Hallberg
Auditors: WIPFLI LLP WAUSAU WISCONSIN

LOCATIONS

HQ: GRAEBEL HOLDINGS, INC.
  16346 AIRPORT CIR, AURORA, CO 800111558
Phone: 303 214-6683
Web: WWW.GRAEBEL.COM

HISTORICAL FINANCIALS
Company Type: Private

Income Statement				FYE: December 31
	REVENUE ($ mil.)	NET INCOME ($ mil.)	NET PROFIT MARGIN	EMPLOYEES
12/20	912	7	0.8%	1,771
12/17	96	1	1.2%	—
12/16	90	3	3.6%	—
12/15	94	5	5.9%	—
Annual Growth	57.5%	6.1%	—	—

2020 Year-End Financials
Return on assets: 5.6%   Cash ($ mil.): 13
Return on equity: 24.8%
Current ratio: 1.20

GRAHAM ENTERPRISE, INC.

EXECUTIVES

Pres, John C Graham
V Pres, Eugene W Graham III
SEC, Matthew X Graham
Coo, Patrick T Graham
Administrator, Matthew Graham
Fuel Accounting Manager, Ashley Flament
Senior Vice President, Brian D Wente
Chief Information Officer, Keyur Bhatt
Manager, Lance Caldwell
Merchandise Coordinator, Marcelo Reyes
Director of Information Techno, Michael Bee
Auditors: FGMK LLC BANNOCKBURN ILLINO

LOCATIONS

HQ: GRAHAM ENTERPRISE, INC.
  750 BUNKER CT STE 100, VERNON HILLS, IL
  600611864
Phone: 847 837-0777
Web: WWW.GRAHAMEI.COM

HISTORICAL FINANCIALS
Company Type: Private

Income Statement				FYE: December 31
	REVENUE ($ mil.)	NET INCOME ($ mil.)	NET PROFIT MARGIN	EMPLOYEES
12/17	638	12	2.0%	350
12/16	596	6	1.1%	—
12/15	662	11	1.7%	—
12/14	866	8	0.9%	—
Annual Growth	(9.7%)	16.5%	—	—

2017 Year-End Financials
Return on assets: 32.4%   Cash ($ mil.): 6
Return on equity: 47.9%
Current ratio: 1.90

GRANDVIEW HEALTH HOMES, INC.

EXECUTIVES

Pres, Jerry E Boone
Marketing Public Relations Dir, Ann McLaughlin
Chief Purchasing Officer, Andrew Roos
Nursing Home Director, Robert Druckenmiller
Business Office Manager, William Mettler
Quality Control Director, Sue Chrysler
Human Resources Director, Wendy Utt

LOCATIONS

HQ: GRANDVIEW HEALTH HOMES, INC.
  78 WOODBINE LN, DANVILLE, PA 178218020
Phone: 570 275-5240
Web: WWW.GRANDVIEWNR.COM

HISTORICAL FINANCIALS
Company Type: Private

Income Statement				FYE: June 30
	REVENUE ($ mil.)	NET INCOME ($ mil.)	NET PROFIT MARGIN	EMPLOYEES
06/09	1,262	4	0.4%	240
06/99	2	2	89.8%	—
06/98	3	0	11.0%	—
Annual Growth	71.5%	25.8%	—	—

2009 Year-End Financials
Return on assets: 92.2%   Cash ($ mil.): —
Return on equity: —
Current ratio: 1.20

GRANITE SCHOOL DISTRICT

EXECUTIVES

Supt, Martin W Bates
SEC*, Mary Lynn
SEC*, Kathy Goodfellow
Information, Anjanette Anderson
Coordinator, Cindy Dunn
Officer, Brett Walker
Officer, Kevin Hyde
Chief Technology Officer, Stephanie Hamilton
Teacher, Tiffany Rasmussen
Educator, Gayleen Gandy
Teacher, Pietz Cheryl
Auditors: SQUIRE & COMPANY PC OREM UT

LOCATIONS

HQ: GRANITE SCHOOL DISTRICT
  2500 S STATE ST STE 500, SOUTH SALT LAKE, UT
  841153195
Phone: 385 646-5000
Web: WWW.GRANITESCHOOLS.ORG

HISTORICAL FINANCIALS

Company Type: Private

Income Statement				FYE: June 30
	REVENUE ($ mil.)	NET INCOME ($ mil.)	NET PROFIT MARGIN	EMPLOYEES
06/20	693	0	0.0%	8,000
06/19	678	52	7.7%	—
06/18	610	79	13.0%	—
06/17	571	9	1.7%	—
Annual Growth	6.6%	(74.9%)		

GRANITE TELECOMMUNICATIONS LLC

Granite Telecommunications carves out an increasing block of telecommunications services to commercial clients in the US and Canada. The company is a wholesaler of local and long distance telephone service as well as broadband internet connections with more than 1.3 million lines provided by network operators. It serves corporate clients many of whom run offices in multiple states offering them no account transfer charges and no term or volume contracts on telephone service. Granite also designs and installs network cabling and security systems and provides loss prevention and risk management services.

Operations

The company serves more than 4800 corporate clients in more than a half a million locations. Its customers include most of the US Fortune 100 companies and its customer retention rate is more than five times higher than the industry average. It has about 1.4 million phone lines; about 1.3 billion lines are business lines and 65000 are data lines. The company uses copper wiring found in traditional telecommunication networks which provide reliable and cost-effective service. Granite's subsidiary Granite Guard is a leading provider of loss prevention and risk management services solely for businesses.

Geographic Reach

Granite serves clients across Canada and the US from offices in Florida Massachusetts Georgia Illinois New York Texas and Rhode Island. It is based in Quincy Massachusetts.

Sales and Marketing

Granite's customers include PepsiCo Toys R Us Quality Distribution Jenny Craig Cardinal Health Southwest Airlines Brookdale Senior Living and Agrium.

Financial Performance

The company reported in 2016 that is annual revenue was more than $1.25 billion and that its revenue increased by more than $100 million.

Strategy

Expanding beyond its role as a reseller of telecom services Granite has rolled out its own Granite Grid. It's a fiber-based network with voice and data services for hospitals shopping malls and other multi-tenant buildings. The Granite-installed and maintained network offers better internet service. Simon Property Group one of the US's biggest mall operators has wired its properties to Granite Grid.

Granite has added clients with expansions in Florida and Georgia where it has built new facilities. It also built a new building at its Quincy Massachusetts headquarters to accommodate more employees.

EXECUTIVES

Mng MBR, Robert Hale Jr
Svp and Coo, Rand Currier
Vice President of Operations, Paul Stutzman
Mng MBR, John Prinner
Mng MBR, Mark Prendergast
Vp Transformation/Strategicaff, Sana Sheikh
Senior Premier Account Analyst, Kevin Ford
Customer Representativ, Michael Fitzgerald
Cfo, Richard Wurman
Executive of Information Techn, Oadnaha Yelmanchili
Staff, Julie Sweklo

LOCATIONS

HQ: GRANITE TELECOMMUNICATIONS LLC
100 NEWPORT AVENUE EXT # 1, QUINCY, MA 021712126
Phone: 617 933-5500
Web: WWW.GRANITENET.COM

PRODUCTS/OPERATIONS

Products and Services

Voice
Managed Solutions
Data
Network Integration
Granite Grid

COMPETITORS

5linx	Rogers Communications
Acn Inc.	Sprint Communications
At&t	Verizon
Bce	World Communications
Earthlink	

HISTORICAL FINANCIALS

Company Type: Private

Income Statement				FYE: December 31
	REVENUE ($ mil.)	NET INCOME ($ mil.)	NET PROFIT MARGIN	EMPLOYEES
12/12	736	187	25.5%	2,116
12/11	609	143	23.5%	—
12/10	517	109	21.2%	—
Annual Growth	19.3%	31.0%		—

2012 Year-End Financials

Return on assets: 110.5%   Cash ($ mil.): 45
Return on equity: 394.1%
Current ratio: 1.40

GREAT RIVER ENERGY

Great River Energy is the second largest electric power supplier in Minnesota and one of the largest generation and transmission cooperatives in the country. The utility provides wholesale electricity to 1.7 million through nearly 30 distribution cooperatives. It operates some 4800 miles of transmission lines and has more than 3500 MW of generation capacity that consists of a diverse mix of baseload and peaking power plants including coal and natural gas as well as wind and solar generation facilities. The company also owns or partially owns more than 100 transmission substations. Approximately one-third of the people in Minnesota receive their electricity from a cooperative. Just like their counterparts in agriculture or housing cooperative utilities are owned by the members they serve.

Operations

Great River Energy serves members through a diverse portfolio of power supply resources and dependable transmission system all of which are part of the region's energy market.

As part of its efforts to increase its green energy output Great River owns Blue Flint Ethanol which includes of approximately 75-80 million-gallon ethanol refinery that uses process steam produced at Great River Energy Coal Creek Station.

Overall electric revenue account for over 90% of the company's sales while other operating revenue accounts for the rest.

Geographic Reach

The company provides power to cooperatives which in turn serve customers in Minnesota (headquarters) and Wisconsin.

Sales and Marketing

Great River Energy provides reliable affordable and environmentally responsible wholesale electricity to 28 member-owner cooperatives that serve more than 700000 members served (or around 1.7 million people).

Financial Performance

Utility operating revenues ended the year at $980.9 million which was down $9.7 million from 2019. While member sales remained strong low energy market prices reduced nonmember revenue in the MISO market and drove an overall revenue decrease in 2020.

In 2020 the company had a net loss of $129.1 million a $134.3 million decrease from the previous year.

The company's cash at the end of 2020 was $231.5 million. Operating activities generated $139.7 million while investing activities used $81.5 million mainly for utility plant additions. Financing activities used another $67.4 million primarily for repayments of long-term obligations.

Strategy

Great River Energy's Integrated Resource Plan (IRP) provides a comprehensive view of the company's resource plans for the next 15 years. The plan represents its intent to reliably meet the company's members' energy needs in a cost-effective and environmentally responsible manner. Its preferred resource plan continues to position its power generation portfolio toward a lower-carbon future and includes additional wind generation. The company's plan continues to rely on energy efficiency and conservation measures. It also highlights the company's innovative electrification and grid modernization initiatives.

Company Background

In 2013 the company signed a deal with Tangshan Shenzhou Manufacturing Company to make Great River Energy's DryFining technology (for more efficient coal use in power stations) available to utilities in China.

It is also cut costs and increasing efficiency at its own power plants. In 2012 these measures saved Great River Energy more than $8 million.

In 2012 Great River bought the remaining 51% of Blue Flint Ethanol it didn't already own. The move added to its production capabilities and helped push the company to record production that year.

The utility was formed in 1999 through the combination of two Minnesota utilities Cooperative Power and United Power Association.

EXECUTIVES

Pres-Ceo, David Saggau
Board Chm, Michael Thorson
V Pres-Cfo, Larry Schmid
Board V Chm, Bruce Leino
Board Treas, Robert Thompson
V Pres, Eric Olsen
V Pres, Greg Ridderbusch
V Pres, Jim Jones
V Pres, Kandance Olsen
V Pres, Rick Lancaster
V Pres, Will Kaul
Auditors: DELOITTE & TOUCHE LLP MINNEA

LOCATIONS

HQ: GREAT RIVER ENERGY
12300 ELM CREEK BLVD N, MAPLE GROVE, MN
553694718
Phone: 763 445-5000
Web: WWW.GREATRIVERENERGY.COM

PRODUCTS/OPERATIONS

2014 Sales

	% of total
Member	83
Non-member	7
Other	7
Nonutility operations Excluding non-controlling Interest	3
Total	**100**

2014 Sales

	$ mil.	% of total
Electric revenue	952	93
Other operating revenue	68	7
Total	**1,020**	**100**

COMPETITORS

Aep	Entergy
Basin Electric Power	Southern Company
Black Hills	Xcel Energy
Dte	

HISTORICAL FINANCIALS

Company Type: Private

Income Statement				FYE: December 31
	REVENUE ($ mil.)	NET INCOME ($ mil.)	NET PROFIT MARGIN	EMPLOYEES
12/18	1,295	8	0.7%	850
12/17	1,270	18	1.4%	—
12/16	1,022	21	2.1%	—
12/15	983	15	1.5%	—
Annual Growth	9.6%	(17.8%)	—	—

2018 Year-End Financials

Return on assets: 0.2%   Cash ($ mil.): 276
Return on equity: 1.0%
Current ratio: 1.30

GREENSTONE FARM CREDIT SERVICES ACA

One of the largest associations in the Farm Credit System GreenStone offers FARM CREDIT SERVICES (FCS) provides short intermediate and long-term loans; equipment and building leases; appraisal services; and life and crop insurance to farmers in Michigan and Wisconsin. It serves about 15000 members and has nearly 40 locations. Through an alliance with AgriSolutions a farm software and consulting company Greenstone provides income tax planning and preparation services farm business consulting and educational seminars. FCS Mortgage provides residential loans for rural properties as well as loans for home improvement construction and refinancing.

EXECUTIVES

Pres-Ceo, David B Armstrong
Exec V Pres*, Jack W Kelly
Chief Credit Officer*, Paul Anderson
Sr V Pres*, Steve Junglas
Exec V Pres*, Travis Jones
Exec V Pres*, Peter Lemmer
Exec V Pres*, Melissa Stolicker
Customer Representativ, Anne Howard
Customer Representativ, Dalene Strong
NW Manager, Mike Schneidewind
Regional Vice President, Cindy Birchmeier
Auditors: PRICEWATERHOUSECOOPERS LLP MI

LOCATIONS

HQ: GREENSTONE FARM CREDIT SERVICES ACA
3515 WEST RD, EAST LANSING, MI 488237312
Phone: 517 324-0213
Web: WWW.GREENSTONEFCS.COM

COMPETITORS

Country Financial	Rabobank Group
Fb Bancorp	

HISTORICAL FINANCIALS

Company Type: Private

Income Statement				FYE: December 31
	ASSETS ($ mil.)	NET INCOME ($ mil.)	INCOME AS % OF ASSETS	EMPLOYEES
12/20	10,967	270	2.5%	380
12/07	4,317	69	1.6%	—
12/06	3,691	63	1.7%	—
Annual Growth	8.1%	10.8%	—	—

GROSSMONT HOSPITAL FOUNDATION

EXECUTIVES

Ex Dir, Elizabeth Morgante
Director of Case Management, Mike Murphey
Doctor, Roxanne Hon
Auditors: ERNST & YOUNG US LLP SAN DIEG

LOCATIONS

HQ: GROSSMONT HOSPITAL FOUNDATION
5555 GROSSMONT CENTER DR, LA MESA, CA
919423077
Phone: 619 740-4200
Web: WWW.SHARP.COM

HISTORICAL FINANCIALS

Company Type: Private

Income Statement				FYE: September 30
	REVENUE ($ mil.)	NET INCOME ($ mil.)	NET PROFIT MARGIN	EMPLOYEES
09/16	738	65	8.9%	6
09/09	5	0	8.5%	—
09/08	5	0	16.8%	—
09/01	1	3	314.9%	—
Annual Growth	54.5%	21.8%	—	—

2016 Year-End Financials

Return on assets: 6.9%   Cash ($ mil.): 43
Return on equity: 8.5%
Current ratio: 2.40

GROUP O, INC.

The "O" in Group O stands for optimization. It also stands for Ontiveros the family that leads this company. Founded by chairman Robert Ontiveros Group O is one of the largest Hispanic-owned companies in the US. It helps big businesses improve their operations through three divisions: marketing packaging and supply chain. It offers everything from direct mail creation to shrink wrap procurement to warehousing and distribution and business intelligence. It has served clients from various industries including food and beverage (Kerry) consumer goods (P&G) manufacturing (Johnson Controls) pharmaceutical (Bristol-Myers Squibb) and telecommunications (AT&T).

Operations

Group O is a diversified business process outsourcing provider specializing in marketing supply chain packaging and business analytics products.

The company's supply chain division mainly serves heavy equipment and high technology OEMs while its packaging division targets manufacturers and distributors in need of streamlining their packaging processes. It procures and distributes bags stretch films tapes and other materials and also repairs calibrates and upgrades equipment to optimize performance.

Its SMART Audit reporting tool provides real-time reports that monitor production and spending across a plant network so that companies can take appropriate cost reduction actions. Meanwhile its marketing division offers a range of service offerings including marketing analytics customer rewards programs direct mail and e-mail marketing outsourced printing and a customer call center.

The company's Business Analytics unit has experts that can guide companies that seek to make sense out of unstructured and structured data - providing strategists and decision-makers with new insights into customer behavior while maximizing both new and existing channels. The team guides the creation implementation and management of tools in the latest applications and platforms across a comprehensive spectrum of existing systems.

Geographic Reach

Group O maintains a national network of more than 20 facilities mostly concentrated in the Midwest (Illinois Iowa and Minnesota) and Texas. Other sales offices and warehouses are located in California Nevada Pennsylvania and various southern states. It also works with more than 7000 suppliers in more than 30 countries.

Sales and Marketing

The company serves FORTUNE 500 clients across a broad range of industries including food and beverage telecommunications manufacturing consumer packaged goods retail financial services pharmaceutical healthcare technology energy and the public sector.

Strategy

In 2014 Group O launched a new website for its O-vations service offering which is aimed at helping companies optimize the design and operation of enterprise-scale reward programs. Key services range from program design and management technology integration operations and communications value-added services and reporting and analytics.

That year the company also opened its Business Analytics unit in Hyderabad India. The team helps generate customer acquisition and loyalty marketing insights that clients can then use to make better business decisions.

Company Background

Ontiveros established Group O in 1974 as Bi-State Packaging which sold packaging materials and equipment to manufacturers. Today it is one of the top 15 Hispanic-owned businesses in the nation.

EXECUTIVES

Ceo-Pres, Gregg Ontiveros
Cfo, Robert Marriott
V Pres, Chris Ontiveros
Chm, Robert Ontiveros
Vice President, Mike De Cruz
Marketing Manager, Mark Bohman
Customer Staff, Billie Anderson
Coordinator, David Vargas
Sales Representative, Marissa Lundberg
Program Manager, Matthew Dusenberry
Senior Program Manager, Ashley Rowatt
Auditors: HONKAMP KRUEGER & CO PC MO

LOCATIONS

HQ: GROUP O, INC.
4905 77TH AVE E, MILAN, IL 612643250
Phone: 309 736-8100
Web: WWW.GROUPO.COM

PRODUCTS/OPERATIONS

Selected Services

Marketing
Analytics
Consumer and trade fulfillment
Customer call center and workforce management
Direct mail and e-mail optimization
Print management outsourcing
Rewards and loyalty programs
Packaging
Equipment supply and repair (bagging case handling labeling shrinking and stretch wrapping systems)
Materials supply (labels poly bags protective packaging sanitation products shrink and stretch films and tape)
Stretch film equipment auditing
Supply chain
Business process outsourcing
Distribution
Global sourcing
Inventory management
Order management
Supplier management
Warehousing

Selected Industries Served

Food and Beverage
Telecommunications
Manufacturing
Consumer Packaged Goods
Financial Services
Pharmaceutical
Health care
Technology

COMPETITORS

Brightstar Corp.   Ozburn-hessey

Ceva Logistics U.s.   Logistics
Fedex Supply Chain   The Bernd Group
Jay Group   Ups Supply Chain
Kenco Logistics   Solutions
Services   Weber Logistics

HISTORICAL FINANCIALS

Company Type: Private

Income Statement

	REVENUE ($ mil.)	NET INCOME ($ mil.)	NET PROFIT MARGIN	EMPLOYEES
12/13	569	5	1.0%	1,066
12/05	240	5	2.2%	—
Annual Growth	11.4%	0.9%		

FYE: December 31

2013 Year-End Financials

Return on assets: 87.9%   Cash ($ mil.): 7
Return on equity: 1.0%
Current ratio: 0.90

GROVE ELK UNIFIED SCHOOL DISTRICT

EXECUTIVES

Supt, Steven Ladd
Assc Supt*, Richard Odegaard
School Counselor, Jerome Orgeron
Nurse, Alyson Gonda
Parent Volunteer Coordinator, Barbara Malana
Speech Therapist, Mary Salzano
Maintenance Shop Supervisor, Rob Teresi
Administrative Team Member, David Gordon
Administrative Assistant, Joanna Corrigan
Library Technician, Rebecca Santos
Teacher, Alegna Atkins
Auditors: CROWE HORWATH LLP SACRAMENTO

LOCATIONS

HQ: GROVE ELK UNIFIED SCHOOL DISTRICT
9510 ELK GROVE FLORIN RD, ELK GROVE, CA 956241801
Phone: 916 686-5085
Web: WWW.EGUSD.NET

HISTORICAL FINANCIALS

Company Type: Private

Income Statement

	REVENUE ($ mil.)	NET INCOME ($ mil.)	NET PROFIT MARGIN	EMPLOYEES
06/17	741	65	8.8%	5,600
06/07	560	(30)	—	—
06/06	0	0	—	—
06/03	454	19	4.4%	—
Annual Growth	3.6%	8.9%	—	—

FYE: June 30

GROWMARK, INC.

GROWMARK is an agricultural cooperative serving about 400000 customers across North America. It provides agronomy energy facility engineering and construction products and services as well as grain marketing and risk management services. It owns the FS trademark which is used by member cooperatives. Handles more than 3.2 million tons annually the company also operates a full-line seed company SEEDWAY and provides grain facility planning and grain marketing services. In addition to secure warehousing in facilities GROWMARK also provides truck barge and rail transport unloading and inventory control. The company has an extensive network of fertilizer terminals throughout the Midwest and Ontario.

Operations

GROWMARK delivers high quality agronomy and energy products as well as premium services from expert advisors. Its long-term relationships with manufacturers and refiners coupled with the company's extensive terminal network means GROWMARK has access to a broad and reliable supply of fertilizers fuel and propane. The company also offers private label crop protection products and proprietary brands of corn and soybean seeds.

In addition GROWMARK also provides grain marketing services through its subsidiary MID-CO COMMODITIES and has partnership with COFCO International. Its commercial construction provides equipment facilities and services that improve the operating efficiency of the company's customers. It is equipped to provide system consultations through complete turnkey construction services such as consultation development planning construction and operation. GROWMARK logistics includes brokerage services specializing in transporting and storing liquid fuel propane anhydrous ammonia bulk and packaged motor oils and crop inputs including seed liquid and dry fertilizer and bulk and packaged crop protection products while its Electronic Payments Network keeps pace with regulatory and market demands for bank cards fleet cards DEBIT cards gift cards ACH/electronic check conversion and PC/web-based payments. Lastly GROWMARK Agronomy Equipment has national account relationships with John Deere Case IH AGCO and Caterpillar to provide its customers with competitive pricing and service from local dealer on application equipment tractors loaders construction equipment and small equipment.

GROWMARK's high performing product lines include proprietary brands FS InVISION FS HiSOY FS Wheat FS Alfalfa as well as distribution agreements with DEKALB Asgrow and NK.

Geographic Reach

GROWMARK is headquartered in Bloomington Illinois and serves customers in about 35 US states and Ontario Canada.

Its SEEDWAY business has about 25 office and warehouse locations in California Vermont South Carolina Mexico New York Pennsylvania Texas and Florida among others.

Sales and Marketing

GROWMARK is serving agriculture and energy cooperatives retailers grain companies and other business customers of all industries including freight brokerage and credit card processing.

Mergers and Acquisitions

In early 2022 GROWMARK acquired the remaining ownership interest in AgriVisor a full-service agricultural risk management and marketing services firm. This comes after GROWMARK purchased Illinois Agricultural Association's ownership interest in AgriVisor in late 2021. AgriVisor delivers in-depth market analysis and recommendations to more than 1000 producers across North America. Using extensive relationships with grain elevators farm insurance brokerages farm bureaus ag research firms and other ag advisory firms to stay ahead of industry trends the company leverages collective buying power and pricing strategies on crop insurance and other innovative services such as its Crossover Solutions.

Company Background

GROWMARK traces its history back to 1920 and the establishment of local cooperatives by Farm Bureau members. One of those cooperatives Farm Bureau Service Company of Iowa in the early 1960s merged with Illinois Farm Supply Company (founded in 1927) to form the foundation of what is today GROWMARK. The GROWMARK name started being used in 1980.

EXECUTIVES

Chb-Pres, John Reifsteck
Ceo, Jim Spradlin
Sr V Pres, Brent Ericson
V Pres-Gen Counsel, Brent Bostrom
V Pres-Energy & Logistics, Carol Kitchen
V Pres-Retail Bus, Barry Schmidt
V Pres-Agronomy, Mark Orr
V Pres-Cfo, Wade Mittelstadt
Vice President, Human Resource, Ann Kafer
V Pres-Midwest, Mike Turner
V Pres-General Counsel, Bill Covey
Auditors: RSM US LLP PEORIA ILLINOIS

LOCATIONS

HQ: GROWMARK, INC.
1701 TOWANDA AVE, BLOOMINGTON, IL 617012057
Phone: 309 557-6000
Web: WWW.GROWMARK.COM

COMPETITORS

Adm	Marathon Oil
Agri Industries	Nc Hybrids
Ag Processing Inc.	Orscheln Farm And Home
Bp	Pfister Hybrid Corn
Barkley Seed	Pioneer Hi-bred
Bayer Cropscience	Rabo Agrifinance
Chs	Sakata Seed
Cargill	Seed Enterprises
Chevron	Southern States
Costco Wholesale	Terra Nitrogen
Debruce Grain	Wal-mart
Exxon Mobil	Wilbur-ellis

HISTORICAL FINANCIALS

Company Type: Private

Income Statement				FYE: August 31
	REVENUE ($ mil.)	NET INCOME ($ mil.)	NET PROFIT MARGIN	EMPLOYEES
08/20	7,541	68	0.9%	8,641
08/19	8,745	75	0.9%	—
08/18	8,522	65	0.8%	—
08/17	7,291	115	1.6%	—
Annual Growth	1.1%	(16.0%)	—	—

2020 Year-End Financials

Return on assets: 2.6%
Return on equity: 6.1%
Current ratio: 1.80
Cash ($ mil.): 78

GRUMA CORPORATION

Gruma is the American subsidiary of giant Mexican food company Gruma S.A.B. de C.V. and the leading tortilla and corn flower producer in the US. The company manufactures and distributes corn flour corn tortillas and related products such as wraps and corn chips through roughly 20 production plants. The company runs the world's largest tortilla plant in Los Angeles; that facility has a production capacity of 25 million tortillas per day. Its highly recognizable brand names include Mission Calidad and Guerrero tortillas and Maseca corn flour. Gruma is its parent company's largest revenue producer.

Operations

Gruma Corporation which generates nearly 60% of its parent's total revenue operates through two divisions — Mission Foods which produces tortillas and related products and Azteca Milling which produces nixtamalized corn flour.

Mission Foods manufactures corn and wheat tortillas and related products (which include tortilla chips) mainly under the MISSION GUERRERO and CALIDAD brand names in the United States. By continuing to build MISSION into a strong national brand oriented to every type of consumer GUERRERO into a strong Hispanic consumer focused brand and CALIDAD as its value brand in tortillas and chips the company expects to increase Mission Foods' market penetration brand awareness and profitability. Azteca Milling manufactures nixtamalized corn flour in the US under the MASECA brand and to a lesser extent under its value brand TORTIMASA.

Geographic Reach

The US-based Gruma Corporation maintains more than 20 tortilla and other plants in the US and six plants located in Amarillo Edinburg and Plainview Texas; Evansville Indiana; Henderson Kentucky; and Madera California.

Sales and Marketing

Its Mission Foods' products are marketed in both retail and food service channels. In the US retail customers represented approximately 80% of its sales volume including supermarkets mass merchandisers membership stores and smaller independent stores. Its food service customers include major chain restaurants food service distributors schools hospitals and the military. Azteca Milling sold approximately 30% of its nixtamalized corn flour sales volume to Mission Foods' plants in the US. Azteca Milling's third-party customers consist largely of other tortilla manufacturers corn chip producers retail customers and wholesalers.

Financial Performance

Revenue increased some 12% for Gruma Corporation in 2011 as compared to 2010 thanks to sales growth volume and price increases spurred by higher raw-material costs.

EXECUTIVES

Chm, Juan A Gonzalez Moreno
Pres, Javier Velez Bautista
V Pres, Felipe Rubio Lamas
Dir, Homero Huerta Moreno
SEC, Salvador Vargas Guajardo
Asst SEC, David A Salazar Cavazos
Treas, Dan Burke
Fleet Staff, Christine A Syed
Maintenance, Antonio Villa
Maintenance Supervisor, Ben Torrey
National Account Manager, Carrie Simmons

LOCATIONS

HQ: GRUMA CORPORATION
5601 EXECUTIVE DR STE 800, IRVING, TX 750382508
Phone: 972 232-5000
Web: WWW.MISSIONFOODS.COM

PRODUCTS/OPERATIONS

Selected Brands and Products

Guerrero
Chicharron de Cerdo
Tortillas de Harina (Original and Butter)
Tortillas de Maíz Blanco
Tostadas Norte?as Clásicas
Tostadas Caseras Doraditas
Mission Foods

96% Fat Free Heart Healthy tortillas
All Natural Spicy Bean dip
Caramel Twists
Carb Balance tortillas
Cheddar Cheese dip
Chicharrones (Original BBQ Habanero and Picante)
Cinnamon Twists
Chunky Salsa Medium
Corn tortilla
Flour tortillas
Guacamole dip
Jumbo Taco shells
Life Balance tortillas
Multi-Grain Flour tortillas
Organic Stone-Ground tortilla chips
Pork Cracklins Plain Tenders
Restaurant Style Tortilla Triangles (Cilantro Lime Premium White Corn and Salsa Roja)
Restaurant Style Tortilla Rounds
Salsa Con Queso
Salsa Verde Medium
Sliced Nacho Jalape?o Peppers
Taco and tostada shells
Wraps (Original Garden Spinach Jalapeno Cheddar Multi-Grain Sun-dried Tomato Basil and Zesty Garlic Herb)

COMPETITORS

Azteca Foods	Horizon Milling
Bimbo Bakeries	La Gloria Foods
Bob's Red Mill Natural Foods	La Reina
	La Tortilla Factory
Bunge Milling	Minsa
C.h. Guenther & Son	Ole' Mexican Foods
Casa De Oro Foods	Organic Milling
Don Pancho Authentic Mexican Foods	Ruiz Mexican Foods
	Star Of The West
Flowers Foods	Taco Bell
Frito-lay	Tumaro's Gourmet Tortillas
General Mills	
Grupo Bimbo	Tyson Foods
Hodgson Mill	

HISTORICAL FINANCIALS

Company Type: Private

Income Statement				FYE: December 31
	REVENUE ($ mil.)	NET INCOME ($ mil.)	NET PROFIT MARGIN	EMPLOYEES
12/19	2,202	224	10.2%	7,000
12/16	2,023	179	8.9%	—
12/15	2,086	152	7.3%	—
Annual Growth	1.4%	10.2%	—	—

2019 Year-End Financials

Return on assets: 13.6%
Return on equity: 19.7%
Current ratio: 2.80
Cash ($ mil.): 76

GUILDNET, INC.

EXECUTIVES

Ceo, Alan R Morse
Chairman, James M Dubin
Treasurer, Lawrence E Goldschmidt
Secretary, Robert B Okun
Optometrist, Laura Sperazza
Administrative Assistant, Angela Rosario
Neurologist, Helen Chang
Occupational Medicine Speciali, Inna Babaeva
Auditors: KPMG LLP NEW YORK NY

LOCATIONS

HQ: GUILDNET, INC.
   15 W 65TH ST, NEW YORK, NY 100236601
Phone: 212 769-6200
Web: WWW.LIGHTHOUSEGUILD.ORG

HISTORICAL FINANCIALS

Company Type: Private

Income Statement				FYE: December 31
	REVENUE ($ mil.)	NET INCOME ($ mil.)	NET PROFIT MARGIN	EMPLOYEES
12/15	950	(24)	—	377
12/14	826	1	0.1%	—
12/13	672	45	6.8%	—
12/12	433	42	9.8%	—
Annual Growth	29.9%	—	—	—

2015 Year-End Financials

Return on assets: (-8.5%)   Cash ($ mil.): 12
Return on equity: (-19.4%)
Current ratio: 1.40

GUILFORD COUNTY SCHOOL SYSTEM

EXECUTIVES

Supt, Sharon L Contreras
Co-Interim Supt*, Nora K Carr
CIO*, Terrance Young
Superintendent, Sharon Contreras
Coordinator, April Dixon
Executive of Information Techn, Eric Brown
Security Staff, Les Allison
Coordinator, Todd Baldwin
Library Media Specialist, Betty Denny
5th Grade Teacher, Emily Harris
Assistant, Enid Barnum

LOCATIONS

HQ: GUILFORD COUNTY SCHOOL SYSTEM
   712 N EUGENE ST, GREENSBORO, NC 274011622
Phone: 336 370-8100
Web: WWW.GCSNC.COM

HISTORICAL FINANCIALS

Company Type: Private

Income Statement				FYE: June 30
	REVENUE ($ mil.)	NET INCOME ($ mil.)	NET PROFIT MARGIN	EMPLOYEES
06/11	692	(0)	—	10,000
06/09	0	(0)	—	—
06/03	0	0	—	—
06/02	546	69	12.8%	—
Annual Growth	2.7%	—	—	—

2011 Year-End Financials

Return on assets: —   Cash ($ mil.): 28
Return on equity: (-0.1%)
Current ratio: 1.10

GUNDERSEN LUTHERAN ADMINISTRATIVE SERVICES INC.

EXECUTIVES

Ceo, Jeff Thompson
V Pres*, Wendy Williams
V Pres*, Gregory Prairie
SEC*, Brian Rude
Tres*, Wendy Lommen
Doctor, David Morrison
Auditors: ERNST & YOUNG US LLP CHICAGO

LOCATIONS

HQ: GUNDERSEN LUTHERAN ADMINISTRATIVE
   SERVICES INC.
   1900 SOUTH AVE, LA CROSSE, WI 546015467
Phone: 608 782-7300
Web: WWW.GUNDERSENHEALTH.ORG

HISTORICAL FINANCIALS

Company Type: Private

Income Statement				FYE: December 31
	REVENUE ($ mil.)	NET INCOME ($ mil.)	NET PROFIT MARGIN	EMPLOYEES
12/19	771	(59)	—	6,000
12/18	841	40	4.8%	—
12/17	716	(38)	—	—
Annual Growth	3.8%	—	—	—

2019 Year-End Financials

Return on assets: (-5.8%)   Cash ($ mil.): 136
Return on equity: —
Current ratio: 0.40

GUNDERSEN LUTHERAN MEDICAL CENTER, INC.

At the heart of the Gundersen Lutheran health system Gundersen Lutheran Medical Center serves residents of nearly 20 counties that stretch across the upper Midwest. The clinical campus for the University of Wisconsin's medical and nursing schools operates a 325-bed teaching hospital with a Level II Trauma and Emergency Center. Focused on caring for patients in western Wisconsin the hospital boasts several specialty services such as bariatrics behavioral health cancer care orthopedics palliative care pediatrics rehabilitation and women's health. The physician-led not-for-profit medical center is affiliated with a group of regional clinics and specialty centers.

Operations

Gundersen Lutheran Medical Center has a staff of some 800 doctors dentists and other professionals. As part of Gundersen Lutheran (also known as Gundersen Health System) the hospital's sister entities include the Gundersen Clinic and the Gundersen Lutheran Administrative Services entity.

In 2013 the Gundersen Health System reported 1437 births 17000 surgeries and 278000 outpatient hospital visits.

Geographic Reach

From its main campus in La Crosse Wisconsin as well as a satellite outpatient center in Onalaska the hospital serves communities located in 19 counties throughout western Wisconsin northeastern Iowa and southeastern Minnesota.

Strategy

The Gundersen Lutheran organization expands though partnerships such as an alliance with the Allen Hospital in Iowa to enhance regional cardiovascular services in 2013. The medical center is also working to upgrade its infrastructure to enable 100% energy independence in 2014.

To offer advanced training to residents and physicians Gundersen Lutheran Medical Center developed and opened a high-tech training center in 2012. The Cleary Kumm Simulation and Training Labs offer mock operating rooms and simulation labs for use by local doctors and nationwide medical professionals for training or conferences. Gundersen Lutheran Medical Center is banking on the simulation and training facility to draw interest talent and outside funds.

Company Background

Gundersen Lutheran Medical Center was founded in 1995 through the merger of Gunderson Clinic and Lutheran Hospital-La Crosse. The Lutheran Hospital opened in 1902.

EXECUTIVES

Ceo, Jeffery Thompson
Contrl, Scott Moebius
Chief Learning Officer, Mary Ellen McCartney
Vp Team 1 and Regional, Mary Jo Klos
Vp, Team 1 and Regiona, Sigurd B Gundersen III
Database Administrator, Kate H Walsh
Neonatologist, Suzanne Toce
Inpatient Personnel Coordinato, Jacob Ellefsen
Nurse Recruiter, Erin Schmitt
Senior Vice President, Gerald Arndt
Executive Recruiter, Kim Jackson
Auditors: KPMG LLP MINNEAPOLIS MN

LOCATIONS

HQ: GUNDERSEN LUTHERAN MEDICAL CENTER, INC.
   1900 SOUTH AVE, LA CROSSE, WI 546015467
Phone: 608 782-7300
Web: WWW.GUNDERSENHEALTH.ORG

PRODUCTS/OPERATIONS

Selected Services
Advance care planning
Apnea
Audiology
Autism Spectrum Disorder
BioBank
Brain disorders
Cardiac services
Children's health
Cleft Lip & Palate Clinic
Endocrinology
Hospice
Eye care
Gynecology
Hand surgery
Heart Institute
LASIK eye surgery
Massage
Neck surgery
Neurosciences
Oral and maxillofacial surgery
Pediatrics
Radiation oncology
Rehabilitation
Urgent care
Urology
Weight management
Wound care

COMPETITORS

Dean Health Systems Inc.
Franciscan Skemp Healthcare
Luther Midelfort
Mayo Clinic
Meriter Health Services
Ministry Health Care
Olmsted Medical
Sacred Heart Hospital
Tomah Memorial Hospital
University Of Wisconsin Hospital And Clinics

HISTORICAL FINANCIALS

Company Type: Private

Income Statement				FYE: December 31
	REVENUE ($ mil.)	NET INCOME ($ mil.)	NET PROFIT MARGIN	EMPLOYEES
12/19	1,275	216	17.0%	4,500
12/18	1,073	117	10.9%	—
12/17	1,071	112	10.5%	—
12/15	980	60	6.1%	—
Annual Growth	6.8%	37.9%	—	—

2019 Year-End Financials

Return on assets: 13.1%
Return on equity: 13.2%
Current ratio: 30.20
Cash ($ mil.): —

GWINNETT COUNTY BOARD OF EDUCATION

EXECUTIVES

Chairperson, Robert McClure
Accounting Staff, Kathy Stillwell
Teacher, Laurie Pitcock
School Psychologist, Larris Boston
Auditors: MAULDIN & JENKINS LLC ATLANT

LOCATIONS

HQ: GWINNETT COUNTY BOARD OF EDUCATION
437 OLD PEACHTREE RD NW, SUWANEE, GA
300242978
Phone: 678 301-6000

HISTORICAL FINANCIALS

Company Type: Private

Income Statement				FYE: June 30
	REVENUE ($ mil.)	NET INCOME ($ mil.)	NET PROFIT MARGIN	EMPLOYEES
06/20	2,263	14	0.7%	298
06/19	2,071	118	5.7%	—
06/18	1,973	(55)	—	—
06/17	1,868	(2)	—	—
Annual Growth	6.6%	—	—	—

2020 Year-End Financials

Return on assets: 0.4%
Return on equity: —
Current ratio: 2.90
Cash ($ mil.): 128

GWINNETT HOSPITAL SYSTEM, INC.

Auditors: KPMG LLP ATLANTA GA

LOCATIONS

HQ: GWINNETT HOSPITAL SYSTEM, INC.
1000 MEDICAL CENTER BLVD, LAWRENCEVILLE,
GA 300467694
Phone: 678 343-3428
Web: WWW.GWINNETTMEDICALCENTER.ORG

HISTORICAL FINANCIALS

Company Type: Private

Income Statement				FYE: June 30
	REVENUE ($ mil.)	NET INCOME ($ mil.)	NET PROFIT MARGIN	EMPLOYEES
06/18	731	12	1.7%	2,050
06/17	729	29	4.1%	—
06/16	735	(31)	—	—
06/15	698	15	2.2%	—
Annual Growth	1.5%	(6.3%)	—	—

2018 Year-End Financials

Return on assets: 1.4%
Return on equity: 2.6%
Current ratio: 2.60
Cash ($ mil.): 54

H. J. BAKER SULPHUR, LLC

EXECUTIVES

Pres, Mark Whittemore
Project Manager, Rick Bloom
Auditors: GRANT THORNTON LLP HOUSTON
T

LOCATIONS

HQ: H. J. BAKER SULPHUR, LLC
1450 LAKE ROBBINS DR # 500, THE WOODLANDS,
TX 773803258
Phone: 346 372-3455
Web: WWW.HJBAKER.COM

HISTORICAL FINANCIALS

Company Type: Private

Income Statement				FYE: December 31
	REVENUE ($ mil.)	NET INCOME ($ mil.)	NET PROFIT MARGIN	EMPLOYEES
12/08	878	26	3.0%	27
12/07	273	4	1.5%	—
12/05	170	(0)	—	—
Annual Growth	72.8%	—	—	—

2008 Year-End Financials

Return on assets: 17.3%
Return on equity: 75.7%
Current ratio: 1.40
Cash ($ mil.): 19

H. LEE MOFFITT CANCER CENTER AND RESEARCH INSTITUTE HOSPITAL, INC.

The H. Lee Moffitt Cancer Center and Research Institute founded in 1986 is a National Cancer Institute-designated Comprehensive Cancer Center located on the Tampa campus of the University of South Florida. The institute carries it out its stated mission of "contributing to the prevention and cure of cancer" through patient care research and education. It operates a 210-bed medical and surgical facility as well as outpatient treatment programs and a blood and marrow transplant program. Its research programs include study in the areas of molecular oncology immunology risk assessment health outcomes and experimental therapeutics.

Operations

The Moffitt Cancer Center sees more than 9000 cancer inpatients each year; it also handles some 328000 outpatient visits annually. In addition to its 40-bed blood and marrow transplant center which performs 400 annual transplants the hospital includes more than a dozen operating rooms and extensive diagnostic radiology and radiation therapy labs. The Cancer Screening and Prevention Center offers genetic testing for certain kinds of hereditary cancers (breast ovarian colon and melanoma).

The Moffitt Research Institute conducts a wide range of cancer studies and some of its drug discovery research programs are managed through partnerships with pharmaceutical companies and other research laboratories. The research institute also relies on funding grants from organizations such as the National Institutes of Health. It has received more than $80 million in grant funding and participated in some 300 clinical trials.

The Moffitt Cancer Center likewise has educational and health care alliances with a number of Florida hospitals and colleges including a three-way cancer care and research partnership with Shands HealthCare and the University of Florida. Through its affiliated network program (the Moffitt Oncology Network) Moffitt works with community doctors and centers across Florida to provide enhanced cancer services throughout the state. It also operates a number of outpatient clinics in surrounding areas.

Geographic Reach

Through its main campus and numerous outpatient sites Moffitt Cancer Center primarily serves residents of seven Florida counties: Hernando Hillsborough Manatee Pasco Pinellas Polk and Sarasota. It also serves patients from other areas of Florida and neighboring states.

Sales and Marketing

HMO and PPO plans account for about 65% of patient service revenues while reimbursements from Medicare and Medicaid plans account for another 32% of sales.

Financial Performance

Revenue at Moffitt Cancer Center and Research Institute increased 1% to $779 million in 2013 from $772 the previous year due to higher patient service revenues. After a net loss in 2012 the institute reported net income of $26 million due to an increase in net assets and non-operating gains. Cash from operations also grew by $77 million due to the net income increase and cash generated from an estimated third-party settlement.

Strategy

Moffitt Cancer Center conducts expansion and facility improvement projects to enhance services for its cancer patients. For instance it launched construction of a new $74 million outpatient facility at the current McKinley office site in 2013; the location is near the main campus and will provide surgery infusion imaging research and other services. It also formed a partnership with Space Coast Cancer Center Boca Raton Regional Hospital Advinus Therapeutics and Lehigh Valley Health Network to improve cancer care for all the organizations.

EXECUTIVES

Vp/Cfo, Yvette Tremonti
Ex V Pres-Ctr Dir*, Thomas Sellers
Dir*, Willam S Dalton
Pres-Coo-Ex Vp*, Jack Kolosky
Evp-Coo*, Sarabdeep Singh
Director Cell-Based Therapies, James J Mul
Stewardship Officer, Jessica Skinner
Project Coordinator Design, Mark Lyon
Public Relations Account Coord, Nicole Drone
Director, Rebecca Young
Receiving Clerk, Bryan Montes
Auditors: GRANT THORNTON LLP TAMPA FLO

LOCATIONS

HQ: H. LEE MOFFITT CANCER CENTER AND RESEARCH INSTITUTE HOSPITAL, INC.
12902 USF MAGNOLIA DR, TAMPA, FL 336129416
Phone: 813 745-4673
Web: WWW.MOFFITT.ORG

PRODUCTS/OPERATIONS

Selected Services

Chemotherapy

Diagnosis
Emotional Support
Integrative Medicine
Labwork Scans and Biopsy
Other Patient Services
Pain Management
Radiation
Screening and Genetics
Spiritual Support
Surgical Care
Well-Being

Selected Research Fields

Basic Science Division
 Cancer Imaging and Metabolism
 Drug Discovery
 Immunology
 Integrated Mathematical Oncology
 Molecular Oncology
 Tumor Biology
Population Science Division
 Biostatistics and Bioinformatics
 Cancer Epidemiology
 Health Outcomes & Behavior

COMPETITORS

All Children's Hospital	Mayo Clinic Jacksonville
Baptist Hospital Of Miami	Memorial Sloan-kettering
Bay Medical Center	Oak Hill Hospital
Boca Raton Regional Hospital	Roswell Park Cancer Institute
Dana-farber	Sacred Heart Health System
Fox Chase Cancer Center	South Georgia Medical Center
Jackson County Hospital Of Florida	St. Vincent's Health

Md Anderson Cancer Center System
Manatee Memorial Hospital

HISTORICAL FINANCIALS

Company Type: Private

Income Statement   FYE: June 30

	REVENUE ($ mil.)	NET INCOME ($ mil.)	NET PROFIT MARGIN	EMPLOYEES
06/21	1,515	295	19.5%	4,200
06/20	1,353	287	21.3%	—
06/18	1,020	167	16.4%	—
06/14	855	50	5.9%	—
Annual Growth	8.5%	28.9%	—	—

2021 Year-End Financials

Return on assets: 96.4%   Cash ($ mil.): —
Return on equity: 156.3%
Current ratio: 2.10

H. LEE MOFFITT CANCER CENTER AND RESEARCH INSTITUTE, INC.

EXECUTIVES

Pres, William Dalton
Svp-Cdio*, Edmondo Robinson
Vp-CIO*, Elizabeth Lindsay-Wood
Project Coordinator, Donna Cosenzo
Scientist, Thinh Cao
Assistant Professor, Alfredo A Santillan
Manager, Lee Anne Corbin
Assistant Professor, Andrew W Carroll
Pathologist, Santo V Nicosia
Scientist, Shelten G Yuen
Scientist, Andrew Myers
Auditors: GRANT THORNTON LLP TAMPA FLO

LOCATIONS

HQ: H. LEE MOFFITT CANCER CENTER AND RESEARCH INSTITUTE, INC.
12902 USF MAGNOLIA DR, TAMPA, FL 336129416
Phone: 813 745-4673
Web: WWW.MOFFITT.ORG

HISTORICAL FINANCIALS

Company Type: Private

Income Statement   FYE: June 30

	REVENUE ($ mil.)	NET INCOME ($ mil.)	NET PROFIT MARGIN	EMPLOYEES
06/21	1,827	186	10.2%	1,239
06/20	1,655	121	7.3%	—
06/19	1,509	111	7.4%	—
06/18	1,310	178	13.6%	—
Annual Growth	11.7%	1.5%	—	—

2021 Year-End Financials

Return on assets: 8.2%   Cash ($ mil.): 412
Return on equity: 15.2%
Current ratio: 2.20

HAGGEN, INC.

Haggen showers shoppers in the Pacific Northwest with salmon coffee and other essentials. Formerly one of the area's largest independent grocers Haggen operated some 130 supermarkets in Washington and Oregon as well as California Nevada and Arizona. Most of the stores were acquired from Albertsons in late 2014. In late 2015 Haggen filed for Chapter 11 bankruptcy protection to allow it to reorganize around a reduced number of locations and in 2016 the company agreed to sell its remaining core stores to Albertsons. The chain was founded in 1933 in Bellingham Washington.

Operations

Haggen runs its retail business under two banner names: Haggen Food & Pharmacy and TOP Food & Drug.

Geographic Reach

Haggen serves customers primarily in Washington but also in Oregon.

Strategy

In late 2014 the company announced it would purchase 146 Vons Pavilions Albertsons and Safeway stores being sold as part of the pending merger of Albertsons and Safeway. More than 80 of the new stores are located in California.

Aiming to boost its business and strengthen its competitive position the grocery operator whittled down its stores portfolio in 2013 to about 20 locations from 30 by shuttering underperforming stores. It's also rebranding many of its TOP Food & Drug stores as Northwest Fresh. The Northwest Fresh theme emphasizes local products new service departments and departments named after local geographic references. The supermarket chain is rebannering all of its TOP stores under the Haggen name and new theme to reinforce its local roots and differentiate itself from its national competition.

Having been a customer since 2007 Haggen also extended a supply partnership with Unified Grocers through 2018.

Focused on brick-and-mortar efforts Haggen had set aside its e-commerce initiative. To keep up with the Joneses of supermarket fortune Haggen partnered with ShopEaze.com (an e-commerce service provider) which failed leaving Haggen without an online store. Awards and Recognition

Industry publication Supermarket News ranks Haggen one of the 75 largest grocery chains in the US. It's also the Northwest's largest independent grocer.

Company Background

Haggen traces its roots back to 1933 when Ben Haggen alongside his wife Dorothy and brother-in-law Doug Clark launched the Economy Food Store in Bellingham Washington with a combined investment of $1100. They later moved and changed the name to White House Market before moving to yet another location in 1957 and adopting the name Haggen's Thriftway.

EXECUTIVES

Pres, John Clougher
Cfo-Cio-V Pres*, Ron Stevens
V Pres*, John Turley
Co-Chb*, Donald Haggen
Co-Chb*, Richard Haggen
V Pres*, Clement Stevens
V Pres*, Derrick Anderson
Treas*, Blake Barnett
Director of Retail Support, Rob Tutor
Senior Financial Analyst, Sean Echevarria
Director Human Resources, Derek Anderson
Auditors: MOSS ADAMS LLP

LOCATIONS

HQ: HAGGEN, INC.
2211 RIMLAND DR STE 300, BELLINGHAM, WA
982265699
Phone: 360 733-8720
Web: WWW.HAGGEN.COM

2014 Stores

Washington		15
Oregon		2
Total	**0**	**17**

COMPETITORS

Costco Wholesale	Smart & Final
Fred Meyer Stores	Target Corporation
Grocery Outlet	Trader Joe's
Quality Food	Wal-mart
Supervalu	Walgreen
Safeway	Winco Foods

HISTORICAL FINANCIALS

Company Type: Private

Income Statement   FYE: December 31

	REVENUE ($ mil.)	NET INCOME ($ mil.)	NET PROFIT MARGIN	EMPLOYEES
12/07	787	8	1.1%	3,900
12/06	758	6	0.9%	—
12/05	164	0	—	—
Annual Growth	—20237.1%		—	—

2007 Year-End Financials

Return on assets: 4.9%   Cash ($ mil.): 6
Return on equity: 1.1%
Current ratio: 0.30

HAMILTON CHATTANOOGA COUNTY HOSPITAL AUTHORITY

The Chattanooga-Hamilton County Hospital Authority (dba Erlanger Health System) offers a broad range of health service operations including the T.C. Thompson Children's Hospital a cancer treatment facility and centers devoted to heart treatment trauma and eye care. The system comprises five hospital campuses in Tennessee with some 810 acute care beds as well as 50 long-term care beds. A teaching center for the University of Tennessee College of Medicine Erlanger provides tertiary care for a region that includes southeastern Tennessee northern Georgia northern Alabama and western North Carolina.

Operations

Erlanger is the tri-state region's only Level One Trauma Center providing the highest level of trauma care for adults. The Children's Hospital at Erlanger houses the region's only Level III Neonatal Intensive Care Unit as well as a pediatric trauma team Emergency Center and Pediatric Intensive Care Unit

The hospital system treats more than 300000 patients every year. In 2014 Erlanger had 30394 inpatient admissions 230765 outpatient visits to physician practices and 28810 surgical patients. Some 3067 children were admitted to Children's Hospital and 43192 received treatment in the Emergency Department and outpatient surgery.

The LIFE FORCE air ambulance service is is equipped with two EC-135 aircraft capable of sin-

gle pilot IFR and two Bell 407 aircraft. LIFE FORCE transported 1419 patients in 2014.

Geographic Reach

The Erlanger Health System is a multi-hospital system with five hospitals based in Chattanooga: the University Hospital Children's Hospital at Erlanger Erlanger North Hospital Erlanger East Hospital and Erlanger Bledsoe Hospital located in Pikeville Tennessee. Its LIFE FORCE air ambulance service is stationed in Chattanooga and Sparta in Tennessee and in Calhoun and Blue Ridge in Georgia.

Financial Performance

Medicare accounted for 33% of Erlanger's net patient revenues in fiscal 2014; Commercial insurance 31%; and Medicaid 22%.

Company Background

To extend its patient reach Erlanger entered into a management contract with Hutcheson Hospital located in North Georgia in 2011.

Erlanger was founded in 1889 through the generosity of French nobleman Baron Frederic Emile d'Erlanger who held financial interests in a number of railroads in the region. He donated $5000 (more than $4 million in today's dollars) for a new hospital. It opened with 72 beds in 1899.

EXECUTIVES

Chm, Linda Moss Mines
Vice Chm, Sheila Boyington
Pres, James Brexler
Ex V Pres-Coo, Charlesetta Woodard-Thompson
Sr V Pres-Chief Nursing Office, Rachel Harris
Secretary, Gerald Webb
Coo, Robert Maloney Jr
Int Cfo, Lynn Dejaco
Program Director, Amar Singh
Executive Director CHI, Darwin Koller
Chief Administrator, Debbie Shepherd

LOCATIONS

HQ: HAMILTON CHATTANOOGA COUNTY HOSPITAL
AUTHORITY
975 E 3RD ST, CHATTANOOGA, TN 374032173
Phone: 423 778-7000
Web: WWW.ERLANGER.ORG

PRODUCTS/OPERATIONS

Selected Campuses

Dodson Avenue Community Health Center
Erlanger Bledsoe Campus
Erlanger East Campus
Erlanger Medical Center
Erlanger North Campus
Southside Community Health Center
T.C. Thompson Children's Hospital

Selected Medical Services

Breast Imaging
Cancer Services
Cardiology
Chattanooga Lifestyle Center
Community Health Centers
Craniofacial Center
Erlanger Metabolic and Bariatric Surgery Center
Erlanger Pharmacy
Gastroenterology
Heart
Home Health (ContinuCare)
HouseCalls
Hypertension Management Center
Imaging Services
LIFE FORCE
Neurobehavioral and Memory Services
Orthopedics
Radiology
Respiratory Services
Rheumatology
Robotic Surgery
Sleep Disorders Center
Stroke
The Weight Loss Program

Trauma Services
Urgent Care - Adult
Urology
UT Erlanger Kidney Transplant Center
Weight Management
Women's Services
WorkForce Corporate Health
Wound Care and Hyperbaric Oxygen center

COMPETITORS

Catholic Health Initiatives	Saint Thomas Rutherford Hospital
Community Health Systems	Southern Hills Vanderbilt University Medical Center
Hutcheson Medical	
Parkridge Medical Center	

HISTORICAL FINANCIALS

Company Type: Private

Income Statement   FYE: June 30

	REVENUE ($ mil.)	NET INCOME ($ mil.)	NET PROFIT MARGIN	EMPLOYEES
06/21	1,044	37	3.6%	4,700
06/20	1,021	29	2.9%	—
06/18	973	26	2.8%	—
06/17	888	13	1.6%	—
Annual Growth	4.1%	28.4%		

2021 Year-End Financials

Return on assets: 3.9%   Cash ($ mil.): 211
Return on equity: 10.2%
Current ratio: 1.40

HARBOR-UCLA MEDICAL CENTER

LOCATIONS

HQ: HARBOR-UCLA MEDICAL CENTER
1000 W CARSON ST, TORRANCE, CA 905022059
Phone: 310 222-2301
Web: WWW.EMEDHARBOR.EDU

HISTORICAL FINANCIALS

Company Type: Private

Income Statement   FYE: June 30

	REVENUE ($ mil.)	NET INCOME ($ mil.)	NET PROFIT MARGIN	EMPLOYEES
06/16	637	(268)	—	3,000
06/15	607	(287)	—	—
Annual Growth	5.0%	—		—

2016 Year-End Financials

Return on assets: (-33.1%)   Cash ($ mil.): 9
Return on equity: —
Current ratio: 1.40

HARLEE MANOR, INC.

EXECUTIVES

Pres, Hardie A Beloff
V Pres*, Leland Beloff

SEC*, Geraldine Barbeau-Leonard
Treasurer, Jean Beloff
Health Care Director, Jennifer Bail

LOCATIONS

HQ: HARLEE MANOR, INC.
218 N DIAMOND ST, CLIFTON HEIGHTS, PA
190181507
Phone: 610 544-2200
Web: WWW.HARLEEMANOR.COM

HISTORICAL FINANCIALS

Company Type: Private

Income Statement   FYE: June 30

	REVENUE ($ mil.)	NET INCOME ($ mil.)	NET PROFIT MARGIN	EMPLOYEES
06/09	1,164	62	5.4%	151
06/98	8	0	6.3%	—
Annual Growth	55.9%	53.6%	—	—

2009 Year-End Financials

Return on assets: 48.8%   Cash ($ mil.): —
Return on equity: 821.7%
Current ratio: 1.80

HARRIS COUNTY FIRE MARSHAL

EXECUTIVES

Exec Dir, Gary K Trietsch
Customer Staff, Jonnie Bryant
Revenue, Nancy Chamroeun
Senior Staff Engineer, John Tyler
Engineer, Douglas Emery
Plaza Clerk, Mahogany Ganey
Web Project Management, Frank Hunt
Executive Director, Gary Trietsch
Cto, Mark Pierce
Manager Senior Consultant, Timothy Lagerstrom
Assistant, Tammy Beck

LOCATIONS

HQ: HARRIS COUNTY FIRE MARSHAL
7701 WILSHIRE PLACE DR, HOUSTON, TX
770405326
Phone: 713 587-7800
Web: WWW.HCFMO.NET

HISTORICAL FINANCIALS

Company Type: Private

Income Statement   FYE: February 28

	REVENUE ($ mil.)	NET INCOME ($ mil.)	NET PROFIT MARGIN	EMPLOYEES
02/19	829	310	37.4%	3
02/18	740	224	30.4%	
Annual Growth	12.1%	38.1%	—	—

2019 Year-End Financials

Return on assets: 6.7%   Cash ($ mil.): 325
Return on equity: 17.0%
Current ratio: 4.80

HARRISON MEDICAL CENTER

EXECUTIVES

Pres-Ceo, Scott Bosch
Exec V Pres*, Adar Palis
Sr V Pres*, Patty Cochrell
Sr V Pres*, Forrest G Ehlinger
Sr V Pres*, Mariel S Kagan
SEC*, James Smalley
Chief Officer, Michael R Anderson
Payroll Staff, Charlie Sanchez
Scientist, Mitch Hopson
Internal Medicine Practitioner, Adeel R Seyal
Coordinator, Christine Wayman

LOCATIONS

HQ: HARRISON MEDICAL CENTER
2520 CHERRY AVE, BREMERTON, WA 983104229
Phone: 360 744-6510
Web: WWW.ADVANTAGERESUME.NET

HISTORICAL FINANCIALS

Company Type: Private

Income Statement   FYE: June 30

	REVENUE ($ mil.)	NET INCOME ($ mil.)	NET PROFIT MARGIN	EMPLOYEES
06/20	610	133	21.9%	2,400
06/16	433	45	10.6%	—
06/15*	398	56	14.1%	—
04/12	345	(22)	—	—
Annual Growth	7.4%	—	—	—

*Fiscal year change

2020 Year-End Financials

Return on assets: 12.0%   Cash ($ mil.): 146
Return on equity: 16.1%
Current ratio: 1.70

HARTFORD HEALTHCARE CORPORATION

Hartford Health Care provides a variety of health services to the descendants of our founding fathers. Founded in 1854 the health care system operates a network of hospitals behavioral health centers nursing and rehabilitation facilities medical labs and numerous community programs for residents in northern Connecticut. Medical specialties range from orthopedics and women's health to cancer and heart care. Hartford Health Care's flagship facility is the Hartford Hospital an 870-bed teaching hospital affiliated with the University of Connecticut Medical School. Its network also includes MidState Medical Center (some 155 beds) Windham Hospital (145 beds) and The Hospital of Central Connecticut (415 beds).

Operations

Hartford Health Care provides primary and specialty care services through partnerships with several physician practice organizations and specialist facilities including diagnostic imaging centers and mental health facilities. The company provides medical laboratory services including pathology genetic testing and other diagnostic services through its Clinical Laboratory Partners affiliate.

It also provides long-term care through Central Connecticut Senior Health Services as well as home health services through VNA HealthCare.

Financial Performance

In 2013 Hartford Health Care reported a 2% rise in revenue from $1.7 million to $2.1 million due to increased patient service revenue.

Strategy

As it becomes increasingly challenging for hospitals to remain independently profitable in an unstable economic climate especially as health reform changes take effect Hartford has been working to expand its footprint in the Connecticut health care market. In 2012 Hartford Health Care formed an alliance with Backus Corporation which operates the Backus Hospital and other medical care centers in eastern Connecticut. Backus gained access to Hartford's broader resources but continues to manage its own day-to-day operations.

In 2014 Hartford Health Care broke ground on a new 90000-square-foot cancer center at The Hospital of Central Connecticut.

EXECUTIVES

Ceo, Jeffrey A Flaks
Cfo*, Charles L Johnson III
Sr V Pres*, Margaret Marchak
Sr V Pres-Finance-Treas*, Richard Stys
Sr V Pres*, Gerald Boisvert
Exec V Pres*, David Whitehead
Exec V Pres*, Tracy Church
Treasurer, Shanan Harkness
Plant Operations, Chris Bibeau
Administrative Associate, Crestina Walker
Director, Cynthia Heller
Auditors: ERNST & YOUNG LLP HARTFORD C

LOCATIONS

HQ: HARTFORD HEALTHCARE CORPORATION
1 STATE ST FL 19, HARTFORD, CT 061033102
Phone: 860 263-4100
Web: WWW.HARTFORDHEALTHCARE.ORG

PRODUCTS/OPERATIONS

2013 Sales

	$ mil.	% of total
Net patient revenue	1,906	90
Other operating revenue	211	10
Net asets released from restrctions for operations	10	-
Total	2,128	100

Selected Facilities

Alliance Occupational Health
Central Connecticut Senior Health Services
Clinical Laboratory Partners
Eastern Rehabilitation Network
Hartford Hospital (acute care)
Hartford Medical Group (primary care)
The Hospital of Central Connecticut (acute care)
Institute of Living (research and psychiatric care)
MidState Medical Center (acute care)
Natchaug Hospital (mental health facility)
Rushford (mental health treatment centers)
VNA HealthCare (home health)
Windham Hospital (acute care)

COMPETITORS

Baystate Medical Center
Berkshire Health Systems
Bristol Hospital
Connecticut Children's Medical Center
Griffin Health
Lawrence & Memorial Hospital
Saint Francis Hospital And Medical Center
St. Vincent's Health Services
University Of Connecticut Health Center
Waterbury Hospital
Western Connecticut Health Network
Yale New Haven Health System
Yale-new Haven Hospital Saint Raphael Campus

HISTORICAL FINANCIALS
Company Type: Private

Income Statement				FYE: September 30
	REVENUE ($ mil.)	NET INCOME ($ mil.)	NET PROFIT MARGIN	EMPLOYEES
09/20	4,280	108	2.5%	12,500
09/19	3,541	(101)	—	—
09/18	3,072	410	13.4%	—
09/15	297	(37)	—	—
Annual Growth	70.4%	—	—	—

2020 Year-End Financials
Return on assets: 1.9%   Cash ($ mil.): 724
Return on equity: 4.5%
Current ratio: 1.70

HARTFORD HOSPITAL

EXECUTIVES
Pres-Ceo, Jeffrey A Flaks
V Pres, Gerry J Boisvert
Sr V Pres, Luis Tavares
Cfo, Tom Marchozzi
Coordinator, Betsy Centeno
Scientist, Michal Assaf
Health Professional, Gada M Abdelhafiz
Scientist, Pamela Tessier
Regional Vice-President, Barry Kriesberg
Coordinator, David Bailey
Assistant Chief, David Chung
Auditors: ERNST & YOUNG LLP HARTFORD

LOCATIONS
HQ: HARTFORD HOSPITAL
  80 SEYMOUR ST, HARTFORD, CT 061028000
Phone: 860 545-5000
Web: WWW.HARTFORDHOSPITAL.ORG

HISTORICAL FINANCIALS
Company Type: Private

Income Statement				FYE: September 30
	REVENUE ($ mil.)	NET INCOME ($ mil.)	NET PROFIT MARGIN	EMPLOYEES
09/20	1,808	61	3.4%	7,500
09/17	1,283	96	7.6%	—
09/16	1,031	76	7.5%	—
09/15	993	64	6.5%	—
Annual Growth	12.7%	(1.0%)	—	—

2020 Year-End Financials
Return on assets: 2.9%   Cash ($ mil.): 200
Return on equity: 6.1%
Current ratio: 2.60

HARVARD BUSINESS SCHOOL PUBLISHING CORPORATION

EXECUTIVES
Pres-Ceo, David Wan
Evp-Coo*, Raymond Carvey
Cfo*, Paul Bills
Vice-President Engineering, Patrick McManus
Customer Support Specialist (i, Jason Gerdom
Senior Manager, Jennifer Long
Customer Support Speci, Evan Ginja
Marketing Manager, Lisa Glynn
Assistant Professor of Finance, Boris Vallee
Marketing and Communications, Cathy Hutchinson
Associate Director, Elizabeth Kozik
Auditors: LB PRICEWATERHOUSECOOPERS LLP

LOCATIONS
HQ: HARVARD BUSINESS SCHOOL PUBLISHING CORPORATION
  20 GUEST ST STE 700, BRIGHTON, MA 021352063
Phone: 617 783-7400
Web: WWW.HARVARDBUSINESS.ORG

HISTORICAL FINANCIALS
Company Type: Private

Income Statement				FYE: June 30
	REVENUE ($ mil.)	NET INCOME ($ mil.)	NET PROFIT MARGIN	EMPLOYEES
06/19	925	11	1.2%	390
06/15	207	2	1.2%	—
06/10	139	1	1.0%	—
06/09	141	1	0.7%	—
Annual Growth	20.7%	26.5%	—	—

2019 Year-End Financials
Return on assets: 0.2%   Cash ($ mil.): 105
Return on equity: 0.2%
Current ratio: —

HARVARD MANAGEMENT PRIVATE EQUITY CORPORATION

EXECUTIVES
Pres, Jane L Mendillo
Treas, Robert A Ettl
Human Resources Senior Analyst, Emily Cummings
Human Resources Staff Assistan, Jonathan Mascia
Human Resources Senior, Patricia Lowe
Assistant Vice President, Charisma Madamba
Assistant Vice President, Drew Hussar
Associate Administrative Assis, Julie Notaro
Attending Physician Department, Katherine Janeway
Assistant Professor Department, Randolph Watnick
Manager III, Suzanna Tran
Auditors: RSM MCGLADREY INC CHICAGO IL

LOCATIONS
HQ: HARVARD MANAGEMENT PRIVATE EQUITY CORPORATION
  600 ATLANTIC AVE STE 1500, BOSTON, MA 022102203
Phone: 617 523-4400
Web: WWW.HARVARDUNIVERSITY.COM

HISTORICAL FINANCIALS
Company Type: Private

Income Statement				FYE: June 30
	REVENUE ($ mil.)	NET INCOME ($ mil.)	NET PROFIT MARGIN	EMPLOYEES
06/20	2,389	2,025	84.7%	6
06/17	663	477	71.9%	—
06/10	1,661	(611)	—	—
Annual Growth	3.7%	—	—	—

HARVARD MEDICAL FACULTY PHYSICIANS AT BETH ISRAEL DEACONESS MEDICAL CENTER, INC.

EXECUTIVES
Ceo, Stuart A Rosenberg
V Pres*, Edward L Grab
Director, Mary Leupold
Neurologist, Robles Lillian
Emergency Medicine, Richard E Wolfe
Auditors: LB DELOITTE TAX LLP JERICHO

LOCATIONS
HQ: HARVARD MEDICAL FACULTY PHYSICIANS AT BETH ISRAEL DEACONESS MEDICAL CENTER, INC.
  375 LONGWOOD AVE STE 3, BOSTON, MA 022155395
Phone: 617 632-9755
Web: WWW.HMFPHYSICIANS.ORG

HISTORICAL FINANCIALS
Company Type: Private

Income Statement				FYE: September 30
	REVENUE ($ mil.)	NET INCOME ($ mil.)	NET PROFIT MARGIN	EMPLOYEES
09/19	553	8	1.6%	800
09/15	487	1	0.3%	—
09/14	460	14	3.2%	—
09/08	22	2	11.6%	—
Annual Growth	33.8%	11.8%	—	—

2019 Year-End Financials
Return on assets: 3.5%   Cash ($ mil.): 32
Return on equity: 5.4%
Current ratio: 2.00

HAWAI I PACIFIC HEALTH

Hawaii may be paradise but even in paradise's some residents get sick. That's when Hawai'i Pacific Health (HPH) surfs in to save the day. HPH is a not-for-profit health care system consisting of four hospitals (Kapi'olani Medical Center for Women & Children Pali Momi Medical Center Straub Clinic & Hospital and Wilcox Memorial Hospital) across the islands with a combined capacity of 550 beds. The system offers a full array of tertiary specialty and acute care services through its hospitals which also serve as teaching and research centers as well as about 50 outpatient centers. Specialized services offered by HPH include cardiac care maternity services oncology orthopedics and pediatric care.

Operations

HPH supplies a wide range of primary and specialty medical services through its physician organizations. The Kapi'olani Medical Specialists group for instance comprises more than 100 physicians and partners with Kapi'olani Medical Center for Women & Children to care for patients from infancy through adulthood. The center also functions as the women's health and pediatric teaching hospital for the University of Hawaii School of Medicine. Its Visiting Specialists group provides care to the islands where HPH doesn't have primary care facilities.

Strategy

The system has partnered with Surgical Care Affiliates to build an outpatient surgical center in Honolulu in an effort to meet growing demand there. The center dubbed Surgicare of Hawai'i offers an array of medical services including orthopedics pain management ophthalmology general surgery and podiatry.

In 2010 the hospital system embarked on a 6-year $580 million master facility plan to expand and improve some of its primary hospital locations. The first stage included new intensive care units and parking capacity at the Kapi'olani Medical Center.

Company Background

The organization was formed through the 2001 merger of three entities: Kapi'olani Health Straub Clinic & Hospital and Wilcox Health System. Committed to supporting Hawaiian culture and values HPH and its member hospitals honor the Hawaiian language and its use of diacritical marks the glottal stop and the macron (okina and kahako).

EXECUTIVES

Pres-Ceo, Raymond Vara
Exec V Pres-Cmo*, Kenneth B Robbins
Exec V Pres*, Gail Lerch
Cfo-Treas*, David Okabe
Exec V Pres-CIO*, Steve Robertson
Exec V Pres-Gen Counsel*, Bob Ching
Chief Operating Officer, Travis Clegg
Director, Raquel Craven
Coordinator, Alyson Emde
Coordinator, Charlotte Geronimo
Patient Safety and Quality, Brandon Wong
Auditors: ERNST & YOUNG LLP DENVER CO

LOCATIONS

HQ: HAWAI I PACIFIC HEALTH
55 MERCHANT ST STE 2500, HONOLULU, HI
968134306
Phone: 808 949-9355
Web: WWW.HAWAIIPACIFICHEALTH.ORG

PRODUCTS/OPERATIONS

Selected Facilities
Kapi'olani Medical Center for Women & Children (Honolulu)
Kaua'i Medical Clinics (Kaua'i)
Pali Momi Medical Center (Aiea)
Straub Clinic & Hospital (Honolulu)
Straub Family Health Centers (Honolulu)
Visiting Specialists (Hilo Kaua'i Lana'i Maui Moloka'i Walmea)
Wilcox Memorial Hospital (Lihue Kaua'i)

COMPETITORS

Adventist Health System West
Kuakini Health System
Queen's Medical Center
Rehabilitation Hospital Of The Pacific

HISTORICAL FINANCIALS

Company Type: Private

Income Statement   FYE: June 30

	REVENUE ($ mil.)	NET INCOME ($ mil.)	NET PROFIT MARGIN	EMPLOYEES
06/20	1,369	(48)		5,400
06/18	1,351	130	9.7%	—
06/17	1,290	153	11.9%	—
06/15	159	0	0.3%	—
Annual Growth	53.8%	—	—	—

2020 Year-End Financials
Return on assets: (-2.3%)   Cash ($ mil.): 284
Return on equity: (-4.8%)
Current ratio: 1.80

HCL AMERICA INC.

EXECUTIVES

Dir, Shiv Nadar
Dir, Prateek Aggarwal
Dir, C Vijayakumar
Dir, Anoop Tiwari
Dir, Robin Abrams
Ceo, Manish Anand
Technical Lead, Pooja Manocha
Associate General Manager, Anand Vidhani
Consultant, Anchal Singhal
Area Sales Director, Arvind Chopra
Vice President, Ayut Patel
Auditors: SR BATLIBOI & CO LLP CAMAC

LOCATIONS

HQ: HCL AMERICA INC.
330 POTRERO AVE, SUNNYVALE, CA 940854194
Phone: 408 733-0480
Web: WWW.HCL.COM

HISTORICAL FINANCIALS

Company Type: Private

Income Statement   FYE: March 31

	REVENUE ($ mil.)	NET INCOME ($ mil.)	NET PROFIT MARGIN	EMPLOYEES
03/17*	3,559	130	3.7%	11,993
06/15	2,815	53	1.9%	—
06/14	2,353	0	0.0%	—
06/13	2,075	35	1.7%	—
Annual Growth	14.4%	37.9%	—	—

*Fiscal year change

2017 Year-End Financials
Return on assets: 8.8%   Cash ($ mil.): 4
Return on equity: 20.2%
Current ratio: 1.10

HDR ENGINEERING, INC.

EXECUTIVES

Ceo, George A Little
Pres, Eric L Keen
Coo, George Little
Cfo, Terence C Cox
Exec V Pres, Terry Cox
Treas, Chad M Hartnett
SEC, Louis J Pachman
Human Resources Manager, Kaitlyn Gonet
Administrator II, Leonard Mollak
Auditors: ERNST & YOUNG LLP CHICAGO I

LOCATIONS

HQ: HDR ENGINEERING, INC.
1917 S 67TH ST, OMAHA, NE 681062973
Phone: 402 399-1000
Web: WWW.HDRINC.COM

HISTORICAL FINANCIALS

Company Type: Private

Income Statement   FYE: December 29

	REVENUE ($ mil.)	NET INCOME ($ mil.)	NET PROFIT MARGIN	EMPLOYEES
12/18	1,399	107	7.7%	6,111
12/17	1,707	73	4.3%	—
12/16	1,748	89	5.1%	—
12/15	1,218	100	8.2%	—
Annual Growth	4.7%	2.3%	—	—

2018 Year-End Financials
Return on assets: 9.7%   Cash ($ mil.): 25
Return on equity: 13.1%
Current ratio: 3.90

HDR, INC.

With projects ranging from restoring the Pentagon and the Everglades to working on the Hoover Dam Bypass project HDR has left its mark on the US. HDR is an architecture engineering and consulting firm that specializes in such projects as bridges water- and wastewater-treatment plants and hospitals. The company also provides mechanical and plumbing services construction and project management and utilities planning. It has operation in nearly 15 countries and has offices in more than 200 global locations. The employee-owned company was founded as Henningson Engineering in 1917 to build municipal plants in the rural Midwest.

Operations

HDR's offers architecture services such as branding infrastructure interior landscape & site as well as lighting designs. Its real estate services includes acquisition and relocation project and property management and site and alignment analysis. Other programs and services includes asset management facility management economics and finance services and environmental sciences services (which includes acoustics noise vibration and ecosystem restoration) among others.

Geographic Reach

Headquartered in Omaha Nebraska HDR has operations in the Americas (US and Canada) Asia Pacific (Australia China India and Singapore) Europe (Denmark Germany Netherlands and the UK) and the Middle East.

Sales and Marketing

HDR's markets include defense & intelligence education health industrial power justice power & energy tech transportation and urban community among others. It has performed design and engineering work for a number of clients including: Shirley Ryan AbilityLab Kitsap Transit Road 13 Winery iKure Tucson Water and Allina Health Systems.

Strategy

HDR strives to do things better and stretch further. From its internal processes to the work it delivers and from the projects it does to the careers it enables. It is also conscious of its environmental impact as evidenced by ranking ninth for top environmental firms by revenue. HDR also believes that sustainability and resiliency make fiscal sense as sustainable resilient projects last longer can save money in the long term and can withstand unique shocks and hazards.

The company also continues to design and engineer big infrastructure projects for city and state governments. In September 2020 HDR was selected by the Southern California Regional Rail Authority to provide program management services for Phase 1 of the transformative Southern California Optimizes Rail Expansion program.

Earlier that year HDR celebrated the opening of the photon science laboratory building fit-out project at SLAC National Accelerator Laboratory Arrillaga Science Center in Menlo Park California. HDR led the 65000-sf major interior and utility systems fit-out which expands SLAC's photon science program.

Not only is HDR expanding its facilities but also its philanthropic efforts through its HDR Foundation. In mid-2020 HDR Foundation announced its expansion to Canada which broadens the reach of the foundation and offers support to its Canadian employees.

EXECUTIVES

Chm-Ceo, Eric Keen
Pres-Coo, Charles O'Reilly
Cfo, Galen Meysenburg
Treas, Kathleen Heaney
Secretary, Jody Debs
Accounting Staff, Adriana Alba
Accounting Staff, Tamela Cross
Vice-President, Louis Pachman
Staff, Rex Kernodle
Human Resources Director, Susan V Sandt
Scientist, Alexandria Snyder
Auditors: ERNST & YOUNG LLP CHICAGO IL

LOCATIONS

HQ: HDR, INC.
   1917 S 67TH ST, OMAHA, NE 681062973
Phone: 402 399-1000
Web: WWW.HDRINC.COM

PRODUCTS/OPERATIONS

Selected Mergers and Acquisitions

FY2015
Brentwood Tennessee-based Infrastructure Corporation
   of America (ICA)
FY2103
   Rice Daubney (Australia architecture design for
   healthcare retail defense markets)
FY2012

Stetson Engineering (Wyoming projects in water sewer storm water hydrology and transportation)
FY2011
   Amnis Engineering (Canada)
   Cooper Medical (Healthcare design/build specialist)
   HydroQual (New Jersey water resource management)
   Schiff Associates (California engineering)
FY2009
   Devine Tarbell & Associates (Maine now named HDR|DTA)
   iTrans Consulting (Toronto-based engineering firm)

Selected Markets

Architecture
   Academic
   Civic
   Corporate
   Healthcare
   Justice
   Science and Technology
Energy
   Oil and Gas
   Power Delivery
   Power Generation
   Renewable Energy
Federal
   Federal Architecture
   Federal Engineering
   Federal Planning
   Federal Environmental
   Federal Energy
   Federal Construction
   HDR SeaPort-e
Private Land Development
   Commercial
   Industrial
   Institutional
   Residential
   Resorts and Hotels
Resource Management
   Community Planning & Consulting
   Environmental Sciences & Permitting
   Fisheries Science & Design
   Mining
   Natural Resource Management
   Waste Management and Industrial
Transportation
   Aviation
   Freight Rail
   Highways and Local Roads
   Maritime
   Transit
Water
   Water
   Wastewater
   Water Planning
   Industrial

Selected Services

Analytical consulting
Architectural design
Coastal engineering and restoration
Consulting
Design/build
Environmental monitoring
Finished water storage facility services
Interior design
Landscape architecture
Master planning
Power facility engineering
Pump stations and flow control
Security services
Utility master planning and modeling
Water resources
Water treatment systems

COMPETITORS

Aecom
Black & Veatch
Brown And Caldwell
Epstein
Fuscoe Engineering
Gensler
Geotechnics
Hbe Corporation
Hks Inc.
Interior Architects
Jacobs Engineering
Kpa Associates

Kimley-horn And Associates
Lee Burkhart Liu
Leo A Daly
Mcg Architects
Mwh Global
Michael Baker
Nasland Engineering
Perkowitz + Ruth
Rmjm
Rtkl Associates
Saic Energy Environment & Infrastructure
Stv
Tetra Tech
The Austin Company
Western Summit Constructors
Willdan Group

HISTORICAL FINANCIALS

Company Type: Private

Income Statement				FYE: December 29
	REVENUE ($ mil.)	NET INCOME ($ mil.)	NET PROFIT MARGIN	EMPLOYEES
12/18	1,762	115	6.5%	10,000
12/17	2,362	82	3.5%	—
12/16	2,230	90	4.0%	—
12/15	2,132	74	3.5%	—
Annual Growth	(6.1%)	15.9%	—	—

2018 Year-End Financials

Return on assets: 7.8%   Cash ($ mil.): 283
Return on equity: 20.1%
Current ratio: 2.00

HEALTH FIRST SHARED SERVICES, INC.

Health First works to keep Florida's Space Coast denizens in tip-top shape. The not-for-profit health system operates four hospitals in Brevard County. Health First's biggest hospital is Holmes Regional Medical Center in Melbourne with more than 500 beds. Its Cape Canaveral Hospital and Palm Bay Community Hospital have 150 and 60 beds respectively. Its Viera Hospital is a 100-bed acute-care hospital. The system also runs outpatient clinics a home health service and a physicians group. Its for-profit subsidiary Health First Health Plans is the county's largest insurer with about 60000 commercial members and 23000 Medicare members.

Operations

The company operates four hospitals (Holmes Regional Medical Center Palm Bay Hospital Cape Canaveral Hospital and Viera Hospital) and offers a wide variety of health insurance plan options for patients in Brevard and Indian River Counties. Health First is the largest multi-specialty physician group on Florida's Space Coast. It also operates to Brevard County's only trauma center and a number of outpatient and wellness services including four pro-health and fitness centers.

Geographic Reach

Health First operates four hospitals and a health insurance company in Brevard County Florida.

Strategy

To expand its capacity Health First makes complementary acquisitions and pursues organic growth.

In 2103 Health First opened of a new center for fracture care at Health First Holmes Regional Medical Center and the center for joint replacement at Health First Viera Hospital. That year it formed a new Small Group Preferred Provider Organization (PPO) Plan offering increased flexibility when it comes to out-of-network coverage and fulfilling the needs of employer groups in its service area.

Mergers and Acquisitions

In 2012 the company acquired Melbourne Internal Medicine Associates (250 physician providers based in Melbourne) to increase patient quality safety and the patient experience. The entity was renamed the Health First Medical Group in 2013.

Company Background

In 2011 Health First partnered with Nemours to expand pediatric care in Brevard County. That year Health First Health Plans opened a new Vero Beach office to serve residents of Indian River County and launch its Medicare Advantage plans to the rest of Indian River County.

Despite an ongoing lawsuit with Wuesthoff Health System (which claims that Health First has an unfair monopoly of hospital services in Brevard County) the company forged ahead with construction of its fourth hospital in the county the Viera hospital campus. The Medical Plaza at Viera Health Park which will includes offices for multi-specialty physicians and a diagnostic/imaging center opened in 2010. And the park's centerpiece Viera Hospital a 100-bed acute-care hospital opened in 2011.

Health First was founded in 1995 through a merger of regional hospitals. The Brevard Hospital (now Holmes Regional Medical Center) first opened in 1937.

EXECUTIVES

Pres-Ceo, Steve Johnson
Chb, James Shaw
V Chb, Russell E Fischer
Exec V Pres-Coo, Larry F Garrison
Sr V Pres-Cfo, Robert C Galloway
V Pres-Ctrl, Roberta B Stoner
CIO, William Walders
Registered Nurse, Roy Bell
Coordinator, Maria Trieste
Coordinator, Sandy Grutta
Coordinator, Vicki Madnick
Auditors: RSM US LLP CHICAGO IL

LOCATIONS

HQ: HEALTH FIRST SHARED SERVICES, INC.
6450 US HIGHWAY 1, ROCKLEDGE, FL 329555747
Phone: 321 434-4300
Web: WWW.HF.ORG

Selected facilities
Cape Canaveral Hospital (Cocoa Beach)
Holmes Regional Medical Center (Melbourne)
Palm Bay Community Hospital (Palm Bay)
Viera Hospital (Viera)

COMPETITORS

Adventist Health System Sunbelt Healthcare
Aetna
Cigna
Florida Blue
Hca
Orlando Health
Osceola Regional Medical Center
Tenet Healthcare
Wuesthoff Health System

HISTORICAL FINANCIALS
Company Type: Private

Income Statement | | | | FYE: September 30

	REVENUE ($ mil.)	NET INCOME ($ mil.)	NET PROFIT MARGIN	EMPLOYEES
09/15	1,255	19	1.6%	6,900
09/14	1,136	90	7.9%	—
09/13	1,059	51	4.8%	—
09/11	129	(0)	—	—
Annual Growth	76.5%	—	—	—

2015 Year-End Financials
Return on assets: 1.2%   Cash ($ mil.): 152
Return on equity: 2.7%
Current ratio: 4.30

HEALTH PARTNERS PLANS, INC.

Health Partners wants to partner up with Pennsylvanians in need of health care. It is one of a few hospital-owned health maintenance organizations in the nation providing free and low-cost high-quality health insurance through its Medicaid Medicare and CHIP plans. The company is a not-for-profit health plan that provides health benefits to over 280000 members in the Philadelphia area. Its Health Partners Medicare plans offer three Medicare Advantage plans in the twelve-county area all of which provide more benefits than Original Medicare with no or low monthly plan premiums. Its KidzPartners program is provided in partnership with the state of Pennsylvania's Children's Health Insurance Program (CHIP). Its provider network includes over 6400 primary and specialty care doctors and more than 40 hospitals in the region. Health Partners was founded in 1984 by a group of hospitals in the Philadelphia area.

EXECUTIVES

Pres, William S George
Sr V Pres*, Debra Kircher
Cfo*, Martin J Brill
Treas*, Karen Armtrong
Sr Vp*, Don Daddario
Sr Vp*, Judy B Harrington
Coo*, Elaine Markezin
Sr Vp*, Vicki Sessoms
Coosvp Operations*, Lisa Getzfrid
Cfo*, Kevin Clancy
Coordinator, Laura Weiglein
Auditors: KPMG LLP PHILADELPHIA PENNSY

LOCATIONS

HQ: HEALTH PARTNERS PLANS, INC.
901 MARKET ST STE 500, PHILADELPHIA, PA 191074496
Phone: 215 849-9606
Web: WWW.HEALTHPARTNERSPLANS.COM

COMPETITORS

Aetna
Cigna
Gateway Health Plan
Health Net
Highmark
Independence Blue Cross
Keystone Mercy
Unitedhealth Group

HEALTH QUEST SYSTEMS, INC.

EXECUTIVES

Ceo, Denise George
V Pres, Mary Ann Keppel
Sr V Pres, Ron Tatelbaumm
Sr V Pres, David Ping
Cfo, Yann Kepple
Sr V Pres, Ann Armater
Coordinator, Cheryl Mathieu
Information Specialist, Lew Hulse
Internal Medicine Practitioner, Christopher Panettieri
Coordinator, Carissa Sharp
Chief of Medicine, Imtiaz Mallick
Auditors: PRICEWATERHOUSECOOPERS LLP N

LOCATIONS

HQ: HEALTH QUEST SYSTEMS, INC.
54 PAGE PARK DR, POUGHKEEPSIE, NY 126032584
Phone: 845 475-9500
Web: WWW.NUVANCEHEALTH.ORG

HISTORICAL FINANCIALS
Company Type: Private

Income Statement | | | | FYE: December 31

	REVENUE ($ mil.)	NET INCOME ($ mil.)	NET PROFIT MARGIN	EMPLOYEES
12/14	796	5	0.6%	2,000
12/13	706	103	14.6%	—
12/12	692	8	1.2%	—
Annual Growth	7.3%	(21.3%)	—	—

2014 Year-End Financials
Return on assets: 0.6%   Cash ($ mil.): 75
Return on equity: 1.2%
Current ratio: 3.10

HISTORICAL FINANCIALS
Company Type: Private

Income Statement | | | | FYE: December 31

	REVENUE ($ mil.)	NET INCOME ($ mil.)	NET PROFIT MARGIN	EMPLOYEES
12/14	910	(8)	—	620
12/13	1,000	(0)	—	—
12/12	1,034	(1)	—	—
Annual Growth	(6.2%)	—	—	—

2014 Year-End Financials
Return on assets: (-2.9%)   Cash ($ mil.): 60
Return on equity: (-10.8%)
Current ratio: 0.90

HEALTH RESEARCH, INC.

Health Research Inc. (HRI) knows where the money is. The group is a not-for-profit organization that helps the New York State Department of Health and its affiliated Roswell Park Cancer Institute solicit evaluate and administer financial support. Sources of that support come from federal and state government sources other non-profits and businesses. HRI's Technology Transfer office also assists the Department of Health in sharing its research findings with other public and private institutions and finding ways to create biomedical technologies through private sector development. HRI was founded in 1953 and has administered $7 billion over its lifetime.

EXECUTIVES

Exec Dir, Cheryl A Mattox
Exec Dir*, Cheryl Mattox
Law Specialist, Nicole McMillin
Scientist, Vincent Escuyer
Administrative Assistant II, Catherine Janese
Graduate Research Assistant, Trisha Winchester
Senior Operations Clerk Accts, Domenica Terry
Research Scientist, Gene Shackmann
Director of Information Techno, John Bintz
Biostatistician, Lawrence Schoen
Microbiology Researcher, Maureen Shail
Auditors: BONADIO & CO LLP ALBANY NE

LOCATIONS

HQ: HEALTH RESEARCH, INC.
150 BROADWAY STE 280, MENANDS, NY 122042732
Phone: 518 431-1200
Web: WWW.HEALTHRESEARCH.ORG

HISTORICAL FINANCIALS

Company Type: Private

Income Statement				FYE: March 31
	REVENUE ($ mil.)	NET INCOME ($ mil.)	NET PROFIT MARGIN	EMPLOYEES
03/20	1,326	506	38.2%	1,400
03/15	677	22	3.3%	—
03/14	703	13	1.9%	—
03/13	665	25	3.9%	—
Annual Growth	10.3%	52.8%	—	—

2020 Year-End Financials

Return on assets: 66.5%   Cash ($ mil.): 154
Return on equity: 82.0%
Current ratio: —

HEALTHPARTNERS, INC.

EXECUTIVES

Pres-Ceo, Mary Brainerd
Exec V Pres-Chief Mktg Offcr*, Andrea Walsh
Cfo*, David A Dziuk
Cfo*, Penny Cermak
Svp-Chief People Officer*, Delinda Washington
Coordinator, Renee Hannan
Team Leader Appl, Chao Nguyen
Admin Asst, Kristi Brandt
Project Coordinator, Lesley Pereira
Information Specialist, Milagros Ogania
Information Specialist, Pierre Gingerichboberg
Auditors: KPMG LLP MINNEAPOLIS MINNESO

LOCATIONS

HQ: HEALTHPARTNERS, INC.
8170 33RD AVE S, BLOOMINGTON, MN 554254516
Phone: 952 883-6000
Web: WWW.HEALTHPARTNERS.COM

HISTORICAL FINANCIALS

Company Type: Private

Income Statement				FYE: December 31
	REVENUE ($ mil.)	NET INCOME ($ mil.)	NET PROFIT MARGIN	EMPLOYEES
12/20	7,033	374	5.3%	22,000
12/19	7,251	278	3.8%	—
12/18	7,061	143	2.0%	—
12/97	1,247	(2)	—	—
Annual Growth	7.8%	—	—	—

2020 Year-End Financials

Return on assets: 5.8%   Cash ($ mil.): 1,583
Return on equity: 10.4%
Current ratio: 2.10

HEARTLAND CO-OP

Heartland Co-op has no need to go against the grain. The cooperative offers agricultural products and services for its central Iowa member/farmers. Heartland operates more than 50 grain elevators and service centers. It offers agronomy products and services such as seed treatments and alfalfa fertilization; grain drying storage and merchandising; petroleum products for farm vehicles and home heating; livestock and pet feed; and personal and crop credit and financing. Headquartered in West Des Moines Heartland was formed in 1987 when cooperatives in Dallas Center Minburn and Panora merged. Heartland which has grown to more than 5400-members merged with Farm Service Company of Council Bluffs in 2013.

Operations
Heartland Co-op operates more than 60 cooperatives in Iowa.

Geographic Reach
Iowa-based Heartland Co-op operates across its home state in the cities of Blairstown Luzerne Chelsea Elberon Conroy Hartwick Marengo Malcom and Montezuma.

Strategy
Heartland Co-op has grown through consolidation and mergers with many smaller cooperatives.

Mergers and Acquisitions
Heartland Co-op acquired Farm Service Company (FSC) in Council Bluffs Iowa in August 2013. The combination of the two extended Heartland's reach westward in Iowa. The corporate offices of the combined operation remains in West Des Moines in Central Iowa.

It sold its service station business in 2012 as it was deemed non-core.

EXECUTIVES

Pres, Arthur L Churchill
Manager, Jeff Jones
Staff, Jonathan Lewis
Marketing, Shawn Devooght
Location Manager, Lowell Finley
Sales Agronomist, Bob Follis
Director of Information Techno, Dave Cunitz
Sales Agronomist, Kyle Dop
Sales Agronomist, Tyler Hetzel
Information, Jason Anderson
Location Manager, Larry Hansen
Auditors: BERGAN PAULSEN & COMPANY PC

LOCATIONS

HQ: HEARTLAND CO-OP
2829 WESTOWN PKWY STE 350, WEST DES MOINES, IA 502661340
Phone: 515 225-1334
Web: WWW.HEARTLANDCOOP.COM

PRODUCTS/OPERATIONS

Selected Products & Services
Crop Nutrition
Seed Solutions
Precision Ag Services
Agronomy Services
Crop Protection Products

COMPETITORS

Adm	Farmers Cooperative
Ag Processing Inc.	Society
Chs	Five Star Co-op
Cargill	Ivesco
Farm Service	Orscheln Farm And Home
Cooperative	Pioneer Hi-bred
Farmers Cooperative	Pro-fac
Company	West Central Co-op

HISTORICAL FINANCIALS

Company Type: Private

Income Statement				FYE: June 30
	REVENUE ($ mil.)	NET INCOME ($ mil.)	NET PROFIT MARGIN	EMPLOYEES
06/19	867	17	2.0%	678
06/18	901	20	2.2%	—
06/17	932	17	1.9%	—
06/16	854	15	1.9%	—
Annual Growth	0.5%	3.5%	—	—

HEARTLAND PAYMENT SYSTEMS, LLC

Heartland Payment Systems (HPS) a wholly owned subsidiary of Global Payments Inc. makes sure plastic-card transactions don't get lost along their way. The company performs credit debit and prepaid card processing services at some 300000 locations nationwide. Its client list includes restaurants retailers convenience stores and professional service providers. The Heartland Payroll Solutions segment provides payroll processing such as check printing and direct deposit for more than 10000 customers. Other markets for the firm include K-12 school nutrition programs and payment processing for colleges and universities. Global Payments bought Heartland for $4.3 billion in 2016.

Sales and Marketing
Heartland Payment Systems clients include small businesses midsize companies enterprise organizations restaurants retailers convenience stores and professional service providers.

Mergers and Acquisitions

EXECUTIVES

Ceo, Robert O Carr
Co-Pres*, Michael A Lawler
Co-Pres*, David Gilbert
Cfo*, Samir Zabaneh
Clo-Gen Counsel*, Charles Kallenbach
Coo*, Conan Lane
Cbo*, Michael McMillan
Cso*, Marty Moretti

Cso*, John R South
Cao*, Joseph E White
Cto*, Bryan Thompson
Auditors: DELOITTE & TOUCHE LLP PHILADE

LOCATIONS

HQ: HEARTLAND PAYMENT SYSTEMS, LLC
10 GLENLAKE PKWY STE 324, ATLANTA, GA
303283495
Phone: 609 683-3831
Web: WWW.HEARTLANDPAYMENTSYSTEMS.COM

PRODUCTS/OPERATIONS

Products:
Billing Solutions
E-Commerce
Gift Cards
Internet of Things
Lending
Loyalty Program
Mobile Ordering
Mobile Payment
Payroll Services
Point of Sale
Processing
School Nutrition
School Payment

COMPETITORS

Banc Of America	Fifth Third
Merchant Services	First Data
Cardtronics	Fiserv
Chase Paymentech	Fujitsu America
Solutions	Total System Services
Comdata	Vantiv
Deluxe Corporation	Wells Fargo
Echo Inc.	Ipayment
Elavon	
Fidelity National	
Information Services	

HISTORICAL FINANCIALS

Company Type: Private

Income Statement				FYE: December 31
	REVENUE ($ mil.)	NET INCOME ($ mil.)	NET PROFIT MARGIN	EMPLOYEES
12/15	2,682	84	3.2%	3,734
12/14	2,311	31	1.4%	—
12/13	2,135	78	3.7%	—
12/12	2,013	66	3.3%	—
Annual Growth	10.0%	8.4%		

2015 Year-End Financials

Return on assets: 5.5%   Cash ($ mil.): 56
Return on equity: 25.2%
Current ratio: 0.90

HEARTLAND REGIONAL MEDICAL CENTER

Heartland Regional Medical Center strives for healthy hearts minds and bodies in the US heartland. The acute care hospital a subsidiary of Heartland Health provides medical services to residents of St. Joseph Missouri and some 20 surrounding counties in northwest Missouri southeast Nebraska and northeast Kansas. Heartland Regional Medical Center encompasses specialty centers for trauma and long-term care acute rehabilitation cancer heart disease and birthing. As part of the services provided by the medical center Heartland Regional Medical Center offers services such as arthritis pain and wound treatments as well as home health and hospice care.

Geographic Reach

Operating in Missouri Heartland Regional Medical Center serves the residents and visitors of its home state as well as those in Nebraska and Kansas. Altogether the medical center caters to a more than 20-county area.

Financial Performance

In fiscal 2012 as compared to 2011 Heartland Regional Medical Center's revenue rose some 8% and its net income saw a 31% boost.

Strategy

As part of its operations Heartland Regional Medical Center partners with several managed care organizations such as Aetna CCN Managed Care Coventry Healthcare and Blue Cross Blue Shield of Kansas City to give its patients payment options for its health services. In 2012 Heartland Regional Medical Center developed an accountable care organization. It's a participant in the Medicare Shared Savings Program and enters into other similar shared savings arrangements with commercial self-insured or other third-party payors.

In recent years the medical facility has been investing in growing its footprint. Heartland Regional Medical Center is funding a $55-million expansion project that includes adding a handful of new operating rooms and renovating 10 more.

EXECUTIVES

Chm, Alfred L Purcell
Ceo*, Mark Laney
SEC*, John Wilson
Data Warehouse Arch, Andrew Bramlage
Chief of Pediatrics, Carmen Ford
Chief of Radiology, David Mena
Physical Therapy Director, Elena Schultz
Utilization Review Director, Elizabeth Jalbert
Records Director, Ellen Ellis
Director of Home SE, James McMillen
Laboratory Director, Jennifer Sapp
Auditors: BLD LLP KANSAS CITY MISSOUR

LOCATIONS

HQ: HEARTLAND REGIONAL MEDICAL CENTER
5325 FARAON ST, SAINT JOSEPH, MO 645063488
Phone: 816 271-6000
Web: WWW.MYMLC.COM

PRODUCTS/OPERATIONS

Selected Services

Appendectomy

Cholecystectomy
Colon Resection
Hernia Repair
Nephrectomy
Assisted Vaginal Hysterectomy
Peritoneal Dialysis Catheter Placement
Pyloromyotomy
Tubal Ligation
Abdominal Perineal Resection
Adrenalectomy
Colostomy
Gastric Banding
Gastric Bypass
Gastric Sleeve
Gastrostomy Tube Placement
Laser Lysis of Adhesions/Endometriosis
Nissan Fundoplication
Salpingo-Oophorectomy
Prostatectomy

COMPETITORS

Ascension Health	Shawnee Mission
Bjc Healthcare	Medical Center
Catholic Health	Sisters Of Charity Of
Initiatives	Leavenworth
Children's Mercy	Truman Medical Centers

Hospital	University Of Kansas
Coxhealth	Medical Center
Mercy Health	
Saint Luke's Health	
System	

HISTORICAL FINANCIALS

Company Type: Private

Income Statement				FYE: June 30
	REVENUE ($ mil.)	NET INCOME ($ mil.)	NET PROFIT MARGIN	EMPLOYEES
06/21	672	47	7.1%	4,000
06/20	714	84	11.8%	—
06/19	645	38	5.9%	—
06/18	639	64	10.1%	—
Annual Growth	1.7%	(9.6%)	—	—

HELM FERTILIZER CORPORATION (FLORIDA)

EXECUTIVES

Pres, Dale Miller
Cfo, Chris Carollo
Dir, Hans Christian Sievers
Auditors: ISRAELOFF TRATTNER & CO PC

LOCATIONS

HQ: HELM FERTILIZER CORPORATION (FLORIDA)
401 E JACKSON ST STE 1400, TAMPA, FL 336025264
Phone: 813 621-8846
Web: WWW.US.HELMCROP.COM

HISTORICAL FINANCIALS

Company Type: Private

Income Statement				FYE: December 31
	REVENUE ($ mil.)	NET INCOME ($ mil.)	NET PROFIT MARGIN	EMPLOYEES
12/13	611	5	0.9%	28
12/12	947	11	1.2%	—
12/11	1,056	10	1.0%	—
12/10	667	6	1.0%	—
Annual Growth	(2.9%)	(6.7%)	—	—

2013 Year-End Financials

Return on assets: 7.6%   Cash ($ mil.): —
Return on equity: 24.4%
Current ratio: 1.40

HENDRICKS COUNTY HOSPITAL

EXECUTIVES

Jd, Ceo, Kevin P Speer
Cfo, Isadore Rivas
Assistant, Anita Dieckmann

Coordinator, Stephanie Jones
Manager, Stacey Bulla
Director of Wellness and Popul, Jennifer Bates
Associate Health Nurse Registe, Lisa Kincaid
Assistant, Amanda Smith
Family Nurse Practitioner, Carolyn Harris
Pathologist Assistant Cytotech, Amy Estes
Public Relations Specialist, Carrie Meyer
Auditors: BLUE & CO LLC INDIANAPOLIS

LOCATIONS

HQ: HENDRICKS COUNTY HOSPITAL
  1000 E MAIN ST, DANVILLE, IN 461221991
Phone: 317 745-4451
Web: WWW.DANVILLEPEDS.COM

HISTORICAL FINANCIALS

Company Type: Private

Income Statement				FYE: December 31
	REVENUE ($ mil.)	NET INCOME ($ mil.)	NET PROFIT MARGIN	EMPLOYEES
12/19	747	13	1.8%	1,700
12/18	605	(25)	—	—
12/17	550	39	7.1%	—
12/16	530	43	8.2%	—
Annual Growth	12.1%	(32.5%)	—	—

2019 Year-End Financials

Return on assets: 1.9% Cash ($ mil.): 20
Return on equity: 3.1%
Current ratio: 1.30

HENNEPIN COUNTY

EXECUTIVES

County ADM, David Hough
Project Engineer Project Manag, Megan Huang
Psychiatrist, Ngozi Wamuo
Administrator Assistant, Rachelle Tait
Audiologist, Tricia Iten-Maly
Coordinator, Moriah Legvold
Information Technology Team ME, Chantha Sok
Information Technology Applica, Charles Windhorst
Administrator, Denise Stewart
Analyst, Duachi Her
Information Technology Team ME, Greg Gaurkee
Auditors: RSM US LLP MINNEAPOLIS MINNE

LOCATIONS

HQ: HENNEPIN COUNTY
  300 S 6TH ST, MINNEAPOLIS, MN 554870999
Phone: 612 348-3000
Web: WWW.HENNEPIN.US

HISTORICAL FINANCIALS

Company Type: Private

Income Statement				FYE: December 31
	REVENUE ($ mil.)	NET INCOME ($ mil.)	NET PROFIT MARGIN	EMPLOYEES
12/20	1,897	(4)	—	10,246
12/18	17	38	222.5%	—
12/17	1,618	(95)	—	—
12/16	1,469	55	3.7%	—
Annual Growth	6.6%			

HENNEPIN HEALTHCARE SYSTEM, INC.

EXECUTIVES

Ceo, Jennifer Decubellis
Coordinator, Jennifer Kelley
Coordinator, Kris Hoplin
Gastroenterologist, Aaron Brosam
Internist, Danielle Haselby
Nephrologist, David Dahl
Otolaryngologist, George Goding
Infectious Disease Specialist, Kay Schwebke
Geriatrician, Mariam Anwar
Hospitalist, Melanie Lo
Orthopedic Surgeon, Nancy Luger

LOCATIONS

HQ: HENNEPIN HEALTHCARE SYSTEM, INC.
  701 PARK AVE, MINNEAPOLIS, MN 554151623
Phone: 612 873-3000
Web: WWW.HENNEPINHEALTHCARE.ORG

HISTORICAL FINANCIALS

Company Type: Private

Income Statement				FYE: December 31
	REVENUE ($ mil.)	NET INCOME ($ mil.)	NET PROFIT MARGIN	EMPLOYEES
12/18	950	13	1.4%	5,000
12/17	1,011	(19)	—	—
Annual Growth	(6.0%)	—	—	—

2018 Year-End Financials

Return on assets: 1.7% Cash ($ mil.): 38
Return on equity: 55.5%
Current ratio: 2.00

HENRY FORD HEALTH SYSTEM

Founded in 1915 by auto pioneer Henry Ford Henry Ford Health System is one of the leading healthcare provider and not-for-profit corporation and is comprised of hospitals medical centers and the Henry Ford Medical Group which includes more than 1200 physicians practicing in over 40 specialties. The system's five hospitals — including the flagship Henry Ford Hospital (877-bed) the Henry Ford Wyandotte Hospital (360-bed) and Henry Ford Allegiance Health (420-bed). Health Alliance Plan (HAP) a Henry Ford subsidiary is a Michigan-based nonprofit health plan that provides health coverage to individuals and companies of all sizes.

Operations

Henry Ford Health System is comprised of hospitals medical centers and the largest in the Henry Ford Medical Group which includes 1200 physicians practicing over 40 specialties.

The system flagship is the Henry Ford Hospital in Detroit a level 1 Trauma Center recognized for clinical excellence in cardiology cardiovascular surgery neurology neurosurgery orthopedics sports medicine multi-organ transplants and cancer treat-

ment. Henry Ford Allegiance Health is a Level II Trauma Center and a teaching hospital center with a thriving Graduate Medical Education program. Henry Ford Macomb Hospital - Clinton Township provides comprehensive acute and tertiary care; specialty services include a Heart & Vascular Institute Joint Replacement Center Henry Ford Cancer Institute a Women's Health Center with a Birthing Center that features roughly 20 labor delivery and post-partum suites. Henry Ford West Bloomfield Hospital provides the highest quality safety clinical excellence integrative services and innovation a unique environment that encourages wellness and provides access information to support and wellness offerings such as Demonstration Kitchen Live Well Shoppe and Greenhouse. Henry Ford Wyandotte Hospital offers a full range of services such as 24-hours emergency care adult mental health services birthing center general medicine neurosurgical services physical therapy and rehabilitation surgery and more.

Geographic Reach

Henry Ford Health System is based in Detroit Michigan.

Company Background

Automaker Henry Ford founded Henry Ford Hospital in 1915.

The Health Alliance Plan became part of the Henry Ford Health System in 1986.

In 2016 Allegiance Health which operated a hospital and other health facilities in Jackson joined the Henry Ford Health System and began operating as Henry Ford Allegiance Health.

EXECUTIVES

Pres-Ceo, Wright Lassiter III
Pres*, Gail L Warden
Exec V Pres, Mark A Kelley
Coo*, Robert Riney
V Pres-Chief Human Resources O*, Kathy Oswald
Cfo*, James M Connelly
Svp-Cso*, Carladenise Edwards
Svp-Chief Mktg Comm & Exp Offi*, Heather Geisler
Division Head of Research Radi, Svend Freytag
Safety, Eric Bacigal
Director of Radiation Physics, Indrin Chetty
Auditors: DELOITTE & TOUCHE LLP DETROI

LOCATIONS

HQ: HENRY FORD HEALTH SYSTEM
  1 FORD PL, DETROIT, MI 482023450
Phone: 313 916-2600
Web: WWW.HENRYFORD.COM

HOSPITAL LOCATIONS
Henry Ford Allegiance Health
Henry Ford Hospital
Henry Ford Kingswood Hospital
Henry Ford Macomb Hospital - Clinton Township
Henry Ford West Bloomfield Hospital
Henry Ford Wyandotte Hospital

PRODUCTS/OPERATIONS

SELECTED SERVICES
Bariatric Surgery
Cancer
Heart & Vascular
Neurology & Neurosurgery
OptimEyes
Orthopedic Surgery
Primary Care
Transplant Services

COMPETITORS

Ascension Health	Omnicare Health Plan
Beaumont Health System	St. John Health
Crittenton Hospital	Total Health Care
Detroit Medical Center	Trinity Health (novi)
Garden City Hospital	University Of Michigan
Harper-hutzel Hospital	Health System
Mclaren Health Care	
Mount Clemens Regional	
Medical Center	

HISTORICAL FINANCIALS

Company Type: Private

Income Statement				FYE: December 31
	REVENUE ($ mil.)	NET INCOME ($ mil.)	NET PROFIT MARGIN	EMPLOYEES
12/18	5,853	89	1.5%	23,000
12/17	5,977	203	3.4%	—
12/14	1,513	(13)	—	—
12/13	4,517	135	3.0%	—
Annual Growth	5.3%	(8.0%)		

2018 Year-End Financials

Return on assets: 2.0% Cash ($ mil.): 556
Return on equity: 4.2%
Current ratio: 1.50

HENRY MODELL & COMPANY, INC.

Operating as Modell's Sporting Goods retailer Henry Modell & Company sells sporting goods fitness equipment apparel and brand-name athletic footwear. It is America's oldest family-owned and -operated sporting goods retailer. Its top brands are Asics Champion Adidas and Smith's to name a few. It also offers fan gear such as jerseys for football. It also boasts an online presence at Modells.com.

Operations

The company offers various products including but not limited to: sports and activities sporting goods athletic footwear active apparel accessories and fan shop. It also offers equipment used for strength cardio bikes outdoor activities games and more.

Sales and Marketing

Modell's markets and sells its products through its stores and online.

Hungarian immigrant Morris Modell first sold menswear from a Lower East Side pushcart in New York City before he founded Henry Modell & Company in 1889. Led by CEO Mitchell Modell the company is operated by the fourth generation of the Modell family.

Company Background

Hungarian immigrant Morris Modell first sold menswear from a Lower East Side pushcart in New York City before he founded Henry Modell & Company in 1889. Led by CEO Mitchell Modell the company is operated by the fourth generation of the Modell family.

EXECUTIVES

Chb-Chm, Mitchell B Modell
Customer Representativ, Marie Sully
Buyer Mens Apparel, Judy Dezabala
Director of Replenishment, Rostislav Shternberg
Manager, Corinne Ribiere
Manager, Jackie Collins

Community Marketing, John Borrelli
As400 Operator, Mark Brown
Solution, Muhammad Ashraf
Project Manager, Rachel Linn
Manager, Business Intelligence, Annie Duncan
Auditors: BDO USA LLP NEW YORK NY

LOCATIONS

HQ: HENRY MODELL & COMPANY, INC.
498 7TH AVE FL 20, NEW YORK, NY 100186738
Phone: 212 822-1000
Web: WWW.MODELLS.COM

2016 Locations

	No.
New York	71
New Jersey	38
Pennsylvania	18
Maryland	9
Connecticut	6
Massachusetts	7
Virginia	5
District of Columbia	2
New Hampshire	2
Delaware	1
Rhode Island	1
Total	**160**

PRODUCTS/OPERATIONS

Selected Product Categories

Accessories
Apparel
Baseball
Basketball
Boxing/martial arts
Camping/hiking
Cycling
Electronics/optics
Fan shop-pro/college
Field hockey
Fishing
Fitness
Football
Footwear
Games
Golf
Ice/roller hockey
In-Line/roller skating
Lacrosse
Optics/telescopes
Outdoor recreation
Paintball
Pilates
Racquetball/squash
Roller hockey
Rugby
Running
Scooters
Skateboarding
Snow sports
Soccer
Softball
Tennis
Water recreation
Winter recreation
Wrestling
Yoga

COMPETITORS

Athleta	Hat World
Dick's Sporting Goods	Olympia Sports
Dunham's	Sports Authority
Eastern Mountain	Target Corporation
Sports	Wal-mart
Foot Locker	

HISTORICAL FINANCIALS

Company Type: Private

Income Statement				FYE: February 2
	REVENUE ($ mil.)	NET INCOME ($ mil.)	NET PROFIT MARGIN	EMPLOYEES
02/13*	607	0	0.1%	5,430
01/12	570	(3)	—	—
01/11	558	(7)	—	—
Annual Growth	4.3%	—	—	—

*Fiscal year change

2013 Year-End Financials

Return on assets: 0.3% Cash ($ mil.): 3
Return on equity: 1.7%
Current ratio: 1.10

HIGHER EDUCATION COORDINATING BOARD, TEXAS

EXECUTIVES

President, Raymund Paredes
Accounting Staff, Ai-Ching Reed
Accounting Staff, Charlie Cannon
Accounting Staff, Daniel Flores
Accounting Staff, Jannice Smith
Accounting Staff, Manuel Ortiz
Accounting Staff, Susan Schroeder
Accountant, Angela Burnett
Information Specialist, Heidi Langdon
Information Technology Manager, Linda Barrera
Director of Policy, Holly Kosiewicz

LOCATIONS

HQ: HIGHER EDUCATION COORDINATING BOARD, TEXAS
1200 E ANDERSON LN, AUSTIN, TX 787521706
Phone: 512 427-6100
Web: WWW.THECB.STATE.TX.US

HISTORICAL FINANCIALS

Company Type: Private

Income Statement				FYE: August 31
	REVENUE ($ mil.)	NET INCOME ($ mil.)	NET PROFIT MARGIN	EMPLOYEES
08/18	1,732	73	4.2%	290
08/03	1,116	(42)	—	—
08/02	0	0	—	—
08/01	0	36	—	—
Annual Growth	—	4.3%	—	—

HILAND DAIRY FOODS COMPANY., LLC

Hiland Dairy Foods is a farmer-owned dairy foods company that offers dairy products including ice cream milk butter cheese and eggnog. It has expanded beyond dairy and has a wide variety of other beverages such as Red Diamond Tea lemonade and fresh juices. Hiland runs more than 15 processing plants and has over 50 distribution centers across the region. It partners with a larger dairy co-operative Prairie Farms Dairy to market and sell products. Beyond dairy Hiland supplies juices bottled milk and coffee as well as tea water and other to-go drinks. It features limited-run specialty items such as peanut butter banana ice cream. Hiland was founded in 1938.

Operations

It is a full-service dairy with a bulging products portfolio that includes the ubiquitous milk cartons as well as ice cream yogurt cheese sour cream dairy-based dips whipping cream butter cheese and orange juice. The company's products are free of antibiotics and artificial growth hormones.

Geographic Reach

Springfield MO-based Hiland serves customers in several states including Arkansas Kansas Iowa Missouri Nebraska Oklahoma and Texas. To support its operations the cooperative boasts more than 15 plants in Arkansas Kansas Missouri Nebraska Oklahoma and Texas and operates over 50 distribution centers.

Sales and Marketing

Hiland uses social media such as Facebook Twitter Instagram and Pinterest to connect with its consumers and to promote dairy foods through blog posts photography and other original content.

EXECUTIVES

MBR, Gary Aggus
Prin*, Woody Rogers
Fleet Manager, John Aldred
Supervisor, Fred White
Plant Manager, Alan Adams
Purchasing Agent, Karen Gilbert
Qa Quality Control Manager, Greg Helbig
Transportation Manager, John Gervais
Human Resources Director, Randy Hyde
Sales Representative, Rob Ballowe
General Sales Manager, Ted Barlows
Auditors: BKD LLP SPRINGFIELD MO

LOCATIONS

HQ: HILAND DAIRY FOODS COMPANY., LLC
1133 E KEARNEY ST, SPRINGFIELD, MO 658033435
Phone: 417 862-9311
Web: WWW.HILANDDAIRY.COM

Selected Plant Locations
Chandler Oklahoma
Fayetteville Arkansas
Fort Smith Arkansas
Kansas City Missouri
Little Rock Arkansas
Norfolk Nebraska
Norman Oklahoma
Omaha Nebraska
Springfield Missouri
Tyler Texas
Wichita Kansas

PRODUCTS/OPERATIONS

Selected Products
Butter
Cheese
Cottage cheese
Cravé;latté; (milk and coffee)
Creams/Half-and-Half
Dips
Egg nog
Egg substitute
Fruit-flavored drinks
Ice cream
Juice
Lactose-free milk
Lemonade

Milk
Sour cream
Tea
To-go drinks
Water
Yogurt

COMPETITORS

Agri-mark	Land O'lakes
Associated Milk	Mmpa
Producers	Nestl ©
Blue Bell	Oberweis Dairy
Conagra	Organic Valley
Dairylea	Saputo
Dean Foods	Sargento
Dreyer's	Smith Dairy
Fonterra	Snapple
Great Lakes Cheese	Wells' Dairy
Hornell Brewing	

HISTORICAL FINANCIALS
Company Type: Private

Income Statement   FYE: September 30

	REVENUE ($ mil.)	NET INCOME ($ mil.)	NET PROFIT MARGIN	EMPLOYEES
09/11	958	8	0.9%	1,350
09/10	588	24	4.2%	—
09/09	559	39	7.0%	—
Annual Growth	30.8%	(53.0%)	—	—

2011 Year-End Financials

Return on assets: 2.7%	Cash ($ mil.): 19
Return on equity: 3.9%	
Current ratio: 2.30	

HILL FIRE PROTECTION, LLC

EXECUTIVES

MBR, Michelle Colyar
Sales Project Manager, Jim Lynch
Sales Representative, Patricia Colar

LOCATIONS

HQ: HILL FIRE PROTECTION, LLC
11045 GAGE AVE, FRANKLIN PARK, IL 601311437
Phone: 847 288-5100
Web: WWW.HILLGRP.COM

HISTORICAL FINANCIALS
Company Type: Private

Income Statement   FYE: December 31

	REVENUE ($ mil.)	NET INCOME ($ mil.)	NET PROFIT MARGIN	EMPLOYEES
12/11	5,669	185	3.3%	100
12/10	2,568	80	3.1%	—
Annual Growth	120.7%	130.7%	—	—

2011 Year-End Financials

Return on assets: 7.3%	Cash ($ mil.): 480
Return on equity: 11.4%	
Current ratio: 2.60	

HILLSBOROUGH COUNTY SCHOOL DISTRICT

EXECUTIVES

Chm, April Griffin
Superintendent*, Maryellen Elia
V Chm*, Cindy Stuart
MBR*, Susan L Valdes
MBR*, Sally Harris
MBR*, Melissa Snively
Building and Grounds Director, Chris Farkas
Technology Specialist, Stephen Filingeri
Director of Mis Is, Pansy Houghton
Teacher Ese, Kelsy Brown
Administrative Assistant, Stacey Dowse
Auditors: KPMG LLP TAMPA FL

LOCATIONS

HQ: HILLSBOROUGH COUNTY SCHOOL DISTRICT
901 E KENNEDY BLVD, TAMPA, FL 336023502
Phone: 813 272-4000
Web: WWW.HILLSBOROUGHSCHOOLS.ORG

HISTORICAL FINANCIALS
Company Type: Private

Income Statement   FYE: June 30

	REVENUE ($ mil.)	NET INCOME ($ mil.)	NET PROFIT MARGIN	EMPLOYEES
06/16	2,133	(59)	—	25,000
06/15	2,042	(110)	—	—
06/14	1,984	(45)	—	—
06/13	1,878	(44)	—	—
Annual Growth	4.3%	—	—	—

2016 Year-End Financials

Return on assets: (-1.8%)	Cash ($ mil.): 113
Return on equity: (-7.6%)	
Current ratio: —	

HMH HOSPITALS CORPORATION

Hackensack University Medical Center (HUMC) is an acute care teaching and research hospital that serves northern New Jersey and parts of New York. The hospital has about 775 beds and staffs more than 2200 medical professionals. HUMC administers general medical surgical emergency and diagnostic care. The center also includes specialized treatment centers including a children's hospital a women's hospital a cancer center and a heart and vascular hospital. HUMC is part of the Hackensack University Health Network which also includes a physician practice group and a joint venture that operates two community hospitals. In 2016 the network merged with Meridian Health to create Hackensack Meridian Health.

Operations

HUMC helps train future dentists and doctors through its affiliation with the University of Medicine and Dentistry of New Jersey. It expanded its education programs in 2012 by partnering with the Stevens Institute of Technology to offer joint biomedical training programs.

The hospital also performs research through the David Joseph Jurist Research Center for Tomorrow's Children. The center has roughly 475 research programs in operation at any given time.

Financial Performance

Medicare accounts for 29.5% of HUMC's funding; HMOs 28%; and Blue Cross 28%.

Strategy

The company grows organically and through acquisitions partnerships and affiliations.

To expand its services HUMC broke ground on a $35 million project to expand and renovate its trauma and emergency facilities in 2012 (scheduled to open in 2015).

Hackensack University Health Network is increasing its partnerships and affiliations with other regional care providers following the trend of US hospitals seeking to improve and lower the cost of health care through shared services and resources. The network partnered up with Texas-based LPH Hospital Group in 2012 to reenovate the Pascack Valley Hospital (now HackensackUMC Pascack) in Westwood New Jersey. Hackensack took over the bankrupt facility's ER back in 2007 and in 2012 the joint venture launched a $90 million project to revamp the rest of the 130-bed acute-care community hospital. It reopened in 2013.

Hackensack University Health Network also formed a joint venture with an area physician group to open two ambulatory surgery centers in 2012 and it entered a collaboration with CVS Health's MinuteClinic to open new urgent care centers.

That year HUMC formed a joint venture partnership with community physicians and United Surgical Partners International to buy and operate ambulatory surgery centers in Bergen County: Hackensack Endoscopy Center and the Endoscopy Center of Bergen County.

Mergers and Acquisitions

In 2015 the Hackensack University Health Network agreed to merge with fellow New Jersey care provider Meridian Health. The combined system to be named Hackensack Meridian Health will have 11 hospitals and two children's hospitals. The deal which is one of a number of consolidation efforts by hospitals in the state is pending regulatory approval.

Company Background

To simplify its operations HUMC sold its hospice operations to Amedisys in 2011. The health provider previously sold its home health agency to Amedisys in 2009 to generate revenue and control costs after struggling with financial losses throughout the year due to declining admissions.

HUMC completed construction of its new John Theurer Cancer Center in late 2010 giving it one of the largest comprehensive cancer centers in the US. The center includes diagnostic and treatment units that focus on specific types of cancers.

HUMC was founded as a hospital in 1888 with 12 beds.

EXECUTIVES

Pres-Ceo, Robert Charles Garrett
Exec Vpres-Coo-Cso*, Ketul J Patel
Pres-Cfo*, Robert Glenning
Chm-Heart & Vascular Hosp, Joseph E Parrillo
Customer Staff, Elizabeth C Cooper
Coordinator, Elizabeth Vega
Coordinator, Christine Pilz
Controller, James De Rosa
Health Professional, Mariette Y Amadi
Staff, Paul Lizotte
Accounting Manager, Christopher Clarke
Auditors: PRICEWATERHOUSECOOPERS LLP NE

LOCATIONS

HQ: HMH HOSPITALS CORPORATION
343 THORNALL ST, EDISON, NJ 088372206
Phone: 201 996-2000
Web: WWW.HACKENSACKUMC.ORG

PRODUCTS/OPERATIONS

Selected Services

Donna A. Sanzari Women's Hospital
Emergency Services
Heart & Vascular Hospital
Hospital Services
John Theurer Cancer Center
Joseph M. Sanzari Children's Hospital
Medical
Specialized
Surgical
Tackle Kids Cancer

Selected Facilities

Donna A. Sanzari Women's Hospital
Hackensack University Medical Center Mountainside
Hackensack University Medical Center Pascack
Heart & Vascular Hospital
John Theurer Cancer Center
Joseph M. Sanzari Children's Hospital
Tomorrows Children's Institute for Cancer and Blood Disorders

COMPETITORS

Bergen Regional Medical
Bronx-lebanon Hospital
Continuum Health Partners
Englewood Hospital And Medical Center
Hospital For Special Surgery

Lenox Hill Hospital
Montefiore Medical
Newyork-presbyterian Healthcare
Newark Beth Israel Medical Center
St. Joseph's Healthcare System
Valley Health System

HISTORICAL FINANCIALS

Company Type: Private

Income Statement   FYE: December 31

	REVENUE ($ mil.)	NET INCOME ($ mil.)	NET PROFIT MARGIN	EMPLOYEES
12/18	3,999	220	5.5%	1,100
12/16	1,707	41	2.4%	—
12/15	1,357	83	6.1%	—
12/14	1,309	106	8.1%	—
Annual Growth	32.2%	19.9%	—	—

2018 Year-End Financials

Return on assets: 5.7%   Cash ($ mil.): 202
Return on equity: 8.6%
Current ratio: 1.50

HMO MINNESOTA

EXECUTIVES

Eo, Andrew Czajkowski
Chb*, Jonathon Killmer
Cfo*, Tim Peterson

LOCATIONS

HQ: HMO MINNESOTA
3535 BLUE CROSS RD, SAINT PAUL, MN 551221154
Phone: 952 456-8434

HISTORICAL FINANCIALS

Company Type: Private

Income Statement   FYE: December 31

	REVENUE ($ mil.)	NET INCOME ($ mil.)	NET PROFIT MARGIN	EMPLOYEES
12/16	1,839	(156)	—	36
12/15	918	52	5.7%	—
12/14	850	85	10.1%	—
12/09	978	30	3.1%	—
Annual Growth	9.4%			

2016 Year-End Financials

Return on assets: (-18.2%)   Cash ($ mil.): 108
Return on equity: (-36.6%)
Current ratio: —

HMS HOLDINGS LLC

EXECUTIVES

Chb-Pres-Ceo, William C Lucia
Exec V Pres-Cfo-Treas, Jeffrey S Sherman
Exec V Pres Hr-Chief ADM Offic, Tracy A South
Exec V Pres-General Counsel-Co, Meredith W Bjorck
Coo, Douglas Williams
Chief Tech Offic, Jacob Sims
CHR & Compliance Offic, David Alexander
Chief Marketing & Strategy Off, Maria Perrin
Dir, Robert Becker
Dir, Craig R Callen
Dir, William F Miller III
Auditors: GRANT THORNTON LLP DALLAS TE

LOCATIONS

HQ: HMS HOLDINGS LLC
5615 HIGH POINT DR # 100, IRVING, TX 750382434
Phone: 214 453-3000
Web: WWW.HMS.COM

COMPETITORS

Accretive Health
Activehealth Management
Allscripts
Argus
Corvel
Expert Global Solutions
Hp Enterprise Services
Healthcare Holdings
Maximus

Magellan Medicaid Administration
Mckesson
Medassets
Optumninsight
Prgx
Performant
Quality Systems
Verisk Health
Athenahealth

HISTORICAL FINANCIALS

Company Type: Private

Income Statement   FYE: December 31

	REVENUE ($ mil.)	NET INCOME ($ mil.)	NET PROFIT MARGIN	EMPLOYEES
12/20	673	70	10.4%	3,100
12/19	626	87	13.9%	—
12/18	598	54	9.2%	—
12/17	521	40	7.7%	—
Annual Growth	8.9%	20.5%	—	—

2020 Year-End Financials

Return on assets: 5.3%   Cash ($ mil.): 207
Return on equity: 7.4%
Current ratio: 4.90

HOAG MEMORIAL HOSPITAL PRESBYTERIAN

Serving California's Orange County population Hoag Memorial Hospital Presbyterian boasts several hospitals and even more clinics to cater to area residents. The not-for-profit health care system is home to two acute care hospitals nine health centers nearly 15 urgent care centers and a network of more than 1700 physicians. Its hospitals include Hoag Hospital Irvine Hoag Orthopedic Institute and Hoag Hospital Newport Beach in Southern California. Combined these hospitals have some 600 beds and provide a comprehensive range of medical and surgical services with specialized expertise in a number of areas such as cancer heart and vascular neurosciences women's health and orthopedics.

Operations

As part of its operations Hoag operates a pair of hospitals ? Hoag Hospital Irvine and Hoag Hospital Newport Beach ? as well as nine health centers located in Aliso Viejo Costa Mesa Foothill Ranch Huntington Beach Irvine Tustin and Newport Beach.

Hoag offers a comprehensive blend of health care services that includes six institutes providing specialized services in the following areas: cancer heart and vascular neurosciences women's health digestive health and orthopedics through Hoag's affiliate Hoag Orthopedic Institute.

Hoag Medical Group is a physician group with specialties in Internal Medicine Family Medicine Pediatrics Geriatrics Diabetes Endocrinology Sports Medicine Rheumatology Allergy & Immunology Infectious Disease and HIV Medicine. The group offers same day appointments provides access to the Hoag network of services and specialists and accepts most major insurance plans. With approximately 100 allied health members more than 30000 inpatients and 450000 outpatients choose Hoag each year.

Geographic Reach

Based in California Hoag operates in about 40 locations.

Company Background

In 2013 Hoag formed an affiliation with St. Joseph Health a Catholic-sponsored health network with operations in three states. The two Hoag hospitals were combined into a new regional network known as Covenant Health Network which also includes five nearby St. Joseph facilities. The Hoag and St. Joseph facilities retain their independent identities and religious affiliations.

Hoag was Founded in 1952.

EXECUTIVES

Pres-Ceo, Robert Braithwaite
Sr V Pres, Flynn A Andrizzi
Ophthalmologist, Richard Weiss
Records Director, Leslie Scarborough
Emergency Medicine Specialist, William Park
Information Technology Analyst, Barbara Garabedian
Director Staff, Carolyn Edwards
Assistant Vice President Speci, Cathy Major
Accounts Payable, Joan Rivero
Executive Director, Laura Morrelli
Family Practice, Bassil Aish

LOCATIONS

HQ: HOAG MEMORIAL HOSPITAL PRESBYTERIAN
1 HOAG DR, NEWPORT BEACH, CA 926634162
Phone: 949 764-4624
Web: WWW.HOAG.ORG

COMPETITORS

Adventist Health System West
Anaheim Regional Medical Center
Children's Hospital Of Orange County
Citrus Valley Health Partners
Dignity Health
Long Beach Memorial Memorial Health Services
Pasadena Hospital Association
Saddleback Memorial Medical Center
St. Joseph Hospital Of Orange
St. Jude Medical Center
Tenet Healthcare
Torrance Memorial Medical Center
Trinity Health (novi)
Western Medical Center - Santa Ana

HISTORICAL FINANCIALS

Company Type: Private

Income Statement

	REVENUE ($ mil.)	NET INCOME ($ mil.)	NET PROFIT MARGIN	EMPLOYEES
06/16	894	100	11.2%	3,800
06/15	822	107	13.1%	
/*	0	0	—	—
Annual Growth	—	—	—	—

FYE: June 30

*Fiscal year change

2016 Year-End Financials

Return on assets: 3.0%
Return on equity: 5.1%
Current ratio: 1.20

Cash ($ mil.): 189

HOBBY LOBBY STORES, INC.

Hobby Lobby is the largest privately owned arts-and-crafts retailer in the world. The craft-and-fabric retailer operates more than 900 stores in the US in more than 45 states selling arts and crafts supplies baskets beads candles frames home-decorating accessories and silk flowers. Hobby Lobby Hobby Lobby also maintains offices in Hong Kong Shenzhen and Yiwu China. In addition the company operates Mardel Christian and Education Supply which sells Christian educational and homeschooling products. CEO David Green who owns the company founded Hobby Lobby in 1972 and operates it according to biblical principles including closing shop on Sunday.

Operations

Hobby Lobby offers more than 70000 items featuring home decor seasonal decor tableware floral art supplies craft supplies yarn fabric jewelry making and hobbies among others. The company works with trusted brands such as DMC Vintaj Crayola Revell Tim Holtz and more.

Geographic Reach

Hobby Lobby's headquarters include more than 10 million-square-feet of manufacturing distribution and an office complex in Oklahoma City.

EXECUTIVES

Ceo, David Green
Pres*, Steven Green
Cfo*, Jon Cargill

SEC Treas*, Mart Green
Application Developer, Aaron Patton
General Manager, Chuck Kane
Assistant Director Crime Inves, David Williams
Network Manager, Matt Bowan
Director Human Resources, Sue Cleveland
Buyer, Tandy Blagg
Buyer Crafts, Barbara Young

LOCATIONS

HQ: HOBBY LOBBY STORES, INC.
7707 SW 44TH ST, OKLAHOMA CITY, OK 731794899
Phone: 405 745-1100
Web: WWW.HOBBYLOBBY.COM

PRODUCTS/OPERATIONS

Selected Products

Arts and crafts supplies
Baskets
Candles
Cards
Furniture
Home accent pieces
Jewelry-making supplies
Needlework
Party supplies
Picture frames and framing
Scrapbooking supplies
Seasonal items
Sewing materials (fabric patterns notions)
Silk flowers
Toys
Wearable art

Selected Affiliates

Hemispheres (home furnishings and accessories stores)
Mardel Christian Office & Educational Supply (Christian materials office supplies and educational products)

COMPETITORS

A.c. Moore
Burnes Home Accents
Garden Ridge
Hancock Fabrics
Jo-ann Stores
Kirkland's
Michaels Companies
Old Time Pottery
Target Corporation
Wal-mart

HISTORICAL FINANCIALS

Company Type: Private

Income Statement

	REVENUE ($ mil.)	NET INCOME ($ mil.)	NET PROFIT MARGIN	EMPLOYEES
12/17	4,544	352	7.8%	23,000
12/06	196	58	29.5%	—
12/04	1,363	88	6.5%	—
12/03	150	58	39.0%	—
Annual Growth	27.5%	13.7%	—	—

FYE: December 31

2017 Year-End Financials

Return on assets: 11.2%
Return on equity: 20.8%
Current ratio: 2.10

Cash ($ mil.): —

HOLY CROSS HEALTH, INC.

EXECUTIVES

Pres-Ceo, Kevin Sexton
Cfo*, Anne D Gillis
Chief Advocacy Officer*, Eileen Cahill
V Pres*, Patrick Connely

Coo*, Stonish Pierce
Obstetrician, Ronald D Jacobs
Ophthalmology, Benjamin D Magno
Gynecology/Obstetrics, Angela D Thompson
Obstetrician, Oluyemisi O Famuyiwa
Home Health Care Director, Margaret Hadley Sr
Information Technology Manager, Patricia Okolie

LOCATIONS

HQ: HOLY CROSS HEALTH, INC.
 1500 FOREST GLEN RD, SILVER SPRING, MD
 209101460
Phone: 301 754-7000
Web: WWW.HOLYCROSSHEALTH.ORG

HISTORICAL FINANCIALS
Company Type: Private

Income Statement				FYE: June 30
	REVENUE ($ mil.)	NET INCOME ($ mil.)	NET PROFIT MARGIN	EMPLOYEES
06/20	628	48	7.7%	3,270
06/18	561	43	7.7%	—
06/16	434	28	6.6%	—
Annual Growth	9.7%	13.9%	—	—

2020 Year-End Financials

Return on assets: 4.7%   Cash ($ mil.): —
Return on equity: 10.2%
Current ratio: 1.30

HONORHEALTH

EXECUTIVES

Ceo, Todd Laporte
Chb*, Robert C Johnson
V Chb*, Gary J Goodman
Pres*, Max Poll
SEC*, Julian L Fruhling
Exec V Pres*, Gary Baker
Sr V Pres*, James F Burke
Sr V Pres*, Alan B Kelly
Treas*, F Michael Geddes
Svp-Cfo*, Paul Briggs
Member*, Jennifer Miller
Auditors: ERNST & YOUNG US LLP PHOENIX

LOCATIONS

HQ: HONORHEALTH
 8125 N HAYDEN RD, SCOTTSDALE, AZ 852582463
Phone: 480 324-7215
Web: WWW.HONORHEALTH.COM

HISTORICAL FINANCIALS
Company Type: Private

Income Statement				FYE: December 31
	REVENUE ($ mil.)	NET INCOME ($ mil.)	NET PROFIT MARGIN	EMPLOYEES
12/17	1,817	44	2.5%	14,000
12/14*	900	25	2.9%	—
09/09	847	4	0.5%	—
09/08	812	(17)	—	—
Annual Growth	9.4%	—	—	—

*Fiscal year change

2017 Year-End Financials

Return on assets: 2.1%   Cash ($ mil.): 96
Return on equity: 3.9%
Current ratio: —

HOOSIER ENERGY RURAL ELECTRIC COOPERATIVE INC

Who's yer daddy? In terms of providing electricity for many Indianans (and some residents of Illinois) that would be Hoosier Energy Rural Electric Cooperative which provides wholesale electric power to 18 member distribution cooperatives in 59 central and southern Indiana counties and 11 counties in southeastern Illinois. These electric cooperatives serve 300000 consumers (650000 residents businesses industries and farms) in a 18000 sq. ml. service area. Hoosier Energy operates six power plants and a 1720-mile transmission system and maintains the Tuttle Creek Reservoir in Southwest Indiana. Hoosier Energy is part of the Touchstone Energy network of electric cooperatives.

Operations

Hoosier Energy operates coal- natural gas- and renewable energy-generation plants. It delivers electricity via a 1720-mile transmission network including 21 major substations and more than 350 delivery points.

Geographic Reach

The company delivers power to member distribution cooperatives in central and southern Indiana and southeastern Illinois.

Financial Performance

In 2013 the power coop's revenues increased by 3% due to higher member revenues and increased sales of electricity. Net income grew by 1% as the result of higher revenues and slight decrease in maintenance costs.

Strategy

To advance its push for more renewable sources Hoosier Energy is pursuing cost-effective generating projects and supply contracts including the Clark-Floyd Landfill Methane Generation plant which has four landfill/coal bed methane projects and which has purchased power agreements for wind and hydropower. These measures are expected to provide 7% of member energy sales annually.

Its recent capital projects include a $400 million multi-year upgrade of the Merom Station investing $18 million in power delivery projects to support growth and reliability and continuing progress toward renewable energy goals with the commercial operation of the Osprey Point coalbed methane plant and the Livingston landfill-methane plant.

Company Background

In 2011 the coop was operating a 2.5 MW landfill methane generation facility in addition to buying 25 MW of wind energy.

Expanding its geographic coverage in 2011 Hoosier Energy began to supply power to the Wayne-White Counties Electric Cooperative when that coop's contract with an independent power supplier ended. The distribution coop serves 13500 residential farm and business consumers in 11 counties in southeastern Illinois.

Hoosier Energy was formed in 1948 as part of the nationwide rural electrification drive initiated by the Roosevelt administration in the 1930s.

EXECUTIVES

Chb, Charlie Meier
Ceo*, J Steven Smith
Pres*, James S Weimer
SEC*, Herbert C Haggard
Mgr*, Brady Mann

Coordinator, Jonathan Bolin
Manager, Fredrick Hamilton
Purchasing Manager, Pat Hayne
Manager, Tom Van Paris
Accountant Team Leader, Amy Parrish
Area Coordinator Serv, Brandon Moore
Auditors: DELOITTE & TOUCHE LLP INDIAN

LOCATIONS

HQ: HOOSIER ENERGY RURAL ELECTRIC
 COOPERATIVE INC
 2501 S COOPERATIVE WAY, BLOOMINGTON, IN
 474035175
Phone: 812 876-2021
Web: WWW.HOOSIERENERGY.COM

PRODUCTS/OPERATIONS

2012 Sales

	$ mil.	% of total
Members	532	82
Nonmembers	115	18
Other	0	-
Total	**647**	**100**

Member Cooperatives

Member Cooperatives
Bartholomew County REMC
Clark County REMC
Decatur County REMC
Daviess-Martin County REMC
Dubois REC Inc.
Harrison REMC
Henry County REMC
Jackson County REMC
Johnson County REMC
Orange County REMC
RushShelby Energy
South Central Indiana REMC
Southeastern Indiana REMC
Southern Indiana Power
Utilities District of Western Indiana REMC
Wayne-White Counties Electric Cooperative
WIN Energy REMC
Whitewater Valley REMC

COMPETITORS

Ipalco Enterprises   Indiana Municipal
Indiana Michigan Power   Power Agency

HISTORICAL FINANCIALS
Company Type: Private

Income Statement				FYE: December 31
	REVENUE ($ mil.)	NET INCOME ($ mil.)	NET PROFIT MARGIN	EMPLOYEES
12/12	647	27	4.3%	475
12/11	649	30	4.7%	—
12/09	575	16	2.9%	—
Annual Growth	4.1%	18.9%	—	—

2012 Year-End Financials

Return on assets: 1.6%   Cash ($ mil.): 50
Return on equity: 11.0%
Current ratio: 1.50

HORRY COUNTY SCHOOL DISTRICT

EXECUTIVES

Supt, Dr Rick Maxey
Accounting Staff, Patsy Johnson
Health Professional, Marti Graves

Case Manager, Hope Lupo
Case Management Specialist, Josue Valentin
Nutrition Manager, Kimberly Johnson
Director, Kristin Wilson
School Resource Officer Horry, Lcpl Anderson
Director of Network, Peggy Vickery
Supervisor, Robin Vaughn
Clerk of Court Administrative, Tania Bellamy
Auditors: MCGREGOR & COMPANY LLP
COLUM

LOCATIONS

HQ: HORRY COUNTY SCHOOL DISTRICT
335 FOUR MILE RD, CONWAY, SC 295264506
Phone: 843 488-6700
Web: WWW.HORRYCOUNTYSCHOOLS.NET

HISTORICAL FINANCIALS

Company Type: Private

Income Statement				FYE: June 30
	REVENUE ($ mil.)	NET INCOME ($ mil.)	NET PROFIT MARGIN	EMPLOYEES
06/19	585	(8)	—	5,000
06/18	548	(42)	—	—
06/17	520	(140)	—	—
06/16	494	218	44.2%	—
Annual Growth	5.8%	—	—	—

2019 Year-End Financials

Return on assets: (-0.6%)   Cash ($ mil.): 250
Return on equity: —
Current ratio: 2.30

HOSPITAL OF THE UNIVERSITY OF PENNSYLVANIA

EXECUTIVES

Dir, Pamela Mack-Brooks
Coordinator, Alvaro Talavera
Coordinator, Cherlyn Bynum
Coordinator, Denise Amaro
Coordinator, Pete Caldwell
Assistant Professor, Rajat Deo
Assistant Professor, Dennis Hadjiliadis
Nurse Practitioner, Diana Van Houten
Assistant Professor, Lachlan Smith
Coordinator, Barbara Lopez
Staff, Diane Frain

LOCATIONS

HQ: HOSPITAL OF THE UNIVERSITY OF
PENNSYLVANIA
3400 SPRUCE ST OFC, PHILADELPHIA, PA
191044208
Phone: 215 662-4000
Web: WWW.PENNMEDICINE.ORG

HISTORICAL FINANCIALS

Company Type: Private

Income Statement				FYE: June 30
	REVENUE ($ mil.)	NET INCOME ($ mil.)	NET PROFIT MARGIN	EMPLOYEES
06/16	2,236	283	12.7%	2,737
06/15	2,164	320	14.8%	—
Annual Growth	3.3%	(11.5%)	—	—

2016 Year-End Financials

Return on assets: 9.3%   Cash ($ mil.): 1,091
Return on equity: 13.2%
Current ratio: 9.90

HOUCHENS INDUSTRIES, INC.

Houchens Industries is listed by Forbes as one of the largest 100% employee-owned companies in the world. The diversified company runs some 400 retail grocery convenience and neighborhood markets across around 15 US states. That includes conventional supermarkets under the Houchens Food Giant IGA Tampico and Pan-Oston banners. In addition Houchens is an extremely diversified company with businesses in more than eleven industries. Houchens Industries was originally founded in Glasgow Kentucky by Ervin G. Houchens in 1917 as Houchens Foods.

Operations

Houchens operates about 25 companies including Cohen's Food Giant IGA Save a Lot and more. It also operates about 10 franchises such as Cinnabon Carvel Ace and Subway to name a few.

The company's manufacturing businesses include Stephens Pipe & Steel a leading maker and distributor of fence materials.

Geographic Reach

Based in Kentucky Houchens Industries operates more than 400 retail grocery convenience and neighborhood market stores across around 15 states.

Company Background

Founded by Ervin Houchens as BG Wholesale in rural Kentucky in 1917 Houchens has been owned by its employees since 1988.

EXECUTIVES

Chairman Of The Board, Chief Executive Officer, Dion Houchins
Auditors: BKD LLP BOWLING GREN KENTUC

LOCATIONS

HQ: HOUCHENS INDUSTRIES, INC.
700 CHURCH ST, BOWLING GREEN, KY 421011816
Phone: 270 843-3252
Web: WWW.HOUCHENSINDUSTRIES.COM

PRODUCTS/OPERATIONS

Selected Operations

American Sun Systems (tanning salon supplier)
Blake Hart Taylor & Wiseman (insurance)
Buehler's Buy Low (grocery retail)
Cohen's Fashion Optical (optical stores)
Food Giant (grocery retail)
Hilliard Lyons (financial services)
Houchens Markets (grocery retail)
IGA (licensed grocery retail)
Insurance Specialists (insurance)
Jr. Food Stores (convenience stores)
Price Less Foods (grocery retail)
Save-A-Lot (licensed grocery retail)
Scotty's (asphalt paving)
Sheldon's Express Pharmacy (drugstores)
Southern Recycling Inc. (recycling)
Stewart-Richey Construction Inc. (construction management)
Taco Del Mar (fast-food)
Tampico (juice)
TS Trucking (hauling)
Van Meter Insurance (insurance benefits)
White's Fresh Foods (grocery retail)

COMPETITORS

7-eleven	Meijer
Aldi	Mott's
Ameriprise	Nestl ©
Cvs	Ocean Spray
Charles Schwab	Odwalla
Citigroup	Old Orchard
Citrus World	Raymond James
Cumberland Farms	Financial
Dole Food	Rite Aid
Dr Pepper Snapple	Sheetz
Group	Southeastern Grocers
E*trade Financial	Sunkist
E. W. James	Sunny Delight
Edward D. Jones	Td Ameritrade
Fmr	Thorntons Inc.
Faygo	Tree Top
Goya	Tropicana
John Hancock Financial	Visionworks Of America
Services	Wal-mart
Jugos Del Valle Usa	Walgreen
K-va-t Food Stores	Weis Markets
Kroger	Welch's
Luxottica Retail	

HISTORICAL FINANCIALS

Company Type: Private

Income Statement				FYE: September 29
	REVENUE ($ mil.)	NET INCOME ($ mil.)	NET PROFIT MARGIN	EMPLOYEES
09/18*	2,613	29	1.1%	16,000
10/16	2,987	104	3.5%	—
10/15	3,212	99	3.1%	—
Annual Growth	(6.7%)	(33.4%)	—	—
*Fiscal year change				

2018 Year-End Financials

Return on assets: 1.7%   Cash ($ mil.): 117
Return on equity: 2.3%
Current ratio: 2.10

HOUSING DEVELOPMENT AUTHORITY, MICHIGAN STATE

EXECUTIVES

Chairperson, Steven Arwood
V Chmn*, Bernard Glieberman
Coordinator, Jared Boll
Coordinator, Jeff Westra
Coordinator, Justin Logsdon
Coordinator, Linda Hegstrom
Coordinator, Randall McKinney

Budget Specialist, Mary Cupp
Director of Legal Affairs, Clarence Stone
Grants Manager, Joelle Letts
Administrative Assistant, Juliann Kline
Auditors: PLANTE & MORAN PLLC EAST LAN

LOCATIONS

HQ: HOUSING DEVELOPMENT AUTHORITY,
MICHIGAN STATE
735 E MICHIGAN AVE, LANSING, MI 489121474
Phone: 517 373-8370
Web: WWW.MITALENT.ORG

HISTORICAL FINANCIALS

Company Type: Private

Income Statement				FYE: June 30
	REVENUE ($ mil.)	NET INCOME ($ mil.)	NET PROFIT MARGIN	EMPLOYEES
06/20	701	26	3.7%	320
06/19	684	25	3.7%	—
06/18	633	9	1.5%	—
Annual Growth	5.3%	66.5%	—	—

2020 Year-End Financials

Return on assets: 0.5% Cash ($ mil.): 381
Return on equity: 3.5%
Current ratio: —

HOUSTON INDEPENDENT SCHOOL DISTRICT

EXECUTIVES

Supt, Grenita Lathan
Accounting Staff*, Glenn Reed
SEC-Treas*, Diana Davila
Int Cao*, Yolanda Rodriguez
Coo*, Wanda Paul
Accounting Staff, Stephanie Matlock
Executive Officer, Manuel Rodriguez
Accounting Staff, David Clardy
Special Education Teacher, Carol Franklin
Coach, Kathleen Suedel
Teacher Coach, Brian Fortenberry
Auditors: WEAVER AND TIDWELL LLP HO

LOCATIONS

HQ: HOUSTON INDEPENDENT SCHOOL DISTRICT
4400 W 18TH ST, HOUSTON, TX 770928501
Phone: 713 556-6000
Web: WWW.HOUSTONISD.ORG

HISTORICAL FINANCIALS

Company Type: Private

Income Statement				FYE: June 30
	REVENUE ($ mil.)	NET INCOME ($ mil.)	NET PROFIT MARGIN	EMPLOYEES
06/21	2,846	(7)	—	22,440
06/20	2,699	(131)	—	—
06/18	2,695	(250)	—	—
06/17	2,329	(39)	—	—
Annual Growth	5.1%	—	—	—

2021 Year-End Financials

Return on assets: (-0.1%) Cash ($ mil.): 4
Return on equity: (-0.4%)
Current ratio: —

HOUSTON METHODIST ST. JOHN HOSPITAL

EXECUTIVES

Ceo, Marc L Boom
Chm, Ewing Werlein Jr
Treas, Carlton E Baucum
SEC, Gregory V Nelson
Manager, Enrica De Rosa
Information Specialist, Larry Tomazinis
Director, Mariana Pope
Information Technology Field S, Billy Koch
Director of Health Information, John Stewart
Chief Information Offi, Nicholas Desai
Research Operations Manager, Hanh H Hoang
Auditors: DELOITTE & TOUCHE LLP HOUSTO

LOCATIONS

HQ: HOUSTON METHODIST ST. JOHN HOSPITAL
18300 HOUSTON METHDST DR, HOUSTON, TX
770586302
Phone: 281 333-5503
Web: WWW.HOUSTONMETHODIST.ORG

HISTORICAL FINANCIALS

Company Type: Private

Income Statement				FYE: December 31
	REVENUE ($ mil.)	NET INCOME ($ mil.)	NET PROFIT MARGIN	EMPLOYEES
12/20	5,302	870	16.4%	4
12/19	5,225	1,275	24.4%	—
12/17	3,887	681	17.5%	—
12/16	3,746	338	9.0%	—
Annual Growth	9.1%	26.7%	—	—

2020 Year-End Financials

Return on assets: 6.9% Cash ($ mil.): 995
Return on equity: 9.8%
Current ratio: 1.20

HOWARD COUNTY OF MARYLAND (INC)

EXECUTIVES

County Executive, Calvin Ball
Chief Administrator Officer*, Raquel Sanodo
Dep Chief of Staff*, Candace Dodson-Reed
Attorney, Marna McLendon
Coordinator, Chris Eatough
Captain, Rick Leonard
Creative Manager, Beth Vessey
Director of Policy, Carl Delorenzo
Planning Specialist Recycling, Gemma Evans
Emergency Management Specialis, Michael Hinson

Chief Innovation Officer, Angela L Cabellon
Auditors: CLIFTONLARSONALLEN LLP
BALTIM

LOCATIONS

HQ: HOWARD COUNTY OF MARYLAND (INC)
3430 COURT HOUSE DR, ELLICOTT CITY, MD
210434300
Phone: 410 313-2195
Web: WWW.HOWARDCOUNTYMD.GOV

HISTORICAL FINANCIALS

Company Type: Private

Income Statement				FYE: June 30
	REVENUE ($ mil.)	NET INCOME ($ mil.)	NET PROFIT MARGIN	EMPLOYEES
06/19	1,335	(25)	—	3,463
06/18	1,298	76	5.9%	—
06/17	1,274	6	0.5%	—
06/16	1,247	(24)	—	—
Annual Growth	2.3%	—	—	—

2019 Year-End Financials

Return on assets: (-0.5%) Cash ($ mil.): 408
Return on equity: (-2.0%)
Current ratio: —

HPS LLC

EXECUTIVES

Mng MBR, Matt Thompson
Cfo-MBR*, Thomas J La Pres
Tres-MBR*, Joseph Schodde
Treas-MBR*, Dwith Gascho
Customer Representativ, Tracy Keeler
Regional Sales Manager, Brian Smith
Member Resources, David Gregory
Regional Sales Manager, Bryan Brauer
Developer, Katie Hayward
Direct Source Int Design Assis, Robin Tagg
Accounting Assistant, Sharon Demond
Auditors: MEYNARD TOLMAN & VENLET PC

LOCATIONS

HQ: HPS LLC
3275 N M 37 HWY, MIDDLEVILLE, MI 493339126
Phone: 269 795-3308
Web: WWW.HPSGPO.COM

HISTORICAL FINANCIALS

Company Type: Private

Income Statement				FYE: June 30
	REVENUE ($ mil.)	NET INCOME ($ mil.)	NET PROFIT MARGIN	EMPLOYEES
06/19	899	0	0.1%	38
06/18	782	0	0.1%	—
06/16	1,032	0	0.1%	—
06/15	960	0	0.1%	—
Annual Growth	(1.6%)	(4.7%)	—	—

2019 Year-End Financials

Return on assets: 4.0% Cash ($ mil.): 4
Return on equity: 5.3%
Current ratio: 2.00

HUMBLE INDEPENDENT SCHOOL DISTRICT

EXECUTIVES

Supt, Guy M Sconzo
Nurse, Lorraine Cano
Counselor, Carol Reiner
Coordinator, Sukari Stredit-Thomas
Registrar, Selene Greff
Assistant Principals Secretary, Frances Harris
Nurse, Karen Gorgol
Assistant, Bethany Harper
Registrar, Alejandra Sanchez
Prin, Angela D Conrad
Life Skills Teacher, Linne Querubin
Auditors: WHITLEY PENN LLP HOUSTON TEX

LOCATIONS

HQ: HUMBLE INDEPENDENT SCHOOL DISTRICT
10203 BIRCHRIDGE DR, HUMBLE, TX 773382200
Phone: 281 641-1000
Web: WWW.HUMBLE.K12.TX.US

HISTORICAL FINANCIALS

Company Type: Private

Income Statement				FYE: June 30
	REVENUE ($ mil.)	NET INCOME ($ mil.)	NET PROFIT MARGIN	EMPLOYEES
06/21	612	63	10.4%	5,000
06/20	559	90	16.1%	—
06/19	546	132	24.3%	—
06/18	490	(67)	—	—
Annual Growth	7.7%	—	—	—

HUNTER ROBERTS CONSTRUCTION GROUP LLC

EXECUTIVES

Ceo, James C McKenna
Sr V Pres*, John Alicandri
Executive Vice President*, Kevin Barrett
V Pres*, Mark Lamble
V Pres*, Alex Craig
V Pres*, Dan Dirscherl
V Pres Proj Exec*, Brian Aronne
V Pres-Dir of Purchasing*, Tim Dillon
Exec V Pres-Gen Mgr NY*, Paul Andersen
Vp of Finance*, Robert Belitz
V Pres*, Chuck Petrusky
Auditors: GRASSI & CO JERICHO NEW YOR

LOCATIONS

HQ: HUNTER ROBERTS CONSTRUCTION GROUP LLC
55 WATER ST FL 51, NEW YORK, NY 100413201
Phone: 212 321-6800
Web: WWW.HRCG.COM

HISTORICAL FINANCIALS

Company Type: Private

Income Statement				FYE: December 31
	REVENUE ($ mil.)	NET INCOME ($ mil.)	NET PROFIT MARGIN	EMPLOYEES
12/13	762	3	0.4%	260
12/12	706	1	0.2%	—
12/10	458	7	1.7%	—
Annual Growth	18.4%	(26.8%)	—	—

2013 Year-End Financials

Return on assets: 1.4%   Cash ($ mil.): 61
Return on equity: 6.4%
Current ratio: 1.20

HUNTINGTON HOSPITAL

LOCATIONS

HQ: HUNTINGTON HOSPITAL
100 W CALIFORNIA BLVD, PASADENA, CA 911053010
Phone: 626 397-5000
Web: WWW.HUNTINGTONHOSPITAL.ORG

HISTORICAL FINANCIALS

Company Type: Private

Income Statement				FYE: December 31
	REVENUE ($ mil.)	NET INCOME ($ mil.)	NET PROFIT MARGIN	EMPLOYEES
12/17	654	15	2.3%	3,500
12/16	646	6	0.9%	—
12/15	551	3	0.7%	—
12/14	513	1	0.4%	—
Annual Growth	8.4%	102.0%	—	—

2017 Year-End Financials

Return on assets: 1.7%   Cash ($ mil.): 11
Return on equity: 2.6%
Current ratio: 3.30

HUNTSVILLE HOSPITAL HEALTH SYSTEM

EXECUTIVES

Ceo, David Spillers
Coo*, Jeff Samz
Pres-Coo*, Tracy Doughty

LOCATIONS

HQ: HUNTSVILLE HOSPITAL HEALTH SYSTEM
101 SIVLEY RD SW, HUNTSVILLE, AL 358014470
Phone: 256 265-1000
Web: WWW.HUNTSVILLEHOSPITAL.ORG

HUNTSVILLE UTILITIES

EXECUTIVES

Pres, William C Pippin
Staff, Mike Coranet
Executive Assistant, Beverly Wilson

LOCATIONS

HQ: HUNTSVILLE UTILITIES
112 SPRAGINS ST NW, HUNTSVILLE, AL 358014902
Phone: 256 535-1200
Web: WWW.HSVUTIL.ORG

HISTORICAL FINANCIALS

Company Type: Private

Income Statement				FYE: June 30
	REVENUE ($ mil.)	NET INCOME ($ mil.)	NET PROFIT MARGIN	EMPLOYEES
06/16	864	98	11.4%	112
06/15	799	100	12.6%	—
Annual Growth	8.1%	(2.4%)	—	—

2016 Year-End Financials

Return on assets: 7.0%   Cash ($ mil.): 186
Return on equity: 9.7%
Current ratio: 2.10

HISTORICAL FINANCIALS

Company Type: Private

Income Statement				FYE: September 30
	REVENUE ($ mil.)	NET INCOME ($ mil.)	NET PROFIT MARGIN	EMPLOYEES
09/20	604	36	6.1%	634
09/19	629	32	5.1%	—
09/18	525	18	3.6%	—
09/11	493	10	2.1%	—
Annual Growth	2.3%	14.9%	—	—

2020 Year-End Financials

Return on assets: 3.4%   Cash ($ mil.): 24
Return on equity: 6.0%
Current ratio: 2.90

HURON HEALTH CARE CENTER, INC

EXECUTIVES

Admin, Amy Donaldson
Minimum Data Set Coordinator, Shelly Shaffer
Nursing Home Director, Trisha Brown
Lpn Unit Manager, Melinda Knisley

LOCATIONS

HQ: HURON HEALTH CARE CENTER, INC
1920 CLEVELAND RD W, HURON, OH 448391211
Phone: 419 433-4990

HISTORICAL FINANCIALS
Company Type: Private

Income Statement
FYE: December 31

	REVENUE ($ mil.)	NET INCOME ($ mil.)	NET PROFIT MARGIN	EMPLOYEES
12/09	584	58	10.0%	37
12/98	3	0	—	—
12/97	3	3	97.8%	—
12/96	3	0	—	—
Annual Growth	48.0%	—	—	—

2009 Year-End Financials
Return on assets: 999.9% Cash ($ mil.): —
Return on equity: 999.9%
Current ratio: 2.20

HY-VEE, INC.

Hy-Vee is one of the largest privately-owned US supermarket chains despite serving some modestly sized towns in the Midwest. The company runs more than 280 stores in eight Midwestern states. It distributes products to its stores through several subsidiaries including Amber Pharmacy D & D Foods Florist Distributing Hy-Vee Construction Midwest Heritage Perishable Distributors of Iowa and Vivid Clear RX. Hy-Vee is synonymous with quality variety convenience healthy lifestyles culinary expertise and superior customer service. Charles Hyde and David Vredenburg founded the employee-owned company in 1930. It takes its name from a combination of its founders' names.

Operations
Hy-Vee offers beverages fresh frozen health and beauty household and laundry ready to go meals pastries cakes and baby products. Through its subsidiaries Hy-Vee established a distribution system that secures the highest quality merchandise and transports its products quickly and efficiently to its customers.

Geographic Reach
Iowa-based Hy-Vee operates more than 280 retail stores in Illinois Iowa Kansas Minnesota Missouri Nebraska South Dakota and Wisconsin. The company has distribution centers in Chariton Iowa and Cherokee Iowa with a third perishable operation in Ankeny Iowa.

Sales and Marketing
Hy-Vee sell its products through online and its own groceries located in eight Midwestern states in the US.

EXECUTIVES
Ceo, Randy Edeker
Evp, Cfo, and Treasurer*, Mike Skokan
SEC*, Michael Jurgens
Coo-Vice Chm*, Jay Marshall
Evp-Chief Merchandising Office*, Darren Baty
Cdo*, Jason Buhrow
Cmo*, Daniel Fick
V Pres, Rose E Kleyweg Mitchell
Mgr, Lindsay Knoop
Programmer Analyst, Gary Stevens
Coordinator, Sara Mitchell

LOCATIONS
HQ: HY-VEE, INC.
  5820 WESTOWN PKWY, WEST DES MOINES, IA 502668223
Phone: 515 267-2800
Web: WWW.HY-VEE.COM

PRODUCTS/OPERATIONS

Selected Subsidiaries
D & D Foods Inc. (salads dips and meats)
Florist Distributing Inc. (flowers plants and florist supplies)
Hy-Vee Construction L.C. (construction)
Hy-Vee Pharmacy Solutions (specialty pharmacy services)
Hy-Vee Weitz Construction L.C. (construction)
Lomar Distributing Inc. (specialty foods)
Midwest Heritage Bank FSB (banking)
Perishable Distributors of Iowa Ltd. (meat fish seafood and ice cream)

COMPETITORS
Aldi	Niemann Foods
Associated Wholesale Grocers	Rite Aid
Ball's Food	Roundy's
Cvs	Supervalu
Casey's General Stores	Save-a-lot Food Stores
Fareway Stores	Target Corporation
Kmart	Wal-mart
Kroger	Walgreen

HISTORICAL FINANCIALS
Company Type: Private

Income Statement
FYE: September 30

	REVENUE ($ mil.)	NET INCOME ($ mil.)	NET PROFIT MARGIN	EMPLOYEES
09/20	11,449	0	—	83,000
09/19	10,672	0	—	—
09/18*	10,290	0	—	—
12/16	9,842	0	—	—
Annual Growth	3.9%	—	—	—
*Fiscal year change

2020 Year-End Financials
Return on assets: —   Cash ($ mil.): 59
Return on equity: —
Current ratio: 0.90

HYUNDAI TRANSYS GEORGIA POWERTRAIN, INC.

EXECUTIVES
Ceo, Sam Ho Cha
SEC*, Taeeuk Kim
Cfo*, Changyoung Kim
Purchasing Specialist, Darren Wiker
Fin & Acct Specialist, Do Hyun Lee
Machining Leader, Jason Aikens
Assistant Manager, Jin Kwak
Associate Professor, Carmello Chris
Senior Specialist J Gen Ral AF, Semin Chun
Manager Maintenance, Eunsu Choi
Auditors: PK LLP OPELIKA ALABAMA

LOCATIONS
HQ: HYUNDAI TRANSYS GEORGIA POWERTRAIN, INC.
  6801 KIA PKWY, WEST POINT, GA 318334937
Phone: 706 902-6800
Web: WWW.HYUNDAI-TRANSYS.COM

HISTORICAL FINANCIALS
Company Type: Private

Income Statement
FYE: December 31

	REVENUE ($ mil.)	NET INCOME ($ mil.)	NET PROFIT MARGIN	EMPLOYEES
12/16	1,134	7	0.6%	500
12/15	1,230	12	1.0%	—
12/14	1,250	11	0.9%	—
12/13	1,220	11	0.9%	—
Annual Growth	(2.4%)	(14.3%)	—	—

2016 Year-End Financials
Return on assets: 2.5%   Cash ($ mil.): 22
Return on equity: 6.0%
Current ratio: 1.70

ICE DATA SERVICES, INC.

Interactive Data Corporation has something vital to the information superhighway — the information. Its subscription services provide financial market data analytics and related services to financial institutions active traders and individual investors. Interactive Data conducts business through two segments: Institutional Services and Active Trader Services. Products include Interactive Data Fixed Income Analytics (fixed-income portfolio analytics for institutions) Interactive Data Pricing and Reference Data (securities information for institutions) and Interactive Data Desktop Solutions (real-time market data for individuals). Private-equity firms Silver Lake and Warburg Pincus agreed to sell IDC to Intercontinental Exchange in 2015.

Operations
The company conducts business through two segments: Pricing and Reference Data and Trading Solutions. Its Pricing and Reference Data segment accounted for about 70% of its revenue in fiscal 2012 while its Trading Solutions segment contributed the other 30% of revenue.

Geographic Reach
Interactive Data has operations in the US Europe and Asia Pacific. About 30% of sales come from outside the US.

Sales and Marketing
To support the sales efforts of its businesses the company implemented a range of promotional and lead-generating campaigns such as publishing white papers direct mail and email initiatives advertising in leading industry publications participating in targeted industry conferences and other public relations tactics.

Financial Performance
In fiscal 2012 the company's total revenue increased by about $12.4 million or 1.4% compared to fiscal 2011. Interactive Data reported slightly more than $880 million in revenue for fiscal 2012 after it claimed $867.7 million for fiscal 2011.

HISTORY
Data Broadcasting was formed in 1992 as the successor to the Financial News Network a bankrupt financial cable TV network. Alan Hirschfield former CEO of Twentieth Century Fox and Columbia Pictures and Allan Tessler experienced in restructuring businesses were brought in; they sold many of Financial News' assets but held onto two information services DBC West (stock data for private investors) and Shark Information Services (serving professional traders).

The company expanded its services and markets through key acquisitions. In 1994 it bought Computer Sports World (online sports data) and Capital Management Sciences (fixed-income data and analysis). The following year Data Broadcasting bought and merged with its chief rival (Broadcast International) bought a stake in Internet Financial Network (online distributor of SEC filings) and sold Shark. These transactions also hurt earnings in 1996.

Data Broadcasting acquired international news provider Federal News Service Group in 1997. It also put its InStore Satellite Network and CheckRite International business services divisions up for sale to focus on information services and fund future acquisitions. National Data Corporation a provider of transaction processing services bought CheckRite International in 1998; InStore Satellite was a tougher sell but finally went to Muzak in 1999. Also that year MarketWatch.com a financial news Web site operated by Data Broadcasting and CBS went public (each company retained a 34% stake). (MarketWatch.com later changed its name to MarketWatch in 2004 and was sold to Dow Jones & Company in 2005.) Data Broadcasting later sold its AgCast business to closely held agricultural publisher The Farm Journal.

In 2000 UK media company Pearson took a 60% stake in Data Broadcasting in exchange for its global equities information business Financial Times Asset Management. Former Pearson executives Stephen Hill and Stuart Clark took over as chairman and CEO respectively. Data Broadcasting later sold its DBC Sports unit (including odds maker Las Vegas Sports Consultants) to former SportsLine.com subsidiary VegasInsider. Also that year Data Broadcasting acquired Thomson Financial's security data business (Muller Data Corporation).

In early 2001 Data Broadcasting sold its stake in MarketWatch.com to Pearson. It later changed its name to Interactive Data Corporation. The following year the company purchased Merrill Lynch's security data business (Merrill Lynch Securities Pricing Service). Interactive Data purchased McGraw-Hill's S&P ComStock (now called Interactive Data Real-Time Services) a provider of financial data news historical information and software applications for $115 million in cash and added Hyperfeed Technologies' consolidated data feed business in 2003.

The following year Interactive Data acquired the assets of FutureSource a provider of real-time futures and commodities data and in 2005 it bought IS.Teledata a provider of customized financial information portals and terminals. IS.Teledata was subsequently renamed Interactive Data Managed Solutions.

In a move to expand its revenue from consumer-oriented services the company acquired online stock information provider Quote.com from search portal Lycos (owned by Korea's Daum Communication) for about $30 million in 2006. The acquired business which includes investment community message board Raging Bull operates as part of Interactive Data's eSignal division.

In 2007 the company grew when it acquired the market data division of Xcitek. The purchase added North American corporate actions information such as reorganization cost basis and class action data to its In

EXECUTIVES

Pres, Scott A Hill
Treasurer, Martin Hunter
Secretary, Octavia Spencer
Vice President, Chuck Adkins
Vice President Information TEC, Scott Caudell
Director Evaluated Op, Steve Miano
Oracle Database Administrator, Sudhir Patel
Senior Relationship Manager, Kevin Mulvey

Global Data Administration Man, Nick Benkovich
Director, Joseph Greiner
Manager, Lisa Dizenzo

LOCATIONS

HQ: ICE DATA SERVICES, INC.
  32 CROSBY DR STE 100, BEDFORD, MA 017301448
Phone: 781 687-8500
Web: WWW.THEICE.COM

HISTORICAL FINANCIALS
Company Type: Private

Income Statement				FYE: December 31
	ASSETS ($ mil.)	NET INCOME ($ mil.)	INCOME AS % OF ASSETS	EMPLOYEES
12/13	3,968	33	0.8%	2,600
12/12	3,962	1	0.0%	—
12/11	4,093	(29)	—	—
Annual Growth	(1.5%)	—	—	—

2013 Year-End Financials

Return on assets: 0.8%   Sales ($ mil): 905
Return on equity: 2.8%

IDEA PUBLIC SCHOOLS

EXECUTIVES

Chm, Mike Rhodes
Pres*, Thomas E Torkelson
V Pres-Fin*, Carlo Hershberger
SEC*, Gabriel Puente
Exec SEC*, Rose Marquez
Treas*, Bill Carrera
Acting Coo*, Collin Sewell
Human Resource, Vernice Carino
Software Developer, Edison Coronado
Senior Vice President of Schoo, Cassandra Flores
Accounts Payable, Dian Gomez
Auditors: RSM US LLP SAN ANTONIO TEXA

LOCATIONS

HQ: IDEA PUBLIC SCHOOLS
  2115 W PIKE BLVD, WESLACO, TX 785960054
Phone: 956 377-8000
Web: WWW.IDEAPUBLICSCHOOLS.ORG

HISTORICAL FINANCIALS
Company Type: Private

Income Statement				FYE: June 30
	REVENUE ($ mil.)	NET INCOME ($ mil.)	NET PROFIT MARGIN	EMPLOYEES
06/21	850	79	9.3%	2,381
06/20	677	57	8.5%	—
06/19	532	39	7.4%	—
Annual Growth	26.4%	41.4%	—	—

2021 Year-End Financials

Return on assets: 4.3%   Cash ($ mil.): 276
Return on equity: 24.5%
Current ratio: 2.30

IDEMIA IDENTITY & SECURITY USA LLC

Idemia Identity & Security USA (formerly MorphoTrust USA) has operated in the US for nearly half a century developing technologies and products that enhance national security while simplifying lives of Americans.It is a global leader in Augmented Identity for an increasingly digital world. It is administered managed and operated by US staff on US soil for all services provided to US government customers at the federal state local and tribal levels.

Operations

The company is the leading driver's license provider in the US. It ensures prevention of fraudulent duplicate licenses and provides secure identity documents meeting federal requirements. It also offers public safety through its biometric systems and customer support center. In addition it also offers enrollment services as well as identity-related solutions.

Geographic Reach

Headquartered in Reston Virginia the company also has office locations in Billerica and Anaheim California; Brentwood Tennessee; Bloomington Minnesota; Fort Wayne Indiana; and Des Moines Iowa.

Sales and Marketing

The company caters to US government customers at the federal state local and tribal levels.

EXECUTIVES

Ceo, Donald Scott
Cfo, Laurent Lacroix
Security Staff, Jim Kottas
Coordinator, Kenny Labarge
Senior Software Engineer, David V Faulkner
Vp Human Resources NA, Karen Gregory
Cfo Nort America, Jim Bottorff
Vice President, Ben Mallen
Director, Leevi Raassina
Business Specialis, Nick Sash
Accts Receivable Mgr, Diane Grochmal

LOCATIONS

HQ: IDEMIA IDENTITY & SECURITY USA LLC
  11951 FREEDOM DR STE 1800, RESTON, VA 201905642
Phone: 703 775-7800
Web: WWW.IDEMIA.COM

PRODUCTS/OPERATIONS

Selected Products and Services

Biometric-based access control to buildings and restricted areas
Biometric recognition technologies that accurately identify individuals
Enrollment centers for processing pre-employment background checks
Secure credentials that serve as proof of identity
Solving critical issues facing US intelligence and national security

COMPETITORS

3m Cogent	Edentify
Acsys Biometrics	Entrust Datacard
Allied Security Innovations	Imageware Systems
Cssn	Secugen
Cross Match Technologies	Security First
De La Rue	Ultra-scan
	Verint Systems

Income Statement				FYE: December 31
	REVENUE ($ mil.)	NET INCOME ($ mil.)	NET PROFIT MARGIN	EMPLOYEES
12/16	708	(7)	—	1,600
12/15	604	0	—	—
Annual Growth	17.1%	—	—	—

2016 Year-End Financials

Return on assets: (-0.5%)   Cash ($ mil.): 73
Return on equity: (-0.7%)
Current ratio: 1.70

IHC HEALTH SERVICES, INC.

EXECUTIVES

Pres-Ceo, William Nelson
Svp-Cfo*, Bert Zimmerli
V Pres-Pres*, Charles Sorenson
Chief Staff, Steven Vannorman
Surgery Director, Brent Hardy
Food Manager, Brent Lamoreaux
Biomedical Engineer, Bryan White
Emergency Medicine Specialist, Stanford Benson
Library Dir, Pamella Asquith
Diagnostic Radiologist, Steven Davis
Purchasing Manager, John Taylor
Auditors: KPMG LLP SALT LAKE CITY UTAH

LOCATIONS

HQ: IHC HEALTH SERVICES, INC.
1380 E MEDICAL CENTER DR, ST GEORGE, UT
847902123
Phone: 435 251-2992
Web: WWW.DIXIEREGIONAL.COM

HISTORICAL FINANCIALS
Company Type: Private

Income Statement				FYE: December 31
	REVENUE ($ mil.)	NET INCOME ($ mil.)	NET PROFIT MARGIN	EMPLOYEES
12/20	7,742	1,335	17.2%	4,000
12/19	6,947	888	12.8%	—
12/18	6,037	317	5.3%	—
12/17	5,483	884	16.1%	—
Annual Growth	12.2%	14.7%	—	—

2020 Year-End Financials

Return on assets: 8.5%   Cash ($ mil.): 298
Return on equity: 14.4%
Current ratio: 1.30

ILLINOIS STATE OF TOLL HIGHWAY AUTHORITY

The Illinois State Toll Highway Authority (ISTHA) is trying to give Illinois drivers a little relief from congestion making their morning and afternoon commutes easier to swallow. The department maintains and operates about 275 miles of interstate tollways in 12 Northern Illinois counties. ISTHA is mid-way through its 10-year $6.3 billion Congestion-Relief Program which is conducting major improvements including rebuilding widening and extending tollway segments; converting toll plazas to provide non-stop toll collection for I-PASS users; opening additional tollway oases; and adding electronic over-the-road signs to improve communication with tollway users.

EXECUTIVES

Pres, John Mitola
Cfo*, Mike Colsch
Acting Exec Dir*, Michael King
Coordinator, Vicky Czuprynski
Chief of Information Technolog, Joseph Kambich
Information Technology Manager, Christine Benn
Communications Supervisor, Thomas Andruscavage
Administrator, Robert Godsil
General Manager Performance ME, Michael Catolico
Engineer, Rocco Zucchero
Chief of Business, Shana Whitehead
Auditors: MCGLADREY & PULLEN LLP SCHAU

LOCATIONS

HQ: ILLINOIS STATE OF TOLL HIGHWAY AUTHORITY
2700 OGDEN AVE, DOWNERS GROVE, IL 605151703
Phone: 630 241-6800
Web: WWW.ILLINOISTOLLWAY.COM

HISTORICAL FINANCIALS
Company Type: Private

Income Statement				FYE: December 31
	REVENUE ($ mil.)	NET INCOME ($ mil.)	NET PROFIT MARGIN	EMPLOYEES
12/20	1,260	124	9.8%	1,750
12/19	1,484	374	25.2%	—
12/18	1,436	353	24.6%	—
12/17	1,398	356	25.5%	—
Annual Growth	(3.4%)	(29.6%)	—	—

2020 Year-End Financials

Return on assets: 1.0%   Cash ($ mil.): 1,035
Return on equity: 4.0%
Current ratio: 1.80

ILWU-PMA WELFARE TRUST

EXECUTIVES

Prin, Michael Ouchida
Auditors: PRICEWATERHOUSECOOPERS LLP SA

LOCATIONS

HQ: ILWU-PMA WELFARE TRUST
1188 FRANKLIN ST STE 101, SAN FRANCISCO, CA
941096852
Phone: 415 673-8500
Web: WWW.BENEFITPLANS.ORG

Income Statement				FYE: June 30
	REVENUE ($ mil.)	NET INCOME ($ mil.)	NET PROFIT MARGIN	EMPLOYEES
06/18	738	(4)	—	9
06/17	738	5	0.8%	—
06/15	676	27	4.1%	—
06/14	624	(21)	—	—
Annual Growth	4.3%	—	—	—

2018 Year-End Financials

Return on assets: (-2.4%)   Cash ($ mil.): 5
Return on equity: (-4.6%)
Current ratio: 1.80

IMPERIAL IRRIGATION DISTRICT

Imperial Irrigation District (IID) keeps the lights on and the water flowing. A public agency IID is the six largest public power utility in the state of California providing generation transmission and distribution services to more than 145000 residential commercial and industrial customers. It is also the largest irrigation district in the US with more than 3000 miles of canals and drains delivering water to active farmland and providing wholesale water to local municipalities primarily in the Southern California desert corridors of Imperial Valley and Coachella Valley. The district is governed by a five-member board of directors elected by district residents.

Financial Performance

IID saw its revenues increase 6% from $530 million in 2011 to $562 million in 2012. The growth was driven by a 12% surge in water revenue; this was due to a rise in water transfer rates and a volume increase in water transferred to the San Diego County Water Authority and the Coachella Valley Water District of about $5 million. Power revenues also climbed 4% in 2012 due to a spike in energy sales mainly from residential customers.

Strategy

In the area of renewable energy IID is part of a statewide effort to significantly increase solar energy development and production by the year 2017. In 2011 it announced a public-private partnership with renewable energy generators. The partnership involves the signing of interconnection and transmission service agreements among IID CalEnergy Generation 8minuteenergy Ormat Technologies and the Los Angeles Department of Water and Power. It's the first step in a renewable energy transmission expansion plan to increase capacity enough to support more than a dozen renewable energy construction projects.

In addition IID offers a variety of programs to assist its customers in reducing their personal energy consumption including rebates for buying select energy efficient products online home energy audits and funding for residential projects that involve installing solar technologies such as photovoltaic (PV) systems.

Company Background

Founded in 1911 IID acquired properties from the financially struggling California Development Company and its Mexican subsidiary. By 1922 it had purchased 13 mutual water companies each of which had developed and operated distribution canals in the Imperial Valley. Principal water customers today include farm operators and municipalities that treat the water and resell it to their residential and business customers. The district entered the power business in 1936 to utilize the hydroelectric generation of the All-American Canal. Since that time IID has added geothermal natural gas coal and solar to its energy generation portfolio. Its electric services account for majority of IID's annual revenues.

EXECUTIVES

Pres, Stephen Benson
Pres*, Anthony Sanchez
V Pres*, Stella Mendoza
V Pres*, Mike Abatti
Ceo*, Keven Kelly
V Pres*, Norma Sierra Galindo
Superintendent, Manuel S Hernandez
Accounting Staff, Amie Ramirez
Manager, David Escobar
Technical Manager, Andres S Avila
Supervisor, Maribel Garcia
Auditors: MOSS ADAMS LLP PORTLAND OREG

LOCATIONS

HQ: IMPERIAL IRRIGATION DISTRICT
  333 E BARIONI BLVD, IMPERIAL, CA 922511773
Phone: 800 303-7756
Web: WWW.IID.COM

HISTORICAL FINANCIALS

Company Type: Private

Income Statement — FYE: December 31

	REVENUE ($ mil.)	NET INCOME ($ mil.)	NET PROFIT MARGIN	EMPLOYEES
12/20	705	115	16.4%	1,300
12/19	642	51	8.0%	—
12/18	615	48	7.9%	—
12/17	634	3	0.5%	—
Annual Growth	3.6%	228.3%	—	—

2020 Year-End Financials

Return on assets: 4.1%
Return on equity: 6.4%
Current ratio: 2.40
Cash ($ mil.): 136

INDEPENDENT PHARMACY COOPERATIVE

EXECUTIVES

Pres, Don Anderson
Director of Marketing/Sales, Linda Reedy Sr
Human Resources Executive, Michelle R Johnson
Sales Associate, Nicole Burbach
Sales Associate, Tammy Riley
Marketing Coordinator, Emily Gutgesell
Administration Staff, Susan Oechsner
Vice President, Finance and Ad, Devin Millard
Regional Director SE, Zach Barth
Member Manager, Carrie Brooks
Director of Marketing, Mindy Herrmann
Auditors: GRANT THORNTON LLP APPLETON

LOCATIONS

HQ: INDEPENDENT PHARMACY COOPERATIVE
  1550 COLUMBUS ST, SUN PRAIRIE, WI 535903901
Phone: 800 755-1531
Web: WWW.IPCRX.COM

HISTORICAL FINANCIALS

Company Type: Private

Income Statement — FYE: December 31

	REVENUE ($ mil.)	NET INCOME ($ mil.)	NET PROFIT MARGIN	EMPLOYEES
12/16	1,427	30	2.1%	160
12/14	1,052	2	0.2%	—
12/13	1,058	2	0.2%	—
12/11	806	1	0.2%	—
Annual Growth	12.1%	73.9%	—	—

2016 Year-End Financials

Return on assets: 12.5%
Return on equity: 60.7%
Current ratio: 1.20
Cash ($ mil.): 40

INDEPENDENT SCHOOL DIST 625

EXECUTIVES

Spdt, Joe Gothard
Mgmt Specialist, Andrew Mosca
Executive of Information Techn, Cathy Bloomquist
Executive of Information Techn, Jim Litwin
Accounting Staff, Shirley Davis
Accounting Staff, Patty Kelly
Accounting Staff, Gloria Thompson
Director, Traci Gauer
Bus/Finance/Purchasing Directo, Brad Miller
Athletic Director, Laura Ranum
Assistant Superintendent, Omoyefe Agbamu
Auditors: MALLOY MONTAGUE KARNOWSKI R

LOCATIONS

HQ: INDEPENDENT SCHOOL DIST 625
  360 COLBORNE ST, SAINT PAUL, MN 551023228
Phone: 651 767-8100
Web: WWW.SPPS.ORG

HISTORICAL FINANCIALS

Company Type: Private

Income Statement — FYE: June 30

	REVENUE ($ mil.)	NET INCOME ($ mil.)	NET PROFIT MARGIN	EMPLOYEES
06/20	743	125	16.9%	6,500
06/19	732	(83)	—	—
06/18	711	17	2.5%	—
06/17	706	49	7.0%	—
Annual Growth	1.7%	36.2%	—	—

INDEPENDENT SUPPLIERS GROUP, INC.

EXECUTIVES

Ceo, Michael Gentile
Ceo, Michael Maggio
Cfo, Jeff Matthews
Assistant Controller Payroll H, Roxanne Kehl
Evp Sales and Marketing, Charles Forman
Vice President, Merchandising, Jill Oneill
Rebate Merchandise Manager, Kelly Layden
Office Manager, Marie Schmidt
Marketing Administrator, Maureen Modelski
Director, Tom Ashburn
Auditors: GREENWALT CPAS INC INDIANAP

LOCATIONS

HQ: INDEPENDENT SUPPLIERS GROUP, INC.
  5600 N RIVER RD STE 700, ROSEMONT, IL 600185165
Phone: 847 699-3330
Web: WWW.ISG.COOP

HISTORICAL FINANCIALS

Company Type: Private

Income Statement — FYE: December 31

	REVENUE ($ mil.)	NET INCOME ($ mil.)	NET PROFIT MARGIN	EMPLOYEES
12/19	635	29	4.7%	26
12/18	223	5	2.3%	—
12/12	192	6	3.1%	—
12/09	167	3	1.9%	—
Annual Growth	14.3%	25.0%	—	—

2019 Year-End Financials

Return on assets: 42.8%
Return on equity: 521.4%
Current ratio: 1.10
Cash ($ mil.): 7

INDIANA UNIVERSITY

EXECUTIVES

Staff, Emily Tenney
Director of Training, Andrew Shea
Director of Special Projects, Beth Feickert
Marketing Manager, Damen Morris
Director of Communications, Deborah Galyan
Office of Marketing, Joel Fosha
Assistant Director of Events, John Bower
General Manager, Jose Fajardo
Clinical Assistant Professor, Lesa Huber
Professor of Philosophy, Adam Leite
Faculty, Marc Bilodeau

LOCATIONS

HQ: INDIANA UNIVERSITY
  1020 E KIRKWOOD AVE, BLOOMINGTON, IN 474057103
Phone: 812 855-7581
Web: WWW.IU.EDU

HISTORICAL FINANCIALS
Company Type: Private

Income Statement				FYE: June 30
	REVENUE ($ mil.)	NET INCOME ($ mil.)	NET PROFIT MARGIN	EMPLOYEES
06/14	2,195	201	9.2%	31
06/13	2,146	189	8.8%	—
Annual Growth	2.3%	6.3%	—	—

2014 Year-End Financials
Return on assets: 10.0%   Cash ($ mil.): 313
Return on equity: 9.2%
Current ratio: 1.10

INFIRMARY HEALTH SYSTEM, INC.

EXECUTIVES

Ceo, D Mark Nix
Pres*, E Chandler Bramlett
Director Information Technolog, Peter Finnorn
Technical Specialist, Tom White
Prin, William Broughton
Human Resources Information MA, Stephanie Andrews
Chief Strategy Officer, Alan Whaley
Director of Radiology, Anthony Mosley
Coordinator, Alex Oditt
Coordinator, Allan Farnum
Information Specialist, Anne Glesie

LOCATIONS

HQ: INFIRMARY HEALTH SYSTEM, INC.
5 MOBILE INFIRMARY CIR, MOBILE, AL 366073513
Phone: 251 435-3030
Web: WWW.INFIRMARYHEALTH.ORG

HISTORICAL FINANCIALS
Company Type: Private

Income Statement				FYE: March 31
	REVENUE ($ mil.)	NET INCOME ($ mil.)	NET PROFIT MARGIN	EMPLOYEES
03/21	902	192	21.3%	5,000
03/20	839	(65)	—	—
03/19	783	(4)	—	—
03/18	727	35	4.8%	—
Annual Growth	7.5%	76.0%	—	—

2021 Year-End Financials
Return on assets: 17.1%   Cash ($ mil.): 145
Return on equity: 36.2%
Current ratio: 3.70

INLAND COUNTIES REGIONAL CENTER, INC.

EXECUTIVES

Ceo, Carol A Fitzgibbons
Exec Dir*, Carol Fitzgibbons
Director, Denise Fanelli

Office Assistant, Stephen Hughes
Counselor, Charlotte Gill
Counselor, Brad Onomura
Counselor, Darith Ung
Manager, Elizabeth Stroh
Counselor, Karuna Tek
Manager, Mary Hernandez
Program Manager, Mia Gurri
Auditors: WINDES INC LONG BEACH CA

LOCATIONS

HQ: INLAND COUNTIES REGIONAL CENTER, INC.
1365 S WATERMAN AVE, SAN BERNARDINO, CA 924082804
Phone: 909 890-3000
Web: WWW.INLANDRC.ORG

HISTORICAL FINANCIALS
Company Type: Private

Income Statement				FYE: June 30
	REVENUE ($ mil.)	NET INCOME ($ mil.)	NET PROFIT MARGIN	EMPLOYEES
06/20	641	15	2.3%	586
06/19	557	(0)	—	—
06/18	502	(0)	—	—
06/17	463	(39)	—	—
Annual Growth	11.5%	—	—	—

2020 Year-End Financials
Return on assets: 9.4%   Cash ($ mil.): 43
Return on equity: —
Current ratio: 1.10

INNOVATIVE AG SERVICES CO.

EXECUTIVES

Ceo, Rick Vaughan
Pres*, Randy Blake
1st Vp*, Paul Cook
Cfo*, Brenda Hoefler
Human Resources Staff, Marilyn E Ewing
Associate Director, Allen Jaspers
Vice President of Human Resour, Carla Elliott
Associate Director, Jeff Lindsay
Facilities, Jon Keninger
Vice President of Agronomy, Tim Krausman
Network Administrator, Jason Welter
Auditors: MERIWETHER WILSON & COMPANY

LOCATIONS

HQ: INNOVATIVE AG SERVICES CO.
2010 S MAIN ST, MONTICELLO, IA 523107707
Phone: 319 465-3501
Web: WWW.INNOVATIVEAG.COM

HISTORICAL FINANCIALS
Company Type: Private

Income Statement				FYE: August 31
	REVENUE ($ mil.)	NET INCOME ($ mil.)	NET PROFIT MARGIN	EMPLOYEES
08/19	597	9	1.6%	500
08/18	649	11	1.8%	—
08/17	615	15	2.6%	—
08/16	682	10	1.6%	—
Annual Growth	(4.4%)	(4.6%)	—	—

2019 Year-End Financials
Return on assets: 3.2%   Cash ($ mil.): 1
Return on equity: 6.0%
Current ratio: 1.80

INOVA HEALTH CARE SERVICES

EXECUTIVES

Chm, Nicholas Carosi
Pres, John Knox Singleton
V Pres, Richard C Magenheimer
V Pres, James Hughes
V Pres, H Patrick Walters
SEC, Shannon Sinclair
Tres, Lydia Thomas
SEC, Tony Nader
Vice-President Information Ser, Maggie Cornett
Coordinator, Roxanne Wright
Chief of Emergency Room, Robert Cates

LOCATIONS

HQ: INOVA HEALTH CARE SERVICES
8110 GATEHOUSE RD 200E, FALLS CHURCH, VA 220421217
Phone: 703 289-2000
Web: WWW.INOVA.ORG

HISTORICAL FINANCIALS
Company Type: Private

Income Statement				FYE: December 31
	REVENUE ($ mil.)	NET INCOME ($ mil.)	NET PROFIT MARGIN	EMPLOYEES
12/13	2,134	145	6.8%	13,000
12/09	1,663	200	12.0%	—
12/03	1,012	46	4.6%	—
12/02	1	(0)	—	—
Annual Growth	96.8%	—	—	—

2013 Year-End Financials
Return on assets: 3.9%   Cash ($ mil.): 203
Return on equity: 7.8%
Current ratio: 0.30

INOVA HEALTH SYSTEM FOUNDATION

Inova Health Foundation provides financial support and assistance to the Inova Health System which operates a network of not-for-profit community hospitals in northern Virginia. It also supports home health services heart care programs clinical research and trials emergency and urgent care centers outpatient services and destination institutes. To raise funds for the hospital system the foundation organizes fundraising monthly giving Inova visionaries gifts of stocks and corporate giving. Donors can also make contributions through the Inova website.

Operations

Money raised by the foundation supports programs at Inova Health. As the leading nonprofit healthcare system in the region it welcomes partnerships with individuals and organizations who share its commitment to providing world-class healthcare to each person in every community it has the privilege to serve. Areas of research include cancer heart and vascular disease obesity trauma surgery pediatrics and neuroscience.

Geographic Reach

Virginia-based Inova Health System operates five health facilities in Virginia.

EXECUTIVES

Ceo, John Knox Singleton
Chm, Stephen Cumbie
Exec V Pres, Loring Flint
Exec V Pres, Marshall Ruffin
SEC, Anthony Nader
Coo, Mark Stauder
Cfo, Alice H Pope
Cao, Kylenne Green
Executive Asst, Carol Gerard
Specialist, Annual, Alexandra Obrand
Specialist, Gift, Amalia Arbulu

LOCATIONS

HQ: INOVA HEALTH SYSTEM FOUNDATION
8110 GATEHOUSE RD 200E, FALLS CHURCH, VA
220421217
Phone: 703 289-2069
Web: WWW.FOUNDATION.INOVA.ORG

HISTORICAL FINANCIALS
Company Type: Private

Income Statement   FYE: December 31

	REVENUE ($ mil.)	NET INCOME ($ mil.)	NET PROFIT MARGIN	EMPLOYEES
12/19	821	762	92.9%	16,000
12/17	765	717	93.6%	—
12/15	2,972	234	7.9%	—
Annual Growth	(27.5%)	34.3%	—	—

2019 Year-End Financials
Return on assets: 13.3%   Cash ($ mil.): 1
Return on equity: 23.0%
Current ratio: 12.40

INSPUR SYSTEMS, INC.

EXECUTIVES

Pres, Ziliang Leon Zheng
Cfo*, Meng Zhu
General Manager, Dolly Wu
Sr Business Manage, Ali Irani
Marketing Supervisor, Nat Dai
Auditors: CG UHLENBERG LLP FREMONT C

LOCATIONS

HQ: INSPUR SYSTEMS, INC.
1501 MCCARTHY BLVD, MILPITAS, CA 950357420
Phone: 800 697-5893
Web: WWW.INSPURSYSTEMS.COM

HISTORICAL FINANCIALS
Company Type: Private

Income Statement   FYE: December 31

	REVENUE ($ mil.)	NET INCOME ($ mil.)	NET PROFIT MARGIN	EMPLOYEES
12/20	617	5	0.9%	300
12/18	410	3	0.8%	—
12/17	180	(0)	—	—
12/16	65	(0)	—	—
Annual Growth	75.1%	—	—	—

2020 Year-End Financials
Return on assets: 2.9%   Cash ($ mil.): 22
Return on equity: 49.5%
Current ratio: 1.00

INTEGRIS BAPTIST MEDICAL CENTER, INC.

INTEGRIS Baptist Medical Center seeks integrity by caring for citizens from across the state of Oklahoma. The Oklahoma City-based medical center is the flagship hospital of the not-for-profit INTEGRIS Health system. With about 510 beds INTEGRIS Baptist is home to specialty care facilities for burns women's and children's health infertility stroke treatment cardiac care organ transplantation cancer treatment and more. The company also has centers for wellness hearing sleep disorders senior health and weight loss and it provides medical training and residency programs. INTEGRIS Baptist Medical Center opened its doors in 1959 with 200 beds.

EXECUTIVES

Pres, Chris Hammes
Cfo*, Wentz J Miller
Coordinator, Dorothy Welcome
Internal Medicine Practitioner, Kristopher Lepere
Senior It Project Manager, Catherine Miller
Central Sterile Supervisor, Cynthia Gideon
Materials Manager, Sonya Roddy
Clinical Nurse Manager, Ann-Marie McCormick
Operations Manager, Hussain Walliani
Registered Nurse Staff, Lacey Thompson
Director Case Management, Linda Hollan

LOCATIONS

HQ: INTEGRIS BAPTIST MEDICAL CENTER, INC.
3300 NW EXPRESSWAY, OKLAHOMA CITY, OK
731124418
Phone: 405 949-3011
Web: WWW.INTEGRISOK.COM

PRODUCTS/OPERATIONS

Selected Centers and Services
Advanced Cardiac Care
Anticoagulation Clinics
Bariatrics
Bennett Fertility Institute
Bones and Joints
Breast Care
Burn Center
Cancer Care
Cardiology
Case Management
Children's Health
Comprehensive Breast Center of Oklahoma
Continuing Medical Education
Corporate Assistance Program
Diabetes

Diagnostic Services
Digestive Health
Emergency Department
Fertility
General Heart Care
General Pediatrics
Home Care
Hospice
Hospitalist Program
Hough Ear Institute
Hyperbaric Medicine and Wound Care
James R. Daniel Cerebrovascular and Stroke Center
Jim Thorpe Rehabilitation Center
Labor and Delivery
Men's Health
Nazih Zuhdi Transplant Institute
Neonatal Intensive Care Unit (NICU)
Orthopedics
PACER Fitness Center
Pastoral Care
Pediatric Intensive Care Unit (PICU)
Pediatric Neurology
Pharmacy
Radiology Services
Senior Health
Sleep Disorders Center of Oklahoma
Stroke Center
Surgical Services
TeleHealth
Urogynecology
Weight Loss

COMPETITORS

Deaconess Health Care
Hillcrest Medical Center
Jackson County Memorial Hospital
Marian Health System
Mercy Health
Norman Regional Health
Ssm Health Care
Saint Francis Health System
Texas Health Denton
Universal Health Services

HISTORICAL FINANCIALS
Company Type: Private

Income Statement   FYE: June 30

	REVENUE ($ mil.)	NET INCOME ($ mil.)	NET PROFIT MARGIN	EMPLOYEES
06/21	1,051	192	18.3%	2,700
06/20	950	(14)	—	—
06/18	814	67	8.3%	—
06/16	701	6	1.0%	—
Annual Growth	8.4%	94.6%	—	—

2021 Year-End Financials
Return on assets: 9.3%   Cash ($ mil.): 239
Return on equity: 26.0%
Current ratio: 6.60

INTEGRIS HEALTH, INC.

INTEGRIS Health is the state's largest Oklahoma-owned health system and one of the largest private employees and with hospitals rehabilitation centers physician clinics mental health facilities fitness centers and more. The company one of Oklahoma's largest not-for-profit health care organization operates around 15 hospitals in Oklahoma City. The hospitals provide services including primary care breast health cancer care gynecology surgery lung care transplant and rehabilitation & physical care and more. INTEGRIS also operates specialty facilities for the treatment of pain management rheumatology and neurology and for rehabilitation & physical therapy. The company operates with more than 100 primary care and specialty clinics statewide and provide medical care for all ages with high-qualified physicians.

Operations

Operations include INTEGRIS Baptist Medical Center (the system's largest with 508 beds) INTEGRIS South Oklahoma City (dba INTEGRIS Southwest Medical Center 369 beds) and INTEGRIS Health Edmond INTEGRIS Baptist Regional Health Center INTEGRIS Bass Baptist Health Center and INTEGRIS Grove Hospital.

INTEGRIS Health has approximately 1400 physicians in its system.

Geographic Reach

INTEGRIS Health is based in Oklahoma City and operates 16 hospitals led in the Oklahoma City area by INTEGRIS Baptist Medical Center and INTEGRIS Southwest Medical Center.

Sales and Marketing

INTEGRIS Health markets its products and services through its website portal such as Breast Health Cancer Care and Children's Health Fertility Care Gynecology Heart & Vascular Home Care &Hospice and more.

EXECUTIVES

Exec Dir, Michael Hatch
Ceo, Bruce Lawrence
Cfo, David Hadley
Coo, Chris Hammes
Exec Dir, Molly Ross
Engineer, Orlan Fisher
Clinical Manager of Kidney, Roberta Graham
Application Coordinator Epic O, Sarah Bennett
Physician Assistant, Sarah Henderson
Engineer, Shawn Mize
MD, Shirin Mohammad
Auditors: KPMG LLP OKLAHOMA CITY OK

LOCATIONS

HQ: INTEGRIS HEALTH, INC.
3300 NW EXPWY, OKLAHOMA CITY, OK 731124418
Phone: 405 949-6066
Web: WWW.INTEGRISOK.COM

PRODUCTS/OPERATIONS

2015 Sales

	$ mil.	% of total
INTEGRIS Baptist Medical Center Inc.	635	39
INTEGRIS South Oklahoma City Hospital Corporation	244	15
INTEGRIS Rural Health Inc.	227	14
INTEGRIS Health Edmond	48	3
All others	459	29
Eliminations	(229.7)	-
Total	**1,384**	**100**

Selected Facilities

Baptist Medical Center
Baptist Regional Health Center
Bass Baptist Health Center
Blackwell Regional Hospital
Canadian Valley Regional Hospital
Cancer Institute of Oklahoma
Clinton Regional Hospital
Grove General Hospital
Health Edmond
Hospice House
Jim Thorpe Rehabilitation
Marshall County Medical Center
Mayes County Medical Center
Mental Health Spencer
Seminole Medical Center
Southwest Medical Center

COMPETITORS

Ardent Health Services
Deaconess Health Care
Fairview Health
Healtheast Care System
Hillcrest Medical
  Center
Marian Health System
Mercy Health
Norman Regional Health
Saint Francis Health
  System
St. John Health System

HISTORICAL FINANCIALS

Company Type: Private

Income Statement — FYE: June 30

	REVENUE ($ mil.)	NET INCOME ($ mil.)	NET PROFIT MARGIN	EMPLOYEES
06/21	2,250	300	13.3%	9,500
06/20	2,077	(172)	—	—
06/19	1,950	11	0.6%	—
06/18	1,673	53	3.2%	—
Annual Growth	10.4%	77.6%	—	—

2021 Year-End Financials

Return on assets: 8.3%
Return on equity: 21.6%
Current ratio: 2.60

Cash ($ mil.): 342

INTERMOUNTAIN HEALTH CARE INC

Intermountain Healthcare is a team of 41000 caregivers that serve the healthcare needs of people across the Intermountain West primarily in Utah Idaho and Nevada. In addition a not-for-profit health system based in Salt Lake City Utah with clinics a medical group affiliate networks hospitals homecare telehealth health insurance plans and subsidiaries such as SelectHealth Saltzer Health and Intermountain Healthcare. It has about 2400 physicians advanced practice providers 3800 affiliated physicians. In addition the not-for-profit health system operates 24 hospitals (includes virtual hospital) telehealth services practice providers a six-state area and some 215 clinics. Intermountain also has an insurance arm named SelectHealth covering around 900000 people in three states.

Operations

Intermountain Healthcare's hospitals provides services such as neuroscience cancer care heart care pediatrics surgical services and women's health. Intermountain Healthcare and Huntsman Cancer Institute at the University of Utah have formed an alliance to fight cancer and focusing on research.

The group also operates urgent care clinics under the InstaCare and KidsCare banners.

Geographic Reach

Salt Lake City Utah-based Intermountain Healthcare serves the health care needs of Utah Nevada and Idaho residents.

Sales and Marketing

Intermountain Healthcare market its services through its websites.

Company Background

Intermountain was formed in 1975 when the Church of Jesus Christ of Latter Day Saints donated 15 hospitals to local communities.

EXECUTIVES

Chb, Scott Anderson
Chb, Bruce Reese
Chb, Gail Miller
Pres-Ceo, Marc Harrison
V Pres, Albert R Zimmerli Sr
V Pres, Douglas J Hammer
V Pres, Daniel L Zuhlke
V Pres, Ryan Smith
Coo, Laura S Kaiser

Coo, Robert W Allen
Svp, Clo, Greg Matis
Auditors: KPMG LLP SALT LAKE CITY UTAH

LOCATIONS

HQ: INTERMOUNTAIN HEALTH CARE INC
36 S STATE ST STE 1600, SALT LAKE CITY, UT 841111633
Phone: 801 442-2000
Web: WWW.INTERMOUNTAINHEALTHCARE.ORG

PRODUCTS/OPERATIONS

2016 Sales

	$ mil.	% of total
Net patient services	4,368	57
Non-patient activities	3,010	40
Non-operating income	237	3
Total	**7,617**	**100**

Selected Hospitals

Alta View Hospital (Sandy UT)
American Fork Hospital (Utah)
Bear River Valley Hospital (Tremonton UT)
Cassia Regional Medical Center (Burley ID)
Delta Community Medical Center (Utah)
Dixie Regional Medical Center (St. George UT)
Fillmore Community Medical Center (Utah)
Garfield Memorial Hospital (Panguitch UT)
Heber Valley Medical Center (Heber City UT)
Intermountain Medical Center (Murray UT)
LDS Hospital (Salt Lake City)
Logan Regional Hospital (Orem UT)
McKay-Dee Hospital Center (Ogden UT)
  McKay-Dee Behavioral Health Institute
Orem Community Hospital (Utah)
Park City Medical Center (Park City UT)
Primary Children's Medical Center (Salt Lake City)
Riverton Hospital (Riverton UT)
Sanpete Valley Hospital (Mt. Pleasant UT)
Sevier Valley Hospital (Richfield UT)
TOSH - The Orthopedic Specialty Hospital (Murray UT)
Utah Valley Regional Medical Center (Provo UT)
Valley View Medical Center (Cedar City UT)

COMPETITORS

Christus Health
Encompass Health
Hca
Lifepoint Health
Ogden Regional Medical
  Center
Regence Bluecross
  Blueshield Of Utah
St. Mark's
University Of Utah
  Hospitals & Clinics

HISTORICAL FINANCIALS

Company Type: Private

Income Statement — FYE: December 31

	REVENUE ($ mil.)	NET INCOME ($ mil.)	NET PROFIT MARGIN	EMPLOYEES
12/20	10,082	1,571	15.6%	35,000
12/19	8,812	1,212	13.8%	—
12/18	7,724	420	5.4%	—
12/17	6,940	1,061	15.3%	—
Annual Growth	13.3%	14.0%	—	—

2020 Year-End Financials

Return on assets: 8.9%
Return on equity: 14.7%
Current ratio: 1.20

Cash ($ mil.): 381

INTERNATIONAL RESCUE COMMITTEE, INC.

EXECUTIVES

Pres-Ceo, David Miliband
General Counsel*, Ricardo Castro
Cfo*, Danusia Dzierzbinski
Project Coordinator, Emelina Cesheshyan
Procurement Staff, Sherif Blaku
Country Director, Jason Phillips
Senior Program Officer, Natalia Lopez
Senior Project Manager, Quentin Scott
Director, Hugh Dwyer
Finance Project Manager, Kamanie Dookiesingh
Chief Information Officer, Charles Popper
Auditors: KPMG LLP NEW YORK NY

LOCATIONS

HQ: INTERNATIONAL RESCUE COMMITTEE, INC.
122 E 42ND ST, NEW YORK, NY 101680002
Phone: 212 551-3000
Web: WWW.THEIRC.ORG

HISTORICAL FINANCIALS

Company Type: Private

Income Statement				FYE: September 30
	REVENUE ($ mil.)	NET INCOME ($ mil.)	NET PROFIT MARGIN	EMPLOYEES
09/19	785	10	1.3%	8,000
09/18	744	2	0.3%	—
09/17	753	44	5.9%	—
09/14	562	9	1.7%	—
Annual Growth	6.9%	1.9%	—	—

2019 Year-End Financials

Return on assets: 2.7%   Cash ($ mil.): 126
Return on equity: 4.6%
Current ratio: 1.60

INTERNATIONAL WIRE GROUP, INC.

International Wire Group (IWG) bares it all in the wire business. Through three divisions — Bare Wire Products Engineered Products - Europe and High Performance Conductors — IWG makes multi-gauge bare silver- nickel- and tin-plated copper wire as well as engineered wire products and performance conductors. The company's customers (General Cable is one of its largest) include suppliers and OEMs. IWG's wire products are used in industrial/energy consumer electronics aerospace and defense medical electronics automotive and appliance applications.

Operations

The company's Bare Wire Products (or conductors) are used to transmit digital video and audio signals or conduct electricity and are sold to more than 1000 insulated wire manufacturers and various industrial OEMs for use in computer and data communications products general industrial energy appliances automobiles and other applications.

IWG's Engineered Products - Europe makes bare copper wire products which are sold to a diverse customer base of various OEMs in Europe.

Its High Performance Conductors include tin nickel and silver plated copper and copper alloy conductors including standard and customized conductors as well as specialty film insulated conductors and miniature tubing products.

Subsidiaries include US-based Continental Cordage a leading maker of braided wire for a wide range of commercial military and industrial applications and Tresse Metallique J. Forissier SAS and Italtrecce leading European makerd of bare copper wire products.

Geographic Reach

The company maintains 18 manufacturing plants and two distribution facilities in the US and Europe (Belgium France Italy and Poland). IWG makes the majority of its sales in the US.

Sales and Marketing

IWG serves customers in the electrical appliances power supplies aircraft railway and automotive system sectors. The volatile pricing of raw materials especially copper is a lingering concern for IWG. The company depends on four leading suppliers for copper and does not have long-term supply contracts with any of them creating concern about the reliability of IWG's copper supply chain. Many of the company's customers have their own captive (in-house) wire production facilities and they could exclusively turn to those facilities reducing orders to IWG.

Mergers and Acquisitions

In late 2019 International Wire Group (IWG) bought New York-based Owl Wire & Cable (Owl) from Marmon Holdings. The deal expands IWG's copper wire manufacturing footprint.

EXECUTIVES

Chb, Rodney D Kent
Sr V Pres-Cfo-Sec*, Glenn J Holler
V Pres Fin*, Donald F Dekay
V Pres Purchasing & Logistics*, Geoff Kent
Customer Representativ, Brett Charbonneau
Executive Assistant, Lauren Badger

LOCATIONS

HQ: INTERNATIONAL WIRE GROUP, INC.
12 MASONIC AVE, CAMDEN, NY 133161202
Phone: 315 245-2000
Web: WWW.INTERNATIONALWIREGROUP.COM

PRODUCTS/OPERATIONS

Selected Products

Bare wire products
  Bare and tin-plated copper wire (or conductors)
    Engineered
  Bare copper wire (to conduct electricity)
High performance conductors
  Conductors

COMPETITORS

A.e. Petsche	Nexans
Cerro Wire	Okonite
Driver-harris	Owl Wire & Cable
Encore Wire	Prestolite Wire
Leoni	Republic Wire
Ls Cable	Southwire
Loos & Co.	

HISTORICAL FINANCIALS

Company Type: Private

Income Statement				FYE: December 31
	REVENUE ($ mil.)	NET INCOME ($ mil.)	NET PROFIT MARGIN	EMPLOYEES
12/08	736	6	0.9%	1,600
12/07	730	15	2.2%	—
12/06	1,789	0	—	—
Annual Growth	—	13597.3%	—	—

2008 Year-End Financials

Return on assets: 1.8%   Cash ($ mil.): 7
Return on equity: 3.6%
Current ratio: 2.10

INVACARE CORPORATION (TW)

LOCATIONS

HQ: INVACARE CORPORATION (TW)
39400 TAYLOR PKWY, NORTH RIDGEVILLE, OH
440356270
Phone: 440 329-6000
Web: WWW.INVACARE.COM

HISTORICAL FINANCIALS

Company Type: Private

Income Statement				FYE: December 31
	REVENUE ($ mil.)	NET INCOME ($ mil.)	NET PROFIT MARGIN	EMPLOYEES
12/11	1,801	(4)	—	45
12/10	1,722	25	1.5%	—
12/09	1,693	41	2.4%	—
Annual Growth	3.1%	—	—	—

2011 Year-End Financials

Return on assets: (-0.3%)   Cash ($ mil.): 34
Return on equity: (-0.7%)
Current ratio: 1.80

IOWA HEALTH SYSTEM

Iowa Health System (IHS) which does business as UnityPoint is an integrated health care system that operates more than 20 acute care hospitals in large communities throughout Iowa as well as parts of western Illinois and Madison Wisconsin. UnityPoint also supports more than 15 rural hospitals and it manages about 300 physician clinics located in rural and suburban areas. The system's hospitals provide general medical-surgical care as well as care in a number of medical specialties such as cardiovascular disease mental health and home health services.

Operations

In 2014 the system had about 155000 patient admissions facilitated 20000 births and saw a total of some 4.5 million patients.

Geographic Reach

UnityPoint Health includes a dozen hospitals in 10 Iowa cities four in Illinois and another in Wisconsin. Its largest geographic markets served are

Anamosa Cedar Rapids Des Moines Dubuque Fort Dodge Sioux City and Waterloo Iowa; the Quad Cities/Muscatine region in Iowa and Illinois; Peoria Illinois; and Madison Wisconsin.

Strategy

The health system operates many of its member hospitals through affiliation agreements where it provides administration contracting billing legal recruitment information technology and other central services. The health system expands by adding new affiliation agreements and by building new health facilities.

UnityPoint Health struck a major merger agreement with South Dakota-based Sanford Health in 2019 but the deal was terminated later that year. The combination would have created a massive health network with more than 75 hospitals in 26 states.

Company Background

Iowa Health System (IHS) was founded in 1993. In 2013 the network rebranded itself UnityPoint to showcase its mission to be a point of unity for patient care and its expansion to include health care facilities in other states including Illinois and Wisconsin.

EXECUTIVES

Int Ceo, Sue Thompson
Cfo, Mark Johnson
V Pres-General Counsel, Denny Drake
Treas, Mike Stone
Dir, Mike Williams
Dir, Ronald Klosterman
SEC, Steven Herwig D O
Vice-President Information Ser, Scott Whitson
Assistant Professor, Joellen Kubik
Executive Asst, Karen Reynolds
Assistant Professor, Adisa Kudumovic
Auditors: KPMG LLP MINNEAPOLIS MN

LOCATIONS

HQ: IOWA HEALTH SYSTEM
1776 WEST LAKES PKWY # 400, WEST DES MOINES, IA 502668377
Phone: 515 241-6161
Web: WWW.UNITYPOINT.ORG

PRODUCTS/OPERATIONS

Selected Facilities

Metropolitan Hospitals
  Allen Memorial Hospital Corporation (Waterloo Iowa)
  Iowa Lutheran Hospital (Des Moines Iowa)
  Iowa Methodist Medical Center (Des Moines Iowa)
  Blank Children's Hospital (Des Moines Iowa)
  Methodist Medical Center of Illinois (Peoria Illinois)
  Methodist West Hospital (West Des Moines Iowa)
  St. Luke's Hospital (Cedar Rapids Iowa)
  St. Luke's Regional Medical Center (Sioux City Iowa)
  Jones Regional Medical Center (Anamosa Iowa)
  The Finley Hospital (Dubuque Iowa)
  Trinity Bettendorf (Bettendorf Iowa)
  Trinity Moline (Moline Illinois)
  Trinity Muscatine (Muscatine Iowa)
  Trinity Regional Medical Center (Fort Dodge Iowa)
  Trinity Rock Island (Rock Island Illinois)
Rural Hospitals
  Buena Vista Regional Medical Center (Storm Lake Iowa)
  Clarke County Hospital (Osceola Iowa)
  Community Memorial Hospital (Sumner Iowa)
  Greater Regional Medical Center (Creston Iowa)
  Greene County Medical Center (Jefferson Iowa)
  Grundy County Memorial Hospital (Grundy Center Iowa)
  Guthrie County Hospital (Guthrie Center Iowa)
  Guttenberg Municipal Hospital (Guttenberg Iowa)
  Humboldt County Memorial Hospital (Humboldt Iowa)
  Loring Hospital (Sac City Iowa)
  Pocahontas Community Hospital (Pocahontas Iowa)

COMPETITORS

Avera Health
Blessing Hospital
Chi Health
Genesis Health System
Mcdonough District Hospital
Mercy Health Network
Methodist Health System
Osf Healthcare System

HISTORICAL FINANCIALS

Company Type: Private

Income Statement				FYE: December 31
	REVENUE ($ mil.)	NET INCOME ($ mil.)	NET PROFIT MARGIN	EMPLOYEES
12/17	4,157	229	5.5%	18,923
12/16	4,054	148	3.7%	—
Annual Growth	2.5%	54.4%	—	—

2017 Year-End Financials

Return on assets: 4.1%
Return on equity: 6.8%
Current ratio: 1.50
Cash ($ mil.): 251

IOWA PHYSICIANS CLINIC MEDICAL FOUNDATION

EXECUTIVES

Pres-Ceo, Sanjeeb Khatua
Pres, Daniel P Allen
Cfo, Robin McNichols
SEC, Kenneth W Anderson
Trainer, Jenna Larson
Pulmonologist, Muhammad Anwer
Director of Finance, Shelley Maynard

LOCATIONS

HQ: IOWA PHYSICIANS CLINIC MEDICAL FOUNDATION
8101 BIRCHWOOD CT UNIT N, JOHNSTON, IA 501312930
Phone: 515 471-9200
Web: WWW.UNITYPOINT.ORG

HISTORICAL FINANCIALS

Company Type: Private

Income Statement				FYE: December 31
	REVENUE ($ mil.)	NET INCOME ($ mil.)	NET PROFIT MARGIN	EMPLOYEES
12/17	600	17	3.0%	1,000
12/00	76	(13)	—	—
12/99	8	2	31.3%	—
12/98	61	(19)	—	—
Annual Growth	12.8%	—	—	—

2017 Year-End Financials

Return on assets: 8.6%
Return on equity: 26.0%
Current ratio: 2.30
Cash ($ mil.): 11

IOWA STATE UNIVERSITY OF SCIENCE AND TECHNOLOGY

Home to the Cyclones athletics teams Iowa State University of Science and Technology (ISU) can be a whirlwind experience for some. ISU is a public land-grant institution offering higher education courses and programs with an emphasis on science technology and related areas. ISU's eight colleges offer more than 100 undergraduate degrees and nearly 200 fields of study leading to graduate and professional degrees. The university has an enrollment of more than 31000 students and charges more than $7720 in tuition and fees for resident students for two semesters.

Operations

In fiscal 2012 Iowa State received $360.2 million in grants contracts co-operative agreements and gifts of which about 60% is utilized for research purpose. The university's research park has about 20000 square feet of incubators space including office and laboratories.

Geographic Reach

The university enrolls students from 50 states and more than 100 countries.

Financial Performance

The 6% increase in revenues in 2012 was due to higher tuition and fees sales and services of educational activities and auxiliary enterprise revenues. The tuition revenue increase was to a 5% hike in the resident tuition rate coupled with record enrollments. The increase in sales and services of educational activities was due to large one-time events ISU farms and the Vet Diagnostic Lab. ISU's auxiliary enterprises reported revenue growth thanks to new revenue sources and a record number of students in the residence system.

ISU's net income increased by 47% in 2012 thanks to higher operating expenses and a decline in non-operating revenues. Non-operating revenues decreased $24.4 million thanks to an $11 million decrease in funding from education appropriations. Investment income also dropped $16.3 million or 49% mainly due to an unrealized loss in the value of investments.

Company Background

Chartered as Iowa Agriculture College in 1858 the school first officially opened for classes in 1869. Among ISU's notable alumni is scientist and inventor George Washington Carver.

EXECUTIVES

Pres, Wendy Wintersteen
Exec V Pres, Jonathan Wickert
Sr V Pres, Pamela Cain
Assoc V-Pres-Business and Fin, Pam Cain
Coordinator, Doan Schmitz
Coordinator, Jody Larson
Assistant Director, Nate Postma
Scientist, Ryan Ott
Assistant Professor, Valentina Salotti
Assistant Professor, Jon Rouse
Law Specialist, Beth White
Auditors: MARLYS K GASTON CPA DES MOI

LOCATIONS

HQ: IOWA STATE UNIVERSITY OF SCIENCE AND TECHNOLOGY
515 MORRILL RD, AMES, IA 500112105
Phone: 515 294-6162
Web: WWW.IASTATE.EDU

PRODUCTS/OPERATIONS

Colleges
Agriculture and Life Sciences
Business
Design
Engineering
Graduate
Human Sciences
Liberal Arts and Sciences
Veterinary Medicine

HISTORICAL FINANCIALS

Company Type: Private

Income Statement				FYE: June 30
	REVENUE ($ mil.)	NET INCOME ($ mil.)	NET PROFIT MARGIN	EMPLOYEES
06/20	936	43	4.6%	5,800
06/19	952	97	10.2%	—
06/18	948	58	6.2%	—
06/17	920	77	8.4%	—
Annual Growth	0.6%	(17.8%)	—	—

2020 Year-End Financials
Return on assets: 1.7%   Cash ($ mil.): 174
Return on equity: 2.5%
Current ratio: 2.60

IRVINE UNIFIED SCHOOL DISTICT

EXECUTIVES

Superintendent, Terry Walker
Ceo*, Michael B Regele
High School Teacher, Haley Dawson
Supervisor, Jennifer Razo
Payroll Technician, Nathan Taylor
Safety Security Techii, Alex Cuevas
Teacher, Kathy Raths
Health Clerk, Anne Josey
Athletic Director Wrestling Co, John Phillips
6th Grade Teacher, Kelly Montplaisir
Special Education Analyst, Kitty Fyfe
Auditors: VAVRINEK TRINE DAY & CO LL

LOCATIONS

HQ: IRVINE UNIFIED SCHOOL DISTICT
  5050 BARRANCA PKWY, IRVINE, CA 926044698
Phone: 949 936-5000
Web: WWW.IUSD.ORG

HISTORICAL FINANCIALS

Company Type: Private

Income Statement				FYE: June 30
	REVENUE ($ mil.)	NET INCOME ($ mil.)	NET PROFIT MARGIN	EMPLOYEES
06/20	672	85	12.6%	2,212
06/19	513	4	0.9%	—
06/18	497	(1)	—	—
06/17	380	138	36.5%	—
Annual Growth	20.9%	(15.1%)	—	—

J M SMITH CORPORATION

J M Smith Corporation is the third-largest privately-held company in South Carolina operating industry-leading healthcare and technology business units including Smith Drug Company which provides purchasing and distribution services in more than 30 US states and RxMedic Systems a pharmacy automation manufacturer. Founded in 1925 by James M. Smith Sr. as a single community pharmacy in Asheville North Carolina the company supplies services and technology to organizations across the US.

Operations

J M Smith operates industry-leading healthcare and technology business units: Smith Drug Company and RxMedic Systems.

Smith Drug Company a full-line distributor of pharmaceuticals medical equipment (HME/DME) over-the-counter medicines gifts and sundries to pharmacies and long-term care facilities.

Rxmedic Systems is a pharmacy automation manufacturer driven to provide the best products that pharmacy automation has to offer.

Geographic Reach

Based in Spartanburg South Carolina J M Smith's headquarters and regional offices span the entire US. Smith Drug has five distribution centers in more than 30 states primarily in the southern US as well as Washington DC and the Virgin Islands.

Company Background

In 2010 Smith expanded by acquiring health equipment manufacturing firm RxMedic. Through the purchase the company entered the automated dispensing system market.

J M Smith was founded in 1943 by drugstore proprietor James Smith and is run by the Smith family.

EXECUTIVES

Pres-Ceo, Paula Harper Bethea
Vice President, Robert Barrett
Cfo, Philip Ryan
Cto, Kevin Welch
National Sales Manager, Jim Hancock
Regional Sales Manager, Scott Wilson
Account Representative, Sheila Reynolds
Project Manager Human Resource, Amy Thyen
Tech, David Phipps
Senior Buyer, Debbie Brown
Marketing Strategy and Communi, Heidi Jameson

LOCATIONS

HQ: J M SMITH CORPORATION
  101 W SAINT JOHN ST # 305, SPARTANBURG, SC 293065150
Phone: 864 542-9419
Web: WWW.JMSMITH.COM

Selected Office Locations
Altamonte Springs FL
Brandon MS
Columbia SC
Dallas TX
Fairmont WV
Gray ME
Hermitage PA
Houston TX
Indianapolis IN
Lexington KY
Mechanicsburg PA
Miami FL
Morrisville GA
Paragould AR

Perry GA
Pleasant Hill MO
Richmond VA
Seattle WA
Spartanburg SC
St. Paul MN
Sturbridge MA
Valdosta GA
Valencia CA
Wake Forest NC

PRODUCTS/OPERATIONS

Selected Divisions
Integral Solutions Group
Norgenix Pharmaceuticals
QS/1
RxMedic
Smith Drug Company
Smith Premier Services

COMPETITORS

Amerisourcebergen	Hp Enterprise Services
Cvs	Kinray
Cardinal Health	Mckesson
Express Scripts	Pharmerica
Fiserv	
H. D. Smith Wholesale Drug	

HISTORICAL FINANCIALS

Company Type: Private

Income Statement				FYE: February 28
	REVENUE ($ mil.)	NET INCOME ($ mil.)	NET PROFIT MARGIN	EMPLOYEES
02/15	2,566	47	1.8%	235
02/14	2,370	38	1.6%	—
02/13	2,362	26	1.1%	—
Annual Growth	4.2%	33.8%	—	—

2015 Year-End Financials
Return on assets: 8.1%   Cash ($ mil.): 142
Return on equity: 16.0%
Current ratio: 1.60

J.E. DUNN CONSTRUCTION COMPANY

From first building designs to the last brick J.E. Dunn Construction helps make building plans a done deal. The contractor offers general construction services construction management and design/build services nationwide. It's known for its work on campus health care and commercial projects including the BayCare Health System CHI Health - Creighton University Medical Center - Bergan Mercy Seaton Hall/Regnier Hall Decatur High School and Ron Clark Academy. Founded in 1924 the company is one of Kansas City's top commercial construction firms and has been listed as one of the nation's top 20 general building companies. It operates as a subsidiary of J.E. Dunn Construction Group.

Operations

JE Dunn has ranked as one of the top 20 largest general building companies in the US. It offers services such as virtual design & construction augmented reality smart building solutions robotics as well as wearable technology including tool assist personal safety access to data as job aids and visualization. JE Dunn also operates a real estate investment through its subsidiary JE Dunn Capital Partners.

It counts several noteworthy projects among its portfolio such as Cerner Innovations Campus Omaha Capitol District Restoration Hardware The Thompson Hotel Minnesota State Capitol Lenexa Civic Center and Minnesota Children's Museum Renovation and Addition.

Geographic Reach
Based in Kansas City Missouri JE Dunn operates nearly 25 offices throughout the US.

Sales and Marketing
JE Dunn works on projects for clients in several sectors including projects related to: science and technology corporate environments healthcare hospitality government and military energy and utility education and multifamily residential properties among others.

Financial Performance
While full financial information of the privately-held company were not available the company reported that it brings in annual revenue of $3.6 billion as of early 2019. Its revenues in 2019 rose to $4.3 billion representing the company's consistent revenue growth over the years.

Strategy
J.E. Dunn Construction Company has been busy working on a variety of different projects in recent years. In 2020 J.E. Dunn completed the seven-story 350000-square-foot new Johnson County Courthouse which replaced the aging overcrowded existing courthouse by consolidating the Tenth Judicial District Court District Attorney and supporting spaces into a distinctive civic building. The team plans to finish installing systems and ancillary furniture in November. Johnson County staff will begin occupying the courthouse by September and the building is intended to open to the public in the first quarter of 2021.

Earlier that year it started construction on the new General Leonard Wood Army Community Hospital a $295 million state-of-the-art 52-acre hospital complex that when completed in 2024 will replace the current hospital facility.

J.E. Dunn also worked on the $40 million Minnehaha County Jail expansion which added 329 beds and new administration space which will solve a long-standing space problem. J.E. Dunn worked with Henry Carlson Construction JLG Architects and BWBR Architects for this project.

Company Background
John Ernest Dunn (Ernie) founded JE Dunn Construction Company in Kansas City Missouri in 1924. In the past JE Dunn grew through acquisitions purchasing RJ Griffin & Co. (Atlanta) in 2000 Witcher Construction (Minneapolis) in 1990 and Drake Construction (Portland Oregon) in 1992.

EXECUTIVES

Chb, Stephen D Dunn
V Chb, William H Dunn Sr
Exec Vp-Sec-Clo, Casey S Halsey
Ceo-Pres, Gordon E Landsford III
Vice Pres/Asst SEC, Robert P Dunn
Senior Engineer, Barbara G Hachey
Prin, Kathy Disney
Cfo, Beth A Soukup
Superintendent, Robert Ryan
Senior Project Coordinator, Sharon Weidner
Cntrl, Melanie Tucker
Auditors: KPMG LLP KANSAS CITY MO

LOCATIONS

HQ: J.E. DUNN CONSTRUCTION COMPANY
  1001 LOCUST ST, KANSAS CITY, MO 641061904
Phone: 816 474-8600
Web: WWW.JEDUNN.COM

PRODUCTS/OPERATIONS

Selected Project Delivery Methods
Competitive Bid
Construction Management (Agency)
Design-Build
General Contracting/CM At Risk
Integrated Project Delivery
Project Management

COMPETITORS

Adolfson & Peterson Inc.	H.j. Russell
Barnhart	Hensel Phelps Construction
Boran Craig Barber Engel	Korte
C.f. Jordan	M. A. Mortenson
Core Construction	Medco Construction
Clarkson Construction	Skanska Usa Building
Flintco	Turner Corporation
	Weitz

HISTORICAL FINANCIALS
Company Type: Private

Income Statement				FYE: December 31
	REVENUE ($ mil.)	NET INCOME ($ mil.)	NET PROFIT MARGIN	EMPLOYEES
12/17	2,945	0	—	1,635
12/16	2,909	0	—	
12/15	2,909	0	—	
12/14	2,242	0	—	
Annual Growth	9.5%	—	—	—

2017 Year-End Financials

Return on assets: —
Return on equity: —
Current ratio: 1.10

Cash ($ mil.): 29

J.E. DUNN CONSTRUCTION GROUP, INC.

Owned by descendants of founder John Ernest Dunn J.E. Dunn Construction Group operates as the holding company for a group of construction firms and JE Dunn Capital Partners its real estate investment subsidiary. Founded in 1924 it builds institutional commercial and industrial structures nationwide. It also provides construction and program management and design/build services. J.E. Dunn Construction which is among the largest US general builders was one of the first contractors to offer the construction management delivery method. Some of its major projects have included an IRS facility and the world headquarters for H&R Block both located in Kansas City Missouri.

Operations
The company provides virtual design and construction augmented reality smart building solutions with advanced technology. Every project J.E. Dunn undertakes involves a multitude of moving parts such as equipment commissioning delivery scheduling construction process coordination safety planning and others. From programming through preconstruction and construction building information modelling and virtual design construction play a major role in all projects. The company-designed technology provides web-based collaboration on design documents digital models virtual estimates and other project documentation.

Its smart building solutions group is a key component of the company's overall business strategy and is fully integrated into its core construction operations.

Geographic Reach
Headquartered in Kansas City Missouri J.E. Dunn operates about 25 offices across the nation. It has offices in Georgia Texas North Carolina Colorado Iowa Missouri Minnesota Tennessee Oklahoma Nebraska Arizona Oregon Kansas and North Dakota.

Sales and Marketing
The company works on corporate environments mission critical correctional and justice and mixed use and retail projects among others.

Company Background
A bigwig particularly in the Midwest the group regularly bids on federal government projects. J.E. Dunn won a major contract from the US Army Corps of Engineers to build a regional correctional facility at Fort Leavenworth Kansas that replaced smaller prisons in Texas Kentucky and Oklahoma.

In 2012 the company earned the designation of having the first ever LEED Gold Certified building in downtown Kansas City.

The descendants of John Ernest Dunn hold a majority stake in the company.

EXECUTIVES

Ceo, Gordon Lansford III
Pres-Ceo, Terrence P Dunn
Chb, Stephen D Dunn
Vice Chair, William H Dunn Sr
Exec V Pres-Clo-Sec, Casey S Halsey
V Pres-Asst SEC, Robert P Dunn
Asst SEC, Barbara Hachey
Cfo, Beth Soukup
Evp and Cfo, Gordon E Lansford III
Project Engineer, Jay Lance
Administrative Assistant, Michelle Andersen
Auditors: KPMG LLP KANSAS CITY MISSOUR

LOCATIONS

HQ: J.E. DUNN CONSTRUCTION GROUP, INC.
  1001 LOCUST ST, KANSAS CITY, MO 641061904
Phone: 816 474-8600
Web: WWW.JEDUNN.COM

PRODUCTS/OPERATIONS

Selected Group Companies
JE Dunn Midwest
JE Dunn North Central
JE Dunn Northwest
JE Dunn Rocky Mountain
JE Dunn South Central
R.J. Griffin & Company

Selected Services
Preconstruction
  Constructability review
  Feasibility studies
  Market analysis
  Mechanical electrical plumbing review
  Preconstruction estimating
  Quality control
  Risk management
  Scheduling
Construction
  Change order management
  Labor relations
  Progress monitoring
  Quality control and testing
Post Construction
  Commissioning
  Final closeout
  Lien releases
  One-year walkthrough
  Operations and maintenance manuals

COMPETITORS

Alberici	Skanska Usa Building

Clark Enterprises
Hensel Phelps
 Construction
Hunt Construction
Mccarthy Building

Sundt
Turner Corporation
Tutor Perini
Weitz
Whiting-turner

HISTORICAL FINANCIALS
Company Type: Private

Income Statement				FYE: December 31
	REVENUE ($ mil.)	NET INCOME ($ mil.)	NET PROFIT MARGIN	EMPLOYEES
12/19	4,329	0	—	2,080
12/15	2,910	0	—	—
12/14	2,243	0	—	—
12/13	2,243	0	—	—
Annual Growth	11.6%	—	—	—

JACKSON ELECTRIC MEMBERSHIP CORPORATION

Jackson EMC distributes electricity to more than 197800 individual customers (more than 210200 meters) in 10 counties around Atlanta and in northeastern Georgia. The majority of customers are residential with commercial and industrial customers accounting for 42% of fiscal year 2013 revenues. One of the largest nonprofit power cooperatives in the US and the largest electric cooperative in Georgia Jackson EMC is owned by its members. The cooperative's generation and transmission partners include Oglethorpe Power Corp. Georgia Systems Operation and Georgia Transmission Corp.

Operations
Jackson EMC operates 86 substations and more than 13550 miles of power line.

Financial Performance
In fiscal 2013 the coop reported a revenue increased of 1%. Net income declined slightly by 0.3%. That year the non-profit coop returned $5.5 million in margin refunds to nearly 201000 members.

Strategy
Among other initiatives Jackson EMC is promoting conservation and green energy options as a way to slow energy growth and reduce greenhouse gas emissions. Initiatives include advocating the use of more efficient light bulbs and the widespread use of solar panels for power generation.

Company Background
Although the county of Jackson is named after a Georgia statesman from the Revolutionary War era Jackson Electric Membership Corporation (Jackson EMC) can trace its roots more directly to US president Franklin Roosevelt whose frequent trips to Warm Springs alerted him to the shortage of affordable electric power outside of major cities. Jackson EMC was founded in 1938 as part of the Roosevelt government's national rural electrification drive.

EXECUTIVES

Ceo, Randall Pugh
Cfo*, Greg Keith
Coo*, Roy Stowe
Executive Officer, Douglas Smith
Training Director, Tim Sweat

Land Management Manager, Chip Jakins
Engineer I, Chris Garrish
Employee Director, Gina Mixon
Accounting Analyst, Jane Mixon
Gainesville District Executive, Jill Talley
Warehouse Clerk, Josh Nix
Auditors: MCNAIR MCLEMORE MIDDLEBROOKS

LOCATIONS
HQ: JACKSON ELECTRIC MEMBERSHIP CORPORATION
850 COMMERCE RD, JEFFERSON, GA 305493329
Phone: 706 367-5281
Web: WWW.JACKSONEMC.COM

HISTORICAL FINANCIALS
Company Type: Private

Income Statement				FYE: May 31
	REVENUE ($ mil.)	NET INCOME ($ mil.)	NET PROFIT MARGIN	EMPLOYEES
05/21	593	36	6.2%	445
05/20	585	37	6.4%	—
05/19	571	29	5.1%	—
05/18	548	37	6.8%	—
Annual Growth	2.7%	(0.8%)	—	—

2021 Year-End Financials
Return on assets: 3.1%
Return on equity: 6.8%
Current ratio: 1.60

Cash ($ mil.): 58

JACKSON HEALTHCARE, LLC

Jackson Healthcare can help find physicians to work at hospitals and help keep track of patients as they enter and leave hospitals. Its staffing businesses offer job search recruiting and placement services for physicians and other health care professionals; provide anesthesiologists; and coordinate the work of traveling nurses. Jackson Healthcare's physician job boards attract thousands of visitors per month giving it a reputation for filling openings quickly. Subsidiary Patient Placement Systems manages patient flow through the medical system and Care Logistics provides patient tracking software. Richard Jackson formed the company in 1978.

Operations
Jackson Healthcare operates more than a dozen subsidiaries and operations units and serves more than 7 million patients spread throughout 1300 health care facilities.

Subsidiaries and divisions include Premier Anesthesia Jackson Therapy Partners LucumTenens.com Jackson Nurse Professionals and Jackson & Coker. Other operations include AdvancedPractice.com Jackson Surgical Assistants Jackson Pharmacy Professionals Tyler & Company and Parker HealthcareIT.

Its health care software and technology portfolio is managed by Care Logistics and Patient Placement Systems.

Mergers and Acquisitions
Jackson Healthcare's growth strategy involves acquiring other staffing businesses to augment its geographical reach. In 2014 it purchased Sullivan Healthcare Consulting (SHC) a Michigan-based firm focused on improving the performance of the hospital's perioperative suite.

EXECUTIVES
Chb-Ceo, Richard L Jackson
Pres, R Shane Jackson
Cfo, Douglas B Kline
SEC, Dennis Stockwell
CIO, Ryan Esparza
Cfo, Leslie Kurtz
Gen Coun, Jay D Mitchell
Chief Academic Officer, Mary Jane Stevens
Executive Officer, Leigh Pace
Coordinator, Diana Clark
Staff, Lakethia Bragg

LOCATIONS
HQ: JACKSON HEALTHCARE, LLC
2655 NORTHWINDS PKWY, ALPHARETTA, GA 300092280
Phone: 770 643-5500
Web: WWW.JACKSONHEALTHCARE.COM

PRODUCTS/OPERATIONS

Selected Subsidiaries and Operating Units
Jackson Healthcare Staffing
  AdvancedPractice.com (a full-service locum tenens agency dedicated to physician assistants and nurse practitioners)
  Healthcare Staffing Technologies (provider of career concierge sites in the healthcare market)
  HealthIT Project Managers (provider of experienced IT project management contractors to hospitals)
  Jackson & Coker (locum tenens and permanent recruitment firm for physicians)
  Jackson Nurse Professionals (specializes in the placement of registered nurses in healthcare settings nationwide)
  Jackson Pharmacy Professionals (national pharmacy-only staffing and recruiting company)
  Jackson Surgical Assistants (staffing of certified surgical assistants to surgeons and hospitals)
  Jackson Therapy Partners (staffing of rehabilitation therapists and other allied healthcare professionals)
  LocumTenens.com (locum tenens physician recruitment agency)
  Parker HealthcareIT (provider of supplemental IT staffing)
  Premier Anesthesia (anesthesia department management company)
Jackson Healthcare Technology
  Care Logistics (firm that helps hospitals transform their operations to deliver hospital efficiency)
  Patient Placement Systems (supplier of continuing care provider software)

COMPETITORS

Amn Healthcare	Gentiva
Atc Healthcare	Kelly Services
Adecco	Manpowergroup
Chg Healthcare	On Assignment
Comphealth	Rehabcare
Cross Country Healthcare	Teamstaff
	Inventiv Health

HISTORICAL FINANCIALS
Company Type: Private

Income Statement				FYE: December 31
	REVENUE ($ mil.)	NET INCOME ($ mil.)	NET PROFIT MARGIN	EMPLOYEES
12/17	949	99	10.5%	949
12/16	838	93	11.1%	—
12/15	696	70	10.2%	—
12/07	384	18	4.8%	—
Annual Growth	9.5%	18.4%	—	—

2017 Year-End Financials
Return on assets: 25.6%
Return on equity: 132.6%
Current ratio: 3.60

Cash ($ mil.): 65

JACKSON-MADISON COUNTY GENERAL HOSPITAL DISTRICT

EXECUTIVES

Pres-Ceo, James Ross
Chm*, Phil Bryant
Cfo*, Jeffrey Blankenship
Coordinator, Trisha Ross
Director, Angela Holmes
Information Technology Manager, Currie Higgs
Senior Vice President of Devel, Karl Misulis
Cme Coordinator, Cathy Brown
Director of Property Managemen, Lester Sands
Senior Human Resources General, Yvette Forrest
Manager, David Aherrera

LOCATIONS

HQ: JACKSON-MADISON COUNTY GENERAL HOSPITAL DISTRICT
620 SKYLINE DR, JACKSON, TN 383013923
Phone: 731 541-5000
Web: WWW.WTH.ORG

HISTORICAL FINANCIALS

Company Type: Private

| Income Statement | | | FYE: June 30 |
	REVENUE ($ mil.)	NET INCOME ($ mil.)	NET PROFIT MARGIN	EMPLOYEES
06/16	597	10	1.8%	6,000
06/15	554	20	3.7%	—
06/04	429	37	8.6%	—
06/03	307	247	80.4%	—
Annual Growth	5.3%	(21.4%)	—	—

2016 Year-End Financials

Return on assets: 1.2%   Cash ($ mil.): 20
Return on equity: 2.3%
Current ratio: 3.70

JACKSONVILLE ELECTRIC AUTHORITY

As long as sparks are flying in Jacksonville everything is A-OK with JEA. The community-owned not-for-profit utility provides electricity to 438000 customers in Jacksonville and surrounding areas in northeastern Florida. Managing an electric system that dates back to 1895 JEA has a net generating capacity of 3747 MW. It owns an electric system with five primarily fossil-fueled generating plants. JEA also gets 12.8 MW of generating capacity from two methane-fueled landfill plants. The company resells electricity to other utilities including NextEra Energy. JEA also provides water and wastewater services; it serves 321600 water customers and 247500 wastewater customers.

Operations

JEA is the largest community-owned utility in Florida and the eighth largest in the US.

The company operates in four segments: the Electric System and Bulk Power Supply System; the St. Johns River Power Park System System; the Water and Sewer System; and the District Energy System.

The Electric System operates five generating plants in Florida (and holds a stake in a power plant in Georgia) and all transmission and distribution facilities including more than 745 miles of transmission lines and more than 6500 miles of distribution lines. It purchases power locally from a solar field and a landfill gas facility. This segment accounted for 77% of the company's 2014 revenues.

JEA's Water System consists of 134 artesian wells that tap into the Floridan aquifer. Water is distributed through 37 water treatment plants and more than 4300 miles of water lines. Wastewater is collected through more than 3800 miles of wastewater collection lines and treated at seven regional treatment plants.

The company's operations are funded by three enterprise funds: the Electric Enterprise Fund the Water and Sewer Fund and the District Energy System The Electric Enterprise Fund is comprised of the JEA Electric System Bulk Power Supply System and St. Johns River Power Park System.

Geographic Reach

The cooperative serves customers in Northeast Florida.

Financial Performance

In 2014 JEA's revenues increased by 3% due to a 3% growth in electric sales as the result of higher consumption (primarily 4.3% in residential sales). Water and sewer sales increased by 1% related to a rise in customers and District Energy System sales increased by 2%. Approximately 47% of JEA's electric 2014 revenues came from its 375000 residential customers 50% from 48000 commercial and industrial customers and 3% from one wholesale customer.

The company's net income increased by 97% due to higher investment returns and a decline in loss from interest on debt.

JEA's operating cash flow decreased by 4% due to higher payments to suppliers.

Strategy

To help meet state regulations for carbon emission control JEA plans to get 10% of its energy requirements from nuclear energy by 2018 and 30% by 2030. In this regard JEA has signed a purchase power agreement to get 206 MW from a nuclear plant beginning in 2016 and is pursuing additional purchased power contracts.

JEA is also building out more fossil fuel capacity.

Company Background

The electric utility grew from a department of city of Jacksonville into an independent authority created by city and county government consolidation in 1967. In 1997 the water and sewer systems (which had been operated by the city since 1880) were also placed under JEA management.

In 2011 it completed the Greenland Energy Center which included two 175-MW natural gas-fired combustion turbines.

EXECUTIVES

Ceo, Jay Stowe
V Pres*, Mike Brost
V Pres*, Brian Roche
Exec Pres*, James Chancellor
Exec V Pres*, James Dickenson
Mng Dir*, Walter Bussells
CIO*, Ron Baker
Cfo*, Melissa Dykes
Chief Legal Officer*, Jody Brooks
Vp*, Kurt Wilson
Int Chief Comp Officer*, Steve Tuten
Auditors: ERNST & YOUNG LLP JACKSONVILL

LOCATIONS

HQ: JACKSONVILLE ELECTRIC AUTHORITY
21 W CHURCH ST FL 1, JACKSONVILLE, FL 322023152
Phone: 904 665-6000
Web: WWW.JEA.COM

PRODUCTS/OPERATIONS

2014 Sales

	$ mil.	% of total
Electric	1,431	77
Water & wastewater	383	21
District Energy System	8	-
Other	38	2
Total	**1,861**	**100**

COMPETITORS

Chesapeake Utilities	Seminole Electric
Florida Power & Light	Southern Company
Florida Public Utilities	Teco Energy
Nextera Energy	United Water Inc.
Progress Energy	Utilities Inc.

HISTORICAL FINANCIALS

Company Type: Private

| Income Statement | | | | FYE: September 30 |
	REVENUE ($ mil.)	NET INCOME ($ mil.)	NET PROFIT MARGIN	EMPLOYEES
09/18	1,789	126	7.1%	2,356
09/17	1,875	254	13.6%	—
09/16*	1,782	210	11.8%	—
06/09	1,319	71	5.4%	—
Annual Growth	3.4%	6.5%	—	—

*Fiscal year change

2018 Year-End Financials

Return on assets: 1.5%   Cash ($ mil.): 441
Return on equity: 4.6%
Current ratio: 4.20

JACO OIL COMPANY

Jaco Oil Company is jockeying for its piece of the convenience store pie. The company's Fastrip Food Stores subsidiary operates more than 50 convenience stores and gas stations primarily in and around Bakersfield California but also in Arizona. Besides offering customers traditional convenience-store fare which includes coffee milk beer snacks tobacco and the like the Fastrip chain stocks a full range of grocery items and provides in-store financial service centers. Financial services include check cashing payday loans wire transfer services via The Western Union Company refund anticipation loans and other services at many locations. Jaco Oil Company was founded in 1970.

Operations

The company operates nearly 50 stores in Bakersfield and Kern counties as well as in Fresno Sacramento and the Chico area. It also has four stores in Arizona located in Bullhead Casa Grande and Nogales. As part of its business Jaco Oil offers food beverages and financial services such as payday loans wire transfer services and tax preparation services.

Geographic Reach

Jaco Oil owns and operates gasoline service stations and convenience stores in the Western US.

Strategy

Fastrip works to distinguish itself from other convenience store chains by stocking a complete assortment of grocery items including such staples as sugar flour salt cake mix and even green beans. The chain bills itself as a Mini Grocery Store a strategy that other retailers including Dollar General and drugstore-giant Walgreen have adopted. It's also always open (24/7/365).

EXECUTIVES

Ceo, T J Jamieson
V Pres*, Charles Mc Can
SEC-Treas*, Lee Jamieson
Cfo*, Brian Busacca
Auditors: MOSS ADAMS LLP LOS ANGELES

LOCATIONS

HQ: JACO OIL COMPANY
   3101 STATE RD, BAKERSFIELD, CA 933084931
Phone: 661 393-7000
Web: WWW.JACO.HOST

2013 Stores

	No.
California	49
Arizona	4
Total	**53**

PRODUCTS/OPERATIONS

Selected Services
Check cashing
EBT
Ice
Liquior
Lottery
Money orders
Money transfers
Phone cards
Quick serve restaurant
Restrooms
WIC

Selected Products
Alcoholic beverages
Beverages
Coffee
Dairy
Food
Fountain drinks
Groceries
Snacks
Tobacco products

COMPETITORS

7-eleven	Ralphs Grocery
Chevron	Stater Bros.
Couche-tard	Vons
Dollar General	Walgreen
Exxon Mobil	

HISTORICAL FINANCIALS
Company Type: Private

Income Statement				FYE: December 31
	REVENUE ($ mil.)	NET INCOME ($ mil.)	NET PROFIT MARGIN	EMPLOYEES
12/20	555	20	3.7%	350
12/19	657	25	3.9%	—
12/18	636	19	3.1%	—
12/17	506	13	2.7%	—
Annual Growth	3.1%	14.9%	—	—

2020 Year-End Financials
Return on assets: 11.1%   Cash ($ mil.): 111
Return on equity: 13.0%
Current ratio: 2.20

JARDEN LLC

EXECUTIVES

Ceo, Debra A Crew
Chm, Patrick D Campbell
Pres, Ravi Saligram
Vp Human Resources, Brian Stull
Director Marketing, Fernando Pacheco
Senior Channel Marketing Manag, Sarah Chirillo
Data Analyst, Aileen Wall
It Procurement Specialist, Alicia Miastkowski
Manager of Vulnerability, Andre Shields
Data Maintenance Lead, Ann Normington
Sr Manager Consumer, Barbara Thorpe
Auditors: PRICEWATERHOUSECOOPERS LLP NE

LOCATIONS

HQ: JARDEN LLC
   221 RIVER ST, HOBOKEN, NJ 070305989
Phone: 201 610-6600
Web: WWW.NEWELLBRANDS.COM

HISTORICAL FINANCIALS
Company Type: Private

Income Statement				FYE: December 31
	REVENUE ($ mil.)	NET INCOME ($ mil.)	NET PROFIT MARGIN	EMPLOYEES
12/15	8,603	146	1.7%	17,000
12/14	8,287	242	2.9%	—
12/13	7,355	203	2.8%	—
12/12	6,696	243	3.6%	—
Annual Growth	8.7%	(15.6%)	—	—

2015 Year-End Financials
Return on assets: 1.0%   Cash ($ mil.): 1,298
Return on equity: 3.6%
Current ratio: 2.00

JEFFERSON COUNTY SCHOOL DISTRICT NO. R-1

EXECUTIVES

Supt, Dan McMinimee
Supt*, Cindy Stevenson
Office Aid, Grease Butte
Coordinator, Mary J Abbott
Secretary Director, Christine Thomas
Director Special Education, Dawn Loge Greer
Director, Veronica Lee
Warehouse Manager, Mel Trimmer
Postsecondary Workforce Readin, Suzanne Ellis
Math, Amy Peddy
Cafeteria Manager, Balinda Blatnik
Auditors: CLIFTONLARSONALLEN LLP BROOMF

LOCATIONS

HQ: JEFFERSON COUNTY SCHOOL DISTRICT NO. R-1
   1829 DENVER WEST DR # 27, GOLDEN, CO 804013120
Phone: 303 982-6500
Web: WWW.JEFFCOPUBLICSCHOOLS.ORG

HISTORICAL FINANCIALS
Company Type: Private

Income Statement				FYE: June 30
	REVENUE ($ mil.)	NET INCOME ($ mil.)	NET PROFIT MARGIN	EMPLOYEES
06/20	1,016	(55)	—	12,000
06/19	960	368	38.4%	—
06/18	848	(4)	—	—
06/17	808	(40)	—	—
Annual Growth	7.9%			

2020 Year-End Financials
Return on assets: (-2.7%)   Cash ($ mil.): 17
Return on equity: —
Current ratio: —

JEFFERSON PARISH SCHOOL BOARD INC

EXECUTIVES

Pres, Mark Morgan
Attorney, Jack Grant
Director of Transportation, Brandon Williams
Office Manager, Gwen Kerner
General Manager, Tiffany Kuhn
Chief Legal Counsel, Patricia Adams
Auditors: MIKE B GILLESPIE CPA JENNIN

LOCATIONS

HQ: JEFFERSON PARISH SCHOOL BOARD INC
   501 MANHATTAN BLVD, HARVEY, LA 700584443
Phone: 504 349-7803
Web: WWW.JPSCHOOLS.ORG

HISTORICAL FINANCIALS
Company Type: Private

Income Statement				FYE: June 30
	REVENUE ($ mil.)	NET INCOME ($ mil.)	NET PROFIT MARGIN	EMPLOYEES
06/11	556	3	0.7%	1,987
06/09	501	(70)	—	—
06/08	521	22	4.2%	—
Annual Growth	2.2%	(43.9%)	—	—

2011 Year-End Financials
Return on assets: 0.7%   Cash ($ mil.): 242
Return on equity: 1.5%
Current ratio: —

JERSEY CENTRAL POWER & LIGHT COMPANY

New Jersey native son Bruce Springsteen may be The Boss but Jersey Central Power & Light (JCP&L) electrifies more fans than he does every day. The company a subidiary of multi-utility holding company FirstEnergy transmits and distributes electricity to 1.1 million homes and businesses in 13 counties in central and northern New Jersey. JCP&L operates 22670 miles of distribution lines; its 2550-mile transmission system is overseen by regional transmission organization (RTO) PJM Interconnection. The utility also has some power plant interests.

Operations
The company provides regulated electric transmission and distribution services. JCP&L also has an ownership interest in a hydroelectric generating facility.

Geographic Reach
JCP&L conducts business in 3200 square miles of east central northern and western New Jersey. The area it serves has a population of approximately 2.7 million.

Financial Performance
Revenues decreased by 18% in 2011 due to a rate adjustment for all customer classes and lower power deliveries. The lower power delivery to residential customers was the result of decreased weather-related usage in 2011. Lower distribution deliveries to commercial and industrial customers that year reflected the impact of economic conditions in JCP&L's service territory. A decrease in retail generation revenues was due to lower generation power sales in all customer classes primarily due to an increase in customers shopping around for alternative providers. Wholesale generation revenues decreased due to a drop in PJM spot market energy sales.

JCP&L's net income decreased by 39% in 2011 due to lower revenues offset by reductions in purchased power costs and amortization of regulatory assets.

Company Background
The utility was organized under the laws of the State of New Jersey in 1925.

EXECUTIVES

Pres-Ceo, Donald M Lynch
Cfo-Cao-Controller*, Marlene A Barwood
Director, Ernest J Novak Jr
Director, Jesse T Williams Sr
Vp Corporate Risk and Chief R, William D Byrd
V Pres External Affairs, Mark A Jones
Customer Staff, Sandra Rudolph
Vp-Operations, Alex Patton
Manager Feu Process, Bret Ingram
General Manager, Chad Hampson
Assistant Business Analyst, Rachel Greer
Auditors: PRICEWATERHOUSECOOPERS LLP C

LOCATIONS

HQ: JERSEY CENTRAL POWER & LIGHT COMPANY
76 S MAIN ST, AKRON, OH 443081812
Phone: 800 736-3402
Web: WWW.FIRSTENERGYCORP.COM

PRODUCTS/OPERATIONS

Selected Services
Electrical services
Outdoor lighting
Professional tree services

COMPETITORS

Conectiv Power Delivery	Public Service Electric And Gas
New Jersey Natural Gas	South Jersey Gas
Orange & Rockland Utilities	Southern Company Gas

HISTORICAL FINANCIALS
Company Type: Private

Income Statement   FYE: December 31

	REVENUE ($ mil.)	NET INCOME ($ mil.)	NET PROFIT MARGIN	EMPLOYEES
12/17	1,801	115	6.4%	1,413
12/16	1,787	80	4.5%	—
12/11	2,495	144	5.8%	—
12/10	3,027	192	6.3%	—
Annual Growth	(7.1%)	(7.1%)	—	—

2017 Year-End Financials
Return on assets: 1.3%   Cash ($ mil.): 251
Return on equity: 3.6%
Current ratio: 2.20

JEWISH COMMUNAL FUND

EXECUTIVES

Pres, Teena Lerner
V Pres, Susan F Dickman
Sr V Pres, Jose Virella
Director of Grants, Karla Floris
Chief Operations Officer, Beth Wohlgelernter
Contribution Coordinator, Wanda Gutierrez
Director, Tamar Snyder
Associate Director, Financial, Igor Musayev
Accounting Manager, Rachel Redlich
Auditors: EISNERAMPER LLP NEW YORK NY

LOCATIONS

HQ: JEWISH COMMUNAL FUND
575 MADISON AVE STE 703, NEW YORK, NY 100228591
Phone: 212 752-8277
Web: WWW.JCFNY.ORG

HISTORICAL FINANCIALS
Company Type: Private

Income Statement   FYE: June 30

	REVENUE ($ mil.)	NET INCOME ($ mil.)	NET PROFIT MARGIN	EMPLOYEES
06/20	585	36	6.2%	14
06/19	822	355	43.3%	—
06/18	511	65	12.9%	—
06/17	461	55	12.0%	—
Annual Growth	8.2%	(13.0%)	—	—

2020 Year-End Financials
Return on assets: 1.9%   Cash ($ mil.): 119
Return on equity: 1.9%
Current ratio: 118.20

JFK HEALTH SYSTEM, INC.

JFK Health System provides medical services in a tri-county area in central New Jersey through flagship facility JFK Medical Center. The hospital has about 500 acute care beds and is one of the Garden State's major health care facilities. Included in the medical center complex are JFK Johnson Rehabilitation Institute JFK New Jersey Neuroscience Institute and a number of outpatient care and imaging centers. Other JFK Health System facilities provide primary and specialty services as well as senior living home health and hospice care. In 2017 JFK Health agreed to merge with Hackensack Meridian; the combined system will operate 15 hospitals in New Jersey.

Operations
JFK Health System's Hartwyck Nursing Convalescent and Rehabilitation Centers are located at three additional sites. Combined they house more than 500 beds for nursing home sub-acute rehabilitation and respite-care patients. One of the units is the only center in the state and one of very few in the country offering specialty care for Huntington's disease patients.

Geographic Reach
JFK Health System serves patients in the central New Jersey counties of Middlesex Union and Somerset.

Strategy
JFK Health System regularly expands and upgrades its facilities and its medical equipment to keep pace with modern health care needs. For instance in 2011 JFK Medical Center began construction of a three-story ER pavilion on top of its existing emergency department.

Company Background
Formerly Solaris Health the not-for-profit system took the JFK Health System name in 2011 to align with its flagship facility. It previously took on the Solaris name in 1997 when JFK Medical Center (founded in 1967) and Muhlenberg Regional Medical Center (founded in 1894) merged. The Muhlenberg inpatient operations were discontinued in 2008 victim of an economically declining population base. JFK sold Muhlenberg to Community Healthcare Associates in 2018.

EXECUTIVES

Pres-Ceo, Raymond Fredericks
Chm*, Dr Michael Kleiman
Plant Manager, Mark Di Geronimno
Coordinator, John Schenk
Osteopathic Physician, Richard Malone
Media Relations Mgr, Mary Jo Layton
Neuroscience Supervisor, Zahra Jiwani
Interior Designer, Asid Persico
or Network Administrato, Bill Thorpe
Director Cardiac, Jim Lindquist
Project Director, Keith Cicerone

LOCATIONS

HQ: JFK HEALTH SYSTEM, INC.
80 JAMES ST, EDISON, NJ 088203938
Phone: 732 321-7000
Web: WWW.JFKHEALTHSYSTEM.ORG

HISTORICAL FINANCIALS
Company Type: Private

Income Statement   FYE: December 31

	REVENUE ($ mil.)	NET INCOME ($ mil.)	NET PROFIT MARGIN	EMPLOYEES
12/18	591	128	21.7%	6,735
12/17	0	(0)	—	—
12/15	0	0	—	—
12/14	0	0	—	—
Annual Growth	—	—	—	—

2018 Year-End Financials
Return on assets: 33.7%   Cash ($ mil.): 35
Return on equity: 74.5%
Current ratio: 0.70

JOBSOHIO BEVERAGE SYSTEM

EXECUTIVES

Controller, Julie Battles

LOCATIONS

HQ: JOBSOHIO BEVERAGE SYSTEM
41 S HIGH ST STE 150, COLUMBUS, OH 432156115
Phone: 614 224-6446
Web: WWW.JOBSOHIO.COM

HISTORICAL FINANCIALS

Company Type: Private

Income Statement				FYE: June 30
	REVENUE ($ mil.)	NET INCOME ($ mil.)	NET PROFIT MARGIN	EMPLOYEES
06/20	596	(17)	—	12
06/19	1,284	(126)	—	—
06/17	444	4	1.0%	—
Annual Growth	10.3%	—	—	—

2020 Year-End Financials

Return on assets: (-1.3%)   Cash ($ mil.): 227
Return on equity: —
Current ratio: 2.00

JOHN C. LINCOLN HEALTH NETWORK

John C. Lincoln Health Network takes care of the health of John Q. Public in Arizona. The not-for-profit health care network serves the northern Phoenix area and is home to two hospitals: John C. Lincoln Deer Valley Hospital with more than 200 beds and John C. Lincoln North Mountain Hospital with roughly 260 beds (the Valley's first Magnet nursing hospital an accredited Chest Pain Center and the host of a Level 1 Trauma Center). The system also features a children's care facility various physician and dental clinics a food bank and assisted living facilities for the elderly all operating under the Desert Mission moniker. John C. Lincoln Health Network is part of the Scottsdale Lincoln Health Network along with Scottsdale Healthcare.

Operations

John C. Lincoln Health Network has a staff of about 1100 physicians.

In addition to its hospital locations the network includes physician practices for primary and specialty care as well as medical imaging and research centers. John C. Lincoln's facilities serve about 750000 patients each year and provide specialty services in fields including cardiology pulmonary care neuroscience and women's health. The Deer Valley Hospital is also home to Mendy's Place the North Valley's only 24-hour hospital emergency center exclusively for children and an accredited Chest Pain Center.

In 2012 John C. Lincoln Health Network had 748019 patient visits to its hospitals and physicians and specialty practices; 26868 exams at the breast health and research center; and 8719 adult day health care visits.

Its specialized medical services includes heart care pulmonary care neurosciences emergency care and a Breast Health and Research Center. Community services include Desert Mission Food Bank a dental clinic for uninsured children a resource center for families in crisis and a child care center. The John C. Lincoln Health Foundation conducts philanthropic efforts.

The health system's Desert Mission Food Bank distributed roughly 41000 emergency food boxes to members of its community in 2012. Other locations providing community outreach services include the Community Health Center Children's Dental Clinic Lincoln Learning Center Adult Day Health Care and Neighborhood Renewal. The Marley House Behavioral Health Clinic provides mental health and related services for children and adults on a sliding scale basis in English and Spanish.

Strategy

In 2013 John C. Lincoln expanded its infrastructure opening the John C. Lincoln Sonoran Health and Emergency Center a new emergency center and outpatient clinic in Phoenix. The $18 million project includes an emergency department medical practice and diagnostic imaging facilities.

Upgrading its technology in 2012 John C. Lincoln Deer Valley Hospital added the da Vinci Si Robotic Surgical System. To help it improve its medical record keeping that year the health system's primary care offices launched JCL Connect electronic health records software.

Mergers and Acquisitions

To strengthen its footing in the Arizona marketplace in 2014 John C. Lincoln formed an affiliation with Scottsdale Healthcare. The combined networks operating under the moniker Scottsdale Lincoln Health Network include five hospitals with some 3700 affiliated physicians and an extensive outpatient services network.

Company Background

The hospital gained its first real funding in 1933 from millionaire entrepreneur John C. Lincoln the founder of Lincoln Electric.

LOCATIONS

HQ: JOHN C. LINCOLN HEALTH NETWORK
2500 E DUNLAP AVE, PHOENIX, AZ 85020
Phone: 602 870-6060

Hospitals

Deer Valley Hospital: Phoenix Arizona
North Mountain Hospital: Phoenix Arizona

PRODUCTS/OPERATIONS

Selected Centers and Services

Breast Health and Research Center
Cancer Treatment
Cardiac Care
Deep Vein Thrombosis Program
Emergency Care
Heartburn Program
Level I Trauma Center
Medical Imaging
Neurosciences
Orthopedics
Outpatient Surgery Centers
Pediatrics
Pulmonary Program
Reconstructive Plastic Surgery
Scarless Surgery
Uterine Fibroid Treatment
Varicose Vein Treatment

COMPETITORS

Banner Health	Scottsdale Healthcare
Community Health Systems	Universal Health Services
Dignity Health	University Of Arizona

Flagstaff Medical Center
Northern Arizona Healthcare
Phoenix Children's Hospital
Health Network
Yuma Regional Medical Center

HISTORICAL FINANCIALS

Company Type: Private

Income Statement				FYE: December 31
	REVENUE ($ mil.)	NET INCOME ($ mil.)	NET PROFIT MARGIN	EMPLOYEES
12/13	584	44	7.6%	3,500
12/12	509	32	6.4%	—
12/11	486	17	3.6%	—
12/10	551	19	3.5%	—
Annual Growth	2.0%	31.3%	—	—

2013 Year-End Financials

Return on assets: 4.7%   Cash ($ mil.): 40
Return on equity: 7.6%
Current ratio: 1.30

JOHN MUIR HEALTH

John Muir Health provides health care throughout the scenic San Francisco Bay area. The John Muir Health Walnut Creek Medical Center has about 555 beds and that serves as Contra Costa County's only designated trauma center. The John Muir Health Concord Medical Center has about 245 beds. Both are recognized as the finest centers for neurosciences orthopedics cancer care cardiovascular care and high-risk obstetrics. The John Muir Behavioral Health Center is a nearly 75-bed psychiatric hospital. John Muir Health also offers home health rehabilitation and wellness programs.

Operations

John Muir Health's network of outpatient facilities include physical therapy and occupational therapy centers as well as specialty pediatric women's health and diabetes centers. The system also includes medical imaging centers.

John Muir Health's other areas of specialty include general surgery robotic surgery weight-loss surgery rehabilitation and critical care.

The system has more than 1000 physicians associated with the John Muir Health Physician Network. The John Muir Medical Group's approximately 350 clinician members work within the John Muir Health System's hospitals urgent care and outpatient clinics in multiple specialties mostly in primary care.

John Muir Health partners include Optum Canopy Health UCSF Medical Center San Ramon Regional Medical Center Stanford Children's Health Blue Cross Blue Shield of California and Health Net of California.

Geographic Reach

John Muir Health's facilities are located throughout Contra Costa county and part of Alameda and Solano counties.

Company Background

John Muir Health was formed from the 1997 merger of the John Muir Medical Center (the Walnut Creek Campus which dates back to 1965) and the Mt. Diablo Medical Center (now the Concord Campus dating back to 1930 as the Concord Hospital).

EXECUTIVES

Ceo, Calvin Knight
Prin*, Ken Meehan
Pres*, Michael S Thomas
Pres*, Jane A Willemsen
Director, Stuart B Shikora
Coordinator, Cynthia Miller
Coordinator, Susan Carter
Coordinator, Karen Mayor
Procurement Staff, Eric Drumm
Coordinator, Rocio Garcia
Clinical Director, Jeanette Moore
Auditors: KPMG LLP SAN FRANCISCO CALIF

LOCATIONS

HQ: JOHN MUIR HEALTH
1601 YGNACIO VALLEY RD, WALNUT CREEK, CA
945983122
Phone: 925 947-4449
Web: WWW.JOHNMUIRHEALTH.COM

PRODUCTS/OPERATIONS

Selected California Locations

Behavioral Health Center (Concord)
Breast Health Center (Walnut Creek)
Caring Hands Volunteer Program (Walnut Creek)
Clinical Research Centers (Concord)
Diabetes Center (Walnut Creek)
Garret Thrift Shop (Walnut Creek)
John Muir Medical Center (Concord)
John Muir Medical Center (Walnut Creek)
John Muir Outpatient Center (Brentwood Tice
  Valley/Rossmoor)
Medical Imaging (Brentwood Concord San Ramon
  Walnut Creek)
MuirLab (Regional)
Occupational Medicine (Brentwood Concord Walnut
  Creek)
Physical Rehabilitation Center (Concord Pleasant Hill)
Urgent Care Centers (Brentwood Concord San Ramon
  Walnut Creek)
Women's Health Center (Walnut Creek)
Wound Care Center (Walnut Creek)

Selected Services

Behavioral Health
Cancer
Cardiovascular Services
Chemical Dependency
Children's Services
Emergency Services
Lab Services
Medical Imaging
Orthopedics
Neurosciences
Physical Rehabilitation
Pregnancy & New Parent
Primary Care
Urgent Care

COMPETITORS

Alta Bates Summit Medical Center
California Pacific Medical Center
Children's Hospital & Research Center At Oakland
Community Hospital Of The Monterey Peninsula
Dignity Health
Healdsburg District Hospital
Hill Physicians Medical Group
Marin General Hospital
Mills-peninsula Health Services
Sequoia Healthcare District
Stanford Health Care
Sutter Health
Tenet Healthcare
The Palo Alto Medical Foundation
Ucsf Medical
Valleycare Health System

HISTORICAL FINANCIALS

Company Type: Private

Income Statement   FYE: December 31

	REVENUE ($ mil.)	NET INCOME ($ mil.)	NET PROFIT MARGIN	EMPLOYEES
12/20	2,106	178	8.5%	2,200
12/17	1,831	92	5.0%	—
12/16	1,734	107	6.2%	—
Annual Growth	5.0%	13.5%	—	—

2020 Year-End Financials

Return on assets: 4.8%   Cash ($ mil.): 222
Return on equity: 7.9%
Current ratio: 1.60

JOHNS HOPKINS ALL CHILDREN'S HOSPITAL, INC.

Johns Hopkins All Children's Hospital has about 260 beds all dedicated to the health of west-central Florida's children. With roughly 200 pediatric physician specialists on board the hospital offers its young patients (infants children and teens) a variety of services including a Neonatal Intensive Care Unit for premature and "at-risk" infants. Its heart bone marrow and kidney transplant programs are nationally renowned. The teaching hospital is also affiliated with the University of South Florida College of Medicine. All Children's Hospital is a member of the Johns Hopkins Medicine network.

Operations

The hospital handles about 8000 inpatient visits each year as well as 45000 emergency room and 400000 outpatient visits. All Children's Hospital has expanded its services over the years to include specialty cancer cystic fibrosis cardiology neurology and cleft palate programs. The organization also includes several satellite outpatient care centers; its All Children's Specialty Physicians group practice organization includes 100 doctors with 15 general and specialist programs.

Geographic Reach

As a referral center for children All Children's draws patients from throughout Florida all 50 states and 36 foreign countries. Most of its patients come from the Florida counties of Hillsborough Manatee Pinellas Pasco and Sarasota.

Outpatient facilities are located in towns including Aquatics Brandon East Lake Fort Myers Lakeland Lakewood Ranch Pasco Sertoma Sarasota South Tampa and Tampa.

Financial Performance

All Children's Hospital revenue increased 7% to $425 million in 2014 as patient service income and investment earnings rose.Net income slipped 4% to $33 million that year on higher contributions to affiliates and increased operating expenses including salaries and benefits.

Cash flow from operations fell 14% to $39 million that year.

Strategy

All Children's has focused on strengthening and expanding services including new pediatric stroke and thrombosis (clotting disorder) programs launched in 2013. The following year it opened its 11th outpatient care center (in South Tampa

Florida). Through its affiliation with other Johns Hopkins entities the pediatric facility is also increasing its research activities.

Company Background

The hospital became a fully integrated part of the Johns Hopkins Health System (the operating health organization of Johns Hopkins Medicine) through a non-cash transaction in 2011. Under terms of the agreement Florida residents remained a majority of the All Children's governing board thereby ensuring local control and staffing and day-to-day operations would not change drastically. The deal gave All Children's access to the Johns Hopkins extensive educational and research resources. It also gave Johns Hopkins a dedicated pediatric facility something it previously lacked.

The hospital traces its roots to the American Legion Hospital for Crippled Children which was opened in 1927 in St. Petersburg to treat children suffering from polio and other diseases.

EXECUTIVES

Ceo, Jonathan Ellen
Treasurer*, J Kenneth Coppedge
Chairman of Board*, Mark Stroud
Cfo*, Douglas Myers
Cfo-Vp*, Chris Whitby
Associate Director, Raquel Hernandez
Coordinator, Anne Oliver
Assistant Professor, Erica Sibinga
Coordinator, Suzanne Anderson
Coordinator, Waleska Lozada
Emergency Medicine Specialist, James V Hillman

LOCATIONS

HQ: JOHNS HOPKINS ALL CHILDREN'S HOSPITAL,
INC.
501 6TH AVE S, SAINT PETERSBURG, FL 337014634
Phone: 727 898-7451
Web: WWW.HOPKINSALLCHILDRENS.ORG

PRODUCTS/OPERATIONS

Selected Affiliates

ACHPOB Inc.
All Children's Hospital Foundation Inc.
All Children's Research Institute Inc. (ACRI)
Kids Home Care Inc.
Pediatric Physician Services Inc.
SurgiKid of Florida Inc.
West Coast Neonatology Inc.

Selected Services

Acute Care Rehabilitation
Allergy/ Immunology
Anesthesiology
Applied Behavior Analysis (ABA)
Asthma Coalition
Audiology: Hearing and Hearing Aid Services
Autism Center
Blood and Marrow Transplant (BMT)
Cancer and Blood Disorders
CanSurvive Clinic
Cardiology and Cardiovascular Surgery
Child Life Services
Craniofacial and Craniomaxillofacial
Critical Care
Early Steps
Emergency Medicine
Endocrinology & Diabetes
Fit4AllKids
Fit4AllMoms
Gastroenterology Nutrition and Hepatology
General Pediatrics
Genetics
Healthy Start
Hematology/ Oncology
Hospitalists
Infectious Disease
Kids Home Care
Minimally Invasive Surgery
Music Therapy at All Children's Hospital
Neonatal Surgery
Neonatology

Nephrology
Neurology
Neuropsychiatry
Neuroscience Institute
Nutrition
Obstetrics/ Gynecology
Occupational Therapy Services
Ophthalmology
Orthopaedic and Scoliosis Surgery
Otolaryngology and Cochlear Implant Program
Pathology and Laboratory Medicine
Pediatric Developmental Medicine
Pediatric General Surgery
Perinatology
Physical Therapy Services
Plastic and Reconstructive Surgery
Psychiatry
Pulmonology
Radiology and Neuroradiology
Rehabilitation Services
Retail Pharmacy
Rheumatology
SAFE KIDS
Safe Routes to School
Speech-Language Pathology Services
Sports Medicine
STEPS to a Healthier Florida
Stroke Program
Thoracic Surgery
Thrombosis Program
Transport Team
Trauma Services
Urology

COMPETITORS

Baycare Health System
Bayfront Health
Florida Hospital Tampa Bay Division
Florida Hospital Waterman
H. Lee Moffitt Cancer Center & Research Institute
Kindred Healthcare
Manatee Memorial Hospital
Mayo Clinic Jacksonville
Miami Children's Hospital
Northside Hospital And Heart Institute
Shriners Hospitals For Children
St. Anthony's Hospital
Tampa General Hospital

HISTORICAL FINANCIALS

Company Type: Private

Income Statement				FYE: June 30
	REVENUE ($ mil.)	NET INCOME ($ mil.)	NET PROFIT MARGIN	EMPLOYEES
06/21	540	144	26.8%	2,325
06/16	400	21	5.4%	—
06/15	408	(1)	—	—
Annual Growth	4.8%	—	—	—

2021 Year-End Financials

Return on assets: 12.5%   Cash ($ mil.): 46
Return on equity: 18.8%
Current ratio: 1.50

JOHNS HOPKINS BAYVIEW MEDICAL CENTER, INC.

If you've just been pulled from the bay like an old empty crab trap Johns Hopkins Bayview might be the first place you're taken. One of five member institutions in the Johns Hopkins Health System Johns Hopkins Bayview Medical Center is a com-munity teaching hospital. Its Baltimore-based op-erations include a neonatal intensive care unit as well as centers devoted to trauma geriatrics sleep disorders and weight management. It also features the state's only regional burn center. The facility in-cludes a meditation labyrinth for patients families and staff to walk. Established in 1773 the medical center has more than 560 beds.

Operations

As an academic teaching hospital all of the physicians at Johns Hopkins Bayview are also full-time faculty at the Johns Hopkins School of Med-icine. Students from The Johns Hopkins University School of Nursing also come to the medical center for hospital-based instruction in acute and long term care.

EXECUTIVES

Pres, Steven J Kravet
Vice President*, Craig Brodian
V Pres-Fin-Treas*, L Kenneth Grabill II
V Pres-Hr*, Joan H Williams
V Pres*, Cheryl Koch
Officer*, David Strapelli
Associate Professor of Plastic, Scott Lifchez
Copy Editor, Abbey Becker
Superintendent, Carla Cunningham
Senior Director Care Managemen, Carol Sylvester
Chief Operating Officer, Charles Reuland
Auditors: PRICEWATERHOUSECOOPERS LLP BA

LOCATIONS

HQ: JOHNS HOPKINS BAYVIEW MEDICAL CENTER, INC.
4940 EASTERN AVE, BALTIMORE, MD 212242735
Phone: 410 550-0100
Web: WWW.HOPKINSMEDICINE.ORG

PRODUCTS/OPERATIONS

Selected services
Primary Care Services
  General Internal Medicine
  Obstetrics/Gynecology
  Pediatrics
Specialty Services
  Bariatrics
  Burn
  Cardiology
  Clinical Nutrition
  Dermatology
  Endocrinology
  Gastroenterology
  General Surgery
  Hematology/Oncology
  Imaging (X-ray mammography ultrasound etc)
  Minor Surgery
  Neurodiagnostic Lab
  Neurology
  Ophthalmology
  Otolaryngology (ear nose and throat)
  Orthopaedics
  Plastic Surgery
  Podiatry
  Urology
  Vascular Lab

COMPETITORS

Franklin Square
  Hospital Center
Gbmc
Good Samaritan
  Hospital Of Maryland
Harbor Hospital
Levindale Hospital
Lifebridge Health
Sinai Hospital Of
  Baltimore
St. Agnes Healthcare
St. Joseph Medical
  Center
University Of Maryland
  Medical System

HISTORICAL FINANCIALS

Company Type: Private

Income Statement				FYE: June 30
	REVENUE ($ mil.)	NET INCOME ($ mil.)	NET PROFIT MARGIN	EMPLOYEES
06/21	716	91	12.7%	3,300
06/20	669	(41)	—	—
06/19	648	(39)	—	—
06/18	628	12	1.9%	—
Annual Growth	4.5%	96.1%	—	—

2021 Year-End Financials

Return on assets: 20.2%   Cash ($ mil.): 23
Return on equity: 130.2%
Current ratio: 1.10

JOHNS HOPKINS HEALTHCARE LLC

EXECUTIVES

Prin, Robert Neall
Business Administrator, Salma Riaz
Program Manager, Tami Wlajnitz
Administrative Coordinator, Tammy Watkins
Sales Customer, Terrina Bean
Lan Administrator Information, Tim Collins
Field Supervisor, William Holmes
Human Resources, Linda Evans
Coordinator, Yvonne Bonner
Information Specialist, Sara McElligott
Administrative Assistant, Leah Adams

LOCATIONS

HQ: JOHNS HOPKINS HEALTHCARE LLC
7231 PARKWAY DR STE 100, HANOVER, MD 210762331
Phone: 410 424-4400
Web: WWW.EHP.ORG

HISTORICAL FINANCIALS

Company Type: Private

Income Statement				FYE: June 30
	REVENUE ($ mil.)	NET INCOME ($ mil.)	NET PROFIT MARGIN	EMPLOYEES
06/21	2,580	30	1.2%	520
06/20	2,412	26	1.1%	—
06/19	2,248	(18)	—	—
06/18	2,125	6	0.3%	—
Annual Growth	6.7%	71.2%	—	—

2021 Year-End Financials

Return on assets: 4.6%   Cash ($ mil.): 135
Return on equity: 17.1%
Current ratio: 0.60

JOHNS HOPKINS HOSPITAL

EXECUTIVES

Pres, Ronald Peterson
Cfo, Ronald Werthman
Ophthalmologist, Albert Jun
Health Professional, Tonya Bradley
Physical Therapist, Perticone Greg
Director of Pharmacy, Rhiannon Fitzsimmons
General Surgeon, Jeffrey Lukish
Genetics Specialist, Tao Wang
Investment Officer, Greg Miller
Dermatology, Bernard Cohen
Administrative Coordinator, Pamela Thompson
Auditors: PRICEWATERHOUSECOOPERS LLP BA

LOCATIONS

HQ: JOHNS HOPKINS HOSPITAL
 1800 ORLEANS ST, BALTIMORE, MD 212870010
Phone: 410 550-0730
Web: WWW.HOPKINSMEDICINE.ORG

HISTORICAL FINANCIALS

Company Type: Private

Income Statement				FYE: June 30
	REVENUE ($ mil.)	NET INCOME ($ mil.)	NET PROFIT MARGIN	EMPLOYEES
06/20	2,617	(202)	—	12,000
06/19	2,527	(64)	—	—
06/18	2,422	98	4.1%	—
06/16	1,968	80	4.1%	—
Annual Growth	7.4%	—	—	—

2020 Year-End Financials

Return on assets: (-6.2%)   Cash ($ mil.): 41
Return on equity: (-17.8%)
Current ratio: 1.10

JOHNS HOPKINS UNIVERSITY

Founded in 1876 The Johns Hopkins University has established its reputation by molding itself in the image of a European research institution. While renowned for its School of Medicine the private university offers more than 400 academic programs spanning fields of study including arts and sciences business engineering and international studies. The university enrolls more than 29000 full- and part-time students throughout nine academic divisions. Johns Hopkins has about a half-dozen campuses in Maryland and Washington DC as well as facilities in China and Italy. The student-teacher ratio is 10:1. The affiliated Johns Hopkins Health System treats more than 3920 patients from approximately 145 countries in its facilities based in the US.

Operations

Johns Hopkins University actively prepares students to be global leaders and citizens to take part in international learning activities. With a proud tradition of leadership in education research service and patient care around the globe the university promotes intellectual discovery through academic exchanges programs abroad collaborative research and cooperative agreements.

Keenly focused on research Johns Hopkins is engaged in a range of disciplines including health and medicine social sciences humanities the arts natural sciences engineering and technology. Projects include researching alternatives to animal testing disease treatments and chemical and biomolecular engineering topics among others.

The Johns Hopkins University offers graduate programs in business finance and real estate through its relatively new Carey Business School.

Notable alumni of the school include 28th US president Woodrow Wilson Michael Bloomberg and horror film director Wesley Craven.

Geographic Reach

Johns Hopkins University boasts three major campuses in Baltimore as well as single campus locations in (Montgomery County) Maryland and Washington DC. Johns Hopkins also operates facilities in the Baltimore-Washington area and abroad in Nanjing China and Bologna Italy.

Financial Performance
Mergers and Acquisitions

In mid-2020 Johns Hopkins finalized the purchase of 555 Pennsylvania Ave. NW in Washington DC which will become a state-of-the art university facility for research education and public engagement that allows every academic division of the institution to have a presence in the nation's capital increasing the university's ability to bring its research and expertise to national and global policy-making debates. The facility will become a vibrant hub for research education and convenings representing a rare alignment of its mission of sharing knowledge with the world and the ongoing growth of the Pennsylvania Avenue corridor.

EXECUTIVES

Pres, Ronald J Daniels
Office Clerk, Daniel Ledford
Veterinary Surgery Technician, Kristy Koenig
Postdoctoral Fellow, Lindsay Hayes
Research Associate, Ravi Anchoori
Assistant Professor, Mir Hossain
Project Leader, Alfonso Del Valle
Scientist, Charles Young
Assistant Professor, David M Loeb
Law, Stephen Marchetti
Assistant Professor, Gregory Riggins
Auditors: KPMG LLP BALTIMORE MARYLAND

LOCATIONS

HQ: JOHNS HOPKINS UNIVERSITY
 3400 N CHARLES ST, BALTIMORE, MD 212182680
Phone: 410 516-8000
Web: WWW.JHU.EDU

PRODUCTS/OPERATIONS

Selected Schools and Colleges

Bloomberg School of Public Health
Carey Business School
Krieger School of Arts and Sciences
Peabody Institute
School of Advanced International Studies
School of Education
School of Medicine
School of Nursing
Whiting School of Engineering

Selected Centers and Institutes

American Institute for Contemporary German Studies
Bloomberg School of Public Health Department of Health Policy and Management Fall Institute in Barcelona Spain
Bloomberg School of Public Health Research Centers
Center for Africana Studies
Center for Communication Programs
Center for Constitutional Studies and Democratic Development
Center for Clinical Global Health Education
Center for Global Health
Center for International Business and Public Policy
Center for Language Education
Center for Talented Youth
Center for Transatlantic Relations
Central Asia Caucasus Institute
Foreign Policy Institute
Hopkins Nanjing Center
Institute for Global Studies in Culture Power and History
Institute for Policy Studies
Johns Hopkins SAIS Bologna Center
Office of Global Nursing
SAIS Research Centers
Summer Language Institute
The Institute for Johns Hopkins Nursing
Yeung Center for Collaborative China Studies

Selected Campuses

Columbia Center - Columbia Maryland
East Baltimore Campus - Baltimore
Harbor East - Downtown Baltimore
Homewood Campus - Baltimore
Hopkins-Nanjing Center - Nanjing Jiangsu Province People's Republic of China
Johns Hopkins University Applied Physics Laboratory - Laurel MD; Baltimore and Washington
Johns Hopkins University Zanvyl Krieger School of Arts & Sciences Advanced Academic Programs - Washington DC
Montgomery County Center - Rockville Maryland
Nitze School of Advanced International Studies (SAIS) - Washington D.C
Peabody Campus - Baltimore
School of Advanced International Studies - Bologna Italy

HISTORICAL FINANCIALS

Company Type: Private

Income Statement				FYE: June 30
	REVENUE ($ mil.)	NET INCOME ($ mil.)	NET PROFIT MARGIN	EMPLOYEES
06/21	6,659	3,427	51.5%	37,600
06/20	6,470	903	14.0%	—
06/19	6,410	2,017	31.5%	—
06/18	6,020	705	11.7%	—
Annual Growth	3.4%	69.4%	—	—

2021 Year-End Financials

Return on assets: 19.0%   Cash ($ mil.): 2,656
Return on equity: 25.3%
Current ratio: —

JOHNSON & JOHNSON PATIENT ASSISTANCE FOUNDATION INC

EXECUTIVES

Prin, Nancy Moyer

LOCATIONS

HQ: JOHNSON & JOHNSON PATIENT ASSISTANCE FOUNDATION INC
 1 JOHNSON AND JOHNSON PLZ, NEW BRUNSWICK, NJ 089330001
Phone: 732 524-1394
Web: WWW.JJPAF.ORG

HISTORICAL FINANCIALS

Company Type: Private

Income Statement				FYE: December 31
	REVENUE ($ mil.)	NET INCOME ($ mil.)	NET PROFIT MARGIN	EMPLOYEES
12/14	787	(16)	—	19
12/13	741	13	1.8%	—
12/10	425	(6)	—	—
12/09	355	(2)	—	—
Annual Growth	17.2%	—	—	—

2014 Year-End Financials

Return on assets: (-23.4%)   Cash ($ mil.): 31
Return on equity: (-23.4%)
Current ratio: —

JOHNSON CONTROLS FIRE PROTECTION LP

SimplexGrinnell handles emergencies well. The company provides integrated security alarm fire suppression healthcare communications and emergency lighting systems. SimplexGrinnell reaches some 1 million customers in the US and Canada through more than 150 district offices located in the Americas Europe Asia and other regions. In addition to providing security and fire related products SimplexGrinnell operates a service division devoted to test and inspection preventive maintenance central station monitoring and emergency services. The company's clients include members of local state and federal government agencies corporations oil and gas companies hospitals and educational facilities.

Operations

The company's communications segment provides mass notification and commercial paging as well as intercom and other sound systems. The company also provides healthcare communications such as infant security nurse call and emergency alert units.

Strategy

SimplexGrinnell launched a new website to give its customers a fast and convenient way to purchase many of its products that do not require installation support.

EXECUTIVES

Ceo, George R Oliver
Pres, Robert Chauvin
Exec V Pres, Larry Costello
V Pres, Chris Maxie
Program Inspector, Robert Schwartz
Designer, Bob Kehrer
Accounting Staff, Chad Lamoureux
Designer, Alan Mahaffie
Program Inspector, Joseph Vereb
Senior Oracle DBA, Dawood Mahmood
Operations Manager, Mark Rossi

LOCATIONS

HQ: JOHNSON CONTROLS FIRE PROTECTION LP
6600 CONGRESS AVE, BOCA RATON, FL 334871213
Phone: 561 988-7200
Web: WWW.TYCOSIMPLEXGRINNELL.COM

PRODUCTS/OPERATIONS

Selected Products and Services

Fire Detection and Alarm

Control Panels
Notification
Network Solutions
Smoke Detector and Carbon Monoxide Detection
Sound and Communication
Healthcare Communications
Emergency Communications
Public Address and Intercom
Sound Reinforcement
Telephone Networks
Integrated Security
Access Control
Intrusion Detection
Property Surveillance
Mass Notification
Fire Sprinkler and Suppression
Fire Extinguisher
Special Hazards
Sprinkler

COMPETITORS

Api Group
Brink's
Cosco Fire Protection
Honeywell International
Ingersoll-rand Security Technologies
Protection One

HISTORICAL FINANCIALS

Company Type: Private

Income Statement				FYE: September 30
	REVENUE ($ mil.)	NET INCOME ($ mil.)	NET PROFIT MARGIN	EMPLOYEES
09/16	1,871	182	9.7%	9,500
09/09	1,750	0	—	—
Annual Growth	1.0%	—	—	—

JOHNSON CONTROLS, INC.

Climate control for offices Johnson Controls manufactures installs and services energy-efficient heating ventilation and air conditioning (HVAC) systems. Its products cover everything needed to make a place of work comfortable and safe to be in extending to fire detection and suppression and security measures such as electronic card site access. Originally an American company Johnson Controls completed a reverse merger with Cork-based Tyco International and is now domiciled in Ireland (although the US remains its largest market by far). The company sold its car battery manufacturing operations in 2018 to Brookfield Business Partners.

Operations

JCI operates through 230 wholly- and majority-owned manufacturing or assembly plants. Its building efficiency business segment designs control systems and mechanical equipment as well as services non-residential properties in about 52 countries. About 65% of this segment's sales are derived from HVAC products and control systems for construction and retrofit markets and the other half from services. Branded products include the Metasys control system and York chillers. This segment is looking to such emerging markets as China and the Middle East for strong sales.

The company's power solutions business claims it is the largest lead-acid automotive battery producer in the world. JCI holds an edge over other battery companies as it is not locked into an alliance with any specific automaker allowing it to

play the field. Its 60 manufacturing and assembly facilities are located in about 22 countries and produce lead-acid batteries as well as AGM (absorbent glass mat) battery technology and lithium-ion batteries used in hybrid vehicles. About 75% of the company's batteries are sold in the automotive replacement sector with the rest going to OEMs. Power solutions is ready to benefit from vertical integration for lead recycling and a shift in its product mix to AGM technology.

Automotive experience designs and manufactures interior products and systems for passenger cars and light trucks including vans pick-up trucks and sport/crossover utility vehicles. The business produces automotive interior systems for OEMs and operates approximately 230 wholly- and majority-owned manufacturing or assembly plants with operations in 32 countries worldwide.

Geographic Reach

JCI operates through more than 1500 locations worldwide. Nearly 45% of its total sales come from the US; other major markets include Germany (9%) and other countries in Europe (20%).

Sales and Marketing

JCI's main customers include the biggest names in the industry: Ford Daimler Fiat Chrysler Toyota and GM . The company sells its control systems mechanical equipment and services through its extensive global network of sales and service offices. Some building controls products and mechanical systems are also sold to distributors of air-conditioning refrigeration and commercial heating systems throughout the world.

Financial Performance

JCI's revenues dipped 1% to $36.9 billion in 2016 as it posted its first net loss in seven years. The marginal revenue decrease for 2016 was driven by lower sales from its automotive experience business and the unfavorable impact of foreign currency translation of $754 million.

The net loss of $847 million JCI suffered in 2016 was due to an increase in the income tax provision additional separation and transaction costs and mounting restructuring and impairment costs. Most of these costs were affiliated with the company's $16.5 billion purchase of Tyco International in late 2016.

Strategy

JCI is looking to streamline its business by selling and spinning off non-core operations. In late 2015 it completed the sale of its Global Workplace Solutions (GWS) business to CBRE Group for $1.5 billion. GWS is a worldwide provider of facilities management services.

In addition the company spun off its global automotive seating components and systems operations into a publicly traded company called Adient Inc. in October 2016.

Mergers and Acquisitions

The company often grows its product portfolio through the use of acquisitions. In a sweeping move for the home-products industry in early 2016 JCI purchased Tyco International for $16.5 billion. The combined company will boast revenues of up to $32 billion.

HISTORY

Professor Warren Johnson developed the electric telethermoscope in 1880 so that janitors at Whitewater Wisconsin's State Normal School could regulate room temperatures without disturbing classrooms. His device the thermostat used mercury to move a heat element that opened and shut a circuit. Milwaukee hotelier William Plankinton believed in the invention and invested $150000 to start production.

The two men formed Johnson Electric Service Company in 1885. They sold the marketing installation and service rights to concentrate on manufacturing. Johnson also invented other devices such as tower clocks and he experimented with the telegraph before becoming intrigued with the automobile and beginning production of steam-powered cars. He won the US Postal Service 's first automotive contract but never gained support within his own company. Johnson continued to look elsewhere for financing until his death in 1911.

The renamed Johnson Services regained full rights to its thermostats in 1912 and sold its other businesses. During the Depression it produced economy systems that regulated building temperatures. Johnson Services became a public company in 1940. During WWII it aided the war effort building weather-data gatherers and radar test sets.

In the 1960s Johnson Services began developing centralized control systems for temperature fire alarm lighting and security regulation. The company was renamed Johnson Controls in 1974.

EXECUTIVES

Chb-Ceo, George Oliver
Exec V Pres-Cfo*, Brian Stief
V Pres-Gen Counsel-Sec*, Brian Cadwallader
V Pres-Corp Contrl*, Suzanne M Vincent
Cpo-V Pres of Controls Operati*, Michael Bartschat
Installation Coordinator, Dewayne Broome
Designer, Duane Iverson
Human Resources Data Analyst, Eric Niemi
Auditor Audit, Erling Antonsen
Vice President, Andy Cheung
Promotion Manager, Bobby Morshed
Auditors: PRICEWATERHOUSECOOPERS LLP MI

LOCATIONS

HQ: JOHNSON CONTROLS, INC.
   5757 N GREEN BAY AVE, GLENDALE, WI 532094408
Phone: 800 382-2804
Web: WWW.JOHNSONCONTROLS.COM

HISTORICAL FINANCIALS
Company Type: Private

Income Statement				FYE: September 30
	REVENUE ($ mil.)	NET INCOME ($ mil.)	NET PROFIT MARGIN	EMPLOYEES
09/15	37,179	1,679	4.5%	105,000
09/14	42,828	1,335	3.1%	—
09/13	42,730	1,297	3.0%	—
Annual Growth	(6.7%)	13.8%	—	—

2015 Year-End Financials
Return on assets: 5.7%   Cash ($ mil.): 597
Return on equity: 15.9%
Current ratio: 1.10

JOINT SCHOOL DISTRICT NO. 28-J OF THE COUNTIES OF ADAMS AND ARAPAHOE

EXECUTIVES

Supt, Rico Munn
Contrl*, Gina Lanier
Chief Operating Officer, Anthony Sturges
Executive Officer, Matthew Eckert
Coordinator, Stephanie Gianneschi
Literacy Coach Teacher Leader, Kayla Cook
Teacher, Janelle Flanscha
Assistant Executive Director, Shelia Siegert
Director, Sherry Hon
Director, Ashley Morgan
Technology, Brett Frank
Auditors: BKD LLP DENVER COLORADO

LOCATIONS

HQ: JOINT SCHOOL DISTRICT NO. 28-J OF THE COUNTIES OF ADAMS AND ARAPAHOE
   15701 E 1ST AVE STE 106, AURORA, CO 800119037
Phone: 303 365-5810
Web: WWW.AURORAK12.ORG

HISTORICAL FINANCIALS
Company Type: Private

Income Statement				FYE: June 30
	REVENUE ($ mil.)	NET INCOME ($ mil.)	NET PROFIT MARGIN	EMPLOYEES
06/21	680	39	5.8%	6,000
06/20	608	24	4.0%	—
06/19	555	6	1.2%	—
06/18	492	(8)	—	—
Annual Growth	11.4%	—	—	—

2021 Year-End Financials
Return on assets: 3.2%   Cash ($ mil.): 174
Return on equity: —
Current ratio: 2.60

KADLEC REGIONAL MEDICAL CENTER

Kadlec Regional Medical Center is an acute care hospital facility serving southeastern Washington and northeastern Oregon. In addition to providing comprehensive medical surgical and emergency services the hospital provides neonatal intensive care cardiopulmonary rehabilitation interventional cardiology neurology cancer care and other specialist services. Not-for-profit Kadlec Regional has some 270 inpatient beds including pediatric intensive intermediate and critical care capacity. It also operates outpatient physician offices and clinics in surrounding areas.

Operations
Kadlec Regional's cardiovascular programs include open heart surgery and interventional cardi-

ology. The hospital also operates an all-digital outpatient imaging center and the region's only level III neonatal intensive care unit (NICU). Kadlec was is also designated as a Level 1 Cardiac Center and a Level 2 Stroke Center. Area specialist practices include centers for dermatology colorectal surgery nephrology pediatrics women's health ENT (ear nose and throat) and foot and ankle practices. Kadlec Regional also operates satellite urgent care and family practice clinics.

The Kadlec Neuroscience Center offers a wide range of services to treat and diagnose conditions related to the brain spine spinal cord & peripheral nervous system.

In 2013 the hospital reported more than 2700 births 66000 emergency department visits and about 15000 admissions.

That year Kadlec Regional provided $27 million in charity care.

Geographic Reach
Kadlec Regional has hospital and clinic locations in Hermiston Kennewick Pasco Pendleton Prosser and Richland.

Financial Performance
The hospital reported revenue of $312 million in 2012 consisting of $305 million in net patient service earnings and other revenue of some $7.5 million. Kadlec Regional brought in profits of some $29 million.

Strategy
The hospital has undergone aggressive expansion efforts adding a new patient tower with diagnostic outpatient and intermediate care and surgery rooms. Kadlec Regional is enhancing its specialty service units in fields to attract specialists and increase revenue.The organization launched a $10 million project to expand its NICU unit in 2013. It will add 27 private and semi-private rooms and new observation gathering and lactation areas.

It is also expanding outpatient service facilities such as a new $19 million three-story specialty physician practice office that opened in Richland in 2013. The new building increases collaboration between various surgical and medical specialists in the Kadlec Regional clinic network.

The year the company also expanded its emergency room offerings through the opening of the Kadlec ER in Kennewick. The new 15-bed ER is the first in the region to operate as a freestanding facility like traditional hospital-based ERs.

Mergers and Acquisitions
Kadlec Regional also absorbs other area providers. In 2013 Inland Cardiology Associates become part of the Kadlec Regional health system. The region's largest independent group of experienced cardiologists Inland provides comprehensive invasive noninvasive and interventional services throughout southeast Washington and northeast Oregon.

Company Background
In 2011 it partnered with the nearby PMH Medical Center to increase collaboration and specialist referrals between the two hospitals. The partnership extends the reach of Kadlec Regional's medical specialists to additional communities and brings PMH online with Kadlec Regional's electronic health record system. Both hospitals remained independently run.

The hospital system was founded in 1944.

EXECUTIVES

Ceo, Lane Savitch
Pres*, Rand Wortman
V Pres-Cfo*, Julie Meek
V Pres*, Jeffrey Clark
V Presis*, Dave Roach
V Pres-Cor Coun*, Bill Wingo
V Pres-Found*, Larry Christensen

V Pres*, Dale Hoekema
Coordinator, Antoinette Burnside
Compliance and Privacy Officer, Jennie Martin
Practice Administrator, Linda Moran

LOCATIONS

HQ: KADLEC REGIONAL MEDICAL CENTER
888 SWIFT BLVD, RICHLAND, WA 993523514
Phone: 509 946-4611
Web: WWW.KADLEC.ORG

PRODUCTS/OPERATIONS

Selected Services
The Birth Center
Bloodless Medicine and Surgery
Cancer Care
Cardiac Care
Cardiac Catheterization
CardioPulmonary Rehabilitation
Cardiovascular and Thoracic Surgery
CaringBridge
Clinical Decision Unit
Coumadin Clinic
Diabetes Learning Center
Diagnostic Imaging
Don and Lori Watts Pediatric Center
Emergency Department
Emergency Room-Kennewick
Home Health Care
Imaging
Inpatient Rehabilitation and Therapy
Intensive Care Unit
Joint Care Center
Kadlec Academy
Kadlec Healthy Ages
Kadlec Medical Associates
Neonatal Intensive Care Unit
Occupational Medicine
Occupational Therapy
Ostomy Support Group
Outpatient Imaging Center
Outpatient Procedures
Physical Therapy
Planetree
Rehabilitation and Therapy Services
Speech Therapy
Urgent Care
Water Therapy
Wound Healing Center

COMPETITORS

Adventist Health System West	Providence St. Joseph Health
Asante Health System	Salem Hospital
Legacy Health System	Wenatchee Valley Medical Center
Peacehealth	Yakima Valley Memorial
Providence Health & Services-washington	

HISTORICAL FINANCIALS

Company Type: Private

Income Statement				FYE: December 31
	REVENUE ($ mil.)	NET INCOME ($ mil.)	NET PROFIT MARGIN	EMPLOYEES
12/18	640	51	8.0%	2,668
12/17	595	87	14.7%	—
12/16	534	9	1.9%	—
12/15	504	(7)	—	—
Annual Growth	8.3%	—	—	—

2018 Year-End Financials
Return on assets: 8.6%
Return on equity: 19.5%
Current ratio: 2.00
Cash ($ mil.): 18

KAISER FDN HEALTH PLAN OF COLORADO

Auditors: PRICEWATERHOUSECOOPERS LLP PH

LOCATIONS

HQ: KAISER FDN HEALTH PLAN OF COLORADO
1 KAISER PLZ STE 15L, OAKLAND, CA 946123610
Phone: 510 271-6611

HISTORICAL FINANCIALS

Company Type: Private

Income Statement				FYE: December 31
	REVENUE ($ mil.)	NET INCOME ($ mil.)	NET PROFIT MARGIN	EMPLOYEES
12/19	4,344	258	6.0%	12
12/13	3,197	115	3.6%	—
12/09	2,374	32	1.4%	—
Annual Growth	6.2%	23.1%	—	—

2019 Year-End Financials
Return on assets: 15.5%
Return on equity: 41.2%
Current ratio: 0.20
Cash ($ mil.): 10

KAISER FOUNDATION HOSPITALS INC

Kaiser Foundation Hospitals is on a roll. The hospital group operates nearly 40 acute care hospitals and 680 medical offices in eight states (California Colorado Georgia Hawaii Maryland Oregon Virginia and Washington) and Washington D.C. The company's largest presence is in California where the majority of its hospitals are located. Kaiser Foundation Hospitals employs more than 21000 physicians representing all medical specialties. Kaiser Foundation Hospital's doctors group is controlled by Permanente Medical Groups and its HMO is offered through Kaiser Foundation Health Plan. Altogether the group provides care for about 11.7 million members.

Operations
Kaiser Foundation Hospitals works with other organizations to tackle such issues as obesity access to care and violence. It also works to promote health in the communities it serves through wellness programs.

In 2016 Kaiser Foundation Hospitals logged 44 million office visits. It facilitated 106000 births performed 129000 surgeries and filled 90 million prescriptions.

Sales and Marketing
Company Background
Kaiser Foundation Hospitals was founded in 1945.

EXECUTIVES

Ceo-Chm, Gregory A Adams
Sr Vp*, Anthony Barreta
Evp Cfo*, Kathy Lancaster
Evp, Group Pres-Coo*, Janet Liang
Svp-Cco*, Catherine Hernandez
Chief Information Technology O*, Diane Comer

Rn, Lisa Liu
Benefits Communication Manager, Dominic Bohbot
Business Relationship Manager, Janice Adams
Area Vice President, Neal Miller
Senior Project Manager, Teddy Chien

LOCATIONS

HQ: KAISER FOUNDATION HOSPITALS INC
1 KAISER PLZ, OAKLAND, CA 946123610
Phone: 510 271-6611
Web: WWW.KAISERCENTER.COM

PRODUCTS/OPERATIONS

Selected Hospitals
Antioch Medical Center
Fremont Medical Center
Fresno Medical Center
Hayward Medical Center
Manteca Medical Center
Modesto Medical Center
Oakland Medical Center
Redwood City Medical Center
Richmond Medical Center
Roseville Women and Children's Center
San Jose Medical Center
Santa Clara Medical Center
Sacramento Medical Center
South San Francisco Medical Center
South Sacramento Trauma Center
Santa Rosa Medical Center
San Francisco Medical Center
San Rafael Medical Center
Vacaville Medical Center
Vallejo Medical Center
Walnut Creek Medical Center
Baldwin Park Medical Center
Downey Medical Center
Fontana Medical Center
Los Angeles Medical Center
Moreno Valley Community Hospital
Orange County - Anaheim Medical Center
Orange County - Irvine Medical Center
Panorama City Medical Center
Riverside Medical Center
San Diego Medical Center
Harbor City (South Bay Medical Center)
Woodlands Hills Medical Center
West Los Angeles Medical Center
Sunnyside Medical Center (Portland Oregon area)
Moanalua Medical Center (Hawaii)

COMPETITORS

Adventist Health System West	Dignity Health
Ascension Health	Hca
Banner Health	Lifepoint Health
Christus Health	Sutter Health
Catholic Health Initiatives	Tenet Healthcare
Community Health Systems	The Cleveland Clinic
	Universal Health Services

HISTORICAL FINANCIALS

Company Type: Private

Income Statement				FYE: December 31
	REVENUE ($ mil.)	NET INCOME ($ mil.)	NET PROFIT MARGIN	EMPLOYEES
12/09	14,795	429	2.9%	175,668
12/08	0	0	99.0%	—
12/05	9,852	774	7.9%	—
Annual Growth	10.7%	(13.7%)	—	—

2009 Year-End Financials
Return on assets: —
Return on equity: 2.9%
Current ratio: —
Cash ($ mil.): 57

KALEIDA HEALTH

Kaleida Health provides a kaleidoscope of services to residents of western New York. The health system operates five acute care hospitals including Buffalo General Hospital and Gates Vascular Institute (combined with about 550 beds) The Women & Children's Hospital of Buffalo (200) DeGraff Memorial Hospital (70) and Millard Fillmore Suburban Hospital (260). Community health needs are met through a network of some 80 medical clinics. Kaleida Health also operates skilled nursing care facilities and provides home health care through its Visiting Nursing Association. To help train future medical professionals Buffalo General Hospital is a teaching affiliate of the State University of New York.

Operations

Kaleida Health is also home to the Deaconess Center and Waterfront long-term care facilities. Along with primary care the system's network of outpatient centers offers medical and surgical subspecialty care dental and oral surgery services and behavioral health and outpatient alcohol treatment services. Kaleida Health also operates the Pediatric Trauma Center and Pediatric HIV/AIDS Center for the Western New York (WNY).

In 2012 the health system had 55125 inpatient discharges 158902 emergency department visits and 2.3 million clinic and lab visits.

Financial Performance

The company's revenues grew by 3% to $1.2 billion in 2012 thanks to higher net patient service revenues and other revenues (including increases from a medical resident tax refund and HITECH incentive funds). It reported that 37% of net patient service revenues came from Medicare; 21% from New York State Medicaid; and 38% from commercial insurance plans.

Kaleida Health saw net income of $52 million in 2012 (compared to a net loss in 2011) as the result of higher revenues and an increase in investment returns (including a gain from a net change in unrealized gains and losses on investments).

Strategy

In an effort to draw in more patients to the eight communities in which it already operates in the US Kaleida Health has become one of a handful of US medical providers to market itself to patients north of the border in Canada. The organization launched a marketing campaign in Ontario over the years that included a website aimed at pulling in Canadian patients seeking bariatric care for obesity gastrointestinal services (such as colonoscopies) joint replacement or spinal surgery pediatric care and radiology services. Overall Kaleida is focused on attracting Canadian patients who can either pay out-of-pocket or patients seeking non-emergency services covered in the US by the Ontario Health Insurance Program.

Growing its operations in 2013 The Kaleida Health Laboratories (which performs more than 4 million tests a year) opened four new patient service centers in New York (Tonawanda Lancaster Buffalo and Cheektowaga).

Teaming up with Olean General Hospital (OGH) in 2013 Kaleida Health and OGH opened their new interventional cardiac catheterization lab joint-venture in the Southern Tier of New York.

Kaleida Health and The University at Buffalo opened a new 10-story vascular institute and research building in 2012. The $291 million Gates Vascular Institute and the University at Buffalo's Clinical and Translational Research Center integrates Kaleida Health's physicians and UB researchers in a collaborative effort to deliver clinical care investigate the causes of a wide range of human diseases and spin-off new biotechnology businesses and jobs.

In 2012 Kaleida Health's Visiting Nursing Association of Western New York received regulatory approval to expand into four additional counties.

To raise cash in 2013 Kaleida Health sold the former Millard Fillmore Gates Circle Hospital to TM Montante Development for commercial development.

Mergers and Acquisitions

In 2013 The Visiting Nursing Association of Western New York was selected as the provider of choice to buy the Livingston County Certified Home Health Agency. In 2012 it was selected as the provider of choice to purchase the Wyoming Certified Home Health Agency.

Company Background

Along with trying to grab a share of the Canadian market Kaleida is working to renovate and refurbish its current locations to draw in more patients. In late 2011 the system completed renovations of its maternity services at Women & Children's Hospital of Buffalo. The new Mother-Baby Unit offers 14 additional single rooms with private showers and enhanced amenities. The health system underwent another complete renovation that serves as an additional Mother-Baby Unit as well as inpatient beds for the Perinatal Center gynecology and other women's services.

EXECUTIVES

Ceo, Robert Nesselbush
Pres*, Jody L Lomeo
Evp-Coo*, Donald Boyd
Evp-Cmo*, David P Hughes
Sr Vp- Chief of Staff*, Michael P Hughes
Evp-CNE*, Cheryl Klass
Evp-Chief Human Resources Offi*, Jerry Venable
Evp-Cfo*, Robert J Nesselbush
Svp-CIO*, Robert Diamond
Ceo, Robert Nesselbush
Evp-Cfo*, Paul Belter
Auditors: KPMG LLP ALBANY NY

LOCATIONS

HQ: KALEIDA HEALTH
726 EXCHANGE ST, BUFFALO, NY 142101484
Phone: 716 859-5600
Web: WWW.KALEIDAHEALTH.ORG

PRODUCTS/OPERATIONS

Selected Facilities
Buffalo General Hospital (Buffalo)
Deaconess Center (Buffalo)
DeGraff Memorial Hospital (North Tonawanda)
Gates Vascular Institute (Buffalo)
Millard Fillmore Suburban Hospital (Williamsville)
VNA Home Care Services (Allegany County Chautauqua County Erie County Genesee County Niagara County)
Women and Children's Hospital of Buffalo (Buffalo)

Selected Services
Admissions
Adult Day Services
Allergy & Immunology Clinic
Anesthesia
Bariatric Program
Bereavement Services
Blood Draw Labs
Breast Reconstruction Surgery Information
Buffalo Niagara MRI Center
Cardiac Program
Center for Asthma & Environmental Exposure
Center for Wound Care
Chest Pain Center
Colorectal Surgery
Community Health Department
DeGraff Skilled Nursing Facility
Diabetes-Endocrinology Center of Western New York
Dialysis Treatments
Diversity & Inclusion
Ear Nose and Throat Center/Otolaryngology
Easy Referrals
Emergency Department
Epilepsy Family Planning Center
Gastroenterology
Geriatric Center of Western New York
Hernia Center
Imaging Services
Immunology Laboratory
Laboratory and Pathology
Maternity Services
Minimally Invasive Surgery
Minor Surgery
Multiple Sclerosis
Neonatology
Neuropsychology
Neurosciences
Neurosurgery and Procedures
Obstetrics and Gynecology
Occupational Therapy
Orthopedics
Parkinson's Disease Comprehensive Movement Disorder Center
Pastoral Care
Personal Care Services
Personal Response System (Lifeline)
Pharmacy - High Street
Pharmacy Pharmacy - Suburban Family Pharmacy
Pharmacy Residency Program
Physical Therapy Prenatal Testing
Primary Care
Rehabilitation Medicine - Acute Medical
Rehabilitation Rehabilitation Services
Retinal
Surgical Services
Robotic Surgery
School Based Health Centers
Security
Speech Therapy - Outpatient
Spirit of Women
Stroke Program
Subacute Rehabilitation
Surgical Services
Telehealth Home Monitoring
The Greater Buffalo
United Accountable Healthcare
Urology Services
Vascular Lab
Vascular Services
Visiting Nursing Association of WNY
VNA Diabetes Program
Women's Services
Wound Care

COMPETITORS

Catholic Health System
Ellis Hospital
Hamot Medical Center
Kane Community Hospital
Lifetime Health
Oneida Healthcare Center
Suny Upstate Medical University
St. Joseph's Hospital Health Center
St. Peter's Health Partners
St. Vincent Health System
Titusville
United Health Services Hospitals
Upstate University Hospital At Community General

HISTORICAL FINANCIALS
Company Type: Private

Income Statement				FYE: December 31
	REVENUE ($ mil.)	NET INCOME ($ mil.)	NET PROFIT MARGIN	EMPLOYEES
12/17	1,331	60	4.5%	9,000
12/13	1,139	(14)	—	—
12/09	1,155	75	6.5%	—
Annual Growth	1.8%	(2.7%)	—	—

2017 Year-End Financials
Return on assets: 4.3%   Cash ($ mil.): 16
Return on equity: 19.6%
Current ratio: 1.40

KANSAS DEPARTMENT OF TRANSPORTATION

The Kansas Department of Transportation (KDOT) helps connect the dots with residents who love to travel the 140000-plus miles across the Sunflower State. The agency focuses on providing a transportation system for citizens in the state by offering a wide range of services such as maintaining roads and bridges transportation planning and designing construction projects. The department also provides federal fund program administration as well as administrative support travel information and programs in traffic safety. KDOT traces its roots to the organization of interstate travel in 1917.

Strategy

The agency hopes to bring in additional revenue and preserve and expand its state's road bridge and highway infrastructure through its $7.8 billion T-WORKS program in effect from fiscal year end 2011 through 2020. It includes $2.7 billion in new revenues from registration fees for heavy trucks and a sales tax deposit that begins in 2014. KDOT will spend at least $8 million in each of Kansas' 105 counties during T-WORKS' administration. KDOT plans for the program to create 175000 jobs over the course of the next 10 years.

EXECUTIVES

Secretary, Richard Carlson
Coordinator, Scott Shields
Bridge Inspector Team Leader, Ed Burdiek
Gis Manager, Kyle Gonterwitz
Chief Global Strategist, Amanda Baxter
Transportation, Andrea Barnes
Engineer, G Comstock
Public Affairs Manager, Kirk Hutchinson
Transportation, Michael Slief
Bridge Management Engineer, Paul Kulseth
It Project Manager, Rick Baker
Auditors: CLIFTONLARSONALLEN LLP
  BROOM

LOCATIONS

HQ: KANSAS DEPARTMENT OF TRANSPORTATION
  700 SW HARRISON ST # 500, TOPEKA, KS
  666033964
Phone: 785 296-3501
Web: WWW.KSDOT.ORG

HISTORICAL FINANCIALS

Company Type: Private

Income Statement				FYE: June 30
	REVENUE ($ mil.)	**NET INCOME** ($ mil.)	**NET PROFIT MARGIN**	**EMPLOYEES**
06/21	1,624	21	1.3%	3,000
06/20	1,540	104	6.8%	—
06/19	1,583	312	19.7%	—
06/18	1,476	265	18.0%	—
Annual Growth	3.3%	(56.9%)	—	—

2021 Year-End Financials

Return on assets: 0.1% Cash ($ mil.): 653
Return on equity: 0.2%
Current ratio: —

KANSAS STATE UNIVERSITY

K-State is a big deal in the Little Apple. Located in Manhattan Kansas (aka the Little Apple) Kansas State University (K-State) is a land grant institution that has an enrollment of some 24000 students. It offers more than 250 undergraduate majors 65 master's degrees 45 doctoral degrees and more than 20 graduate certificate programs. Major fields of study include agriculture technology and veterinary medicine. Notable alumni include former White House press secretary Marlin Fitzwater and actor Gordon Jump. Along with the University of Kansas and other universities technical schools and community colleges in the state K-State is governed by The Kansas Board of Regents.

Operations

With a student-to-faculty ratio of 20:1 K-State ranks among top US colleges and has one of the highest levels of prestigious scholarship winners (including Rhodes Marshall and Truman scholars) in the US. The university also has several notable research organizations in fields including agriculture and genetic science.

K-State is also big on sports and is part of the Big 12 Conference of collegiate athletics.

Geographic Reach

K-State has its main campus on 670-acres in Manhattan Kansas. It also has satellite campuses in Salina and Olathe. It also has agricultural and research centers at five Kansas locations. The university's students come from all 50 US states and more than 90 countries.

Financial Performance

K-State increased revenues by 9% to $541 million in 2012 due to higher income from student fees; government and non-government grants and contracts (for research and athletic activities); and auxiliary enterprises. Net income decreased 24% to $47 million due to higher operating expenses and lower non-operating revenues which was attributed to lower state appropriation levels and higher interest expenses.

Strategy

K-State is expanding its facilities and programs to meet the needs of its students. It completed the first $22 million phase of its National Bio and Agro-Defense Facility in 2012 as well as work on a new student recreational housing classroom and athletics facilities. In 2011 it added a new bachelor's degree program in social work. It also expanded its partnership with the Chinese scholarship council to allow additional students from China to study at K-State.

Company Background

K-State was established in 1858 as Bluemont Central College; five years later it was one of the first colleges in the US to be designated a land-grant school.

EXECUTIVES

Pres, Richard B Myers
Provost and Senior Vice Presid*, April Mason
Accounting Staff, Jenny Imhoff
Digital & Social Media Directo, Jay Alloway
Scientist, Christopher M Sorensen
Payroll Staff, Donnita Nelson
Scientist, George Marchin
Scientist, Marietta R White
Scientist, Maureen J Gorman
Scientist, Neena Kanwar
Scientist, Vijayalakshmi Iyer

LOCATIONS

HQ: KANSAS STATE UNIVERSITY
  ANDERSON HALL 110 1301 MI, MANHATTAN, KS
  66506
Phone: 785 532-6011
Web: WWW.K-STATE.EDU

PRODUCTS/OPERATIONS

Selected Colleges and Departments

College of Agriculture
  Agricultural Economics
  Agronomy
  Animal Sciences and Industry
  Entomology
  Food Science Institute
  Grain Science and Industry
  Plant Pathology
College of Architecture Planning and Design
  Architecture
  Interior Architecture and Product Design
  Landscape Architecture/Regional and Community
  Planning
College of Arts and Sciences
  Aerospace Studies
  American Ethnic Studies
  Art
  Biochemistry
  Chemistry
  Economics
  English
  Geography
  Geology
  History
  International and Area Studies
  Journalism and Mass Communications
  Kinesiology
  Mathematics
  Military Science
  Modern Languages
  Music
  Philosophy
  Physics
  Political Science
  Psychology
  Statistics
  Women's Studies
College of Business Administration
  Accounting
  Finance
  Management
  Marketing
College of Education
  Educational Leadership
  Elementary Education
  Secondary Education
  Special Education Counseling and Student Affairs
College of Engineering
  Architectural Engineering and Construction Science
  Biological and Agricultural Engineering
  Chemical Engineering
  Computing and Information Science
  Electrical and Computer Engineering
  Mechanical and Nuclear Engineering
College of Human Ecology
  Apparel Textiles and Interior Design
  Gerontology
  Human Nutrition
College of Technology and Aviation
  Arts Sciences and Business
  Aviation Technology
College of Veterinary Medicine
  Anatomy and Physiology
  Clinical Sciences

HISTORICAL FINANCIALS

Company Type: Private

Income Statement				FYE: June 30
	REVENUE ($ mil.)	**NET INCOME** ($ mil.)	**NET PROFIT MARGIN**	**EMPLOYEES**
06/17	620	50	8.2%	5,168
06/10	459	50	11.0%	—
06/09	420	10	2.6%	—
Annual Growth	5.0%	21.4%	—	—

KATY INDEPENDENT SCHOOL DISTRICT

EXECUTIVES

Pres, Bryan Michalsky
Pres-SEC*, Rebecca Fox
Katy Isd Board of Trustees Mem*, Henry Dibrell
V Pres*, Joe M Adams
Supt*, Alton Fraley
Treas*, Charles Griffin
Cfo*, William L Moore
Coordinator, Howard Grimet
Reading Specialist, Janet Sutherland
Teacher, Brandy Williams
Student Publications Advisor, Ed Larsen

LOCATIONS

HQ: KATY INDEPENDENT SCHOOL DISTRICT
6301 S STADIUM LN, KATY, TX 774941057
Phone: 281 396-6000
Web: WWW.KATYISD.ORG

HISTORICAL FINANCIALS
Company Type: Private

Income Statement				FYE: August 31
	REVENUE ($ mil.)	NET INCOME ($ mil.)	NET PROFIT MARGIN	EMPLOYEES
08/20	1,060	47	4.5%	6,631
08/19	993	17	1.8%	—
08/18	922	0	0.1%	—
08/16	841	15	1.9%	—
Annual Growth	6.0%	31.4%	—	—

KAWEAH DELTA HEALTH CARE DISTRICT GUILD

EXECUTIVES

Ceo, Donna Archer
Ceo*, Lindsay K Mann
V Pres-Cfo*, Gary Herbst
Auditing Manager, Suzy Plummer
Network Administrator, Christine Johns
Senior Information, Mark Wiseman
Regulatory Affairs Manager, Lisa Wass
Information Technology Adminis, Stuart Goings
Chief Operating Officer, Thomas Rayner
Database Analyst, Crystal Clark
Director, Leland Beggs
Auditors: MOSS ADAMS LLP STOCKTON CAL

LOCATIONS

HQ: KAWEAH DELTA HEALTH CARE DISTRICT GUILD
400 W MINERAL KING AVE, VISALIA, CA 932916237
Phone: 559 624-2000
Web: WWW.KDHCD.ORG

HISTORICAL FINANCIALS
Company Type: Private

Income Statement				FYE: June 30
	REVENUE ($ mil.)	NET INCOME ($ mil.)	NET PROFIT MARGIN	EMPLOYEES
06/21	776	13	1.8%	3,200
06/20	734	(6)	—	—
06/19	751	28	3.8%	—
06/18	710	28	4.1%	—
Annual Growth	3.0%	(21.6%)	—	—

KBR WYLE SERVICES, LLC

Like its acronym name suggests SGT (aka Stinger Ghaffarian Technologies) is used to taking military orders; in this case very specific technical ones. An engineering services firm SGT provides aerospace engineering project management IT systems development and related services to NASA the US Navy the US Air Force and other primarily military-related government entities through contracts. The company also offers science-related services such as earth climate and planetary modeling and analysis. SGT's facilities are located near airfields and other military facilities.

Geographic Reach
SGT operates a more than dozen offices including in Houston Cleveland and Los Angeles White Sands (New Mexico) and Wallops Island (Virginia).

Sales and Marketing
The company serves the aerospace and aeronautics sectors in addition to civilian agencies and national security entities.

Strategy
SGT grows by signing contracts and working with other partners. In early 2017 it won a $45 million contract to support the National Oceanic and Atmospheric Administration (NOAA). Under the contract SGT will support the National Mesonet Program which brings non-federal meteorological data sources to NOAA for use in operations at weather forecast offices and numerical modeling information at the National Centers for Environmental Protection. To achieve this SGT is working in partnership with Earth Networks Weather Telematics WeatherFlow Synoptic Data Corp. Sonoma Technology Inc. Panasonic Avionics Corp. and the University of Oklahoma.

Company Background
SGT was founded in 1994 by Harold Stinger and Kam Ghaffarian.

EXECUTIVES

Pres, William Bright
Coo*, Dave Wolt
Cfo*, Joseph Morway
Evp*, Terry Tarbell
Chief Strategy Ofcr*, Charlie Goorevich

Chief Hr Ofcr*, Shelley Johnson
Consultant, Jim Wiedman
Director of Contracts, Julie Smith
Desk Technician, Kevin Kelsch
Digital Content Manager, Lawrence Page
Space Station Robotics Instruc, Linda Pope
Auditors: GRANT THORNTON LLP MCLEAN VI

LOCATIONS

HQ: KBR WYLE SERVICES, LLC
7701 GREENBELT RD STE 400, GREENBELT, MD 207706521
Phone: 301 614-8600
Web: WWW.KBR.COM

COMPETITORS

Ball Aerospace	Qss Group
Caci International	Sierra Nevada Corp
Cdi Government Services	Techshot
Digital Fusion	United Space Alliance
Lockheed Martin Space Systems	

HISTORICAL FINANCIALS
Company Type: Private

Income Statement				FYE: September 30
	REVENUE ($ mil.)	NET INCOME ($ mil.)	NET PROFIT MARGIN	EMPLOYEES
09/15	570	23	4.2%	2,300
09/13	416	15	3.7%	—
09/12	374	9	2.4%	—
09/08	292	8	2.8%	—
Annual Growth	10.0%	16.3%	—	—

KENNESTONE HOSPITAL AT WINDY HILL, INC.

Kennestone cures kidney stones and other ailments for residents of Cobb County Georgia. Well-Star Kennestone Hospital has more than 630 beds and a full range of specialty services. The hospital's physicians provide cardiac care inpatient and outpatient surgery and rehabilitation trauma diabetes care oncology dialysis and home health care. The hospital also operates centers specializing in women's health senior living facilities diagnostic clinics and a wellness and fitness center. WellStar Kennestone Hospital is part of the not-for-profit WellStar Health System which operates hospitals and other medical facilities throughout Georgia.

Operations
WellStar Kennestone Hospital is the anchor of the group's WellStar Kennestone Regional Medical Center division. WellStar Kennestone Hospital handles about 37000 inpatient admissions each year as well as more than 400000 outpatient appointments and 120000 emergency room visits. It also conducts about 23000 inpatient and outpatient surgeries and 9000 births annually and operates a level II regional trauma center. The hospital has been recognized in a number of specialist fields such as orthopedics neurology and gastroenterology.

Geographic Reach

Located in Marietta Georgia WellStar Kennestone Hospital primary serves northern and central Cobb County.

Strategy

The hospital is undergoing renovation and expansion efforts including construction of a new hospital tower with all private patient rooms; the tower was completed and opened in early 2013. Two years later the hospital opened a new inpatient pediatric unit. It also began renovations of its cancer center.

WellStar Kennestone also regularly upgrades its medical technology systems and tools such as robotic surgery systems and data management programs.

EXECUTIVES

Ceo, Thomas E Hill
Cfo*, Dick Stovall
Scientist, Pat Abruzzo
Information Specialist, Rishi Gupta
Internal Medicine Practitioner, Robin Klein
Obstetrician Gynecologist, Amberly Winley
Staff Pharmacist, Nathan Stripling
Manager, Aj Kassim
Information Technology Influen, Ben Alfred
MD, Gunter Kurrle
Registered Nurse, Jennifer Lowe

LOCATIONS

HQ: KENNESTONE HOSPITAL AT WINDY HILL, INC.
677 CHURCH ST NE, MARIETTA, GA 300601101
Phone: 770 793-5000
Web: WWW.WELLSTAR.ORG

COMPETITORS

Adventist Health System Sunbelt Healthcare
Children's Healthcare Of Atlanta
Dekalb Medical
Emory Healthcare
Grady Health System
Northside Hospital
Piedmont Healthcare
Redmond Regional Medical Center
Regency Hospital
Shepherd Center
Sunlink Health Systems
The Fulton-dekalb Hospital Authority
West Georgia Health System

HISTORICAL FINANCIALS

Company Type: Private

Income Statement				FYE: June 30
	REVENUE ($ mil.)	NET INCOME ($ mil.)	NET PROFIT MARGIN	EMPLOYEES
06/15	821	106	12.9%	2,950
06/05	481	54	11.2%	—
06/04	877	50	5.7%	—
06/03	792	24	3.1%	—
Annual Growth	0.3%	12.9%	—	—

2015 Year-End Financials

Return on assets: 20.5%   Cash ($ mil.): —
Return on equity: 38.2%
Current ratio: 8.90

KENNESTONE HOSPITAL INC

Auditors: PRICEWATERHOUSECOOPERS LLP PH

LOCATIONS

HQ: KENNESTONE HOSPITAL INC
805 SANDY PLAINS RD, MARIETTA, GA 300666340
Phone: 770 792-5023
Web: WWW.WELLSTAR.ORG

HISTORICAL FINANCIALS

Company Type: Private

Income Statement				FYE: June 30
	REVENUE ($ mil.)	NET INCOME ($ mil.)	NET PROFIT MARGIN	EMPLOYEES
06/15	948	182	19.2%	15
06/14	836	113	13.5%	—
06/13	791	123	15.6%	—
06/10	800	123	15.5%	—
Annual Growth	3.5%	8.0%	—	—

2015 Year-End Financials

Return on assets: 29.0%   Cash ($ mil.): —
Return on equity: 48.5%
Current ratio: 8.60

KERN HIGH SCHOOL DST

EXECUTIVES

Supt, Donald E Carter
Principal, Robert Schneider
Principal, Jim Caswell
Payroll Staff, Gregory Vasquez
Superintendent, Don Carter
Substitute Teacher, Damien Lomack
Categorical Programs Administr, Krista Twist
Coordinator, Anthony Lopez
Payroll Supervisor, Diane Haddock
Science Teacher, Judy Farris
Purchasing Agent, Lloyd Fries
Auditors: CROWE LLP SACRAMENTO CALIFO

LOCATIONS

HQ: KERN HIGH SCHOOL DST
5801 SUNDALE AVE, BAKERSFIELD, CA 933097908
Phone: 661 827-3100
Web: WWW.KERNHIGH.ORG

HISTORICAL FINANCIALS

Company Type: Private

Income Statement				FYE: June 30
	REVENUE ($ mil.)	NET INCOME ($ mil.)	NET PROFIT MARGIN	EMPLOYEES
06/20	676	(51)	—	2,000
06/19	677	(43)	—	—
06/18	557	40	7.3%	—
06/17	518	40	7.8%	—
Annual Growth	9.3%	—	—	—

KETTERING MEDICAL CENTER

EXECUTIVES

Ceo, Jarrod McNaughton
Pres, Fred Manchur
V Pres, Roy Chew
V Pres, Walter Sackett
Cfo, Russell Wetherell
SEC, Terri Day
Coordinator, Kara Paxson
Human Resources Executive, Edward Mann
Recruiter, Gloria Hopkins
General Surgeon, Christa Siebenburgen
Human Resources Manager, Dave Evans
Auditors: CLARK SCHAEFER HACKETT & CO D

LOCATIONS

HQ: KETTERING MEDICAL CENTER
3535 SOUTHERN BLVD, KETTERING, OH 454291298
Phone: 937 298-4331
Web: WWW.KETTERINGHEALTH.ORG

HISTORICAL FINANCIALS

Company Type: Private

Income Statement				FYE: December 31
	REVENUE ($ mil.)	NET INCOME ($ mil.)	NET PROFIT MARGIN	EMPLOYEES
12/19	946	122	13.0%	3,100
12/09	531	40	7.6%	—
12/04	628	40	6.4%	—
12/03	568	561	98.6%	—
Annual Growth	3.2%	(9.1%)	—	—

2019 Year-End Financials

Return on assets: 8.0%   Cash ($ mil.): 5
Return on equity: 14.1%
Current ratio: 0.20

KEY FOOD STORES CO-OPERATIVE, INC.

Key Food Stores Co-Operative is a friend to independent New York area grocers. The co-op provides retail support and other services to 150 independently owned food retailers in the New York City area. Key Food's member-owners run stores mainly in Brooklyn and Queens but also in the other boroughs and surrounding counties. It operates stores primarily under the Key Food banner but it also has Key Food Marketplace locations that feature expanded meat deli and produce departments. In addition the co-op supplies Key Foods-branded products to member stores. Among its members are Pick Quick Foods Dan's Supreme Super Markets Gemstone Supermarkets and Queens Supe rmarkets. Key Foods was founded in 1937.

Geographic Reach

Staten Island-based Key Food Stores Co-Operative operates supermarkets across the five boroughs and on Long Island in upstate New York and in New Jersey and Pennsylvania.

Financial Performance

Key Foods Stores has annual sales of about $1.5 billion.

Strategy

Key Food has been expanding in Queens and Brooklyn and on Long Island after scaling back in Manhattan — where many of its stores were converted to Duane Reade drugstores as the pharmacy chain expanded and took over individual locations. To that end in late 2013 the regional grocer launched a new banner called Urban Market in Brooklyn. The 16000-square foot store in Williamsburg was the co-op's 150th location. The cooperative is expanding aggressively adding more than 30 locations under the Key Food Key Fresh & Natural and Food Dynasty banners including stores in Harlem and the Bronx. It also recently reopened a store in Coney Island that was destroyed by Hurricane Sandy in 2012.

EXECUTIVES

Ceo, Dean Janeway
Chb*, Lawrence Mandel
Pres, Richard Grobman
V Pres, Salvatore Bonavita
SEC*, Sam Obeid
Treas, Anthony Bileddo
Asst SEC, Benjamin Levine
Coordinator, Marnique Ortiz
Information Technology Project, Michaele Domnisch
Vice President Finance, Sharon Konzelman
Vice President, George Knobloch
Auditors: ANCHIN BLOCK & ANCHIN LLP N

LOCATIONS

HQ: KEY FOOD STORES CO-OPERATIVE, INC.
100 MATAWAN RD STE 100 # 100, MATAWAN, NJ 077473913
Phone: 718 370-4200
Web: WWW.KEYFOOD.COM

PRODUCTS/OPERATIONS

Selected Banners
Food Dynasty
Food World
Holiday Farms
Key Food
Key Food Marketplace
Key Fresh & Natural
Locust Valley
Milford Farms
Urban Market
Vitelio's Marketplace

COMPETITORS

A&p
D'agostino
Supermarkets
Food Emporium

Fresh Direct
Gristede's Foods
King Kullen Grocery
Walgreen

HISTORICAL FINANCIALS

Company Type: Private

Income Statement				FYE: April 25
	REVENUE ($ mil.)	NET INCOME ($ mil.)	NET PROFIT MARGIN	EMPLOYEES
04/15	893	(0)	—	84
04/14	753	0	0.0%	—
04/11	537	(0)	—	—
04/10	0	0	—	—
Annual Growth	—	—	—	—

2015 Year-End Financials

Return on assets: (-0.6%)   Cash ($ mil.): 4
Return on equity: (-2.7%)
Current ratio: 1.10

KFHP OF THE MID-ATLANTIC STATES INC.

Auditors: PRICEWATERHOUSECOOPERS LLP PH

LOCATIONS

HQ: KFHP OF THE MID-ATLANTIC STATES INC.
1 KAISER PLZ 15L, OAKLAND, CA 946123610
Phone: 510 271-6611

HISTORICAL FINANCIALS

Company Type: Private

Income Statement				FYE: December 31
	REVENUE ($ mil.)	NET INCOME ($ mil.)	NET PROFIT MARGIN	EMPLOYEES
12/13	2,511	(13)	—	2
12/09	2,089	(10)	—	
Annual Growth	4.7%	—	—	—

2013 Year-End Financials

Return on assets: 7.1%   Cash ($ mil.): 7
Return on equity: (-0.5%)
Current ratio: 0.60

KGBO HOLDINGS, INC

Total Quality Logistics sets a high standard for moving merchandise. The third-party logistics (non-asset based) provider specializes in arranging freight transportation using reefers (refrigerated trucks) vans and flatbeds — moving in excess of 500000 loads each year. The trucking brokerage company serves more than 7000 clients across the US Canada and Mexico ranging from small businesses to Fortune 500 organizations. Founded in 1997 by company president Ken Oaks Total Quality Logistics (TQL) has contracts with carriers that include single owner operators and large fleets. Customers have included Kroger Dole Food and Laura's Lean Beef.

Operations

The company began as a produce shipper — not a popular item for most brokers because it is perishable — and expanded into flatbed shipments and other dry freight. As a non-asset-based business TQL does not own trucks or warehouses nor does it employ drivers. Rather it arranges for independent carrier companies and owner/operators to transport its customers' freight; TQL manages the shipment while it is on the road. Additionally the company has no expensive overhead and is not limited by fleet size equipment or shipping routes allowing more flexibility for its customers.

Geographic Reach

TQL largely caters to customers in the Greater Cincinnati Area where it has nearly five offices. It has about 25 satellite locations located in Chicago; Cleveland; Charlotte North Carolina; Charleston South Carolina; Detroit; Indianapolis; Denver; Columbus Ohio; Houston; Lexington Kentucky; Louisville; Nashville Tennessee; Orlando Florida; Dayton Ohio; Erlanger Kentucky; Pittsburgh; Tampa; and Austin Texas.

Sales and Marketing

The company serves more than 10000 customers and 50000 carriers across North America

to move more than 800000 loads each year. Customers include Dole Food Wholesalers and Kroger.

Financial Performance

TOL posted $1.6 billion in annual sales for 2013 up from the $1.4 billion it posted the previous year. With no expense overhead to bog down its balance sheet the company has enjoyed three straight years of sizable growth.

Strategy

TQL grows its business by gradually launching additional locations and sales offices in key cities across the country. In 2013 it expanded its sales office in Charlotte North Carolina and moved its operations in Lexington Kentucky to a larger space. Also that year TQL launched a new sales office in Orlando Florida. In 2012 the company opened new offices in the key metropolitan areas of Cleveland Detroit and Pittsburgh. In 2014 it announced plans to launch a new office in Nashville Tennessee.

EXECUTIVES

Pres, Kenneth Oaks
Controller, Kate Lucas Stump
Distribution/Shipping/Transpor, Aaron Schaeffer
Logistics Account Executive, Alexander Izsak
National Sales Recruiter, Collin Saylor
Senior Account Executive, Iyer Amruthur
Logistics Account Executive Tr, Matt Graves
Logistics Account Executive, Preston Lovingood
Logistics Account Executive, Stephen Schlater
Logistics Account Executive, Thurgood Burkscoats
Logistics Account Executive, Timothy Leslie
Auditors: BARNES DENNIG & CO LTD CI

LOCATIONS

HQ: KGBO HOLDINGS, INC
4289 IVY POINTE BLVD, CINCINNATI, OH 452450002
Phone: 513 831-2600

COMPETITORS

Alliance Shippers
C.h. Robinson Worldwide
Echo Global
Miq Logistics
Roadrunner Transportation Systems
Ryder System
Schneider Logistics
Transplace
Ups Supply Chain Solutions

HISTORICAL FINANCIALS

Company Type: Private

Income Statement				FYE: December 30
	REVENUE ($ mil.)	NET INCOME ($ mil.)	NET PROFIT MARGIN	EMPLOYEES
12/12	1,387	0	—	4,077
12/11	1,046	0	—	—
12/10	762	0	—	—
Annual Growth	34.9%	—	—	—

KIEWIT BUILDING GROUP INC.

EXECUTIVES

Pres-Ceo, Joseph R Lempka
Sr V Pres*, Michael J Colpack

Sr V Pres*, Ronald C Duce
Sr V Pres*, J D Vetter
Sr V Pres*, Kevin P Welker
Sr V Pres*, Lance K Wilhelm
V Pres*, Becky S Golden
V Pres*, Raymond D Hallquist
V Pres*, Michael J Piechoski
V Pres*, Herb J Reuss
V Pres*, Tobin A Schropp
Auditors: KPMG LLP OMAHA NE

LOCATIONS

HQ: KIEWIT BUILDING GROUP INC.
160 INVERNESS DR W # 110, ENGLEWOOD, CO
801125004
Phone: 402 977-4500
Web: WWW.KIEWIT.COM

HISTORICAL FINANCIALS

Company Type: Private

Income Statement				FYE: December 29
	REVENUE ($ mil.)	NET INCOME ($ mil.)	NET PROFIT MARGIN	EMPLOYEES
12/12	649	12	1.9%	1,047
12/11	860	85	10.0%	—
12/10	1,280	124	9.7%	—
Annual Growth	(28.8%)	(68.3%)	—	—

2012 Year-End Financials

Return on assets: 4.5%
Return on equity: 9.2%
Current ratio: 1.80
Cash ($ mil.): 47

KIEWIT CORPORATION

EXECUTIVES

Ceo, Bruce E Grewcock
Exec V Pres, Richard W Colf
Exec V Pres, Douglas E Patterson
Exec V Pres, Scott L Cassels
Sr V Pres, Steven Hansen
Treas, Stephen S Thomas
SEC, Michael F Norton
Major Project Mana, Joe Wingerter
Career, Heather Semple
Law Specialist, Simson Chan
Superintendent, Gary Dyer
Auditors: KPMG LLP OMAHA NE

LOCATIONS

HQ: KIEWIT CORPORATION
1550 MIKE FAHEY ST, OMAHA, NE 681024722
Phone: 402 342-2052
Web: WWW.KIEWIT.COM

HISTORICAL FINANCIALS

Company Type: Private

Income Statement				FYE: December 28
	REVENUE ($ mil.)	NET INCOME ($ mil.)	NET PROFIT MARGIN	EMPLOYEES
12/13	11,826	796	6.7%	10,441
12/12	11,220	512	4.6%	—
12/11	10,381	796	7.7%	—
Annual Growth	6.7%	(0.0%)	—	—

KIEWIT INDUSTRIAL GROUP INC

EXECUTIVES

Pres, Douglas E Patterson
Ex V Pres, Richard A Lanoha
Auditors: KPMG LLP OMAHA NE

LOCATIONS

HQ: KIEWIT INDUSTRIAL GROUP INC
3555 FARNAM ST, OMAHA, NE 681313311
Phone: 402 342-2052
Web: WWW.KIEWIT.COM

HISTORICAL FINANCIALS

Company Type: Private

Income Statement				FYE: December 28
	REVENUE ($ mil.)	NET INCOME ($ mil.)	NET PROFIT MARGIN	EMPLOYEES
12/13	3,474	241	6.9%	20
12/12	3,397	110	3.2%	—
12/11	2,445	118	4.8%	—
12/10	2,546	173	6.8%	—
Annual Growth	10.9%	11.5%	—	—

2013 Year-End Financials

Return on assets: 13.8%
Return on equity: 26.4%
Current ratio: 1.80
Cash ($ mil.): 324

KIEWIT INFRASTRUCTURE CO.

EXECUTIVES

Pres, Bruce Grewcock
Prin, Scott L Cassels
Exec V Pres, H E Adams
Exec V Pres, David J Miles
Snr V Pres, Parke D Ball
Snr V Pres, Craig A Briggs
Cfo, Michael J Piechoski
V Pres, Stephen P Allen
V Pres, Michael K Breyer
Cntrl, Michael J Whetstine
Asst Cntrl, Jean Dulmaine

LOCATIONS

HQ: KIEWIT INFRASTRUCTURE CO.
1550 MIKE FAHEY ST, OMAHA, NE 681024722
Phone: 402 346-8535
Web: WWW.KIEWIT.COM

HISTORICAL FINANCIALS

Company Type: Private

Income Statement				FYE: December 31
	REVENUE ($ mil.)	NET INCOME ($ mil.)	NET PROFIT MARGIN	EMPLOYEES
12/12	857	55	6.5%	9,000
12/11	1,127	74	6.6%	—
12/10	3,516	269	7.7%	—
Annual Growth	(50.6%)	(54.6%)	—	—

2012 Year-End Financials

Return on assets: 6.9%
Return on equity: 10.3%
Current ratio: 2.30
Cash ($ mil.): —

KIEWIT INFRASTRUCTURE SOUTH CO.

EXECUTIVES

Pres, David J Miles
V Pres, Jeffrey P Petersen
V Pres, Randall P Sanman
V Pres, Keith N Sasich
V Pres, S Van Groves
V Pres, Howard L Barton Jr
V Pres, Stephen Paul Carter Jr
V Pres, Timothy J Cleary
V Pres, Ricardo Cummings
V Pres, William D Glaser
V Pres, Mark D Langford
Auditors: KPMG LLP OMAHA NEBRASKA

LOCATIONS

HQ: KIEWIT INFRASTRUCTURE SOUTH CO.
13119 OLD DENTON RD, FORT WORTH, TX
761772403
Phone: 402 342-2052
Web: WWW.KIEWIT.COM

HISTORICAL FINANCIALS

Company Type: Private

Income Statement				FYE: December 29
	REVENUE ($ mil.)	NET INCOME ($ mil.)	NET PROFIT MARGIN	EMPLOYEES
12/12	549	85	15.6%	333
12/11	901	135	15.0%	—
12/10	1,009	126	12.6%	—
Annual Growth	(26.2%)	(17.8%)	—	—

2012 Year-End Financials

Return on assets: 21.0%
Return on equity: 39.7%
Current ratio: 2.00
Cash ($ mil.): 127

KIEWIT INFRASTRUCTURE WEST CO.

EXECUTIVES

Pres, Scott L Cassels
Exec V Pres, H E Adams
Exec V Pres, David J Miles
Exec V Pres, Alfredo E Sori
Sr V Pres, Jeffrey P Petersen
Sr V Pres, Eric M Scott

Sr V Pres, A T Skoro
Sr V Pres, Matt L Swinton
Sr V Pres, Eugene D Van Wagner III
Sr V Pres, J D Vetter
Sr V Pres, Jamie D Wisenbaker
Auditors: KPMG LLPOMAHA NEBRASKA

LOCATIONS

HQ: KIEWIT INFRASTRUCTURE WEST CO.
3555 FARNAM ST, OMAHA, NE 681313311
Phone: 402 342-2052
Web: WWW.KIEWIT.COM

HISTORICAL FINANCIALS

Company Type: Private

Income Statement				FYE: December 29
	REVENUE ($ mil.)	NET INCOME ($ mil.)	NET PROFIT MARGIN	EMPLOYEES
12/12	1,512	(126)	—	2,625
12/11	1,209	85	7.1%	—
12/10	945	31	3.3%	—
Annual Growth	26.5%			

2012 Year-End Financials

Return on assets: (-13.5%)   Cash ($ mil.): 152
Return on equity: (-47.1%)
Current ratio: 1.20

KIMBALL HILL INC

LOCATIONS

HQ: KIMBALL HILL INC
5999 NEW WILKE RD STE 306, ROLLING MEADOWS, IL 600084503
Phone: 847 364-7300

HISTORICAL FINANCIALS

Company Type: Private

Income Statement				FYE: September 30
	REVENUE ($ mil.)	NET INCOME ($ mil.)	NET PROFIT MARGIN	EMPLOYEES
09/07	900	(220)	—	900
09/05	1,146	86	7.6%	—
09/04	927	55	6.0%	—
09/03	786	37	4.8%	—
Annual Growth	3.4%	—	—	—

2007 Year-End Financials

Return on assets: (-25.0%)   Cash ($ mil.): 31
Return on equity: (-144.4%)
Current ratio: —

KING COUNTY PUBLIC HOSPITAL DISTRICT 2

EXECUTIVES

Ceo, Bob Malte
Sr V Pres*, Neil Johnson
V Pres*, Jack Handley
Scientist, Deanne Gilbert
Chief of Medicine, James D Brown

Director, Francis X Riedo
Senior Recruiter, Jon Rheinheimer
Pharmacist, Margo Hollenbeck
Pharmacist, Michael Higginson
Educator, Mary Dennison
Director of Strategic Marketin, Sasha Weiler
Auditors: KPMG LLP SEATTLE WASHINGTON

LOCATIONS

HQ: KING COUNTY PUBLIC HOSPITAL DISTRICT 2
12040 NE 128TH ST, KIRKLAND, WA 980343013
Phone: 425 899-2769
Web: WWW.EVERGREENHEALTH.COM

HISTORICAL FINANCIALS

Company Type: Private

Income Statement				FYE: December 31
	REVENUE ($ mil.)	NET INCOME ($ mil.)	NET PROFIT MARGIN	EMPLOYEES
12/17	713	14	2.0%	2,400
12/16	597	(3)	—	—
12/15	565	3	0.7%	—
12/06	273	16	6.2%	—
Annual Growth	9.1%	(1.4%)	—	—

2017 Year-End Financials

Return on assets: 2.1%   Cash ($ mil.): 44
Return on equity: 4.4%
Current ratio: 1.70

KING'S DAUGHTERS HEALTH SYSTEM, INC.

EXECUTIVES

Ceo, Fred Jackson
SEC*, Sheryl Mahaney
Treasurer*, Jeff Treasure
Director, Ray Mecca
Directors, Charlie Borders
Network Engineer, Greggory Howard
Manager, Larry Sites
Director of Student Education, Mark Detherage
Occupational Medicine, Rhonda Heaberlin
Director, Tammy Conley
Residency Coordinator, Tonia Hall
Auditors: BAKER TILLY VIRCHOW KRAUSE LLP

LOCATIONS

HQ: KING'S DAUGHTERS HEALTH SYSTEM, INC.
2201 LEXINGTON AVE, ASHLAND, KY 411012843
Phone: 606 408-4000
Web: WWW.KINGSDAUGHTERSHEALTH.COM

HISTORICAL FINANCIALS

Company Type: Private

Income Statement				FYE: September 30
	REVENUE ($ mil.)	NET INCOME ($ mil.)	NET PROFIT MARGIN	EMPLOYEES
09/20	547	14	2.7%	4,200
09/19	505	(4)	—	—
09/18	485	(1)	—	—
09/17	475	3	0.8%	—
Annual Growth	4.8%	59.6%	—	—

2020 Year-End Financials

Return on assets: 2.1%   Cash ($ mil.): 37
Return on equity: 5.4%
Current ratio: 1.00

KLEIN INDEPENDENT SCHOOL DISTRICT

EXECUTIVES

Supt, Bret A Champion
Pres, Steven E Smith
V Pres, Ronnie K Anderson
SEC, Stephen J Szymczak
Building) Instructional Office, Pat Braunagel
Accounting Staff, Heather Cummings
Coordinator, Karri Clark
Coordinator, Kim Huseman
Transportation Router, Melanie Dean
Assistant, Tanya Brogger
Administrative Assistant, Abel Huffman
Auditors: HEREFORD LYNCH SELLARS & KIR

LOCATIONS

HQ: KLEIN INDEPENDENT SCHOOL DISTRICT
7200 SPRING CYPRESS RD, SPRING, TX 773793215
Phone: 832 249-4000
Web: WWW.KLEINISD.NET

HISTORICAL FINANCIALS

Company Type: Private

Income Statement				FYE: August 31
	REVENUE ($ mil.)	NET INCOME ($ mil.)	NET PROFIT MARGIN	EMPLOYEES
08/19	622	39	6.3%	5,691
08/18	594	2	0.4%	—
08/17	548	8	1.5%	—
08/16	539	(135)	—	—
Annual Growth	4.9%	—	—	—

2019 Year-End Financials

Return on assets: 2.3%   Cash ($ mil.): 271
Return on equity: —
Current ratio: —

KMM TELECOMMUNICATIONS

EXECUTIVES

Ceo, Katherine McConvey
Cfo*, Kofi Badu
Pres*, Nick Shanker
Corporate Communications Staff*, Sarah McNab
Accnt, Brad Van Kalsbeck
Employee, Botero Alba
Vice President, Operational Ex, Debbie Smith
Employee, Orozco Ashley
Vice-President Sales, Pat Healy
Employee, Steve Halverson
Auditors: DORFMAN ABRAMS MUSIC LLC SAD

LOCATIONS

HQ: KMM TELECOMMUNICATIONS
1900 LAKEWAY DR STE 100, LEWISVILLE, TX
750576012
Phone: 888 566-2677
Web: WWW.KMMCORP.NET

HISTORICAL FINANCIALS

Company Type: Private

Income Statement				FYE: December 31
	REVENUE ($ mil.)	NET INCOME ($ mil.)	NET PROFIT MARGIN	EMPLOYEES
12/08	868	13	1.5%	190
12/07	789	17	2.2%	—
12/06	483	0	0.0%	—
Annual Growth	34.0%	70961.0%	—	—

2008 Year-End Financials

Return on assets: 13.3%   Cash ($ mil.): 3
Return on equity: 57.5%
Current ratio: 1.30

KNIGHTS OF COLUMBUS

Good Knight! The Knights of Columbus is a men who lead serve protect and defend whether it is are giving out Coats for Kids lending a hand in disaster relief efforts supporting local pregnancy centers by donating ultrasound machines or providing top-quality financial products.. The fraternal organization is also a force to be reckoned with in the insurance world providing life insurance annuities and long-term care insurance to its members and their families. In addition the group manages the Knights of Columbus Museum in New Haven Connecticut. The group was founded in 1882 by Father Michael J. McGivney.

Operations

The company offers charity insurance investments programs scholarships and churchloans to its members. Charity is at the heart of its work and faith. One hundred percent of the donation goes directly to support the Knights of Columbus charitable cause of choice. Its insurance products have included permanent life insurance term life insurance retirement annuities long-term care and disability insurance. It also offers a suite of faith-based investment solutions specifically designed for Catholic investors such as mutual funds separate accounts. Model portfolios and target date portfolios. In addition the Knights of Columbus has been helping young people. It provided nearly $1 million in scholarships to students attending colleges universities and seminaries. It also offers ChurcLoan to any Church institution that is affiliated with the Catholic community in the United States United States Territories and Canada.

Geographic Reach

The Knights of Columbus is headquartered in New Haven Connecticut.

Company Background

The Knights of Columbus was founded in New Haven by Father Michael J. McGivney in 1882 and has been selling insurance since its founding.

EXECUTIVES

Supreme Knight, Carl A Anderson
V Pres*, Robert Tracz
Asst SEC*, Charles Maurer
Gen Counsel*, John Marrella
Treas*, Logan Ludwig
Assistant Vice President of AP, Niki Kratzert

Coordinator, Barb Fuks
Managing Editor, Alton Pelowski
Agent, Marc Madore
Field Agent, Will Britten
Customer Manager, Kathryn Perrelli
Auditors: SEWARD AND MONDE CPA'S NORTH

LOCATIONS

HQ: KNIGHTS OF COLUMBUS
1 COLUMBUS PLZ STE 1700, NEW HAVEN, CT
065103326
Phone: 203 752-4000
Web: WWW.KOFC.ORG

HISTORICAL FINANCIALS

Company Type: Private

Income Statement				FYE: December 31
	ASSETS ($ mil.)	NET INCOME ($ mil.)	INCOME AS % OF ASSETS	EMPLOYEES
12/13	20,534	113	0.6%	2,300
12/12	19,401	127	0.7%	—
12/11	18,026	81	0.4%	—
12/10	16,861	86	0.5%	—
Annual Growth	6.8%	9.5%	—	—

2013 Year-End Financials

Return on assets: 0.6%   Sales ($ mil): 2,115
Return on equity: 6.0%

KNOXVILLE UTILITIES BOARD

Providing utility services to residential and business customers has proven to be an excellent idea for Knoxville Utilities Board (KUB) an independent agency that serves the city of Knoxville and surrounding areas. The multi-utility provides services to 196500 electric 96920 gas 77600 water and 68740 wastewater customers. The company accesses electric power from the Tennessee Valley Authority. KUB's natural gas supply comes from the East Tennessee Natural Gas pipeline. It also maintains five treatment plants which provide water and wastewater services.

Operations

In 2013 the company was operating 1324 miles of wastewater mains 1407 miles of water mains 5265 miles of electric service lines and 69 substations and 2295 miles of natural gas mains.

Geographic Reach

The company serves 440000 customers in Knoxville and parts of seven surrounding counties.

Financial Performance

In 2013 KUB's operating revenues grew by 7%. Electric Division operating revenue increased $27.4 million thanks to a 1% rise in sales volumes and electric rate increases. Gas Division revenues grew 20% thanks to 14% rise in natural gas sales volumes. Water Divisionrevenue increased by 1.4% due tomwater rate increases. The Wastewater Division revenues were $4.1 million higher than in 2012 thanks to a rate increase.

Strategy

KUB is engaged in a long term plan to renovate its aging infrastructure. The push began the mid-1990s with a focus on upgrading Knoxville's water tanks distribution pipelines and the its water treatment plants.

Company Background

The agency was founded by the City of Knoxville in 1939. The utility's electric system is one of the nation's most dependable reporting a 99.9% uninterrupted service rating.

EXECUTIVES

Ceo, Mintha Roach
Exec V Pres*, Bill Elmore
V Pres*, Mark Walker
Sr V Pres*, Susan Edwards
Sr V Pres*, Eddie Black
V Pres*, Mike Bolin
Plant Superintendent, Jimmy England
Supervisor, Kevin Keaton
Customer Representativ, Amy Branch
Staff, Dale Grubbs
Electrical Engineer, Gordon Bryant
Auditors: COULTER & JUSTUS PC KNOXVI

LOCATIONS

HQ: KNOXVILLE UTILITIES BOARD
445 S GAY ST, KNOXVILLE, TN 379021125
Phone: 865 594-7531
Web: WWW.KUB.ORG

HISTORICAL FINANCIALS

Company Type: Private

Income Statement				FYE: June 30
	REVENUE ($ mil.)	NET INCOME ($ mil.)	NET PROFIT MARGIN	EMPLOYEES
06/21	822	75	9.2%	500
06/20	803	78	9.7%	—
06/19	815	65	8.0%	—
06/18	815	63	7.8%	—
Annual Growth	0.3%	5.9%	—	—

2021 Year-End Financials

Return on assets: 2.9%   Cash ($ mil.): 119
Return on equity: 5.9%
Current ratio: 1.70

KOOTENAI HOSPITAL DISTRICT

EXECUTIVES

Prin, Jon Ness
Cfo*, Kim Webb
V Pres*, Jeremy S Evans
Accounting Staff, Jenny Lea
Chief Staff, Thomas Nickol
Physician Recruitment Manager, Brian S Jerome
Phlebotomist, Daphne Kaiser
Coordinator, Megan Clevenger
Physician, Cody Reese
Recruiter, Julie Pickup
Registered Nurse, Rita Webb

LOCATIONS

HQ: KOOTENAI HOSPITAL DISTRICT
2003 KOOTENAI HEALTH WAY, COEUR D ALENE, ID
838146051
Phone: 208 625-4000
Web: WWW.KH.ORG

Company Type: Private

Income Statement				FYE: December 31
	REVENUE ($ mil.)	NET INCOME ($ mil.)	NET PROFIT MARGIN	EMPLOYEES
12/20	693	48	7.0%	2,776
12/18	550	17	3.1%	—
12/17	506	35	6.9%	—
12/16	467	15	3.4%	—
Annual Growth	10.4%	32.4%	—	—

2020 Year-End Financials

Return on assets: 5.5%
Return on equity: 8.7%
Current ratio: 2.50
Cash ($ mil.): 169

KPH HEALTHCARE SERVICES, INC.

EXECUTIVES

Chb, Craig Painter
Pres, John Marraffa
Exec V Pres, Stephen McCoy
V Pres, Michael Burgess
V Pres Real Estate, David C McClure
Auditing Manager, Julie Park
Chief Technology Officer, Pavi Chigateri
Pharmacist, Cynthia Krake
Third Party Administrator, Lisa Weir
Director Operations, Russell Simpson
Pharmacist, John Krake
Auditors: DANNIBLE & MCKEE LLP SYRACUS

LOCATIONS

HQ: KPH HEALTHCARE SERVICES, INC.
29 E MAIN ST, GOUVERNEUR, NY 136421401
Phone: 315 287-3600
Web: WWW.KPHHEALTHCARESERVICES.COM

HISTORICAL FINANCIALS

Company Type: Private

Income Statement				FYE: December 31
	REVENUE ($ mil.)	NET INCOME ($ mil.)	NET PROFIT MARGIN	EMPLOYEES
12/20	1,589	41	2.6%	3,900
12/19	1,542	51	3.3%	—
Annual Growth	3.0%	(17.9%)	—	—

2020 Year-End Financials

Return on assets: 7.6%
Return on equity: 19.0%
Current ratio: 1.90
Cash ($ mil.): 38

KRAMM HEALTHCARE CENTER, INC.

EXECUTIVES

Pres, Jeffrey Kramm
Activities Director, Mindy Bartholomew

LOCATIONS

HQ: KRAMM HEALTHCARE CENTER, INC.
743 MAHONING ST, MILTON, PA 178472232
Phone: 570 742-2681
Web: WWW.PARTYBUSES.NET

HISTORICAL FINANCIALS

Company Type: Private

Income Statement				FYE: June 30
	REVENUE ($ mil.)	NET INCOME ($ mil.)	NET PROFIT MARGIN	EMPLOYEES
06/09	925	98	10.7%	330
06/00	5	0	3.8%	—
06/98	1	0	—	—
06/97	4	0	1.8%	—
Annual Growth	56.0%	80.8%	—	—

2009 Year-End Financials

Return on assets: 688.1%
Return on equity: 582.5%
Current ratio: 1.10
Cash ($ mil.): —

KRATON POLYMERS U.S. LLC

EXECUTIVES

Chief Financial Officer, Executive Vice President, Treasurer, Atanas Atanasov
Chief Human Resource Officer, Senior Vice President, Melinda Conley
Director, Karen Twitchell

LOCATIONS

HQ: KRATON POLYMERS U.S. LLC
15710 JOHN F KENNEDY BLVD # 300, HOUSTON, TX 770322347
Phone: 281 504-4700
Web: WWW.KRATON.COM

HISTORICAL FINANCIALS

Company Type: Private

Income Statement				FYE: December 31
	REVENUE ($ mil.)	NET INCOME ($ mil.)	NET PROFIT MARGIN	EMPLOYEES
12/08	1,226	28	2.3%	520
12/07	1,089	(43)	—	—
12/06	0	0	—	—
12/05	975	166	17.1%	—
Annual Growth	7.9%	(44.6%)	—	—

2008 Year-End Financials

Return on assets: 6.1%
Return on equity: 2.3%
Current ratio: 1.10
Cash ($ mil.): 101

KRUEGER INTERNATIONAL, INC.

Krueger International is one of the world's leading contract furniture manufacturers in the industry. The company which does business as KI makes ergonomic seating cabinets sleepers occasional tables and other furniture used by businesses healthcare organizations government agencies and educational institutions. It offers everything from benches and beds to desks and tables not to mention shelving filing systems and movable walls. KI markets its products through sales representatives furniture dealers architects and interior designers worldwide. Founded in 1941 KI is 100% employee-owned.

Operations

KI operates a variety of subsidiaries including KI Europe KI Canada KI India KI China and KI Australia (Sebel). The company provides delivery and furniture installation services worldwide. Its service program includes space planning on-site project management furniture reconfiguration special inside delivery and coordination of product staging and a dedicated transportation fleet. KI also offers the option to purchase furniture according to what fits to its clients' ordering and fulfillment process whether direct or via a third party.

KI also owns Pallas Textiles and Spacesaver. Pallas Textiles which operates out of Wisconsin creates textile products for contract upholstery panel systems and wall-coverings healthcare environments and casements. Spacesaver also located in Wisconsin makes high-density mobile storage systems for office institutional and industrial applications and is a major supplier of steel shelving systems rotary storage systems and storage accessories.

KI's products include seating tables desks architectural walls pods files and storage casegoods dormitory furniture school library furniture auditorium and lecture hall furniture and accessories among others.

Geographic Reach

Based in Wisconsin KI sells its products worldwide and operates manufacturing facilities showrooms and sales offices in the US Canada China and India as well as throughout Europe Middle East America and Asia. It currently operates six manufacturing facilities in the US and Canada. The company has subsidiaries based in Europe Canada India Australia and China. Its showrooms are in several metropolitan areas across the US Toronto and London.

Sales and Marketing

KI sells its products globally through furniture dealers sales representatives architects and interior designers. It primarily serves the educational university workplace healthcare business and government markets.

The company has district sales offices around the world and also boasts showrooms in metropolitan areas to display its products to potential business and individual customers.

Strategy

KI's entries into foreign markets are varied. Entries include exporting licensing joint ventures and foreign direct investments where appropriate. Services are provided through fulfillment partners in established and emerging markets.

KI continues to differentiate itself and establish enduring relationships throughout the world by personalizing products and service solutions to the specific needs of each customer through its unique design and "Market of One" manufacturing philosophy.

Company Background

The company has expanded its network of showrooms in the US and abroad over the years. KI added a showroom in Houston in 2010 to boost its US presence which includes about 10 locations in half a dozen states. To better serve its Asian and European customers the company operates through a showroom in Shanghai China. KI has international showrooms in London Malaysia Mexico Puerto Rico and Toronto. To support its growth KI completed a $3.3-million 100000-sq.-ft. plant expansion in 2012 to reduce costs and streamline its business. The move boosts its manufacturing shipping receiving and warehousing space.

As its showroom presence grew KI also formed new sales partnerships. The company tapped Heartland Furniture Group a contract furniture representative in 2011 to take care of existing customer accounts and broker sales in Kansas Missouri and southern Illinois.

It's also looked to acquisitions to extend the reach of its business. In 2011 KI purchased Sebel Furniture Limited from GWA Group Ltd. a top supplier of building fixtures in Australia. The $24 million deal has given KI a foothold in the commercial furniture business in Australia New Zealand the UK and Hong Kong.

EXECUTIVES

Ceo, Brian Krenke
Chm*, Richard J Resch
Cfo-Treas*, Nick Guerrieri
Asst SEC*, Michael J Pum
Asst SEC*, Guy Patzke
SEC*, Robert M Charles
V Pres*, Dean Lindsley
Engineering Manager, Thomas Vollrath
Project Manager Midwest, Craig Nehasil
Project Engineer, David Liegeois
Coordinator, David Stirdivant
Auditors: BAKER TILLY VIRCHOW KRAUSE LL

LOCATIONS

HQ: KRUEGER INTERNATIONAL, INC.
1330 BELLEVUE ST, GREEN BAY, WI 543022197
Phone: 920 468-8100
Web: WWW.KI.COM

PRODUCTS/OPERATIONS

Selected Products
Auditorium seating
Beds
Benches
Bookcases
Carrels
Chairs
Desks
File cabinets
Lecterns
Movable walls
Planters
Power and data connections
Receptacles
Recliners
Residence hall furniture
Sleepers
Special events seating
Stools
Tables

COMPETITORS

Abco Office Furniture	Kewaunee Scientific
Allsteel	Kimball International
Bretford	Knoll Inc.
Cfgroup	La-z-boy
Columbia Manufacturing	Norstar Office
Edsal Manufacturing	Products

Global Group	Sagus
Hni	Steelcase
Haworth Inc.	Trendway
Herman Miller	Virco Mfg.
Inscape Corp	

HISTORICAL FINANCIALS

Company Type: Private

Income Statement				FYE: December 31
	REVENUE ($ mil.)	NET INCOME ($ mil.)	NET PROFIT MARGIN	EMPLOYEES
12/15	617	53	8.6%	2,300
12/11	649	56	8.8%	—
12/10	40	0	—	—
Annual Growth	—	1047.2%	—	—

2015 Year-End Financials

Return on assets: 19.5%   Cash ($ mil.): 4
Return on equity: 92.6%
Current ratio: 1.10

KWIK TRIP, INC.

Midwesterners who need to make a quick trip to get gas or groceries cigarettes or donuts race on over to Kwik Trip stores. Kwik Trip owns and operates more than 600 Kwik Trip and Kwik Star convenience stores in Iowa Minnesota and Wisconsin. Kwik Trip owns in-house dairy and bakery operations and makes many of its products in-house; popular products include Glazers donuts and Karuba Coffee. All Kwik Trip stores built since 1990 are owned by Convenience Store Investments a separate firm which leases the land and stores to Kwik Trip. Kwik Trip which opened its first store in 1965 in Eau Claire Wisconsin is owned by the family of CEO Don Zietlow.

Operations

To supply its stores with baked goods and other foods Kwik Trip operates a 60000-square-foot commissary and research facility at its headquarters in southwestern Wisconsin. The bakery produces the Kwickery Bake Shoppe line of bagels buns cookies donuts muffins and more and its dairy packages the Nature's Touch brand of fresh milk ice cream orange juice and water. The company has opened a new 65000-square-foot dairy facility in its hometown of La Crosse to supply its own stores (and those owned by others) with ice cream yogurt and other dairy products. Longer term the company hopes to develop its own plastic bottle manufacturing plant. Food service currently accounts for about a third of the company's annual profit ahead of fuel.

Kwik Trip vertically integrates by processing its own gasoline and producing and packaging products to be sold in its convenience stores.

Subsidiary Convenience Transportation LLC provides transportation to the company. Since 2006 Kwik Trip has also partnered with Marshfield Food Safety LLC a full-service microbiological laboratory that provides third-party on-site food safety laboratory services.

Geographic Reach

The company operates in Iowa Minnesota and Wisconsin.

Strategy

Kwik Trip's main route to growth is opening new stores. It's currently adding store at a rate of roughly 40 each year.

The company is always looking at ways to improve its food and drink offering. Initiatives have included a new line of take-home meals produced

each day in house and a tie-up with delivery service EatStreet that allows customers near select locations to order up to 400 items.

Company Background

The John Hansen family founded Kwik Trip in Eau Claire Wisconsin in 1965. In 2000 the Hansens sold their interest in Kwik Trip to the Zietlow family for $120 million. The two families had jointly owned Kwik Trip since 1972.

EXECUTIVES

Pres, Don Zietlow
Vp and Director Petroleum Oper*, Steve Zietlow
V Pres*, Robert Thorud
V Pres*, Steve Loehr
V Pres*, Greg Olson
V Pres*, Thomas Reinhart
Treas*, Scott Teigen
Telecommunications Staff, Jo Neve
Production, Mike Byington
Human Resources Director, Tom Reinhart
Other Is It Technology Profess, Kristy Herlitzka
Auditors: MCGLADREY & PULLEN LLP MINNE

LOCATIONS

HQ: KWIK TRIP, INC.
1626 OAK ST, LA CROSSE, WI 546032308
Phone: 608 781-8988
Web: WWW.KWIKTRIP.COM

PRODUCTS/OPERATIONS

Selected Banners
Hearty Platter
Kwik Star
Kwik Trip
Tobacco Outlet Plus

COMPETITORS

7-eleven	Denny's
Brinker	Exxon Mobil
Carlson Restaurants	Hy-vee
Casey's General Stores	Krause Gentle
Chevron	Northern Tier Energy
Couche-tard	Roundy's
Cub Foods	

HISTORICAL FINANCIALS

Company Type: Private

Income Statement				FYE: September 27
	REVENUE ($ mil.)	NET INCOME ($ mil.)	NET PROFIT MARGIN	EMPLOYEES
09/08	3,640	23	0.7%	10,500
09/04	1,887	24	1.3%	—
09/03	1,651	24	1.5%	—
Annual Growth	17.1%	(0.2%)	—	—

2008 Year-End Financials

Return on assets: 3.6%   Cash ($ mil.): 1
Return on equity: 20.3%
Current ratio: 0.70

LADENBURG THALMANN FINANCIAL SERVICES INC.

Ladenburg Thalmann Financial Services is a wholly-owned subsidiary of Advisor Group Holdings Inc. which is owned by private investment funds sponsored by Reverence Capital Partners LLC. Ladenburg's subsidiaries include industry-leading independent advisory and brokerage (IAB) firms Securities America Triad Advisors Securities Service Network Investacorp and KMS Financial Services as well as Premier Trust Ladenburg Thalmann Asset Management Highland Capital Brokerage a leading independent life insurance brokerage company and full-service annuity processing and marketing company and Ladenburg Thalmann & Co. Inc. an investment bank.

Geographic Reach

Based in New York Ladenburg Thalmann has branch offices in Boca Raton and Naples Florida; Calabasas California; and Melville New York.

Sales and Marketing

Ladenburg Thalmann has relationships with over 1000 institutional investors and provide targeted results-driven corporate access through non-deal road shows one-day forums one-on-one meetings specialized industry events conference calls and site visits for its corporate clients.

Ladenburg Thalmann serves also middle-market public companies across various industry vertical including healthcare & life sciences yield-oriented securities (BDCs REITs MLPs) energy power & infrastructure and telecom media & technology.

EXECUTIVES

Chief Financial Officer, Senior Vice President, Brett Kaufman, $350,000 total compensation
President, Chief Executive Officer, Director, Jamie Price
Director, Ahmed Hassanein
Senior Vice President - Corporate And Regulatory Affairs, Joseph Giovanniello, $325,000 total compensation
Auditors: EISNERAMPER LLP NEW YORK NEW

LOCATIONS

HQ: LADENBURG THALMANN FINANCIAL SERVICES INC.
4400 BISCAYNE BLVD FL 12, MIAMI, FL 331373212
Phone: 305 572-4100
Web: WWW.LADENBURG.COM

PRODUCTS/OPERATIONS

2017 Sales

	$ mil.	% of total
Commissions	536	42
Advisory fees	560	44
Investment banking	46	4
Interest & dividends	25	2
Principal transactions	0	.
Service fees & other	98	8
Total	**1,268**	**100**

2017 Sales

	$ mil.	% of total
Independent Advisory & Brokerage	1,140	90
Ladenburg	66	5
Insurance Brokerage	57	5
Corporate	4	.
Total	**1,268**	**100**

COMPETITORS

Citigroup Global Markets	Lpl Financial
Detwiler Fenton	Morgan Stanley
Investors Capital Holdings	National Holdings
Jpmorgan Chase	Sage Advisory Services
	Ubs Financial Services

HISTORICAL FINANCIALS

Company Type: Private

Income Statement — FYE: December 31

	REVENUE ($ mil.)	NET INCOME ($ mil.)	NET PROFIT MARGIN	EMPLOYEES
12/19	1,469	22	1.5%	1,512
12/18	1,391	33	2.4%	—
12/17	1,268	7	0.6%	—
12/16	1,106	(22)	—	—
Annual Growth	**9.9%**	—	—	—

2019 Year-End Financials

Return on assets: 2.7%
Return on equity: 9.4%
Current ratio: —

Cash ($ mil.): 248

LAFAYETTE GENERAL MEDICAL CENTER, INC.

Serving the people of Acadiana (southern Louisiana) Lafayette General Medical Center (LGMC) provides general inpatient medical and surgical care as well as specialized trauma care and neonatal intensive care. The nonprofit hospital which has 365 beds also offers a cancer center home health services outpatient care occupational medicine and mental health care. As part of umbrella group Lafayette Health LGMC is affiliated with Lafayette General Surgical Hospital Lafayette General Southwest St. Martin Hospital Acadia General Hospital University Hospital and Clinics and Abrom Kaplan Memorial Hospital. It's also a teaching hospital for LSU. Non-profit foundation Lafayette General Foundation supports and governs Lafayette Health.

Operations

LGMC has evolved from a six-bed sanitarium that opened in 1911 to become the region's only community-owned and managed hospital. The 10-floor hospital now has larger rooms bathrooms and showers. It has also updated the Louisiana Extended Care Hospital its long-term acute care unit as well as its adult emergency department. New pediatric treatment and waiting areas were added to the emergency department and a new in-patient rehab unit was created. In 2013 LGMC became a teaching hospital for nearby Louisiana State University (LSU).

A strong community member LGMC not only makes financial contributions to further medical education and research it also coordinates events and provides free screenings to the public it serves.

Strategy

Like many health care providers facing reforms in the industry the hospital is developing a new patient-centered model of care delivery using evidenced-based practices and collaboration between patients their families and clinical ancillary and support staff members to improve outcomes and gain efficiencies. LGMC has been the first hospital in the area to bring in new technology like the DaVinci robotic surgical system to offer wifi access hospital-wide and to continuously upgrade and expand its facilities.

EXECUTIVES

Exec Dir, Caroline Huval
Svp-Coo*, Al Patin
Assistant Vice President Human, Wendy Alexander
Chief Crna, Cameron Chappuis
Neonatologist, David De Iulio
Director, Lee Perry
Director, John Kleyla
Hospitalist, Norris Guidry
Internist, Shema Abraham
Anesthesiologist, William Jarrell
Director, Marie Lukaszeski
Auditors: LAPORTE APAC METAIRIE LA

LOCATIONS

HQ: LAFAYETTE GENERAL MEDICAL CENTER, INC.
1214 COOLIDGE BLVD, LAFAYETTE, LA 705032621
Phone: 337 289-7991
Web: WWW.OCHSNERLG.ORG

COMPETITORS

Baton Rouge General	Lifepoint Health
Christus St. Frances Cabrini Hospital	Our Lady Of Lourdes Women & Children's Hospital
Hca	

HISTORICAL FINANCIALS

Company Type: Private

Income Statement — FYE: September 30

	REVENUE ($ mil.)	NET INCOME ($ mil.)	NET PROFIT MARGIN	EMPLOYEES
09/19	559	44	8.0%	1,626
09/18	480	45	9.4%	—
09/17	465	44	9.5%	—
09/16	454	50	11.2%	—
Annual Growth	**7.1%**	**(4.4%)**	—	—

2019 Year-End Financials

Return on assets: 8.6%
Return on equity: 9.3%
Current ratio: 3.00

Cash ($ mil.): 3

LAHEY CLINIC HOSPITAL, INC.

EXECUTIVES

Ceo, Howard R Grant JD
Ceo, David Barrett
Chm, Bernard Gordon
V Chm, John Libertino
V Pres, Donna Cameron
Director of Comm & Mktg, Scott V Hartman
Internal Medicine Practitioner, Anu Diddee
Ophthalmologist, Paul R Cotran
Laboratory Director, Barbara Sacco
Director Education, Donna Ales
Information Technology Manager, Elizabeth Gardner

LOCATIONS

HQ: LAHEY CLINIC HOSPITAL, INC.
  41 MALL RD, BURLINGTON, MA 018050002
Phone: 781 273-5100
Web: WWW.LAHEY.ORG

HISTORICAL FINANCIALS

Company Type: Private

Income Statement				FYE: September 30
	REVENUE ($ mil.)	NET INCOME ($ mil.)	NET PROFIT MARGIN	EMPLOYEES
09/15	816	(17)	—	1
09/14	800	(0)	—	—
09/13	774	228	29.5%	—
09/12	796	192	24.1%	—
Annual Growth	0.8%	—	—	—

2015 Year-End Financials

Return on assets: (-2.3%)
Return on equity: (-12.0%)
Current ratio: 2.40

Cash ($ mil.): 105

LAKE WASHINGTON SCHOOL DISTRICT

EXECUTIVES

Supt, Chip Kimball
Coordinator, Shannon Parthemer
Coordinator, Wynn Spaulding
Kindergarten, Russell Laura
Elementary Music Teacher, Amanda Andrews
Technology Manager, Matt Palmer
4th Grade Teacher, Sara Holmes
Manager, Ella Nordby
Project Manager, Thomas Allen
Teacher, Abbie Delong
Associate Director, Brian Buck

LOCATIONS

HQ: LAKE WASHINGTON SCHOOL DISTRICT
  16250 NE 74TH ST, REDMOND, WA 980527817
Phone: 425 936-1200
Web: WWW.LWSD.ORG

HISTORICAL FINANCIALS

Company Type: Private

Income Statement				FYE: August 31
	REVENUE ($ mil.)	NET INCOME ($ mil.)	NET PROFIT MARGIN	EMPLOYEES
08/20	583	38	6.7%	3,100
08/16	385	176	45.7%	—
Annual Growth	10.9%	(31.5%)	—	—

2020 Year-End Financials

Return on assets: 2.3%
Return on equity: 6.8%
Current ratio: —

Cash ($ mil.): 300

LAKELAND REGIONAL HEALTH SYSTEMS, INC.

EXECUTIVES

Pres-Ceo, Danielle Drummond
Vp-Coo, Sarah Bhagat
Exec Vp-Cfo, Evan C Jones
Vp & Chief Public Relations, Timothy J Boynton
Svp & Chief Hr, Scott W Dimmick
Evp & Chief Nurse Executive, Janet Fansler
Vp & Chief Analytics Officer, Caroline Gay
Vp Finance, Lance Green
Exec Dir & Chief Academic Offi, Graham F Greene
Evp & Chief Legal Officer, Jonn D Hoppe
Svp & Chief Strategy Officer, Deana Nelson
Auditors: KPMG LLP TAMPA FL

LOCATIONS

HQ: LAKELAND REGIONAL HEALTH SYSTEMS, INC.
  1324 LAKELAND HILLS BLVD, LAKELAND, FL 338054543
Phone: 863 687-1100
Web: WWW.MYLRH.ORG

HISTORICAL FINANCIALS

Company Type: Private

Income Statement				FYE: September 30
	REVENUE ($ mil.)	NET INCOME ($ mil.)	NET PROFIT MARGIN	EMPLOYEES
09/14	685	67	9.9%	3,124
09/13	24	(13)	—	—
09/12	582	67	11.6%	—
Annual Growth	8.5%	0.4%	—	—

2014 Year-End Financials

Return on assets: 7.2%
Return on equity: 10.9%
Current ratio: 1.40

Cash ($ mil.): 22

LAKELAND REGIONAL MEDICAL CENTER, INC.

Lakeland Regional Medical Center (LRMC) serves Florida's Polk County (roughly between Kissimmee and Tampa) through an acute care hospital with approximately 850 beds. Among its specialty services are cardiac care cancer treatment senior care urology emergency medicine orthopedics women's and children's health care and surgery. LRMC also operates general care and specialty outpatient clinics. Additionally the hospital provides medical training programs for radiology specialists. Its LRMC Foundation offers financial support for indigent patients facing ongoing treatment.

Operations

LRMC is part of Lakeland Regional Health System a not-for-profit organization that also includes Lakeland Regional Cancer Center Lakeland Regional Family Health Center and Lakeland Regional Health Medical Group.

Annually LRMC has more than 41000 admissions and performs more than 15000 surgeries. Its emergency department treats more than 200000 patients each year.

Financial Performance

Revenue in 2014 totaled $633 million (representing 92% of Lakeland Regional Health System's revenue) while net income totaled $67 million.

LRMC funds its activities through charges to patients for inpatient and outpatient services as well as from non-hospital activities such as its cafeteria gift and uniform shops and physicians' answering service. Although the hospital also receives payment from federal agencies such as Medicaid and Medicare they along with other managed care entities have cut their reimbursement levels causing LRMC's charity care levels to increase.

Strategy

The hospital has been undergoing facility and data systems improvement efforts to enhance care and increase efficiencies. It recently expanded its intensive care department and upgraded technology in areas including radiology orthopedics and chemotherapy.

In 2014 Lakeland Regional Health System announced plans to build an eight-story women and children pavilion at LRMC. The $250 million addition will include 300000 sq. ft. of space including 32 private rooms for mothers and newborns a 30-bed neonatal intensive care unit 64 private rooms for women's surgical and medical care three surgical suites and 12 private suites for labor delivery and recovery. It will also have an education and conference center. The pavilion is expected to open in 2017.

EXECUTIVES

Ceo, Elaine C Thompson
Pres, Timothy J Regan
V Pres, Lance Green
Health Professional, Kelly King
Internal Medicine Practitioner, Kyaw Min
Law Specialist, Laura Simmons
Chief of Medicine, Timothy Gompf
Training and Direc, Jackie Wallis
Chief of Medicine, Joy Jackson
Coordinator, Alease Christie
Health Professional, Alexis Ferguson
Auditors: PERSHING YOAKLEY & ASSOCIATES

LOCATIONS

HQ: LAKELAND REGIONAL MEDICAL CENTER, INC.
  1324 LAKELAND HILLS BLVD, LAKELAND, FL 338054500
Phone: 863 687-1100
Web: WWW.MYLRH.ORG

PRODUCTS/OPERATIONS

Selected Facilities

Lakeland Regional Cancer Center
Lakeland Regional Medical Center (LRMC) Foundation
Lakeland Regional Orthopedics Associates
Lakeland Regional Rehabilitation and Sports Medicine Clinic

Selected Services and Centers

Emergency
Family health center
Gastroenterology
Heart center
Mental health & addictions
Neurosurgery
Nursing
Oncology care
Orthopedic care
Palliative care
Pharmacy
Rehabilitation and sports medicine clinic
Robotic surgery
School of radiologic technology
Stroke center
Surgery
Trauma services
Women and children
Wound center

COMPETITORS

Adventist Health System Sunbelt Healthcare
All Children's Hospital
Baptist Health South Florida
Baycare Health System
Bayfront Health
Desoto Memorial
Florida Hospital Tampa Bay Division
Hca
Manatee Memorial Hospital
Sarasota Memorial Health Care
Tampa General Hospital
Winter Haven Hospital

HISTORICAL FINANCIALS
Company Type: Private

Income Statement				FYE: September 30
	REVENUE ($ mil.)	NET INCOME ($ mil.)	NET PROFIT MARGIN	EMPLOYEES
09/19	905	65	7.3%	3,100
09/16	790	84	10.7%	—
09/15	674	68	10.2%	—
09/14	618	66	10.8%	—
Annual Growth	7.9%	(0.3%)	—	—

2019 Year-End Financials
Return on assets: 7.7%
Return on equity: 16.4%
Current ratio: 0.40
Cash ($ mil.): —

LAMEX FOODS INC.

EXECUTIVES

Ceo, Phillip O Wallace
Pres*, Steven Anderson
V Pres*, Mark Barrett
Sr Dir*, Mark Ryder
Trading Manager, Robert Lucas
Export Coordinator, Danielle Waterhouse
Business Management, Paul Wallace
Key Account Manager, Andy Gillquist
Logistics Coordinator, Alex Radtke
Operations Controller, Billy Thompson
Imports Team Lead, Danielle Behling

LOCATIONS

HQ: LAMEX FOODS INC.
8500 NORMANDALE LAKE BLVD, BLOOMINGTON,
MN 554373813
Phone: 952 844-0585
Web: WWW.LAMEXFOODS.EU

HISTORICAL FINANCIALS
Company Type: Private

Income Statement				FYE: March 31
	REVENUE ($ mil.)	NET INCOME ($ mil.)	NET PROFIT MARGIN	EMPLOYEES
03/15	592	7	1.3%	80
03/05	103	1	1.0%	—
03/04	76	0	0.9%	—
Annual Growth	20.4%	24.8%	—	—

2015 Year-End Financials
Return on assets: 7.2%
Return on equity: 20.8%
Current ratio: 1.50
Cash ($ mil.): —

LANE INDUSTRIES INCORPORATED

EXECUTIVES

Pres-Dir, Mark Schiller
Pres-Dir, Robert Alger
Treas-Asst SEC, Vincent Caiola
Dir-SEC, Gianfranco Catrini
Exec V Pres, Kirk Junco
V Pres, David Benton
Exec V Pres, Mike Cote
SEC, Carol Gallagher
Treas, Mark Tomkalski
Auditors: KPMG LLP HARTFORD CT

LOCATIONS

HQ: LANE INDUSTRIES INCORPORATED
90 FIELDSTONE CT, CHESHIRE, CT 064101212
Phone: 203 235-3351

HISTORICAL FINANCIALS
Company Type: Private

Income Statement				FYE: December 31
	REVENUE ($ mil.)	NET INCOME ($ mil.)	NET PROFIT MARGIN	EMPLOYEES
12/18	856	(68)	—	4,500
12/17	1,592	14	0.9%	—
12/16	1,292	36	2.8%	—
12/15	1,197	(13)	—	—
Annual Growth	(10.6%)	—	—	—

2018 Year-End Financials
Return on assets: (-6.9%)
Return on equity: (-13.8%)
Current ratio: 1.80
Cash ($ mil.): 137

LEE MEMORIAL HEALTH SYSTEM FOUNDATION, INC.

Not feeling so bright in the Sunshine State? Lee Memorial Health System can help. Serving residents of Fort Myers and surrounding areas in Southwestern Florida's Lee County the community-owned not-for-profit health care system is home to four acute care hospitals (with a total of more than 1400 beds) a home health agency a 112-bed nursing home and numerous outpatient treatment and diagnostic centers. The flagship Lee Memorial Hospital also houses a 60-bed inpatient rehabilitation hospital and the HealthPark Medical Center location includes a dedicated 100-bed children's hospital. Lee Memorial Health Systems' corporate services include pre-employment screenings drug screens and wellness programs.

Operations

The system's facilities include the flagship Lee Memorial Hospital (355 beds) HealthPark Medical Center (270 beds) Gulf Coast Medical Center (350 beds) and Cape Coral Hospital (290 beds). Lee Memorial Health System employs more than 1200 doctors including primary and specialty care practitioners that are members of the affiliated Lee Physician Group. Patient service revenues account for nearly all of the company's revenues.

Lee Memorial Hospital is the only level II trauma center between Tampa and Miami.

Altogether the system has more than 1 million patient contacts each year.

Geographic Reach

Three of the systems' hospitals are located in Fort Myers Florida. Its fourth hospital (Cape Coral Hospital) is located in Cape Coral Florida.

Sales and Marketing

Medicare payments accounted for a third of the system's net patient service revenues in fiscal 2014 while Medicaid accounted for 15%. Self-pay accounted for 26% followed by managed care (20%) and commercial insurance (6%).

Financial Performance

Revenue increased 8% to $1.4 billion in fiscal 2014 (ended September) as net patient service revenues grew. This in turn led to an increase in net income which grew 31% to $158 million. Decreased interest expenses also helped boost profits.

Cash flow from operations increased 49% to $225 million that year largely due to cash received from patient care services.

Strategy

Lee Memorial Health System is a not-for-profit organization that proclaims its fiscal mission is to reinvest its profits back into the community it serves through facility and equipment upgrades and other measures. The system has undertaken a number of expansion projects at its hospitals in recent years to add specialty services and private patient rooms and has also opened a number of new community outpatient centers. In addition it is enhancing existing facilities to improve quality safety and financial performance.

In 2015 the system approved a $315 million expansion plan that will add 275 patient beds to Gulf Coast Medical Center. Construction on the project is expected to begin in 2017.

Lee Memorial Health System is also upgrading its IT systems to provide coordinated and efficient care. It has installed electronic health record programs (using EHR software from Epic Systems) at most of its facilities and it is improving other tools to streamline business systems and improve health care delivery processes.

Company Background

Tracing its roots to 1916 Lee Memorial Health System is a public health care system created by special act of the Florida Legislature in 1963. Its governing board is composed of 10 members elected by the public.

EXECUTIVES

Pres-Ceo, James R Nathan
Sr V Pres-Strategic Officer*, C B Rebsamen
CIO*, Rick Schooler
Cno*, Jennifer Higgins
Section Chief of Endocrinology, Richard J J Weiss
Compliance Staff, Nina Norman
Chief of Medicine, C B Resamen
Chief of Medicine, Mary Magno
Executive of Information Techn, Randy Grams
Director of Pharmacy, Steve Kessinger
Financial Analyst, Caleb Baker
Auditors: PRICEWATERHOUSECOOPERS LLP

LOCATIONS

HQ: LEE MEMORIAL HEALTH SYSTEM FOUNDATION, INC.
2776 CLEVELAND AVE, FORT MYERS, FL 339015864
Phone: 239 343-2000
Web: WWW.LEEHEALTH.ORG

PRODUCTS/OPERATIONS

2014 Sales by Segment

	$ mil.	% of total
Lee Memorial Hospital	682	50
Gulf Coast Memorial Center	302	22
Cape Memorial Hospital	206	15
Physicians	133	10
Health Park Care Center	13	1
Lee Memorial Home Health	8	1
Lee Memorial Health System Foundation	3	-
Lee County Trauma Services District	3	-
Lee Community Health Care	1	-
Other	9	1
Total	**1,363**	**100**

Selected Florida Hospitals
Blood Centers
Cardiac Care (Heart Services)
Community Health Centers/United Way Houses
Convenient Care
Emergency Services
Home Health Services
The Kidney Transplant Center
Lee Physician Group
Mental Health Services
Neuroscience Services
Nursing Home
Occupational Health Services
Orthopedic and Spine Services
Palliative Services
Patient Services
Pediatric Services
Pulmonary Services
Rehabilitation Services
Sleep Disorder Center
Surgical Services
Volunteer Services
Wellness and Nutrition Services
Women's Health Services
Wound Care and Hyperbaric Medicine

COMPETITORS

Adventist Health System Sunbelt Healthcare
All Children's Hospital
Baycare Health System
Bayfront Health
Desoto Memorial
H. Lee Moffitt Cancer Center & Research Institute
Hca
Nch Healthcare
Sarasota Memorial Health Care
St. Joseph's-baptist Health Care
Tampa General Hospital

HISTORICAL FINANCIALS
Company Type: Private

Income Statement

				FYE: September 30
	REVENUE ($ mil.)	NET INCOME ($ mil.)	NET PROFIT MARGIN	EMPLOYEES
09/18	1,789	101	5.6%	7,870
09/04	585	46	8.0%	—
09/03	522	50	9.8%	—
09/02	477	7	1.6%	—
Annual Growth	**8.6%**	**17.4%**	**—**	**—**

2018 Year-End Financials
Return on assets: 4.1%   Cash ($ mil.): 33
Return on equity: 6.6%
Current ratio: 5.40

LEE MEMORIAL HOSPITAL, INC.

EXECUTIVES

President, Jim Nathan
Coordinator, Shari Trivett
Executive Officer, Ken Szymanski
Health Professional, Furhan Qureshi
Internal Medicine Practitioner, Iasmina Jivanov
Internal Medicine Practitioner, Nadia Parchment
Family Practitioner, Asif Azam
Assistant Property Management, Brock Billman
Information Technology Staff, Connie Bowles
Assistant Manager, Clarice Bongiovanni
Customer Representativ, Emil J Zalesak

LOCATIONS

HQ: LEE MEMORIAL HOSPITAL, INC.
2776 CLEVELAND AVE, FORT MYERS, FL 339015855
Phone: 239 343-2000
Web: WWW.LEEHEALTH.ORG

HISTORICAL FINANCIALS
Company Type: Private

Income Statement

				FYE: September 30
	REVENUE ($ mil.)	NET INCOME ($ mil.)	NET PROFIT MARGIN	EMPLOYEES
09/14	688	163	23.8%	1,159
09/13	632	135	21.4%	—
09/12	613	105	17.3%	—
Annual Growth	**6.0%**	**24.4%**	**—**	**—**

2014 Year-End Financials
Return on assets: 10.8%   Cash ($ mil.): 32
Return on equity: 21.1%
Current ratio: 7.30

LEGACY EMANUEL HOSPITAL & HEALTH CENTER

Legacy Emanuel Hospital and Health Center part of the Legacy Health System provides acute and specialized health care to residents of Portland Oregon and surrounding communities. The 420-bed teaching hospital's operations include centers devoted to trauma treatment burn care oncology birthing neurosurgery orthopedics and cardiology. It also houses a pediatric hospital and operates the region's Life Flight Network service which is owned by a consortium of local hospitals. Legacy Emanuel's emergency department handles more than 15600 visits every year.

Operations
Legacy Emanuel's trauma and burn centers are level I designated facilities meaning they receive severe trauma and burn cases from other area hospitals. The hospital's burn center is the only one of its kind in an area stretching from Seattle to Sacramento and Salt Lake City. Other specialist facilities at Legacy Emanuel include its maternity center and its diagnostic imaging and screening units.

The medical center sees more than 18000 inpatients each year. Its staff includes about 140 full-time doctors and dentists as well as 700 full-time registered nurses. The Randall Children's Hospital located within Legacy Emanuel has about 600 affiliated pediatricians and specialists on its staff and handles about 100000 patient encounters each year including 20000 emergency room visits.

Strategy
The hospital has undergone massive expansion efforts. The hospital has completed construction of the new Randall Children's Hospital facilities making it one of the largest pediatric facilities in the state. The new pediatric center is four times as large as the past facilities. Other expansion efforts in recent years include new acute and intensive care capacity.

Company Background
To expand its medical transportation services Legacy Emanuel and other owners of LFN teamed up to purchase 15 new helicopters in 2012.

Legacy Emanuel Hospital was established in 1912 by the Lutheran Church.

EXECUTIVES

Ceo-Pres, George J Brown
Administrative Assistant, Mary Ann McNulty
Executive Director, Lisa Harris
Coordinator, Amy Lyons
Project Manager, Barri Stiber
Pediatrician, Kelsie Storm
Maternal Newborn Specialist, Lauren Rose
Pediatrician, Linnea Wittick
Doctor, Marc Legras
Internist, Smitha Chadaga

LOCATIONS

HQ: LEGACY EMANUEL HOSPITAL & HEALTH CENTER
2801 N GANTENBEIN AVE, PORTLAND, OR 972271623
Phone: 503 413-2200
Web: WWW.LEGACYHEALTH.ORG

PRODUCTS/OPERATIONS

Selected Centers and Services
Burn care
Cancer care
Children's care
Diabetes and nutrition
Emergency services
Family birth center
Gardens
High-risk obstetrics
Imaging
Injury prevention
Intensive care
Interventional and diagnostic cardiology
Level I trauma center
Life flight network
Maternal-fetal medicine
Neurology and neurosurgery including spine surgery
Orthopedics
Pediatrics
Rehabilitation (inpatient and outpatient)
Radiation oncology
Stroke
Surgery (including minimally invasive surgery)
Vascular clinic
Wound and ostomy clinic
Wound care and outpatient burn clinic

COMPETITORS

Adventist Health System West	Peacehealth
Asante Health System	Peacehealth Southwest Medical Center
Dignity Health	Providence St. Joseph Health
Kadlec Regional Medical Center	Salem Hospital

Company Type: Private

Income Statement				FYE: March 31
	REVENUE ($ mil.)	NET INCOME ($ mil.)	NET PROFIT MARGIN	EMPLOYEES
03/20	977	(49)	—	3,619
03/17	778	(12)	—	
03/15	705	29	4.2%	
03/14	649	30	4.8%	
Annual Growth	7.0%	—	—	—

LEGACY HEALTH

Legacy Health is a locally owned nonprofit health system that offers a unique blend of health services across the Portland/Vancouver metro area and mid-Willamette Valley. Its services range from wellness and urgent care to dedicated children's services and advanced medical centers for patients of all ages. It operates half a dozen hospitals including Legacy Emanuel Medical Center and Legacy Good Samaritan Medical Center as well as the Randall Children's Hospital at Legacy Emanuel. Legacy Health has more than 70 primary care specialty and urgent care clinics and its facilities provide such services as acute and critical care behavioral health and outpatient and health education programs. It also operates labs research and hospice.

Operations

Legacy Health has nearly 3000 doctors and providers. Its hospitals include Legacy Emanuel Medical Center Randall Children's Hospital Legacy Good Samaritan Medical Center Legacy Meridian Park Medical Center Legacy Mount Hood Medical Center Legacy Silverton Medical Center and Legacy Salmon Creek Medical Center in Washington.

With more than 800 care providers Legacy Medical Group is comprised of more than 50 primary care clinics and specialty practices and doctors who specifically care for hospitalized patients.

Geographic Reach

Portland Oregon-based Legacy Health operates six advanced medical centers in Portland Vancouver Gresham Tualatin and Silverton.

Company Background

Legacy Health was founded through the 1989 merger of HealthLink and Good Samaritan Hospital.

EXECUTIVES

Ceo, George J Brown
Sr V Pres*, Carol Bradley Rn
Sr V Pres*, Maureen Bradley
Sr V Pres*, Rob Dewitt
Sr V Pres*, Trent Green
Treas*, Kelly A Higgins
Administrative Assistant To Ho, Rebecca Cohen
Analyst, Sandy Sippel
Strategic Planning Consultant, Vinay Prasad
Director, Christopher S Thoming
Director, David Brauer-Rieke
Auditors: KPMG LLP PORTLAND OREGON

LOCATIONS

HQ: LEGACY HEALTH
1919 NW LOVEJOY ST, PORTLAND, OR 972091503
Phone: 503 415-5600
Web: WWW.LEGACYHEALTH.ORG

PRODUCTS/OPERATIONS

Selected Facilities

Hospitals
Legacy Emanuel Medical Center (Portland Oregon)
Legacy Good Samaritan Medical Center (Portland Oregon)
Legacy Meridian Park Medical Center (Tualatin Oregon)
Legacy Mount Hood Medical Center (Gresham Oregon)
Legacy Salmon Creek Medical Center (Vancouver Washington)
Randall Children's Hospital At Legacy Emanuel (Portland Oregon)
Clinics
Legacy Medical Group - Fisher's Landing
Legacy Medical Group - Good Samaritan
Legacy Medical Group - Lake Oswego
Legacy Medical Group - Salmon Creek Family Medicine (Vancouver Washington)
Legacy Medical Group - Salmon Creek Internal Medicine (Vancouver Washington)
Legacy Medical Group - West Linn
Legacy Med

COMPETITORS

Adventist Health System West	Oregon Health & Science University
Asante Health System	Peacehealth
Kadlec Regional Medical Center	Providence St. Joseph Health
Kaiser Foundation Hospitals	Salem Hospital

HISTORICAL FINANCIALS

Company Type: Private

Income Statement				FYE: March 31
	REVENUE ($ mil.)	NET INCOME ($ mil.)	NET PROFIT MARGIN	EMPLOYEES
03/21	2,265	363	16.0%	10,675
03/20	2,336	(42)	—	
03/19	2,219	84	3.8%	
03/18	2,117	100	4.7%	
Annual Growth	2.3%	53.6%	—	—

2021 Year-End Financials

Return on assets: 10.2%
Return on equity: 16.9%
Current ratio: 2.30
Cash ($ mil.): 563

LEHIGH GAS CORPORATION

LOCATIONS

HQ: LEHIGH GAS CORPORATION
702 HAMILTON ST STE 203, ALLENTOWN, PA 181012469
Phone: 610 791-3800

HISTORICAL FINANCIALS

Company Type: Private

Income Statement				FYE: December 31
	REVENUE ($ mil.)	NET INCOME ($ mil.)	NET PROFIT MARGIN	EMPLOYEES
12/07	1,034	4	0.5%	200
12/05*	53	(0)	—	
06/04	116	1	1.2%	
Annual Growth	72.5%	36.5%	—	—

*Fiscal year change

Return on assets: 2.5%
Return on equity: 46.7%
Current ratio: 0.80
Cash ($ mil.): 1

LEHIGH VALLEY HEALTH NETWORK, INC.

Lehigh Valley Health Network (LVHN) is a not-for-profit health care provider operates through nine full-service hospital campuses. LVHN serves as a regional referral center for trauma and burn care and organ transplantation as well as specialty care such as cardiology women's health and pediatric surgery. LVHN also boasts a network of physician practices and community health centers as well as home health and hospice units. Through Lehigh Valley Physician Group LVHN has more than 2000 primary care and specialty physicians as well as more than 800 advanced practice clinicians. HNL Lab Medicine provides an extensive range of laboratory tests from the most critical medical applications to simple pre-employment drug screenings.

Operations

The company's hospitals provide care in about 95 specialist fields including pediatric care burn treatment trauma care organ transplant emergency care general surgery and neurology. Its children's hospital includes inpatient emergency and specialist units. LVHN conducts medical training programs and performs research in a range of different areas including cancer cardiovascular and infectious disease; a number of these programs are conducted through partnership with University of South Florida's Morsani College of Medicine. In addition LVHN offers a full-time three-year non-resident RN diploma nursing program at Joseph F. McCloskey School of Nursing at Lehigh Valley Health Network in Schuylkill County.

Lehigh Valley Reilly Children's Hospital is the only children's hospital in the Lehigh Valley. The Children's Hospital offers both inpatient and ambulatory care a children's ER the J.B. and Kathleen Reilly Children's Surgery Center in Salisbury Township more than 30 pediatric specialists and numerous child-specific services such as rehab and burn care.

Overall net patient service generates some 95% of total revenue and other supporting operations account for the remaining 5%.

Geographic Reach

LVHN operates more than 20 offices and lab and imaging services located in an eight-county territory in Pennsylvania.

Its HNL Lab Medicine is located in a dozens of convenient locations in Pennsylvania.

Financial Performance

The company's revenue for fiscal 2021 increased to $3.4 billion compared from the prior year with $3.1 billion.

EXECUTIVES

Pres-Ceo, Elliot J Sussman
Chb, J B Relly
V Pres-Support Services, Stuart Paxton
Ceo, Ronald Swinfard
Svp-Chief Philanthropy Officer, Liv Vesely
Coordinator, Cathy Fuhrman
Internal Medicine Practitioner, Gina Verdetti
Coordinator, Gloribel Nieves
Internal Medicine Practitioner, Jeffrey Faidley

Lvpg Clinical Educator Clinica, Rob Mangano
Coordinator, Gwen Rosenberger
Auditors: KPMG LLP PHILADELPHIA PENNSY

LOCATIONS

HQ: LEHIGH VALLEY HEALTH NETWORK, INC.
1247 S CEDAR CREST BLVD # 105, ALLENTOWN, PA
181036298
Phone: 610 402-8000
Web: WWW.LVHN.ORG

PRODUCTS/OPERATIONS

Selected Facilities

Community Health Centers
  Hamburg Community Health Center
  Lehigh Valley Health Center at Bath
  Lehigh Valley Health Center at Bethlehem Township
  Lehigh Valley Health Center at Hellertown
  Lehigh Valley Health Center at Kutztown
  Lehigh Valley Health Center at Saucon Valley
  Lehigh Valley Health Center at Trexlertown
  Upper Bucks Health & Diagnostic Center (in
  partnership with Grand View Hospital Quakertown)
Hospitals
  Lehigh Valley Hospital - 17th St. (short-stay hospital
  Salisbury Township in Allentown)
  Lehigh Valley Hospital - Cedar Crest (Allentown)
  Lehigh Valley Hospital - Muhlenberg (Bethlehem)

COMPETITORS

Abington Memorial Hospital
Ascension Health
Community Health Systems
Doylestown Hospital
Grand View
Main Line Health System
Mercy Health System
Moses Taylor Hospital
North Philadelphia Health System
Pennsylvania Hospital
Reading Hospital And Medical Center
Sacred Heart Hospital Of Allentown
Shore Memorial Hospital
St. Luke's University Health Network
Tenet Healthcare
University Of Pennsylvania Health System
Wyoming Valley Health Care System

HISTORICAL FINANCIALS

Company Type: Private

Income Statement				FYE: June 30
	REVENUE ($ mil.)	**NET INCOME** ($ mil.)	**NET PROFIT MARGIN**	**EMPLOYEES**
06/21	3,437	700	20.4%	12,000
06/20	3,129	2	0.1%	—
06/19	2,978	118	4.0%	—
06/18	2,739	106	3.9%	—
Annual Growth	7.8%	87.2%	—	—

2021 Year-End Financials

Return on assets: 13.6%
Return on equity: 26.9%
Current ratio: 1.30
Cash ($ mil.): 476

LELAND STANFORD JUNIOR UNIVERSITY

The Leland Stanford Junior University better known as simply Stanford University is one of the top universities in the US. It boasts respected programs across seven schools and about 20 interdisciplinary institutes such as business engineering law and medicine among others. Stanford serves about 17245 students (taught by nearly 2280 faculty members) from all 50 US states and approximately 55 other countries. Its student-teacher ratio sits at about 5:1. A private institution Stanford is supported through an endowment of some $28.9 billion one of the largest in the US. The university was established in 1885 by Leland Stanford Sr. It was named after his son Leland Stanford Jr.

Operations

Stanford University is widely recognized as one of the top US research universities and sports a host of laboratories and research centers including the Stanford Institute for Economic Policy Research and the Stanford Linear Accelerator Center. Its faculty members include around 35 Nobel Prize winners a handful of Pulitzer Prize winners and about 35 MacArthur fellows.

The university also offers nearly 35 varsity sports and about 35 club sports; it boasts around 125 NCAA team championships.

Geographic Reach

Stanford is located in the heart of California's Silicon Valley known worldwide as an epicenter for technology and research ventures. Google (headquartered in Silicon Valley) got its start at Stanford when Sergey Brin and Larry Page developed the page-rank algorithm while they were still computer science graduate students.

The university is located on 8180 contiguous acres and has almost 700 major buildings.

Strategy

To further widen its student resources Stanford has recently completed renovation and construction efforts on some 40 campus buildings and added a number of new faculty and fellowship positions. The university is also exploring options to establish a satellite-applied science and engineering campus in another US city. In addition Stanford is examining whether it might begin to offer courses through an online platform.

In 2017 Stanford launched a new major in aeronautics and astronautics (allowing students to work with unmanned aerial vehicles satellites autonomous systems and other flight technologies).

HISTORY

In 1885 Leland Stanford Sr. and his wife Jane established Leland Stanford Junior University in memory of their son Leland Jr. who had died of typhoid at age 15. Stanford made his fortune selling provisions to California gold miners and as a major investor in the Central Pacific Railroad one of the two companies that built the first transcontinental railway. It was Stanford who connected the tracks laid eastward by Central Pacific and westward by Union Pacific with a gold railway spike in 1869. He also served as California's governor and as a US senator.

The Stanfords donated more than 8000 acres of land from their own estate to establish an unconventional university one that was coeducational and nondenominational with a focus on preparing students for a profession. Stanford opened its doors in 1891 to a freshman class of 559 students. It awarded its first degrees four years later and among the graduates was future US president Herbert Hoover.

Leland Stanford Sr. died in 1893 and in 1903 Jane Stanford turned the university over to the board of trustees. After weathering significant damage in 1906 from the Great San Francisco Earthquake the university established a law school in 1908 and its medical school five years later.

During WWI the university mobilized half of its students into the Students' Army Training Corps. The School of Education was established in 1917 followed by the School of Engineering and Graduate School of Business eight years later. In 1933 a rule limiting the number of women admitted to Stanford was abolished.

Wallace Sterling who became president of the university after WWII initiated the transformation of Stanford into a world-class institution with a reputation for teaching and research. Under Sterling the university initiated development on the Stanford Research Park.

In 1958 Stanford opened its first overseas campus (near Stuttgart Germany) and the Stanford Medical Center was completed the following year. The university created a computer science department in 1965 and two years later opened the Stanford Linear Accelerator Center dedicated to physics research.

Donald Kennedy became president in 1980. The next year students voted to abandon the university's official mascot the "Indians" in response to concerns raised by Native American students. The nickname "Cardinal" was adopted in its place. The term refers to the school's color cardinal red.

Also during Kennedy's tenure it was revealed that Stanford had overcharged the Office of Naval Research for indirect costs associated with research. The scandal led to Kennedy's resignation in 1992 and in 1994 the Office of Naval Research and the university settled a related lawsuit for $1.2 million and a stipulation that Stanford had not committed any wrongdoing. Gerhard Casper succeeded Kennedy as president.

In 1997 Stanford and the University of California at San Francisco combined their teaching hospitals in a public/private merger. Two years later after the controversial experiment had harmed both hospitals' financial pictures the merger was terminated and the two hospitals agreed to go their separate ways.

In 1999 Casper announced his intention to resign as president. The school tapped provost John Hennessy as his replacement. Soon after his appointment in 2000 Hennessey launched a campaign to raise $1 billion. Former Stanford professor and Netscape co-founder Jim Clark donated $150 million later that year to support Stanford's biomedical engineering and sciences program. The school also launched a new company SKOLAR which developed an online search engine for the medical industry.

EXECUTIVES

Pres*, Marc Tessier-Lavigne
V Pres*, Debra Zumwalt
Cfo*, Randall S Livingston
Prin*, John Hennessy
Director, Sally Benson
Director of Facilities, Sandy Meyer
Staff Scientist, Sasha Novokhatski
Director, Teresa Janeway
Associate Director of Real Est, Tiffany Griego
Scientist, Hendrik J Vreman
Assistant Professor, Marion Buckwalter
Auditors: PRICEWATERHOUSECOOPERS LLP SA

LOCATIONS

HQ: LELAND STANFORD JUNIOR UNIVERSITY
450 JANE STANFORD WAY, STANFORD, CA
943052004
Phone: 650 723-2300
Web: WWW.STANFORD.EDU

PRODUCTS/OPERATIONS

2014 Sales

	$ mil.	% of total
Healthcare services	3,942	50
Sponsored reseach support	1,266	16
Investment income	1,181	15
Student income	533	7
Special program fee and other income	641	7
Gifts	212	3
Net assets released from restrictions	146	2
Total	**7,924**	**100**

Selected Schools

Undergraduate
  School of Earth Sciences
  School of Engineering
  School of Humanities and Sciences
Graduate
  School of Business
  School of Earth Sciences
  School of Education
  School of Engineering
  School of Humanities and Sciences
  School of Law
  School of Medicine

Selected Interdisciplinary Research Centers

Alliance for Innovative Manufacturing at Stanford
Center for Computer Research in Music and Acoustics
Center for Integrated Facility Engineering
Center for Integrated Systems

Selected Laboratories Centers and Institutes

Center for Research on Information Storage Materials
Center for the Study of Language and Information
Edward L. Ginzton Laboratory
Institute for International Studies
Institute for Research on Women and Gender
John and Terry Levin Center for Public Service and
  Public Interest Law
Stanford Center for Buddhist Studies
Stanford Humanities Center
Stanford Institute for Economic Policy Research
W.W. Hansen Experimental Physics Laboratory

Selected Medical Research Facilities

Center for Biomedical Ethics
Center for Research in Disease Prevention
Human Genome Center
Richard M. Lucas Center for Magnetic Resonance
  Spectroscopy & Imaging
Sleep Disorders Center
Other Selected Research Facilities
Hoover Institution on War Revolution and Peace
Hopkins Marine Station
Martin Luther King Jr. Papers Project
Stanford Linear Accelerator Center

HISTORICAL FINANCIALS

Company Type: Private

Income Statement				FYE: August 31
	REVENUE ($ mil.)	NET INCOME ($ mil.)	NET PROFIT MARGIN	EMPLOYEES
08/20	12,455	1,983	15.9%	15,000
08/19	12,262	1,961	16.0%	—
08/18	11,311	2,653	23.5%	—
08/17	5,604	2,972	53.0%	—
Annual Growth	30.5%	(12.6%)	—	—

2020 Year-End Financials

Return on assets: 3.2%   Cash ($ mil.): 3,142
Return on equity: 4.2%
Current ratio: —

LENOX HILL HOSPITAL

LOCATIONS

HQ: LENOX HILL HOSPITAL
210 E 64TH ST FL 4, NEW YORK, NY 100657471
Phone: 212 472-8872
Web: WWW.LENOXHILL.ORG

HISTORICAL FINANCIALS

Company Type: Private

Income Statement				FYE: December 31
	REVENUE ($ mil.)	NET INCOME ($ mil.)	NET PROFIT MARGIN	EMPLOYEES
12/16	960	21	2.3%	41
12/15	885	6	0.7%	—
Annual Growth	8.5%	244.8%	—	—

2016 Year-End Financials

Return on assets: 1.8%   Cash ($ mil.): —
Return on equity: 4.7%
Current ratio: 0.80

LESTER E. COX MEDICAL CENTERS

Lester E. Cox Medical Centers (dba CoxHealth) is the area leader in health care and community involvement. CoxHealth's network includes six acute care hospitals (with nearly 1015 licensed beds) five ERs and more than 80 physician clinics. Centers for cardiac care cancer treatment orthopedics and women's health are among CoxHealth's specialized care options. In addition to a wide range of treatments and services CoxHealth contributes millions each year to community outreach medical education and research foundation grants donations and other contributions to the community. The organization was named after its primary fundraiser in the 1940s.

Operations

Each year CoxHealth handles about 1.5 million clinic visits; approximately 267780 emergency urgent care and trauma visits; nearly 37730 ambulance services; and more than 4135 births. Its hospitals include Cox Medical Center South Cox Medical Center Branson Cox North Hospital Cox Monett Hospital Meyer Orthopedic and Rehabilitation Hospital CoxHealth at Home Home Parenteral Services and Ferrell-Duncan Clinic. Its specialty clinics include centers for cancer orthopedics cardiovascular care women's and children's health outpatient surgery and diagnostic imaging.

Geographic Reach

Springfield Missouri-based CoxHealth has primary and specialty care providers located in more than 80 clinics across the region. Serving approximately 25 counties CoxHealth's major facilities are in Branson Monett and Springfield Missouri.

Sales and Marketing

CoxHealth primarily serves families children women seniors and athletes.

Strategy

CoxHealth strives to improve its services and the health of its community. The system typically grows by adding or expanding facilities. CoxHealth is building a super clinic in 2020 bringing a new level of care to the Republic community with this addition. The super clinic will replace CoxHealth's current facility in Republic and is the health system's fourth super clinic.

CoxHealth also consolidated Crighton Olive Dunn Surgical Group in late 2020. The consolidated clinic which will be rebranded as CoxHealth Vein Center will offer a variety of outpatient procedures including vein ablations microphlebectomies and sclerotherapy as well as other general surgical services and diagnostic imaging.

CoxHealth and North Arkansas Regional Medical Center (NARMC) collaborated to expand health care access for residents of North Central Arkansas jointly opening a new medical facility in Harrison so residents can continue to receive exceptional primary care while increasing access to specialists close to home. CoxHealth also opened a new Cardiovascular Observation Unit at Cox South responding to the growing need for cardiovascular services.

Company Background

CoxHealth was founded as Burge Deaconess Hospital in 1908. It became Lester E. Cox Medical Centers in 1968 following the death of Cox a St. Louis businessman who led a series of major fundraising campaigns in the 1940s critical to the survival and growth of the hospital.

EXECUTIVES

Ceo, Steven D Edwards
V Chm, William Turner
Cfo, Jake McWay
Exec SEC, Vickie Nelson
Analyst, Janet Ellison
Accounting Staff, Joy Hoskins
Information Specialist, Jim Walton
Director, Amy Lea
Cardiology Director, James Ceaser
Director of Volunteer, Barbara Frogue
Information Technology Manager, Jeff Sanders

LOCATIONS

HQ: LESTER E. COX MEDICAL CENTERS
1423 N JEFFERSON AVE, SPRINGFIELD, MO 658021917
Phone: 417 269-3000
Web: WWW.COXHEALTH.COM

PRODUCTS/OPERATIONS

Selected Services

Air Care
Alzheimer's Disease
Behavioral Health
Brain and Spine Disorders
Breast Care
Cancer Services
Children's Health
Diabetes
Dialysis
Ear Nose and Throat (ENT)
Emergency Department
Fitness Centers
Food and Nutrition
Heart and Vascular
Home Health
Hyperbaric Medicine and Wound Care
Neuroscience
Occupational Medicine
Orthopedics
Parenting
Parkinson's Clinic
Pharmacy
Physical Medicine
Pregnancy
Radiology
Rehabilitation
Respiratory Care
Robotic Surgery
Sleep Disorders
Smoking Cessation
Specialty Services
Sports Medicine
Stroke

Trauma Services
Urgent Care
Weight Loss
Wellness Consultations
Women's Health
Workers' Compensation

COMPETITORS

Ascension Health	Shawnee Mission
Bjc Healthcare	Medical Center
Catholic Health	Sisters Of Charity Of
Initiatives	Leavenworth
Children's Mercy	St. Anthony's Medical
Hospital	Center
Hca	Tenet Healthcare
Mercy Health	Truman Medical Centers
Mercy Hospital	Universal Health
Springfield	Services
Saint Luke's Health	University Of Kansas
System	Medical Center

HISTORICAL FINANCIALS

Company Type: Private

Income Statement   FYE: September 30

	REVENUE ($ mil.)	NET INCOME ($ mil.)	NET PROFIT MARGIN	EMPLOYEES
09/14	898	50	5.6%	11,170
09/13	858	105	12.3%	—
09/12	843	66	7.9%	—
Annual Growth	3.2%	(13.0%)	—	—

2014 Year-End Financials

Return on assets: 3.6%   Cash ($ mil.): 61
Return on equity: 7.3%
Current ratio: 2.00

LEVI STRAUSS & CO.

Levi Strauss & Co. (LS&CO) is a global manufacturer of brand-name clothing LS&CO sells jeans and sportswear under the Levi's Dockers Signature by Levi Strauss and Denizen labels in more than 110 countries. The company distributes its brand products through approximately 50000 retail stores worldwide which includes 3100 brand-dedicated stores and shop-in-shops. It designs markets and sells ? directly or through third parties and licensees ? products that include jeans pants tops shorts skirts dresses jackets footwear and related accessories for men women and children. About 45% of the company total revenue comes from US operation. Founded In 1853 Levi Strauss opened a wholesale dry goods business in San Francisco that became known as Levi Strauss & Co.

HISTORY

Levi Strauss arrived in New York City from Bavaria in 1847. In 1853 he joined his brother-in-law David Stern in San Francisco selling dry goods to the gold rushers. Shortly after a prospector told Strauss of miners' problems in finding sturdy pants. Strauss made a pair out of canvas for the prospector; word of the rugged pants spread quickly.

Strauss continued his dry-goods business in the 1860s. During this time he switched the pants' fabric to a durable French cloth called serge de Nimes soon known as denim. He colored the fabric with indigo dye and adopted the idea from Nevada tailor Jacob Davis of reinforcing the pants with copper rivets. In 1873 Strauss and Davis produced their first pair of waist-high overalls (later known as jeans). The pants soon became de rigueur for lumberjacks cowboys railroad workers oil drillers and farmers.

Strauss continued to build his pants and wholesaling business until he died in 1902. Levi Strauss & Co. passed to four Stern nephews who carried on their uncle's jeans business while maintaining the company's philanthropic reputation.

After WWII Walter Haas and Peter Haas (a fourth-generation Strauss family member) assumed leadership of LS&CO. In 1948 they ended the company's wholesaling business to concentrate on Levi's clothing. In the 1950s Levi's jeans ceased to be merely functional garments for workers; they became the uniform of American youth. In the 1960s LS&CO. added women's attire and expanded overseas.

The company went public in 1971. That year it added a women's career line and bought Koret sportswear (sold in 1984). By the mid-1980s profits declined. Peace Corps-veteran-turned-McKinsey-consultant Robert Haas (Walter's son) grabbed the reins of LS&CO. in 1984 and took the company private the next year (he became chairman in 1989). He also instilled a touchy-feely corporate culture often at odds with the bottom line.

In 1986 LS&CO. introduced Dockers casual pants. The company's sales began rising in 1991 as consumers forsook the designer duds of the 1980s for more practical clothes. LS&CO. says seven out of every 10 American men own a pair of Dockers. However LS&CO. missed out on the birth of another trend: the split between the fashion sense of US adolescents and their Levi's-loving baby boomer parents.

In 1996 the company introduced Slates dress slacks. That year LS&CO. bought back nearly one-third of its stock from family and employees for $4.3 billion. Grappling with slipping sales and debt from the buyout in 1997 LS&CO. closed 11 of its 37 North American plants laying off 6400 workers and 1000 salaried employees; it granted generous severance packages even to those earning minimum wage.

In 1998 citing improved labor conditions in China LS&CO. announced it would step up its use of Chinese subcontractors. Further restructuring added a third of its European plants to the closures list that year. LS&CO.'s sales fell 13% in fiscal 1998. Also that year Haas handed his CEO title to Pepsi executive Philip Marineau; Haas remained chairman.

LS&CO. closed 11 of 22 remaining North American plants in 1999. It also unleashed several new jeans brands that eschewed the company's one-style-fits-all approach of old.

In April 2002 LS&CO. announced it would close six of its last eight US plants and cut 20% of its worldwide staff (3300 workers). In September 2003 it cut another 5% of its global staff (650 workers). That month the company opened its first girls-only store located in Paris. In December LS&CO. replaced CFO Bill Chiasson with an outside turnaround specialist.

Pinpointing 2006 as the best time to step down as the company's chief executive Philip Marineau retired at the end of 2006. John Anderson president of LS&CO.'s Asia/Pacific division and head of the firm's global supply chain unit replaced Marineau as president and CEO.

Levi Strauss chairman Robert Haas retired in 2008 after 18 years in that role. His successor was Dryer's ice cream executive T. Gary Rogers who became the first leader in the company's history who was not a descendant of the founder. In August 2008 CFO Hans Ploos van Amstel left the company the and was replaced by Heidi Manes its corporate controller and principal accounting officer.

Looking to gain a more active role in its store business LS&CO. in July 2009 bought the operating rights for more than 70 Levi's and Dockers Outlet locations from store operator Anchor Blue Retail Group which had filed for bankruptcy for $72 million. Anchor Blue said the US recession and drop in consumer spending especially among teens severely affected its financial performance. LS&CO. said the acquisition will enable it to better manage its brands' positioning.

Rogers retired in late 2009 and Richard Kauffman became chairman.

EXECUTIVES

Independent Director, Patricia Pineda
Chief Financial Officer, Executive Vice President, Harmit Singh, $882,308 total compensation
Independent Director, Spencer Fleischer
Independent Director, Jenny Ming
Executive Vice President, President - Brands, Jennifer Sey
Independent Chairman Of The Board, Robert Eckert
President, Chief Executive Officer, Director, Charles Bergh, $1,414,423 total compensation
Independent Director, Troy Alstead
Executive Vice President And General Counsel, Seth Jaffe
Executive Vice President, Chief Commercial Officer, Seth Ellison, $775,769 total compensation
Independent Director, Jill Beraud
Executive Vice President, President - Levi Strauss Americas, Marc Rosen
Executive Vice President, Chief Operations Officer, Elizabeth O'Neill, $720,192 total compensation
Independent Director, Joshua Prime
Independent Director, Yael Garten
Independent Director, Elliott Rodgers
Principal Accounting Officer, Global Controller, Lisa Stirling
Auditors: PRICEWATERHOUSECOOPERS LLP SA

LOCATIONS

HQ: LEVI STRAUSS & CO.
1155 BATTERY ST, SAN FRANCISCO, CA 941111264
Phone: 415 501-6000
Web: WWW.LEVISTRAUSS.COM

2018 Stores	#
Americas region	268
Europe region	300
Asia/Pacific region	256
Total	**0** **697**

2018 Sales	$ mil.	% of total
Americas	3,042	55
Europe	1,646	29
Asia/Pacific region	886	17
Total	**5,575**	**100**

PRODUCTS/OPERATIONS

2018 Sales	% of total
Levi's brand	86
Dockers brand	7
Signature by Levi Strauss & Denizen brands	7
Total	**100**

Selected Brands

Denizen
Dockers
    Dockers Alpha Khaki
    Dockers for Men
    Dockers for Women
Levi's
    Levi's 501 Original
    Levi's 505 Straight

Levi's 511 Skinny
Levi's 513 Slim
Levi's 514 Slim Straight
Levi's Curve ID
Signature by Levis Strauss & Co.
Intro
Waterless
Wellthread
Wasteless

COMPETITORS

Abercrombie & Fitch	Nautica Apparel
American Eagle	Nine West
Outfitters	Oshkosh B'gosh
Benetton	Oxford Industries
Calvin Klein	Pvh
Diesel Spa	Perry Ellis
Fubu	International
Fast Retailing	Ralph Lauren
Fruit Of The Loom	Sean John
Guess?	Target Corporation
Haggar	The Gap
Hugo Boss	True Religion Apparel
Inditex	Under Armour
J. Crew	Vf Corporation
Jockey International	Victoria's Secret
Joe's Jeans	Stores
Kmart	Wacoal
Kohl's	Wal-mart
Lands' End	Warnaco Group
Macy's	Adidas
Nike	

HISTORICAL FINANCIALS
Company Type: Private

Income Statement				FYE: November 25
	REVENUE ($ mil.)	NET INCOME ($ mil.)	NET PROFIT MARGIN	EMPLOYEES
11/18	5,575	285	5.1%	14,800
11/17	4,904	284	5.8%	—
11/16	4,552	291	6.4%	—
11/15	4,494	209	4.7%	—
Annual Growth	7.4%	10.8%	—	—

2018 Year-End Financials

Return on assets: 8.1%   Cash ($ mil.): 713
Return on equity: 42.7%
Current ratio: 2.20

LEXA INTERNATIONAL CORPORATION

EXECUTIVES

Chb-Pres, Antonia Axson Johnson
V Chb, P Goeran Ennerfelt
V Pres-Contrl, Charles W Seitz
V Pres, John Pascale
Quality Control Manager, Elias Flessas
Vp, Finance and Administration, Sally Sarsfield
Legal Administrator and Secret, Tammany Patrick
Auditors: CITRIN COOPERMAN & COMPANY LL

LOCATIONS

HQ: LEXA INTERNATIONAL CORPORATION
1 LANDMARK SQ STE 407, STAMFORD, CT
069012601
Phone: 203 326-5200

HISTORICAL FINANCIALS
Company Type: Private

Income Statement				FYE: December 31
	REVENUE ($ mil.)	NET INCOME ($ mil.)	NET PROFIT MARGIN	EMPLOYEES
12/09	2,598	6	0.2%	1,204
12/08	4,312	4	0.1%	—
12/07	4,003	(21)	—	—
Annual Growth	(19.4%)			

2009 Year-End Financials

Return on assets: 0.6%   Cash ($ mil.): 43
Return on equity: 3.1%
Current ratio: 1.80

LEXINGTON COUNTY HEALTH SERVICES DISTRICT, INC.

EXECUTIVES

Pres, Michael Biediger
V Pres*, Melinda P Kruzner
Coo*, Tod Augsburger
Internal Audit, Jason McKinney
Senior Major Gifts Officer, Beth Wingard
Vp Marketing and Public Relati, Charles Wendt
Infection Control Manager, Janet Foster
Auditors: KPMG LLP ATLANTA GA

LOCATIONS

HQ: LEXINGTON COUNTY HEALTH SERVICES DISTRICT, INC.
2720 SUNSET BLVD, WEST COLUMBIA, SC
291694810
Phone: 803 791-2000
Web: WWW.LEXMED.COM

HISTORICAL FINANCIALS
Company Type: Private

Income Statement				FYE: September 30
	REVENUE ($ mil.)	NET INCOME ($ mil.)	NET PROFIT MARGIN	EMPLOYEES
09/10	576	59	10.4%	6,000
09/09	528	57	10.9%	—
09/08	491	35	7.2%	—
Annual Growth	8.3%	29.8%	—	—

2010 Year-End Financials

Return on assets: 7.3%   Cash ($ mil.): 170
Return on equity: 11.6%
Current ratio: 4.70

LEXINGTON MEDICAL CENTER

Lexington Medical Center is a not-for-profit health care organization serving the residents of South Carolina's Lexington County. Established in 1971 the medical center has some 415 beds and provides general emergency surgical and diagnostic services. Specialty services include cancer treatment cardiovascular care women's health and rehabilitation. Lexington Medical Center also operates a skilled nursing center as well as a network of affiliated community health centers urgent care clinics and affiliated physician practices. The hospital is managed by the Lexington County Health Service District.

Operations

The 414-bed facility is home to the largest extended-care facility in the Carolinas. It sees about 100000 emergency department visits each year.

Altogether the Lexington Medical Center's network of facilities — which includes six community clinics an occupational health center an Alzheimer's care center and 60 doctors' offices — employs some 5900 health professionals.

Strategy

Lexington Medical Center is expanding its facilities to better serve the growing population in its service territory. In 2015 it opened a new cardiac rehabilitation program at its Irmo Medical Park campus. The program — the first of its kind in the area — provides services to patients with a history of heart attack angioplasty heart failure heart transplant bypass surgery or the like.

In 2014 Lexington's physician practice opened a third sleep lab where clinicians can diagnose such conditions as hypersomnia insomnia narcolepsy restless leg syndrome snoring and sleep apnea.

EXECUTIVES

Pres-Ceo, Tod Augsburger
Sr V Pres-Cfo*, Melinda Kruzner
Emergency Medicine Specialist, Patrick M O'Malley
Coordinator, Sarah Walker
Health Professional, Hope Wisniewski
Family Practitioner, Benjamin Askins
Outcomes Coordinator, Cathy Jashinsky
Director of Materials Manageme, Douglas McCullough
Internist, Gilbert L Rogers
Assistant Director Patient Fin, Pam James
Oncologist, Theresa Altman
Auditors: KPMG LLP ATLANTA GA

LOCATIONS

HQ: LEXINGTON MEDICAL CENTER
2720 SUNSET BLVD, WEST COLUMBIA, SC
291694810
Phone: 803 791-2000
Web: WWW.LEXMED.COM

PRODUCTS/OPERATIONS

Selected Services
Patient Care
Alzheimer's Care
Birth Center
Extended Care
Family Medicine
General Surgery
Imaging
Laboratory & Pathology
Occupational Health
Weight-Loss Surgery
Health & Wellness
Community Health Screenings
Health Directions Wellness Center
Nutrition Therapy
Sleep Solutions

Selected Facilities
Community Medical Centers
LMC Batesburg-Leesville
LMC Chapin
LMC Gilbert
LMC Irmo

LMC Lexington
LMC Swansea
Hospital Units
 Alzheimers Care Center
 Birth Center
 Cancer Center
 Emergency Care
 Extended Care
 Heart Center
 Obesity Surgery Center
 Urgent Care
 Women's Services

COMPETITORS

Carolinas Healthcare
 System
Carolinas Hospital
 System
Georgetown Hospital
 System
Grand Strand Regional
 Medical Center

Laurens County
 Hospital
Mcleod Health
Palmetto Health
Upstate Affiliate

HISTORICAL FINANCIALS
Company Type: Private

Income Statement   FYE: September 30

	REVENUE ($ mil.)	NET INCOME ($ mil.)	NET PROFIT MARGIN	EMPLOYEES
09/17	953	(9)	—	5,616
09/16	906	21	2.3%	—
09/15	863	86	10.0%	—
09/14	781	95	12.2%	—
Annual Growth	6.8%	—	—	—

2017 Year-End Financials
Return on assets: (-0.6%)   Cash ($ mil.): 173
Return on equity: (-3.2%)
Current ratio: 2.80

LHH CORPORATION

When Manhattanites are looking for health care many of them head for the hill: Lenox Hill Hospital to be exact. The 650-bed facility provides care to patients on Manhattan's Upper East Side — about 45% of its patient base is from Manhattan the rest from surrounding boroughs. Services include cardiac care high-risk obstetrics pediatrics and orthopedics and sports medicine. Lenox Hill serves as a teaching affiliate for NYU Medical Center and also owns Manhattan Eye Ear and Throat Hospital a provider of specialty care for vision hearing and speech disorders. Today it's part of North Shore-Long Island Jewish Health System.

Operations
As part of the North Shore-LIJ system Lenox Hill has access to the larger organization's resources. North Shore-LIJ one of the largest health care providers in New York State; Lenox Hill is its first hospital in the New York metropolitan area.

Lenox Hill Hospital operates a handful of outpatient locations that provide medical surgical and specialized services. Its center for mental health administers a wide range of inpatient and ambulatory psychiatric services for adults and children. To provide quality services to a diverse population Lenox Hill provides multi-lingual translators.

The hospital treats more than 325000 patients a year.

Geographic Reach
The hospital serves patients from Manhattan and surrounding neighborhoods from two campuses in New York City and one in Westchester County.

Financial Performance
In 2012 Lenox Hill reported revenues of $729 million and a net loss of $37 million.

Strategy
Lenox Hill Hospital has also expanded in recent years by opening primary care center and urgent care centers in Manhattan and upgrading and enhancing some of its existing facilities such as its emergency care center to accommodate a growing number of patients. In 2012 it opened a new pediatric inpatient care unit for general and surgical care as well as new head and neck and cranial base surgery centers. In 2013 it opened a new reproduction clinic for fertility services.

Expanding its medical services outside of North Shore-LIJ system's 16 hospitals and into community settings in 2013 Lenox Hill opened the 3200-sq.-ft. Heart and Vascular Institute in Yorktown Heights — the first facility for the hospital system in Westchester County.

In 2012 Lenox Hill became the first in the New York area to perform minimally invasive heart valve replacement.

Company Background
US News & World Report has ranked Lenox Hill as one the top 50 in Cardiology and Heart Surgery and Ear Nose and Throat facilities in the US and among the top 10 hospitals in New York state.

In 2010 the hospital expanded its service offerings by adding palliative care to its medical roster. The services are aimed at relieving pain symptoms and stress related to serious illness. In many cases palliative care specialists provide care to patients who are not eligible for or don't want hospice care when facing a fatal illness.

It performed the first coronary angioplasty in the US (in 1978) and the first angiocardiogram (in 1938).

The hospital was established in 1857 as the German Dispensary.

EXECUTIVES

Exec Dir, Franck Danza
R&a, Paul Zabetakis
Scientist, V A Subramanian
Nephrology, Maria V Devita
Information Specialist, Tony Karran
Laboratory Director, Chiara Sugrue
Plastic Surgeon, Oren Lerman
Director Clinic, Oana Vele
Physician Dermatology, Andrew Woolrich
Nicu Registered Nurse, Aileen Miclat
Registered Nurse, Alison Bottenhofer

LOCATIONS

HQ: LHH CORPORATION
 100 E 77TH ST, NEW YORK, NY 100751850
Phone: 212 434-2000
Web: WWW.LENOXHILL.NORTHWELL.EDU

PRODUCTS/OPERATIONS

Selected Services
Bariatric surgery
Cardiothoracic surgery
Cardiovascular care
Colorectal surgery
Critical care
Maternal and child health
Manhattan Ear Eye and Throat Institute
Mental health
Neurosurgery
Palliative care
Pathology
Plastic and reconstructive surgery
Primary care
Radiology
Rehabilitation
Robotic surgery

COMPETITORS

Beth Israel Medical Center
Bronx-lebanon Hospital
Catholic Health Services Of Long Island
Catholic Healthcare System
Lutheran Healthcare
Maimonides Medical Center
Memorial Sloan-kettering
Montefiore Medical
New York City Health And Hospitals
Newyork-presbyterian Hospital

HISTORICAL FINANCIALS
Company Type: Private

Income Statement   FYE: December 31

	REVENUE ($ mil.)	NET INCOME ($ mil.)	NET PROFIT MARGIN	EMPLOYEES
12/18	1,064	73	6.9%	2,955
12/16	960	21	2.3%	—
12/14	790	3	0.4%	—
Annual Growth	7.7%	119.1%	—	—

2018 Year-End Financials
Return on assets: 5.8%   Cash ($ mil.): 2
Return on equity: 12.9%
Current ratio: 1.10

LIBERTY UNIVERSITY, INC.

EXECUTIVES

Cfo, Don Moon
Sr V Pres*, Mark Hine
Cao*, Ronald E Hawkins
Coo*, Randy Smith Randy Smith
SEC*, David M Corry
Vice President of University S, Trey Falwell
Project Coordinator, William Mailand
Assistant Professor, Bruce M Kirk
Assistant Professor, Danielle E Scholten
Assistant Professor, Michael R Mitchell
Accounting Staff, Michael Ohemeng-Dapaah
Auditors: BDO USA LLP ATLANTA GA

LOCATIONS

HQ: LIBERTY UNIVERSITY, INC.
 1971 UNIVERSITY BLVD, LYNCHBURG, VA 245150002
Phone: 434 582-2000
Web: WWW.LIBERTY.EDU

HISTORICAL FINANCIALS
Company Type: Private

Income Statement   FYE: June 30

	REVENUE ($ mil.)	NET INCOME ($ mil.)	NET PROFIT MARGIN	EMPLOYEES
06/21	1,153	551	47.8%	7,200
06/20	1,043	213	20.4%	—
06/19	989	316	32.0%	—
06/18	896	276	30.8%	—
Annual Growth	8.7%	25.9%	—	—

2021 Year-End Financials
Return on assets: 14.0%   Cash ($ mil.): 414
Return on equity: 15.9%
Current ratio: —

LIFEBRIDGE HEALTH, INC.

LifeBridge Health links patients to healthcare. Serving the Baltimore region the not-for-profit company operates two general hospitals — Sinai Hospital of Baltimore and Northwest Hospital — with specialties including oncology neurology pediatrics and sports medicine. The LifeBridge Health network also provides long-term care at the Levindale Hebrew Geriatric Center and Hospital (nursing subacute and adult day care services) and the Courtland Gardens Nursing & Rehabilitation Center. Altogether the health system boasts some 1190 beds. LifeBridge's Health Wellness division includes a health and fitness program and community fitness center.

Operations

Sinai Hospital is a teaching hospital with residency programs for medical students training at Johns Hopkins University and University of Maryland. Levindale also serves as a teaching facility for medical dental nursing and social work students pursuing training to serve geriatric populations.

EXECUTIVES

Ceo, Neil M Meltzer
Chb*, Howard Weiss
Sr V Pres*, Aric Spitulnik
Cfo*, David Krajewski
Associate Program Director, Anthony Castelbuono
Director of Patient Care Servi, Bonnie Hartley Faust
Division Head, Fouad Abbas
Radiologist, Karen Song
Director Oncology, Mayer Gorbaty
Foreman, P Jay
Clinical Training Director, S Testa
Auditors: KPMG LLP BALTIMORE MD

LOCATIONS

HQ: LIFEBRIDGE HEALTH, INC.
2401 W BELVEDERE AVE, BALTIMORE, MD
212155216
Phone: 410 601-5653
Web: WWW.LIFEBRIDGEHEALTH.ORG

PRODUCTS/OPERATIONS

Selected Locations
Courtland Gardens Nursing & Rehabilitation Center
Levindale Hebrew Geriatric Center and Hospital
Northwest Hospital
Sinai Hospital

Selected Services
Bariatric and Minimally Invasive Surgery
Brain & Spine Institute
Cancer Institute
Hospitalist Program
Rubin Institute for Advanced Orthopedics
Vascular Institute

COMPETITORS

Anne Arundel Medical Center	Johns Hopkins Health System
Ascension Health	Medstar Health
Bon Secours Health	Medstar Union Memorial Hospital
Franklin Square Hospital Center	University Of Maryland Medical System
Gbmc	

HISTORICAL FINANCIALS
Company Type: Private

Income Statement — FYE: June 30

	REVENUE ($ mil.)	NET INCOME ($ mil.)	NET PROFIT MARGIN	EMPLOYEES
06/20	1,662	54	3.3%	6,000
06/19	1,610	65	4.1%	—
06/17	1,527	111	7.3%	—
06/15	145	0	0.5%	—
Annual Growth	62.8%	134.1%	—	—

2020 Year-End Financials
Return on assets: 2.1%
Return on equity: 4.1%
Current ratio: 2.00
Cash ($ mil.): 251

LIMETREE BAY TERMINALS LLC

HOVENSA brings together US and Latin American know-how and operations to handle oil products in the US Virgin Islands. HOVENSA is a joint venture of Hess and Venezuelan oil giant PDVSA (its major crude oil supplier). Once the largest private employer in the US Virgin Islands the company operated a 500000-barrels-per-day crude oil refinery on St. Croix along with two specialized oil processing complexes a 150000-barrels-per-day fluid catalytic cracking unit and a 58000-barrels-per-day delayed coker unit. However the St. Croix refinery had run up losses for years; it was shut down in 2012 and was put up for sale in 2013.

Strategy

Citing high operating and maintenance costs (the refinery was fueled by oil not the cheaper natural gas) and the growth of lower-cost refineries in emerging markets HOVENSA has posted $1.3 billion in losses since 2009. As a result the company decided to cut its losses by converting the refinery into an oil storage terminal which can take advantage of St. Croix's strategic location. Its 55-ft. deep harbor enables it to receive crude oil tanker deliveries from Venezuela and around the world. The storage terminal employs about 100 workers. The shutdown of the refinery resulted in more than 2000 employes being laid off.

Company Background

In 2009 the global economic downturn depressed demand for oil caused a dip in production and prompted the company to lay off 270 employees (about 21% of its total contract workers).

Crude thoughput has declined steadily at HOVENSA due to weaker refining margins and planned and unplanned maintenance from 402000 barrels per day (bpd) in 2009 to 390000 bpd in 2010 to 284000 bpd in 2011.

Auditors: ERNST & YOUNG LLP NEW YORK N

LOCATIONS

HQ: LIMETREE BAY TERMINALS LLC
1 ESTATE HOPE, CHRISTIANSTED, VI 00820
Phone: 340 692-3000

COMPETITORS

Chevron	Royal Dutch Shell
Conocophillips	Sunoco
Exxon Mobil	Valero Energy
Marathon Oil	

LINCOLN MEDICAL AND MENTAL HEALTH CENTER

EXECUTIVES

Exec Dir, Milton Nunez
Infectious Disease Specialist, Chung Kim
Doctor, Karen Hennessey
Obstetrician Gynecologist, Manisha Jain
Emergency Medicine Specialist, Andaleeb H Raja
Geriatrician, Dilshad F Chagla
Emergency Medicine Specialist, Moira McCarty
General Surgeon, Rushi Shah
Obstetrician Gynecologist, Sandra A Semple
Psychologist, Michael Fraser
Gastroenterologist, Sulaiman Azeez

LOCATIONS

HQ: LINCOLN MEDICAL AND MENTAL HEALTH CENTER
234 E 149TH ST, BRONX, NY 104515504
Phone: 718 579-5000
Web: WWW.NYCHEALTHANDHOSPITALS.ORG

HISTORICAL FINANCIALS
Company Type: Private

Income Statement — FYE: June 30

	REVENUE ($ mil.)	NET INCOME ($ mil.)	NET PROFIT MARGIN	EMPLOYEES
06/16	616	120	19.6%	3,406
06/15	530	20	3.9%	—
Annual Growth	16.2%	488.5%		

2016 Year-End Financials
Return on assets: 14.0%
Return on equity: 50.4%
Current ratio: 1.40
Cash ($ mil.): —

HISTORICAL FINANCIALS
Company Type: Private

Income Statement — FYE: December 31

	REVENUE ($ mil.)	NET INCOME ($ mil.)	NET PROFIT MARGIN	EMPLOYEES
12/09	10,048	(451)	—	1,300
12/08	17,479	94	0.5%	—
Annual Growth	(42.5%)	—	—	—

2009 Year-End Financials
Return on assets: 3.2%
Return on equity: (-4.5%)
Current ratio: 0.20
Cash ($ mil.): 77

LOMA LINDA UNIVERSITY MEDICAL CENTER

EXECUTIVES

Ceo, Richard H Hart
Pres, James Jesse
V Pres, Richard Catalano
Tres, Noni Patchett
Associate Professor, Standford Shu
Assistant Professor, Andy Lampkin
Assistant Professor, Aijaz Hashmi
Assistant Professor, Alexander Chien
Assistant Professor, Catherine Tan
Assistant Professor, Cheryl Imes
Assistant Professor, Cinda Nauertz
Auditors: ERNST & YOUNG LLP IRVINE CA

LOCATIONS

HQ: LOMA LINDA UNIVERSITY MEDICAL CENTER
11234 ANDERSON ST, LOMA LINDA, CA 923542871
Phone: 909 558-4000
Web: WWW.LLUH.ORG

HISTORICAL FINANCIALS

Company Type: Private

Income Statement   FYE: June 30

	REVENUE ($ mil.)	NET INCOME ($ mil.)	NET PROFIT MARGIN	EMPLOYEES
06/21	1,511	145	9.6%	5,766
06/20*	1,439	71	4.9%	—
12/16	1,776	128	7.3%	—
12/15	846	(413)	—	—
Annual Growth 12.3%		—	—	—

*Fiscal year change

2021 Year-End Financials

Return on assets: 3.5%   Cash ($ mil.): 180
Return on equity: 13.1%
Current ratio: 1.70

LONG BEACH MEDICAL CENTER

Long Beach Medical Center (LBMC) is an old-timer in the Long Beach health care market. A subsidiary of Memorial Care LBMC provides a full range of health services to residents of the Long Beach California area. Services include primary emergency diagnostic surgical therapeutic and re-habilitative care. The hospital is home to centers for treatment of cancer heart stroke and women's and children's health concerns. It also provides home and hospice care programs as well as occupational health services. Through Outpatient Wound Healing Center LBMC provides full-services wound care for adults and children in Los Angeles County and Orange County.

EXECUTIVES

Ceo, John Bishop
Pres-Ceo*, Barry Arbuckle PHD
Sr V Pres- Cno*, Judy Fix

Sr V Pres-CIO*, Scott Joslyn
V Pres*, Thomas Poole
Cfo-Cpo*, Wendy Dorchester
Coo*, Tamra Kaplan
Coo*, Suize Reinsvold
Executive Secretary, Donna L Gorman
Coordinator, Catherine Fagen
Neurologist, Randolph B Shey

LOCATIONS

HQ: LONG BEACH MEDICAL CENTER
2801 ATLANTIC AVE FL 2, LONG BEACH, CA
908061701
Phone: 562 933-2000
Web: WWW.MEMORIALCARE.ORG

PRODUCTS/OPERATIONS

Selected Institutes and Centers
Certified Comprehensive Stroke Center
Long Beach Adult & Pediatric Sleep Center
MemorialCare Breast Center at Long Beach Medical Center
MemorialCare Heart & Vascular Institute
MemorialCare Imaging Center
MemorialCare Joint Replacement Center
MemorialCare Rehabilitation Institute
MemorialCare Todd Cancer Institute
Spine Center at Long Beach Memorial
Trauma Center at Long Beach Medical Center

Selected Services
Blood Donation Center
Diabetes Care
Digestive Care
Emergency Department
Gynecological Care at Long Beach Medical Center
Lung & Respiratory Care
Minimally Invasive Surgery at Long Beach Memorial
Palliative Care Program at Long Beach Medical Center
Pharmacy at Long Beach Medical Center
Robotic-Assisted Surgery at Long Beach Memorial
Surgical Care
Wound Healing & Hyperbaric Medicine at Long Beach Medical Center

COMPETITORS

Adventist Health System West
Aptium Oncology
Brotman Medical Center
Cedars-sinai Medical Center
Dignity Health
Good Samaritan Hospital (los Angeles)
Hca
Hoag Memorial Hospital
Hollywood Presbyterian Medical Center
Methodist Hospital Of Southern California
Newhall Memorial Hospital
Pasadena Hospital Association
Providence Health System Southern California
Sutter Health
Tenet Healthcare
Torrance Memorial Medical Center
Trinity Health (novi)
Western Medical Center - Santa Ana

HISTORICAL FINANCIALS

Company Type: Private

Income Statement   FYE: June 30

	REVENUE ($ mil.)	NET INCOME ($ mil.)	NET PROFIT MARGIN	EMPLOYEES
06/18	633	63	10.1%	6,000
06/16	618	88	14.4%	—
06/15	624	93	15.0%	—
06/11	1,083	63	5.9%	—
Annual Growth	(7.4%)	0.1%	—	—

2018 Year-End Financials

Return on assets: 4.8%   Cash ($ mil.): —
Return on equity: 5.3%
Current ratio: 11.70

LONG ISLAND JEWISH MEDICAL CENTER

Long Island Jewish Medical Center serves the western edge of Long Island and the eastern edge of the greater metropolitan New York area. The medical center campus includes Long Island Jewish Hospital a general acute care hospital; Cohen Children's Medical Center of New York Hospital which provides a full range of pediatric care services; and The Zucker Hillside Hospital a psychiatric hospital for patients of all ages. The medical center's staff includes 1200 physicians. Long Island Jewish Medical Center is the primary clinical and medical training facility of Northwell Health.

Operations
The Long Island Jewish Medical Center's main activities are centered at the Long Island Jewish Hospital which provides emergency diagnostic surgical inpatient and outpatient services. The hospital has centers for cancer treatment cardiac surgery and women's health as well as units specializing in hearing loss stroke recovery sleep disorders and hemophilia treatment. As an affiliate of Hofstra University the Long Island Jewish Hospital also provides graduate medical education programs.

Geographic Reach
Long Island Jewish Medical Center is located on a 48-acre campus on the border of New York's Queens and Nassau counties about 15 miles east of Manhattan.

Strategy
To enhance services provided to residents of the growing New York City metropolitan area Long Island Jewish Medical Center is conducting expansion efforts on its facilities. In 2012 it opened a new $300 million 10-story inpatient tower (containing 160 private patient rooms) at the Long Island Jewish Hospital. The project increased the hospital's overall capacity and added women's health cardiovascular care and wellness centers.

EXECUTIVES

Ceo, Michael J Dowling
Coordinator, Jennifer Graff
Internal Medicine Practitioner, Deyun Yang
Assistant Professor, Kenneth J Nichols
Internal Medicine Practitioner, Lauren D Block
Internal Medicine Practitioner, Pranisha Gautam
Safety Manager, Clifford Jarvis
Emergency Medicine Specialist, Jeremy Seelinger-Devey
Anp, Renee S Cooke
Records Director, Patricia Hennelly
Physician Ed, Robert Gochman

LOCATIONS

HQ: LONG ISLAND JEWISH MEDICAL CENTER
27005 76TH AVE, NEW HYDE PARK, NY 110401496
Phone: 516 465-2600
Web: WWW.LIJED.COM

PRODUCTS/OPERATIONS

Selected Facilities
Long Island Jewish Hospital (490 beds)
The Steven and Alexandra Cohen Children's Medical Center (160 beds)
The Zucker Hillside Hospital (240 beds)

Selected Services
Anesthesiology
Cardiac Services
Center for Maternal-Fetal Health
Dental Medicine
Emergency Medicine

Medicine
Neurosciences
Obstetrics
Ophthalmology
Orthopaedic Surgery
Otolaryngology
Pathology
Radiation Oncology
Radiology
Rehabilitation
Surgery
Thoracic Surgery
Urogynecology
Urology: The Arthur Smith Insitute for Urology

COMPETITORS

Catholic Health Services Of Long Island
Mercy Medical Center (ny)
North Shore University Hospital
Nuhealth
St. Francis Hospital Roslyn
Winthrop-university Hospital

HISTORICAL FINANCIALS

Company Type: Private

Income Statement				FYE: December 31
	REVENUE ($ mil.)	NET INCOME ($ mil.)	NET PROFIT MARGIN	EMPLOYEES
12/18	2,448	56	2.3%	1,214
12/17	2,222	154	6.9%	—
12/16	2,093	162	7.8%	—
12/15	1,524	44	2.9%	—
Annual Growth	17.1%	7.6%	—	—

2018 Year-End Financials

Return on assets: 2.0%   Cash ($ mil.): 1
Return on equity: 8.4%
Current ratio: 2.00

LONG ISLAND POWER AUTHORITY

The long and short of it is that Long Island Power Authority (LIPA) owns the electric transmission and distribution system on Long Island that delivers power to more than 1.1 million retail customers. The company's network which is managed and operated by the National Grid USA consists of nearly 14000 miles of overhead and underground lines. LIPA offers energy conservation products and services as well as incentive programs to encourage customers to purchase energy from "green" (environmentally friendly) power generation sources. LIPA is a municipally owned not-for-profit utility company.

EXECUTIVES

Pres-Ceo, Matthew Cohen
Gen Counsel-Sec*, Lynda Nicolino
V Pres-Envrnm Affrs*, Michael Deering
V Pres-Cfo*, Herbert L Hogue
V Pres*, Kenneth Kane
Procurement Director, Maria Gomes
Manager Customer Operations Ov, Timothy Lederer
Administrative Assistant, Anthony Ciorra
Auditor, Kristin Leung
Independent Technology, Paul Capel
Vice President, Kathleen Mitterway
Auditors: KPMG LLP NEW YORK NEW YORK

LOCATIONS

HQ: LONG ISLAND POWER AUTHORITY
    333 EARLE OVINGTON BLVD # 403, UNIONDALE, NY 115533606
Phone: 516 222-7700
Web: WWW.LIPOWER.ORG

PRODUCTS/OPERATIONS

Energy Conservation Products and Services
Commercial energy analysis
Construction and renovation incentives
Energy Star labeled homes program
Geothermal rebates
HVAC upgrades
Lighting and appliance solutions
Peak demand reduction programs
Residential energy affordability program
Residential energy audit
Solar Pioneer program
Wind energy development initiatives

COMPETITORS

Avangrid   New York Power
Ch Energy   Authority
Con Edison

HISTORICAL FINANCIALS

Company Type: Private

Income Statement				FYE: December 31
	REVENUE ($ mil.)	NET INCOME ($ mil.)	NET PROFIT MARGIN	EMPLOYEES
12/20	3,900	18	0.5%	100
12/19	3,516	24	0.7%	—
12/18	3,576	22	0.6%	—
12/16	3,399	(26)	—	—
Annual Growth	3.5%	—	—	—

2020 Year-End Financials

Return on assets: 0.1%   Cash ($ mil.): 266
Return on equity: 3.5%
Current ratio: 1.50

LOS ANGELES COUNTY OFFICE OF EDUCATION

EXECUTIVES

Ceo, Rudell S Freer
Pres*, Rebecca J Turrentine
V Pres*, Katie Braude
E-Business Point of Contact, Roberta Gerarde
Executive Officer, Ronald Reynolds
Director, Dotti Ysais
Risk Management Officer, Sergio Cazorla
Financial Advisory, Jeff Young
Custodial Operations Superviso, Jhowel Mercado
Senior Specialist, Joseph Oporto
Administrative Office, Keith Crafton
Auditors: EIDEBAILLY LLP RANCHO CUCAMON

LOCATIONS

HQ: LOS ANGELES COUNTY OFFICE OF EDUCATION
    9300 IMPERIAL HWY, DOWNEY, CA 902422813
Phone: 562 922-6111
Web: WWW.BTPLACOE.COM

HISTORICAL FINANCIALS

Company Type: Private

Income Statement				FYE: June 30
	REVENUE ($ mil.)	NET INCOME ($ mil.)	NET PROFIT MARGIN	EMPLOYEES
06/19	621	38	6.2%	4,000
06/18	657	22	3.4%	—
06/17	646	17	2.6%	—
06/16	661	7	1.2%	—
Annual Growth	(2.1%)	71.2%	—	—

LOS ANGELES DEPARTMENT OF WATER AND POWER

The Los Angeles Department of Water and Power (LADWP) keeps the movie cameras running and the swimming pools full. The largest municipally owned utility in the US LADWP provides electricity to approximately 1.4 million residential and business customers and water to some 681000 customers. The company has net dependable capacity of about 8010 MW from a diverse mix of energy resources; it also buys and sells wholesale power. As a revenue-producing proprietary department the LADWP transfers a portion of its annual estimated electric revenues to the City of Los Angeles general fund.

Operations
LADWP's operations are financed solely by the sale of water and electric services. The department has about 125 tanks and reservoirs ranging in size from 10000 to 60 billion gallons and a storage capacity of approximately 323820 acre feet. Nine aqueduct reservoirs provide some 95% of the Water system's storage capacity while major and minor distribution reservoirs and tanks provide the remaining nearly 5%. It also has about 85 pump stations a distribution main of around 7335 miles of pipe.

The company has about 35 generation plants with some 1.6 MW of city-owned energy storage approximately 21.5 MW of utility-scale battery energy storage and some 1244 MW of pumped hydro storage. About 35% of power resources come from renewable energy over 25% from natural gas about 25% from nuclear around 20% from coal and nearly 5% from large hydroelectric.

Geographic Reach
The company is based in Los Angeles California.

Sales and Marketing
The company delivers reliable safe water and electricity to some 4 million residents and businesses in Los Angeles. LADWP also provides its around 681000 water customers and some 1.4 million electric customers with quality service at competitive prices.

Financial Performance
LADWP's operations are entirely financed by the sale of water and electric services. For fiscal 2020 the multi-utility transferred $230 million of its annual electric revenues to the City of Los Angeles general fund. Operating revenue decreased $264 million mainly due to a decrease of $203 million in total from retail customers a $50 million

decrease in wholesale and other revenue and a $9.7 million increase of uncollectable accounts.

LADWP's operating revenue from its Water System in fiscal 2020 increased by $22 million or 2% from fiscal year 2019 primarily due to increase in pass-through rates as a result of higher capital expenditures and operating and maintenance expenses for Water Quality projects.

Strategy

LADWP continues to provide the city with reliable water and power service in a cost effective and environmentally responsible manner. In late 2020 LADWP teamed up with the California Air Resources Board (CARB) to offer the California Clean Fuel Reward (CCFR) a point-of-sale price reduction of up to $1500 for the purchase or lease of any eligible new battery electric or plug-in hybrid vehicle from a participating automotive retailer. In addition to accessing the CCFR LADWP residential customers could apply for EV incentives for used EVs and charging stations through the Department's "Charge Up L.A." rebate program.

LADWP also offered a new energy management program that allowed customers to save energy and support a cleaner more reliable power grid by enrolling their smart thermostats. LADWP Power Savers is the energy management program for residential and small business electric customers to help lower and manage their energy costs while reducing strain on the power grid during periods of high energy demand. At the same time the program supports LADWP's Clean Grid LA initiative by providing a clean energy alternative to using natural gas "peaker" plants to maintain reliability when energy use spikes.

Company Background

LADWP was founded in 1902.

EXECUTIVES

Gen Mgr, Martin Adams
Gen Mgr*, David H Wright
Coo*, Martin L Adams
Gen Counsel*, Joseph A Brajevich
Senior Assistant General Manag, Richard F Harasick
Senior Assistant General Mgr, Reiko A Kerr
Senior Assistant General Mgr, Andrew C Kendall
Chief Administrative Officer, Donna I Stevener
Interim Cfo, Ann M Santilli
Chief Sustainability Officer, Nancy Sutley
Manager Customer, Caroline McKnight
Auditors: KPMG LLP LOS ANGELES CA

LOCATIONS

HQ: LOS ANGELES DEPARTMENT OF WATER AND POWER
111 N HOPE ST, LOS ANGELES, CA 900122607
Phone: 213 367-1320
Web: WWW.LADWP.COM

COMPETITORS

Aes	Edison International
American States Water	Pg&e Corporation
Avista	Sacramento Municipal
California Water	Utility
Service	Sempra Energy
Calpine	Southwest Water
Duke Energy	

HISTORICAL FINANCIALS

Company Type: Private

Income Statement

| | | NET | NET | |
| | REVENUE | INCOME | PROFIT | |
	($ mil.)	($ mil.)	MARGIN	EMPLOYEES
06/17	1,118	140	12.6%	9,500
06/11	3,125	57	1.8%	—
06/10	812	67	8.3%	—
Annual Growth	4.7%	11.1%	—	—

FYE: June 30

2017 Year-End Financials

Return on assets: 1.4%   Cash ($ mil.): 320
Return on equity: 4.5%
Current ratio: 1.20

LOS ANGELES LOMOD CORPORATION

EXECUTIVES

Pres, Nancy Wesoff
Dir*, Lucelia Hooper
President*, Connie Loyola
Principal*, Ben Besley
Principal*, Erica Jacquez
Manager, Blanca Vasquez
Sr Quality Assurance, Carina Espinoza
Sr Compliance Specialist, Daisy Zuniga
Sr Quality Assurance, Dianna Jimenez
Sr Quality Assurance, Erika Cedeno
Compliance Specialist, Jose Aguilar
Auditors: MACIAS GINI & O'CONNELL LLP L

LOCATIONS

HQ: LOS ANGELES LOMOD CORPORATION
2600 WILSHIRE BLVD, LOS ANGELES, CA 900573400
Phone: 213 252-2510
Web: WWW.LOMOD.ORG

HISTORICAL FINANCIALS

Company Type: Private

Income Statement

| | | NET | NET | |
| | REVENUE | INCOME | PROFIT | |
	($ mil.)	($ mil.)	MARGIN	EMPLOYEES
12/18	575	14	2.5%	44
12/17	534	12	2.4%	—
12/13	405	6	1.5%	—
12/09	356	5	1.4%	—
Annual Growth	5.5%	12.3%	—	—

FYE: December 31

2018 Year-End Financials

Return on assets: 34.9%   Cash ($ mil.): 37
Return on equity: 35.2%
Current ratio: —

LOS ANGELES UNIFIED SCHOOL DISTRICT

EXECUTIVES

Superintendent, Michelle King
Superintendent*, Steve Zimmer
Assistant, Kathryn De Sensi
Superintendent, Dr John Deasy
Coordinator, Esparza Monica
Coordinator, Ana-Maria Madero
Coordinator, Beatriz Lopez
Staff, Betty Moore
Coordinator, Chris Oswald
Project Coordinator, Diana Diaz
Coordinator, Jennifer Di Lorenzo

LOCATIONS

HQ: LOS ANGELES UNIFIED SCHOOL DISTRICT
333 S BEAUDRY AVE STE 209, LOS ANGELES, CA 900175141
Phone: 213 241-1000
Web: WWW.LAUSD.NET

HISTORICAL FINANCIALS

Company Type: Private

Income Statement

| | | NET | NET | |
| | REVENUE | INCOME | PROFIT | |
	($ mil.)	($ mil.)	MARGIN	EMPLOYEES
06/20	9,378	160	1.7%	65,231
06/09	0	0	—	—
06/06	0	0	—	—
06/05	0	0	20.1%	—
Annual Growth	92.6%	63.5%	—	—

FYE: June 30

2020 Year-End Financials

Return on assets: 0.7%   Cash ($ mil.): 5,888
Return on equity: —
Current ratio: —

LOUDOUN COUNTY PUBLIC SCHOOL DISTRICT

EXECUTIVES

Supt, Eric Williams
Coordinator, Mark Taylor
Assistant Superintendent, Mary V Kealy
Coordinator, Paige Neeley
Sergeant, Linda Cerniglia
Information Technology Manager, Andrew Leith
Education Specialist, Hollister Davidson
Counselor, Colleen Hurley
Teacher, Abed Kirrish
Director, Anthony Royse
Supervisor of Applications Dev, Don Bell
Auditors: CHERRY BEKAERT LLP TYSONS COR

LOCATIONS

HQ: LOUDOUN COUNTY PUBLIC SCHOOL DISTRICT
21000 EDUCATION CT, BROADLANDS, VA 201485526
Phone: 571 252-1000
Web: WWW.LCPS.ORG

HISTORICAL FINANCIALS
Company Type: Private

Income Statement				FYE: June 30
	REVENUE ($ mil.)	NET INCOME ($ mil.)	NET PROFIT MARGIN	EMPLOYEES
06/16	1,130	14	1.3%	6,900
06/15	1,080	19	1.8%	—
Annual Growth	4.7%	(28.6%)	—	—

LOUISIANA CHILDRENS MEDICAL CENTER, INC

EXECUTIVES

Pres-Ceo, Mary Perrin
Cfo, Jenny Barnett-Sarpalius
Coordinator, Susan Wack MBA
Coordinator, Jennifer Turner
Chief Administrative Officer, Ayame Dinkler
Svphuman Resources, Chad Courrege
Vpsupply Chain Management, James Ludwig
Chief Legal Officer, Jody Martin
Vppopulation Health Network De, Meg Vitter
Chief Strategy Officer, Robert Eli
Physician, Scott Zander

LOCATIONS

HQ: LOUISIANA CHILDRENS MEDICAL CENTER, INC
1100 POYDRAS ST STE 2500, NEW ORLEANS, LA
701632500
Phone: 504 896-9581
Web: WWW.LCMCHEALTH.ORG

HISTORICAL FINANCIALS
Company Type: Private

Income Statement				FYE: December 31
	REVENUE ($ mil.)	NET INCOME ($ mil.)	NET PROFIT MARGIN	EMPLOYEES
12/18	1,617	(34)	—	6,100
12/14	21	0	—	—
12/13*	926	285	30.8%	—
03/13	500	10	2.1%	—
Annual Growth	21.6%	—	—	—

*Fiscal year change

2018 Year-End Financials

Return on assets: (-1.3%)   Cash ($ mil.): 104
Return on equity: (-2.3%)
Current ratio: 1.20

LOUISVILLE-JEFFERSON COUNTY METRO GOVERNMENT

Louisville is so much more than bourbon baseball bats and horse races. The largest city in Kentucky Louisville counts about 600000 people in the urban area which has the same parameters as Jefferson County. Louisville is home to liquor company Brown-Forman; Hillerich & Bradsby maker of Louisville Slugger baseball bats; and Churchill Downs where the Kentucky Derby is held. In addition Louisville has a few Fortune 500 companies in the city - fast food operator YUM! Brands and health care companies Humana and Kindred.

EXECUTIVES

Mayor, Greg Fischer
Cfo*, Daniel Frockt
Assistant Director, Bart Irwin
Assistant Director, Griffin Torrance
Business Accountant II, Molli M Duff
Personnel Supervisor I, Bobbi Morrison
Buyer II, Larr Smith
Engineer I, Tony Kelly
Secretary, Cecli M Bandy
Director, Eri C Friedlander
Senior Social Worker, Sherr Brooks
Auditors: CROWE HORWATH LLP LOUISVILLE

LOCATIONS

HQ: LOUISVILLE-JEFFERSON COUNTY METRO
GOVERNMENT
527 W JEFFERSON ST # 400, LOUISVILLE, KY
402022814
Phone: 502 574-2003
Web: WWW.JEFFERSONCOUNTYCLERK.ORG

HISTORICAL FINANCIALS
Company Type: Private

Income Statement				FYE: June 30
	REVENUE ($ mil.)	NET INCOME ($ mil.)	NET PROFIT MARGIN	EMPLOYEES
06/20	860	26	3.1%	6,500
06/19	873	(38)	—	—
06/18	825	14	1.8%	—
06/17	797	11	1.5%	—
Annual Growth	2.6%	30.8%	—	—

2020 Year-End Financials

Return on assets: 0.3%   Cash ($ mil.): 428
Return on equity: 1.1%
Current ratio: —

LOWER COLORADO RIVER AUTHORITY

The Lower Colorado River Authority serves customers and communities throughout Texas by managing the lower Colorado River; generating and transmitting electric power; providing a clean reliable water supply; and offering outdoor adventures at more than 40 parks along the Colorado River from the Texas Hill Country to the Gulf Coast. LCRA and its employees are committed to fulfilling its mission to enhance the quality of life of the Texans it serves through water stewardship energy and community service. LCRA was created by the Texas Legislature in 1934 and receives no state appropriations.

Operations
The LCRA has pursued two complementary goals — providing reliable low-cost utility and public services and ensuring the protection of the area's natural resources. In the latter role the LCRA owns or operates more than 40 public recreation areas comprising more than 11000 acres. It also monitors the water quality and levels of the lakes formed by its dams.

Geographic Reach
The company was based Austin Texas.

Sales and Marketing
The company offers business opportunities land development and land parks concessionaires.

Company Background
The company was founded in 1934 by State Legislature

EXECUTIVES

Chm, Timothy Timmerman
Exec V Pres*, John Hofmann
Exec V Pres*, Bill Lauderback
Cfo*, Richard Williams
Exec Asst*, Allison Millard
Executive Officer, Rosemary Rust
Benefits Coordinator, Melissa Deleon
Supervisor, Hydro Operations C, Bill Barr
Business Analyst, Leslie Kearns
Senior Information Security AR, Barry Moody
Superintendent, Brandon Mathis
Auditors: BAKER TILLY VIRCHOW KRAUSE LLP

LOCATIONS

HQ: LOWER COLORADO RIVER AUTHORITY
3700 LAKE AUSTIN BLVD, AUSTIN, TX 787033504
Phone: 512 473-3200
Web: WWW.LCRA.ORG

PRODUCTS/OPERATIONS

Selected Subsidiaries and Affiliates
Fayette Power Project (coal-fired power generating units)
GenTex Power Corporation (power generation)
LCRA Transmission Services Corporation (power transmission services)

HISTORICAL FINANCIALS
Company Type: Private

Income Statement				FYE: June 30
	REVENUE ($ mil.)	NET INCOME ($ mil.)	NET PROFIT MARGIN	EMPLOYEES
06/15	1,021	15	1.5%	1,800
06/12	1,261	101	8.0%	—
06/11	1,185	48	4.1%	—
06/10	1,244	110	8.9%	—
Annual Growth	(3.9%)	(32.5%)	—	—

2015 Year-End Financials

Return on assets: 0.3%   Cash ($ mil.): 182
Return on equity: 1.2%
Current ratio: 1.20

LOYOLA UNIVERSITY MEDICAL CENTER

EXECUTIVES

Ceo, Roger Spoelman
Pres, Mary Elizabeth Cleary
V Pres, John B Hart
Internal Medicine Practitioner, Joshua D Evans
Internal Medicine Practitioner, Julia Brown
Staff, Vinny Gossain
Coordinator, Denise Gabriele
Oral and Maxillofacial Surgeon, Jelada Huff
Internal Medicine Practitioner, Lindsey E
 Tengerstrom
Assistant Professor, Toni Pak
Internal Medicine Practitioner, Ebinehita
 Arhebamen

LOCATIONS

HQ: LOYOLA UNIVERSITY MEDICAL CENTER
 2160 S 1ST AVE, MAYWOOD, IL 601533328
Phone: 708 216-9000
Web: WWW.LOYOLAFITNESS.ORG

HISTORICAL FINANCIALS

Company Type: Private

Income Statement				FYE: June 30
	REVENUE ($ mil.)	NET INCOME ($ mil.)	NET PROFIT MARGIN	EMPLOYEES
06/20	1,581	81	5.2%	81
06/15	1,210	19	1.6%	
Annual Growth	5.5%	33.3%	—	—

2020 Year-End Financials

Return on assets: 4.6%   Cash ($ mil.): 14
Return on equity: 35.7%
Current ratio: 1.00

LOYOLA UNIVERSITY MEDICAL CENTER

Auditors: PRICEWATERHOUSECOOPERS LLP WA

LOCATIONS

HQ: LOYOLA UNIVERSITY MEDICAL CENTER
 2160 S 1ST AVE, MAYWOOD, IL 601533328
Phone: 708 216-9000
Web: WWW.LOYOLAHEALTH.ORG

HISTORICAL FINANCIALS

Company Type: Private

Income Statement				FYE: June 30
	REVENUE ($ mil.)	NET INCOME ($ mil.)	NET PROFIT MARGIN	EMPLOYEES
06/11	938	14	1.6%	4
06/10	917	8	0.9%	—
Annual Growth	2.3%	75.7%	—	—

2011 Year-End Financials

Return on assets: —   Cash ($ mil.): 65
Return on equity: 1.6%
Current ratio: 0.30

LOYOLA UNIVERSITY OF CHICAGO INC

Loyola University is a Jesuit Catholic university with a reach that extends far beyond the Windy City. In addition to its three Chicago-area campuses the university also maintains an undergraduate campus in Italy and a study center in Beijing China. Loyola University's nearly 14765 students can choose from more than 80 undergraduate nearly 100 master's a dozen doctoral and more than 140 graduate professional and certificate programs. With nearly 1390 full-time faculty and staff members the not-for-profit school has a 15:1 student-teacher ratio. Notable alumni include actor Bob Newhart and writer Sandra Cisneros. Established in 1870 by a group of Jesuit priests the university turned its medical center into a separate subsidiary in 1995.

Operations

The university's undergraduate offers major and minor programs including accounting advertising and public relations biochemistry criminal justice and criminology economics film and digital media and theology among others. It also offers graduate and professional education such as arts and sciences biomedical sciences & medicine business continuing and professional studies (adult) education law nursing pastoral studies and social work.

Undergraduate students work with advisors in Academic Advising. Graduate students are advised differently depending on their school and program. These schools include The Graduate School Quinlan School of Business Institute of Pastoral Studies Marcella Niehoff School of Nursing School of Continuing and Professional Studies School of Education and School of Social Work.

Geographic Reach

Headquartered in Illinois Loyola University three Chicago campuses include Lake Shore Water Tower and Health Sciences as well as the John Felice Rome Center in Italy. It is home to a dozen schools and colleges that include arts and sciences business administration communication education graduate studies law medicine nursing continuing and professional studies and social work.

Loyola also features course locations in Beijing China and Saigon-Ho Chi Minh City Vietnam.

Sales and Marketing

Loyola University uses social media channels such as Facebook Twitter and YouTube to connect with the students faculty staff and Alumni.

Strategy

The Loyola University Chicago created Plan 2020. Plan 2020 is a framework to focus its energies on improving the quality of education so its students are prepared to be agents of change affecting their families careers and communities.

Plan 2020 has four institutional priorities: student access and success faculty development programs for societal needs and local and global partnerships.

For the first institutional priority strategies include recruitment of and retaining underserved students and making programs for student success.

For the second priority recruitment retaining and development of faculty for social justice will be of focus.

For the third priority strategies include collaboration for the reduction of health disparities the advancement of STEM and sustainability and addressing injustice and violence.

Lastly to promote local and global partnerships the university will develop community outreach programs and expand global engagement.

Company Background

Founded in 1870 by Arnold Damen S.J. as St. Ignatius College the college was originally located at West Twelfth Street next to Holy Family Church the current location of St. Ignatius College Prep. In 1909 St. Ignatius College was re-chartered by the State of Illinois as Loyola University and in 1922 the University moved operations from West Twelfth Street to Sheridan and Devon in the Rogers Park neighborhood. College classes had been offered at the Rogers Park campus since 1912 and Loyola Academy opened on the property in 1909.

EXECUTIVES

Pres, Jo Ann Rooney
Asst V Pres-Fin, Cynthia J H Redman
Assistant Professor, Annie Thomas
Assistant Professor, Maria Derylo
Information Technology/Interne, Greg Small
Director Campus Ministry, Chris Murphy
Professor of Psychology, Catherine Haden
PHD, Janis Fine
Information Technology Team ME, Saundra
 Harrison
Security Officer, Bernadette Aviles
Board Member, Carolyn Saari
Auditors: DELOITTE & TOUCHE LLP CHICAG

LOCATIONS

HQ: LOYOLA UNIVERSITY OF CHICAGO INC
 1032 W SHERIDAN RD, CHICAGO, IL 606601537
Phone: 773 274-3000
Web: WWW.LUC.EDU

PRODUCTS/OPERATIONS

Selected Schools & Colleges

College of Arts and Sciences
Graduate School of Business
Institute of Pastoral Studies
Marcella Niehoff School of Nursing
Quinlan School of Business
School of Communication
School of Continuing and Professional Studies
School of Education
School of Law
School of Social Work
Stritch School of Medicine
The Graduate School

HISTORICAL FINANCIALS

Company Type: Private

Income Statement				FYE: June 30
	REVENUE ($ mil.)	NET INCOME ($ mil.)	NET PROFIT MARGIN	EMPLOYEES
06/21	554	301	54.5%	10,500
06/20	611	23	3.8%	—
06/19	614	78	12.8%	—
06/18	594	109	18.4%	—
Annual Growth	(2.3%)	40.2%	—	—

2021 Year-End Financials

Return on assets: 12.0%   Cash ($ mil.): 106
Return on equity: 15.2%
Current ratio: —

LUCILE SALTER PACKARD CHILDREN'S HOSPITAL AT STANFORD

EXECUTIVES

Pres-Ceo, Christopher Dawes
Cfo*, Timothy W Carmack
Coordinator, Arlene Sheehan
Coordinator, Sonja Avery
Chief Information Security Off, Auston Davis
Coordinator, Carrie Johnson
Coordinator, Erin Murphy
Coordinator, Jennifer Cctc
Occupational Specia, Quiara Smith
Senior Human Resources General, Alexis Silver
Licensed Vocational Nurse, Ann Hepner
Auditors: PRICEWATERHOUSECOOPERS LLP BO

LOCATIONS

HQ: LUCILE SALTER PACKARD CHILDREN'S
HOSPITAL AT STANFORD
725 WELCH RD, PALO ALTO, CA 943041601
Phone: 650 497-8000
Web: WWW.STANFORDCHILDRENS.ORG

HISTORICAL FINANCIALS
Company Type: Private

Income Statement				FYE: August 31
	REVENUE ($ mil.)	NET INCOME ($ mil.)	NET PROFIT MARGIN	EMPLOYEES
08/20	2,064	95	4.6%	1,100
08/19	1,959	99	5.1%	—
08/18	1,637	22	1.4%	—
08/17	1,486	227	15.3%	—
Annual Growth	11.6%	(25.2%)	—	—

2020 Year-End Financials
Return on assets: 2.3%   Cash ($ mil.): 354
Return on equity: 3.6%
Current ratio: 2.20

LUKOIL PAN AMERICAS, LLC

EXECUTIVES

Ceo, Timothy Bullock
Manager, Alexandra Krylova
Controller Risk Manager, Paul Carroll
Managing Director, Simon Fenner
Executive Officer, Eliecer Palacios
Hr Business Partner, Glory Perazzo
Design, Kenny Fong
Financial Manager Controller, Linda Raynor
Business, Richard Lloyd
Risk Analyst, Thomas Petrosino
Accounts Receivable Specialist, Valentina Lytle

LOCATIONS

HQ: LUKOIL PAN AMERICAS, LLC
1095 AVENUE OF THE AMERIC, NEW YORK, NY
100366797
Phone: 646 562-3600
Web: WWW.LITASCO.COM

HISTORICAL FINANCIALS
Company Type: Private

Income Statement				FYE: December 31
	REVENUE ($ mil.)	NET INCOME ($ mil.)	NET PROFIT MARGIN	EMPLOYEES
12/08	4,745	5	0.1%	77
12/07	4,717	3	0.1%	—
12/06	3,021	23	0.8%	—
12/05	2,788	21	0.8%	—
Annual Growth	19.4%	(37.8%)	—	—

2008 Year-End Financials
Return on assets: —   Cash ($ mil.): 1
Return on equity: 0.1%
Current ratio: 0.40

LUMINIS HEALTH ANNE ARUNDEL MEDICAL CENTER, INC

The ill and infirm get the royal treatment at Anne Arundel Medical Center. The full-service acute-care hospital serves the residents of Anne Arundel Calvert Prince George's and Queen Anne counties in Maryland. With about 425 beds the hospital administers care for women's health oncology pediatrics (it has a level III neonatal intensive care unit) neurology orthopedics and cardiovascular care. The medical center also has weight loss sleep disorder and rehabilitation centers. Anne Arundel which opened its doors in 1902 and is part of the Anne Arundel Health System has expanded its service offerings through various affiliations with regional specialty and primary care clinics. It also has a partnership with Johns Hopkins Medicine.

Operations
With more than 1000 staff members Anne Arundel handles some 26000 inpatient visits and 102000 outpatient visits per year. It also manages more than 5000 births and 93000 emergency room visits.

Johns Hopkins and the not-for-profit Anne Arundel share some services faculty and patients through their collaboration. They also operate a joint outpatient urgent-care facility. Additionally the two organizations work together to perform clinical research projects and conduct physician graduate medical education programs.

Geographic Reach
In addition to its 57-acre Annapolis campus Anne Arundel has outpatient centers in Bowie Kent Island Odenton Pasadena and Waugh Chapel.

Sales and Marketing
In 2014 Medicare payments accounted for about one-third of net patient revenues.

Financial Performance
In 2014 revenue grew 3% to $591 million as net patient services revenues increased. However net income fell 23% to $42 million due to a decline in non-operating income (investment earnings). Cash flow from operations spike 188% to $56 million as cash generated from patient receivables prepaid expenses and other sources rose.

Strategy
Anne Arundel has in recent years added new facilities to better keep up with a continued growth in demand for health care services throughout its service area. In 2015 it opened the second phase of its Pasadena Pavilion adding physical therapy orthopedics and sports medicine capabilities. It also opened a new FastCare walk-in clinic in a grocery store/pharmacy in Annapolis. In 2014 the system opened an outpatient mental health clinic in Annapolis which provides services for patients 13 years of age and older.

In 2013 Anne Arundel opened a training center — the James and Sylvia Earl Simulation to Advance Innovation and Learning (SAIL) Center — to enhance its medical education programs and improve the quality and safety of care in the region. It also opened the Hackerman-Patz House that year to provide an affordable and convenient housing option for families of patients.

Also in 2013 the organization was designated as a Medicare accountable care organization (ACO) by the US government. ACOs work to coordinate care for Medicare patients to improve quality and reduce expenses.

EXECUTIVES

Chb, Florence B Kurdle
V Chb*, James F McEncaney Jr
Pres*, Martin L Doordan
V Pres-Fin*, Bill Hughes
R V Pres, Joseph D Moser
Pres*, Stephen L Clarke
V Pres*, Shirley J Knelly
SEC*, Patricia Troy
Treas*, John M Suit II
Cso*, Paula Widerlite
Fo*, Bob Reilly
Auditors: SC&H TAX & ADVISORY SERVICES L

LOCATIONS

HQ: LUMINIS HEALTH ANNE ARUNDEL MEDICAL
CENTER, INC
2001 MEDICAL PKWY, ANNAPOLIS, MD 214013773
Phone: 443 481-1000
Web: WWW.AAHS.ORG

PRODUCTS/OPERATIONS

Selected Centers and Services
Blood Donor Center
Breast Center
Cardiac Cath Lab
Chest Pain Center
DeCesaris Cancer Institute
Diabetes Wound and Hyperbaric Center
Diagnostic Imaging
Heart and Vascular Institute
Joint Center
Laboratory
Pediatrics
Rehabilitation
Research Institute
Sleep Disorder Center
Spine Center
Stroke Center
Surgery
Women's and Children's Center

COMPETITORS

Ascension Health	Johns Hopkins Medicine
Bon Secours Health	Lifebridge Health
Dimensions Healthcare	Medstar Health
Franklin Square	Sinai Hospital Of
Hospital Center	Baltimore
Gbmc	St. Agnes Healthcare
Harbor Hospital	University Of Maryland
Johns Hopkins Health	Medical System
System	

HISTORICAL FINANCIALS

Company Type: Private

Income Statement   FYE: June 30

	REVENUE ($ mil.)	NET INCOME ($ mil.)	NET PROFIT MARGIN	EMPLOYEES
06/19	579	17	2.9%	1,890
06/15	526	39	7.6%	—
06/14	492	20	4.1%	—
06/13	493	16	3.4%	—
Annual Growth	2.7%	0.3%	—	—

2019 Year-End Financials

Return on assets: 1.8%   Cash ($ mil.): 9
Return on equity: 4.0%
Current ratio: 0.90

MAGELLAN PIPELINE COMPANY, L.P.

EXECUTIVES

Ptnr-Pres-Ceo, Don Wellendorf
Ptnr-V Pres-Tres,, Jeff Holman
Analyst, Tj Simmons
Facility Maintenance Superviso, Kevan Heil
Tech, Dan Sotelo
Technician Senior, Todd Huls
Corrosion Technician II, Jeff Saehler
Scada Analyst, Mike Cochran
Senior Representative, Tim Kassen
Director, Doug Chabino
Senior Manager, Eduardo Nunez

LOCATIONS

HQ: MAGELLAN PIPELINE COMPANY, L.P.
1 WILLIAMS CTR, TULSA, OK 741720140
Phone: 918 574-7000
Web: WWW.MAGELLANLP.COM

HISTORICAL FINANCIALS

Company Type: Private

Income Statement   FYE: December 31

	REVENUE ($ mil.)	NET INCOME ($ mil.)	NET PROFIT MARGIN	EMPLOYEES
12/17	828	396	47.9%	435
12/16	911	339	37.2%	—
Annual Growth	(9.1%)	17.0%	—	—

2017 Year-End Financials

Return on assets: 18.5%   Cash ($ mil.): 15
Return on equity: 20.9%
Current ratio: 0.60

MAIMONIDES MEDICAL CENTER

Maimonides Medical Center a not-for-profit hospital offers emergency medicine surgical procedures psychiatric treatment and other traditional hospital services to patients in Brooklyn New York. Its Maimonides Children's Hospital provides full array of pediatric subspecialties. Maimonides is home to the most advanced team of orthopedic specialists in the region at its Bone and Joint Center. It also manages pain for patients in ways that minimize the risk of opioid addiction. Its Acute Care for the Elderly (ACE) Geriatric Unit provides an interdisciplinary approach to care for older patients helping to ease their hospitalization.

Sales and Marketing

Maimonides is the hometown hospital of Brooklyn Nets and the Brooklyn Cyclones.

Company Background

Maimonides Medical Center traces its roots to the New Utrecht Dispensary which opened in 1911. The medical center later merged with Beth Moses and United Israel Zion hospitals in 1947. It is named after 12th-century philosopher Rabbi Moshe Ben Maimon.

EXECUTIVES

Chb, Martin D Payson
Pres-Ceo*, Pamela Brier
Exec V Pres-Coo*, Dominque Stanzione
Exec V Pres-Cfo*, Robert Naldi
Chief Information Officer*, Walter Fahey
Chief Information Security Off, Gabriel Sando
Coordinator, Maryann Corley
Scientist, Chris Miquel
Scientist, Jorge Brea
Internal Medicine Practitioner, Kamaldeen Agoro
Internal Medicine Practitioner, Kelly E Teagle

LOCATIONS

HQ: MAIMONIDES MEDICAL CENTER
4802 10TH AVE, BROOKLYN, NY 112192916
Phone: 718 581-0598
Web: WWW.MAIMO.ORG

PRODUCTS/OPERATIONS

2014 Sales

	$ mil.	% of total
Net patient revenue less provision for bad debts	1,001	95
Net assets released from restrictions	0	-
Other revenue	48	5
Total	**1,051**	**100**

Selected Services

Adult Primary Care
Ambulatory Health Services
Bay Parkway Multi-Specialty
Manfredi Family Health Center
Newkirk Family Health Center
Outpatient Eye Clinic
Pediatric Primary Care
Primary Health Services
Sheepshead Bay
Women's Primary Care Services

COMPETITORS

Beth Israel Medical	Lutheran Healthcare
Center	Montefiore Medical
Bronx-lebanon Hospital	New York City Health
Brookdale University	And Hospitals
Hospital	New York Methodist
Brooklyn Hospital	Hospital
Center	Newyork-presbyterian
Catholic Healthcare	Hospital
System	North Shore University

Continuum Health	Hospital
Partners	Suny Downstate
Jamaica Hospital	Staten Island
Medical Center	University Hospital
Kingsbrook Jewish	Wyckoff Heights
Medical Center	Medical Center
Long Island College	
Hospital	

HISTORICAL FINANCIALS

Company Type: Private

Income Statement   FYE: December 31

	REVENUE ($ mil.)	NET INCOME ($ mil.)	NET PROFIT MARGIN	EMPLOYEES
12/19	1,304	7	0.6%	6,382
12/17	958	19	2.0%	—
12/16	940	20	2.2%	—
12/15	890	(2)	—	—
Annual Growth	10.0%	—	—	—

2019 Year-End Financials

Return on assets: 0.5%   Cash ($ mil.): 77
Return on equity: 1.6%
Current ratio: 1.40

MAIN LINE HEALTH SYSTEM

Main Line Health is a not-for-profit network that includes four acute care hospitals a drug and alcohol recovery treatment center home care outpatient centers a physician network and a biomedical research organization all serving the greater Philadelphia area. Its hospitals — Lankenau Medical Center Bryn Mawr Hospital Paoli Hospital and Riddle Hospital — are accredited as primary stroke care centers comprehensive breast centers and chest pain centers. Other specialties include diabetes and endocrinology orthopedics and cardiovascular care. Bryn Mawr Hospital offers residency programs in family practice radiology and surgical podiatry. Main Line Health was founded in 1985.

Operations

Main Line Hospitals include The Bryn Mawr Hospital; The Lankenau Hospital; Paoli Hospital); Lankenau Institute of Medical Research; Main Line Diversified Services; Bryn Mawr Rehabilitation Hospital and other related organizations. TJUH includes Thomas Jefferson University Hospitals (Thomas Jefferson University Hospital and its subsidiaries; the Jefferson Hospital for Neuroscience and the Methodist Hospital Division.)

Thomas Jefferson University Hospitals has 969 licensed acute care beds and provides services in at five locations - the main hospital facility and Jefferson Hospital for Neuroscience both in Center City Philadelphia; Methodist Hospital in South Philadelphia; Jefferson at the Navy Yard just past the sports complex; and Jefferson-Voorhees in South Jersey. Magee Rehabilitation Hospital is a physical rehabilitation hospital specializing in the treatment of spinal cord injury brain injury stroke and orthopedic. Main Line Health offers a range of medical surgical obstetric pediatric psychiatric and emergency services.

Financial Performance

The company's revenues increased by 5% in fiscal 2012 due to a growth in patient services and other revenues. The patient services revenues increase was primarily due to a growth in Medicare and Medical Assistance fee-for-service program revenues. The increase in other income was due to receipts received for the initial payment of the incentive relating to Main Line Health implementing an electronic health records program as part of the American Recovery and Reinvestment Act of 2009.

Net income increased by 2% in fiscal 2012 primarily due to higher revenues.

Strategy

Jefferson Health System has realigned its relationship with former member Aria Health (formerly Frankford Health Care System) after the two organizations decided they too could better serve customers as separate entities. While Aria Health is no longer a direct member of the Jefferson Health System the two health networks maintain an affiliate relationship through which they collaborate in some areas of care.

EXECUTIVES

Pres-Ceo, Jack Lynch
Sr V Pres*, Thomas Mendicino
Hris Analyst, Michelle Massaro
Event Marketing Specialist, Karen Rawlings
Lead Recruiter, Cheryl Remolde
Manger Graphic Designer, Damien Lubeski
Disability, Donna Monaco
Recruiter, Katie Kealey
Senior Recruiter, Lindsey Breiner
Director, Physician Rel, Lorraine Placido
Senior Compensation Analyst, Mark Benner

LOCATIONS

HQ: MAIN LINE HEALTH SYSTEM
240 N RADNOR CHESTER RD, RADNOR, PA 190875170
Phone: 610 225-6200
Web: WWW.MAINLINEHEALTH.ORG

COMPETITORS

Abington Memorial Hospital
Albert Einstein Healthcare Network
Crozer-keystone Health System
Lvhn
Lancaster General
Memorial Hospital (pa)
Mercy Health System
North Philadelphia Health System
Tuhs
University Of Pennsylvania Health System
Virtua Health

HISTORICAL FINANCIALS

Company Type: Private

Income Statement

FYE: June 30

	REVENUE ($ mil.)	NET INCOME ($ mil.)	NET PROFIT MARGIN	EMPLOYEES
06/21	1,984	510	25.7%	17,485
06/20	1,781	(17)	—	—
06/19	1,769	21	1.2%	—
06/18	1,742	267	15.4%	—
Annual Growth	4.4%	24.0%	—	—

2021 Year-End Financials

Return on assets: 10.4%
Return on equity: 16.0%
Current ratio: 2.30

Cash ($ mil.): 138

MAIN LINE HOSPITALS, INC.

Bryn Mawr Hospital a member of the Main Line not-for-profit health network is an acute care facility providing a variety of inpatient and outpatient services in the western suburbs of Philadelphia. With some 320 beds Bryn Mawr Hospital is recognized nationally for its orthopedic program. Founded in 1893 by Dr. George Gerhard the teaching hospital also provides cancer cardiac surgical pediatric reproductive health diagnostic imaging psychiatric bariatric and wound care services. The hospital also operates the Main Line Health Center outpatient facility (which includes a comprehensive breast center) in Newtown Square.

Operations

Based in Bryn Mawr Pennsylvania Bryn Mawr Hospital boasts specialized departments such as a Comprehensive Breast Center; Wound Healing Center at Bryn Mawr Hospital; Outpatient Imaging Center; Center for Reproductive Medicine; Cancer Center; Main Line Health Heart Center; Center for Addictive Diseases; Level III Neonatal Intensive Care Unit; and Nemours Pediatric Partners at Bryn Mawr Hospital. The hospital also operates an outpatient health center in Newton Square Pennsylvania.

Bryn Mawr Hospital admits some 18000 patients annually performing around 4800 inpatient and 6800 outpatient surgeries. It provides care to more than 2000 newborns and receives some 47000 emergency department visits each year.

Strategy

Main Line Health in 2015 announced plans to invest $200 million to modernize Bryn Mawr Hospital. The initiative is the most significant renovation ever for the hospital and it includes plans to build a five-story patient-care pavilion and convert all patient rooms to private rooms.

Like many hospitals Bryn Mawr Hospital aims to expand its outpatient services and connect to medical practices. The practice helps to boost the number of referrals to its facility and grow physician relations throughout the community.

Bryn Mawr Hospital collaborates with Nemours/Alfred I. duPont Hospital for Children to provide 24/7 pediatric care for the pediatric inpatient unit and the pediatric emergency department with added board-certified emergency medicine physicians. In 2015 the hospital formed a partnership with Lifecycle WomanCare to provide specialized care to pregnant and postpartum families in the community.

EXECUTIVES

Ceo, Leland I White
Ceo*, Jack Lynch
Pres*, Andrea Gilbert
Sr V Pres*, Brian T Corbett
Cfo*, Michael J Buongiorno
Staff, Robert Rose
Staff, Sharon K Sweinberg
Director, Mary McKay
Health Professional, Cheryl E Clarkin
Chief of Medicine, Donald C Arthur
Project Manager Information Te, Eugene Smith

LOCATIONS

HQ: MAIN LINE HOSPITALS, INC.
130 S BRYN MAWR AVE, BRYN MAWR, PA 190103121
Phone: 610 526-3000
Web: WWW.MAINLINEHEALTH.ORG

COMPETITORS

Abington Memorial Hospital
Albert Einstein Healthcare Network
Christiana Care
Crozer-keystone Health System
Doylestown Hospital
Memorial Hospital (pa)
Moses Taylor Hospital
North Philadelphia Health System
Tenet Healthcare
University Of Pennsylvania Health System
Virtua Memorial

HISTORICAL FINANCIALS

Company Type: Private

Income Statement

FYE: June 30

	REVENUE ($ mil.)	NET INCOME ($ mil.)	NET PROFIT MARGIN	EMPLOYEES
06/21	1,485	194	13.1%	5,840
06/20	1,345	11	0.8%	—
06/19	1,323	58	4.4%	—
06/18	1,193	100	8.4%	—
Annual Growth	7.6%	24.6%	—	—

2021 Year-End Financials

Return on assets: 4.8%
Return on equity: 6.7%
Current ratio: 3.40

Cash ($ mil.): 75

MAINE MEDICAL CENTER

EXECUTIVES

Ceo, Richard W Petersen
Pres, Jeffrey D Sanders
Coo, Jennifer McCarthy
Cfo, Lugene Inzana
Vice President, Brian Noyes
Pediatrics, Christina Manning
Geriatrician, Heidi Wierman
Annual Giving Manager, Kathleen Leahy
Grants Officer, Lisa Dyk
Bbch Philanthropy Specialist, Meaghan McNamara
Philanthropy Manager, Nichole Greaves
Auditors: BAKER NEWMAN & NOYES LLC PORT

LOCATIONS

HQ: MAINE MEDICAL CENTER
576 SAINT JOHN ST, PORTLAND, ME 041022710
Phone: 207 780-0020
Web: WWW.MAINEHEALTH.ORG

HISTORICAL FINANCIALS

Company Type: Private

Income Statement

FYE: September 30

	REVENUE ($ mil.)	NET INCOME ($ mil.)	NET PROFIT MARGIN	EMPLOYEES
09/20	1,671	(5)	—	14
09/19	1,622	74	4.6%	—
09/18	1,564	164	10.5%	—
Annual Growth	3.3%	—	—	—

2020 Year-End Financials
Return on assets: (-0.4%)   Cash ($ mil.): 1
Return on equity: (-1.7%)
Current ratio: 2.50

MAINEGENERAL HEALTH

EXECUTIVES

Ceo-Pres, Charles Hays
Cfo*, Michael Koziol
Coo*, Paul Stein
Surgical Computer Admi, Celeste Theriault
Purchasing Coordinator, James Derouche
Staff, Kathi Rodrigue
Manager, Rae Dennis
Director, Kelli Mayfield
Clinical Analyst, Lori Tuttle
Information Technology Project, Donna Plourde
Orthopedic Surgeon, Stuart Aitken
Auditors: BAKER NEWMAN NOYES LLC
PORTLA

LOCATIONS

HQ: MAINEGENERAL HEALTH
35 MEDICAL CENTER PKWY # 20, AUGUSTA, ME
043308160
Phone: 207 626-1000
Web: WWW.MAINEGENERAL.ORG

HISTORICAL FINANCIALS
Company Type: Private

Income Statement				FYE: June 30
	REVENUE ($ mil.)	NET INCOME ($ mil.)	NET PROFIT MARGIN	EMPLOYEES
06/20	575	31	5.6%	3,800
06/17	10	1	14.8%	—
06/15	11	0	4.5%	—
06/12	440	(2)	—	—
Annual Growth	3.4%	—	—	—

2020 Year-End Financials
Return on assets: 4.2%   Cash ($ mil.): 29
Return on equity: 11.5%
Current ratio: 1.10

MAINEHEALTH

Maine Medical Center (MMC) is the flagship hospital of MaineHealth which is an integrated health network comprising a dozen local hospital and other health facilities that touch central southern and western Maine and eastern New Hampshire. MMC is a not-for-profit medical center consists of a tertiary care community hospital The Barbara Bush Children's Hospital and outpatient clinics. Specialty services include cancer care geriatrics emergency medicine cardiovascular care rehabilitation neurology orthopedics and women's health. Through its partnership with the Tufts University School of Medicine the 640-bed teaching hospital provides a variety of medical education and training programs. MMC also conducts research through the Maine Medical Center Research Institute. The medical center was founded in 1874.

Operations

MMC boasts a large ever-expanding outpatient segment that provides day surgery cardiac catheterization laboratory services and rehabilitation services. It also operates about 20 inpatient and outpatient clinics. MMC provides preventive and consultation services including the MMC Pre-Operative Readiness Education Program ? Preadmission Testing Unit MMC Wound Healing & Hyperbarics and NorDx laboratory services.

The medical center is one of the largest employers in its service territory with a workforce of some 9600. Its Maine Medical Partners is a group of primary care and specialty medical practices. Its The Barbara Bush Children's Hospital is a full-service children's hospital with some 115 beds. MMC also provides more than 20% of charity care for uninsured or underinsured patients in the state.

Geographic Reach

Located in Portland the MMC serves the northern New England area.

EXECUTIVES

Pres-Ceo, Andrew T Mueller
CIO, Daniel Nigrin
Trustee, Patricia Stogsdill
Director, Barbara Grillo
Clinical Trial Project Manager, Brad Gallant
Credentialing Manager, Heather Owens
MD Office Manager, Peter Marro
Quality Program Manager, Sandra Daigle
Vice President, Miriam A Leonard
Physician, Sandra Stevens
Radiology, Mary Duffy
Auditors: KPMG LLP BOSTON MA

LOCATIONS

HQ: MAINEHEALTH
22 BRAMHALL ST, PORTLAND, ME 041023134
Phone: 207 662-0111
Web: WWW.MAINEHEALTH.ORG

PRODUCTS/OPERATIONS

Selected Specialty Centers
Cancer Institute
Cardiovascular Institute
Emergency Medicine
Family Birth Center
Joint Replacement Center
Neuroscience Institute
The Barbara Bush Children's Hospital

COMPETITORS

Eastern Maine Healthcare Systems	Mainegeneral Health
Franklin Community Health Network	Mercy Health System Of Maine
Maine Coast Memorial Hospital	St. Joseph Healthcare

HISTORICAL FINANCIALS
Company Type: Private

Income Statement				FYE: September 30
	REVENUE ($ mil.)	NET INCOME ($ mil.)	NET PROFIT MARGIN	EMPLOYEES
09/20	2,884	283	9.8%	2,000
09/19	2,717	5	0.2%	—
09/18	2,523	205	8.2%	—
09/17	1,236	152	12.4%	—
Annual Growth	32.6%	22.8%	—	—

2020 Year-End Financials
Return on assets: 6.6%   Cash ($ mil.): 547
Return on equity: 13.8%
Current ratio: 3.90

MAINEHEALTH SERVICES

MaineHealth provides health care to residents of central southern and western Maine. The health system's facilities include Maine Medical Center Spring Harbor Hospital and Stephens Memorial Hospital (part of Western Maine Health). MaineHealth also operates long-term care facilities a home health care service physician practices medical laboratories and other health care service units. The company's Synernet subsidiary provides administrative and group purchasing services for MaineHealth's members and other health care organizations.

Operations

Other MaineHealth affiliates include MidCoast Health Services PenBay Healthcare and St. Mary's Regional Medical Center. The New England Rehabilitation Hospital is a joint venture with HealthSouth. Many of the company's hospital affiliates are governed by independent boards but receive administrative planning capital and group purchasing benefits as members of MaineHealth.

Strategy

In 2013 two of MaineHealth's affiliated hospitals — Miles Memorial Hospital (part of Miles Health Care) and St. Andrews Hospital — merged to form a two-campus hospital operating as LincolnHealth. The hospital continues to be governed by the independent Lincoln County Healthcare board of trustees.

In 2009 the nonprofit hospital Southern Maine Medical Center (SMMC) became a full member of MaineHealth. The hospital had been affiliated with MaineHealth for several years. As a full member of MaineHealth SMMC gained access to planning consulting capital and group purchasing benefits while remaining an independently governed entity. MaineHealth aimed to enhance its care services and lower health care costs through the agreement.

MaineHealth also moved to expand its network further by agreeing to acquire a 50-bed community hospital Goodall Hospital in Sanford Maine in 2009; however the merger was canceled after the FTC raised concerns over possible antitrust violations.

EXECUTIVES

V Pres, Mark Harris
V Pres Ops & Treasurer*, Frank G McGinty
Mgr, Mary Ann Miro
Doctor, Heather P McClelland
Engineer, Guy Bolduc
Manager, Steve O'Kusky
Manager, Hillary M Berry
Director Rehab, Wendy E Osgood
Program Manager, Gloria Neault
Manager, Jeffrey Chapman
Interim Director, Brooke Curran
Auditors: KPMG LLP BOSTON MASSACHUSETT

LOCATIONS

HQ: MAINEHEALTH SERVICES
110 FREE ST, PORTLAND, ME 041013576
Phone: 207 661-7010
Web: WWW.MAINEHEALTH.ORG

PRODUCTS/OPERATIONS

Members and Affiliates
HomeHealth Visiting Nurses of Southern Maine
Intellicare (joint venture)

LincolnHealth Miles Campus (aka Miles Health
Care/Miles Memorial Hospital affiliate)
LincolnHealth St. Andrews Campus (aka St. Andrews
Hospital affiliate)
MaineGeneral Health (affiliate)
Maine Medical Center
Maine Physician Hospital Organization (MPHO)
MidCoast Health Services (affiliate)
New England Rehabilitation Hospital (joint venture)
NorDx
PenBay Healthcare (affiliate)
St. Andrews Hospital & Healthcare Center
Southern Maine Medical Center (affiliate)
Spring Harbor Hospital
Stephens Memorial Hospital/Western Maine Health Care
St. Mary's Regional Medical Center (affiliate)
Synernet

COMPETITORS

Eastern Maine
Healthcare Systems
Franklin Community
Health Network
Maine Coast Memorial
Hospital

Mainegeneral Health
Mercy Health System Of
Maine
St. Joseph Healthcare

HISTORICAL FINANCIALS
Company Type: Private

Income Statement   FYE: September 30

	REVENUE ($ mil.)	NET INCOME ($ mil.)	NET PROFIT MARGIN	EMPLOYEES
09/19	2,717	5	0.2%	7,000
09/08	23	(0)	—	—
09/99	493	30	6.2%	—
09/98	1,001	0	—	—
Annual Growth	4.9%	—	—	—

2019 Year-End Financials

Return on assets: 0.2%   Cash ($ mil.): 292
Return on equity: 0.3%
Current ratio: 4.00

MANAGEMENT & TRAINING CORPORATION

Management & Training Corporation (MTC)
prepares prison inmates for re-entry into society.
It provides a variety of academic vocational and
social-skills training in rehabilitation-oriented private prisons. Its holistic education model offers
programs to help inmates avoid substance abuse
as they also boost their engagement in community
service find work and increase their cognitive skills.
As part of its services MTC operates about 25 Job
Corps centers more than 20 correctional facilities
nearly 15 prison and detention medical departments some five detention centers and two workforce development sites around the world.

Operations
MTC operates through four divisions: Correctional Education & Training MTC Medical and
Economic & Social Development. It currently educates and trains more than 14000 students provides safe and secure rehabilitation and transition
services to nearly 29000 residents and detainees
and provides healthcare to more than 16000 residents and detainees.

The company's MTC Medical unit provides vital
healthcare and wellness services to people at its
correctional facilities and detention centers. It is

comprised of doctors nurses and other healthcare
professionals and provides approximately 47450
dental evaluations and services to promote proper
dental hygiene. It conducts some 37160 comprehensive mental health visits to provide appropriate
services and about 53060 physicals performed to
promote overall health and wellness. Its Economic
& Social Development division provides training
in entrepreneurship and innovation to more than
20740 technical school students.

Geographic Reach
The company's main offices are located in Centerville Utah and has regional office in Texas and
Washington DC. MTC operates correctional facility
contracts in Arizona Florida Idaho Ohio Mississippi
and Texas. It also operates two international corrections in Rainsbrook Secure Training Centre (in
the UK) and Parklea Correctional Centre in Australia.

Sales and Marketing
MTC clients including the Federal Bureau of
Prisons Immigration & Customs Enforcement US
Marshals Service and state departments of corrections. It also provided workforce training to USAID
the World Bank the United Nations regional development banks and national governments.

Company Background
MRC was founded in 1981.

EXECUTIVES

Pres-Chm-Ceo, Scott Marquardt JD
V Chm*, Jane Marquardt
Sr V Pres-Cfo-Treas*, Dan Marquardt
Sr V Pres Training Program, John Pedersen
Sr V Pres*, Sergio Molina
SEC*, Michael Petrogeorge
Sr Vp*, Leanne Bertsch
Human Resources Manager, Carol Westbroek
Director, Brian Goodwin
Administrative Assistant, Teresa Anderson
Director Corporate Communicati, Issa Arnita
Auditors: KPMG LLP SALT LAKE CITY UTAH

LOCATIONS

HQ: MANAGEMENT & TRAINING CORPORATION
500 N MARKET PLACE DR # 100, CENTERVILLE, UT
840141711
Phone: 801 693-2600
Web: WWW.MTCTRAINS.COM

PRODUCTS/OPERATIONS

Selected Services
Communicate through formal and informal channels
Develop custom training for students clients & offenders
Manage facilities
Provide community connections
Provide data solutions

COMPETITORS

Avalon Correctional Services
Community Education Centers
Conmed Healthcare
Corizon
Corrections Corporation Of America
G4s
Geo Group
Mhm Services
Res-care
Wexford Health

HISTORICAL FINANCIALS
Company Type: Private

Income Statement   FYE: December 31

	REVENUE ($ mil.)	NET INCOME ($ mil.)	NET PROFIT MARGIN	EMPLOYEES
12/20	907	54	6.0%	9,500
12/15	753	30	4.0%	—
12/13	735	50	6.9%	—
12/12	704	45	6.5%	—
Annual Growth	3.2%	2.2%	—	—

2020 Year-End Financials

Return on assets: 14.9%   Cash ($ mil.): 53
Return on equity: 25.6%
Current ratio: 1.80

MANAGEMENT-ILA MANAGED HEALTH CARE TRUST FUND

EXECUTIVES

MGT, Jason Cury
Accounting Director, Robin Csabon
Auditors: DESENA & COMPANY CPAS EAST
HA

LOCATIONS

HQ: MANAGEMENT-ILA MANAGED HEALTH CARE
TRUST FUND
111 BROADWAY FL 5, NEW YORK, NY 100061901
Phone: 212 766-5700
Web: WWW.MILAMHCTF.COM

HISTORICAL FINANCIALS
Company Type: Private

Income Statement   FYE: December 31

	REVENUE ($ mil.)	NET INCOME ($ mil.)	NET PROFIT MARGIN	EMPLOYEES
12/17	675	64	9.6%	3
12/14	492	(39)	—	—
12/13	491	24	5.0%	—
Annual Growth	8.3%	27.3%	—	—

2017 Year-End Financials

Return on assets: 6.9%   Cash ($ mil.): 28
Return on equity: 7.5%
Current ratio: 1.90

MANN+HUMMEL FILTRATION TECHNOLOGY INTERMEDIATE HOLDINGS INC.

Affinia Group Intermediate Holdings caters to
car drivers with a natural affinity for parts. The

company is a leading designer manufacturer and distributor of aftermarket vehicular components. Affinia's slew of products — primarily oil and air filters ball joints idler arms steering components and suspension parts — are made for passenger cars; SUVs; light medium and heavy trucks; and off-highway vehicles. Its well-known brand names including McQuay-Norris Nakata ecoLAST Raybestos and WIX are sold in 70 countries. It primarily serves the US and South American markets.

Geographic Reach

Affinia has operations in North and South America Europe and Asia spanning nearly 12 countries. It manufactures and distributes products in 11 countries and sells into more than 70 countries. The US accounts for 42% of the company's sales; Brazil is its second-largest market generating 30%.

Sales and Marketing

Affinia's largest customers include aftermarket distributors NAPA (22% of total sales) and CARQUEST (6%). Other customers include AutoZone O'Reilly Auto Parts and Canadian Tire . The company derived 97% of its 2013 net sales from the on and off-highway replacement products and services industry.

Financial Performance

The company saw its revenues jump 8% from 2012 to 2013. The growth for 2013 was driven by a 9% increase in its filtration segment due to increased sales in its North American and Asia operations driven by increased volume as a result of market growth and new business with existing customers. European sales increased in 2013 due to higher sales in Poland along with favorable currency translation effects in Poland. Increased Venezuela filter sales were the main contributor to the increase in South America sales.

Affinia posted net income of $10 million in 2013 after posting net losses in 2011 and 2012. The positive net income for 2013 was attributed to the absence of losses from discontinued operations as opposed to other years.

Strategy

With the sale of its Brake North America and Asia group in 2012 and the announced signing of an agreement to sell its Chassis group in 2014 the company is focused on operating strictly as a Filtration segment and Affinia South America segment company. (Affinia agreed to sell its chassis operations to Federal-Mogul in January 2014.)

Company Background

Affinia got its start in 2004. Private-equity firm Cypress and OMERS (Ontario Municipal Employees Retirement System) a Canadian pension fund bought the auto replacement parts business of Dana Holding Corporation to form Affinia. In mid-2010 Affinia filed to go public but remains privately owned.

EXECUTIVES

Pres-Ceo, Keith A Wilson
Sr V Pres-Cfo-Treas, Steven P Klueg
CIO, Karl J Westrick
Sr V Pres Hr, Kay Teixeira
Sr Vpres-General Counsel-Sec, David E Sturgess
Senior Manager, Carl McMaken
Management, Horace Love
Director, Human Resources, Keith Clark
Auditors: DELOITTE & TOUCHE LLP CHARLOT

LOCATIONS

HQ: MANN+HUMMEL FILTRATION TECHNOLOGY INTERMEDIATE HOLDINGS INC.
1 WIX WAY, GASTONIA, NC 280546142
Phone: 704 869-3300
Web: WWW.WIXFILTERS.COM

HISTORICAL FINANCIALS

Company Type: Private

Income Statement — FYE: December 31

	REVENUE ($ mil.)	NET INCOME ($ mil.)	NET PROFIT MARGIN	EMPLOYEES
12/15	899	(72)	—	6,262
12/14	1,396	82	5.9%	—
12/13	1,361	10	0.7%	—
12/12	1,453	(102)	—	—
Annual Growth	(14.8%)	—	—	

2015 Year-End Financials

Return on assets: (-12.2%)
Return on equity: —
Current ratio: 0.90

Cash ($ mil.): 28

MAP INTERNATIONAL (INC.)

EXECUTIVES

Ceo-Pres, Steve Stirling
Int Pres-Ceo*, Chok-Pin Foo
Cfo*, Daniel C Reed
Chm*, Immanuel Phangaraj
VCM*, Edwin G Corr
SEC*, Ingrid M Mail
Asst SEC*, Carrene G Rosser
Prin*, Michael J Nyenhuis
Coordinator, Connie Reed
Executive Director, John Reid
Human Resources, Lindsey Holland
Auditors: CAPIN CROUSE LLP LAWRENCEVILL

LOCATIONS

HQ: MAP INTERNATIONAL (INC.)
4700 GLYNCO PKWY, BRUNSWICK, GA 315256901
Phone: 912 265-6010
Web: WWW.MAP.ORG

HISTORICAL FINANCIALS

Company Type: Private

Income Statement — FYE: September 30

	REVENUE ($ mil.)	NET INCOME ($ mil.)	NET PROFIT MARGIN	EMPLOYEES
09/20	588	(129)	—	200
09/19	590	28	4.8%	—
09/18	575	11	2.1%	—
09/17	598	(40)	—	—
Annual Growth	(0.6%)	—	—	

2020 Year-End Financials

Return on assets: (-131.5%)
Return on equity: (-132.9%)
Current ratio: 105.90

Cash ($ mil.): 3

MARICOPA COUNTY SPECIAL HEALTH CARE DISTRICT

EXECUTIVES

Ceo, Steve Purves
Executive Assistant To CHI*, Stacy Westbrook
Admin*, David Villasenor
Chief Human Resources Officer*, Jenny Marchiniak
Dir Research, Jeffrey N Joyce PH D
Chief Operating Officer, Bill Van Askie
Senior Programming Analyst, Damian Van Cleaf
Accounting Staff, Merrenda Salazar
Coordinator, Kristine Turlock
Coordinator, Sabrina Soto
Information Specialist, Betty Battese

LOCATIONS

HQ: MARICOPA COUNTY SPECIAL HEALTH CARE DISTRICT
2601 E ROOSEVELT ST, PHOENIX, AZ 850084973
Phone: 602 344-5011

HISTORICAL FINANCIALS

Company Type: Private

Income Statement — FYE: June 30

	REVENUE ($ mil.)	NET INCOME ($ mil.)	NET PROFIT MARGIN	EMPLOYEES
06/20	548	19	3.6%	4,000
06/19	507	51	10.1%	—
06/18	510	93	18.3%	—
Annual Growth	3.7%	(54.0%)	—	

2020 Year-End Financials

Return on assets: 1.5%
Return on equity: 7.1%
Current ratio: 3.00

Cash ($ mil.): 210

MARINA DISTRICT DEVELOPMENT COMPANY, LLC

EXECUTIVES

Pres-Coo, Tom Ballance
MBR, Bob Boughner
MBR, Auggie Cipollini
Pres-Coo, Melonie Johnson
V Pres of Fin, Hugh Turner
Executive Officer, Cassie Fireman
Vice President, Jason Lyons
Assistant Executive Steward, Enrique Villanueva
Box Office Assistant Manager, Alexa Destefano
Senior Buyer, Heather Herold
Labor Relations Manager, Marisa Kocher

HQ: MARINA DISTRICT DEVELOPMENT COMPANY, LLC
1 BORGATA WAY, ATLANTIC CITY, NJ 084011946
Phone: 609 317-1000
Web: WWW.BORGATA.MGMRESORTS.COM

HISTORICAL FINANCIALS
Company Type: Private

Income Statement				FYE: December 31
	REVENUE ($ mil.)	NET INCOME ($ mil.)	NET PROFIT MARGIN	EMPLOYEES
12/10	738	44	6.0%	7,000
12/09	777	108	13.9%	—
12/08	830	83	10.0%	—
Annual Growth	(5.7%)	(27.1%)	—	—

2010 Year-End Financials
Return on assets: 3.1%   Cash ($ mil.): 42
Return on equity: 9.6%
Current ratio: 0.80

MARITZ HOLDINGS INC.

Maritz Holdings designs employee incentive and reward programs including incentive travel rewards and customer loyalty programs. The company also plans corporate trade shows and events and offers traditional market research services such as the creation of product launch campaigns. Its programs are designed to help its clients improve workforce quality and customer satisfaction. The company operates through a number of subsidiaries including Maritz Motivation (services for marketing sales HR) Maritz Automotive (helping clients and partners' sales) Maritz Global Events (meeting and event industry professionals) and Maritz Travel (planners sales operations and procurement). The company is owned by Steve Maritz.

HISTORY

Edward Maritz an entrepreneur of Swiss-French descent founded the E. Maritz Jewelry Manufacturing Company in St. Louis in 1894. By 1900 the wholesaler and manufacturer of men's and women's jewelry was supplying retail jewelers across the South and West. By 1921 Maritz had become a major importer of Swiss watches which it sold to retail jewelers under the Merit Cymrex and Record brands. In the 1920s the company added diamond jewelry and silverware to its product mix. Edward Maritz died in 1929.

To drum up new business during the Depression Edward's son James began trying to sell watches and jewelry to large corporations for use as sales and service awards pioneering the incentive market. The first sale for a nationwide employee incentive campaign was to Caradine Hat a St. Louis hatmaker in 1930. In 1948 Maritz handled a $2 million incentive program for Chevrolet.

In 1950 the Maritz family split the business into two operations. Brother Lloyd handled the jewelry business (it died in 1955 when Lloyd died); James took over the incentive operations which flourished. In the 1950s James expanded his company's offerings to include merchandise awards and in 1958 travel incentive awards (arranged through the newly acquired Holiday House Travel Center of Detroit). The enterprise adopted the corporate name Maritz Inc. in 1961. During the 1960s and early 1970s Maritz made a series of acquisitions closely allied with its motivation endeavors including Lee Creative Research the nucleus of what would become its market research operations (1973). The organization expanded internationally with the opening of Maritz offices in the UK and Mexico in 1974.

In 1980 the company acquired the Wilding division of Bell & Howell which it merged with another unit to form Maritz Communications Co. James died in 1981. Maritz beefed up its travel operations in the 1980s acquiring corporate travel agency Traveler's Service (St. Louis 1981) Byfield Travel (Chicago 1984) Beverly Hills Travel (Los Angeles 1986) and Travel Counselors International (Virginia 1986).

These acquisitions led to record sales in 1989 but sliding results in the early 1990s prompted the company to streamline its operations by cutting overlapping units. After a family boardroom tussle in 1993 William Maritz expanded his control by buying out his sister's 50% stake in the company and putting his two sons on the board. His son Stephen Maritz subsequently took over as president.

As part of its international expansion strategy Maritz acquired The Research Business Group the UK's largest independently owned marketing research firm (1993) and BLC the largest performance-improvement company in France (1994). In 1997 the company established an office in Manila its first in Asia.

In 1998 William Maritz stepped down as CEO and retained the title of chairman; his son Stephen succeeded him. In 1998 and 1999 the company boosted its international presence with acquisitions in Canada (group travel firm Partners in Performance marketing research firm Thompson Lightstone & Co.) and the Netherlands (Maritz B.V.).

Facing heat from online incentive programs the company launched its own online service e-Maritz in 2000. It also started Heybridge an e-commerce subsidiary that helps small and midsized businesses sell over the Internet. In 2001 Maritz purchased Librix Learning an online learning company.

The following year it purchased travel and incentive business McGettigan (later to be renamed Martiz McGettigan) to add depth to its client offerings. Also that same year Peter and Philip Maritz (brothers of chairman and CEO Steve Maritz) sued the company purportedly seeking a greater role in managing the family business. In the summer of 2003 the brothers again filed suit against Steve alleging that the purchase of McGettigan cost $10 million more than what was originally presented to the board. Peter and Philip's suits are an attempt to cash out of the family business — which they feel lost value because of the McGettigan purchase — at a better price than they'd get now.

In early 2004 Maritz sold its data collection unit Delve to St. Louis-based Bush O'Donnell Capital Partners. The same year Maritz sold its TQ3 Travel Solutions division to Carlson Wagonlit Travel.

Steve Maritz became the sole owner of the company in 2006 after buying out his other family members' shares.

Maritz also expanded its product offerings and geographic reach in 2008 when it acquired Cascade Promotion Corporation a marketing and fulfillment business operating out of Boston Las Vegas and St. Louis. With Cascade catering to the gaming and technology industries the buyout gave Maritz access to growing niche markets.

Making ground into what it considers a high-growth market Maritz solidified its position in the prepaid card sector in 2010 when it acquired full ownership of American Express Incentive Services (AEIS). For more than a decade AEIS operated as a joint venture between Maritz and a subsidiary of American Express. AEIS is an independent issuer of prepaid products such as cards and American Express Travelers Cheques on the American Express network. The products are used for employee recognition consumer promotions and sales incentives.

EXECUTIVES

Ceo, Steve Maritz
Cfo*, Rick Ramos
Dir*, Paula Voss
General Counsel, Derek Mays
Division Vice-President, Lisa Weaner
Manager, Debbie Cullen
Manager, Neal Thompson
Director, Bruce Smart
Senior Executive Vice Presiden, John F Risberg
Information Technology Manager, Ron Hunskaker
Director, Susan O'Neal
Auditors: KPMG LLP ST LOUIS MISSOURI

LOCATIONS

HQ: MARITZ HOLDINGS INC.
1375 N HIGHWAY DR, FENTON, MO 630990001
Phone: 636 827-4000
Web: WWW.MARITZ.COM

PRODUCTS/OPERATIONS

Selected Services
Marketing Research
  Custom marketing research
  Customer satisfaction and customer value analysis
  Data collection (focus groups telephone interviews)
  Maritz Polls and Maritz Research Reports
  Syndicated buyer research
  Telecommunications research
Performance Improvement
  Communications
  e-Learning
  Fulfillment
  Internet consulting
  Loyalty marketing
  Measurement and feedback
  Rewards and recognition
Travel
  Consulting services
  Corporate travel management
  Group travel services
  Travel award programs

COMPETITORS

Franklin Covey	J.d. Power
Gallup	Jtb Corp.
Giftcertificates.com	Kantar Group
Harris Interactive	Motivcom
Ims Health	Nielsen
Information Resources Inc.	Orc International

HISTORICAL FINANCIALS
Company Type: Private

Income Statement				FYE: March 31
	REVENUE ($ mil.)	NET INCOME ($ mil.)	NET PROFIT MARGIN	EMPLOYEES
03/20	1,303	54	4.2%	2,500
03/19	1,326	2	0.2%	—
03/18	1,263	(9)	—	—
03/17	1,217	(30)	—	—
Annual Growth	2.3%	—	—	—

2020 Year-End Financials
Return on assets: 7.6%   Cash ($ mil.): 189
Return on equity: 80.1%
Current ratio: 1.00

MARQUETTE UNIVERSITY

A member of the Association of Jesuit Colleges and Universities Marquette University provides undergraduate graduate and professional courses and programs. It specializes in business engineering arts and sciences nursing law dentistry and other fields. The university offers undergraduates some 75 majors and 65 minors and post-graduate students about 50 doctoral and master's degree programs. With an enrollment of more than 11700 students Marquette University boasts a student/faculty ratio of 14:1. Its student population consists of students from all 50 US states and nearly 70 countries. Founded in 1881 the university is named after French missionary explorer Father Jacques Marquette.

Operations

Marquette University an independent coeducational and not-for-profit institution of higher learning and research consists of a dozen separate colleges and schools.

Geographic Reach

Based in Milwaukee Wisconsin the Marquette University campus attracts students across the nation and from nearly 70 countries worldwide.

Financial Performance

The educational institution logged a marginal 1% increase in revenue in fiscal 2012 as compared to 2011 due to rising tuition and fees contributions government and private grants and endowment income used in operations. Net income during the same reporting period dropped some 90% thanks to increases in operating expenses and declines in endowment gains in excess of the amount designated for current operations (net other).

Strategy

To boost its healthcare presence the Marquette University College of Nursing opened the Wheaton Franciscan Healthcare Center for Clinical Simulation in late 2012. The facility features a six-bed hospital suite with a pair of intensive care rooms two medical surgical rooms one pediatrics room and one labor and delivery suite.

EXECUTIVES

Pres, Rev Scott Pilarz
V Pres-Fin-Cfo*, John C Lamb
Board of Trustees, Richard Burke
Dir State Relations, Mary Czech - Mrochinski
Assistant Professor, Sandra Hunter
Coordinator, William R Elliott
Manager, Dax J Phillips
Security Staff, Joseph Secanky
Senior Financial Analyst, Michelle L Cook
Assistant Vice President For S, Jeff Janz
Administrative Assistant, Irene Cvetich
Auditors: KPMG LLP MILWAUKEE WI

LOCATIONS

HQ: MARQUETTE UNIVERSITY
1250 W WISCONSIN AVE, MILWAUKEE, WI 532332225
Phone: 414 288-7250
Web: WWW.MARQUETTE.EDU

PRODUCTS/OPERATIONS

Selected Schools and Colleges

College of Business Administration
College of Education
College of Engineering
College of Health Sciences
College of Nursing
College of Professional Studies
Graduate School
Graduate School of Management
Helen Way Klingler College of Arts and Sciences
J. William and Mary Diederich College of Communications
Law School
School of Dentistry

HISTORICAL FINANCIALS
Company Type: Private

Income Statement   FYE: June 30

	REVENUE ($ mil.)	NET INCOME ($ mil.)	NET PROFIT MARGIN	EMPLOYEES
06/20	679	53	7.9%	3,000
06/18	463	57	12.4%	—
06/17	434	67	15.4%	—
06/15	548	48	8.8%	—
Annual Growth	4.4%	2.2%	—	—

2020 Year-End Financials

Return on assets: 3.2%   Cash ($ mil.): 211
Return on equity: 4.7%
Current ratio: 0.90

MARSHFIELD CLINIC, INC.

Marshfield Clinic is a private group medical practice that operates more than 50 medical locations across Wisconsin. The network provides primary and tertiary care through its more than 700 physicians who represent about 80 medical specialties. Through two hospitals — the 25-bed Flambeau Hospital and the 40-bed Lakeview Medical Center — and dozens of clinics Marshfield annually serves roughly 380000 patients and handles 3.8 million patient encounters. Other parts of the network include Marshfield Laboratories and Security Health Plan of Wisconsin as well as medical education and research organizations.

Operations

Marshfield Clinic's Security Health Plan of Wisconsin provides a variety of health insurance options to more than 200000 members in much of central northern and western Wisconsin. The Marshfield Clinic organization also includes Marshfield Labs one of the largest private practice full-service laboratory systems in the nation conducting more than 25 million tests annually.

Flambeau Hospital is a 25-bed Critical Access Hospital and provides 24-hour care for inpatient and outpatient services emergency ambulance services and home health & hospice service. Flambeau Hospital is jointly sponsored by Ministry Health Care and Marshfield Clinic.

Lakeview Medical Center is a 40-bed nonprofit community hospital and provides 24-hour care for inpatient and outpatient services and emergency ambulance services. Lakeview Medical Center integrates modern design and technology with a calm healing environment.

Marshfield Clinic runs about 50 general and specialty medical clinics and dental offices in its service territory. It also has an outreach services program that collaborates with 1200 medical sites to provide care in surrounding regions.

The Marshfield Clinic Education Foundation programs for medical school graduates are internal medicine pediatrics dermatology and surgery. The company's research division Marshfield Clinic Research Foundation focuses on clinical research health and safety human genetics epidemiology and biomedical informatics.

Geographic Reach

Marshfield Clinic operates about 50 clinic locations and two hospitals in central western and northern Wisconsin. Its main hospital campuses are located in Park Falls and Rice Lake.

Sales and Marketing

Features of the Security Health Plan include contacting members through reminder mailings and personal phone calls to aid with their health maintenance. Additionally affiliated home health nurses visit members at home or in the hospital to answer their questions about their medications or care and to provide needed resources for their recuperation.

Strategy

In 2015 CareCloud and Marshfield Clinic Information Services a healthcare IT company established from within the Marshfield Clinic announced a partnership to deliver a joint cloud-based solution to help improve the clinical financial and administrative outcomes of large ambulatory medical practices. The two parties have joined together MCIS' clinical solutions - including a physician-designed electronic health record (EHR) patient portal and population health management tool with CareCloud's practice management and medical billing software and services. The integrated solution which also includes unified customer implementation and support is optimized for the requirements of large practices across dozens of specialties. MCIS has collaborated with Marshfield Clinic to build a physician-designed cloud-based clinical solution that reflects our successful experiences supporting a renowned multi-specialty group of more than 700 physicians.

Marshfield Clinic has a rich history in health information technology and software development. The Clinic has used a computer-based electronic health record for more than 20 years. Cattails Software Suite Marshfield Clinic's homegrown electronic health record was developed in conjunction with Clinic providers and the Information Systems Department. Cattails Software Suite played a significant role in the Clinic's success in the Centers for Medicare and Medicaid Services' Physician Group Practice project. Marshfield Clinic improved patient care while lowering health care costs during the five-year project - saving the Medicare program more than $118 million.

In 2015 the company expanded outpatient services provided in the Ambulatory Surgery Center in Marshfield adding skilled nursing care in the East Wing of its Marshfield campus. Similar plans to lower the total cost of care have been designed for all of its mission-critical centers.

The second phase of the plan includes construction of a new hospital of the future in Marshfield. A smaller more smartly-designed and more energy efficient high-tech facility will allow for highly-specialized care that requires a hospital setting.

The organization also advances its patient care through a collaboration with Cleveland Clinic. Together the organizations conduct research and development programs on new medical innovations.

Company Background

Marshfield Clinic announced the formation of a new subsidiary Marshfield Clinic Information Services in 2013. The unit will use the organizations health IT expertise to help other care providers implement electronic health record (EHR) systems and other population health management software programs and services.

The clinic was founded in 1916.

EXECUTIVES

Pres, Brian H Ewert
V Pres, Douglas Reding
Cfo, Gary Jankowski
V Pres, C Todd Stewart
Treas, Mark A Lepage
Urology Specialist, Gregory A Anderson
Ophthalmologist, Richard B Patchett
Director Facilities and Proper, James D Colburn
Dir Buss Devlopment, Victoria L Strobel
Accounting Staff, Debra Brock
Cardiology, Julie A Meyer
Auditors: KPMG LLP MINNEAPOLIS MN

LOCATIONS

HQ: MARSHFIELD CLINIC, INC.
1000 N OAK AVE, MARSHFIELD, WI 544495702
Phone: 800 782-8581
Web: WWW.MARSHFIELDCLINIC.ORG

HISTORICAL FINANCIALS

Company Type: Private

Income Statement				FYE: September 30
	REVENUE ($ mil.)	NET INCOME ($ mil.)	NET PROFIT MARGIN	EMPLOYEES
09/15	1,211	24	2.0%	363
09/09	1,062	78	7.4%	—
09/08*	102	6	5.9%	—
06/06	813	23	2.9%	—
Annual Growth	4.5%	0.5%	—	—

*Fiscal year change

2015 Year-End Financials

Return on assets: 2.3%   Cash ($ mil.): 96
Return on equity: 4.5%
Current ratio: 0.70

MARTIN MEMORIAL MEDICAL CENTER, INC

EXECUTIVES

Pres, Mark Robitaille
V Pres-Cfo*, L Mark Cocorullo
Treas*, John Lowenberg
Secr*, James Orr III
Sr V Pres*, Donna H Griffith
V Pres*, Craig Chindemi
Cfo*, Chuck Cleaver
Chief of Pediatric, Kristen Walker
Executive Officer, Cindy Pingolt
Coordinator, Ellon Allen
Coordinator, Sara Beem

LOCATIONS

HQ: MARTIN MEMORIAL MEDICAL CENTER, INC
200 SE HOSPITAL AVE, STUART, FL 349942346
Phone: 772 287-5200
Web: WWW.MARTINHEALTH.ORG

HISTORICAL FINANCIALS

Company Type: Private

Income Statement				FYE: September 30
	REVENUE ($ mil.)	NET INCOME ($ mil.)	NET PROFIT MARGIN	EMPLOYEES
09/19	599	31	5.2%	2,972
09/18	506	20	4.0%	—
09/17	490	26	5.3%	—
09/14	910	545	59.9%	—
Annual Growth	(8.0%)	(43.6%)	—	—

2019 Year-End Financials

Return on assets: 4.5%   Cash ($ mil.): 23
Return on equity: 11.2%
Current ratio: 0.30

MARTIN PRODUCT SALES LLC

EXECUTIVES

Pres, Ruben S Martin III
MBR-V Pres*, Chris Booth
Coo*, Randall L Tauscher
Exec V Pres*, Robert D Bondurant

LOCATIONS

HQ: MARTIN PRODUCT SALES LLC
4200 STONE RD, KILGORE, TX 756626935
Phone: 903 983-6200
Web: WWW.THEMARTINCOMPANIES.COM

HISTORICAL FINANCIALS

Company Type: Private

Income Statement				FYE: December 31
	REVENUE ($ mil.)	NET INCOME ($ mil.)	NET PROFIT MARGIN	EMPLOYEES
12/07	1,204	8	0.7%	206
12/02*	156	1	0.7%	—
06/01	260	3	1.4%	—
06/99	132	0	0.2%	—
Annual Growth	27.8%	46.7%	—	—

*Fiscal year change

2007 Year-End Financials

Return on assets: 2.0%   Cash ($ mil.): 5
Return on equity: 21.2%
Current ratio: 1.80

MARTIN RESOURCE MANAGEMENT CORPORATION

Martin Resource Management likes to push around petroleum products. The employee-owned company's flagship affiliate Martin Midstream Partners offers transportation storage marketing and logistics management services for petroleum products including sulfur sulfur derivatives fuel oil liq-uefied petroleum gas asphalt and other bulk tank liquids primarily in the southern US. Martin Resource also manufactures and markets fertilizer and other processed sulfur products. Through its Martin Energy Services unit the company offers inland marine fuel supply and offshore support services. Other units include The Brimrock Group (sulfur) Cross Oil Refining & Marketing and Martin Asphalt.

Operations

Each year the company markets more than 250 million gallons of diesel fuel and lubricants along the Gulf Coast and 1.5 million barrels of naphthenic lubricants and base oils across the US. In addition Martin Resource also provides surface transportation services for products such as molten sulfur sulfuric acid fuel oil natural gas liquids (NGLs) asphalt paper mill liquids and other bulk tank liquids.

The company's more than $550 million of assets include a fleet of truck trailers and tractors. Its Martin Transport subsidiary has about 25 terminals in the Southeast and Southern US with more than 850 trucks and 1200 trailers. Martin Product Sales LLC markets and distributes petroleum-based products including asphalt fuel oil and sulfuric acid.

Martin Resource owns a 28.0% limited partnership interest and a 2% general partnership interest in its flagship operating company Martin Midstream Partners. Its Martin Energy Services subsidiary offers marine fuel supply and offshore support services.

Sales and Marketing

The company's customers include agriculture petrochemical petroleum and utility companies.

Strategy

Martin Resource markets oil and gas and by-products through facilities located throughout the Gulf Coast region. It acquires other companies or forms joint ventures to develop its portfolio. It also redistributes operating assets to its major subsidiaries to improve their performance.

In 2013 Canadian subsidiary Brimrock signed an engineering service agreement with Keyera to act as the engineering management and technology provider for Keyera's planned sulphur forming and materials handling facilities upgrade.

That year Martin Resource sold a 49% voting interest in MMGP Holdings LLC a newly-formed sole member of Martin Midstream GP LLC the general partner of Martin Midstream Partners to Alinda Capital Partners.

In 2012 Martin Midstream Partners also sold its East Texas and Northwest Louisiana natural gas gathering and processing assets to CenterPoint Energy Field Services for $275 million.

Streamlining its businesses in 2012 the company formed Martin Energy Services LLC combining the entities of Midstream Fuel Service LLC L & L Oil and Gas Services L.L.C. and PEPCO into one entity for improved service and growth.

Mergers and Acquisitions

In 2013 Martin Midstream Partners' subsidiary Martin Operating Partnership L.P bought Kansas City Missouri-based NL Grease LLC a grease manufacturer that specializes in private-label packaging of commercial and industrial greases.

Boosting its NGL handling capabilities that year Martin Midstream Partners purchased six liquefied petroleum gas pressure barges and two commercial push boats from affiliates of Florida Marine Transporters for $51 million.

In 2012 Martin Midstream Partners acquired Gulf Coast fuels and lubricants provider Talen's Marine & Fuel LLC. The transactions boosted the company's marine terminal infrastructure adding ten marine terminals between Houston/Galveston and Port Fourchon in Louisiana with total tankage of 300000 barrels and an additional 4000 feet of water-accessible bulkhead.

In 2012 Martin Midstream Partners bought the remaining equity interests in Redbird Gas Storage LLC for $150 million. (In 2011 Martin Resource and Martin Midstream Partners formed the Redbird Gas Storage natural gas storage joint venture to invest in Cardinal Gas Storage Partners a joint venture between Redbird and Energy Capital Partners focused on the development of natural gas storage facilities across North America).

Company Background

The acquisition of L & L Oil and Gas L.L.C. by Midstream Fuel Service in 2011 increased Martin Resources' capability along the U.S. Gulf Coast to 31 facilities for offshore fuels lubricants and logistical services including land based commercial and industrial fuels and lubricants.

In 2011 Martin Resource and Martin Midstream Partners formed the Redbird Gas Storage natural gas storage joint venture to invest in Cardinal Gas Storage Partners. Cardinal is a joint venture between Redbird and Energy Capital Partners that is focused on the development construction operation and management of natural gas storage facilities across North America.

To raise cash and boost the Martin Midstream Partners' storage segment in 2011 Martin Resource sold 13 terminals to that unit for $36.5 million.

Founded in 1951 by R. S. Martin Jr. Martin Resource also holds a stake in Ican Energy an LPG distributor. To raise cash and increase its financial flexibility in 2002 the company spun off a portion of its assets.

EXECUTIVES

Pres, Ruben S Martin III
V Pres*, Douglas Towns
Cfo*, Bob Bondurant
Sr V Pres Opers, Scot A Shoup
Coordinator, Darren Volle
Coordinator, Connie Adams
Manager of Rail Transportation, Tali Wilkinson
R Andamp, Juan Hermosillo
Information Technology Develop, Ben Roberts
Tax Accountant, Tabitha Staley
Manager Mechanical Integrity, Colin Bryant
Auditors: KPMG LLP DALLAS TEXAS

LOCATIONS

HQ: MARTIN RESOURCE MANAGEMENT CORPORATION
4200 STONE RD, KILGORE, TX 756626935
Phone: 903 983-6200
Web: WWW.THEMARTINCOMPANIES.COM

PRODUCTS/OPERATIONS

Selected Companies

Altec Environmental Consulting
Commercial & Industrial Fuels & Lubricants
Commercial & Industrial Tanks & Equipment
Cross Oil Refining & Marketing Inc.
Marine Lubricants & Specialty Products
Martin Crude Marketing Company
Martin Energy Services LLC
Martin Product Sales LLC
Martin Transport Inc
Roddey engineering services Inc.

COMPETITORS

Enterprise Products	Penn Octane
George Warren	Sun Coast Resources
Global Partners	Williams Companies
Gulf Oil	

HISTORICAL FINANCIALS

Company Type: Private

Income Statement   FYE: December 31

	REVENUE ($ mil.)	NET INCOME ($ mil.)	NET PROFIT MARGIN	EMPLOYEES
12/15	2,493	27	1.1%	2,300
12/11	2,985	37	1.3%	—
12/09	1,537	23	1.5%	—
12/08	2,903	5	0.2%	—
Annual Growth	(2.1%)	24.9%		

2015 Year-End Financials

Return on assets: 1.5%   Cash ($ mil.): 13
Return on equity: 6.9%
Current ratio: 1.80

MARTIN'S POINT HEALTH CARE, INC.

EXECUTIVES

Ceo-Pres, David Howes
Chb*, Robert Moore
Cfo*, Daniel Chojnowski
Coordinator, Elizabeth Chadbourne
Coordinator, INA Levasseur
Coordinator, Jeanne Richards
Coordinator, Sheryl Fossett
Administrative Project Coordin, Kacey Parquette
Senior Human Resource Business, Terry K Sphr
Payroll Administrator, John Carter
Senior Consultant, Christine Torraca
Auditors: BAKER NEWMAN & NOYES PORTLAND

LOCATIONS

HQ: MARTIN'S POINT HEALTH CARE, INC.
331 VERANDA ST STE 1, PORTLAND, ME 041035544
Phone: 207 774-5801
Web: WWW.MARTINSPOINT.ORG

HISTORICAL FINANCIALS

Company Type: Private

Income Statement   FYE: December 31

	ASSETS ($ mil.)	NET INCOME ($ mil.)	INCOME AS % OF ASSETS	EMPLOYEES
12/16	386	17	4.6%	839
12/14	351	3	1.0%	—
12/13	345	10	3.0%	—
12/09	247	30	12.2%	—
Annual Growth	6.6%	(7.2%)	—	—

2016 Year-End Financials

Return on assets: 4.6%   Sales ($ mil): 704
Return on equity: 6.6%

MARYLAND AND VIRGINIA MILK PRODUCERS COOPERATIVE ASSOCIATION, INCORPORATED

Milk is "Mar-VA-lous" for the members of the Maryland & Virginia Milk Producers Cooperative Association. Known as Maryland & Virginia the co-op processes and sells milk for nearly 1500 member/farmers with dairy herds in the southeastern US and mid-Atlantic region. Maryland & Virginia produces fluid milk ice cream and cultured dairy products for retail sale under the Marva Maid Maola and Valley Milk brands. Its butter condensed milk and milk-powder products are sold primarily to food manufacturers. As a co-op it also offers agricultural supplies to its members. Maryland & Virginia operates three fluid-milk processing plants a manufacturing plant and an equipment-supply warehouse.

Operations

Maryland & Virginia operates three fluid processing plants a single manufacturing plant and a farm supply equipment division. It also owns a majority stake in Valley Milk LLC. The co-op transports more than 300 tanker truckloads of milk daily to nearly 30 different plants. Member farms range in size from fewer than 100 cows to more than 2000. Combined Maryland & Virginia members produce three billion pounds of milk annually.

Geographic Reach

The co-op gets its milk from member farmers in Delaware Florida Georgia Kentucky Maryland North Carolina Ohio Pennsylvania South Carolina Tennessee Virginia and West Virginia. Its fluid processing plants are located in Newport News Virginia; Landover Maryland; and New Bern North Carolina. It has manufacturing facilities in Laurel Maryland and Strasburg Virginia and a warehouse in Frederick Maryland.

Sales and Marketing

In addition to supermarkets the co-op counts customers such as Walgreens Starbucks Sheetz convenience stores and Dairy Queen among its customers.

Financial Performance

The co-op's revenue decreased by 5% to $1.3 billion in 2012 versus $1.4 billion in 2011 due to a decline in milk dairy and other products as well as sales of equipment and supplies partially offset by an increase in sales of its members' and non-members' raw milk. Despite the decline in sales the Maryland & Virginia reported a profit of $5.5 million in 2012 versus a loss of $2.8 million the prior year. Like other milk producers Maryland & Virginia has been contending with sluggish milk sales due to decreasing milk consumption beginning in the 1970s.

EXECUTIVES

Pres, Dwayne Myers
Cfo, Jorge Gonzalez
Treas, Jay Bryant

Corp SEC, Barbara Campbell
V Pres, R Graybeal
V Pres, Richard Mosemann
Operations Manager, Craig Gentry
Milk Marketing, Troye Cooper
Chief Operating Officer, Brian Linney
Payroll Accounting Specialist, Brenda Phillips
Vice President, Grant Gayman
Auditors: HERLIEM & COMPANY INC
READING

LOCATIONS

HQ: MARYLAND AND VIRGINIA MILK PRODUCERS
COOPERATIVE ASSOCIATION, INCORPORATED
1985 ISAAC NEWTON SQ W, RESTON, VA 201905031
Phone: 703 742-6800
Web: WWW.MDVAMILK.COM

COMPETITORS

Associated Milk	Dairylea
Producers	Dean Foods
Dairy Farmers Of	Foremost Farms
America	Land O'lakes
Dairy Manufacturers	

HISTORICAL FINANCIALS
Company Type: Private

Income Statement			FYE: December 31
	REVENUE ($ mil.)	NET INCOME ($ mil.)	NET PROFIT MARGIN	EMPLOYEES
12/12	1,296	5	0.4%	550
12/11	1,362	(2)	—	—
12/10	1,219	8	0.7%	—
Annual Growth	3.1%	(20.4%)	—	—

2012 Year-End Financials
Return on assets: 3.4% Cash ($ mil.): —
Return on equity: 14.9%
Current ratio: 0.80

MARYLAND DEPARTMENT OF TRANSPORTATION

Traveling in Maryland? You can thank (or curse) the Maryland Department of Transportation (MDOT). MDOT is responsible for building operating and maintaining a safe and seamless transportation network that includes highway transit maritime and aviation facilities. The Department of Transportation is organized along various administrative groups including the Maryland Motor Vehicle Administration Transit Administration Port Administration Aviation Administration and Highway Administration. MDOT annual budget of about $1.5 billion is funded through the state's Transportation Trust Fund and federal aid.

EXECUTIVES

SEC, Pete K Rahn
SEC*, John Porcari
Prin*, Donald A Halligan
Prin*, Robert Ehrlich
Bay Bridge Facility Administra, Richard Jaramillo
Coordinator, Cathy Kahl
Coordinator, Colleen Johnson
Treasurer, Bill Oliver

Assistant Manager, Jane Shock-Osborn
Deputy Director, Sandy Hertz
Member, Steven Miles
Auditors: CLIFTONLARSONALLEN LLP BALTI

LOCATIONS

HQ: MARYLAND DEPARTMENT OF TRANSPORTATION
7201 CORPORATE CENTER DR, HANOVER, MD
210761415
Phone: 410 865-1037
Web: WWW.MDOT.MARYLAND.GOV

HISTORICAL FINANCIALS
Company Type: Private

Income Statement			FYE: June 30
	REVENUE ($ mil.)	NET INCOME ($ mil.)	NET PROFIT MARGIN	EMPLOYEES
06/20	4,791	(210)	—	1,000
06/19	4,609	229	5.0%	—
06/18	4,407	(189)	—	—
06/17	4,490	85	1.9%	—
Annual Growth	2.2%	—	—	—

MARYLAND TRANSPORTATION AUTHORITY

EXECUTIVES

Governor, Larry Hogan
Security Agent, Amanda Moran
Administrative Assistant, Britney Grammer
Technical, Carmine Picarelli
Functional Analyst, Donna Singfield
Tech, Ganine Steffe
Programmer, Gregory Jones
Project Manager, Heather Amick Lowe
Qa Supervisor, Heather Vitas
Asset Manager, John Privot
Police Officer, Justin Ambush

LOCATIONS

HQ: MARYLAND TRANSPORTATION AUTHORITY
2310 BROENING HWY STE 150, BALTIMORE, MD
212246673
Phone: 410 537-7833
Web: WWW.MARYLAND.GOV

HISTORICAL FINANCIALS
Company Type: Private

Income Statement			FYE: June 30
	REVENUE ($ mil.)	NET INCOME ($ mil.)	NET PROFIT MARGIN	EMPLOYEES
06/20	733	210	28.7%	77
06/19	862	321	37.2%	—
06/18	862	309	35.9%	—
06/17	869	332	38.3%	—
Annual Growth	(5.5%)	(14.1%)	—	—

2020 Year-End Financials
Return on assets: 2.6% Cash ($ mil.): 248
Return on equity: 4.1%
Current ratio: 2.50

MASHANTUCKET PEQUOT GAMING ENTERPRISE INC

EXECUTIVES

Pres-Ceo, Jason Guyot
Information Specialist, Ronald Guy
Director, Joseph Macrino
Information, Mark Thornton
Housekeeping Supervisor, Cherri Augustine
Hvac Manager, Dave Waznowicz
Production Manager, Don Costello
Security Manager, Edward Demarco
Audio Visual Supervisor, Everett Maggs
Senior Marketing Executive, Linda Rondeau
Assistant Slot Shift Manager, Marilee McMahan
Auditors: DELOITTE & TOUCHE LLP HARTFO

LOCATIONS

HQ: MASHANTUCKET PEQUOT GAMING ENTERPRISE
INC
350 TROLLEY LINE BLVD, MASHANTUCKET, CT
063383830
Phone: 860 312-3465
Web: WWW.FOXWOODSMEETINGSANDEVENTS.COM

HISTORICAL FINANCIALS
Company Type: Private

Income Statement			FYE: September 30
	REVENUE ($ mil.)	NET INCOME ($ mil.)	NET PROFIT MARGIN	EMPLOYEES
09/19	787	(40)	—	2
09/18	828	(46)	—	—
Annual Growth	(5.0%)	—	—	—

2019 Year-End Financials
Return on assets: (-5.8%) Cash ($ mil.): 47
Return on equity: (-7.1%)
Current ratio: 0.80

MASS GENERAL BRIGHAM INCORPORATED

Mass General Brigham is an integrated academic healthcare system. Mass General Brigham connects a full continuum of care across a system of academic medical centers community and specialty hospitals a health insurance plan physician networks community health centers home care and long-term care services. Mass General Brigham is a non-profit organization that is committed to patient care research teaching and service to the community. In addition Mass General Brigham is one of the nation's leading biomedical research organizations and a principal teaching affiliate of Harvard Medical School.

Operations

The nearly 15-member institutions encompass a range of health care organizations including Brigham and Women's Hospital which is comprised of nearly 795 bed teaching hospitals of Harvard Medical School; Brigham and Women's Faulkner Hospital which is comprised of a 171-bed non-profit community teaching hospital offering complete medical surgical and psychiatric care as well as a full complement of emergency ambulatory and diagnostic services; and Martha's Vineyard Hospital is a critical access not-for-profit community hospital on the island of Martha's Vineyard.

In addition to its academic medical centers Mass General also operates COVID-19 vaccination centers rehabilitation community health centers urgent care and outpatient healthcare centers.

Sales and Marketing
Mass General Brigham serves 1.5 million patients.

Strategy
In late 2021 Mass General Brigham joined with leaders from Kraft Sports + Entertainment to announce Mass General Brigham will now serve as the official sports medicine sponsor of the New England Patriots New England Revolution and Gillette Stadium. As part of this expanded relationship Mass General Brigham is opening the Mass General Performance and Research Center at Patriot Place in 2022. Representatives from Mass General Brigham and Kraft Sports + Entertainment gathered at Gillette Stadium on December 15 as part of this announcement.

Company Background
Partners HealthCare was founded in 1994 through the merger of Brigham and Women's Hospital and Massachusetts General Hospital.

EXECUTIVES

Pres-Ceo, Anne Klibanski
V Pres-Legal Counsel, Brent L Henry
V Pres, Peter K Markell
Chb, John M Conners Jr
Prin, Neil Buckley
Coo, Ron Walls
Cfo-Treas, Niyum Gandhi
Evp, David F M Brown
Technical Manager, Mgh, Scott Thomas
Director Manager Department He, Robert Castaldo
Anesthesiologist, Robert A Peterfreund

LOCATIONS

HQ: MASS GENERAL BRIGHAM INCORPORATED
800 BOYLSTON ST STE 1150, BOSTON, MA 021998123
Phone: 617 278-1000
Web: WWW.MASSGENERALBRIGHAM.ORG

PRODUCTS/OPERATIONS

2014 Sales

	$ mil.	% of total
Net patient service revenue	7,042	65
Premium revenue	1,622	15
Direct academic and research	1,225	11
Indirect academic and research	353	3
Other revenue	662	6
Total	**10,906**	**100**

COMPETITORS

Baystate Health	Milford Regional
Boston Medical Center	Medical Center
Cambridge Health	Northeast Health
Alliance	System
Cape Cod Healthcare	Southcoast Hospitals
Cape Cod Hospital	Group
Care New England	Steward Health Care
Caregroup	Universal Health
Children's Hospital	Services
Boston	

HISTORICAL FINANCIALS
Company Type: Private

Income Statement
FYE: September 30

	REVENUE ($ mil.)	NET INCOME ($ mil.)	NET PROFIT MARGIN	EMPLOYEES
09/15	11,665	(916)	—	67,000
09/10	8	(0)	—	—
09/08	551	(44)	—	—
Annual Growth	54.7%	—	—	—

2015 Year-End Financials

Return on assets: (-6.1%)   Cash ($ mil.): 621
Return on equity: (-15.1%)
Current ratio: 2.30

MASSACHUSETTS BAY TRANSPORTATION AUTHORITY

EXECUTIVES

Chm, John R Jenkins
Ceo-Gen Mgr*, Luis M Ramirez
Treas-Contrl*, Paul Brandley
Exec Dir*, Alan G Macdonald
Coordinator, John Ford
Sergeant, Paul Carroll
Procurement Staff, Judi Kidd
Procurement Staff, Karen Love
Director of Environmental Comp, Janis Kearney
Software Quality Assurance Jun, Anthony Leoni
Operations Control Center Supe, Brian Hoey
Auditors: KPMG LLP BOSTON MA

LOCATIONS

HQ: MASSACHUSETTS BAY TRANSPORTATION AUTHORITY
MBTA 10 PARK PLZ STE 3910, BOSTON, MA 02116
Phone: 617 222-3106
Web: WWW.MBTA.COM

HISTORICAL FINANCIALS
Company Type: Private

Income Statement
FYE: June 30

	REVENUE ($ mil.)	NET INCOME ($ mil.)	NET PROFIT MARGIN	EMPLOYEES
06/19	777	459	59.1%	6,100
06/18	764	408	53.4%	—
06/06*	379	(23)	—	—
12/05	0	0	—	—
Annual Growth	—	—	—	—
*Fiscal year change				

2019 Year-End Financials

Return on assets: 3.5%   Cash ($ mil.): 296
Return on equity: 18.6%
Current ratio: 0.80

MASSACHUSETTS DEPARTMENT OF TRANSPORTATION

The Massachusetts Department of Transportation (MassDOT) oversees the operations essential for the massive job of moving people and goods throughout the Commonwealth. In 2009 the former Massachusetts Executive Office of Transportation merged with other state agencies to form MassDOT. The unified organization operates in four divisions: highway; transit; aeronautics; and the registry of motor vehicles. In addition to its regulatory responsibility MassDOT also provides research planning and information services relevant to the state's transportation system.

EXECUTIVES

Ceo, Stephanie Pollack
Executive Assistant, Kathleen Quirk
Administrator, Kevin Lopez
Director, Lisa Strout
General Manager, Paul Garrity
Information Technology Manager, Paul Jay
Senior Project Manager, Abhishek Gupta
Director, Augie Grace
Assistant Director, Edvard Duffaut
Administrative Assistant, Jillian Melito
Independent Director, Kathleen A Theoharides

LOCATIONS

HQ: MASSACHUSETTS DEPARTMENT OF TRANSPORTATION
10 PARK PLZ STE 4160, BOSTON, MA 021163979
Phone: 857 368-4636
Web: WWW.MALEGISLATURE.GOV

HISTORICAL FINANCIALS
Company Type: Private

Income Statement
FYE: June 30

	REVENUE ($ mil.)	NET INCOME ($ mil.)	NET PROFIT MARGIN	EMPLOYEES
06/20	3,114	58	1.9%	6,100
06/18	2,957	1	0.1%	—
06/17	2,984	(107)	—	—
06/16	3,235	15	0.5%	—
Annual Growth	(0.9%)	38.4%	—	—

MASSACHUSETTS HOUSING FINANCE AGENCY

EXECUTIVES

Chb, Michael J Dirrane
Chm*, Ronald A Homer
Exec Dir*, Thomas R Gleason
Treas*, Andris J Silins
Prin*, Tom O'Brien
Cfo*, Michael Fitzmaurice

Staff, Tyrone Reed
Real Estate Conultant, Kristin Olsen
Vp-Homeownership Programs, Mounzer M Aylouche
Business Officer E, Angelo Nuby
Marketing Analyst, Deanna Ramsden

LOCATIONS

HQ: MASSACHUSETTS HOUSING FINANCE AGENCY
1 BEACON ST FL 4, BOSTON, MA 021083132
Phone: 617 854-1000
Web: WWW.MASSHOUSING.COM

HISTORICAL FINANCIALS

Company Type: Private

Income Statement   FYE: June 30

	ASSETS ($ mil.)	NET INCOME ($ mil.)	INCOME AS % OF ASSETS	EMPLOYEES
06/21	6,316	39	0.6%	325
06/20	5,948	149	2.5%	—
06/18	5,460	6	0.1%	—
Annual Growth	5.0%	87.2%	—	—

2021 Year-End Financials

Return on assets: 0.6%   Sales ($ mil): 266
Return on equity: 2.6%

MASSACHUSETTS INSTITUTE OF TECHNOLOGY

Massachusetts Institute of Technology (MIT) is an academic community for undergraduate and graduate for education research and innovation. MIT is providing its students with an education that combines rigorous academic study and discovery of support of intellectual stimulation of a diverse campus community. MIT has more than 11250 students from all 50 states and the District of Columbia three territories and about 120 foreign nations in the academic year ending 2020-2021. The school's student teacher ratio is 3:1 (undergraduates). Founded in 1865 MIT is integral part of host city Cambridge.

Operations

Research flourishes in its 30 departments across five schools and one college as well as in dozens of centers labs and programs that convene experts across disciplines to explore new intellectual frontiers and attack important societal problems. MIT's on-campus research capabilities are enhanced through the work of MIT Lincoln Laboratory the Woods Hole Oceanographic Institution active research relationships with industry and a wide range of global collaborations. In this work the MIT Libraries serve as a crucial partner and a source of important research in their own right.

MITx the Institute's portfolio of massively open online courses offers flexible access to a range of interactive courses developed and taught by instructors from MIT. Another MIT innovation ? the MicroMasters credential ? is increasingly recognized by industry leaders hiring new talent. And MIT's original digital learning option OpenCourseWare continues to offer teachers and learners worldwide the materials for more than 2450 MIT courses freely available online.

Geographic Reach

MIT is based in Cambridge Massachusetts.

Company Background

MIT has some extraordinary alumni who include former chairman of the Federal Reserve Ben Bernanke former US Representative Pete Stark former National Economic Council chairman Lawrence H. Summers and former Council of Economic Advisors chairwoman Christina Romer. Outside of politics MIT alumni founded or cofounded several notable companies such as Intel Hewlett-Packard Texas Instruments Qualcomm Bose and Campbell Soup.

EXECUTIVES

Pres, L Rafael Reif
Exec V Pres, Israel Ruiz
V Pres, Kirk Kolendrander
Director, V Bove
Executive Officer, David Reed
Scientist, Lance Koutny
Scientist, Richard Petrasso
Scientist, Stanley Gershwin
Staff, Virginia Such
Scientist, Heidi Greulich
Information, Steven Saito
Auditors: PRICEWATERHOUSECOOPERS LLP BO

LOCATIONS

HQ: MASSACHUSETTS INSTITUTE OF TECHNOLOGY
77 MASSACHUSETTS AVE, CAMBRIDGE, MA 021394307
Phone: 617 253-1000
Web: WWW.WEB.MIT.EDU

PRODUCTS/OPERATIONS

2014 Sales

	$ mil.	% of total
Reseach revenue	1,528	49
Support from investment	625	20
Tuition and similar revenue	324	10
Fee and services	176	6
Gifts	162	5
Auxiliary enterprises	120	4
Other program	117	4
Net asset reclassification	69	2
Total	**3,124**	**100**

Schools and Areas of Study

Schools and Areas of Study
School of Architecture and Planning
  Architecture
  Media Arts and Sciences
  Urban Studies and Planning
School of Engineering
  Aeronautics and Astronautics
  Biological Engineering
  Chemical Engineering
  Civil and Environmental Engineering
  Electrical Engineering and Computer Science
  Engineering Systems Division
  Materials Science and Engineering
  Mechanical Engineering
  Nuclear Science and Engineering
School of Humanities Arts and Social Sciences
  Anthropology
  Comparative Media Studies
  Economics
  Foreign Languages and Literatures
  History
  Humanities
  Linguistics and Philosophy
  Literature
  Music and Theater Arts
  Political Science
  Science Technology and Society
  Writing and Humanistic Studies
Sloan School of Management
  Management
School of Science
  Biology
  Brain and Cognitive Sciences

Chemistry
Earth Atmospheric and Planetary Sciences
Mathematics
Physics
Whitaker College of Health Sciences and Technology
  Harvard-MIT Division of Health Sciences and Technology
MIT-WHOI Joint Program in Oceanography and Applied
  Ocean Science and Engineering
Degrees Offered
Bachelor of Science (SB)
Master of Architecture (MArch)
Master of Business Administration (MBA)
Master in City Planning (MCP)
Master of Engineering (MEng)
Master of Finance (MFin)
Master of Science (SM)
Engineer (degree designates the field)
Doctor of Philosophy (PhD)
Doctor of Science (ScD)

HISTORICAL FINANCIALS

Company Type: Private

Income Statement   FYE: June 30

	REVENUE ($ mil.)	NET INCOME ($ mil.)	NET PROFIT MARGIN	EMPLOYEES
06/21	3,945	12,229	310.0%	12,000
06/20	3,950	1,447	36.7%	—
06/19	3,931	1,252	31.8%	—
06/18	3,626	2,391	65.9%	—
Annual Growth	2.8%	72.3%	—	—

2021 Year-End Financials

Return on assets: 28.8%   Cash ($ mil.): 345
Return on equity: 33.6%
Current ratio: —

MASSACHUSETTS PORT AUTHORITY

Massachusetts Port Authority (Massport) operates three airports: Boston Logan International Hanscom Field and Worcester Regional. Logan is home to 50 airlines and is New England's largest airport and the first port of call for many international flights entering the US. (It accounts for the majority of Massport's revenues.) Hanscom Field operates as the region's main aviation airport and offers niche commercial services while Worcester Regional primarily supports commercial flight services. Massport also oversees various waterfront properties of the Port of Boston. The agency was created by the Commonwealth of Massachusetts in 1956. The governor of Massachusetts appoints the agency's board members.

Operations

Massport's business consists of two distinct operating departments: Aviation and the Port. Logan airport catered to 29.4 million aviation passengers and 369000 cruise passengers in 2013. Its shipping operations serviced more than 110000 containers of products at its port.

Financial Performance

Massport's net revenues have steadily climbed over the years. Revenues jumped 2% from $1.78 billion in 2012 to $1.83 billion in 2013 thanks mainly to parking concession ground services and other revenue from nearly 125000 more passengers at Logan. The overall revenue increase for 2013 was generated by operating revenues exceeding operating expenses by $2.4 million.

EXECUTIVES

Ceo, Thomas P Glynn
Chb*, Mark Robinson
Cfo*, John Pranckevicius
Cso*, Harold H Shaw
Secretary, Rita Hannon
Payroll Staff, Anita Jansky
Compliance Staff, Gregory Short
Director Human Resources, David M Gambone
Sergeant, Chris Ryan
Junior Buyer, Heather Fife
Procurement Specialist, Judith Miskinis
Auditors: ERNST & YOUNG LLP BOSTON MA

LOCATIONS

HQ: MASSACHUSETTS PORT AUTHORITY
  1 HARBORSIDE DR STE 200, BOSTON, MA
  021282905
Phone: 617 561-1600
Web: WWW.MASSPORT.COM

HISTORICAL FINANCIALS

Company Type: Private

Income Statement				FYE: June 30
	REVENUE ($ mil.)	NET INCOME ($ mil.)	NET PROFIT MARGIN	EMPLOYEES
06/20	824	104	12.6%	1,102
06/15	662	107	16.2%	—
Annual Growth	4.5%	(0.6%)	—	—

2020 Year-End Financials

Return on assets: 1.8%
Return on equity: 4.1%
Current ratio: 3.10
Cash ($ mil.): 82

MASSACHUSETTS SCHOOL BUILDING AUTHORITY

EXECUTIVES

Exec Director, Katherine Craven
Accounting Staff, Audrey Cushman
Senior Project Manager, Gregory Brunell
Senior Project Manager, Richard Hudson
Executive Board Member, Matthew Deninger
Assistant Project Manager, Chizoba Ezeigwe
Senior Project Manager, Greg Brunell
Project Manager, Kevin Sullivan
Assistant Project Manager, Rachel O 'brien
Project Manager, Zhanna Pekelis

LOCATIONS

HQ: MASSACHUSETTS SCHOOL BUILDING
  AUTHORITY
  40 BROAD ST STE 500, BOSTON, MA 021094371
Phone: 617 720-4466
Web: WWW.MASSSCHOOLBUILDINGS.ORG

HISTORICAL FINANCIALS

Company Type: Private

Income Statement				FYE: June 30
	REVENUE ($ mil.)	NET INCOME ($ mil.)	NET PROFIT MARGIN	EMPLOYEES
06/19	998	270	27.0%	8
06/18	891	252	28.3%	—
06/17	828	148	17.9%	—
06/16	908	237	26.1%	—
Annual Growth	3.2%	4.4%	—	—

MASSACHUSETTS WATER RESOURCES AUTHORITY

EXECUTIVES

Chm, Richard K Sullivan Jr
Exec Dir*, Fred Laskey
Coo*, Michael Hornbrook
Cfo*, Rachel Madden
SEC*, Joseph C Foti
Senior Analyst, Michael Farmer
Senior Program Manager, Daniel Nvule
Manager It Security Architectu, Paula Weadick
Senior Administrator, Caren Sekenski
Project Leader, Kristen Hall
Supervisor, Lewis Boynton
Auditors: CLIFTONLARSONALLEN LLP
  BOSTON

LOCATIONS

HQ: MASSACHUSETTS WATER RESOURCES
  AUTHORITY
  100 1ST AVE, BOSTON, MA 021292043
Phone: 617 242-6000
Web: WWW.MWRA.COM

HISTORICAL FINANCIALS

Company Type: Private

Income Statement				FYE: June 30
	REVENUE ($ mil.)	NET INCOME ($ mil.)	NET PROFIT MARGIN	EMPLOYEES
06/21	786	(39)	—	1,200
06/20	778	(40)	—	—
06/18	738	(39)	—	—
06/17	716	(37)	—	—
Annual Growth	2.3%	—	—	—

2021 Year-End Financials

Return on assets: (-0.6%)
Return on equity: (-2.7%)
Current ratio: 2.10
Cash ($ mil.): 69

MAXIFACIAL DENTAL SURGERY

Auditors: ERNST & YOUNG US LLP INDIAN

LOCATIONS

HQ: MAXIFACIAL DENTAL SURGERY
  1 MEDICAL CENTER DR, LEBANON, NH 037561000
Phone: 603 650-5000
Web: WWW.HITCHCOCK.ORG

HISTORICAL FINANCIALS

Company Type: Private

Income Statement				FYE: September 30
	REVENUE ($ mil.)	NET INCOME ($ mil.)	NET PROFIT MARGIN	EMPLOYEES
09/09	1,147	27	2.4%	7,500
09/06	913	15	1.7%	—
Annual Growth	7.9%	20.7%	—	—

2009 Year-End Financials

Return on assets: 2.3%
Return on equity: 10.6%
Current ratio: 1.30
Cash ($ mil.): 40

MAXIM HEALTHCARE SERVICES, INC.

Maxim Healthcare aims to promote good health by offering medical staffing and home health care as well as immunizations and other wellness services to clients nationwide. Its healthcare staffing and workforce management solutions are focused on hospitals schools government programs correction facilities and managed care organizations. Maxim Healthcare's consultants are available 24 hours a day seven days a week to provide assistance for clients. The company which operates from approximately 150 locations nationwide was established in 1988.

Operations

Maxim Healthcare's companies include Maxim Healthcare Staffing and Maxim Healthcare Services.

Maxim Healthcare Staffing connects the nation's top healthcare talent with a variety of organizations. It specializes in creating meaningful career opportunities for healthcare professionals including nurses allied health professionals locum tenens travel nurses medical coders and more.

Maxim Healthcare Services offers in-home skilled nursing physical rehabilitation companion care respite care and behavioral care for people with illnesses or disabilities.

Geographic Reach

Maryland-based Maxim Healthcare has approximately 150 offices in more than 35 US states.

Sales and Marketing

Maxim Healthcare's compassionate patient care and staffing experienced healthcare professionals has made the company as an established resource in the healthcare industry. The company provides its services to elderly chronically ill disabled recuperating and pediatric patients.

EXECUTIVES

Ceo, William Butz
V Pres*, Jacqueline Baratian
V Pres*, Toni Jean Lisa
V Pres*, W John Langley
Coo*, Paula Sotir
CIO*, Kevin Apperson
Chief Experience Officer*, Julie Judge
Staffing Coordinator, Christy Peacock
Senior Project Specialist, Steven Weigley
Recruiting Coordinator, Wendy Wood
Benefits Manager, Beverly Hardin
Auditors: PRICEWATERHOUSECOOPERS LLP
  BA

LOCATIONS

HQ: MAXIM HEALTHCARE SERVICES, INC.
  7227 LEE DEFOREST DR, COLUMBIA, MD 210463236
Phone: 410 910-1500
Web: WWW.MAXIMHEALTHCARE.COM

PRODUCTS/OPERATIONS

Selected Services

Allied Health staffing
Facility nurse staffing
Flu and wellness services
Government services
Health information services
International nursing
Home healthcare
HME/pharmacy services
Habilitation services
Physician services
Travel nursing

Selected Divisions

CareFocus
CareFocus Companion Services
Centrus Premier Homecare
Logix Healthcare Search Partners
Maxim Coders
Maxim Government Services
Maxim Health Information Services
Maxim Health Systems
Maxim Healthcare Services (Homecare)
Maxim Home Health Resources
Maxim Pediatric Services
Maxim Physician Resources
Maxim Staffing Solutions - Administrative Staffing
Maxim Staffing Solutions - Allied Health
Maxim Staffing Solutions - Nurse Staffing
Orbis Clinical
Reflectx Services
StaffAssist
TimeLine Recruiting
TravelMax

COMPETITORS

American Homepatient
Apria Healthcare
Cross Country
  Healthcare
Medstaff
Medsearch Staffing
  Services

Phs Correctional
  Healthcare
Team Health
Teamstaff

HISTORICAL FINANCIALS

Company Type: Private

Income Statement				FYE: December 31
	REVENUE ($ mil.)	NET INCOME ($ mil.)	NET PROFIT MARGIN	EMPLOYEES
12/17	1,510	38	2.5%	35,000
12/15	1,382	11	0.8%	—
12/14	1,269	4	0.4%	—
12/13	1,226	(1)	—	—
Annual Growth	5.3%	—	—	—

2017 Year-End Financials

Return on assets: 14.2%   Cash ($ mil.): 8
Return on equity: 71.1%
Current ratio: 1.40

MAYER ELECTRIC SUPPLY COMPANY, INC.

Mayer Electric Supply helps to light up those southern nights. The company is one of the nation's largest distributors of electrical supplies with about 50 branch locations in the southeastern US. It offers some 40000 items made by leading manufacturers such as 3M GE Littelfuse and Schneider Electric. Products include conduit circuit breakers controls and switches fire and safety products LED and low-voltage lighting systems motors power tools transformers and wire and cable. Mayer Electric supplies customers in the construction datacomm government industrial and utility industries. The Collat family including CEO Nancy Collat Goedecke owns Mayer Electric.

Operations

Besides distributing electrical supplies Mayer Electric offers several services. Its Mayer Project Management group works to lower cost for construction contractors by providing on-site storage and inventory management. Other services include lamp and battery recycling conduit bending and threading and wire and cable cutting. The company also specializes in factory automation energy efficiency and datacomm systems.

Geographic Reach

Mayer Electric serves customers through locations in Alabama Florida Georgia Mississippi the Carolinas Texas Tennessee and Virginia.

Sales and Marketing

The electrical supplies distributor serves multiple customer segments including those in the construction government industrial datacomm and utility industries through about 51 branch locations across US Southeast.

Strategy

Growing its geographic presence in 2013 Mayer Electric opened a branch location in the Houston area.

Mergers and Acquisitions

Looking to expand further in the southeastern US Mayer Electric in 2012 acquired Mustang Electric Supply based outside Dallas in Lewisville Texas. Established in 1998 Mustang Electric serves commercial and residential contractors across the Dallas and Fort Worth area allowing Mayer Electric to expand to the dynamic and lucrative Dallas market. The purchase included Mustang Electric's 40000-sq.-ft. facility in Lewisville.

Company Background

The recession hit companies like Mayer Electric hard as residential and commercial construction efforts were backburnered. Sales for Mayer Electric dropped by about 21% in 2009 compared to the prior year. Rather than responding by laying off employees or shuttering branches the company planned for break-even results or a small loss for the year. Indeed the company made a small profit in 2009.

Mayer Electric was founded in 1930.

EXECUTIVES

Chb-Ceo, Nancy Collat Goedecke
Pres*, Wes Smith
Exec V Pres*, Glenn Goedecke

Executive Officer, Mike Dunaway
Staff, Steve Poremba
Outside Sales, Brian Miller
Customer Supervisor, Corey Isbell
Counter Sales, Jack Davidson
Sales Support, Kristopher Holmes
Counter Sales, Max Maddox
Accounting Manager, Nathan Harr
Auditors: WARREN AVERETT BIRMINGHAM AL

LOCATIONS

HQ: MAYER ELECTRIC SUPPLY COMPANY, INC.
  3405 4TH AVE S, BIRMINGHAM, AL 352222300
Phone: 205 583-3500
Web: WWW.MAYERELECTRIC.COM

PRODUCTS/OPERATIONS

Selected Services

Basic distributor services
Construction partner
Maintenance repair and operations

Selected Products

Ballasts
Batteries
Cable and wire
Circuit breakers
Conduit
Factory automation products
Fan boxes
Fasteners
Fuses
LED lighting systems
Lenses
Lighting fixtures
Locks
Low-voltage lighting systems
Meters
Motors
Panelboards
Power supplies
Relays
Switches
Surge protection devices
Terminal blocks
Tools
Transformers
Voltage regulators

COMPETITORS

Anixter International
Consolidated
  Electrical
Crescent Electric
  Supply
Gexpro
Graybar Electric

Independent Electric
  Supply
Rexel Inc.
W.w. Grainger
Wesco International
Wholesale Supply Group

HISTORICAL FINANCIALS

Company Type: Private

Income Statement				FYE: January 2
	REVENUE ($ mil.)	NET INCOME ($ mil.)	NET PROFIT MARGIN	EMPLOYEES
01/21*	1,067	11	1.1%	900
12/19	1,138	14	1.2%	—
12/18	1,072	11	1.1%	—
12/17	911	11	1.2%	—
Annual Growth	5.4%	0.9%	—	—

*Fiscal year change

2021 Year-End Financials

Return on assets: 3.3%   Cash ($ mil.): —
Return on equity: 12.0%
Current ratio: 1.10

MAYO FOUNDATION FOR MEDICAL EDUCATION AND RESEARCH

EXECUTIVES

Pres-Ceo, William Litchy
Pres and Ceo*, John H Noseworthy
Operations Administrator, Adrienne Palmer Fache
Senior Analyst Programmer, Craig Robert Stancl
Information, Gerhardt Hartke
Information Technology/Telecom, Jeralyn Waller Smith
Information Project Sp, Joe Woodie
Information Unit Head, Karen Laures
Assistant To Chief Technology, Kristin Olson
Information, Calvin Beebe
Network, Christina Ellenburg

LOCATIONS

HQ: MAYO FOUNDATION FOR MEDICAL EDUCATION AND RESEARCH
200 1ST ST SW, ROCHESTER, MN 559050001
Phone: 507 284-2511
Web: WWW.MAYO.EDU

HISTORICAL FINANCIALS
Company Type: Private

Income Statement   FYE: December 31

	REVENUE ($ mil.)	NET INCOME ($ mil.)	NET PROFIT MARGIN	EMPLOYEES
12/13	1,069	6	0.6%	60,000
12/05	5,802	505	8.7%	—
12/03	4,822	348	7.2%	—
12/02	0	0	—	—
Annual Growth	—	—	—	—

2013 Year-End Financials
Return on assets: 75.4%   Cash ($ mil.): 496
Return on equity: 0.6%
Current ratio: 0.70

MCCARTHY BUILDING COMPANIES, INC.

McCarthy Building Companies is one of the top privately-held builders in the US. McCarthy Building Companies Inc. has a long history of building facilities that drive greater value. From exceptional levels of quality and safety to ease of maintenance over time It is firmly committed to helping its clients and partners achieve the short- and long-term strategic goals of every project it does. Contracts include heavy construction projects and transportation expertise (bridges and highways and road construction) commercial projects (retail and office buildings) and more. Founded by Timothy McCarthy in 1864 the company is 100% employee owned.

Operations
The company builds a wide array of projects including advanced technology & manufacturing aviation commercial education government healthcare heavy civil & transportation hospitality & entertainment industrial parking ports & marine terminals renewable energy research laboratory and water & wastewater projects.

Geographic Reach
Headquartered in Saint Louis McCarthy Building Companies has offices in Atlanta Georgia; Austin Dallas Houston Texas; Denver Colorado; Collinsville Illinois; Overland Park Kansas; Las Vegas Nevada; Los Angeles Newport Beach Sacramento San Diego San Francisco and San Jose California; Omaha Nebraska; and Phoenix Arizona.

Sales and Marketing
The company's clients include some of the well-known companies such as Banner Health Ameren Cornell University Dairy Farmers of America Delta Airlines Eli Lilly & Company Genetech Kaiser Permanente Lifescan Metropolitan Transit Authority NRG Energy Occidental Petroleum Pfizer Sigma-Aldrich Toyota University of Arizona Walt Disney Imagineering and Yuma Regional Medical Center and among others.

EXECUTIVES

Ceo, Raymond Sedey
Pres-Coo*, Scott Wittkop
Evp-Cfo*, J Douglas Audifred
Sr Vp-Sec-Gen Counsel*, Matthew Lawson
RES SW Div*, Justin Kelton
Evp-Pres California Div*, Michael Myers
Evp-Pres Nopac Div*, Shaun Sleeth
Evp-Pres Central Div*, John Buescher
Asst SEC-Vp Accounting*, Jan Pallares
Evp-Pres Southern Division*, Joe Jouvenal
Pres Houston Division, Jim Stevenson
Auditors: RUBINBROWN LLP SAINT LOUIS M

LOCATIONS

HQ: MCCARTHY BUILDING COMPANIES, INC.
12851 MANCHESTER RD, SAINT LOUIS, MO 631311802
Phone: 314 968-3300
Web: WWW.MCCARTHYBUILDINGCOMPANIES.COM

PRODUCTS/OPERATIONS

Selected Markets

Commercial
Education K-12
Health care
Heavy/civil/transportation
Higher education
High performance/green
Hospitality/entertainment
Industrial
Native American
Parking structures
Science and technology
Water/wastewater

Selected Services
Negotiated general contracting
Construction management
Hard bid (lump sum contract for services)
Design/build
Construction management/general contracting

COMPETITORS

Alberici	Korte
Barton Malow	Peter Kiewit Sons'
Bechtel	Primus Builders
Clayco	S. M. Wilson
Dpr Construction	Skanska
Gilbane	Swinerton
Hbe Corporation	Turner Corporation
Hensel Phelps Construction	Tutor Perini

HISTORICAL FINANCIALS
Company Type: Private

Income Statement   FYE: December 31

	REVENUE ($ mil.)	NET INCOME ($ mil.)	NET PROFIT MARGIN	EMPLOYEES
12/20	4,706	0	—	4,332
12/19	4,513	0	—	—
12/18	3,852	0	—	—
12/17	3,574	0	—	—
Annual Growth	9.6%	—	—	—

2020 Year-End Financials
Return on assets: —   Cash ($ mil.): 706
Return on equity: —
Current ratio: 1.40

MCCARTHY HOLDINGS, INC.

EXECUTIVES

Ceo, Raymond J Sedey
Pres-Coo*, Scott Wittkop
Exec V Pres-Cfo*, J Douglas Audiffred
Sr V Pres-Gen Counsel-Sec*, Matthew Lawson
Vp Treasury-Asst SEC*, Danel Dillon
Project Engineer, Austin Everett
Superintendent, Edward Meade
Assistant Superintendent, Eric Fletcher
R Accountant Specialist, Eugenia Duff
Project Engineer Einformation, Jaren Murphy
Divisonal Accountant, Jennifer Foster
Auditors: RUBINBROWN LLP SAINT LOUIS M

LOCATIONS

HQ: MCCARTHY HOLDINGS, INC.
12851 MANCHESTER RD, SAINT LOUIS, MO 631311802
Phone: 314 968-3300
Web: WWW.MCCARTHY.COM

HISTORICAL FINANCIALS
Company Type: Private

Income Statement   FYE: December 31

	REVENUE ($ mil.)	NET INCOME ($ mil.)	NET PROFIT MARGIN	EMPLOYEES
12/20	4,784	0	—	4,957
12/19	4,591	0	—	—
12/18	3,925	0	—	—
12/17	3,666	0	—	—
Annual Growth	9.3%	—	—	—

2020 Year-End Financials
Return on assets: —   Cash ($ mil.): 113
Return on equity: —
Current ratio: 1.30

MCHS HOSPITALS INC

EXECUTIVES

Prin, Jerard J Jensen

Physical Therapy Director, Amy Pearson
Chief Financial Officer, James Braun
Security Manager, Robert Pflanz

LOCATIONS

HQ: MCHS HOSPITALS INC
1000 N OAK AVE, MARSHFIELD, WI 544495703
Phone: 715 389-3258

HISTORICAL FINANCIALS

Company Type: Private

Income Statement				FYE: September 30
	REVENUE ($ mil.)	NET INCOME ($ mil.)	NET PROFIT MARGIN	EMPLOYEES
09/18	629	17	2.8%	23
09/17	82	(4)	—	
Annual Growth	665.0%	—	—	—

2018 Year-End Financials

Return on assets: 2.6%   Cash ($ mil.): 10
Return on equity: 17.8%
Current ratio: —

MCLANE COMPANY, INC.

McLane Company is one of the largest wholesale suppliers of grocery and food products in the US serving some 46000 retail locations. It buys sells and delivers more than 50000 different consumer products to customers and nearly 110000 locations across the US such as convenience and discount stores mass merchandisers wholesale clubs and drug stores among others. Through McLane Grocery and McLane Foodservice the company operates more than 80 distribution centers and one of the nation's largest private fleets. In addition McLane provides spirits wine beer and nonalcoholic beverages distribution through its subsidiary Empire Distributors Inc. McLane is a wholly owned unit of Berkshire Hathaway Inc.

Operations

McLane offers a wide range of industry-leading supply chain solutions. It operates through three business units: grocery distribution foodservice distribution and alcoholic beverage distribution. In addition the company also offers proven third-party supply chain management solutions.

McLane's grocery and foodservice divisions along with numerous subsidiaries deliver more than 10 billion pounds of merchandise to customers annually. Through Empire Distributors the company offers more than 15000 unique products and sells over 10 million cases of beverages annually.

Geographic Reach

McLane has an extensive distribution network of some 80 facilities across the country. Its headquarters and grocery operations are based in Temple Texas while its foodservice operation is based in Carrollton Texas.

The company supplies alcoholic beverages throughout the southeastern US and in Colorado through distribution centers in Colorado Georgia North Carolina and Tennessee.

Sales and Marketing

McLane is a leading supplier to convenience stores; other customers include discount and drug stores bars chain restaurants mass merchants wholesale clubs and more.

Strategy

McLane continues to strengthen its business partnerships. In 2020 the company renewed its multi-year service agreement with RaceTrac Pe-

troleum Inc. The relationship dates back to 1996 and McLane's distribution services encompass all convenience store categories including tobacco grocery candy snacks and store supplies. McLane helps RaceTrac pursue its growth strategy by leveraging its purchasing power geographic distribution and product assortment allowing RaceTrac to offer competitive pricing across all of its stores.

McLane also renewed its multi-year contract with EG America. EG America will continue to utilize McLane's scale of 24 grocery distribution centers across the US to provide excellent service to all of its locations except for Cumberland Farms and Fastrac which self-distribute.

Company Background

Starting as a family-owned grocery store in 1894 McLane expanded into wholesale distribution in the early 1900s. The McLane family including former Houston Astros owner Drayton McLane sold the business to Wal-Mart Stores in the 1990s. Conglomerate Berkshire Hathaway acquired McLane Company in 2003 for about $1.5 billion.

EXECUTIVES

Pres-Ceo, Tony Frankenberger
Evp Administration, James L Kent
Pres Grocery Distrib, Mike Youngblood
Pres Foodservice Distrib, Tom Zatina
Pres Info Sys, Penny Echelberger
Sr V Pres Sls & Mktg, Stuart Clark
V Pres Acctg Fin & Tax, Kevin J Koch
V Pres-Gen Couns, Len Mewhinney
V Pres People Division, Janann Williams
Pres-Mclane Foodservice, Susan Adzick
Transportation Manager, Ernest Smith

LOCATIONS

HQ: MCLANE COMPANY, INC.
4747 MCLANE PKWY, TEMPLE, TX 765044854
Phone: 254 771-7500
Web: WWW.MCLANECO.COM

COMPETITORS

Amcon Distributing	Maines
Associated Wholesale	Performance Food Group
Grocers	Reinhart Foodservice
Ben E. Keith	Supervalu
C&s Wholesale	Southern Glazer's Wine
Core-mark	And Spirits
Eby-brown	Sysco
Gsc Enterprises	Us Foods
Golden State Foods	United Natural
Gordon Food Service	Wakefern Food
H. T. Hackney	

HISTORICAL FINANCIALS

Company Type: Private

Income Statement				FYE: December 30
	REVENUE ($ mil.)	NET INCOME ($ mil.)	NET PROFIT MARGIN	EMPLOYEES
12/16*	48,016	0	—	20,128
01/16	48,144	0	—	
12/12	37,389	0	—	
01/09	29,800	0	—	
Annual Growth	6.1%	—	—	—

*Fiscal year change

2016 Year-End Financials

Return on assets: —   Cash ($ mil.): 122
Return on equity: —
Current ratio: 1.40

MCLEOD REGIONAL MEDICAL CENTER OF THE PEE DEE, INC.

EXECUTIVES

Chb, Ronnie Ward
Ceo*, Robert L Colones
Procurement Staff, George Nixon
Executive Officer, Brad Willbanks
Internal Medicine Practitioner, Mahendrabhai Patel
Internal Medicine Practitioner, Worku Wondafrash
Information Technology Directo, Jaime Hayes
MD, Thomas Spencer
Chief Operating Officer, Tom Hartley
Shift Supervisor, Alicia Council
Professional, Richard Bryant
Auditors: KPMG LLP GREENSBORO NC

LOCATIONS

HQ: MCLEOD REGIONAL MEDICAL CENTER OF THE PEE DEE, INC.
555 E CHEVES ST, FLORENCE, SC 295062617
Phone: 843 777-2000
Web: WWW.MCLEODHEALTH.ORG

HISTORICAL FINANCIALS

Company Type: Private

Income Statement				FYE: September 30
	REVENUE ($ mil.)	NET INCOME ($ mil.)	NET PROFIT MARGIN	EMPLOYEES
09/19	784	91	11.7%	5,000
09/15	607	72	11.8%	
Annual Growth	6.6%	6.1%	—	—

2019 Year-End Financials

Return on assets: 4.4%   Cash ($ mil.): 23
Return on equity: 5.5%
Current ratio: 0.40

MCNAUGHTON-MCKAY ELECTRIC CO.

McNaughton-McKay is a wholesale distributor of electrical supplies through its office in Germany and several offices in the US. One of the largest employee-owned companies in the US McNaughton-McKay distributes an array of product lines from manufacturers such as nVent Hoffman Sylvania Panduit Appleton Sola HD and Rockwell Automation to name a few. It is a full line electrical distributor of products ranging from pipe and wire to complex automation control systems for everyone from small electrical contractors to large scale manufacturers. It sells to the construction lighting motion networking and industrial automation markets.

Operations

The company offers products such as Rockwell automation alarms security & signaling audio & video batteries & accessories cable trays & struts chemicals lubricants & paints conduit fittings and more. Its services and solutions include predictive and preventive maintenance mechatronics lighting renewable energy visualization and enclosure modification among others.

Geographic Reach

McNaughton-McKay Electric Company is headquartered in Madison Heights Michigan with over 25 locations across five states and one sale office in Germany.

Sales and Marketing

In addition to industrial automation commercial markets McNaughton-McKay supports construction drives lighting motion networking safety and visualization. McNaughton-McKay's customers include supplyFORCE Edge Global Supply and Vantage Group to name a few.

Company Background

Founded in 1910 the Bull and McNaughton families ran McNaughton-McKay until 2006. It established a sales office in Germany in 2004.

EXECUTIVES

Ceo, Donald D Slominski
President, Mark Borin
Executive Vp, Sales and Market, J Christopher Majni
Executive Vp and Cfo, John D Kuczmanski
Vice President, Human Resource, Carol A Hoefler
Coo, Walt Reynolds
Technical Support Engineer, Anthony Verdaglio
Employee, Cagle Sharon
Accounts Payable Specialist, Cari Skrinner
Warehouse Associate, Christopher Sevener
Payroll Analyst, Cindy Quick-Wasik
Auditors: KPMG LLP

LOCATIONS

HQ: MCNAUGHTON-MCKAY ELECTRIC CO.
1357 E LINCOLN AVE, MADISON HEIGHTS, MI 480714126
Phone: 248 399-7500
Web: WWW.MC-MC.COM

PRODUCTS/OPERATIONS

Selected Products
Bar code scanners and systems
Communication input/output (I/O) networks
Computers and peripherals
Convenience panels (cables and equipment)
Cordsets
Data-collection terminals and software
Drives and motor controllers
Engineered products
I/O products (AC/DC modules)
Motion-control products
  CNC controls
  Servos
  Spindles
Motors (AC)
PLC processors
Radio-frequency identification (RFID) products
Safety products
  Gate switches
  Light curtains
  Mats
  Relays
Sensors
Software
Vision products (inspection equipment)

COMPETITORS

Anixter International	Kendall Electric
Border States Electric	Madison Electric
Consolidated	Medler Electric
Electrical	Onesource Distributors
Crescent Electric	Rexel Inc.
Supply	Summit Electric Supply
Dealers Electrical	Steiner Electric
Electrocomponents	Stuart C. Irby
Graybar Electric	W.w. Grainger
Hite Company	Wesco International

HISTORICAL FINANCIALS

Company Type: Private

Income Statement   FYE: December 31

	REVENUE ($ mil.)	NET INCOME ($ mil.)	NET PROFIT MARGIN	EMPLOYEES
12/20	1,335	0	—	1,400
12/19	1,515	0	—	—
12/16	724	0	—	—
12/15	702	0	—	—
Annual Growth	13.7%	—	—	—

2020 Year-End Financials

Return on assets: —   Cash ($ mil.): 9
Return on equity: —
Current ratio: 3.20

MED AMERICA HEALTH SYSTEMS CORPORATION

EXECUTIVES

Pres, T G Breitenbach
SEC*, Dale Creech
Cfo*, Timothy Jackson
Coordinator, Evan Ichikawa
Coordinator, Kimiko Johnson
Vice-President, Diane Ewing
Finance Manager, Fatou K Ndoye
It Application Manager, Fred Barker
Patient Access Manager, Idongesit Ekpo
Account Manager, Paul Sartain
Vice President Cardiovascular, Robin Rutledge

LOCATIONS

HQ: MED AMERICA HEALTH SYSTEMS CORPORATION
1 WYOMING ST, DAYTON, OH 454092722
Phone: 937 223-6192

HISTORICAL FINANCIALS

Company Type: Private

Income Statement   FYE: December 31

	REVENUE ($ mil.)	NET INCOME ($ mil.)	NET PROFIT MARGIN	EMPLOYEES
12/11	919	24	2.7%	10,700
12/10	843	67	8.1%	—
12/08	790	(153)	—	—
Annual Growth	5.1%	—	—	—

2011 Year-End Financials

Return on assets: 1.7%   Cash ($ mil.): 42
Return on equity: 3.5%
Current ratio: 1.90

MEDCO, L.L.C.

EXECUTIVES

Admin, Archie J Chapman
Physical Therapy Rehabilitatio, Kym Longstreet

LOCATIONS

HQ: MEDCO, L.L.C.
3701 DADEVILLE RD, ALEXANDER CITY, AL 350109075
Phone: 256 215-3889
Web: WWW.CHAPMANHEALTHCARE.NET

HISTORICAL FINANCIALS

Company Type: Private

Income Statement   FYE: June 30

	REVENUE ($ mil.)	NET INCOME ($ mil.)	NET PROFIT MARGIN	EMPLOYEES
06/09*	854	(173)	—	225
09/02	4	0	13.6%	—
09/00	2	0	13.7%	—
12/99	0	0	—	—
Annual Growth	—	—	—	—

*Fiscal year change

2009 Year-End Financials

Return on assets: (-999.9%)   Cash ($ mil.): —
Return on equity: (-999.9%)
Current ratio: 1.40

MEDICAL CENTER OF THE ROCKIES

EXECUTIVES

Ceo, George Hayes
Exec Dir*, Laurie Tuka
Asst Gen Council*, Emily Weber
Utilities Management Lead, Ken Chandler
Pathologist, Christopher Bee
Vp For National Security Strat, Gene Renuart
Professor and Chair, George B Boedecker
Vice President Government and, Jeff Thompson
Receptionist, Kathy Venrick
Registered Nurse, Kristy Corkle
Neurosurgeon, Lars Widdel

LOCATIONS

HQ: MEDICAL CENTER OF THE ROCKIES
2500 ROCKY MOUNTAIN AVE, LOVELAND, CO 805389004
Phone: 970 624-2500
Web: WWW.UCHEALTH.ORG

HISTORICAL FINANCIALS

Company Type: Private

Income Statement   FYE: June 30

	REVENUE ($ mil.)	NET INCOME ($ mil.)	NET PROFIT MARGIN	EMPLOYEES
06/20	552	84	15.3%	4,000
06/16	421	61	14.6%	—
06/15	403	68	16.9%	—
Annual Growth	6.5%	4.4%	—	—

2020 Year-End Financials

Return on assets: 15.0%   Cash ($ mil.): 56
Return on equity: 35.7%
Current ratio: 0.40

MEDICAL UNIVERSITY HOSPITAL AUTHORITY

EXECUTIVES

Exec Dir, Patrick Pawley
Auditors: KPMG LLP ATLANTA GA

LOCATIONS

HQ: MEDICAL UNIVERSITY HOSPITAL AUTHORITY
169 ASHLEY AVE, CHARLESTON, SC 294258905
Phone: 843 792-1414
Web: WWW.MUSCHEALTH.ORG

HISTORICAL FINANCIALS
Company Type: Private

| Income Statement | | | FYE: June 30 |
	REVENUE ($ mil.)	NET INCOME ($ mil.)	NET PROFIT MARGIN	EMPLOYEES
06/08	821	(19)		4,000
06/07	749	26	3.5%	—
06/06	0	0		—
Annual Growth	—	—	—	—

2008 Year-End Financials
Return on assets: (-2.2%)   Cash ($ mil.): 14
Return on equity: (-8.3%)
Current ratio: 1.50

MEDSTAR HEALTH, INC.

MedStar Health is a not-for-profit regional healthcare system based in Columbia Maryland and one of the largest employers in the region. MedStar Health runs ten hospitals and about 35 other health-related businesses across Maryland and the Washington DC area. MedStar Health has one of the largest graduate medical education programs in the country training 1150 medical residents annually and is the medical education and clinical partner of Georgetown University. With more than 31000 physicians nurses and many other clinical and non-clinical associates MedStar has a comprehensive service offering including emergency services home health care and rehabilitation.

Operations
MedStar operates ten hospitals (MedStar Harbor Hospital MedStar St. Mary's Hospital and MedStar Washington Hospital Center) two clinical research and innovation (MedStar Health Research Institute and MedStar Institute Nurse Association) two home health care (MedStar Health Infusion and MedStar Health Home Care) two managed care (MedStar Family Choice and MedStar Medicare Choice) and two independent senior living (Belverde Green and Woodbourne Woods).

Geographic Reach
MedStar has operations in Maryland and Washington D.C.

EXECUTIVES

Ceo, Kenneth A Samet
Cfo*, Michael J Curran
Chb*, William R Roberts
V Pres*, Robert Divito
Director, Nadine Wethington
Executive Assistant, Sheila Lagnese
Scientist, Paul Eder

Executive Officer, M Drass
Sharepoint Application Develop, Peter Knapp
Chief Information Security Off, Ron Baklarz
Partner of Radiation Oncology, Paul B Fowler
Auditors: KMPG LLP BALTIMORE MD

LOCATIONS

HQ: MEDSTAR HEALTH, INC.
10980 GRANTCHESTER WAY # 700, COLUMBIA, MD 210446108
Phone: 410 772-6500
Web: WWW.MEDSTARHEALTH.ORG

Selected Facilities

Maryland
Franklin Square Hospital Center (Baltimore)
Good Samaritan Hospital (Baltimore)
Harbor Hospital (Baltimore)
Montgomery General Hospital (Olney)
St. Mary's Hospital (Leonardtown)
Union Memorial Hospital (Baltimore)
Washington DC
Georgetown University Hospital
National Rehabilitation Hospital
Washington Hospital Center

PRODUCTS/OPERATIONS

Selected Affiliates/Operations
Clinical Research
    Georgetown University Medical Center (Washington DC)
    MedStar Research Institute (Hyattsville Maryland)
Home Health Care
    MedStar Health VNA (Washington DC)
    MedStar Health Infusion (Elkridge Maryland)
    MGH Community Health (Olney Maryland)
Managed Care
    MedStar Family Choice (Baltimore Maryland)
Nursing Homes/Senior Living
    Franklin Woods (Rosedale Maryland)
    Good Samaritan Nursing Center (Baltimore Maryland)
    Belvedere Green (Baltimore Maryland)
    Woodbourne Woods (Baltimore Maryland)
Primary Care
    MedStar Physician Partners (Washington DC)
Outpatient Surgery Centers
    MedStar Surgery Center (Washington DC)
    Harbor Hospital HealthPark (Pasadena Maryland)
    SurgiCenter at Pasadena (Pasadena Maryland)

COMPETITORS

Adventist Healthcare
Anne Arundel Medical Center
Ascension Health
Bon Secours Health
Carilion Clinic
Children's National Medical Center
Christiana Care
Civista Health
Franklin Square Hospital Center
Gbmc
Harbor Hospital
Inova
Johns Hopkins Health System
Johns Hopkins Medicine
Kaiser Foundation Health Plan Of The Mid-atlantic
Levindale Hospital
Lifebridge Health
Medstar Union Memorial Hospital
Sinai Hospital Of Baltimore
Suburban Hospital
Trinity Health (novi)
University Of Maryland Medical System
Valley Health
Virginia Hospital Center

HISTORICAL FINANCIALS
Company Type: Private

| Income Statement | | | | FYE: June 30 |
	REVENUE ($ mil.)	NET INCOME ($ mil.)	NET PROFIT MARGIN	EMPLOYEES
06/21	6,725	774	11.5%	33,000
06/20	5,788	136	2.4%	—
06/19	5,690	187	3.3%	—
06/18	5,604	324	5.8%	—
Annual Growth	6.3%	33.6%	—	—

2021 Year-End Financials
Return on assets: 9.2%   Cash ($ mil.): 1,523
Return on equity: 25.2%
Current ratio: 1.40

MEDSTAR-GEORGETOWN MEDICAL CENTER, INC.

Medstar-Georgetown Medical Center (dba as Medstar Georgetown University Hospital as a part of MedStar Health) is a 609-bed acute care teaching hospital serving residents of the greater Washington DC area including Maryland and Virginia. The hospital's staff of more than 1100 physicians represents a wide range of medical specializations including cardiology oncology neurology/neurosurgery and surgical transplantation. Medstar Georgetown provides a comprehensive array of inpatient outpatient surgical and rehabilitative care services. The hospital is part of a local network of affiliated primary care providers.

Operations
Medstar Georgetown's Transplant Institute is one of a handful of centers in the US that offers living-donor liver transplants; it opened a new medical space in 2014. Also Georgetown Neurosciences is the sixth unit nationwide to provide CyberKnife stereotactic radiosurgery for the treatment of tumors and lesions of the brain neck and spine.

Strategy
In 2015 Medstar Georgetown submitted a letter of intent with the District of Columbia State Health Planning and Development Agency seeking approval to modernize its existing medical facility by constructing a new state-of-the-art medical surgical pavilion. The pavilion will house surgical critical care and emergency departments as well as related administrative functions.

In 2014 MedStar Georgetown became the first center in Washington DC to perform a two-level artificial disc replacement in a patient's neck.

Company Background
In 2011 Medstar Georgetown became the first health system in the area to offer bloodless surgery to patients who prefer not to receive someone else's blood usually for religious reasons. There are three primary approaches to performing bloodless surgeries: before during and after surgery. Before surgery the hospital gives the patient medications such as iron supplements or epoprotein to boost the blood's hemoglobin level. During surgery the hospital is precise as it can be with its surgical techniques to limit blood loss and there are anesthesia techniques to lower blood pressure so patients bleed less. There is also a machine called Cell Saver that is used during surgery that collects blood lost suctions it into a canister washes and filters it and then returns it directly into the patient

as a product that is about 60-percent pure red blood cells. After surgery medications are used to raise blood levels and medical providers avoid taking multiple blood draws for blood tests.

The hospital was founded in 1898 to promote health through education research and patient care. The current hospital/medical center was opened in 1947.

EXECUTIVES

Exec Dir, Joy Drass
Cfo*, Pipper Williams
Neurosurgeon, Jean-Marc Voyadzis
Nurse Technician, Ryan Goldschmidt
Internist, Faiza Niaz
Information Analyst II, James W Gunter
Materials, Sheila Merritt
Regional Chief, Thomas Watson
Team Leader, Donna M Lucia
Project Manager, Nadine Heron
Research Associate, Nick Prindeze

LOCATIONS

HQ: MEDSTAR-GEORGETOWN MEDICAL CENTER, INC.
3800 RESERVOIR RD NW, WASHINGTON, DC 200072113
Phone: 202 444-2000
Web: WWW.MEDSTARGEORGETOWN.ORG

PRODUCTS/OPERATIONS

Selected Services
Anesthesiology
Audiology
Bloodless Medicine and Surgery Program
Bone Marrow Transplant
Breast Cancer
Breast Health Program
Cancer Care
Cardiology
Cerebrovascular Center
Colon and Rectal Surgery
Ear Nose and Throat (ENT)
Emergency Urgent Care and Trauma
Endocrinology
Epilepsy
Family Medicine
Fracture Liaison
Head and Neck Cancer
Headache Center
Hematology
Hospital Medicine
Huntington Disease Center
Hyperbaric Oxygen Therapy
Ophthalmology
Orthopaedics
Ostomy Clinic
Otolaryngology
Pastoral Care
Pediatrics
Pharmacy
Physical Medicine
Plastic Surgery
Primary Care
Prostate Cancer

COMPETITORS

Adventist Healthcare
Bon Secours Health
Calvert Memorial Hospital
Children's National Medical Center
Chindex International
Dimensions Healthcare
Doctors Community Hospital
Inova Alexandria Hospital
Providence St. Joseph Health
Suburban Hospital
Upper Chesapeake Health

HISTORICAL FINANCIALS
Company Type: Private

Income Statement   FYE: June 30

	REVENUE ($ mil.)	NET INCOME ($ mil.)	NET PROFIT MARGIN	EMPLOYEES
06/16	801	104	13.1%	4,000
06/15	774	98	12.7%	—
06/11	809	43	5.4%	—
06/10	782	45	5.8%	—
Annual Growth	0.4%	15.0%	—	—

2016 Year-End Financials
Return on assets: 23.6%
Return on equity: 31.3%
Current ratio: 1.90
Cash ($ mil.): 5

MEGLOBAL AMERICAS INC.

EXECUTIVES

Pres, Ramesh Ramachandran
Cfo, Niklaus Meier
Treas, Sumit Pathak

LOCATIONS

HQ: MEGLOBAL AMERICAS INC.
2150 TOWN SQUARE PL # 750, SUGAR LAND, TX 774791465
Phone: 844 634-5622

HISTORICAL FINANCIALS
Company Type: Private

Income Statement   FYE: December 31

	REVENUE ($ mil.)	NET INCOME ($ mil.)	NET PROFIT MARGIN	EMPLOYEES
12/13	596	10	1.7%	15
12/12	597	13	2.2%	—
12/11	743	20	2.7%	—
Annual Growth	(10.4%)	(29.9%)	—	—

2013 Year-End Financials
Return on assets: 13.6%
Return on equity: 107.6%
Current ratio: 1.10
Cash ($ mil.): 5

MELLANOX TECHNOLOGIES, INC.

EXECUTIVES

Chb-Pres-Ceo, Eyal Waldman
V Pres Engineering, Roni Ashuri
Coo, Shai Cohen
V Pres Architecture-Cto, Michael Kagan
Cfo, Michael Gray
V Pres Worldwide Sls, Marc Sultzbaugh
Vp-Quality & Reliability, Ayelet Margalit-Ilovich
Vice-President Business Develo, Chris Shea
Customer Staff, Einav Ezra

Vice-President of Business, Alon Webman
Engineer, Shahar Shavit
Auditors: KOST FORER GABBAY AND KASIERER

LOCATIONS

HQ: MELLANOX TECHNOLOGIES, INC.
2530 ZANKER RD, SAN JOSE, CA 951311127
Phone: 408 970-3400
Web: WWW.NVIDIA.COM

HISTORICAL FINANCIALS
Company Type: Private

Income Statement   FYE: December 31

	REVENUE ($ mil.)	NET INCOME ($ mil.)	NET PROFIT MARGIN	EMPLOYEES
12/19	1,330	205	15.4%	876
12/18	1,088	134	12.3%	—
12/17	863	(19)	—	—
12/16	857	18	2.2%	—
Annual Growth	15.8%	122.9%	—	—

2019 Year-End Financials
Return on assets: 9.7%
Return on equity: 12.4%
Current ratio: 3.70
Cash ($ mil.): 77

MEMORIAL HEALTH CARE SYSTEM, INC.

EXECUTIVES

Pres, James M Hobson
Pres*, Shawn Morrow
Sr V Pres*, Debra L Moore
Cfo*, Cheryl A Sadro
V Pres*, Leigh Bertholf
V Pres*, Diona Brown
Auditors: CATHOLIC HEALTH INITIATIVES E

LOCATIONS

HQ: MEMORIAL HEALTH CARE SYSTEM, INC.
2525 DESALES AVE, CHATTANOOGA, TN 374041161
Phone: 423 495-2525
Web: WWW.MEMORIAL.ORG

HISTORICAL FINANCIALS
Company Type: Private

Income Statement   FYE: June 30

	REVENUE ($ mil.)	NET INCOME ($ mil.)	NET PROFIT MARGIN	EMPLOYEES
06/20	564	(30)	—	8,800
06/16	545	22	4.1%	—
06/15	527	34	6.6%	—
06/14	557	25	4.6%	—
Annual Growth	0.2%	—	—	—

2020 Year-End Financials
Return on assets: (-3.7%)
Return on equity: (-6.1%)
Current ratio: 1.40
Cash ($ mil.): 33

MEMORIAL HEALTH SERVICES

MemorialCare is a nonprofit integrated delivery system which includes four premier hospitals ? Long Beach Medical Center Miller Children's & Women's Hospital Long Beach Orange Coast Medical Center and Saddleback Medical Center; medical groups ? MemorialCare Medical Group and Greater Newport Physicians; a health plan ? Seaside Health Plan; and numerous outpatient health centers imaging centers surgery centers and dialysis centers throughout Orange and Los Angeles Counties. The MemorialCare 55+ Program is a unique program for adults 55 and older that provides easy access to health and wellness information resources and exclusive perks free of cost to members.

Operations
MemorialCare Medical Group includes 1700 physicians specializing in internal medicine family medicine obstetrics-gynecology and pediatrics; specialties like oncology cardiology pulmonology gastroenterology surgery and urgent care.

Geographic Reach
MemorialCare has convenient outpatient health centers urgent care centers imaging centers breast centers surgical centers physical therapy centers and dialysis centers throughout Orange and Los Angeles Counties.

Sales and Marketing
In addition to multiple locations throughout Orange County MemorialCare Medical Group offers Urgent Care Centers that are open 365 days a year Telephone Advice Nurses available 24 hours a day 7 days a week; and Lab and X-ray services available on-site at most locations.

EXECUTIVES

Pres, Barry Arbuckle
Chief Strategy Officer*, Diane Laird
CIO-Treas*, Rick Graniere
Cfo*, Karen Testman
Gen Counsel*, Terri Cammarano
Cto*, Helen Macfie
Cfo*, Aaron Coley
Trauma Surge Coordinator/ Trau, Desiree Thomas
Safety Coordinator, Joann Smith
Pulmonary Diseases, Mark M Chung
Gynecology/Obstetrics, John K Yee
Auditors: PRICEWATERHOUSECOOPERS LLP LO

LOCATIONS

HQ: MEMORIAL HEALTH SERVICES
17360 BROOKHURST ST # 160, FOUNTAIN VALLEY, CA 927083720
Phone: 714 377-2900
Web: WWW.MEMORIALCARE.ORG

Selected Facilities
Long Beach Memorial Medical Center (Long Beach California)
Miller Children's Hospital (Long Beach California)
Community Hospital (Long Beach California)
Orange Coast Memorial Medical Center (Fountain Valley California)
Saddleback Memorial Medical Center (San Clemente California)
Saddleback Memorial Medical Center (Laguna Hills California)
MemorialCare Medical Group (regional)
MemorialCare HealthExpress (regional)
MemorialCare Imaging Centers (regional)
Memorial Prompt Care (regional)

PRODUCTS/OPERATIONS

Selected Services
Blood Donation
Diabetes Care
Heart and Vascular Care
Joint Replacement
Neonatal Intensive Care
Rehabilitation and Therapy
Wellness Care
Cancer Care
Gynecological Care
Imaging and Radiology
Maternity Care
Orthopedic Care
Stroke Care
Wound Healing
Breast Care
Express Care
Hyperbaric Medicine
Laboratory Services
Pediatric Care
Surgical Care
Women's Care

COMPETITORS

Adventist Health System West
Cedars-sinai Medical Center
Childrens Hospital Los Angeles
Community Health Systems
Dignity Health
Good Samaritan Hospital (in)
Good Samaritan Hospital (los Angeles)
Hca
Healthcare Partners
Hollywood Presbyterian Medical Center
Lifepoint Health
Methodist Hospital Of Southern California
Pasadena Hospital Association
Prospect Medical
Providence St. Joseph Health
St. Jude Medical Center
Sutter Health
Tenet Healthcare
Trinity Health (novi)
Western Medical Center - Santa Ana

HISTORICAL FINANCIALS

Company Type: Private

Income Statement				FYE: June 30
	REVENUE ($ mil.)	NET INCOME ($ mil.)	NET PROFIT MARGIN	EMPLOYEES
06/21	2,580	770	29.8%	6,000
06/20	2,556	(52)	—	—
06/19	2,438	208	8.6%	—
06/18	2,232	101	4.5%	—
Annual Growth	5.0%	96.8%	—	—

2021 Year-End Financials
Return on assets: 14.9%   Cash ($ mil.): 255
Return on equity: 23.2%
Current ratio: 0.90

MEMORIAL HEALTH SERVICES GROUP RETURN

EXECUTIVES

Senior Manager, Ryan Gil
Research Analyst, Dena Freeman
Director, Robert Hunn
Corporate Accounting Manager, Laline Gutierrez
Auditors: MOSS ADAMS LLP SAN FRANCISCO

LOCATIONS

HQ: MEMORIAL HEALTH SERVICES GROUP RETURN
17360 BROOKHURST ST, FOUNTAIN VALLEY, CA 927083720
Phone: 714 377-3002
Web: WWW.MEMORIALCARE.ORG

HISTORICAL FINANCIALS

Company Type: Private

Income Statement				FYE: June 30
	REVENUE ($ mil.)	NET INCOME ($ mil.)	NET PROFIT MARGIN	EMPLOYEES
06/18	2,340	73	3.1%	5
06/17	2,253	87	3.9%	—
06/15	2,302	135	5.9%	—
06/14	2,048	68	3.3%	—
Annual Growth	3.4%	1.7%	—	—

2018 Year-End Financials
Return on assets: 3.3%   Cash ($ mil.): 14
Return on equity: 4.1%
Current ratio: 1.10

MEMORIAL HEALTH, INC.

Auditors: DIXON HUGHES GOODMAN LLP ASHE

LOCATIONS

HQ: MEMORIAL HEALTH, INC.
4700 WATERS AVE, SAVANNAH, GA 314046220
Phone: 912 350-8000
Web: WWW.MEMORIALHEALTH.COM

HISTORICAL FINANCIALS

Company Type: Private

Income Statement				FYE: December 31
	REVENUE ($ mil.)	NET INCOME ($ mil.)	NET PROFIT MARGIN	EMPLOYEES
12/16	581	(38)	—	4,500
12/14	42	(11)	—	—
12/13	24	0	—	—
Annual Growth	185.6%	—	—	—

2016 Year-End Financials
Return on assets: (-6.8%)   Cash ($ mil.): 16
Return on equity: (-28.3%)
Current ratio: 1.50

MEMORIAL HERMANN HEALTH SYSTEM

EXECUTIVES

Ceo-Pres, David Callender
Chb*, Wh Easter III
Chief of Medicine, Todd M Price
Coordinator, Melissa Aing
Obstetrics, Jennifer Weber
Director of Business Developme, Amanda Spielman

Head of Cardiology, Byron Auzenne
Chief Operating Engineer, Dennis Fults
Chief Administrative Officer, Keith Alexander
Quality Assurance Director, David Stowers
Application Analyst, Cassandra Morrissey
Auditors: ERNST & YOUNG LLP HOUSTON T

LOCATIONS

HQ: MEMORIAL HERMANN HEALTH SYSTEM
929 GESSNER RD STE 1900, HOUSTON, TX
770242317
Phone: 713 242-3000
Web: WWW.MEMORIALHERMANN.ORG

HISTORICAL FINANCIALS

Company Type: Private

Income Statement				FYE: June 30
	REVENUE ($ mil.)	NET INCOME ($ mil.)	NET PROFIT MARGIN	EMPLOYEES
06/21	6,924	1,511	21.8%	14,000
06/20	5,792	248	4.3%	—
06/19	5,528	270	4.9%	—
06/18	5,258	318	6.1%	—
Annual Growth	9.6%	68.1%	—	—

2021 Year-End Financials

Return on assets: 14.3%   Cash ($ mil.): 881
Return on equity: 26.5%
Current ratio: 1.10

MEMORIAL HOSPITAL CORPORATION

Memorial Hospital tries to keep good health more than a memory for the patients in its care. The hospital is a 520-bed general hospital which provides a range of children's and adult healthcare services and specialties including cardiac care cancer treatment trauma care women's services pediatric medicine and rehabilitation. The hospital has about 700 physicians on its medical staff. Memorial Hospital also includes the 100-bed Memorial Hospital North and Children's Hospital Colorado as well as outpatient clinics throughout the Colorado Springs area. In 2012 it became an affiliate of University of Colorado Health.

Operations

In 2013 alone the Memorial Hospital Auxiliary gave more than $76000 to Memorial Hospital to assist with equipment purchases and education to 17 different departments.

Geographic Reach

The hospital system has more than a dozen facilities throughout the Pikes Peak region of Colorado.

Strategy

In 2013 Memorial Hospital doubled the number of physicians in its medical group hiring specialists in cardiology oncology thoracic surgery neuroscience trauma breast surgery and other areas. That year it also secured achieved Primary Stroke Center Accreditation and Chest Pain Center Accreditation with PCI two distinguished designations of quality.

UCHealth spent about $37 million in 2013 on new technology repairs and other improvements at Memorial Hospital. In 2013 Memorial Hospital introduced new electronic medical records system allows patients to access lab results consult with physicians make appointments and conduct other medical-related activities online.

Company Background

In 2012 the hospital was named as the Official Hospital of the Colorado Springs US Olympic Training Center.

Memorial Hospital has been working to reduce expenses by increasing operational efficiencies. The health system was recognized by Thomson Reuters in 2010 for its efficiency measures as it cut spending by $35 million in three years. The company considered converting itself into an independent not-for-profit to allow for further financial flexibility and expansion outside of the Colorado Springs area.

In order for Memorial Hospital to become an independent operation it would have had to exit the Public Employees Retirement Association (PERA) the retirement fund currently responsible for its employee pensions. The two organizations were at odds over how much Memorial Hospital should have to pay in order to exit the fund. PERA estimated that about $245 million would cover Memorial Hospital's obligations to the fund; Memorial Hospital's estimate was between $25 and $50 million. The disparity led Memorial Hospital to table plans to exit PERA indefinitely.

The hospital system was established in 1904.

EXECUTIVES

Ceo, Mike Scialdone
Coo*, Bill Mohon
Vp Quality, Oda Roozeboom
Vice President Sales, Char Longwell
Vice President Finance, Michael Ryan
Trauma Manager Cns, Lynn Andersen
Patient Representative Team Le, Sarah Benavides
Registered Nurse, Dena Pena
Financial Analyst, Kelsey Totsch
Human Resources, Linda Ortiz
Director of Compliance, Renee Willis

LOCATIONS

HQ: MEMORIAL HOSPITAL CORPORATION
1400 E BOULDER ST. COLORADO SPRINGS, CO
809095599
Phone: 719 365-5000
Web: WWW.UCHEALTH.ORG

COMPETITORS

Banner Health	The Memorial Hospital
Centura Health	University Of Colorado
Exempla Healthcare	Hospital
Healthone	Valley View Hospital
Poudre Valley Health System	

HISTORICAL FINANCIALS

Company Type: Private

Income Statement				FYE: June 30
	REVENUE ($ mil.)	NET INCOME ($ mil.)	NET PROFIT MARGIN	EMPLOYEES
06/21	1,150	128	11.2%	2,438
06/20	1,037	49	4.8%	—
06/19	1,051	97	9.3%	—
06/16	693	25	3.7%	—
Annual Growth	10.6%	38.1%	—	—

2021 Year-End Financials

Return on assets: 12.2%   Cash ($ mil.): 27
Return on equity: 35.5%
Current ratio: 1.10

MEMORIAL HOSPITAL FOR CANCER AND ALLIED DISEASES

EXECUTIVES

Ceo, Craig B Thompson
Finance Manager, Brendan Phalan

LOCATIONS

HQ: MEMORIAL HOSPITAL FOR CANCER AND ALLIED DISEASES
1275 YORK AVE, NEW YORK, NY 100656094
Phone: 212 639-2000
Web: WWW.MSKCC.ORG

HISTORICAL FINANCIALS

Company Type: Private

Income Statement				FYE: December 31
	REVENUE ($ mil.)	NET INCOME ($ mil.)	NET PROFIT MARGIN	EMPLOYEES
12/14	2,035	71	3.5%	5,000
12/08	1,236	(51)	—	—
Annual Growth	8.7%	—	—	—

2014 Year-End Financials

Return on assets: 3.5%   Cash ($ mil.): —
Return on equity: 7.4%
Current ratio: 0.90

MEMORIAL MEDICAL CENTER

If you've lost the spring in your step and need a little care Memorial Medical Center will be there. As the flagship facility for Memorial Health System in Springfield Illinois this acute care and teaching hospital provides a wide range of medical and surgical services as well as emergency medicine and outpatient care. Its myriad specialties include cardiovascular maternity cancer care behavioral health orthopedic rehabilitation and burn treatment services. The hospital which sees 25000 inpatients per year also has special surgical divisions for bariatric procedures and organ transplants. The 500-bed hospital is a teaching affiliate of the Southern Illinois University (SIU) School of Medicine.

EXECUTIVES

Pres, Edgar J Curtis
Coo*, Douglas Rahn
Chief of Medicine, Robert L Vautrain
Audiologist, Lori Faber
Coordinator, Stacie Skelton
Emergency Medicine Specialist, Christopher Inabnit
Physical Therapy Director, Jason Beeler
Director, Jennifer Davis
Radiology, John Ecker
Emergency Medicine Specialist, John Holland
Staff Coordinator, Kim Bradbury
Auditors: ERNST & YOUNG LLP ST LOUIS

MEMORIAL SLOAN-KETTERING CANCER CENTER

Memorial Sloan-Kettering Cancer Center (MSKCC) is the world's oldest and largest private cancer center for patient care innovative research and outstanding educational programs. The center includes about 500 In-patient beds and more than 1400 physicians more than 3900 nurses more than 22800 inpatient stays and more than 781900 outpatient visits. Memorial Hospital specializes in bone-marrow transplants radiation therapy and chemotherapy. It also offers programs in cancer prevention diagnosis treatment research and education. The Sloan Kettering Institute conducts medical and clinical laboratory research on cancer biology genetics cell biology chemical biology immunology structural biology and more. In addition to the main cancer center and research facilities in New York City MSKCC operates clinics in New York New Jersey and Long Island.

Operations

Memorial Sloan-Kettering Cancer Center's departments and divisions comprise physicians nurses researchers and other professionals. The Department of Anesthesiology & Critical Care Medicine provides expert multidisciplinary care to MSK's inpatients and outpatients 24 hours a day seven days a week. The Department comprises four services ? Anesthesiology Critical Care Medicine Pain and Respiratory Therapy. Its Anesthesiology Service is responsible for all forms of anesthesia administered for both inpatient and outpatient procedures. Its Critical Care Medicine (CCM) Service provides care for patients in the adult medical-surgical Intensive Care Unit (ICU) in collaboration with other clinical departments. Its Pain Service provides acute chronic and interventional pain management consultation and services to both inpatients and outpatients and its Respiratory Therapy Service provides care for both adult and pediatric patients.

The Division of Subspecialty Medicine in the department of medicine provides general medical care to patients undergoing cancer treatment at memorial Sloan Kettering. Department of Neurology is a leader in treatment of central nervous system and tumors and neurological complications of cancers. Department of Pediatrics is a multidisciplinary center for excellence for treatment of children teenager and young adults with cancer and blood disorders. Division of Hematologic Malignancies is dedicated for treating patients with a variety of blood cancers as well as some benign hematologic diseases and more.

Geographic Reach

Memorial Sloan-Kettering Cancer Center is based in New York NY United States. The cancer care facilities are located in New York City Long Island Westchester County and New Jersey.

The company maintains one of the world's most dynamic programs of cancer research with more than 120 research laboratories that are focused on better understanding every type of the disease. Memorial Sloan Kettering is also home to about 40 state-of-the-art core facilities.

Sales and Marketing

Memorial Sloan-Kettering Cancer Center market its products and services by offering advanced education and training for postdoctoral researchers and graduate students. In addition to laboratory research training Memorial Sloan Kettering Cancer Center offer extensive professional development services and joint program with Weill Cornell Medical College and The Rockefeller University and plus resources of New York City and diverse opportunities for trainees and students.

Strategy

Research at the Sloan Kettering Institute (SKI) ? Memorial Sloan Kettering's basic research arm ? is dedicated to understanding the biology of cancer through eight major research programs. Investigators at SKI collaborate with Memorial Hospital physician-scientists ? a partnership that helps speed important research findings from the laboratory to the patient.

Memorial Hospital's extensive research program includes areas that focus on basic laboratory research translational research that bridges discoveries made in the laboratory and those made in the clinic and mathematical and computational research directed at analyzing and interpreting biomedical data.

Company Background

Memorial Hospital was founded in 1884 as the New York Cancer Center by a group that included John and Charlotte Astor. Sloan Kettering Institute was founded in 1945 by Alfred Sloan and Charles Kettering to research new cancer cures; the institute was located adjacent to Memorial Hospital. The two entities formed a coordinating corporate entity (Memorial Sloan Kettering Cancer Center) in 1960 and officially merged in 1980.

EXECUTIVES

Pres-Ceo, Craig B Thompson
Chb, Douglas A Warner III
Exec V Pres-Coo, Katherine Martin
Exec V Pres-Cfo, Michael P Gutnick
Evp and General Counsel, Jorge Lopez
Treas, Clifton S Robbins
V Pres, Kerry Bessey
V Pres, Murray F Brennan
V Pres, Eric Cottington
Cdo-Hd Tech, Claus Torp Jensen
CIO, Atefeh Riazi
Auditors: ERNST & YOUNG US LLP INDIANAP

LOCATIONS

HQ: MEMORIAL SLOAN-KETTERING CANCER CENTER
1275 YORK AVE, NEW YORK, NY 100656007
Phone: 212 639-2000
Web: WWW.MSKCC.ORG

PRODUCTS/OPERATIONS

2013 Sales

	$ mil.	% of total
Patient care	2,367	78
Grants and contracts	202	7
Other	455	15
Total	**3,025**	**100**

COMPETITORS

Aptium Oncology
City Of Hope
Columbia University
Continuum Health
 Partners
Dana-farber
Fox Chase Cancer
 Center
Johns Hopkins Medicine
Md Anderson Cancer
 Center
Mayo Clinic
New York City Health
 And Hospitals

Newyork-presbyterian
 Healthcare
Northwell Health
Partners Healthcare
Roswell Park Cancer
 Institute
Sandford Burnham
 Institute
St. Jude Children's
 Research Hospital
Wistar Institute

HISTORICAL FINANCIALS

Company Type: Private

Income Statement				FYE: December 31
	REVENUE ($ mil.)	NET INCOME ($ mil.)	NET PROFIT MARGIN	EMPLOYEES
12/19	5,561	302	5.4%	9,325
12/17	4,499	314	7.0%	—
12/13	582	0	0.2%	—
12/09	2,105	(195)	—	—
Annual Growth	10.2%	—	—	—

2019 Year-End Financials
Return on assets: 2.6%   Cash ($ mil.): 833
Return on equity: 4.3%
Current ratio: 1.00

MENTOR GRAPHICS CORPORATION

Mentor Graphics lends a hand to guide engineers who design electronic components. The company is a leading global developer of electronic design automation (EDA) software and systems used by engineers to design simulate and test electronic components such as integrated circuits (IC's) wire harness systems and printed circuit boards (PCBs). Products include PADS (PCB design) Nucleus (operating system) and Calibre (IC design). Its software is used to design components for such products as computers and wireless handsets. Clients come from the aerospace IT telecommunications and increasingly transportation industries. Mentor Graphics was acquired by Siemens for $4.5 billion in 2017.

Operations

Mentor Graphics creates system and software products most of which are sold through term software license contracts. It also provides service and support including professional services consulting training and other services.

Geographic Reach

Based in Wilsonville Oregon Mentor Graphics has US research and development operations in Colorado Washington Alabama and Massachusetts. It also conducts R&D in Armenia Egypt France Germany Hungary India Israel Pakistan Poland Russia Taiwan and the UK.

Sales and Marketing
Financial Performance

Mentor Graphics reported increases in revenue and profit in 2017 (ended January). The company's sales rose 9% to $1.3 billion in 2017 from 2016 and profit shot up 60% to $155 million for the year. The company had robust growth in all geographic markets except for the US its biggest market with about 40% of sales. Japan was particularly strong in 2017 with sales jumping more than 35% while sales rose about 15% each in the Pacific Rim and Europe. The company credited the overseas growth to the timing of contract renewals and blamed the North America decline of 3% on weaker sales of emulation hardware systems and a slower rate of contract renewals for the year.

The 60% rise in profit to $1.3 billion in 2017 resulted from higher sales combined with lower special charges in 2017 from 2016. The higher profit helped boost cash flow from operations to $322 million in 2017 from $228 million in 2016.

Strategy

Mentor Graphics is moving to apply its processes to new businesses. The automotive business is one example. It has grown to 20% of Mentor Graphics' revenue in several years. The company is keen on driving its products into other transportation areas such as the design of electronic components in airplanes and trains.

Mergers and Acquisitions

HISTORY

Mentor Graphics was founded in 1981 by a group from instrument maker Tektronix to market desktop computers to design engineers. Throughout the 1980s the company was a leader in electronic design automation (EDA) software but the early 1990s found it in trouble. Revenues fell because of delays in upgrade releases and a worldwide recession.

In 1992 Mentor Graphics began phasing out hardware sales further disrupting operations. Texas Instruments veteran Walden Rhines became CEO in 1993. That year the company acquired CheckLogic a maker of testing software for integrated circuit (IC) design. By 1994 cost-cutting and product line restructuring returned Mentor to profitability.

The company bought ANACAD which developed design software for analog and mixed-signal ICs and Model Technology a very-high-density logic simulation tool firm in 1994. It acquired 14 more companies in 1995 and 1996 including embedded software tool developer Microtec Research (1996) which moved Mentor into the market for software development tools.

Auditors: KPMG LLP PORTLAND OREGON

LOCATIONS

HQ: MENTOR GRAPHICS CORPORATION
8005 SW BOECKMAN RD, WILSONVILLE, OR 970707777
Phone: 503 685-7000
Web: WWW.NEW.SIEMENS.COM

2016 Sales

	$ mil.	% of total
United States	488	41
Europe	254	22
Japan	87	7
Pacific Rim	335	29
Other	15	1
Total	**1,181**	**100**

PRODUCTS/OPERATIONS

2017 Sales

	$ mil.	% of total
System and software	794	62
Service & support	488	38
Total	**1,282**	**100**

Selected Products

Embedded software development
  Compilers
  Debugger
  Real-time operating system
Integrated circuit (IC) design and verification
  Analog/mixed signal
  Custom design
  Design-for-test
  Field-programmable gate array/application-specific IC design
  Formal verification
  High-capacity circuit simulation
  Interconnect modeling
  Physical optimization
  Physical verification & manufacturability
  Resolution enhancement technologies
  Static timing
  Synthesis
Printed circuit board design and analysis
  Design tools
  Digital high-speed
  Integration interfaces and viewers
  Layout
  Library management
  Radio-frequency/mixed-signal
  Simulation and analysis
System-level design and verification
  Accelerated system verification
  Cabling design and analysis
  Design creation
  Digital simulation
  Hardware emulation and simulation
  Intellectual property
  Process management
  System-on-a-chip
  Web-based development system

COMPETITORS

Ansys	Interra Systems
Axiom Design	Intrinsix
Altium	Pdf Solutions
Autodesk	Qnx Software Systems
Blue Ridge Numerics	Silvaco
Cadence Design	Synopsys
Collabnet	Wind River Systems
Green Hills Software	Zuken

HISTORICAL FINANCIALS

Company Type: Private

Income Statement				FYE: January 31
	REVENUE ($ mil.)	NET INCOME ($ mil.)	NET PROFIT MARGIN	EMPLOYEES
01/17	1,282	154	12.1%	5,700
01/16	1,180	94	8.0%	—
01/15	1,244	145	11.7%	—
01/14	1,156	153	13.3%	—
Annual Growth	3.5%	0.3%		

2017 Year-End Financials

Return on assets: 6.8%   Cash ($ mil.): 441
Return on equity: 11.3%
Current ratio: 1.30

MERCY CARE

Mercy Care is a not-for-profit provider of managed health care services in Arizona. The Mercy Care Plan provides these services under a contract with the Arizona Health Care Cost Containment System the state of Arizona's Medicaid program. The plan provides health coverage and prescription drug benefits to some 300000 members. The company founded in 1985 is affiliated with St. Joseph's Hospital & Medical Center (which is part of Catholic Healthcare West) Dignity Health and Carondelet Health Network. The plan is administered by health care management firm Schaller Anderson.

Operations

Mercy Care provides coverage to families children the elderly and the developmentally disabled. In addition to traditional HMO coverage the company also offers disease management and preventative health care services.

Along with the Centers for Medicare & Medicaid Services (CMS) Mercy Care provides qualified members with medical and prescription drug benefits. Its Mercy Care Long Term Care (MCLTC) offers services to those covered by the AHCCCS Arizona Long Term Care System (ALTCS) which accounts for 22% of revenue.

The Division of Developmental Disabilities Long Term Care serves members who are enrolled through the Arizona Department of Economic Security/Division of Development Disabilities (DES/DDD) which generates approximately 2% of SCHN's revenue. Through a contract with the DES/DDD the company provides medical care to qualified members.

Geographic Reach

Mercy Care serves the Arizona counties of Maricopa Pima Graham Greenlee and Cochise providing covered services to enrolled members.

Sales and Marketing

As part of its business Mercy Care provides patients with prescriptions through retail pharmacies mail order pharmacies home infusion pharmacies long-term care pharmacies and Indian Health Service/Tribal/Urban Indian Health Program (I/T/U) pharmacies.

Financial Performance

Mercy Care logged a 10% decline in revenue in 2012 as compared to 2011. The provider points to a decrease in capitation premiums delivery/HIV AIDS supplement reinsurance and third-party recoveries for the double-digit drop. During the same reporting period SCHN posted a $7.5 million net loss thanks to revenue decreases paired with increases in investment fees and unrealized losses on investments incurred by the company during 2012.

EXECUTIVES

Ceo, Mark Fisher
Director of Community Relation, Jim Grosso
Network Account Manager, Cathrine Farnham
Director of Customer O, Cathy Waldbillig
Case Manager Long Term Care, Shannon Denning
Network Account Manager, William Henderson
Network Account Manager, Jim Sohn
Network Account Manager, John Schneider
Network Account Manager, Robin Migliorino
Vice President of Health Plan, John Monte
Management, Murrell Kennedy

LOCATIONS

HQ: MERCY CARE
4500 E COTTON CENTER BLVD, PHOENIX, AZ
850408895
Phone: 602 263-3000
Web: WWW.MERCYCAREAZ.ORG

COMPETITORS

Aetna   Health Net
Blue Cross Blue Shield   Unitedhealth Group
  Of Arizona
Cigna Healthcare Of
  Arizona

HISTORICAL FINANCIALS

Company Type: Private

Income Statement				FYE: June 30
	REVENUE ($ mil.)	NET INCOME ($ mil.)	NET PROFIT MARGIN	EMPLOYEES
06/20	3,796	65	1.7%	500
06/14	1,808	41	2.3%	—
06/12	1,747	28	1.6%	—
06/11	1,939	58	3.0%	—
Annual Growth	7.7%	1.2%	—	—

2020 Year-End Financials

Return on assets: 8.6%   Cash ($ mil.): 188
Return on equity: 17.8%
Current ratio: —

MERCY CHILDREN'S HOSPITAL

Children's Mercy is a leading independent children's health organization dedicated to holistic care translational research breakthrough innovation and educating the next generation of caregivers. The system has two hospitals three urgent care facilities and a campus featuring primary care offices and more than 15 specialty clinics. Among its specialized services are diabetes and endocrinology genetics heart surgery neonatology and rehabilitation. Founded in 1897 it has completed some 19290 surgical cases about 4620 medical transports and saw nearly 12545 admissions through its around 385 inpatient beds.

Operations

Children's Mercy has a medical staff of roughly 785 pediatric specialists. Its main campus Children's Mercy Adele Hall has around 385 beds.

The system performs roughly 19290 surgeries annually; it has around 4620 medical transports as well as nearly 12545 admissions in 2020. It also has about 81505 telemedicine visits during the year.

Geographic Reach

Children's Mercy Adele Hall is the only Level I pediatric trauma center between Kansas Missouri where it is headquartered.

Company Background

Children's Mercy is a not-for-profit free-standing pediatric health system that offers low-income families a low- or no-cost health plan through the Take CARE benefit plans.

EXECUTIVES

Pres, Randall L O'Donnell
Exec V Pres-Cfo*, Dwight Hyde
Exec V Pres*, Karen Cox
Exec V Pres*, Sandra Aj Lawrence
Exec V Pres*, Charles C Roberts
Exec V Pres*, Jo Stueve
Director of Patient Care Servi, Janis Smith
Director, Brian Wicklund
Doctor of Medicine, Lisa L Schroeder
Doctor of Medicine, Milton Fowler
Director of Transport Operatio, Sherry McCool

LOCATIONS

HQ: MERCY CHILDREN'S HOSPITAL
2401 GILLHAM RD, KANSAS CITY, MO 641084619
Phone: 816 234-3000
Web: WWW.CHILDRENSMERCY.ORG

Selected locations
Children's Mercy Adele Hall Campus (Kansas City MO)
Children's Mercy Blue Valley (Overland Park KS)
Children's Mercy Broadway (Kansas City)
Children's Mercy College Boulevard (Overland Park KS)
Children's Mercy East (Independence MO)
Children's Mercy Hospital Kansas (Overland Park KS)
Children's Mercy Northland (Kansas City MO)
Children's Mercy Olathe (Olathe KS)
Children's Mercy West (Kansas City KS)
Children's Mercy Sports Medicine Center at Village West
  (Kansas City KS)

COMPETITORS

Ascension Health   Shriners Hospitals For
Coxhealth   Children
Liberty Hospital   Sisters Of Charity Of
Saint Luke's Health   Leavenworth
  System   Truman Medical Centers
Shawnee Mission   University Of Kansas
  Medical Center   Medical Center

HISTORICAL FINANCIALS

Company Type: Private

Income Statement				FYE: June 30
	REVENUE ($ mil.)	NET INCOME ($ mil.)	NET PROFIT MARGIN	EMPLOYEES
06/20	1,614	91	5.7%	7,000
06/16	1,020	35	3.5%	—
06/15	978	79	8.1%	—
06/13	9	(0)	—	—
Annual Growth	109.6%	—	—	—

2020 Year-End Financials

Return on assets: 3.6%   Cash ($ mil.): 125
Return on equity: 4.9%
Current ratio: 2.40

MERCY GENERAL HEALTH PARTNERS

EXECUTIVES

Pres-Ceo, Roger Spoelman
Cfo*, Mary Boyd
Internal Medicine Practitioner, Ernest Vera-
  Vazquez
Coordinator, Estella Rohm
Coordinator, Michelle Howard
Coordinator, Candace Coleman
Internal Medicine Practitioner, Osman Ahmedfiqi
Support Coordinator, Kelly Jacobs
Director Building, Lee Tencate
Board Member, Richard Wilcox
Staff Nurse, Paul Copeland

LOCATIONS

HQ: MERCY GENERAL HEALTH PARTNERS
1500 E SHERMAN BLVD, MUSKEGON, MI 494441849
Phone: 231 728-4032
Web: WWW.MERCYHEALTH.COM

HISTORICAL FINANCIALS

Company Type: Private

Income Statement				FYE: June 30
	REVENUE ($ mil.)	NET INCOME ($ mil.)	NET PROFIT MARGIN	EMPLOYEES
06/20	692	(30)	—	2,000
06/09	215	(0)	—	—
Annual Growth	11.2%	—	—	—

2020 Year-End Financials

Return on assets: (-3.7%)   Cash ($ mil.): —
Return on equity: (-14.5%)
Current ratio: 0.60

MERCY HEALTH

Mercy Health formerly known as the Sisters of Mercy Health System provides a range of health care and social services through its network of facilities and service organizations. The organization operates some 35 acute care hospitals (including four specialty heart hospitals and two children's hospitals) with more than 4200 licensed beds as well as 700 clinics and outpatient facilities in four Midwestern states. Its hospital groups include facilities for nursing homes medical practices and outpatient centers. Mercy Health also operates Resource Optimization & Innovation (ROi) its industry-leading health care supply chain organization and health outreach organizations in Louisiana Mississippi and Texas.

Operations

Mercy Health also operates three rehabilitation hospitals and two orthopedic hospitals. The system has more than 2000 Mercy Clinic physicians.

In 2014 Mercy Health had 150696 acute inpatient discharges; 158911 inpatient and outpatient surgeries; 631444 emergency department visits; 23213 births; and nearly 8.4 million outpatient visits.

Geographic Reach

The system operates in Arkansas Kansas Missouri and Oklahoma.

Mercy Health's outreach efforts include Mercy Ministries of Laredo a group providing primary health care and social services to residents of Laredo Texas. In New Orleans Mercy Health sponsors Mercy Family Center which provides mental health services; in Mississippi it funds a health care advocacy group.

Sales and Marketing

Commercial and other third-party payments accounted for 44% of net patient service revenue while Medicare and Medicaid combined accounted for 51%.

Financial Performance

Mercy Health's operating revenue increased 14% to $4.5 billion in 2014 as net patient and other revenues grew. However the system reported a net loss of $6.5 million that year (versus net income in 2013) as a result of interest rate swap agreement losses and higher expenses as well as lower investment earnings.

Cash flow from operations fell 46% to $354 million in 2014.

Strategy

In 2013 Mercy Health opened new facilities in Missouri (St. Charles and Wentzville) as well as a new heart and vascular center that centralized its outpatient heart and vascular offerings. The following year it opened a new orthopedic hospital in Fort Smith and a 60-bed rehabilitation hospital.

The system acquired Lincoln County Medical Center (renamed Mercy Hospital Lincoln) and its eight affiliated clinics in 2015 expanding its presence in eastern Missouri.

Despite its various expansions the Mercy system experienced the same industry challenges as its health care brethren including escalating medical and pharmaceutical costs and increasing self-pay bad debts (uninsured patients who leave their medical bills unpaid). Several of the health system's facilities have seen a decline in discharges.

Company Background

The organization was founded by the Sisters of Mercy of the St. Louis Regional Community in 1986 and operated under that model until 2008 when its sponsorship was transferred from the Sisters of Mercy of the St. Louis Regional Community to a new entity Mercy Health Ministry. The shift to the new sponsorship organization was made to allow lay members to join the Sisters of Mercy in sponsoring the ministry. It also reflected the growing number of lay people holding executive positions at the system's hospitals and on the board of directors.

EXECUTIVES

Ceo-Pres, Lynn Britton
Evp-Coo, Michael McCurry
Evp-Cfo, Shannon Sock
Vp of Information, Mike Mc Creary
Vp of Operations, Mike Mc Curry
Health Professional, Lora Petty
Chief Information Security Off, David Westman
Chief of Medicine, Edson Carrel
Information, Jon Allen
Executive Director, Ann Rucker
Svp Mission, Brian O'Toole
Auditors: ERNST & YOUNG LLP ST LOUIS

LOCATIONS

HQ: MERCY HEALTH
615 S NEW BALLAS RD, SAINT LOUIS, MO
631418221
Phone: 314 579-6100
Web: WWW.MERCY.NET

Selected Locations

Arkansas
Berryville
Fort Smith
Hot Springs
Ozark

Paris
Rogers
Waldron
Kansas
Columbus
Fort Scott
Independence
Missouri
Aurora
Cassville
Joplin
Lebanon
Mountain View
St. Louis
Springfield
Washington
Oklahoma
Ada
Ardmore
El Reno
Guthrie
Healdton
Kingfisher
Marietta
Oklahoma City
Tishomingo
Watonga

PRODUCTS/OPERATIONS

2014 Sales

	$ mil.	% of total
Net patient service revenue less provision for bad debts	3,838	85
Member revenue	477	11
Other revenue	194	4
Total	**4,510**	**100**

Selected Facilities

Arkansas
Mercy Hospital Berryville
Mercy Hospital Fort Smith
Mercy Hospital Hot Springs
Mercy Hospital Northwest Arkansas
Mercy Hospital of Scott County
Mercy Hospital Ozark
Mercy Hospital Paris
Mercy Hospital Waldron
Kansas
Mercy Health Center
Mercy Hospital Fort Scott
Mercy Hospital Independence
Mercy Maude Norton Hospital Columbus
Missouri
Mercy Hospital Aurora
Mercy Hospital Cassville
Mercy Hospital Joplin
Mercy Hospital Lebanon
Mercy Hospital St. Louis
Mercy Children's Hospital St. Louis
Mercy Heart and Vascular Hospital St. Louis
Mercy Heart Hospital St. Louis
Mercy Rehabilitation Hospital St. Louis
Mercy Hospital Springfield
Mercy Children's Hospital Springfield
Mercy Hospital Washington
Mercy McCune-Brooks Hospital
Mercy St. Francis Hospital
Oklahoma
Arbuckle Memorial Hospital
Mercy Health Love County
Mercy Hospital Ardmore
Mercy Hospital El Reno
Mercy Hospital Healdton
Mercy Hospital Logan County
Mercy Hospital Oklahoma City
Mercy Hospital - Tishomingo
Valley View Regional Hospital
Watonga Municipal Hospital

COMPETITORS

Ascension Health
Bjc Healthcare
Baptist Health
(arkansas)
Barnes-jewish Hospital
Christus Health
Christian Hospital
Community Health
Systems

Ssm Health Care
Saint Luke's Health
System
Shawnee Mission
Medical Center
Sisters Of Charity Of
Leavenworth
St. Anthony's Medical
Center

Coxhealth
Hca
Integris Health
Memorial Hospital
(illinois)
Rehabcare

St. Vincent Health
System
Tenet Healthcare
Universal Health
Services

HISTORICAL FINANCIALS

Company Type: Private

Income Statement

FYE: June 30

	REVENUE ($ mil.)	NET INCOME ($ mil.)	NET PROFIT MARGIN	EMPLOYEES
06/21	7,422	1,330	17.9%	8,800
06/20	6,519	(325)	—	—
06/19	6,509	(32)	—	—
06/18	6,254	243	3.9%	—
Annual Growth	5.9%	76.0%	—	—

2021 Year-End Financials

Return on assets: 12.9%
Return on equity: 26.4%
Current ratio: 1.40
Cash ($ mil.): 1,361

MERCY HEALTH

Mercy Health (formerly Catholic Health Partners) performs acts of healing in Kentucky and Ohio. One of the nation's largest not-for-profit health systems Mercy Health offers health care services through about 450 facilities including 23 hospitals eight homes for the elderly five hospice programs and seven home health agencies. It also operates more than 150 clinics a number of physician practices and a health insurance plan. The system is co-sponsored by the Sisters of Mercy South Central and Mid-Atlantic communities; the Sisters of the Humility of Mary; the Franciscan Sisters of the Poor; and Covenant Health Systems. Mercy Health merged with Maryland-based Bon Secours Health System to create the 43-hospital system Bon Secours Mercy Health in 2018.

Operations

Mercy Health organizes its operations into regions to better serve the communities where its facilities are located. Its acute and non-acute inpatient facilities have a total of more than 6300 beds. The system is affiliated with more than 1800 physicians of various medical and surgical specialties.

Hospitals include St. Elizabeth and St. Joseph Health Centers near Youngstown Ohio; seven Mercy locations in the Toledo Ohio area; Mercy Regional Medical Center near Cleveland; St. Rita's Medical Center in Lima Ohio; Springfield Regional Medical Center and Mercy Memorial Hospital in Springfield Ohio; Anderson Clermont Fairfield Mt. Airy Jewish West and Western Hills hospitals in Cincinnati; and Lourdes Hospital in Paduchah Kentucky.

Its specialized health care services include cancer cardiology radiology laboratory surgical and women's health care. The company also operates HealthSpan a PPO health insurance plan that covers nearly 273000 lives.

Geographic Reach

Mercy Health divides its operations into seven regional markets. North Markets include Mercy in Toledo and Lorain Ohio and Humility of Mary Health Partners in Youngstown Ohio. South Markets include St. Rita's Health Partners Community Mercy Health Partners and Mercy Health Partners in Ohio as well as Mercy Health Partners - Kentucky.

Financial Performance

Mercy Health's revenue increased 14% to $4.5 billion in 2014 on growing net patient service revenue and other revenue. However the system lost a net $6.5 million that year due to interest rate swap agreement losses lower investment earnings and higher operating expenses.

Cash flow from operations dropped in 2014 to $354 million.

Strategy

In 2014 after the Affordable Care Act (which requires insurance companies to provide access to abortion and birth control) took effect Mercy Health spun off its HealthSpan insurance arm to avoid a conflict with church doctrine.

The following year Mercy Health partnered with Akron Ohio-based Summa Health to create Advanced Health Select a network of doctors and medical caregivers in an effort to attract large employers and insurance companies.

Mergers and Acquisitions

In 2018 Mercy Health and Maryland-based Bon Secours Health System merged to create a system with 43 hospitals in seven states. The combined entity has more than 2100 physicians and clinicians working in more than 1000 locations.

EXECUTIVES

Ceo-Pres, John M Starcher Jr
Coordinator, Fiona McCloy
Chief Officer and Pres, Randy Curnow
Scientist, Larry Jackson
Purchasing Agent, Carlos Ballinas
Vice President, Cathy Follmer
Information Technology, David Laytart
Chief Legal Officer, Michael Bezney
Vice President Clinical Soluti, Mike Hibbard
Human Resource Generalist, Yolanda Ross
Pres Lima Market, Ronda Lehman
Auditors: KPMG LLP CINCINNATI OHIO

LOCATIONS

HQ: MERCY HEALTH
  12621 ECKEL JUNCTION RD, PERRYSBURG, OH 435511304
Phone: 513 639-2800
Web: WWW.MERCY.COM

HISTORICAL FINANCIALS
Company Type: Private

Income Statement				FYE: December 31
	REVENUE ($ mil.)	NET INCOME ($ mil.)	NET PROFIT MARGIN	EMPLOYEES
12/18	4,860	(978)	—	1,000
12/17	4,737	456	9.6%	—
Annual Growth	2.6%	—	—	—

MERCY HEALTH CORPORATION

EXECUTIVES

Ceo, Javon R Bea
Asso Cno, Beth Pearson
Chief of Radiology, Kyle Pfeifer
MD, Pablo Morales
Purchasing Director, Adam Yowell
Technician, Danny Breit

Provider Recruiter, Meghan Sreenan
Pharmacy Director, Susan Lee
Registered Nurse Clinic Superv, Jennifer Miley
Inventory Controller, Jerry Henning
Registered Nurse Team, Rebeka Bauer
Auditors: WIPFLI LLP MILWAUKEE WISCON

LOCATIONS

HQ: MERCY HEALTH CORPORATION
  2400 N ROCKTON AVE, ROCKFORD, IL 611033655
Phone: 815 971-5000
Web: WWW.MERCY.COM

HISTORICAL FINANCIALS
Company Type: Private

Income Statement				FYE: June 30
	REVENUE ($ mil.)	NET INCOME ($ mil.)	NET PROFIT MARGIN	EMPLOYEES
06/21	1,163	210	18.1%	2,200
06/19	1,152	50	4.4%	—
06/18	1,014	68	6.7%	—
Annual Growth	4.7%	45.4%	—	—

2021 Year-End Financials
Return on assets: 9.1%
Return on equity: 17.3%
Current ratio: 2.10

Cash ($ mil.): 345

MERCY HEALTH PARTNERS

EXECUTIVES

Pres, Gordon A Mudler
V Pres, David Gingras
Chb, Richard C Lague
Treas, H Richard Morgenstern
SEC, Patrick T Kirk
Staff Rn, Erica Cousins
Staff Physician, Saundra Blanchard
MD, Christine Faser
Employee, Abbey Afienko
Staff Nurse, Amanda Twining
Senior Process Excellence Cons, Brian Weele

LOCATIONS

HQ: MERCY HEALTH PARTNERS
  1675 LEAHY ST STE 101, MUSKEGON, MI 494425538
Phone: 231 728-4032
Web: WWW.MERCYHEALTH.COM

HISTORICAL FINANCIALS
Company Type: Private

Income Statement				FYE: June 30
	REVENUE ($ mil.)	NET INCOME ($ mil.)	NET PROFIT MARGIN	EMPLOYEES
06/18	666	36	5.5%	1,500
06/08	0	0	81.1%	—
06/06	0	0	50.7%	—
06/04	0	(0)	—	—
Annual Growth	96.2%	—	—	—

MERCY HEALTH SERVICES, INC.

EXECUTIVES

Pres, Thomas Mullen
Executive Vice President, John Topper
Senior Vice President, Institu, Claudia Keenan
Chief, David Riseberg
Director, Radiation Oncology, Maria Jacobs
Oncology and Hematolog, Peter Ledakis
Chief Administrative Officer, Regina Figueroa
Senior Vice President,, Scott Spier
Auditors: DIXON HUGHES GOODMAN LLP CHA

LOCATIONS

HQ: MERCY HEALTH SERVICES, INC.
  301 SAINT PAUL ST, BALTIMORE, MD 212022102
Phone: 410 332-9000
Web: WWW.MDMERCY.COM

HISTORICAL FINANCIALS
Company Type: Private

Income Statement				FYE: June 30
	REVENUE ($ mil.)	NET INCOME ($ mil.)	NET PROFIT MARGIN	EMPLOYEES
06/21	861	132	15.4%	1
06/20	774	8	1.0%	—
06/19	766	30	4.0%	—
06/18	737	31	4.2%	—
Annual Growth	5.3%	61.8%	—	—

2021 Year-End Financials
Return on assets: 9.0%
Return on equity: 21.3%
Current ratio: 1.70

Cash ($ mil.): 309

MERCY HEALTH SERVICES-IOWA, CORP.

EXECUTIVES

Ceo, Jack Weiner
Pres-Ceo*, Joseph Swevish
Pres*, Daniel Varnum
Cfo*, James Peppiatt-Combes
Gen Counsel*, Daniel G Hale
Prin*, Scott Leighty
Director, Mary West
Executive Officer, Pat McDermott
Family Practitioner, Rudy Ochs
Family Practitioner, Amanda Truer
Network Administrator, Bob Carroll

LOCATIONS

HQ: MERCY HEALTH SERVICES-IOWA, CORP.
  20555 VICTOR PKWY, LIVONIA, MI 481527031
Phone: 734 343-1000
Web: WWW.TRINITY-HEALTH.ORG

HISTORICAL FINANCIALS
Company Type: Private

Income Statement				FYE: June 30
	REVENUE ($ mil.)	NET INCOME ($ mil.)	NET PROFIT MARGIN	EMPLOYEES
06/18	969	31	3.3%	2,471
06/14	665	2	0.4%	—
06/05	546	23	4.3%	—
Annual Growth	4.5%	2.3%	—	—

MERCY HEALTH SERVICES-IOWA, CORP.

EXECUTIVES

Prin, Robin Edgar
Internal Medicine Practitioner, Natalia F Gabilondo
Vascular Surgeon, Ali Mardan
Finance Business Manager, Connie Morrison
Marketing Director, Jason Monarch
Internist, Patrick Dunlay
Internal Medicine, Muhammad Al Sharif
Desktop, Jeff Schuchard
Womens Health Srv Director, Lori Barkela
Clinical Nutrition Supervisor, Bea Volk
Informatics Manager, Deborah Rickard

LOCATIONS

HQ: MERCY HEALTH SERVICES-IOWA, CORP.
1000 4TH ST SW, MASON CITY, IA 504012800
Phone: 641 428-7000
Web: WWW.MERCYNORTHIOWA.COM

HISTORICAL FINANCIALS
Company Type: Private

Income Statement				FYE: June 30
	REVENUE ($ mil.)	NET INCOME ($ mil.)	NET PROFIT MARGIN	EMPLOYEES
06/11	649	17	2.7%	—
06/10	632	19	3.0%	—
Annual Growth	2.7%	(7.9%)	—	—

2011 Year-End Financials

Return on assets: 2.2%   Cash ($ mil.): 10
Return on equity: 3.5%
Current ratio: 0.40

MERCY HEALTH SYSTEM CORPORATION

EXECUTIVES

Ceo, Javon R Bea
V Pres-Cfo*, Joseph Nemeth
Optometrists, Kevin Walter
Optometrists, Becky Trujillo
Public Relations Director, Ronald Del Ciello
Procurement Staff, Steve Walker

Training and Direc, Wynn Biedermann
Coordinator, Kristin Hansberry
Coordinator, Jennifer Bestland
Patient Account Supervisor, Paula Boyce
Family Practice, Shailesh Virani
Auditors: WIPFLI LLP MILWAUKEE WISCONS

LOCATIONS

HQ: MERCY HEALTH SYSTEM CORPORATION
1000 MINERAL POINT AVE, JANESVILLE, WI 535482940
Phone: 608 741-6891
Web: WWW.MERCYHEALTHSYSTEM.ORG

HISTORICAL FINANCIALS
Company Type: Private

Income Statement				FYE: June 30
	REVENUE ($ mil.)	NET INCOME ($ mil.)	NET PROFIT MARGIN	EMPLOYEES
06/21	633	89	14.1%	2,200
06/20	592	50	8.5%	—
06/16	559	19	3.5%	—
06/15	523	12	2.3%	—
Annual Growth	3.2%	39.7%	—	—

2021 Year-End Financials

Return on assets: 11.5%   Cash ($ mil.): 259
Return on equity: 22.3%
Current ratio: 3.70

MERCY HEALTH SYSTEM OF SOUTHEASTERN PENNSYLVANIA

EXECUTIVES

Chb, Christine McCann
Ceo*, H Ray Welch
Cfo*, Joseph Bradley
Asst Acct, Lia Onell
Scientist, Patricia Daly
Compliance Staff, Maryann L Cannon
Director Info Technology, Charles Welsh
Assistant To President, Janet Borger
Vice President Information TEC, Michael McCreary
Vice President, Brian Hannah
Nurse Manager Mercy Ambulatory, Kathleen Gavin
Auditors: DELOITTE TAX LLP PHILADELPHIA

LOCATIONS

HQ: MERCY HEALTH SYSTEM OF SOUTHEASTERN PENNSYLVANIA
3805 WEST CHESTER PIKE # 10, NEWTOWN SQUARE, PA 190732329
Phone: 610 567-6000
Web: WWW.TRINITYHEALTHMA.ORG

HISTORICAL FINANCIALS
Company Type: Private

Income Statement				FYE: June 30
	REVENUE ($ mil.)	NET INCOME ($ mil.)	NET PROFIT MARGIN	EMPLOYEES
06/18	745	64	8.7%	8,050
06/15	88	10	11.8%	—
Annual Growth	103.6%	83.7%	—	—

MERCY HOSPITAL OKLAHOMA CITY, INC.

EXECUTIVES

Pres, Jim R Gebhart
Dof*, Christopher Hahne
Director of Psychology, S Renee Orcutt
Neonatal Care Director, Amy Gwartney
Safety Director, Chad Larman
Dir of Geriatric Srvs, Gaylene Stiles
Nursing Director, Karyl James
Physician Director of Er, Lance Watson
Human Resources Director, Melinda Sharum
Biomedical Engineer, Michael Dixon
Radiology Director, Peter Ersteniuk
Auditors: PLEUS AND COMPANY LLC CHESTER

LOCATIONS

HQ: MERCY HOSPITAL OKLAHOMA CITY, INC.
4300 W MEMORIAL RD, OKLAHOMA CITY, OK 731208304
Phone: 405 755-1515
Web: WWW.MERCY.NET

HISTORICAL FINANCIALS
Company Type: Private

Income Statement				FYE: June 30
	REVENUE ($ mil.)	NET INCOME ($ mil.)	NET PROFIT MARGIN	EMPLOYEES
06/20	583	71	12.3%	2,302
06/10	312	16	5.2%	—
06/09	287	7	2.7%	—
06/08	1	0	34.7%	—
Annual Growth	60.5%	47.3%	—	—

2020 Year-End Financials

Return on assets: 17.2%   Cash ($ mil.): 12
Return on equity: 28.0%
Current ratio: 6.30

MERCY HOSPITAL SPRINGFIELD

Mercy Hospital Springfield is an 890-bed acute-care hospital in the Mercy Health system. The facility provides health care to southwestern Missouri and northwestern Arkansas and includes the Mercy Children's Hospital Springfield. Other hospital specialties include cardiology and stroke care as well as women's and seniors' health cancer emergency trauma burn neuroscience rehabilitation and sports medicine. In addition to its hospital in Springfield Mercy Hospital Springfield operates a number of community clinics and specialty care centers in the area.

Operations

Mercy Hospital Springfield has about 700 doctors on its medical staff. The center sees some 441000 outpatient visits per year as well as 94000 emergency room visits and 37000 surgeries. It also enables more than 3000 births Specialty units feature a level I trauma and burn center (the highest ranking in the US) a neonatal intensive care unit a nationally certified stroke center and high-tech surgery suites (including da Vinci robotic surgery and CyberKnife radiosurgery centers). It also operates an air ambulance service.

Geographic Reach

The hospital serves patients in southwest Missouri and northwest Arkansas.

Financial Performance

The hospital's revenues decreased by 1% in 2014 due to 1% drop in net patient service revenue (which contributed 98% of the revenue) and a 11% decrease in revenues from other sources.

In 2014 the company provided charity care of about $26 million along with unreimbursed Medicaid expenses of around $17 million.

Strategy

That year Mercy Hospital Springfield opened the 60-bed Mercy Rehabilitation Hospital Springfield which is spread across a 63000-square-feet facility. The new $28 million building allows for more options for patient rehabilitation and will also serve as the region's only burn unit.

In 2014 the company also opened Phase II of its Betty and Bobby Allison Neonatal Intensive Care Unit (NICU) which expands the number of beds under NICU to 46. With this final phase complete Mercy permanently closed its former NICU.

Company Background

Formerly St. John's Regional Health Center the hospital's name changed to Mercy Hospital Springfield in 2012; the move coincided with the parent organization's efforts to to unify its brand identity. (The parent group's named changed as well from Sisters of Mercy Health System to Mercy Health.)

The hospital was founded in 1891 by the Sisters of Mercy.

EXECUTIVES

Ceo, Lynn Britton
Ceo, Kim Day
Pres, John Swope
Exec V Pres, Michael McCurry
Exec V Pres, Shannon Sock
In Education Dir, Carla Weber
Oncology Director, Christopher Estes
Chief Officer, David Merriman
Vice President Finance, Greta Wilcher
Library Dir, Holly Henderson
Infection Prevention Director, Julie Warner

LOCATIONS

HQ: MERCY HOSPITAL SPRINGFIELD
 1235 E CHEROKEE ST, SPRINGFIELD, MO
 658042203
Phone: 417 820-2000
Web: WWW.MERCY.NET

PRODUCTS/OPERATIONS

Selected Services
Bariatric Surgery
Cancer Care
Children's Care
Heart Care
Integrative Medicine
Mother and Baby Care

Neurosciences
Orthopedic and Sport Care
Palliative Care
Pastoral Care
Senior Care
Trauma and Burn Care
Women's Care

COMPETITORS

Ascension Health
Bjc Healthcare
Boone Hospital Center
Catholic Health
 Initiatives
Christian Hospital
Coxhealth

Hca
Heartland Health
Liberty Hospital
Tenet Healthcare
Truman Medical Centers
University Of Kansas
 Medical Center

HISTORICAL FINANCIALS
Company Type: Private

Income Statement				FYE: June 30
	REVENUE ($ mil.)	NET INCOME ($ mil.)	NET PROFIT MARGIN	EMPLOYEES
06/16	1,024	104	10.2%	4,400
06/15	948	93	9.9%	—
06/14	964	42	4.4%	—
06/13	965	87	9.1%	—
Annual Growth	2.0%	6.1%	—	—

2016 Year-End Financials
Return on assets: 24.4%   Cash ($ mil.): 25
Return on equity: 27.5%
Current ratio: 4.60

MERCY HOSPITALS EAST COMMUNITIES

EXECUTIVES

President, Jeffrey Johnston
Vice President*, Paul Hintze
Attorney, Melissa Jackson
Internist, Carolyn L Koenig
Dermatologist, Brooke Shadel
Director of Home SE, Carrie Harrison
Exec Director, Chris Carter
Chief of Pediatrics, John Mantovani
Pediatrics, Joseph Kahn
Cardiac Cath Lab Director, Kevin Politte
Physical Therapy Director, Laura Johnston

LOCATIONS

HQ: MERCY HOSPITALS EAST COMMUNITIES
 615 S NEW BALLAS RD, SAINT LOUIS, MO
 631418221
Phone: 314 251-6000
Web: WWW.MERCY.NET

COMPETITORS

Bjc Healthcare
Memorial Hospital
 (illinois)
Ssm Health Care

St. Anthony's Medical
 Center
St. Luke's Hospital
 (mo)

HISTORICAL FINANCIALS
Company Type: Private

Income Statement				FYE: June 30
	REVENUE ($ mil.)	NET INCOME ($ mil.)	NET PROFIT MARGIN	EMPLOYEES
06/16	1,023	184	18.0%	10,000
06/15	940	132	14.1%	—
06/14	1,177	118	10.1%	—
06/13	840	82	9.8%	—
Annual Growth	6.8%	30.9%	—	—

2016 Year-End Financials
Return on assets: 29.1%   Cash ($ mil.): 22
Return on equity: 31.5%
Current ratio: 4.90

MERCY MEDICAL CENTER, INC.

EXECUTIVES

Chb, Sister Helen Amos
Ceo*, Thomas R Mullen
Exec V Pres-Cfo*, John E Topper
Exec V Pres*, Amy Freeman
Sr V Pres Medical Affairs*, Dr Scott Spier
Coordinator, Rona Kassem
Scientist, Ruth Bates
Internal Medicine Practitioner, Robert G
 Davidson
Coordinator, Eric Barbieri
Coordinator, Erin Pollitt
Internal Medicine Practitioner, Matthew Croley
Auditors: DIXON HUGHES GOODMAN LLP
 CHA

LOCATIONS

HQ: MERCY MEDICAL CENTER, INC.
 345 SAINT PAUL ST, BALTIMORE, MD 212022123
Phone: 410 332-9000
Web: WWW.MDMERCY.COM

HISTORICAL FINANCIALS
Company Type: Private

Income Statement				FYE: June 30
	REVENUE ($ mil.)	NET INCOME ($ mil.)	NET PROFIT MARGIN	EMPLOYEES
06/21	571	118	20.7%	2,139
06/20	510	9	1.8%	—
06/19	511	22	4.4%	—
06/18	502	25	5.1%	—
Annual Growth	4.4%	66.9%	—	—

2021 Year-End Financials
Return on assets: 9.2%   Cash ($ mil.): 297
Return on equity: 23.6%
Current ratio: 1.90

MERCY SCRIPPS HOSPITAL

EXECUTIVES

Prin, Andrew C Ping
Coordinator, Callie Huza
General Surgery, Alan Wittgrove
Manager of Patient Access, Erlinda Medina
Chief Staff, Jerry Glassman
Risk Manager, Kathy Maroni
General Surgery, Kimberly Peck
General Surgery, Mayyas Isho
Registered Dietitian, Eileen Ackerman
General Surgery, Leo Murphy
Hospitalist, Matthew Callahan

LOCATIONS

HQ: MERCY SCRIPPS HOSPITAL
   4077 5TH AVE MER35, SAN DIEGO, CA 921032105
Phone: 619 294-8111
Web: WWW.SCRIPPS.ORG

HISTORICAL FINANCIALS

Company Type: Private

Income Statement				FYE: September 30
	REVENUE ($ mil.)	NET INCOME ($ mil.)	NET PROFIT MARGIN	EMPLOYEES
09/15	750	44	5.9%	73
09/14	623	3	0.6%	—
09/13	700	41	5.9%	—
Annual Growth	3.5%	3.7%	—	—

MERCY WOODSTOCK MEDICAL CENTER

EXECUTIVES

Principal, Napoleon P Abando
Dermatologist, Jeffrey Altman
Orthopedics, Marko Krpan
Vascular Surgeon, Douglas Bryan
Senior Manager, Michelle Grecek
Patient Access Supervisor 191, Tiffany Sobczak
Office Manager, Valerie Johns

LOCATIONS

HQ: MERCY WOODSTOCK MEDICAL CENTER
   2000 LAKE AVE, WOODSTOCK, IL 600987401
Phone: 815 337-7100

HISTORICAL FINANCIALS

Company Type: Private

Income Statement				FYE: June 30
	REVENUE ($ mil.)	NET INCOME ($ mil.)	NET PROFIT MARGIN	EMPLOYEES
06/19	592	23	3.9%	1
06/18	584	25	4.4%	—
Annual Growth	1.4%	(8.6%)	—	—

2019 Year-End Financials

Return on assets: 4.0%   Cash ($ mil.): 84
Return on equity: 9.0%
Current ratio: 3.10

MERIDIAN HOSPITALS CORPORATION

Auditors: PRICEWATERHOUSECOOPERS LLP NE

LOCATIONS

HQ: MERIDIAN HOSPITALS CORPORATION
   1945 ROUTE 33, NEPTUNE, NJ 077534859
Phone: 732 751-7500

HISTORICAL FINANCIALS

Company Type: Private

Income Statement				FYE: December 31
	REVENUE ($ mil.)	NET INCOME ($ mil.)	NET PROFIT MARGIN	EMPLOYEES
12/16	1,667	244	14.7%	5,200
12/15	674	64	9.5%	—
12/09	929	94	10.2%	—
12/08	873	(140)	—	—
Annual Growth	8.4%	—	—	—

2016 Year-End Financials

Return on assets: 9.6%   Cash ($ mil.): 257
Return on equity: 18.4%
Current ratio: 2.80

MESA UNIFIED SCHOOL DISTRICT 4

EXECUTIVES

Supt, Amber Conley
Exec Asst, Alice Swinehart
Department Head, Allison Miller
Secretary, Cheryl Farney
Specialist, Christine Niven
Counselor, Gary Ingle
Technology Director, Karen Procopio
Teacher, Robert Guyton
Elementary, Sandi Kuhn
Technology Director, Keith Parker
Teacher, Christi Barron
Auditors: HEINFELD MEECH & CO PC P

LOCATIONS

HQ: MESA UNIFIED SCHOOL DISTRICT 4
   63 E MAIN ST STE 101, MESA, AZ 852017422
Phone: 480 472-0200
Web: WWW.MPSAZ.ORG

HISTORICAL FINANCIALS

Company Type: Private

Income Statement				FYE: June 30
	REVENUE ($ mil.)	NET INCOME ($ mil.)	NET PROFIT MARGIN	EMPLOYEES
06/20	642	35	5.5%	9,621
06/19	617	39	6.5%	—
06/18	580	8	1.4%	—
06/16	549	(22)	—	—
Annual Growth	4.0%	—	—	—

MESSER CONSTRUCTION CO.

From casinos and courthouses to laboratories and dormitories Messer Construction has built them all. The builder provides commercial construction services (including design/build and project management) for projects in Indiana Kentucky Ohio North Carolina and Tennessee. Messer has done more than $300 million worth of construction with Construction Management Agency. It has clients in the life sciences higher education senior living commercial manufacturing/industrial public and health care sectors among others. Its projects have included the renovation of Michaelman Inc. Advanced Materials Collboration Center & Corporate Campus and Cook Regentec Build-Out & Renovations. Founded in 1932 employee-owned Messer boasts nearly 20% of its annual revenue from design-build projects.

Operations

Messer offers a range of commercial construction services including building information modeling cost planning and estimating integrated project delivery lean construction and safety programs. It also offers prefabrication services such as mechanical/electrical/plumbing services bathroom pods and health care headwall assemblies.

Geographic Reach

Based in Cincinnati Ohio Messer operates regional offices in North Carolina (Charlotte and Raleigh) Ohio (Cincinnati Columbus and Dayton) Indiana (Indianapolis) Tennessee (Knoxville and Nashville) and Kentucky (Lexington and Louisville).

Sales and Marketing

Messer has served customers from a variety of industries including aviation federal/military education industrial science and technology and corporate that including clients such as: Charlotte Douglas International Airport (CDIA) Dayton Airport US Army Corps of Engineer Wright-Patterson Air Force Aisin Automotive Casting DHL Express the Connor Group and Valvoline.

Strategy

Messer continues to work on high-value projects across a wide range of industries in the Midwest particularly in secure industries such as healthcare government and education. One of the projects is the Andrew J Brady ICON Music Center which Messer along with GBBN Architects CMTA Engineers Inc. The Kleingers Group THP Limited Cini-Little Harvey Marshall Berling Associates Dynamix Engineering and WA Architects consulted in. The center is set to open in the fall of 2020.

Messer also acquired EGC Construction an industrial contractor based in Newport Kentucky. One part of Messer Construction's strategy for growth is to increase its industrial and manufacturing work across the Midwest. The purchase of EGC Construction is the first time Messer Construction has acquired another construction company.

Messer's Operations Technology Solutions (OTS) department has been developing virtual mock-ups: problem-solvers and cost-savers that help ensure work is done right the first time. These virtual mock-ups are being used on projects such as the CONRAC at Cincinnati/Northern Kentucky International Airport (CVG).

Mergers and Acquisitions

In mid-2019 Messer Construction completed its acquisition of Kentucky-based EGC Construction an industrial contractor that specializes in design-build services industrial manufacturing processes and manufacturing and medical equipment installation and rigging. With the acquisition Messer gains access to EGC's miscellaneous metal fabrication shop and team of approximately 75 skilled trade professionals with expertise as electrical and millwright workers ironworkers pipefitters carpenters and laborers. Details of the acquisition were not disclosed.

Company Background
Formerly known as Frank Messer & Sons Inc. the company changed its name to Messer Construction Co. in March 2002.

EXECUTIVES

Pres-Ceo, Tim Steigerwald
Fo- Sr V Pres*, E Paul Hitter Jr
Sr V Pres*, Kevin Cozart
Sr V Pres*, Bernard Suer
Coo*, Mark S Luegering
Sr V Pres*, Steven Bestard
Sr V Pres*, Nicholas Apanius
Sr V Pres*, Alex Munoz
Sr V Pres*, Robert Verst
Vp, C Allen Begley Jr
Prin, M W King
Auditors: DELOITTE & TOUCHE LLP CINCINN

LOCATIONS

HQ: MESSER CONSTRUCTION CO.
643 W COURT ST, CINCINNATI, OH 452031511
Phone: 513 242-1541
Web: WWW.MESSER.COM

PRODUCTS/OPERATIONS

Selected Projects
Health Care
  Norton Healthcare
  Knoxville Orthopedic Clinic
Life Sciences
  Indiana University
  University of Kentucky
Higher Education
  Xavier University
  Western Kentucky University
Senior Living
  Graceworks Lutheran Services
  Episcopal Retirement Homes
Commercial
  IGS Energy
  Penn National Gaming
Manufacturing & Industrial
  Aisin Automotive Casting Tennessee Inc.
  DHL Express Inc.
Public/Institutional
  The Ohio Building Authority
  Commonwealth of Kentucky

COMPETITORS

Albert M. Higley	Shook National
Danis	Skanska Usa Building
F.a. Wilhelm	The Austin Company
Gray Construction	Turner Corporation
Hunt Construction	Tutor Perini
Pepper Construction	

HISTORICAL FINANCIALS
Company Type: Private

Income Statement   FYE: September 30

	REVENUE ($ mil.)	NET INCOME ($ mil.)	NET PROFIT MARGIN	EMPLOYEES
09/17	1,092	0	—	1,390
09/15	1,167	0	—	—
09/14	1,029	0	—	—
09/13	831	0	—	—
Annual Growth	7.0%	—	—	—

2017 Year-End Financials
Return on assets: —
Return on equity: —
Current ratio: 1.20
Cash ($ mil.): 83

METALDYNE PERFORMANCE GROUP INC.

Metaldyne designs and supplies a slew of products for engine transmission and driveline applications. The company focuses on powertrain products such as balance shaft modules differential assemblies clutch modules and exhaust components. Other business units make vibration control (dampers isolation pulleys) sintered (connecting rods bearing caps) and forged parts. Customers have included OEMs Chrysler Ford GM and Toyota. Metaldyne in 2017 was acquired by American Axle & Manufacturing (AAM) for $3.3 billion.

Operations
Metaldyne operates in three segments including HHI Holding LLC (HHI; 38% of sales) Metaldyne (32%) and Grede (30%). Metaldyne manufactures highly-engineered metal-based powertrain components for the global light vehicle markets. HHI manufactures highly-engineered metal-based components for the North American light vehicle market.

Grede manufactures cast machined and assembled components for the light commercial and industrial (agriculture construction mining rail wind energy and oil field) vehicle and equipment end-markets.

Geographic Reach
Metaldyne's business is supported by 61 locations dotting 13 countries in Asia Europe South America and North America. The US accounts for 77% of net sales; other major markets include Europe (12%) and other international countries (11%).

Sales and Marketing
Metaldyne targets the global light commercial and industrial vehicle markets. In 2015 Ford Motor General Motors and Fiat Chrysler Automobiles (FCA) accounted for approximately 24% 21% and 15% of its end-customer sales respectively. Other customers included Daimler AG Toyota and Hyundai which together accounted for approximately 9% of its end-customer sales for the year.

Financial Performance
The company has experienced strong revenue growth the last three years. In 2015 revenues climbed by 12% to peak at $3 billion primarily due to a 59% surge in its Grede segment partially offset by declines in its Metaldyne segment. Net income also surged by 72% in 2015 mainly due to a decline in losses related to paying down debt.

The growth in its Grede segment was fueled by its Grede acquisition which contributed approximately $409 million of extra revenue and increased volumes mainly due to light vehicle production volumes. Also a 2% increase in HHI net sales was primarily attributable to increased volumes due to higher North American light vehicle production levels. The decrease in Metaldyne net sales was attributable to unfavorable foreign currency movements net price decreases and lower raw material pass-through.

Mergers and Acquisitions

EXECUTIVES

Pres, Michael K Simonte
Chb, Kevin Penn
Coo, Douglas Grimm
Cfo, Mark Blaufuss
Exec V Pres-Gen Counsel-Sec, Thomas M Dono Jr
Exec V Pres Sls, Russell Bradley
V Pres-Cao-Controller, Gary Ford
Auditors: DELOITTE & TOUCHE LLP DETROIT

LOCATIONS

HQ: METALDYNE PERFORMANCE GROUP INC.
1 TOWNE SQ STE 550, SOUTHFIELD, MI 480763710
Phone: 248 727-1800
Web: WWW.AAM.COM

HISTORICAL FINANCIALS
Company Type: Private

Income Statement   FYE: December 31

	REVENUE ($ mil.)	NET INCOME ($ mil.)	NET PROFIT MARGIN	EMPLOYEES
12/16	2,790	96	3.5%	12,000
12/15	3,047	125	4.1%	—
12/14	2,717	73	2.7%	—
Annual Growth	1.3%	15.0%	—	—

2016 Year-End Financials
Return on assets: 3.0%
Return on equity: 14.3%
Current ratio: 2.00
Cash ($ mil.): 209

METHODIST HEALTH CARE SYSTEM

EXECUTIVES

Pres, Larry L Mathis
Pres*, Mauro Ferrari
V Pres*, S Jeffrey Atcherman
Operations Administrator, Laura Espinosa PHD Rn
Chief of Medicine, Bruce Kennedy
Staff, Korsh Jafarnia
Health Professional, Sherrie Alexander
Scientist, David Raskin
Clinic Manager, Dominique Bookman
Manager of Academic Developmen, Jessica Uriarte
Manager, Melita Howell
Auditors: GRANT THORNTON LLP DALLAS TX

LOCATIONS

HQ: METHODIST HEALTH CARE SYSTEM
6565 FANNIN ST D200, HOUSTON, TX 770302703
Phone: 713 793-1602
Web: WWW.HOUSTONMETHODIST.ORG

METHODIST HEALTHCARE- MEMPHIS HOSPITALS

EXECUTIVES

Ceo, David Baytos
Pres*, Meri Armour
Chief of Medicine, Karen Hopper
Executive Officer, Willeen Hasting
Co-Minimum Data Set Coordinato, Shelly Neal
Scientist, Keeba Hudson
Coordinator, Teresa Berkley
Executive Officer, Cato Johnson
Chief Financial Officer, Chuck Lane
Diagnostic Radiologist, Davis Moser
Manager of Child Life, Lauren McCann
Auditors: DIXON HUGHES GOODMAN LLP
ASHE

LOCATIONS

HQ: METHODIST HEALTHCARE- MEMPHIS
HOSPITALS
1265 UNION AVE, MEMPHIS, TN 381043415
Phone: 901 516-7000
Web: WWW.METHODISTHEALTH.ORG

HISTORICAL FINANCIALS
Company Type: Private

Income Statement				FYE: December 31
	REVENUE ($ mil.)	NET INCOME ($ mil.)	NET PROFIT MARGIN	EMPLOYEES
12/17	2,101	101	4.8%	7,000
12/02	784	(26)	—	—
12/01	717	(28)	—	—
Annual Growth	6.9%	—	—	—

METROHEALTH MEDICAL CENTER

LOCATIONS

HQ: METROHEALTH MEDICAL CENTER
2500 METROHEALTH DR, CLEVELAND, OH
441091900
Phone: 216 778-7800
Web: WWW.METROHEALTH.ORG

HISTORICAL FINANCIALS
Company Type: Private

Income Statement				FYE: December 31
	REVENUE ($ mil.)	NET INCOME ($ mil.)	NET PROFIT MARGIN	EMPLOYEES
12/16	883	(8)	—	6,000
12/15	795	35	4.5%	—
12/14	782	32	4.2%	—
Annual Growth	6.3%	—	—	—

2016 Year-End Financials
Return on assets: (-0.8%) Cash ($ mil.): 11
Return on equity: (-4.9%)
Current ratio: 1.30

METROPOLITAN EDISON COMPANY

Metropolitan Edison is an electric company and it knows a thing or two about serving cities and surrounding communities. The company a subsidiary of holding company FirstEnergy provides electric services to a population of 1.3 million in a 3300-sq. ml. service area in south central and eastern Pennsylvania. Metropolitan Edison or Met-Ed as it is sometimes referred to operates almost 16500 miles of power transmission and distribution lines. Although the company's primary source of electricity is derived from oil-and gas-fired units its York Haven Power Company generates hydroelectric power.

EXECUTIVES

Exec V Pres-Cfo, Mark T Clark
V Pres-Controller-Cao, Harvey L Wagner
Exec V Pres-Gen Counsel, Leila L Vespoli
V Pres-Treas, James F Pearson
Real Estate Conultant, Craig Correll
Supervisor Engineering, Alfred Nerino
Customer Associate, Matthew Kemp
Manager Forestry, Doug Kinyo
Manager Regional Operations, James Frey
Distribution Designer, David Marsh
Adv Human Resources Representa, Carol Lied
Auditors: PRICEWATERHOUSECOOPERS LLP
CL

LOCATIONS

HQ: METROPOLITAN EDISON COMPANY
76 S MAIN ST, AKRON, OH 443081812
Phone: 800 736-3402
Web: WWW.FIRSTENERGYCORP.COM

COMPETITORS

Columbia Gas Of Pennsylvania
Direct Energy
Peco Energy
Ppl Electric

METROPOLITAN GOVERNMENT OF NASHVILLE & DAVIDSON COUNTY

Memphis may have the blues but Nashville has that country sound. Tennessee's second-largest city (with about 600000 people) is home to many recording studios music labels and thousands of working musicians. The city also has a large health care community with two Fortune 500 companies - HCA and Community Health Systems- employing thousands of people.

EXECUTIVES

Mayor, John Cooper
Chief of Staff, Debby D Mason
Staff, Steve Glover
Information Specialist, Kale Lawson
Executive Director, Brenda Ramsey
Information Specialist, Matthew Keaton
Director of Corporate, Amanda Tate
Director Quality, Dan Freudberg
Human Resources Manager, Kent Minich
CPA, Kim McDoniel
Training Manager, Kym Tucker

LOCATIONS

HQ: METROPOLITAN GOVERNMENT OF NASHVILLE
& DAVIDSON COUNTY
100 METRO COURTHOUSE, NASHVILLE, TN 37201
Phone: 615 862-5000
Web: WWW.NASHVILLE.GOV

HISTORICAL FINANCIALS
Company Type: Private

Income Statement				FYE: June 30
	REVENUE ($ mil.)	NET INCOME ($ mil.)	NET PROFIT MARGIN	EMPLOYEES
06/20	2,572	(315)	—	18,000
06/19	2,605	416	16.0%	—
06/18	2,462	(517)	—	—
06/17	2,367	130	5.5%	—
Annual Growth	2.8%	—	—	—

2020 Year-End Financials

Return on assets: (-1.9%)   Cash ($ mil.): 1,646
Return on equity: (-101.8%)
Current ratio: —

METROPOLITAN TRANSPORTATION AUTHORITY

Metropolitan Transportation Authority (MTA) is North America's largest transportation network serving a population of 15.3 million people across a 5000-square-mile travel area surrounding New York City through Long Island southeastern New York State and Connecticut. The MTA network comprises the nation's largest bus fleet and more subway and commuter rail cars than all other US transit systems combined. The MTA's operating agencies are MTA New York City Transit MTA Bus Long Island Rail Road Metro-North Railroad and MTA Bridges and Tunnels.

HISTORY

Mass transit began in New York City in the 1820s with the introduction of horse-drawn stagecoaches run by small private firms. By 1832 a horse-drawn railcar operating on Fourth Avenue offered a smoother and faster ride than its streetbound rivals.

By 1864 residents were complaining that horsecars and buses were overcrowded and that drivers were rude. (Horsecars were transporting 45 million passengers annually.) In 1870 a short subway under Broadway was opened but it remained a mere amusement. Elevated steam railways were built but people avoided them because of the smoke noise and danger from explosions. Cable cars arrived in the 1880s and by the 1890s electric streetcars had emerged.

Construction of the first commercial subway line was completed in 1904. The line was operated by Interborough Rapid Transit (IRT) which leased the primary elevated rail line in 1903 and had effective control of rail transit in Manhattan and the Bronx. In 1905 IRT merged with the Metropolitan Street Railway which ran most of the surface railways in Manhattan giving the firm almost complete control of the city's rapid transit. Public protests led the city to grant licenses to Brooklyn Rapid Transit (later BMT) creating the Dual System. The two rail firms covered most of the city.

By the 1920s the transit system was again in crisis largely because the two lines were not allowed to raise their five-cent fares. With the IRT and BMT in receivership in 1932 the city decided to own and operate part of the rail system and organized the Independent (IND) rail line. Pressure for public ownership and operation of the transit system resulted in the city's purchase of all of IRT's and BMT's assets in 1940 for $326 million.

In 1953 the legislature created the New York City Transit Authority the first unified system. In 1968 two years after striking transit workers left the city in a virtual gridlock the Metropolitan Transit Authority began to coordinate the city's transit activities with other commuter services.

The 1970s and 1980s saw the city's transit infrastructure and service deteriorate as crime accidents and fares rose. But by the early 1990s a modernization program had begun to make im-

provements: Subway stations were repaired graffiti was removed from trains and service was extended. By 1994 the agency said subway crime was down 50% from 1990 and ridership had increased.

The MTA set up a five-year plan in 1995 to cut expenses by $3 billion. Only 18 months later and already two-thirds of the way to reaching the goal the authority said it would cut another $230 million and return the savings to customers as fare discounts. The agency agreed in 1996 to sell Long Island Rail Road's freight operations. The next year it began selling its one-fare/free-transfer Metro-Card Gold.

In 1998 the MTA capital program completed the $200 million restoration of the Grand Central Terminal. The next year the MTA ordered 500 new clean-fuel buses. But the agency suffered a setback when New York State's $3.8 billion Transportation Infrastructure Bond Act which included $1.6 billion for MTA improvements was rejected by voters in 2000.

MTA subway lines in lower Manhattan suffered extensive damage from the September 11 2001 terrorist attacks that destroyed the World Trade Center's twin towers. The attacks left the MTA which was already seeking billions of dollars for improvements faced with $530 million worth of damage.

Confronted with a budget gap for the 2003 fiscal year the MTA authorized the sale of nearly $2.9 billion worth of transportation bonds the largest bond issue in the agency's history. The MTA had hoped the eventual proceeds from the bonds would help stave off a fare increase but in 2003 the agency raised subway and bus fares from $1.50 to $2 among other fare and toll increases.

Angered by issues involving wage hikes health care retirement age and pension costs members of the Transportation Workers Union walked off the job mere days before Christmas in 2005. The strike stranded commuters and stymied New Yorkers eager to shop and celebrate during the holiday season. The strike was estimated to cause a loss of $300 million per day to the city. In the face of heavy fines possible jail terms and the growing ire of would-be commuters the 33000 striking union members agreed to go back to work without a contract after three days of picketing and negotiations resumed. The Metropolitan Transportation Authority and the transit union later reached a contract agreement in which workers pay a portion of their health care costs.

In May 2009 the New York Legislature passed a $2.3 billion bailout package for the MTA which outlines fare increases of 10% in 2009 and 7.5% in 2011 and 2013. The bailout also requires management changes including combining the agency's chairman and CEO positions. Within days after the bailout was passed CEO Elliot Sander stepped down and was replaced on an interim basis by Long Island Rail Road President Helena Williams. New York Governor David Paterson picked Jay Walder a former executive with the London transit system and MTA's former CFO to succeed Sander and Chairman H. Dale Hemmerdinger. Walder was confirmed by the New York Senate in September 2009.

After five years of working toward bringing in cash by selling naming rights the MTA made a $4 million deal with Barclays in June 2009 to have the British bank's moniker added to the Atlantic Avenue-Pacific Street subway station in Brooklyn. The MTA also hopes to sell naming rights on its bus lines bridges and tunnels and to expand other corporate sponsorship and advertising opportunities. In 2008 the agency reached a $1 billion deal with Related Companies for the rights to build a 26-acre office and apartment complex above railyards on Manhattan's West Side but the deal's

closing was pushed back to 2010 due to the financial slump. The MTA also sold an eight-acre plot above the Long Island Rail Road's Brooklyn railyard for $100 million to Forest City Ratner.

EXECUTIVES

Chm, Joseph J Lhota
Pres*, Patrick Foye
Interim Executive Director*, Veronique Hakim
Acting Chairman*, Fernando Ferrer
Chief of Staff*, Zeb Voss
Cfo*, Jaibala Patel
Cao*, Quemuel Arroyo
AIA Fciob Senior Vice Presiden, Virginia Borkoski
Capital Planning Analyst, Adam Hartke
Manager, April Wang
Information Technology, Edward Eberling
Auditors: DELOITTE TOUCHE LLP NEW YOR

LOCATIONS

HQ: METROPOLITAN TRANSPORTATION AUTHORITY
2 BROADWAY, NEW YORK, NY 100042207
Phone: 212 878-7000
Web: WWW.NEW.MTA.INFO

PRODUCTS/OPERATIONS

Selected Operations

Bus
Long Island Bus
MTA Bus Company
New York City Transit
Commuter Rail
Long Island Rail Road
Metro-North Railroad
Staten Island Railway

HISTORICAL FINANCIALS

Company Type: Private

Income Statement				FYE: December 31
	REVENUE ($ mil.)	NET INCOME ($ mil.)	NET PROFIT MARGIN	EMPLOYEES
12/20	4,728	532	11.3%	67,457
12/19	9,043	498	5.5%	—
12/18	8,736	(145)	—	—
12/17	8	(0)	.	—
Annual Growth	716.9%	—	—	—

2020 Year-End Financials

Return on assets: 0.5%   Cash ($ mil.): 782
Return on equity: 10.7%
Current ratio: 1.60

METROPOLITAN WATER RECLAMATION DISTRICT OF GREATER CHICAGO

EXECUTIVES

Exec Dir, Brian Perkovich
V Pres, Kathleen Meany
Chief of Mno, Thomas O Conner
Principal, Jeff Weber
Actng Public Info Coordinat, Mary Carroll
Accounting Staff, Marilyn Torres
Scientist, Weizhe An

Executive Officer, Joe Cannici
Scientist, Ali Oskouie
Program Inspector, Dwayne Logan
Office Support Speci, Jennie Harrell
Auditors: RSM US LLP CHICAGO IL

LOCATIONS

HQ: METROPOLITAN WATER RECLAMATION
DISTRICT OF GREATER CHICAGO
100 E ERIE ST, CHICAGO, IL 606112829
Phone: 312 751-5600
Web: WWW.MWRD.ORG

HISTORICAL FINANCIALS
Company Type: Private

Income Statement			FYE: December 31	
	REVENUE ($ mil.)	NET INCOME ($ mil.)	NET PROFIT MARGIN	EMPLOYEES
12/20	782	88	11.4%	2,259
12/19	792	116	14.7%	—
12/18	755	107	14.2%	—
12/17	719	76	10.6%	—
Annual Growth	2.8%	5.1%	—	—

2020 Year-End Financials
Return on assets: 0.9%   Cash ($ mil.): 143
Return on equity: 1.8%
Current ratio: —

MFA INCORPORATED

Agricultural cooperative MFA brings together 45000 farmers in Missouri and adjacent states. It is a primary manufacturer of livestock feed holding a major market share within its trade territory. It is also a supplier and marketer of plant food and crop protection products. The co-op also provides its members with animal feeds animal-health products and farm supplies. The company's about 105 company-owned MFA Agri Services Centers combined with nearly 25 locally owned MFA affiliates and approximately 400 independent dealers. The company was founded in 1914.

Operations
MFA's services include credit and finance crop insurance health track powercalf precision agronomy among others. MFA's Animal Health division provides its retail operations a good mix of over-the-counter (OTC) labeled medications and vaccines along with the staff at the dealer locations. The crop protection division sells roughly 850 products from over 40 different vendors to meet the demand of producers. This division's products include but are not limited to pesticides - row crops aquatic range/pasture stored grain vineyards and lawn/garden foliar nutrition fertilizer stabilizers adjuvants and seed treatments and biological. Other product offerings include equine farm supply feed lawn and garden and pets among others.

With the combination of its core business subsidiaries and joint ventures the company delivers sales of about one billion dollars annually.

Geographic Reach
The company's corporate office is located in Columbia Missouri. The coop has fertilizer terminals on the Mississippi River as well as on the Missouri and Arkansas rivers.

Sales and Marketing
The coop sells through 400 independent dealers. MFA offers the best products and state-of-the-art services through its MFA Agri Services affiliates and partners. MFA also offers timely wholesale products to agricultural companies.

Company Background
Expanding its assets in 2013 MFA acquired Producers Grain Company's assets in El Dorado Springs Walker Bronaugh and Nevada in Missouri.

The co-op was established in 1914 when seven Missouri farmers got together to buy binder twine.

EXECUTIVES

Ceo, Ernie Verslues
Sr V Pres*, Janice Schuerman
V Pres*, J Brian Griffith
V Pres*, Craig Childs
V Pres*, Alan Wessler
V Pres*, Bill Coen
V Pres Livestock Oprs, Dr Kent Haden
Sales Manager, Teresa Carlson
Sales Manager, Dj Vollrath
Staff, Dale Leeper
Second Vice President Finance, David Moore
Auditors: WILLIAMS KEEPERS LLC JEFFERS

LOCATIONS

HQ: MFA INCORPORATED
201 RAY YOUNG DR, COLUMBIA, MO 652013599
Phone: 573 874-5111
Web: WWW.MFA-INC.COM

COMPETITORS

Adm	Growmark
Andersons	Heartland Co-op
Cargill	Missouri Farm Bureau
Farm Service Cooperative	Orscheln Farm And Home
Farmers Cooperative Company	Tennessee Farmers Co-op
	United Producers

HISTORICAL FINANCIALS
Company Type: Private

Income Statement			FYE: August 31	
	REVENUE ($ mil.)	NET INCOME ($ mil.)	NET PROFIT MARGIN	EMPLOYEES
08/18	1,367	6	0.5%	1,393
08/17	1,373	14	1.0%	—
08/16	1,192	4	0.3%	—
Annual Growth	7.1%	30.1%	—	—

MFA OIL COMPANY

Many farmers appreciate MFA Oil. The energy cooperative controlled by its 40000 farmer-members produces fuel and lubrication products and manages bulk petroleum and propane plants in the Central and Western US. Operating 140 propane plants the company sells more propane for farm use and home heating than any other company in Missouri. It also operates nearly 100 oil and lubricant bulk plants and serves customers in Arkansas Iowa Kansas and Oklahoma. Additionally the company operates 76 convenience stores under the Break Time brand (in Arkansas and Missouri) more than 160 Petro-Card 24 fueling locations and owns 10 Jiffy Lube and a dozen Big O Tire franchises.

Geographic Reach
MFA Oil serves customers in Arkansas Colorado Kansas Kentucky Indiana Iowa Missouri Nebraska Oklahoma Virginia and Wyoming.

Strategy
While not a pure vertically integrated enterprise over time the cooperative has developed multiple complementary business lines to enable it to respond to a wide range of its members' fuel transportation and food service needs. In this tradition in 2011 MFA Oil teamed up with biofuel developer Aloterra Energy to form MFA Oil Biomass LLC. The partnership aims to help farmers to produce a renewable energy crop that can be used as biomass for an alternative cleaner burning energy supply for use in power generation plants as well as a liquid fuel. In 2011 about 250 farmers had signed letters of intent to grow miscanthus (a perennial grass) on more than 21000 acres as part of this initiative.

Mergers and Acquisitions
Expanding its geographic network in 2013 MFA Oil acquired Kansas-based American Petroleum Marketers which distributes fuel to more than 60 Cenex branded sites along with unbranded fuel in six states.

Company Background
MFA Oil has grown well beyond its Missouri roots where it was founded by farmers in 1929. The company's first bulk plant was located at Wright City Missouri.

EXECUTIVES

Int Ceo, Jon Ihler
Chb, Benny Farrell
SEC, Beverly Twellman
Cfo, Robert Condron
Accounts Receivable, Kari Evans
Human Resources Assistant, Beth Bartlett
Accounts Payable Manager, Ashley McVay
Senior Vice President of Retai, Curtis Chaney
Employee Health, Dan Creek
Vice President of Supply, James Greer
Cfo, Jeff Raetz
Auditors: WILLIAMS-KEEPERS LLC COLUMBIA

LOCATIONS

HQ: MFA OIL COMPANY
1 RAY YOUNG DR, COLUMBIA, MO 652013506
Phone: 573 442-0171
Web: WWW.MFAOIL.COM

COMPETITORS

Ag Processing Inc.	Lykins
Green Brick Partners	Shell Oil Products
Green Plains	Valero Energy
Jordan Oil Company	Wilcohess

HISTORICAL FINANCIALS
Company Type: Private

Income Statement			FYE: August 31	
	REVENUE ($ mil.)	NET INCOME ($ mil.)	NET PROFIT MARGIN	EMPLOYEES
08/17	900	8	0.9%	1,500
08/16	800	24	3.1%	—
08/15	1,045	48	4.6%	—
Annual Growth	(7.2%)	(58.4%)	—	—

2017 Year-End Financials
Return on assets: 2.1%   Cash ($ mil.): 22
Return on equity: 2.7%
Current ratio: 2.20

MHM SUPPORT SERVICES

EXECUTIVES

Ceo, Lynn Britton
Auditors: ERNST & YOUNG US LLP CLAYTON

LOCATIONS

HQ: MHM SUPPORT SERVICES
  14528 SOUTH OUTER 40 RD # 100, CHESTERFIELD,
  MO 630175785
Phone: 314 628-3513

HISTORICAL FINANCIALS

Company Type: Private

Income Statement   FYE: June 30

	REVENUE ($ mil.)	NET INCOME ($ mil.)	NET PROFIT MARGIN	EMPLOYEES
06/20	1,018	(86)	—	44,000
06/18	867	0	0.1%	
06/10	326	(39)	—	
Annual Growth	12.0%	—	—	—

2020 Year-End Financials

Return on assets: (-10.1%)   Cash ($ mil.): 136
Return on equity: —
Current ratio: —

MIAMI CHILDREN'S HEALTH SYSTEM MANAGEMENT SERVICES, LLC

EXECUTIVES

Chm, Mario Morgado
Chair Board of Directors, Mario Murgado
V Chm, Michael Fux
Treas-SEC, Tim Birkenstock
Svp-Gen Coun, Jodi B Laurence
Cfo, Arianna Urquia

LOCATIONS

HQ: MIAMI CHILDREN'S HEALTH SYSTEM
  MANAGEMENT SERVICES, LLC
  3100 SW 62ND AVE, MIAMI, FL 331553009
Phone: 305 666-6511
Web: WWW.NICKLAUSCHILDRENS.ORG

HISTORICAL FINANCIALS

Company Type: Private

Income Statement   FYE: December 31

	REVENUE ($ mil.)	NET INCOME ($ mil.)	NET PROFIT MARGIN	EMPLOYEES
12/19	754	(38)	—	22
12/16	688	72	10.5%	—
Annual Growth	3.1%	—	—	—

2019 Year-End Financials

Return on assets: (-2.9%)   Cash ($ mil.): 153
Return on equity: (-5.8%)
Current ratio: 1.90

MIAMI UNIVERSITY

Not that Miami the other one. Named for the Miami Indian Tribe that inhabited the area now known as the Miami Valley Region of Ohio Miami University emphasizes undergraduate study at its main campus in Oxford (35 miles north of Cincinnati) as well as at commuter campuses in Hamilton Middletown and West Chester Ohio and a European Center in Luxembourg. The school offers bachelors masters and doctoral programs in areas including business administration arts and sciences engineering and education. Its student body includes more than 15000 undergraduates on the Oxford campus; 2500 graduate students; and another 5700 students attending satellite campuses. Miami University was established in 1809.

Financial Performance

Miami University's 2011 revenue increased 3% vs. 2010 due to a corresponding increase in undergraduate tuition on its three campuses and a rising rates for room and board. Net income at the public university rose 25% over the same period on higher revenue and lower operating expenses due primarily to a reduction in the number of positions and no salary increases. The rise in tuition for Ohio residents in 2011 was the first in four years. Also investment income rose in 2011 for the second consecutive year.

Company Background

Miami University celebrated its bicentennial in 2009. The school was chartered in February of 1809 by the State of Ohio but the first classses were not held until 1824.

EXECUTIVES

Pres, David Hodge
Dean, School of Engineering An, Marek Doll R
Accounting Staff, Lindsay Hubbard
Assistant Professor, M D Stoel
Accounting Staff, Jeanne L Kolb
Chief Information Security Off, Richard Knowles
Manager, Michael W Dale
Instructor, Michael R Hieber
Program Associate Vice Preside, Agnes A Shea
Professor, Sara L Butler
Assistant Vice President Enter, Troy Travis
Auditors: MCGLADREY LLP CLEVELAND OHIO

LOCATIONS

HQ: MIAMI UNIVERSITY
  501 E HIGH ST, OXFORD, OH 450561846
Phone: 513 529-1809
Web: WWW.MIAMIOH.EDU

HISTORICAL FINANCIALS

Company Type: Private

Income Statement   FYE: June 30

	REVENUE ($ mil.)	NET INCOME ($ mil.)	NET PROFIT MARGIN	EMPLOYEES
06/18	551	184	33.5%	4,925
06/17	544	83	15.4%	—
06/16	522	65	12.5%	—
06/12	440	32	7.5%	—
Annual Growth	3.8%	33.3%	—	—

2018 Year-End Financials

Return on assets: 7.7%   Cash ($ mil.): 85
Return on equity: 15.7%
Current ratio: 6.20

MIAMI VALLEY HOSPITAL

Don't go to Florida looking for this hospital! Miami Valley Hospital (MVH) is an acute care facility serving the residents of Dayton Ohio and surrounding areas through two campuses. MVH and MVH South have roughly 950 beds and offer 50 primary and specialty care practices through its Regional Adult Burn Center the MVH Cancer Center MVH Sports Medicine Center and behavioral health units for outpatient and inpatient chemical dependency therapy and other psychiatric services. MVH also offers Level I trauma services Level III-B NICU adult burn center an air ambulance program and blood marrow and kidney transplant services. The hospital is part of the Premier Health Partners network.

Operations

In addition to MVH the Premier Health Partners network consists of Good Samaritan Hospital (also stationed in Dayton Ohio) Atrium Medical Center in nearby Middletown and Upper Valley Medical Center in Troy. Collectively the multi-hospital health system houses about 1800 inpatient beds and around 65 facilities.

MVH have more than 1100 physicians in more than 70 primary and specialty medical practice areas. It was a 2012 recipient of the HealthGrades Distinguished Hospital Award for Clinical Excellence placing it among the top 5% of hospitals in the US.

In 2012 it had 41555 inpatient admissions; 164140 outpatient visits; 125622 emergency department visits; and oversaw 4000 births.

Financial Performance

Medicare accounted for 40% of the company's 2012 revenues; Medicaid 20%.

Strategy

Over the past few years MVH has focused on upgrading its infrastructure. It has built a $135 million 440000-sq. ft. 11-story heart tower on the south side of the campus and spent $19 million on renovating and expanding its neonatal intensive care unit.

In 2013 it opened its new $6 million 24-hour Emergency Center in Jamestown Ohio to meet the growing demand for emergency care.

In 2013 MVH South opened a $20 million Comprehensive Cancer Center and (in 2012) a new maternity center which includes five labor and delivery suites two surgical suites for c-section deliveries and 16 private after-birthing suites.

Company Background

MVH was formed in 1890.

EXECUTIVES

Pres-Ceo, Jenny M Lewis
Pres*, Mark Shaker
V Pres*, Makkie Clancy
Cfo*, Lisa Bishop
V Pres-Coo*, Barbara Johnson
Health Professional, Jon D Girard
Human Resources, Gretchen Long MBA
Coordinator, Melissa Brook
Obstetrician Gynecologist, Janice Duke
Facilities Technician, Jeremy Greth
Laboratory Director, Lisa Berger

LOCATIONS

HQ: MIAMI VALLEY HOSPITAL
 1 WYOMING ST, DAYTON, OH 454092711
Phone: 937 208-8000
Web: WWW.PREMIERHEALTH.COM

PRODUCTS/OPERATIONS

Campus Locations
Miami Valley Hospital - Dayton OH
Miami Valley Hospital South - Centerville Ohio

Selected Services and Specialties
Ablation (Cardiology)
Access and Transfer Center (physicians)
Alcoholism Drug Dependency and Addiction Treatment
Aneurysm (Neurosciences)
Ankle Surgery
Arterial Interventions
Audiology
Bariatrics/Weight Loss Surgery
Behavioral Services
Biotherapy/Targeted Therapy
Blood and Marrow Transplant Program
Brachytherapy
Brain Conditions and Treatments
Brain Injury Rehabilitation
Breast Cancer Navigators
Breast Center
Breast Center
Brethen Center for Surgical Advancement (physicians)
Bull Family Diabetes Center
Burn Center
Cancer Care
Cancer Care (Oncology)
Cardiac Electrophysiology Lab
Cardiac Rehabilitation
Cardiology
Cardiology
Cardiothoracic Surgery
CareFlight - Medical Transportation
Catheterization Lab Procedures
Center for Sleep and Wake Disorders
Chemoembolization
Chemotherapy and Infusion Therapy
Childbirth Education
Colon Cancer
Colorectal Cancer
Complementary Medicine (Cancer)
Comprehensive Outpatient Rehab Program (CORP)
Counseling/Pastoral Care
Craniectomy (Neuroscience)
Craniotomy (Neuroscience)
Cryoablation
CT scan (Imaging)
Dental Center
Depression/Anxiety Treatment
Diabetes
Dialysis Services
Discectomy
Drug Addiction Treatment
Elder Care
Emergency & Trauma Center (ETC)
Foot Surgery
Fractures (Athletes)
Fusion (spinal treatment)
Gastric Bypass
Genetic Testing
Gynecologic Cancer
Gynecology
Hand Therapy
Head and Neck Cancer
Heart Care
Heart Surgery
High Risk Breast Cancer Center
Hip Surgery
Hormone Therapy
Hospitalists/Medical Professionals
Hyperbaric Oxygen Therapy Center
Image Guided Radiation Therapy (IGRT)
Injury Prevention Center
Inpatient Rehabilitation
Intensity Modulated Radiation Therapy (IMRT)
Intensive Care Unit (ICU)
Interventional Radiology
Joint replacements
Kidney Transplant
Knee Surgery
Kyphoplasty
Leukemia

Lung Cancer
Lymphoma
Mammography Screenings
Maternal-Fetal Medicine
Maternity
Maternity
Medical Professionals/Hospitalists
Medical Transportation - CareFlight
Mental Health Services
Minimally Invasive Surgery
Mother and Baby Services
MRI (Imaging)
Nanoknife
Neonatal Intensive Care
Neuro Rehabilitation
NeuroInterventional Center
Neuroscience
Neurosciences
Nutrition Services
OB-GYN
Obstetrics
Occupational Rehabilitation
Occupational Therapy
Oncology
Organ Transplant
Orthopedics
Orthopedics
Outpatient Physical Therapy
Pain Management
Palliative Care
Pancreatic Cancer
Perinatal Intensive Care
PET Scan (Imaging)
Pharmacy
Physiatry
Physical Therapy
Pre-Admission Testing
Premier HeartWorks
Preventive Cardiology
Prostate Cancer
Pulmonary Services
Radiofrequency ablation
Radiology
Radionuclide scan
Rehabilitation
Rehabilitation Institute of Ohio
Respiratory Care
Robotic Surgery
Shoulder Surgery
Shunt (Neuroscience)
Skin Cancer
Sleep Center
Solitaire Revascularization Device (Neurosciences)
Speech-Language Pathology
Spinal decompression surgery
Spinal disc replacement
Spinal fracture treatment
Spinal tumor surgery
Spine and back injuries (Orthopedics)
Spine Conditions and Treatments (Neuroscience)
Sports Medicine
Sports Medicine
Stereotaxis
Stomach Cancer
Stroke Treatments
Surgery Center
Surgical Oncology
Thoracic Surgery
Throat Cancer
Trauma
Ultrasound (Imaging)
Urological Cancer
Urology
Vascular Services
Venous Interventions
Vertebroplasty
Weight Loss Surgery (Bariatrics)
Weight Loss Surgery/Bariatrics
Wheelchair Clinic
Women's Health
Women's Heart Services
Women's Services
Wound Therapy
X-rays (Imaging)
Y-90 Radioembolization

COMPETITORS

Cincinnati Children's Hospital	Ohiohealth
Deaconess Associations	The Christ Hospital Corporation

Encompass Health	Trihealth
Good Samaritan Hospital (in)	Uc Health
Kettering Health Network	

HISTORICAL FINANCIALS
Company Type: Private

Income Statement				FYE: December 31
	REVENUE ($ mil.)	NET INCOME ($ mil.)	NET PROFIT MARGIN	EMPLOYEES
12/16	809	35	4.4%	8,403
12/15	827	37	4.5%	—
12/14	785	37	4.8%	—
12/07	622	44	7.1%	—
Annual Growth	3.0%	(2.3%)	—	—

2016 Year-End Financials
Return on assets: 2.3%   Cash ($ mil.): 42
Return on equity: 5.2%
Current ratio: 10.00

MIAMI-DADE AVIATION DEPARTMENT

EXECUTIVES

Aviation Dir-Ceo, Lester Sola
Deputy Dir, Ken Pyatt
Chief of Staff, Arlyn Rull
Cfo, Sergio San Miguel
Senior Executive Assistant, Patricia Hernandez
Terminal Operations Agent, Alexandra Diaz-Zablah
Executive Secretary, Tc Cherenek
Supervisor, Alina Exposito
Capital Improvements Manager, Ana Finol
Assistant Aviation Director, Barbara Jimenez
Customer Supervisor, Diana Berron
Auditors: CHERRY BEKAERT TAMPA FLORIDA

LOCATIONS

HQ: MIAMI-DADE AVIATION DEPARTMENT
 13344 SW 108TH STREET CIR, MIAMI, FL 331863424
Phone: 305 876-7000
Web: WWW.AIAMIAMI.ORG

HISTORICAL FINANCIALS
Company Type: Private

Income Statement				FYE: September 30
	REVENUE ($ mil.)	NET INCOME ($ mil.)	NET PROFIT MARGIN	EMPLOYEES
09/16	830	(29)	—	40
09/15	794	(15)	—	—
Annual Growth	4.6%	—	—	—

2016 Year-End Financials
Return on assets: (-0.4%)   Cash ($ mil.): 171
Return on equity: (-3.1%)
Current ratio: 2.00

MICHIGAN MILK PRODUCERS ASSOCIATION

Ice cream and other dairy products might be missing a major ingredient without Michigan Milk Producers Association (MMPA). The dairy cooperative which serves more than 2100 farmers in Michigan Ohio Indiana and Wisconsin produces some 3.9 billion pounds of milk each year. Milk products include sweetened condensed milk instant nonfat milk and dried buttermilk as well as other items the likes of cream cheese butter and ice-cream mixes. With no consumer brands or products MMPA sells its products as ingredients to food makers who sell baby formulas candy ice cream and yogurt. Founded in 1916 the co-op operates a pair of Michigan plants and a merchandise facility.

Operations

As part of its business of serving member-farmers MMPA provides them with product quality incentives testing and customized blending as well as protection against loss from disaster.

Geographic Reach

From its headquarters in Novi Michigan MMPA operates solely in the state of Michigan where it has manufacturing plants in the villages of Ovid and Constantine and a merchandise facility in the Michigan city of Saint Louis. Its farmers are located in Michigan Ohio Indiana and Wisconsin.

EXECUTIVES

Ceo-SEC, John Dilland
Pres*, Kenneth Nobis
Treas*, C Velmar Green
Asst Treas*, Clayton Galarneau
V Pres*, Bob Kran
Director of Credit, Cheryl Schmandt
Director of Management Informa, Andrew Caldwell
Plant Manager, Colt Johnson
Senior Director of Sales, Jim Feeney
Director of Manufacturing, Kaylan Kennel
Office Coordinator, Karen Elmore
Auditors: CLIFTONLARSONALLEN LLP

LOCATIONS

HQ: MICHIGAN MILK PRODUCERS ASSOCIATION
41310 BRIDGE ST, NOVI, MI 483751302
Phone: 248 474-6672
Web: WWW.MIMILK.COM

PRODUCTS/OPERATIONS

Selected Products
Condensed skim milk
Condensed whole milk
Dried buttermilk
Dried whole milk
Ice cream mixes
Instant nonfat dry milk
Nonfat dry milk
Standardized cream
Standardized milk
Sweet condensed milk
Sweet cream butter

COMPETITORS

Associated Milk
  Producers
Dairy Farmers Of
  America
Dean Foods
Foremost Farms

Land O'lakes
Main Street
  Ingredients
Quality Chekd
Saputo

HISTORICAL FINANCIALS

Company Type: Private

Income Statement · FYE: September 30

	REVENUE ($ mil.)	NET INCOME ($ mil.)	NET PROFIT MARGIN	EMPLOYEES
09/11	870	6	0.7%	200
09/10	698	6	1.0%	—
09/09	556	6	1.1%	—
Annual Growth	25.1%	3.2%	—	—

2011 Year-End Financials

Return on assets: 3.8%
Return on equity: 13.4%
Current ratio: 1.50

Cash ($ mil.): 5

MICHIGAN STATE UNIVERSITY

Founded in 1855 Michigan State University (MSU) was the model of a land-grant institution made into law in 1862. MSU and its nearly 49700 students cover a lot of land in East Lansing. The university offers more than 200 programs of study through more than 15 colleges and unrivaled opportunities for undergraduate research. It has extensive programs in core fields including education physics psychology medicine and communications. It is also a leading research university with top-ranked international studies programs. As a highly ranked research university MSU is awarded millions of dollars in research grants each year from public and private entities.

Operations

Michigan State University has more than 100 active research centers and institutes on campus as well as field research sites throughout the state of Michigan. Most are interdisciplinary and several are joint initiatives between Michigan State University and other universities around the world.

With more than 5700 faculty and academic staff members and a student-teacher ratio of about 16:1 MSU is noted by US. News & World Report for its programs in graduate-level elementary and secondary education nuclear physics and industrial and organizational psychology. Its more than 200 undergraduate masters doctoral and certificate programs include accounting biomedical engineering communication finance and educational technology (online program).

Geographic Reach

MSU's 5300-acre main campus is in East Lansing three miles east of Lansing (the capital city of Michigan).

MSU's students hail from all 50 US states as well as 130 other countries. MSU also offers an extensive study abroad program which includes 275 programs in 60 different countries and all seven continents.

Company Background

MSU was founded in 1855 a forerunner of the land-grant college concept under the name Agricultural College of the State of Michigan. The Morrill Act which codified land-grant institutions became law in 1862. MSU became a full university in 1955 as Michigan State University of Agriculture and Applied Science. It changed its name to Michigan State University in 1964.

EXECUTIVES

Chm, Joel I Ferguson

Vice Chm*, Mitch Lyons
Pres*, Samuel Stanley Jr
Int Pres*, Satish Udpa
Svp-CIO*, Melissa Woo
Int Provost-Evp Academic Aff*, Teresa A Sullivan
Gen Counsel-Vp Legal Affairs*, Brian Quinn
Prin*, Shea Bryant
Assistant Professor, Kirill Vaninsky
Associate Professor, Laura J Fair
Assistant Professor, Lee D Ed Kyunghee
Auditors: PLANTE & MORAN PLLC EAST LAN

LOCATIONS

HQ: MICHIGAN STATE UNIVERSITY
426 AUDITORIUM RD, EAST LANSING, MI 488242600
Phone: 517 355-1855
Web: WWW.MSU.EDU

PRODUCTS/OPERATIONS

Selected Colleges and Divisions
College of Agriculture and Natural Resources
College of Arts and Letters
College of Communication Arts and Sciences
College of Education
College of Engineering
College of Human Medicine
College of Law (affiliated)
College of Music
College of Natural Science
College of Nursing
College of Osteopathic Medicine
College of Social Science
College of Veterinary Medicine
Eli Broad College of Business and Eli Broad Graduate School of Management
Honors College
James Madison College
Lyman Briggs College
Residential College in the Arts and Humanities
Undergraduate University Division

HISTORICAL FINANCIALS

Company Type: Private

Income Statement · FYE: June 30

	REVENUE ($ mil.)	NET INCOME ($ mil.)	NET PROFIT MARGIN	EMPLOYEES
06/18	1,986	(246)	—	11,100
06/17	1,931	481	25.0%	—
06/16	1,811	71	3.9%	—
Annual Growth	4.7%	—	—	—

2018 Year-End Financials

Return on assets: (-3.7%)
Return on equity: (-10.5%)
Current ratio: 0.50

Cash ($ mil.): 384

MID-AMERICA PIPELINE COMPANY, LLC

EXECUTIVES

Mng MBR-Pres, J M Collingsworth
MBR, W Randall Fowler
MBR-Sr V Pres, Michael J Knesek
MBR-Treas, Bryan F Bulawa
MBR-SEC, Raymond P Albrecht

LOCATIONS

HQ: MID-AMERICA PIPELINE COMPANY, LLC
1100 LA ST STE 1000, HOUSTON, TX 77002
Phone: 713 880-6500
Web: WWW.ENTERPRISEPRODUCTS.COM

HISTORICAL FINANCIALS
Company Type: Private

Income Statement				FYE: December 31
	REVENUE ($ mil.)	NET INCOME ($ mil.)	NET PROFIT MARGIN	EMPLOYEES
12/17	591	361	61.1%	250
12/16	591	366	62.0%	—
Annual Growth	0.0%	(1.4%)	—	—

MIDCOAST ENERGY PARTNERS, L.P.

Midcoast Energy Partners was formed by Enbridge Energy Partners in 2013 as an investment vehicle to own and grow its natural gas and NGL midstream business. It has minority stakes in Enbridge's network of natural gas and natural gas liquids (NGLs) gathering and transportation systems natural gas processing and treating facilities and NGL fractionation plants in Texas and Oklahoma. Organized as a limited partnership Midcoast Energy Partners is exempt from paying income tax as long as it distributes quarterly dividends to shareholders. It went public in 2013 raising $333 million. In 2017 Enbridge Energy Partners agreed to acquire control of Midcoast Energy Partners.

EXECUTIVES

Pres, Laura Sayavedra
Sr V Pres, Mark A Maki
L.L.C., Gen Ptnr, Midcoast Holdings
Vice President, Stephen J Neyland
Auditors: PRICEWATERHOUSECOOPERS LLP HO

LOCATIONS

HQ: MIDCOAST ENERGY PARTNERS, L.P.
1100 LA ST STE 3300, HOUSTON, TX 77002
Phone: 800 755-5400
Web: WWW.MIDCOASTENERGY.COM

COMPETITORS

Buckeye Partners	Oneok
Dcp Midstream Partners	Sunoco Logistics
Duke Energy	Transcanada
Koch Industries Inc.	Williams Companies
Magellan Midstream	
Martin Midstream Partners	

HISTORICAL FINANCIALS
Company Type: Private

Income Statement				FYE: December 31
	REVENUE ($ mil.)	NET INCOME ($ mil.)	NET PROFIT MARGIN	EMPLOYEES
12/16	1,966	(157)	—	1,250
12/15	2,842	(284)	—	—
12/14	5,894	144	2.4%	—
12/13	5,593	53	1.0%	—
Annual Growth	(29.4%)	—	—	—

2016 Year-End Financials	
Return on assets: (-3.2%)	Cash ($ mil.): 7
Return on equity: (-4.2%)	
Current ratio: 0.50	

MIDDLESEX, COUNTY OF (INC)

EXECUTIVES

Cnty Admin, John Pulomena
Deputy Director, Stephen J Dalina
Freeholder Director, David B Crabiel
County Clerk, Elaine Flynn
Treas, Jim Phillips
Internal Medicine Practitioner, Suzanne Kowalski
Secretary, Edward Testino
Coordinator, Louis Sasso
Sergeant, Paul Miller
Staff, Robert Jandernal
Director of Social Work Servic, Bridget Kennedy
Auditors: HODULIK & MORRISON PA CRANF

LOCATIONS

HQ: MIDDLESEX, COUNTY OF (INC)
75 BAYARD ST, NEW BRUNSWICK, NJ 089012112
Phone: 732 745-3000
Web: WWW.MIDDLESEXCOUNTYNJ.GOV

HISTORICAL FINANCIALS
Company Type: Private

Income Statement				FYE: December 31
	REVENUE ($ mil.)	NET INCOME ($ mil.)	NET PROFIT MARGIN	EMPLOYEES
12/20	689	18	2.7%	2,100
12/19	522	6	1.2%	—
12/17	497	9	2.0%	—
12/16	483	11	2.5%	—
Annual Growth	9.3%	11.6%	—	—

2020 Year-End Financials	
Return on assets: 1.1%	Cash ($ mil.): 122
Return on equity: 2.1%	
Current ratio: —	

MIDMICHIGAN MEDICAL CENTER-MIDLAND

EXECUTIVES

Pres, Currie Scott
V Pres*, Sandy Hermann
V Pres*, Greg Rogers
V Pres*, Francine Padgett
Cfo*, Scott Currie
Chief of Medicine, Jay C Hough
Chief Information Security Off, T Moore
Supervisor, Melissa Chambers
Microbiology Supervisor, Muriel Thurston
Director, Eric Thompson
Nurse Practitioner Urgent Care, Lindsey Elias
Auditors: ANDREWS HOOPER PAVLIK PLC SAG

LOCATIONS

HQ: MIDMICHIGAN MEDICAL CENTER-MIDLAND
4000 WELLNESS DR, MIDLAND, MI 486702000
Phone: 989 839-3000
Web: WWW.MIDMICHIGAN.ORG

HISTORICAL FINANCIALS
Company Type: Private

Income Statement				FYE: June 30
	REVENUE ($ mil.)	NET INCOME ($ mil.)	NET PROFIT MARGIN	EMPLOYEES
06/21	550	173	31.4%	1,404
06/20	519	41	8.0%	—
06/19	476	62	13.0%	—
06/18	427	37	8.7%	—
Annual Growth	8.8%	66.8%	—	—

2021 Year-End Financials	
Return on assets: 16.0%	Cash ($ mil.): 10
Return on equity: 23.3%	
Current ratio: 1.10	

MILES HEALTH CARE, INC

Miles Health Care provides acute and specialty health care service to the residents of Maine's Lincoln County. The not-for-profit company operates Miles Memorial Hospital — known as LincolnHealth Miles Campus — a rural medical center with about 40 beds and has emergency intensive care surgery and birthing departments. In addition Miles Health Care operates outpatient and specialty practice clinics physician practice offices and home health rehabilitation and hospice programs. It also provides long-term senior care through its nursing assisted and independent living facilities. Miles Health Care is a member of Lincoln County Healthcare (LincolnHealth) which is part of the MaineHealth network.

Operations

In addition to the two main hospital campuses LincolnHealth includes physician practices operated by the Lincoln Medical Partners as well as family care and urgent care centers. It also continues to operate nursing home health hospice and assisted-living organizations.

Geographic Reach

The LincolnHealth Miles Campus is located in Lincoln County Maine in the town of Damariscotta (which is north of Portland). The LincolnHealth St. Andrews Campus is located in Boothbay Harbor.

Strategy

Both the Miles and St. Andrews medical centers began using electronic health record (EHR) systems in 2010 which allows doctors to access a patient's past medical and diagnostic experiences to make the best decisions on current treatment plans and avoid duplication. Such EHR systems are part of an initiative to lower the cost of medical care in the US.

Company Background

Miles Health Care was established in 1941. Miles has historically been governed by a board of trustees (the Lincoln County Healthcare Board of Trustees) that also oversee the nearby St. Andrews Hospital; as an independently governed member of MaineHealth Miles has received planning consulting capital and group purchasing benefits. In

2013 St. Andrews Hospital and Miles Memorial Hospital were officially merged to serve as dual campuses of the single LincolnHealth hospital.

EXECUTIVES

Ceo, James Donavan
Administrative Assistant, Dave Phillips
Senior Vice President of Hospi, Cynthia Wade
Accounts Payable Manager, Kelley House
Manager His, Leslie Lindquist
Director Information, Brooks Betts
Physician Assistant, Frank Setchel
Business Office Manager, Gwen Waltz
Chief Officer, Linda S Durst
Vice President Physician Servi, Stacey Miller
Chief Nursing Officer, Jennifer Hunt

LOCATIONS

HQ: MILES HEALTH CARE, INC
35 MILES ST, DAMARISCOTTA, ME 045434047
Phone: 207 563-1234
Web: WWW.MAINEHEALTH.ORG

PRODUCTS/OPERATIONS

Selected Centers and Services
Chase Point Adult Day Services
Chase Point Assisted Living
Cove's Edge
Emergency Services
Family Support Services
General Surgery
Internal Medicine
Mammography
Miles & St. Andrews Home Health & Hospice
Miles Family Medicine
MMH BabyNet
Obstetrics
Orthopedic Services
Pediatric Services
Schooner Cove
Senior Services
Waldoboro Family Medicine
Wellness and Rehabilitation
Wiscasset Family Medicine
Women's Services

COMPETITORS

Eastern Maine
  Healthcare Systems
Mainegeneral Health

Mercy Health System Of
  Maine
St. Joseph Healthcare

HISTORICAL FINANCIALS
Company Type: Private

| Income Statement | | | FYE: September 30 | |
	REVENUE ($ mil.)	NET INCOME ($ mil.)	NET PROFIT MARGIN	EMPLOYEES
09/09	1,042	12	1.2%	800
09/08	14	0	3.9%	—
09/06	58	3	5.9%	—
09/05	52	(0)	—	—
Annual Growth	111.6%	—	—	—

2009 Year-End Financials

Return on assets: 112.3%
Return on equity: 494.4%
Current ratio: 1.30

Cash ($ mil.): —

MILLS-PENINSULA HEALTH SERVICES

With health facilities south of San Francisco Mills-Peninsula Health Services provides care to communities in and around Burlingame California. The not-for-profit health care group includes the 240-bed Mills-Peninsula Medical Center an acute-care hospital in Burlingame; Mills Health Center an outpatient diagnostic surgery and rehabilitation facility in San Mateo; and physician practice offices in surrounding areas. The facilities provide specialty services such as cancer care cardiovascular therapy behavioral health radiology respiratory care and senior services. Mills-Peninsula Health Services is part of the Sutter Health network.

Operations
Along with sister company Palo Alto Medical Foundation Mills-Peninsula forms the Peninsula Coastal Region division of Sutter Health. Together the organizations operate collaborative medical clinic and physician practice locations.

Geographic Reach
Mills-Peninsula Health Services operates facilities in Burlingame and San Mateo in California.

Financial Performance
Mills-Peninsula Health Services reported revenues of $611 million (7% of the parent company's net revenues) in 2013.
Its net income in 2013 was $53 million.

Strategy
Through the contribution of donors in 2014 the Mills-Peninsula Women's Center replaced all its digital mammography units with digital breast tomosynthesis allowing it to provide 3D mammography for breast cancer screenings at no extra cost to patients.
The hospital enhanced its surgical capabilities in 2013 with the addition of a da Vinci Si robotic system for surgical procedures.
That year Mills-Peninsula's Dorothy E. Schneider Cancer Center introduced a new cancer treatment Xofigo (Radium-223 dichloride) for patients with advanced-stage prostate cancer that has metastasized to the bones but not other organs.

Company Background
The organization opened the doors on its newly constructed Mills-Peninsula Medical Center in Burlingame in 2011. The $618 million project added a new 240-bed main hospital facility (to replace the aging Peninsula Medical Center facility) with all private patient rooms as well as a 180000 sq. ft. medical office building and a parking garage. The new hospital is compliant with California's new earthquake safety requirements.
The Peninsula facility was founded as a public hospital district in 1954. The two hospitals merged in 1985 and became part of Sutter Health the following year.
Founded in 1908 the Mills hospital was named for philanthropist Elizabeth Mills Reid who helped to fund the medical facility.

Auditors: ERNST & YOUNG US LLP SAN DIEG

LOCATIONS

HQ: MILLS-PENINSULA HEALTH SERVICES
1501 TROUSDALE DR, BURLINGAME, CA 940104506
Phone: 650 696-5400
Web: WWW.MILLS-PENINSULA.ORG

PRODUCTS/OPERATIONS

Selected Services
Arthritis & Osteoporosis
Behavioral Health
Birth Center
Cancer Center
Cardiovascular
Children's Services
Psychiatric Emergency
Senior Services
Obesity Surgery
Orthopedic Surgery
Women's Center

COMPETITORS

Alta Bates Summit
  Medical Center
California Pacific
  Medical Center
Dignity Health
Good Samaritan
  Hospital (san Jose)

John Muir Health
Marin General Hospital
Sequoia Healthcare
  District
The Palo Alto Medical
  Foundation
Ucsf Medical

HISTORICAL FINANCIALS
Company Type: Private

| Income Statement | | | | FYE: December 31 |
	REVENUE ($ mil.)	NET INCOME ($ mil.)	NET PROFIT MARGIN	EMPLOYEES
12/13	609	54	8.9%	2,200
12/09	533	56	10.6%	—
12/02	274	18	6.6%	—
12/01	398	0	0.0%	—
Annual Growth	3.6%	172.8%	—	—

2013 Year-End Financials

Return on assets: 12.6%
Return on equity: 8.9%
Current ratio: 0.10

Cash ($ mil.): 20

MILTON HERSHEY SCHOOL & SCHOOL TRUST

EXECUTIVES

Owner, Milton Hershey
Auditors: PRICEWATERHOUSECOOPERS LLP PH

LOCATIONS

HQ: MILTON HERSHEY SCHOOL & SCHOOL TRUST
711 CREST LN, HERSHEY, PA 170338903
Phone: 717 520-1100
Web: WWW.HERSHEYTRUST.COM

HISTORICAL FINANCIALS
Company Type: Private

| Income Statement | | | | FYE: July 31 |
	REVENUE ($ mil.)	NET INCOME ($ mil.)	NET PROFIT MARGIN	EMPLOYEES
07/18	1,069	784	73.4%	16
07/17	469	198	42.2%	—
07/12	386	180	46.7%	—
07/10	211	3	1.6%	—
Annual Growth	22.4%	97.8%	—	—

2018 Year-End Financials

Return on assets: 5.6%
Return on equity: 5.7%
Current ratio: —

Cash ($ mil.): 72

MILWAUKEE PUBLIC SCHOOLS (INC)

EXECUTIVES

Supt, Darienne Driver
Cfo*, Gerald Pace
Personnel Dir*, Daniel Chanen
Comptroller*, Lawanda Baldwin
Principal, Deborah Bell
Principal, Martha Wheeler-Fair
Principal, Jewell Riano
Principal, Daniel J Donder
Social Worker, Cathy Klein
Staff, Carmen M Rahming
Programmer, Steve Schnelz
Auditors: BAKER TILLY VIRCHOW KRAUSE LL

LOCATIONS

HQ: MILWAUKEE PUBLIC SCHOOLS (INC)
   5225 W VLIET ST, MILWAUKEE, WI 532082698
Phone: 414 475-8393
Web: WWW.MPS.MILWAUKEE.K12.WI.US

HISTORICAL FINANCIALS

Company Type: Private

Income Statement				FYE: June 30
	REVENUE ($ mil.)	NET INCOME ($ mil.)	NET PROFIT MARGIN	EMPLOYEES
06/19	1,199	(22)	—	14,154
06/18	1,196	2	0.2%	
06/17	1,182	9	0.8%	
06/16	1,178	(0)	—	
Annual Growth	0.6%	—	—	—

MINERS INCORPORATED

Miner's is a family-owned chain of about 30 grocery stores in Michigan North Dakota northern Minnesota and Wisconsin. Most of the company's stores fly the Super One Foods banner but there are a few under the U-Save Foods and Marketplace Foods names. Following the acquisition of seven Jubilee and Festival Foods stores in Minnesota from Plaza Holding Co. Miner's converted the stores to its Super One Foods banner most of which are located in Minnesota. Miner's also has a wholesale grocery operation in Duluth. Miner's was founded by Anton and Ida Miner who started out selling groceries out of their tavern in Grand Rapids Michigan in the 1930s. In 1943 they built the family's first store Miner's Market.

Geographic Reach

Minnesota is the regional grocery chain's largest market home to 21 of its 31 stores. Wisconsin and Michigan are each home to about five locations. The grocery chain has a single store North Dakota.

Financial Performance

Miner's rang up an estimated $437 million in sales in fiscal 2013 (ended June).

Strategy

Miner's takes a measured approach to growth combining occasional acquisitions with organic growth. Its newest location is a 59000-square-foot Super One Foods store slated to open in 2014 in Superior Wisconsin.

Mergers and Acquisitions

In May 2011 Miner's upped its store count with the acquisition of four family-owned Paulson's Super Valu grocery stores in northern Minnesota and Wisconsin.

Prevented by Minnesota law from selling alcohol in grocery stores the company recently bought two liquor stores in Cloquet and Duluth.

EXECUTIVES

Ceo-Pres, James A Miner Sr
Treas*, Theresa Lorentz
Information Specialist, Jason Kearney
Manager District, Michael Peterson
Director Loss Prevention, Mike Utecht
Information Technology Directo, Bill Rulla
Vice President Operations, Bob Halvorson
Manager, Don Olson
Merchandise Manager District, Roger Nordby
Buyer Delicatessen, Stephanie Licari
Manager, Tyree Johnson
Auditors: RSM US LLP DULUTH MINNESOTA

LOCATIONS

HQ: MINERS INCORPORATED
   5065 MILLER TRUNK HWY, HERMANTOWN, MN
   558111442
Phone: 218 729-5882
Web: WWW.SUPERONEFOODS.COM

2014 Stores

	No.
Minnesota	21
Michigan	5
Wisconsin	4
North Dakota	1
Total	**31**

PRODUCTS/OPERATIONS

2014 Stores

	No.
Super One Foods	27
U-Save Foods	2
Country Market	1
Marketplace Foods	1
Total	**31**

COMPETITORS

Cub Foods	Roundy's
Iga	Spartannash
Kroger	Target Corporation
Meijer	Wal-mart

HISTORICAL FINANCIALS

Company Type: Private

Income Statement				FYE: June 24
	REVENUE ($ mil.)	NET INCOME ($ mil.)	NET PROFIT MARGIN	EMPLOYEES
06/17	548	26	4.8%	2,300
06/12	501	31	6.3%	
06/11	475	30	6.4%	
06/10	463	27	5.8%	
Annual Growth	2.4%	(0.5%)	—	—

2017 Year-End Financials

Return on assets: 10.7%   Cash ($ mil.): 7
Return on equity: 15.4%
Current ratio: 1.80

MINNEAPOLIS PUBLIC SCHOOL DISTRICT

EXECUTIVES

Suptd, Michael Goar
Supt*, Bernadeia Johnson
Payroll Staff, Diane Woolridge
Occupational Specia, Laura Wilcox
Payroll Staff, Stacy Swain
Coordinator, Ben Mulhern
Research Assistant, Eric V Berk
Coordinator, Matthew Branch
Occupational Specia, Nancy Bradehoft
Information Specialist, Jeremiah Bohn
Coordinator, Max Athorn
Auditors: BERGAN KDV LTD MINNEAPOLIS

LOCATIONS

HQ: MINNEAPOLIS PUBLIC SCHOOL DISTRICT
   1250 W BROADWAY AVE, MINNEAPOLIS, MN
   554112533
Phone: 612 668-0200
Web: WWW.MPLS.K12.MN.US

HISTORICAL FINANCIALS

Company Type: Private

Income Statement				FYE: June 30
	REVENUE ($ mil.)	NET INCOME ($ mil.)	NET PROFIT MARGIN	EMPLOYEES
06/16	709	(25)	—	9,000
06/15	685	116	17.1%	
06/05	441	18	4.2%	
06/04	632	(42)	—	
Annual Growth	1.0%	—	—	—

MISSION HOSPITAL REGIONAL MEDICAL CENTER INC

EXECUTIVES

Ceo, Seth Peigen
Financial Executive, Kenn Mc Farland
Coordinator, Maryann Hubbard
Emergency Medicine, Kenneth Kwon
Gastroenterology, Habib Rahman
Cardiology, Michael Gault
Cardiovascular Disease, David T Kawanishi
Emergency Medicine, James Keany
MD, Lauren Dwinell
Vice President, Mark Jablonski
MD, Elwyn Rexinger
Auditors: ERNST & YOUNG US LLP SAN DIEG

LOCATIONS

HQ: MISSION HOSPITAL REGIONAL MEDICAL
   CENTER INC
   27700 MEDICAL CENTER RD, MISSION VIEJO, CA
   926916426
Phone: 949 364-1400
Web: WWW.MISSION4HEALTH.COM

	REVENUE ($ mil.)	NET INCOME ($ mil.)	NET PROFIT MARGIN	EMPLOYEES
				FYE: June 30
06/16	547	28	5.3%	2,600
06/15	516	23	4.5%	—
06/10	500	50	10.1%	—
06/09	355	12	3.5%	—
Annual Growth	6.4%	13.0%	—	—

2016 Year-End Financials

Return on assets: 4.9% Cash ($ mil.): 38
Return on equity: 10.5%
Current ratio: 1.40

MISSION HOSPITAL, INC.

Its mission is clear and bold: Improve the health of all in western North Carolina. Mission Hospital is a 760-bed regional referral center serving the western quarter of North Carolina and portions of adjoining states. A not-for-profit community hospital system Mission is located in Asheville on two adjoining campuses: Memorial and St. Joseph's. It provides tertiary-level services in neurosciences cardiac care trauma care surgery pediatric medicine and women's services and has a medical staff of more than 540. It also includes the Mission Children's Hospital. Mission Hospital is the flagship hospital of Mission Health System which is being acquired by HCA Healthcare for $1.5 billion.

Geographic Reach

Mission Health System serves patients in western North Carolina.

Sales and Marketing

Medicare accounts for some 40% of Mission Hospital's net patient service revenue; Medicaid account for around for 30% and self-pay and other third-party payors account for the rest.

Financial Performance

Revenue increased 6% to $119 million in 2014 on higher net patient service earnings. Those gains plus higher investment returns led to a 12% increase in net income to $1.2 million.

After posting an operating cash outflow in 2013 Mission Hospital had a cash inflow of $0.9 million in 2014 as less cash was used towards net patient accounts receivable.

Strategy

Mission Hospital has been actively expanding and modernizing its facilities in recent years. It built a surgery registration and waiting area to ease patient comfort as they wait to be seen at the Memorial Campus. It also opened a four-story facility to provide more surgery suites and patient beds for Mission Hospital. In order to increase patient satisfaction the hospital opened a new surgery registration and waiting area at its Memorial Campus.

Mission Hospital places great focus on genetic medicine. It has an entire department dedicated to the study of genetics genetic therapy and the study of fetal alcohol spectrum disorders.

Mission Health partnered with Western Carolina University to provide a graduate certification program in Healthcare Innovation Management. The program which began in 2013 is a component of Mission Health's budding Center for Innovation established to foster a spirit of advancement in healthcare throughout western North Carolina. The program consists of four courses over a period

of 21 months and is open to all Mission Health employees. Students who complete the program which is fully funded by Mission Health will earn credit towards bachelor's and master's degrees.

Company Background

Mission Hospital was formed in 1996 from the partnership (and eventual merger) of Memorial and St. Joseph's hospitals.

EXECUTIVES

Ceo, Chad Patrick
Pres*, Joseph Damore
Ceo*, Ronald A Paulus
Sr V Pres*, Charles F Ayscue
Human Resources Representative, Teresa McCarthy
Human Resources Representative, Dan McFatter
Chief Staff, Alan S Baumgarten
Allergy and Immunology, John Van Wye
Business Manager Senior, Cora McPherson
Hospitalist, Lisa Ryan

LOCATIONS

HQ: MISSION HOSPITAL, INC.
    509 BILTMORE AVE, ASHEVILLE, NC 288014601
Phone: 828 213-1111
Web: WWW.MISSIONHEALTH.ORG

PRODUCTS/OPERATIONS

Surgical Services
General Surgery
Minimally Invasive Surgery
Outpatient Surgery
Prepare for Surgery
Robotic Surgery
Surgery at Mission Hospital
Surgery Guide
Programs of Service
Endoscopy
Genetics
Integrative Healthcare
Mother and Baby
Outpatient Care Centers
Sleep Center
Urology
Weight Management Center
Wound Healing and Hyperbarics
Support Services
Chronic Medical Conditions
Long-Term Acute Care
Laboratory
Pastoral Care Services
Pharmacy
Psychiatric Services
Radiology (Imaging) Services
Rehabilitation Services
Research Institute
Respiratory Therapy
Senior Services and Geriatrics

COMPETITORS

Blue Ridge Healthcare
Caromont
Carolinas Healthcare System
Duke University Health System
Haywood Regional Presbyterian Healthcare
Unc Hospitals

HISTORICAL FINANCIALS
Company Type: Private

	REVENUE ($ mil.)	NET INCOME ($ mil.)	NET PROFIT MARGIN	EMPLOYEES
				FYE: September 30
09/15	1,019	91	9.0%	10,000
09/14	936	64	6.9%	—
09/13	942	71	7.6%	—
09/12	861	86	10.0%	—
Annual Growth	5.8%	2.0%	—	—

MISSISSIPPI STATE UNIVERSITY

While agriculture is at its roots Mississippi State University's (MSU) is today a four-year university offering approximately 150 undergraduate majors and pre-professional programs as well as master's educational specialist and doctorate degree programs at a dozen colleges and schools. It confers more than 4300 degrees annually and has an enrollment of more than 20870 students at its main campus in Starkville and a regional campus in Meridian. More than three-quarters of its student body hail from Mississippi. MSU was created by the Mississippi Legislature in 1878 as The Agricultural and Mechanical College of the State of Mississippi.

EXECUTIVES

Pres, Mark E Keenum
Evp-Provost*, David Shaw
Chro*, Nancy L Siegert
Executive Officer, Terry Kiser
Coordinator, Janice Pettus
Principal, Michael Murphy
Assistant Professor, Jun Liao
Coordinator, Anne Skinner
Scientist, Justin Thornton
Coordinator, Peter Hudson
Scientist, Walter Diehl III

LOCATIONS

HQ: MISSISSIPPI STATE UNIVERSITY
    245 BARR AVE MCRTHUR HL MCRTHUR HALL,
    MISSISSIPPI STATE, MS 39762
Phone: 662 325-2302
Web: WWW.MSSTATE.EDU

HISTORICAL FINANCIALS
Company Type: Private

	REVENUE ($ mil.)	NET INCOME ($ mil.)	NET PROFIT MARGIN	EMPLOYEES
				FYE: June 30
06/20	547	68	12.6%	4,500
06/19	525	71	13.6%	—
06/18	489	29	6.0%	—
06/17	461	18	4.0%	—
Annual Growth	5.9%	55.1%	—	—

2020 Year-End Financials

Return on assets: 4.2% Cash ($ mil.): 219
Return on equity: 11.1%
Current ratio: 4.80

MISSOURI BAPTIST MEDICAL CENTER

EXECUTIVES

Pres, John Antes
V Pres-Cfo*, Gary McLaughlin
Vpres*, Timothy Ranney
Vpres*, Douglas Black
Vpres*, Sandra Young
Vpres*, Tim Mislan

Director of Mis/Is, Rosa Davila
Food Director, Terri Powell
Pastoral Care Director, Alan Runge
Oncologist, Gary Ratkin
Manager Sterile Processing, Sara Vinson

LOCATIONS

HQ: MISSOURI BAPTIST MEDICAL CENTER
3015 N BALLAS RD, SAINT LOUIS, MO 631312329
Phone: 314 996-5155
Web: WWW.MISSOURIBAPTIST.ORG

HISTORICAL FINANCIALS
Company Type: Private

Income Statement | | | | FYE: December 31

	REVENUE ($ mil.)	NET INCOME ($ mil.)	NET PROFIT MARGIN	EMPLOYEES
12/18	584	15	2.6%	1,670
12/17	600	18	3.0%	—
12/16	570	25	4.5%	—
12/15	511	15	3.0%	—
Annual Growth	4.6%	(0.1%)	—	—

2018 Year-End Financials
Return on assets: 4.4%   Cash ($ mil.): —
Return on equity: 4.8%
Current ratio: 4.20

MISSOURI CITY OF KANSAS CITY

You may not be in Kansas anymore but you could still be in Kansas City . Situated opposite Kansas City Kansas is the city of Kansas City Missouri the state's largest city with a population of about 460000. Its council-manager form of government is made up of 12 members presided over by the mayor. The city manager serves and advises the council and prepares the annual budget for council consideration as well as enforces municipal laws and ordinances and manages city operations. With more than 200 fountains within 320 square miles its official nickname is the "City of Fountains." Incorporated in 1850 it is home to the Chiefs and Royals and is famous for barbeque.

EXECUTIVES

Mayor, Sly James
Asst Atty, William Geary
Dept Dir, Franklyn Pogge
City, Galen Beaufort
Csr, Elyssa Dodd
Sr Admin Asst, Taylor Dalena
City Clerk, Millie Crossland
City Mgr, Wayne Cauthen
Dir of Fin, Dwanda Gunger
Commanding Officer, Diane Mozzicato
Relocation Assistant, Carmen Wheeler
Auditors: ALLEN GIBBS & HOULIK LC WIC

LOCATIONS

HQ: MISSOURI CITY OF KANSAS CITY
414 E 12TH ST STE 105, KANSAS CITY, MO
641062705
Phone: 816 513-1313
Web: WWW.HELLOKANSASCITY.COM

HISTORICAL FINANCIALS
Company Type: Private

Income Statement | | | | FYE: April 30

	REVENUE ($ mil.)	NET INCOME ($ mil.)	NET PROFIT MARGIN	EMPLOYEES
04/20	1,150	42	3.7%	8,000
04/19	1,150	(22)	—	—
04/18	1,085	13	1.2%	—
04/17	1,058	(9)	—	—
Annual Growth	2.8%	—	—	—

2020 Year-End Financials
Return on assets: 0.4%   Cash ($ mil.): 1,115
Return on equity: 1.0%
Current ratio: —

MISSOURI DEPARTMENT OF TRANSPORTATION

Missouri has come a long way since its first byway Three Notch Road was built in 1735 and MoDOT has had a lot to do with the progress. The Missouri Department of Transportation (MoDOT) oversees one of the nation's largest state highway systems. Specifically it designs builds and maintains the 32000-plus miles of highway and some 10000 bridges and administers federal and state programs that affect public transit and air water and rail transportation throughout the state. MoDOT is governed by the six-member Missouri Highways and Transportation Commission. The agency that became MoDOT got its start when the Missouri Legislature established a job for a state highway engineer in 1907.

EXECUTIVES

Dir, Dave Nichols
Transportation Planner*, Machelle Watkins
SEC*, Sharon Monroe
Compensation Manager, Paul Imhoff
Program Manager, Amy Wilson
Program Manager, Denise Fennewald
Program Manager, Eileen Rackers
Program Manager, Harry Gilmore
Assistant Const, Jay Bestgen
Program Manager, Melissa Wilbers
General Manager Purch, Rebecca Jackson
Auditors: BKD LLP SPRINGFIELD MO

LOCATIONS

HQ: MISSOURI DEPARTMENT OF TRANSPORTATION
105 W CAPITOL AVE, JEFFERSON CITY, MO
651016811
Phone: 573 751-2551
Web: WWW.MODOT.ORG

PRODUCTS/OPERATIONS

Selected Services and Operations
Commnity Services
   Adopt-A-Highway
   Being Green
   Economic Impact Analysis
   Local Programs
   Memorial Designation Programs
   Partnership Development
   Planning and Policy Group
   Request a Speaker
   Roadside Vegetation Management
   Scenic Byways
   Sponsor-A-Highway

   Stormwater Pollution Reporting
   Transportation Enhancements
   Work-Zone Safety Awareness
Engineering Services
   Bridge Engineering Assistance Program
   Traffic Engineering Assistance Program
Travel Services
   Carpool Connections
   Commuter Lots
   Gateway Guide
   Intelligent Transportation Systems
   Kansas City Scout
   Missouri Rest Area Guide
   Motorist Assist
   Online Traveler Information Map
   Ozark Traffic Information
   Snow Plowing info — priorities driving tips and more

HISTORICAL FINANCIALS
Company Type: Private

Income Statement | | | | FYE: June 30

	REVENUE ($ mil.)	NET INCOME ($ mil.)	NET PROFIT MARGIN	EMPLOYEES
06/17	2,213	(107)	—	6,295
06/09	2,142	(357)	—	—
06/05	0	0	—	—
Annual Growth	—	—	—	—

2017 Year-End Financials
Return on assets: (-0.3%)   Cash ($ mil.): 735
Return on equity: (-0.4%)
Current ratio: 2.60

MMR CONSTRUCTORS, INC.

EXECUTIVES

Pres, James B Rutland
V Pres*, Tom Welborn
SEC-Treas*, Donald Fairbanks
Manager, John Salisbury
Superintendant, Barry Lewis
Hsande Coordinator, Furnell Hankton
Site Manager, Herbie Bordelon
Office Manager, Irina Lee
Project Coordinator, Kirt Thibodeaux
Acct Clerk, Megan Adams
Director of Information Techno, Robert Benoit
Auditors: MADDOX & ASSOCIATES APC BATO

LOCATIONS

HQ: MMR CONSTRUCTORS, INC.
15961 AIRLINE HWY, BATON ROUGE, LA 708177412
Phone: 225 756-5090
Web: WWW.MMRGRP.COM

HISTORICAL FINANCIALS
Company Type: Private

Income Statement | | | | FYE: December 31

	REVENUE ($ mil.)	NET INCOME ($ mil.)	NET PROFIT MARGIN	EMPLOYEES
12/20	556	42	7.6%	4,000
12/19	772	30	3.9%	—
12/18	775	25	3.3%	—
12/17	581	16	2.9%	—
Annual Growth	(1.5%)	36.6%	—	—

2020 Year-End Financials
Return on assets: 7.8%   Cash ($ mil.): 2
Return on equity: 15.3%
Current ratio: 3.90

MMR GROUP, INC.

That murmur you hear could be the gentle hum of a properly functioning power system. MMG Group provides electrical and instrumentation construction maintenance management and technical services for clients in the oil and gas manufacturing chemical and power generation industries around the world. It also offers services in offshore marine and platform environments. Its Power Solutions division constructs onsite power-generation systems in industrial plants and other facilities. The group primarily operates in the Gulf of New Mexico. Founded in 1990 MMG is 100% management owned and has served such clients as Chevron Shell BP Merck Air Liquide DuPont and 3M.

Operations

MMR Group's provides four main services: electrical and instrumentation contracting safety services panel fabrication and communications.

MMR's electrical and instrumentation contractors work on projects throughout the US and overseas. To ensure its projects are completed on time and within budget its personnel has support and management control systems and emphasizes planning scheduling progress tracking and labor analysis.

The MMR Offshore Safety Services division specializes in disaster prevention and safety helping with navigation fire and gas detection suppression products paging and alarm systems level one cathodic protection inspections and other related services.

For panel fabrication services MMR stages tests and designs control systems that best fit client needs.

The MMR ProCom division is in charge of precommissioning commissioning and start-Up activities for both MMR Group construction projects and for outside clients interested in turning their facilities construction into a safe and reliable operation seamlessly.

Geographic Reach

MMR operates out of some 20 offices spread across North and South America with most of its offices in Texas Louisiana and California. The company works on projects all over the world with foreign affiliate offices in Calgary Canada; Cartagena Colombia; Puerto la Cruz Venezuela; and Port of Spain Trinidad & Tobago.

Sales and Marketing

MMR serves a variety of markets including: alternative energy exploration and production chemical and petrochemical industrial and manufacturing oil and gas power generation and waste and water treatment among others.

Some of the company's panel fabrication clients have included Shell Pipeline Chevron Pipeline Enbridge Pipeline AGI Services Cimitation Engineering ExxonMobil Keystone Engineering W.S. Nelson Engineering and Entergy among others.

Depending on the project and client's preference MMR operates on all types of fixed-price and cost-plus contracts.

Strategy

The company continues to expand its operations to accommodate more projects. In 2014 the company built a 19-office administration building along with a 6000 square-foot warehouse facility to support the influx of new projects going on in the Golden Triangle area between Beaumont TX and Lake Charles LA.

EXECUTIVES

Pres, James B Rutland
V Pres*, Thomas O Welborn
SEC-Treas*, Donald W Fairbanks
Information Specialist, Meagan L Bourgeois
Internal Medicine Practitioner, Garrett Benoit
Coordinator, Brandon Legrange
Director, Darryl Sockwell
Clerk, Kathleen Thompson
Manager, Kevin Alexander
Vice President Marketing, Grady Saucier
Senior Network Engineer, David Nezat
Auditors: MADDOX & ASSOCIATES APC BATO

LOCATIONS

HQ: MMR GROUP, INC.
   15961 AIRLINE HWY, BATON ROUGE, LA 708177412
Phone: 225 756-5090
Web: WWW.MMRGRP.COM

PRODUCTS/OPERATIONS

Selected Services

Instrumentation
   Air supply installation
   Control room equipment installation
   Instrument installation
   Process leads
   Panel fabrication
   Signal wiring
Electrical
   Controls
   Electrical equipment setting
   Grounding
   Lighting
   Power distribution
Technical
   Calibration
   Commissioning
   Detail design
   High voltage testing
   Instrument procurement
   Loop check
   Maintenance
   Start up assistance
   System analysis

Selected Divisions

MMR Constructors
MMR International
MMR Power Solutions
MMR Offshore Services
MMR Technical Services
Southwestern Power Group

COMPETITORS

Alberici	Myr Group
Emcor	Matrix Service
Fisk Electric	Turner Industries
Industrial Specialty Contractors	

HISTORICAL FINANCIALS

Company Type: Private

Income Statement				FYE: December 31
	REVENUE ($ mil.)	NET INCOME ($ mil.)	NET PROFIT MARGIN	EMPLOYEES
12/20	564	36	6.4%	4,000
12/19	783	23	3.0%	—
12/18	786	17	2.2%	—
12/17	618	9	1.5%	—
Annual Growth	(3.0%)	55.9%	—	—

2020 Year-End Financials

Return on assets: 7.1%   Cash ($ mil.): 2
Return on equity: 15.3%
Current ratio: 1.50

MODERN WOODMEN OF AMERICA

No need to pitch a tent to have Modern Woodmen in your camp. One of the largest fraternal benefit societies in the US Modern Woodmen of America provides annuities life insurance and other financial savings products to more than 740000 members through some 1000 agents. The group founded in 1883 is organized into "camps" (or chapters) that provide financial social recreational and service benefits to members. Founder Joseph Cullen Root chose the society's name to compare pioneering woodmen clearing forests to men using life insurance to remove the financial burdens their families could face upon their deaths.

Operations

The organization claims some approximately 2500 chapters nationwide provide opportunities for members to take part in educational social and volunteer activities; nearly 300 summit chapters offer activities for members age 55 and over; and more than 800 youth service clubs which are led by adult member volunteers.

In addition to financial services the organization offers life insurance for member families include term life insurance plans specifically designed for children and young adults and permanent life insurance plans with a minimum insurance amount of $50000. Its annuities services include Max-Provider for retirement savings variable annuity for multiple investment options and single premium immediate annuity. In addition to life insurance and annuities the company offers retirement accounts including IRAs college savings plans investment assistance and other insurance products. Modern Woodmen has $20.4 million in life insurance in force.

Subsidiary MWA Financial Services offers securities and advisory products. The MWABank (dba Modern Woodmen Bank) division provides retail banking services.

Geographic Reach

Based in Rock Island Illinois the organization has nearly 500 home offices and operates throughout the US. It has agents in more than 45 regions throughout 45 states.

Financial Performance

In 2019 Modern Woodmen had $17.34 billion in assets. This was higher than the $16.5 billion reported in 2018 as bonds and stocks both increased.

Net income for the same year was $89.5 million which was lower than the $109.9 million reported the year prior. The decrease was mainly due to lower realized capital gains.

Cash at the end of the year for the company was $363.4 million. Net cash provided by operating activities was $189.2 million while cash used for investments was $299.9 million.

Strategy

Modern Woodmen manages its assets so that changes in the financial markets ? recessions depressions or periods of inflation ? have minimal effect. Modern Woodmen is also careful not to follow investment fads. To build its investment portfolio its financial management team follows these principles: High-quality investments; Diversified investments; and Competitive rates of return.

Assets are invested primarily in high-quality low-risk investments. As of December 31 2019 approximately 99.7 percent of bonds were of high or medium quality.

Company Background

Although Modern Woodmen's roots are tangled with Woodmen of the World Life Insurance Society the two fraternal benefit societies are not related. Modern Woodmen of America was founded in 1883.

EXECUTIVES

Pres, W Kenneth Massey
Gen Counsel*, Darcy G Callas
Treas*, Nick S Coin
SEC*, Gerald Odean
Supervisor, Tina Schindler
General Counsel, Darcy Callas
Programmer Analyst, Barb Haertjens
Financial Representative, Brian Moreno
Sales, Joe Feeney
Managing Partner, Matthew Ward
Vice President of It, Becky Hansen

LOCATIONS

HQ: MODERN WOODMEN OF AMERICA
1701 1ST AVE, ROCK ISLAND, IL 612018779
Phone: 309 793-5537
Web: WWW.MODERNWOODMEN.ORG

PRODUCTS/OPERATIONS

Selected Products
Annuities (fixed immediate and variable; through MWA
  Financial Services)
Banking (MWABank)
  Certificates of Deposit
  Checking and savings accounts
  Credit cards and gift cards
  First mortgage and refinancing home loans
  Home equity loans
Insurance (through MWAGIA)
  Dental and vision insurance
  Disability income insurance
  Group employee benefits
  Group voluntary benefits
  Impaired risk life insurance
  International life and health insurance
  Long-term care insurance
  Major medical insurance
  Medicare supplement insurance
Investment (through MWA Financial Services)
  Brokerage services
  College savings plans
  Mutual funds
  Retirement plans
Life Insurance
  Term life insurance
  Term life insurance for children
  Universal life insurance
  Whole life insurance

COMPETITORS

Allstate	Reliance Standard
Massmutual	Royal Neighbors Of
Metlife	America
Nationwide Financial	State Farm
New York Life	Thrivent Financial
Northwestern Mutual	Woodmen Of The World
Prudential	Life Insurance

HISTORICAL FINANCIALS

Company Type: Private

Income Statement				FYE: December 31
	ASSETS ($ mil.)	NET INCOME ($ mil.)	INCOME AS % OF ASSETS	EMPLOYEES
12/07	8,318	96	1.2%	480
12/06	7,928	99	1.3%	—
Annual Growth	4.9%	(2.6%)	—	—

2007 Year-End Financials

Return on assets: 1.2%   Sales ($ mil): 1,065
Return on equity: 8.2%

MODIVCARE SOLUTIONS, LLC

LogistiCare is a go-between for getting from your house to the doctor's office and back. The company brokers non-emergency transportation services for commercial health plans government entities (such as state Medicaid agencies) and hospitals throughout the US. Using its nearly 20 call centers and a network of some 1500 independent contracted transportation providers the company coordinates the medical-related travel arrangements of its clients' members. In addition it contracts with local school boards to coordinate transportation for special needs students. The company provides more than 26 million trips each year for clients in some 40 states. LogistiCare is a subsidiary of Providence Service.

Operations

LogistiCare also known as Charter LCI has contracts with clients including metro transit authorities HMOs and commercial insurance firms. Other services include finance and consulting to help companies with billing management and claims adjudication customer reimbursement risk management and discount programs for patients requesting noncovered services. LogistiCare's eligibility and authorization services include call screening to determine client-provided benefit criteria as well as screening to determine type of transport needed.

The company operates more than a dozen regional call centers that match incoming requests with subcontracted transportation providers including local taxi and ambulance companies. Transportation customers often include the elderly or those with disabilities that prevent self-transportation.

Strategy

A major part of LogistiCare's growth strategy is to secure contracts with state and local authorities to become the sole Medicaid or Medicare transportation provider. It scored one such contract in late 2010 with Sussex County Delaware. Under terms of that agreement LogistiCare became the statewide broker for all Medicaid medical transportation.

EXECUTIVES

Ceo, Dan Greenleaf
Ceo*, Dan Greenleafe
Coo*, Kenny Wilson
Cfo*, Heath Sampson
CIO*, Walt Meffert
Cco*, Jody Kepler
Corporate Information Technolo, Eric Lorne
Svp-Program & Prod Mgmnt, Andres Salinas
Director of Human Resources, Michael Johnson
Administrator, Alex Batista
Director Operations, Edmundo Hinds
Auditors: KPMG LLP ATLANTA GEORGIA

LOCATIONS

HQ: MODIVCARE SOLUTIONS, LLC
6900 E LAYTON AVE # 1200, DENVER, CO 802373656
Phone: 404 888-5831
Web: WWW.MODIVCARE.COM

PRODUCTS/OPERATIONS

Selected Services
Billing and claims management
Call center management
Credentialing
Data management and reporting
Eligibility and authorization services
Logistics
Non-emergency transportation management
  (ambulatory/livery vans wheel chair vans stretcher
  vans)
Provider payment
Quality assurance

COMPETITORS

Amr	National Express Group
Coach Usa	Safe Ride Services
Firstgroup America	Veolia Transportation
Mv Transportation	

HISTORICAL FINANCIALS

Company Type: Private

Income Statement				FYE: December 31
	REVENUE ($ mil.)	NET INCOME ($ mil.)	NET PROFIT MARGIN	EMPLOYEES
12/17*	1,318	35	2.7%	3,794
04/17	1,234	44	3.6%	—
12/15	1,083	40	3.7%	—
12/14	884	71	8.1%	—
Annual Growth	14.2%	(21.0%)	—	—

*Fiscal year change

2017 Year-End Financials

Return on assets: 19.1%   Cash ($ mil.): 26
Return on equity: 73.8%
Current ratio: 1.10

MOHEGAN TRIBAL GAMING AUTHORITY

EXECUTIVES

President, Chief Executive Officer, Ray Pineault
Chief Marketing Officer, David Martinelli
Senior Vice President, Chief Information Officer, Mark Rosa
Chief Financial Officer, Senior Vice President, Carol Anderson
Auditors: DELOITTE & TOUCHE LLP HARTFOR

LOCATIONS

HQ: MOHEGAN TRIBAL GAMING AUTHORITY
1 MOHEGAN SUN BLVD, UNCASVILLE, CT 063821355
Phone: 860 862-8000
Web: WWW.MOHEGANSUN.COM

HISTORICAL FINANCIALS

Company Type: Private

Income Statement				FYE: September 30
	REVENUE ($ mil.)	NET INCOME ($ mil.)	NET PROFIT MARGIN	EMPLOYEES
09/21	1,228	7	0.6%	11,000
09/20	1,114	(162)	—	—
09/19	1,388	(2)	—	—
09/18	1,355	131	9.7%	—
Annual Growth	(3.2%)	(61.8%)	—	—

2021 Year-End Financials

Return on assets: 0.3%   Cash ($ mil.): 149
Return on equity: —
Current ratio: 0.70

MONMOUTH MEDICAL CENTER INC.

Monmouth Medical Center is a 530-bed tertiary care teaching hospital providing comprehensive health care to residents of central New Jersey. The not-for-profit medical center offers services ranging from orthopedics diagnostics and obstetric care to surgery dentistry and geriatric services. The medical center campus also includes a children's hospital a cancer center a neuroscience institute an outpatient care clinic and hospice and home health facilities. Monmouth Medical Center is a teaching affiliate of the Rutgers-Robert Wood Johnson Medical School. The hospital is part of the RWJBarnabas Health network.

Operations

Monmouth Medical Center handles 19000 inpatient admissions each year as well as 49000 emergency room visits. Its outpatient clinic handles some 126000 appointments annually. The hospital has 700 doctors representing 60 specialties on its staff.

Geographic Reach

Monmouth Medical Center is located on about 20 acres in Long Branch New Jersey near the Atlantic Ocean. The campus includes the main 16-wing hospital and and about 16 other buildings including resident physician dwellings a day care center a medical education and training facility and a Ronald McDonald House.

The hospital serves a territory consisting of Monmouth Ocean and Middlesex counties with a total of about one million residents. It has outpatient locations in Colts Neck Howell Long Branch Ocean Township and Shrewsbury.

Strategy

The hospital has conducted recent expansion projects including additions of new a new cancer center surgical suites and a family center. In 2013 it opened a new postpartum wing and newborn nursery as well as a larger neonatal ICU. Monmouth Medical Center also extended its pediatric and oncology programs by forming partnerships with other area hospitals in 2012.

Company Background

Monmouth Medical Center was founded in 1887. It has expanded over the years to provide a number of specialist services including high-tech offerings such as robotic surgery. Parent Barnabas Health merged with Robert Wood Johnson Health in 2016 to form RWJBarnabas.

EXECUTIVES

Ceo, Eric Carney
Exec Dir*, Frank Vozos
SEC*, Frank Ciesla
Cfo*, David McClung
Executive of Information Techn, Michael Kordelski
Health Professional, Maureen A Tumolo
Child Psychology, Emilya Fardman
Health Professional, Wael Ghali
Administrative Director of RAD, Karen Mount
Vice President of Supply Chain, Robert Carretta
Vice President of Patient Care, Sari Kaplon
Auditors: KPMG LLP NEW YORK NY

LOCATIONS

HQ: MONMOUTH MEDICAL CENTER INC.
300 2ND AVE, LONG BRANCH, NJ 077406395
Phone: 732 222-5200
Web: WWW.RWJBH.ORG

PRODUCTS/OPERATIONS

Selected Centers and Services

Anesthesiology Services
Behavioral Health Network
Brain Tumor Center (David S. Zocchi)
The Breast Center (Jacqueline M. Wilentz Comprehensive)
Burn Center
Cancer Services
Cardiac Services
Cardiac Surgery
Children's Hospital at Monmouth (Pediatrics)
Cleft Palate Center
Cord Blood Banking Program
Cosmetic Surgery
Cranmer Ambulatory Surgery Center
Critical Care Services
Diabetes Education - Center for Diabetes Education
Dental Medicine
Diagnostic Imaging Services
The Eisenberg Family Center
Emergency Services
Epilepsy Monitoring Program
Extracorporeal Membrane Oxygenation Program (ECMO)
The Gamma Knife Center
Geriatric Emergency Medicine (GEM) Unit
Geriatric Health Center
Head & Neck Surgery
Hernias Repair Institute for the Treatment of Complex
HIV/AIDS Program
Home Health Care
Home Infusion Care
Hospice
Hyperbaric Oxygen Therapy
Integrative Medicine (Center for)
Joint Replacement and Spine Center
Medical Records
Medical Alert/Lifeline
Medicine (Department of)
Minimally Invasive Surgery
Monmouth Family Health Center
Neonatal Intensive Care Unit (Regional Newborn Center)
Neuroscience Institute
Nutritional Counseling
Obstetrics/Gynecological Services
Occupational Medicine
Orthopaedic Services
Outpatient Services Location
Pain Management Program
Palliative Care
Pastoral Care
Pathology & Laboratory Services
Pediatric Services
Pediatric Subspecialty Center at Toms River The
Pediatric Surgery
Pharmacy Department
Plastic Surgery
Podiatry Services
Pre-Admission Testing Services
Psychiatric Services
Pulmonary Services
Radiation Oncology
Rehabilitation Services
Renal Services
Renal Transplantation
Respiratory Services
Robotic Surgery
Senior Services Program
Sleep Disorders Center
Spine Center
Surgical Services
Total Joint Replacement
Urogynecology
Urology
Valerie Fund Cancer Center (Pediatrics)
Vascular Surgery
The Weight Loss Institute of New Jersey
Wound Treatment Center

COMPETITORS

Atlantic Health	Saint Peter's
Bergen Regional	University Hospital
Medical	Shore Memorial
Capital Health System	Hospital
Centrastate Healthcare	St. Joseph's
System	Healthcare System
Hackensack Meridian	Trinitas Regional

Health	Medical Center
Princeton Healthcare	Valley Health System

HISTORICAL FINANCIALS
Company Type: Private

Income Statement
FYE: December 31

	REVENUE ($ mil.)	NET INCOME ($ mil.)	NET PROFIT MARGIN	EMPLOYEES
12/19	556	5	1.0%	2,400
12/18	546	43	8.0%	—
12/17	529	52	10.0%	—
12/16	399	46	11.5%	—
Annual Growth 11.7%	(50.5%)	—	—	—

2019 Year-End Financials

Return on assets: 0.7%   Cash ($ mil.): —
Return on equity: 1.6%
Current ratio: 2.90

MONOGRAM FOOD SOLUTIONS, LLC

Monogram Food Solutions is focused on M E A and T. As a manufacturer of meat and meat snack products the company produces beef jerky sausage hot dogs bacon and other processed food items. Its brands include Circle B King Cotton and Trail's Best Meat Snacks. Through several special licensing agreements Monogram Food Solutions also sells Jeff Foxworthy Jerky Products NASCAR Jerky and Steak Strips and Bass Pro Uncle Buck's Licensed Products. The company which distributes its products nationwide operates facilities in Minnesota Indiana and Virginia. Founded in 2004 Monogram Food Solutions was formed through the merger of assets (King Cotton and Circle B) previously owned by Sara Lee Corp.

Geographic Reach

From its headquarters in Memphis Tennessee Monogram Food Solutions directs the operation of additional facilities in (Chandler) Minnesota (Muncie and Bristol) Indiana and (Martinsville) Virginia. The company distributes its products nationwide.

Strategy

Licensing agreements have helped Monogram Food Solutions build a firm foundation for its business. Aside from its deal with Bass Pro Shops and Jeff Foxworthy the company enjoys licensing partnerships with Johnsonville Sausage and Glory Foods. Its alliance with Johnsonville Sausage inked in 2012 gave Monogram Food Solutions the go-ahead to produce and market Johnsonville Deli Bites Bacon Jerky and other meat snacks innovations.

Beginning in 2010 the company began manufacturing and selling meat snacks for the energy drink maker DNA Beverages Corporation under the DNA brand. Geared toward a younger consumer the DNA beef products gives Monogram a larger demographic for its products.

Mergers and Acquisitions

Since its founding the company has quickly built itself up by buying established meat product manufacturers and processing plants. In 2009 it acquired three companies including beef jerky maker Wild Bill's Foods and Al Pete's Meats (and the Pete's Pride brand name). It also acquired the Hannah's Bull's O'Brien's and Dakota meat snack brands from meat processing company American Foods Group.

In late 2012 Monogram Food Solutions purchased Hinsdale Farms of Bristol Indiana. As one of the nation's largest makers of corn dogs Hinsdale also has a hand in serving retail private label customers and co-packing for other manufacturers. The deal added a fourth manufacturing plant for processing meat. As part of the acquisition Monogram Food Solutions is working to integrate the Hinsdale business into its manufacturing and sales systems.

EXECUTIVES

MBR, Wes Jackson
MBR, Karl Schledwitz
MBR, Ches Jackson
MBR, David Dunavant
MBR, Don Brunson
MBR, Rob Shuster
Sr Analyst, Jocelyn Brown
Staff, Kevin Kuechenmeister
Coordinator, Stacey Bollin
Chief Procurement and Logistic, Jeffrey Modica
Finance, Rob S Shuster
Auditors: MAYER HOFFMAN MCCANN PC MEM

LOCATIONS

HQ: MONOGRAM FOOD SOLUTIONS, LLC
530 OAK COURT DR STE 400, MEMPHIS, TN 381173735
Phone: 901 685-7167
Web: WWW.MONOGRAMFOODS.COM

PRODUCTS/OPERATIONS

Selected Brands
Circle B
Hannah's
King Cotton
O'Brien's Meat Snacks/Sausages
Wild Bill's

COMPETITORS

Bridgford Foods	Hormel
Carl Buddig	Jerky Snack Brands
Clemens Family	Link Snacks
Corporation	Oberto Sausage Company
Conagra	Weaver Meats

HISTORICAL FINANCIALS

Company Type: Private

Income Statement   FYE: January 2

	REVENUE ($ mil.)	NET INCOME ($ mil.)	NET PROFIT MARGIN	EMPLOYEES
01/21*	819	25	3.1%	790
12/19	747	(4)	—	—
12/18	647	11	1.7%	—
12/17	640	2	0.4%	—
Annual Growth	8.5%	114.8%	—	—

*Fiscal year change

2021 Year-End Financials

Return on assets: 6.6%   Cash ($ mil.): —
Return on equity: 19.1%
Current ratio: 1.30

MONONGAHELA POWER COMPANY

Electricity flows from Monongahela Power (Mon Power) just like the river the utility was named after. The company services approximately 388000 residential and commercial customers in a service area of 13000 sq. mi. in West Virginia. Mon Power along with West Penn Power and Potomac Edison comprise the Allegheny Power arm of Allegheny Energy which is now part of FirstEnergy. In 2013 Mon Power owned or controlled 3580 MW of generating capacity. The company is contractually obligated to supply Potomac Edison with sufficient power to meet that company's power load obligations in West Virginia.

Operations
Mon Power provides generation transmission and distribution services. Its infrastructure includes 25390 miles of distribution lines and more than 2125 miles of transmission lines.

Geographic Reach
The utility's service area includes Northern Central and Southeastern West Virginia.

Strategy
In 2013 the parent company invested about $131 million in Mon Power and planned to invest about $233 million more in 2014 to help Mon Power expand its operations.

In a transfer of assets within FirstEnergy's West Virginia-based operations to improve efficiencies in 2013 Mon Power sold its 8% share of the Pleasants power plant at its fair market value of $73 million to Allegheny Energy Supply. In return Allegheny Energy Supply sold its 80% stake in the Harrison plant to Mon Power at its book value of $1.2 billion.

To lower carbon emissions in 2012 Mon Power shut down three aging coal-fired power plants in West Virginia: Albright Willow Island and Rivesville.

Company Background
The company is a subsidiary of Allegheny Energy which is owned by FirstEnergy.

Mon Power was incorporated in Ohio in 1924.

EXECUTIVES

Chb-Ceo, Paul J Evanson
V Pres*, Philip L Goulding
Pres*, David E Flitman
Contrl*, Thomas R Gardner
V Pres-SEC*, Hyun Park
Cfo*, Jeffrey David Serkes
Associate Business Analyst, Jane Campbell
Auditors: PRICEWATERHOUSECOOPERS LLP CL

LOCATIONS

HQ: MONONGAHELA POWER COMPANY
5001 NASA BLVD, FAIRMONT, WV 265548248
Phone: 800 686-0022
Web: WWW.FIRSTENERGYCORP.COM

COMPETITORS

Appalachian Power	Dominion Transmission
Buckeye Power	Ohio Edison
Dominion Hope	Ohio Valley Electric

HISTORICAL FINANCIALS

Company Type: Private

Income Statement   FYE: December 31

	REVENUE ($ mil.)	NET INCOME ($ mil.)	NET PROFIT MARGIN	EMPLOYEES
12/17	1,619	69	4.3%	4,000
12/16	1,613	66	4.1%	
Annual Growth	0.3%	4.5%	—	—

2017 Year-End Financials

Return on assets: 1.6%   Cash ($ mil.): 76
Return on equity: 5.4%
Current ratio: 1.80

MONSTER BEVERAGE 1990 CORPORATION

LOCATIONS

HQ: MONSTER BEVERAGE 1990 CORPORATION
1 MONSTER WAY, CORONA, CA 928797101
Phone: 951 739-6200
Web: WWW.MONSTERBEVCORP.COM

HISTORICAL FINANCIALS

Company Type: Private

Income Statement   FYE: December 31

	REVENUE ($ mil.)	NET INCOME ($ mil.)	NET PROFIT MARGIN	EMPLOYEES
12/17	3,369	820	24.4%	2,001
12/16	3,049	712	23.4%	—
12/15	2,722	546	20.1%	—
12/14	2,464	483	19.6%	—
Annual Growth	11.0%	19.3%	—	—

2017 Year-End Financials

Return on assets: 17.1%   Cash ($ mil.): 528
Return on equity: 21.1%
Current ratio: 3.70

MONTAGE HEALTH

EXECUTIVES

Pres-Ceo, Steven Packer
V Pres*, Terril Lowe
V Pres-Fin*, Laura Zehm
V Pres*, Cynthia Peck
V Pres*, Tim Nylen
Dentist, Diane Day DDS
Doctor, George H Penn
Radiologist, Kristine W Leatherberry
Urologist, Craig Stauffer
Director of Lipid Serv, Diane Sobkowicz
Analyst, Francis Allard
Auditors: MOSS ADAMS LLP SAN FRANCISCO

LOCATIONS

HQ: MONTAGE HEALTH
23625 HOLMAN HWY, MONTEREY, CA 939405902
Phone: 831 625-4830
Web: WWW.MONTAGEHEALTH.ORG

HISTORICAL FINANCIALS

Company Type: Private

Income Statement				FYE: December 31
	REVENUE ($ mil.)	NET INCOME ($ mil.)	NET PROFIT MARGIN	EMPLOYEES
12/19	784	143	18.3%	2,003
12/17*	145	139	95.9%	—
11/11	450	23	5.2%	—
Annual Growth	7.2%	25.4%	—	—

*Fiscal year change

2019 Year-End Financials

Return on assets: 8.4%   Cash ($ mil.): 76
Return on equity: 11.8%
Current ratio: 1.60

MONTEFIORE MEDICAL CENTER

The primary teaching hospital of the Albert Einstein College of Medicine Montefiore offers medical education programs. Montefiore Medical Center attends to the health care needs of residents across the Bronx Westchester and the Hudson Valley. Montefiore Einstein Center for Cancer Care a Montefiore Center of Excellence delivers advanced patient-centered multidisciplinary care designed to maximize treatment outcomes while optimizing the quality of life for each patient. Children's Hospital at Montefiore (CHAM) a premier academic children's hospital nationally renowned for its clinical excellence innovative research and commitment to training the next generation of pediatricians and pediatric subspecialists. Montefiore Medical Center was founded in 1884 by Jewish philanthropists.

Operations

As the teaching hospital for Albert Einstein College of Medicine Montefiore provides postgraduate training for more than 1250 residents across some 90 accredited residency and fellowship programs.

Through Montefiore Care Management the company uses a global prepayment or similar strategies to manage care for 200000 individuals for hospital care rehabilitation outpatient care professional services home care mental health counseling community-based services remote patient monitoring and other programs.

Montefiore and Einstein are among about three dozen academic medical centers nationwide to be awarded the Clinical and Translational Science Award (CTSA) by the National Institutes of Health.

Geographic Reach

Montefiore operations throughout the Bronx Westchester and the Hudson Valley. It has nearly 50 primary care locations throughout the New York metropolitan area.

Strategy

Montefiore's partnership with Einstein advances clinical and translational research to accelerate the pace at which new discoveries become the treatments and therapies that benefit patients. Together the two institutions are among 38 academic medical centers nationwide to be awarded a prestigious Clinical and Translational Science Award (CTSA) by the National Institutes of Health.

The second-largest medical residency program in the country with 1251 residents and fellows across 89 programs Montefiore provides the doctors of tomorrow a unique opportunity for education and training in one of the most diverse urban areas in the country ? one where the population is global the disease burden is high and the need for quality care is great.

The partnership is further strengthened by the dual appointments of faculty and physicians across both organizations?enhancing synergies and collaborations for research teaching and patient care.

Company Background

Founded in 1884 to treat tuberculosis patients Montefiore has a long history of responding to community health crises including lead poisoning and AIDS. In response to rising needs in the community Montefiore opened a community clinic with the aim of vaccinating young women for HPV a sexually transmitted disease that can cause cervical cancer.

EXECUTIVES

Ceo, Steven M Safyer
Evp and Coo*, Philip O Ozuah
Evp Finance and Cfo*, Joel A Perlman
Sr V Pres*, Alfredo Cabrera
Sr V Pres*, Lynn Richmond
Physician, Syed Abbas
Physician, Talat Syed
Technical Lead, Tammi Reel-Davis
Physician, Tanuja Devaraj
Obstetrician Gynecologist, Tracy Grossman
Assistant Professor, Uma Tejwani
Auditors: ERNST & YOUNG US LLP NEW YORK

LOCATIONS

HQ: MONTEFIORE MEDICAL CENTER
111 E 210TH ST, BRONX, NY 104672401
Phone: 718 920-4321
Web: WWW.MONTEFIORE.ORG

PRODUCTS/OPERATIONS

Selected Services

Allergy & Immunology
Arthritis & Joint Disease (Rheumatology)
Blood (Hematology)
Bones Muscles & Joints Orthopaedics)
Brain (Neurology)
Centers of Excellence
Dentistry & Oral Surgery
Dermatology
Diabetes Hormones Metabolism (Endocrinology)
Diagnostics & Testing (Pathology)
Digestive & Liver Dieases (Gastroenterology)
Elder Care (Geriatrics)
Emergency Medicine
Eyes (Opthalmology and Visual Sciences)
Family and Social Medicine
General Internal Medicine
Headache Center
HIV/AIDS
Home Care
ICU (Critical Care Medicine)
Infectious Diseases
Internal Medicine
Kidney Disease (Nephrology)
Lungs (Pulmonary Medicine)
Neurosurgery
OB/GYN & Women's Health
Otorhinolaryngology - Head and Neck Surgery
Pain Management & Anesthesiology
Pediatrics
Pharmacy Services
Primary Care
Psychiatry and Behavioral Sciences
Radiology
Rehabilitation Medicine
Sleep-Wake Disorders Center
Surgery
Surgical Services (All)
Urology
Wound Care (Hyperbaric Medicine)

Selected Facilities

Greene Medical Arts Pavilion (outpatient care)
Mercy Community Care (outpatient care)
Montefiore Medical Group (23 Bronx and Westchester locations)
Montefiore Medical Park (outpatient care)
Moses Division Hospital (or Henry and Lucy Moses Division)
The Children's Hospital at Montefiore
North Division (formerly Our Lady of Mercy Medical Center)
Weiler Division Hospital (or Jack D. Weiler Hospital)

COMPETITORS

Beth Israel Medical Center
Bronx-lebanon Hospital
Brookdale University Hospital
Brooklyn Hospital Center
Catholic Healthcare System
Jamaica Hospital Medical Center
Kingsbrook Jewish Medical Center
Lenox Hill Hospital
Maimonides Medical Center
New York City Health And Hospitals
Newyork-presbyterian Healthcare
Northwell Health
Phelps Memorial Hospital Center
Suny Downstate
Winthrop-university Hospital

HISTORICAL FINANCIALS

Company Type: Private

Income Statement				FYE: December 31
	REVENUE ($ mil.)	NET INCOME ($ mil.)	NET PROFIT MARGIN	EMPLOYEES
12/19	4,196	38	0.9%	11,000
12/17	3,762	43	1.2%	—
12/16	2,690	42	1.6%	—
Annual Growth	16.0%	(2.8%)	—	—

2019 Year-End Financials

Return on assets: 0.9%   Cash ($ mil.): 404
Return on equity: 5.3%
Current ratio: 0.90

MONTGOMERY COUNTY, MARYLAND

EXECUTIVES

County Executive, Marc Elrich
Pres*, Hans Riemer
Exec Dir*, Linda Herman
Prin*, Amy Moskowitz
Captain, Dan Ogren
Captain, Gary Rebsch
Captain, Mike Green
Program Inspector, Brian Keeler
Coordinator, Michael Brown
Coordinator, Paulina Alvarado
Deputy Chief of Staff, Sharon St Pierre
Auditors: SB & COMPANY LLC OWINGS MILL

LOCATIONS

HQ: MONTGOMERY COUNTY, MARYLAND
101 MONROE ST FL 15, ROCKVILLE, MD 208502503
Phone: 240 777-8220
Web: WWW.MONTGOMERYCOUNTYMD.GOV

HISTORICAL FINANCIALS
Company Type: Private

Income Statement				FYE: June 30
	REVENUE ($ mil.)	NET INCOME ($ mil.)	NET PROFIT MARGIN	EMPLOYEES
06/20	4,464	(248)	—	7,400
06/18	4,203	217	5.2%	—
06/17	4,191	52	1.3%	—
06/16	3,874	(89)	—	—
Annual Growth	3.6%	—	—	—

2020 Year-End Financials
Return on assets: (-1.6%)
Return on equity: (-13.3%)
Current ratio: —
Cash ($ mil.): 163

MONUMENT HEALTH RAPID CITY HOSPITAL, INC.

EXECUTIVES
Chm, Tom Morrison
Ceo, Charles E Hart
Exec V Pres, Joseph Sluka
Treas, Roy Dishman
Coo, Timothy Sughrue
Information, Bill Stockmann
Staff, Clinton Oyler
Staff, Teresa Lemmer
Compliance Staff, Sabine Colton
Applications Supervisor, Christopher Brandner
Anesthesiologist, John Butz
Auditors: EIDE BAILLY LLP MINNEAPOLIS

LOCATIONS
HQ: MONUMENT HEALTH RAPID CITY HOSPITAL, INC.
353 FAIRMONT BLVD, RAPID CITY, SD 577017375
Phone: 605 755-1000
Web: WWW.MONUMENT.HEALTH

HISTORICAL FINANCIALS
Company Type: Private

Income Statement				FYE: June 30
	REVENUE ($ mil.)	NET INCOME ($ mil.)	NET PROFIT MARGIN	EMPLOYEES
06/20	799	31	4.0%	4,258
06/19	808	49	6.2%	—
06/09	0	0	—	—
Annual Growth	89.5%	—	—	—

2020 Year-End Financials
Return on assets: 2.5%
Return on equity: 4.2%
Current ratio: 0.70
Cash ($ mil.): 151

MORSE OPERATIONS, INC.

Morse Operations (dba Ed Morse Automotive Group) has been selling cars and trucks long enough to know the code of the road. It owns about a dozen new car dealerships across Florida most of them operating under the Ed Morse name. Dealerships house more than 15 franchises and 10 domestic and import car brands including Cadillac Fiat Chevrolet Buick GMC Scion Honda Mazda and Toyota. The company's Bayview Cadillac in Fort Lauderdale is one of the world's largest volume sellers of Cadillacs. Morse Operations also sells used cars provides parts and service and operates a fleet sales division. Founder and auto magnate the late Ed Morse entered the automobile business in 1946 with a 20-car rental fleet.

Operations
Ed Morse Fleet Sales offers vehicles from about 10 different brands including Honda Cadillac Fiat Chevrolet Buick GMC Scion Mazda and Toyota. To date annual fleet sales have reached 100000 vehicles.

Fleet customers include daily rental companies such as National Car Rental Avis and Alamo Rent A Car.

Geographic Reach
The dealership network serves customers throughout Florida along the East and West coasts and in Central Florida.

EXECUTIVES
Pres-Chm, Edward Morse III
Pres-Coo, Carmine Colella
Prin, Dennis Macinnes
Exec V Pres, Rany Hoffman
Manager, Mike Byrne
Marketing Director, Anita Evans
Manager, Eduardo Marquez
Director of Advertising, Maleia Satterlee
Director of Ecommerce, Peter Deiser
Auditors: CROWE LLP FORT LAUDERDALE FL

LOCATIONS
HQ: MORSE OPERATIONS, INC.
2850 S FEDERAL HWY, DELRAY BEACH, FL 334833216
Phone: 561 276-5000
Web: WWW.EDMORSE.COM

PRODUCTS/OPERATIONS
Selected Dealerships
Brandon Auto Mall
Ed Morse Auto Plaza - Port Richey
Ed Morse Bayview Cadillac
Ed Morse Cadillac - Delray Beach
Ed Morse C
Ed Morse C
Ed Morse Delray Toyota/Scion
Ed Morse Honda Blue Heron
Ed Morse M
Ed Morse Sawgrass

COMPETITORS
Autonation
Braman Management
Buchanan Automotive
Ferman Automotive
Holman Enterprises
Island Lincoln-mercury
Jm Family Enterprises
March/hodge
Penske Automotive Group
Scott-mcrae

HISTORICAL FINANCIALS
Company Type: Private

Income Statement				FYE: December 31
	REVENUE ($ mil.)	NET INCOME ($ mil.)	NET PROFIT MARGIN	EMPLOYEES
12/20	1,290	17	1.4%	925
12/18	1,125	(0)	—	—
12/17	1,019	4	0.4%	—
12/16	1,334	9	0.7%	—
Annual Growth	(0.8%)	16.8%	—	—

2020 Year-End Financials
Return on assets: 2.8%
Return on equity: 17.1%
Current ratio: 1.20
Cash ($ mil.): 54

MORTON PLANT HOSPITAL ASSOCIATION, INC.

EXECUTIVES
Pres, Brandon May
V Pres-Oprs-Adm*, Hal Ziecheck
Doctor, Margaret Ann Kelleher
Doctor, Michael Starsiak
Obstetrician Gynecologist, David D Desper Jr
Registrar 1, Dianna Biscoglia
Rn, Michelle Mdevivo
Director, Sally Judiscak
Chief Administrative Officer, Lou Galdieri
Director of Laboratory, Pam Pound
Infection Prevention Director, Suzanne Chandler

LOCATIONS
HQ: MORTON PLANT HOSPITAL ASSOCIATION, INC.
300 PINELLAS ST, CLEARWATER, FL 337563892
Phone: 727 462-7000
Web: WWW.BAYCARE.ORG

HISTORICAL FINANCIALS
Company Type: Private

Income Statement				FYE: December 31
	REVENUE ($ mil.)	NET INCOME ($ mil.)	NET PROFIT MARGIN	EMPLOYEES
12/19	852	67	7.9%	3,000
12/16	555	83	14.9%	—
12/15	107	(8)	—	—
12/13	598	49	8.3%	—
Annual Growth	6.1%	5.2%	—	—

2019 Year-End Financials
Return on assets: 5.6%
Return on equity: 5.8%
Current ratio: 3.10
Cash ($ mil.): —

MOSAIC HEALTH SYSTEM

Heartland Health provides medical care in the heart of the Midwest. The integrated health care system serves residents of northwest Missouri as well as bordering areas of Kansas and Nebraska. Its flagship facility is Heartland Regional Medical Center a 350-bed acute-care hospital that features an emergency room and Level II trauma center as well as specialty care programs in heart disease cancer and obstetrics. Heartland Health also provides primary care through a multi-specialty medical practice (Heartland Clinic) and it offers home health hospice and long-term care services from the primary medical center facility. The company's Community Health Improvement Solutions unit is an HMO health insurer.

Strategy

In 2012 Heartland Health joined the Mayo Clinic Care Network which will enable to it to tap the knowledge and expertise of Mayo Clinic physicians to better serve its patients.

Company Background

Heartland Health was formed in 1984 through the merger of two St. Joseph Missouri hospital: Methodist Medical Center and St. Joseph's Hospital. The two facilities trace their roots back to 1924 and 1861 respectively.

EXECUTIVES

Ceo, Mark Laney
Pres*, Lowell Kruse
V Pres-Cfo*, John Wilson
Chairman*, Alfred L Purcell
Asst SEC*, Karen Dittemore
Asst Treas-Contrl*, Douglas Brandt
Cmo*, Robert Permet
Chm*, David Solanski
Coo*, Cut Kretzinger
Staff, C R Shumann III
Staff, Monica Ray
Auditors: RSM US LLP DAVENPORT IOWA

LOCATIONS

HQ: MOSAIC HEALTH SYSTEM
  5325 FARAON ST, SAINT JOSEPH, MO 645063488
Phone: 816 271-6000
Web: WWW.MYMLC.COM

PRODUCTS/OPERATIONS

Selected Affiliates
Atchison Hospital (Atchison KS)
Community Hospital (Fairfax MO)
Community Medical Center (Falls City NE)
Dental Clinic (St. Joseph MO)
Laser Cosmedic Center (Platte City MO)
North Kansas City Hospital (North Kansas City MO)
The Surgery Center (St. Joseph MO)

COMPETITORS

Ascension Health
Bjc Healthcare
Blue Cross And Blue Shield Of Kansas City
Catholic Health Initiatives
Children's Mercy Hospital
Coxhealth
Hca
Mercy Health
Mercy Hospital Springfield
Saint Luke's Health System
Shawnee Mission Medical Center
Sisters Of Charity Of Leavenworth
Truman Medical Centers
University Of Kansas Medical Center

HISTORICAL FINANCIALS
Company Type: Private

Income Statement   FYE: June 30

	REVENUE ($ mil.)	NET INCOME ($ mil.)	NET PROFIT MARGIN	EMPLOYEES
06/21	780	221	28.4%	32,000
06/20	778	75	9.6%	—
06/19	688	85	12.4%	—
06/18	667	64	9.6%	—
Annual Growth	5.3%	51.2%	—	—

2021 Year-End Financials

Return on assets: 15.1%   Cash ($ mil.): 77
Return on equity: 21.9%
Current ratio: 8.90

MOTION PICTURE INDUSTRY HEALTH PLAN

EXECUTIVES

Prin, David Wescoe
Chief Human Resources Officer, Rita Van Vranken
Director, Client Relations, Ed Brown
Chief Officer, Janice Spinner
Senior Director, Retirement Be, Charan Singh
Chief Financial Officer, David Camp
Editor, Gary Salvador
Auditors: MILLER KAPLAN ARASE LLP NORTH

LOCATIONS

HQ: MOTION PICTURE INDUSTRY HEALTH PLAN
  11365 VENTURA BLVD, STUDIO CITY, CA 916043148
Phone: 818 769-0007

HISTORICAL FINANCIALS
Company Type: Private

Income Statement   FYE: December 31

	ASSETS ($ mil.)	NET INCOME ($ mil.)	INCOME AS % OF ASSETS	EMPLOYEES
12/13	856	60	7.1%	34
12/09	543	(75)	—	—
Annual Growth	12.0%	—	—	—

2013 Year-End Financials

Return on assets: 7.1%   Sales ($ mil.): 732
Return on equity: 18.7%

MOUNT CARMEL HEALTH PLAN MEDIG

LOCATIONS

HQ: MOUNT CARMEL HEALTH PLAN MEDIG
  6150 E BROAD ST, COLUMBUS, OH 432131574
Phone: 614 546-3138
Web: WWW.MEDIGOLD.COM

HISTORICAL FINANCIALS
Company Type: Private

Income Statement   FYE: December 31

	REVENUE ($ mil.)	NET INCOME ($ mil.)	NET PROFIT MARGIN	EMPLOYEES
12/16	571	(20)	—	4
12/13	423	37	8.8%	—
Annual Growth	10.5%	—	—	—

2016 Year-End Financials

Return on assets: (-7.1%)   Cash ($ mil.): 55
Return on equity: (-14.2%)
Current ratio: 3.40

MOUNT CARMEL HEALTH PLAN, INC.

EXECUTIVES

Prin, Ginny Gale

LOCATIONS

HQ: MOUNT CARMEL HEALTH PLAN, INC.
  6150 E BROAD ST, COLUMBUS, OH 432131574
Phone: 614 546-4300
Web: WWW.MEDIGOLD.COM

HISTORICAL FINANCIALS
Company Type: Private

Income Statement   FYE: December 31

	REVENUE ($ mil.)	NET INCOME ($ mil.)	NET PROFIT MARGIN	EMPLOYEES
12/18	582	47	8.1%	45
12/17	614	32	5.3%	—
Annual Growth	(5.3%)	44.2%	—	—

2018 Year-End Financials

Return on assets: 14.0%   Cash ($ mil.): 99
Return on equity: 21.8%
Current ratio: 2.30

MOUNT CARMEL HEALTH SYSTEM

Mount Carmel Health System cares for the sick in the greater Columbus area and central Ohio. The health care system boasts 1500 physicians at three general hospitals and a specialty surgical hospital offering a comprehensive range of medical and surgical services including cardiovascular care. Mount Carmel Health also operates outpatient centers including primary care and specialty physicians' practices and it offers home health care services. The hospital group is part of Trinity Health one of the largest Catholic health care systems in the US.

Operations

Mount Carmel's facilities include the acute care Mount Carmel East Mount Carmel West and Mount Carmel St. Ann's hospitals as well as the Mount Carmel New Albany a surgical hospital specializing in orthopedic neurological and musculoskeletal treatments. The system also operates several freestanding emergency and surgery centers and other outpatient and community care centers. Its HealthProviders subsidiary manages about two dozen primary care and specialty practices with more than 100 physicians in central Ohio.

In the realm of education Mount Carmel Health operates six medical residency programs for physicians and its Mount Carmel College of Nursing is one of the largest in the state.

Strategy

In 2015 Mount Carmel announced that it was investing more than $700 million in a major expansion. The investment includes big projects at three Mount Carmel campuses: Mount Carmel East Mount Carmel Grove City and Mount Carmel West. Mount Carmel East will begin a $310 million modernization in 2015 to be completed in phases through 2019.

That year the company signed an agreement with HealthSouth to begin construction on a new inpatient rehabilitation hospital in Westerville Ohio. The 60-bed hospital will be a joint venture between HealthSouth and Mount Carmel and will provide specialized rehabilitative care to patients who have experienced stroke trauma brain and orthopedic injuries or other major illnesses or injuries. Construction on the 60000-square-foot hospital is expected to be completed in early 2017. When the new hospital opens Mount Carmel will relocate its existing 24-bed unit at Mount Carmel West to the new facility.

Company Background

In 2012 the company launched a $110 million facilities improvement project (Project GRACE) which includes the renovation of the St. Ann's hospital. Mount Carmel Health plans for the upgraded St. Ann's facility to serve as a regional medical center.

In 2010 Mount Carmel completed construction of a new freestanding emergency center in the town of Canal Winchester through a partnership with Fairfield Medical Center. The center features both general emergency and pediatric urgent care facilities. In time the center might expand into a larger hospital facility.

Mother M. Angela and Sister M. Rufina Dunn of the Congregation of the Sisters of the Holy Cross of Notre Dame founded Mount Carmel in 1886.

EXECUTIVES

Ceo, Michael Englehart
Pres*, Douglas H Stine
Reproductive Endocrinology, Dennis R Blose
Neurologist, Gerald S Steiman
Neurological Surgeon, Gregory Z Mavian
Neurologist, Jean Vike
Director, Jeffrey Sams
Lab Technician, Jennifer Ruark
Director Human Resources, Kathryn Smith
Coordinator, Kelly W Holmes
Pharmacist, Pamela Purtee

LOCATIONS

HQ: MOUNT CARMEL HEALTH SYSTEM
  6150 E BROAD ST, COLUMBUS, OH 432131574
Phone: 614 234-6000
Web: WWW.MOUNTCARMELHEALTH.COM

PRODUCTS/OPERATIONS

Selected Facilities

Hospitals
  Mount Carmel East
  Mount Carmel New Albany
  Mount Carmel St. Ann's
  Mount Carmel West
Other Facilities
  Anticoagulation Centers
  Atrial Fibrillation Center
  Cardiac Rehabilitation
  Diley Ridge Medical Center
  Mount Carmel Grove City Medical Center
  Geriatrics Center
  Health Centers
  Heart Failure Centers
  Home Medical Equipment
  Imaging Centers
  Mount Carmel Medical Group
  Occupational Health Centers
  Outpatient Cancer Treatment
  Outpatient Labs
  Physician Offices
  Rehab and Sports Medicine Services
  Sleep Medicine
  Surgery Centers
  Urgent Care Centers
  Women's Health Centers
  Wound Centers

COMPETITORS

Adena Health System
Fairfield Medical Center
Genesis Healthcare System (ohio)
Licking Memorial Health Systems
Nationwide Children's Hospital
Ohiohealth
Regency Hospital

HISTORICAL FINANCIALS

Company Type: Private

Income Statement				FYE: June 30
	REVENUE ($ mil.)	NET INCOME ($ mil.)	NET PROFIT MARGIN	EMPLOYEES
06/20	1,345	1	0.1%	8,000
06/18	1,911	157	8.2%	—
06/15	1,267	131	10.4%	—
06/14	1,223	94	7.7%	—
Annual Growth	1.6%	(50.3%)	—	—

2020 Year-End Financials
Return on assets: 0.1%   Cash ($ mil.): 6
Return on equity: 0.1%
Current ratio: —

MOUNT CARMEL HEALTH SYSTEM

EXECUTIVES

Ceo, Jay Kasey
Vice-President, Bruce Lucas
Information Specialist, Mike Croyle
Internal Medicine Practitioner, John Weiss
Information Specialist, Terri Theibert
Information Specialist, Tanya Hartshorn

Hematologist, Timothy Moore
Information Specialist, Jaime Capestany
Administrative Assistant, Linda Barkhurst
Manager, Mike Oross
Pacs Administrator, Lisa Gardner

LOCATIONS

HQ: MOUNT CARMEL HEALTH SYSTEM
  5300 N MEADOWS DR, GROVE CITY, OH 431232546
Phone: 614 234-5000
Web: WWW.MOUNTCARMELHEALTH.COM

HISTORICAL FINANCIALS

Company Type: Private

Income Statement				FYE: June 30
	REVENUE ($ mil.)	NET INCOME ($ mil.)	NET PROFIT MARGIN	EMPLOYEES
06/16	743	33	4.5%	1
06/15	707	47	6.7%	—
Annual Growth	5.1%	(29.5%)	—	—

2016 Year-End Financials
Return on assets: 6.6%   Cash ($ mil.): 39
Return on equity: 7.6%
Current ratio: 3.00

MOUNT SINAI MEDICAL CENTER OF FLORIDA, INC.

Mount Sinai Medical Center is the largest private independent not-for-profit teaching hospital in South Florida. The medical center which boasts more than 670 licensed beds provides general medical and surgical care as well as specialty care in cardiology (Mount Sinai Heart Institute) neuroscience oncology orthopedics pulmonology radiology and other fields. It also participates in clinical research studies and drug trials with an emphasis on cancer heart and lung conditions. It maintains an inpatient behavioral health unit and houses the Wien Center for Alzheimer's disease and memory disorders diagnosis and research the largest such facility in the region.

Operations

Mount Sinai Medical Center has about 25 operating suites and more than 700 physicians. Its medical specialties include cardiology endocrinology urology internal medicine cancer diagnostics and care gastroenterology and sleep lab. Mount Sinai's Centers of Excellence combine technology research and academics to provide innovative and comprehensive care in cardiology neuroscience oncology and orthopaedics. It works together with New York's prestigious Columbia University to create the Mount Sinai Heart Institute and the Columbia University Division of Urology at Mount Sinai the only Ivy League-affiliated programs in South Florida. These programs combine the strengths of two leaders in cardiovascular and urological care enhancing the outstanding level of service and providing greater access to state-of-the-art technology research and treatment options.

Geographic Reach

Reaching beyond its main South Florida campus the Mount Sinai Medical Center also operates a multi-specialty physicians' clinic emergency care and diagnostic center in nearby Aventura. It also operates physicians' clinics in Key Biscayne Hialeah Key West Marathon Miami Shores Midtown Skylake Sunny Isles Beach and two satellite locations in Coral Gables.

Company Background

Mount Sinai Medical Center of Florida was founded in 1949 by a group of philanthropists and concerned citizens.

EXECUTIVES

Pres-Ceo, Steven Sonenreich
Chb*, Wayne Chaplain
Exec Vp of Oper-Cfo*, Alex Mendez
Chief Operating Officer*, Angel Pallin
Accounts Coordinator, Aicia Jerez
Executive of Information Techn, Tom Gillette
Coordinator, Carroll Robitaille
Assistant Vice President of Nu, Maryse Dufresne
Human Resources Manager, Paul Katz
Pulmonary Supervisor, Carlos Gonzalez
Wien Center Research Manager, Maria G Custo

LOCATIONS

HQ: MOUNT SINAI MEDICAL CENTER OF FLORIDA, INC.
4300 ALTON RD, MIAMI BEACH, FL 331402948
Phone: 305 674-2121
Web: WWW.MSMC.COM

PRODUCTS/OPERATIONS

Florida Locations
MOUNT SINAI MEDICAL CENTER (MAIN CAMPUS): Miami Beach
MOUNT SINAI AVENTURA EMERGENCY ROOM PHYSICIAN OFFICES CANCER CENTER AND DIAGNOSTIC CENTER: Aventura
MOUNT SINAI KEY BISCAYNE PHYSICIAN OFFICES: Key Biscayne
MOUNT SINAI CORAL GABLES DIAGNOSTIC CATHETERIZATION LAB: Coral Gables
MOUNT SINAI PRIMARY & SPECIALTY CARE CORAL GABLES: Coral Gables
MOUNT SINAI HIALEAH: Hialeah

COMPETITORS

Baptist Health South Florida	Miami Children's Hospital
Broward Health	Tenet Healthcare
Hca	University Of Miami Hospital
Jackson Health System	

HISTORICAL FINANCIALS

Company Type: Private

Income Statement				FYE: December 31
	REVENUE ($ mil.)	NET INCOME ($ mil.)	NET PROFIT MARGIN	EMPLOYEES
12/16	560	19	3.5%	3,225
12/15	533	38	7.2%	—
12/14	530	17	3.2%	—
12/13	584	42	7.3%	—
Annual Growth	(1.4%)	(22.9%)	—	—

2016 Year-End Financials
Return on assets: 2.8%   Cash ($ mil.): 255
Return on equity: 8.7%
Current ratio: 3.30

MOUNT SINAI ST. LUKE'S.

EXECUTIVES

Pres, Frank Cracolici
Sr V Pres*, Robert Catalano
Research Manager*, Anthony Grillo
Manager, Jeff Horvath
Coordinator, Christella Watts
Assistant Professor, Preetika Mukherjee
Lab Manager, Mary Ellen Nusbaum
Director, Michelle Dunn
Ed Director, Debbie Gulecki
Staff, Debbie Wu
Coordinator, Maribel Fiol
Auditors: ERNST & YOUNG US LLP INDIANAP

LOCATIONS

HQ: MOUNT SINAI ST. LUKE'S.
1111 AMSTERDAM AVE, NEW YORK, NY 100251716
Phone: 212 523-4000
Web: WWW.MOUNTSINAI.ORG

HISTORICAL FINANCIALS

Company Type: Private

Income Statement				FYE: December 31
	REVENUE ($ mil.)	NET INCOME ($ mil.)	NET PROFIT MARGIN	EMPLOYEES
12/19	1,348	(22)	—	6,000
12/16	901	53	5.9%	—
12/15	859	61	7.1%	—
12/14	1,160	(17)	—	—
Annual Growth	3.0%	—	—	—

2019 Year-End Financials
Return on assets: (-1.6%)   Cash ($ mil.): 167
Return on equity: (-32.5%)
Current ratio: 1.80

MPHASIS CORPORATION

EXECUTIVES

Ceo-Pres, Vikas Gurugunti
Cfo, Ganesh Murthy
SEC, A Sivaram Nair
Chief Corporate, Dinesh Venugopal
Exec V Pres, Eric Winston
Attorney, Anuj Shah
Information Technology Project, Gregory Bailey
Executive Officer, John Bahadur
Executive Officer, Ann Weaver
Senior Manager Payroll, Bhushan Sathvik
Associate Vice President, Subrato Mozumdar
Auditors: GRANT THORNTON BHARAT LLP BEN

LOCATIONS

HQ: MPHASIS CORPORATION
460 PARK AVE S RM 1101, NEW YORK, NY 100167315
Phone: 212 686-6655
Web: WWW.MPHASIS.COM

HISTORICAL FINANCIALS

Company Type: Private

Income Statement				FYE: March 31
	REVENUE ($ mil.)	NET INCOME ($ mil.)	NET PROFIT MARGIN	EMPLOYEES
03/20	597	15	2.6%	2,000
03/19	584	29	5.0%	—
Annual Growth	2.3%	(47.5%)	—	—

2020 Year-End Financials
Return on assets: 5.0%   Cash ($ mil.): 16
Return on equity: 12.2%
Current ratio: 1.30

MULTI-COLOR CORPORATION

Multi-Color Corporation is a global label solutions supporting a number of the world's most prominent brands including leading producers of home and personal care wine and spirits food and beverage healthcare and specialty consumer products. The company serves international brand owners in the North American Latin American EMEA and Asia Pacific regions with a comprehensive range of the latest label technologies. With operations in more than 25 countries worldwide Multi-Color also provides a specialized label solutions including pressure sensitive shack cut and stack and heat transfer.

Operations

Multi-Color provides a wide range of products for the packaging needs of customers and is one of the world's largest producers of high quality pressure sensitive in-mold and heat transfer labels and a major manufacturer of cut and stack roll fed aluminum and shrink sleeve labels.

The company also offers the right label solution including creative development label production and application and packaging durability. It also provides custom durables and technical such as customer foams gaskets and insulator decal and digital braille. In addition to in-mold labels pressure sensitive labels and shrink sleeves Multi-Color also offers premium label solutions that will differentiate its clients' products from the competition and attract more customers. Lastly the company also provides extended text labels security label and smart label solutions.

Geographic Reach

Headquartered in Ohio Multi-Color also has approximately 80 manufacturing facilities located in North America Latin America EMEA and Asia Pacific.

Sales and Marketing

Multi-Color sells to a broad range of automotive and chemicals beverage durables and technical food and dairy personal care and beauty healthcare wine and spirits home care and laundry.

Strategy

Platinum Equity announced today the signing of a definitive agreement to sell Multi-Color Corporation (MCC) a global leader in label solutions to affiliates of Clayton Dubilier & Rice ("CD&R"). Financial terms of the transaction were not disclosed.

In connection with the transaction CD&R also announced it has signed a definitive agreement to acquire Fort Dearborn from Advent International and that it intends to combine MCC and Fort Dearborn to create a global label solutions company serving consumer packaged goods companies worldwide. The transactions are expected to close by the end of 2021 subject to customary regulatory approvals and other conditions.

Mergers and Acquisitions

In mid-2021 Multi-Color and Hexagon have signed a binding Sale and Purchase Agreement whereby MCC will acquire 100% of the shares in Hexagon. The acquisition includes Hexagon subsidiaries Hally Labels AU Label Partners AU Adhesif Labels NZ Hally Labels NZ Kiwi Labels NZ & Rapid Labels NZ.

In early 2021 Multi-Color acquired the Australia-based Herrods a leading provider of in-mould label (IML) solutions in Australia and New Zealand. The acquisitions expands MCC's in-mould labeling network creates new foothold for growth in Asia Pacific region. Financial terms of the transaction were not disclosed.

EXECUTIVES

Ceo-Pres, Kevin Kwilinski
V Pres-Cfo, Sharon E Birkett
Prin, Timothy P Lutz
Manager Engineering, Aron Kratky
Lab Technician, Brittany Pelgen
Customer Team Member, Carli Ritner
Business Analyst, Diana Cotton
Vice President, Greg Myers
Prepress Technician, James Howell
National Account Manager, Jeff Lozen
Payroll Specialist, Katie Brady
Auditors: GRANT THORNTON LLP DETROIT M

LOCATIONS

HQ: MULTI-COLOR CORPORATION
4053 CLOUGH WOODS DR, BATAVIA, OH 451032587
Phone: 513 381-1480
Web: WWW.MCCLABEL.COM

2015 Sales

	$ mil.	% of total
US	512	58
Australia	63	7
Italy	57	5
Other International	177	30
Total	**810**	**100**

PRODUCTS/OPERATIONS

Selected Products and Services

Labels
Heat transfer
In-mold
Neck bands
Peel-away
Pressure sensitive
Re-sealable
Shrink sleeve

COMPETITORS

Fort Dearborn	Outlook Group
H. S. Crocker	Ws Packaging Group

HISTORICAL FINANCIALS

Company Type: Private

Income Statement   FYE: March 31

	REVENUE ($ mil.)	NET INCOME ($ mil.)	NET PROFIT MARGIN	EMPLOYEES
03/19	1,725	(28)	—	8,400
03/18	1,300	71	5.5%	—
03/17	923	61	6.6%	—
03/16	870	47	5.5%	—
Annual Growth	25.6%	—	—	—

2019 Year-End Financials

Return on assets: (-1.1%)   Cash ($ mil.): 57
Return on equity: (-4.6%)
Current ratio: 1.90

MULTICARE HEALTH SYSTEM

MultiCare Health System is a not-for-profit health system that serves the residents in the southern Puget Sound region and southwestern Washington. Altogether the system's some 10 hospitals have more than 1785 beds. The largest facility Tacoma General boasts more than 435 beds and provides specialized cancer cardiac orthopedic and trauma care in addition to general medical and surgical care. Other medical centers include Good Samaritan Hospital (with approximately 375 beds) Allenmore Hospital (some 130 beds) Auburn Regional Medical Center (approximately 195 beds) and Mary Bridge Children's Hospital (more than 80 beds). Wellfound Behavioral Health Hospital is an independently operated joint venture of Multi-Care and CHI Franciscan Health.

Operations

MultiCare has more than 1800 staff physician specialists. In addition to its more than 10 hospitals the health system also operates numerous inpatient care primary care virtual care urgent care dedicated pediatric care and specialty services ? including MultiCare Behavioral Health Network MultiCare Indigo Urgent Care Mary Bridge Children's Hospital & Health Network a comprehensive regional network of health services for children Pulse Heart Institute MultiCare Rockwood Clinic the largest multispecialty clinic in the Inland Northwest region.

Tacoma General Hospital operates a wide range of essential health care services including a 24-hour Emergency Department the MultiCare Regional Cancer Center Family Birth Center and the region's largest most advanced NICU as well as leading-edge cardiac neurological orthopedic robotic and traditional surgical care. Tacoma General also offers Level II Adult Trauma Center and Level IV NICU. The nationally accredited in neonatal transport services and provides care and transportation for more than 750?800 premature infants annually. Mary Bridge Children's Hospital & Health Center operates a Pediatric Intensive Care Unit Pediatric Heart Center Center for Childhood Safety Child Abuse Intervention Programs and outpatient specialty clinics.

Geographic Reach

MultiCare serves patients in more than 230 primary care specialty care and urgent care clinics in Pierce King Kitsap Thurston Snohomish and Spokane counties.

EXECUTIVES

Pres-Ceo, William G Robertson
V Pres-Fin Cfo*, Vince Schmitz
Sr V Pres*, Lois I Bernstein
Exec V Pres*, Florence Chang
Sr V Pres*, Theresa M Boyle
Sr V Pres*, Sarah M Horsman
Chief of Medicine, William Crabb
Coordinator, Kathleen Floyd

Information Technology Manager, Barbara Smith
Technologist, Loree Peters
Registered Nurse, Michelle Rippe
Auditors: KPMG LLP SEATTLE WASHINGTON

LOCATIONS

HQ: MULTICARE HEALTH SYSTEM
316 MRTIN LTHER KING JR W, TACOMA, WA 984054252
Phone: 253 403-1000

PRODUCTS/OPERATIONS

Selected Facilities

Hospitals
Allenmore Hospital (Tacoma)
Auburn Medical Center (Auburn)
Good Samaritan Hospital (Puyallup)
Mary Bridge Children's Hospital and Health Center (Tacoma)
Tacoma General Hospital (Tacoma)
Other facilities
Allenmore Medical Center
Auburn MultiCare Clinic
Covington MultiCare Clinic
Lakewood Urgent Care Clinic
Kent MultiCare Clinic
MultiCare Home Services
Spanaway MultiCare Clinic
Tacoma Family Medicine
University Place Urgent Care Clinic
Westgate Urgent Care Clinic

Selected Services

Adult Day Health
Behavioral Health
Boutique
Breast Health
Cancer Center
Center for Healthy Living
Children's Therapy Unit
Community Programs
CyberKnife Radiosurgery
Diabetes Services
Ear Nose and Throat
Emergency and Urgent Care
Family Birth Centers
Geriatric Psychiatric Center
Health Care Resource Center
Heart Care
Home Health and Hospice
Immunization Clinic
Infusion Center
Institute for Research & Innovation
Laboratories Northwest
Maternal-Fetal Medicine
Medical Imaging
Nephrology
Neonatal Intensive Care Unit
Neurosciences
Nutrition
OB/GYN
Occupational Medicine
Orthopedics
Pain Management
Palliative Medicine
Perinatal Outreach Program
Pharmacy
Physical Therapy
Podiatry
Primary Care Clinics
Pulmonary Care
Pulmonary Rehabilitation
Rehabilitation
Robotic Technology
Senior Services
Sexual Assault Services
Spa
Sports Medicine
Surgical Services
Tobacco Cessation
Transfusion Free Medical and Surgical Program
Urology
Weight Loss and Wellness
Wound Healing Center

COMPETITORS

Catholic Health
  Initiatives
Franciscan Health
  System
Harrison Medical
  Center
Overlake Hospital
Peacehealth

Providence St. Joseph
  Health
Seattle Children's
  Hospital
Swedish Health
  Services
Yakima Valley Memorial

HISTORICAL FINANCIALS

Company Type: Private

Income Statement — FYE: December 31

	REVENUE ($ mil.)	NET INCOME ($ mil.)	NET PROFIT MARGIN	EMPLOYEES
12/20	3,367	311	9.2%	6,510
12/19	3,234	336	10.4%	—
12/18	2,922	34	1.2%	—
12/17	2,416	347	14.4%	—
Annual Growth	11.7%	(3.6%)	—	—

2020 Year-End Financials

Return on assets: 5.2%
Return on equity: 9.6%
Current ratio: 2.60
Cash ($ mil.): 946

MUNICIPAL ELECTRIC AUTHORITY OF GEORGIA

With more juice than a ripe Georgia peach the Municipal Electric Authority of Georgia (MEAG Power) supplies wholesale electric power. The authority has a generating capacity of 2069 MW through its interests in nuclear and fossil-fueled plants. Some 49% of the energy MEAG Power delivered in 2012 came from its nuclear plants. MEAG Power transmits electricity to 48 municipal and one county distribution systems across Georgia that in turn serve some 600000 consumers. It utilizes a transmission network that is co-owned by all the power suppliers in Georgia although it is considering joining a regional transmission organization (RTO) to further defray costs.

Operations

MEAG Power owns more than 1300 miles of high-voltage transmission lines and almost 200 substations. It also provides value-added services including management infrastructure and marketing support to its member municipalities energy marketers and other utilities.

The company generates most of its revenues from Project One (ownership stakes in nine generating units other owned transmission plants and working capital). Higher member billings for operating expenses related to fuel and nuclear operations lifted MEAG Power's revenues and net income in 2010.

Geographic Reach

The company serves 49 communities across Georgia.

Financial Performance

In 2012 MEAG Power's revenues increased by 8% thanks to higher participant billings related to a planned reduction in trust transfers as well as an increase in debt service related to environmental improvements to the coal operations and higher contract energy sales. These gains were partially offset by lower participant billings for maintenance and fuel expenses.

That year the company's net income increased by 351% as the result of higher net sales and decreased operating costs.

Strategy

With Georgia restricted in its natural potential for solar and wind power development MEAG Power is pushing hard for the expansion of nuclear power as a clean energy alternative to coal.

In a major breakthrough in 2012 the Nuclear Regulatory Commission approved a Combined Construction and Operating License for units 3 and 4 of the Vogtle plant (near Waynesboro Georgia) the first such license ever approved for a US nuclear plant and the first federal go-ahead for nuclear plant construction since 1978.

In 2013 MEAG Power completed a basemat of structural concrete for the nuclear island at the Vogtle Unit 4 nuclear expansion site the second of two units under construction at Plant Vogtle.

Company Background

In 2009 the Georgia Public Service Commission gave the go ahead for the expansion of the nuclear-powered Vogtle Electric Generating Plant which is co-owned by MEAG Power and in 2010 MEAP Power sold $2.7 billion in bonds to fund this expansion.

EXECUTIVES

Pres-Ceo, James E Fuller
V Pres*, William J Yearta
Tres*, Steve A Rentfrow
Mayor, Patrick C Bowie
Mayor, L Keith Brady
Director of Information Techno, Ron King
Senior Designer, Philip Johnson
Manager, Jerry Heeren
Controller, Andy Sharp
Transmission Administra, Aaron Hammers
Fuels Manager, Bret Griffin
Auditors: PRICEWATERHOUSECOOPERS LLP AT

LOCATIONS

HQ: MUNICIPAL ELECTRIC AUTHORITY OF GEORGIA
  1470 RIVEREDGE PKWY, ATLANTA, GA 303284640
Phone: 770 563-0300

COMPETITORS

Aep
Dominion Energy
Duke Energy
North Carolina
  Electric Membership
Oglethorpe Power

Progress Energy
Santee Cooper
Southern Company
Southern Company Gas
Tva

HISTORICAL FINANCIALS

Company Type: Private

Income Statement — FYE: December 31

	REVENUE ($ mil.)	NET INCOME ($ mil.)	NET PROFIT MARGIN	EMPLOYEES
12/20	639	23	3.6%	150
12/19	648	17	2.7%	—
12/18	681	(4)	—	—
12/17	623	0	—	—
Annual Growth	0.9%	—	—	—

2020 Year-End Financials

Return on assets: 0.2%
Return on equity: —
Current ratio: 1.60
Cash ($ mil.): 5

MUNSON HEALTHCARE

Munson Healthcare is a not-for-profit health care system serving residents in northern Michigan. Its flagship facility is Munson Medical Center in Traverse City a regional referral hospital with about 390 beds offering specialty services including cancer treatment behavioral health cardiac care and orthopedics. Munson Healthcare also has management agreements and other types of affiliations with about a dozen other hospitals in the region. In addition Munson Healthcare operates urgent care and community clinics home health care and hospice agencies an ambulance service and the Northern Michigan Supply Alliance a supply chain management group co-owned with Trinity Health.

Operations

Munson Healthcare is composed of eight hospitals located throughout northern Michigan - Charlevoix Area Hospital (Charlevoix) Kalkaska Memorial Health Center (Kalkaska) Mercy Hospital Cadillac (Cadillac) Mercy Hospital Grayling (Grayling) Munson Medical Center (Traverse City) Otsego Memorial Hospital (Gaylord) Paul Oliver Memorial Hospital (Frankfort) and West Shore Medical Center (Manistee). Services are also available at Munson Community Health Center (Traverse City) and Mercy Community Health Center (Prudenville). Munson Healthcare also works closely with Alpena General Hospital in Alpena and War Memorial Hospital in Sault St. Marie.

In addition to its hospital operations Munson Healthcare also offers in-home care through Munson Home Health and Munson Hospice and Palliative Care. Other specialty services and resources include speech and hearing clinics physical rehabilitation CAT scans magnetic resonance imaging and cardiac catheterization.

Munson Healthcare provides direct access to nearly 800 physicians representing more than 50 specialties.

Eah year the system sees some 22500 admissions performs some 8000 inpatient and 7000 outpatient surgeries and has some 51000 emergency department visits.

Geographic Reach

The health care system offers a continuum of health care services to people in 24 Michigan counties.

Strategy

To better provide services to region residents Munson Healthcare partnered with critical access hospital Mackinac Straits Health System in 2015. The affiliation is focused on improving health care services in rural northern Michigan.

Munson Healthcare is also forming an air ambulance joint venture between its North Flight EMS Air Division and Spectrum Health's Aero Med. The venture to be named North Flight Aero Med will provide critical care air emergency transport services in northern Michigan. It will begin operating in 2016.

Company Background

Munson Healthcare was founded in 1915.

EXECUTIVES

Ceo, Ed Ness
Pres, Al Pilong
Chm, Dan Wolf
Chm, John Pelizzari
SEC, Bob Sprunk
Treas, Connie Deneweth
Treas, Christina Macinnes
Asst Treas, Paul Sharilla
Treas, Dan McDavid
Cmo, Walt Noble

Corporate Vp Affairs M, David S McGreaham
Auditors: PLANTE & MORAN PLLC TRAVERSE

LOCATIONS

HQ: MUNSON HEALTHCARE
  1105 SIXTH ST, TRAVERSE CITY, MI 496842345
Phone: 800 252-2065
Web: WWW.MUNSONHEALTHCARE.ORG

PRODUCTS/OPERATIONS

Selected Michigan Facilities

	Charlevoix
	Kalkaska M
	Mercy Hosp
	Mercy Hosp
Munson Community Health Center - Traverse City	
Munson Hospice House - Traverse City	
Munson Manor Hospitality House - Traverse City	
Munson Medical Center - Traverse City	
Northwest Michigan Surgery Center - Traverse City	
	Otsego Mem
	Paul Olive
Smith Family Breast Health Center - Traverse City	
	West Shore

Medical Specialties
Bariatric Surgery
Behavioral Health
Bleeding Disorders Center
Cancer Services
Diabetes
Dialysis
Emergency Services
Hearing Clinic
Heart and Vascular Services
Hospice and Palliative Care
Occupational Health and Medicine
Orthopedics
Senior's Health
Sleep Disorders Center
Stroke Care
Teen's Health
Urgent Care
Urology
Women and Children

COMPETITORS

Borgess Health	Mclaren Health Care
Covenant Healthcare	Spectrum Health
Genesys Regional	Trinity Health (novi)
Medical Center	Zeeland Community
Hurley Medical Center	Hospital

HISTORICAL FINANCIALS

Company Type: Private

Income Statement				FYE: June 30
	REVENUE ($ mil.)	NET INCOME ($ mil.)	NET PROFIT MARGIN	EMPLOYEES
06/21	1,258	260	20.7%	4,000
06/20	1,144	39	3.4%	—
06/18	1,039	142	13.7%	—
06/17	940	160	17.1%	—
Annual Growth	7.5%	12.8%	—	—

2021 Year-End Financials

Return on assets: 13.6%   Cash ($ mil.): 203
Return on equity: 20.8%
Current ratio: 2.70

MUNSON MEDICAL CENTER

EXECUTIVES

Pres-Ceo, Matt Wille
Cfo*, Edward Carlson
Coo*, Derk Pronger
Manager, Christopher Layne
Manager, Eric Warren
Project Coordinator, Jennifer Satchwell
Internal Medicine Practitioner, John C Lorentson
Occupational Specia, Kristine A Siemer
Certified Cardiographic Techni, Linda Becker
Pharmacist, Mark Heindl
Oncology, Robert Prust

LOCATIONS

HQ: MUNSON MEDICAL CENTER
  1105 SIXTH ST, TRAVERSE CITY, MI 496842386
Phone: 231 935-6000
Web: WWW.MUNSONHEALTHCARE.ORG

HISTORICAL FINANCIALS

Company Type: Private

Income Statement				FYE: June 30
	REVENUE ($ mil.)	NET INCOME ($ mil.)	NET PROFIT MARGIN	EMPLOYEES
06/20	704	66	9.5%	3,100
06/16	533	67	12.7%	—
06/15	509	60	11.9%	—
06/10	441	28	6.4%	—
Annual Growth	4.8%	9.0%	—	—

2020 Year-End Financials

Return on assets: 5.9%   Cash ($ mil.): 391
Return on equity: 10.5%
Current ratio: 2.40

MUNSTER MEDICAL RESEARCH FOUNDATION, INC

EXECUTIVES

Pres-Ceo, Donald S Powers
Treas*, George E Watson
Admin*, Edward Robinson
SEC*, Palmer C Singleton
V Pres*, Joseph Morrow
Chm*, Frankie L Fesko
Prin*, James J Richards
SEC*, William A Hasse III
Treas*, David E Wickland
Coordinator, Carol Hernandez
Law Specialist, Cathy Reese
Auditors: ERNST & YOUNG LLP

LOCATIONS

HQ: MUNSTER MEDICAL RESEARCH FOUNDATION, INC
  901 MACARTHUR BLVD, MUNSTER, IN 463212901
Phone: 219 836-1600

HISTORICAL FINANCIALS

Company Type: Private

Income Statement				FYE: June 30
	REVENUE ($ mil.)	NET INCOME ($ mil.)	NET PROFIT MARGIN	EMPLOYEES
06/21	607	(9)	—	2,000
06/20	541	(104)	—	—
06/19	537	1	0.2%	—
06/18	548	74	13.5%	—
Annual Growth	3.4%	—	—	—

2021 Year-End Financials

Return on assets: (-3.2%)   Cash ($ mil.): —
Return on equity: (-5.6%)
Current ratio: 1.00

MV TRANSPORTATION, INC.

Need to supply transportation by bus? MV Transportation will run your bus system so you don't have to. The company operates more than 200 contracts to offer fixed-route and shuttle bus services as well as paratransit (transportation of people with disabilities) and transportation of Medicaid beneficiaries. Its customers consist primarily of transit authorities and other state and local government agencies responsible for public transportation. MV Transportation operates in more than 130 locations spanning 28 US states and in British Columbia Canada and Saudi Arabia; overall the company maintains a fleet of about 7000 vehicles. MV Transportation was founded in 1975.

Geographic Reach

MV Transportation and its subsidiaries joint ventures partnerships and affiliates operate more than 130 locations in 28 states the District of Columbia two Canadian Provinces and Saudi Arabia.

Sales and Marketing

The company provides its transportation services to cities counties municipalities and other jurisdictional entities as well as for private corporations non-profit agencies and community organizations. Some of its customers include Corpus Christi Regional Transportation Authority (B-Line paratransit and shuttle services) Ashland Public Transit (the curb-to-curb demand response transit service) Capital Area Transit System and Ashtabula County Transportation System (paratransit services).

Strategy

The company relies on the signing of year-long contracts and joint ventures for growth. In 2013 MV Transportation received a four-year contract to continue operation of the City of Irvine's iShuttle service; Irvine's iShuttle provides morning and evening peak-hour service along four routes connecting the Irvine Metrolink Station the Tustin Metrolink Station John Wayne Airport Irvine Spectrum and the Irvine Business Complex (IBC).

To expand its presence and experience in Qatar MV Transportation in 2013 opened its newest business venture in Doha Qatar: MV Global Transport Logistics WLL (MVGTL). In addition MVGTL signed an agreement with passenger transportation provider Mowasalat to provide planning scheduling and event management for the numerous events in Doha.

In early 2012 MV Transportation signed its first contract to manage a bus system outside North

America when it made a two-year agreement to coordinate an operation of more than 400 buses carrying Saudi Arabian Oil employees in the Middle Eastern kingdom. Striving to extend its international reach even further the company purchased Transportation Management Services UK Limited (TMSUK) a few months later. The deal allowed MV Transportation to enter a niche market as TMSUK designs and operates transportation systems for special events worldwide.

EXECUTIVES

Ceo, Thomas A Egan
Coo, Kevin A Klika
Co-Interim Cfo, Erin Niewinski
Co-Interim Cfo-Treas, Gary Richardson
Chb, Lisa Winston Hooks
General Consul, Ted Navitskas
Chief Sales Officer, Scott Sosnowski
Cntrl, Jessica Furey
Vice-President Information Ser, Chris Ruhig
Chief Human Resources, Jarrett Andrews
Dispatcher, Debbie Briant

LOCATIONS

HQ: MV TRANSPORTATION, INC.
2711 N HASKELL AVE # 1500, DALLAS, TX 752042911
Phone: 972 391-4600
Web: WWW.MVTRANSIT.COM

PRODUCTS/OPERATIONS

Selected Services
Bid committee consultation
Emergency evacuation planning
Global mobility and unique technology assets
International transport and logistics solutions
Logistics and security staffing
Paratransit and multimodal transport
Parking management and valet services
Sustainability transport initiatives
Traffic control planning staffing and consultation
Transport planning and operations
VIP fleet services

COMPETITORS

Coach Usa   National Express Group
Firstgroup America   Veolia Transportation
Logisticare

HISTORICAL FINANCIALS

Company Type: Private

Income Statement				FYE: December 31
	REVENUE ($ mil.)	NET INCOME ($ mil.)	NET PROFIT MARGIN	EMPLOYEES
12/09	706	23	3.3%	224
12/08	645	(2)	—	—
12/07	422	0	—	—
Annual Growth	29.3%	—	—	—

2009 Year-End Financials
Return on assets: 12.3%   Cash ($ mil.): 6
Return on equity: 94.1%
Current ratio: 1.50

MVP HEALTH PLAN, INC.

MVP Health Plan also know as MVP Health Care provides health insurance and employee benefits to its more than 700000 members in upstate New York New Hampshire and Vermont. MVP a not-for-profit organization offers a variety of plans including HMO PPO and indemnity coverage as well as dental plans health accounts and Medicare Advantage plans. Subsidiary MVP Select Care provides third-party administration (TPA) services for self-insured employers. MVP Health Care was founded in 1983 as Mohawk Valley Physicians' Health Plan.

Geographic Reach
MVP Health Care operates regional service and support offices across New York Vermont and New Hampshire. New York State is its largest service area. The firm has offices in Binghamton Fishkill Schenectady Syracuse Rochester and Utica New York as well as in Manchester New Hampshire; and Williston Vermont.

The company's provider network includes 19000 doctors in its three-state service territory; the firm also provides its members with access to about 500000 providers in other states through a partnership with CIGNA.

Sales and Marketing
The company uses a direct sales force as well as brokerages and call centers to sell its products. Its customers include individuals Medicare and Medicaid participants and employer groups.

Financial Performance
MVP Health Care revenue increased 18% to $2.9 billion in 2014; that growth was bolstered by the integration of Hudson Health Plan (acquired in 2013) as well as commercial and government membership growth. Medicaid Managed Care membership grew 21% that year.

Despite that growth the company lost a net $13.6 million.

Strategy
In addition to acquiring other area providers MVP Health Care widens its product offerings to attract a diversified customer base adding new non-employer group options (individual and high-deductible plans) and new small employer group products. It is has also launched new financial and preventative care tools including flexible spending accounts and disease management programs. Cutting policy prices has helped boost membership numbers as well.

The company also partners with health care providers to provide better care for its members as well as developing programs to target specific segments of the population.

MVP Health Care utilizes new technologies to cut its own operating costs. Recent initiatives include launching an e-commerce/plan administration platform creating virtual medical records with area health information organizations and supporting the Taconic Health Information Network and Community (an independent physician practice association).

EXECUTIVES

Pres-Ceo, David Oliker
Pres-Ceo*, Denise Gonick
Exec V Pres*, Karla Austen
Exec V Pres*, Allen J Hinkle
Execv Pres*, Patrick Glavey
Evp and Cfo*, Mark Fish
Chief of Information Technolog, Marilyn Horaszewski
Core Admin Mana, William Peat
Management Vice-President, Dale Hockel
Licensed Mvp Medicare Products, Pamela Kennedy
Programmer Analyst, Todd Cramer
Auditors: PRICEWATERHOUSECOOPERS LLP HA

LOCATIONS

HQ: MVP HEALTH PLAN, INC.
625 STATE ST, SCHENECTADY, NY 123052260
Phone: 518 370-4793
Web: WWW.MVPHEALTHCARE.COM

PRODUCTS/OPERATIONS

Selected Products
Alternative Funding Arrangements
Deferred Deductible Plans
Defined Contribution Plans
EPOs and PPOs
Health Spending Accounts
High-Deductible Health Plans
HMOs
Medicare Advantage Plans
Regional Plan Options

COMPETITORS

Affinity Health
Blue Cross And Blue Shield Of Vermont
Cigna
Capital District Physicians' Health Plan
Emblemhealth
Excellus Bluecross Blueshield
Fallon Community Health Plan
Fidelis Care New York
Healthplus Amerigroup
Healthfirst
Independent Health
Lifetime Healthcare
Unitedhealth Group
Healthnow New York Inc

HISTORICAL FINANCIALS

Company Type: Private

Income Statement				FYE: December 31
	ASSETS ($ mil.)	NET INCOME ($ mil.)	INCOME AS % OF ASSETS	EMPLOYEES
12/15	589	11	1.9%	1,500
12/14	540	(26)	—	—
Annual Growth	9.2%	—	—	—

2015 Year-End Financials
Return on assets: 1.9%   Sales ($ mil): 1,573
Return on equity: 2.7%

MWH GLOBAL, INC.

MWH Global is an environmental engineering construction and management firm that specializes in water-related projects or "wet infrastructure." The company's typical projects include building water treatment or desalination plants water transmission systems or storage facilities. MWH also provides general building services for transportation energy mining ports and waterways and industrial projects. The company is active in some 35 countries and serves governments public utilities and private sector clients. Affiliates of the employee-owned company include software provider Innovyze and business and government relations firm mCapitol. Canadian Engineering firm Stantec acquired MWH Global for $795 million in May 2016.

Geographic Reach
When it comes to projects MWH Global lives up to its name. The Colorado-based firm operates from 180 offices in 35 countries on six continents in the Americas the Asia/Pacific region the Middle East Africa and Europe.

Sales and Marketing

MWH Global seeks projects in five main markets including: the energy and power; water and wastewater; natural resources and mining; ports waterways and coastal; industrial and commercial transportation; and oil and gas markets.

It also does work for local regional and federal governments; US federal clients; public and private utilities; financial institutions; and insurance companies.

Strategy

MWH Global has kept busy in recent years working on a series of high-profile design and construction projects around the globe.

In 2015 the company continued its design-build work on the $7 billion Panama Canal Third Set of Locks project which will double the canal's capacity by the time its completed at the end of the year. The company also continued working with international electricity and gas company National Grid on the largest energy infrastructure program in the UK.

In late-2014 through a joint venture with Costain MWH Global signed on to a 200 million ($325 million) contract to provide design and build services for Southern Water's water and wastewater infrastructure and non-infrastructure assets program in Southeast England; part of Southern Waters' 3 billion ($5 billion) business plan for 2015-2020. Around the same time MWH Global completed its nearly two-decade-long Huanza Hydroelectric project in the Andes Mountains which now provides 92 Megawatts of electricity to some 90000 households in Peru.

In mid-2014 the South Florida Water Management District awarded MWH Global with a master services agreement to help implement the $880 million Restoration Strategies Regional Water Quality Plan which is part of the state's long-term strategy to restore the Everglades. In 2012 the Qatar Public Works Authority appointed MWH to design a drainage master plan in Qatar which will provide a road map for future investment into water and wastewater treatment and other water-related infrastructure programs over the next 50 years.

EXECUTIVES

Ceo, Alan J Krause
Cfo*, David G Barnes
Chief Legal Officer-Gen Counse*, Jeffrey D'Agosta
Chief Comm Ofcr*, Meg Vanderlaan
Chief Information Officer*, Claire Rutkowski
Chief Strategy Officer*, David A Smith
Project Manager, David Rush
Associate General Counsel, Donald K Blackwell
Vice President, Geoffrey Carthew
Project Manager, Jeff Coleman
Deputy Director, Jennifer Jones
Auditors: DELOITTE & TOUCHE LLP DENVER

LOCATIONS

HQ: MWH GLOBAL, INC.
370 INTERLOCKEN BLVD # 300, BROOMFIELD, CO 800218009
Phone: 303 533-1900
Web: WWW.STANTEC.COM

PRODUCTS/OPERATIONS

Selected Services

Construction
Airports
General building
Industrial
Highways bridges roads
Marine and port facilities
Engineering and technical services

Facilities development
Government relations
Program management and management consulting
Research and testing
Renewable energy and sustainability
Chemical and soil remediation
Hazardous waste
Hydroelectric power
Non-hydro renewable energy
Power distribution and transmission lines
Thermal power
Risk assessment
Specialized consulting services
Water and environment
Dams and reservoirs
Landfills biosolids
Sanitary/storm sewers conveyance pumping stations
Water resources planning management
Water treatment and desalination plants
Water transmission lines aqueducts
Waste water planning and management

COMPETITORS

Aecom	Peter Kiewit Sons'
Bechtel	Severn Trent
Black & Veatch	Siemens Water
Camp Dresser Mckee	Technologies
Ea Engineering	Tetra Tech
Engie	Veolia Environnement
Fluor	Ws Atkins
Jacobs Engineering	Zachry Inc.
Kbr	

HISTORICAL FINANCIALS
Company Type: Private

Income Statement				FYE: January 1
	REVENUE ($ mil.)	NET INCOME ($ mil.)	NET PROFIT MARGIN	EMPLOYEES
01/16*	1,318	35	2.7%	6,700
12/05	946	0	—	—
01/03	975	942	96.6%	—
12/01	774	19	2.6%	—
Annual Growth	3.9%	4.3%	—	—

*Fiscal year change

2016 Year-End Financials

Return on assets: 5.4%   Cash ($ mil.): 68
Return on equity: 19.1%
Current ratio: 1.40

NANA DEVELOPMENT CORPORATION

EXECUTIVES

Pres, Helvi Sandvik
Chairman*, Luke Sampson
Chairperson*, Lester Hadley
President*, Sandvik Helvi K
Sr V Pres*, Stan Fleming
V Pres*, Thomas Kevin E
Sr Vice President*, Jacquelyn R Luke
Secretary*, Dood Lincoln
Treasurer*, Henry Horner
Vice President*, Selina Moose
Vice President*, Charles J Greene
Auditors: KPMG LLP ANCHORAGE AK

LOCATIONS

HQ: NANA DEVELOPMENT CORPORATION
909 W 9TH AVE, ANCHORAGE, AK 995013322
Phone: 907 265-4100
Web: WWW.NANA.COM

HISTORICAL FINANCIALS
Company Type: Private

Income Statement				FYE: September 30
	REVENUE ($ mil.)	NET INCOME ($ mil.)	NET PROFIT MARGIN	EMPLOYEES
09/08	1,018	1	0.2%	3,000
09/07	833	7	0.8%	—
09/06	30	31	104.1%	—
09/00	119	0	0.6%	—
Annual Growth	30.7%	11.4%	—	—

2008 Year-End Financials

Return on assets: 0.3%   Cash ($ mil.): 37
Return on equity: 4.0%
Current ratio: 2.10

NANA REGIONAL CORPORATION, INC.,

EXECUTIVES

Prin, Wayne Westlake
Ceo*, Marie Green
Prin*, Kevin Thomas
Coo*, Lori Henry
Information Specialist, Justin Yeoman
Vice President Shareholder Rel, Gia Hanna
Employee, Anderson Heidi
Program Manager, Bernard Warrington
Manager, Betty Sheldon
Program Manager, Cyrus Snyder
Senior Manager, Damon Schaeffer

LOCATIONS

HQ: NANA REGIONAL CORPORATION, INC.,
3150 C ST STE 150, KOTZEBUE, AK 99752
Phone: 907 442-3301
Web: WWW.NANA.COM

HISTORICAL FINANCIALS
Company Type: Private

Income Statement				FYE: September 30
	REVENUE ($ mil.)	NET INCOME ($ mil.)	NET PROFIT MARGIN	EMPLOYEES
09/09	1,257	17	1.4%	4,650
09/08	1,175	29	2.5%	—
09/07	975	37	3.8%	—
Annual Growth	13.6%	(32.4%)	—	—

2009 Year-End Financials

Return on assets: 2.3%   Cash ($ mil.): 23
Return on equity: 7.0%
Current ratio: 1.60

NAPLES COMMUNITY HOSPITAL INC

EXECUTIVES

Pres-Ceo, Phillip C Dutcher
Cfo*, Rick Wyles

Cso*, Mike Riley
M.D., Cmo*, Frank Astor
Interim Coo*, Jonathan Kling
Coordinator, Jeanie McCree
Coordinator, Lawrence Lasky
Administrative Director, Sheila Phillips
Program Director, Rob Leyden
Payroll Supervisor, Karen Labin
Chief Financial Officer, Michael Stephens
Auditors: RSM US LLP MIAMI FLORIDA

LOCATIONS

HQ: NAPLES COMMUNITY HOSPITAL INC
350 7TH ST N, NAPLES, FL 341025754
Phone: 239 436-5000
Web: WWW.NCHMD.ORG

HISTORICAL FINANCIALS

Company Type: Private

Income Statement — FYE: September 30

	REVENUE ($ mil.)	NET INCOME ($ mil.)	NET PROFIT MARGIN	EMPLOYEES
09/19	656	9	1.5%	3,300
09/18	472	38	8.2%	—
09/17	472	38	8.2%	—
09/15	443	38	8.6%	—
Annual Growth	10.3%	(29.0%)	—	—

2019 Year-End Financials

Return on assets: 1.1%   Cash ($ mil.): 13
Return on equity: 1.4%
Current ratio: 1.70

NARRAGANSETT ELECTRIC COMP

LOCATIONS

HQ: NARRAGANSETT ELECTRIC COMP
642 GEORGE WASHINGTON HWY, LINCOLN, RI
028654244
Phone: 401 335-6238

HISTORICAL FINANCIALS

Company Type: Private

Income Statement — FYE: December 31

	REVENUE ($ mil.)	NET INCOME ($ mil.)	NET PROFIT MARGIN	EMPLOYEES
12/17	1,387	121	8.8%	6
12/16	1,269	84	6.7%	—
Annual Growth	9.3%	43.0%	—	—

2017 Year-End Financials

Return on assets: 2.6%   Cash ($ mil.): 8
Return on equity: 6.1%
Current ratio: 0.70

NASSUA COUNTY INTERIM FINANCE AUTHORITY

EXECUTIVES

Exec Dir, Richard Luke
Executive Director, Evan Cohen
Auditors: RSM US LLP NEW YORK NEW YORK

LOCATIONS

HQ: NASSUA COUNTY INTERIM FINANCE AUTHORITY
170 OLD COUNTRY RD # 205, MINEOLA, NY
115014322
Phone: 516 248-2828
Web: WWW.NASSAUCOUNTYNY.GOV

HISTORICAL FINANCIALS

Company Type: Private

Income Statement — FYE: December 31

	REVENUE ($ mil.)	NET INCOME ($ mil.)	NET PROFIT MARGIN	EMPLOYEES
12/19	1,173	(2)	—	6
12/18	1,133	(0)	—	—
12/17	1,095	(5)	—	—
12/16	1	140	12831.1%	—
Annual Growth	924.2%	—	—	—

2019 Year-End Financials

Return on assets: (-1.3%)   Cash ($ mil.): —
Return on equity: —
Current ratio: —

NATIONAL ASSOCIATION OF LETTER CARRIERS

EXECUTIVES

Pres, Fredric V Rolando
SEC*, Maria Licalzi
Treas*, Jane E Broendell
Administrative Assistant, Cindy Chaney
Director of Governmental Affai, Paul Swartz
Research Assistant, Holly Feldman-Wiencek
Assistant To President, J Sims
Director, Ron Watson
Administrative Assistant, Susan Wellhausen
Data Entry Clerk, Treva Koonce
Auditors: BOND BEEBE PC BETHESDA MD

LOCATIONS

HQ: NATIONAL ASSOCIATION OF LETTER CARRIERS
100 INDANA AVE NW STE 709, WASHINGTON, DC
20001
Phone: 202 393-4695
Web: WWW.NALC.ORG

HISTORICAL FINANCIALS

Company Type: Private

Income Statement — FYE: March 31

	REVENUE ($ mil.)	NET INCOME ($ mil.)	NET PROFIT MARGIN	EMPLOYEES
03/14*	1,406	97	6.9%	533
12/13	0	0	17.9%	—
12/11	0	0	67.4%	—
03/10	1	0	28.8%	—
Annual Growth	436.7%	275.8%		

*Fiscal year change

2014 Year-End Financials

Return on assets: 10.5%   Cash ($ mil.): 245
Return on equity: 20.1%
Current ratio: —

NATIONAL CHRISTIAN CHARITABLE FOUNDATION, INC.

EXECUTIVES

Prin, Terra Parker
Treasurer, David D Johnson
Vice President, George Cox
Chief Information Officer., Amy Garrett
Vice President., Marsha Walker
Gift Planning Team, Don Etheridge
Chief Information Officer, Dan Brown
Asset Manager, Amy Rogier
Vice President, David Parsley
Director of Giver, Natalie Taylor
Director of Giver, Sandi Banister
Auditors: NATIONAL CHRISTIAN CHARITABLE

LOCATIONS

HQ: NATIONAL CHRISTIAN CHARITABLE
FOUNDATION, INC.
11625 RAINWATER DR # 500, ALPHARETTA, GA
300098674
Phone: 404 252-0100
Web: WWW.NCFGIVING.COM

HISTORICAL FINANCIALS

Company Type: Private

Income Statement — FYE: December 31

	REVENUE ($ mil.)	NET INCOME ($ mil.)	NET PROFIT MARGIN	EMPLOYEES
12/16	1,413	306	21.7%	2
12/11	665	141	21.3%	—
12/09	396	50	12.7%	—
Annual Growth	19.9%	29.4%	—	—

2016 Year-End Financials

Return on assets: 14.9%   Cash ($ mil.): 457
Return on equity: 15.1%
Current ratio: —

NATIONAL COLLEGIATE ATHLETIC ASSOCIATION

The National Collegiate Athletic Association (NCAA) supports the intercollegiate sports activities of around 1000 member colleges and universities. A not-for-profit organization the NCAA administers scholarship and grant programs enforces conduct and eligibility rules and works to support and promote the needs of student athletes. The association is known for its lucrative branding and television deals such as those surrounding the popular "March Madness" tournament for Division I men's basketball. Seeking reform of athletics rules and regulations officials from 13 schools formed the Intercollegiate Athletic Association of the United States in 1906. The organization took its current name in 1910.

Financial Performance

NCAA revenue in fiscal 2013 (ended August) was $913 million up 5% versus the prior year most of which came from the rights agreement with CBS Sports and Turner Broadcasting. Indeed about 80% of the NCAA's revenue come from television and marketing rights fees generated primarily from the Division I men's basketball championship. Another 12% comes from championships and NIT tournaments including ticket and merchandise sales.

About 96% of NCAA revenue is distributed directly to the Division I membership or to support championships or programs that benefit student-athletes. The remaining 4% goes for central services such as building operations and salaries not related to particular programs.

Strategy

In a major shift the NCAA in 2019 allowed student-athletes to receive compensation when their names images or likenesses are used for commercial purposes. The organization changed its rules on student-athletes after California passed a law allowing compensation (effective in 2023) following a lawsuit. The NCAA has long adamantly prohibited any payment of college athletes (other than scholarships) to preserve their amateur status. The NCAA's three major divisions were left to set rules governing compensation.

EXECUTIVES

Pres, Mark A Emmert
Customer Staff, Melody Lawrence
Accounting Staff, Morgan Sanders
Project Coordinator, Reggie Krow
Accounting, Dean Schmollinger
Assistant Coordinator, Evelyn Gross
Managing Director, Jackie Campbell
Executive Assistant, Amy Huston
Associate Director, Amy L Reis
Associate Director of Academic, Charnele Kemper
Senior Web Developer, Colin Chappell
Auditors: CROWE LLP INDIANAPOLIS IN

LOCATIONS

HQ: NATIONAL COLLEGIATE ATHLETIC ASSOCIATION
700 W WASHINGTON ST, INDIANAPOLIS, IN
462042710
Phone: 317 917-6222
Web: WWW.NCAA.ORG

PRODUCTS/OPERATIONS

2013 Revenues

	% of total
Television & marketing rights fees	80
Championships & NIT tournaments	12
Investments	4
Sales & services	3
Contributions facilities & other	1
Total	**100**

HISTORICAL FINANCIALS

Company Type: Private

Income Statement

FYE: August 31

	REVENUE ($ mil.)	NET INCOME ($ mil.)	NET PROFIT MARGIN	EMPLOYEES
08/19	1,118	70	6.3%	508
08/18	1,064	27	2.5%	—
08/17	1,061	104	9.9%	—
08/16	995	(403)	—	—
Annual Growth	3.9%	—	—	—

2019 Year-End Financials

Return on assets: 11.5%   Cash ($ mil.): 15
Return on equity: 15.7%
Current ratio: 0.50

NATIONAL GRAPE CO-OPERATIVE ASSOCIATION, INC.

Well of course grape growers want to hang out in a bunch! The more than 1090 grower/owner-members of the National Grape Cooperative harvest Concord and Niagara grapes from almost 50000 acres of vineyards. The plucked produce supplies the coop's wholly owned subsidiary Welch Foods. Welch Foods makes and sells fruit-based juices jams jellies and spreads under the Welch's and Bama brands in the US and nearly 50 other countries. Offerings include fresh eating grapes distributed by C.H. Robinson Worldwide as well as dried fruit and frozen juice pops. The grape growers own vineyards in Pennsylvania Michigan New York Ohio Washington and Ontario Canada which produce some 300000 tons of grapes annually.

HISTORY

Looking for a steady supply of grapes for his processing plant in 1945 Russian immigrant Jack Kaplan convinced 900 grape growers to join the newly formed National Grape Cooperative. Also that year Welch Foods' parent company decided to spin off its purple fruit interests and Kaplan purchased a controlling interest. Welch's — a competitor at the time — had been started in 1869 when Dr. Thomas Welch a tee totaling dentist created an unfermented Concord grape wine to be used for nonalcoholic communions. The juice was coolly received at first but the advent of Prohibition helped push the company to the forefront of the fruit-drink industry.

While Kaplan had purchased his interest in Welch's with the intention of combining it with the National Grape Co-op it wasn't until the mid-1950s that the two could agree on the acquisition. Welch's product line grew throughout the 1960s and 1970s including the 1972 introduction of red

grape and white grape juices. A glut of grapes depressed prices in the 1980s but the co-op rebounded by the 1990s.

In 1994 the co-op acquired jam and jelly maker BAMA Foods from Borden. Daniel Dillon became CEO of Welch's in 1995 and Fredrick Kalian was named president of the co-op the next year. Yakima Valley Grape Producers joined National Grape Co-op in 1997 adding new growers and more grapes to meet a growing demand spurred in part by newly discovered health benefits of purple and white grape juice. (Welch's helped fund the research.)

New products and increased advertising helped boost juice sales dramatically in 1998 and 1999. Fresh table grapes distributed by C.H. Robinson Worldwide were also introduced in 1999 and by 2000 were available nationwide. In 2001 the company announced it would be cutting up to 100 jobs — its first layoffs in more than two decades — due to slowing sales.

In 2003 the company introduced new variations of its products including single-serving juices (Welsh Squeezables). This along with increased marketing and new packaging have seen its sales growing during the last two years. Expansion in grocery channels and the introduction of low-calorie items and shrink-pack products led to further sales gains in 2004.

EXECUTIVES

Pres, Randolph Graham
V Pres, Joseph C Falcone
Asst SEC, Vivian S Y Tseng
V Pres, Harold Smith
Dir, Jerry A Czebotar
Dir, Jon Hinkleman
Employee, Arcelia Hultberg
General Manager, Brent Roggie
Executive Administrative Assis, Ivis Edgerton
Employee, Kimberly Lynch
Auditors: KPMG LLP BOSTON MA

LOCATIONS

HQ: NATIONAL GRAPE CO-OPERATIVE ASSOCIATION, INC.
71 E MAIN ST, WESTFIELD, NY 147871342
Phone: 716 326-5200
Web: WWW.WELCHS.COM

COMPETITORS

B&g Foods	Hornell Brewing
Big Heart Pet Brands	Izze
Chiquita Brands	Mondelez International
Coca-cola	Monster Beverage
Constellation Brands	Nestl © Usa
Cranberries Limited	Ocean Spray
Dole Food	Pepsico
Dr Pepper Snapple Group	Procter & Gamble
Fresh Del Monte Produce	Smucker
Goya	Snapple
	Tropicana

HISTORICAL FINANCIALS

Company Type: Private

Income Statement

FYE: August 31

	REVENUE ($ mil.)	NET INCOME ($ mil.)	NET PROFIT MARGIN	EMPLOYEES
08/12	649	74	11.5%	1,325
08/11	640	74	11.6%	—
08/10	658	82	12.6%	—
Annual Growth	(0.7%)	(5.1%)	—	—

2012 Year-End Financials

Return on assets: 19.8%   Cash ($ mil.): 4
Return on equity: 999.9%
Current ratio: 1.50

NATIONAL RAILROAD PASSENGER CORPORATION

National Railroad Passenger Corporation better known as Amtrak has been riding the rails for more than 40 years. Amtrak is the US' intercity passenger rail provider and its only high-speed rail operator. More than 30 million passengers travel on Amtrak every year on more than 300 daily trains. It connects 46 states Washington DC and three provinces in Canada. Its network consists of about 21000 route miles of track most of which is owned by freight railroads. Amtrak also operates commuter rail systems on behalf of several states and transit agencies. Owned by the US government through the US Department of Transportation Amtrak depends on subsidies from the federal government to operate.

HISTORY

US passenger train travel peaked in 1929 with 20000 trains in operation. But the spread of automobiles bus service and air travel cut into business and by the late 1960s only about 500 passenger trains remained running in the country. In 1970 the combined losses of all private train operations exceeded $1.8 billion in today's dollars. That year Congress passed the Rail Passenger Service Act which created Amtrak to preserve America's passenger rail system. Although railroads were offered stock in the corporation for their passenger equipment most just wrote off the loss.

Amtrak began operating in 1971 with 1200 cars most built in the 1950s. Although the company lost money from the outset ($153 million in 1972) it continued to be bankrolled by Uncle Sam despite much criticism. Amtrak ordered its first new equipment in 1973 the year it also began taking over stations yards and service staff. The company didn't own any track until 1976 when it purchased hundreds of miles of right-of-way track from Boston to Washington DC.

After a 1979 study showed Amtrak passengers to be by far the most heavily subsidized travelers in the US Congress ordered the company to better utilize its resources. The 1980s saw Amtrak leasing its rights-of-way along its tracks in the Northeast corridor to telecommunications companies which installed fiber-optic cables and beginning mail and freight services for extra revenue.

In the early 1990s Amtrak faced a number of challenges: Midwest flooding falling airfares and safety concerns over a number of rail accidents particularly the 1993 wreck of the Sunset Limited near Mobile Alabama in which 47 people were killed (the worst accident in Amtrak's history). In 1994 Amtrak's board of directors (at Congress' behest) adopted a plan to be free of federal support by 2002. In 1995 the company began planning high-speed trains for its heavily traveled East Coast routes.

In 1997 Amtrak finalized agreements to buy the high-speed cars and locomotives central to its self-sufficiency plan. It also began increasing its freight hauling and had its first profitable offering: the Metroliner route between New York and Washington DC.

Amtrak's board of directors was replaced by Congress in 1997 with a seven-member Reform Board appointed by President Clinton. Chairman and president Thomas Downs resigned that year and Tommy Thompson then governor of Wiscon-

sin took over as chairman. Former Massachusetts governor Michael Dukakis was named vice chairman and George Warrington stepped in as Amtrak's president and CEO.

Technical problems in 1999 delayed Amtrak's introduction of the Acela high-speed train in the Northeast until late 2000 when service began in the Boston-Washington corridor. In 2001 Amtrak pitched a 20-year plan involving an annual outlay of $1.5 billion in federal funds for expanding and modernizing its passenger service to help alleviate highway and airport congestion nationwide.

Thompson left the Amtrak board in 2001 after he was named US secretary of health and human services.

Realizing Amtrak would not meet its end-of-the-year deadline to be self-sufficient in 2002 the Amtrak Reform Council sent a proposal to Congress that Amtrak be divided into three groups: one to oversee operations and funding a second to maintain certain Amtrak-owned tracks and properties and a third to operate trains. It also called for competition to be allowed on some passenger routes within two to three years.

Also in 2002 Warrington resigned and was replaced by David Gunn who formerly headed the metropolitan transit systems in New York and Toronto. Gunn began moving to cut costs and he worked to secure new federal money to avert a threatened shutdown of rail service in July 2002. In 2004 the company exited the mail-carrying business which had not been profitable.

Gunn was fired in November 2005 however and chief engineer David Hughes was named interim president and CEO. He left the company after Alexander Kummant was made president and CEO in September 2006.

The Passenger Rail Investment and Improvement Act of 2008 gives five annual grants to Amtrak amounting to $9.8 billion for fiscal years 2009 through 2013. Another boon came in the form of $1.3 billion of stimulus money earmarked for Amtrak by the American Recovery and Reinvestment Act (ARRA) of 2009 which authorizes the Federal Railroad Administration to make the funds available to Amtrak by grant agreement. About $446.8 million will be used for capital security grants including life safety improvements. Another $884 million will go toward the repair rehabilitation or upgrade of railroad assets and infrastructure and toward capital projects that expand rail capacity including the rehabilitation of rolling stock. The Obama administration promised an ongoing investment of about $1 billion annually for high-speed rail projects.

A record 28.7 million passengers rode on Amtrak in fiscal 2010. While impressive the company also had a history of recurring operating losses. Although total revenues increased about 7% in 2010 compared to 2009 Amtrak reported fairly comparable net losses in both years.

EXECUTIVES

Pres-Ceo, Richard H Anderson
Exec V Pres-Gen Counsel-Corp S, Eleanor D Acheson
Sr Exec V Pres, Stephen J Gardner
Exec V Pres-Chief Mktg and Com, J Timothy Griffin
Exec V Pres-Chief Safety Offce, Kenneth Hylander
Exec V Pres- Coo, Scot Naparstek
Exec V Pres-Cao, Dj Stadtler
Exec V Pres-CIO, Christian Zacariassen
Evp-Chief Mktg & Comml Officer, Roger Harris
Acting Director, Frank Gallello
Procurement Staff, Marylin Jamisom
Auditors: ERNST & YOUNG LLP TYSONS VA

LOCATIONS

HQ: NATIONAL RAILROAD PASSENGER CORPORATION
1 MASSACHUSETTS AVE NW, WASHINGTON, DC 200011401
Phone: 202 906-3000
Web: WWW.AMTRAKOIG.GOV

PRODUCTS/OPERATIONS

2014 Sales

	% of total
Passenger related	78
Commuter	4
Other	18
Total	**100**

2014 Sales

	% of total
Ticket	69
State Contribution	7
Food Beverage	4
Others	20
Total	**100**

COMPETITORS

Airtran Airways
American Airlines Group
Delta Air Lines
Frontier Airlines
Greyhound
Jetblue
Port Imperial Ferry Corp.
Southwest Airlines
Trailways Transportation System
United Continental

HISTORICAL FINANCIALS

Company Type: Private

Income Statement				FYE: September 30
	REVENUE ($ mil.)	NET INCOME ($ mil.)	NET PROFIT MARGIN	EMPLOYEES
09/20	2,430	(1,679)	—	18,650
09/19	3,503	(880)	—	—
09/18	3,386	(817)	—	—
Annual Growth (15.3%)		—	—	—

2020 Year-End Financials

Return on assets: (-8.8%)
Return on equity: (-13.4%)
Current ratio: 2.20
Cash ($ mil.): 409

NATURAL GAS PIPELINE COMPANY OF AMERICA LLC

EXECUTIVES

MBR-Pres, David Devine
Mng MBR*, Richard D Kinder
MBR*, Scott Parker
MBR-Cfo*, Jim Saunders
MBR-Exec V Pres*, Steve Kean
MBR*, Charles Schwager
MBR*, Joseph Listengart
Engineer Pipeline Senior, Fredrik Sultan
Senior Administrator, Robert L Gamble

LOCATIONS

HQ: NATURAL GAS PIPELINE COMPANY OF AMERICA LLC
1001 LOUISIANA ST, HOUSTON, TX 770025089
Phone: 713 369-9000
Web: WWW.KINDERMORGAN.COM

HISTORICAL FINANCIALS

Company Type: Private

Income Statement   FYE: December 31

	REVENUE ($ mil.)	NET INCOME ($ mil.)	NET PROFIT MARGIN	EMPLOYEES
12/17	679	130	19.2%	1,747
12/16	613	121	19.7%	—
Annual Growth	10.8%	8.0%	—	—

2017 Year-End Financials

Return on assets: 6.7%   Cash ($ mil.): 15
Return on equity: 9.7%
Current ratio: 1.50

NAVIGATE AFFORDABLE HOUSING PARTNERS, INC

EXECUTIVES

Ceo, Lisa McCarroll
Coo*, Julie Reynolds
Acct*, Tammy Cantrell
Receptionist, Rhonda Thurman
Deputy Director, Admi, Rob McLaughlin
Administration Coordi, Tim Shearer
Auditors: KASSOUF & CO PC BIRMINGHAM A

LOCATIONS

HQ: NAVIGATE AFFORDABLE HOUSING PARTNERS, INC
1827 1ST AVE N STE 100, BIRMINGHAM, AL 352033137
Phone: 205 445-2800
Web: WWW.NAVIGATEHOUSING.COM

HISTORICAL FINANCIALS

Company Type: Private

Income Statement   FYE: December 31

	REVENUE ($ mil.)	NET INCOME ($ mil.)	NET PROFIT MARGIN	EMPLOYEES
12/19	605	9	1.5%	49
12/17	573	8	1.5%	—
12/16	540	(12)	—	—
12/13	498	(6)	—	—
Annual Growth	3.3%	—	—	—

2019 Year-End Financials

Return on assets: 21.2%   Cash ($ mil.): 33
Return on equity: 21.4%
Current ratio: 105.80

NAVY EXCHANGE SERVICE COMMAND

Before Old Navy there was the Navy Exchange Service Command (NEXCOM). Active-duty military personnel reservists retirees and their family members can shop and gas up at more than 100 Navy Exchange (NEX) retail stores (brand-name and private-label merchandise ranging from apparel to home electronics) more than 150 NEXCOM Ships Stores (basic necessities) and its 100-plus Uniform Support Centers (the sole source of authorized uniforms). NEXCOM also runs about 40 Navy Lodges (motels) in the US and about half a dozen foreign countries. NEXCOM receives tax dollars for its shipboard stores but it is otherwise self-supporting. Most of the profits fund morale welfare and recreational programs (MWR) for sailors.

Geographic Reach

Navy Exchange Service Command has more than 100 NEX stores on land in the US Cuba Africa Europe the Middle East Japan and China.

Strategy

Since the government lifted restrictions on the types of items sold at the stores allowing more expensive furniture jewelry and televisions sales have been on the rise at NEX stores. NEXCOM has also been adding stores at home and abroad. In fall 2013 it opened a Fleet Store in Jebel Ali Dubai to serve sailors stationed in and around Dubai as well as military personnel passing through the area aboard ship.

To better compete with online rivals Walmart.com Target.com Amazon.com BestBuy.com and others in 2013 NEX expanded its Price Match Policy to match their prices.

EXECUTIVES

Ceo, Robert J Bianchi
Coo*, Michael P Good
Cfo*, Laurie P Hasten
Treas*, Thomas McDonald
Controllor*, Gerald Outar
Law Specialist, Nancy Haas
Staff, Cleveland Rogers
Network Manager, Tim Anthony
Coordinator, Charles Early
Law Specialist, Kia Coleman
Law Specialist, Kim Sherman

LOCATIONS

HQ: NAVY EXCHANGE SERVICE COMMAND
3280 VIRGINIA BEACH BLVD, VIRGINIA BEACH, VA 234525799
Phone: 757 631-3696
Web: WWW.MYNAVYEXCHANGE.COM

PRODUCTS/OPERATIONS

2014 Sales

	% of total
Total Sales	95
Income from Concessions net	2
Contributed Services	3
Other Revenue	0
Total	**100**

PRODUCT DEPARTMENTS

PRODUCT DEPARTMENTS
For The Home
Electronics
Shoes
Beauty
Women
Men

Kids
Navy pride
Handbags and accessories

COMPETITORS

7-eleven	Target Corporation
Amazon.com	Value City Furniture
Best Buy	Wal-mart
Kmart	

HISTORICAL FINANCIALS

Company Type: Private

Income Statement   FYE: February 3

	REVENUE ($ mil.)	NET INCOME ($ mil.)	NET PROFIT MARGIN	EMPLOYEES
02/18*	2,617	32	1.2%	14,000
01/17	2,574	45	1.8%	—
01/16	2,635	73	2.8%	—
01/11	2,749	68	2.5%	—
Annual Growth	(0.7%)	(10.3%)	—	—

*Fiscal year change

NCH CORPORATION

NCH Corporation is a global leader in industrial commercial and institutional maintenance products and services and one of the largest companies in the world to sell such products through direct marketing. The company makes and sells chemical maintenance repair and supply products including all kinds of cleaners for customers in more than 50 countries throughout the world. NCH markets its products through a direct sales force to companies in industrial commercial and infrastructure markets. Other products include pet care supplies plumbing parts. Founded in 1919 leadership of the company remains in the hands of the Levy family descendants of the founding father Milton P. Levy Senior.

Operations

The company's major areas of focus include producing products for the industrial cleaning and maintenance pet care plumbing specialty industries supply and water treatment and remediation markets.

The company's divisions include: water treatment solutions plumbing industrial and institutional maintenance parts washing lubrication and biologicals.

Subsidiaries in NCH's Chemical Specialties division produce cleaners degreasers lubricants grounds care housekeeping and water treatment products. Its plumbing products group provides plumbing supplies that include thousands of parts and products for repair replacement remodeling and new construction. Other subsidiaries include Pure Solve a parts washing service.

NCH sells its products directly through a number of wholly owned subsidiaries many of which are engaged in the maintenance products business. It include Certified Chemsearch Chem-Aqua and Danco.

Geographic Reach

NCH has operations throughout the world. The company has representatives in six continents. Its sales and service teams serve customers in North America Latin America Europe Asia Australia and India. NCH also has wholly owned subsidiaries in more than 50 countries. The company is headquartered in Irving Texas.

Sales and Marketing

NCH sells to industrial commercial and institutional customers. Its products are distributed nationally through home centers and hardware stores. The company has organization of direct sales representatives and it sells its products through direct marketing. The Plumbing Products group provides supplies for the do-it-yourself consumer and the OEM market.

Company Background

Founded in 1919 NCH Corporation is a global leader in industrial commercial and institutional maintenance products and services and one of the largest companies in the world to sell such products through direct marketing.

HISTORY

NCH was established in 1919.

Salesman Milton Levy founded National Disinfectant Co. in Dallas in 1919 to make disinfectants insecticides and soaps. The company's offerings grew in the 1930s to include Everbrite a top-selling industrial floor wax. Levy's sons Irvin Lester and Milton Jr. worked for the company as teenagers and took over its management after their father's death in 1946.

National Disinfectant expanded geographically in the 1950s and 1960s opening its first branch office in St. Louis in 1956. The company changed its name to National Chemsearch in 1960 to reflect its diversity. It also expanded into Europe and Latin America. National Chemsearch went public in 1965. Acquisitions boosted its product line to about 250 items by 1970. The company shortened its name to NCH in 1978.

NCH expanded its marketing to include catalog sales direct mail and telemarketing in 1986. It opened a South Korean plant in 1992. Troubled economies in Mexico and Venezuela hurt profits in 1994 and the next year NCH began work on a long-term business strategy that envisioned third-generation Levy family members moving into higher executive ranks.

Softened currency rates in Europe and Asia contributed to a decrease in profits for fiscal 1999. That year NCH focused on strengthening its customer relationships by boosting sales staff training and implementing an Internet-based corporate network.

In 2000 Irvin Levy became the company's chairman and NCH sold its electronic components business. The next year the company shut down its direct broadcast satellite equipment operations. In February 2002 the Levys took the company private by purchasing the 43% of the company that they didn't already own. The brothers originally offered a 20% premium to buy the shares but were greeted by lawsuits from shareholders who claimed they were taking advantage of a depressed market. The Levys settled the suits by upping the offer by $120 million.

In 2012 subsidiaries Chem-Aqua and Nephros signed a non-exclusive distributor agreement for Chem-Aqua to distribute Nephros's innovative ultrafilters in North America. The addition of Nephros ultrafilters to Chem-Aqua's product line allows both companies to offer their institutional customers a comprehensive multi-barrier approach for the prevention of waterborne infection.

EXECUTIVES

Pres-Chm, Irvin Levy
Exec V Pres-Cfo*, Christopher T Sortwell
Exec V Pres*, Levy John
V Pres*, Donald L Jones
Treas*, Irena Ki
Vice President of Marketing, Kevin Jones
Vice President Information TEC, Leonard Brown
Assistant Vice President, Donna Cagler

Senior Vice President of Sales, Frank Pellegrini
Senior Vice President of Globa, Jeff Saunders
Treasurer, Mark Hoesten
Auditors: PRICEWATERHOUSECOOPERS LLP DA

LOCATIONS

HQ: NCH CORPORATION
2727 CHEMSEARCH BLVD, IRVING, TX 750626454
Phone: 972 438-0211
Web: WWW.NCH.COM

PRODUCTS/OPERATIONS

Selected Operations and Products

Chemical Specialties
  Cleaning chemicals
  Deodorizers
  Floor and carpet care products
  HVAC products
  Lubricants
  Oil production facility chemicals
  Paint
  Paint removers
  Water-treatment chemicals
Landmark Direct
  First-aid supplies
  Workplace signage and productivity products
Pet Care
Partsmaster Group
  Cutting tools
  Electrical products
  Fasteners
  Welding alloys
Plumbing Products Group
  Plumbing products for new construction
  Plumbing repair and replacement parts
Industrial and Institutional Maintenance
Industrial and commercial cleaning
Industrial Repair and maintenance
Drains Grease Traps and lift stations
Lubrication and coolants
Equipment and supplies
Parts washing
Grounds Care
Personal hygiene
Pet Care
Training pads
Stain and Odor Removers
Cleaners and Disinfectants
Allergy Relief and shed Control
Grooming products
Plumbing
Sinks
Faucets
Tub & Showers
Toilets
Drains
Specialty Industrial Supply
High Performance Cutting Tools
Welding
Abrasives
Compounds
Fasteners
Electrical and Automotive
Shop Supplies
Storage Hardware
Tools
Water Treatment Solutions
Boiler
Cooling Towers
Colsed Recirculation Systems
Biocides and Algaecides
Cleaner/Descalers
Equipment
Wastewater and Bio Remediation

COMPETITORS

Church & Dwight	H.b. Fuller
Cintas	Illinois Tool Works
Clariant	Pioneer Corporation
Danaher	Quaker Chemical
Detrex	Safety-kleen
Ecolab	Wd-40

HISTORICAL FINANCIALS

Company Type: Private

Income Statement — FYE: April 30

	REVENUE ($ mil.)	NET INCOME ($ mil.)	NET PROFIT MARGIN	EMPLOYEES
04/19	1,005	26	2.6%	8,500
04/12	1,045	6	0.6%	—
04/11	952	6	0.7%	—
Annual Growth	0.7%	18.5%	—	—

2019 Year-End Financials

Return on assets: 4.3%   Cash ($ mil.): 26
Return on equity: 13.5%
Current ratio: 2.20

NEBRASKA MEDICINE

EXECUTIVES

Pres, Bradley E Britigan
SEC*, James Linder
Treas*, Bruce Grewcock
Drug Policy Coordinator, Jenel Proksel
Drug Policy Coordinator, Jenny Van Moorleghem
Utilization Management Lead, Karie Eberhardt
Administrative Assistant, Mary Stenzel
Nurse Practitioner, Rachael Schmidt
Clinical Education Coordinator, Shaylene Michaels
Database Analyst, Andrew Novak
Registered Nurse, Jill Petersen

LOCATIONS

HQ: NEBRASKA MEDICINE
987400 NEBRASKA MED CTR, OMAHA, NE 681980001
Phone: 402 559-8650
Web: WWW.NEBRASKAMED.COM

HISTORICAL FINANCIALS

Company Type: Private

Income Statement — FYE: June 30

	REVENUE ($ mil.)	NET INCOME ($ mil.)	NET PROFIT MARGIN	EMPLOYEES
06/20	1,786	61	3.4%	15,200
06/19	1,662	80	4.8%	—
06/18	1,514	58	3.9%	—
Annual Growth	8.6%	2.2%	—	—

2020 Year-End Financials

Return on assets: 2.7%   Cash ($ mil.): 212
Return on equity: 5.9%
Current ratio: 2.70

NEBRASKA PUBLIC POWER DISTRICT

Nebraska Public Power District (NPPD) electrifies the Cornhusker State. The government-owned electric utility the largest in the state provides power in 86 of the state's 93 counties. The firm has a generating capacity of about 3130 MW and operates more than 5200 miles of transmission lines. NPPD distributes electricity to about 89000 retail customers in 81 cities and towns; it also provides power to about 1 million customers through wholesale power contracts with more than 50 towns and 25 public power districts. In addition NPPD purchases electricity from the federally owned Western Area Power Administration and operates a surface water irrigation system.

Operations

The company uses multiple sources including nuclear steam mixed wind hydro and diesel to generate power.

NPPD's revenues comes from wholesale power supply agreements with 50 towns and 25 rural public power districts and rural cooperatives who rely totally or partially on NPPD's electrical system. NPPD also serves about 81 communities at the retail level.

Financial Performance

Revenues for 2013 increased by 2% due mostly to rate increases and sales to other utilities. Net income jumped 30% on the revenue increase and reduced costs. Cash from operations followed suit and rose nearly $100 million.

Strategy

Faced with growing long-term demand for electricity along with pressure to keep prices low NPPD has implemented plans to increase transmission capacity. With a goal of getting of 15% it energy from renewable sources by 2025 the company is exploring alternative fuel sources for future plants. With 45% of NPPD's energy supply coming from coal in 2011 the company was looking to cleaner alternatives such as wind power and biomass in order to meet stricter environmental regulations. In 2014 it signed a deal to purchase wind power from Sempra a move that put it within sight of its goal to have 10% of its power generation come from renewable sources.

Company Background

NPPD was formed in 1970 through the merger of three public utilities: Consumers Public Power District Platte Valley Public Power and Irrigation District and Nebraska Public Power System.

EXECUTIVES

Pres-Ceo, Thomas Kent
Exec Vp-Cfo*, Traci Bender
V Pres-Cco*, Ken Curry
Exec Vp-Gen Counsel*, John McClure
Vp Corp Strategy & Innovation*, Tim Arlt
Vp-CIO*, Robyn Tweedy
Analyst, Darin Anderson
Assistant Maintenance Manager, Matt C Hug
Customer Team Member, Nicole Brumbaugh
Electrical Engineer, Doug Jebens
Advertising, Christy Avery
Auditors: PRICEWATERHOUSECOOPER LLP CH

LOCATIONS

HQ: NEBRASKA PUBLIC POWER DISTRICT
1414 15TH ST, COLUMBUS, NE 686015226
Phone: 877 275-6773
Web: WWW.NPPD.COM

PRODUCTS/OPERATIONS

2013 Sales

	$ mil.	% of total
Wholesale	584	53
Retail	294	27
Other	227	20
Total	**1,106**	**100**

COMPETITORS

Basin Electric Power	Omaha Public Power
Berkshire Hathaway	Tri-state Generation
Energy	And Transmission
Northwestern	

HISTORICAL FINANCIALS

Company Type: Private

Income Statement				FYE: December 31
	REVENUE ($ mil.)	NET INCOME ($ mil.)	NET PROFIT MARGIN	EMPLOYEES
12/20	1,103	95	8.7%	1,900
12/19	1,074	89	8.3%	—
12/18	1,144	82	7.2%	—
12/17	1,101	71	6.5%	—
Annual Growth	0.0%	10.4%	—	—

2020 Year-End Financials

Return on assets: 2.1%   Cash ($ mil.): 23
Return on equity: 5.5%
Current ratio: 2.90

NEVADA SYSTEM OF HIGHER EDUCATION

You can gamble on a solid academic foundation with The Nevada System of Higher Education (NSHE). The system oversees Nevada's public colleges and institutions. NSHE encompasses eight institutions: the University of Nevada Las Vegas; the University of Nevada Reno; Nevada State College; community colleges Truckee Meadows Great Basin College College of Southern Nevada and Western Nevada College; and environmental research arm Desert Research Institute (DRI). The system which enrolls some 106000 students is governed by the Nevada Board of Regents consisting of 13 members elected for six-year terms.

Financial Performance

Total operating revenue fell 4% in 2012 as an increase in NSHE's largest segment (student tuition and fees) was not enough to offset double-digit declines in federal state and local grants and contracts. The rise in tuition and fees resulted from an increase in tuition rates to offset an enrollment decrease.

Strategy

In late 2013 NSHE announced a partnership to establish medical schools at the University of Nevada Las Vegas and Reno campuses.

EXECUTIVES

Ceo, Daniel Klaich
Administrative Assistant II, Dennis Thieme
Associate Professor English, Jeffrey Jablonski
Assistant Professor, Natalie Berman
Acting Pres Wstrnnevadacollege, P Mark Ghan
Editor, Doug Smith
Executive, Emily Dyer
Internal Medicine Practitioner, Jihye Park
Graduate Student Teaching Assi, Armin Saraei
Unlvino Student Manager, Jackie Watson
Network Manager, Chris Gaub
Auditors: GRANT THORNTON LLP SAN JOSE

LOCATIONS

HQ: NEVADA SYSTEM OF HIGHER EDUCATION
2601 ENTERPRISE RD, RENO, NV 895121666
Phone: 775 784-4901
Web: WWW.NSHE.NEVADA.EDU

HISTORICAL FINANCIALS

Company Type: Private

Income Statement				FYE: June 30
	REVENUE ($ mil.)	NET INCOME ($ mil.)	NET PROFIT MARGIN	EMPLOYEES
06/19	982	(6)	—	8,000
06/18	953	116	12.2%	—
06/17	1,115	140	12.6%	—
06/16	1,055	48	4.6%	—
Annual Growth	(2.4%)	—	—	—

2019 Year-End Financials

Return on assets: (-0.2%)   Cash ($ mil.): 175
Return on equity: (-0.4%)
Current ratio: 2.90

NEW ENGLAND PETROLEUM LIMITED PARTNERSHIP

EXECUTIVES

Ptnr, Gary Kaneb
Auditors: PRICEWATERHOUSECOOPERS LLP B

LOCATIONS

HQ: NEW ENGLAND PETROLEUM LIMITED PARTNERSHIP
6 KIMBALL LN STE 400, LYNNFIELD, MA 019402685
Phone: 617 660-7400

HISTORICAL FINANCIALS

Company Type: Private

Income Statement				FYE: December 31
	REVENUE ($ mil.)	NET INCOME ($ mil.)	NET PROFIT MARGIN	EMPLOYEES
12/12	1,081	4	0.4%	25
12/11	998	3	0.3%	—
12/10	568	2	0.5%	—
Annual Growth	37.9%	32.5%	—	—

2012 Year-End Financials

Return on assets: 7.7%   Cash ($ mil.): 2
Return on equity: 13.5%
Current ratio: 2.40

NEW JERSEY TRANSPORTATION TRUST FUND AUTHORITY

EXECUTIVES

Commissioner, James Weinstein
Scientist, Katie Lynch
Auditors: MERCADIEN PC PRINCETON NJ

LOCATIONS

HQ: NEW JERSEY TRANSPORTATION TRUST FUND AUTHORITY
1035 PARKWAY AVE, EWING, NJ 086182309
Phone: 609 530-2035
Web: WWW.NJ.GOV

HISTORICAL FINANCIALS

Company Type: Private

Income Statement   FYE: June 30

	REVENUE ($ mil.)	NET INCOME ($ mil.)	NET PROFIT MARGIN	EMPLOYEES
06/20	2,348	(362)	—	1
06/19	2,272	(364)	—	—
06/18	1,676	(859)	—	—
06/17	1,338	(532)	—	—
Annual Growth	20.6%	—	—	—

2020 Year-End Financials

Return on assets: (-1.8%)   Cash ($ mil.): 889
Return on equity: (-149.5%)
Current ratio: —

NEW JERSEY TURNPIKE AUTHORITY INC

The New Jersey Turnpike Authority operates two toll-supported highways the New Jersey Turnpike and the Garden State Parkway. The New Jersey Turnpike runs for 148 miles from the Delaware River Bridge at the southern end of the state to the George Washington Bridge that connects New Jersey with New York. The turnpike includes about 10 rest stops or service areas named for former New Jersey residents such as Alexander Hamilton Vince Lombardi and Walt Whitman. The Garden State Parkway runs for 173 miles and spans the length of New Jersey's Atlantic coastline.

HISTORY

After almost seven years of construction Garden State Parkway's Driscoll Bridge was opened in May 2009. The $225 million project included constructing a new span and rehabilitating two existing spans bumping the Driscoll Bridge up to 15 lanes — more than any other US bridge. The Driscoll Bridge connects Woodbridge Township to Sayreville and is traveled by some 300000 vehicles daily.

New Jersey Turnpike Authority New Jersey Transit the Port Authority of New York and New Jersey had committed $5.7 billion toward an $8.7 billion new mass transit tunnel beneath the Hudson River — the first such project in a century. Work began in 2009 on the almost four-mile tunnel known as the Mass Transit Tunnel (MTT) which was to double the rail capacity between New Jersey and New York but the project was cancelled in 2010.

EXECUTIVES

Chb, Jamie Fox
Ceo*, Ronald Gravino
Treas*, Michael R Dupont
Commissioner*, Frank X Mc Dermott
Coo*, John F O Hern
Exec Dir*, Veronique Hakim
Commissioner*, Harold L Hodes
Commissioner*, Raymond M Pocino
Commissioner*, Ulises E Diaz
Assistant, Irene Volkmann
Assistant Chief, Robert Fischer
Auditors: KPMG LLP SHORT HILLS NJ

LOCATIONS

HQ: NEW JERSEY TURNPIKE AUTHORITY INC
1 TURNPIKE PLZ, WOODBRIDGE, NJ 070955195
Phone: 732 750-5300
Web: WWW.NJTA.COM

HISTORICAL FINANCIALS

Company Type: Private

Income Statement   FYE: December 31

	REVENUE ($ mil.)	NET INCOME ($ mil.)	NET PROFIT MARGIN	EMPLOYEES
12/20	1,528	(50)	—	2,400
12/19	1,743	191	11.0%	—
12/18	1,753	209	12.0%	—
12/17	1,698	329	19.4%	—
Annual Growth	(3.4%)	—	—	—

2020 Year-End Financials

Return on assets: (-0.3%)   Cash ($ mil.): 290
Return on equity: (-9.4%)
Current ratio: 2.00

NEW PRIME, INC.

Specialized carrier New Prime (which does business simply as Prime) provides refrigerated flatbed tanker and intermodal trucking services throughout North America through over 11600 remotely monitored temperature-controlled trailers. Prime has been an innovative regional and Over the Road (OTR) trucking company paving the way for the rest of the trucking industry. A subsidiary Prime Floral uses the parent company's refrigerated equipment and facilities to serve the flower industry. In addition to its freight-hauling operations Prime provides logistics services including freight brokerage. The company was founded in 1970.

Operations

Prime with a fleet of over 6100 trucks operates through four divisions.

Prime's liquid bulk fleet (Tanker Division) consists of over 300 trucks and over 500 tank trailers with capacities of 6800 7000 or 7250 gallons. The company's Refrigerated Division has over 6500 trucks and over 11700 remotely monitored temperature-controlled trailers. It is a carrier that can ship fresh produce fresh cut floral pharmaceuticals fresh or frozen meats or any other dry or temperature-controlled freight. Flatbed division is focused on hauling freight from pipe and steel to drywall and roofing materials and more. Prime's Intermodal fleet is a direct link to virtually every market across the continent.

The company also offers two leasing options lease and lease purchase.

Geographic Reach

The company serves customers in North America. Based in Springfield Missouri Prime operates US terminals in Colorado Texas Pennsylvania and Utah. Additionally it has facilities in Indiana Georgia Florida Oregon and California.

Sales and Marketing
Company Background

Prime was founded in 1970 by Robert Low who continues to serve as Prime's president.

EXECUTIVES

Pres, Robert Low
Cfo*, Dean Hoedl
Coordinator, Andrea Mueller
Coordinator, Trish Mitchell
Fleet Manager, Scott McKnight
Operations Manager, Stan Auman
Logistics Coordinator, Zach Goodman
Coordinator, Cody Burke
Logistics Coordinator, Chris Weldy
Cash Management, Thomas Dee
Chef, Chris Freeman

LOCATIONS

HQ: NEW PRIME, INC.
2740 N MAYFAIR AVE, SPRINGFIELD, MO 658035084
Phone: 800 321-4552
Web: WWW.PRIMEINC.COM

COMPETITORS

Boyd Bros. Transportation	Comcar Frozen Food Express
C.h. Robinson Worldwide	Kllm Transport Services
C.r. England Central Refrigerated Service	Marten Transport Quality Distribution Stevens Transport

HISTORICAL FINANCIALS

Company Type: Private

Income Statement   FYE: March 31

	REVENUE ($ mil.)	NET INCOME ($ mil.)	NET PROFIT MARGIN	EMPLOYEES
03/17*	1,653	116	7.1%	6,775
04/16	1,598	133	8.3%	—
03/12	1,022	60	6.0%	—
04/11	941	47	5.0%	—
Annual Growth	9.8%	16.2%	—	—

*Fiscal year change

2017 Year-End Financials

Return on assets: 12.7%   Cash ($ mil.): —
Return on equity: 32.2%
Current ratio: 0.40

NEW WORLD FUND

EXECUTIVES

Admn, Michael W Stockton

LOCATIONS

HQ: NEW WORLD FUND
333 S HOPE ST FL 53, LOS ANGELES, CA 900711418
Phone: 213 486-9200

HISTORICAL FINANCIALS

Company Type: Private

Income Statement				FYE: October 31
	REVENUE ($ mil.)	NET INCOME ($ mil.)	NET PROFIT MARGIN	EMPLOYEES
10/20	595	3,579	601.2%	2
10/19	792	8,314	1049.1%	—
10/18	404	(94)	—	—
Annual Growth	21.3%	—	—	—

2020 Year-End Financials

Return on assets: 7.8%   Cash ($ mil.): 90
Return on equity: 7.9%
Current ratio: —

NEW YORK CITY HEALTH AND HOSPITALS CORPORATION

New York City Health and Hospitals Corporation (NYC H+H) operates health care facilities in all five boroughs of New York City. The NYC H+H health plan MetroPlus offers low no cost health insurance to eligible people living in Manhattan Brooklyn Queens Staten Island and Bronx. NYC H+H operates a network of around 10 acute care hospitals (including Bellevue the nation's oldest public hospital) large diagnostic and treatment centers skilled nursing centers long-term care facilities and a home health care agency. NYC H+H also operates more than 70 community-based clinics and provides medical services to New York City's correctional facilities.

Operations

NYC H+H has five facilities:

NYC Health + Hospitals/Cooler which provides high quality short-term rehabilitation therapy and long-term skilled nursing services and from specialized rehabilitation equipment to expert wound care.

The NYC Health + Hospitals/Gouverneur is the 295-bed skilled nursing facility that provides medical nursing and rehabilitative care in an atmosphere of dignity and compassion and provide full spectrum of care for children and adults.

NYC Health + Hospitals/Carter provides safe and superior quality care across the continuum of long-term acute and skilled nursing care with clinical excellence and patient focused philosophy.

NYC Health + Hospitals/McKinney offer short-term rehabilitation services long-term skilled nursing care specialized care for serious injuries and medically complex services.

NYC Health + Hospitals/Sea View provides 24 hours medical and nursing care patients and residents have access to specialty services and highest quality of rehabilitation and long-term skilled nursing services.

Geographic Reach

NYC H+H operates health care facilities in New York's Manhattan Brooklyn Queens Bronx and Staten Island boroughs.

Sales and Marketing

NYC H+H's MetroPlus health plan provides low to no-cost insurance to more than 500000 customers in New York. It insures many New York City government employees.

HISTORY

The City of New York in 1929 created a department to manage its hospitals for the poor. During the Depression more than half of the city's residents were eligible for subsidized care and its public hospitals operated at full capacity.

Four new hospitals opened in the 1950s but the city was already having trouble maintaining existing facilities and attracting staff (young doctors preferred private insurance-supported hospitals catering to the middle class). Meanwhile technological advances and increased demand for skilled nurses made hospitals more expensive to operate. The advent of Medicaid in 1965 was a boon for the system because it brought in federal money.

In 1969 the city created the New York City Health and Hospitals Corporation (HHC) to manage its public health care system — and it was hoped to distance it from the political arena. But HHC was still dependent on the city for funds arousing criticism from those who had hoped for more autonomy. A 1973 state report claimed "the people of New York City are not materially better served by the Health and Hospitals Corporation than by its predecessor agencies."

City budget shortfalls in the mid-1970s led to cutbacks at HHC including nearly 20% of staff. Later in the decade several hospitals closed and some services were discontinued. Ed Koch became mayor in 1978 and gained more control over HHC's operations. Struggles between his administration and the system led three HHC presidents to resign by 1981. That year Koch crony Stanley Brezenoff assumed the post and helped transform HHC into a city pseudo-department.

The early 1980s brought greater prosperity to the system. Reimbursement rates and collections procedures improved allowing HHC to upgrade its record-keeping and its ambulatory and psychiatric care programs. In the late 1980s sharp increases in AIDS and crack addiction cases strained the system and a sluggish economy decreased city funding. Criticism mounted in the early 1990s with allegations of wrongful deaths dangerous facilities and lack of Medicaid payment controls. HHC lost patients to managed care providers and revenues plummeted. In 1995 a city panel recommended radically revamping the system.

Faced with declining revenues and criticism from Mayor Rudolph Giuliani that HHC was "a jobs program" the company began cutting jobs and consolidating facilities in 1996. Under Giuliani's direction HHC made plans to sell its Coney Island Elmhurst and Queens hospital centers. In 1997 the New York State Supreme Court struck down Giuliani's privatization efforts saying the city council had a right to review and approve each sale. In 1998 Giuliani continued to seek to restructure HHC and the agency itself contended it was making progress toward its restructuring goals which were aimed at giving HHC more autonomy as well as more fiscal responsibility. In anticipation of a budget shortfall that year the system laid off some 900 support staff employees. In 1999 the state court of appeals ruled HHC could not legally lease or sell its hospitals.

In 2000 HHC launched an effort to improve its physical infrastructure by beginning the rebuilding and renovation of facilities in Brooklyn Manhattan and Queens. The organization also began converting to an electronic (and thus more efficient) clinical information system. In 2001 HHC forged ahead with further restructuring initiatives. It introduced the Open Access plan a cost-cutting measure designed to expedite the processes involved in outpatient visits.

In 2006 Mayor Michael Bloomberg committed $16 million in funds toward the treatment of those affected by exposure to toxic fumes and dust from

the 2001 attacks on the World Trade Center. Together with the city HHC established the WTC Environmental Health Center at Bellevue Hospital; treatment was made available at little or no charge to the patient.

EXECUTIVES

Pres, Ramanathan Raju
Executive Director, Lincoln ME, Jos R S Nchez
Director, Gretchen Van Wye
Svp, Queens Network, Anne Marie Sullivan
Svp, Information Technology An, Norberto Robles
Coordinator, Peter Carrubba
Evp and Coo, Antonio Martin
Executive Director, Joel Bondy
Assistant Vice President, Laura Free
Assistant, Marty Preston
Executive Director, Gouverneur, Mendel Hagler
Auditors: KPMG LLP NEW YORK NY

LOCATIONS

HQ: NEW YORK CITY HEALTH AND HOSPITALS CORPORATION
125 WORTH ST RM 514, NEW YORK, NY 100134006
Phone: 212 788-3321
Web: WWW.NYCHEALTHANDHOSPITALS.ORG

HHC Networks

Central Brooklyn Family Health Network
  Dr. Susan Smith McKinney Nursing and Rehabilitation Center
  East New York Diagnostic & Treatment Center
  Kings County Hospital Center
Generations Plus Northern Manhattan Health Network
  Harlem Hospital Center
  Lincoln Medical and Mental Health Center
  Metropolitan Hospital Center
  Morrisania Diagnostic & Treatment Center
  Renaissance Health Care Network Diagnostic & Treatment Center
  Segundo Ruiz Belvis Diagnostic & Treatment Center
North Bronx Healthcare Network
  Jacobi Medical Center
  North Central Bronx Hospital
North Brooklyn Health Network
  Cumberland Diagnostic & Treatment Center
  Woodhull Medical and Mental Health Center
Queens Health Network
  Elmhurst Hospital Center
  Queens Hospital Center
South Brooklyn and Staten Island Health Network
  Coney Island Hospital
  Sea View Hospital Rehabilitation Center & Home
South Manhattan Healthcare Network
  Bellevue Hospital Center
  Gouverneur Healthcare Services

PRODUCTS/OPERATIONS

2018 Sales

	$ mil.	% of total
Net patient services	6,216	80
Net appropriations from City of New York	787	10
Grants	652	9
Other	105	1
Total	**7,761**	**100**

Selected Services

Alcohol and Opioid Use Disorder
Asthma Care
Bariatric Services
Breast Health
Burn Care
Cancer Care
Cardiology
Child Health and Pediatrics
Colon Cancer Screening
Deaf and Hard-of-Hearing
Dental Care
Depression
Diabetes Care
Farmers Market
Flu Vaccination
Geriatric Services

HIV/AIDS Care
HPV Vaccine
Hyptertension
Language/Translation Services
LGBTQ Services
Men's Health
Mental Health
Neonatal Intensive Care
Obstetrics & Gynecology
Palliative Care
Parkinson's Disease
Pediatrics
Quit Smoking
Rehab Services
Victims of Domestic Violence
Sexual Response Assault Teams
Sickle Cell Disease
Sleep Disorder Labs
Stroke Prevention and Care
Telehealth Initiatives
Trauma Centers
Vision Care
Women's Health
WTC Environmental Health Center
Youth Health

COMPETITORS

Beth Israel Medical
  Center
Catholic Healthcare
  System
Columbia University
Continuum Health
  Partners
Cornell University

Lenox Hill Hospital
Memorial
  Sloan-kettering
Montefiore Medical
Nyu
Newyork-presbyterian
  Healthcare
Northwell Health

HISTORICAL FINANCIALS

Company Type: Private

Income Statement				FYE: June 30
	REVENUE ($ mil.)	NET INCOME ($ mil.)	NET PROFIT MARGIN	EMPLOYEES
06/17	9,550	(193)	—	35,700
06/02	4,285	(118)	—	—
06/01	4,287	(71)	—	—
06/00	4,083	9	0.2%	—
Annual Growth	5.1%	—	—	—

2017 Year-End Financials

Return on assets: (-2.8%)   Cash ($ mil.): 1,184
Return on equity: —
Current ratio: 1.00

NEW YORK CITY SCHOOL CONSTRUCTION AUTHORITY

EXECUTIVES

Pres-Ceo, Nina Kubota
Exec V Pres*, Ross J Holden
Sr V Pres*, Samir Eid
Manager B It, Samir Patel
Manager, Carmen Mateo
Information Specialist, Scott Lindeman
Contractor, Martina Davis
Managing, Arti Shah
Chief Plan Examiner, David Choy
Design Project Manager, Emad Asaad

Information Technology Technic, Constantin Petrof
Auditors: PRICEWATERHOUSECOOPER LLP NE

LOCATIONS

HQ: NEW YORK CITY SCHOOL CONSTRUCTION AUTHORITY
3030 THOMSON AVE FL 3, LONG ISLAND CITY, NY 111013019
Phone: 718 472-8000
Web: WWW.NYCSCA.ORG

HISTORICAL FINANCIALS

Company Type: Private

Income Statement				FYE: June 30
	REVENUE ($ mil.)	NET INCOME ($ mil.)	NET PROFIT MARGIN	EMPLOYEES
06/14	2,190	(410)	—	600
06/13	1,840	(494)	—	—
Annual Growth	19.0%	—	—	—

2014 Year-End Financials

Return on assets: (-16.8%)   Cash ($ mil.): 74
Return on equity: (-24.4%)
Current ratio: —

NEW YORK CITY TRANSIT AUTHORITY

New York City Transit Authority has your ticket to ride in the Big Apple. Known as MTA New York City Transit it provides subway and bus transportation throughout New York City's five boroughs. It is the primary agency of the MTA and the largest public transportation system in North America. Its subway system — which includes more than 6300 subway cars 468 stations and 660 miles of track — serves more than 5.5 million passengers a day day on 238 local six select bus service and 61 express routes in the five boroughs. Its more than 5700 buses transport some 2.6 million riders each day. The agency also operates the Staten Island Railway system.

Operations

New York City Subways and Buses is comprised of two agencies of the MTA regional transportation network - MTA New York City Transit Transit and MTA Bus. The regional network also includes MTA Staten Island Railway (part of NYC Transit's Department of Subways) MTA Long Island Rail Road MTA Metro-North Railroad MTA Bridges and Tunnels and MTA Capital Construction.

MTA New York City Transit and its subsidiary Manhattan and Bronx Surface Transit Operating Authority provide subway and public bus service within New York City's five boroughs.

In 2013 MTA New York City Transit's total ridership was 2.4 billion up 62 million or 2.7% from 2012. After including 44 million of lost ridership from Superstorm Sandy in 2012 the company's 2013 ridership increased by 0.8% with a subway ridership increase of 19 million or 1.1% and no change in bus ridership.

Geographic Reach

The company serves customers in Brooklyn the Bronx Manhattan and Queens and Staten Island

Financial Performance

Rebounding from the effects of Superstorm Sandy on ridership (which resulted in lost revenues of $52 million) in 2013 MTA New York City Transit's revenues from fares increased by 9%. In 2014 its operating budget was $10.1 billion.

Strategy

MTA New York City Transit's parent company the MTA has been plagued by operating losses. To mitigate its losses the MTA has in recent years raised fares cut jobs and decreased service on its buses and subway lines. It has also sought to raise its non-operating revenues by seeking increased government funding.

With the help of federal stimulus and other funding MTA New York City Transit has been making capital improvements to its systems. Projects have included the construction of the Second Avenue Subway and renovations at the Fulton Street Transit Center and other stations throughout the system.

In 2013 the company broke ground on a new MTA Staten Island Railway station. The 27-month construction project the first such project to include a parking lot will replace the existing Atlantic and Nassau Stations in the Tottenville section of the borough.

Company Background

New York City Transit Authority was formed in the 1950s by New York's legislature; the city's transit system dates back to the early 1900s.

EXECUTIVES

Int Pres, Sarah Feinberg
Exec V Pres*, Barbara Spencer
Prin*, Thomas F Prendergast
Prin*, Fernando Ferrer
Prin*, Andrew Albert
Executive, Emily Morgan
Management, Barbara L Tischler
Engineer, Aruna Dalal
Senior Director Marketing, Bill Patterson
Manager, Jimmy Choi
Maintenance Supervisor, Joseph Pero
Auditors: PRICEWATERHOUSECOOPERS LLP ST

LOCATIONS

HQ: NEW YORK CITY TRANSIT AUTHORITY
2 BROADWAY FL 18, NEW YORK, NY 100043357
Phone: 718 330-1234
Web: WWW.NEW.MTA.INFO

HISTORICAL FINANCIALS

Company Type: Private

Income Statement				FYE: December 31
	REVENUE ($ mil.)	NET INCOME ($ mil.)	NET PROFIT MARGIN	EMPLOYEES
12/19	5,060	1,049	20.7%	47,956
12/18	4,892	985	20.1%	—
12/17	4,911	(287)	—	—
Annual Growth	1.5%	—	—	—

2019 Year-End Financials

Return on assets: 2.1%   Cash ($ mil.): 48
Return on equity: 4.4%
Current ratio: 0.80

NEW YORK HOTEL TRADES COUNCIL AND HOTEL ASSOCIATION OF NEW YORK CITY HEALTH CENTER, INC.,

EXECUTIVES

Chb, Joseph E Spinnato
Ceo*, Robert Greenstan
Pres*, Peter Ward
Cfo*, Harry Veras
Support, Lydia Ortizlugo
Coordinator, Sadye Stern
Manager, Chris Cheung
Top Computer Executive (cio, John Brisco
Director Admistrative, Andrew Windsor
Administrative Assistant, Elizabeth Acevedo
Pharmacist, Sharyn Rachev
Auditors: ARMAO LLP GARDEN CITY NY

LOCATIONS

HQ: NEW YORK HOTEL TRADES COUNCIL AND
HOTEL ASSOCIATION OF NEW YORK CITY HEALTH
CENTER, INC.,
305 W 44TH ST, NEW YORK, NY 100365407
Phone: 212 586-6400
Web: WWW.HOTELFUNDS.ORG

HISTORICAL FINANCIALS

Company Type: Private

Income Statement				FYE: December 31
	REVENUE ($ mil.)	NET INCOME ($ mil.)	NET PROFIT MARGIN	EMPLOYEES
12/19	540	(21)	—	1,000
12/18	500	12	2.5%	—
12/17	272	44	16.3%	—
12/16	565	121	21.5%	—
Annual Growth	(1.5%)	—	—	—

2019 Year-End Financials

Return on assets: (-5.8%)   Cash ($ mil.): 14
Return on equity: (-6.5%)
Current ratio: 560.30

NEW YORK POWER AUTHORITY

The New York Power Authority (NYPA) is America's largest state power organization with around 15 generating facilities. Some 80% of the power that NYPA produces is from hydropower resources. The company generates and transmits some 25% of New York's electricity. NYPA owns hydroelectric and fossil-fueled generating facilities and it operates more than 1400 circuit-miles of transmission lines. State and federal regulations shape NYPA's diverse customer base which includes large and small businesses not-for-profit organizations community-owned electric systems and rural electric cooperatives and government entities. NYPA is owned by the State of New York.

Operations

The company's principal operating revenues are generated from the power sales (some 60% of sales) wheeling of power (nearly 30%) and transmission (some 10%). Revenues are recorded when power is delivered or service is provided. Customers' meters are read and bills are rendered monthly. Wheeling charges are for costs the Authority incurred for the transmission and/or delivery of power and energy to customers over transmission lines owned by other utilities.

Geographic Reach

The company serves customers throughout New York State various public corporations in Southeastern New York within the metropolitan area of New York City (SENY Governmental Customers) and certain out-of-state customers.

Sales and Marketing

NYPA's over 1400 customers include businesses; local county and state government entities; and around 50 municipal electric systems and rural electric cooperatives.

Financial Performance

Operating revenues of $2.3 billion in 2020 were $105 million or 4% lower than the $2.4 billion in 2019 primarily due to lower market-based energy sales resulting from lower market prices and the pass through of lower power costs to customers as well as lower customer consumption attributable to the COVID-19 pandemic environment partially offset by higher generation at both our hydro and fossil fuel plants resulting in a higher volume sold in the market.

The Authority had a net loss of $17 million for the year ended December 31 2020 compared to $23 million net income in 2019 a decrease of $40 million (174%). The decrease was primarily due to lower operating income of $31 million (28%) and lower non-operating revenues of $20 million (43%).

The company's cash at the end of 2020 was $947 million. Operating activities generated $196 million. Investing activities and financing activities provided another $491 million and $16 million respectively.

Strategy

In December 2020 the Authority's Board of Trustees approved its strategic plan VISION2030 which focuses on preserving the value of its hydropower assets; leading the transition away from natural gas while ensuring system reliability; rapidly developing new transmission assets to meet market needs; partner with customers' and the state to help meet energy goals; and reimagine the New York State Canals System. The Authority's strategic plan will also ensure the continuation of its evolution to a digital utility; ensure long-term environmental social and governance (ESG) performance; the commitment to Diversity Equity and Inclusion (DE&I); the incorporation of resiliency into all of NYPA; and the on-going focus on employee development through Resource Alignment initiatives.

HISTORY

The Power Authority of the State of New York (aka New York Power Authority or NYPA) was established in 1931 by Gov. Franklin Roosevelt to gain public control of New York's hydropower resources. The utility's major power plants came on line with the opening of the St. Lawrence-Franklin D. Roosevelt Power Project (1958) and the Niagara Power Project (1961). The Blenheim-Gilboa Pumped Storage Power Project opened in 1973.

In the mid-1970s NYPA shifted to nuclear power when it opened the James A. FitzPatrick Nuclear Power Plant (1975) and the Indian Point 3 Nuclear Power Plant (1976). The company then opened gas- and oil-powered plants: the Charles Poletti Power Project (1977) and the Richard M. Flynn Power Plant (1994).

In 1998 the authority allocated low-cost electricity to five companies that planned to invest $104 million in business expansions in western New York. The company suffered a loss in 1999 in part from reduced hydro generation and a drop in investment earnings. In 2000 NYPA sold its two nuclear plants (1800 MW of capacity) to utility holding company Entergy for $967 million.

The company completed the installation of 11 gas-powered turbines at various locations in New York City and on Long Island in 2001; the program was initiated to prevent expected energy shortages that summer but it also helped maintain power in areas of the city during the September 11 terrorist attacks.

In 2013 The Village of Lake Placid unveiled a new hybrid-electric shuttle bus that will make commuting on public transportation quieter and cleaner. Financing for the bus was made possible through NYPA's Municipal Electric-Drive Vehicle Program which provides financial assistance to New York municipal utilities to facilitate the replacement of less fuel-efficient vehicles in order to advance the state's clean energy goals. That year NYPA added seven more hybrids and one more EV to its fleet bringing the total number of electric drive vehicles to 79. It also purchased just over 40000 gallons of B20 biodiesel which earned the Power Authority 17 Alternative Fuel Vehicle credits under the Department of Energy's Energy Policy Act that will be used to purchase additional hybrid and plug-in hybrid vehicles.

EXECUTIVES

Ceo-Pres, Gil C Quiniones
Coo*, Edward A Welz
Cfo*, Adam Barsky
Exec V Pres-Gen Counsel*, Justin E Driscoll
Chief Auditor*, Jennifer Faulkner
Sr V Pres*, James F Pasquale
Sr V Pres of Hr and Shared Ser*, Kristine Pizzo
Sr V Pres-Wholesale Commercial*, Jill C Anderson
Sr V Pres-Chief Risk Officer*, Soubhagya Parija
V Pres-Sr Advisor To Pres and*, Rocco Iannarelli
Senior Analyst, Surendra Grover
Auditors: KPMG LLP NEW YORK NY

LOCATIONS

HQ: NEW YORK POWER AUTHORITY
250 MARTINE AVE APT 2E, WHITE PLAINS, NY
106013410
Phone: 914 681-6200
Web: WWW.NYPA.GOV

PRODUCTS/OPERATIONS

2014 Sales

	$ mil.	% of total
Power sales	2,396	76
Wheeling charges	614	19
Transmission charges	165	5
Total	**3,175**	**100**

Selected Operations

Transmission Control Facility
  Frederick R. Clark Energy Center (Oneida County)
Fossil-Fueled Plants
  Charles Poletti Power Project (New York City)
  Richard M. Flynn Power Plant (Suffolk County)
  PowerNow! Turbines (11 units in New York City and Long Island)
Hydropower Plants
  Blenheim-Gilboa Pumped Storage Power Project (Schoharie County)
  Niagara Power Project (Niagara County)

St. Lawrence-Franklin D. Roosevelt Power Project (St. Lawrence County)
Small Hydropower Plants
  Ashokan Project (Ulster County)
  Crescent Plant (Albany and Saratoga Counties)
  Gregory B. Jarvis Plant (Oneida County)
  Kensico Project (Westchester County)
  Vischer Ferry Plant (Saratoga and Schenectady counties)

COMPETITORS

Avangrid	National Grid Usa
Ch Energy	Rochester Gas And
Con Edison	Electric
Enbridge	Transcanada
Entergy	

HISTORICAL FINANCIALS
Company Type: Private

Income Statement				FYE: December 31
	REVENUE ($ mil.)	NET INCOME ($ mil.)	NET PROFIT MARGIN	EMPLOYEES
12/20	2,265	(17)		2,237
12/19	2,370	26	1.1%	—
12/18	2,689	102	3.8%	—
12/17	2,573	119	4.6%	—
Annual Growth	(4.2%)	—	—	—

2020 Year-End Financials
Return on assets: (-0.2%)   Cash ($ mil.): 219
Return on equity: (-0.4%)
Current ratio: 1.10

NEW YORK PRESBYTERIAN HOSPITAL WEILL CORNELL UNIVERSITY MEDICAL CENTER

EXECUTIVES

Pres, Steven Corwin
Exec V Pres-Coo, Laura Forese
Sr V Pres-Cmo, Craig Albanese
Sr V Pres-Ciso, Jennings Aske
Sr V Pres-CIO, Daniel Barchi
Sr V Pres-Cfo, Michael Breslin
S V Pres-Clo, Mary Beth Claus
Branch/Division/Department Hea, Janet Parisi
Administrator, David Weir
Administrator, Suzan Toro
Research Scientist, Catherine Liu

LOCATIONS

HQ: NEW YORK PRESBYTERIAN HOSPITAL WEILL CORNELL UNIVERSITY MEDICAL CENTER
525 E 68TH ST, NEW YORK, NY 100654870
Phone: 212 746-8115
Web: WWW.NYP.ORG

HISTORICAL FINANCIALS
Company Type: Private

Income Statement				FYE: December 31
	REVENUE ($ mil.)	NET INCOME ($ mil.)	NET PROFIT MARGIN	EMPLOYEES
12/15	4,505	265	5.9%	5
12/12	75	21	28.2%	—
Annual Growth	290.4%	131.8%	—	—

2015 Year-End Financials
Return on assets: 3.9%   Cash ($ mil.): 227
Return on equity: 7.6%
Current ratio: 2.20

NEW YORK STATE CATHOLIC HEALTH PLAN, INC.

Fidelis Care hopes for always faithful health plan members. The New York State Catholic Health Plan which does business as Fidelis Care serves more than 921000 residents in some 60 counties across the state including the New York City area. The church-sponsored plan's provider network includes more than 63000 physicians hospitals and other health care professionals and facilities. Fidelis Care provides managed Medicaid Medicare and state-sponsored family and children's Health Plus plans as well as long-term care and behavioral health coverage.

Operations
The company boasts an overall statewide member retention rate of more than 78% with a s Child Health Plus retention rate of more than 85%.

Geographic Reach
Fidelis Care's regional offices are located in Rego Park Queens (Greater Metropolitan); Albany (Northeast); Syracuse (Central); and Buffalo (Western) with satellite offices in Poughkeepsie Rochester and Suffern.

Sales and Marketing
The health plan has expanded its membership by seeking new low-income patients who lack coverage. In addition to direct sales efforts Fidelis Care tries to maintain a presence at health centers frequented by its target audience partnering with neighborhood clinics to hold free health screenings and Health Plus enrollment information sessions.

Enroll NY a new website sponsored by not-for-profit organization Hudson Center for Health Equity & Quality is also connecting Fidelis Care and other Medicaid providers with potential customers. In 2013 Fidelis Care began selling through the New York State of Health insurance exchange marketplace.

To bosst membership in 2013 the company ran the "I Want Fidelis Care' campaign (which promoted Fidelis Care as a health care resource) in English and Spanish. TV was added to the media buy in the New York City and Buffalo regions. It also established a social media presence on Facebook Twitter YouTube and Google+.

Financial Performance
Fidelis Care reported gross revenues of $4.1 billion in 2013 up from $3.3 billion in 2012.

Strategy
The company is expanding its office to keep up with demand. In 2014 it opened Ridgewood Com-

munity Office; in 2013 it completed of?ce expansion projects in the Albany and Syracuse regional of?ces and the satellite of?ce in Suffern and opened new community of?ces in Flushing (Queens) the Bronx and Bath (Steuben County).

Forecasting substantial growth in 2014 with the enrollment of more than 120000 new members the company announced plans to add more than 75 new information technology jobs at its Buffalo regional office.

In 2013 Fidelis Care moved into 12 new counties with the Medicare Advantage program highlighted by the opportunity to serve residents of western New York for the ?rst time. It also made plans to expand into Seneca Yates and Jefferson counties in 2014 and served additional Managed Long Term Care members as part of the State's phased-in expansion of mandatory enrollment in counties beyond New York City.

Fidelis Care has grown by expanding rapidly into new counties in New York including a number of growth measures in the Medicare marketplace during 2012 and 2013. The health plan's recent activity includes completing construction of Fidelis Care's new operations center and offices in Getzville (Erie County) and the launch of its new provider portal (Provider Access Online). Other growth measures include a 2012 partnership with DentaQuest to promote dental checkups; it also launched a new member portal for members to access benefit information. In 2013 the company gained approval to be a qualified health plan provider on the official New York State of Health marketplace.

Fidelis Care regularly evaluates and broadens its plan offerings. Recent additions include its Fidelis Care at Home managed long-term care offering; the behavioral health and developmental disabilities coverage options; and its fully integrated dual advantage plans (for consumers with both Medicare and Medicaid coverage).

Company Background
The church-sponsored plan was founded in 1993 by the bishops of New York's Roman Catholic dioceses and the Catholic Medical Center of Brooklyn and Queens.

EXECUTIVES

Ceo, Rev Patrick J Frawley
Exec V Pres, David P Thomas
Cfo, Thomas Halloran
Security Manager, Doug Schuler
Assistant Vice President, Erick Moncayo
Marketing Supervisor, Felicia Johnson
Regional Market Manager, Humberto Trimino
Information Technology Manager, Jack Toepfer
Supervisor, Jared Connor
Director, Justin Smith
Assistant Vice President Provi, Maryjean Valigorsky
Auditors: LB DELOITTE TAX LLP JERICHO

LOCATIONS

HQ: NEW YORK STATE CATHOLIC HEALTH PLAN, INC.
9525 QUEENS BLVD, REGO PARK, NY 113744510
Phone: 888 343-3547
Web: WWW.CENTENE.COM

PRODUCTS/OPERATIONS

Selected Plans
Child Health Plus
Dual Advantage
Family Health Plus
Fidelis Care at Home (managed long-term care)
Medicaid Advantage Plus (managed long-term care)
Medicaid Managed Care
Medicare Advantage
New York State of Health

COMPETITORS

Aetna
Affinity Health
Anthem
Cigna
Capital District Physicians' Health Plan
Emblemhealth
Health Net
Healthplus Amerigroup
Healthfirst
Healthplex
Humana
Independent Health
Lifetime Healthcare
Mvp Health Plan
Unitedhealth Group
Vytra Healthcare
Healthnow New York Inc

HISTORICAL FINANCIALS

Company Type: Private

Income Statement				FYE: December 31
	REVENUE ($ mil.)	NET INCOME ($ mil.)	NET PROFIT MARGIN	EMPLOYEES
12/14	5,304	271	5.1%	1,625
12/10	1,920	51	2.7%	—
12/09	1,435	27	1.9%	—
12/08	1,068	3	0.4%	—
Annual Growth	30.6%	103.1%	—	—

2014 Year-End Financials

Return on assets: 12.4%
Return on equity: 22.3%
Current ratio: 9.10

Cash ($ mil.): 948

NEW YORK STATE ENERGY RESEARCH AND DEVELOPMENT AUTHORITY

EXECUTIVES

Ceo, Richard Kauffman
Project Coordinator, Harith Saam
Director of Marketing and Deve, Susan Moyer

LOCATIONS

HQ: NEW YORK STATE ENERGY RESEARCH AND DEVELOPMENT AUTHORITY
17 COLUMBIA CIR, ALBANY, NY 122035156
Phone: 518 862-1090
Web: WWW.NYSERDA.NY.GOV

HISTORICAL FINANCIALS

Company Type: Private

Income Statement				FYE: March 31
	REVENUE ($ mil.)	NET INCOME ($ mil.)	NET PROFIT MARGIN	EMPLOYEES
03/21	1,204	(1)	—	1
03/20	1,287	32	2.5%	—
Annual Growth	(6.4%)	—	—	—

NEW YORK STATE HOUSING FINANCE AGENCY

EXECUTIVES

Pres-Ceo, Stephen J Hunt
Chb*, Judd S Levy
Sr V Pres*, Ralph J Madalena
Sr V Pres*, Bernard H Abramowitz
Sr V Pres*, Robert M Drillings
Sr V Pres*, James Angley
Vice President, Mark Flescher
Executive Deputy Commissioner, Betsy Mallow
Senior Vice President of Singl, Dina Levy
Chief of Staff, Gabriella Green
Senior Network Engineer, Jimmy Chan
Auditors: ERNST & YOUNG LLP NEW YORK N

LOCATIONS

HQ: NEW YORK STATE HOUSING FINANCE AGENCY
641 LEXINGTON AVE FL 4, NEW YORK, NY 100224503
Phone: 212 688-4069
Web: WWW.HCR.NY.GOV

HISTORICAL FINANCIALS

Company Type: Private

Income Statement				FYE: October 31
	REVENUE ($ mil.)	NET INCOME ($ mil.)	NET PROFIT MARGIN	EMPLOYEES
10/20	549	90	16.5%	131
10/18	553	187	33.9%	—
10/17	400	112	28.0%	—
10/16	279	77	27.7%	—
Annual Growth	18.4%	4.1%	—	—

2020 Year-End Financials

Return on assets: 0.5%
Return on equity: 8.2%
Current ratio: 2.60

Cash ($ mil.): 52

NEW YORK UNIVERSITY

The setting and heritage of New York University (NYU) make it one of the nation's most popular educational institutions. With about 53600 students attending its nearly 20 schools and colleges NYU is among the largest private schools in the US. Its Tisch School of the Arts is well-regarded and its law school and Leonard N. Stern School of Business are among the foremost in the country. One of the most prominent and respected research universities in the world featuring top-ranked academic programs and accepting fewer than one-in-five undergraduates NYU's students come from nearly every state and about 135 countries. The school was founded in 1831.

Operations

NYU reports its financials in two segments ? NYU Langone Health and University. The latter segment is composed of the NYU Langone Health System (Health System) and its two medical schools: the NYU Robert I. Grossman School of Medicine (NYUGSoM) and NYU Long Island School of Medicine (collectively the NYU Schools of Medicine).

NYU Langone Health operates two hospitals Kimmel Pavilion and Tisch Hospital which together have nearly 845 beds. It also operates the 225-bed NYU Langone Orthopedic Hospital the 450-bed NYU Langone Hospital in Brooklyn and several ambulatory care facilities. The segment brings in nearly 75% of NYU's total revenue.

The University includes nearly 20 colleges and divisions including schools of art and sciences law dentistry business mathematical sciences fine arts professional studies public services social work and engineering. NYU also operates NYU Abu Dhabi and NYU Shanghai a joint venture with East China Normal University. The University segment accounts for about 25% of NYU's total revenue.

Overall patient care accounts for more than 55% of NYU's total operating revenue.

Geographic Reach

Along with its campuses in New York NYU operates degree-granting campuses in Abu Dhabi and Shanghai. It also has more than 10 global academic centers in Africa Asia Europe and the Americas and research programs in more than 25 countries.

Sales and Marketing
Financial Performance

Company revenue for fiscal 2020 increased to $12.77 billion compared from the prior year with $12.76 billion.

Cash held by the company at the end of fiscal 2020 increased to $3.5 billion. Cash provided by operations and financing activities were $1.7 billion and $810.0 million. Cash used for investing activities was $1.5 billion mainly for Purchases of investments.

Company Background

In 1831 Albert Gallatin who'd served as Secretary of the Treasury under Thomas Jefferson and James Madison announced his plans to establish NYU. His vision was to create a center of higher learning that would be available to all regardless of nationality religion or social background. In 1832 NYU's first classes were held at Clinton Hill in Lower Manhattan.

HISTORY

New York University was founded by several prominent New Yorkers in 1831. The school held its first classes the following year in rented rooms on the corner of Beekman and Nassau streets then moved to a building in Washington Square in 1835. It established its law school that year. NYU started its school of medicine in 1841 followed by the school of engineering and science (1854). Postgraduate studies in arts and science (its first coeducational program) began in 1886.

NYU's enrollment jumped from fewer than 2000 in 1900 to 28000 in 1930. After a lull during the Depression and WWII the campus boomed again in the postwar years. During the 1950s the university began focusing on improving academics rather than on increasing enrollment. It created a school of the arts in 1965 and in the early 1970s it completed the Elmer Holmes Bobst Library. However a cash crunch during that decade almost forced the school into bankruptcy.

President Jay Oliva took the reins in 1981 and focused on transforming NYU from a largely commuter college into a global university. The school began a campaign to raise $1 billion in 1984 but earmarked the funds for campus improvements rather than swelling its endowment. During the late 1980s NYU opened several new dormitories and conference spaces. In 1994 British historian and collector Sir Harold Acton bequeathed to the school his Tuscany estate — five art-filled villas overlooking Florence Italy.

In 1996 NYU's Medical Center began talks with Mount Sinai Medical Center aimed at merging their hospitals and medical schools. The talks fell apart in early 1997 but the following year the two sides agreed to merge hospitals and keep their medical schools distinct. Also in 1998 NYU formed NYU On-Line Inc. a for-profit subsidiary to develop and sell specialized Internet courses to other schools training centers and students; the venture was subsequently folded in late 2001. During 1999 contributions to the school approached $250 million. That year however two upper-level school officials were fired following allegations of improper use of university money.

Oliva retired as president in 2002 and was replaced by John Sexton former School of Law dean. In 2004 Sexton announced that NYU would give $1 million to New York City towards renovation of Washington Square Park (the school annually gives some $200000 for the park's ongoing maintenance).

EXECUTIVES

Pres, Andrew D Hamilton
Exec V Pres, Martin Dorph
Sr V Pres-Cfo, Stephanie Pianka
CIO, Kathleen E Jacobs
Sr V Pres-CIO, Len Peters
Vice Chancellor For Regional C, Mari T Westermann
Svp, General Counsel, and Secr, Bonnie S Brier
Trustee, Mariuccia Zerilli-Marim
Executive Officer, Adam Waldman
Executive Officer, Brian Squibb
Director of Finance, Christina De Haven
Auditors: PRICEWATERHOUSECOOPERS LLP NE

LOCATIONS

HQ: NEW YORK UNIVERSITY
70 WASHINGTON SQ S, NEW YORK, NY 100121019
Phone: 212 998-1212
Web: WWW.NYU.EDU

PRODUCTS/OPERATIONS

2018 Sales

	$ mil.	% of total
Patient care	6,981	60
Tuition & fees	1,852	16
Grants & contracts	1,011	9
Auxiliary enterprises	505	4
Hospital affiliations	342	3
Endowment distribution	169	2
Contributions	168	2
Net assets from restrictions	121	1
Insurance premiums earned	115	1
Return on short-term investments	16	-
Programs & other	272	2
Total	**11,556**	**100**

2018 Sales

	$ mil.	% of total
NYU Langone Health	8,298	72
University	3,267	28
Adjustments	(10.3)	-
Total	**11,556**	**100**

Selected Schools and Colleges

College of Arts and Science (founded 1832)
College of Dentistry (1865)
Courant Institute of Mathematical Sciences (1934)
Gallatin School of Individualized Study (1972)
Graduate School of Arts and Science (1886)
Leonard N. Stern School of Business (1900)
Robert F. Wagner Graduate School of Public Service (1938)
School of Continuing and Professional Studies (1934)
School of Law (1835)
School of Medicine (1841)
School of Social Work (1960)
Steinhardt School of Culture Education and Human Development (1890)
Tisch School of the Arts (1965)

NEW YORK UNIVERSITY

EXECUTIVES

Pres, John Sexton
Proj Dir*, Yamilee Bazile
Assistant Professor, Satarupa Dasgupta
Assistant Professor, Cristina Vatulescu
General Practitioner, Emanuela Corielli
General Practitioner, Steven David
Adjunct Instructor, William Hewitt
Assistant Professor of Marketi, Raluca Ursu
Professor of Social Work, Gary Holden
Professor of Social Work, Jeffrey Seinfeld
Clinical Placement Nurse Manag, Marigold Martinez
Auditors: PRICEWATERHOUSECOOPERS LLP NE

LOCATIONS

HQ: NEW YORK UNIVERSITY
433 1ST AVE RM 619, NEW YORK, NY 100104067
Phone: 212 998-5813
Web: WWW.HEARTBREAKDREAMS.COM

HISTORICAL FINANCIALS

Company Type: Private

Income Statement   FYE: August 31

	REVENUE ($ mil.)	NET INCOME ($ mil.)	NET PROFIT MARGIN	EMPLOYEES
08/12	4,016	53	1.3%	30
08/10	3,376	149	4.4%	
08/09	2,970	(172)	—	
Annual Growth	**10.6%**	—	—	—

2012 Year-End Financials

Return on assets: 0.7%   Cash ($ mil.): 982
Return on equity: 1.4%
Current ratio: 0.70

NEWARK BETH ISRAEL MEDICAL CENTER INC.

Part of the RWJBarnabas network Newark Beth Israel Medical Center is a 670-bed acute-care regional referral hospital. The facility serves residents of Newark and surrounding areas in northern New

Jersey. The hospital offers services including primary diagnostic emergency surgical and rehabilitative care. It is home to specialized programs such as kidney transplantation cancer care dentistry sleep disorders geriatrics and women's health services. Newark Beth Israel Medical Center also houses the Children's Hospital of New Jersey and the Saint Barnabas Heart Center. The research and teaching hospital has a medical staff of more than 800 physicians.

Operations

Newark Beth Israel Medical Center along with sister hospital Saint Barnabas Medical Center has a teaching and research affiliation with the New Jersey Medical School (part of the University of Medicine and Dentistry of New Jersey). The hospital also has training programs with other regional schools.

Parent Barnabas Health merged with Robert Wood Johnson Health in 2016 to form RWJBarnabas.

EXECUTIVES

Exec Dir-Pres-Ceo, Paul Mertz
Chb*, Francis Giantomasi
Coo*, Kenneth Tyson
Cfo*, Veronica Zichner
Chief Equity Officer*, Atiya Jaha-Rashidi
Coordinator, Brigitte King
Chief of Medicine, Don Greenfield
Coordinator, Joanne Loeb
Coordinator, Lisa Tremayne
Coordinator, Stefanie Kelly
Chief of Medicine, Todd Phillips
Auditors: WITHUMSMITHBROWN PC MORRISTOW

LOCATIONS

HQ: NEWARK BETH ISRAEL MEDICAL CENTER INC.
201 LYONS AVE, NEWARK, NJ 071122027
Phone: 973 926-7000
Web: WWW.RWJBH.ORG

PRODUCTS/OPERATIONS

Selected Departments and Centers

Barnabas Health Heart Center
Center for Geriatric Health Care
Center for Women's Health
Children's Hospital of New Jersey
Cohen Comprehensive Cancer and Blood Disorder Center
Lung Center
Pacemaker and Defibrillator Center
Palliative Care Program
Regional Perinatal Center
Radiology
Robotic Surgery Center
Renal Transplantation
Sleep Disorders Center

COMPETITORS

Atlanticare
Atlantic Health
Bergen Regional Medical
Centrastate Healthcare System
Children's Specialized Hospital
Chilton Medical Center
East Orange General Hospital
Englewood Hospital And Medical Center
Hackensack Meridian Health
Hackensack University Medical Center
Newton Medical Center
Robert Wood Johnson University Hospital
Robert Wood Johnson University Hospital At Rahway
St. Joseph's Healthcare System
The Valley Hospital
Virtua Health
Winthrop-university Hospital

HISTORICAL FINANCIALS

Company Type: Private

Income Statement   FYE: August 31

	REVENUE ($ mil.)	NET INCOME ($ mil.)	NET PROFIT MARGIN	EMPLOYEES
08/16	8,500	177	2.1%	21,000
08/11	5,172	563	10.9%	
08/06	2,148	195	9.1%	—
Annual Growth	**14.7%**	**(1.0%)**	—	—

2016 Year-End Financials

Return on assets: 1.1%   Cash ($ mil.): 1,033
Return on equity: 2.4%
Current ratio: —

Company Type: Private

Income Statement				FYE: December 31
	REVENUE ($ mil.)	NET INCOME ($ mil.)	NET PROFIT MARGIN	EMPLOYEES
12/19	660	(33)	—	3,000
12/18	645	19	3.1%	—
12/17	545	35	6.5%	—
12/16	539	27	5.2%	—
Annual Growth	7.0%	—	—	—

2019 Year-End Financials

Return on assets: (-6.1%)   Cash ($ mil.): 1
Return on equity: (-19.2%)
Current ratio: 3.80

NEWARK CORPORATION

Newark offers all sorts of electronic goods in one place and in places all across the Americas. The company doing business as Newark element14 distributes some 4.4 million electronic components and supplies including semiconductors passive devices electrical equipment connectors wire and cable optoelectronics test and measurement instruments and tools. It is also a source for companies needing parts compliant with the Restrictions of Hazardous Substances order in the European Union. Customers are electronics design engineers maintenance technicians and other electronics buyers. Newark element14 is a subsidiary of Premier Farnell a top UK electronic and industrial parts supplier.

Operations

Newark element14 also offers such services as re-calibration custom panel meters and cable assemblies and re-reeling as well as procurement and stockroom services.

The company stocks more than 500 brands from companies the likes of Analog Devices AVX Cypress Semiconductor Freescale Microchip and Texas Instruments.

Geographic Reach

The company operates in North America.

Sales and Marketing

Like its parent Newark element14 maximizes the Internet for selling and customer service purposes with a growing emphasis on electronics design engineering (EDE). Newark element14's EDE customers can access a website that offers collaborative design tools; the company also maintains a dedicated website just for US federal government customers. In addition to its websites Newark element14 operates a customer contact center has a dedicated sales force and offers a print catalog of its products.

Strategy

As part of its business Newark element14 regularly rolls out new products through partnerships with other companies. In 2014 for instance it launched the MagniV S12ZVML-MINIBRD variable-speed motor-control development kit alongside Freescale as well as the Tektronix TBS1000B Series digital storage oscilloscopes. Newark element14 also introduced three new Fluke Thermal Image cameras to its test and measurement portfolio to help boost a technician's productivity while in the field.

Expanding its distribution agreements also keeps Newark element14 growing. In 2014 the company became an authorized distributor of Wurth Electronics items. Wurth specializes in components circuit boards and intelligent systems.

Company Background

Newark was originally established in 1934 as Newark Electric Company a supplier of radio parts — the name of the Chicago-based company's way of recognizing Newark New Jersey as the home of the the first radio station in the US. Newark Electric first published a catalog of parts in 1948. The company went public in 1960 on the American Stock Exchange (now NYSE MKT) changing its name to Newark Electronics Corporation. In 1968 the company was acquired by Premier Industrial Corporation a Cleveland-based distributor. Premier Industrial merged in 1996 with Farnell Electronics plc to become Premier Farnell. Newark and element14 (another Premier Farnell company) combined in 2011 to create Newark element14.

EXECUTIVES

Pres, Dan Hill
V Pres*, Steven Webb
Vice Pres, Thomas Mayfield
V Pres, General Counsel & Secr, Joseph R Daprile
Treasurer & Asst Secretary, Paul M Barlak
Attorney, Rachael Sroda
Call Center Manager, Bill Totzke
Quotations, Cheryl Perry
Senior Manager, Dawn Richter
Manager, Debbie Tomkiell
Account Representative, Diane Arndt

LOCATIONS

HQ: NEWARK CORPORATION
300 S RIVERSIDE PLZ # 220, CHICAGO, IL 606066613
Phone: 773 784-5100
Web: WWW.NEWARK.COM

PRODUCTS/OPERATIONS

Selected Product Categories
Automation and process control
Batteries and chargers
Cable wire and assemblies
Chemicals and adhesives
Circuit protection
Connectors
Crystals and oscillators
Electrical
Enclosures racks and cabinets
Fans heat sinks and HVAC
Fasteners and mechanical
LED technologies
Office and computer
Optoelectronics and displays
Passive components
Power and line protection
Security and audio visual
Semiconductors
Sensors and transducers
Static control and site safety
Switches and relays
Test measurement and inspection
Tools and production supplies
Transformers

COMPETITORS

Arrow Electronics   Future Electronics
Avnet   Rexel Inc.
Davis Instruments   Trek Equipment
Eaco

Company Type: Private

Income Statement				FYE: February 1
	REVENUE ($ mil.)	NET INCOME ($ mil.)	NET PROFIT MARGIN	EMPLOYEES
02/15	543	24	4.5%	834
02/14	541	23	4.4%	—
02/13	580	20	3.5%	—
Annual Growth	(3.2%)	9.6%	—	—

NEWMARK & COMPANY REAL ESTATE, INC.

Newmark & Company Real Estate (dba Newmark Knight Frank or NKF) is one of the world's top commercial real estate advisory firms it provides leasing advisory global corporate services investment sales and capital markets property and facilities management program and project management consulting and valuation and advisory services to investors corporations and property owners worldwide. Newmark also offers facility management services overseeing a portfolio of properties across the globe. Together with its London-based partner Knight Frank NKF operates more than 430 offices across six continents.

Operations

The company provides real estate brokerage appraisal and valuation portfolio and property management mortgage brokerage loan servicing consultancy advisory and facilities and construction management services. Other services include tenant representation + strategic planning owner representation and investment sales + advisory services.

Property management division provides superior operations and services for all classes of commercial and investment properties worldwide. Its services include accounting and financial reporting employee experience operational efficacies specialty facilities management customer service energy and sustainability services project management services tenant experience data center services engineering and maintenance services and receivership services.

Its retail services team comprises the most elite solution providers in the industry.

Sales and Marketing

NKF serves a diverse array of industries including small and large public and private owners developers institutional investors international luxury labels mass merchandisers local retailers quick-service restaurants and fine-dining establishments. It counts several big names among its list of clients including AEW Boston Properties Credit Suisse Equinox GNC J. Crew Michael Kors and Under Armour.

Company Background

EXECUTIVES

Ceo, Barry M Gosin
Chm, Jeffrey R Gural
Pres, James D Kuhn
Cfo, Michael J Rispoli
Pres New York Tri-State Region, David A Falk
Capital, David L Noonan
Managing, Patrick Duffy
Accounts Receivable Specialist, Ashley Stevens
Director, Aaron Gillespie

Associate, Conrad Jacobs
Payroll Tax Manager Payroll MA, Debra
Whiteside

LOCATIONS

HQ: NEWMARK & COMPANY REAL ESTATE, INC.
125 PARK AVE, NEW YORK, NY 100175529
Phone: 212 372-2000
Web: WWW.NEWMARKKNIGHTFRANK.COM

Selected Locations
North America
US
Canada
Mexico
Europe
Asia-Pacific
Africa
Middle East

PRODUCTS/OPERATIONS

Selected Services
Leasing Advisory
Global Corporate Services
Investment Sales and Capital Markets
Retail
Industrial
Consulting
Program and Project Management
Facilities Management
Property Management
Landauer Valuation & Advisory
Residential Construction Services
Specialty Practice Groups
Data Center Consulting
Global Gaming Group
Global Healthcare
Government
Hotels
Law Firm Advisory
Loan Sale Advisory
Multi-Housing Group
Not-For-Profit Advisory
Retail Occupier Services
Self Storage Group

COMPETITORS

Breslin Realty   Eastdil Secured
Development Corp.   Greiner-maltz
Cbre Group   Jones Lang Lasalle
Colliers International   Lend Lease
Cushman & Wakefield   Lincoln Property

HISTORICAL FINANCIALS

Company Type: Private

Income Statement				FYE: December 31
	ASSETS ($ mil.)	NET INCOME ($ mil.)	INCOME AS % OF ASSETS	EMPLOYEES
12/16	860	53	6.3%	2,250
12/15	694	139	20.1%	—
12/14	234	0	—	—
Annual Growth 91.7%	—	—	—	—

2016 Year-End Financials
Return on assets: 6.3%   Sales ($ mil): 1,058
Return on equity: 10.2%

NEWPORT CORPORATION

Newport makes lasers vacuum instruments vibration isolation and optical tables and isolation systems. It makes products that are used around the world in such fields as scientific research microelectronics life and health sciences industrial manufacturing and defense/security. In addition Newport has built a strong history of partnering with OEM customers delivering solutions from subassemblies to full solutions including design testing and manufacturing. Established in 1969 as Newport Research Corporation the company is a wholly owned subsidiary of MKS Instruments Inc.

Operations
Newport offers products such as motion optomechanics optics light light analysis tables and isolation and vacuum instruments under leading brands such as ILX Lightwave New Focus Oriel Instruments Ophir Richardson Gratings MKS Instruments and Spectra-Physics.

Geographic Reach
US plants are located in California (headquarters) Massachusetts Montana New York and Utah. Internationally its plants are located in developed and emerging markets in Austria China France Germany Israel and Romania. In addition the company has direct sales offices located in the US Austria China France Germany Japan Israel Singapore South Korea Taiwan and the UK.

Sales and Marketing
Newport uses a direct sales force as well as an international network of independent distributors and sales representatives.

EXECUTIVES

Pres, Seth Bagshaw
SEC*, Kathleen Burke
Treas*, Derek D'Antilio
Facilities Manager, Kevin Williams
Information Technology Staff, Dave Bell
Manufacturing Engineer Sr Staf, Larry Mayhew
Senior Director, Todd Hultsman
Vice President, Greg Reischlein
Sen Manufacturing Engineer, Hans Albert
Prod Marketing, Herman Chui
Staff Field Engineer, Joe Shapiola
Auditors: DELOITTE & TOUCHE LLP COSTA M

LOCATIONS

HQ: NEWPORT CORPORATION
1791 DEERE AVE, IRVINE, CA 926064814
Phone: 949 863-3144
Web: WWW.NEWPORT.COM

2016 Sales

	$ mil.	% of total
US	231	38
Asia	170	28
Europe	157	26
Other regions	44	8
Total	**602**	**100**

PRODUCTS/OPERATIONS

2016 Sales

	$ mil.	% of total
Photonics & precision technologies	249	41
Lasers	192	32
Optics	160	27
Total	**602**	**100**

COMPETITORS

Adept Technology	Manz
Agilent Technologies	Nikon
Allied Motion	Nordson
Technologies	Oclaro
Anritsu	Palomar Technologies
Carl Zeiss	Parker-hannifin
Coherent Inc.	Renishaw
Corning	Rockwell Automation
Danaher	Roper Technologies

Exfo	Spectris
Horiba	Trumpf
Ii-vi	Thermo Fisher
Ipg Photonics	Scientific
Jenoptik	Viavi Solutions
Kinetic Systems	Zygo

HISTORICAL FINANCIALS

Company Type: Private

Income Statement				FYE: January 3
	REVENUE ($ mil.)	NET INCOME ($ mil.)	NET PROFIT MARGIN	EMPLOYEES
01/15*	605	35	5.8%	2,480
12/13	560	15	2.8%	—
12/12	595	(89)	—	—
Annual Growth 0.8%	—	—	—	—

*Fiscal year change

2015 Year-End Financials
Return on assets: 6.1%   Cash ($ mil.): 46
Return on equity: 9.9%
Current ratio: 2.90

NEWYORK-PRESBYTERIAN/BROOKLYN METHODIST

New York Methodist Hospital is a not-for-profit acute-care teaching hospital serving Brooklyn residents. Established in 1881 as the Methodist Episcopal Hospital the facility has more than 650 licensed beds. It offers a full range of medical services including primary and emergency care as well as specialty services such as women's health cancer cardiovascular pediatric geriatric and behavioral health. The hospital also operates satellite clinics in surrounding areas. A member of New York-Presbyterian Healthcare System New York Methodist is a teaching hospital affiliated with Cornell University's Weill Medical College.

Operations
New York Methodist Hospital handles about 40000 inpatient admissions and 100000 emergency department visits each year as well as 24000 surgeries and 5000 births. It also processes about 200000 laboratory sample processes annually.

New York Methodist Hospital includes specialty institutes in about 10 fields including pulmonary medicine cancer care and vascular health. In addition to providing inpatient care the organization operates some 10 primary and specialty outpatient centers. It also runs a number of graduate medical programs including programs affiliated with professional training schools in the areas of radiography medical technology radiation therapy and paramedics.

Geographic Reach
New York Methodist Hospital's main campus is in the Park Slope neighborhood of Brooklyn. It has several outpatient centers in other parts of Brooklyn as well.

Strategy
To expand care for area residents New York Methodist is adding new specialist programs and equipment. For instance in 2012 the hospital added a robotic-assisted surgery program for bariatric procedures. It also opened a new wound

care and hyperbaric oxygen therapy center for hard-to-heal wounds. In addition in 2013 the hospital moved its sleep disorder center into a new facility.

EXECUTIVES

Chb, James Perkins
Vchb*, Sharon Greenberger
President*, Richard Liebowitz
Doctor, Izabella R Mullokandov
Coordinator, Maria Rivera
Internal Medicine Practitioner, Adnan Raza
Internal Medicine Practitioner, Ahmad Hakimzada
Internal Medicine Practitioner, Ajoke Bamisile
Internal Medicine Practitioner, Ali Mahjoub
Internal Medicine Practitioner, Michael Megally
Internal Medicine Practitioner, Miguel Jennings
Auditors: ERNST & YOUNG LLP NEW YORK N

LOCATIONS

HQ: NEWYORK-PRESBYTERIAN/BROOKLYN METHODIST
506 6TH ST, BROOKLYN, NY 112153609
Phone: 718 780-3000

COMPETITORS

Beth Israel Medical Center
Bronx-lebanon Hospital
Brookdale University Hospital
Catholic Healthcare System
Kingsbrook Jewish Medical Center
Lutheran Healthcare
Maimonides Medical Center
New York City Health And Hospitals
Northwell Health
Suny Downstate
Winthrop-university Hospital

HISTORICAL FINANCIALS

Company Type: Private

Income Statement				FYE: December 31
	REVENUE ($ mil.)	NET INCOME ($ mil.)	NET PROFIT MARGIN	EMPLOYEES
12/19	962	123	12.8%	4,929
12/16	788	145	18.5%	—
12/15	732	88	12.1%	—
Annual Growth	7.1%	8.6%	—	—

2019 Year-End Financials

Return on assets: 6.3%   Cash ($ mil.): 74
Return on equity: 11.6%
Current ratio: 1.20

NEWYORK-PRESBYTERIAN/QUEENS

The New York Hospital Medical Center of Queens aims to provide care that's fit for royalty. Better known as the New York Hospital Queens the acute care hospital has about 520 beds and provides both primary and tertiary care. Specialist services include cancer cardiovascular pediatric obstetric surgical and dental care. The medical center also operates about a dozen outpatient clinics and care centers that offer such services as family health kidney dialysis rehabilitation and dental care as well as home health care services. New York Hospital Queens is part of the NewYork-Presbyterian Healthcare System.

EXECUTIVES

Pres-Ceo, Stephen S Mills
Sr V Pres-Cfo*, Kevin Ward
Exec V Pres*, John E Sciortino
Exec V Pres*, Stephen Rimar
Sr V Pres*, Kevin J Ward
Sr V Pres*, Michaelle Williams
Procurement Staff, Jed Golden
Chief Engineer, David Harris
Office Manager, Nancy Garcia
Anesthesiologist, Alizabeth Acevedo
Internist, Brigit Palathra
Auditors: ERNST & YOUNG LLP NEW YORK N

LOCATIONS

HQ: NEWYORK-PRESBYTERIAN/QUEENS
5645 MAIN ST, FLUSHING, NY 113555045
Phone: 718 670-2000

PRODUCTS/OPERATIONS

Selected Services and Centers
Ambulatory Patient Care Facilities
Anesthesiology
Cancer Center
Cardiothoracic Surgery
Center for Dental and Oral Medicine
Children's Health (Pediatrics)
Emergency Medicine
Heart and Vascular Center
Neuroscience Institute
Obstetrics and Gynecology
Orthopaedics and Rehabilitation
Pathology and Laboratories
Primary Care and Specialties
Radiation Oncology
Radiology
Surgery
Women's Health

COMPETITORS

Catholic Healthcare System
Continuum Health Partners
Jamaica Hospital Medical Center
Newyork-presbyterian Hospital
Nyack Hospital
Southside Hospital
Winthrop-university Hospital

HISTORICAL FINANCIALS

Company Type: Private

Income Statement				FYE: December 31
	REVENUE ($ mil.)	NET INCOME ($ mil.)	NET PROFIT MARGIN	EMPLOYEES
12/19	841	(2)	—	2,380
12/17	846	5	0.6%	—
12/14	669	14	2.1%	—
12/05	457	10	2.3%	—
Annual Growth	4.4%	—	—	—

2019 Year-End Financials

Return on assets: (-0.3%)   Cash ($ mil.): 13
Return on equity: (-3.1%)
Current ratio: 1.10

NFP CORP.

Through a network of subsidiaries and affiliates NFP provides commercial and personal insurance corporate benefits products and wealth management services to businesses and individuals in the US Puerto Rico Canada and the Europe. NFP enables client success through the expertise of over 6600 global employees investments in innovative technologies and enduring relationships with highly rated insurers vendors and financial institutions. NFP is the 5th largest benefits broker by global revenue.

Operations

NFP is organized along three business segments. Its Individual Solutions provides life insurance wealth management and personal risk. Corporate Benefits offers employee executive and retirement benefits products and HR consulting services to commercial clients. Property and Casualty provides claims management reinsurance occupational health and safety professional liability and workers' compensations.

Geographic Reach

New York-headquartered NFP has offices throughout the US and Puerto Rico Canada and Europe.

Sales and Marketing

NFP serves a wide range of industries including aviation communication media and technology healthcare and life sciences municipalities and public entities education financial institutions real estate nonprofit organizations power and utility companies and transportation logistics and distribution.

Mergers and Acquisitions

In late 2021 NFP acquired Improved Funding Techniques Inc. (IFTI) a third-party administrator (TPA) with an internal RIA offering a consolidated solution for designing implementing and administering retirement plans for privately owned business. The acquisition adds scale to its retirement business and expands its footprint in the New York metro area and around the country. The acquisition also advances NFP's existing internal TPA expertise while adding complementary defined benefit plan capabilities that can be leveraged across the entire organization.

In 2021 NFP acquired Foster Park Brokers Inc. (Foster Park). With the addition of Foster Park one of Western Canada's largest independent insurance brokerages NFP is adhering to its strategic plan of building a unified national platform that provides superior expertise and advice to clients and reinforcing our people first culture for all employees.

Also in late 2021 NFP acquired Connecticut-based Insurance Provider Group LLC (IPG) a P&C insurance broker that provides commercial brokerage services primarily to small to medium sized businesses. In acquiring IPG NFP adds scale as it expands its P&C presence in its Northeast region particularly in Connecticut. IPG will complement NFP's existing expertise and capabilities in commercial risk management personal lines P&C and employee benefits.

Company Background

In 2013 Chicago-based private equity investment firm Madison Dearborn Partners took NFP private in a $1.4 billion deal.

EXECUTIVES

Chairman Of The Board, Chief Executive Officer, Douglas Hammond, $425,000 total compensation
Executive Vice President, Head Of Insurance Brokerage And Consulting, Edward O'Malley
President, Chief Operating Officer, Director, Michael Goldman, $325,000 total compensation
Chief Financial Officer, Executive Vice President, Brett Schneider
Chief Human Resource Officer, Executive Vice President, Ginnette Quesada-Kunkel
Vice President - Commercial Lines, Robert Beauchamp

LOCATIONS

HQ: NFP CORP.
340 MADISON AVE FL 21, NEW YORK, NY 101730401
Phone: 212 301-4000
Web: WWW.NFP.COM

COMPETITORS

Aon	Marsh & Mclennan
Blackrock	Northwestern Mutual
Brown & Brown	Old Mutual (us)
First Commonwealth	Raymond James
Financial	Financial
Gallagher	Securities America
Hub International	The Lockton Companies
Lpl Financial	Usi
M Financial Group	Willis Towers Watson

HISTORICAL FINANCIALS

Company Type: Private

Income Statement — FYE: December 31

	ASSETS ($ mil.)	NET INCOME ($ mil.)	INCOME AS % OF ASSETS	EMPLOYEES
12/11	894	36	4.1%	5,063
12/10	893	42	4.8%	—
12/09	970	(493)	—	—
12/08	1,543	14	1.0%	—
Annual Growth	(16.6%)	35.5%	—	—

2011 Year-End Financials

Return on assets: 4.1% Sales ($ mil.): 1,013
Return on equity: 9.1%

NHK INTERNATIONAL CORPORATION

EXECUTIVES

Ceo, Hideto Enomoto
Sales Associate, Mark Sakata
Information Technology Manager, James Green
Sales Account Manager, Yayoi Akamatsu
Administrative Assistant, Cheryl Mason
Project Manager, Jeff Schaad
Senior Information ADM, Andrew Jahn
Purchasing Manager, Austin Shearer
Sales Manager, Midori Siegfried
Maintenance Technician, Robert Wargowsky
Engineer, Steven Deboer
Auditors: ERNST & YOUNG LLP LOUISVILLE

LOCATIONS

HQ: NHK INTERNATIONAL CORPORATION
46855 MAGELLAN DR, NOVI, MI 483772451
Phone: 248 926-0111
Web: WWW.NHKINTERNATIONAL.COM

HISTORICAL FINANCIALS

Company Type: Private

Income Statement — FYE: March 31

	REVENUE ($ mil.)	NET INCOME ($ mil.)	NET PROFIT MARGIN	EMPLOYEES
03/16	894	12	1.4%	200
03/15	842	(13)	—	—
03/14	739	17	2.4%	—
03/13	688	14	2.1%	—
Annual Growth	9.1%	(4.4%)	—	—

2016 Year-End Financials

Return on assets: 2.8% Cash ($ mil.): 3
Return on equity: 6.1%
Current ratio: 1.00

NICHOLAS PROPERTIES & DEVELOPMENTS, INC.

EXECUTIVES

Ceo, Nicholas J Zinni
Auditors: HW & COMPANY LPA

LOCATIONS

HQ: NICHOLAS PROPERTIES & DEVELOPMENTS, INC.
160 E WASHINGTON ST # 194, CHAGRIN FALLS, OH 440223060
Phone: 216 296-9469

HISTORICAL FINANCIALS

Company Type: Private

Income Statement — FYE: December 31

	ASSETS ($ mil.)	NET INCOME ($ mil.)	INCOME AS % OF ASSETS	EMPLOYEES
12/20*	656	494	75.4%	8
11/18	77	32	41.8%	—
12/16	118	23	19.8%	—
12/14	19	0	1.3%	—
Annual Growth	79.4%	250.9%	—	—

*Fiscal year change

2020 Year-End Financials

Return on assets: 75.4% Sales ($ mil.): 775
Return on equity: 134.8%

NIELSEN HOLDINGS PLC

EXECUTIVES

Independent Executive Chairman Of The Board, James Attwood
Chief Human Resource Officer, Laurie Lovett, $469,423 total compensation
Non-executive Independent Director, Robert Pozen
Non-executive Independent Director, Harish Manwani
Non-executive Independent Director, Guerrino De Luca
Non-executive Independent Director, Javier Teruel
Non-executive Independent Director, Lauren Zalaznick
Non-executive Independent Director, Karen Hoguet
Chief Legal And Corporate Affairs Officer, George Callard, $573,010 total compensation
Non-executive Independent Director, Nancy Tellem
Non-executive Independent Director, Thomas Castro
Chief Operating Officer, Karthik Rao

Non-executive Independent Director, Janice Mazza
Chief Financial Officer, Principal Accounting Officer, Linda Zukauckas, $704,923 total compensation
Director, Jonathan Miller
Chief Marketing And Communications Officer, Jamie Moldafsky
Director, Stephanie Plaines
Corporate Controller, Henry Iglesias
Chief Executive Officer, Director, David Kenny, $1,268,250 total compensation
Chief Commercial Officer, Us, Peter Bradbury
Chief Growth Officer And President, International, Sean Cohan

LOCATIONS

HQ: NIELSEN HOLDINGS PLC
85 BROAD ST, NEW YORK, NY 100042434
Phone: 646 654-5000

HISTORICAL FINANCIALS

Company Type: Private

Income Statement — FYE: December 31

	REVENUE ($ mil.)	NET INCOME ($ mil.)	NET PROFIT MARGIN	EMPLOYEES
12/15	6,172	575	9.3%	43,061
12/14	6,288	381	6.1%	—
12/13	5,703	736	12.9%	—
12/12	5,612	273	4.9%	—
Annual Growth	3.2%	28.2%	—	—

2015 Year-End Financials

Return on assets: 16.4% Cash ($ mil.): 357
Return on equity: 9.3%
Current ratio: 0.90

NOBLE HOLDING (U.S.) CORPORATION

Auditors: PRICEWATERHOUSECOOPERS LLP H

LOCATIONS

HQ: NOBLE HOLDING (U.S.) CORPORATION
3135 S DAIRY ASHFORD, SUGAR LAND, TX 77478
Phone: 281 276-6100
Web: WWW.NOBLECORP.COM

HISTORICAL FINANCIALS

Company Type: Private

Income Statement — FYE: December 31

	REVENUE ($ mil.)	NET INCOME ($ mil.)	NET PROFIT MARGIN	EMPLOYEES
12/15	3,352	607	18.1%	3,744
12/14	3,232	83	2.6%	—
12/13	4,234	935	22.1%	—
Annual Growth	(11.0%)	(19.4%)	—	—

2015 Year-End Financials

Return on assets: 4.7% Cash ($ mil.): 511
Return on equity: 8.2%
Current ratio: 1.40

NORTH ADVOCATE SIDE HEALTH NETWORK

EXECUTIVES

Chief Executive, Kenneth J Rojek
Coordinator, San Wilson
Staff Nurse, Becky Brakel
Engineer, Kerry Kost
Director, Laura Kucyk
Manager of Inpatient Adult, Laurie Shellito
Manager of Human Resources, Len Pawelski
Executive Director Neuroscienc, Rae Salus
Manager, Adam Bloom
Rn, Anna Chernyavskaya
Manager of Design, Bradley Mayer

LOCATIONS

HQ: NORTH ADVOCATE SIDE HEALTH NETWORK
836 W WELLINGTON AVE, CHICAGO, IL 606575147
Phone: 773 296-5699
Web: WWW.ADVOCATEHEALTH.COM

HISTORICAL FINANCIALS

Company Type: Private

Income Statement				FYE: December 31
	REVENUE ($ mil.)	NET INCOME ($ mil.)	NET PROFIT MARGIN	EMPLOYEES
12/19	776	116	15.0%	1,600
12/15	487	97	19.9%	—
12/08	317	29	9.3%	—
Annual Growth	8.5%	13.3%	—	—

2019 Year-End Financials

Return on assets: 12.9%   Cash ($ mil.): 15
Return on equity: 14.7%
Current ratio: —

NORTH AMERICAN LIGHTING, INC.

North American Lighting offers travelers a beacon of safety through the fog. The company is an independent manufacturer of vehicle lighting products in North America. Operating through four assembly plants and one technology center the company produces a line-up of headlamps signal lamps and fog lamps. Its forward-lighting products include mercury-free high intensity discharge (HID) headlamps and the Adaptive Front Lighting System (AFS). Among its signal lamps are rear-combo and license plate lamps. Its products are tailored to the designs of large auto makers and local Japanese automakers. Founded in 1983 North American Lighting is a subsidiary of Japan-based KOITO MANUFACTURING.

Geographic Reach

North American Lighting is stationed in Paris Illinois and has four manufacturing plants in Illinois and one in Alabama. Its technology research center resides in Michigan while a tool plan is located in Indiana.

Sales and Marketing

North American Lighting sells its products primarily to vehicle manufacturers in North America. It provides headlights and taillights to Toyota Nissan General Motors and Honda.

Financial Performance

The company generated 16% of its parent's revenue total in 2014. Revenues for the North American segment also skyrocketed by almost 20% in 2014 due to higher demand in the auto sector which resulted in increased automobile production.

Strategy

Like most players in the manufacturing sector North American Lighting's strategy for growth involves the expansion of its manufacturing capacity. It also attracts additional clients through new product launches. In 2013 the company invested $50 million to expand its plant in Edgar County Illinois by building a 200000 sq. ft. addition and purchasing new equipment for added production lines.

In 2014 the company also began production at its North American Lighting Mexico S.A. de C.V. (Mexican manufacturing plant) which was established in 2012 to expand automobile production throughout Mexico.

EXECUTIVES

Ceo, Takashi Ohtake
Pres*, Jun Toyota
V Pres*, Naoshi Misawa
SEC-Treas*, Kirk Gadberry
V Pres*, Kem Cooley
V Pres*, Kishore Ahuja
Asst SEC*, Theodore Cornell
Program Manager, Keith Blain
Maintenance Supervisor, Dave Sullens
Supplier Quality Engineer, Jeff Akeman
Lab Supervisor, Ben Robinson

LOCATIONS

HQ: NORTH AMERICAN LIGHTING, INC.
2275 S MAIN ST, PARIS, IL 619442963
Phone: 217 465-6600
Web: WWW.NAL.COM

COMPETITORS

Delphi Automotive Systems	Robert Bosch
Hella	Valeo
	Visteon

HISTORICAL FINANCIALS

Company Type: Private

Income Statement				FYE: December 31
	REVENUE ($ mil.)	NET INCOME ($ mil.)	NET PROFIT MARGIN	EMPLOYEES
12/17	1,466	111	7.6%	2,200
12/11	297	13	4.4%	—
12/10	297	13	4.4%	—
Annual Growth	25.6%	35.6%	—	—

2017 Year-End Financials

Return on assets: 16.2%   Cash ($ mil.): 77
Return on equity: 22.9%
Current ratio: 2.10

NORTH BROWARD HOSPITAL DISTRICT

North Broward Hospital District which operates as Broward Health takes care of shark bites and more. The taxpayer-supported not-for-profit health system serves the coastal city of Fort Lauderdale and the northern two-thirds of Broward County Florida with four acute care hospitals and a host of community-based centers. Flagship hospital Broward General Medical Center has more than 700 beds and features the Chris Evert Children's Hospital; all of the hospitals together have more than 1500 beds. Broward Health boasts about 30 additional facilities including family health and surgery centers and home health and hospice programs.

Operations

The Broward Health system also includes teaching hospital Broward Health Medical Center facilities such as Broward Health North and Broward Health Imperial Point Broward Health Community Services and Broward Health Physician Group. The company also operates urgent care clinics.

With more than 1200 physicians Broward Health typically sees some 62500 admissions 283000 emergency department visits 267000 outpatient visits and 17000 outpatient clinic visits each year. It also delivers some 6000 babies annually.

Broward Health is controlled by a seven-member board of commissioners appointed by Florida's governor. As a safety-net health provider in its service territory the system's hospitals receive property tax-based funding for the charity care they provide. The rest of Broward County is served by a second public hospital system South Broward Hospital District. (The county's dual structure goes back to the 1950s.)

Geographic Reach

The company has more than 50 locations across Broward County.

Sales and Marketing

Managed care accounts for more than half of Broward Health's net patient revenues; Medicare and Medicaid combined make up more than 20%.

Financial Performance

In fiscal 2014 revenue grew 2% to $971 million due to growth in net patient service revenues. Net income rose 20% that year on higher investment gains and a decline in interest expenses. The system reported an operating cash outflow to $80 million (versus $27 million in 2013) as less cash was generated from third-party payers and patients.

Strategy

Broward Health looks to improve services by adding new or renovating existing facilities in its system. For example in 2014 it opened a new Adult Cancer Infusion Center at Broward Health Medical Center (featuring an outdoor healing garden); it also opened AJ Acker Virtual Hospital with interactive patient simulators at Broward Health North for training purposes. It broke ground on a $70 million renovation of Broward Health North that will add more operating rooms and expand the emergency department. In 2015 it was given approval to expand Broward Health Coral Springs.

EXECUTIVES

Ceo, Heather Havericak
Pres*, Beverly Capasso
Coo*, Paul Echelard
Cfo*, Robert Martin
Corp Hr Officer*, Kiera Page
Vp-Chief Compliance & Privacy*, Nicholas Hartfield
Cfo*, Paul C Schwarzkopf
Cfo*, Kim Braxl Cole
Chief Information Officer*, Katherine Ross
Cfo*, Laura Thomas
Chief Human Resources Officer*, Deven Silverman
Auditors: WARREN AVERETT LLC BIRMINGHA

LOCATIONS

HQ: NORTH BROWARD HOSPITAL DISTRICT
1800 NW 49TH ST, FORT LAUDERDALE, FL
333093092
Phone: 954 473-7010
Web: WWW.BROWARDHEALTH.ORG

PRODUCTS/OPERATIONS

2014 Sales

Patient care	$ mil.	% of total
Broward Health Medical Center	432	44
Broward Health North	207	21
Broward Health Imperial Point	100	10
Broward Health Coral Springs	140	15
Other	96	10
Eliminations	(5.9)	7
Total	**971**	**100**

Selected Services

Bariatric Surgery
Barrett's Esophagus
Behavioral Health
Broward Health Complete
Cancer Services
Cardiac Services
Children's Diagnostic & Treatment Center
Clinical Trials
Colorectal Services
Concussion Care
Diabetes
Digestive Health
Dysphagia
Emergency Services
Endoscopic Sinus Surgery
Home Health & Hospice Services
International Services
Liver Transplant
Maternity Place
Men's Health
Neurology
Orthopedic Services
Ostomy
Outpatient Services
Pediatric Services
Pharmacy
Primary Care
Senior Services
Sickle Cell Day Unit
Single Incision Laparoscopic Surgery (SILS)

Selected Facilities

Hospitals
　Broward General Medical Center (Fort Lauderdale)
　Coral Springs Medical Center (Coral Springs)
　Imperial Point Medical Center (Fort Lauderdale)
　North Broward Medical Center (Deerfield Beach)
Other Facilities
　Chris Evert Children's Hospital (Fort Lauderdale)
　Broward Health Physician Group (Fort Lauderdale)
　Broward Health Weston (Weston)
　Gold Coast Home Health & Hospice Services (Fort Lauderdale)
　Seventh Avenue Family Health Center (Fort Lauderdale)

COMPETITORS

Baptist Health South Florida
Boca Raton Regional Hospital
Continucare
Hca
Holy Cross Hospital Fort Lauderdale
Jackson Health System
Jupiter Medical Center
Larkin Community Hospital
Mount Sinai Medical Center Of Florida
South Broward Hospital District
University Of Miami Hospital

HISTORICAL FINANCIALS

Company Type: Private

Income Statement　　　　　　　　　　　FYE: June 30

	REVENUE ($ mil.)	NET INCOME ($ mil.)	NET PROFIT MARGIN	EMPLOYEES
06/18	1,035	120	11.6%	7,000
06/17	1,025	33	3.3%	—
06/16	1,014	(12)	—	—
06/08	1,335	67	5.0%	—
Annual Growth	(2.5%)	6.0%	—	—

2018 Year-End Financials

Return on assets: 7.1%　　　Cash ($ mil.): 121
Return on equity: 13.3%
Current ratio: 3.60

NORTH CAROLINA BAPTIST HOSPITAL

EXECUTIVES

Ceo-Pres, Eugene A Woods
Professor, Jeff Weiner
Nurse Manager, Jennifer Ingle
Supervisor, Jennifer Jenkins
Administrative Team Member, Kim Crews
Assistant Professor of Interna, Nancy Denizard-Thomps
Data Analyst, Tina Coble
Vascular Surgeon, Yoshio Otaki
Director Shareholder, Jana Newsome
Human Resources, Dottie Jones
Radiology, James Ball
Auditors: KPMG LLP GREENSBORO NORTH CA

LOCATIONS

HQ: NORTH CAROLINA BAPTIST HOSPITAL
MEDICAL CENTER BLVD, WINSTON SALEM, NC
271570001
Phone: 336 716-2011
Web: WWW.WAKEHEALTH.EDU

HISTORICAL FINANCIALS

Company Type: Private

Income Statement　　　　　　　　　　　FYE: June 30

	REVENUE ($ mil.)	NET INCOME ($ mil.)	NET PROFIT MARGIN	EMPLOYEES
06/21	2,062	319	15.5%	12,563
06/20	1,887	8	0.5%	—
06/19	1,762	8	0.5%	—
06/18	1,633	60	3.7%	—
Annual Growth	8.1%	73.7%	—	—

2021 Year-End Financials

Return on assets: 12.4%　　　Cash ($ mil.): 73
Return on equity: 20.7%
Current ratio: 1.60

NORTH CAROLINA BAPTIST HOSPITAL FDN

Auditors: DIXON HUGHES GOODMAN LLP ASHE

LOCATIONS

HQ: NORTH CAROLINA BAPTIST HOSPITAL FDN
MEDICAL CTR BLVD, WINSTON SALEM, NC
271570001
Phone: 336 716-4445

HISTORICAL FINANCIALS

Company Type: Private

Income Statement　　　　　　　　　　　FYE: June 30

	REVENUE ($ mil.)	NET INCOME ($ mil.)	NET PROFIT MARGIN	EMPLOYEES
06/18	1,795	(6)	—	16
06/17	0	(0)	—	—
06/15	1	0	33.5%	—
06/11	1	0	32.2%	—
Annual Growth	170.8%	—	—	—

2018 Year-End Financials

Return on assets: (-0.4%)　　　Cash ($ mil.): 35
Return on equity: (-0.6%)
Current ratio: —

NORTH CAROLINA ELECTRIC MEMBERSHIP CORPORATION

It's a cooperative effort: North Carolina Electric Membership Corporation (NCEMC) generates and transmits electricity to the state's 26 electric cooperatives (more than 2.5 million people) in 93 of 100 North Carolina counties. The co-op owns more than 600 MW of generating capacity through four primarily natural gas peak load generators plus a 61.5% stake in Catawba Nuclear Station Unit 1 and a 31% stake in the Catawba Nuclear Station in South Carolina. It also buys power from Progress Energy American Electric Power and other for-profit utilities. NCEMC's member cooperatives serve more than 950000 metered businesses and homes in North Carolina. The wholesale co-op also operates an energy operations center.

EXECUTIVES

Ceo, Joe Brannon
Cfo, Lark James
Administrative Assistant, Sibyl Murchison
Purchasing Agent, Larry Hicks
Coordinator, Mike Johnson
Programmer Analyst, Jason Stoddard
Creative Director, Tara Verna
Manager of Energy Operations, Richard McCall
Director of Community Developm, Eddie Miller
Finance, Alice Ward
Computer Network Admini, Beth Berry
Auditors: ERNST & YOUNG LLP RALEIGH NC

LOCATIONS

HQ: NORTH CAROLINA ELECTRIC MEMBERSHIP CORPORATION
3400 SUMNER BLVD, RALEIGH, NC 276162950
Phone: 919 872-0800
Web: WWW.NCELECTRICCOOPERATIVES.COM

PRODUCTS/OPERATIONS

Subsidiaries
North Carolina Association of Electric Cooperatives (NCAEC training programs)
The Tarheel Electric Membership Association Inc. (TEMA purchasing and materials supply)
North Carolina Cooperatives
Albemarle Electric Membership Corporation
Blue Ridge Electric Membership Corporation
Brunswick Electric Membership Corporation
Cape Hatteras Electric Cooperative
Carteret-Craven Electric Cooperative
Central Electric Membership Corporation
Edgecombe-Martin County Electric Membership Corporation
EnergyUnited
Four County Electric Membership Corporation
French Broad Electric Membership Corporation
Halifax Electric Membership Corporation
Haywood Electric Membership Corporation
Jones-Onslow Electric Membership Corporation
Lumbee River Electric Membership Corporation
Pee Dee Electric Membership Corporation
Piedmont Electric Membership Corporation
Pitt & Greene Electric Membership Corporation
Randolph Electric Membership Corporation
Roanoke Electric Cooperative
Rutherford Electric Membership Corporation
South River Electric Membership Corporation
Surry-Yadkin Electric Membership Corporation
Tideland Electric Membership Corporation
Tri-County Electric Membership Corporation
Union Power Cooperative
Wake Electric Membership Corporation

COMPETITORS

Aep	Progress Energy
Dominion Energy	Scana
Duke Energy	Santee-Cooper
Meag Power	Tva

HISTORICAL FINANCIALS
Company Type: Private

Income Statement				FYE: December 31
	REVENUE ($ mil.)	NET INCOME ($ mil.)	NET PROFIT MARGIN	EMPLOYEES
12/20	1,092	29	2.7%	188
12/19	1,219	30	2.5%	—
12/18	1,188	30	2.5%	—
12/17	1,017	23	2.3%	—
Annual Growth	2.4%	8.4%	—	—

2020 Year-End Financials
Return on assets: 1.3%   Cash ($ mil.): 206
Return on equity: 10.2%
Current ratio: 1.40

NORTH DAKOTA UNIVERSITY SYSTEM

EXECUTIVES

Information, Jerry Olson
Residence Hall Director, Chelsee Rohmiller
Director of Event Operations, Colin Bailey
Associate Professor, Kelly Buettner-Schmid

Vice Chair, Casey Ryan
Director of Finance, David Krebsbach
Director, Human Resources, Jane Grinde
Chief Compliance Officer, Karol Riedman
Director, Katie Fitzsimmons
Software Developer, Aldrin Simpron
Assistant Professor, Allison Sadowsky
Auditors: ROBERT R PETERSON STATE AUDI

LOCATIONS

HQ: NORTH DAKOTA UNIVERSITY SYSTEM
2000 44TH ST S STE 301, FARGO, ND 581037434
Phone: 701 231-6326
Web: WWW.NDUS.EDU

HISTORICAL FINANCIALS
Company Type: Private

Income Statement				FYE: June 30
	REVENUE ($ mil.)	NET INCOME ($ mil.)	NET PROFIT MARGIN	EMPLOYEES
06/20	690	(11)	—	46
06/19	709	8	1.2%	—
06/18	713	19	2.8%	—
06/17	702	66	9.5%	—
Annual Growth	(0.6%)	—	—	—

2020 Year-End Financials
Return on assets: (-0.5%)   Cash ($ mil.): 219
Return on equity: (-0.8%)
Current ratio: 3.30

NORTH DAKOTA UNIVERSITY SYSTEM FOUNDATION

EXECUTIVES

Princ, Hamid Augustine Shirvani
Chancellor, William Goetz
Presi, Kirsten Diederich
V Pres, Terry Hjelmstad
Gis Coordinator, Subhro Mitra
Information Profession, Carol Tschakert
Scientist, Erin Koval
Scientist, Thomas Glass
Assistant Professor, Annie X Tangpong
Coordinator, David Dodds
Assistant Professor, David Newman
Auditors: ROBERT R PETERSON FARGO NORT

LOCATIONS

HQ: NORTH DAKOTA UNIVERSITY SYSTEM FOUNDATION
600 E BOULEVARD AVE # 215, BISMARCK, ND 585050601
Phone: 701 328-2960
Web: WWW.NDUS.EDU

HISTORICAL FINANCIALS
Company Type: Private

Income Statement				FYE: June 30
	REVENUE ($ mil.)	NET INCOME ($ mil.)	NET PROFIT MARGIN	EMPLOYEES
06/20	690	(11)	—	252
06/19*	709	8	1.2%	—
12/17	78	59	76.1%	—
06/17	1,252	66	5.3%	—
Annual Growth	(18.0%)			

*Fiscal year change

2020 Year-End Financials
Return on assets: (-0.5%)   Cash ($ mil.): 219
Return on equity: (-0.8%)
Current ratio: 3.30

NORTH EAST INDEPENDENT SCHOOL DISTRICT COUNCIL OF PARENT TEACHER ASSOCIATION

EXECUTIVES

Supt, Brian G Gottardy
Bd Pres, Beth Plummer
Bd V Pres, Susan Galindo
Bd SEC, Sandy Hughey
Occupational Specia, Gayla Aguilar
Corrections Officer, Andres De Leon
Occupational Specia, Katherine Farrimond
Executive of Information Techn, Betsy Williams
Executive of Information Techn, Dawn Gembler
Director of Operations, Juan De Losntos
Facilities Specialist, Cindy Salazar
Auditors: ABIP PC SAN ANTONIO TEXAS

LOCATIONS

HQ: NORTH EAST INDEPENDENT SCHOOL DISTRICT COUNCIL OF PARENT TEACHER ASSOCIATION
8961 TESORO DR, SAN ANTONIO, TX 782176209
Phone: 210 407-0359
Web: WWW.NEISD.NET

HISTORICAL FINANCIALS
Company Type: Private

Income Statement				FYE: June 30
	REVENUE ($ mil.)	NET INCOME ($ mil.)	NET PROFIT MARGIN	EMPLOYEES
06/20	768	38	5.0%	10,000
06/19	744	(41)	—	—
06/18	759	23	3.0%	—
06/17	747	(2)	—	—
Annual Growth	0.9%	—	—	—

2020 Year-End Financials
Return on assets: 1.8%   Cash ($ mil.): 273
Return on equity: —
Current ratio: —

NORTH KANSAS CITY HOSPITAL

EXECUTIVES

Ceo, Peggy Schmitt
Cfo*, Henry Seybold
Coo*, Kerri Jenkins
Director of Manufacturing, Tim Ford
Vice President, Dawn Bryant
Member To Board of Trustee, James Hake
Vice President, Kristen Guillaume
Purchasing Supervisor, Barbara Wolfgeher
Database Administrator, Brenda Pratt
Radiology Operations Superviso, Cheryl Bondank
Accounting Supervisor, Dan Pratt
Auditors: BKD LLP KANSAS CITY MISSOUR

LOCATIONS

HQ: NORTH KANSAS CITY HOSPITAL
   2800 CLAY EDWARDS DR, NORTH KANSAS CITY, MO
   641163220
Phone: 816 691-2000
Web: WWW.NKCH.ORG

HISTORICAL FINANCIALS

Company Type: Private

Income Statement   FYE: June 30

	REVENUE ($ mil.)	NET INCOME ($ mil.)	NET PROFIT MARGIN	EMPLOYEES
06/18	586	6	1.1%	3,100
06/16	484	31	6.6%	—
06/15	462	35	7.6%	—
06/11	419	22	5.3%	—
Annual Growth	4.9%	(16.7%)	—	—

2018 Year-End Financials

Return on assets: 0.8%   Cash ($ mil.): 24
Return on equity: 1.0%
Current ratio: 1.50

NORTH MEMORIAL HEALTH CARE

North Memorial Health Care fights illness in the Twin Cities. Established in 1939 as Victory Hospital the health care network is home to North Memorial Medical Center a 520-bed hospital that features a Level I trauma center and the Humphrey Cancer Center. The hospital also operates specialty centers for cardiovascular care orthopedics pediatrics and women's health as well as an emergency vehicle fleet of more than 125 ambulances and nearly 10 helicopters. The adjacent outpatient center provides oncology radiation and imaging services. North Memorial Health Care also has a network of primary and specialty care clinics in the Twin Cities region and it provides home health and hospice services.

Strategy

North Memorial Health fights illness in the Twin Cities. Started as a single hospital in 1954 North Memorial Health is home to North Memorial Health Hospital and Maple Grove Hospital. It has over 350 care providers and more than 6000 team members. The hospital also operates specialty centers for cardiovascular care orthopedics pediatrics

and women's health as well as an emergency vehicle fleet of more than 125 ambulances and nearly 10 helicopters. The adjacent outpatient center provides oncology radiation and imaging services. Serves more than 55000 customers monthly North Memorial Health also has a network of nearly 25 primary and specialty care clinics in the Twin Cities region and it provides home health and hospice services.

EXECUTIVES

Pres-Ceo, Loren Taylor
Exec V Pres-Coo*, David W Cress
V Pres*, M Kaye Foley
Cfo*, Patrick Boran
CIO*, Bradford Newton
Gastroenterologist, Agata Bednarz
Internist, Alireza Khakbaznejad
Emergency Medicine Specialist, Brenden Wilde
Revenue Analyst, Cheryl Manthey
Hrms Administrator Ultipro, Dustin Kuklenz
Gastroenterologist, Joseph Schowalter

LOCATIONS

HQ: NORTH MEMORIAL HEALTH CARE
   3300 OAKDALE AVE N, MINNEAPOLIS, MN
   554222900
Phone: 763 520-5200
Web: WWW.NORTHMEMORIAL.COM

PRODUCTS/OPERATIONS

Selected Locations

Heart & Vascular Center - Maple Grove - Maple Grove Minnesota
Heart & Vascular Clinic - Buffalo - Buffalo Minnesota
Heart & Vascular Clinic - Monticello - Monticello Minnesota
Hope Chest Breast Center - Robbinsdale Minnesota
Humphrey Cancer Center - Robbinsdale Minnesota
Maple Grove Hospital - Maple Grove Minnesota
Maternal Fetal Medicine - Maple Grove - Maple Grove Minnesota
North Memorial Clinic Brooklyn Center - Brooklyn Center Minnesota
North Memorial Clinic Brooklyn Park - Brooklyn Park Minnesota
North Memorial Clinic Camden - Maple Grove - Maple Grove Minnesota
North Memorial Clinic Camden - Minneapolis - Minneapolis Minnesota
North Memorial Clinic Camden - Plymouth - Plymouth Minnesota
North Memorial Clinic Elk River - Elk River Minnesota
North Memorial Clinic Golden Valley - Golden Valley Minnesota
North Memorial Clinic Maple Grove - Maple Grove Minnesota
North Memorial Clinic Minnetonka - Minnetonka Minnesota
North Memorial Clinic Northeast - Minneapolis Minnesota
North Memorial Clinic Plymouth City Center - Plymouth Minnesota
North Memorial Clinic Silver Lake Clinic - St. Anthony - St. Anthony Minnesota
North Memorial Clinic Silver Lake Clinic - Blaine - Blaine Minnesota
North Memorial Medical Center - Robbinsdale Minnesota
North Memorial Urgent Care - Maple Grove - Maple Grove Minnesota
North Memorial Urgent Care - Roseville - Roseville Minnesota
Outpatient Imaging Center - Robbinsdale Minnesota
Outpatient Psychiatric Clinic - Robbinsdale Minnesota
Rehabilitation Services - Robbinsdale Minnesota
Rehabilitation Services - Maple Grove Minnesota
Rehabilitation Services - Elk River Minnesota
Residential Hospice - Brooklyn Center Minnesota
Sleep Health Center - Maple Grove Minnesota
Sleep Health Center - Robbinsdale Minnesota
Urgent Care - Blaine Minnesota

Selected Services

Acupuncture
Acute Concussion Clinic
Acute Inpatient Rehabilitation
Air Care
Ambulance Services
Anterior Hip Replacement
Balance Center
Breast Health
Breast Milk Depot
CACE Unit
Cancer Education & Support
Cancer Treatment
Cardiac Rehabilitation
Cardiology
Cardiology Clinic Services
Complex Heart Procedures and Interventional Services
Computed Tomography - CT
Dermatology
Diabetes Education
Domestic Abuse Victim Advocacy - SafeJourney
Emergency Department
EMS Education
Endovenous Laser Treatment (EVLT) for Varicose Veins
Family Birth Center
Family Medicine
Gastroenterology
General Radiology
Genetics Program
Geriatric Care
Gift Shop
Grief and Loss Support
Group Physical Therapy
Gynecology

COMPETITORS

Allina Hospitals
Bethesda Hospital
Catholic Health Initiatives
Centracare Health
Children's Hospitals And Clinics Of Minnesota
Fairview Health
First Care
Healtheast Care System
Mayo Clinic
Methodist Hospital (mn)
Park Nicollet Health Services
Regions Hospital
Scmc
St. John's Hospital (minnesota)
St. Luke's Hospital (mn)
University Of Minnesota Medical Center

HISTORICAL FINANCIALS

Company Type: Private

Income Statement   FYE: December 31

	REVENUE ($ mil.)	NET INCOME ($ mil.)	NET PROFIT MARGIN	EMPLOYEES
12/18	720	(16)	—	5,180
12/17	651	(28)	—	—
12/16	721	(0)	—	—
12/13	735	51	7.0%	—
Annual Growth	(0.4%)	—	—	—

NORTH MISSISSIPPI HEALTH SERVICES, INC.

North Mississippi Health Services (NMHS) isn't contained by its name: The health system also provides health care to residents of northwestern Alabama. NMHS includes half a dozen community hospitals including its flagship North Mississippi Medical Center in Tupelo. North Mississippi Medical Clinics a regional network of more than 30 primary and specialty clinics; and nursing homes.

Combined the facilities have nearly 1000 beds designated for acute long term and nursing care. Specialty services include home health and long-term care inpatient and outpatient behavioral health and treatment centers for cancer and digestive disorders. NMHS also operates outpatient care and wellness clinics in the region.

Operations

During 2014 NMHS handled about 30000 inpatient visits as well as more than 128000 emergency room visits and some 345000 outpatient care visits. It also conducted about 24000 surgeries at its various facilities. Its outpatient centers include more than 30 primary and specialty care clinics in Mississippi and Alabama operated through the North Mississippi Medical Clinics division as well as more than half a dozen wellness centers.

Geographic Reach

In all NMHS serves two dozen counties across the two states. In addition to its main hospital in Tupelo NMHS operates health centers in communities including Eupora Iuka Pontotoc and West Point Mississippi and in Hamilton Alabama. It also manages a center in Calhoun City Mississippi. Its Baldwyn Nursing Facility is located in Baldwyn Mississippi.

Financial Performance

Flagship North Mississippi Medical Center (NNMC)'s revenues increased by 6% due to a growth in net patient revenues. Medicare and Medicaid together accounted for about 50% of net patient revenues; managed care and commercial 25%; Blue Cross 14%; self-pay 10%; and Health Link 1%.

NNMC reported net loss of $14 million in 2014 over net income in 2013 due to pension-related changes.

NNMC's operating cash flow increased by 256% that year.

Mergers and Acquisitions

In 2018 North Mississippi Health Services agreed to buy Gilmore Memorial Hospital out of bankruptcy. It will pay $10.5 million for the Armory Mississippi hospital including the assumption of liabilities and financial commitments.

EXECUTIVES

Chb, Jim Kelley
Ceo, Shane Spees
Pres-Ceo, John Heer
Treas, Joe Reppert
SEC, Bruce Toppin
Cfo, Sharon Nobles
Vice Pres, Steven Blaylock
Account Representative, Sam Michael
Charge Nurse, Meagan Waldrip
Chief Human Resources Officer, Sondra Davis
Manager Nurse, Cera Bates

LOCATIONS

HQ: NORTH MISSISSIPPI HEALTH SERVICES, INC.
830 S GLOSTER ST, TUPELO, MS 388014934
Phone: 662 377-3000
Web: WWW.NMHS.NET

Selected Locations

Baldwyn Nursing Facility (Baldwyn Mississippi)
Calhoun County Medical Clinic (managed facility; Calhoun Mississippi)
NMMC-Eupora (Eupora Mississippi)
NMMC-Hamilton (Hamilton Alabama)
NMMC-Iuka (Iuka Mississippi)
NMMC-Pontotoc (Pontotoc Mississippi)
NMMC-Tupelo (Tupelo Mississippi)
NMMC-West Point (West Point Mississippi)
North Mississippi Medical Clinics (NMMCI regional)

PRODUCTS/OPERATIONS

Selected Facilities and Services

Acute Stroke Unit
Advanced Wound Center and Hyperbarics
Bariatric Center
Behavioral Health Center
Breast Care Center
Cancer Center
Center for Digestive Health
Community Health
Critical Care Unit
CRNA Program
Diabetes Treatment Center
Emergency Services
Family Medicine Residency Center
Heart Institute
Home Health and Hospice
Hospitalists
Joint Replacement Center
Le Bonheur Specialty Clinics
Medical Imaging
North Mississippi Surgery Center
Outpatient Infusion
Pain Management Center
Pastoral Care
Physician Specialties
Radiology
Rehabilitation Services
Respiratory Therapy
Skilled Nursing Facility
Sleep Disorders Center
Surgical Services
Tupelo Wellness Center
Vein Center
Volunteer Services
Women's Hospital
Women's and Children Services

COMPETITORS

Baptist Memorial Health Care
Community Health Systems
Delta Regional Medical Center
Forrest General Hospital
Hca
Memorial Hospital At Gulfport
Methodist Healthcare
Natchez Regional Medical Center
North Mississippi Medical
Shelby County Health Care
Southwest Mississippi Regional Medical Center

HISTORICAL FINANCIALS

Company Type: Private

Income Statement				FYE: September 30
	REVENUE ($ mil.)	NET INCOME ($ mil.)	NET PROFIT MARGIN	EMPLOYEES
09/17	898	26	3.0%	6,000
09/16	893	30	3.4%	—
09/15	860	19	2.2%	—
09/14	779	(14)	—	—
Annual Growth	4.9%	—	—	—

2017 Year-End Financials

Return on assets: 2.2%   Cash ($ mil.): 36
Return on equity: 3.4%
Current ratio: 4.00

NORTH SHORE UNIVERSITY HEALTH SYSTEM

LOCATIONS

HQ: NORTH SHORE UNIVERSITY HEALTH SYSTEM
2650 RIDGE AVE, EVANSTON, IL 602011700
Phone: 847 570-2640
Web: WWW.NORTHSHORE.ORG

HISTORICAL FINANCIALS

Company Type: Private

Income Statement				FYE: September 30
	REVENUE ($ mil.)	NET INCOME ($ mil.)	NET PROFIT MARGIN	EMPLOYEES
09/15	1,419	55	3.9%	3
09/14	1,397	148	10.6%	—
09/13	1,815	238	13.1%	—
Annual Growth	(11.6%)	(51.7%)	—	—

2015 Year-End Financials

Return on assets: 1.7%   Cash ($ mil.): 62
Return on equity: 3.0%
Current ratio: 0.60

NORTH SHORE UNIVERSITY HOSPITAL

North Shore University Hospital (NSUH) knows you shouldn't have to leave the island for quality health care. The Long Island hospital has more than 800 beds devoted to adult and pediatric medicine rehabilitation stroke care women's health orthopedics urology wound healing dentistry and trauma emergency services among other areas. The hospital is home to specialist institutes for cancer care and cardiology. It also serves as a campus for the Hofstra Northwell Shool of Medicine. NSUH is part of Northwell Health.

Operations

The not-for-profit NSUH operates numerous satellite community health centers that provide primary surgery psychiatric dental and specialty care including the Schwartz Ambulatory Surgery Center. Its Stern Family Center for Extend Care and Rehabilitation has about 250 beds; NSUH also includes a Katz Women's Hospital (one of two in the system). The hospital provides comprehensive care in all health care specialties including organ transplant services. In addition the hospital operates mobile health vehicles and conducts educational and wellness programs for area residents.

NSUH has a staff of more than 6000 specialist and subspecialist physicians nurses and other medical workers. It handles about 50000 inpatient visits 90000 emergency room visits 20000 surgeries and 6000 births each year.

NSUH has medical health professional and nursing school affiliations with about 15 colleges and universities. Programs include residencies postgraduate training and fellowships.

Geographic Reach

Strategy

NSUH and the larger Northwell Health system tend to grow through the acquisitions of smaller campuses and mergers with other systems. This allows the hospital to gain operating efficiency through vertical integration bargaining power with vendors and a more diversified revenue stream.

In 2017 NSUH opened the Sandra Atlas Bass Heart Hospital for advanced cardiac care. The facility will be the first on Long Island to offer heart transplants and the sixth in New York State (which has a very high number of transplant candidates on its waiting list).

As part of its efforts to bring cutting-edge health care to the community it serves the hospital began offering 3D-printed titanium spinal implants in 2017. These synthetic implants approved in the US in 2016 are made with titanium powder rather than from a donor or from the patient's own body and manufactured using a 3D-printing process.

EXECUTIVES

Pres, Michael J Dowling
Cno*, Irene Macyk
Project Coordinator, Christopher Martin
Coordinator, Melissa Robinson
Executive Vice President and P, Lawrence G Smith
Poct Supervisor, Cathy Drechsel
Senior Executive Assistant, Amy Mulvey
Manager, Cathleen Reis
Manager, Mary Parker
Supervisor, Patricia McDonald
Director, Venice M Vanhuse

LOCATIONS

HQ: NORTH SHORE UNIVERSITY HOSPITAL
300 COMMUNITY DR, MANHASSET, NY 110303876
Phone: 516 562-0100
Web: WWW.NORTHWELL.EDU

PRODUCTS/OPERATIONS

Selected Centers and Services
Bariatric Services
Cancer Institute
Cardiovascular and Thoracic Services
Colorectal Surgery
Emergency Department / Trauma Services
Fertility and Reproductive Services
Geriatric and Palliative Medicine
Infectious Diseases / AIDS Research
Kidney Transplantation
Laparoendoscopic Single-Site Surgery
Military/Veterans Services
Minimally Invasive Robotic Surgery
Neuroscience
Obstetrics and Gynecology
Orthopaedics
Pain Management
Pediatric Services
Radiation Medicine
Travel Immunization
Urology Services
Wound Care

COMPETITORS

Brookhaven Memorial Hospital Medical Center
Catholic Health Services Of Long Island
Catholic Healthcare System
Long Island College Hospital
Maimonides Medical Center
New York City Health And Hospitals
Newyork-presbyterian Healthcare
Winthrop-university Hospital

HISTORICAL FINANCIALS
Company Type: Private

Income Statement   FYE: December 31

	REVENUE ($ mil.)	NET INCOME ($ mil.)	NET PROFIT MARGIN	EMPLOYEES
12/18	1,883	38	2.1%	5,000
12/17	1,826	191	10.5%	—
12/16	1,795	171	9.6%	—
12/15	1,617	37	2.3%	—
Annual Growth	5.2%	1.3%	—	—

2018 Year-End Financials
Return on assets: 1.9%   Cash ($ mil.): 31
Return on equity: 3.8%
Current ratio: 3.00

NORTH SHORE-LONG ISLAND JEWISH HEALTH CARE

EXECUTIVES

Prin, Filippo Petti
Information Technology/Interne, Phil Leonardi
Project Manager, Cathlyn Fagan
Director Research, Michael Ryan

LOCATIONS

HQ: NORTH SHORE-LONG ISLAND JEWISH HEALTH CARE
972 BRUSH HOLLOW RD 5TH, WESTBURY, NY 115901740
Phone: 516 876-6611

HISTORICAL FINANCIALS
Company Type: Private

Income Statement   FYE: December 31

	REVENUE ($ mil.)	NET INCOME ($ mil.)	NET PROFIT MARGIN	EMPLOYEES
12/14	719	(34)	—	2
12/13	633	(33)	—	—
12/09	351	(2)	—	—
Annual Growth	15.4%	—	—	—

2014 Year-End Financials
Return on assets: (-1.9%)   Cash ($ mil.): 74
Return on equity: (-7.7%)
Current ratio: 0.50

NORTH TEXAS MUNICIPAL WATER DISTRICT

EXECUTIVES

Pres, Darwin Whiteside
V Pres*, Joe Joplin
SEC*, Terry Sam Anderson

Exec Dir*, Tom Kula
Scientist, Rachel Blakey
Program Inspector, Manual Rivas
Information, Jodi Hall
Human Resources Technician, Laura E Benfield
Admin Technician, Amanda Gaffaney
Administrative Assistant, Amy Parks
Assistant Instrumentation Supe, Bradley Gebhard
Auditors: WEAVER AND TIDWELL LLP DA

LOCATIONS

HQ: NORTH TEXAS MUNICIPAL WATER DISTRICT
501 E BROWN ST, WYLIE, TX 750984406
Phone: 972 442-5405
Web: WWW.NTMWD.COM

HISTORICAL FINANCIALS
Company Type: Private

Income Statement   FYE: September 30

	REVENUE ($ mil.)	NET INCOME ($ mil.)	NET PROFIT MARGIN	EMPLOYEES
09/20	572	134	23.5%	670
09/19	516	167	32.4%	—
09/18	484	117	24.3%	—
09/17	439	129	29.4%	—
Annual Growth	9.2%	1.4%	—	—

2020 Year-End Financials
Return on assets: 2.1%   Cash ($ mil.): 124
Return on equity: 7.7%
Current ratio: —

NORTH TEXAS TOLLWAY AUTHORITY

The North Texas Tollway Authority (NTTA) operates a toll system consisting of about 90 miles of roadway. Facilities include the Dallas North Tollway the President George Bush Turnpike the Addison Airport Toll Tunnel the Mountain Creek Lake Bridge and the Sam Rayburn Tollway. The authority serves four counties in the Dallas-Fort Worth area. A predecessor agency the Texas Turnpike Authority was created by the Texas Legislature in 1953; the NTTA was created by the Legislature in 1997 to take over for the turnpike authority in Collin Dallas Denton and Tarrant counties.

EXECUTIVES

Chairman, Kenneth Barr
Interim Executive Director*, Gerry Carrigan
Director and Incident M, Marty Leg
Director of Finance, Armando Garza
Maintenance Support Manager, Floyd Spencer
Information Specialist, Chris Tobias
Customer Specialist II, Patricia Nelson
Applications Manage, Brad Rhodes
Customer Specialist II, Rocio Aguero
Accountant, Santesia Washington
Customer Specialist, Joshua Davis
Auditors: CROWE HORWATH LLP DALLAS TEX

LOCATIONS

HQ: NORTH TEXAS TOLLWAY AUTHORITY
5900 W PLANO PKWY STE 100, PLANO, TX 750934695
Phone: 214 461-2000
Web: WWW.NTTA.ORG

HISTORICAL FINANCIALS
Company Type: Private

Income Statement				FYE: December 31
	REVENUE ($ mil.)	NET INCOME ($ mil.)	NET PROFIT MARGIN	EMPLOYEES
12/20	785	(1)	—	733
12/16	741	93	12.6%	—
12/13	551	(99)	—	—
12/12	0	(126)	—	—
Annual Growth	—	—	—	—

2020 Year-End Financials
Return on assets: —
Return on equity: (-0.5%)
Current ratio: 1.60

Cash ($ mil.): 39

NORTHEAST GEORGIA MEDICAL CENTER, INC.

EXECUTIVES

Ceo, Carol Burrell
V Pres*, Tracy Vardeman
V Pres*, Anthony Williamson
V Pres*, Paul Vervalin
Cfo*, Anthony M Herdener
Oncology, Jack T Griffeth
Internal Medicine Practitioner, Ernest T Kamara
Coordinator, Jason Grady
Internal Medicine Practitioner, Getachew Iyasu
Internal Medicine Practitioner, Erine Raybon
Internal Medicine Practitioner, Kolawole Atandeyi
Auditors: PYA P C KNOXVILLE TN

LOCATIONS

HQ: NORTHEAST GEORGIA MEDICAL CENTER, INC.
743 SPRING ST NE, GAINESVILLE, GA 305013715
Phone: 770 219-9000
Web: WWW.NGHS.COM

HISTORICAL FINANCIALS
Company Type: Private

Income Statement				FYE: September 30
	REVENUE ($ mil.)	NET INCOME ($ mil.)	NET PROFIT MARGIN	EMPLOYEES
09/19	1,328	162	12.2%	3,053
09/18	1,266	113	9.0%	—
09/17	1,152	7	0.7%	—
09/16	1,024	45	4.5%	—
Annual Growth	9.1%	52.4%	—	—

2019 Year-End Financials
Return on assets: 8.8%
Return on equity: 23.5%
Current ratio: 0.10

Cash ($ mil.): 15

NORTHEASTERN UNIVERSITY

Since 1898 Northeastern University has been educating students in Boston and beyond. Northeastern is a private nonprofit school that offers undergraduate and graduate degree programs. It is home to more than 35 specialized research and education centers. The graduate programs offers professional doctorates masters certificates and all other programs. Undergraduate education offers accounting biology business administration computer science engineering and more.

Operations
Northeastern offered programs include Dialogue Civilization Programs Global Co-op Global Engagement Program Global Quest Incoming Exchange Program N.U. in Semester In Study Abroad Specialized Entry Program and more.

The school also boasts extensive research centers and institutes.

Geographic Reach
Northeastern's students hail from about 148 countries. The university has study abroad programs in locations including Argentina Costa Rica France China Germany and the UK (among many others).

In addition to its main campus in Boston Northeastern has satellite graduate schools in Charlotte North Carolina Seattle California London Silicon Valley Portland Maine Vancouver and Toronto.

Sales and Marketing
Northeastern University program such as Global Engagement Program Incoming Exchange Program N.U. In Semester In Study Abroad Specialized Entry Programs are offered in the company websites.

Strategy
Northeastern University has adopted endowment investment and spending policies that attempt to provide a predictable stream of funding to programs supported by its endowment while seeking to maintain the purchasing power of endowment assets. To achieve its long-term rate of return objectives the university relies on a total return strategy in which investment returns are achieved through both capital appreciation (realized and unrealized gains) and current yield (interest and dividends).

EXECUTIVES

Pres, Joseph Aoun
Sr V Pres*, James Bean
Sr V Pres*, Philomena Mantella
Sr V Pres*, Michael Armini
Treas*, Thomas Nedell
Sr V Pres*, Ralph Martin
Sr V Pres*, Diane Macgillivray
Chief of Staff*, James R Hackney
Administrator, Kelly Basner
Journalism Professor, Matthew Carroll
Digital Marketing Manager, Sarah Woodward
Auditors: PRICEWATERHOUSECOOPERS LLP BO

LOCATIONS

HQ: NORTHEASTERN UNIVERSITY
360 HUNTINGTON AVE, BOSTON, MA 021155000
Phone: 617 373-2000
Web: WWW.NORTHEASTERN.EDU

PRODUCTS/OPERATIONS

Selected Schools & Colleges
Bouvé: College of Health Sciences
College of Arts Media and Design
College of Computer and Information Science
College of Engineering
College of Professional Studies
College of Science
College of Social Sciences and Humanities
D'Amore-McKim School of Business
School of Law

HISTORICAL FINANCIALS
Company Type: Private

Income Statement				FYE: June 30
	REVENUE ($ mil.)	NET INCOME ($ mil.)	NET PROFIT MARGIN	EMPLOYEES
06/21	1,551	53	3.4%	4,175
06/20	1,523	193	12.7%	—
06/19	1,405	229	16.4%	—
06/18	1,306	163	12.5%	—
Annual Growth	5.9%	(31.1%)	—	—

2021 Year-End Financials
Return on assets: 1.1%
Return on equity: 2.0%
Current ratio: —

Cash ($ mil.): 534

NORTHERN INDIANA PUBLIC SERVICE COMPANY LLC

Northern Indiana Public Service Company (NIPSCO) can shine a little light on the topic of Hoosiers. The largest subsidiary of utility holding company NiSource NIPSCO has more than 457000 electricity customers and more than 786000 natural gas customers. The utility has three coal-fired power plants with 2540 MW of generating capacity. On the power side of the business NIPSCO generates transmits and distributes electricity to the northern part of Indiana and engages in electric wholesale and transmission transactions. The company operates approximately 13000 miles of electric transmission and distribution lines and 16000 miles of gas mains.

Operations
NIPSCO's three operating power facilities have a net capability of 2540 MW. It also owns and operates Sugar Creek a combined cycle gas turbine plant with a 535 MW capacity four gas-fired generating units with a net capability of 206 MW and two hydroelectric generating plants with a net capability of 10 MW. During 2012 NIPSCO generated 74.1% and purchased 25.9% of its electric requirements.

Geographic Reach
NIPSCO Gas is the largest natural gas distribution company in Indiana and NIPSCO Electric which serves customers in 20 counties is the state's #2 power distribution company behind Duke Energy Indiana.

Strategy
NIPSCO is promoting incentive plans to help customers save money through energy efficiency programs including appliance rebates for the installation of more energy efficient water heaters and other electric appliances and for automated

air-conditioning cycling (cutting use for limited periods during peak loads). Other incentives are available for weatherizing energy audits and green construction projects.

In 2011 the company increased residential customer rates by 5%. The rate increase was in part a way to compensate for a decline in usage and revenues as a result of the global recession.

In 2011 NiSource companies Northern Indiana Fuel & Light and Kokomo Gas were consolidated with and into NIPSCO in order to improve operating efficiencies.

EXECUTIVES

Pres, Mike Hooper
V Pres*, Jon D Veurink
Sr V Pres Trans & Eng'g*, Timothy A Dehring
V Pres Fx Compliance-Corp SEC*, Gary W Pottorff
Cfo*, Pete Disser
Vp-Comm. & External Affairs, Jennifer Montague
Senior Vice President, Dan Douglas
Executive Director, Debora Owen
Chief Accounting Officer, Jeffrey Grossman
Damage Prevention Coordinator, Kevin Miller
Administrative Manager, Ralph Rosenbrock

LOCATIONS

HQ: NORTHERN INDIANA PUBLIC SERVICE COMPANY LLC
801 E 86TH AVE, MERRILLVILLE, IN 464106271
Phone: 800 464-7726
Web: WWW.NISOURCE.COM

PRODUCTS/OPERATIONS

Selected Services
Call 811 Before You Dig
Commercial and Industrial Services
DependaBill
Dusk to Dawn Streetlights
Extra Service Protection
Green Power
IN-Charge Electric Vehicle Program
Meter Reading
NIPSCO Choice Program
NIPSCO Connect
Price Protection Service
Residential Builder and Developer Services
Selling Your Clean Energy
Smart Grid Technology
Start or Stop Gas and Electric Services
Trees and Power Lines
Wood Stove Changeout Program

COMPETITORS

Aep	Ipalco Enterprises
Citizens Energy	Indiana Michigan Power
Dominion Energy	Vectren
Duke Energy Indiana	

HISTORICAL FINANCIALS
Company Type: Private

Income Statement				FYE: December 31
	REVENUE ($ mil.)	NET INCOME ($ mil.)	NET PROFIT MARGIN	EMPLOYEES
12/17	2,418	226	9.3%	3,096
12/16	2,252	178	7.9%	—
/	0	0	—	—
Annual Growth	—	—	—	—

2017 Year-End Financials
Return on assets: 3.2%   Cash ($ mil.): 7
Return on equity: 9.0%
Current ratio: 0.50

NORTHERN NATURAL GAS COMPANY

Northern Natural Gas (NNG) keeps the pipes gassed up. The company operates 14600 miles of natural gas pipeline stretching from the Permian Basin in Texas to Michigan's Upper Peninsula. It also provides transportation and storage services to more than 80 utilities and a number of other customers. The company has 6.3 billion cu. ft. per day market area peak capacity and its three natural gas storage facilities have a total capacity of 75 billion cu. ft. including 4 billion cu. ft. of liquefied natural gas (LNG). NNG which was formed in 1930 is an indirect subsidiary of Berkshire Hathaway Energy.

Operations
The company provides cross-haul and grid transportation between other interstate and intrastate pipelines in the Permian Anadarko Hugoton and Midwest areas.

NNG offers firm and interruptible transportation services storage services as well as other transportation related services that are available to customers as a reliable and flexible supply source to meet short-and long-term market demands.

Geographic Reach
Omaha Nebraska-bsed NNG accesses natural gas supply in the Mid-Continent Rocky Mountain and Western Canadian basins. Its northern service unit (Market Area) delivers gas supply to customers in Illinois Iowa Kansas Michigan Minnesota Nebraska South Dakota and Wisconsin.

The company's pipeline system stretches across over 10 states from the Permian Basin in Texas to Michigan's Upper Peninsula providing access to five of the major natural gas supply regions in North America.

Sales and Marketing
NNG offers its products for utilities and numerous producers energy marketing companies and industrial end-users.

Company Background
NNG was established in 1930 in Omaha to serve 44 communities in Iowa Kansas and Nebraska. Its more recent history includes a takeover by Dynegy in 2002 from the pipeline unit's former parent bankrupt energy giant Enron. The deal was part of Dynegy's proposed acquisition of Enron which was subsequently called off. To strengthen its own balance sheet Dynegy ended up selling NNG to MidAmerican Energy (which later became Berkshire Hathaway Energy) that year.

In 2011 NNG brought in 13 billion cu. ft. of new gas supply to its northern system from tight sand formations in Oklahoma and Texas.

EXECUTIVES

Pres, Mark A Hewett
Dir*, Gregory E Abel
Dir*, Mike Loeffler

LOCATIONS

HQ: NORTHERN NATURAL GAS COMPANY
1111 S 103RD ST, OMAHA, NE 681241072
Phone: 402 398-7700
Web: WWW.NORTHERNNATURALGAS.COM

COMPETITORS

Enbridge	Oneok Partners
Kinder Morgan Energy Partners	Transcanada
	Williams Companies

HISTORICAL FINANCIALS
Company Type: Private

Income Statement				FYE: December 31
	REVENUE ($ mil.)	NET INCOME ($ mil.)	NET PROFIT MARGIN	EMPLOYEES
12/17	693	170	24.6%	1,055
12/16	636	159	25.0%	—
12/07	663	161	24.3%	—
12/06	633	142	22.5%	—
Annual Growth	0.8%	1.7%	—	—

2017 Year-End Financials
Return on assets: 4.6%   Cash ($ mil.): 20
Return on equity: 10.8%
Current ratio: 1.00

NORTHSHORE UNIVERSITY HEALTHSYSTEM

NorthShore University HealthSystem is an integrated healthcare delivery system. NorthShore operates six hospitals a home care organization and a Medical Group with some 900 primary and specialty care physicians. With about 375 beds NorthShore's Evanston Hospital has teaching and research programs as well as capabilities for trauma cancer and cardiology. NorthShore also includes Glenbrook Hospital (about 175 beds) Highland Park Hospital (140 beds) Swedish Hospital (about 310 beds) and Skokie Hospital (roughly 125 beds). NorthShore is affiliated with the University of Chicago Pritzker School of Medicine. The NorthShore Research Institute focuses on clinical and translational research including leadership in clinical trials and medical informatics.

Operations
Each of NorthShore's hospitals is known for a certain specialty. Evanston for example specializes in cancer and cardiac care; Glenbrook Hospital is known for advanced technology for the treatment of gastrointestinal disorders; Highland Park Hospital is the site of the first open heart surgery in the region; Swedish Hospital provides the full range of comprehensive health and wellness services; Northwest Community Hospital houses a Level III NICU Level II Trauma Center and a dedicated pediatric emergency department and Skokie Hospital is known for its expertise in cardiac care and orthopedics. Each year the hospitals see more than 200400 emergency room visits.

The Neaman Center for Personalized Medicine at NorthShore is a comprehensive precision medicine organization utilizing genetic testing to help inform patients' care including disease prevention and treatment.

NorthShore also operates a hospital-based not-for-profit home and hospice services agency that offers the full spectrum of home and hospice care including skilled nursing physical and occupational therapy and home medical equipment.

Geographic Reach
Based in Evanston Illinois NorthShore has some 140 medical offices across the region.

EXECUTIVES

Chief Compliance Officer, Harry Jones
Chief Operating Officer, Sean O'Grady
President, Chief Executive Officer, Gerald
  Gallagher
Chief Information Officer, Steven Smith
Chief Financial Officer, Doug Welday
Auditors: DELOITTE TAX LLP MINNEAPOLIS

LOCATIONS

HQ: NORTHSHORE UNIVERSITY HEALTHSYSTEM
1301 CENTRAL ST, EVANSTON, IL 602011613
Phone: 847 570-2000
Web: WWW.NORTHSHORE.ORG

COMPETITORS

Advocate Health Care	Metrosouth Medical
Central Dupage	Northwest Community
Hospital	Healthcare
Children's Hospital Of	Northwestern Memorial
Chicago	Healthcare
Community Health	Rockford Health System
Systems	Rush System For Health
Mercy Hospital And	University Of Chicago
Medical Center	Medical Center

HISTORICAL FINANCIALS

Company Type: Private

Income Statement				FYE: September 30
	REVENUE ($ mil.)	NET INCOME ($ mil.)	NET PROFIT MARGIN	EMPLOYEES
09/19	1,883	172	9.1%	9,000
09/18	2,153	197	9.2%	—
09/09	1,085	(71)	—	—
09/08	26	0	0.4%	—
Annual Growth	47.5%	95.3%	—	—

2019 Year-End Financials

Return on assets: 4.4%   Cash ($ mil.): 72
Return on equity: 7.0%
Current ratio: —

NORTHSIDE HOSPITAL, INC.

Northside Hospital is committed to health wellness community and offers all benefits of high-touch quality care close to home and the best in class health care delivery including: North Side Hospital Cancer Institute (NHCI) top two community cancer programs and the largest and most comprehensive cancer hospital network in Georgia. NHCI Cancer Research Program one of the largest community-based oncology/hematology programs. All of Northside's hospitals are full-service acute-care facilities that provide specialty care including cancer care surgery radiology and women's health. Northside Hospital which opened in 1970.

Operations

Northside hospitals has grown over the years expanding across 25 counties with five acute-care hospitals over 250 outpatient facilities 4000 providers and 24500 employees.

Northside Hospital handles about 4300 patient visits annually at its facilities. The organization's cancer treatment division partners with the Cancer Support Community of Atlanta to provide mental health social and educational services to cancer patients and survivors as well as family members and friends.

Geographic Reach

Northside Hospital's three campuses are located in Atlanta Forsyth and Cherokee Georgia.

Sales and Marketing

Northside Hospital offers their products services through its MyOneChart patient portal to which patients can easily access their personal health information.

Strategy

Northside Hospital has opened a new Sleep Disorders Center in Gainesville. The brand new state-of-the-art sleep lab features the latest diagnostic technology and includes many upgrades for each patient's room. It is the first of its kind to the Gainesville area.

At all Northside Hospital Sleep Disorders Centers Northside's highly specialized team of sleep professionals utilizes the latest software and technology in diagnosing and treating sleep/wake disorders. In addition each center offers portable in-home sleep studies Continuous Positive Airway Pressure (CPAP) set-ups and troubleshooting with personalized instruction and fitting.

Mergers and Acquisitions

In 2020 Northside acquired ChoiceOne Urgent Care of Gwinnet and will partner with the Nashville-based Urgent Care Group to manage and operate three locations in the Gwinnet County Georgia area.

EXECUTIVES

Ceo, Robert T Quattrocchi
Human Resources Director, Barbara Schipani
Plastic Surgery, Joel Alexander
Plastic Surgery, Philip H Beegle
Operations Assistant, Jennifer Wheeler
Director of Womens, Melissa Sisson
Him Director, Victoria Andrews
Chief of Orthopedic Surgery, Douglas Murray
Manager, Ernie Fuller
Gynecology, Eva Arkin
Physician Rheumatologist, Gary Myerson

LOCATIONS

HQ: NORTHSIDE HOSPITAL, INC.
1000 JOHNSON FERRY RD, ATLANTA, GA 303421611
Phone: 404 851-8000
Web: WWW.NORTHSIDE.COM

Selected Locations
Alpharetta Medical Campus
Dunwoody Cancer Center
Imaging at Peachtree Dunwoody
Medlock Bridge Imaging
Meridian Park Plaza
Northside Hospital Doctors Center
Northside Hospital-Atlanta
Northside Hospital-Cherokee
Northside Hospital-Forsyth
Northside-Forsyth Outpatient Surgery Center
Northside Sugar Hill Imaging (Buford)
Pediatric Center at Northside/Alpharetta
Roswell Cancer Center
Townelake Medical Office/Riverstone Imaging

COMPETITORS

Children's Healthcare	Piedmont Healthcare
Of Atlanta	Regency Hospital
Dekalb Medical	Shepherd Center
Emory Healthcare	Sunlink Health Systems
Grady Health System	The Fulton-dekalb
Gwinnett Health System	Hospital Authority
Northeast Georgia	Wellstar Health System
Health System	

HISTORICAL FINANCIALS

Company Type: Private

Income Statement				FYE: September 30
	REVENUE ($ mil.)	NET INCOME ($ mil.)	NET PROFIT MARGIN	EMPLOYEES
09/18	2,081	265	12.8%	8,000
09/17	2,002	301	15.0%	—
09/16	1,897	157	8.3%	—
09/15	1,733	223	12.9%	—
Annual Growth	6.3%	6.0%	—	—

2018 Year-End Financials

Return on assets: 10.6%   Cash ($ mil.): 448
Return on equity: 14.8%
Current ratio: 4.40

NORTHSIDE INDEPENDENT SCHOOL DISTRICT

EXECUTIVES

Supt, John Folks
Supt, Brian T Woods
Pres, Robert Blount Jr
Trustee, Katie N Reed
SEC, Bennie L Cole
Principal, Ellen Sutton
General, Lora Mathison
Manager, Joe Delgadillo
Coordinator, Derek Howorth
Secretary, Alma Lira
Teacher, Anne Flores
Auditors: RSM US LLP SAN ANTONIO TEXAS

LOCATIONS

HQ: NORTHSIDE INDEPENDENT SCHOOL DISTRICT
5900 EVERS RD, SAN ANTONIO, TX 782381606
Phone: 210 397-8770
Web: WWW.NISD.NET

HISTORICAL FINANCIALS

Company Type: Private

Income Statement				FYE: August 31
	REVENUE ($ mil.)	NET INCOME ($ mil.)	NET PROFIT MARGIN	EMPLOYEES
08/20	1,292	(150)	—	13,698
08/19	1,223	4	0.3%	—
08/18	1,203	57	4.8%	—
08/17	1,152	75	6.5%	—
Annual Growth	3.9%	—	—	—

2020 Year-End Financials

Return on assets: (-4.7%)   Cash ($ mil.): 580
Return on equity: —
Current ratio: 6.00

NORTHWEST DAIRY ASSOCIATION

Northwest Dairy Association (NDA) members milk a lot of cows. The dairy cooperative's 550-plus member/farmers ship 7.2 billion pounds of milk annually which is processed by the co-op's subsidiary Darigold and packaged and sold under the Darigold label. NDA produces fluid and cultured dairy products including milk butter cottage cheese sour cream and yogurt that altogether generate some $2 billion in sales. It also makes bulk butter and cheese milk powder and whey products. The co-op caters to several sectors nationwide. Its customers include food retailers and wholesalers as well as foodservice and food-manufacturing companies. The association's membership spans half a dozen US states.

Operations
The cooperative's Darigold subsidiary operates a dozen processing facilities across the Northwestern US.

Geographic Reach
NDA members are located in Washington Oregon Idaho Montana California and Utah.

Sales and Marketing
Through Darigold NDA makes and markets a full line of dairy-based products for retail foodservice and commodity and specialty markets.

Financial Performance
The dairy cooperative logged nearly $2.5 billion in revenue in 2012 up from just shy of $2.1 billion the prior year. While NDA earned more revenue its assets declined from $579 million to $548 million.

Mergers and Acquisitions
NDA added Country Classic Dairies to its operations in 2010. Its Montana-based business churn out Darigold-branded products with help from its 30 member/farmers. Securing the Country Classics business added some 160 million pounds of milk a year (more than half of Montana's milk supply) to the co-op's total production. NDA and Country Classic's union was the culmination of the two businesses' longtime working relationship (at one time Country Classic used the Darigold name to market its products).

EXECUTIVES

Ceo, Jim Werkhoven
Pres, James Wegner
V Pres, Steve Rowe
SEC-Treas, Randy Lindley
Corporate Health, Erin Allen
Corporate Counsel, Kristi Keene
Chief Operating Officer, Grant Kadavy
Supply Chain Specialist, Frank Kelly
Executive Officer, Marie-Claude Milot
Sr Environmental, Health, and, Scott Algate

LOCATIONS

HQ: NORTHWEST DAIRY ASSOCIATION
5601 6TH AVE S STE 300, SEATTLE, WA 981082545
Phone: 206 284-7220
Web: WWW.DARIGOLD.COM

PRODUCTS/OPERATIONS

Selected Products

Consumer
Butter
Buttermilk
Cottage cheese
Cream
Half and half
Milk
Sour cream
Whipping cream
Yogurt
Ingredients
Bleached sweet dry whey
Colored cheddar cheese
Cultured skim milk powder
Milk protein concentrate
Monterey Jack cheese
Nonfat dry milk
Salted sweet cream butter
Skim milk powder
Sweet cream buttermilk powder
Unsalted butter
Whey protein concentrate

COMPETITORS

Associated Milk Producers	Dean Foods
Berkeley Farms	Humboldt Creamery
California Dairies Inc.	Land O'lakes
Dairy Farmers Of America	Straus Family Creamery
	Tillamook County Creamery Association

HISTORICAL FINANCIALS

Company Type: Private

Income Statement   FYE: March 31

	REVENUE ($ mil.)	NET INCOME ($ mil.)	NET PROFIT MARGIN	EMPLOYEES
03/08	2,207	87	4.0%	1,300
03/07	1,450	12	0.9%	—
03/04	1,297	(6)	—	—
03/03	1,140	2	0.2%	—
Annual Growth	14.1%	107.0%	—	—

2008 Year-End Financials

Return on assets: 17.7%   Cash ($ mil.): 10
Return on equity: 41.5%
Current ratio: 1.80

NORTHWEST FARM CREDIT SERVICES

Customer-owned financial cooperative Northwest Farm Credit Services is an agricultural lender that provides financial services to farmers ranchers agribusinesses commercial fishermen timber producers and rural home owners in Alaska Idaho Montana Oregon and Washington. The company has a network of around 45 branches and offers a broad range of flexible loan programs to meet the needs of people in the agriculture business. Northwest Farm Credit also provides leasing services appraisal services and life mortgage disability and crop insurance as well as legal advocacy and assistance to customers in need. It is part of the Farm Credit System a network of lenders serving the US agriculture industry.

Operations
The credit union provides financing and related services to farmers ranchers agribusinesses commercial fishermen timber producers rural homeowners and crop insurance customers. Northwest Farm Credit provides $10.3 billion in loans. Farm Credit System a nationwide network of borrower-owned lending institutions of which it is part provides $205 billion in loans to rural America.

Geographic Reach
Northwest Farm Credit serves customers through 45 offices located in Idaho Alaska Montana Oregon and Washington.

Sales and Marketing
Northwest Farm Credit finances farmers ranchers agribusinesses commercial fishermen timber producers and rural homeowners as well as farm-related businesses agricultural cooperatives and rural utilities.

Financial Performance
In 2015 the company's net revenue increased by 5% due to higher net interest income driven by increased loan volume.

Northwest Farm Credit's net income rose by 12% due to higher net revenues and a decrease in income tax expense.

In 2015 the company's operating cash inflow increased by 19%.

Strategy
The company plans to continue to fund lending operations primarily through its borrowing relationship with CoBank (a fellow Farm Credit System member) and from retained earnings.

Mergers and Acquisitions
In 2014 the company expanded its operations in Montana by buying Culbertson State Agency's crop insurance portfolio.

Company Background
The US Congress created the Farm Credit System in 1916 to meet the financial needs of farmers ranchers and cooperatives who invest as well as borrow from the institutions within the system. All Farm Credit System members are regulated by the Farm Credit Administration.

EXECUTIVES

Ceo, Phil Dipofi
Assistant Vice President Loan Coordinator, Sophie Conley
Communications Specialist, Jennifer Rohrer
Communications Specialist, Debra N Strohmaier N
Senior Risk Management Analyst, Erica Sphuler
Director Employment, Wanda Todd
Vice President, Carol L Sobson
Vice President Appraisal Servi, Joe Moore
Relationship Manager, Cody Hendrix
Vice President Internal Contro, Don Bellamy
Relationship Manager, Michael Mills
Auditors: PRICEWATERHOUSECOOPERS LLP S

LOCATIONS

HQ: NORTHWEST FARM CREDIT SERVICES
2001 S FLINT RD, SPOKANE, WA 992249198
Phone: 509 838-2429
Web: WWW.NORTHWESTFCS.COM

PRODUCTS/OPERATIONS

2015 Sales

	$ mil.	% of total
Interest Income	412	82
Patronage income	52	11
Financially Related Services	19	4
loans and other fee	6	1
Other non-interest income	11	2
Total	502	100

COMPETITORS

Bank Of America	U.S. Bancorp
First Interstate	Wells Fargo
Idaho Independent Bank	Zions Bancorporation
Keycorp	
Northwest Bancorporation	

HISTORICAL FINANCIALS

Company Type: Private

Income Statement				FYE: December 31
	ASSETS ($ mil.)	NET INCOME ($ mil.)	INCOME AS % OF ASSETS	EMPLOYEES
12/13	9,604	236	2.5%	500
12/12	9,471	187	2.0%	—
12/11	8,696	159	1.8%	—
Annual Growth	5.1%	22.0%	—	—

2013 Year-End Financials

Return on assets: 2.5%   Sales ($ mil): 460
Return on equity: 13.5%

NORTHWESTERN MEMORIAL HOSPITAL

EXECUTIVES

Ceo, Dean Harrison
Pres, Richard J Gannotta
Cfo, Peter McCanna
Chb, William J Brodsky
Neurosurgeon, Lisa Krammer
Call Center Supervisor, John Robinson
Vice President, Alfred Torrence
Director, Cindy A Parker
Communications Manage, Reginald Ervin
Associate Professor of Surgery, Gregory Dumanian
MD, Jenny Kim

LOCATIONS

HQ: NORTHWESTERN MEMORIAL HOSPITAL
251 E HURON ST, CHICAGO, IL 606113055
Phone: 312 926-2000
Web: WWW.NM.ORG

HISTORICAL FINANCIALS

Company Type: Private

Income Statement				FYE: August 31
	REVENUE ($ mil.)	NET INCOME ($ mil.)	NET PROFIT MARGIN	EMPLOYEES
08/15	1,337	198	14.8%	5,800
08/10	1,380	64	4.7%	—
08/09	1,304	4	0.3%	—
Annual Growth	0.4%	87.7%	—	—

NORTHWESTERN UNIVERSITY

With its main campus in the Chicago suburb of Evanston Northwestern University (NU) serves its approximately 21000 students through about a dozen schools and colleges such as the Medill School of Journalism and the McCormick School of Engineering and Applied Sciences. Its Chicago campus houses the schools of law and medicine as well as several hospitals of the McGaw Medical Center. With a faculty of more than 3300 the school has a student-to-teacher ratio of about 6:1. NU is home to several research centers and community outreach programs; it also has a branch in Qatar. It is the only private member of the Big Ten conference; varsity sports include soccer football basketball and fencing.

Operations

Among NU's top-ranked programs are its law school medical school and its engineering program. Its Kellogg Graduate School of Management consistently ranks among the nation's top five business schools by Business Week and U.S. News & World Report. Its journalism and drama programs produced such alumni as Charlton Heston Gary Marshall and Julia Louis-Dreyfus. The late US Supreme Court Justice John Paul Stevens is also a former Wildcat.

NU spends approximately $893 million in annual sponsored research funds (and some $434 million National Institute of health funding) conducting research at more than 50 university research institutes and centers (and over 90 school-based research centers) in areas such as materials science biomedical engineering African studies performance studies and marketing. The school has earned recognition for its research in mesostructures neonatal biotechnology nanotechnology biomedical and materials sciences. NU partners have included the Argonne National Laboratory Fermilab and local universities.

Geographic Reach

NU's main campus encompasses about 240 acres in Evanston. The university also operates in Chicago as well as its education center in Qatar. In addition the company has more than 70 international partners in over 30 countries.

Company Background

Northwestern University's Methodist founders met in 1850 to create an institution of higher learning serving the original Northwest Territory. The university was chartered in 1851 and two years later it acquired 379 acres of property north of Chicago on Lake Michigan. The town of Evanston was later named after John Evans one of the school's founders.

HISTORY

Northwestern University's Methodist founders met in 1850 to create an institution of higher learning serving the original Northwest Territory. The university was chartered in 1851 and two years later it acquired 379 acres of property north of Chicago on Lake Michigan. The town of Evanston was later named after John Evans one of the school's founders.

Classes began in the fall of 1855 with two professors and 10 students. By 1869 Northwestern had more than 100 students and began to admit women. In 1870 Northwestern signed an affiliation agreement with the Chicago Medical College (founded 1859) and three years later it joined with the original University of Chicago (no relation to the current institution) to create the Union College of Law. When the University of Chicago closed in 1886 due to financial difficulties Northwestern took control of the law school. The university reorganized in 1891 consolidating its affiliated professional schools (dentistry law medicine and pharmacy) into the university.

By 1900 Northwestern had become the third-largest university in the US (after Harvard and Michigan) with an enrollment of 2700. During the 1920s the university created the Medill School of Journalism named for Joseph Medill founder of the Chicago Tribune. In 1924 the school's athletic teams adopted the nickname Wildcats and two years later the university completed the primary buildings that form its Chicago campus. North-western suffered a drop in enrollment during the Depression but after WWII it saw student numbers swell as veterans took advantage of the GI Bill. Expansion continued throughout the 1960s and 1970s.

In 1985 the school and the City of Evanston began developing a research center to attract more high-tech industries to the area. The university's graduate school of business achieved national prominence in 1988 after it was ranked #1 in the US by Business Week. In 1995 Northwestern's football team forever the doormat of the Big 10 achieved national fame when it won the conference championship.

In 1998 faculty member Professor John Pople won the Nobel Prize in Chemistry the first Nobel Prize awarded to a faculty member while teaching at the university.

Northwestern won a significant legal battle in 1998 when a judge ruled that the university was not obligated to pay a faculty member simply because he had been granted tenure.

The university's dental school closed its doors in 2001 citing the difficulties posed for private schools in providing a competitive dental education.

EXECUTIVES

Pres, Morton Schapiro
Pres*, Schapiro Morton
Exec V Pres*, Nim Ehinniah
Crco*, Luke Figora
Chief Admissions Officer, Chris Van Nostrand
Assistant Vice President Publi, Bruce Lewis
Business Admin, Chad Bergmann
Coordinator, Mick McCall
Coordinator, Pam Bonnevier
Executive Officer, Scott Devine
Assistant Vice President of PR, Megan Blackwelder
Auditors: KPMG LLP CHICAGO IL

LOCATIONS

HQ: NORTHWESTERN UNIVERSITY
633 CLARK ST, EVANSTON, IL 602080001
Phone: 847 491-3741
Web: WWW.NORTHWESTERN.EDU

PRODUCTS/OPERATIONS

Selected Programs
Continuing and Professional Programs
Graduate Programs
Pre-Collegiate Programs
Undergraduate Programs

Selected Schools and Colleges
Bienen School of Music
Feinberg School of Medicine
The Graduate School
Kellogg School of Management
McCormick School of Engineering and Applied Science
Medill School of Journalism Media Integrated Marketing Communications
Northwestern in Qatar
School of Communication
School of Continuing Studies
School of Education and Social Policy
School of Law
Weinberg College of Arts and Science

HISTORICAL FINANCIALS

Company Type: Private

Income Statement				FYE: August 31
	REVENUE ($ mil.)	NET INCOME ($ mil.)	NET PROFIT MARGIN	EMPLOYEES
08/18	2,464	560	22.7%	5,954
08/17	2,309	668	29.0%	—
Annual Growth	6.7%	(16.2%)	—	—

2018 Year-End Financials
Return on assets: 3.6%   Cash ($ mil.): 185
Return on equity: 4.6%
Current ratio: —

NORTON HOSPITALS, INC

EXECUTIVES

Pres, Steven A Williams
SEC*, Robert B Azar
Treas*, Michael W Gough
V Pres*, Russell F Cox
SEC*, Theodore T Myre Jr
Internal Medicine Practitioner, Deep Ajmani
Information Manager, Joy Karrer
Human Resources Director, Judy Settle
Human Resources Director, Kevin Guthrie
Internal Medicine Practitioner, Sergio Cardinali
Administrator, Jamie Mattingly

LOCATIONS

HQ: NORTON HOSPITALS, INC
200 E CHESTNUT ST, LOUISVILLE, KY 402021831
Phone: 502 629-8000
Web: WWW.NORTONHEALTHCARE.COM

HISTORICAL FINANCIALS
Company Type: Private

Income Statement   FYE: December 31

	REVENUE ($ mil.)	NET INCOME ($ mil.)	NET PROFIT MARGIN	EMPLOYEES
12/15	1,712	137	8.0%	1,500
12/14	1,577	187	11.9%	—
Annual Growth	8.6%	(26.7%)	—	—

2015 Year-End Financials
Return on assets: 8.0%   Cash ($ mil.): —
Return on equity: 8.6%
Current ratio: 2.20

NOVA SOUTHEASTERN UNIVERSITY, INC.

Nova Southeastern University (NSU) gives a whole new meaning to "school of sharks." NSU whose mascot is the deep sea predator has an enrollment of approximately 20435 students and offers a variety of undergraduate graduate and professional academic programs. NSU offers degrees in several medical disciplines (osteopathic medicine pharmacy optometry and pediatrics) marine biology business law education and computer science. The not-for-profit independent school operates seven campuses in the Miami-Fort Lauderdale area several health centers and an oceanographic center. Founded in 1964 Nova University merged with Southeastern University of the Health Sciences in 1994 to become Nova Southeastern University.

Operations
In addition to its more than 150 undergraduate and graduate programs NSU also operates The

University School a pre-K through 12th grade college preparatory day school. The university's Mailman Segal Institute for Early Childhood Studies is a multidisciplinary demonstration and professional training center for education research and the advancement of knowledge in early childhood parenting and autism across the life span. Located at the Jim & Jan Moran Family Center Village the center offers educational programs clinical services and academic programs in collaboration with other NSU divisions.

Geographic Reach
NSU is a distance education pioneer (it was the one of the first US university to offer graduate programs online) offering classes on the Internet as well as at seven regional campuses in Florida and Puerto Rico.

Strategy
As universities do NSU regularly invests in facility upgrades to meet the growing needs of its students. In 2020 the university constructed the Alan B. Levan | NSU Broward Center of Innovation scheduled to open its doors in July 2021. The Levan Center of Innovation is the continuation of a long-standing public-private partnership with NSU and Broward County and will occupy the entire fifth floor of NSU's Alvin Sherman Library making it one of the largest of its kind in the nation occupying 54000-square-feet of space.

Company Background
Founded in 1964 Nova University merged with Southeastern University of the Health Sciences in 1994 to become Nova Southeastern University.

EXECUTIVES

Chm, Robert Steele
Pres*, Dr George Larbury
Cfo-Vp Finance*, Alyson Silva
Vp Clinical Operations, Kelly Gregg
Svp Translational RES/Econ Dev, H Thomas Temple
V Pres-Facilities, Jessica Brumley
Vp-of Facilities Management, Daniel Alfonso
Contrl, Roger La Casse
Dean, College of Pharmacy, Andr S Malav
Trustee, Zachariah P Zachariah
Chief Financial Officer, Henry Del Riego
Auditors: LB KPMG LLP GREENSBORO NC

LOCATIONS

HQ: NOVA SOUTHEASTERN UNIVERSITY, INC.
3301 COLLEGE AVE, DAVIE, FL 333147796
Phone: 954 262-7300
Web: WWW.NOVA.EDU

HISTORICAL FINANCIALS
Company Type: Private

Income Statement   FYE: June 30

	REVENUE ($ mil.)	NET INCOME ($ mil.)	NET PROFIT MARGIN	EMPLOYEES
06/20	777	24	3.1%	2,500
06/15	678	45	6.7%	—
Annual Growth	2.8%	(11.9%)	—	—

2020 Year-End Financials
Return on assets: 1.5%   Cash ($ mil.): 70
Return on equity: 2.6%
Current ratio: 0.30

NOVANT HEALTH, INC.

Novant Health is an integrated system of physician practices hospitals outpatient centers and more. Novant Health is a not-for-profit integrated system of around 20 medical centers and more than 2400 physicians in more than 800 locations and numerous outpatient surgery centers medical plazas rehabilitations programs diagnostic imaging centers and community health outreach programs. In 2021 Novant Health completed the $5.3 billion acquisition of new Hanover Regional Medical Center. The company was formed in 1997.

Operations
Novant Health provides services such as behavioral health cancer care heart & vascular inpatient services neurology & neurosurgery orthopedic care pediatric care primary care and more.

Geographic Reach
Novant Health has dual headquarters in Winston-Salem and Charlotte North Carolina; it provides health care services to more than 800 locations.

Sales and Marketing
Novant Health market its products and services through its websites such as emergency urgent & walk in care behavioral health cancer care heart & vascular and more.

Mergers and Acquisitions
In 2021 Novant Health completed the $5.3 billion acquisition of new Hanover Regional Medical Center. Novant received a final approval Oct. by 4-1 New Hanover Board of commissioner vote to acquire the 59-year-old health-care system through an asset purchase.

Company Background
Novant Health was formed in 1997 by a merger of Carolina Medicorp Presbyterian Healthcare and Thomasville Medical Center.

EXECUTIVES

Chief Financial Officer, Executive Vice President, Fred Hargett
President, Chief Executive Officer, Carl Armato
Chief Operating Officer, Executive Vice President, Jeffery Lindsay
Executive Vice President, Chief Diversity, Inclusion And Equity Officer, Tanya Blackmon
Executive Vice President, Chief Administrative Officer, Frank Emory
Auditors: PRICEWATERHOUSECOOPERS LLP GR

LOCATIONS

HQ: NOVANT HEALTH, INC.
2085 FRONTIS PLAZA BLVD, WINSTON SALEM, NC 271035614
Phone: 336 277-1120
Web: WWW.NOVANTHEALTH.ORG

PRODUCTS/OPERATIONS

Selected Health Facilities
Brunswick Community Hospital (Supply North Carolina)
Forsyth Medical Center (Winston-Salem North Carolina)
Franklin Regional Medical Center (Louisburg North Carolina)
Kerner's Medical Center (Kernersville North Carolina)
Medical Park Hospital (Winston-Salem North Carolina)
The Oaks at Forsyth (residental long-term care; Winston-Salem North Carolina)
Presbyterian Hospital (Charlotte North Carolina)
Presbyterian Hemby Children's Hospital
Presbyterian Hospital Huntersville (Huntersville North Carolina)
Presbyterian Hospital Matthews (Charlotte North Carolina)
Presbyterian Orthopaedic Hospital (Charlotte North Carolina)

Rowan Regional Medical Center (Salisbury North Carolina)
Springwood Care Center (residental long-term care; Winston-Salem North Carolina)
Thomasville Medical Center (Thomasville North Carolina)
Upstate Carolina Medical Center (Gaffney South Carolina)

Selected Services
Assisted living
Behavioral health
Blood services
Breast health
Cancer
Children's services
Clinical research
Corporate health & wellness
Critical care
Diabetes
Emergency
Employer services
Heart & vascular
Hospice
Imaging
Infusion services
Inpatient services
Laboratory services
Orthopedics
Pain management
Pastoral care
Pharmacy
Rehabilitation
Respiratory services
Sickle cell
Sleep health
Sports medicine
Stroke & neurosciences
Supportive care
Surgery
Urgent and express care
Weight loss services
Wellness programs and services
Women's health
Women's heart health
Wound care

COMPETITORS

Alamance Regional Medical Center	High Point Regional Health System
Bon Secours Health	New Hanover Regional Medical Center
Carilion Clinic	Rex Healthcare
Caromont	Riverside Health System (virginia)
Carolinas Healthcare System	Rowan Regional Medical Center
Carolinas Medical Center-northeast	Sentara Healthcare
Cone Health	Unc Hospitals
Davis Regional Medical Center	Upstate Affiliate
Duke University Health System	Vidant Health
Hca	Wakemed

HISTORICAL FINANCIALS
Company Type: Private

Income Statement				FYE: December 31
	REVENUE ($ mil.)	NET INCOME ($ mil.)	NET PROFIT MARGIN	EMPLOYEES
12/20	5,682	383	6.7%	13,800
12/19	5,434	547	10.1%	—
12/18	4,985	109	2.2%	—
12/17	167	(142)	—	—
Annual Growth	223.6%	—	—	—

2020 Year-End Financials
Return on assets: 4.4%   Cash ($ mil.): 711
Return on equity: 7.7%
Current ratio: 1.50

NOVANT MEDICAL GROUP INC

EXECUTIVES

Vice President, Mark Higdon
Clinical Nurse Specialist, Mary Muehl
Regional Trauma Program Manage, Philip Angelo

LOCATIONS

HQ: NOVANT MEDICAL GROUP INC
2085 FRONTIS PLAZA BLVD, WINSTON SALEM, NC 271035614
Phone: 336 718-2803

HISTORICAL FINANCIALS
Company Type: Private

Income Statement				FYE: December 31
	REVENUE ($ mil.)	NET INCOME ($ mil.)	NET PROFIT MARGIN	EMPLOYEES
12/17	852	(76)	—	17
12/15	709	(63)	—	—
12/14	641	(39)	—	—
12/13	591	(41)	—	—
Annual Growth	9.6%	—	—	—

2017 Year-End Financials
Return on assets: (-51.0%)   Cash ($ mil.): —
Return on equity: —
Current ratio: 1.10

NOVARTIS PHARMACEUTICALS CORPORATION

As part of the Innovative Medicines Division of Swiss drug giant Novartis AG Novartis Pharmaceuticals Corporation (NPC) helps with the development manufacturing marketing and sales of its parent company's products in the US. Its product lines address a range of ailments including cardiovascular and respiratory diseases central nervous system disorders cancers bone and skin conditions infectious diseases and organ transplant complications. NPC's key products include tumor growth inhibitor Gleevec high blood pressure drug Diovan and attention deficit disorder therapies Focalin and Ritalin. NPC markets its products through an in-house sales team.

Operations
NPC is part of Novartis' Innovative Medicines Division which handles the group's growing portfolio of patented medicines. The Innovative Medicines Division is further divided into two global business units: Novartis Oncology and Novartis Pharmaceuticals. Novartis Pharmaceuticals is composed of six divisions: Ophthalmology; Established Medicines; Neuroscience; Immunology Hepatology and Dermatology; Respiratory; and Cardio-Metabolic.

Geographic Reach
NPC parent Novartis AG operates some 65 manufacturing sites around the world. US sales account for around 35% of its total revenue.

Sales and Marketing
NPC and the broader Innovative Medicines Division have some 3000 field force representatives including supervisors and administrative staff. In general Novartis sells its prescription drugs to wholesale distributors retail distributors hospitals and clinics government entities and managed care organizations. It markets certain products in the US through online television newspaper and magazine advertising.

Strategy
NPC widens its offerings in the US market through a number of methods including internal research programs licensing agreements and acquisitions. In 2015 the company received approval from the US FDA for its Cosentyx product for the treatment of moderate-to-severe plaque psoriasis in adults eligible for systemic therapy (drug absorbed through the bloodstream) or phototherapy (light therapy).

As part of its parent's efforts to focus on eye care generics and innovative pharmaceuticals NPC remains a vital part of Novartis' growth strategy. One area of growing interest is oncology; in 2015 Novartis acquired certain cancer-fighting products and pipeline compounds from GlaxoSmithKline.

Mergers and Acquisitions
In 2016 Novartis acquired the Oklahoma-based Selexys Pharmaceuticals which specializes in hematologic and inflammatory disorder treatments for some $665 million.

Company Background
In 2016 Novartis AG restructured its Pharmaceuticals Division creating two business units: Novartis Pharmaceuticals and Novartis Oncology. Those units now comprise the group's Innovative Medicines Division of which NPC is a part.

EXECUTIVES

Pres, Marie-France Tschudin
Sr V-Pres-Cmo*, Nancy Lurker
Pres*, Andre Wyss
V Pres*, Yves Teirlynck
V Pres*, Julie Kane
Coo*, Alex Gorsky
V-Pres-Cfo*, Gary E Rosenthal
Cfo*, Helen Boudreau
Director, Kenneth Wong
Marketing, Kevin Herbst
Clinical Scientist, Kudsia Hafeez
Auditors: PRICEWATERHOUSECOOPERS LLP-BR

LOCATIONS

HQ: NOVARTIS PHARMACEUTICALS CORPORATION
1 HEALTH PLZ, EAST HANOVER, NJ 079361016
Phone: 862 778-8300
Web: WWW.NOVARTIS.COM

HISTORICAL FINANCIALS
Company Type: Private

Income Statement				FYE: December 31
	REVENUE ($ mil.)	NET INCOME ($ mil.)	NET PROFIT MARGIN	EMPLOYEES
12/16	49,436	6,698	13.5%	7,000
12/15	49,440	17,794	36.0%	—
12/13	58,831	9,292	15.8%	—
Annual Growth	(5.6%)	(10.3%)	—	—

2016 Year-End Financials
Return on assets: 5.1%   Cash ($ mil.): 7,007
Return on equity: 8.9%
Current ratio: 1.10

NOVO CONSTRUCTION, INC.

EXECUTIVES

Ceo, James C Fowler
Pres*, Jim Fowler
SEC*, Robert Williamson
Superintendent, Dave Fournier
Director, Brian Cronin
Superintendent, Bill Young
Project Accountant, Pilar Bonilla
Superintendant, Alan Buzzetta
Project Engineer, Ben Helms
Foreman, Ken Romero
Project Engineer, James Falvey

LOCATIONS

HQ: NOVO CONSTRUCTION, INC.
1460 OBRIEN DR, MENLO PARK, CA 940251432
Phone: 650 701-1500
Web: WWW.NOVOCONSTRUCTION.COM

HISTORICAL FINANCIALS

Company Type: Private

Income Statement				FYE: October 31
	REVENUE ($ mil.)	NET INCOME ($ mil.)	NET PROFIT MARGIN	EMPLOYEES
10/19	872	8	1.0%	133
10/18	684	7	1.1%	—
10/17	603	5	0.9%	—
10/16	577	6	1.1%	—
Annual Growth	14.8%	11.4%	—	—

2019 Year-End Financials

Return on assets: 2.4%   Cash ($ mil.): 93
Return on equity: 95.0%
Current ratio: 1.00

NPC RESTAURANT HOLDINGS, LLC

NPC International is the prince of pepperoni in a pizza empire. The world's largest franchisee of Pizza Hut restaurants NPC owns and operates more than 1275 pizza restaurants and delivery kitchens in about 30 states. The quick-service eateries located mostly in such southern states as Alabama Florida Georgia and Tennessee serve a variety of pizza styles as well as such items as buffalo wings and pasta. The pizza parlors are franchised from YUM! Brands the world's largest fast-food restaurant company. NPC was founded in 1962 by former chairman Gene Bicknell who was one of the first Pizza Hut franchisees. The company was acquired by private equity group NPC International Holdings in late 2011.

Operations

NPC runs more than 20 Wendys restaurants in addition to its large stable of pizza places. As a franchisee NPC gets the benefit of operating restaurants under a popular and well known name. It pays YUM! Brands royalties and fees in exchange for the right to use the Pizza Hut brand and other intellectual property. Typically local operators are also held to certain standards regarding food and service quality.

Strategy

NPC has grown to such a large size primarily through a series of acquisitions mostly corporate-run locations. In 2012 it snapped up 36 Pizza Hut units located primarily in Florida for roughly $19 million from Pizza Hut Inc. The deal enabled NPC to strengthen its position in its largest geographical market.

While NPC doesn't own the Pizza Hut chain as its largest franchisee the company can exert a certain amount of influence in how the fast-food business operates. It called upon YUM! Brands to improve its Pizza Hut marketing strategy while sales were slumping amid the economic downturn. The company spends 6% of its revenue on national and local advertising demonstrating its commitment to Pizza Hut operations and advertising strategy.

NPC's revenue improved in 2010 and 2011 partly as a result of promoting its value-priced menu items as a way to gain market share from competing chains including Domino's and Papa John's. (Within its local markets NPC competes against #1 Domino's franchisee RPM Pizza and Papa John's operator PJ United.)

EXECUTIVES

Chb-Pres-Ceo, James K Schwartz
V Pres Fin-Cfo, Troy D Cook
Sr V Pres-Head of Oprs, D Blayne Vaughn
Sr V Pres Mktg, Linda L Sheedy
Cao, Jason P Poenitske
Auditors: KPMG LLP KANSAS CITY MISSOUR

LOCATIONS

HQ: NPC RESTAURANT HOLDINGS, LLC
7300 W 129TH ST, OVERLAND PARK, KS 662132631
Phone: 913 327-5555
Web: WWW.NPCINTERNATIONAL.COM

COMPETITORS

Boddie-noell	Pj United
Burger King	Papa John's
Captain D's	Rpm Pizza
Carrols	Sbarro
Chick-fil-a	Sonic Corp.
Domino's	Subway
Hardee's	Tacala
Interfoods	United States Beef
K-mac	Valenti Management
Krystal	Wendy's
Little Caesar's	West Quality Foods
Mcdonald's	

HISTORICAL FINANCIALS

Company Type: Private

Income Statement				FYE: December 27
	REVENUE ($ mil.)	NET INCOME ($ mil.)	NET PROFIT MARGIN	EMPLOYEES
12/16	1,236	8	0.7%	29,000
12/15	1,223	6	0.5%	—
12/14	1,179	1	0.1%	—
12/13	1,094	29	2.7%	—
Annual Growth	4.2%	(33.5%)	—	—

2016 Year-End Financials

Return on assets: 0.7%   Cash ($ mil.): 13
Return on equity: 3.1%
Current ratio: 0.40

NUTRISYSTEM, INC.

EXECUTIVES

Pres-Ceo, Dawn M Zier
Chb*, Michael J Hagan
Pres, Stephen Mikulak
Exec V Pres-Cfo, Michael P Monahan
Exec V Pres-Cmo, Keira Krausz
Vice President, Jennifer Hartnett
Sales Representative, Jennifer Stopyra
Director Application Developme, Joe McPherson
Ux Designer, Joseph Fang
Director of Food, Judy Kim
Associate Online Marketing Man, Justine Bartholomew
Auditors: KPMG LLP PHILADELPHIA PENNSY

LOCATIONS

HQ: NUTRISYSTEM, INC.
600 OFFICE CENTER DR, FORT WASHINGTON, PA 190343232
Phone: 215 706-5300
Web: WWW.NUTRISYSTEM.COM

HISTORICAL FINANCIALS

Company Type: Private

Income Statement				FYE: December 31
	REVENUE ($ mil.)	NET INCOME ($ mil.)	NET PROFIT MARGIN	EMPLOYEES
12/18	691	58	8.5%	606
12/17	696	57	8.3%	—
12/16	545	35	6.5%	—
12/15	462	26	5.7%	—
Annual Growth	14.3%	30.9%	—	—

2018 Year-End Financials

Return on assets: 28.7%   Cash ($ mil.): 22
Return on equity: 40.0%
Current ratio: 2.90

OAKLAND UNIFIED SCHOOL DISTRICT

EXECUTIVES

Coordinator, Marcus Silvi
Coordinator, Adimu Madyun
Teacher, Barbara Cone
Project Coordinator, Neena Bawa
Vice, Donnell Mayberry
Community School Program Manag, Glendy Cordero
Educator, Tara Austin
Administrative Assistant, Ana Navarro
Financial Analyst, Angel Burr
Nurse Manager, Belinda Campbell
Secretary, Christina Miller

LOCATIONS

HQ: OAKLAND UNIFIED SCHOOL DISTRICT
1000 BROADWAY FL 4, OAKLAND, CA 946074099
Phone: 510 434-7790
Web: WWW.OUSD.ORG

Company Type: Private

Income Statement				FYE: June 30
	REVENUE ($ mil.)	NET INCOME ($ mil.)	NET PROFIT MARGIN	EMPLOYEES
06/19	731	(69)	—	7,200
06/18	677	(45)	—	—
06/17	658	(2)	—	—
06/06	0	0	—	—
Annual Growth	—	—	—	—

OCEAN SPRAY CRANBERRIES, INC.

Known for its blue-and-white wave logo Ocean Spray Cranberries is a top US maker of canned bottled and shelf-stable juice drinks. Structured as a cooperative Ocean Spray is owned by more than 700 cranberry and grapefruit growers in North and South America. It produces juice drinks by blending cranberries with other fruits typically ranging from apples to blueberries at its processing facilities. The company's other products include fresh and dried cranberries sauces snacking energy sparkling and supplements along with fresh citrus fruits. Ocean Spray sells its products through food retailers foodservice providers distributors and food makers worldwide. The vibrant agricultural company was founded in 1930.

Operations

The world's leading producer of cranberry juices juice drinks and dried cranberries and the best-selling brand in the North American bottled juice category's original products remain most popular: Ocean Spray Jellied Cranberry Sauce and Ocean Spray Cranberry Juice Cocktail.

The company partners with key stakeholders including Feeding America and others.

Geographic Reach

Headquartered in Massachusetts Ocean Spray has operations in Pennsylvania Nevada Wisconsin Washington Texas and Chile.

While it primarily harvests in the Northeast cranberries also grow in other parts of North and South America from Massachusetts to New Jersey Oregon to Washington Wisconsin parts of British Columbia and Quebec and Chile.

Through its global network of distributors across North America Europe Africa South America Middle East Asia and Australia the company sells its products to more than 70 countries worldwide.

Sales and Marketing

In addition to healthcare restaurants and bars the company also serves in retail schools and travel and leisure sectors. The company's variety of product offerings are available in grocery convenience drug and club stores throughout the world as well as on various online retailers.

HISTORY

Ocean Spray Cranberries traces its roots to Marcus Urann president of the Cape Cod Cranberry Company. In 1912 Urann who became known as the "Cranberry King" began marketing a cranberry sauce that was packaged in tins and could be served year-round. Inspired by the sea spray that drifted off the Atlantic and over his cranberry bogs

Urann dubbed his concoction Ocean Spray Cape Cod Cranberry Sauce.

It didn't take long for other cranberry growers to make their own sauces and rather than compete the Cranberry King consolidated. In 1930 Urann merged his company with A.D. Makepeace Company and with Cranberry Products forming a national cooperative called Cranberry Canners. During the 1940s it added growers in Wisconsin Oregon and Washington and to reflect its new scope changed its name to National Cranberry Association.

Canadian growers were added to the fold in 1950. Urann retired in 1955 and two years later the co-op introduced its first frozen products. To take advantage of the popular Ocean Spray brand name in 1959 the company changed its name to Ocean Spray Cranberries.

EXECUTIVES

Ceo-Pres, Tom Hayes
Dir, Peter P Dhillon
Cfo, Daniel Cunha
Cco-Generl Manager-Internal &, Celina LI
Marketing Manager, Adena Barber
Business Analyst, Aimee Dauphinee
Manager, Alan Friberg
Senior Business Analyst, Amy Witkowski
Assistant Customer Marketing M, Angela Offerman
Scientist, Antelmo Santos
Corporate Counsel, Becca Griffin
Auditors: PRICEWATERHOUSECOOPERS LLP BO

LOCATIONS

HQ: OCEAN SPRAY CRANBERRIES, INC.
 1 OCEAN SPRAY DR, MIDDLEBORO, MA 023490001
Phone: 508 946-1000
Web: WWW.OCEANSPRAY.COM

PRODUCTS/OPERATIONS

Selected Brands & Products
Dried fruit
 Craisins Blueberry Juice Infused Dried Cranberries
 Craisins Cherry Juice Infused Dried Cranberries
 Craisins Original Dried Cranberries
 Craisins Pomegranate Juice Infused Dried Cranberries
 Craisins Snack Packs
 Craisins Trail Mix - Cranberry & Chocolate
 Craisins Trail Mix - Cranberry Fruit & Nut
Fresh Produce
 Clementines
 Cranberries
 Grapefruit
 Lemons
 Limes
 Oranges
 Tangerines
Instant oatmeal
 Cranberry
 Cranberry Honey Multigrain
 Cranberry Orange Muffin
 Cranberry Pomegranate
Juice
 100% Juice Blends
 Blueberry Juice Drinks
 Cran;Energy Energy Juice Drinks
 Cranberry Juice Cocktails
 Cranberry Juice Drink Blends
 Diet Juice Drinks
 Fruit & Veggie Juice
 Fruit & Veggie Juice Drinks
 Grapefruit Juice
 Grapefruit Juice Drinks
 Juice Drinks
 Light Juice Drinks
 On the Go Juice
 On the Go Juice Drinks
 Sugar-Free Drink Mixes

 White Cranberry Juice Drinks
Sauces
 Jellied cranberry sauce
 Whole berry cranberry sauce

COMPETITORS

A. Duda & Sons	Freshco
Arcade Industries	Jugos Del Valle Usa
Cherry Central	Mariani Packing
Cooperative Inc.	Meridian Nut Growers
Chiquita Brands	Naked Juice
Citrus World	National Grape
Coca-cola	Cooperative
Coloma Frozen Foods	Nestl © Usa
Cranberries Limited	Odwalla
Dole Food	Shoreline Fruit
Dundee Citrus Growers	Sunsweet Growers
Edinburg Citrus	Tampico Beverages
Fresh Del Monte	Tropicana
Produce	Wonderful Company

HISTORICAL FINANCIALS

Company Type: Private

Income Statement				FYE: August 31
	REVENUE ($ mil.)	NET INCOME ($ mil.)	NET PROFIT MARGIN	EMPLOYEES
08/17	1,660	272	16.4%	2,000
08/16	1,706	334	19.6%	—
08/15	1,719	317	18.5%	—
Annual Growth	(1.7%)	(7.4%)	—	—

2017 Year-End Financials

Return on assets: 16.1%   Cash ($ mil.): 11
Return on equity: 81.6%
Current ratio: 2.30

OCHSNER CLINIC FOUNDATION

EXECUTIVES

Pres, Warner Thomas
Exec V Pres, Scott Posecai
Nurse, Bonnie Foto
Director of Supply Chain, Clifford C Harlan
Rn, Dennis Pfefferle
Information Technology Influen, Russell Rebstock
Administrative Assistant Facil, Sarah Kevorkian
Rn Director, Stacie Falati
Manager, Stacy Martinez
Radiology Purchasing Coordinat, Clayton Pistorius
Human Resources Specialist, Julie Miller
Auditors: ERNST & YOUNG US LLP FORT WOR

LOCATIONS

HQ: OCHSNER CLINIC FOUNDATION
 1514 JEFFERSON HWY, JEFFERSON, LA 701212483
Phone: 504 842-3000
Web: WWW.OCHSNER.ORG

HISTORICAL FINANCIALS
Company Type: Private

Income Statement				FYE: December 31
	REVENUE ($ mil.)	NET INCOME ($ mil.)	NET PROFIT MARGIN	EMPLOYEES
12/17	8,405	128	1.5%	10,500
12/14	2,196	(16)	—	
12/13	5,550	52	0.9%	
12/12	4,829	12	0.3%	
Annual Growth	11.7%	60.1%		

2017 Year-End Financials
Return on assets: 4.9% Cash ($ mil.): 306
Return on equity: 13.3%
Current ratio: 0.60

OCHSNER HEALTH SYSTEM

Auditors: ERNST & YOUNG LLP NEW ORLEANS

LOCATIONS
HQ: OCHSNER HEALTH SYSTEM
1516 JEFFERSON HWY, NEW ORLEANS, LA 701212429
Phone: 504 842-3483
Web: WWW.OCHSNER.ORG

HISTORICAL FINANCIALS
Company Type: Private

Income Statement				FYE: December 31
	REVENUE ($ mil.)	NET INCOME ($ mil.)	NET PROFIT MARGIN	EMPLOYEES
12/16	2,812	55	2.0%	19,000
12/15	2,592	63	2.5%	
Annual Growth	8.5%	(13.2%)	—	—

2016 Year-End Financials
Return on assets: 2.4% Cash ($ mil.): 121
Return on equity: 7.8%
Current ratio: 1.40

OHIO EDISON COMPANY

Ohio Edison has taken a shine to the folks in the Buckeye state. The company distributes electricity to a population of about 2.3 million (more than 1 million customers) in a 7000 sq. ml. area of central and northeastern Ohio. Ohio Edison a unit of FirstEnergy also has 5955 MW of generating capacity from interests in primarily fossil-fueled and nuclear generation facilities and it sells excess power to wholesale customers. The utility's power plants are operated by sister companies FirstEnergy Nuclear and FirstEnergy Generation. Subsidiary Pennsylvania Power Company provides electric service to communities in a 1100 sq. ml. area of western Pennsylvania which has a population of approximately 400000.

Operations
Ohio Edison and Pennsylvania Power provide regulated electric distribution services and procure of generation services. Ohio Edison operates more than 30460 miles of distribution lines and 500 miles of transmission lines.

Geographic Reach
Ohio Edison and Pennsylvania Power conduct business in portions of Ohio and Pennsylvania.

Financial Performance
Revenues decreased by 11% in 2011 due to lower retail generation revenues partially offset by higher distribution and wholesale generation revenues. Retail generation revenues decreased primarily due to a drop in energy sales caused from an increase in customers shopping for alternative power providers and lower average prices across all customer classes.

Ohio Edison's net income decreased by 17% in 2011 due to lower revenues partially offset by lower purchased power costs.

Strategy
In 2011 parent FirstEnergy acquired Allegheny Energy in a $8.5 billion deal that grew FirstEnergy's generation capacity and dramatically boosted the company's position as a leading regional energy provider.

Company Background
FirstEnergy and Ohio Edison reached a settlement in 2005 with the federal government to reduce harmful emissions from its Ohio power generating plants; in addition to fines Ohio Edison has been mandated to pledge $25 million for wind power biomass and other alternative energy sources. In 2009 Ohio Edison began retrofitting two units at its Shadyside Ohio power plant to burn wood and other biomass materials in order to lower its greenhouse gas output.

EXECUTIVES
Sr V Pres-Cfo, James F Pearson
V Pres-Controller*, Harvey L Wagner
Engineering Supervisor, Chris Hixon
Board Member, Ernest Novak
Supervisor Reg Operations Line, Jeffery Akers
Supervisor Reg Operations West, Damian Wess
Supervisor Reg Operations Line, Darren Puffinburger
Adv Customer Specialis, Eric Weisenberger
Supervisor, Jim Pitchford
Manager, Transportation, Larry Lallathin
Auditors: PRICEWATERHOUSECOOPES LP CLEV

LOCATIONS
HQ: OHIO EDISON COMPANY
76 S MAIN ST BSMT, AKRON, OH 443081817
Phone: 800 736-3402
Web: WWW.FIRSTENERGYCORP.COM

COMPETITORS

Columbia Gas Of Ohio	Ohio Power
Dpl	Vectren Energy
Dominion East Ohio	Delivery Of Ohio
Duke Energy Ohio	

HISTORICAL FINANCIALS
Company Type: Private

Income Statement				FYE: December 31
	REVENUE ($ mil.)	NET INCOME ($ mil.)	NET PROFIT MARGIN	EMPLOYEES
12/16	1,394	150	10.8%	1,190
12/11	1,633	128	7.8%	
12/10	1,836	157	8.6%	
12/09	2,516	122	4.9%	
Annual Growth	(8.1%)	3.0%	—	—

OHIO STATE UNIVERSITY PHYSICIANS, INC.

EXECUTIVES
President, Doug Rund
Vice President-Operations*, Pam Edson
Human Resources Specialist, Paula Vagnier
Marketing and Communications, Cheryl Petrilla
Value Stream Leader, Janice Pierpoint
Assistant Director of Donor RE, Brittany Stricklen-Hilly
Senior Director, Emily Fijol
Information Technology, Michael Thompson
Patient Account Representative, Shawn Reeve

LOCATIONS
HQ: OHIO STATE UNIVERSITY PHYSICIANS, INC.
700 ACKERMAN RD STE 600, COLUMBUS, OH 432021559
Phone: 614 947-3700
Web: WWW.OSUPHYSICIANS.COM

HISTORICAL FINANCIALS
Company Type: Private

Income Statement				FYE: June 30
	REVENUE ($ mil.)	NET INCOME ($ mil.)	NET PROFIT MARGIN	EMPLOYEES
06/20	606	8	1.4%	99
06/17	500	29	6.0%	
Annual Growth	6.7%	(35.0%)	—	—

2020 Year-End Financials
Return on assets: 2.9% Cash ($ mil.): 182
Return on equity: 4.0%
Current ratio: —

OHIOHEALTH CORPORATION

OhioHealth is a nationally recognized not-for-profit charitable healthcare outreach of the United Methodist Church. The not-for-profit system runs a dozen of hospitals including OhioHealth Riverside Methodist Hospital OhioHealth Grant Medical Center and OhioHealth Doctors Hospital. All told OhioHealth has 200-plus ambulatory sites hospice home health medical equipment and other services spanning more than 45 Ohio counties. OhioHealth offers urgent care physical rehabilitation diagnostic imaging and sleep diagnostics services. OhioHealth Physician Group includes 800 primary care physicians and 400 advance practice providers in more than 50 specialties.

Operations
In addition to offering patient care OhioHealth also operates the OhioHealth Research & Innovation Institute which coordinates research throughout the health system including conducting clinical trials of new drugs and medical devices. The system also operates The Center for Medical Education a medical training facility that among other technologies offers human patient simulators on which medical professionals can practice new procedures in various clinical situations.

OhioHealth has some 35000 associates physicians and volunteers.

Geographic Reach
Based in Ohio OhioHealth provide health services in more than 45 counties.

Strategy
In late 2021 OhioHealth Doctors Hospital purchased the medical office building across the street from the hospital located at 5109 West Broad Street. Renovations for that building will follow. Starting in January 2022 OhioHealth will begin planning and design work for a complete renovation within the recently purchased medical office building attached to the hospital located at 5131 Beacon Hill Road. The investment will bring more outpatient services to the west side allowing Doctors Hospital to recruit new physicians and improve the patient experience.

This investment brings the OhioHealth commitment to nearly $75 million dollars over a little more than a decade ensuring patients have access to the right care at the right time and most importantly at the right place.

Company Background
The health system traces its roots back to 1892 when Protestant Hospital (now known as Riverside Methodist Hospital) opened. The system initially organized as U.S. Health Corporation in 1984 later took on the OhioHealth name in 1997.

EXECUTIVES

Pres-Ceo, David Blom
Sr V Pres-Cfo*, Michael W Louge
Sr V Pres*, Robert P Millen
Sr V Pres*, Donna Hanly
Sr V Pres*, Michael S Bernstein
Sr V Pres*, Steve Garlock
Prin*, Earl Barnes
Coo*, John McWhorter
Sr V Pres*, Cynthia Latney
Executive Officer, Jane Berkebile
Chief Officer, Bruce Vanderhoff
Auditors: DELOITTE TAX LLP INDIANAPOL

LOCATIONS

HQ: OHIOHEALTH CORPORATION
3430 OHHALTH PKWY FL 5 FLR 5, COLUMBUS, OH 43202
Phone: 614 788-8860
Web: WWW.OHIOHEALTH.COM

PRODUCTS/OPERATIONS

Selected Facilities

Owned
Doctors Hospital (Columbus)
Doctors Hospital Nelsonville (Nelsonville)
Dublin Methodist Hospital (Dublin)
Grady Memorial Hospital (Delaware)
Grant Medical Center (Columbus)
Hardin Memorial Hospital (Kenton)
Marion General Hospital (Marion)
O'Bleness Memorial Hospital (Athens)
Riverside Methodist Hospital (Columbus)
Affiliated
Blanchard Valley Medical Center
Galion Community Hospital (Galion)
Genesis Healthcare System (Zanesville)
Knox Community Hospital
Morrow County Hospital (Mt. Gilead)
Samaritan Regional Health System (Ashland)
Southern Ohio Medical Center (Portsmouth)

COMPETITORS

Adena Health System
Fairfield Medical Center
Licking Memorial Health Systems
Mount Carmel Health
Nationwide Children's Hospital
Regency Hospital
Select Medical

HISTORICAL FINANCIALS
Company Type: Private

Income Statement   FYE: June 30

	REVENUE ($ mil.)	NET INCOME ($ mil.)	NET PROFIT MARGIN	EMPLOYEES
06/19	3,388	542	16.0%	15,000
06/18	4,045	519	12.8%	—
06/17	3,792	631	16.6%	—
06/14	2,179	354	16.3%	—
Annual Growth	9.2%	8.9%	—	—

2019 Year-End Financials
Return on assets: 7.8%
Return on equity: 11.5%
Current ratio: 0.40
Cash ($ mil.): 132

OHIOHEALTH CORPORATION GROUP RETURN

EXECUTIVES

Nurse Manager, Anne Keller
Registered Nurse, Paul Newsome
Auditors: DELOITTE TAX LLP CINCINNATI

LOCATIONS

HQ: OHIOHEALTH CORPORATION GROUP RETURN
180 E BROAD ST, COLUMBUS, OH 432153707
Phone: 614 544-4052
Web: WWW.OHIOHEALTH.COM

HISTORICAL FINANCIALS
Company Type: Private

Income Statement   FYE: June 30

	REVENUE ($ mil.)	NET INCOME ($ mil.)	NET PROFIT MARGIN	EMPLOYEES
06/18	1,334	(98)	—	8
06/17	1,204	(77)	—	—
06/14	600	(85)	—	—
06/13	563	(55)	—	—
Annual Growth	18.8%	—	—	—

2018 Year-End Financials
Return on assets: (-9.0%)
Return on equity: (-14.1%)
Current ratio: 1.40
Cash ($ mil.): 42

OHIOHEALTH RIVERSIDE METHODIST HOSPITAL

EXECUTIVES

Pres-Ceo, Brian D Jepson
Sr V Pres*, Steve Markovitch
Director of Information Techno, Vandhana V Veerni
Information Specialist, Anne Rhodes
Information Specialist, Elizabeth Queen
Information Specialist, Jeanne Walker
Chief of Medicine, Mark Davis
Physician, Peter George
Director of Radiology, Dennis Horn
Family Practitioner, Michelle Taylor
Team Leader, Corey Hamilton

LOCATIONS

HQ: OHIOHEALTH RIVERSIDE METHODIST HOSPITAL
3535 OLENTANGY RIVER RD, COLUMBUS, OH 432143908
Phone: 614 566-5000
Web: WWW.OHIOHEALTH.COM

HISTORICAL FINANCIALS
Company Type: Private

Income Statement   FYE: June 30

	REVENUE ($ mil.)	NET INCOME ($ mil.)	NET PROFIT MARGIN	EMPLOYEES
06/16	1,207	190	15.8%	944
06/15*	19	0	2.3%	—
12/01	49	(1)	—	—
12/00	0	0	—	—
Annual Growth	—	—	—	—

*Fiscal year change

2016 Year-End Financials
Return on assets: 28.3%
Return on equity: —
Current ratio: 0.50
Cash ($ mil.): —

OKLAHOMA STATE UNIVERSITY

Oooooklahoma where the... students come to learn! Oklahoma State University is the flagship campus of its namesake (OSU) system which also includes OSU-Tulsa OSU-Oklahoma City OSU-Okmulgee the OSU Center for Health Sciences in Tulsa the OSU College of Veterinary Medicine and the Oklahoma Agricultural Experiment Station. OSU offers courses in a variety of disciplines and confers undergraduate graduate doctoral and professional degrees in everything from agriculture and the arts to business and engineering. Altogether the system boasts an enrollment of about 36000 students across its five campuses; its student-teacher ratio is about 17:1.

Geographic Reach
Operating across Oklahoma OSU's several campus locations include three branch campuses a Center for Health Sciences College of Veterinary Medicine and Oklahoma Agricultural Experiment Station.

Financial Performance
The Oklahoma university has seen its revenue rise for the past several years due to organic growth. OSU logged an 11% increase in revenue in 2012 as compared to 2011 thanks to increases from tuition and fees grants and contracts auxiliary enterprises and other operating revenue. Net income meanwhile slipped by 14% during the same reporting period attributable to increases in compensation and employee benefits contractual services scholarships and fellowships depreciation expense supplies and materials and other operating expenses.

Strategy

One of OSU's biggest financial contributors is alumnus and oil and gas tycoon T. Boone Pickens who over the years has given the school more than $500 million. Pickens' 2010 donation of $100 million went toward the school's $1 billion fundraising campaign that was used to endow scholarships and fellowships for students as well as attract and retain professors upgrade facilities and create new programs. Pickens is the campaign's honorary chairman.

Company Background

OSU was founded in 1890 as the Oklahoma Territorial Agricultural and Mechanical College (A&M). The first students were enrolled the following year; the school operated as Oklahoma A&M until 1957 when it changed its name to Oklahoma State University to reflect the fact that its curriculum had grown to include a wide range of subjects. Following the name change the OSU began establishing campuses starting with the Stillwater campus and then the OSU-Institute of Technology in Okmulgee (1946) OSU-Oklahoma City (1961) OSU-Tulsa (1984) and the Center for Health Sciences also in Tulsa (1988).

EXECUTIVES

Pres, Burns Hargis
Accounting Staff, Brendon Daft
Staff, Cary Fox
Assistant Professor, Jane Vogler
Assistant Professor, Stephen Nemeth
Exec Asst To Pres, Debbie Lane
Assistant Professor, Pamela Lloyd
Staff, Krista Curry
Staff Associate Vice President, Virginia Wyckoff
Social Director, Jeremy Brown
Staff, Lawrence Hynson
Auditors: BKD LLP SPRINGFIELD MISSOUR

LOCATIONS

HQ: OKLAHOMA STATE UNIVERSITY
401 WHITEHURST HALL, STILLWATER, OK 740781030
Phone: 405 744-5000
Web: WWW.AGRICULTURE.OKSTATE.EDU

PRODUCTS/OPERATIONS

Selected Colleges
Agricultural Sciences and Natural Resources
Arts and Sciences
Education
Engineering Architecture and Technology
Human Sciences
Spears School of Business
Center for Veterinary Health Sciences
Graduate College
Honors College

HISTORICAL FINANCIALS
Company Type: Private

Income Statement				FYE: June 30
	REVENUE ($ mil.)	NET INCOME ($ mil.)	NET PROFIT MARGIN	EMPLOYEES
06/20	842	115	13.8%	8,882
06/19	904	95	10.6%	—
06/18	802	8	1.1%	—
06/17	815	40	5.0%	—
Annual Growth	1.1%	42.1%	—	—

2020 Year-End Financials
Return on assets: 4.5%   Cash ($ mil.): 134
Return on equity: 10.6%
Current ratio: 2.70

OLD DURA, INC.

EXECUTIVES

Ceo, Lynn Tilton
Exec V Pres, Jim Gregory
Exec V Pres, Franois Stouvenot
Exec V Pres, Martin Becker
Exec V Pres, Mario Buttino
Vp-Treas, Kathleen Birney
Marketing Director Europe, Anne Cara
Cfo, James Gregory
Engineering Supervisor, Jason Matta
It Manager, Jeffrey Zimmerman

LOCATIONS

HQ: OLD DURA, INC.
1780 POND RUN, AUBURN HILLS, MI 483262752
Phone: 248 299-7500
Web: WWW.DURAAUTO.COM

HISTORICAL FINANCIALS
Company Type: Private

Income Statement				FYE: December 31
	REVENUE ($ mil.)	NET INCOME ($ mil.)	NET PROFIT MARGIN	EMPLOYEES
12/07	1,894	(472)	—	3
12/06	2,090	(910)	—	—
12/05	2,344	1	0.1%	—
12/04	2,492	11	0.5%	—
Annual Growth	(8.7%)	—	—	—

2007 Year-End Financials
Return on assets: (-45.1%)   Cash ($ mil.): 93
Return on equity: —
Current ratio: 1.20

OMAHA PUBLIC POWER DISTRICT

EXECUTIVES

Chb, Anne McGuire
Pres-Ceo*, Gary Gates
V Chm*, Del B Weber
SEC*, John K Green
Treas*, Michael J Cavanaugh
Treas*, Frederick J Ulrich
Executive Administrative Assis, Rose Kruse
Human Resources Business Partn, Angela Carter
Supervisor Operations, Brandon Cotarelo
Electrical Designer Co, Chad Oltman
Supervisor, Hallie Rodis
Auditors: BKD LLP OMAHA NEBRASKA

LOCATIONS

HQ: OMAHA PUBLIC POWER DISTRICT
444 S 16TH ST, OMAHA, NE 681022247
Phone: 402 636-2000
Web: WWW.OPPD.COM

HISTORICAL FINANCIALS
Company Type: Private

Income Statement				FYE: December 31
	REVENUE ($ mil.)	NET INCOME ($ mil.)	NET PROFIT MARGIN	EMPLOYEES
12/20	1,083	74	6.8%	2,300
12/19	1,160	86	7.5%	—
Annual Growth	(6.6%)	(14.9%)	—	—

2020 Year-End Financials
Return on assets: 1.3%   Cash ($ mil.): 26
Return on equity: 5.6%
Current ratio: 2.00

OMAHA PUBLIC SCHOOLS

EXECUTIVES

Supt, Cheryl Logan
Controller, Dr Liz Standish
Assist Superintendent, Dr Dennis Pool
Coordinator, Suann Witt
Assistant, Jennifer Schlapia
Health Professional, Kari Caddell
Project Coordinator, Lesley Dean
Coordinator, Lisa Thompson
Special Education, Aaron Brooker
School Nurse, Andrea Lostaglia-Hosko
Computer Technology Teacher, Angela Reick
Auditors: SEIM JOHNSON LLP OMAHA NEBR

LOCATIONS

HQ: OMAHA PUBLIC SCHOOLS
3215 CUMING ST, OMAHA, NE 681312000
Phone: 402 557-2120
Web: WWW.OPS.ORG

HISTORICAL FINANCIALS
Company Type: Private

Income Statement				FYE: August 31
	REVENUE ($ mil.)	NET INCOME ($ mil.)	NET PROFIT MARGIN	EMPLOYEES
08/18	763	20	2.7%	8,000
08/17	720	33	4.7%	—
08/16	693	(41)	—	—
08/15	626	126	20.3%	—
Annual Growth	6.9%	(45.4%)	—	—

2018 Year-End Financials
Return on assets: 1.4%   Cash ($ mil.): 305
Return on equity: —
Current ratio: —

ONEOK PARTNERS, L.P.

For ONEOK Partners it's OK to have three businesses: natural gas pipelines; gas gathering and processing; and natural gas liquids (NGLs). Its pipelines include Midwestern Gas Transmission Guardian Pipeline Viking Gas Transmission and OkTex Pipeline. The ONEOK affiliate operates

17100 miles of gas-gathering pipeline and 7600 miles of transportation pipeline as well as gas processing plants and storage facilities (with 52 billion cu. ft. of capacity). It also owns one of the US's top natural NGL systems (more than 7200 miles of pipeline). In 2017 41%-owner ONEOK agreed to buy the stock of ONEOK Partners that it did not already own for $9.3 billion in a stock deal. Operations ONEOK Partners operates in three business segments: natural gas gathering and processing; natural gas pipelines; and natural gas liquids. Geographic Reach The company gathers and processes natural gas in the Mid-Continent region which includes the NGL-rich Cana-Woodford Shale and Granite Wash formations the Mississippian Lime formation of Oklahoma and Kansas and the Hugoton and Central Kansas Uplift Basins of Kansas. The Natural Gas Pipelines segment owns and operates regulated natural gas transmission pipelines natural gas storage facilities and natural gas gathering systems for nonprocessed gas. It also provide interstate natural gas transportation and storage service. The company's interstate natural gas pipeline assets transport natural gas through pipelines in North Dakota Minnesota Wisconsin Illinois Indiana Kentucky Tennessee Oklahoma Texas and New Mexico. Its Natural gas liquids assets provide nondiscretionary services to producers that consist of facilities that gather fractionate and treat NGLs and store NGL products primarily in Oklahoma Kansas and Texas. It also owns or has stakes in natural gas liquids gathering and distribution pipelines in Oklahoma Kansas Texas Wyoming and Colorado and terminal and storage facilities in Missouri Nebraska Iowa and Illinois. In addition it owns natural gas liquids distribution and refined petroleum products pipelines in Kansas Missouri Nebraska Iowa Illinois and Indiana that connect the company's Mid-Continent assets with Midwest markets including Chicago.

Financial Performance

Revenues decreased by 10% in 2012 due to lower net realized natural gas and NGL product prices offset partially by higher natural gas and NGL sales volumes from completed capital projects. The increase in natural gas supply resulting from the development of nonconventional resource areas in North America and a warmer than normal winter caused natural gas prices to drop. NGL prices particularly ethane and propane also decreased in 2012 due primarily to increased NGL production and an increase in available supply. Propane prices also were affected by a warmer than normal winter.

ONEOK Partners' net income grew by 7% in 2012 thanks to lower costs of sales and fuels and lower interest expenses.

Strategy

The company pursues a strategy of building up its fee-based earnings coupled with organic growth and complementary acquisitions in both conventional oil and gas and unconventional (shale plays).

It is looking to increase NGL volumes gathered and fractionated in its NGL segment and natural gas volumes processed in its natural gas gathering and processing segment as producers continue to develop NGL-rich resource plays in the Mid-Continent and Rocky Mountain areas.

In 2012 ONEOK Partners announced plans to invest up to $360 million to grow its projects in the Woodford Shale formation.

Company Background

ONEOK Partners was formed in 2006 when ONEOK spun off its gathering and processing NGLs pipelines and storage businesses for $3 billion following that company's acquisition of Northern Border Partners (which was founded in 1993). Building out its assets in 2007 the company acquired an interstate pipeline system from Kinder Morgan Energy Partners for $300 million.

EXECUTIVES

Pres-Ceo, Terry K Spencer
Evp-Cfo, Walter S Hulse III
Svp,naturalgasgathering&procce, Michael A Fitzgibbons
Employee, Sydney L Mitchell

LOCATIONS

HQ: ONEOK PARTNERS, L.P.
100 W 5TH ST STE LL, TULSA, OK 741034298
Phone: 918 588-7000
Web: WWW.ONEOK.COM

PRODUCTS/OPERATIONS

Natural Gas Pipelines

Midwestern Gas Transmission Company
Viking Gas Transmission Company
Guardian Pipeline
OkTex Pipeline Company
ONEOK Gas Transportation
ONEOK Gas Gathering
ONEOK Gas Storage
ONEOK WesTex Transmission
ONEOK Texas Gas Storage
Mid Continent Market Center
ONEOK Transmission Company
Natural Gas Gathering & Processing
Crestone Energy Ventures
ONEOK Field Services
ONEOK Rockies Midstream

COMPETITORS

Enbridge	Panhandle Eastern Pipe
Kinder Morgan Energy	Line
Partners	Transcanada

HISTORICAL FINANCIALS

Company Type: Private

Income Statement   FYE: December 31

	REVENUE ($ mil.)	NET INCOME ($ mil.)	NET PROFIT MARGIN	EMPLOYEES
12/16	8,918	1,072	12.0%	2,364
12/15	7,761	597	7.7%	—
12/14	12,191	911	7.5%	—
Annual Growth	(14.5%)	8.5%	—	—

2016 Year-End Financials

Return on assets: 6.9%
Return on equity: 17.4%
Current ratio: 0.40

Cash ($ mil.): —

ORANGE AND ROCKLAND UTILITIES INC

Orange and Rockland Utilities (O&R) operates under the auspices of its big city cousin holding company Consolidated Edison (Con Edison). O&R's subsidiaries Rockland Electric and Pike County Power & Light operate in southeastern New York and adjacent portions of New Jersey and Pennsylvania. The utilities distribute electricity to more than 301800 customers in about 100 communities in those three states and deliver natural gas more than to 128000 customers in New York and Pennsylvania. O&R's transmission and distribution facilities include 5550 miles of overhead and underground power distribution lines 560 miles of transmission lines and more than 1850 miles of gas pipeline.

Operations

O&R and its two utility subsidiaries Rockland Electric Company and Pike County Light & Power Co. deliver power and gas to customers in three states. The electricity O&R sold to its customers in 2011 was purchased under firm power contracts or through the wholesale electricity markets administered by the NYISO and PJM Interconnection LLC.

Geographic Reach

The company serves a population of approximately 750000 in seven counties in New York northern New Jersey and northeastern Pennsylvania. About 75% of O&R's power customers are in the state of New York.

Financial Performance

O&R's revenues increased by 5% in 2011 mainly due to lower purchased power costs and a decrease in gas purchased for resale.

Strategy

As a way to attract more businesses to its New York service area in 2011 O&R doubled the discount on its electric delivery rate (up from 10% to 20% for five years) for qualified companies.

The company is investing heavily in upgrading its aging infrastructure. In late 2010 the company announced plans to invest $2.6 million over a 13 month period to replace 11800 feet of 60-year-old 4-inch steel gas underground distribution pipe with 8-inch plastic gas pipe across Orange and Rockland counties.

Company Background

When deregulation arrived in O&R's territory in 1999 the energy company exited its power generation activities and sold itself to Con Edison.

EXECUTIVES

Pres, John McAvoy
Pres*, William G Longhi
V Pres*, Francis Peverly
Human Resources Representative, Marion Gaglione

LOCATIONS

HQ: ORANGE AND ROCKLAND UTILITIES INC
1 BLUE HILL PLZ STE 20, PEARL RIVER, NY 109653100
Phone: 845 352-6000
Web: WWW.ORU.COM

PRODUCTS/OPERATIONS

2011 Sales

	$ mil.	% of total
Electric	641	75
Gas	214	25
Total	**855**	**100**

Subsidiaries

Subsidiaries
Pike County Light & Power Company
Rockland Electric Company

COMPETITORS

Avangrid	Niagara Mohawk
Delmarva Power	Ppl Corporation
Enbridge	Public Service
National Fuel Gas	Enterprise Group
New Jersey Resources	

HISTORICAL FINANCIALS
Company Type: Private

Income Statement				FYE: December 31
	REVENUE ($ mil.)	NET INCOME ($ mil.)	NET PROFIT MARGIN	EMPLOYEES
12/16	653	59	9.1%	1,060
12/05	824	50	6.1%	—
12/04	703	46	6.5%	—
12/03	727	45	6.2%	—
Annual Growth	(0.8%)	2.1%		

2016 Year-End Financials
Return on assets: 2.1%
Return on equity: 9.2%
Current ratio: 0.50

Cash ($ mil.): —

ORANGE COUNTY HEALTH AUTHORITY, A PUBLIC AGENCY

EXECUTIVES

Ceo, Richard Chambers
Ceo, Michael Schrader
Chief Medical Officer, Richard Helmer
Chief Operating Officer, Ladan Khamseh
Chief Counsel, Gary Crockett
Chief Administrative Officer, Kim Cunningham
General Counsel, George L Root
Telecommunications Admi, Chris Williams
Coordinator, Barbara Collins
Information Specialist, Faye Heidari
Public Relations Manager, Claudia Hernandez

LOCATIONS

HQ: ORANGE COUNTY HEALTH AUTHORITY, A
PUBLIC AGENCY
505 CITY PKWY W, ORANGE, CA 928682924
Phone: 714 246-8500
Web: WWW.CALOPTIMA.ORG

HISTORICAL FINANCIALS
Company Type: Private

Income Statement				FYE: June 30
	REVENUE ($ mil.)	NET INCOME ($ mil.)	NET PROFIT MARGIN	EMPLOYEES
06/09	1,078	(17)	—	432
06/05	812	(24)	—	—
06/04	0	0	—	—
06/03	756	1	0.2%	—
Annual Growth	6.1%	—	—	

2009 Year-End Financials
Return on assets: (-5.2%)
Return on equity: (-13.3%)
Current ratio: 1.00

Cash ($ mil.): 81

ORANGE COUNTY TRANSPORTATION AUTHORITY

Public transportation in sunny Orange County California is overseen by the Orange County Transportation Authority (OCTA). The OCTA is the main provider of bus services in its 800-sq.-mi. territory which is home to more than 3 million people. In cooperation with the Southern California Regional Rail Authority the OCTA oversees Metrolink commuter rail service in Orange County. The agency also operates a 10-mile toll road and issues permits to taxi operators. Revenue from a half-cent local sales tax allows the agency to pay for road improvement and mass transit projects.

Operations
OCTA builds designs operates plans maintains and regulates the robust transportation network within Orange County. In addition to the four modes of transportation (transit driving bicycling and walking) OCTA oversees paratransit services taxi services light rail commuter rail and high-occupancy managed lanes.

It operates rail service for OCTA centers on Metrolink Southern California's commuter rail system linking residential communities to employment and activity centers. Metrolink is operated by the Southern California Regional Rail Authority- a joint powers authority of five member agencies representing the counties of Los Angeles Orange Riverside San Bernardino and Ventura. OCTA is one of the five member agencies that administers Orange County Metrolink activities.

The 91 Express Lanes is a four-lane 10-mile toll road built in the median of California's Riverside Freeway (SR-91) between the Orange/Riverside County line and the SR-55.

Geographic Reach
The company is located in Southern California - south of Los Angeles County north of San Diego County and west of Riverside and San Bernardino counties.

Financial Performance
OCTA's rail budget for fiscal year 2015-16 consists of both operating and capital expenses. Operating expenses in FY 2015-16 are budgeted at $31.6 million while capital expenditures are anticipated to reach $100.4 million. The FY 2015-16 rail capital projects. The organization saw a decline in its budget for FY 2015-16 due to drop in passenger fares and state assistance federal capital assistance grants.

(OCTA uses its revenue primarily in salaries and benefits professional services and capital expenditure).

Strategy
The 2014 - 2019 OCTA Strategic Plan takes a comprehensive forward-looking approach to address Orange County's transportation needs during the next five years.(OCTA maintains a Long-Range Transportation Plan updated every four years to account for new planning efforts as well as changes in demographics economic conditions and available sources of transportation funding).

In the FY 2015-16 budget $6.9 million of Measure M funds deposited in the General Fund are being used to fund the final work on the West County Connectors project.

After four years in the making OCTA marked the completion of the $297 million West County Connector project in 2014 which will bring congestion relief where three major freeways (Interstate 405 Interstate 605 and State Route 22) converge.

In 2014 OCTA purchased 400 new buses for fixed-route and ACCESS services. This purchase combined with the in-process repainting of the existing fleet presents a cost-effective opportunity to explore new branding concepts for Orange County bus services.

Company Background
OCTA was formed in 1991 in a consolidation of seven transportation agencies.

EXECUTIVES

Ceo, Darrell Johnson
Dir*, Don Hansen
Director, Charles V Smith
Digital Marketing Specialist, Jacqueline Moon
Office Specialist Assistant, Leslie Tuiteleleapaga
Vanpool Administrator, Tracy McConnell
Coach Operator, Anthony McCollough
Programmer Analyst, Bob Stwalley
Store Supervisor, David Rosenkranz
Executive Assistant V, Elizabeth Wade
Bussiness Unit Analyst Associa, Esther Jimenez
Auditors: VAVRINEK TRINE DAY & CO LL

LOCATIONS

HQ: ORANGE COUNTY TRANSPORTATION AUTHORITY
550 S MAIN ST, ORANGE, CA 928684506
Phone: 714 636-7433
Web: WWW.OCTA.NET

PRODUCTS/OPERATIONS

2014 Sales

	$ mil.	% of total
Sales taxes	451	93
Unrestricted investment earning	18	4
Property taxes	12	3
Other	0	-
Total	**482**	**100**

Selected Services
91 Express Lanes toll facility
Bus transit service
Freeway improvements funding
Freeway Service Patrol
Long-range planning
Measure M2 administration
Metrolink rail service
Rideshare options
Street and road improvements grants
Taxi administration program
Vanpool subsidies

HISTORICAL FINANCIALS
Company Type: Private

Income Statement				FYE: June 30
	REVENUE ($ mil.)	NET INCOME ($ mil.)	NET PROFIT MARGIN	EMPLOYEES
06/20	708	(87)	—	1,050
06/18	634	(53)	—	—
06/17	611	54	9.0%	—
06/16	600	67	11.2%	—
Annual Growth	4.2%	—	—	

OREGON DEPARTMENT OF TRANSPORTATION

The Oregon Department of Transportation (ODOT) helps move people and goods across the state. The agency strives to provide a safe and efficient transportation system — including highway rail and public transit — for its residents. The department is responsible for construction and maintenance of highways and bridges improving public transportation services reducing traffic crashes and ensuring equal access for low-income and elderly citizens as well as people with disabilities. Its division of driver and motor vehicles (DMV) provides vehicle registration driver licenses and ID cards. The agency also tries to decrease the impact that its transportation system has on air and water quality.

EXECUTIVES

Dir, Mathew Garrett
Coordinator, Basil Christopher
Chief Human Resources Officer, Madilyn Zike
Manager, Central Operations, Anna Giddens-Reed
Interim Program Manager, Maint, Daniel Ohrn
Customer Manager, Dianna Price-Eastburn
Assistant Project Manager, Jennifer Pearce
Manager, Facilities, Randy Gengler
Business Assistant, Tom Fuller

LOCATIONS

HQ: OREGON DEPARTMENT OF TRANSPORTATION
355 CAPITOL ST NE MS21, SALEM, OR 973013871
Phone: 503 378-5849
Web: WWW.OREGON.GOV

HISTORICAL FINANCIALS

Company Type: Private

Income Statement				FYE: June 30
	REVENUE ($ mil.)	NET INCOME ($ mil.)	NET PROFIT MARGIN	EMPLOYEES
06/19	2,260	56	2.5%	4,800
06/18	2,017	23	1.2%	—
06/05	0	0	—	—
06/03	461	(198)	—	—
Annual Growth	10.4%	—	—	—

2019 Year-End Financials

Return on assets: 3.6%
Return on equity: 5.7%
Current ratio: 2.40

Cash ($ mil.): 958

OREGON HEALTH & SCIENCE UNIVERSITY MEDICAL GROUP

Oregon Health & Science University (OHSU) is Oregon's only academic health center and distinguished nationally as a research university dedicated solely to advancing health sciences. OHSU focuses on discoveries to prevent and cure diseases on education that prepares the health care and health science professionals of the future and on patient care that incorporates the latest advances. OSHU operates OSHU Hospital; OHSU Doernbecher Children's Hospital Hillsboro Medical Center (formerly Tuality Healthcare); Adventist Health Portland; and clinics across Oregon. OHSU traces its roots to 1867 when members of the medical department at Willamette University began the first formal medical students to its Salem campus.

Geographic Reach

OSHU has facilities in Marquam Hill Campus Portland (with more than 35 major buildings OHSU Hospital Kohler Pavilion and Doernbecher Children's Hospital) South Waterfront Campus Portland (includes five major buildings) and West Campus Hillsboro (OHSU's Oregon National Primate Research Center and The Vaccine and Gene Therapy Institute).

Sales and Marketing

About 95% of its health care patients are from Oregon.

EXECUTIVES

Pres, Joseph Robertson Jr
V Pres*, Deborah Golden-Epplelein
Cfo*, Lawrence J Furnstahl
Health Professional, Rebecca Harrison
Cataloger and Libraria, Carla Pealer
Director, Oregon National Prim, Nancy L Haigwood
Director, Vollum Institute, Richard H Goodman
Director, Rom N Hern Ndez
Accounting Staff, Peggy Schmidt
Assistant Professor, Abraham Furman
Assistant Professor, Beth Edmunds
Auditors: KPMG LLP PORTLAND OREGON

LOCATIONS

HQ: OREGON HEALTH & SCIENCE UNIVERSITY MEDICAL GROUP
3181 SW SAM JACKSON PK RD, PORTLAND, OR 972393011
Phone: 503 494-8311
Web: WWW.OHSU.EDU

PRODUCTS/OPERATIONS

Selected schools

School of Dentistry
School of Medicine
School of Nursing
School of Pharmacy (with Oregon State University)
School of Science & Engineering

HISTORICAL FINANCIALS

Company Type: Private

Income Statement				FYE: June 30
	REVENUE ($ mil.)	NET INCOME ($ mil.)	NET PROFIT MARGIN	EMPLOYEES
06/20	3,313	(13)	—	19,500
06/19	3,178	251	7.9%	—
06/18	3,050	259	8.5%	—
06/17	2,846	222	7.8%	—
Annual Growth	5.2%	—	—	—

2020 Year-End Financials

Return on assets: (-0.2%)
Return on equity: (-0.4%)
Current ratio: 2.30

Cash ($ mil.): 422

OREGON STATE LOTTERY

The Oregon State Lottery operates the Beaver State's lottery and other state-run games of chance. It offers traditional lotto numbers games and instant-win tickets and it operates video lottery and video poker machines. Oregon also takes part in the multistate Powerball drawing. About 65% of the lottery's profits are channeled into public education programs while the rest is used to fund economic development projects state parks and other government programs. Oregon created its lottery in 1984.

EXECUTIVES

Comm, Chris Telfer
Comm*, Elisa Dozono
Comm*, Mary Wheat
Comm*, Raul Valdivia
Comm*, Liz Carle
Dir*, Barry Pack
Coordinator, Sharon Ingram
Coordinator, James B Scheppke
Senior Information Security An, John McKean
Manager, Lea Dymoke
Administrator, Micah Rosier

LOCATIONS

HQ: OREGON STATE LOTTERY
500 AIRPORT RD SE, SALEM, OR 973015068
Phone: 503 540-1000
Web: WWW.OREGONLOTTERY.ORG

COMPETITORS

California State Lottery
Multi-state Lottery
Washington State Lottery

HISTORICAL FINANCIALS

Company Type: Private

Income Statement				FYE: June 30
	REVENUE ($ mil.)	NET INCOME ($ mil.)	NET PROFIT MARGIN	EMPLOYEES
06/20	1,145	(11)	—	420
06/19	1,347	7	0.5%	—
06/18	1,302	(14)	—	—
06/16	1,230	61	5.0%	—
Annual Growth	(1.8%)	—	—	—

2020 Year-End Financials

Return on assets: (-1.8%)
Return on equity: (-4.3%)
Current ratio: 1.40

Cash ($ mil.): 172

OREGON UNIVERSITY SYSTEM

Auditors: CLIFTONLARSONALLEN LLP GREENW

LOCATIONS

HQ: OREGON UNIVERSITY SYSTEM
, EUGENE, OR 97403
Phone: 541 737-0827
Web: WWW.OUS.EDU

Company Type: Private

Income Statement				FYE: June 30
	REVENUE ($ mil.)	NET INCOME ($ mil.)	NET PROFIT MARGIN	EMPLOYEES
06/14	1,782	83	4.7%	26,000
06/13	1,701	14	0.8%	—
06/12	1,657	10	0.6%	—
06/08	1,251	80	6.4%	—
Annual Growth	6.1%	0.6%	—	—

2014 Year-End Financials

Return on assets: 9.8% Cash ($ mil.): 456
Return on equity: 4.7%
Current ratio: 1.30

ORLANDO HEALTH, INC.

Orlando Health Orlando Health is a not-for-profit healthcare organization with $7.6 billion of assets under management that serves the southeastern US. It has about 3200 beds that includes some15 wholly-owned hospitals and emergency departments; rehabilitation services cancer institutes heart institutes physician offices for adults and pediatrics and more. Its flagship facility the Orlando Regional Medical Center is a Level 1 trauma center and provides comprehensive acute care services in a range of specialties. Orlando Health is also home to the only state-accredited Level 2 Adult Trauma Center in the St. Petersburg region at Bayfront Health St. Petersburg. Orlando Health Winnie Palmer Hospital for Women & Babies houses the nation's largest neonatal intensive care unit.

Operations

Diagnostic services include pathology and laboratory medicine radiology and diagnostic imaging and nuclear medicine with an array of invasive and noninvasive testing such as angiography bone density scan CT scan mammography MRI ultrasound and X-ray.

In addition to diagnostic services Orlando Health provide a comprehensive range of outpatient medical services in an environment that offers more convenience and less stress for its patients and families. Outpatient services include advanced catheterization surgical and endoscopic procedures neurodiagnostics cardiology wound care and rehabilitation therapy.

Orlando Health hospitals are Bayfront Health St. Petersburg Orlando Health Arnold Palmer Hospital for Children Orlando Health Dr. P. Phillips Hospital Orlando Health ? Health Central Hospital Orlando Health Horizon West Hospital Orlando Health Orlando Regional Medical Center; Orlando Health South Lake Hospital; Orlando Health South Seminole Hospital Orlando Health St. Cloud Hospital and Orlando Health Winnie Palmer Hospital for Women & Babies.

Orlando Health operates the National Training Center for Olympic athletes and the Orlando Health Network which is recognized as one of the largest and highest performing clinically integrated networks in the region. The system's Graduate Medical Education (GME) program hosts more than 350 residents and fellows including more than 40 who are enrolled at Bayfront Health St. Petersburg.

Geographic Reach

Based in Orlando Florida Orlando Health has eight primary facility locations within Central Florida.

Sales and Marketing

Orlando Health served nearly 160000 inpatients and nearly 3.6 million outpatients.

Mergers and Acquisitions

In 2021 Orlando Health acquires Leesburg-based FHV health for undisclosed price. The multispecialty medical group has 19 physicians and 10 locations including primary care cardiology practices and urgent care facilities in Lake Sumton Marion counties. The acquisition will expand its presence in those three counties and advance FHV Health's ability.

Company Background

In 2012 Arnold Palmer Hospital added an outpatient rehabilitation center.

The health system expanded its network in 2012 by acquiring the 170-bed Health Central Hospital and its associated facilities in Ocoee Florida for $181 million. Orlando Health further expanded through the purchase of Physician Associates a professional practice organization in 2013.

Orlando Health was founded in 1918.

EXECUTIVES

Ceo, David Strong
Cfo, Bernadette Spong
Coo, Jamal Hakim
Sr V Pres, Mildred Beam
Information Consultant, Yaira Nicolet
Physician, Clark Davenport
Network Administrator, Dale Houser
Doctor, Dean Johnston
Him Operations Manager, Dean Ritchey
Physician, Deepak Vivek
Biomedical Engineer, Diana Savickas
Auditors: GRANT THORNTON LLP ORLANDO F

LOCATIONS

HQ: ORLANDO HEALTH, INC.
52 W UNDERWOOD ST, ORLANDO, FL 328061110
Phone: 407 841-5111
Web: WWW.ORLANDOHEALTH.COM

PRODUCTS/OPERATIONS

2014 Sales

	$ mil.	% of total
Net patient service revenue less provision for bad debts	2,010	95
Other revenue	103	5
Net assets released from restrictions	4	.
Total	**2,118**	**100**

Selected Facilities

Arnold Palmer Hospital for Children (Orlando)
Dr. P. Phillips Hospital (formerly Orlando Regional Sand Lake Hospital Orlando)
Health Central Hospital (Ocoee)
Lucerne Pavilion (Orlando)
M. D. Anderson Cancer Center Orlando
Orlando Health Heart Institute
Orlando Health Rehabilitation Institute
Orlando Regional Medical Center
South Lake Hospital (50% affiliate Clermont)
South Seminole Hospital (Longwood)
St. Cloud Regional Medical Center (20% affiliate)
Winnie Palmer Hospital for Women & Babies (Orlando)

Selected Specialties

Cancer care (at M. D. Anderson Cancer Center Orlando)
Emergency and trauma care
Heart and vascular
Neurosciences
Oncology/hematology
Orthopedic and sports medicine
Surgery
Women's services

Selected Services

Anesthesiology
Brain Injury Rehabilitation Center (BIRC)
Endocrinology (diabetes)
Endoscopy
Epilepsy care
Home health care
Infectious diseases
Internal medicine
Laboratory and pathology Services
Mammography
Memory Disorder Center
MRI
Multiple sclerosis treatment
Nephrology
Nuclear medicine
Ophthalmology
Otolaryngology (Ears Nose Throat)
Pain management
Patient and family counseling
Pediatric outpatient surgery
Pulmonary medicine
Radiology and diagnostic imaging
Rehabilitation and physical therapy

COMPETITORS

Adventist Health System Sunbelt Healthcare
All Children's Hospital
Baptist Health South Florida
Baptist Health System
Community Health Systems
Florida Hospital Heartland
Florida Hospital Waterman
Hca
Health First
Holmes Regional Medical Center
Mayo Clinic Jacksonville
Mount Sinai Medical Center Of Florida
Munroe Regional Health System
Nemours Foundation
Ocala Regional Medical Center
Osceola Regional Medical Center
St. Vincent's Health System
Uf&shands

HISTORICAL FINANCIALS

Company Type: Private

Income Statement				FYE: September 30
	REVENUE ($ mil.)	NET INCOME ($ mil.)	NET PROFIT MARGIN	EMPLOYEES
09/19	2,756	508	18.5%	23,000
09/14	1,663	231	13.9%	—
09/13	1,576	115	7.3%	—
09/10	1,700	91	5.4%	—
Annual Growth	5.5%	21.0%	—	—

2019 Year-End Financials

Return on assets: 11.4% Cash ($ mil.): 438
Return on equity: 20.3%
Current ratio: 0.50

ORLEANS PARISH SCHOOL DISTRICT

EXECUTIVES

Supt, Stanley Smith
Ceo-Supt*, Alphonse G Davis
Coo*, Roger Reese
Principal, Victor Gordon
Security Officer, Jade Fisher
Auditors: LA PORTE METAIRIE LA

LOCATIONS

HQ: ORLEANS PARISH SCHOOL DISTRICT
3520 GEN DE GAULLE STE 5, NEW ORLEANS, LA
70114
Phone: 504 304-3520
Web: WWW.FCWCS.ORG

HISTORICAL FINANCIALS

Company Type: Private

Income Statement   FYE: June 30

	REVENUE ($ mil.)	NET INCOME ($ mil.)	NET PROFIT MARGIN	EMPLOYEES
06/19	626	10	1.6%	7,062
06/17	433	(0)	—	—
06/16	473	46	9.8%	—
06/05	419	19	4.7%	—
Annual Growth	2.9%	(4.7%)	—	—

2019 Year-End Financials

Return on assets: 0.5%   Cash ($ mil.): 33
Return on equity: 0.6%
Current ratio: —

OSF HEALTHCARE SYSTEM

OSF Healthcare helps patients who are feeling oh-so-frail in northern Illinois and southwestern Michigan. OSF Healthcare system includes 11 acute care hospitals and one long-term care facility that combined are home to more than 1500 beds and offer a full spectrum of inpatient and outpatient medical and surgical services. The system's primary care physician network consists of about 650 physicians at more than 105 locations throughout its service area. Subsidiary OSF Home Care provides hospice home visit and equipment services and OSF Saint Francis provides ambulance pharmacy and health care management services. The not-for-profit system is a subsidiary of the Sisters of The Third Order of St. Francis.

Operations

Along with its various acute care hospitals OSF Healthcare provides urgent care through its OSF PromptCare locations. PromptCare administers a range of services including labs MRI ultrasound and primary and specialty care.

The company also has two colleges of nursing — Saint Francis Medical Center College of Nursing in Peoria Illinois; and the Saint Anthony College of Nursing in Rockford Illinois.

The system had some 58000 inpatient admissions; 1.3 million outpatient visits; and 254000 emergency department visits in 2014.

Financial Performance

In 2014 gross patient services revenue totaled $6.9 billion.

Strategy

OSF Healthcare has an incubation collaboration with the University of Illinois College of Medicine at Peoria. The venture dubbed Jump Trading Simulation and Education Center was established in 2013 to focus on advances in education research and innovation. It has been involved in such activities as funding 3-D printing for surgical procedures and exposing high school students to medical training experiences.

EXECUTIVES

Ceo, Robert Sehring
Cmo*, Harley Brooks
Ceo Northern Region, Carol Friesen
Consultant, Dick Brooks
Executive Officer, Judith Duva
Staff, Marc Matulis
Corporate Office Site Director, Mike Redd
Executive Officer, Ruth Clift
Senior Vice President, Robert Sawicki
Auditors: KPMG LLP CHICAGO ILLINOIS

LOCATIONS

HQ: OSF HEALTHCARE SYSTEM
800 NE GLEN OAK AVE, PEORIA, IL 616033200
Phone: 309 655-2850
Web: WWW.OSFHEALTHCARE.ORG

PRODUCTS/OPERATIONS

Selected Clinical Services

Cancer Care
Diabetes & Endocrinology
Emergency Services
Heart & Vascular
Home Health
Hospice
Neurosciences
Pediatrics
Primary Care
Rehabilitation
Surgery
Transplant Services
Weight Loss Management
Women's Health

Selected Support Services

Advance Care Planning
Clinical Research
Equipment Technology Services
Home Infusion Pharmacy
Home Medical Equipment
Mobile Medical Systems
OSF Life Flight
Retail Services
Skilled Nursing Network
System Laboratory
Telehealth

Selected Facilities

OSF Holy Family Medical Center (Monmouth IL)
OSF Saint Anthony Medical Center (Rockford IL)
OSF Saint Clare Home (Peoria Heights IL)
OSF Saint Elizabeth Medical Center (formerly Ottawa Regional Hospital Ottowa IL)
OSF Saint Francis Medical Center (Peoria IL)
OSF Saint James - John W. Albrecht Medical Center (Pontiac IL)
OSF St. Mary Medical Center (Galesburg IL)
OSF St. Francis Hospital (Escanaba MI)
OSF St. Joseph Medical Center (Bloomington IL)

COMPETITORS

Advocate Bromenn	Rush-copley Medical
Centegra Health System	Center
Central Dupage	Swedishamerican Health
Hospital	System
Covenant Healthcare	University Of Chicago
Genesis Health System	Medical Center
Mcdonough District	University Of Michigan
Hospital	Health System
Memorial Health System	Wheaton Franciscan
Northwestern Memorial	Services
Healthcare	

HISTORICAL FINANCIALS

Company Type: Private

Income Statement   FYE: September 30

	REVENUE ($ mil.)	NET INCOME ($ mil.)	NET PROFIT MARGIN	EMPLOYEES
09/19	2,622	354	13.5%	4,360
09/18	2,826	155	5.5%	—
09/17	2,561	144	5.7%	—
09/16	2,422	99	4.1%	—
Annual Growth	2.7%	52.9%	—	—

2019 Year-End Financials

Return on assets: 9.3%   Cash ($ mil.): 136
Return on equity: 24.2%
Current ratio: 2.50

OU MEDICINE, INC.

EXECUTIVES

Prin, Steven Davis
Prin, Amy Sine
Prin, Armand Paliota
Vice President, Renee Landry
Manager, Chris Wallace
Administrator, Joel Peebles
Manager, Kristian Brown
Information Technology Directo, Jobi Stitt
Customer Care Associate, Aimee Kelso
Recruiter, Brittany Kooyman
Chief Legal Counsel, Christy Hendricks
Auditors: ERNST & YOUNG LLP OKLAHOMA C

LOCATIONS

HQ: OU MEDICINE, INC.
700 NE 13TH ST, OKLAHOMA CITY, OK 731045004
Phone: 405 271-6035
Web: WWW.OUHEALTH.COM

HISTORICAL FINANCIALS

Company Type: Private

Income Statement   FYE: June 30

	REVENUE ($ mil.)	NET INCOME ($ mil.)	NET PROFIT MARGIN	EMPLOYEES
06/21	1,415	(27)	—	2,900
06/20	1,298	48	3.7%	—
06/19	1,213	12	1.0%	—
Annual Growth	8.0%	—	—	—

2021 Year-End Financials

Return on assets: (-1.4%)   Cash ($ mil.): 277
Return on equity: (-12.4%)
Current ratio: 2.00

OUR LADY OF THE LAKE HOSPITAL, INC.

Our Lady of the Lake Regional Medical Center reaches out to Baton Rouge residents with a helping hand. Participating in teaching programs for LSU and Tulane medical schools the medical center has some 800 inpatient beds and includes trauma emergency surgery general medical and specialty care centers for conditions including heart disease cancer orthopedics and ENT (ear nose and throat) disorders. Our Lady of the Lake also includes a Children's Hospital two nursing homes and an independent-living facility and it offers outpatient services at its main campus and at satellite facilities throughout the greater Baton Rouge area.

Operations

The hospital's family of services include an 800-bed Regional Medical Center; a dedicated Children's Hospital; a 350-provider Physician Group primary care network free-standing emergency room in Livingston Parish; an outpatient imaging and surgery centers; Assumption Community Hospital; a network of urgent care clinics; and Our Lady of the Lake College.

Our Lady of the Lake is a primary teaching site for graduate medical education programs and serves 45000 inpatients and 350000 outpatients a year.

The company has more than 850 doctors. Some 70% of its physicians and other professional medical staff members are board certified and in nearly one-third of the hospital system's medical specialty areas 100% of the physicians and other professionals are board certified.

Strategy

As a major facility in the Baton Rouge area Our Lady of the Lake has been expanding its services in the region in recent years. In 2015 Our Lady of the Lake Children's Hospital opened its first pediatric specialty clinic outside of the Baton Rouge area offering specialized outpatient care for pediatric gastroenterology patients.

In 2014 the company opened a new children's emergency room and expanded its adult emergency department.

Company Background

In 2012 the hospital constructed a freestanding emergency room facility in the suburban community of Livingston Louisiana. It is also building a new nine-story patient tower to the main hospital campus; the tower will house the heart and vascular center as well as an expanded ER and a new level 1 regional trauma center and will be completed in late 2013.

Our Lady of the Lake has also expanded its education programs. For instance it added a pediatric residency program in 2010. The hospital also moved to extend its relationship with LSU that year by agreeing to become the primary clinical site for the LSU medical school. The agreement came as LSU considered whether to build a replacement hospital for its aging teaching facility and coincides with the Our Lady of the Lake expansion projects. The partnership launched a new psychiatric residency program in 2012.

Our Lady of the Lake was founded in 1923 by the Franciscan Missionaries of Our Lady.

EXECUTIVES

Ceo-Pres, K Scott Wester
Chb, Charles Valluzzo
Staff, Griffith R Bryan Jr
Director Surgical, Pedrina Blouin
Associate Program Director, Amy Wood
Program Coordinator, Tiffany Johnson
Physician, Joseph Laughlin
Doctor, Roberta Vicari
MD, James E Craven

LOCATIONS

HQ: OUR LADY OF THE LAKE HOSPITAL, INC.
7777 HENNESSY BLVD, BATON ROUGE, LA
708084300
Phone: 225 765-6565
Web: WWW.FOUNDATION.OLOLRMC.COM

PRODUCTS/OPERATIONS

Selected Services

Advanced Wound and Ostomy Clinic
Cancer
Children's Hospital
Critical Care
Diabetes & Nutrition Center
Emergency Services
Endoscopy Center
Hearing and Balance Center
Heart & Vascular Institute
Imaging Services
Laboratory and Diagnostics
Lake Express Check-In
LSU Health Baton Rouge
Mental and Behavioral Health
Neurology Neurosurgery and Stroke
Orthopedics
Palliative Care
Pharmacy
Rehabilitation Center
Respiratory Care
Senior Services
St. Anthony's Home
Surgery
Trauma Center
Urgent Care
Voice Center
Weight Loss

COMPETITORS

Christus St. Frances	Our Lady Of Lourdes
Cabrini Hospital	River Parishes
Dynacq Healthcare	Hospital
General Health System	Woman's Hospital
Lane Regional Medical	
Center	

HISTORICAL FINANCIALS
Company Type: Private

Income Statement				FYE: June 30
	REVENUE ($ mil.)	NET INCOME ($ mil.)	NET PROFIT MARGIN	EMPLOYEES
06/20	1,526	(18)	—	1,800
06/19	1,467	33	2.3%	—
06/18	1,254	103	8.2%	—
06/16	895	(89)	—	—
Annual Growth	14.3%	—	—	—

2020 Year-End Financials

Return on assets: (-0.7%)   Cash ($ mil.): 383
Return on equity: (-1.6%)
Current ratio: 1.90

OVERLAKE HOSPITAL ASSOCIATION

EXECUTIVES

Prin, Diane Sperry
Coordinator, Lisa Sato
Nurse Manager, Jody Burnell
Coordinator, Jennifer Fischer
Registered Nurse, Anastasia Samsonov
Admitting Manager, Jill Salsbury
Therapist, Svetlana Young
Senior Analyst, Caroline Curtis
Nurse Manager, Carolyn Holmes
Director, Edward Chun
Social Worker, Janice Noble
Auditors: KPMG LLP SEATTLE WA

LOCATIONS

HQ: OVERLAKE HOSPITAL ASSOCIATION
1035 116TH AVE NE, BELLEVUE, WA 980044604
Phone: 425 688-5000
Web: WWW.OVERLAKEHOSPITAL.ORG

HISTORICAL FINANCIALS
Company Type: Private

Income Statement				FYE: June 30
	REVENUE ($ mil.)	NET INCOME ($ mil.)	NET PROFIT MARGIN	EMPLOYEES
06/21	607	91	15.1%	95
06/20	579	(0)	—	—
06/19	574	48	8.4%	—
06/18	559	41	7.4%	—
Annual Growth	2.8%	30.1%	—	—

2021 Year-End Financials

Return on assets: 7.7%   Cash ($ mil.): 25
Return on equity: 13.0%
Current ratio: 1.00

OVERLAKE HOSPITAL MEDICAL CENTER

Over the lake and through the sound to Overlake Hospital Medical Center we go! The not-for-profit hospital provides health care services to residents of Bellevue Washington in the Puget Sound region. The nearly 350-bed facility provides comprehensive inpatient and outpatient services ranging from cancer care and surgery to specialized senior care. Overlake also operates a number of outpatient clinics providing primary care urgent care and specialty care such as weight loss surgery. The organization also provides patients with health and wellness programs addressing issues like women's and children's health.

Operations

The medical center has more than 1000 physicians on staff and runs Centers of Excellence in cardiac care cancer care surgical services women's and infants' care and emergency and Level III trauma care. The facility is home to a 24-hour urgent care clinic an anticoagulation clinic and a breast screening center. Overlake also operates numerous outpatient clinics providing primary care urgent care and specialty care.

Geographic Reach

Overlake provides health care services to residents of Bellevue Washington and the entire Puget Sound region. It operates clinics on its main campus in Bellevue as well as in Redmond and in Issaquah and on Mercer Island.

Sales and Marketing

In 2014 Medicare payments accounted for 27% of net patient revenues followed by group health organizations (17%) Premera (13%) and Regence (12%).

Financial Performance

Overlake's revenues increased by 2% to $433 million in 2014 as the result of higher net patient revenues and contribution revenues.

Net income rose 50% to $60 million that year primarily due to income from change in net unrealized gains on investments. Cash flow from operations fell 3% to $47 million as more cash was used in net clinic accounts receivable pledges receivable prepaid expenses and other long-term receivables.

Strategy

Increasing demand in the region has led the hospital to invest in expansions and equipment upgrades that include more emergency treatment capabilities and an on-campus helistop for trauma patients being airlifted to the area.

Along with its expansion and construction projects Overlake is investing in new technology to keep the health system in line with its competitors and to improve patient care. It is adding endoscopic video towers to its operating rooms to facilitate improved views of surgical procedures and is also moving to digitize all of its facilities with electronic health records.

In 2013 it opened the new $17.4 million David and Shelley Hovind Heart & Vascular center. The new 19200-sq.-ft. facility brings cardiac and vascular services together in one location.

Overlake has also focused on adding new primary care clinics and expanding its physician network to serve patients in locations closer to where they live and work.

Company Background

Overlake founded in 1960 is led by CEO Craig Hendrickson a veteran health care executive.

EXECUTIVES

Prin, Gregory Collins
Physician, IB Odderson
Network Manager, Charles Jackson
Director Surgical Nurs, Christina Armstrong
Plastic Surgeon, Christine Nygaard
Executive Vice President, David Schultz
Principle, Kalle Kang
Plastic Surgeon, Kimberly Lu
Plastic Surgeon, Marshall Partington
Executive Assistant, Colleen White
Ophthalmologist, James J McMillan
Auditors: KPMG LLP SEATTLE WA

LOCATIONS

HQ: OVERLAKE HOSPITAL MEDICAL CENTER
1035 116TH AVE NE, BELLEVUE, WA 980044687
Phone: 425 688-5000
Web: WWW.OVERLAKEHOSPITAL.ORG

Selected Locations

Outpatient Rehabilitation Services
Outpatient Surgery (park in the West Garage; Outpatient Surgery is located on the first floor of the West Garage.)
Overlake Bellevue Campus and Overlake Medical Clinics Medical Tower
Overlake Medical Clinics Downtown Bellevue
Overlake Medical Clinics Issaquah
Overlake Medical Clinics Kirkland
Overlake Medical Clinics Redmond
Urgent Care Clinic in Issaquah
Urgent Care Clinic in Redmond

PRODUCTS/OPERATIONS

2014 Sales

	$ mil.	% of total
Net patient service revenue	419	97
Other operating revenue	11	3
Contribution revenue	2	—
Total	**433**	**100**

Selected Medical Services

Breast Health Services
Cancer Center at Overlake
Cardiac Center at Overlake
Clinical Trials
Emergency & Trauma Center
Medical Imaging
Overlake Medical Clinics
Surgical Services
Weight Loss Surgery
Women's & Infants' Center

COMPETITORS

Catholic Health Initiatives	Providence St. Joseph Health
Franciscan Health System	Seattle Children's Hospital
Harrison Medical Center	Swedish Health Services
Kaiser Permanente Wa	University Of Washington
Multicare Health System	Yakima Valley Memorial
Peacehealth	

HISTORICAL FINANCIALS

Company Type: Private

Income Statement   FYE: June 30

	REVENUE ($ mil.)	NET INCOME ($ mil.)	NET PROFIT MARGIN	EMPLOYEES
06/21	601	86	14.4%	2,450
06/20	574	(3)	—	—
06/19	570	45	8.0%	—
06/18	555	39	7.1%	—
Annual Growth	**2.7%**	**30.1%**	**—**	**—**

2021 Year-End Financials

Return on assets: 7.5%   Cash ($ mil.): 22
Return on equity: 12.8%
Current ratio: 1.00

PACE UNIVERSITY

Students can learn at their own pace at Pace University which offers certificate programs as well as undergraduate graduate and doctoral degrees through half a dozen schools: arts and sciences business computer science and information systems education law and nursing. Altogether the school is home to 100 undergraduate majors offering roughly 30 undergraduate and graduate degrees 50 master's programs and four doctoral programs. Nearly 13000 students attend the university's three New York campuses (Lower Manhattan Pleasantville-Briarcliff and White Plains). Pace was founded in 1906 by the brothers Homer and Charles Pace as a co-educational business school called Pace Institute.

Operations

The school has an endowment of more than $100 million. Besides its three New York campuses the university also offers courses online and at a location in midtown Manhattan.

Geographic Reach

Pace boasts campus locations in New York City and in Westchester County.

Financial Performance

The university logged a 3% increase in revenue in 2012 as compared to 2011 due to a boost in contributions as well as tuition and fees net government grants and contracts. Net income meanwhile dropped by 160% during the same reporting period thanks to rises in expenses and unrealized depreciation in fair value of derivative instruments in 2012 vs. appreciation in 2011.

Company Background

In 1948 Pace began its transformation into its current incarnation as a liberal arts and sciences college.

EXECUTIVES

Pres, Stephen J Friedman
Chb*, Rob Sands
SEC-Legal Counsel*, Stephen Brodsky
Cfo*, Robert C Almon

Cfo*, Toby Weiner
Chief Diversity Officer*, Tiffany Hamilton
Programmer, Sarah Shamilov
Analyst, Stephen Salbod
Dean, Pforzheimer Honors Colle, Susan Dinan
Dean of Admissions, Todd E Heilman
Coordinator, Whitney Brown
Auditors: KPMG LLP NEW YORK NY

LOCATIONS

HQ: PACE UNIVERSITY
1 PACE PLZ, NEW YORK, NY 100381598
Phone: 212 346-1956
Web: WWW.PACE.EDU

HISTORICAL FINANCIALS

Company Type: Private

Income Statement   FYE: June 30

	REVENUE ($ mil.)	NET INCOME ($ mil.)	NET PROFIT MARGIN	EMPLOYEES
06/20	597	14	2.5%	1,862
06/16	393	14	3.7%	—
06/14	492	26	5.4%	—
06/13	326	20	6.2%	—
Annual Growth	**9.0%**	**(4.4%)**	**—**	**—**

2020 Year-End Financials

Return on assets: 2.1%   Cash ($ mil.): 22
Return on equity: 4.7%
Current ratio: 0.20

PACIFIC COAST PRODUCERS

Fruits seafood sauces and organic tomato puree — rather than movies — are the creative output of this particular group of Pacific Coast Producers. The cooperative markets the apricots grapes peaches pears and tomatoes grown by its approximately 160 California-based members. It turns the produce into private-label canned fruit sauces and juices and sells them to the retail and foodservice industries. Pacific Coast Producers typically serves retailers the likes of Albertson's Aldi Kroger Safeway SUPERVALU Whole Foods and Wal-Mart as well as the US Department of Agriculture. The company founded in 1971 operates three production sites and one distribution center in California.

Operations

The cooperative boasts three food-processing facilities in California as well as distribution centers in California and Washington.

Geographic Reach

From its base in Lodi California Pacific Coast Producers grows its fruits in California and sells them nationwide.

Sales and Marketing

Pacific Coast Producers sells the products it grows and processes to retailers and foodservice operators nationwide as well as to the US Department of Agriculture.

Financial Performance

As one of California's premier private label packers Pacific Coast Producers has logged annual sales in excess of $535 million plus $100 million in alliance income.

Strategy

Pacific Coast Producers has expanded its warehouse space in Lodi to improve efficiency and boost capacity. The move cost the company $23 million. It expanded its distribution center by 50% to meet rising demand for canned food.

The cooperative serves tomato processor Morning Star through a sales and marketing alliance it formed with the company in 2009. As part of the collaboration Pacific Coast Producers provides canned tomatoes to the retail and foodservice industries.

EXECUTIVES

Ceo, Daniel L Vincent
V Pres*, Peter C Wtulich
V Pres*, Andrew K Russick
V Pres*, Mona Shulman
Treas*, Zeb Rocha
Cfo*, Matthew Strong
Retail Sales Manager, Tami Gross
Human Resources Manager, Tara Bahtka
Information Security M, Jeannette Anderson
Administrative Assistant, Jean Roberts
Assistant Sales Manager, Ashley Ganas
Auditors: KPMG LLP SACRAMENTO CALIFORN

LOCATIONS

HQ: PACIFIC COAST PRODUCERS
  631 N CLUFF AVE, LODI, CA 952400756
Phone: 209 367-8800
Web: WWW.PACIFICCOASTPRODUCERS.COM

PRODUCTS/OPERATIONS

Selected Products

Apricots

Catsup
Chili Sauces
Chunky Mixed Fruit
Concentrated Crushed Tomatoes
Diced Style Tomatoes
Extra Heavy Concentrated Crushed Round Tomato Puree
Formulated Pizza Sauces
Fruit Cocktail
Fruit for Salad
Fruit Mix
Ground Tomatoes
Marinara Sauces
Non-Formulated Pizza Sauce
Organic Tomatoes
Peaches
Pears
Random Cut / Strip Style Tomatoes
Seafood Sauces
Stewed Style Tomatoes
Tomato Juice
Whole Peeled Tomatoes

COMPETITORS

Big Heart Pet Brands	Hain Celestial
Campbell Soup	Hanover Foods
Cento	Heinz
Conagra	Norpac
Dole Food	Pictsweet
General Mills	Seneca Foods
Glory Foods	

HISTORICAL FINANCIALS

Company Type: Private

Income Statement				FYE: May 31
	REVENUE ($ mil.)	NET INCOME ($ mil.)	NET PROFIT MARGIN	EMPLOYEES
05/21	864	47	5.5%	1,000
05/20	911	27	3.0%	—
05/19	806	14	1.8%	—
05/18	668	22	3.4%	—
Annual Growth	9.0%	27.5%	—	—

2021 Year-End Financials

Return on assets: 8.6%   Cash ($ mil.): 2
Return on equity: 17.7%
Current ratio: 1.80

PACIFIC PREMIER BANK

EXECUTIVES

Pres-Ceo, Steven R Gardner
Chb*, Jeff C Jones
Sr V Pres-Cfo*, Kent Smith
Sr Exec Vpres-Cfo*, Ronald J Nicolas Jr
Cro*, Michael Karr
Evp-Cco*, Donn Jakosky
Evp-Chief Acctg Officer*, Lori Wright
Senior Vice President Director, Thomas Galindo
Desk Manager, Robert Prater
Vp Information Technology, Dinorah Roggero
Credit Analyst, Carol Hiegl

LOCATIONS

HQ: PACIFIC PREMIER BANK
  17901 VON KARMAN AVE # 1, IRVINE, CA 926146297
Phone: 714 431-4000
Web: WWW.PPBI.COM

HISTORICAL FINANCIALS

Company Type: Private

Income Statement				FYE: December 31
	ASSETS ($ mil.)	NET INCOME ($ mil.)	INCOME AS % OF ASSETS	EMPLOYEES
12/17	8,022	68	0.9%	104
12/16	4,035	44	1.1%	—
12/15	2,782	29	1.1%	—
12/14	2,033	18	0.9%	—
Annual Growth	58.0%	54.0%	—	—

2017 Year-End Financials

Return on assets: 0.9%   Sales ($ mil): 298
Return on equity: 5.1%

PAN AMERICAN HEALTH ORGANIZATION INC

EXECUTIVES

Pres, Mirta Periago
Cfo, Esteban Alzamora
Information Specialist, Claudia Ortiz
Information Specialist, Douglas Alvarado
Coordinator, Farida Kerouani
Human Resources, Paul De La
Coordinator, Alessandra Senisse
Coordinator, Fatima W Marinho
Information Specialist, Manuel A Mijango
Marketing Manager, Eleana Villanueva
Director, Marcelo D'Agostino

LOCATIONS

HQ: PAN AMERICAN HEALTH ORGANIZATION INC
  525 23RD ST NW, WASHINGTON, DC 200372825
Phone: 202 974-3000
Web: WWW.PAHO.ORG

HISTORICAL FINANCIALS

Company Type: Private

Income Statement				FYE: December 31
	REVENUE ($ mil.)	NET INCOME ($ mil.)	NET PROFIT MARGIN	EMPLOYEES
12/09	1,268	101	8.0%	1,500
12/06	541	84	15.7%	—
Annual Growth	32.9%	6.2%	—	—

2009 Year-End Financials

Return on assets: 0.9%   Cash ($ mil.): 351
Return on equity: 8.0%
Current ratio: 14.00

PANDUIT CORP.

Panduit creates leading-edge physical electrical network infrastructure and AV solutions for enterprise-wide environments from the data center to the telecom room from the desktop to the plant floor. Products include cabling connectors copper wire fiber-optic components cabinets and racks grounding systems outlets terminals and other electrical components. Panduit's products are used in data centers office buildings single pair Ethernet wire harness and other settings. With approximately 2000 patents the privately held company also serves about 90% of the Fortune 100 companies.

Operations

Panduit provides infrastructure products and services for data networks and electrical power applications. Its industrial electrical and network infrastructure ensures smart scalable and efficient connectivity solutions. The company designs builds installs and services innovative solutions ranging from data centers and office facilities to plant floors and processing lines.

In addition to wire termination fiber optic systems power environmental security and connectivity hardware and wire routing management and protection Panduit also offers audio visual monitoring signs labels and identification among others.

With nearly 20 laboratories the company's world-class innovation center houses research design analysis prototyping testing and manufacturing capabilities that lead to smarter solutions.

Geographic Reach

Headquartered in Illinois Panduit operates across the US Canada Europe Middle East and Africa Latin America and Asia Pacific.

Sales and Marketing

Panduit serves customers in education healthcare oil and gas renewable energy transportation food and beverage and financial industries.

Strategy

In early 2021 as bandwidth speeds continue to increase 200G/400G applications are becoming commonplace in high performance data center environments requiring enhanced capabilities at the rack level. Panduit launched the CSConnector a high-density fiber connector solution that optimizes the data center for next generation applications. Its compact size enables breakout mode options and improves compute density for 25G-400G deployments. The CS Connector is available for unitary Singlemode and Multimode fiber options.

Around the same time Panduit Corp. signed a partner agreement with Cailabs a French deep tech company and global leader in light beam shaping for the global rights to integrate Cailabs technology within Panduit's innovative OneModeTM product portfolio. This is a far-reaching partnership that includes among other elements of the relationship exclusive use of the technology for the K-12 (kindergarten through 12th grade) education market in the United States.

Panduit's OneMode is a passive media converter allowing the deployment of 10 Gbps 50 Gbps and faster using existing multimode fibers by eliminating modal dispersion. This innovation provides a flexible and affordable solution that reduces the investment in upgrading the multimode cabling infrastructure. Regardless of the network topology OneMode can transport 10 Gbps or more and can support the evolution in network traffic without long complex and expensive new cable deployment. OneMode is attractive to the K-12 university healthcare enterprise industrial and other campus markets because they do not need to trench or rip and replace with new fiber to upgrade their network infrastructure.

Company Background

Panduit was established in 1955 by Jack Caveney Sr.Its first product was the Panduct Wiring Duct.

EXECUTIVES

Pres-Ceo, Dennis Renaud
V Pres*, Michael Kenny
Sr Analyst, Ed Piccirilli
Executive of Information Techn, Robert Saindon
Customer Staff, Brian Corse
Assistant Chief, Kevin Hoffmeyer
Staff, Vytas Vaitkus
Payroll Staff, Felicia Rangel
Territory Account Executive, Jeff Angus
Safety Manager, Kevin McHugh
Manufacturing Engineering Mana, Clark
Porterfield
Auditors: GRANT THORNTON

LOCATIONS

HQ: PANDUIT CORP.
18900 PANDUIT DR, TINLEY PARK, IL 604873600
Phone: 708 532-1800
Web: WWW.PANDUIT.COM

PRODUCTS/OPERATIONS

PRODUCTS
Cabinets Thermal Management Racks and Enclosures
Cable and Wire Bundling
Cable Routing and Pathways
Copper Systems
Fiber Systems
Grounding
Identification
Japan Market Only Products
Power Distribution and Environmental Monitoring
Product Promotions
Safety and Security
Software and Hardware
Tools
Wire Routing Protection and Insulation
Wire Termination
SOFTWARE/INTELLIGENCE
DCIM
6 Zone; Methodology
Data Center Management
Enterprise Management
Intelligent Hardware
Intelligent Software
SmartZone Overview
PROFESSIONAL SERVICES
Case Studies
Industrial Automation Services
Safety Services

COMPETITORS

Amphenol	Ortronics
Avaya	Rit Technologies
Commscope	Schneider Electric
Corning	Siemens Ag
Molex	Te Connectivity
Optical Cable	

HISTORICAL FINANCIALS

Company Type: Private

Income Statement — FYE: December 31

	REVENUE ($ mil.)	NET INCOME ($ mil.)	NET PROFIT MARGIN	EMPLOYEES
12/16	937	0	—	5,110
12/15	924	0	—	—
12/14	973	0	—	—
Annual Growth	(1.9%)	—	—	—

PAREXEL INTERNATIONAL CORPORATION

PAREXEL International is in the business of improving the world's health. From clinical trials to regulatory consulting and market access its therapeutic technical and functional ability is underpinned by a deep conviction in what it does. It is done through a suite of services that help life science and biopharmaceutical customers across the globe transform scientific discoveries into new treatments for patients. In 2021 PAREXEL completes separation of Parexel Informatics and Medical Imaging Business. As part of the separation Parexel Informatics will become Calyx.

Operations

Through its Clinical Development solutions Parexel offers a variety of clinical research services that bring together its global clinical and regulatory expertise with proprietary technologies.

Parexel's Regulatory & Access consulting organization includes around 100 former regulators and HTA assessors.

Parexel will continue to leverage Calyx's (formerly Integrated Technologies) Medical Imaging Clinical Trial Management Systems (CTMS) Electronic Data Capture (EDC) Interactive Response Technology (IRT) and Regulatory Information Management (RIM) solutions moving forward as part of the company's clinical development offerings.

Its outsourcing services includes Parexel Functional Service Provider (FSP) Model and Strategic Partnerships.

Parexel's other solutions are Medical and Scientific Services; and Real-World Evidence.

Geographic Reach

Headquartered near Boston Massachusetts and in Durham North Carolina Parexel has offices that support clients in over 100 countries around the world. It also has global study locations in Baltimore and Los Angeles as well as London and Berlin.

Financial Performance

After years of steady growth PAREXEL's revenue increased less than 1% to $2.4 billion in fiscal 2017 (ended June). Service revenues for the PC segment rose 11% thanks largely to the acquisition

of consulting firm Health Advances. The CRS and PI segments remained flat that year. Geographically revenues grew in the Americas and the Asia/Pacific region but fell 5% in EMEA.

As operating costs and expenses (including restructuring charges incurred as part of a corporate reorganization) increased net income fell 31% to $107.3 million in 2017. Cash flow from operations increased 17% to $306.4 million; this increase was due to factors including a decrease in accounts receivable and an increase in accounts payable.

Strategy

In early 2021 Parexel completed the separation of its Parexel Informatics and Medical Imaging business. The strategic move is designed to simplify and streamline Parexel's business strategy and customer relationships while best positioning both organizations for continued long-term growth and success. As part of the separation Parexel Informatics will become Calyx. Parexel will continue to leverage Calyx's Medical Imaging Clinical Trial Management Systems (CTMS) Electronic Data Capture (EDC) Interactive Response Technology (IRT) and Regulatory Information Management (RIM) solutions moving forward as part of the company's clinical development offerings. Calyx will be privately held by the same ownership group that has owned Parexel since 2017.

Mergers and Acquisitions

In early 2020 Model Answers a consultancy firm based in Brisbane Queensland Australia. The company's expertise and proven approach will enhance the operational scale and global footprint of Parexel's Clinical Pharmacology Modeling and Simulation offering to drive more informed and efficient drug development.

Company Background

Founders Josef von Rickenbach a health care and international products specialist and Anne Sayigh a chemist and regulatory affairs specialist started PAREXEL in 1982 to provide regulatory consulting services to pharmaceutical firms. Its name referred to 16th-century Swiss physician Theophrastus Bombastus von Hohenheim — better known as Paracelsus the father of empirical chemistry.

Through a series of acquisitions PAREXEL entered new markets including biostatistics and data management medical marketing and health consulting.

The company went public in 1995 and was taken private again in 2017.

HISTORY

Founders Josef von Rickenbach a health care and international products specialist and Anne Sayigh a chemist and regulatory affairs specialist started PAREXEL in 1982 to provide regulatory consulting services to pharmaceutical firms. Its name referred to 16th-century Swiss physician Theophrastus Bombastus von Hohenheim — better known as Paracelsus the father of empirical chemistry.

In 1988 PAREXEL bought Consulting Statisticians and moved into the biostatistics and data management market. The next year it went international with the purchase of the biostatistics and data management division of McDonnell Douglas Information Systems. In 1991 PAREXEL augmented its European operations with the acquisition of German contract researcher AFB Arzneimittelforschung — a move that paid off in rising sales.

PAREXEL went public in 1995. In the following two years it bought six health consulting firms including State and Federal Associates and medical marketing firm Rescon with the intention of boosting its ability to get its clients' products on the market. The company continued its acquisition spree in 1998; this time European marketing and research companies were on the shopping list. Competitor Covance was set to buy PAREXEL in 1999 then called off the deal when investors balked.

The company announced in 2000 that it would lay off more than 400 workers after Novartis cancelled a major contract. That year the company formed new alliances with such companies as NeuroRecovery Research Phenome Sciences and Prevention Concepts. PAREXEL also bought a full-service clinical pharmacology unit in the UK from GlaxoWellcome (now GlaxoSmithKline) as well as a majority stake in FARMOVS a clinical pharmacology research business and laboratory in South Africa.

In 2001 the company formed Perceptive Informatics a subsidiary focused on developing Internet-based information management systems. To strengthen its clinical trial management services PAREXEL bought software developer FW Pharma Systems in 2003. In 2006 it purchased US-based Behavioral and Medical Research LLC for $69 million to expand its research services.

EXECUTIVES

Ceo, Jamie Macdonald
Pres-Coo*, Mark A Goldberg
Sr V Pres-Cfo*, Simon Harford
Sr V Pres-Chief Hr Officer*, Michelle Graham
Sr V Pres-Cso*, Sy Pretorius
Sr V Pres-Gen Counsel-Sec*, Douglas A Batt
Evp-Cfo*, Greg Rush
Svp-Chief Hr Officer*, Michele Fournier
Associate Director of Technolo, Stephen Fogarasi
Executive Assistant, Tammy Musto
Director, Thomas Dougan
Auditors: ERNST & YOUNG LLP BOSTON MAS

LOCATIONS

HQ: PAREXEL INTERNATIONAL CORPORATION
275 GROVE ST STE 3101, AUBURNDALE, MA 024662281
Phone: 617 454-9300
Web: WWW.PAREXEL.COM

COMPETITORS

Albany Molecular Research
Bioclinica
Charles River Laboratories
Covance
Datatrak International
Icon
Inc Research
Iqvia
Pharmanet Development Group
Pharmaceutical Product Development
Research Pharmaceutical Services
Wuxi Pharmatech
Eresearchtechnology
Inventiv Health

HISTORICAL FINANCIALS
Company Type: Private

Income Statement				FYE: June 30
	REVENUE ($ mil.)	NET INCOME ($ mil.)	NET PROFIT MARGIN	EMPLOYEES
06/16	2,426	154	6.4%	18,900
06/15	2,330	147	6.3%	—
06/14	2,266	129	5.7%	—
Annual Growth	3.5%	9.5%	—	—

2016 Year-End Financials
Return on assets: 7.6% Cash ($ mil.): 248
Return on equity: 24.5%
Current ratio: 1.50

PARISH OF JEFFERSON

EXECUTIVES

Pres, Michael Yenni
Accounting Staff, Donna Richoux
Information Technology Divisio, Danielle Shirk
Acct Mgr, Clifford Smith Jr
Council Member District 5, Jennifer Van Vrancken
Fins Administrative Assistant, Kathleen Fradella
Personell Director, Kathy Frey
Assistant Finance Director, Kerry Schrieffer
Chief Financial Officer, Paul Rivera
Exec Director, Brenda Campos
Council Clerk, Karen Oseguera
Auditors: CARR RIGGS & INGRAM LLC MET

LOCATIONS

HQ: PARISH OF JEFFERSON
200 DERBIGNY ST, GRETNA, LA 700535850
Phone: 504 364-2600
Web: WWW.JEFFPARISH.NET

HISTORICAL FINANCIALS
Company Type: Private

Income Statement				FYE: December 31
	REVENUE ($ mil.)	NET INCOME ($ mil.)	NET PROFIT MARGIN	EMPLOYEES
12/20	641	111	17.3%	3,217
12/19	588	281	47.8%	—
12/18	561	(4)		—
12/17	561	146	26.1%	—
Annual Growth	4.5%	(8.8%)	—	—

2020 Year-End Financials
Return on assets: 2.7% Cash ($ mil.): 138
Return on equity: 4.6%
Current ratio: 13.40

PARK NICOLLET CLINIC

EXECUTIVES

Exec V Pres, David K Wessner
V Pres-Cfo*, William F Telleen
V Pres, Rodney R Dueck
Md- Ceo*, David Abelson
Chief Financial Officer, Sheila Mc Millan
Doctor, John A Reichert
Doctor, Monica Norwick
Doctor, Rachel Hub
Podiatrist, Stephanie Sanders
Doctor of Medicine, Eric Locher
Doctor of Medicine, Andrew Klein
Auditors: DELOITTE TAX LLP MINNEAPOLIS

LOCATIONS

HQ: PARK NICOLLET CLINIC
3800 PARK NICOLLET BLVD, MINNEAPOLIS, MN 554162527
Phone: 952 993-3123
Web: WWW.PARKNICOLLET.COM

HISTORICAL FINANCIALS
Company Type: Private

Income Statement				FYE: December 31
	REVENUE ($ mil.)	NET INCOME ($ mil.)	NET PROFIT MARGIN	EMPLOYEES
12/20	858	(24)	—	1,300
12/19	921	13	1.5%	—
Annual Growth	(6.8%)	—	—	—

2020 Year-End Financials
Return on assets: (-6.3%) Cash ($ mil.): —
Return on equity: (-10.3%)
Current ratio: 1.50

PARKLAND COMMUNITY HEALTH PLAN, INC., A PROGRAM OF DALLAS COUNTY HOSPITAL

EXECUTIVES

Ceo, Rob Smith
Director of Provider Relations, Patricia Carney
Executive Assistant, Kathy Rose
Auditors: BRUCE E BERNSTEIN & ASSOC PC

LOCATIONS

HQ: PARKLAND COMMUNITY HEALTH PLAN, INC., A PROGRAM OF DALLAS COUNTY HOSPITAL
1341 W MOCKINGBIRD LN 1150E, DALLAS, TX 752474974
Phone: 214 266-2100
Web: WWW.PARKLANDHOSPITAL.COM

HISTORICAL FINANCIALS
Company Type: Private

Income Statement				FYE: December 31
	REVENUE ($ mil.)	NET INCOME ($ mil.)	NET PROFIT MARGIN	EMPLOYEES
12/18	577	(9)	—	2
12/17	541	17	3.3%	—
12/15	527	(32)	—	—
12/13	519	27	5.2%	—
Annual Growth	2.1%	—	—	—

2018 Year-End Financials
Return on assets: (-6.4%) Cash ($ mil.): 138
Return on equity: (-10.7%)
Current ratio: 2.50

PARSONS ENVIRONMENT & INFRASTRUCTURE GROUP INC.

A unit of Parsons Corporation Parsons Commercial Technology Group (PARCOMM) provides project management engineering construction design maintenance and related services for industrial and commercial projects. The company's clients include firms in the telecommunications health care manufacturing defense petroleum and chemical industries. PARCOMM also completes projects for schools colleges and government entities. Specialized services include industrial environmental remediation factory modernization and developing state vehicle inspection and compliance programs. PARCOMM operates throughout the US and the world.

EXECUTIVES

Dir, George L Ball
SEC*, Clyde E Ellis Jr
Cfo*, Leslie Bradley
Energy Infrastructure Sector, Paul Gallagher
Chief Corporate Affairs Office, Virginia Grebbien

LOCATIONS

HQ: PARSONS ENVIRONMENT & INFRASTRUCTURE GROUP INC.
  4701 HEDGEMORE DR, CHARLOTTE, NC 282093281
Phone: 704 529-6246
Web: WWW.PARSONS.COM

COMPETITORS

Bechtel   Halliburton
Fluor   Jacobs Engineering

HISTORICAL FINANCIALS

Company Type: Private

Income Statement   FYE: July 29

	REVENUE ($ mil.)	NET INCOME ($ mil.)	NET PROFIT MARGIN	EMPLOYEES
07/14*	684	(12)	—	1,205
12/12	684	(12)	—	
12/11	443	(57)	—	
Annual Growth 15.6%		—	—	—

*Fiscal year change

2014 Year-End Financials

Return on assets: (-1.9%)   Cash ($ mil.): 24
Return on equity: (-3.1%)
Current ratio: 1.30

PASADENA HOSPITAL ASSOCIATION, LTD.

No need to hunt for medical care if you're near Huntington Hospital. The not-for-profit Pasadena Hospital Association which does business as Huntington Hospital provides health care to residents of the San Gabriel Valley in Southern California. The hospital boasts some 625 beds and offers acute medical and surgical care and community services in a number of specialties including cardiology gastroenterology women's and children's health orthopedics and neurology. It engages in clinical cancer research (as well as diagnosis and treatment) through the Huntington Cancer Center. The hospital is also a teaching facility for the University of Southern California (USC) Keck School of Medicine.

Operations

As part of its operations the California hospital runs The Stroke Center Heart and Vascular Center Huntington Hospital Cancer Center Regional Neonatal Intensive Care Unit Prenatal High Risk Unit and Pediatric Intensive Care Unit. The hospital is the only level II trauma center and level III NICU in the San Gabriel Valley.

Through its partnership with USC Huntington Hospital offers graduate medical education in areas such as general surgery and internal medicine. Its Huntington Cancer Center partners with area physicians (including some affiliated with USC and UCLA) and the City of Hope medical center to provide comprehensive oncology services and research potential new cancer treatments.

The hospital has 900 physicians and more than 1200 nurses. In 2013 it had about 26000 inpatient admissions more than 216000 outpatient visits and helped deliver more than 3300 babies. Huntington Hospital provided a $92.9 million in community benefits that year.

Geographic Reach

Huntington Hospital serves the health care needs of those who reside in and around Southern California's San Gabriel Valley.

Sales and Marketing

The medical center is working to upgrade its information technology systems including the addition of an electronic health record (EHR) system.

Financial Performance

Huntington Hospital's revenues rose by 3% in 2013 thanks to an increase in patient services and revenues.

The hospital recorded a net loss of $10 million that year due to higher expenses (including salaries employees benefits and other costs).

Strategy

The company is pursuing infrastructure and services expansion and innovation to keep up with demand.

In 2014 Huntington Hospital collaborated with Anthem Blue Cross and six of its fellow leading hospitals in Los Angeles and Orange counties to form Anthem Blue Cross Vivity a new insurance entity.

In 2013 the hospital signed a deal with Shriners Hospitals for Children- Southern California to provide inpatient surgical services for its pediatric patients.

Huntington Hospital completed renovating its existing emergency facility in 2013. The project to increase patient capacity up to 80000 and increase diagnostic facilities came about in response to growing levels of ER visits.

Company Background

Huntington Hospital broke ground several years ago on an $80-million expansion effort to double the size of its emergency department. The project has included building a new portion that was completed in 2012.

Upgrading its technology to increase efficiency in 2012 Huntington Hospital launched a multi-year project to replace and upgrade its computer information system with new system (Huntington Access Network Knowledge) to manage the hospital's clinical and financial software.

In a medical innovation in 2012 the hospital became the first hospital in Southern California to offer an Ekso Bionics' technology enabling patients with lower-extremity paralysis or weakness to stand and walk.

Huntington Hospital was founded in 1892.

EXECUTIVES

Ceo, Lori J Morgan
Chm*, Lois Matthews
Ceo-Pres*, Stephen A Ralph
Exec V Pres*, Jim Noble
Sr V Pres*, Jane Haderlein
Sr V Pres*, Paula Verrette
Sr V Pres*, Bonnie Kass
Chb*, Paul Ouyang
Treas*, Leonard M Marangi
Sr V Pres-Cfo*, Steven L Mohr
Executive Officer, John Mangoni
Auditors: ERNST & YOUNG US LLP IRVINE

LOCATIONS

HQ: PASADENA HOSPITAL ASSOCIATION, LTD.
  100 W CALIFORNIA BLVD, PASADENA, CA 911053010
Phone: 626 397-5000
Web: WWW.HUNTINGTONHOSPITAL.ORG

PRODUCTS/OPERATIONS

Selected Services

Ambulatory Care/Dispensary
Angiography
Anticoagulation Clinic
Asthma Education and Management
Bariatric Surgery
Breast Cancer Program
Cardiac Catheterization Lab
Cardiac Electrophysiology (EP)
Cardiac Rehabilitation
Cardiac Screening and Diagnostics
Cardiothoracic Surgery
Community Outreach
CT Scanning (Type 2) Diabetes Prevention and Management
Epilepsy and Brain Mapping
Gastroenterology
Genetic Counseling
Geriatric Assessment Clinic
Gynecological Cancer Program
Heart and Vascular Services
Neurophysiology
Neuroradiology
Neurosciences
Neurosurgery
Obstetrics
Orthopedics
Ostomy Clinic
Pediatric Obesity Prevention
Prenatal High Risk Unit
Prostate Cancer Program
Radiation Oncology
Urology
Uterine Artery Embolization (UAE)

COMPETITORS

Adventist Health   Dignity Health
  System West   Glendale Adventist
Cedars-sinai Medical   Medical Center
  Center   Memorial Health
Citrus Valley Health   Services
  Partners   Tenet Healthcare

HISTORICAL FINANCIALS

Company Type: Private

Income Statement   FYE: December 31

	REVENUE ($ mil.)	NET INCOME ($ mil.)	NET PROFIT MARGIN	EMPLOYEES
12/16	695	8	1.2%	2,800
12/15	593	0	0.0%	
Annual Growth 17.2%	3278.7%		—	—

2016 Year-End Financials
Return on assets: 0.9% Cash ($ mil.): 12
Return on equity: 1.5%
Current ratio: 0.60

PASADENA INDEPENDENT SCHOOL DISTRICT

EXECUTIVES

Pres, Mariselle Quijano-Lerma
Supt*, Dr Kirk Lewis
V Pres*, Vickie Morgan
SEC*, Fred Roberts
Pomeroy Secretary, Mayra Rodriguez
Teacher, Melinda Connolly
Executive Director of Grants, Olivia Smith-Daugherty
Finance Executive, Patty Huffman
Teacher, Annie Sargent
Chief Financial Officer, Carla Merka
Cte Director, Sarah Wrobleski
Auditors: WHITLEY PENN HOUSTON TEXAS

LOCATIONS

HQ: PASADENA INDEPENDENT SCHOOL DISTRICT
1515 CHERRYBROOK LN, PASADENA, TX 775024099
Phone: 713 740-0000
Web: WWW.PASADENAISD.ORG

HISTORICAL FINANCIALS
Company Type: Private

Income Statement				FYE: August 31
	REVENUE ($ mil.)	NET INCOME ($ mil.)	NET PROFIT MARGIN	EMPLOYEES
08/20	660	(29)	—	5,000
08/19	696	30	4.3%	—
08/18	680	99	14.7%	—
08/17	606	(93)	—	—
Annual Growth	2.8%	—	—	—

PATERSON PUBLIC SCHOOL DISTRICT

EXECUTIVES

Supt, Jacqueline Jones
Supt*, Donnie W Evans
Vice Paterson Public, Cosmo Braico
Supervisor, Karen Bernard
Accounting, Kennia Fulgencio
Teacher Nurse, Marie Simeus
Assistant, Ronnie Estrict
School Social Worker, Roseann Brizan
Secretary Administrative, Tairis Colon
Office Manager, Andrea Sierra
Educator, Cecilia Frederick-Otool
Auditors: LERCH VINCI & HIGGINS LLP F

LOCATIONS

HQ: PATERSON PUBLIC SCHOOL DISTRICT
90 DELAWARE AVE, PATERSON, NJ 075031804
Phone: 973 321-0980

HISTORICAL FINANCIALS
Company Type: Private

Income Statement				FYE: June 30
	REVENUE ($ mil.)	NET INCOME ($ mil.)	NET PROFIT MARGIN	EMPLOYEES
06/20	661	(12)	—	3,055
06/19	642	(6)	—	—
06/18	602	(4)	—	—
06/17	601	1	0.3%	—
Annual Growth	3.2%	—	—	—

2020 Year-End Financials
Return on assets: (-2.9%) Cash ($ mil.): 21
Return on equity: (-9.7%)
Current ratio: —

PCL CONSTRUCTION ENTERPRISES, INC.

PCL Construction Enterprises is the contractor to call on for commercial and civil construction concerns. The company serves as the parent to half a dozen US construction companies: PCL Construction Services PCL Civil Constructors PCL Construction PCL Industrial Services PCL Industrial Construction and Nordic PCL Construction. The companies serve as the operating entities for PCL one of Canada's largest general contracting groups. Having completed projects in nearly every US state PCL Construction Enterprises is active in the commercial institutional multi-family residential heavy industrial and civil construction sectors. PCL first entered the US construction market in 1975.

Operations
PCL Construction Enterprises and its subsidiaries work on a variety of projects. PCL Construction Enterprises has completed bridges water and wastewater systems manufacturing plants office buildings and restaurants nationwide.

Like many construction companies PCL was hit by the economic recession. Backlogs were lacking and new projects became tougher to win due to an increase in competition. Contracts with water wastewater and renewable energy projects and universities have helped PCL Construction Enterprises through the downturn.

Geographic Reach
Denver-based PCL Construction Enterprises through its half a dozen operating units concentrates on commercial civil and industrial construction projects located in the US.

Its parent's work spans the US Canada the Caribbean and Australia.

Sales and Marketing
PCL caters to customers in three primary sectors: commercial buildings civil infrastructure and heavy industrial construction. Clients have included the Alaska Railroad Corporation US Army Corps of Engineers Shaw Constructors and OUC-The Reliable One.

Its markets span big cities in Alaska Georgia California North Carolina Texas Colorado Hawaii Minnesota Florida Arizona and Washington.

EXECUTIVES

Sr V Pres, Shaun P Yancey
Exec V Pres*, Al E Troppmann
Regional V Pres*, Luis S Ventoza
V Pres-Fin-Sec-treas*, Michael J Kehoe
Information Specialist, Brandon Sato
Project Manager, Aidan Felzien
Executive Assistant, Angela Walker
Building Manager, Blair Trigg
Project Coordinator, Branden Svienson
Project Manager, Brian Paskuski
Hse Supervisor, Mark Ducey

LOCATIONS

HQ: PCL CONSTRUCTION ENTERPRISES, INC.
2000 S COLO BLVD STE 2-50, DENVER, CO 80222
Phone: 303 365-6500

PRODUCTS/OPERATIONS

Selected Operating Companies
Nordic PCL Construction Inc.
PCL Civil Constructors Inc.
PCL Construction Inc.
PCL Construction Services Inc.
PCL Industrial Construction Co.
PCL Industrial Services Inc.

COMPETITORS

Adolfson & Peterson Inc.	M. B. Kahn
Andersen Construction	Skanska Usa Civil
Brasfield & Gorrie	Suffolk Construction
C.w. Driver	Tic Holdings
Dimeo Construction	Torix General
Fci Constructors	Contractors
Fluor	Turner Corporation
Gilbane Building Company	

HISTORICAL FINANCIALS
Company Type: Private

Income Statement				FYE: October 31
	REVENUE ($ mil.)	NET INCOME ($ mil.)	NET PROFIT MARGIN	EMPLOYEES
10/10	1,616	23	1.5%	3,300
10/09	2,182	52	2.4%	—
10/08	2,315	84	3.7%	—
Annual Growth	(16.4%)	(47.2%)	—	—

2010 Year-End Financials
Return on assets: 4.2% Cash ($ mil.): 95
Return on equity: 17.6%
Current ratio: 1.20

PEACEHEALTH

PeaceHealth is a not-for-profit Catholic health system that serves residents in Washington Oregon and Alaska. In all PeaceHealth has some 16000 caregivers and a multi-specialty medical group practice with more than 1100 physicians. It also has ten medical centers in both rural and urban communities throughout the Northwest. Its medical centers include PeaceHealth Ketchikan Medical Center PeaceHealth St. Joseph Medical Center PeaceHealth St. John Medical Center Sacred Heart Medical Center (two campuses) Cottage Grove Community Hospital Peace Harbor Hospital PeaceHealth Peace Island Medical Center and PeaceHealth Southwest Medical Center.

Operations

PeaceHealth reported more than 66800 inpatient admissions and roughly 1.5 million outpatient registrations as well as almost 2 million patient encounters with its medical group. It had more than 7000 infant births and more than 309500 emergency department visits annually.

Geographic Reach

Based in Vancouver Washington PeaceHealth has operations in Washington Oregon and Alaska.

Company Background

PeaceHealth was formed in 1923 by the Sisters of St. Joseph of Peace who opened the Little Flower Hospital in Ketchikan named after Saint Teresa. The Sisters of St. Joseph of Peace had previously opened St. Joseph Hospital in Bellingham in 1891.

PeaceHealth and Southwest Washington Health System merged in early 2011 boosting PeaceHealth's hospital holdings from six to eight with the addition of the two-campus Southwest Washington Medical Center in Vancouver Washington.

Under terms of the affiliation Southwest Washington Health System became part of PeaceHealth allowing Southwest to benefit from its larger peer's medical and financial resources. The move allows both health systems to increase the scope of services they offer in Washington State where Southwest Washington Health System also operates clinics a medical group and a foundation through which it conducts fundraising efforts.

EXECUTIVES

Ceo, Charles Prosper
Coo, Beth O'Brien
V Pres, Andrea Nenzel
SEC, Anne Hayes
Treas, Prill Ron
Coo, Elliot Kuida
Coordinator, Beth Getman
Director Information Technolog, Brian Churchill
Coordinator, Colby Hagen
Chief Nursing Officer, Heather Wall
Regional Vice-President, James Farley

LOCATIONS

HQ: PEACEHEALTH
1115 SE 164TH AVE, VANCOUVER, WA 986839324
Phone: 360 788-6841
Web: WWW.PEACEHEALTH.ORG

PRODUCTS/OPERATIONS

2013 Sales

	$ mil.	% of total
Patient service revenue	1,984	92
Premium revenue	93	4
Other operating revenue	94	4
Total	**2,171**	**100**

Selected Hospitals

PeaceHealth Ketchikan Medical Center (Ketchikan Alaska)
Cottage Grove Community Hospital (Cottage Grove Oregon)
Peace Harbor Hospital (Florence Oregon)
PeaceHealth Peace Island Medical Center (Friday Harbor Washington)
PeaceHealth Southwest Medical Center (Vancouver Washington)
PeaceHealth St. John Medical Center (Longview Washington)
PeaceHealth St. Joseph Medical Center (Bellingham Washington)
Sacred Heart Medical Center at RiverBend (Springfield Oregon)
Sacred Heart Medical Center University District (Eugene Oregon)
Other Operations
PeaceHealth Laboratories (locations throughout Oregon and Washington)

PeaceHealth Medical Group (operates in Alaska Oregon and Washington)

COMPETITORS

Alaska Native Tribal Health Consortium	Providence St. Joseph Health
Franciscan Health System	Seattle Children's Hospital
Hca	South Peninsula Hospital
Harrison Medical Center	Swedish Health Services
Immediate Care	Tenet Healthcare
Multicare Health System	Yakima Valley Memorial
Overlake Hospital	

HISTORICAL FINANCIALS
Company Type: Private

Income Statement
FYE: June 30

	REVENUE ($ mil.)	NET INCOME ($ mil.)	NET PROFIT MARGIN	EMPLOYEES
06/14	2,249	114	5.1%	6,690
06/09	1,372	(88)	—	
06/06	1,048	103	9.8%	—
Annual Growth	**10.0%**	**1.3%**	**—**	**—**

2014 Year-End Financials

Return on assets: 3.3%   Cash ($ mil.): 549
Return on equity: 6.5%
Current ratio: 0.70

PEDERNALES ELECTRIC COOPERATIVE, INC.

Created by Texas ranchers and business owners Pedernales Electric Cooperative provides electricity services in the Texas Hill Country. The company the largest electric cooperative in the US purchases its electricity from wholesale providers primarily the Lower Colorado River Authority (LCRA) and transmits and distributes it to about 209350 cooperative members (or more than 247810 individual customer meters). Pedernales Electric Cooperative operates more than 17450 miles of power line and maintains 290000 wooden utility poles in its service area.

Geographic Reach

The cooperative serves a customer base spread across 24 counties in Central Texas (8100 sq. miles an area larger than the state of Massachusetts).

Financial Performance

In 2012 the company's revenues decreased by 3% as the result of unfavorable weather conditions weakening demand for power (despite an increase of 5500 new customers). Net income decreased 24% driven by lower net sales.

Strategy

A member of the American Wind Energy Association Pedernales Electric Cooperative is committed to move toward conservation and cleaner energy (to meet clean air standards) and has a renewable energy goal of 30% of energy from renewable sources by 2020. The coop contracts with AEP Energy Partners to buy wind power produced at the South Trent Wind Farm near Sweetwater Texas. In all the wind-power purchase is expected to power up 22000 to 27000 homes.

In 2013 company upgraded the electric system in the Canyon Lake area manually converting more than 1900 transformers to accept higher voltage to better serve the growing energy needs of nearly 2600 coop members in the Clear Water Estates Tamarack Shores Scenic Terrace Linda Ledges Hancock Oak Hills and Rocky Creek Ranch subdivisions.

Company Background

As part of reforming its operations following a financial scandal in 2009 Pedernales Electric Cooperative became one of the first electric distribution cooperatives in the US to broadcast its Board meetings live on the Internet. In 2009 the cooperative ratified the first member advisory panel (on energy conservation and renewable energy use) in Pedernales Electric Cooperative's history.

Pedernales Electric Cooperative was founded in 1938 with the help of local landowner (and later US president) Lyndon Johnson.

EXECUTIVES

Ceo, John Hewa
Accounting Staff, Mike Mowrey
Supervisor, Darryl Harvey
Administrative Assistant, Andrew Dunn
District Manager, Archie Lopez
Manager, Martin Benavidez
Manager, Eddie Dauterive
Member Planner, Cynthia Lehoski
Procurement Specialist, Dayna Thompson
Administrative Assistant, Karla Williams
Supervisor, Steven Kilmer
Auditors: BOLINGER SEGARS GILBERT AND MO

LOCATIONS

HQ: PEDERNALES ELECTRIC COOPERATIVE, INC.
201 S AVENUE F, JOHNSON CITY, TX 786362072
Phone: 830 868-7155
Web: WWW.PEC.COOP

HISTORICAL FINANCIALS
Company Type: Private

Income Statement
FYE: December 31

	REVENUE ($ mil.)	NET INCOME ($ mil.)	NET PROFIT MARGIN	EMPLOYEES
12/11	589	6	1.1%	741
12/10	550	53	9.8%	—
12/09	578	57	10.0%	—
Annual Growth	**0.9%**	**(66.5%)**	**—**	**—**

2011 Year-End Financials

Return on assets: 0.5%   Cash ($ mil.): 27
Return on equity: 1.6%
Current ratio: 0.20

PENNSYLVANIA - AMERICAN WATER COMPANY

Pennsylvania-American Water distributes water and provides wastewater services to a population of more than 2 million people in some 390 communities across Pennsylvania. The company serves 635000 water customers and 17500 wastewater customers. It operates about 35 water treatment plants six wastewater facilities and 9800 miles of pipeline. Pennsylvania-American Water's service territory covers some three dozen Pennsylvania counties. The utility the largest regulated water and wastewater service provider in Pennsylvania is a subsidiary of New Jersey-based American Water Works.

Operations

Pennsylvania-American Water also has 85 well stations and treats and delivers about 216 millions of gallons of water each day. In addition it operates 70 groundwater treatment facilities which process water sourced from more than 100 groundwater wells and maintains 250 treated water storage facilities 280 pumping stations and 60 dams.

Geographic Reach

The utility's primarily service areas include Mechanicsburg Mon Valley Norristown Pittsburgh Scranton Washington and Wilkes-Barre.

Financial Performance

Pennsylvania-American Water represents about a fifth of its parent company's sales; in 2011 it reported $516 million in revenue from Pennsylvania.

Mergers and Acquisitions

The utility expands its reach in Pennsylvania by picking up smaller water systems; in 2012 it completed six such acquisitions including a Monroe County system serving the Fernwood Resort and a Pike County system serving about 100 residents.

EXECUTIVES

Pres, Kathy Pape
V Pres*, William C Kelvinton
SEC*, Velma A Redmond
Treas*, Stephen F Analdo
Information Technology Support, James P Oehling
Domino Administrator, Jill Breneman
Senior Developer, Richard Watts
Counsel, Susan Simms
Senior Financial Analyst, Jim Alexander
Electrical Design Engineer, Eric Boyer
Manager, Dean Tawana

LOCATIONS

HQ: PENNSYLVANIA - AMERICAN WATER COMPANY
852 WESLEY DR, MECHANICSBURG, PA 170554436
Phone: 800 565-7292
Web: WWW.PAWC.COM

COMPETITORS

Aqua America · · · · · · · · · · · Utilities Inc.
United Water Inc.

HISTORICAL FINANCIALS

Company Type: Private

Income Statement   FYE: December 31

	REVENUE ($ mil.)	NET INCOME ($ mil.)	NET PROFIT MARGIN	EMPLOYEES
12/17*	661	160	24.3%	1,007
06/14	589	127	21.7%	—
03/14	584	128	22.0%	—
12/13	571	122	21.4%	—
Annual Growth	3.7%	7.1%	—	—

*Fiscal year change

2017 Year-End Financials

Return on assets: 3.5%   Cash ($ mil.): 3
Return on equity: 5.6%
Current ratio: 0.20

PENNSYLVANIA ELECTRIC COMPANY

Pennsylvania Electric (Penelec) has elected to provide power to the people of the Keystone State. The company distributes power to a population of 1.6 million in a 17600-square-mile portion of northern western and south-central Pennsylvania. The utility operates more than 20170 miles of distribution and more than 2700 transmission lines. The Waverly Electric Light & Power Company a subsidiary of Penelec provides electric services to a population of about 8400 in Waverly New York. Penelec is an operating subsidiary of regional utility power player FirstEnergy.

EXECUTIVES

Exec V Pres-Cfo, Mark T Clark
Exec V Pres-Gen Counsel, Leila L Vespoli
V Pres-Controller-Cao, Harvey L Wagner
V Pres-Treas, James F Pearson
Vice President, Controller, Jason J Lisowski
Auditors: PRICEWATERHOUSECOOPERS LLP CL

LOCATIONS

HQ: PENNSYLVANIA ELECTRIC COMPANY
2800 POTTSVILLE PIKE, AKRON, OH 44308
Phone: 800 545-7741
Web: WWW.FIRSTENERGYCORP.COM

COMPETITORS

Columbia Gas Of · · · · · · Peco Energy
Pennsylvania · · · · · · · · · · Ppl Electric
Direct Energy · · · · · · · · · Peoples Natural Gas

HISTORICAL FINANCIALS

Company Type: Private

Income Statement   FYE: December 31

	REVENUE ($ mil.)	NET INCOME ($ mil.)	NET PROFIT MARGIN	EMPLOYEES
12/17	893	95	10.7%	896
12/16	904	88	9.8%	—
12/10	1,539	59	3.9%	—
12/09	1,448	65	4.5%	—
Annual Growth	(5.9%)	4.9%	—	—

2017 Year-End Financials

Return on assets: 2.2%   Cash ($ mil.): —
Return on equity: 7.8%
Current ratio: 1.20

PENNSYLVANIA HIGHER EDUCATION ASSISTANCE AGENCY

PHEAA is a national provider of student financial aid services serving millions of students and thousands of schools through its loan guaranty loan servicing financial aid processing outreach and other student aid programs. PHEAA conducts its student loan servicing operations nationally as FedLoan Servicing and American Education Serv-

ices (AES). PHEAA operates its digital technology division as Avereo. PHEAA's earnings are used to support its public service mission and to pay its operating costs including administration of the PA State Grant and other state-funded student aid programs. Created in 1963 by the Pennsylvania General Assembly the Pennsylvania Higher Education Assistance Agency (PHEAA) has evolved into one of the nation's leading student aid organizations.

EXECUTIVES

Chb, William F Adolph Jr
Ceo*, James L Preston
V Pres*, Stephanie Foltz
V Pres*, Nathan Hench
V Pres*, Todd E Mosko
V Pres*, Matthew D Sessa
Purchasing Vice-President, Donna Orris
Staff, Erica Eshelman
Payroll Staff, Michelle McCoy
Human Resources Representative, Tom Rineer
Regional Director, Amy Sloan
Auditors: ERNST & YOUNG LLP MCLEAN VA

LOCATIONS

HQ: PENNSYLVANIA HIGHER EDUCATION ASSISTANCE AGENCY
1200 N 7TH ST, HARRISBURG, PA 171021419
Phone: 717 720-2700
Web: WWW.PHEAA.ORG

PRODUCTS/OPERATIONS

2015 sales

	$ mil.	% of total
Non-interest		
Servicing fees	308	50
Retention of collections on defaulted loans net	130	21
Federal fees	20	3
Other	(1.2)	-
Interest		
Loans	155	25
Investments	5	1
Total	619	100

COMPETITORS

Bank Of America · · · · · · First Marblehead
Discover · · · · · · · · · · · · · · Keycorp
Educational Funding Of · · Sallie Mae
The South · · · · · · · · · · · · Suntrust

HISTORICAL FINANCIALS

Company Type: Private

Income Statement   FYE: June 30

	REVENUE ($ mil.)	NET INCOME ($ mil.)	NET PROFIT MARGIN	EMPLOYEES
06/13*	671	155	23.2%	2,700
03/12	436	68	15.7%	—
Annual Growth	53.8%	127.6%	—	—

*Fiscal year change

2013 Year-End Financials

Return on assets: 1.7%   Cash ($ mil.): 88
Return on equity: 16.4%
Current ratio: 5.60

PEPPER CONSTRUCTION COMPANY

EXECUTIVES

Ceo, J David Pepper
President, Kenneth Egidi
Exec Pres, James A Nissen
Cfo, Chris Averill
Manager, Atul Raj
Safety Coordinator, Danny Torres
Assistant Superintendent, Joe Mildice
Assistant To Atul Raj, Lori Brown
Coordinator of Marketing, Rebecca Wagner
Project Accounting Assistant, Janice Alvarado
Senior Vice President Director, Jay Jacobsmeyer
Auditors: BKD LLP OAKBROOK TERRACE IL

LOCATIONS

HQ: PEPPER CONSTRUCTION COMPANY
643 N ORLEANS ST, CHICAGO, IL 606543690
Phone: 312 266-4700
Web: WWW.PEPPERCONSTRUCTION.COM

HISTORICAL FINANCIALS

Company Type: Private

Income Statement — FYE: September 30

	REVENUE ($ mil.)	NET INCOME ($ mil.)	NET PROFIT MARGIN	EMPLOYEES
09/20	737	10	1.4%	900
09/17	704	14	2.1%	—
09/16	805	20	2.5%	—
09/15	709	10	1.5%	—
Annual Growth	0.8%	(0.3%)	—	—

2020 Year-End Financials

Return on assets: 5.2%
Return on equity: 20.2%
Current ratio: 1.30

Cash ($ mil.): 46

PEPPER CONSTRUCTION GROUP, LLC

Pepper Construction Group spices up the construction business with a little of this and a pinch of that. The company provides general contracting and construction management services for commercial office education entertainment health care and institutional clients as well as waterworks projects. (Health care projects account for about 50% of Pepper's revenue.) Its client list includes UBS Northwestern University University of Notre Dame Texas Heart Institute Loyola University Medical Center and NASA. Pepper Construction Group has divisions in Illinois Indiana Ohio and Texas. Stanley F. Pepper founded the company in Chicago in 1927. The group is owned by his family and employees of the firm.

Operations

The company's Pepper Environmental Technologies unit provides environmental services. Green building has become a large part of Pepper Construction's operations. Its Green Team of certified professionals have helped construct more than 2.9 million sq. ft. of eco-friendly space. The Green Team has built the Apple Computer flagship store HSBC Chicago North and Kohl's Children's Museum.

The firm's Pepper-Lawson Waterworks group constructs water purification plants for municipal clients including Houston and Missouri City Texas.

Geographic Reach

Chicago-based Pepper Construction comprises four geographic divisions: Illinois; Indiana; Ohio; and Texas. Overall the company is active in about 20 states mostly in the central and northeastern states.

EXECUTIVES

Chm, Dave Pepper
V Pres-Assist SEC*, Stephanie Vitner
Sr V Pres-Gen Counselor-Sec*, Timothy F Sullivan
Evp-Cfo*, Chris Averill
Senior Business Unit Accountan, Kelly Hampton
Project Coordinator, Caitlin Poe
Superintendent, Kevin Lally
Auditors: BKD LLP OAKBROOK TERRACE IL

LOCATIONS

HQ: PEPPER CONSTRUCTION GROUP, LLC
643 N ORLEANS ST, CHICAGO, IL 606543690
Phone: 312 266-4700
Web: WWW.PEPPERCONSTRUCTION.COM

PRODUCTS/OPERATIONS

Selected Operations

Pepper Construction Group LLC (Chicago Illinois)
Pepper Construction Co. (Chicago Illinois)
Pepper Construction Co. of Indiana (Indianapolis Indiana)
Pepper Construction Co. of Ohio LLC (Dublin Ohio)
Pepper Environmental Technologies Inc. (Barrington Illinois)
Pepper-Lawson Construction LP (Houston Texas)
Pepper-Lawson Waterworks LLC (Houston Texas)

COMPETITORS

Barton Malow	Graycor
Bulley & Andrews	M. A. Mortenson
C. G. Schmidt	Mccarthy Building
Charles Pankow Builders	Power Construction
Clark Enterprises	Turner Corporation
Gilbane	Walbridge Aldinger
	Walsh Group

HISTORICAL FINANCIALS

Company Type: Private

Income Statement — FYE: September 30

	REVENUE ($ mil.)	NET INCOME ($ mil.)	NET PROFIT MARGIN	EMPLOYEES
09/20	1,254	22	1.8%	1,100
09/16	1,179	23	2.0%	—
09/15	1,110	9	0.9%	—
09/11	911	15	1.7%	—
Annual Growth	3.6%	4.2%	—	—

2020 Year-End Financials

Return on assets: 5.8%
Return on equity: 29.5%
Current ratio: 1.20

Cash ($ mil.): 74

PERISHABLE DISTRIBUTORS OF IOWA, LTD.

EXECUTIVES

Pres, Dan Wampler
Exec V Pres*, Linda Sharp
Director, Ronald Pearson
Logistics Coordinator, Cory Breese
Human Resources Executive, Janel Jones
Operations Manager, Joe McConnell
Tran Manager, Keith Lyman
Assistant Vice President of Tr, Kevin Gass
Truck Shop Manager, Mark Choate
Director, Mark Kloberdanz
Programmer Analyst, Rich Dressen

LOCATIONS

HQ: PERISHABLE DISTRIBUTORS OF IOWA, LTD.
2741 SE PDI PL, ANKENY, IA 500213958
Phone: 515 965-6300
Web: WWW.CONTACTPDI.COM

HISTORICAL FINANCIALS

Company Type: Private

Income Statement — FYE: September 30

	REVENUE ($ mil.)	NET INCOME ($ mil.)	NET PROFIT MARGIN	EMPLOYEES
09/18*	1,346	38	2.9%	687
10/17	1,343	35	2.6%	—
10/16	1,307	33	2.6%	—
09/15	1,248	31	2.5%	—
Annual Growth	2.5%	7.3%	—	—

*Fiscal year change

2018 Year-End Financials

Return on assets: 25.9%
Return on equity: 55.2%
Current ratio: 1.30

Cash ($ mil.): 15

PERMANENT UNIVERSITY FUND

LOCATIONS

HQ: PERMANENT UNIVERSITY FUND
221 W 6TH ST STE 1700, AUSTIN, TX 787013451
Phone: 512 225-1600

HISTORICAL FINANCIALS

Company Type: Private

Income Statement — FYE: August 31

	REVENUE ($ mil.)	NET INCOME ($ mil.)	NET PROFIT MARGIN	EMPLOYEES
08/21	8,724	7,588	87.0%	5
08/20	2,215	1,550	70.0%	—
08/19	1,035	953	92.1%	—
08/18	1,906	1,964	103.0%	—
Annual Growth	66.0%	56.9%	—	—

PETER KIEWIT SONS', INC.

Kiewit is one of North America's largest construction and engineering companies. The company is active in building industrial mining oil gas chemicals power transportation water and wastewater. It builds everything from roads and dams to high-rise office towers and power plants. Kiewit focuses on projects located throughout the US Canada and Mexico. Specializes in mine management production infrastructure construction and maintenance its mining experience includes constructing infrastructure performing mine services or contract mining in coal copper diamond gold nickel platinum potash and rare earth mines throughout North America. Founded in 1884 Kiewit is owned by employees and Kiewit family members.

Operations

Kiewit provides engineering construction procurement foundations development services and decarbonization solutions.

It delivers more than 1000 oil gas and chemical projects. As a premier contractor in the North American power industry Kiewit has installed more than 125000 MW of capacity and consistently ranks among the Engineering News-Record top five power contractors. Its diverse expertise includes renewable hydrogen and fossil-fuel energy generation energy storage of all types carbon capture technologies as well as transmission and distribution. In addition its successful track record includes the construction and upgrade of interstates; highways and bridges; rail lines and rail yards; urban mass transit systems; and airport runways taxiways and associated facilities.

The company's other capabilities include preconstruction general contracting building information modeling construction management engineering sustainability and self-performed scopes of work. Kiewit's procurement and supply chain management experts leverage more than $9 billion in annual procurement spend over a large network of nationwide and local vendors. Its foundations provide a diverse scope of integrated geotechnical solutions including all types of deep foundations ground improvement and earth retention services. It provides engineering and construction services for alternative and renewable energy and fuels as well as carbon capture projects. Its recent experience includes wind turbines power transmission networks that deliver renewable electricity hydrogen production facilities and the largest carbon capture and sequestration facility in the US.

Geographic Reach

Based in Omaha Nebraska Kiewit operates across the US (more than 85 locations) Canada (about 10 locations) and Mexico (two locations).

Sales and Marketing

Kiewit serves a diverse array of industries including building industrial mining oil gas and chemical power transportation and water.

Company Background

The sons of Dutch immigrants Peter and Andrew Kiewit founded masonry contractor Kiewit Brothers in 1884 in Omaha Nebraska. Following the dissolution of the partnership in 1904 Peter continued as the company's sole proprietor. In 1931 ? 17 years after Peter's death ? his son Peter reorganized the business as Peter Kiewit Sons'.

HISTORY

Born to Dutch immigrants Peter Kiewit and brother Andrew founded Kiewit Brothers a brick-

yard in 1884 in Omaha Nebraska. By 1912 two of Peter's sons worked at the yard which was named Peter Kiewit & Sons. When Peter Kiewit died in 1914 his son Ralph took over and the firm took the name Peter Kiewit Sons'. Another son Peter joined Ralph at the helm in 1924 after dropping out of Dartmouth and later took over.

During the Depression Kiewit managed huge federal public works projects and in the 1940s it focused on war-related emergency construction projects.

One of the firm's most difficult projects was top-secret Thule Air Force Base in Greenland above the Arctic Circle. For more than two years 5000 men worked around the clock beginning in 1951; the site was in development for 15 years. In 1952 the company won a contract to build a $1.2 billion gas diffusion plant in Portsmouth Ohio. It also became a contractor for the US interstate highway system (begun in 1956).

Peter Kiewit died in 1979 after stipulating that the largely employee-owned company should remain under employee control and that no one employee could own more than 10%. His 40% stake when returned to the company transformed many employees into millionaires. Walter Scott Jr. whose father had been the first graduate engineer to work for Kiewit took charge. Scott made his mark by parlaying money from construction into successful investments.

When the construction industry slumped Kiewit began looking for other investment opportunities and in 1984 it acquired packaging company Continental Can Co. (selling off noncore insurance energy and timber assets). Continental was saddled with a 1983 class action lawsuit alleging that it had plotted to close plants and lay off workers before they were qualified for pensions. In 1991 Kiewit agreed to pay $415 million to settle the lawsuit. In the face of a consolidating packaging industry the company sold Continental in the early 1990s.

In 1986 Kiewit loaned money to a business group to build a fiber-optic loop in Chicago; by 1987 it had launched MFS Communications to build local fiber loops in downtown districts. In 1992 Kiewit split its business into two pieces: the construction group which was strictly employee-owned; and a diversified group to which it added a controlling stake in phone and cable TV company C-TEC in 1993. That year Kiewit took MFS public; by 1995 it had sold all its shares and the next year MFS was bought by telecom giant WorldCom.

In 1996 Kiewit assisted CalEnergy (now MidAmerican Energy) in a hostile $1.3 billion takeover of the UK's Northern Electric. Kiewit got stock in CalEnergy and a 30% stake in the UK electric company all of which it sold to CalEnergy in 1998.

That year Kiewit spun off its telecom and computer services holdings into Level 3 Communications. Scott who had been hospitalized the year before for a blood clot in his lung stepped down as CEO and Ken Stinson CEO of Kiewit Construction Group took over Peter Kiewit Sons'.

In 1999 Kiewit acquired a majority interest in Pacific Rock Products a construction materials firm in Canada. Kiewit spun off its asphalt concrete and aggregates operations in 2000 as Kiewit Materials. Also that year the company created Kiewit Offshore Services to focus on construction for the offshore drilling industry. In 2001 the company acquired marine construction firm General Construction Company (GCC). The next year it expanded its offshore business further by buying a Canadian subsidiary from oil and gas equipment services company Friede Goldman Halter which was trying to emerge from bankruptcy.

Kiewit made history in 2002 for the fastest completion of a project of its type when it completed the rebuilding of Webbers Falls I-40 Bridge in Oklahoma at the end of July. (The bridge had collapsed in May after being hit by a pair of barges resulting in 14 fatalities.)

In 2004 Kiewit greatly increased its coal sales and reserves with the acquisition of the Buckskin Mine in Wyoming from Arch Coal.

Kiewit underwent a changing of the guard at the end of 2004 when 22-year veteran Bruce Grewcock took the reins as the company's fourth CEO since its founding. Stinson stayed on as the company's chairman.

In 2008 the group acquired TIC Holdings a heavy industrial construction and engineering firm.

Through its Kiewit Power Engineers Co. the company was contracted by Plutonic Energy Corporation and GE Energy Financial Services to work on the 235 MW hydroelectric Toba Montrose project one of British Columbia's largest renewable energy projects (completed around 2011).

In 2013 Kiewit entered the Australian market through a joint venture agreement that involves as $247 million engineer-procure-construct contract for a wet front end and ore wash plant situated at the Cloudbreak Mine in Northwest Australia. Fortescue Metals Group is the previous owner of Cloudbreak prior to the handover in early 2013.

EXECUTIVES

Pres-Ceo, Bruce E Grewcock
Exec V Pres, Douglas E Patterson
Exec V Pres, Richard W Colf
Sr V Pres-Cfo, Michael J Piechoski
Sr V Pres-Sec-Gen Counsel, Tobin A Schropp
Phoenix District Mngr, Doug Duplisea
Program Inspector, Ben Honig
Staff, Norma King
Real Estate Conultant, Paul White
Graphic Designer, Meriam Harvey
Vice President of Human Resour, Michael Geary
Auditors: KPMG LLP OMAHA NEBRASKA

LOCATIONS

HQ: PETER KIEWIT SONS', INC.
1550 MIKE FAHEY ST, OMAHA, NE 681024722
Phone: 402 342-2052
Web: WWW.KIEWIT.COM

Selected Locations

US
Alaska
Arizona
Arkansas
California
Colorado
Florida
Georgia
Hawaii
Idaho
Illinois
Iowa
Kansas
Louisiana
Maryland
Massachusetts
Minnesota
Nebraska
Nevada
New Jersey
New York
North Carolina
Oregon
Tennessee
Texas
Utah
Virginia
Washington
Wyoming
Australia

Western Australia
Canada
  Alberta
  British Columbia
  Manitoba
  Newfoundland
  New Brunswick
  Ontario
  Quebec
  Saskatchewan

PRODUCTS/OPERATIONS

Selected Locations

US
Alaska
Arizona
California
Colorado
Florida
Georgia
Hawaii
Illinois
Iowa
Kansas
Maryland
Massachusetts
Minnesota
Nebraska
Nevada
New Jersey
New York
North Carolina
Oregon
Texas
Utah
Virginia
Washington
Wyoming
Canada
  Alberta
  British Columbia
  Newfoundland
  Ontario
  Quebec
Mexico
  Mexico City

Selected Subsidiaries and Affiliates
Aero Automatic Sprinkler
Cherne Contracting Corporation
Continental Fire Sprinkler Company
Kiewit Australia
Kiewit Bridge & Marine
Kiewit Building Group
Kiewit Energy Company.
Kiewit Engineering Group Inc.
Kiewit Infrastructure Co.
Kiewit Infrastructure South Co.
Kiewit Infrastructure West Co.
Kiewit Mining Group
Dry Valley/No. Rassmussen Ridge Mines
Buckskin Mining Company
San Miguel Mine
Walnut Creek Mining Company
Kiewit Offshore Services Ltd..
Kiewit Power Constructors Co.
Kiewit Power Engineers
Kiewit Texas Construction L.P.

COMPETITORS

Abb	Lane Construction
Ames Construction	Pcl Constructors
Balfour Beatty	Parsons Corporation
Infrastructure	Raytheon
Bechtel	Rio Tinto Plc
Black & Veatch	Skanska Usa Civil
Fluor	Turner Corporation
Granite Construction	Tutor Perini
Halliburton	Walsh Group
Hubbard Group	Whiting-turner
Jacobs Engineering	Williams Companies
Kbr	

HISTORICAL FINANCIALS

Company Type: Private

Income Statement   FYE: December 29

	REVENUE ($ mil.)	NET INCOME ($ mil.)	NET PROFIT MARGIN	EMPLOYEES
12/12	11,220	515	4.6%	14,700
12/11	10,381	790	7.6%	—
12/10	9,938	789	7.9%	—
Annual Growth	6.3%	(19.2%)	—	—

2012 Year-End Financials

Return on assets: 7.6%   Cash ($ mil.): 1,447
Return on equity: 13.2%
Current ratio: 1.90

PETRO STAR INC.

Petro Star is an oil refining and fuel marketing shining star that brings heating fuel and energy (heating oil diesel and aviation and marine fuels) to the citizens of the communities in the vast cold and lonely expanses of the US' largest state Alaska. It operates refineries at North Pole and Valdez and distributes fuels and lubricants throughout Interior Alaska Dutch Harbor Kodiak and Valdez. Started in 1984 by a group of petroleum industry veterans the company built its first refinery operations along the Trans-Alaska Pipeline at North Pole Alaska. Petro Star is a subsidiary of Arctic Slope Regional Corp.

Operations

The company's divisions are Refining; Retail; Lubricants; Marine Fuel; Heating Fuel; Aviation; and Port of Alaska.

Refining operates two refineries: the 60000 barrel-per-day Petro Star Valdez refinery which produces jet fuel JP-8 JP-5 marine diesel heating fuel and turbine fuel; and the North Pole refinery approximately 22000-barrel-per-day facility producing heating fuel kerosene diesel jet fuels and asphalt base oil.

Its retail division is engaged in retail stores selling its products (North Pacific Fuel and Sourdough Fuel). It operates several gas stations and convenience stores throughout the state offering fuel food groceries and propane sales for customer's convenience.

Petro Star Lubricants is a bulk lube repackaging company offering several product lines and provide technical services for all of the company's product lines.

Marine offers marine fueling as well as supplies such as pumps hoses and nozzles.

Heating Fuel distributes locally produced heating and diesel fuel directly from the company's refineries in North Pole and Valdez to locations throughout Alaska.

Aviation is a supplier of jet fuel for the Ted Stevens International Airport for both commercial and corporate aircraft.

Petro Star distributes ultra low sulfur diesel jet fuel and gasoline at Terminal 1 at the Port of Alaska.

Geographic Reach

Headquartered in Alaska Petro Star operates in Kodiak Dutch Harbor Valdez St Paul Fairbanks Anchorage and an additional offices in Seattle.

Sales and Marketing

The company's customers include aviation residential commercial industrial marine and military.

Company Background

The company has expanded through acquisitions including fuel distribution firm Sourdough Fuel (in 1986) as well as the 1991 purchase of Alaska Lube and Fuel (now Petro Star Lubricants). Kodiak Sales (in 1997) and North Pacific Fuel (in 1998).

In 2008 Petro Star secured a $158.7 million aviation fuel contract from the Defense Logistics Agency.

EXECUTIVES

Pres, Douglas L Chapados
Coo*, Jim Boltz
V Pres*, Don Castle
Dir*, Nancy Gore
Treas*, Tracy Steelman
Dir*, Rock Rex
Dir*, Glenn Richard
Executive Officer, John Rense
Executive Officer, Lila Moto
Executive Officer, Thomas Bourdon
Executive Officer, Lisa Lewis

LOCATIONS

HQ: PETRO STAR INC.
  3900 C ST STE 802, ANCHORAGE, AK 995035963
Phone: 907 339-6600
Web: WWW.PETROSTAR.COM

COMPETITORS

Exxon Mobil   Valero Energy
Tesoro

HISTORICAL FINANCIALS

Company Type: Private

Income Statement   FYE: December 31

	REVENUE ($ mil.)	NET INCOME ($ mil.)	NET PROFIT MARGIN	EMPLOYEES
12/08	992	0	—	300
12/03	291	3	1.2%	—
12/02	267	1	0.7%	—
12/01	279	3	1.1%	—
Annual Growth	19.9%	—	—	—

2008 Year-End Financials

Return on assets: —   Cash ($ mil.): 106
Return on equity: —
Current ratio: 1.90

PETROCARD, INC.

EXECUTIVES

Ceo-Pres, Laura Yellig
Chm*, Joseph Chythlook
V Pres*, Jack Mowreader
Treas*, Andrew Rewolinski
Senior Financial Analyst, Rebecca Benson
Chief Information Officer, Roger Hall
Branch Manager, David Harris
Fuel Consultant, Ryan McShane
Fuel Consultant, Leif Johnston
Fuel Consultant, Colleen Vogel
Credit Manager, Heath McMorris

LOCATIONS

HQ: PETROCARD, INC.
  730 CENTRAL AVE S, KENT, WA 980326109
Phone: 253 852-7801
Web: WWW.PETROCARD.COM

HISTORICAL FINANCIALS

Company Type: Private

Income Statement   FYE: March 31

	REVENUE ($ mil.)	NET INCOME ($ mil.)	NET PROFIT MARGIN	EMPLOYEES
03/12	1,173	0	0.1%	190
03/11	948	3	0.4%	—
03/10	791	3	0.4%	—
Annual Growth	21.7%	(50.7%)	—	—

2012 Year-End Financials

Return on assets: 0.6%   Cash ($ mil.): 1
Return on equity: 1.7%
Current ratio: 1.00

PETROLEUM TRADERS CORPORATION

Petroleum Traders Corporation barters with fuel. The company provides wholesale gasoline diesel fuel and heating oil to fuel distributors government agencies and other large consumers of fuel such as businesses with vehicle fleets. The largest pure wholesale fuel distributor in the country Petroleum Traders operates and trades in 44 US states. It supplies #1 and #2 low sulfur diesel fuels biodiesel high sulfur heating oil and kerosene and conventional ethanol and reformulated blends of gasoline in regular midgrade and premium octane ratings.

Operations

Petroleum Traders focuses on supplying wholesale diesel and gasoline exclusively in the US offering a range of turnkey wholesale diesel fuel and wholesale gasoline fuel services.

Sales and Marketing

The company provides discount fuel to commercial government and wholesale customers. In the commercial space it services the trucking construction railroad mining and manufacturing industries as well as utilities and private fleets.

Strategy

Petroleum Traders parlays its hedging experience into fuel cost management for its customers via firm pricing cap programs collars and fuel swaps.

Company Background

The company was founded in 1979.

EXECUTIVES

Pres-Ceo, Michael Himes
Asst Ceo*, Vicki Himes
V Pres*, Linda Stephens
SEC*, Glenn Moonen
Vice President, Vicky Himes
Accounting Staff, Shawn Harris
Human Resources Manager, Jen Bynum
Business, Scott Wake
Accounting Team Member, Jon McIntosh
Sales Assistant, Cassandra Minich
Senior Account Executive Contr, Joseph Jurczak
Auditors: BADEN GAGE & SHROEDER LLC FO

LOCATIONS

HQ: PETROLEUM TRADERS CORPORATION
  7120 POINTE INVERNESS WAY, FORT WAYNE, IN
  468047928
Phone: 260 432-6622
Web: WWW.PETROLEUMTRADERS.COM

COMPETITORS

George Warren   Petro Holdings
Gulf Oil   Sun Coast Resources
Martin Resource
  Management

HISTORICAL FINANCIALS

Company Type: Private

Income Statement   FYE: June 30

	REVENUE ($ mil.)	NET INCOME ($ mil.)	NET PROFIT MARGIN	EMPLOYEES
06/21	1,241	12	1.0%	142
06/19	2,030	39	1.9%	
06/18	1,815	11	0.6%	—
06/17	1,606	19	1.2%	—
Annual Growth	(6.2%)	(10.7%)	—	—

2021 Year-End Financials

Return on assets: 5.3%   Cash ($ mil.): 115
Return on equity: 7.3%
Current ratio: 3.70

PGA TOUR, INC.

The PGA TOUR is the world's premier membership organization for touring professional golfers co-sanctioning tournaments on the PGA TOUR PGA TOUR Champions Korn Ferry Tour PGA TOUR Latinoam ©rica Mackenzie Tour-PGA TOUR Canada and Forme Tour. Each PGA TOUR player has earned a position on the priority-ranking system that is used to select full-field open tournaments. Its major championships are the Masters Open Championship and PGA Championship. The PGA TOUR was formed in 1968 by a splinter faction of the PGA of America.

Geographic Reach

Headquartered in Florida the PGA TOUR holds events in the US Canada Latin America and China among others.

EXECUTIVES

Coo, Edward L Moorhouse
Comm*, Timothy W Finchem
Pres-Chm*, Richard J Ferris
Exec V Pres-Coo*, W William Calfee
Exec V Press-Cfo*, Charles L Zink
Sr V Press-Public Rel-Communic*, Robert J
 Combs
Sr V Press-Coo of Pga Tour*, Henry Hughes
Sr V Press-Tel-Prod-media*, Donna G Orender
Sr V Press-Fin & Admin*, Ronald E Price
V Press-V Chm*, Will Mann
V Press-Coo of Sr Pga Tour*, Jeff Monday
Auditors: PRICEWATERHOUSECOOPERS LLP
 JA

LOCATIONS

HQ: PGA TOUR, INC.
  100 TPC BLVD, PONTE VEDRA BEACH, FL 320823167
Phone: 904 285-3700
Web: WWW.PGATOUR.COM

COMPETITORS

Fifa   Pga
Lpga   Professional Bowlers
Major League Baseball   Association
Major League Soccer   Usta
Nba   Wta Tour
Nfl

HISTORICAL FINANCIALS

Company Type: Private

Income Statement   FYE: December 31

	REVENUE ($ mil.)	NET INCOME ($ mil.)	NET PROFIT MARGIN	EMPLOYEES
12/13	1,075	34	3.2%	3,563
12/06	894	3	0.3%	—
12/05	875	4	0.5%	—
12/04	802	3	0.4%	—
Annual Growth	3.3%	29.4%	—	—

2013 Year-End Financials

Return on assets: 1.6%   Cash ($ mil.): 149
Return on equity: 3.7%
Current ratio: —

PHILADELPHIA CONSOLIDATED HOLDING CORP.

Because each industry has its own unique set of risks Philadelphia Insurance Companies and its subsidiaries specialize in designing and underwriting commercial property/casualty insurance. Its niche clients include rental car companies (for that insurance they always want to sell you at the counter) not-for-profits health and fitness centers and day-care facilities. Its specialty lines include loss-control policies and liability coverage for such professionals as lawyers doctors accountants dog groomers and even insurance claims adjusters. Philadelphia Insurance Companies is a subsidiary of Tokio Marine Holdings.

Geographic Reach

Philadelphia Insurance Companies' operating subsidiaries Philadelphia Insurance and Philadelphia Indemnity Insurance sell and service policies through a network of independent agents and about 50 regional offices that stretch across the US. With its new-found backing from Tokio Marine the insurer has access to broader distribution avenues in the US and overseas.

Sales and Marketing

In addition to commercial property and casualty insurance the company also sells personal coverage for collectible cars and homeowners flood insurance.

Strategy

Philadelphia Insurance Companies has been enhancing its information technology systems. The firm is working to upgrade its back-office infrastructure for more efficient handling of billing claims accounting and data management functions.

EXECUTIVES

Jr. Ch, James J Maguire
Ceo, Robert D O'Leary
Exec V Pres, Brian O'Reilly
Exec V Pres, Karen A Gilmer-Pauciello
Exec V Pres, William J Benecke
Auto Liability Supervisor, Mark Diseroad
Business Operations Analyst I, Thomas Smart
Coordinator, Elisa Pileggi
Assistant Vice President Talen, Fay Maffei
Staff, Fran Deeming
Assistant Vice President Suret, Richard Kukosky

LOCATIONS

HQ: PHILADELPHIA CONSOLIDATED HOLDING CORP.
1 BALA PLZ STE 100, BALA CYNWYD, PA 190041401
Phone: 610 617-7900
Web: WWW.PHLY.COM

PRODUCTS/OPERATIONS

Selected Products

Commercial and Personal Property/Casualty Insurance
Adoption agencies
Adult day care
Amateur sports
Antique collector car
Apartments
Auto leasing/rental program
Boat dealers
Bowling centers
Builder's exchange
Builders' risk
Business auto fleet
Camp operators
Child care centers
Consulting foresters
Contractor environmental coverage
Crime protection plus
Entertainment
Environmental
Fairs and fairgrounds
Festivals
Film production
Flood
Golf and country clubs
Health fitness and wellness
Home health care
Homeowners association
Hospice
Hotels
Life and business coaches
Loss control
Medical facilities and hospitals
Motorsports
Museums
Non-profit and social service organizations
Nursing homes
Office parks
Outdoor recreation
Performing arts
Pest control services
Professional sports
Public entities
Real rstate dchedules
Religious organizations
RV parks and campgrounds
Schools
Security services (The Guardian)
Shopping centers
Special events
Substance abuse rehabilitation facilities
Temporary staffing agencies
Volunteer fire department
Zoos
Liability
Accountants professional liability
Allied Health professional liability
Business owners
Cyber security liability
Employed lawyers professional liability
Employment practices stand alone
Excess liability
Miscellaneous professional liability (Affinity Pro)

COMPETITORS

Aig	Liberty Mutual
American Financial Group	Markel
	North Pointe
Cna Financial	Rli
Hagerty Insurance	State Farm
Hanover Insurance	Travelers Companies

HISTORICAL FINANCIALS

Company Type: Private

Income Statement — FYE: December 31

	ASSETS ($ mil.)	NET INCOME ($ mil.)	INCOME AS % OF ASSETS	EMPLOYEES
12/16	9,719	347	3.6%	1,374
12/15	9,047	323	3.6%	
Annual Growth	7.4%	7.5%	—	—

PHOENIX CHILDREN'S HOSPITAL, INC.

Phoenix Children's Hospital (PCH) invests in the health of the next generation. Founded in 1983 one of the largest pediatric healthcare systems in the country provides a comprehensive range of medical services specifically for children and adolescents in the greater Phoenix area. The hospital has about 1000 specialists who deliver care across more than 75 subspecialties including emergency care childhood cancers hematology neuroscience heart disease trauma and orthopedics. It also operates a newborn intensive care unit (NICU) at its main campus. PCH has several pediatric outpatient care centers in surrounding Phoenix suburbs.

EXECUTIVES

Pres-Ceo, Robert Meyer
Cfo*, Craig McKnight
Child Neurology, Robert D Little
Director, Dino R Camu EZ
Chief of Dentistry, Jack A Buhrow
Coordinator, Diane Depietro
Coordinator, Theresaterri Moore
Coordinator, Nancy Salzwedel
Infection Control Director, Scott Ostdiek
Law Specialist, Shari Krueger
Orthopedist, Richard Shindell

LOCATIONS

HQ: PHOENIX CHILDREN'S HOSPITAL, INC.
1919 E THOMAS RD, PHOENIX, AZ 850167710
Phone: 602 546-1000
Web: WWW.PHOENIXCHILDRENS.ORG

PRODUCTS/OPERATIONS

2014 Sales

	$ mil.	% of total
Net patient service revenue	691	95
Net assets released from restrictions used for operations	10	2
Donations gifts & contributions	8	1
Other operating revenue	15	2
Total	**725**	**100**

Selected Center of Excellence

Barrow Neurological Institute at Phoenix Children's Hospital
Center for Cancer and Blood Disorders
Center for Pediatric Orthopaedics
Level One Pediatric Trauma Center
Neonatal Intensive Care
Phoenix Children's Heart Center

COMPETITORS

Banner Health	Scottsdale Healthcare
Dignity Health	Shriners Hospitals For

Flagstaff Medical Center
John C. Lincoln Health Network
Northern Arizona Healthcare
Children
University Of Arizona Health Network

HISTORICAL FINANCIALS

Company Type: Private

Income Statement — FYE: December 31

	REVENUE ($ mil.)	NET INCOME ($ mil.)	NET PROFIT MARGIN	EMPLOYEES
12/14	661	26	4.1%	3,000
12/13	655	31	4.9%	
12/11	498	(5)	—	
12/09	408	106	26.1%	
Annual Growth	10.1%	(24.1%)		—

2014 Year-End Financials

Return on assets: 2.4%   Cash ($ mil.): 130
Return on equity: 8.8%
Current ratio: 4.50

PHYSICIAN AFFILIATE GROUP OF NEW YORK PC

EXECUTIVES

Pres, Bijan Safai
M.d, Ceo, Luis R Marcos
Coo, Michael J Chambers
Cfo, Anthony Mirdita
Benefits Coordinator, Jesenia Rivas
Director, Joseph Monteleone
Human Resources Generalist, Carolina Castro-Nicho
Pediatrician, Kerry Godfrey
Budget Analyst, Anil Singh
Affiliation Director, Christine Ber
General Counsel, Diana G Voigt

LOCATIONS

HQ: PHYSICIAN AFFILIATE GROUP OF NEW YORK PC
55 W 125TH ST FL 10, NEW YORK, NY 100274516
Phone: 646 672-3651
Web: WWW.PAGNY.ORG

HISTORICAL FINANCIALS

Company Type: Private

Income Statement — FYE: June 30

	REVENUE ($ mil.)	NET INCOME ($ mil.)	NET PROFIT MARGIN	EMPLOYEES
06/19	745	21	2.8%	75
06/15	524	(0)		
Annual Growth	9.2%	—	—	—

2019 Year-End Financials

Return on assets: 45.6%   Cash ($ mil.): 46
Return on equity: 45.6%
Current ratio: —

PIEDMONT HOSPITAL, INC.

Those feeling ill in Atlanta can count on Piedmont Healthcare for help. Founded in 1905 the not-for-profit organization's flagship facility is Piedmont Atlanta an acute care hospital with about 645 beds. Piedmont Atlanta provides general and most advanced medical-surgical care including open-heart surgery organ transplantation and neurosurgery. Also part of the Piedmont family are Piedmont Fayette Hospital with more than 280 beds; Piedmont Mountainside Hospital a 52-bed community hospital of the North Georgia; and the Piedmont Physicians Group a network of more than 290 primary care physicians and over 85 cardiovascular specialists operating in about 25 offices across Metro Atlanta and North Georgia.

Operations

Piedmont Healthcare also operates Piedmont Newnan Hospital a 154-bed acute-care community hospital in Coweta County Georgia with a medical staff of more than 300 physicians and a 236-bed not-for-profit acute care community hospital Piedmont Henry Hospital. In addition to Piedmont Walton Hospital a 77-bed not-for-profit community hospital in Monroe Georgia and serves as the sole hospital provider for the Walton County community it also operates Piedmont Rockdale Hospital and Piedmont Columbus Regional.

Each year the system serves around 2 million patients performing nearly 88370 surgeries completing more than 380 organ transplants and handling more than 627230 emergency department visits. It also sees about 1 million outpatients and around 16745 infant deliveries annually.

Geographic Reach

Piedmont Healthcare serves communities across approximately 800 locations.

Sales and Marketing

Piedmont Healthcare serves approximately 2.7 million patients and communities that comprise 70% of Georgia's population.

EXECUTIVES

Ceo, Leslie Les A Donahue
V Pres, Mark Cohen
SEC, Jay D Mitchell
Cfo, Charlie Hall
Coo, William D Knopf
Emergency Medicine Specialist, James V Robertson
Payroll Staff, Dejanelle N Gower
Coordinator, Deberah Williams
Chief Officer, Leigh S Hamby
Chief Strategy & Performance I, Michelle Fisher
Phlebotomist, Michael Higginbotham

LOCATIONS

HQ: PIEDMONT HOSPITAL, INC.
1968 PEACHTREE RD NW, ATLANTA, GA 303091285
Phone: 404 605-5000
Web: WWW.PIEDMONT.ORG

PRODUCTS/OPERATIONS

2014 Sales

	$ mil.	% of total
Net patient service revenue	1,595	96
Other revenue	62	4
Total	**1,657**	**100**

Selected Operations

Piedmont Atlanta
Piedmont Fayette Hospital (Fayetteville)

Piedmont Henry Hospital (Stockbridge)
Piedmont Mountainside Hospital (Jasper)
Piedmont Newnan Hospital (Newnan)
Piedmont Physicians Group (metropolitan Atlanta)

COMPETITORS

Children's Healthcare Of Atlanta	Northside Hospital
Dekalb Medical	Shepherd Center
Emory Healthcare	Tenet Healthcare
Grady Health System	Universal Health Services

HISTORICAL FINANCIALS

Company Type: Private

Income Statement

FYE: June 30

	REVENUE ($ mil.)	NET INCOME ($ mil.)	NET PROFIT MARGIN	EMPLOYEES
06/20	1,110	128	11.6%	6,419
06/16	918	60	6.5%	—
06/15	857	66	7.8%	—
06/10	689	75	11.0%	—
Annual Growth	**4.9%**	**5.4%**	**—**	**—**

2020 Year-End Financials

Return on assets: 7.3%   Cash ($ mil.): 28
Return on equity: 17.5%
Current ratio: 0.20

PIGGLY WIGGLY ALABAMA DISTRIBUTING CO., INC.

EXECUTIVES

Ceo-Pres, David Bullard
Director of Operations, Dale Reynolds
Manager, Human Resources, Dana Curtis
Admin, Shaunta Brown
Auditors: DENT BAKER & COMPANY LLP BI

LOCATIONS

HQ: PIGGLY WIGGLY ALABAMA DISTRIBUTING CO., INC.
2400 J TERRELL WOOTEN DR, BESSEMER, AL 350202272
Phone: 205 481-2300
Web: WWW.PWADC.NET

HISTORICAL FINANCIALS

Company Type: Private

Income Statement

FYE: July 29

	REVENUE ($ mil.)	NET INCOME ($ mil.)	NET PROFIT MARGIN	EMPLOYEES
07/11	772	0	0.1%	500
07/10	837	0	0.0%	—
07/09	830	0	0.0%	—
Annual Growth	**(3.5%)**	**85.6%**	**—**	**—**

2011 Year-End Financials

Return on assets: 0.5%   Cash ($ mil.): 4
Return on equity: 1.7%
Current ratio: 1.70

PIH HEALTH WHITTIER HOSPITAL

EXECUTIVES

Ceo, James R West
Cfo, Anita Chou
Cno, Ramona Pratt
Doctor, John R Hamilton
Dentist, Sue Ponce
Chaplain, Bruce Whyte
Administrative Coordinator RES, Mary Ladewig
Records Director, Nancy Stoner
Physician Assistant, Paula Meyer
Rn, Sasitorn Tanpradith
Business Office Director, Cole Christianson

LOCATIONS

HQ: PIH HEALTH WHITTIER HOSPITAL
12401 WASHINGTON BLVD, WHITTIER, CA 906021006
Phone: 562 698-0811
Web: WWW.PIHHEALTH.ORG

HISTORICAL FINANCIALS

Company Type: Private

Income Statement

FYE: September 30

	REVENUE ($ mil.)	NET INCOME ($ mil.)	NET PROFIT MARGIN	EMPLOYEES
09/19	651	59	9.2%	3,150
09/14	495	18	3.8%	—
09/13	491	81	16.7%	—
09/12	419	69	16.6%	—
Annual Growth	**6.5%**	**(2.1%)**	**—**	**—**

2019 Year-End Financials

Return on assets: 4.6%   Cash ($ mil.): —
Return on equity: 8.5%
Current ratio: 0.20

PIKEVILLE MEDICAL CENTER, INC.

Taking a nasty fall while hiking the rugged Appalachians will likely land you at Pikeville Medical Center (PMC). Serving patients in eastern Kentucky the hospital boasts more than 260 beds and provides a full range of inpatient outpatient and surgical services. PMC's centers and departments handle a number of specialties such as diagnostic imaging echocardiogram neurosurgery cancer care and bariatric surgery. Employing some 350 physicians PMC also operates a rehabilitation hospital a home health agency and outpatient family practice and specialty clinics as well as a physician residency program. PMC first opened on Christmas Day in 1924.

Operations

Pikeville Kentucky-based PMC offers more than 400 services.

Strategy

PMC is rapidly expanding its services and facilities to keep pace with the needs of area residents. In recent years it has added such new services as pulmonary rehabilitation plastic surgery and orthopedic trauma. In addition the hospital launched a $150 million expansion project that will add an 11-story outpatient center (including physician practices and surgery suites) and a 10-story parking garage. Additional expansion efforts have included opening new outpatient cancer diagnostic pain management and primary care clinics.

An active participant in clinical trials and studies PMC works to expand its research opportunities for patients and physicians. In 2013 the hospital began new treatment for patients with Paroxysmal Atrial Fibrillation (Afib) using Medtronic's Arctic Front Advance Cardiac Cryoballoon System.

Since 2012 when it inked a Medicaid contract with Coventry PMC has contracts with all three providers: Coventry Wellcare and Kentucky Spirit. PMC become member of the Mayo Clinic Care Network in 2013. The agreement gives PMC providers access to Mayo Clinic resources including its online point-of-care information system and its electronic consulting process that connects physicians with Mayo Clinic specialists on questions of diagnosis therapy or care management.

EXECUTIVES

Ceo-Pres, Walter E May
V Pres*, Ronald Burchett
SEC-Treas*, Joe Dean Anderson
Vp*, Michelle Hagy
Chief Operating Officer*, Debbie Puckett
Vp*, Peggy Rasnick Justice
Coo*, Juanita Deskins
Cfo*, Michelle Hagey
Occupational Specia, Alisa Bowers
Scientist, Sharon Weddington
Chief of Medicine, Ihari Malempati
Auditors: PERSHING YOAKLEY & ASSOCIATES

LOCATIONS

HQ: PIKEVILLE MEDICAL CENTER, INC.
  911 BYPASS RD, PIKEVILLE, KY 415011689
Phone: 606 218-3500
Web: WWW.PIKEVILLEHOSPITAL.ORG

PRODUCTS/OPERATIONS

Selected Services
Bariatric Surgery
Breast Care Center
Critical Care
Diagnostics
Diabetes Education
Ear Nose & Throat (Otolaryngology)
Emergency
Endocrinology
Family Practice
Gastroenterology
Gynecology/Obstetrics
Family Practice Clinic
Heart Institute
Heart Failure/Coumadin Clinic
Home Health
Home Medical Equipment
Inpatient
Infectious Disease
Laboratory Services
Leonard Lawson Cancer Center
Neonatology
Nephrology
Neurosurgery
Ophthalmology
Other Patient Services
Orthopedic Surgery
Palliative Care
Pediatrics
Pharmacy
Plastic & Reconstructive Surgery
Pulmonary Clinic
Radiology
Rehabilitation
Residency Program
Rheumatology
Sleep
Urology
Women and Childrens' Services
Wound Care Center

COMPETITORS

Appalachian Regional Healthcare	Norton Community Hospital
Clinch Valley Medical Center	Norton Healthcare
Community Health Systems	Russell County Medical Center
Highlands Health	University Of Kentucky Chandler Hospital

HISTORICAL FINANCIALS
Company Type: Private

Income Statement   FYE: September 30

	REVENUE ($ mil.)	NET INCOME ($ mil.)	NET PROFIT MARGIN	EMPLOYEES
09/20	568	17	3.0%	2,527
09/19	547	5	1.1%	—
09/18	524	(14)	—	—
09/16	489	29	5.9%	—
Annual Growth	3.8%	(12.3%)	—	—

2020 Year-End Financials

Return on assets: 2.4%   Cash ($ mil.): 277
Return on equity: 5.8%
Current ratio: 3.00

PILKINGTON NORTH AMERICA, INC.

Pilkington North America has a clear view of the US glass market. The company manufactures and markets glass and glazing products primarily for the automotive and building industries. Benefits of its glass include fire protection noise control solar heat control and thermal insulation. A majority of its sales come from automotive glass sold to the original equipment and replacement markets. More than a quarter of sales are made from building glass geared at homeowners and architects. A small but growing part of its business focuses on specialty glass used in solar energy conversion. Pilkington North America is a subsidiary of Pilkington plc which operates as part of Japanese glass giant Nippon Sheet Glass.

Geographic Reach
Pilkington North America manages six float glass lines in the US (where molten glass is poured on a bed of molten tin to ensure flat surface and uniform thickness) more than half a dozen automotive glass fabrication facilities in the US Canada and Mexico and a network of more than 100 US wholesale centers that distribute automotive replacement glass products.

Its six float glass lines including Rossford Ohio (2); Laurinburg North Carolina (2); Ottawa Illinois (1); Lathrop California (1). Products are shipped from its distribution centers in Columbus Ohio and Phoenix Arizona to external retailers and wholesale customers.

Sales and Marketing
The company provides glass products and glazing systems to automotive original equipment manufacturers of light vehicles buses trucks and specialized and utility vehicles; and glass products and accessories for replacing and repairing windshields and other glass parts to automotive glass replacement aftermarket sectors. Pilkington North America also serves homeowners architects and other window manufacturers and offers its products to retailers and wholesalers.

Automotive products (57% OEMs and 43% for automotive glass replacement) account for 70% of total sales; architectural products account for the remaining 30%. Products are shipped from its distribution centers in Phoenix and Columbus Ohio to external retailers and wholesale customers.
Strategy
In line with its parent's strategy a key focus for Pilkington North America's future is expanding its solar energy portfolio within its building products segment. The company anticipates an increase in volumes and that sales of solar energy glass will contribute a significant portion of those higher volumes. Although some of its float glass production lines were suspended during the economic crisis some have since been converted into solar energy lines and are coming back on stream to support its expansion particularly in photovoltaics.

Product introductions are also a key part of Pilkington North America's growth strategy. In 2014 it introduced Pilkington MirroView 50/50 which enhances the standard MirroView's visual performance for a brightly lit environment such as a store or showroom and Pilkington OptiView Pro a nonconductive anti-reflection coating especially designed for touch screen applications. In 2013 the company introduced Optiwhite which widens the color choice.

EXECUTIVES

Ceo-Pres, Richard Altman
Accounting Staff, David Reid
Marketing Director, Bill George
Payroll Staff, Trisha Walter
Senior Manager Benefits Planni, Marcie Kaminski
Chief Technical Officer, Dan Vermilya
Treas, Jeffrey Bowman
Research Associate, Scott Wilson
Purchasing Manager, David Lind
Recruiter, Julie Steel
Human Resources Specialist, Kim Wisniewski

LOCATIONS

HQ: PILKINGTON NORTH AMERICA, INC.
  811 MADISON AVE FL 3, TOLEDO, OH 436045688
Phone: 419 247-3731
Web: WWW.PILKINGTON.COM

PRODUCTS/OPERATIONS

Selected Products and Brands

Decoration
  Texture glass (18 pattern designs)
Fire protection
  Pyrodur (fire-resistant and radiant heat-protected glass)
  Pyrostop (fire-resistant insulating glass)
Glass systems
  Planar (structural glass system for architects)
  Profilit (exterior glazing glass)
Noise control
  Optiphon (laminated glass with high sound insulation)
Self-cleaning
  Activ Clear (clear float glass with self-cleaning properties)
Solar control
  Arctic Blue (tinted glass)
  Eclipse Advantage (solar control and thermal insulation glass)
  EverGreen (tinted glass)
  Solar-E (solar control and thermal insulation glass)
  SuperGrey (gray-colored solar control float glass)
Solar energy
  NSG TEC (coated glass for photovoltaic technologies)
  Sunplus (extra clear patterned glass for solar energy conversion)
  Optiwhite (extra clear float glass for solar energy conversion)
Special applications
  Mirropane (interior glass to create";infinity" mirror effects)

TEC Glass (electrically conductive glass for flat panel
displays heated glass and oven doors)
Thermal insulation
Energy Advantage (energy-efficient window glass)
OptiFloat (float glass)
Spacia (medium thermal insulation glass)

COMPETITORS

Apogee Enterprises	Saint-gobain
Asahi Glass	Schott Corporation
Cardinal Glass	Taylor Made Group
Guardian Glass	Viracon
Ppg Industries	

HISTORICAL FINANCIALS
Company Type: Private

Income Statement   FYE: March 31

	REVENUE ($ mil.)	NET INCOME ($ mil.)	NET PROFIT MARGIN	EMPLOYEES
03/08	967	(11)	—	3,747
03/07	913	(17)	—	
03/04	931	31	3.4%	—
Annual Growth	1.0%	—	—	—

2008 Year-End Financials
Return on assets: 12.3% Cash ($ mil.): —
Return on equity: (-1.2%)
Current ratio: 0.50

PIMA COUNTY

EXECUTIVES

Admin, Chuck Huckelberry
Information Specialist, Ed Sander
Customer Staff, Dana Moore
Environmental Officer, Jim Faas
Supervisor District 5, Richard Elias
Special Staff Assistant, Spencer Graves
Sergeant, Charles Lopiccolo
Detective, Jeremy Butcher
EDP Project Supervisor, Brandy Elliott
Information Technology Team ME, David Dargan
Chief Counsel, Edith Croxen
Auditors: STATE OF ARIZONA-DEBBIE
  DAVENP

LOCATIONS

HQ: PIMA COUNTY
  130 W CONGRESS ST FL 6, TUCSON, AZ 857011332
Phone: 520 724-9999
Web: WWW.WEBCMS.PIMA.GOV

HISTORICAL FINANCIALS
Company Type: Private

Income Statement   FYE: June 30

	REVENUE ($ mil.)	NET INCOME ($ mil.)	NET PROFIT MARGIN	EMPLOYEES
06/17	873	17	2.0%	7,500
06/16	863	2	0.3%	
06/13	789	(13)	—	
Annual Growth	2.6%			

2017 Year-End Financials
Return on assets: 0.4% Cash ($ mil.): 521
Return on equity: 0.9%
Current ratio: —

PINNACLE HEALTH HOSPITAL

EXECUTIVES

Ceo, Roger Longenderfer
Sr V Pres-Treas-Cfo*, William Pugh
Administrator*, Philip Guarneschelli
Law Specialist, John Warner
Coordinator, Andrea Flowers
Assistant Practice Manager, Michael Briner
Pain Management Specialist, Robert S Rankin
Family Practitioner, David Metzger
Internist, Julie Worthington
Podiatrist, Lauren Pruner
Director of Operations Lebanon, Oneida Deluca
Auditors: BAKER TILLY VIRCHOW KRAUSE
  LLP

LOCATIONS

HQ: PINNACLE HEALTH HOSPITAL
  4300 LONDONDERRY RD, HARRISBURG, PA
  171095317
Phone: 717 782-3131
Web: WWW.PINNACLEHEALTH.ORG

HISTORICAL FINANCIALS
Company Type: Private

Income Statement   FYE: June 30

	REVENUE ($ mil.)	NET INCOME ($ mil.)	NET PROFIT MARGIN	EMPLOYEES
06/14	759	94	12.5%	4,800
06/13	733	105	14.4%	—
06/08	0	0	14.6%	—
06/05	0	0	—	
Annual Growth	—	—	—	—

2014 Year-End Financials
Return on assets: 10.0% Cash ($ mil.): 1
Return on equity: 25.5%
Current ratio: 0.30

PITT COUNTY MEMORIAL HOSPITAL, INCORPORATED

Vidant Medical Center is an acute health services
facility that serves the vibrant community of
Greenville North Carolina and surrounding areas.
The 909-bed regional referral hospital's specialty
divisions include Vidant Children's Hospital East
Carolina Heart Institute a rehabilitation center and
the outpatient Vidant SurgiCenter. Other services
include oncology transplant women's health orthopedic behavioral care and home health and hospice care units. The center also serves as a teaching
facility for East Carolina University's Brody School
of Medicine. Vidant Medical Center (formerly Pitt
County Memorial Hospital) is a member of University Health Systems of Eastern Carolina (dba Vidant Health).

Operations
In addition to serving as a primary teaching facility for the Brody School of Medicine Vidant Medical Center provides clinical training for East Car-

olina University's allied health and nursing programs. About 2000 students complete clinical programs at the medical center and its affiliated Vidant
Health facilities each year.
Its subsidiary PMI Inc. offers property management services.
Altogether Vidant Medical Center serves more
than 1.4 million people across its 29-county service
area. Boasting a clinical staff of more than 500
physicians and 1200 nurses the medical center in
2013 tended to more than 46000 inpatients and
more than 275000 outpatients. Its emergency department visits reached 121000-plus in 2013.
Geographic Reach
Vidant Medical Center provides care to patients
in a 29-county service territory in eastern North
Carolina. It operates as a regional referral center
for smaller community hospitals in the area taking
on complex care cases in its specialized fields of
medicine.
Strategy
To enhance its service offerings to area residents
the Vidant Health organization regularly updates
its facilities through capital improvement projects.
In addition to basic equipment and infrastructure
upgrades in 2011 the hospital completed phase
one of an expansion project at the Vidant Medical
Center that aims to improve the hospital's pediatric
and cancer care capabilities.
To signify its mission to enhance the quality of
life in its service territories in 2012 University
Health Systems of Eastern Carolina began operating as Vidant Health and the Pitt County Memorial
Hospital was renamed as Vidant Memorial Hospital.

EXECUTIVES

Pres, Brian Floyd
Ceo*, Dave McRae
Registered Nurse, Susan Cash
Pta Licensed Physical Therapis, Mary Pabst
Dietetic Internship Coordinato, Ruth Schneider
Academic Appointments Associat, Wilson Rw
Police Chief of Support Servic, Tim Nelson
Coordinator, Linda McDanie
Coordinator, Linda McDaniel
Coordinator, Anita Harrison
Human Resources Information MA, Diane
  Hobbs
Auditors: RSM US LLP MINNEAPOLIS MINNE

LOCATIONS

HQ: PITT COUNTY MEMORIAL HOSPITAL,
  INCORPORATED
  2100 STANTONSBURG RD, GREENVILLE, NC
  278342832
Phone: 252 847-4100
Web: WWW.VIDANTHEALTH.COM

PRODUCTS/OPERATIONS

Selected Services
Asthma Program (Pediatric)
Audiology
Behavioral & Mental Health
Cancer Care
Child Life
Children's Care
Children's Emergency Department
Children's Hospital
Community Health Programs
CyberKnife
Diagnostic Imaging
Diabetes
Emergency Services
Endoscopy Services
Gamma Knife

Adventist Health System Sunbelt Healthcare
Bon Secours Health
Carolinas Healthcare System
Duke University Health System
Novant Health
Sentara Healthcare
Tenet Healthcare
Unc Hospitals
Upstate Affiliate

HISTORICAL FINANCIALS
Company Type: Private

Income Statement				FYE: September 30
	REVENUE ($ mil.)	NET INCOME ($ mil.)	NET PROFIT MARGIN	EMPLOYEES
09/20	1,974	58	3.0%	15,000
09/18	1,201	131	10.9%	—
09/15	1,066	79	7.5%	—
09/14	1,025	79	7.8%	—
Annual Growth	11.5%	(5.0%)	—	—

2020 Year-End Financials
Return on assets: 2.4% Cash ($ mil.): 111
Return on equity: 4.8%
Current ratio: 1.90

PITTSBURGH SCHOOL DISTRICT

EXECUTIVES

Supt, Linda Lane
Teacher, Ashley Filotei
Teacher, Laura Saxon
School Staff, Patricia Evans
Teacher, Takisha Miyares
Auditors: MAHER DUESSEL PITTSBURGH PEN

LOCATIONS

HQ: PITTSBURGH SCHOOL DISTRICT
341 S BELLEFIELD AVE, PITTSBURGH, PA
152133552
Phone: 412 622-3500
Web: WWW.PGHSCHOOLS.ORG

HISTORICAL FINANCIALS
Company Type: Private

Income Statement				FYE: December 31
	REVENUE ($ mil.)	NET INCOME ($ mil.)	NET PROFIT MARGIN	EMPLOYEES
12/20	715	3	0.5%	1,808
12/19	707	(21)	—	—
12/18	690	(19)	—	—
12/17	674	(4)	—	—
Annual Growth	2.0%	—	—	—

2020 Year-End Financials
Return on assets: 0.4% Cash ($ mil.): 51
Return on equity: —
Current ratio: 2.70

PLACID HOLDING COMPANY

EXECUTIVES

Pres, Dan Robinson
V Pres, Larry Doty
V Pres, Ron Hurst
Manager, Daniel Robinson
Auditors: HEIN & ASSOCIATES LLP DALLAS

LOCATIONS

HQ: PLACID HOLDING COMPANY
1601 ELM ST STE 3900, DALLAS, TX 752014708
Phone: 214 880-8479

HISTORICAL FINANCIALS
Company Type: Private

Income Statement				FYE: December 31
	REVENUE ($ mil.)	NET INCOME ($ mil.)	NET PROFIT MARGIN	EMPLOYEES
12/13	4,929	47	1.0%	2
12/02	532	3	0.6%	—
12/01	579	18	3.1%	—
12/00	564	5	1.0%	—
Annual Growth	18.1%	17.5%	—	—

2013 Year-End Financials
Return on assets: 7.5% Cash ($ mil.): 51
Return on equity: 12.8%
Current ratio: 1.40

PLACID REFINING COMPANY LLC

A calm presence in the volatile oil and gas industry Placid Refining owns and operates the Port Allen refinery in Louisiana which converts crude oil into a number of petroleum products including diesel ethanol gasoline liquid petroleum gas jet fuel and fuel oils. Placid Refining's refinery has the capacity to process 80000 barrels of crude oil per day. The company is one of the largest employers and taxpayers in West Baton Rouge Parish. Placid Refining which is controlled by Petro-Hunt distribute fuels across a dozen states in the southeastern US from Texas to Virginia and is a major supplier of jet fuel to the US military.

EXECUTIVES

Pres, Daniel Robinson
V Pres, Ron Hurst
Treasurer, Barry Joffrion
Manager, Accounts Payable, Leeann Maze
Auditors: HEIN & ASSOCIATES LLP DALLAS

LOCATIONS

HQ: PLACID REFINING COMPANY LLC
2101 CEDAR SPRINGS RD, DALLAS, TX 752012104
Phone: 214 880-8479
Web: WWW.PLACIDREFINING.COM

COMPETITORS

Citgo Refining And
  Chemicals
Nustar Energy

United Refining
Valero Energy

HISTORICAL FINANCIALS
Company Type: Private

Income Statement				FYE: December 31
	REVENUE ($ mil.)	NET INCOME ($ mil.)	NET PROFIT MARGIN	EMPLOYEES
12/13	4,929	47	1.0%	200
12/11	4,699	4	0.1%	—
12/10	3,686	39	1.1%	—
12/06	2,925	128	4.4%	—
Annual Growth	7.7%	(13.1%)	—	—

2013 Year-End Financials
Return on assets: 4.2% Cash ($ mil.): 42
Return on equity: 1.0%
Current ratio: 1.10

PLAINS COTTON COOPERATIVE ASSOCIATION

Plainly speaking most of the US cotton used by textile mills worldwide starts with the Plains Cotton Cooperative Association (PCCA). The farmer-owned co-op markets millions of bales annually for members in Oklahoma Kansas and Texas. To obtain a competitive price for their cotton PCCA takes advantage of Telmark LP's access to The Seam an online cotton marketplace that continually updates cotton prices buyer data and more. The co-op operates cotton warehouses in Texas Oklahoma and Kansas. PCCA sold its textile and apparel operations in 2014 to focus exclusively on cotton marketing and warehousing. Formed in 1953 PCCA's customers include Replay Urban Outfitters and Abercrombie & Fitch.

Operations

PCCA is a member of the American Apparel Producers' Network Amcot the National Cotton Council of America the National Council of Textile Organizations the Texas Agricultural Coop Council and The International Cotton Association.

Geographic Reach

Lubbock Texas-based Plains Cotton Cooperative Association owns half a dozen cotton warehouses in Kansas Oklahoma and Texas. Its Telmark LP business is also headquartered in Lubbock.

Financial Performance

The cooperative which distributed more than $22 million to its members posted total net margins of $10.4 million from its fiscal 2012-2013 operations. Despite a small crop during the reporting period PCCA saw its cotton marketing and warehouse divisions post profits. It was also helped by its IT division and support services. Feeling the drag of the US economy and unemployment the co-op's textile and apparel division focused on cutting costs.

Strategy

To better focus on its core cotton marketing and warehousing businesses PCCA sold its textile and apparel division to American Textile Holdings LLC (AmTex) in June 2014. The sale gave AmTex control of all the operations of American Cotton Growers (ACG) denim mill in Littlefield Texas and Denimatrix S.A. in Guatemala.

EXECUTIVES

Pres-Ceo, Kevin Brinkley
Chm*, Eddie Smith
Exec V Pres-Fin & Treas*, Sam Hill
Auditors: CROWE LLP DALLAS TEXAS

LOCATIONS

HQ: PLAINS COTTON COOPERATIVE ASSOCIATION
3301 E 50TH ST, LUBBOCK, TX 794044331
Phone: 806 763-8011
Web: WWW.PCCA.COM

PRODUCTS/OPERATIONS

Selected Sales and Services
Buying cotton
Cotton gins
  Gin bookkeeping
  Gin patronage
  Marketing and invoicing
  Scale ticket software
  Support and training
  Technology solutions
Cotton producers
  Agent gins
  Cash marketing
  marketing contracts
  Pool marketing
Warehousing

COMPETITORS

Alabama Farmers	J.g. Boswell Co.
Cooperative	Parkdale Mills
Calcot	Staplcotn
Dunavant Enterprises	Weil Brothers Cotton
Greenwood Mills	
International Cotton	
Marketing	

HISTORICAL FINANCIALS
Company Type: Private

Income Statement				FYE: June 30
	REVENUE ($ mil.)	NET INCOME ($ mil.)	NET PROFIT MARGIN	EMPLOYEES
06/16	892	23	2.7%	170
06/15	975	25	2.6%	—
Annual Growth	(8.6%)	(7.7%)	—	—

PLAINS PIPELINE, L.P.

EXECUTIVES

Ceo, Greg L Armstrong
V Pres, Harry N Pefanis
Exec V Pres, Al Swanson

LOCATIONS

HQ: PLAINS PIPELINE, L.P.
333 CLAY ST STE 1600, HOUSTON, TX 770024101
Phone: 713 646-4100
Web: WWW.PLAINSALLAMERICAN.COM

HISTORICAL FINANCIALS
Company Type: Private

Income Statement				FYE: December 31
	REVENUE ($ mil.)	NET INCOME ($ mil.)	NET PROFIT MARGIN	EMPLOYEES
12/17	935	783	83.7%	200
12/16	780	621	79.6%	—
Annual Growth	19.9%	26.1%	—	—

2017 Year-End Financials
Return on assets: 8.9%   Cash ($ mil.): 8
Return on equity: 17.4%
Current ratio: 0.40

PLAN INTERNATIONAL, INC.

EXECUTIVES

Ceo, Rose Caldwell
Director, Brittney Rocourt
IMC Team Coordinator, Cathie Cabral
Country Wash Advisor, Edgar Viterbo
Marketing and Acquisition, Jennifer Trainor
Senior Director, Jill Nosach
Manager Global Applications, Max Charman
Zone Coordinator Kissidougou P, Michel Kamano
Chief Marketing Officer, Shanna Marzilli
Director Coordinator, Dini Widiastuti
Senior Vice President of Progr, John Glover
Auditors: DYL & PERILLO INC PROVIDENCE

LOCATIONS

HQ: PLAN INTERNATIONAL, INC.
155 PLAN WAY STE A, WARWICK, RI 028861099
Phone: 401 294-3693
Web: WWW.PLAN-INTERNATIONAL.ORG

HISTORICAL FINANCIALS
Company Type: Private

Income Statement				FYE: June 30
	REVENUE ($ mil.)	NET INCOME ($ mil.)	NET PROFIT MARGIN	EMPLOYEES
06/15	684	(5)	—	7
06/14	657	(5)	—	—
06/12	601	29	4.9%	—
06/10	531	93	17.6%	—
Annual Growth	5.2%	—	—	—

2015 Year-End Financials
Return on assets: (-2.2%)   Cash ($ mil.): 185
Return on equity: (-3.1%)
Current ratio: 6.60

PLAN INTERNATIONAL, INC.

EXECUTIVES

Ceo, Anne-Birgitte Albrectsen
Administrative Officer, Marli Kaufmann
Auditors: DYL & PERILLO INC PROVIDENCE

LOCATIONS

HQ: PLAN INTERNATIONAL, INC.
228 E 45TH ST FL 15, NEW YORK, NY 100173344
Phone: 401 738-5600
Web: WWW.PLAN-INTERNATIONAL.ORG

HISTORICAL FINANCIALS
Company Type: Private

Income Statement				FYE: June 30
	REVENUE ($ mil.)	NET INCOME ($ mil.)	NET PROFIT MARGIN	EMPLOYEES
06/20	612	(48)	—	16
06/18	660	33	5.0%	—
Annual Growth	(3.6%)	—	—	—

2020 Year-End Financials
Return on assets: (-17.8%)   Cash ($ mil.): 168
Return on equity: (-26.4%)
Current ratio: 5.80

PLANO INDEPENDENT SCHOOL DISTRICT

EXECUTIVES

Exec Dir, Mark Allen
Spdt, Richard Matkin
Deputy Supt, Jeff Bailey
Assoc Supt, Jim Hirsch
Assistant, Mark De Hertogh
Coordinator, Suzana Spina
Registered Nurse, Amy Cimino
Nurse, Ashly Taylor
Assistant, Brittany Drake
Pace Teacher, David Edmondson
Nurse, Elizabeth Bond
Auditors: WEAVER AND TIDWELL LLP DA

LOCATIONS

HQ: PLANO INDEPENDENT SCHOOL DISTRICT
2700 W 15TH ST, PLANO, TX 750757524
Phone: 469 752-8100
Web: WWW.PISD.EDU

HISTORICAL FINANCIALS
Company Type: Private

Income Statement				FYE: June 30
	REVENUE ($ mil.)	NET INCOME ($ mil.)	NET PROFIT MARGIN	EMPLOYEES
06/20	871	(61)	—	5,610
06/19	928	(74)	—	—
06/18	840	34	4.1%	—
06/17	775	288	37.2%	—
Annual Growth	4.0%	—	—	—

PLY GEM HOLDINGS, INC.

Ply Gem brings out a new side of homes. The company makes and supplies exterior building materials used in home construction and renovation primarily in the US. Its products have included vinyl siding aluminum windows and doors stone veneer and fence and railing. Subsidiaries include Variform (vinyl siding) Its brands offer a broad selection of quality building products that includes nearly everything on the outside of a house. These products lead the industry as the #1 in windows vinyl siding and metal accessories with an un-matched portfolio backed by industry-leading warranties. Every product is rigorously tested to ensure exceptional durability and performance for every region or climate. Limitless color design and texture options are intended to work together to create custom curb appeal.

IPO

Operations

Ply Gem offers a wide array of products including siding windows patio doors stone fence and railing shutters and accents gutters as well as trim and moulding. The company's Home Design Visualizer is the ultimate tool for design inspiration and discovery. Its siding products have included vinyl solar defense insulated steel and aluminum lap siding shake and shingle siding and vertical siding. Customers can also choose from window styles offered by Ply Gem such as double hung single hung casement as well as door styles including sliding swinging multi-sliding and french doors.

Geographic Reach

The company is headquartered in North Carolina.

Mergers and Acquisitions

EXECUTIVES

Pres-Ceo, Gary E Robinette
Exec V Pres-Cfo-Sec, Shawn K Poe
Exec V Pres-Coo, John C Wayne
Chief Accounting Officer, Bryan Boyle
Pres, Siding Group, John L Buckley
Pres, US Windows & Doors, Arthur W Steinhafel
Customer Staff, Karen Brown
Sr Vp of Hr, David N Schmoll
Innovation Officer, Lee Clark-Sellers
Director Benefits, Steven Brown
Distribution, Cindy Meyer
Auditors: KPMG LLP RALEIGH NORTH CAROL

LOCATIONS

HQ: PLY GEM HOLDINGS, INC.
5020 WESTON PKWY STE 400, CARY, NC 275132322
Phone: 919 677-3900
Web: WWW.PLYGEM.COM

2017 Sales

	$ mil.	% of total
United States	1,849	90
Canada	202	10
Other foreign countries	3	-
Total	**2,056**	**100**

PRODUCTS/OPERATIONS

2017 Sales

	$ mil.	% of total
Windows & Doors	1,086	53
Sliding Fencing & Stone	970	47
Total	**2,056**	**100**

Selected Brands

Variform Siding
Napco Siding
Mastic Siding
Mitten Siding
Performance Siding
Georgia-Pacific
Canyon Stone
Simonton Windows
Great Lakes Window
Durabuilt
Leaf Relief
Leaf Relief Snap Tight
Leaf Smart
Leaf Logic
Ply Gem Shutters & Accents
Ply Gem Fence & Rail
Ply Gem Gutters

Ply Gem Roofing
Ply Gem Stone
Ply Gem Trim & Moulding
Ply Gem Windows & Doors

Selected Products

Fence & Rail
Gutters
Siding
Steel Siding
Stone Veneer
Trim
Windows and Doors

COMPETITORS

Alsco
Andersen Corporation
Arconic
Armstrong World
  Industries
Associated Materials
Atrium
Certainteed
Harvey Industries
Jeld-wen

Louisiana-pacific
Mi Windows And Doors
Masco
Owens Corning
Pella
Royal Group
Simonton Windows Inc.
Therma-tru
Trex Company

HISTORICAL FINANCIALS

Company Type: Private

Income Statement				FYE: December 31
	REVENUE ($ mil.)	NET INCOME ($ mil.)	NET PROFIT MARGIN	EMPLOYEES
12/17	2,056	68	3.3%	9,000
12/16	1,911	75	3.9%	—
12/15	1,839	32	1.8%	—
12/14	1,566	(31)	—	—
Annual Growth	9.5%	—	—	—

2017 Year-End Financials

Return on assets: 5.2%
Return on equity: 83.4%
Current ratio: 1.70

Cash ($ mil.): 71

POLK COUNTY

EXECUTIVES

Chm, Todd Dantdler
Commissioner*, Sam Johnson
Commissioner*, Jack Myers
Commissioner*, Bob English
Commissioner*, Wandy Wilkinson
Commissioner*, Jane Reed
Comptroller*, Stacy M Butterfield
Tax Collector, Joe Tetter
Property Appraiser, Marsha Faux
Commissioner, Bob Gernert Jr
Attorney, Mark Carpanini

LOCATIONS

HQ: POLK COUNTY
330 W CHURCH ST, BARTOW, FL 338303760
Phone: 863 534-6000
Web: WWW.POLK-COUNTY.COM

HISTORICAL FINANCIALS

Company Type: Private

Income Statement				FYE: September 30
	REVENUE ($ mil.)	NET INCOME ($ mil.)	NET PROFIT MARGIN	EMPLOYEES
09/18	602	48	8.0%	3,600
09/15	508	1	0.3%	—
09/12	593	(39)	—	—
09/09	589	(68)	—	—
Annual Growth	0.2%	—	—	—

2018 Year-End Financials

Return on assets: 1.0%
Return on equity: 1.3%
Current ratio: —

Cash ($ mil.): —

POLK COUNTY SCHOOL DISTRICT

EXECUTIVES

Spdt, Jacqueline Byrd
Occupational Specia, Amy Radano
Associate Superintendent, Michael Perrone Jr
Director of Charter Schools, Melissa Brady
Teacher, Sarah Sojos
Mathematics Teacher, Deborah Craig
Payroll Clerk Specialist, Ann Rentz
School Social Worker, Shannon Gillespie
Senior Manager, Angela Bottom
Music Teacher, Jessica Fredricks
Teacher, Kara Holt
Auditors: CHERRY BEKAERT LLP ORLANDO F

LOCATIONS

HQ: POLK COUNTY SCHOOL DISTRICT
1915 S FLORAL AVE, BARTOW, FL 338307124
Phone: 863 534-0500
Web: WWW.POLKSCHOOLSFL.COM

HISTORICAL FINANCIALS

Company Type: Private

Income Statement				FYE: June 30
	REVENUE ($ mil.)	NET INCOME ($ mil.)	NET PROFIT MARGIN	EMPLOYEES
06/14	871	(5)	—	5,124
06/13	827	(40)	—	—
06/12	821	(42)	—	—
Annual Growth	3.0%	—	—	—

2014 Year-End Financials

Return on assets: (-0.4%)
Return on equity: (-0.6%)
Current ratio: —

Cash ($ mil.): 69

POPULATION SERVICES INTERNATIONAL

Population Services International (PSI) goes far beyond the scope of its name. Founded in 1970 to promote global family planning PSI has established social programs that use local networks in low-income regions to distribute such lifelines as insecticide-treated mosquito nets iodized salt snake boots and insect repellent along with condoms contraceptives and pregnancy test kits. The group prides itself on using business principals to confront health issues in more than 65 countries worldwide. It reportedly has averted 4.2 million unintended pregnancies some 29 million malaria cases and provided 1.8-plus million clients with of HIV testing and counseling. PSI is also active ensuring safe water supplies.

EXECUTIVES

Ceo-Pres, Karl Hofmann
Chief Hr Officer*, Brandon Guzzone
Sr V-Pres-Coo*, Judith Heichelheim
Sr. V-Press- Chief Strategy An*, Michael Holsher
Sr. V-Press-Cfo*, Kin Schwarts
Dir. Institute and Foundation*, Mark Adam
General Counsel*, Katie Burnette
Managing Director*, Douglas Call
V Pres-Global Marketing*, Nikki Charman
Sr V-Pres- Wash and Chief Evid*, Desmond Chavasse
Dir-Grants & Contract*, Karen Conley

LOCATIONS

HQ: POPULATION SERVICES INTERNATIONAL 1120 19TH ST NW STE 600, WASHINGTON, DC 200363605
Phone: 202 785-0072
Web: WWW.PSI.ORG

HISTORICAL FINANCIALS
Company Type: Private

Income Statement				FYE: December 31
	REVENUE ($ mil.)	NET INCOME ($ mil.)	NET PROFIT MARGIN	EMPLOYEES
12/13	584	4	0.8%	455
12/01	121	(0)	—	—
12/00	96	3	3.4%	—
Annual Growth	14.8%	2.9%	—	—

2013 Year-End Financials
Return on assets: 10.1%   Cash ($ mil.): 210
Return on equity: 0.8%
Current ratio: 0.60

PORT OF LOS ANGELES

EXECUTIVES

Exec Dir, Gene Seroka
Port Police Sergeant, David Clements
Port Police Officer III, William Yocham
Accounting Rec Supervisor I, Brenda Aubert
Real Estate Officer, David Castillo
Clerk, Lachelle Washington
Sergeant, Michael Belo
Consultant, Ryan Kolanz
Vice President, Edward Renwick
Port Police Officer III, Arthur Kurkowski
Senior Security Officer, Damon Lankford
Auditors: MACIAS GINI & O'CONNELL LLP L

LOCATIONS

HQ: PORT OF LOS ANGELES 425 S PALOS VERDES ST, SAN PEDRO, CA 907313309
Phone: 310 732-3508
Web: WWW.PORTOFLOSANGELES.ORG

HISTORICAL FINANCIALS
Company Type: Private

Income Statement				FYE: June 30
	REVENUE ($ mil.)	NET INCOME ($ mil.)	NET PROFIT MARGIN	EMPLOYEES
06/21	572	128	22.5%	63
06/20	467	58	12.5%	—
06/19	506	168	33.3%	—
06/18	490	93	19.0%	—
Annual Growth	5.2%	11.3%	—	—

2021 Year-End Financials
Return on assets: 2.6%   Cash ($ mil.): 1,012
Return on equity: 3.5%
Current ratio: 6.20

PORTLAND PUBLIC SCHOOLS

EXECUTIVES

Superintendent, Carole Smith
Interim Chief of Staff, Alexander Perrins
Facilities, Adam Napier
Teacher, Allen Lauraine
Assistant Director, Ben Dandeneau
Board Clerk, Caren Huson
Third Grade, Chris Meeker
School Psychologist, Diane Lewis
Grade, Elizabeth Draper
Teacher, Joshua Zeller
Teacher, Karen Allen
Auditors: TALBOT KORVOLA & WARWICK LLP

LOCATIONS

HQ: PORTLAND PUBLIC SCHOOLS 501 N DIXON ST, PORTLAND, OR 972271876
Phone: 503 916-2000
Web: WWW.PPS.NET

HISTORICAL FINANCIALS
Company Type: Private

Income Statement				FYE: June 30
	REVENUE ($ mil.)	NET INCOME ($ mil.)	NET PROFIT MARGIN	EMPLOYEES
06/20	973	358	36.8%	5,244
06/19	922	(133)	—	—
06/18	882	336	38.1%	—
06/17	770	(127)	—	—
Annual Growth	8.1%	—	—	—

2020 Year-End Financials
Return on assets: 17.7%   Cash ($ mil.): 262
Return on equity: 178.4%
Current ratio: 6.30

POUDRE VALLEY HEALTH CARE, INC.

Providing health care is what this Poudre Valley is all about. The not-for-profit Poudre Valley Health System (PVHS) cares for residents of Colorado western Nebraska and southern Wyoming through the Poudre Valley Hospital and the Medical Center of the Rockies. With a total of about 440 beds the two hospitals offer general medical and surgical services and trauma care. They also offer treatment centers for specialties including cancer heart brain and spine disorders. PVHS is home to the Mountain Crest Behavioral Healthcare Center which administers mental health and substance abuse treatment. PVHS is part of the Health District of Northern Larimer County; it is also part of University of Colorado Health.

Operations
The Poudre Valley Hospital features 270 patient beds while the Medical Center of the Rockies has a capacity of about 170 beds. Beyond its primary hospital campuses the health system also operates several outpatient clinics and a family medicine center that hosts a rural medicine residency program. Altogether PVHS has more than 550 physicians practicing in more than 40 specialty fields.

In addition to its joint operating agreement with the University of Colorado Hospital PVHS has formed collaborative care partnerships with local organizations including a local laser eye surgery center numerous outpatient centers for rehabilitation surgery and infusion therapy as well as home health care and home supply companies.

Geographic Reach
PVHS serves residents of Estes Park Fort Collins Greeley and Loveland Colorado as well as Larimer and Weld Counties. The system also serves customers from Cheyenne and Laramie Wyoming and Scottsbluff Nebraska.

Strategy
The organization has held a long tradition of partnering with numerous local organizations to expand its service offerings. To create a broader health organization for the Rocky Mountain region PVHS formed a joint operating agreement with University of Colorado Hospital in 2012. Together the systems are known as University of Colorado Health and are governed by a single board of directors. The hospitals continue to operate under their existing names.

Other growth efforts include the construction of a new $14.5 million emergency care center in 2012 and the opening of a new 12-bed women's and children's unit at Medical Center of the Rockies in 2013.

In 2013 it also opened the 36000-sq.-ft. Indian Peaks Medical Center in Frederick at an estimated cost of $20 million to $30 million. It includes cardiology and diagnostics departments.

Company Background
The organization was founded in 1925. Since 1995 when PVHS reorganized as a private not-for-profit health care organization local property taxes that used to go straight to PVHS have been paid to the Health District of Northern Larimer County which then uses them to fund PVHS' various activities.

EXECUTIVES

Ceo, Rulon Stacey
Pres*, Keving Unger
Manager, Ryan Roberts

Assistant To Vice President, Samantha Hutchinson
MBA Student MBA Biomedical Eng, Sara Andrews
Real Estate Specialist, Steve Houston
Coordinator, Brenda Nicholson
Information Technology Manager, Mike Brachtenbach
Staff Nurse, Rita Stern
Psychologist, Joan Welsh
Surgery Coordinator, Amy Hartman
Auditors: PLANTE & MORAN PLLC DENVER

LOCATIONS

HQ: POUDRE VALLEY HEALTH CARE, INC.
12401 E 17TH AVE STE B132, AURORA, CO 800452589
Phone: 970 495-7000
Web: WWW.UCHEALTH.ORG

PRODUCTS/OPERATIONS

Selected Services
Back Neck and Spine Care
Cancer Care
Diabetes and Endocrinology
Hyperbaric Medicine
Imaging and Radiology
Laboratory Services
Orthopedics
Pain Care and Management
Seniors' Health
Weight and Metabolism
Women's Health
Wound Care

COMPETITORS

Catholic Health Initiatives
Centura Health
Denver Health And Hospital Authority
Exempla Healthcare Healthone
Memorial Health System (colorado)
North Colorado Medical Center
University Of Colorado Hospital
Valley View Hospital
Wyoming Medical Center

HISTORICAL FINANCIALS

Company Type: Private

Income Statement   FYE: June 30

	REVENUE ($ mil.)	NET INCOME ($ mil.)	NET PROFIT MARGIN	EMPLOYEES
06/20	1,266	209	16.5%	2,800
06/19	1,412	340	24.1%	—
06/16	523	92	17.7%	—
06/15	480	98	20.6%	—
Annual Growth	21.4%	16.2%	—	—

2020 Year-End Financials
Return on assets: 6.7%
Return on equity: 8.7%
Current ratio: 3.10
Cash ($ mil.): 381

POWERSOUTH ENERGY COOPERATIVE

Several hundred thousand Alabamans and Floridians get their electric power courtesy of the work of PowerSouth Energy Cooperative which provides wholesale power to its member-owners (16 electric cooperatives and four municipal distribution utilities). Its distribution members provide electric services to almost 417200 customer meters in central and southern Alabama and western Florida. PowerSouth operates a more than 2200-mile power transmission system and has more than 2000 MW of generating capacity from interests in six fossil-fueled and hydroelectric power plants.

Geographic Reach
PowerSouth serves customers in Alabama (39 counties) and Florida (10 counties).

Operations
The company owns and operates six generation facilities and holds ownership interest in an additional facility. Its diverse generating fuel mix includes natural gas coal and water (hydro). It also has compressed air energy storage technology and a disciplined fuel supply hedging program that minimizes the impact of fuel cost increases. In addition PowerSouth maintains long-term purchased power agreements to ensure economic and reliable power supply for its members.

PowerSouth serves the wholesale energy needs of electric cooperatives and municipal electric systems in Alabama and northwest Florida who in turn serve more than a million consumers. PowerSouth is dedicated to providing reliable energy at the lowest possible cost to its members.

Financial Performance
The company's revenues increased by 3% in 2013 primarily due to an increase in member revenues as a result of an increase in energy sales. The remaining increase was due to the surcharges added to the excess demand rate during 2013.

That year PowerSouth's net income decreased by 6% as the result of increased operating costs caused by higher distribution costs and administration and general expenses.

Its operating cash inflow increased to $63.5 million in 2013 (compared to $38.3 million in 2012) due to a rise in account receivables and inventories.

Strategy
To meet future demand and tightening environmental regulations the company is looking to diversify and expand its power production assets with an emphasis on cleaner energy plants. PowerSouth's long-term energy plans include a 20-year contract for 125 MW of nuclear power from two Vogtle Units being built by the Municipal Energy Authority of Georgia near Augusta and due to come onstream in 2016 and 2017. The company is also investing in wind power and biomass-to-energy initiatives.

Company Background
PowersSouth is owned and managed by it 20 distribution members.

The company once provided propane but sold its Cooperative Propane unit in 2011 to focus on its core power businesses.

In 2008 Alabama Electric Cooperative changed its name to PowerSouth Energy Cooperative to better reflect its service territory (Alabama and Florida) and its opportunities for future growth.

Founded in 1941 as Alabama Electric Cooperative the coop promotes a strong economic development program aimed at bringing industry into both Alabama and Florida.

EXECUTIVES

Ceo, Gary Smith
V Pres-Coo*, Damon Morgan
Cfo-V Pres*, Rick Kyle
Vice President Information TEC, Lewis Jeffers
Vice President, Beth Woodard
Mechanical Maintenance Supervi, Wayne Phillips
Trustee, Davis Henson
Buyer I, Benny Cockrell
Fleet Maintenance Supervisor, Chuck Dutton
Programmer Analyst, Amy Turner
Department Secretary, Angela Kelly
Auditors: BKD LLP OKLAHOMA CITY OKLAH

LOCATIONS

HQ: POWERSOUTH ENERGY COOPERATIVE
2027 E THREE NOTCH ST, ANDALUSIA, AL 364212427
Phone: 334 427-3000
Web: WWW.POWERSOUTH.COM

PRODUCTS/OPERATIONS

View Archived What Charts | Edit 2013 Sales

	% of total
Electric	
Cooperatives	93
Municipalities	6
Other	1
Total	**100**

HISTORICAL FINANCIALS

Company Type: Private

Income Statement   FYE: December 31

	REVENUE ($ mil.)	NET INCOME ($ mil.)	NET PROFIT MARGIN	EMPLOYEES
12/20	547	12	2.3%	640
12/19	602	13	2.3%	—
12/18	612	12	2.0%	—
12/17	588	9	1.6%	—
Annual Growth	(2.4%)	9.7%	—	—

2020 Year-End Financials
Return on assets: 0.6%
Return on equity: 3.4%
Current ratio: 1.10
Cash ($ mil.): 152

PRAIRIE FARMS DAIRY, INC.

Prairie Farms Dairy is one of the largest and most successful dairy cooperatives in the Midwest and the South. With more than 700 dairy farmer/members the cooperative offers a full line of retail and food service dairy products. It turns raw milk into fresh fluid cultured and frozen dairy products under the Prairie Farms label. It also makes juices and ice cream novelties. The company's customers include food drug and convenience stores mass merchandisers schools restaurants and other food service operators. Located in Edwardsville Illinois it is the managing partner for joint ventures with smaller regional dairies. It makes its products at nearly 50 manufacturing plants and over 100 distribution facilities which are located throughout the midwestern and southern areas of the US.

Operations
From its over 700 member farms Prairie Farms sources milk products for its array of food products. It produces all varieties of milk butter cottage cheese cream ice cream yogurt and other diary-based products. It also goes outside its core to produce and sell teas juices and iced coffee.

In addition to manufacturing dairy foods co-packing is a big part of Prairie Farms' operation. The company's PFD Supply and GMS Transportation non-dairy subsidiaries distribute products for fast-food chains.

Geographic Reach

Headquartered in Edwardsville Illinois Prairie Farms and its subsidiaries manufacture dairy products at nearly 50 plants and more than 100 distribution facilities in Arkansas Illinois Indiana Iowa Kansas Kentucky Michigan Mississippi Missouri Nebraska Oklahoma Ohio Tennessee Texas and Wisconsin.

Sales and Marketing

Prairie Farms' products are for sale through a variety of retail grocery store foodservice drug club and dollar stores mass merchandiser and school locations in the same states in which it has production facilities. It sells its products under the Prairie Farms brand name and the co-op also sells products through partners Hiland Dairy East Side Jersey Ice Cream Specialties and Turner.

Company Background

The cooperative dates back to 1932 when Illinois farmers formed a statewide organization Illinois Producers Creameries to market and sell cream. In 1938 it became Prairie Farms Dairy.

EXECUTIVES

Ceo, Ed Mullins
Pres of The Brd, Fred Kuenstler
Cfo-Asst SEC, Tom Weber
Cfo, Jason Geminn
V Pres-Data Processing, Ronnie G McMillan
Accounting Staff, Suzy Mertz
Coordinator, Adrianna Bishop
Distribution/Shipping/Transpor, Rob Ruppert
Qa Qc Manager, Karen Frazier
Corporate Ehs Manager, Troy Ferguson
Corporate Fleet Assistant, Aimee McCormick
Auditors: BKD LLP ST LOUIS MO

LOCATIONS

HQ: PRAIRIE FARMS DAIRY, INC.
  3744 STAUNTON RD, EDWARDSVILLE, IL 620256936
Phone: 618 659-5700
Web: WWW.PRAIRIEFARMS.COM

Selected Areas of Distribution
Arkansas
Illinois
Indiana
Iowa
Kansas
Kentucky
Michigan
Mississippi
Missouri
Nebraska
Ohio
Oklahoma
Tennessee
Wisconsin

PRODUCTS/OPERATIONS

Branded Partners
Hiland Dairy Foods Company
Ice Cream Specialties
Madison Farms Butter
Muller-Pinehurst Dairy
Turner Dairy

Selected Products
Butter
Cultured dairy products
  Cottage cheese (regular low fat and fat-free; small and large curd)
  Dips
  Sour cream
  Yogurt (regular low fat and fat-free)
Fluid milk products
  Buttermilk
  Cream
  Egg nog (seasonal)
  Milk (regular low fat and fat-free)
  Flavored milk
Frozen desserts
  Frozen yogurt

Ice cream (regular low fat and fat-free)
  Novelties
  Sherbet
Juices drinks and iced tea

COMPETITORS

Associated Milk Producers	Foremost Farms
Dairy Farmers Of America	Friendly's Ice Cream
	Hp Hood
Darigold Inc.	Land O'lakes
Dean Foods	Quality Chekd
Dreyer's	Rockview Dairies
Farmland Dairies	Wells' Dairy

HISTORICAL FINANCIALS

Company Type: Private

Income Statement   FYE: September 30

	REVENUE ($ mil.)	NET INCOME ($ mil.)	NET PROFIT MARGIN	EMPLOYEES
09/13	1,721	14	0.8%	1,965
09/12	1,649	38	2.4%	—
09/11	1,607	28	1.7%	—
Annual Growth	3.5%	(28.9%)	—	—

2013 Year-End Financials

Return on assets: 1.9%   Cash ($ mil.): 12
Return on equity: 3.4%
Current ratio: 1.20

PRATT CORRUGATED HOLDINGS, INC.

EXECUTIVES

Employee, Stephanie Inman
Auditors: GRANT THORNTON LLP ATLANTA

LOCATIONS

HQ: PRATT CORRUGATED HOLDINGS, INC.
  1800 SARASOT BUS PKWY NE C, CONYERS, GA 300135775
Phone: 770 918-5678

HISTORICAL FINANCIALS

Company Type: Private

Income Statement   FYE: June 30

	REVENUE ($ mil.)	NET INCOME ($ mil.)	NET PROFIT MARGIN	EMPLOYEES
06/21	3,113	128	4.1%	425
06/20	2,649	75	2.9%	—
06/18	2,518	87	3.5%	—
06/17	2,360	65	2.8%	—
Annual Growth	7.2%	18.2%	—	—

2021 Year-End Financials

Return on assets: 7.8%   Cash ($ mil.): 247
Return on equity: 16.6%
Current ratio: 1.40

PRATT INDUSTRIES, INC.

Pratt Industries (USA) doesn't mill around when it comes to recycling and caring for the environment. The company rivals the world's largest manufacturers of recycled paper and packaging and claims to be the 5th largest box manufacturer in the US and the world's largest privately-held 100% recycled paper and packaging company. Pratt has a handful of operating divisions: recycling mills corrugating converting displays packaging systems and national accounts. Its products which include container board and corrugated sheets are sold to clients such as Rubbermaid and Pringles.

Operations

The company operates 32 sheet plants 18 recycling centers 16 corrugating plants seven distribution centers seven displaying facilities four recycled paper mills and one clean energy plant. It operates through the main divisions of Clean Energy Converting Corrugating Display Paper Mills Recycling Logistics Specialty and Strategic Services.

Geographic Reach

Pratt operates some 50 plants in more than 20 US states and Mexico.

Strategy

Pratt has strategically located its manufacturing facilities to reduce freight time and cost and to provide regional design and account management support. The locations enable it to react quickly and decisively to meet the needs of customers.

In 2015 Pratt Industries broke ground on its new $52 million corrugated box factory in Beloit Wisconsin. The 350000 sq. ft. facility due for start-up in early 2016 will sit on a 56-acre site and produce 600 tons of recycled boxes a day at capacity.

Mergers and Acquisitions

In 2015 the company improved its footprint through the purchase of California-based food and agricultural packaging company Robert Mann Packaging (RMP). Pratt paid $60 million for the privately-owned RMP group which has $150 million in annual sales and more than a dozen facilities in the western US and Mexico including a 350000 square-foot box-making plant in Salinas California. The deal gave the company a nationwide footprint throughout the US with manufacturing sites stretching from New York to the West Coast.

Company Background

The company was founded in 1948 by Leon Pratt grandfather of Anthony Pratt.

EXECUTIVES

Ceo, Brian McPheely
V Pres*, Gary Byrd
V Pres-SEC*, David J Kyles
Coo*, David Dennis
Cfo*, Stephen Ward
Designer, Fernando Arreola
Coordinator, Luke Rock
Vice President Purchasing and, Danielle Roszko
Controller, Alan Welch
Design Manager, Brent Hise
Account Manager, David Roberts
Auditors: GRANT THORNTON LLP ATLANTA

LOCATIONS

HQ: PRATT INDUSTRIES, INC.
  1800 SARASOT BUS PKWY NE S, CONYERS, GA 300135775
Phone: 770 918-5678
Web: WWW.PRATTINDUSTRIES.COM

PRODUCTS/OPERATIONS

Selected Divisions
Converting
Corrugating
Displays
Mills
National Accounts
Packaging Systems
Recycling

Selected Products and Services
Bagging
  Merchandise bags
  Polypropylene bags
  Poly-tubing
  Seal-top bags
  Static shielded bags
Carton Closure/Sealing
  Adhesives
  Double coated tape
  Duct tape
  Filament tape
  Foam tape
  Foil tape
  Masking tape
  Poly-strapping
  Pressure sensitive carton sealing tape
  Staples
  Steel Strapping
  Teflon tape
  Water activate carton sealing tape
Cushioning/Void Fill
  Air dunnage bags
  Bubble wrap
  Cellulose wadding
  Foam-N-Place
  Honeycomb
  Kraft wrap
  Loose fill foam
  Newsprint
  Polyethylene foam
  Polypropylene foam
Edge/Corner Protection
  Angleboard
  Anglewrap
  Cornerboard
  Form-A-Board
  Protect-A-Board
  Protect-A-Wrap
  Stackmaster
  Strap protectors
Labeling and Coding
  Cleaners
  Inks
  Labels
  Ribbons
Mailing and Shipping
  Mailers
  Packing list envelopes
  Shipping tubes and tags
Unitization
  Poly pallet covers
  Poly pallet shrink bags
  Poly top sheets
  Poly-strapping
  Shrink bundling
  Steel strapping
  Stretch film
Visual Packaging
  Blister packaging
  Clamshells
  Polyolefin shrinkfilm
  PVC shrink bands
  Skin packaging
  Skin packaging film

COMPETITORS

Georgia-pacific
Green Bay Packaging
International Paper
Interstate Resources
  Inc.
Packaging Corp. Of
  America
Southern Container
Weyerhaeuser

HISTORICAL FINANCIALS
Company Type: Private

Income Statement

	REVENUE ($ mil.)	NET INCOME ($ mil.)	NET PROFIT MARGIN	EMPLOYEES
06/21	3,064	225	7.3%	5,890
06/20	2,612	200	7.7%	—
06/18	2,498	200	8.0%	—
Annual Growth	7.0%	3.9%	—	—

FYE: June 30

2021 Year-End Financials
Return on assets: 7.4%
Return on equity: 16.2%
Current ratio: 2.40
Cash ($ mil.): 707

PRECISION CASTPARTS CORP.

Precision Castparts Corp. (PCC) is the market leader in manufacturing large complex structural investment castings airfoil castings forged components aerostructures and highly engineered critical fasteners for aerospace applications. In addition the Company is the leading producer of airfoil castings for the industrial gas turbine. PCC also manufactures extruded seamless pipe fittings forgings and clad products for power generation and oil & gas applications; commercial and military airframe aerostructures; and metal alloys and other materials to the casting and forging industries. The company is a subsidiary of Berkshire Hathaway. The company was founded in 1947.

HISTORY

The history of Precision Castparts Corp. (PCC) is not as precise as its castings. The Oregon Saw Company was founded in 1949 and sold in 1953; its buyer wanted neither the future PCC nor a power tools unit so the two became Omark Industries. In 1956 a buyer purchased the power tool business but wasn't interested in castings; that operation was spun off as Precision Castparts Corp.

In the early 1950s a group of Oregon Saw's casting employees developed a process for producing parts as large as 60 inches by use of investment casting making products that rivaled the strength of forged and machined parts at a fraction of the cost. After a two-year search they landed their first aerospace customer — Air Research Corp. — with many to follow. The higher operating temperatures generated by aircraft engines led the company to buy a vacuum furnace in 1959 to fabricate parts that could tolerate greater heat; two more vacuum furnaces were added and sales vaulted toward $10 million by 1967. PCC went public in 1968 and continued to grow. In 1976 the company acquired Centaur Cast Alloys (small investment castings UK) to make parts for the European aerospace industry. By that time General Electric (GE) and Pratt & Whitney accounted for most of PCC's business. Edward Cooley who had masterminded the company's growth since incorporation forged ahead with plans to double production capacity.

In 1980 the airline industry crashed but PCC's sales held at about $90 million. Structural airplane products soon picked up and in 1984 the company bought two titanium foundries in France. To diversify it added TRW's cast airfoils (used in aircraft engines and industrial gas turbines) division in

1986. That acquisition renamed PCC Airfoils increased PCC's annual sales by about 80%; sales reached $443 million by 1989.

The company broadened its offerings again in 1991 when it acquired Advanced Forming Technology which made small complex metal-injection molded parts used in everything from adding machines to military ordnance. The early 1990s recession hit the airline industry and sales dropped. Cooley retired as chairman in 1994 and GE veteran William McCormick replaced him. The next year PCC acquired Quamco Inc. (industrial tools and machines). In 1996 PCC flowed into the fluid management market with the acquisition of NEWFLO for about $300 million.

In 1997 PCC spent $437 million to acquire seven more companies that helped boost sales 75% from 1996 levels. The next year it purchased four metalworking companies that served industries other than aerospace. Having reduced dependence on sales to the aerospace industry to just over 50% PCC began consolidating operations and closing plants to reduce costs.

The company continued to diversify through acquisitions in 1999 but it also expanded its aerospace operations with the purchase of Wyman-Gordon a leading maker of advanced metal forgings for the aerospace market. PCC's 2000 acquisitions included the aerospace division of United Engineering Forgings and Germany-based Convey Engineering (heavy-duty valves). The next year the company bought the assets of Netherlands-based Wouter Witzel and the US's Drop Dies and Forgings Company (renamed Wyman-Gordon Cleveland). In 2002 PCC bought the rest of Western Australian Specialty Alloys (casting and forging alloys) for $27.6 million in cash and PCC shares.

In 2003 Precision Castparts' PCC Structurals unit reached a $400 million agreement with Rolls-Royce to supply large titanium and steel castings. That year the company acquired SPS Technologies a producer of fasteners and other metal components for the aerospace automotive and industrial markets. In 2004 subsidiary SPS Aerospace Fasteners signed a four-year deal with Airbus worth about $72 million to supply collars nuts studs and titanium pins to Airbus plants across Europe.

PCC acquired Air Industries Corporation in early 2005. In 2006 PCC bought Special Metals Corporation (SMC) a maker of nickel alloys and super alloys for $295 million in cash and the assumption of $245 million in SMC debt. PCC intended to use SMC's product as raw materials for its own aircraft engine components. SMC also served the automotive chemical and power generation industries.

Later in 2006 PCC bought Shur-Lok Corporation a manufacturer of aerospace fasteners for about $110 million. The acquisition combined with the 2005 purchase of Air Industries Corporation helped to further PCC's desire to grow its airframe fasteners business.

Early in 2007 PCC completed the purchase of GSC a leading maker of aluminum and steel structural investment casting for the aerospace energy and medical markets. It also acquired Cherry Aerospace which expanded its fastener products portfolio.

In 2009 the company acquired Carlton Forge Works which makes aircraft engines for Boeing and Airbus; California-based Arcturus Manufacturing (hammer forging operations) was included in the transaction. PCC also picked up Airdrome Holdings (fluid fittings) Fatigue Technology (cold expansion technology) and Hackney Ladish (forged pipe fittings) in 2009.

In late summer 2011 PPC purchased Primus International a maker of complex metal industrial parts and assemblies. Its products (machined aluminum and titanium components used in aircraft wings fuselages and engine-related assemblies)

cater to Boeing Airbus and other aerospace OEMs. The $900 million deal furthered the company's commitment to the global aerospace industry. In a similar vein the company obtained Unison Engine Components (operating as Tru-Form Rings) from GE Aviation in mid-2011. Tru-Form made flash-welded and cold-rolled rings with jet engine as well as gas turbine applications.

PCC also acquired RathGibson which makes tubing for the oil and gas chemical/petrochemical power-generation and other markets in 2012.

To expand both its Fasteners and Forged Products segments PCC acquired the aerostructures and industrial products businesses of H ©roux-Devtek for about CAD$300 million (about $295.5 million) in 2012. Among other benefits the acquisition expanded the company's product line for such OEMs as Lockheed Bombardier and Gulfstream. PCC also inked a deal to purchase the Synchronous Aerospace Group business of private investment firm Littlejohn & Co. in late 2012.

EXECUTIVES

Pres, Mark Donegan
Cfo-Evp*, Shawn R Hagel
Evp*, Steven G Hackett
SEC*, Ruth A Beyer
Cto*, Mark Roskopf
Cco-Vp*, EMI Donis
Director of Real Estate Servic, Liz Fritzinger
Corporate It Manager, Ronald Kemp
Treasurer, Steven Blackmore
Manager of Cnc Machining Techn, Eric Huhn
University Relations Program M, Karen Garrison
Auditors: DELOITTE & TOUCHE LLP PORTLAN

LOCATIONS

HQ: PRECISION CASTPARTS CORP.
4650 SW MCDAM AVE STE 300, PORTLAND, OR 97239
Phone: 503 946-4800
Web: WWW.PRECAST.COM

PRODUCTS/OPERATIONS

Selected Products and Services

Fasteners
  Advanced forming technology
  E/One (for the disposal of residential sanitary waste)
  J&L fiber services (for pulp and paper industry)
  PCC Precision Tool Group
  SPS aerospace fasteners (for commercial/military aircraft)
  SPS engineered fasteners (high strength for automotive and construction applications)
Forged products
  Special Metals Corporation
  Wyman-Gordon Forgings
Investment Cast Products
  PCC Airfoils (high-temperature blades and vanes)
  PCC Structurals (structural investment castings)
  Specialty materials and alloys (alloys waxes and metal processing for investment casting)

COMPETITORS

Ati Ladish	Hitachi Metals
Allegheny Technologies	Kennametal
Arconic	Lisi
Carpenter Technology	Mettis Aerospace
Chicago Rivet	Souriau Pa&e
Crane Co.	Swagelok
Curtiss-wright	Teleflex
Esco	Thyssenkrupp
Farwest Steel	United Technologies
Corporation	Universal Stainless
Federal Screw Works	V & M Tubes (usa)
Georg Fischer	Volvo Aero
Haynes International	

HISTORICAL FINANCIALS
Company Type: Private

Income Statement				FYE: January 3
	REVENUE ($ mil.)	NET INCOME ($ mil.)	NET PROFIT MARGIN	EMPLOYEES
01/16*	7,002	817	11.7%	30,116
03/15	10,005	1,533	15.3%	—
03/14	9,616	1,784	18.6%	—
03/13	8,377	1,429	17.1%	—
Annual Growth	(5.8%)	(17.0%)	—	—

*Fiscal year change

2016 Year-End Financials
Return on assets: 4.0%   Cash ($ mil.): 343
Return on equity: 7.0%
Current ratio: 3.90

PREMIER HEALTHCARE ALLIANCE, L.P.

EXECUTIVES

MBR-Ceo, Susan Devore
MBR-Chb*, Glenn Steel Jr
MBR-V Chb*, Dennis Vonderfecht
Coo*, Michael Alkire
Cfo*, Craig McKasson
Ceo*, Richard A Norling
Sr V Pres*, Ann D Rhoads
Vice-President Information Ser, Larry D Grandia
Lawson Edi Administrat, Rory Flood
Business Continuity and Disast, David A Shimberg
Data Specialist/Membership Gro, Joseph Lawrence

LOCATIONS

HQ: PREMIER HEALTHCARE ALLIANCE, L.P.
13034 BALNTYN CORP PL, CHARLOTTE, NC 282771498
Phone: 704 357-0022
Web: WWW.PREMIERINC.COM

HISTORICAL FINANCIALS
Company Type: Private

Income Statement				FYE: June 30
	REVENUE ($ mil.)	NET INCOME ($ mil.)	NET PROFIT MARGIN	EMPLOYEES
06/12	590	326	55.3%	199
06/11	679	311	45.8%	—
06/09	1,830	0	—	—
Annual Growth		—18233.3%	—	—

2012 Year-End Financials
Return on assets: 72.7%   Cash ($ mil.): 129
Return on equity: 92.9%
Current ratio: 5.30

PREMISE HEALTH HOLDING CORP.

EXECUTIVES

Ceo, Edward Stuart Clark
Coo, Trent Riley
Cfo, Shannon Farrington
Pres, Jami Doucette
Chief Information Officer, Haden McWhorter
Chief Human Resources Officer, Elizebeth Reimer
Chief Compliance Officer, Dana Fields
Chief Information Security Off, Joey Johnson
Exec V Pres, Peter Vasquez
Exec V Pres, Ed McNamara
Operations, Beth Ratliff
Auditors: RSM US LLP CHICAGO ILLINOIS

LOCATIONS

HQ: PREMISE HEALTH HOLDING CORP.
5500 MARYLAND WAY STE 400, BRENTWOOD, TN 370277048
Phone: 615 468-6562
Web: WWW.PREMISEHEALTH.COM

HISTORICAL FINANCIALS
Company Type: Private

Income Statement				FYE: December 31
	REVENUE ($ mil.)	NET INCOME ($ mil.)	NET PROFIT MARGIN	EMPLOYEES
12/17	685	7	1.0%	4,500
12/16	630	(2)	—	—
12/15	581	0	0.0%	—
12/14	303	(14)	—	—
Annual Growth	31.2%	—	—	—

2017 Year-End Financials
Return on assets: 2.1%   Cash ($ mil.): 37
Return on equity: 6.4%
Current ratio: 2.20

PRESBYTERIAN HOSPITAL

EXECUTIVES

Ceo, Carl Armato
Pres*, Lynn Bodgs
Coordinator, Jacqueline Vaughn
Coordinator, Rachel Karo
Supervisor, Cynthia Jackson

LOCATIONS

HQ: PRESBYTERIAN HOSPITAL
200 HAWTHORNE LN, CHARLOTTE, NC 282042528
Phone: 704 384-4000

HISTORICAL FINANCIALS

Company Type: Private

Income Statement				FYE: December 31
	REVENUE ($ mil.)	NET INCOME ($ mil.)	NET PROFIT MARGIN	EMPLOYEES
12/09	688	68	10.0%	3,100
12/08	500	18	3.7%	
Annual Growth	37.6%	270.7%	—	—

2009 Year-End Financials

Return on assets: —
Return on equity: 10.0%
Current ratio: —

Cash ($ mil.): —

PRESBYTERIAN MEDICAL CENTER OF THE UNIVERSITY OF PENNSYLVANIA HEALTH SYSTEM

EXECUTIVES

Exec Dir, Michele Volpe
Program Director, Jeanmarie Perch
Clinical Assistant Professor O, Michael Colucciello
Staff Nurse, Rasheda Peoples
Internist, Andrew W Maier
PA C, Dawn Carson
Chief of Internal Medicine, Jack Ende
Podiatrist, Paula Gangopadhyay
Infectious Disease Specialist, Richard J Maniglia
Registered Nurse, Samuel Bernstein
Cardiovascular Disease, Theodhor Diamanti

LOCATIONS

HQ: PRESBYTERIAN MEDICAL CENTER OF THE UNIVERSITY OF PENNSYLVANIA HEALTH SYSTEM 51 N 39TH ST, PHILADELPHIA, PA 191042640
Phone: 215 662-8000
Web: WWW.PENNMEDICINE.ORG

HISTORICAL FINANCIALS

Company Type: Private

Income Statement				FYE: June 30
	REVENUE ($ mil.)	NET INCOME ($ mil.)	NET PROFIT MARGIN	EMPLOYEES
06/20	973	66	6.9%	1,370
06/15	546	(0)		
06/14	445	21	4.7%	—
06/13	429	7	1.7%	—
Annual Growth	12.4%	36.7%	—	—

2020 Year-End Financials

Return on assets: 8.2%
Return on equity: 12.9%
Current ratio: —

Cash ($ mil.): 6

PRESIDENT AND BOARD OF TRUSTEES OF SANTA CLARA COLLEGE

Santa Clara University wants its students to achieve clarity. The Jesuit Catholic school California's oldest higher-education institution offers degrees in more than 40 disciplines. Its variety of graduate programs include business engineering law pastoral ministries counseling psychology and education. With more than 8000 students Santa Clara University boasts a student/faculty ratio of 12:1 and support from a $760 million endowment. The university occupies a 106-acre campus and has more than 520 full-time and more than 360 part-time faculty members.

Operations

The educational institution is recognized as the having the fourth-highest graduation rate among all US master's universities. About 61% of students come from California. The remainder are from 33 US states and 19 other countries.

Financial Performance

Its budget reached $387.4 million in 2013-14. The school charges undergraduate students $42156 million per year in tuition and fees.

Company Background

Notable alumni include Oakland mayor and former governor of California Jerry Brown soccer player Brandi Chastain Cirrus Logic chairman Michael Hackworth and winemaker Sam Sebastiani.

Santa Clara University was founded as Santa Clara College in 1851 on the site of Mission Santa Clara de As s the eighth of the original 21 California missions. It became a university in 1925 when the schools of engineering and law were added and became a coeducational institution in 1961.

EXECUTIVES

Chm, Jon R Aboitiz
Pres, Gregory R Bonfiglio Sj
V Pres-University Relations, Robert Gunsalus
Provost, Dennis Jacobs
Prin, Robert J Finocchio Jr
Board of Advisor, Zoe Lofgren
Board of Advisor, Gregg Alton
Board of Trustees, David C Drummond
Board of Trustees, J Terrence Lanni
Board of Trustees, Gregory Bonfiglio
Board of Trustees, Robert Peters
Auditors: MOSS ADAMS LLP STOCKTON CA

LOCATIONS

HQ: PRESIDENT AND BOARD OF TRUSTEES OF SANTA CLARA COLLEGE 500 EL CAMINO REAL, SANTA CLARA, CA 950504776
Phone: 408 554-4000
Web: WWW.SCU.EDU

PRODUCTS/OPERATIONS

Degrees Offered

Undergraduate Degrees
  Bachelor of Arts
  Bachelor of Science
  Bachelor of Science in Commerce
Graduate Degrees
  Business (MBA EMBA MSIS)
  Counseling Psychology (M.A.)
  Education (M.A.)
  Engineering (M.S. Ph.D.)
  Law (J.D. LL.M.)
  Pastoral Ministries (M.A.)

HISTORICAL FINANCIALS

Company Type: Private

Income Statement				FYE: June 30
	REVENUE ($ mil.)	NET INCOME ($ mil.)	NET PROFIT MARGIN	EMPLOYEES
06/20	550	36	6.6%	1,431
06/17	362	104	28.9%	—
06/16	460	16	3.5%	—
06/14	457	65	14.3%	—
Annual Growth	3.1%	(9.4%)	—	—

2020 Year-End Financials

Return on assets: 1.5%
Return on equity: 2.0%
Current ratio: 0.50

Cash ($ mil.): 151

PRINCE GEORGE'S COUNTY PUBLIC SCHOOLS

EXECUTIVES

Ceo, Kevin Maxwell
Assoc Supt Budget & Fin, Dr Kenneth Brown
Health Professional, William Kurtz
Security Staff, Clifford Mack
Staff, Georgene Arneson
Coordinator, Anthony Dean
Coordinator, Karuna Skariah
Teacher, Bryan Pierre
Coordinating Supervisor, Mary Bell
Music Teacher, Amber Abbott
Supervisor, Terry Hamlin
Auditors: CLIFTONLARSONALLEN LLP BALTIM

LOCATIONS

HQ: PRINCE GEORGE'S COUNTY PUBLIC SCHOOLS 14201 SCHOOL LN, UPPER MARLBORO, MD 207722866
Phone: 301 952-6000
Web: WWW.PGCPS.ORG

HISTORICAL FINANCIALS

Company Type: Private

Income Statement				FYE: June 30
	REVENUE ($ mil.)	NET INCOME ($ mil.)	NET PROFIT MARGIN	EMPLOYEES
06/14	1,932	(6)	—	22,000
06/13	1,966	43	2.2%	—
06/11	1,855	3	0.2%	—
06/07	1,627	13	0.8%	—
Annual Growth	2.5%	—	—	—

PRINCE WILLIAM COUNTY PUBLIC SCHOOLS

EXECUTIVES

Supt, Steven Walts
Assistant Superintendent, J Keith Johnson
Safety/Security Director, Ronald Crowe
Tech Prep Coordinator, Douglas Wright
Webmaster, Mary Billingsley
Instructor, Debbie Marchio
Manager Operations, Susan Dooley
Bookkeeper, Joan McGregor
Substitute Specialist, Susan Cox
Marketing, Jim Hoover
Department Chair, Vincent Reese
Auditors: CHERRY BEKAERT LLP TYSONS COR

LOCATIONS

HQ: PRINCE WILLIAM COUNTY PUBLIC SCHOOLS
14715 BRISTOW RD, MANASSAS, VA 201123945
Phone: 703 791-7200
Web: WWW.PWCS.EDU

HISTORICAL FINANCIALS
Company Type: Private

Income Statement				FYE: June 30
	REVENUE ($ mil.)	NET INCOME ($ mil.)	NET PROFIT MARGIN	EMPLOYEES
06/13	1,048	23	2.3%	6,013
06/12	968	(18)	—	—
06/11	887	(66)	—	—
Annual Growth	8.7%	—	—	—

PRISMA HEALTH-UPSTATE

From education and research to primary care and surgery Upstate Affiliate Organization (dba Prisma Health-Upstate formerly Greenville Hospital System) is out to keep residents of the "Golden Strip" (the corridor connecting Charlotte North Carolina and Atlanta) healthy. Originally founded in 1912 the system encompasses eight inpatient hospitals and more than 100 outpatient facilities. Its flagship facility is Prisma Health Greenville Memorial Hospital a referral and academic medical center with more than 800 beds; other facilities include several smaller community hospitals a nursing home and a long-term acute care hospital. Greenville Hospital System merged with Palmetto Health in 2017; the combined system rebranded as Prisma Health in early 2019.

Operations
Prisma Health-Upstate offers a full range of services including a primary care physician network outpatient services and home health care.

The system has teaching affiliations with Medical University of South Carolina and University of South Carolina Medical School and nursing school affiliations with Clemson University and Bob Jones University. Prisma Health-Upstate offers residency programs in about a dozen specialties including internal medicine OB-GYN and vascular surgery. It also performs extensive medical research in partnership with pharmaceutical companies in areas including oncology pediatric oncology women's health cardiology and vascular disease.

Prisma Cancer Institute (formerly GHS Cancer Institute) a regional leader in cancer care offers cancer treatment and prevention trials through the Community Clinical Oncology Program. It also offers Phase 1 clinical trials genetic counseling a blood and marrow transplant program and a number of patient-specific programs.

Financial Performance
GHS reported $2.1 billion in revenues in 2015 primarily from patient services. It posted $32 million in net income.

Strategy
In an effort to reduce unnecessary trips to the emergency room Prisma Health-Upstate has been opening several MD360 urgent care clinics. By diverting patients away from the ER for after-hours and non-emergency health problems GHS hopes to reduce health care costs and increase access to medical care.

Mergers and Acquisitions
In 2017 Greenville Hospital System joined forces with Palmetto Health to create South Carolina's largest health care system. The combined company rebranded itself as Prisma Health in early 2019. Greenville Hospital System became Prisma Health-Upstate.

EXECUTIVES

Co-Ceo, Charles D Beaman Jr
Co-Ceo*, Michael C Riordan
Exec V Pres*, Gregory J Rusnak
Chief Governance Officer*, Joseph J Blake
Chief Nursing Exec-Sr V Pres*, Carolyn Swinton
Chief Health Info Exec, V Pres*, Mark Wess
CIO-Sr V Pres*, Rich Rogers
Social Worker Internal, Amy Abdalla
Pulmonary Diseases, Charles V Mullen
V Pres, Audit Svcs, Chris Hammond
Infection Control Director, Connie C Steed

LOCATIONS

HQ: PRISMA HEALTH-UPSTATE
300 E MCBEE AVE STE 302, GREENVILLE, SC 296012899
Phone: 864 455-1120
Web: WWW.PRISMAHEALTH.ORG

PRODUCTS/OPERATIONS

2015 Sales

	$ mil.	% of total
Net patient services	1,973	96
Other operating revenues	82	4
Total	**2,056**	**100**

Selected Operations
Baptist Easley Hospital (with Palmetto Health Easley)
Greenville Memorial Hospital (tertiary academic and referral medical center)
Greer Memorial Hospital (Greer acute care hospital)
Hillcrest Memorial Hospital (Simpsonville general acute care hospital)
Laurens County Memorial Hospital (Clinton)
North Greenville Hospital (long-term acute care hospital)
Oconee Memorial Hospital (Seneca inpatient and outpatient services)
Patewood Memorial Hospital (Greenville inpatient elective hospital and outpatient center)

Selected Services
Behavioral Health
Cancer Institute
Children's Hospital
Heart & Vascular Institute
Medicine
Orthopaedics & Neurosurgery
Radiology
Rehabilitation
Surgery
Women's Health

COMPETITORS

Anmed Health	Mcg Health
Blue Ridge Healthcare	Novant Health
Bon Secours Health	Piedmont Athens
Caromont	Regional
Doctors Hospital Of Augusta	Spartanburg Regional Healthcare System
Grace Hospital	St. Mary's Health Care
Gwinnett Health System	Walton Rehabilitation
Laurens County Hospital	Hospital

HISTORICAL FINANCIALS
Company Type: Private

Income Statement				FYE: September 30
	REVENUE ($ mil.)	NET INCOME ($ mil.)	NET PROFIT MARGIN	EMPLOYEES
09/13	1,001	80	8.1%	7,200
09/05	789	21	2.7%	—
09/04	789	21	2.7%	—
09/03	754	52	7.0%	—
Annual Growth	2.9%	4.4%	—	—

2013 Year-End Financials
Return on assets: —
Return on equity: 8.1%
Current ratio: —
Cash ($ mil.): —

PRO PETROLEUM LLC

EXECUTIVES

Pres, Marcus Griffin
Treas-Cfo, Don Hayden
Stkhldr, B R Griffin
Controller, Betty Catherman
Operator, Chris Thuran
Operator, Jack Worley
Auditors: GARRETT AND SWANN LLP LUBBOC

LOCATIONS

HQ: PRO PETROLEUM LLC
4710 4TH ST, LUBBOCK, TX 794164900
Phone: 806 795-8785
Web: WWW.PROPETROLEUM.COM

HISTORICAL FINANCIALS
Company Type: Private

Income Statement				FYE: December 31
	REVENUE ($ mil.)	NET INCOME ($ mil.)	NET PROFIT MARGIN	EMPLOYEES
12/15	1,063	5	0.5%	150
12/14	1,701	4	0.3%	—
12/13	1,815	12	0.7%	—
Annual Growth	(23.5%)	(35.6%)	—	—

2015 Year-End Financials
Return on assets: 4.1%
Return on equity: 12.5%
Current ratio: 1.30
Cash ($ mil.): 33

PRODUCE ALLIANCE, L.L.C.

EXECUTIVES

MBR, George Melshenker
MBR, Scott Weber
Exe V Pres, Mike Williams
Partner Executive Vice Preside, Joe Collier
V Pres, Melissa Melshenker Ackerman
Cfo, Rob Feldgreber
Executive Customer Account Man, Gennifer Thompson
Business, Nate Montgomery
Associate General Counsel, Lisa Matyas
Project Coordinator, Bradley Townsend
Sales Team Member, Cory Oleson
Auditors: MILLER COOPER & CO LTD DEE

LOCATIONS

HQ: PRODUCE ALLIANCE, L.L.C.
100 LEXINGTON DR STE 201, BUFFALO GROVE, IL 600896937
Phone: 847 808-3030
Web: WWW.PRODUCEALLIANCE.COM

HISTORICAL FINANCIALS

Company Type: Private

Income Statement				FYE: December 31
	REVENUE ($ mil.)	NET INCOME ($ mil.)	NET PROFIT MARGIN	EMPLOYEES
12/19	572	0	0.0%	75
12/18	504	0	0.1%	—
12/17	441	1	0.3%	—
12/16	381	2	0.7%	—
Annual Growth	14.5%	(56.8%)	—	—

PRODUCTION TECHNOLOGIES, INC.

EXECUTIVES

Chm, John Maclennon
Ceo*, Mark Utley
V Pres*, Michael Lundequam
Purchase Executive, Martha Smith
Marketing Agent, Martha Timmers

LOCATIONS

HQ: PRODUCTION TECHNOLOGIES, INC.
7651 WASHINGTON AVE S, EDINA, MN 554392417
Phone: 952 944-1076
Web: WWW.PTIMN.COM

HISTORICAL FINANCIALS

Company Type: Private

Income Statement				FYE: December 31
	REVENUE ($ mil.)	NET INCOME ($ mil.)	NET PROFIT MARGIN	EMPLOYEES
12/16	3,289	580	17.6%	25
12/15	3,488	719	20.6%	—
12/14	3,880	348	9.0%	—
12/11	4	0	9.8%	—
Annual Growth	280.1%	327.2%	—	—

PROVIDENCE HEALTH & SERVICES

Providence St. Joseph Health was established in 2016 from the merger of Providence Health & Services and St. Joseph Health System . The not-for-profit operates 50 hospitals and more than 800 clinics in seven states in the western US. Its facilities operate under such brands as Swedish Health Services Hoag Memorial Hospital Presbyterian and Covenant Health . It provides health insurance through Providence Health Plans and offers subsidized housing for the low-income elderly and disabled. The young organization has also established the Institute for Mental Health and Wellness to improve access to quality mental health care around the nation.

Operations
In addition to its health care and housing operations Providence St. Joseph operates a small Catholic university in Great Falls Montana called University of Great Falls and a private high school — aptly named Providence High School — in Burbank California.

Geographic Reach
The system has facilities in Alaska California Montana New Mexico Oregon Texas and Washington.

Providence Health International helps respond to health care needs in developing countries by shipping supplies to hospitals and clinics around the world arranging for grants to cover the expense of sending volunteers overseas and offering educational support to health professionals in foreign countries.

Strategy
Even as the organization struggles with higher charity care levels it still has to work to invest in its infrastructure to keep its facilities up-to-date to expand to meet demand and to attract patients. For example Providence Health embarked on a major campus expansion beginning at its Providence Alaska Medical Center to modernize the Newborn Intensive Care Unit (NICU) Prenatal and Mother Baby Units and cardiac surgery program. The project increased the size of the NICU from 47 to 66 beds and added a number of cardiac operating rooms and surgical services. It expanded similar services at its Holy Cross Medical Center in California and is working to convert patient information to electronic patient medical records

In 2014 Providence Health opened the 3000-sq.-ft. Providence Autism Center for Women and Children on Pacific Avenue in Everett.

That year Providence Sacred Heart Medical Center & Children's Hospital broke ground on an expansion and remodel of its adult cardiac intensive care unit (scheduled to open in 2016). The $19.2 million project includes the renovation and modernization of the existing 22-bed unit and the addition of 12 more critical care beds.

In 2016 Providence Health merged with fellow not-for-profit St. Joseph Health System operator of nearly 20 hospitals in California New Mexico and Texas. The combination created a larger provider network of hospitals physician groups and outpatient centers eliminating some overhead expenses in the process. Furthermore by creating economies of scale the new organization will be better positioned to negotiate with health plans.

EXECUTIVES

Ceo, Rod Hochman
Pres- Chief Dev Officer*, Laurie Kelley
Exec V Pres-Cfo*, Todd Hofheins
Technology, Henry Morgan
Coordinator, Mayra Graves
Security Engineering Consultan, Diana Bullion
Admin Assistant, Alex Figueroa
Pharmacy Director, Helen Noonan-Harnsber
Chief Human Resources Officer, Ron Chavira
Executive Director, Terri Warren
Senior Financial Analyst Real, Tuan Nguyen
Auditors: KPMG LLP SEATTLE WA

LOCATIONS

HQ: PROVIDENCE HEALTH & SERVICES
1801 LIND AVE SW, RENTON, WA 980573368
Phone: 425 525-3355
Web: WWW.PROVIDENCE.ORG

HISTORICAL FINANCIALS

Company Type: Private

Income Statement				FYE: December 31
	REVENUE ($ mil.)	NET INCOME ($ mil.)	NET PROFIT MARGIN	EMPLOYEES
12/15	14,433	49	0.3%	130
12/12	280	14	5.3%	—
12/08	7,026	(156)	—	—
12/07	6,348	434	6.8%	—
Annual Growth	10.8%	(23.8%)	—	—

2015 Year-End Financials
Return on assets: 0.3% Cash ($ mil.): 729
Return on equity: 0.6%
Current ratio: 1.40

PROVIDENCE HEALTH & SERVICES - OREGON

EXECUTIVES

Pres-Ceo, John Koster
Sr V Pres-Cfo, Mike Butler
Pres, Rodney Hochman
SEC, Cindy Strauss
Treas, Todd Hofheins
Proj Coordinator, Jeanette Staley
Coordinator, Sandy Tingley
Access Supervisor, Schmidt Susan
Manager Reimbursement, Soderman Shirley
Head of School, Joe Sciuto
Director, Beth Hegde
Auditors: CLARK NUBER PS BELLEVUE WA

LOCATIONS

HQ: PROVIDENCE HEALTH & SERVICES - OREGON
1801 LIND AVE SW, RENTON, WA 980573368
Phone: 425 525-3355
Web: WWW.PROVIDENCE.ORG

HISTORICAL FINANCIALS

Company Type: Private

Income Statement				FYE: December 31
	REVENUE ($ mil.)	NET INCOME ($ mil.)	NET PROFIT MARGIN	EMPLOYEES
12/19	3,823	946	24.8%	103,036
12/17	3,479	781	22.5%	—
12/09	2,057	57	2.8%	—
12/08	73	7	10.5%	—
Annual Growth	43.3%	54.9%	—	—

Return on assets: 26.1%   Cash ($ mil.): 678
Return on equity: 31.5%
Current ratio: 3.70

PROVIDENCE HEALTH & SERVICES-WASHINGTON

EXECUTIVES

Pres-Ceo, Michael Butler
Treas*, Jo Ann Escasa-Haigh
Corp SEC*, Cindy Strauss
Asst Corp SEC*, John Whipple
Asst SEC*, Shannon Dwyer
Asst SEC For Enrollment*, Donald Anderson Jr
Asst Corp SEC*, Tammy Teodosio
Sterile Processing Coordinator, Anna Shannon
Chief Marketing Officer (provi, Brad Garrigues
Physician, Peter Benziger
Auditors: CLARK NUBER PS BELLEVUE WA

LOCATIONS

HQ: PROVIDENCE HEALTH & SERVICES-
WASHINGTON
 1801 LIND AVE SW 9016, RENTON, WA 980573368
Phone: 425 525-3355
Web: WWW.PROVIDENCE.ORG

HISTORICAL FINANCIALS

Company Type: Private

Income Statement				FYE: December 31
	REVENUE ($ mil.)	NET INCOME ($ mil.)	NET PROFIT MARGIN	EMPLOYEES
12/09	3,178	(37)	—	130
12/08	26	(0)	—	—
12/07	6,348	434	6.8%	—
12/06	2,055	113	5.5%	—
Annual Growth	15.6%	—	—	—

2009 Year-End Financials

Return on assets: (-0.8%)   Cash ($ mil.): 314
Return on equity: (-2.4%)
Current ratio: —

PSCU INCORPORATED

PSCU (Payment Systems for Credit Unions) the nation's premier payments CUSO supports the success of 1500 credit unions representing more than 5.4 billion transactions annually. PSCU's payment processing risk management data and analytics loyalty programs digital banking marketing strategic consulting and mobile platforms help deliver possibilities and seamless member experiences. Comprehensive 24/7/365 member support is provided by contact centers located throughout the US. PSCU provides an end-to-end competitive advantage that enables credit unions to securely grow and meet evolving consumer demands. Founded in 1997 PSCU was formed by five leading credit union CEOs from GTE Federal Credit Union Suncoast Schools Federal Credit Union Pinellas County Teachers Credit Union Publix Employees Federal Credit Union and Railroad & Industrial Federal Credit Union.

Geographic Reach

Headquartered in Florida PSCU operates three service centers located in Arizona Nebraska and Michigan. The CU Recovery and The Loan has service center in Minnesota and its Lumin Digital has office located in California. PSCU also maintain office in Iowa.

Financial Performance

PSCU has increased its revenue by 40% between 2017 and 2020. The company's revenue in 2020 were $582.5 million a 17% increase from $499 million the year prior. PSCU had $175.8 million in cash and cash equivalents at the end of 2020.

Strategy

PSCU has a "Digital First" strategy in response to shifting consumer preferences becoming apparent in the digital space with more consumers adopting online banking downloading payment apps and changing the ways in which they interact with their financial institutions. As COVID-19 has fast-tracked these changing preferences with digital banking gaining traction and contactless forms of payments rapidly gaining momentum PSCU has proactively prepared for these shifts in the digital habits of credit union members. The company's transformation from a card processor to an end-to-end solutions provider leaves it well-prepared to assist its Owners in planning for this new reality.

Utilization of PSCU's Digital Xperience (DX) suite continues to expand as digital card management becomes more important than ever in the pandemic environment. Serving more than one million members PSCU's DX platform enables Owner credit unions to effectively compete with big banks while maintaining the personal touch that differentiates credit unions.

PSCU also produced more than 6.8 million new contactless plastics ? the most significant volume in the credit union space ? and delivered them to more than 100 credit unions to support natural and mass reissuance strategies in 2020. In addition PSCU has grown its contact center support. PSCU continues to invest in key resources and innovative tools ? from its Unified Agent Desktop to caller authentication.

Mergers and Acquisitions

In 2020 PSCU acquired Primax business from T.K. Keith Company Inc. Terms of the transaction were not disclosed. Based in Wakefield Mass. Primax has been designing and providing support services for payment card programs for credit unions and community banks throughout the US and the Caribbean. PSCU has transformed its business model and evolved from a transactional processor and reseller of a platform partner's products to an integrated value-add financial technology solution provider.

Company Background

PSCU was formed in 1977 by leaders from Pinellas County Teachers Credit Union and the federal credit unions of GTE Publix Employees Suncoast Schools and Railroad and Industrial.

EXECUTIVES

Ceo, Chuck Fagan
SEC*, Cathie Tierney
Coo*, Tom Gandre
Chairman*, Jeff March
Svp-Chief Sales Officer*, Chris Gunnare
Manager, Jeremiah Lotz
Information Technology Manager, Kelley Skinner
Human Resources Manager, Lesley Trumbull
Lead Ecommerce Account Executi, Jennifer Loveland
Account Executive, Tom Swanson

Senior Analyst, Tricia Blasquez
Auditors: PRICEWATERHOUSECOOPERS LLP
 TA

LOCATIONS

HQ: PSCU INCORPORATED
 560 CARILLON PKWY, SAINT PETERSBURG, FL
 337161294
Phone: 727 572-8822
Web: WWW.PSCU.COM

PRODUCTS/OPERATIONS

Selected Services

Advisors Plus
Credit Solutions
Debit Solutions
eCommerce Solutions
EMV
Prepaid Solutions
Risk Management Solutions
Total Member Care
Technology Tools
PSCU Partnerships/Sponsorships
Credit Union Cherry Blossom Run
Credit Union Student Choice
Filene Research Institute
Financial Service Center Cooperatives (FSCC)
Ongoing Operations
The Colonial Williamsburg Foundation

COMPETITORS

Cuso Financial Services	Raymond James Financial
Fidelity National Information Services	Southwest Corporate Fcu
Lpl Financial	U.s. Central

HISTORICAL FINANCIALS

Company Type: Private

Income Statement				FYE: September 30
	REVENUE ($ mil.)	NET INCOME ($ mil.)	NET PROFIT MARGIN	EMPLOYEES
09/20	582	37	6.4%	2,100
09/18	481	11	2.4%	—
09/16*	458	28	6.1%	—
12/12	377	38	10.2%	—
Annual Growth	5.6%	(0.4%)	—	—

*Fiscal year change

2020 Year-End Financials

Return on assets: 4.1%   Cash ($ mil.): 175
Return on equity: 13.7%
Current ratio: 1.10

PUBLIC EMPLOYEE RETIREMENT SYSTEM, IDAHO

EXECUTIVES

Director, Don Drumd
Information Specialist, Branden Kennah
Deputy Director, Don Drum
Auditors: EIDE BAILLY LLP BOISE IDAHO

HQ: PUBLIC EMPLOYEE RETIREMENT SYSTEM, IDAHO
607 N 8TH ST, BOISE, ID 837025518
Phone: 208 334-3365
Web: WWW.PERSI.IDAHO.GOV

HISTORICAL FINANCIALS

Company Type: Private

Income Statement				FYE: June 30
	REVENUE ($ mil.)	**NET INCOME** ($ mil.)	**NET PROFIT MARGIN**	**EMPLOYEES**
06/20	1,362	243	17.9%	62
06/19	2,221	1,145	51.6%	—
06/18	2,160	1,157	53.6%	—
06/17	2,586	1,625	62.9%	—
Annual Growth	(19.2%)	(46.9%)	—	—

2020 Year-End Financials

Return on assets: 1.2%   Cash ($ mil.): 12
Return on equity: 1.2%
Current ratio: —

PUBLIC HOSPITAL DISTRICT 1 OF KING COUNTY

EXECUTIVES

Admin-Ceo, Richard D Roodman
Cfo*, Michael Bernstein
Comm*, Carole Anderson
Coo*, Paul Hayes
MD, Wuaca Luna
Doctor, Olga V Khait-Palant
Doctor, Shreeketa M Mehta
Anesthesiology, Andrew O Smith
Doctor, Joyce V Gauthier
Anesthesiology, Sidney W Postma
Coordinator, Cheryl Webster
Auditors: KPMG LLP SEATTLE WASHINGTON

LOCATIONS

HQ: PUBLIC HOSPITAL DISTRICT 1 OF KING COUNTY
400 S 43RD ST, RENTON, WA 980555714
Phone: 425 228-3440
Web: WWW.VALLEYMED.ORG

HISTORICAL FINANCIALS

Company Type: Private

Income Statement				FYE: June 30
	REVENUE ($ mil.)	**NET INCOME** ($ mil.)	**NET PROFIT MARGIN**	**EMPLOYEES**
06/19	694	12	1.7%	2,700
06/18	653	40	6.2%	—
06/16	519	11	2.2%	—
Annual Growth	10.1%	1.6%	—	—

2019 Year-End Financials

Return on assets: 1.6%   Cash ($ mil.): 35
Return on equity: 4.4%
Current ratio: 1.60

PUBLIC UTILITY DISTRICT 1 OF SNOHOMISH COUNTY

Keeping its customers' safety is priority No. 1 at Public Utility District No. 1 of Snohomish County Washington (Snohomish County PUD) which distributes electricity to over 360000 electric customers in Washington State. The utility the second largest PUD in the state with over 2200 sq. ml. service area purchases most of its power supply from third parties (Bonneville Power Administration and other producers). It sells surplus power into the wholesale power transactions to balance its supply load. Snohomish County PUD also serves more than 21000 water utility customers.

Operations

Snohomish County PUD's operations consist of three systems: the Electric System the Generation System and the Water System.

The Electric System (about 95% of sales) is made up of electric transmission and distribution system.

The Generation System (some 5%) is composed of the company's Jackson Hydroelectric Project and four smaller hydroelectric projects.

The Water System (less than 5%) is made up of water distribution system.

Overall around 90% of total sales came from its retail sales while wholesale sales and others account for the rest.

Geographic Reach

The company is headquartered in Everett Washington.

Sales and Marketing

The PUD serves three categories of customers: Residential (around 305915) Commercial (about 30795) Industrial (nearly 75) and other (roughly 230).

The company offers a wide range of energy-efficiency solutions for business customers.

Financial Performance

PUD's revenue decreased from $695.8 million in 2018 to $685.7 million in 2019 which resulted from a decrease in wholesale sales and others.

Net income was $82.2 million a 2% increase compared to the previous year.

Cash and cash equivalents at the end of the year were $45.6 million 51% less compared to $45.6 million in the previous year. Cash provided by operating activities was $87.4 million. Financing activities used $142.3 million primarily from capital construction while investing activities provided $5.6 million primarily from sale of special funds and investment securities.

Strategy

In 2019 the PUD completed its first Community Solar project located at the home of the future Microgrid and Clean Energy Technology Center in Arlington. The 500-kilowatt array is the largest community solar project in the state.

With the launch of Community Solar the PUD also awarded its final Planet Power solar energy grants to five community-focused and nonprofit organizations: Eagle Creek Elementary Snohomish County Fire District No. 22 YMCA-Everett Farmer Frog and Camp Killoqua.

Thanks to customer contributions to the Planet Power program through the years an additional 329 kilowatts of solar energy has been added to the PUD's grid across 39 individual projects - 112 kilowatts in 2019 alone.

In addition to the hydropower resources available through Bonneville Power the PUD continued to invest in its own hydroelectric projects. In 2019 the PUD completed the last of the capital improvements specifically identified in the new license for the Henry M. Jackson Hydroelectric Project near Sultan which is capable of supplying power to over 53000 homes. The PUD also continued to invest in and benefit from its four smaller projects at Woods Creek Youngs Creek Calligan Creek and Hancock Creek.

The PUD's other renewable energy resources include long-term contracts for wind projects in Central Washington and Oregon and contracts with locally owned and operated biomass and biodigester facilities.

Company BackgroundIn 2013 solar energy capacity stood at two MW enough to serve 170 homes. More than 350 PUD customers cover part of their electricity needs through their own solar energy units. The PUD's Solar Express program offers financial incentives and technical assistance for solar photovoltaic and solar hot water systems. In 2012 the company amended a power contract with Hampton Lumber (a fuel supplier since 2007) that will boost the level of biomass energy the utility will receive from the lumber company's Darrington plant. The new agreement will allow Snohomish County PUD to receive up to 2.5 MW of energy from Hampton Lumber enough energy to power about 2000 homes. Supported by $15.8 million in matching federal stimulus dollars in 2011 Snohomish County PUD completed its first major project as part of a long-term upgrade of its electric grid with smart grid technology. The upgrade includes the installation of more than 160 miles of fiber optic cable and connecting them to 62 substations two radio sites and other utility buildings. The company began providing water utility service to parts of Snohomish County in 1946. Public Utility District No. 1 of Snohomish County began operating as power utility in 1949 providing publicly owned electric and water utility service to the residents of Snohomish County and Camano Island.

EXECUTIVES

Pres, Kathleen Vaughn
V Pres*, Toni Olson
SEC*, David Aldrich
Senior Manager Distribution, Francisco C Cafm
Customer Team Member, Julia Sennikov
Director, Allison Jubb
Manager, Carolyn Beebe Snopud
Customer Representativ, Chelsea Holte
Manager, Janet Barnes
Customer Accounting, Joe Hovsepian
Senior Accountant, Julie Thompson
Auditors: BAKER TILLY MADISON WI

LOCATIONS

HQ: PUBLIC UTILITY DISTRICT 1 OF SNOHOMISH COUNTY
2320 CALIFORNIA ST, EVERETT, WA 982013750
Phone: 425 257-9288

PRODUCTS/OPERATIONS

2014 Sales

	$ mil.	% of total
Retail sales	554	86
Wholesale sales	59	9
Other	30	5
Total	**645**	**100**

COMPETITORS

Avista
Chelan County Pud
Grant County Public Utility District

Public Utility District No. 1 Of Clark County
Puget Energy
Tacoma Public Utilities

HISTORICAL FINANCIALS
Company Type: Private

Income Statement				FYE: December 31
	REVENUE ($ mil.)	NET INCOME ($ mil.)	NET PROFIT MARGIN	EMPLOYEES
12/20	692	65	9.4%	879
12/19	685	82	12.0%	—
12/18	695	80	11.5%	—
12/17	686	75	11.1%	—
Annual Growth	0.3%	(5.0%)	—	—

PUBLISHING OFFICE, US GOVERNMENT

The US Government Printing Office (GPO) keeps America informed in print and online. The GPO is the Federal government's primary centralized resource for gathering cataloging producing providing and preserving published information in all its forms. Part of the legislative branch the GPO offers Congress the courts and other government agencies centralized services to enable them to easily produce printed documents according to uniform Federal specifications. The GPO also offers the publications for sale to the public and makes them available at no cost through the Federal Depository Library Program. The GPO is run like a business and requires payment from its government customers for services rendered.

EXECUTIVES

Cting Deputy, John Crawford
Cfo*, Steven T Shedd
Deputy*, James Bradley
En Counsel*, Drew Spalding
Chief Public Relations Officer*, Gary Somerset
Acting CIO*, Tracee Boxley
CIO*, Sam Musa
Staff, Juanita Thompson
Auditors: KPMG LLP WASHINGTON DC

LOCATIONS

HQ: PUBLISHING OFFICE, US GOVERNMENT
732 N CAPITOL ST NW, WASHINGTON, DC
204010002
Phone: 202 512-0000
Web: WWW.GPO.GOV

HISTORICAL FINANCIALS
Company Type: Private

Income Statement				FYE: September 30
	REVENUE ($ mil.)	NET INCOME ($ mil.)	NET PROFIT MARGIN	EMPLOYEES
09/20	915	(14)	—	1,880
09/19	937	51	5.5%	—
09/18	874	52	6.0%	—
09/17	874	58	6.7%	—
Annual Growth	1.6%	—	—	—

2020 Year-End Financials
Return on assets: (-1.3%)
Return on equity: (-2.0%)
Current ratio: 2.90
Cash ($ mil.): 660

QUALITY OIL COMPANY, LLC

With more services than your average oil company Quality Oil helps its customers get fueled up cooled off and well rested. And they can smoke if they want to. The company distributes fuel oil and propane to customers in the Winston-Salem area of North Carolina. Quality Oil provides air conditioning and heating equipment service operates 47 convenience stores (Quality Marts) and about 20 service stations and owns hotels in five southern states. In addition the company operates 60 Quality Plus locations at which drivers can buy cigarettes at discount prices. The company also provides Right-a-Way oil change services at many of its gas stations.

Operations
In addition the company's real estate unit (Quality Oil Real Estate) operates a diverse portfolio of retail and hotel sites industrial units residential subdivision developments and a shopping center. Quality Marts and Quality Plus also provide heating and cooling and fleet fueling services.

Geographic Reach
Quality Oil owns and operates four Hampton Inns two Hampton Inn & Suites and one Homewood Suites in the Carolinas Florida Georgia and Virginia. Affiliate Reliable Tank Line LLC transports petroleum products and provides fleet fueling services at 10 locations in North Carolina northern South Carolina eastern Virginia and eastern Tennessee. Quality Oil Heating-Cooling has assets throughout North Carolina and parts of South Carolina Virginia Florida and Tennessee and serves Forsyth County Stokes County Davie County Davidson County Yadkin County Rowan County and Iredell County.

Sales and Marketing
The company markets Shell oil products.

Strategy
To sharpen its competitive edge in 2013 Quality Oil created a new department — Retail Technology — to maintain PDI Pricebook and POS Systems and test and implement future technological developments.

To increase operational efficiency in 2012 Quality Oil installed Professional Datasolutions Inc. (PDI) scanning software at all of its retail outlets.

Mergers and Acquisitions
To complement its existing oil and propane business in 2012 Quality Oil acquired regional gas station and convenience store operator Horn Oil Co. in Mocksville North Carolina.

Company Background
Expanding its store network in 2011 the company opened Quality Mart locations #46 and #47 in Kernersville and Morrisville.

Quality Oil was founded in 1929 by Joe Glenn and Bert Bennett as a Shell oil products distributor and is still owned and operated by descendants of the founders.

EXECUTIVES

Pres, Graham F Bennett
MBR*, Donald McIver
Sr V Pres*, Ernie Rhymer
Sr V Pres*, Buddy Jenkins
Sr V Pres*, Tim Lowman
Sr V Pres*, Andy Sayles
Vice President, Thomas Rieke
Terminal Manager, Ashley Fowler
Technical Support Specialist, Brian Minter
Hr and Recruiting Specialist, Leah Hardy

General Manager, Mary Humphries
Auditors: BUTLER & BURKE LLP WINSTON-S

LOCATIONS

HQ: QUALITY OIL COMPANY, LLC
1540 SILAS CREEK PKWY, WINSTON SALEM, NC
271273705
Phone: 336 722-3441
Web: WWW.QUALITYOILNC.COM

PRODUCTS/OPERATIONS

Selected Brands
Hampton Inn
Quality Heating and Air Conditioning
Quality Mart
Quality Oil Appliance Sales and Service
Quality Oil Commercial Heating and On-Site Fueling
Quality Oil Fuel Oil
Quality Oil Gas Logs and Heaters
Quality Oil Propane
Quality Plus
Reliable Tank Line
Shell Oil products

Selected Mergers and Acquisitions

COMPETITORS

Cumberland Farms	Marriott
E-z Mart Stores	Racetrac Petroleum
Hyatt	Wilcohess

HISTORICAL FINANCIALS
Company Type: Private

Income Statement				FYE: December 31
	REVENUE ($ mil.)	NET INCOME ($ mil.)	NET PROFIT MARGIN	EMPLOYEES
12/09	634	11	1.9%	1,000
12/08	806	27	3.4%	—
12/07	619	10	1.8%	—
12/06	542	15	2.8%	—
Annual Growth	5.4%	(8.1%)	—	—

2009 Year-End Financials
Return on assets: 9.9%
Return on equity: 13.1%
Current ratio: 0.90
Cash ($ mil.): 11

R. DIRECTIONAL DRILLING & UNDERGROUND TECHNOLOGY, INC.

EXECUTIVES

Pres-Ceo, Jose M Ruiz
V Pres of Oprs*, Aurelio Ruiz
V Pres of Sls*, Derek Reeve
Job Coordinator, Denise Lenz
Auditors: KEN DUSSEAU PC

LOCATIONS

HQ: R. DIRECTIONAL DRILLING & UNDERGROUND TECHNOLOGY, INC.
8560 N 77TH DR, PEORIA, AZ 853457969
Phone: 602 374-3173
Web: WWW.DRILLRDD.COM

HISTORICAL FINANCIALS

Company Type: Private

Income Statement				FYE: December 31
	REVENUE ($ mil.)	NET INCOME ($ mil.)	NET PROFIT MARGIN	EMPLOYEES
12/12	7,667	(1,040)	—	61
12/11*	7	2	29.9%	—
09/10	2	0	27.4%	—
Annual Growth	5174.7%	—	—	—

*Fiscal year change

2012 Year-End Financials

Return on assets: (-24.4%)
Return on equity: (-48.7%)
Current ratio: 1.30
Cash ($ mil.): 416

R. E. MICHEL COMPANY, LLC

Blowing hot and cold is good for R.E. Michel. The company is one of the nation's largest wholesale distributors of heating air-conditioning and refrigeration (HVAC-R) equipment parts and supplies. The family-owned and operated firm offers more than 16000 items through about 2 sales offices located across the Southern Mid-Atlantic and Northeastern regions of the country. R.E. Michel ships more than 20000 items each day from its 900000-sq.-ft. distribution center in Maryland. Its Exclusive Supplier Partnership (ESP) program offers customers inventory control advertising and marketing support. R.E. Michel was founded in 1935 as a supplier to the home heating oil burner industry.

Geographic Reach

The HVAC wholesaler maintains a handful of offices to cater to customers located in the Southern US as well as in the Mid-Atlantic and Northeastern regions. Most recently opened offices reside in Ohio California Virginia Florida South Carolina Arizona and Tennessee.

Sales and Marketing

R.E. Michel uses up to 50 trailers to ship its more than 10000 items each day. To this end the company also ships more than 3200 items via the United Parcel Service each week. As part of its business it publishes a 1300 page catalog that includes 20000 catalog line items.

EXECUTIVES

Chb, John Michel
Chairman of The Board, John W H Michel
President, Robert P Michel
Executive Vice President, Ronald D Miller
Senior Vice President, Gene Winters
Secretary—Treasurer, Allison Robinson
Sales Coordinator, Tracy Johnson
Training Coordinator, Paul Murray
Branch, Christopher Schubert
Branch Manager, Sandra Perdue
Sales Tax Coordinator, Tina Vanskiver
Auditors: CLIFTONLARSONALLEN LLP BALTIM

LOCATIONS

HQ: R. E. MICHEL COMPANY, LLC
1 RE MICHEL DR, GLEN BURNIE, MD 210606408
Phone: 410 760-4000
Web: WWW.REMICHEL.COM

PRODUCTS/OPERATIONS

Selected Products & Services

Air conditioning & heating
Indoor air quality
Boilers
Water heating equipment
Hydronic & steam systems
Valves
Pipe & fittings
Fuel oil systems
Gas systems
Chemicals
Refrigeration equipment & supplies
Controls
Electrical supplies
Motors
Air handling products
Venting products
Duct registers & grilles
Tools & test instruments
O.E.M. Parts

COMPETITORS

Emco Corporation	Lowe's
Ferguson Enterprises	Msc Industrial Direct
Gensco	W.w. Grainger
Hd Supply	Winwholesale

HISTORICAL FINANCIALS

Company Type: Private

Income Statement				FYE: December 31
	REVENUE ($ mil.)	NET INCOME ($ mil.)	NET PROFIT MARGIN	EMPLOYEES
12/20	999	57	5.7%	1,948
12/19	939	48	5.2%	—
12/18	898	37	4.1%	—
12/17	804	26	3.2%	—
Annual Growth	7.5%	29.8%	—	—

2020 Year-End Financials

Return on assets: 11.2%
Return on equity: 17.8%
Current ratio: 2.50
Cash ($ mil.): 3

R. M. PARKS, INC.

EXECUTIVES

Ceo, Tim Callison
SEC-Treas, Marilyn Callison
Offc Mgr, Jason Patterson
Accounting Manager, Sherrill Morris
Auditors: GUMBINER SAVETT INC SANTA MO

LOCATIONS

HQ: R. M. PARKS, INC.
1061 N MAIN ST, PORTERVILLE, CA 932571686
Phone: 559 784-2384
Web: WWW.RMPARKSINC.COM

HISTORICAL FINANCIALS

Company Type: Private

Income Statement				FYE: October 31
	REVENUE ($ mil.)	NET INCOME ($ mil.)	NET PROFIT MARGIN	EMPLOYEES
10/18	571	0	0.0%	20
10/17	477	(0)	—	—
10/16	448	0	0.2%	—
10/15	534	0	0.2%	—
Annual Growth	2.3%	(73.9%)	—	—

2018 Year-End Financials

Return on assets: 0.1%
Return on equity: 0.2%
Current ratio: 1.30
Cash ($ mil.): —

R.C. WILLEY HOME FURNISHINGS

R.C. Willey Home Furnishings is the number one place to find exceptional selection value superior service and professional associates in about 15 stores in Utah Nevada California and Idaho. It sells furniture (Broyhill Flexsteel Lane) appliances (GE Maytag) electronics (Sony Samsung) and flooring. The company also sells mattresses (Serta Spring Air Simmons). R.C. Willey is owned by the investment giant Warren Buffett of Berkshire Hathaway. Adding the buying power of the other home furnishings stores he owns across the nation its huge buying power guarantees the lowest price on name-brand merchandise.

Operations

The company is known for its large selection and reliable products such as furniture appliances electronics flooring and matresses under well-known brand names. It carries Broyhill Flexsteel Lane Natuzzi AICO Pulaski Schnadig General Electric Whirlpool LG Maytag Amana KitchenAid Sony Mitsubishi Toshiba LG Samsung Serta Spring Air Simmons and Tempur-Pedic among others.

Geographic Reach

Utah-based R.C. Willey operates about 15 stores in Utah Nevada Idaho and California.

Sales and Marketing

A plus to R.C. Willey Home Furnishings customers the company offers financing through its R.C. Willey Credit Card.

EXECUTIVES

Ceo, Scott L Hymas
Chb, William H Child
Pres, Jeffrey Child
Dir, Curtis K Child
Staff, Mike Parker
Sales Team Member, Brian Stewart
Sales Team Member, Cade Koyle
Buyer, Jennie Towery
Sales Associate, Al Pringle
SEC Treas, Curtis Child
Sales Manager, Douglas Hansen

LOCATIONS

HQ: R.C. WILLEY HOME FURNISHINGS
2301 S 300 W, SOUTH SALT LAKE, UT 841152516
Phone: 801 461-3900
Web: WWW.RCWILLEY.COM

PRODUCTS/OPERATIONS

Selected Products

Appliances

Electronics

Fitness

Flooring

Furniture

Mattresses

COMPETITORS

Abbey Carpet	J. C. Penney Company
Best Buy	La-z-boy
Costco Wholesale	Lowe's
Ethan Allen	Pier 1 Imports
Fry's Electronics	Radioshack
Home Depot	Williams-sonoma

HISTORICAL FINANCIALS

Company Type: Private

Income Statement				FYE: December 31
	REVENUE ($ mil.)	NET INCOME ($ mil.)	NET PROFIT MARGIN	EMPLOYEES
12/17	807	19	2.4%	2,700
12/16	800	26	3.3%	—
12/14	712	17	2.4%	—
12/13	664	15	2.3%	—
Annual Growth	5.0%	6.3%	—	—

2017 Year-End Financials

Return on assets: 2.1%   Cash ($ mil.): 62
Return on equity: 2.5%
Current ratio: 4.10

RADY CHILDREN'S HOSPITAL AND HEALTH CENTER

EXECUTIVES

Pres-Ceo, Donald B Kearns
Cmo*, Irvin A Kaufman
Exec V Pres*, Margareta E Norton
Sr V Pres-Cfo*, Roger G Roux
Coo*, Nicholas Holmes
Coordinator, Giuseppe Principato
Scientist, Andrea Hazen
Coordinator, Carrie Arii
Coordinator, Deborah Ferreira
Coordinator, Maria Guzman
Finance Manager, Alexa Kratze
Auditors: LB KPMG LLP LOS ANGELES CA

LOCATIONS

HQ: RADY CHILDREN'S HOSPITAL AND HEALTH CENTER
   3020 CHILDRENS WAY, SAN DIEGO, CA 921234223
Phone: 858 576-1700
Web: WWW.RCHSD.ORG

HISTORICAL FINANCIALS

Company Type: Private

Income Statement				FYE: June 30
	REVENUE ($ mil.)	NET INCOME ($ mil.)	NET PROFIT MARGIN	EMPLOYEES
06/21	1,336	593	44.4%	4,033
06/20	1,334	(20)	—	—
06/19	1,354	167	12.3%	—
06/18	1,243	205	16.5%	—
Annual Growth	2.5%	42.4%	—	—

2021 Year-End Financials

Return on assets: 17.5%   Cash ($ mil.): 127
Return on equity: 26.8%
Current ratio: 5.40

RADY CHILDREN'S HOSPITAL-SAN DIEGO

Rady Children's Hospital-San Diego handles the big injuries of pint-sized patients. Serving as the region's only pediatric trauma center the nonprofit hospital boasts more than 520 beds. As part of its services Rady Children's Hospital-San Diego offers comprehensive pediatric care including surgical services convalescent care a neonatal intensive care unit and orthopedic services. Across its service area the hospital also operates about 25 satellite centers that provide such primary and specialized care services as physical therapy and hearing diagnostics. Rady Children's Hospital a teaching hospital affiliated with the University of California San Diego Medical School was founded in 1954.

Operations

Rady Children's operates its own 36-bed emergency department — The Sam S. and Rose Stein Emergency Care Center — that each day sees up to 300 patients. It is the only regional emergency center solely dedicated and equipped to care for children. The hospital also operates California's only pediatric skilled nursing facility — The Helen Bernardy Center — to provide 24-hour care to disabled and medically fragile children in a homelike environment.

For treating non-life-or-limb-threatening injuries and illnesses the hospital operates neighborhood urgent care centers in Escondido La Mesa Oceanside and San Diego.

Through its medical school affiliation Rady Children's engages in nearly 500 clinical trials in all pediatric specialties. It collaborates with University of California San Diego the Sanford-Burnham Medical Research Institute The Scripps Research Institute the Salk Institute for Biological Studies and St. Jude Children's Research Hospital. Specialized research facilities on campus include the Autism Discovery Institute the Blair L. Sadler Center for Quality and the Child and Adolescent Services Research Center.

The hospital operates a LEED-certified Acute Care Pavilion which holds a neonatal intensive care unit the Peckham Center for Cancer and Blood Disorders and the Warren Family Surgical Center. It serves those suffering from eating disorders through its inpatient center to allow for intensive psychiatric therapy for patients with anorexia and bulimia and to aid families with home care.

In 2014 the hospital had 18782 inpatient admissions 230383 outpatient visits nearly 85000 emergency department visits and more than 54000 urgent care visits. It performed about 20000 surgeries.

Geographic Reach

Rady Children's Hospital serves as the pediatric medical center that caters to the California region of San Diego Imperial and southern Riverside counties. It has more than 30 offices throughout San Diego and southern Riverside counties with satellite locations in Chula Vista El Centro Encinitas Escondido La Jolla La Mesa Murrieta Oceanside San Diego and Solana Beach.

EXECUTIVES

Ceo, Donald Kearns
Vp-Cao*, Jill Strickland
Chief Officer, Irvin A Kaufman
Coordinator, Mindy Collins
Project Coordinator, Teresa Yang
Ophthalmologist, Colin Scher
Ophthalmologist, David Granet
Ophthalmologist, Henry O'Halloran
Coordinator, Kyla Gonzalez
Purchasing Agent, Glenda C Abalos
Head of Chemistry Lab, Irene Bressanutti

LOCATIONS

HQ: RADY CHILDREN'S HOSPITAL-SAN DIEGO
   3020 CHILDRENS WAY, SAN DIEGO, CA 921234223
Phone: 858 576-1700
Web: WWW.RCHSD.ORG

Selected Satellite Locations

Chula Vista
El Centro
Encinitas
Escondido
La Jolla
La Mesa
Murrieta
Oceanside
San Diego
Solana Beach

PRODUCTS/OPERATIONS

Selected Services

Allergy/Immunology
Attention Deficit Hyperactivity Disorder
Audiology/Hearing
Autism Discovery Institute
Behavioral Health
Brachial Plexus Clinic
Cancer & Blood Disorders
Cardiology
Cardiovascular Surgery
Celiac Disease Clinic
Center for Healthier Communities
Cerebral Palsy Center
Chadwick Center For Children & Families
Child & Adolescent Psychiatry Services (CAPS)
Child & Adolescent Services Research Center (CASRC)
Child Life Services
Children's Care Connection (C3)
Children's Hospital Emergency Transport (CHET)
Cleft Palate Clinic
Craniofacial Disorders
Critical Care
Cystic Fibrosis Center
Dental Surgery
Dermatology
Developmental Evaluation Clinic
Developmental-Behavioral Pediatrics
Developmental Screening & Enhancement Program (DSEP)
Developmental Services
Down Syndrome Center
Eating Disorders/
Medical-Behavioral Disorders Unit
Emergency Medicine
Endocrinology/Diabetes
Fatty Liver Clinic
Feeding Team
Gastroenterology Hepatology & Nutrition

Genetics/Dysmorphology
Heart Institute
Helen Bernardy Center for Medically Fragile Children
Hematology/Oncology
HomeCare
Hospice
Infectious Diseases
Kawasaki Disease Clinic
Kidney/Liver Tranplant Program
Kidney Disease
Laboratory Services/Pathology
Liver Disease
Liver Transplant
Muscle Disease Clinic
Metabolic Medicine
Neonatology
Nephrology
Neurology
Neurosurgery
Newborn Screening Program
Nutrition Clinic
Occupational Therapy
Ophthalmology
Orthopedics
Otolaryngology/ENT
Pain Services
Palliative Care
Pediatric Surgery
Pediatrics & Hospital Medicine
Pharmacy Services
Physical Therapy
Prader-Willi Syndrome Clinic
Psychiatry
Pulmonary/Respiratory Medicine
Radiology
Rehabilitation Medicine
Rheumatology
Sleep Center
Speech/Language Pathology
Spiritual Care
Sports Medicine
Surgery
Toddler School (Alexa's PLAYC)
Trauma Center
Urgent Care
Urology
Weight & Wellness Center

COMPETITORS

All Children's Hospital
Children's Health System
Children's Hospital & Research Center At Oakland
Children's Hospital Of Orange County
Children's Hospital Of Philadelphia
Children's Hospital Of Richmond
Children's Specialized Hospital
Childrens Hospital Los Angeles
Cook Children's Health Care System
Dell Children's Medical Center
Nationwide Children's Hospital
Palomar Health
Scripps Health
Seattle Children's Hospital
Sharp Healthcare
Shriners Hospitals For Children
St. Jude Children's Research Hospital
Sutter Health
Tri-city Healthcare District
Ucsf Medical

HISTORICAL FINANCIALS

Company Type: Private

Income Statement				FYE: June 30
	REVENUE ($ mil.)	NET INCOME ($ mil.)	NET PROFIT MARGIN	EMPLOYEES
06/21	1,254	449	35.8%	2,313
06/20	1,267	73	5.8%	—
06/19	1,300	208	16.0%	—
06/15	522	104	20.1%	—
Annual Growth	15.7%	27.5%	—	—

2021 Year-End Financials

Return on assets: 14.2%   Cash ($ mil.): 126
Return on equity: 22.3%
Current ratio: 5.20

RALEY'S

Raley's has to stock plenty of fresh fruit and great wines — it sells to the people that produce them. The company operates about 130 supermarkets and superstores in California and Nevada. In addition to about 80 flagship Raley's Superstores the company operates about 20 Bel Air Markets (in the Sacramento area) and Nob Hill Foods (an upscale Bay Area chain with some 20 locations). Raley's stores typically offer groceries natural foods and liquor as well as in-store pharmacies. Founded during the Depression by Thomas Porter Raley the company is still owned and run by the Raley family.

Operations

In addition to Raley's Bel Air and Nob Hill supermarkets Raley's operates nearly 10 discount warehouse stores under the Food Source banner in Northern California and Nevada and one Market 5-ONE-5 neighborhood market in downtown Sacramento. The company offers online shopping and delivery in some markets.

Geographic Reach

Raley's approximately 130 stores are located primarily in Central and Northern California with a cluster around its headquarters city of Sacramento. It has about 20 locations in Nevada.

Strategy

Raley's strategy is centered around providing health fresh food at affordable prices. To that end in late 2018 it divested its Aisle 1 fuel stations which are adjacent to Raley's supermarkets to focus on core operations. It has also launched new products to appeal to changing tastes for healthy natural foods and prepared meals including a line of chef-created fresh meal kits vegetable sides (introduced in late 2018). Earlier in 2018 the company removed soda and candy from its check-out stands reducing its overall sugar offerings by 25%.

Raley's has also invested in technology to better serve customers and in 2018 launched a new website and campaign to promote online shopping and introduced a pharmacy mobile app.

Company Background

Raley's traces its roots to Placerville California and the 1935 opening of a grocery store by Tom Raley. The company has grown organically and through acquisitions; it acquired Bel Air Markets in 1992 and Nob Hill Foods in 1998. It remains family-owned.

EXECUTIVES

Ceo, Keith Knopf
Chb-Ceo*, Michael Teel
Cfo-Ctrl*, Ken Mueller
SEC*, Helen Singmaster
Dir*, Michael J Teel
Dir*, Julie Teel
Dir*, Jerry Cook
Cao*, Jennifer Warner
Chief Customer Experience Offi, Deirdre Zimmermann
Payroll Clerk, Jordan Brown
Food Supervising Forem, Ralph Rankin

LOCATIONS

HQ: RALEY'S
500 W CAPITOL AVE, WEST SACRAMENTO, CA 956052696
Phone: 916 373-3333
Web: WWW.RALEYS.COM

2018 Stores

	No.
California	110
Northern Nevada	18
Total	**128**

PRODUCTS/OPERATIONS

2018 Stores

	No.
Supermarkets	
Raley's	78
Nob Hill	20
Bel Air	20
Food Source	8
Other	2
Total	**128**

COMPETITORS

Andronico's Market	Safeway
Costco Wholesale	Save Mart
Food 4 Less Holdings	Trader Joe's
Grocery Outlet	Wal-mart
Kroger	Whole Foods
Lunardi's Super Market	Winco Foods
Ralphs Grocery	

HISTORICAL FINANCIALS

Company Type: Private

Income Statement				FYE: June 30
	REVENUE ($ mil.)	NET INCOME ($ mil.)	NET PROFIT MARGIN	EMPLOYEES
06/12	3,162	(1)	—	14,000
06/10	3,064	0	—	
06/09	0	0	—	
Annual Growth	—	—	—	—

2012 Year-End Financials

Return on assets: (-0.2%)   Cash ($ mil.): 26
Return on equity: (-0.6%)
Current ratio: 0.90

RAYMOND JAMES & ASSOCIATES INC

Does everybody love Raymond James & Associates (RJA)? Raymond James Financial hopes so. RJA is that company's primary subsidiary and one of the largest retail brokerages in the US. The unit provides brokerage financial planning investments and related services to consumers. It performs equity and fixed income sales trading and research for institutional clients in North America and Europe. Its investment banking group provides corporate and public finance debt underwriting and mergers and acquisitions advice. RJA also makes markets for approximately 1000 stocks including thinly traded issues. Planning Corporation of America a wholly-owned subsidiary of RJA sells insurance and annuities.

Operations

RJA is engaged in most aspects of securities distribution and investment banking.

Geographic Reach

The company has more than 200 branches and satellite offices concentrated in the Mid-Atlantic Midwest Southeast and Southwest portions of the US in addition to ten institutional sales offices in Europe.

Sales and Marketing

RJA has many big name clients across dozens of industries. In 2013 Titan Medical announced that it has retained RJA to provide advisory services and present options which could include a possible sale.

Strategy

In 2012 the company's parent completed its acquisition of Morgan Keegan & Co. and MK Holding Inc. from Regions Financial Corporation. Some of the equity capital markets and fixed income operations of were integrated into RJA.

EXECUTIVES

Chb, Thomas A James
Exec V Pres*, Dennis W Zank
Ceo*, Paul Reilly
Exec V Pres*, Bella Loykhter Allaire
Cfo*, Jeffrey P Julien
Branch Manager,svp-Investments, George J Garro
Law, Aaron Shuck
Com Spec, Katy Barrett
Senior Research Analyst Intern, Aaron Kessler
Equity Research Analyst, Ben Brownlow
Vice President Investments, Hall Sumner
Auditors: KPMG LLP TAMPA FLORIDA

LOCATIONS

HQ: RAYMOND JAMES & ASSOCIATES INC
880 CARILLON PKWY, SAINT PETERSBURG, FL 337161100
Phone: 727 567-1000
Web: WWW.RAYMONDJAMES.COM

COMPETITORS

Ameriprise	Janney Montgomery
Charles Schwab	Scott
E*trade Financial	Merrill Lynch
Edward D. Jones	Scottrade
Edward Jones	Td Ameritrade
Fmr	Wells Fargo Advisors

HISTORICAL FINANCIALS

Company Type: Private

Income Statement				FYE: September 30
	ASSETS ($ mil.)	NET INCOME ($ mil.)	INCOME AS % OF ASSETS	EMPLOYEES
09/17	9,917	198	2.0%	10,000
09/16	10,689	145	1.4%	—
09/15	7,893	167	2.1%	—
09/14	6,955	182	2.6%	—
Annual Growth	12.6%	2.8%	—	—

2017 Year-End Financials

Return on assets: 2.0%   Sales ($ mil): 3,255
Return on equity: 7.8%

RAYMOURS FURNITURE COMPANY, INC.

Raymours Furniture is heating up the oft-chilly Northeast doing business as Raymour & Flanigan. The company operates in several states through 94 retail stores including nearly a dozen clearance centers. It sells furniture for just about every room in the house (bedroom dining room home office living room) offering such pieces as bookcases entertainment centers headboards mattresses nightstands recliners sofas and tables. Brands such as Broyhill La-Z-Boy Natuzzi and Tempur Sealy are represented. Raymours is run by founding Goldberg family.

Operations

The company boasts 94 full-line showrooms about a dozen clearance centers 15 customer service centers and four distribution centers in New York New Jersey Pennsylvania Connecticut Massachusetts Delaware and Rhode Island. Raymours also operates more than a dozen customer distribution centers. Its one warehouse property is located in Quakertown Pennsylvania.

Geographic Reach

Based in New York Raymours has become the largest furniture retailer in the Northeast. Through a contractor it provides furniture delivery across the continental US.

Sales and Marketing

Raymours sells its furniture and accessories through its retail stores and online.

Strategy

Following significant expansion in 2008 Raymours has focused in recent years on expanding its presence on the Internet to entice more customers to shop. It added rugs and home decor items such as lamps throw pillows wall art and silk florals to its online furniture catalog. It also extended its furniture delivery area to all states within the continental US through a partnership with a contracted delivery service.

Raymours also expanded its existing partnership with Kathy Ireland Worldwide (led by its namesake model-actress) by adding 10 upholstered pieces to its Kathy Ireland Home furniture collection. The Kathy Ireland pieces are sold exclusively through Raymours.

The company has been expanding its New York distribution center in Rockland County spending some $46 million to purchase and renovate the 839000-sq.-ft. facility which will serve as its primary regional warehouse and distribution hub for the New York New Jersey and Connecticut areas.

In 2015 Raymours purchased the North Oaks Shopping Plaza. The majority of the complex located at 1345 Route 1 South in North Brunswick had been vacant for years. Raymours will become the plaza's new anchor.

Since 2013 Raymours has been prudently adding furniture showrooms in New York one in Brooklyn in 2013 on Fulton Street and another in 2014 in Queens which spans 22000 sq. ft. on multiple levels.

Company Background

Founded in 1947 by brothers Arnold and Bernard Goldberg Raymour & Flanigan is run by president and CEO Neil Goldberg and EVPs Michael and Steven.

EXECUTIVES

Chb-Ceo, Neil Goldberg
Exec V Pres*, Michael Goldberg
Exec V Pres*, Steven Goldberg
Cfo*, James Poole
Coordinator, Marcelino Berrios
Customer Representativ, Phillip Barnett
Inventory Control Manager, Corin McManus
Home Furnishings Consultant, Brian Brown
Senior Buyer of Case Goods, Andrea Sheer
Net Developer, Joey Buczek
Director of Distribution, Benjamin Engstrand
Auditors: GREEN & SEIFTER SYRACUSE NEW

LOCATIONS

HQ: RAYMOURS FURNITURE COMPANY, INC.
7248 MORGAN RD, LIVERPOOL, NY 130904535
Phone: 315 453-2500
Web: WWW.RAYMOUR.NET

PRODUCTS/OPERATIONS

Selected Products

Accents
Area Rugs
Bedrooms
Dining Rooms
Entertainment
Home Decor
Home Office
Living Rooms
Mattresses
Youth Bedrooms

Selected Brands
Berkline
Bernhardt
Broyhill
Cindy Crawford Home
Kathy Ireland Home
La-Z-Boy
Natuzzi
Rowe
Sealy
Stanley Furniture
Stearns & Foster
Tempur-Pedic

COMPETITORS

Abc Home Furnishings
American Signature
Bassett Furniture
Bob's Discount Furniture Bob's Discount Furnitu
Crawford Furniture
Dillard's
Ethan Allen
Euromarket Designs
Jennifer Convertibles
La-z-boy
Room & Board
Rooms To Go
Williams-sonoma

HISTORICAL FINANCIALS

Company Type: Private

Income Statement				FYE: December 29
	REVENUE ($ mil.)	NET INCOME ($ mil.)	NET PROFIT MARGIN	EMPLOYEES
12/07	881	30	3.4%	6,166
12/06	780	23	3.0%	—
12/05	655	21	3.2%	—
Annual Growth	16.0%	20.2%	—	—

2007 Year-End Financials

Return on assets: 13.5%   Cash ($ mil.): —
Return on equity: 38.1%
Current ratio: 1.50

RDO EQUIPMENT CO.

RDO Equipment sells and rents new and used trucks and heavy equipment to customers in the agriculture and construction industries. RDO Equipment operates more than 75 locations across the United States. It offers John Deere agriculture equipment construction and forestry and lawn and land as well as Vermmer Topcon and other top brands. RDO also has partnerships in Africa Australia Mexico Russia and Ukraine making it a total solutions provider and partner to customers around the globe. Ronald Offutt founded the family-owned and operated company in 1968.

Operations

The company offers new and used equipment used agriculture and construction equipment. It offers heavy-duty equipment such as compact excavator electric utility vehicle mower-conditioner tractor disc mower and more. These products are sold under brand names John Deere Vermeer Topcon and other top brands such as Mazzotti Spudnik and Carlson Machine Control.

Geographic Reach

North Dakota-based RDO Equipment has over 75 stores across the US. Outside the US the company operates through partnerships in Africa Australia Mexico Russia and Ukraine as RDO International.

Sales and Marketing

The company offers its products to industries such as agriculture irrigation technology and construction.

Mergers and Acquisitions

I

EXECUTIVES

Chb, Ronald D Offutt
Ceo*, Christi Offutt
*, Allan F Knoll
Treas-Asst SEC*, Thomas K Espel
Cfo*, Steven Dewald
Sales Representative, Jay Charlson
Manager, Kevin Ardary
Credit Analyst, Matthew Stevens
Financial Reporting Manager, Nadine Kruk
Director of Parts Operations S, Sandy Blatter
Sales Team Member, Scott Kvidt
Auditors: PRICEWATERHOUSECOOPERS LLP MI

LOCATIONS

HQ: RDO EQUIPMENT CO.
225 BROADWAY N, FARGO, ND 581024800
Phone: 701 239-8700
Web: WWW.RDOEQUIPMENT.COM

PRODUCTS/OPERATIONS

Selected Brands

Hitachi
John Deete
Sakai
Topcon
Vermeer
Wirtgen

Selected Products

Balers
Chippers
Combines
Dozers
Drills
Excavators
Planters
Scrapers
Tractors
Trenchers
Wheel loaders

COMPETITORS

Briggs Equipment	Komatsu America
Herc Holdings	Mustang Cat
Home Depot	Scott Equipment

HISTORICAL FINANCIALS

Company Type: Private

Income Statement FYE: April 30

	REVENUE ($ mil.)	NET INCOME ($ mil.)	NET PROFIT MARGIN	EMPLOYEES
04/21	2,362	105	4.5%	1,500
04/20	2,242	48	2.1%	—
04/19	2,095	52	2.5%	—
Annual Growth	6.2%	41.8%	—	—

2021 Year-End Financials

Return on assets: 7.3%   Cash ($ mil.): 6
Return on equity: 20.5%
Current ratio: 1.80

READING HOSPITAL

No it's not a square on the game of Monopoly but The Reading Hospital and Medical Center does treat patients in Berks County Pennsylvania and the surrounding area. Operating as Reading Health System the not-for-profit 735-bed medical center provides acute care and rehabilitation programs as well as behavioral and occupational health services. Specialty units include cancer cardiovascular weight management diabetes orthopedic trauma (level II) and women's health centers. In addition to the main hospital the Reading Health System includes Reading Health Rehabilitation Hospital and medical centers in nearby communities as well as laboratory imaging and outpatient centers throughout its region.

Operations

The system also delivers academic clinical training through its School of Health Sciences and Residency programs and operates the 113-acre Highlands at Wyomissing retirement community.

Altogether Reading Health System operates more than 45 locations with roughly 800 combined beds including primary and specialty care centers operated by Reading Health Physician Partners Reading Health Medical Services and the Quick Care and Urgent Care organizations. It employs some 1000 physicians and serves a population of more than 750000 residents. The Reading Health System served about 124400 emergency room patients during 2014; it also handled more than 31000 inpatient discharges and 19000 surgeries.

More than 90% of the company's revenues come from patient care services while residential (rehabilitation) and other services account for the rest.

Geographic Reach

Reading Health System's main hospital campus is located on a 22-building campus on 36 acres in West Reading Pennsylvania.

The system serves Berks County and the surrounding area.

Financial Performance

Reading Health System reported revenues of $901.1 million in fiscal 2014 (ended June) with net income of $62.8 million. Cash flow from operations totaled $30.2 million.

Strategy

Like most other hospitals Reading Health System sees its fair share of uninsured or underinsured patients seeking care at the ER for problems that are often not emergencies which can put a strain on hospital finances. Reading works to divert these patients to its Quick Care and Urgent Care Centers to help reduce some of that burden. The organization is also working to increase the size of its primary care network.

Within the main hospital Reading Health System is working to add new specialists such as interventional neuroradiologists and pediatric hospitalists as well as physicians who specialize in cardiac revascularization and robotic surgery procedures. It is also working to modernize technologies build new facilities and expand partnerships with area health care organizations. For example in 2013 it implemented its Reading HealthConnect electronic health record (EHR) system.

In addition the network broke ground on a $354 million expansion at the main West Reading hospital campus. The facility which is expected to open in 2016 will include new surgery and emergency treatment capacity and will add 150 private patient rooms; the project also includes conversion of existing rooms to private status. In 2015 Reading Health System opened a new family health care center; a new medical facility (featuring primary care physicians' offices imaging services and a laboratory) in Douglassville is also in the works.

Company Background

The Reading Hospital and Medical Center was founded in 1868 as The Reading Dispensary.

EXECUTIVES

Pres, Clint Matthews
Ceo*, David Clint Matthews
V Pres*, Theresa Sucher
Cmo*, Ron Nutting
Cfo*, Mark Reyngoudt
Cno*, Rosemary Wurster
Assistant To Human Resources M, Lori Fiddler
Coordinator, Lynn Burkett
Coordinator, Patti Luckenbill
Staff, Brian Le
Gynecologist, Stephen H Fehnel
Auditors: PRICEWATERHOUSECOOPERS LLP PH

LOCATIONS

HQ: READING HOSPITAL
420 S 5TH AVE, READING, PA 196112143
Phone: 484 628-8000
Web: WWW.READING.TOWERHEALTH.ORG

Selected Pennsylvania Operations

The Reading Health Dispensary (Reading)
The Reading Hospital (West Reading)
Reading Health Medical Services
Reading Health Medical Services at Muhlenberg (Reading)
Reading Health Medical Services at Northern Berks (Hamburg)
Reading Health Medical Services at Spring Ridge (Wyomissing)
Reading Health Medical Services at Wyomissing (Wyomissing)
Reading Health Medical Services at Wyomissing Plaza (Reading)
Reading Health Physicians
Reading Health Rehabilitation Hospital (Wyomissing)
QuickCare Centers (regional)
Urgent Care Centers (regional)

Selected Services

Audiology
Behavioral Health Services
Behavioral Medicine Pain Management
Center for Public Health
Chaplaincy Services
Chest Pain Center
Cleft Palate Clinic
Cochlear Implant Program
da Vinci Surgical System
Diabetes Center
Emergency Services
Epilepsy Monitoring Unit
Family Risk Assessment Program (FRAP)
HelpLine
Hospitalist Program
Infusion Center
Interventional Radiology
Laboratory Services
Library Services
Mammography Services
Nutrition Services
Occupational Health Services
Occupational Therapy
Pain Management
Palliative Care Program
Pediatrics - St' Chris Care
PET/CT Imaging
Physical Therapy
QuickCare -Reading Health Physician Network
Radiology Services
Rehabilitation Services

Respiratory Care
Senior Assessment Program
Sleep Center
Social Service
Speech and Hearing Center
Stroke Center
The Reading Hospital Home Care
Tobacco-Free Wellness Program
Travel Immunization Service
Women's Health Services
Wound Healing and Hyperbaric Medicine Center

COMPETITORS

Ascension Health
Doylestown Hospital
Lvhn
Lancaster General
Main Line Health System
Moses Taylor Hospital
Sacred Heart Hospital Of Allentown
St. Luke's University Health Network
Universal Health Services
University Of Pennsylvania Health System
Wyoming Valley Health Care System

HISTORICAL FINANCIALS

Company Type: Private

Income Statement				FYE: June 30
	REVENUE ($ mil.)	NET INCOME ($ mil.)	NET PROFIT MARGIN	EMPLOYEES
06/09	675	42	6.2%	5,500
06/08	640	50	7.8%	—
06/06	783	0	—	—
Annual Growth	—	—	—	—

2009 Year-End Financials

Return on assets: 5.4%   Cash ($ mil.): 43
Return on equity: 103.7%
Current ratio: 1.80

READING HOSPITAL SERVICES INC

EXECUTIVES

Pres, Charles B Sullivan
V Pres, Scott R Wolfe
SEC, Richard I Mabel
Treas, Steven I Finkel
Coordinator, Alana Strause
Coordinator, Patti Luckenbill
Recruiter, Adriane Hoke
Pharmacist, Roman Gokhman
Receiving Manager, Eugene McGarry
Division Director, Timothy Marks
Administrator, Charles Barbera

LOCATIONS

HQ: READING HOSPITAL SERVICES INC
6TH AND SPRUCE ST, READING, PA 19612
Phone: 610 988-8000
Web: WWW.READING.TOWERHEALTH.ORG

HISTORICAL FINANCIALS

Company Type: Private

Income Statement				FYE: June 30
	REVENUE ($ mil.)	NET INCOME ($ mil.)	NET PROFIT MARGIN	EMPLOYEES
06/20	1,035	63	6.1%	1
06/08	24	(10)	—	—
06/03	0	0	81.7%	—
06/02	0	0	86.3%	—
Annual Growth	53.0%	32.1%	—	—

2020 Year-End Financials

Return on assets: 5.4%   Cash ($ mil.): —
Return on equity: 45.4%
Current ratio: 1.10

REALPAGE, INC.

EXECUTIVES

Chb-Ceo, Stephen Winn
Pres, Ashley Glover
Exec V Pres-Prin, David Monk
Sr V Pres-Prin, Barry Carter
Sr V Pres-Prin, Kurt Twining
Exec V Pres-Cfo, Brian Shelton
Account Manager III, Nate Fish
Senior Revenue Analyst, Patrick Lambert
Implementation Consultant II, Penny Fielder
Network Operation Man, Pj Hall
Network Manager, Queenie Hu
Auditors: ERNST & YOUNG LLP DALLAS TEX

LOCATIONS

HQ: REALPAGE, INC.
2201 LAKESIDE BLVD, RICHARDSON, TX 750824305
Phone: 972 820-3000
Web: WWW.REALPAGE.COM

COMPETITORS

Archibus	Infor Global
Assurant	Moneygram
Chase Paymentech	International
Solutions	Pros Holdings
Communities Group	Sitestuff
First Advantage	Transunion
First Data	Who's Calling
Fiserv	Yardi Systems

HISTORICAL FINANCIALS

Company Type: Private

Income Statement				FYE: December 31
	REVENUE ($ mil.)	NET INCOME ($ mil.)	NET PROFIT MARGIN	EMPLOYEES
12/20	1,158	46	4.0%	7,000
12/19	988	58	5.9%	—
12/18	869	34	4.0%	—
12/17	670	0	0.1%	—
Annual Growth	20.0%	397.1%	—	—

2020 Year-End Financials

Return on assets: 1.3%   Cash ($ mil.): 594
Return on equity: 2.9%
Current ratio: 1.20

RECKSON OPERATING PARTNERSHIP, L.P.

EXECUTIVES

Pres-Ceo, Marc Holliday
Cfo-Cao-Treas, Matthew J Diliberto
Gen Ptnr, Wyoming Acquisition GP LLC
Managing Director, Brett Herschenfeld

LOCATIONS

HQ: RECKSON OPERATING PARTNERSHIP, L.P.
420 LEXINGTON AVE, NEW YORK, NY 101700002
Phone: 212 594-2700
Web: WWW.SLGREEN.COM

HISTORICAL FINANCIALS

Company Type: Private

Income Statement				FYE: December 31
	ASSETS ($ mil.)	NET INCOME ($ mil.)	INCOME AS % OF ASSETS	EMPLOYEES
12/18	7,009	199	2.8%	279
12/17	8,541	198	2.3%	—
12/16	8,754	313	3.6%	—
12/15	8,858	362	4.1%	—
Annual Growth	(7.5%)	(18.1%)	—	—

2018 Year-End Financials

Return on assets: 2.8%   Sales ($ mil): 816
Return on equity: 3.2%

RECTOR & VISITORS OF THE UNIVERSITY OF VIRGINIA

The nation's third president Thomas Jefferson founded the University of Virginia in 1819. Named Rector and Visitors of the University of Virginia the university is known as UVA today. It is said to be Jefferson's proudest achievement and boasts an enrollment of about 23000 students throughout the university's over 10 graduate and undergraduate schools. One of the most prestigious public universities in the US the school has been noted for its law program English department and its more than 175-year-old student-enforced conduct code (the Honor System). The school also includes the University of Virginia Health System which trains future doctors and other health care workers at its Medical Center hospital.

Operations

UVA is an agency of the Commonwealth of Virginia governed by the university's Board of Visitors. The university comprises three divisions: the Academic Division the University of Virginia's College at Wise and the Medical Center Division. Its College at Wise focuses on the humanities arts science and professional disciplines concentrating on instruction research and public service. The Medical Center Division offers both routine and ancillary patient services via its full-service hospital and clinics.

The university which has a 14:1 student-faculty ratio employs some 3200 full-time faculty and research staff supported by approximately 9700 full-time staff members. It runs the College and Graduate School of Arts & Sciences Darden School of Business Frank Batten School of Leadership and Public Policy McIntire School of Commerce as well as the School of Architecture School of Continuing & Professional Studies and School of Data Science among its schools. The university has approximately 16000 undergraduates and some 7800 graduate students.

It offers aerospace engineering biology comparative literature health and wellbeing minor criminal justice education mechanical engineering and religious studies. The university also offers additional academic opportunities such as Air Force ROTC Lifetime Physical Activity Options Interdisciplinary Major Program and University Seminars.

Patient services provide more than 55% of sales student tuition and fees account for nearly 20% sponsored programs bring in about 15% of sales and others represent the remaining.

Geographic Reach

The University of Virginia operates its more than 10 schools and medical center in Charlottesville while its College at Wise is in the Southwest Virginia town of Wise.

Financial Performance

The company's revenue for fiscal 2020 decreased by 2% to $3.9 billion compared from the prior year with $4.0 billion.

Cash held by the company at the end of fiscal 2020 increased to $415.3 billion. Cash provided by financing activities was $486.0 million while cash used for operations and investing activities were $214.4 million and $204.5 million respectively. Main uses of cash were payments to employees and fringe benefits and acquisition and construction of capital assets.

Strategy

The University's financial stability over time enables leaders to develop and execute long-term strategic plans. Despite the global uncertainties of FY2020 UVA made important progress toward the goals identified in the 2030 Plan that were formally approved by the Board of Visitors in August 2019. Successful fundraising efforts continue to bolster financial support for students and faculty through the Bicentennial Scholars and Bicentennial Professors programs.

The University made progress on important capital construction projects in FY2020 opening a new hospital bed tower ahead of schedule and a new upper-class residence hall ? Bond House ? for the start of the academic year continuing work to develop the Brandon Avenue corridor and construct a new facility for Student Health and Wellness completing UVA softball's new home at Palmer Park and advancing long-term plans for the Emmet-Ivy Corridor. In addition the University continues the renovation of the Chemistry Building and Gilmer Hall a project largely funded by the state. In FY2020 the state approved funding for the Alderman Library renewal project which is now under construction and authorized the University to begin the renovation of the Physics Building.

EXECUTIVES

Pres, Teresa A Sullivan

Exec V Pres-Coo, Leonard W Sandridge Jr

Associate Vp-Treasurer, Jim Matteo

Vp and Chief Student Affairs O, Patricia M Lampkin

Executive Director Career Serv, James L McBride Jr

Vp and Cfo, Yoke San L Reynolds

Dean, School of Continuing and, Billy K Cannaday Jr

Vice Provost Pro, Gowher Rizvi

Vice Provost Faculty Developme, Sharon L Hostler

Assistant Professor, Angela Zarling

Assistant Professor, Naomi L Katz

Auditors: WALTER J KUTCHARSKI RICHMOND

LOCATIONS

HQ: RECTOR & VISITORS OF THE UNIVERSITY OF VIRGINIA
1001 EMMET ST N, CHARLOTTESVILLE, VA 229034833
Phone: 434 924-0311
Web: WWW.VIRGINIA.EDU

PRODUCTS/OPERATIONS

Selected Schools
College and Graduate School of Arts & Sciences
Curry School of Education
Darden Graduate School of Business Administration
McIntire School of Commerce
School of Architecture
School of Continuing & Professional Studies
School of Engineering and Applied Science
School of Law
School of Medicine
School of Nursing

HISTORICAL FINANCIALS

Company Type: Private

Income Statement				FYE: June 30
	REVENUE ($ mil.)	NET INCOME ($ mil.)	NET PROFIT MARGIN	EMPLOYEES
06/11	1,909	909	47.6%	13,300
06/10	524	97	18.6%	—
06/08	2,181	312	14.3%	—
06/07	2,121	1,114	52.5%	—
Annual Growth	(2.6%)	(5.0%)	—	—

2011 Year-End Financials

Return on assets: 11.4% Cash ($ mil.): 324
Return on equity: 14.5%
Current ratio: 1.40

REDEEMER HEALTH HOLY SYSTEM

EXECUTIVES

Prin, Terri Crowe

Medicare Coordinator, Carol Noverati

Treasury Manager, David Golden

Business Office Manager, Delores Squillace

In Education Director, Mary Cockerham

LOCATIONS

HQ: REDEEMER HEALTH HOLY SYSTEM
1616 HUNTINGDON PIKE, JENKINTOWN, PA 190468001
Phone: 215 938-4000
Web: WWW.REDEEMERHEALTH.ORG

HISTORICAL FINANCIALS

Company Type: Private

Income Statement				FYE: June 30
	REVENUE ($ mil.)	NET INCOME ($ mil.)	NET PROFIT MARGIN	EMPLOYEES
06/09	2,900	286	9.9%	1
06/99	0	(0)	—	—
Annual Growth	187.6%			

2009 Year-End Financials

Return on assets: 73.5% Cash ($ mil.): 47
Return on equity: 195.9%
Current ratio: 0.80

REDNER'S MARKETS, INC.

Redner's Markets operates about 45 warehouse club-style supermarkets under the Redner's Warehouse Markets banner and more than a dozen Quick Shoppe convenience stores. Most of the company's stores are located in eastern Pennsylvania but the regional grocer also operates several locations in Maryland and Delaware having closed its one New York supermarket. Redner's Warehouse Markets house bakery deli meat produce and seafood departments as well as in-store banks. The employee-owned company was founded by namesake Earl Redner in 1970. It is still operated by the Redner family including chairman and CEO Richard and COO Ryan Redner.

Financial Performance

Redner's Markets rang up an estimated $865 million in sales in fiscal 2012 (ends September) up from about $859 million in sales the previous year.

Strategy

Redner's has been tinkering with its store portfolio shuttering underperforming locations including several in its core Pennsylvania market while building new stores in existing and new markets. The regional chain has grown to four stores each in Delaware and Maryland since entering those markets in 2008 and 2005 respectively. Redner's is also growing its Web presence doubling its online traffic in the first year of a digiral shopper marketing program conducted in partnership with Google Shopping Network.

EXECUTIVES

Pres-Ceo, Ryan Redner

Chb*, Richard E Redner

V Pres-Fin*, Gordon B Hoch

V Pres-Hr*, Robert Mc Donough

Treas*, Gary W Redner

SEC*, Chere Kelly

V Pres*, Michael McNaney

V Pres-It, John W Sweigart

Administrator, Lori Brauer

Director, Perry Hoffmaster

Merchandise Manager, Dick Stiles

Auditors: RKL LLP WYOMISSING PENNSYLV

LOCATIONS

HQ: REDNER'S MARKETS, INC.
3 QUARRY RD, READING, PA 196059787
Phone: 610 926-3700
Web: WWW.REDNERSMARKETS.COM

2012 Warehouse Market Stores

	No.
Pennsylvania	36
Delaware	4
Maryland	4
Total	**44**

PRODUCTS/OPERATIONS

2012 Stores

	No.
Redner's Warehouse Market	44
Quick Shoppe	14
Total	**58**

COMPETITORS

7-eleven	Wal-mart
A&p	Wawa Inc.
Cumberland Farms	Wegmans
Giant Food Stores	Weis Markets
Sheetz	

HISTORICAL FINANCIALS

Company Type: Private

Income Statement

FYE: October 1

	REVENUE ($ mil.)	NET INCOME ($ mil.)	NET PROFIT MARGIN	EMPLOYEES
10/16*	864	4	0.6%	4,800
09/15	884	6	0.7%	—
09/14	902	1	0.2%	—
09/13	892	4	0.5%	—
Annual Growth	(1.1%)	1.8%	—	—

*Fiscal year change

2016 Year-End Financials

Return on assets: 3.0%
Return on equity: 4.0%
Current ratio: 3.40
Cash ($ mil.): 56

REGAL ENTERTAINMENT GROUP

Regal Entertainment Group a subsidiary of the Cineworld Group operates one of the largest and most geographically diverse theatre circuits in the US consisting of more than 7200 screens in almost 550 theatres in more than 45 states along with American Samoa the District of Columbia Guam and Saipan. Provides bonus rewards through its Crown Club card the company partners with Movietickets.com Variety ? The Children's Charities NCM ? America's Movie Network World Travel Services Will Rogers Institute Fandango Elavon and Patricia Neal Rehabilitation Center. The company was founded in 1989.

Operations

Regal Entertainment offers IMAX RealD 3D RPX ScreenX 4DX Auro Recliners and Dolby Atmos.

Geographic Reach

Tennessee-based Regal Entertainment operates in over 45 US states the District of Columbia Guam Saipan and American Samoa. The chain targets midsized metropolitan markets and suburban growth areas of larger cities. It has a large number of theaters in California Florida and New York.

Sales and Marketing

Regal Entertainment employs an interactive marketing program for specific films and concession items to increase attendance and consumption. Its Regal Crown Club loyalty program rewards frequent moviegoers with deals of concessions and more.

The company uses the internet mobile and social media print and multimedia advertising to promote its service. Regal Entertainment conducts special interactive marketing programs for specific films and concessions items.

EXECUTIVES

Ceo, Nisan Cohen
Cfo-Treas-Sr Vp, Vincent Fusco
District Manager, Charles Shaw
District Manager, Shane Mongar
Network Administrator, Shelia Galler
Vice President, Vince Fusco
Film Buyer, Eric Burrell
General Manager, Jake Bishop
Vice President Payroll, Joseph Marlowe
Analyst II, Mike Trabalka
Director, Jessica Stanford
Auditors: KPMG LLP KNOXVILLE TENNESSEE

LOCATIONS

HQ: REGAL ENTERTAINMENT GROUP
101 E BLOUNT AVE STE 100, KNOXVILLE, TN
379201605
Phone: 865 922-1123
Web: WWW.REGMOVIES.COM

PRODUCTS/OPERATIONS

2017 Sales

	$ mil.	% of total
Admissions	2,008	64
Concessions	930	29
Other	224	7
Total	**3,163**	**100**

Selected Operations

Cinemas
  Edwards Theatres
  Regal Cinemas
  United Artists Theatre Company
Theater advertising
  National CineMedia (20%)

COMPETITORS

Amc Entertainment	Marcus Corporation
Alamo Drafthouse	National Amusements
Carmike Cinemas	Netflix
Cinemark	Pacific Theatres
Cineplex	Reading International
Landmark Theatres	Redbox

HISTORICAL FINANCIALS

Company Type: Private

Income Statement

FYE: December 31

	REVENUE ($ mil.)	NET INCOME ($ mil.)	NET PROFIT MARGIN	EMPLOYEES
12/17	3,163	112	3.6%	25,359
12/16	3,197	170	5.3%	—
12/15*	3,127	153	4.9%	—
01/15	2,990	105	3.5%	—
Annual Growth	1.9%	2.2%	—	—

*Fiscal year change

2017 Year-End Financials

Return on assets: 999.9%
Return on equity: —
Current ratio: 0.80
Cash ($ mil.): —

REGENTS OF THE UNIVERSITY OF MICHIGAN

Ranking among the top US public universities Regents of the University of Michigan (or simply University of Michigan) boasts roughly 64300 students in southeast Michigan. Its three campuses in Ann Arbor Dearborn and Flint offer more than 275 undergraduate and graduate degree programs in fields including architecture education law medicine music and social work. The university has a student to faculty ratio of 15:1. The University of Michigan Health System includes three hospitals and more than 125 health clinics/centers.

Operations

The university has about 15 undergraduate schools and colleges offering architecture & urban planning; art & design; business; dental hygiene; education; engineering; information; kinesiology; literature science and the arts (LSA); music theatre & dance; nursing; pharmacy; public health; and public policy. Its graduate programs include certificate doctoral and master's in the areas of anthropology architecture biophysics business chemical biology and criminal study among others.

Geographic Reach

From its primary campuses in southeast Michigan the university attracts students from more than 80 Michigan counties some 50 states and about 140 countries.

Financial Performance

University's revenue for fiscal 2021 increased to $8.4 billion compared from the prior year with $8.0 billion.

Loss for fiscal 2021 decreased to $1.1 billion compared from the prior year with $1.4 billion.

Cash held by the company at the end of fiscal 2021 increased to $19.5 billion. Cash provided by noncapital financing activities was $900.9 million while cash used for operations and capital and related financing activities were $331.3 million and $569.8 million respectively.

Strategy

The University's long-term investment strategy combined with its endowment spending policy serves to insulate operations from expected volatility in the capital markets and provides for a stable and predictable level of spending distributions from the endowment. The success of the University's long-term investment strategy is evidenced by strong returns over sustained periods of time and the ability to limit losses in the face of challenging markets.

EXECUTIVES

Pres, Mary Coleman
V Pres*, Sally J Churchill
Chef Assistant Unions Food Ser, John Layher
Chief Technology Officer, Juan P Bedoya
Professor Emeritus, Judith Becker
Physician Surgery, Lisa Colletti
Claims, Pamella Mitchell
Professor Dbn Casl Social Scie, Patricia K Smith
Professor Lsa Geological Scien, Philip A Meyers
Clinical Assistant Professiona, Karen K Milner
Coordinator Pat Fam Rels, Umh, Kellylee Roth
Auditors: PRICEWATERHOUSECOOPERS LLP DE

LOCATIONS

HQ: REGENTS OF THE UNIVERSITY OF MICHIGAN
503 THOMPSON ST, ANN ARBOR, MI 481091340
Phone: 734 764-1817
Web: WWW.UMICH.EDU

PRODUCTS/OPERATIONS

Selected Academic Units
Architecture and urban planning
Art and design
Business administration
Dentistry
Education
Engineering
Kinesiology
Law
Literature science and the arts
Medicine
Music
Natural resources and environment
Nursing
Pharmacy
Public health
Public policy
Social work

HISTORICAL FINANCIALS

Company Type: Private

Income Statement   FYE: June 30

	REVENUE ($ mil.)	NET INCOME ($ mil.)	NET PROFIT MARGIN	EMPLOYEES
06/20	7,955	(0)	—	34,624
06/19	7,989	522	6.5%	—
06/18	7,466	920	12.3%	—
06/17	7,079	1,275	18.0%	—
Annual Growth	4.0%	—	—	—

2020 Year-End Financials

Return on assets: —   Cash ($ mil.): 1,284
Return on equity: —
Current ratio: 1.70

REGIONAL CENTER OF THE EAST BAY, INC.

EXECUTIVES

Ceo, Kathy Hebert
Case Management Supervisor, Brenda Pineda
Case Manager II, Jonna Hall
File Clerk, Kenneth Chin
Childrens Case Manager, Gwynneth Dunne
Case Manager I Bilingual, Jorge Verduzco
Support Staff, Robin Phillips
Bilingual Case Manager II, Sarah Steinberg
Director Human Resources, Terri Jones
Case Manager II, Julie Whiskeyman
Case Manager II, Lisa Kindblad

LOCATIONS

HQ: REGIONAL CENTER OF THE EAST BAY, INC.
500 DAVIS ST STE 100, SAN LEANDRO, CA
945772758
Phone: 510 618-6100
Web: WWW.RCEB.ORG

HISTORICAL FINANCIALS

Company Type: Private

Income Statement   FYE: June 30

	REVENUE ($ mil.)	NET INCOME ($ mil.)	NET PROFIT MARGIN	EMPLOYEES
06/20	547	37	6.9%	250
06/08	250	(2)	—	—
06/06	199	0	0.0%	—
06/05	184	0	0.0%	—
Annual Growth	7.5%	74.2%		

2020 Year-End Financials

Return on assets: 12.5%   Cash ($ mil.): 42
Return on equity: 999.9%
Current ratio: —

REGIONAL TRANSPORTATION AUTHORITY

EXECUTIVES

Exec Dir, Richard J Bacigalupo
Chb, Thomas J McCraken Jr
Dep Exec Dir-Cfo, Joseph G Costello
Treas, Allan Sharkey
Prin, Julie Gomez
Prin, Carole Brown
Manager, Roxann Galvan
Customer Programs Specialist, Vanessa Alvarez
Senior Financial Analyst, Alejandro Montero
Accountant, Anita Anderson
Programmer Analyst, Xiaoni Wu
Auditors: RSM US LLP CHICAGO ILLINOIS

LOCATIONS

HQ: REGIONAL TRANSPORTATION AUTHORITY
175 W JACKSON BLVD # 1650, CHICAGO, IL
606042711
Phone: 312 913-3200
Web: WWW.RTACHICAGO.ORG

HISTORICAL FINANCIALS

Company Type: Private

Income Statement   FYE: December 31

	REVENUE ($ mil.)	NET INCOME ($ mil.)	NET PROFIT MARGIN	EMPLOYEES
12/19	618	(102)	—	80
12/16	637	(99)	—	—
12/15	805	(77)	—	—
12/14	755	(3)	—	—
Annual Growth	(3.9%)	—	—	—

2019 Year-End Financials

Return on assets: (-12.1%)   Cash ($ mil.): 123
Return on equity: —
Current ratio: 1.70

REGIONS HOSPITAL

Auditors: KPMG LLP MINNEAPOLIS MN

LOCATIONS

HQ: REGIONS HOSPITAL
8170 33RD AVE S, MINNEAPOLIS, MN 554254516
Phone: 952 883-6280
Web: WWW.HEALTHPARTNERS.COM

HISTORICAL FINANCIALS

Company Type: Private

Income Statement   FYE: December 31

	REVENUE ($ mil.)	NET INCOME ($ mil.)	NET PROFIT MARGIN	EMPLOYEES
12/19	847	52	6.2%	47
12/17	790	47	6.0%	—
12/14	691	40	5.9%	—
12/09	515	17	3.4%	—
Annual Growth	5.1%	11.5%	—	—

2019 Year-End Financials

Return on assets: 5.4%   Cash ($ mil.): 184
Return on equity: 8.5%
Current ratio: 3.10

REGIONS HOSPITAL

EXECUTIVES

Pres, Megan Remark
Hematologist Oncologist, Balkrishna N Jahagirdar
Lab Technician, Becky Green
Director PA Residency, Bradley Hernandez
Emergency Medicine Specialist, Casey M Woster
Hematologist Oncologist, Colleen Morton
Trauma Program Manager Coordin, Heidi Altamirano
Director of Risk Management, Jeremy Sundheim
Neurosurgeon, Jon I McIver
Chief Engineer, Josh Knoll
Senior Manager, Michaela Timmers
Auditors: KPMG LLP MINNEAPOLIS MINNESO

LOCATIONS

HQ: REGIONS HOSPITAL
640 JACKSON ST, SAINT PAUL, MN 551012595
Phone: 651 254-3456
Web: WWW.REGIONSHOSPITAL.COM

HISTORICAL FINANCIALS

Company Type: Private

Income Statement   FYE: December 31

	REVENUE ($ mil.)	NET INCOME ($ mil.)	NET PROFIT MARGIN	EMPLOYEES
12/20	819	52	6.4%	469
12/19	847	52	6.2%	—
12/14	636	40	6.4%	—
Annual Growth	4.3%	4.4%	—	—

2020 Year-End Financials

Return on assets: 4.7%   Cash ($ mil.): 306
Return on equity: 7.8%
Current ratio: 2.90

REGIONS HOSPITAL FOUNDATION

If you live around the Twin Cities Regions Hospital can help with your medical needs. The not-for-profit hospital has more than 450 beds and provides acute medical and emergency care services as well as specialty programs in areas including behavioral health rehabilitation burn care cancer cardiovascular orthopedic pediatrics and women's care. Regions Hospital is one of a handful of level I trauma centers in Minnesota and is also a teaching and residency center for the University of Minnesota Medical School. Regions Hospital is part of HealthPartners which operates a network of medical centers and a health plan in the Twin Cities area.

Operations
In 2012 Regions Hospital operated at a 78% occupancy rate with some 25000 inpatient visits. It also handled 78000 emergency center visits 13000 surgeries and some 2500 births. It has about 650 physicians on its staff plus another 800 affiliated doctors who are members of the Health-Partners Medical Group physician practice organization.

The hospital provided some $56 million in community benefits during 2012 including charity care and outreach programs.

Geographic Reach
Regions Hospital serves the St. Paul Minnesota metropolitan area as well as patients from other areas across Minnesota and in western Wisconsin. It also sees visitors from other Midwest states.

Strategy
The hospital has expanded its facilities in recent years to meet the demands of a growing Twin Cities population and address current underserved community health needs. For instance in 2012 Regions Hospital completed construction of a new $36 million eight-story inpatient mental health center with about 100 beds designed to replace its aging mental health facility. In addition in 2009 the hospital wrapped up a $180 million expansion and renovation project that gave it a new 10-story patient tower with 20 new operating rooms more than 35 private patient beds and shell space for further expansion in the future.

In addition the hospital looks to enhance services through new equipment and procedural offerings as well as through partnerships with other area providers.

Company Background
Established in 1872 Regions Hospital became part of the HealthPartners network in 1993.

EXECUTIVES

Pres, Brock Nelson
Cfo*, Greg Klugherz
Internist, Matthew Turner
Admin Secretary Surgical Servi, Monica Knack
Physical Therapist, Robin Peterson

LOCATIONS

HQ: REGIONS HOSPITAL FOUNDATION
640 JACKSON ST, SAINT PAUL, MN 551012595
Phone: 651 254-3456
Web: WWW.REGIONSHOSPITAL.COM

PRODUCTS/OPERATIONS

Selected Specialties and Divisions
Behavioral Health
Birth Center
Breast Health Center
Burn Center
Cancer Care Center
Center for Dementia and Alzheimer's Care
Digestive Care Center
Emergency Center
Heart Center
Level I Trauma Center
Level I Pediatric Trauma Center
Neurosciences
Orthopedics
Palliative Care Unit
Rehabilitation Institute
Spine Center
Stroke Center
Surgery Center

COMPETITORS

Allina Hospitals
Amery Regional Medical Center
Catholic Health Initiatives
Centracare Health
Children's Hospitals And Clinics Of Minnesota
Fairview Health
Gillette Children's
Healtheast Care System
Mayo Clinic
North Memorial Health Care
Olmsted Medical
Paynesville Area Healthcare System

HISTORICAL FINANCIALS
Company Type: Private

Income Statement				FYE: December 31
	REVENUE ($ mil.)	NET INCOME ($ mil.)	NET PROFIT MARGIN	EMPLOYEES
12/12	581	36	6.3%	3,000
12/06	413	4	1.0%	—
12/05	430	12	2.8%	—
12/04	7	0	0.0%	—
Annual Growth	71.3%	320.5%	—	—

2012 Year-End Financials

Return on assets: 6.2%   Cash ($ mil.): 64
Return on equity: 6.3%
Current ratio: 1.70

RENSSELAER POLYTECHNIC INSTITUTE

Rensselaer Polytechnic Institute (RPI) feeds scientific minds. The university offers about 150 bachelor's master's and doctoral degree programs primarily in scientific research and technology fields. With some 7000 undergraduate and graduate students and a student-to-faculty ratio of 15:1 RPI strives to provide interdisciplinary education programs through its five schools (Architecture; Engineering; Humanities Arts and Social Sciences; Management and Technology; and Science). The institute was founded in 1824 and is one of the oldest engineering schools in the country. RPI's main campus is in Troy New York but the institute also has a location in Hartford Connecticut that caters to working professionals.

Operations
RPI strives to provide interdisciplinary programs by balancing students' experiences in the classroom research laboratory and work studio environments. The university's research programs primarily focus on art biotechnology information technology energy and nanotechnology and some of its students' discoveries become the foundation for commercial development efforts through the school's office of technology and commercialization. The institute has 500 full- and part-time faculty members and charges some $45000 in tuition and more than $15000 in additional room board and supply fees.

Geographic Reach
RPI students are enrolled from nearly all US states and more than 60 international countries. The 280-acre main campus is located on a bluff overlooking the Hudson River and the city of Troy New York. The 1250-acre Rensselaer Technology Park has 60 company tenants that partner with RPI on a number of research programs.

Its Hartford Connecticut campus is located on a 15-acre urban site. RPI also has a regional site in Groton Connecticut and an architecture school satellite location in New York City.

Strategy
In recent years RPI has been expanding certain programs under the Rensselaer Plan a concerted effort to turn the university into a full-service technological university. Growth efforts to attract a more diverse student base under the plan include construction of new learning halls living quarters and athletic facilities. RPI is also working to greatly expand its research and entrepreneurship programs.

It opened a new stem cell research center a manufacturing innovation learning lab and the Mercer Laboratory for student exploration and innovation during 2012 as well as the institute-wide Center for Cognition Communication and Culture (CCC).

The institute also expands by adding new degree programs such as sustainability studies and supply chain management offerings added in 2013. It further enhanced programs that year by forming a diagnostic development and learning affiliation with the Icahn School of Medicine at Mount Sinai.

EXECUTIVES

Pres, Shirley Ann Jackson
V Pres-Fin*, Virginia C Gregg
Treas*, David Gaume
Assistant Professor, Khaled N Salama
Assistant Professor, Zhaoran R Huang
Associate Professor, Tong Zhang
Coordinator, Barb Jordan
Assistant Professor, Dan Shawhan
Coordinator, Denise M Posson
Assistant Professor, Dongling Huang
Coordinator, Jennifer Tedesco
Auditors: PRICEWATERHOUSECOOPERS LLP HA

LOCATIONS

HQ: RENSSELAER POLYTECHNIC INSTITUTE
110 8TH ST, TROY, NY 121803522
Phone: 518 276-6000
Web: WWW.RPI.EDU

PRODUCTS/OPERATIONS

Selected Schools
School of Architecture
School of Engineering
School of Humanities Arts and Social Sciences
School of Information Technology and Web Science
School of Management
School of Science

Selected Programs
Aeronautical Engineering
Applied Physics
Architecture
Biochemistry and Biophysics
Bioinformatics and Molecular Biology
Biology
Biomedical Engineering

Business and Management
Chemical Engineering
Chemistry
Civil Engineering
Cognitive Science
Communication
Computer and Systems Engineering
Computer Science
Design Innovation and Society
Economics
Electrical Engineering
Electronic Arts
Electronic Media Arts and Communication
Environmental Engineering
Environmental Science
Games and Simulation Arts and Sciences
Geology
Hydrogeology
Industrial and Management Engineering
Information Technology and Web Science
Interdisciplinary Science
Materials Engineering
Mathematics
Mechanical Engineering
Nuclear Engineering
Philosophy
Physics
Psychology
Science Technology and Society
Sustainability Studies

HISTORICAL FINANCIALS
Company Type: Private

Income Statement   FYE: June 30

	REVENUE ($ mil.)	NET INCOME ($ mil.)	NET PROFIT MARGIN	EMPLOYEES
06/20	653	33	5.2%	1,500
06/17	414	77	18.8%	—
Annual Growth	16.4%	(24.3%)	—	—

2020 Year-End Financials
Return on assets: 2.1%   Cash ($ mil.): 23
Return on equity: 6.5%
Current ratio: 0.20

RESEARCH TRIANGLE INSTITUTE INC

Founded in 1958 Research Triangle Institute operates mainly under its trade name RTI International (RTI) the not-for-profit enterprise conducts research in such areas as advanced technologies environmental resources and medicine. It provides such services and materials testing as well as the software used in laboratories and research projects. Serving the US federal government other governments nonprofits and for-profit companies RTI offers analytical perspectives on public policy and has researchers working in offices around the world.

Geographic Reach
North Carolina-based RTI serves clients in more than 75 countries. RTI also offers multiple teleworking options to its worldwide staff members. RTI's regional offices in Asia Africa and Latin America and the Caribbean serve as operational hubs for projects throughout these regions. The company also maintains a wholly-owned subsidiary in India RTI Health Solutions offices in Europe and dozens of project-specific offices in many of the countries.

Sales and Marketing
The company's clients include government agencies academia foundations global NGOs and commercial companies.

EXECUTIVES
Ceo, E Wayne Holden
Evp and Coo, James J Gibson
Exec V Pres, Tim Gabel
Sr V Pres, G Edward Story
Manager, Senior Contracts, Gillian Gaeta
Senior Public Health Project D, Gretchen Van Vliet
Survey Director, Ilona Johnson
Research Analyst, L D Wagner
Research Public Health Analyst, Youn Lee
Financial Analyst, Lilly Bliss
Associate Director of Market, Maria Fernandez
Auditors: DELOITTE & TOUCHE LLP RALEIGH

LOCATIONS
HQ: RESEARCH TRIANGLE INSTITUTE INC
3040 CORNWALLIS RD, DURHAM, NC 277090155
Phone: 919 541-6000
Web: WWW.RTI.ORG

PRODUCTS/OPERATIONS

Selected Research Areas
Advanced technology research and development
Drug discovery and development
Economic and social
Education and training
Energy
Environmental
Health
International development
Laboratory and chemistry
Statistics
Survey

COMPETITORS
Battelle Memorial   Urban Institute
Qss Group
Sandford Burnham
  Institute

HISTORICAL FINANCIALS
Company Type: Private

Income Statement   FYE: September 30

	REVENUE ($ mil.)	NET INCOME ($ mil.)	NET PROFIT MARGIN	EMPLOYEES
09/20	912	25	2.8%	3,117
09/18	957	(1)	—	—
09/17	972	22	2.4%	—
09/16	884	15	1.8%	—
Annual Growth	0.8%	12.6%	—	—

2020 Year-End Financials
Return on assets: 3.5%   Cash ($ mil.): 55
Return on equity: 5.9%
Current ratio: 2.10

REX HEALTHCARE, INC.

Part of the UNC Health Care UNC REX Healthcare is a not-for-profit health care provider that serves residents of Raleigh and the rest of Wake County North Carolina. Founded in 1894 UNC REX Healthcare includes a medical staff of more than 1100 physicians and 1700 nurses as well as primary and specialty care clinics throughout the area. Its facilities include an acute care hospital

five wellness centers and two skilled nursing facilities. Specialty centers and clinics provide services such as birthing cancer treatment same-day surgery heart and vascular care pain management and sleep disorder therapy. UNC REX also provides home health and mobile emergency medical services. UNC HealthCare also includes affiliate UNC Hospitals.

EXECUTIVES
Ceo, Gary Park
Pres*, David Strong
V Pres-Cfo*, Bernadette Spong
Chm*, A Dale Jenkins
Vp Support, Chad T Lefteris
Pathologist, Stephen V Chiaetta
Property Manager, Lisa H Rosenberg
Team Leader, Douglas Palmer
Clinical Coordinator, Bonnie Aslett
Manager Sleep Disorder Center, Carol Watson
Vice President, Charles Scarantino
Auditors: CLIFTON LARSON ALLEN LLP CHAR

LOCATIONS
HQ: REX HEALTHCARE, INC.
4420 LAKE BOONE TRL., RALEIGH, NC 276077505
Phone: 919 784-3100
Web: WWW.REXHEALTH.COM

PRODUCTS/OPERATIONS

Selected Specialty Services

Oncology
Heart and vascular
Surgical Services: Bariatric Heartburn and GI
Orthopedic Neuro and Spine
Rehabilitation
Emergency and Urgent Care
Women's Services
Wound Healing

COMPETITORS
Carolinas Healthcare   Firsthealth Of The
  System   Carolinas
Cone Health   Morehead Memorial
Cumberland County   Hospital
  Hospital System   Novant Health
Danville Regional   Vidant Health
  Medical Center   Wakemed
Duke University Health
  System

HISTORICAL FINANCIALS
Company Type: Private

Income Statement   FYE: June 30

	REVENUE ($ mil.)	NET INCOME ($ mil.)	NET PROFIT MARGIN	EMPLOYEES
06/20	1,180	(2)	—	5,500
06/13	731	8	1.2%	—
06/12	719	34	4.8%	—
06/11	1,669	0	—	—
Annual Growth	—	—	—	—

2020 Year-End Financials
Return on assets: (-0.2%)   Cash ($ mil.): 430
Return on equity: (-0.4%)
Current ratio: 2.30

RHODE ISLAND HIGHER EDUCATION SAVINGS TRUST

EXECUTIVES

Prin, Marc Lacroix
Collection Manager, Reed McLaren
Director School Relations, Gail Walker
Senior Loan Underwriter, Joseph Morrissey

LOCATIONS

HQ: RHODE ISLAND HIGHER EDUCATION SAVINGS TRUST
560 JEFFERSON BLVD # 100, WARWICK, RI 028861394
Phone: 401 736-1100
Web: WWW.RIOPC.EDU

HISTORICAL FINANCIALS

Company Type: Private

Income Statement				FYE: June 30
	REVENUE ($ mil.)	NET INCOME ($ mil.)	NET PROFIT MARGIN	EMPLOYEES
06/21	1,024	239	23.3%	2
06/19	508	(352)	—	—
06/18	500	(373)	—	—
06/17	0	0	—	—
Annual Growth	—	—	—	—

2021 Year-End Financials

Return on assets: 4.4%   Cash ($ mil.): 5
Return on equity: 4.4%
Current ratio: —

RHODE ISLAND HOSPITAL

EXECUTIVES

Ceo, Margaret Van Bree
Svp-Cno*, Cynthia Danner
Director of Laboratory, Marilyn McAllister
Associate Director, Nicholas Ward
Doctor, Ronald A Delellis
Coordinator, Ann Roberto
Doctor, James M Klinger
Chief of Medicine, John Murphy
Coordinator, Marna Jones
Doctor, Andrew Cohen
Doctor, Dominick H Tammaro Jr

LOCATIONS

HQ: RHODE ISLAND HOSPITAL
593 EDDY ST, PROVIDENCE, RI 029034923
Phone: 401 444-4000
Web: WWW.LIFESPAN.ORG

HISTORICAL FINANCIALS

Company Type: Private

Income Statement				FYE: September 30
	REVENUE ($ mil.)	NET INCOME ($ mil.)	NET PROFIT MARGIN	EMPLOYEES
09/14	1,016	(5)	—	6,400
09/13	1,048	49	4.7%	—
09/07	918	110	12.0%	—
Annual Growth	1.5%	—	—	—

2014 Year-End Financials

Return on assets: (-0.5%)   Cash ($ mil.): 32
Return on equity: (-1.2%)
Current ratio: 1.70

RICELAND FOODS, INC.

Riceland is the world's largest miller and marketer of rice and one of the Mid-South's major soybean processors. It handles more than 125 million bushels of grain a year. Each grains are grown in the US and then shipped to its locations in Missouri and Arkansas to be stored and milled. The company sells white and brown rice plus flavored rice and meal kits under the Riceland and private-label brands. It sells to food retailers food service and food manufacturing companies worldwide. Riceland also makes cooking oils and processes soybeans bran and lecithin and offers rice bran and hulls to pet food makers and livestock farmers as feed and bedding.

Operations

Riceland provides marketing services for rice and soybeans grown by its approximately 5500 farmer-members in Arkansas and Missouri.

It offers ingredient rice rice co-products private label rice PBH rice hulls export rice cooking oils soy products retail rice and foodservice products.

The company provides product in packaging for all applications. From bagged product to product in bulk Riceland can advise what product is best for its clients' business and which packaging is appropriate for the process. This includes 50-lb and 100-lb polywoven bags 2000-lb tote 50000-lb truck loads and 200000-lb railcar loads. Riceland Rice Co-Products have a wide range of applications for animals. Two of its most popular products are defatted rice bran and rice hulls. Its private label rice includes long grain milled rice medium grain milled rice parboiled milled rice brown rice and American Grown Jasmine Rice. Among its wholesale oil products are frying oil soybean salad oil canola salad oil creamy frying shortening butter alternative and clear frying oil.

Riceland's soybean processing plant in Stuttgart Arkansas has provided high-protein soybean meal and soybean hulls (mill run) for nearly 60 years to many Mid-South and Southwestern feed mills and livestock producers along with shipping raw soybeans for the export market. From raw unprocessed soybeans to soybean feed ingredients Riceland offers a full range of industrial soy products.

Geographic Reach

Arkansas-based Riceland's products are sold across the US and to more than 75 foreign destinations.

Sales and Marketing

Riceland provides bulk rice products to club stores and bulk users who have the option of using private label packaging. Rice and oil products are supplied to many of America's leading restaurants fast-food chains and cafeterias. Packaged and flavored rice products are marketed under the Riceland brand. Vegetable oil and shortening products are sold under Riceland and private label brands.

EXECUTIVES

President-Ceo, Daniel Kennedy
Chb, Roger E Pohlner
V Pres-Cfo, Sandra Morgan
Vp - General Counsel & SEC, Andrew Dallas
Sr Vp-Marketing & Risk Managem, Carl W Brothers
Treasurer, Jackie Huguenard
It Internet Support, Terry Ashmore
Warehouse Operator, Tiffany Fawcett
Manager (engineering), Ward Smith
Regional Sales Manager, Whitt Hartz
V Pres, George M Vickers
Auditors: BKD LLP LITTLE ROCK ARKANSA

LOCATIONS

HQ: RICELAND FOODS, INC.
2120 S PARK AVE, STUTTGART, AR 721606822
Phone: 870 673-5500
Web: WWW.RICELAND.COM

PRODUCTS/OPERATIONS

Selected Products

Consumer
  Saffron Yellow Rice Mix
  Rice N Easy Mix Wild Rice
  Long Grain & Wild Mix Rice N Easy Mix
  Broccoli & Cheese Rice N Easy Mix
  Spanish Rice Mix Rice N Easy Mix
  Chicken Rice Mix Rice N Easy Mix
  Long Grain Rice Riceland Extra Long Grain Rice
  Riceland GOLD Perfected Rice
  Riceland Jasmine Rice
  Riceland Natural Brown Rice
  Riceland Plump & Tender Medium Grain Rice
Food Service
  Oil
  Rice
Food Ingredients
  Long grain milled rice
  Long grain brown rice
  Medium grain milled rice
  Parboiled rice
  Broken grains

COMPETITORS

Aarhuskarlshamn	Goya
American Rice	Jfc International
Chs	Lotus Foods
Cereal Byproducts	Louis Dreyfus Group
Connell Company	Producers Rice Mill
Ebro Foods	Riviana Foods
Farmers Rice Milling	Specialty Rice
Farmers' Rice Cooperative	

HISTORICAL FINANCIALS

Company Type: Private

Income Statement				FYE: July 31
	REVENUE ($ mil.)	NET INCOME ($ mil.)	NET PROFIT MARGIN	EMPLOYEES
07/17	941	0	0.0%	1,646
07/16	1,007	5	0.6%	—
07/15	1,122	9	0.9%	—
07/14	1,148	2	0.2%	—
Annual Growth	(6.4%)	(54.4%)	—	—

2017 Year-End Financials

Return on assets: —   Cash ($ mil.): 2
Return on equity: 0.1%
Current ratio: 3.10

RICH PRODUCTS CORPORATION

Rich Products is a family-owned food company which has grown from a niche maker of soy-based whipped toppings and frozen desserts to a leading global US frozen foods maker. The company has developed other products such as toppings and icings and Coffee Rich (non-dairy coffee creamer). It has expanded its product line to include frozen bakery and pizza doughs and ingredients for the food service and in-store bakery markets plus appetizers meals and snacks (Farm Rich) baked goods ice cream cakes (Carvel) seafood (SeaPak) meatballs and barbecue meat. With more than 4000 product types Rich Products has approximately 11000 associates around the world.

Operations
Rich Products offers pizza cake icing and sweet starters beverage and finishing touches desserts bakery product and culinary solutions.

Geographic Reach
US-based Rich Products has operations in over 100 countries worldwide including in South Africa Brazil Mexico China India the UK Istanbul the US and Canada.

Sales and Marketing
The company serves customers in foodservice retail in-store bakery deli and prepared foods among others. In addition to SeaPak FarmRich and Carvel Rich Products' other consumer brands include F'real Byron's Jon Donaire Casa Meatballs Rich Whip and more.

Mergers and Acquisitions
In mid-2021 Rich Products acquired Signature Breads a decades-long leader in specialty breads and rolls. Rich Products will continue to produce key Signature Breads products like baguettes ciabatta and one-of-a-kind sandwich and dinner rolls and the acquisition expands Rich's offerings in the par- and fully baked bread and roll categories.

EXECUTIVES

Vice Chairman Of The Board, Melinda Rich
Chief Financial Officer, Executive Vice President, James Deuschle
Chairman Of The Board, Robert Rich
Executive Vice Chairman, William Gisel
Chief Executive Officer, Richard Ferranti

LOCATIONS

HQ: RICH PRODUCTS CORPORATION
1 ROBERT RICH WAY, BUFFALO, NY 142131701
Phone: 716 878-8000
Web: WWW.RICHS.COM

PRODUCTS/OPERATIONS

Selected Product Categories
Appetizers and snacks
Bakery products
BBQ
Breads and rolls
Cakes & desserts
Cooking creams
Gluten-free and all-natural
Meatballs and pasta
Pizza
Shrimp and seafood
Syrups and soaked cakes
Toppings and icings

Selected Consumer Brands
Byron's
Carvel
Casa
Coffee Rich
Farm Rich
Freal
French Meadow Bakery
Rich's
SeaPak

COMPETITORS

Bakemark	Gorton's
Campbell Soup	Heinz
Canada Bread Company	Hom/ade Foods
Conagra	Nestl ©
Dawn Food Products	Pinnacle Foods
Dean Foods	Schwan's
General Mills	Windsor Foods
Gonnella Baking	

HISTORICAL FINANCIALS
Company Type: Private

Income Statement				FYE: December 31
	REVENUE ($ mil.)	NET INCOME ($ mil.)	NET PROFIT MARGIN	EMPLOYEES
12/12	2,858	0	—	11,713
12/11	2,736	0	—	
12/10	2,465	0	—	
Annual Growth	7.7%	—	—	—

RITE-HITE HOLDING CORPORATION

EXECUTIVES

Chb-Ceo, Michael H White
Pres*, Mark Petri
V Pres*, Clem Maslowski
Cfo*, Mark S Kirkish
Senior Programmer Analyst, Louis Lieberman
Vice President Manager Directo, Ellen Kosidowski
Production Control Supervisor, Kelly Palmer
Operations Manager, Mike Trump
Vice President Manager Directo, Brad Stone
Vice President, Kyle Nelson
Sales Team Member, Bob Wilson

LOCATIONS

HQ: RITE-HITE HOLDING CORPORATION
8900 N ARBON DR, MILWAUKEE, WI 532232451
Phone: 414 355-2600
Web: WWW.RITEHITE.COM

HISTORICAL FINANCIALS
Company Type: Private

Income Statement				FYE: December 31
	REVENUE ($ mil.)	NET INCOME ($ mil.)	NET PROFIT MARGIN	EMPLOYEES
12/20	798	0	—	1,000
12/19	767	0	—	
12/18	779	0	—	
12/05	274	0	—	
Annual Growth	7.4%	—	—	—

RIVER CITY PETROLEUM, INC.

EXECUTIVES

Ceo, Jeanne Haskell
Cfo*, Kurt Schmidl
Information Technology, Chris Gaither
Assistant, Kreidler John
General Manager, Brad Folkins
National Account Manager, Brian Rosser
Government Affairs Manager, Cindy Moua
Supply Coordinator, Jeremy Bautista
Assistant Credit Manager, John Kreidler
Customer Supervisor, Lydia Castellanos
Assistant Staff Accountant, Macie Wightman
Auditors: BFBA LLP SACRAMENTO CALIFOR

LOCATIONS

HQ: RIVER CITY PETROLEUM, INC.
3775 N FREEWAY BLVD # 101, SACRAMENTO, CA 958341959
Phone: 916 371-4960
Web: WWW.RCPFUEL.COM

HISTORICAL FINANCIALS
Company Type: Private

Income Statement				FYE: December 31
	REVENUE ($ mil.)	NET INCOME ($ mil.)	NET PROFIT MARGIN	EMPLOYEES
12/13	655	1	0.2%	55
12/12	579	1	0.2%	—
12/11	656	2	0.4%	—
Annual Growth	(0.1%)	(34.5%)	—	—

2013 Year-End Financials
Return on assets: 2.1%   Cash ($ mil.): 4
Return on equity: 6.0%
Current ratio: 1.30

RIVERSIDE HEALTHCARE ASSOCIATION, INC.

Extra! Extra! Read all about it! Residents of Newport News (and about a dozen other cities in Eastern Virginia) Turn to Riverside Health for Medical Care. The not-for-profit health care provider administers general emergency and specialty medical services from five hospitals Riverside Regional Medical Center Riverside Walter Reed Hospital Riverside Tappahannock Hospital and Riverside Shore Memorial Hospital and Riverside Doctors Hospital as well as a psychiatric hospital a physical rehabilitation facility and retirement communities. Riverside also operates physician offices and medical training facilities. Specialty centers provide home and hospice care cancer treatment and dialysis.

Operations
Combined Riverside's hospitals (including rehabilitation and psychiatric) are home to nearly 1000 beds. Its major hospitals include Riverside Regional Medical Center (450-bed flagship hospital); Riverside Walter Reed Hospital (67-bed acute care facility); Riverside Tappahannock Hospital (67-bed serving the Northern Neck rural area); Riverside Shore Memorial Hospital (143-bed facility); and

Riverside Doctors' Hospital Williamsburg (40 private rooms). It also operates specialty medical facilities including a psychiatric hospital a physical rehabilitation facility and retirement communities.

Geographic Reach

It serves Eastern Virginia including cities of Gloucester Hampton Newport News Poquoson Richmond Tappahannock West Point Williamsburg and Yorktown; Eastern Shore Area of Virginia; Counties of Essex Gloucester Isle of Wight James City King and Queen King William Lancaster Mathews Middlesex New Kent Northumberland Richmond and Surry.

Strategy

To keep up with demand Riverside Health has been upgrading its older facilities and building new ones.

In 2013 the company opened a new hospital the Doctors Hospital in Williamsburg. The 40 room hospital provides acute and emergency care as well as specialty services including cardiology neurology and pulmonary care.

That year Riverside broke ground on the new Riverside Shore Memorial Hospital in Onley which is expected to be completed in late 2015. It will have 57 private inpatient rooms with the ability to add 12 more in the future.

In 2012 Riverside Walter Reed Hospital opened a new intensive care unit.

It is also investing in technology physician expertise and patient services. In 2013 Riverside Shore Medical Center at Metompkin converted to digital mammography equipment offering patients a superior diagnostic tool to film mammograms.

Company Background

The original charter for Riverside dates back to 1915 when the company began as one hospital founded by the community. In 1962 the hospital was relocated to the present site in central Newport News.

EXECUTIVES

Chm, Alan S Witt
V Chm*, Jerold W Allen
Pres*, William B Downey
Exec V Pres-SEC*, Wade D Broughman
Treas*, Walter W Austin Jr
Network Analyst, Terry Street
Director, Christine McKinney
Patient Safety Manager, Kelly Wood
Nutrition Manager, Steven Cristina
Director of Dietary, Jason Houck
Human Resources Decision Suppo, Shaina Moore
Auditors: ERNST & YOUNG LLP RICHMOND V

LOCATIONS

HQ: RIVERSIDE HEALTHCARE ASSOCIATION, INC.
701 TOWN CENTER DR # 1000, NEWPORT NEWS, VA
236064283
Phone: 757 534-7000
Web: WWW.RIVHS.COM

Selected Facilities – Virginia

HOSPITALS
Riverside Behavioral Health Center (Hampton)
Riverside Doctors' Hospital (Williamsburg)
Riverside Regional Medical Center (Newport News)
Riverside Rehabilitation Institute (Williamsburg)
Riverside Tappahannock Hospital (Tappahannock)
Riverside Shore Memorial Hospital (Nassawadox)
Riverside Walter Reed Hospital (Gloucester)
RETIREMENT COMMUNITIES
Patriots Colony (Williamsburg)
Sanders (Gloucester)
Warwick Forest (Newport News)
SURGERY CENTERS
Doctors Surgery Center (Williamsburg)
Peninsula Surgery Center (Newport News)
Riverside Hampton Surgery Center (Hampton)

COMPETITORS

Alleghany Regional Hospital	Franklin Hospital Corp.
Bon Secours Health	Novant Health
Carilion Clinic	Sentara Healthcare
Centra Health Inc.	
Children's Hospital Of The King's Daughters	

HISTORICAL FINANCIALS
Company Type: Private

Income Statement — FYE: December 31

	REVENUE ($ mil.)	NET INCOME ($ mil.)	NET PROFIT MARGIN	EMPLOYEES
12/15	1,149	21	1.8%	8,000
12/14	1,059	(86)	—	—
12/13	1,017	101	10.0%	—
12/12	948	41	4.4%	—
Annual Growth	6.6%	(20.3%)	—	—

2015 Year-End Financials

Return on assets: 1.5%   Cash ($ mil.): 1
Return on equity: 2.9%
Current ratio: 1.50

RIVERSIDE HOSPITAL, INC.

Riverside Hospital operates as Riverside Regional Medical Center a 450-bed acute-care facility that serves the residents of Newport News Virginia. Founded in 1916 the hospital moved to its current 72-acre campus in 1963 providing more than 30 medical specialties including cancer treatment cardiology birthing and diagnostic imaging. It specializes in cardiovascular and neurological surgeries and provides radiosurgery (radiation surgery) through a partnership with the University of Virginia Health System. Its emergency department is a 42-room Level II Trauma Center that treats more than 57000 patients each year. Riverside Hospital is part of the Riverside Health System.

Operations

As part of its operations Riverside Hospital operates a heart center neonatal center 18-bed neonatal intensive care unit cancer care center and radiosurgery center through a partnership with Chesapeake Regional and the University of Virginia Health System. Riverside Hospital works to prevent diagnose and treat diseases of the stomach intestines esophagus pancreas gall bladder liver and biliary tract through its Peninsula Gastroenterology & Riverside Endoscopy Center.

Geographic Reach

Riverside Hospital serves the health care needs of those who reside in and around Newport News Virginia.

EXECUTIVES

Ceo-Pres, William B Downey
SEC*, Wade D Broughman
V Pres*, Mike J Doucette
Treas*, Walter W Austin Jr
Coordinator, Holly Hicks
Internal Medicine Practitioner, Camelia Pana
Surgeon, Laura Cordes
Surgeon, Jeffrey Morrison
Director of Case Management, Fiona Patoux
Administrative Coordinatr, Andrea Bryant

Program Manager Nextgen, Ken Beckerle
Auditors: ERNST YOUNG RICHMOND VA

LOCATIONS

HQ: RIVERSIDE HOSPITAL, INC.
500 J CLYDE MORRIS BLVD, NEWPORT NEWS, VA
236011929
Phone: 757 594-2000
Web: WWW.RIVERSIDEONLINE.COM

PRODUCTS/OPERATIONS

Selected Services
Diagnostic Services
  Cardiac testing
  CT
  Digital mammography
  Electrocardiography
  Magnetic resonance imaging
  Nuclear medicine
  PET
  Ultrasound
Nutrition Services
  Radiosurgery Center
  Leksell Gamma Knife Synergy S Radiosurgery
  Gastroenterology Procedures
  Colonoscopy and polypectomy
  Flexible sigmoidoscopy
  Upper endoscopic exams and therapy
  Endoscopic retrograde cholangiopancreatography (ERCP)
  Percutaneous endoscopic gastrostomy (PEG)
  Capsule/Cam (M2A) study of the small intestine
  Esophageal dilation
  Esophageal and anal manometry
  BRAVO pH study of the esophagus
Pulmonary Rehabilitation
Surgical Services

COMPETITORS

Alleghany Regional Hospital	Franklin Hospital Corp.
Bon Secours Health	Novant Health
Carilion Clinic	Sentara Healthcare
Centra Health Inc.	
Children's Hospital Of The King's Daughters	

HISTORICAL FINANCIALS
Company Type: Private

Income Statement — FYE: December 31

	REVENUE ($ mil.)	NET INCOME ($ mil.)	NET PROFIT MARGIN	EMPLOYEES
12/18	618	61	10.0%	8,000
12/17	611	57	9.4%	—
12/16	636	65	10.3%	—
12/11	466	36	7.8%	—
Annual Growth	4.1%	7.9%	—	—

RIVERSIDE REGIONAL MEDIAL CENTER

EXECUTIVES

Principal, Debbie Davis
Vp of Ambulatory Care, Susan Mc Andrews

LOCATIONS

HQ: RIVERSIDE REGIONAL MEDIAL CENTER
500 J CLYDE MORRIS BLVD, NEWPORT NEWS, VA
236011929
Phone: 757 856-7030
Web: WWW.RIVERSIDEONLINE.COM

HISTORICAL FINANCIALS
Company Type: Private

Income Statement				FYE: December 31
	REVENUE ($ mil.)	NET INCOME ($ mil.)	NET PROFIT MARGIN	EMPLOYEES
12/14	544	73	13.5%	1
12/08	301	0	0.2%	—
Annual Growth	10.4%	123.6%	—	—

RIVERSIDE UNIFIED SCHOOL DISTRICT

EXECUTIVES

Supt, Dr David Hansen
Supt*, Michael H Fine
Pres*, Lynn Carmen Day
V Pres*, Charles L Beaty PHD
Teacher, Candace Mendoza
Teacher, Jenna King
Manager, Marcus A Ridley
Teacher, Matthew Schiller
Teacher, Monica Schalow
Teacher, Neil Schlesener
Teacher, Toni Tautolo
Auditors: NIGRO & NIGRO PC MURRIETA C

LOCATIONS

HQ: RIVERSIDE UNIFIED SCHOOL DISTRICT
3380 14TH ST, RIVERSIDE, CA 925013810
Phone: 951 788-7135
Web: WWW.RIVERSIDEUNIFIED.ORG

HISTORICAL FINANCIALS
Company Type: Private

Income Statement				FYE: June 30
	REVENUE ($ mil.)	NET INCOME ($ mil.)	NET PROFIT MARGIN	EMPLOYEES
06/19	592	(31)	—	3,740
06/18	540	(8)	—	—
06/17	513	75	14.7%	—
06/16	499	18	3.6%	—
Annual Growth	5.8%	—	—	—

2019 Year-End Financials
Return on assets: (-3.0%)   Cash ($ mil.): 258
Return on equity: (-27.5%)
Current ratio: —

RIVERVIEW HOSPITAL

Riverview Hospital (which changed its operating name to Riverside Health in 2014) provides general medical and surgical care to residents in central Indiana. With about 155 beds and 300 physicians representing more than 35 medical specialties the hospital is a full-service facility that offers specialty care in a number of areas including heart disease cancer women's health and orthopedics. Besides its main campus Riverview operates several outpatient facilities including an occupational health center a community health clinic and several rehab and fitness centers.

Operations

The Indiana hospital which admits some 6500 patients each year provides family medicine pediatrics OB/GYN care cardiac care surgery orthopedics and sports medicine cancer care interventional pain management wound care diabetes and endocrinology internal medicine and imaging among other services. Also part of its operations the health care facility runs a community health clinic rehab and fitness centers and an occupational health center.

Its Riverview Medical Group is a network of affiliated primary and specialty care doctors with 20 offices located throughout Hamilton and Tipton counties.

Geographic Reach

Riverview serves patients who reside in Indiana's Hamilton and Tipton Counties particularly the service area north of Indianapolis in central Indiana. It has locations in Carmel Cicero Fishers Noblesville Sheridan Tipton and Westfield.

Strategy

To better reflect the organization's full scope of inpatient and outpatient services in 2014 the hospital changed its name from Riverview Hospital to Riverview Health.

Expanding its services in 2014 the hospital began building the Mugg-Z Caf © an internet caf © and gift shop for elders.

EXECUTIVES

Pres, Seth Warren
Treas*, T H Lee
V Pres*, Joyce Wood
V Pres*, John Paris
V Pres*, Brant Bucciarelli
V Pres*, Brenda Baker
Scientist, Victor Burroughs
Information Specialist, James Reichert
Director of Engineering, Scott Tripp
Clinical Documentation Special, Deb Rood
Pfs Business Office Coordinato, Amy Williams

LOCATIONS

HQ: RIVERVIEW HOSPITAL
395 WESTFIELD RD, NOBLESVILLE, IN 460601434
Phone: 317 773-0760
Web: WWW.RIVERVIEW.ORG

PRODUCTS/OPERATIONS

Selected Services
Cancer Services
Diabetes and Endocrinology
Emergency Services
Heart and Vascular Services
Internal Medicine Services
Laboratory Services
Occupational Health Services
Orthopedic Services
Pediatric Services
Radiology and Imaging Services
Rehabilitation Services
Sleep Disorders Services
Surgery Services
Women's Health Services
Wound Care Services

COMPETITORS

Ascension Health	Iu Health
Community Health Network	Kosciusko Community Hospital
Franciscan Alliance	St. Vincent Health
Henry County Memorial Hospital	Wabash County Hospital

HISTORICAL FINANCIALS
Company Type: Private

Income Statement				FYE: December 31
	REVENUE ($ mil.)	NET INCOME ($ mil.)	NET PROFIT MARGIN	EMPLOYEES
12/18	574	2	0.4%	949
12/17	179	8	4.8%	—
12/16	171	1	1.1%	—
12/15	162	1	0.8%	—
Annual Growth	52.5%	16.4%	—	—

2018 Year-End Financials
Return on assets: 0.5%   Cash ($ mil.): 87
Return on equity: 0.8%
Current ratio: 1.60

ROBERT BOSCH LLC

Robert Bosch LLC is your one-stop shop for German-engineered auto parts appliances and power tools. The company operating four business sectors Mobility Solutions Industrial Technology Consumer Goods and Energy and Building Technology. In additions offer customers a multitude of value-add cross-sector solutions across diversity of industry applications. The company provides expertise in sensor technology systems integration software and services and IoT cloud to offer to customer connected on cross-domain solutions from a single source. Active since 1906 Bosch LLC has grown to around 70 primary North American locations.

Operations

Robert Bosch LLC provides comprehensive expertise in vehicle technology with hardware.

The Mobility Solutions Mobility solutions web portal presents in the areas of connected to mobility automated mobility powertrain and electrified mobility. Bosh offers spare parts to aftermarket and repair shops from new and exchange parts to repair solutions as well repair equipment such as diagnostics software and hardware. In addition provide service-training courses and partner programs for repair shops Bosch offers automobile competence and knowledge to service technicians all over the world. The company eBike Systems develop produce and market products that fascinate people. In addition Rober Bosch offers diagnostics software and hardware training courses and partner programs for repair shops.

Geographic Reach

Robert Bosch LLC has around 70 primary facilities in the US Canada and Mexico.

Sales and Marketing

Robert Bosch LLC's generated sales of $14.4 billion n U. S. Canada and Mexico in 2019.

Strategy

Bosch's objective is to develop innovative useful and exciting products and solutions to enhance its quality of living. At Bosch the company creates technology that is "Invented for life." The company is committed to providing technologies and systems for the four business sectors of Bosch ? Mobility Solutions Energy and Building Technology Industrial Technology and Consumer Goods ? by scouting and collaborating with top universities and industry partners in North America.

Bosch launched BMP384 a robust barometric pressure sensor delivering market leading accuracy in a compact package. Bosch has applied its many years of experience in creating reliable sensors for harsh environments into the design of BMP384.

Bosch teamed up with Microsoft in 2021 to develop a software platform to seamlessly connect cars to the cloud. The goal of this collaboration is to simplify and accelerate the development and deployment of vehicle software throughout a car's lifetime in accordance with automotive quality standards. The new platform based on Microsoft Azure and incorporate software modules from Bosch enables software to be developed and downloaded to the control units and vehicle computers.

EXECUTIVES

MBR, Markus Heyn
MBR, Mike Mansuetti
Chief Financial Officer, Maximiliane Straub
MBR, Erik Dyhrkopp
Treas, Brian Marron
Asst SEC, Heather Schroder
Engineer, Russell Van Pelt
Fin Dir, William A Davis III
North & South AM Chassis Div, Ronaldo Reimer
Site Concept Americas, Michael Jonietz
Pres, Automotive Electronics, Tim Frasier

LOCATIONS

HQ: ROBERT BOSCH LLC
38000 HILLS TECH DR, FARMINGTON HILLS, MI
483313418
Phone: 248 876-1000
Web: WWW.BOSCH.US

PRODUCTS/OPERATIONS

2019 Sales

	% of total
Mobility Solutions	66
Consumer Goods	18
Industrial Technology	10
Energy and Building Technology	6
Other	3
Total	**100**

Selected Products

Automotive Technology
  Aftermarket
  Alternators
  Brake pads
  Car audio products
  Diesel parts
  Filters
  Fuel pumps
  Ignition products
  Oxygen sensors
  Spark plugs
  Spark plug wire sets
  Starters
  Wiper blades
  Original equipment
  Actuators
  Braking and chassis systems
  Car multimedia
  Electrical systems
  Electronic systems
  Powertrain systems - diesel
  Powertrain systems - gasoline
Consumer Goods and Building Technology
  Household appliances
  Cooktops
  Dishwashers
  Ovens
  Washers and dryers
  Power tools
  Angle grinders
  Belt sanders
  Circular saws
  Drill bits
  Drills
  Drywall drivers
  Impact wrenches
  Jigsaws
  Orbit sanders/polishers
  Planers
  Reciprocating saws
  Rotary hammers
  Routers

Screwdriver bits and accessories
Wet/dry vacuums
Security Systems
  Access control
  Communications
  Fire detection
  Security management
  Video surveillance
Thermotechnology
  Indoor climate control (heating and cooling and hot water production)
Industrial Technology
  Drive and control
  Assembly
  Electric drives and controls
  Gears
  Hydraulics
  Linear motion
  Pneumatics
  Packaging
  Confectionary cosmetics and chemicals
  Packaging machines
  Packaging services
  Pharmaceuticals
  Production tools
  Air assembly tools
  Cordless assembly tools
  DC electric assembly tools
  Electric assembly tools
Solar Energy
  Crystalline PV modules
  Solar cells
  Thin-film modules
  Wafers

COMPETITORS

Aisin World Corp.	Lg Electronics
Advanced Security & Controls	Makita
	Molins
Denso America	Motorcar Parts
Dana	Ngk Spark Plugs
Delphi Automotive Systems	Neaton Auto Products
Ge	Stanley Black And Decker
Hitachi Automotive Systems Americas	Visteon
	Whirlpool

HISTORICAL FINANCIALS

Company Type: Private

Income Statement — FYE: December 31

	REVENUE ($ mil.)	NET INCOME ($ mil.)	NET PROFIT MARGIN	EMPLOYEES
12/14	10,474	181	1.7%	12
12/10	6,810	326	4.8%	—
12/09	5,464	59	1.1%	—
Annual Growth	13.9%	25.1%	—	—

2014 Year-End Financials

Return on assets: 2.7%   Cash ($ mil.): 832
Return on equity: 13.0%
Current ratio: 0.90

ROBERT W BAIRD & CO INC

Employee-owned Robert W. Baird & Co. brings mid-western sensibility to the high-flying world of investment banking. The company offers brokerage asset management and investment banking services to middle-market corporations institutional clients municipal and wealthy individuals and families around the world. Its investment banking activities include underwriting and distributing corporate securities mergers and acquisitions capital advisory equity capital markets and institutional sales and trading. The company advises clients on a range of other unique situations such as fairness opinions restructuring takeover defenses and other special situations. Baird manages more than $355 billion in client assets. The company was founded in 1919.

Operations

Baird's Private Wealth Management offers opportunities for financial advisors and client relationship assistants. Its Asset Management business includes Baird Advisors and Baird Equity Asset Management. The company's Equity Capital Markets business is comprised of research equity sales and trading and investment banking while Fixed Income Capital Markets unit consists of fixed income sales and trading and public finance.

Geographic Reach

Headquartered in Wisconsin Baird has offices across the US Europe and Asia.

Sales and Marketing

Baird primarily serves individuals families and public entities throughout the US as well as corporations and institutions worldwide.

Strategy

The company invested in multiple companies recently. In mid-2021 Baird Capital's venture team announced its investment in Forj a leading virtual events and member experience platform for associations and professional community organizations. Baird Capital led the financing round with participation from GCI. The new capital will enable Milwaukee-headquartered Forj to accelerate its growth and investment in developing its innovative platform purpose-built for professional associations and member groups to enable a more fulfilling member experience.

Around the same time Baird Capital's private equity team announced its investment in Azzur Group ("Azzur") one of the nation's fastest-growing life science consultancies. The investment aims to help Azzur accelerate expanding its professional services to the industry including Azzur Cleanrooms on DemandTM. In partnering with Baird Capital Azzur further solidifies its commitment to serving the life science and healthcare industries through the delivery of novel services designed to accelerate therapeutic delivery timelines and empower innovators to start scale and sustain their GxP organizations.

Earlier in 2021 Baird Capital announced that its venture team completed an investment in Appdetex a global brand protection leader and expert in online detection assessment and enforcement of online infringements. Baird Capital led the $12.2 million Series C financing to fuel the company's growth team and market opportunity. Appdetex's existing investors First Analysis Origin Ventures and EPIC Ventures also participated in the financing. Four of the top five World's Most Valuable Brands along with hundreds of other brands depend on Appdetex's brand protection technology and expertise to defend their customer relationships revenue and reputation. With this additional investment Appdetex will enhance its patented technologies and grow its sales and service teams to service its fast-growing customer base and a burgeoning list of partners.

Company Background

Founded in 1919 Baird had been majority-owned by Northwestern Mutual since 1982. However employees bought back the company's stock in a series of purchases that culminated in 2004.

EXECUTIVES

Pres-Ceo, Steve Booth
Chm, Paul E Purcell
Cfo, Terrance Maxwell
SEC-Gen Counsel, Paul L Schultz
Assistant Vice President, Lee Orlowski

Assistant Vice President, Leslie Reinhart
Business Analyst, Lindsey Buchanan
Assistant Vice President Proje, Marla Regan
Administrative Assistant, Marsha Wescott
Assistant Vice President Facil, Marty Young
Assistant Vice President, Mary Walters

LOCATIONS

HQ: ROBERT W BAIRD & CO INC
777 E WISCONSIN AVE FL 29, MILWAUKEE, WI
532025391
Phone: 414 765-3500
Web: WWW.RWBAIRD.COM

PRODUCTS/OPERATIONS

Business Groups
Asset Management
Equity Capital Markets
Fixed Income Capital Markets
Private Equity
Private Wealth Management

COMPETITORS

Citigroup Global Markets	Piper Jaffray
Cowen Group	Raymond James Financial
Goldman Sachs	Stephens
Greenhill	Stifel Financial
Jefferies Group	Thomas Weisel Partners
Morgan Stanley	William Blair

HISTORICAL FINANCIALS

Company Type: Private

Income Statement   FYE: December 31

	ASSETS ($ mil.)	NET INCOME ($ mil.)	INCOME AS % OF ASSETS	EMPLOYEES
12/09	2,063	41	2.0%	2,000
12/08	1,080	36	3.4%	—
12/07	1,712	50	2.9%	—
Annual Growth	9.8%	(8.6%)	—	—

2009 Year-End Financials

Return on assets: 2.0%   Sales ($ mil): 699
Return on equity: 11.2%

ROBERT WOOD JOHNSON UNIVERSITY HOSPITAL, INC.

Robert Wood Johnson University Hospital (RWJUH) is the flagship medical center of the RWJBarnabas health system. The hospital consists of four campuses offering acute and tertiary care services including cardiovascular transplant pediatric trauma cancer neurology and women's health care. Founded in 1884 the facility serves as a teaching center for the Rutgers Robert Wood Johnson Medical School. The hospital is part of the RWJBarnabas Health organization.

Operations

RWJUH has four campuses: RWJUH-New Brunswick RWJUH-Somerset RWJUH-Rahway and RWJUH-Hamilton.

The main RWJUH-New Brunswick campus includes a Level I trauma center a Clinical Neurosciences Center and the Bristol-Myers Squibb Children's Hospital. It also operates the Cancer Hospital of New Jersey which is the main hospital

partner of the Rutgers Cancer Institute of New Jersey. The New Brunswick campus also serves as the primary teaching hospital for the Rutgers Robert Wood Johnson Medical School.

RWJUH operates satellite clinics near its hospital campuses including wellness wound healing laboratory and physical therapy facilities.

The broader RWJBarnabas Health network operates about a dozen hospitals. Outside of the RWJUH facilities major facilities include Monmouth Medical Center Newark Beth Israel Medical Center and Saint Barnabas Medical Center. The system also operates outpatient locations providing ambulatory care behavioral health trauma emergency geriatric pharmacy and home health and hospice care.

Geographic Reach

RWJUH's main campus is in New Brunswick New Jersey; it has other campuses in Somerset Hamilton and Rahway New Jersey. Parent RWJBarnabas operates throughout the state.

Strategy

To widen its operations RWJUH has expanded its main campus facilities; it has also acquired or opened new satellite locations. The main New Brunswick hospital campus launched an emergency department expansion project to increase capacity and reduce wait times in 2017 with scheduled completion in 2020. The facility will help meet a growing need for emergency and trauma care services in Central New Jersey.

As part of a partnership formed in 2018 between parent RWJBarnabas and Rutgers University RWJBarnabas is building a new cancer research facility and a new ambulatory care facility in New Brunswick.

Company Background

RWJUH was founded in 1884. In 2014 Somerset Medical Center was merged into RWJUH adding more than 300 beds and providing RWJUH entry into the Somerset community.

RWJUH's parent company Robert Wood Johnson Health System merged with fellow New Jersey hospital system Barnabas Health in 2015 creating the largest hospital system in New Jersey. The combined entity began operating under the name RWJBarnabas Health.

EXECUTIVES

Pres-Ceo, Bill Arnold
Pres*, John Gantner
Chb*, John Hoffman
Dir of Fin*, Shawn Mayer
Coo*, Alan Lee
Chief of Pediatric, Patricia Whitley- Willia
Director Volunteers/Auxiliary, Margie Mc Donald
Nursing Director, Leigh Schmidt
Social Worker, Augusto Dafonseca
Coordinator, Christine Tricarico
Vice President Is, Robert Irwin
Auditors: KPMG LLP SHORT HILLS NJ

LOCATIONS

HQ: ROBERT WOOD JOHNSON UNIVERSITY
HOSPITAL, INC.
1 ROBERT WOOD JOHNSON PL, NEW BRUNSWICK,
NJ 089011928
Phone: 732 828-3000
Web: WWW.RWJBH.ORG

PRODUCTS/OPERATIONS

Selected Services
Bariatric Surgery
Bloodless Surgery
Cardiothoracic Surgery
Colorectal Surgery
Comprehensive Sleep Disorders Center
Diabetes
Digestive Disorders

Emergency Department
Executive Health Program
Heart Transplantation
Injury Prevention
Kidney and Pancreas Transplantation
Lab Services (blood work and blood collection)
Level 1 Trauma Center
Neurosciences
  Clinical Neurosciences Center
  Deep Brain Stimulation for Movement Disorders
  Laser Ablation for Brain Tumor Treatment
  Neurosurgery
  New Jersey Brain Aneurysm & AVM Program
  Parkinson's Disease Information and Referral Center
  Stroke Center
  The Gamma Knife Center: Advanced Treatment for Brain and Spine
New Jersey Pain Institute at RWJUH
Orthopedic Surgery
Outpatient Radiology: University Radiology at Robert Wood Johnson
Palliative Care Program
Pastoral Care
Pelvic Floor and Incontinence Program
Physical and Occupational Therapy
Prostate Cancer Surgery
Radiation Oncology
  Gynecologic Brachytherapy
  Prostate Brachytherapy
  TomoTherapy
  Total Skin Electron Beam Therapy
Radiology (including CT MRI and ultrasound)
Speech and Hearing Program
The Center for Wound Healing
The Limb Preservation Program
Therapeutic Apheresis
Thoracic Surgery
Vascular Surgery

COMPETITORS

Bergen Regional Medical	Saint Peter's University Hospital
Capital Health System	St. Joseph's Healthcare System
Princeton Healthcare	
Raritan Bay Medical Center	

HISTORICAL FINANCIALS

Company Type: Private

Income Statement   FYE: December 31

	REVENUE ($ mil.)	NET INCOME ($ mil.)	NET PROFIT MARGIN	EMPLOYEES
12/19	1,451	(89)	—	4,674
12/18	1,337	(3)	—	—
12/17	1,249	(59)	—	—
Annual Growth	7.8%	—	—	—

2019 Year-End Financials

Return on assets: (-5.0%)   Cash ($ mil.): —
Return on equity: (-10.7%)
Current ratio: 3.90

ROCHESTER CITY SCHOOL DISTRICT

EXECUTIVES

Supt, Jean C Brizard
Supt*, Bolgen Vargas
RES*, Malik Evans
V-Pres*, Jose Cruz
V Pres*, Van Henri White
MBR-Board of Edu*, Mary Adams
MBR-Board of Edu*, Melisza Campos

MBR-Board of Edu*, Cynthia Elliot
Mgr-Board of Edu*, Willa Powell
Human Resources Secretary II, Annette Ramos
Teacher, Gloria Brooks
Auditors: FREEDMAXICK CPA PC ROCHEST

LOCATIONS

HQ: ROCHESTER CITY SCHOOL DISTRICT
131 W BROAD ST, ROCHESTER, NY 146141103
Phone: 585 262-8100
Web: WWW.RCSDK12.ORG

HISTORICAL FINANCIALS

Company Type: Private

Income Statement				FYE: June 30
	REVENUE ($ mil.)	**NET INCOME** ($ mil.)	**NET PROFIT MARGIN**	**EMPLOYEES**
06/13	708	74	10.6%	5,470
06/11	681	(19)	—	—
Annual Growth	1.9%	—	—	—

2013 Year-End Financials

Return on assets: 8.7%   Cash ($ mil.): 315
Return on equity: 123.6%
Current ratio: —

ROCHESTER GAS AND ELECTRIC CORPORATION

Upstate New York residents count on Rochester Gas and Electric (RG&E) to keep the lights turned on. The regulated utility provides electricity to about 370000 customers and natural gas to 306000 customers. RG&E operates 22500 miles of power transmission and distribution lines and has a generating capacity of approximately 400 MW from interests in fossil-fueled and hydroelectric power plants. RG&E and sister utility company New York State Electric & Gas (NYSEG) are subsidiaries of regional power and gas distribution player Avangrid).

· **Geographic Reach**

RG&E's service territory contains a substantial suburban area and a large agricultural area in parts of nine counties including and surrounding the city of Rochester New York with a population of 1 million.

Financial Performance

The company operates under the Network business of IBERDROLA. The Network business accounted for 25% of IBERDROLA's 2013 revenues; some 28% of Network sales came from US operations. IBERDROLA generated 10% of its total revenues from the US in 2013.

Strategy

To reduce its carbon emissions RG&E along with affiliate NYSEG is pushing green energy options including a wind energy power program whereby residents can choose to have their power supply from wind generated sources.

In 2013 the company announced plans to retire its 18-MW Rochester 9 natural gas-fired combustion turbine as it would be too expensive to repair the equipment failures that forced the unit offline that year.

Company Background

Between 2008 and the end of 2010 NYSEG or RG&E interconnected six landfill gas plants with a total of 26MW of generating capacity three wind farms with 209 wind turbines (381 MW of gener-

ating capacity) in Wyoming and Steuben counties a new 30 MW combined heat and power facility for Cornell University and a lithium-ion battery energy storage facility for AES Corporation.

EXECUTIVES

Pres, Mark S Lynch
Vp-Contrl-Treas*, Joseph J Syta
Executive Officer, Kathleen Case
Staff, Timothy King
Engineer, Mary Masters
Sales Representati, John Blum
Chief Trouble Mechanic, Lawrence Castellano
Claims Manager, Robert Perkins
Associate Engineer, Syed Jamal
RG, Angel Hernandez
Human Resources Manager, Dena Paratore
Auditors: KPMG LLP NEW YORK NEW YORK

LOCATIONS

HQ: ROCHESTER GAS AND ELECTRIC CORPORATION
89 EAST AVE, ROCHESTER, NY 146490002
Phone: 800 295-7323
Web: WWW.RGE.COM

COMPETITORS

Ch Energy	New York Power
Con Edison	Authority
National Fuel Gas	Niagara Mohawk

HISTORICAL FINANCIALS

Company Type: Private

Income Statement				FYE: December 31
	REVENUE ($ mil.)	**NET INCOME** ($ mil.)	**NET PROFIT MARGIN**	**EMPLOYEES**
12/17	850	83	9.8%	865
12/16	1,042	80	7.7%	—
12/10	982	54	5.5%	—
Annual Growth	(2.0%)	6.3%	—	—

2017 Year-End Financials

Return on assets: 2.3%   Cash ($ mil.): —
Return on equity: 8.8%
Current ratio: 1.20

ROCHESTER INSTITUTE OF TECHNOLOGY (INC)

The Rochester Institute of Technology (RIT) is a privately endowed university with nine colleges focused on providing career-oriented education to nearly 18670 students. The school which has a student-faculty ratio of about 13:1 offers approximately 85 bachelor's degree programs in art and design business engineering science and hospitality. RIT also confers more than 75 master's and eight doctorate degrees. The university's National Technical Institute for the Deaf is the first and largest technological college for learners who suffer from hearing loss. RIT which traces its roots back to 1829 counts among its alumni the CEOs of Kodak and The Associated Press.

Operations

RIT's campus serves about 15740 undergraduate and around 2930 graduate students with help from its faculty and staff of more than 4040. More than 900 deaf and hard-of-hearing students live study and work alongside hearing students on the RIT campus. Tuition runs more than $33650 for

general students and more than $17275 for deaf and hard-of-hearing students.

RIT operates a campus in Dubai's Silicon Oasis a not-for-profit global campus technological-focused. The campus serves the university's goal of growing its reputation worldwide and expanding international opportunities for students. RIT Dubai offers undergraduate and graduate degree programs in engineering business information technology and leadership.

Geographic Reach

Spanning some 1300 acres in Rochester New York it has international campuses in China Croatia Dubai and Kosovo. The university's students come from all 50 states and more than 100 nations around the world.

Strategy

RIT has acquired the former Radisson Hotel Rochester Airport located next to its campus on Jefferson Road in Henrietta. RIT will renovate the entire facility and use it for housing students and university guests.

EXECUTIVES

Pres, David C Munson Jr
V Pres*, Ellen Granberg
SEC*, Karen Barrows
Program Director, Adara Wilczak
Acting Director, Jan Reich
Executive Vice President and G, Jennifer Horak
Associate Vice President and O, Kevin Dooley
Associate Vice President, Meredith Smith
Senior Vice President and Regi, Peter Lalley
Vice President's Office, Sandy Johnson
Scientist, Robert Kremens
Auditors: PRICEWATERHOUSECOOPERS LLP RO

LOCATIONS

HQ: ROCHESTER INSTITUTE OF TECHNOLOGY (INC)
1 LOMB MEMORIAL DR, ROCHESTER, NY 146235698
Phone: 585 475-2411
Web: WWW.RIT.EDU

PRODUCTS/OPERATIONS

Selected Colleges

College of Applied Science and Technology
  School of Engineering Technology
  School of International Hospitality and Service
    Innovation
E. Philip Saunders College of Business
B. Thomas Golisano College of Computing and
  Information Sciences
Kate Gleason College of Engineering
College of Health Sciences and Technology
College of Imaging Arts and Sciences
  School for American Crafts
  School of Art
  School of Design
  School of Film and Animation
  School of Media Sciences
  School of Photographic Arts and Sciences
College of Liberal Arts
National Technical Institute for the Deaf
College of Science

Selected Graduate & Undergraduate Programs

Accounting
Applied Networking & Systems Administration
Applied Statistics
Biochemistry
Business
Civil Engineering Technology
Clinical Chemistry
Computer Integrated Machining Technology
Computer Science
Digital Imaging & Publishing Technology
Electrical/Mechanical Engineering Technology
Environmental Science
Finance
Glass & Glass Sculpture
Health Systems Administration

Healthcare Billing & Coding Technology
Imaging Arts: Photography
Industrial & Systems Engineering
Instruction Technology
Management
Medical Illustration
Metals/Jewelry Design
Ophthalmic Optical Finishing Technology
Print Media
Psychology
Service Leadership and Innovation
Voice Communication
Woodworking and Furniture Design

HISTORICAL FINANCIALS
Company Type: Private

Income Statement   FYE: June 30

	REVENUE ($ mil.)	NET INCOME ($ mil.)	NET PROFIT MARGIN	EMPLOYEES
06/18	579	203	35.2%	3,300
06/17	560	74	13.2%	—
06/12	490	16	3.4%	—
06/06	370	45	12.2%	—
Annual Growth	3.8%	13.4%	—	—

2018 Year-End Financials
Return on assets: 10.4%   Cash ($ mil.): 62
Return on equity: 14.2%
Current ratio: —

ROCHESTER REGIONAL HEALTH

EXECUTIVES

Pres, Eric Bieber
Director, Christopher Jordan
Senior Engineer, Craig Unterborn
Director, Daniel Newcomb
Director, Diane Farnsworth
Supervisor, Laura Caceci
Financial Analyst, Lori Falzone
Vice President, Matt Drake
Network Engineer, Matt Kassel
Vice President, Mazie Tai
Compliance Coordinator, Nicole Delgrosso
Auditors: FUST CHARLES CHAMBERS SYRACUS

LOCATIONS

HQ: ROCHESTER REGIONAL HEALTH
100 KINGS HWY S STE 2300, ROCHESTER, NY
146175503
Phone: 585 922-4000
Web: WWW.ROCHESTERREGIONAL.ORG

HISTORICAL FINANCIALS
Company Type: Private

Income Statement   FYE: December 31

	REVENUE ($ mil.)	NET INCOME ($ mil.)	NET PROFIT MARGIN	EMPLOYEES
12/18	2,189	38	1.8%	22,500
12/17	2,059	54	2.6%	—
Annual Growth	6.3%	(28.6%)	—	—

2018 Year-End Financials
Return on assets: 1.8%   Cash ($ mil.): 170
Return on equity: 7.0%
Current ratio: 1.60

ROPER ST. FRANCIS HEALTHCARE

CareAlliance Health Services (doing business as Roper St. Francis Healthcare) operates four hospitals — the 370-bed Roper Hospital the 200-bed Bon Secours St. Francis Hospital the 85-bed Mount Pleasant Hospital and the Roper Rehabilitation Hospital. Besides providing home health services it also operates outpatient emergency primary care and diagnostic facilities. Roper St. Francis Healthcare serves Charleston South Carolina and surrounding communities. Its Roper St. Francis Physician Partners is one of the region's largest physician practices.

Operations
The health system comprises Roper Hospital Bon Secours St. Francis Hospital Roper St. Francis Mount Pleasant Hospital Roper St. Francis Foundation and Roper St. Francis Physicians Network. Altogether it boasts three acute care hospitals with 655-plus beds one specialty hospital 15 centers for outpatient services three industrial medicine sites five emergency rooms and two urgent care centers.

Roper St. Francis Healthcare has a medical staff of some 800 physicians. The Roper St. Francis Physician Partners organization has more than 230 physicians who offer primary and specialty care including family practice internal medicine and pediatrics.

Geographic Reach
Altogether Roper St. Francis Healthcare operates about 90 facilities in seven counties in the lowcountry region of South Carolina.

Strategy
The health system in 2014 signed an agreement with Trendlines Lab to collaborate on the development of new medical device inventions as well as low-cost solutions for clinical problems. The partnership will work to create devices that will address unmet needs identified by physicians and other health care providers.

Company Background
Roper St. Francis Healthcare was formed through the merger of Roper Hospital and Bon Secours St. Francis Hospital in 1998.

Roper St. Francis Physician Partners was formed through the 2009 combination of Roper St. Francis Physicians' Network and Lowcountry Medical Associates.

EXECUTIVES

Pres-Ceo, Jeffrey Dilisi
Sr V Pres*, Bret Johnson
V Pres*, Mark Dickson
V Pres*, Carolyn Donohue
V Pres*, Greg Edwards
Customer Director, Laura Icard
Programmer, Lynn Kress
Diagnostic Radiologist, James Wells
Physician, Francis Akom
Corporate Transcription Manage, Kay Carr
Director of Sports Medicine, Robert Schoderbek
Auditors: DELOITTE & TOUCHE LLP CHARLO

LOCATIONS

HQ: ROPER ST. FRANCIS HEALTHCARE
125 DOUGHTY ST STE 760, CHARLESTON, SC
294035785
Phone: 843 724-2000
Web: WWW.RSFH.COM

Selected South Carolina Facilities
Hospitals
Mt. Pleasant Hospital Campus - Mount Pleasant
Roper Hosp
Roper Rehabilitation Hospital
St. Franci
Outpatient Centers
After Hours Care - James Island
Kiawah-Seabrook Medical & Urgent Care
Roper Hosp
Roper Hospital Ambulatory Surgery & Pain
Management - James Island
Roper Hosp
Roper Hosp
Roper Hosp
Roper Hosptial Diagnostics - Goose Creek
Roper Hosptial Diagnostics - James Island
Roper Hosp
Roper Hosptial Diagnostics - Moncks Corner
Roper Hospital Imaging - Wesley Drive
Roper Hospital Imaging - Wingo Way

COMPETITORS

Beaufort Memorial Hospital	Hca
Conway Medical Center	Medical University Of South Carolina
Georgetown Hospital System	Tenet Healthcare
Grand Strand Regional Medical Center	

HISTORICAL FINANCIALS
Company Type: Private

Income Statement   FYE: December 31

	REVENUE ($ mil.)	NET INCOME ($ mil.)	NET PROFIT MARGIN	EMPLOYEES
12/14	793	(2)	—	6,000
12/09	682	56	8.3%	—
12/08	618	(51)	—	—
Annual Growth	4.3%	—	—	—

2014 Year-End Financials
Return on assets: (-0.3%)   Cash ($ mil.): 54
Return on equity: (-0.7%)
Current ratio: 1.30

ROUND ROCK INDEPENDENT SCHOOL DISTRICT (INC)

EXECUTIVES

Supt, Dr Jess H Chvez
Prin*, Georgia Mill
Supt*, Dr Steven Flores
Information Specialist, Debby Acevedo
Coordinator, Nicole Shannon
Educational Assistant, Connie Swofford
Financial Analyst, Wayne Curry
Cafeteria Manager, Maria Calderon
School Administrator, Jane Miller
French Teacher, Jennie Chao
Position In Technology, Angie Hintz
Auditors: MAXWELL LOCKE & RITTER LLP A

LOCATIONS

HQ: ROUND ROCK INDEPENDENT SCHOOL DISTRICT (INC)
1311 ROUND ROCK AVE, ROUND ROCK, TX 786814941
Phone: 512 464-5000
Web: WWW.ROUNDROCKISD.ORG

HISTORICAL FINANCIALS

Company Type: Private

Income Statement — FYE: June 30

	REVENUE ($ mil.)	NET INCOME ($ mil.)	NET PROFIT MARGIN	EMPLOYEES
06/21	603	(196)	—	4,500
06/19	600	174	29.0%	—
06/18	546	(70)	—	—
06/17	533	(65)	—	—
Annual Growth	3.1%	—	—	—

2021 Year-End Financials

Return on assets: (-11.9%)   Cash ($ mil.): 699
Return on equity: (-189.0%)
Current ratio: —

ROUSE'S ENTERPRISES, L.L.C.

EXECUTIVES

MBR, Anthony J Rouse Sr
MBR*, Donald J Rouse
MBR*, Thomas B Rouse
Director, Ben Russell
Category Manager, Bethany Ber
Accounting, Celeste Hidalgo
Vice President Perishables, James Breuhl
Buyer, Kerry Adams
Director of Information Techno, Malcom Landry
Store Director, Michael Vanamburg
Produce Buyer Category Manager, Morris Patrick
Auditors: TS KEARNS & CO THIBODAUX

LOCATIONS

HQ: ROUSE'S ENTERPRISES, L.L.C.
179 ROUSES DR, SCHRIEVER, LA 703953310
Phone: 985 447-5998
Web: WWW.SHOP.ROUSES.COM

HISTORICAL FINANCIALS

Company Type: Private

Income Statement — FYE: December 29

	REVENUE ($ mil.)	NET INCOME ($ mil.)	NET PROFIT MARGIN	EMPLOYEES
12/10	691	24	3.5%	5,200
12/09	689	21	3.1%	—
12/06	247	11	4.8%	—
Annual Growth	29.4%	19.7%	—	—

2010 Year-End Financials

Return on assets: 15.7%   Cash ($ mil.): 8
Return on equity: 25.8%
Current ratio: 2.00

ROYAL TEN CATE (USA), INC.

EXECUTIVES

Ceo, Loek De Vries
V Pres-Cfo*, Joseph W Averette
SEC*, Henry Hope
Director, David Clarke
Extrusion Manager, Tony Pilgrim
Transportation Coordinator, Ann Spinelli

LOCATIONS

HQ: ROYAL TEN CATE (USA), INC.
365 S HOLLAND DR, PENDERGRASS, GA 305674625
Phone: 706 693-2226
Web: WWW.TENCATEGEO.US

HISTORICAL FINANCIALS

Company Type: Private

Income Statement — FYE: December 31

	REVENUE ($ mil.)	NET INCOME ($ mil.)	NET PROFIT MARGIN	EMPLOYEES
12/13	613	0	—	1,500
12/12	626	0	—	—
12/11	178	0	—	—
Annual Growth	85.2%	—	—	—

2013 Year-End Financials

Return on assets: —   Cash ($ mil.): 8
Return on equity: —
Current ratio: 3.00

RTW RETAILWINDS, INC.

EXECUTIVES

Ceo-Cfo, Sheamus Toal
Senior Counsel, Christina White
Senior Vice President, Dhinora Montalvo
Director, Amanda Burden
Computer Specialist, Angel Aponte
Senior Programmer Analyst, Bella Fogelman
Director of Technology, Chintan Patel
Executive Vice President Desig, David Witkewicz
Controller, John Jones
Associate Staff Analyst, Josefina Hernandez
Assistant Commissioner, Joy Wang
Auditors: BDO USA LLP NEW YORK NEW YO

LOCATIONS

HQ: RTW RETAILWINDS, INC.
330 W 34TH ST FL 9, NEW YORK, NY 100012433
Phone: 212 884-2000
Web: WWW.NYANDCOMPANY.COM

HISTORICAL FINANCIALS

Company Type: Private

Income Statement — FYE: February 1

	REVENUE ($ mil.)	NET INCOME ($ mil.)	NET PROFIT MARGIN	EMPLOYEES
02/20	826	(61)	—	1,460
02/19	893	4	0.5%	—
02/18*	926	5	0.6%	—
01/17	929	(17)	—	—
Annual Growth	(3.8%)	—	—	—

*Fiscal year change

2020 Year-End Financials

Return on assets: (-15.0%)   Cash ($ mil.): 60
Return on equity: (-386.2%)
Current ratio: 0.90

RUDOLPH AND SLETTEN, INC.

Rudolph and Sletten ... the little-known tenth reindeer? More like the elves who built Santa's workshop. The firm is a mainstay of the California construction scene especially Silicon Valley. It has built corporate campuses for Apple Microsoft and Wells Fargo as well as Lucasfilm's Skywalker Ranch production facility. Rudolph and Sletten is one of the US' largest general building contractors with site selection design/build and construction management capabilities. Key projects also include biotech labs hospitals and schools. Onslow "Rudy" Rudolph founded the company in 1959 and was joined by partner Kenneth Sletten in 1962. Rudolph and Sletten is a subsidiary of Tutor Perini Corporation .

Geographic Reach

Redwood City California-based Rudolph and Sletten has regional offices in San Francisco Sacramento Irvine San Diego and Stockton California. The firm is licensed to build in California Arizona Nevada Washington Colorado Idaho Oregon Oklahoma and Texas.

Sales and Marketing

Big name clients have included a number of prestigious institutions such as Childrens Hospital Los Angeles The University of Southern California Genentech and the Monterey Bay Aquarium. The company reports that more than 95% of its business comes from repeat customers.

Financial Performance

California is Rudolph and Slatten's largest market representing an estimated $666 million in revenue in 2013.

Strategy

To capitalize on San Francisco's building boom the firm hired several San Francisco construction veterans in early 2014 to expand its operations there. Rudolph and Sletten is currently working on projects in Mission Bay and the Financial District.

The firm is renowned for its green building practices with nearly half the staff Leadership in Energy and Environmental Design (LEED)-accredited; it aims for 100% accreditation by 2013. Its own corporate headquarters was Gold LEED-certified based on its use of recycled materials energy and water efficiency and sustainable site. Other sustainable projects undertaken by Rudolph and Sletten include the Lawrence Berkeley National Laboratory and the NOAA Fisheries Services Southwest Science Center.

EXECUTIVES

Pres, Jonathan Foad
V Pres*, Michael P Mohrman
Information Specialist, Victor Ladao
Coordinator, Phyllis Avery
Project Manager, Amy Traugot
Coordinator, Courtney Eads
Director Quality, Steve Nielsen
Executive Administrative Assis, Carol Harper
Mechanical Coordinator, Bruce Leidle

Administrative Assistant, Teresa Allen
Senior Marketing Coordinator, Rebecca Kaiser
Auditors: DELOITTE & TOUCHE LLP LOS AN

LOCATIONS

HQ: RUDOLPH AND SLETTEN, INC.
2 CIRCLE STAR WAY FL 4, SAN CARLOS, CA
940706200
Phone: 650 216-3600
Web: WWW.TUTORPERINI.COM

PRODUCTS/OPERATIONS

Major Markets

Biotechnology/pharmaceutical
Commercial office and corporate campuses
Education
Gaming and hospitality
Government
Health care
Industrial
Justice
Sports and entertainment
Technology

Selected Services
Estimating
Scheduling
Value engineering
Constructibility review
Building Information Modeling (BIM)
Construction
Construction management
Project management
Quality control
Disruption management
Commissioning
Self performed work
Sustainable cpnstruction
Safety

COMPETITORS

Charles Pankow Builders	Kitchell
Clark Construction Group	Mccarthy Building Pcl Constructors
Dpr Construction	Summit Builders
Devcon Construction	Swinerton
Hathaway Dinwiddie Construction	Turner Construction Webcor Builders
Hensel Phelps Construction	Whiting-turner

HISTORICAL FINANCIALS

Company Type: Private

Income Statement				FYE: December 31
	REVENUE ($ mil.)	NET INCOME ($ mil.)	NET PROFIT MARGIN	EMPLOYEES
12/16	1,307	14	1.1%	700
12/15	940	7	0.7%	—
12/14	637	3	0.5%	—
12/13	665	(0)	—	—
Annual Growth	25.2%	—	—	—

RUSH UNIVERSITY MEDICAL CENTER

EXECUTIVES

Pres-Ceo, Omar Lateef
Exec V Pres-Coo, Wayne E Keathley
Svp-Cfo, Patricia Steeves O'Neil

Chief of Medicine, David Amsell
Accounting Staff, Donna Ameismeier
General, Fred A Cbet
Dental Assistant Supervisor, George Katsoyannis
Coordinator, Janie Voyles
Staff, John S Weitzner
Doctor, Juan-Miguel Mosquera
Accounting Staff, Mable Kyles
Auditors: DELOITTE & TOUCHE LLP CHICAG

LOCATIONS

HQ: RUSH UNIVERSITY MEDICAL CENTER
1620 W HARRISON ST, CHICAGO, IL 606123801
Phone: 312 942-5000
Web: WWW.RUSH.EDU

HISTORICAL FINANCIALS

Company Type: Private

Income Statement				FYE: June 30
	REVENUE ($ mil.)	NET INCOME ($ mil.)	NET PROFIT MARGIN	EMPLOYEES
06/17	2,267	302	13.3%	8,000
06/16	1,502	83	5.6%	—
06/15	1,408	(22)	—	—
06/14	1,969	208	10.6%	—
Annual Growth	4.8%	13.2%	—	—

2017 Year-End Financials

Return on assets: 7.9%   Cash ($ mil.): 99
Return on equity: 13.7%
Current ratio: 0.90

RYMAN HOSPITALITY PROPERTIES, INC.

Ryman Hospitality Properties (formerly Gaylord Entertainment) consists of resort hotels tethered closely to attractions that appeal to the meetings and conventions market. It includes the Gaylord Opryland Resort & Convention Center in Nashville the Gaylord Palms Resort in Florida (close to Disney World) the Gaylord Texan Resort near Dallas and the Gaylord National Resort and Convention Center in the Washington DC area. Ryman owned assets include a network of five upscale meetings-focused resorts totaling some 9600 rooms that are managed by Marriott under the Gaylord Hotels brand.

HISTORY

The origins of Gaylord Entertainment can be traced back to the Oklahoma Publishing Co. a newspaper publishing company founded by Edward K. Gaylord Ray Dickinson and Roy McClintock in 1903. The publisher of The Daily Oklahoman Oklahoma Publishing branched into radio in 1928 with the purchase of Oklahoma City radio station WKY. With its 1949 creation of Oklahoma City television station WKY-TV Oklahoma Publishing made the leap into television.

Edward K. Gaylord died in 1974 at the age of 101 and his son Edward L. Gaylord was appointed CEO. Under his leadership the company purchased Opryland USA in 1983 — an acquisition that netted it the Grand Ole Opry Opryland Themepark and the Opryland Hotel. Opryland USA also launched country music cable network The Nashville Network that year.

In 1991 the increasingly diverse Oklahoma Publishing spun off its entertainment and broadcast

---

holdings in the form of public company Gaylord Entertainment which established its headquarters in Nashville Tennessee. Gaylord Entertainment acquired a majority interest in cable music network Country Music Television (CMT) the same year. It later expanded CMT into Latin America Asia and the Pacific Rim. CMT also made a brief foray into Europe but that initiative was ended in 1998.

Facing a consolidating entertainment and media landscape Gaylord sold The Nashville Network and the US operations of CMT to Westinghouse (now CBS) in 1997. It also sold television station KSTW that year. The company expanded its reach into Christian music with the purchase of Word Entertainment and its 1997 acquisition of Blanton Harrell Entertainment gave Gaylord a presence in artist management. Terry London was appointed CEO in 1997.

The company closed its Opryland theme park in 1998 in the face of declining attendance and broke ground at the same site for the Opry Mills entertainment shopping and restaurant complex (opened 2000). Gaylord also purchased a Nashville Ramada Inn in 1998 (later renaming it Radisson Hotel at Opryland). With its 1998 acquisition of Paris-based Pandora Investment Gaylord branched into film distribution.

In 1999 the company formed Opryland Hospitality Group to oversee expansion of the Opryland hotel concept across the US. It also sold its last television station KTVT in Dallas/Fort Worth to CBS. Edward K. Gaylord II succeeded his father as chairman in 1999. That year the company launched its Internet division GETdigitalmedia (later renamed Gaylord Digital) and moved online with the purchase of Christian Web sites Musicforce.com and Lightsource.com. Later the same year the company expanded its Internet presence with the purchase of Songs.com a music Web site focused on independent artists. But in late 2000 the company announced it would close its Internet unit. Also in 2000 the company bought Corporate Magic a firm focused on producing entertainment events for corporate audiences.

At the end of 2000 Gaylord sold Musicforce.com to Christian Book Distributors. Following that sale it sold Lightsource.com to LifeAudio.com in early 2001. That year the company sold its film and television production units and announced a restructuring in order to cut costs. It also renamed Opryland Hotels to Gaylord Opryland while expanding into Texas and Florida. Colin Reed was appointed CEO in 2001.

Between 2001 and 2003 Gaylord Entertainment sold Word Entertainment to Warner Music Group the Opry Mills shopping and restaurant complex to The Mills Corporation the Acuff-Rose Music Publishing business to Sony/ATV two of its Nashville radio stations to Cumulus Media and its majority interest in the Oklahoma City Redhawks minor league baseball team.

Edward L. Gaylord officially retired from the company in 2003 at age 83. Also that year the company significantly expanded its hospitality business with the purchase of ResortQuest a vacation and condominium property management firm. In 2004 the Gaylord family sold more than half its shares in the company making Gabelli Funds the majority owner.

In 2005 Gaylord acquired 50% of Corporate Magic a Dallas-based provider of production support for corporate meetings and events. It did so to support its meeting and convention facilities.

The company unloaded its minority interest in minor league hockey team the Nashville Predators in 2005. Two years later it sold ResortQuest to a subsidiary of Leucadia National Corp. for $35 million. Also in 2007 it sold its interest in sporting goods store operator Bass Pro Group. In 2008 the company opened the Gaylord National Resort and

Convention Center in the Washington DC area. The property has some 2000 rooms and approximately 450000 square feet of meeting space.

Also in 2008 Gaylord terminated plans to acquire the Westin La Cantera Resort in San Antonio for about $253 million citing a tough economic environment. In addition the 2008 sale of its ResortQuest subsidiary an online booking service in vacation rentals property management and resort real estate sales fit the company's strategy of selling off assets that aren't related to its Grand Ole Opry or its operations in the meetings and convention market.

In 2009 the company responded to weak earnings by cutting approximately 500 jobs across all areas of the business. Gaylord reported steep dip in profits in 2010 primarily due to harsh flooding in Nashville when the Cumberland River rose to historic levels flowing over protective levees. The flood resulted in property damage and temporary closures at its properties in Nashville causing lost revenues and an increase in expenses. Also in 2010 Gaylord sold its 50% stake in Corporate Magic back to that company's CEO.

The company changed its name to Ryman Hospitality Properties in 2012. It also converted to an REIT and sold the Gaylord brand to Marriott which now manages Ryman's hotel properties and certain other entertainment holdings.

EXECUTIVES

Chairman Of The Board, Chief Executive Officer, Colin Reed, $1,079,012 total compensation

President, Chief Financial Officer, Mark Fioravanti, $572,949 total compensation

Executive Vice President, Chief Accounting Officer, Corporate Controller, Jennifer Hutcheson, $332,748 total compensation

Executive Vice President, Chief Operating Officer - Hotels, Patrick Chaffin, $448,931 total compensation

Executive Vice President, General Counsel, Secretary, Scott Lynn, $380,409 total compensation

Independent Director, Christine Pantoya
Auditors: ERNST & YOUNG LLP NASHVILLE

LOCATIONS

HQ: RYMAN HOSPITALITY PROPERTIES, INC.
1 GAYLORD DR, NASHVILLE, TN 372141207
Phone: 615 316-6000
Web: WWW.RYMANHP.COM

PRODUCTS/OPERATIONS

2015 Sales

	$ mil.	% of total
Hospitality	994	91
Entertainment (previously Opry and Attractions)	97	9
Total	**1,092**	**100**

2015 Sales

	$ mil.	% of total
Food and beverage	461	42
Rooms	404	37
Other hotel revenue	129	12
Entertainment (previously Opry and Attractions)	97	9
Total	**1,092**	**100**

Select Operations

Hospitality
  Gaylord Opryland Resort & Convention Center (Tennessee)
  Gaylord Palms Resort & Convention Center (Florida)
  Gaylord Texan Resort & Convention Center
  Radisson Hotel at Opryland (Tennessee)
Attractions
  Gaylord Springs Golf Links (golf club Tennessee)
  General Jackson Showboat
  Grand Ole Opry

Ryman Auditorium
Wildhorse Saloon
WSM-AM

COMPETITORS

Ckx
Caesars Entertainment
Disney Parks & Resorts
Elvis Presley Enterprises
Herschend Entertainment
Hershey Entertainment
Hilton Worldwide
Kennywood
Las Vegas Sands
Live Nation Entertainment
Mgm Resorts
Marriott
New York Convention Center Operating Corporation
Seaworld
Welk Group

HISTORICAL FINANCIALS

Company Type: Private

Income Statement				FYE: December 31
	ASSETS ($ mil.)	NET INCOME ($ mil.)	INCOME AS % OF ASSETS	EMPLOYEES
12/16	2,405	159	6.6%	177,000
12/15	2,331	111	4.8%	—
12/14	2,413	126	5.2%	—
12/13	2,424	113	4.7%	—
Annual Growth	(0.3%)	12.0%	—	—

2016 Year-End Financials

Return on assets: 6.6%
Return on equity: 43.3%
Sales ($ mil): 1,149

S & B ENGINEERS AND CONSTRUCTORS, LTD.

S & B Engineers and Constructors (S&B) makes it possible for others to burn the midnight oil. The employee-owned company specializes in engineering procurement construction and fabrication services to multiple industries. It primarily focuses on NGL fractionation import / export terminals pipelines petrochemicals & polymers and refining. S&B also flexes its engineering muscle on transportation waste and wastewater and environmental and telecommunications projects for public sector clients. Founded in 1967 by James Slaughter and William Brookshire to serve refineries and other process plants along the Texas and Louisiana gulf coasts the company has expanded services globally with two offices in India.

Operations

The company has divisions that focus on specific geographic areas and services. S&B's Engineers and Constructors division provides engineering procurement and construction services for combustion turbine combined and simple cycle projects as well as environmental AQCS retrofit projects for existing coal plants.

Ford Bacon & Davis does much of its business in the southern US where it takes on engineering and design projects for oil gas and chemical companies. It not only constructs new plants but is often hired to rebuild facilities that have been damaged by fires or explosions.

The firm's Plant Services division provides small capital construction supplemental maintenance

turnaround professional services asset management and other plant services including productivity studies and specialty training. S&B Infrastructure caters to private and government clients — ranging from federal to state to local authorities — while its private sector services extend from land development to industrial to pipeline client needs.

S&B India services its parent company's US clients as well as clients in India and other countries.

Geographic Reach

Houston-based S&B boasts more than five offices throughout Texas (including its modular operation) its Northeast office in Canonsburg Pennsylvania a handful of offices in Louisiana and a single office in Greenville South Carolina also in Morrisville North Carolina and Kingsport Tennessee. S&B India has engineering centers in Bangalore and New Delhi.

Sales and Marketing

The company primarily serves midstream industry which is nearly 30% of its project. The petrochemical and polymers industry accounts 25% of its projects. Other industries includes terminals/transportation refining and power.

EXECUTIVES

Chb, James G Slaughter Jr
Ceo, JW Brookshire
Chm, William A Brookshire
Sr V Pres, Greg Hafer
Exec Dir, Richard L Akin
Evp-Coo, David Taylor
Cfo, Kris Barnhill
Accounting Manager, Aurora Saavedra
Executive Assistant, Shenoa Flack
Project Material Manager, Gary Malloy
Purchasing, Mike Dunnahoe
Auditors: ERNST & YOUNG LLP HOUSTON TX

LOCATIONS

HQ: S & B ENGINEERS AND CONSTRUCTORS, LTD.
7825 PARK PLACE BLVD, HOUSTON, TX 770874697
Phone: 713 645-4141
Web: WWW.SBEC.COM

Selected Locations

US
  Austin TX
    Baton Roug
  El Paso TX
  Fort Worth TX
  Freeport TX
  Greenville SC
  Houston
  Longview TX
  McAllen TX
  Monroe LA
  New Orleans
  San Antonio
India
  Bangalore
  New Delhi

PRODUCTS/OPERATIONS

Selected Projects

Sulfur Tailgas Treating Unit Blaine WA
Crude Upgrade Project El Segundo CA
Pipeline Terminal Project Los Angeles CA
Refinery Revamp Project Bakersfield CA
Fractionation Expansion Project Billings MT
Gas Plant Project Meeker CO
SMR Project Port Arthur TX
ABF Program BP Refinery Texas City
Low Sulfur Gasoline & Diesel Projects Houston TX
Fine Paper Machine Project Kingsport TN

Selected Services

Construction
Engineering
Modules and skids

Plant services
Procurement
Project management

Selected Divisions
Ford Bacon & Davis
S&B India
S&B Infrastructure
S&B Plant Services
S&B Power Division

COMPETITORS

Bechtel	Kbr Building Group
Fluor	Parsons Corporation
Jacobs Engineering	Turner Industries
Kbr	Zachry Inc.

HISTORICAL FINANCIALS
Company Type: Private

Income Statement   FYE: December 31

	REVENUE ($ mil.)	NET INCOME ($ mil.)	NET PROFIT MARGIN	EMPLOYEES
12/18	679	0	—	7,000
12/17	679	0	—	—
12/16	950	0	—	—
Annual Growth	(15.4%)	—	—	—

2018 Year-End Financials
Return on assets: —   Cash ($ mil.): 59
Return on equity: —
Current ratio: 1.50

SACRAMENTO CITY UNIFIED SCHOOL DISTRICT

EXECUTIVES

Supt, Jose Banda
Cfo*, Tom Barrinson
C-Level Human Resources, Robert Garcia
Teacher, Bre Rizzo
K12 Project Manager, Jay Elmquist
Teacher, Chris Congdon
Auditors: CROWE LLP SACRAMENTO CALIFOR

LOCATIONS

HQ: SACRAMENTO CITY UNIFIED SCHOOL DISTRICT
5735 47TH AVE, SACRAMENTO, CA 958244528
Phone: 916 643-7400
Web: WWW.SCUSD.EDU

HISTORICAL FINANCIALS
Company Type: Private

Income Statement   FYE: June 30

	REVENUE ($ mil.)	NET INCOME ($ mil.)	NET PROFIT MARGIN	EMPLOYEES
06/19	690	(57)	—	6,500
06/18	635	(45)	—	—
06/17	625	71	11.5%	—
06/16	656	47	7.2%	—
Annual Growth	1.7%	—	—	—

SACRAMENTO MUNICIPAL UTILITY DISTRICT

The Sacramento Municipal Utility District (SMUD) doesn't want its name to be mud. One of the largest locally owned electric utilities in the US SMUD serves more than 640710 residential and commercial customer meters (a service area population of approximately 1.5 million) in California's Sacramento and Placer counties. SMUD is responsible for the acquisition generation transmission and distribution of electric power to its service area. It began serving Sacramento in 1946.

Operations
The utility operates more than 10910 miles of transmission and distribution lines across its 900-sq.-mi. service area. It gets power from varied sources including hydropower natural-gas-fired generators renewable energy (such as solar and wind power) and purchases power on the wholesale market.

The company has installed some 600000 smart meters at customer locations across its entire service area.

Geographic Reach
SMUD generates transmits and distributes electricity to a territory that includes Sacramento Sacramento County and a small portion of Placer and Yolo Counties.

Sales and Marketing
The company has over 640710 customer contracts in some 1.5 million service area population.

Financial Performance
SMUD's revenue is $1.6 billion similar to the previous year due to fluctuations in the company's segment revenues.Cash and cash equivalents at the end of the year were $308.1 million 21% higher than in the previous year. Cash provided by operating activities was $415.9 million. Financing activities and investing activities used $313.7 million and $4.1 million respectively. Main cash uses were repayments of commercial paper construction expenditures and purchases of securities.

Strategy
In 2019 SMUD continued its partnership with Habitat for Humanity by establishing a 2-year partnership to incentivize electrification and EV-ready homes and install rooftop solar. Building electrification programs resulted in a partnership with D.R. Horton to build more than 100 new all-electric homes. And through SMUD's Smart Homes Program SMUD received commitments from local and national homebuilders to build approximately 1900 new all electric homes by the end of 2022. SMUD has continued to grow its Greenergy program and is now one of the largest of its kind in the nation. Through its economic development program SMUD played a key role in the attraction retention and expansion of several companies in its service territory which led to the creation of over 700 jobs.

As part of the hydro relicensing process SMUD entered into long-term contracts to provide certain services to four different government agencies ? U.S. Department of Interior Bureau of Land Management U.S. Department of Agriculture Forest Service El Dorado County and the California Department of Parks and Recreation. On Dec. 31 2019 and 2018 the liability for these contract payments was $63.4 million and $58.8 million respectively.

SMUD also has a long-term agreement with the Western Area Power Administration (WAPA) to purchase power generated by the Central Valley Project a series of federal hydroelectric facilities operated by the U.S. Bureau of Reclamation.

Company Background
In 2012 SMUD announced that it is the leading utility in the US in terms of new homes which had solar panels installed during construction. The utility commenced the SMUD Solar Smart Homes program in 2006 and had constructed more than 1000 homes with solar panels by 2012.

The company has been delivering power to customers in the region since 1946 but its history goes back to 1923 when citizens voted to create SMUD as a community-owned electric service. However years of engineering studies political battles and legal wrangling delayed SMUD's purchase of PG&E' s local electrical system.

In March 1946 the California Supreme Court denied PG&E's final petition to halt the sale and nine months later SMUD finally began operations.

EXECUTIVES

Ceo, Arlen Orchard
Cfo*, Jim Tracy
Director, Ren E N Taylor
Cntrl, Carry Nethaway
Asst GM, Jim Shelter
Staff, Sheryl Yee
Marketing Specialist II, Caryn Fisher
Network Engineer, Jason Farinsky
Information Technology Supervi, Jason Moreno
Project Manager On Sacramento, Jaspal Deol
Manager Supervisor, Lawrence Gunn
Auditors: BAKER TILLY US LLP MADISON

LOCATIONS

HQ: SACRAMENTO MUNICIPAL UTILITY DISTRICT
6201 S ST, SACRAMENTO, CA 958171818
Phone: 916 452-3211
Web: WWW.SMUD.ORG

PRODUCTS/OPERATIONS

2015 Sales

	% of total
Commercial & industrial	47
Residential	42
Wholesale power	6
Street lighting & other	5
Total	**100**

Selected Products and Services
Conservation programs
Customer billing programs
Diagnostic services
Electric vehicle charging stations
Energy assistance programs
Energy-efficient appliances and equipment
Energy management
Green energy programs
Power quality and environmental services
Security lighting
Shade trees for customers
Solar water heating
Surge protection
Tree trimming

COMPETITORS

Aes	Los Angeles Water And
Avista	Power
Duke Energy	Pg&e Corporation
Edison International	Sempra Energy

HISTORICAL FINANCIALS

Company Type: Private

Income Statement				FYE: December 31
	REVENUE ($ mil.)	NET INCOME ($ mil.)	NET PROFIT MARGIN	EMPLOYEES
12/20	1,587	153	9.7%	2,213
12/19	1,559	78	5.1%	—
12/18	1,595	209	13.1%	—
12/17	1,559	181	11.6%	—
Annual Growth	0.6%	(5.5%)	—	—

2020 Year-End Financials

Return on assets: 2.2%   Cash ($ mil.): 680
Return on equity: 7.8%
Current ratio: 2.80

SADDLE BUTTE PIPELINE LLC

Auditors: HEIN & ASSOCIATES LLP DENVER

LOCATIONS

HQ: SADDLE BUTTE PIPELINE LLC
858 MAIN AVE UNIT 301, DURANGO, CO 813015496
Phone: 970 375-3150
Web: WWW.SBPIPELINE.COM

HISTORICAL FINANCIALS

Company Type: Private

Income Statement				FYE: December 31
	REVENUE ($ mil.)	NET INCOME ($ mil.)	NET PROFIT MARGIN	EMPLOYEES
12/12	689	656	95.2%	30
12/11	69	(10)	—	—
12/10	68	0	0.0%	—
Annual Growth	218.1%	199	13.8%	—

2012 Year-End Financials

Return on assets: 425.5%   Cash ($ mil.): 144
Return on equity: 433.6%
Current ratio: 50.40

SAINT ALPHONSUS REGIONAL MEDICAL CENTER INC.

EXECUTIVES

Pres-Ceo, Sally Jeffcoat
Cco*, Steven Nemerson
Director, Sarah Berg
Managing Partner, Elizabeth Criner
Account Manager, Lois Soito
Chief Officer, Ryan Heyborne
Total Rewards Manager, Cynthia Shehan

Nurse Practitioner, Melissa Dirocco
Associate General Counsel, Michael Woodhouse
Vice-President, Mike Malone

LOCATIONS

HQ: SAINT ALPHONSUS REGIONAL MEDICAL CENTER INC.
1055 N CURTIS RD, BOISE, ID 837061309
Phone: 208 367-6899
Web: WWW.SAINTALPHONSUS.ORG

HISTORICAL FINANCIALS

Company Type: Private

Income Statement				FYE: June 30
	REVENUE ($ mil.)	NET INCOME ($ mil.)	NET PROFIT MARGIN	EMPLOYEES
06/18	937	50	5.4%	40
06/15	37	(5)	—	—
06/14	29	(5)	—	—
06/11	0	(0)	—	—
Annual Growth	—	—	—	—

2018 Year-End Financials

Return on assets: 4.5%   Cash ($ mil.): 208
Return on equity: 6.8%
Current ratio: 3.40

SAINT ALPHONSUS REGIONAL MEDICAL CENTER, INC.

Saint Alphonsus Regional Medical Center makes medical care its primary mission. The 384-bed hospital provides Boise Idaho and the surrounding region (including eastern Oregon and northern Nevada) with general acute and specialized health care services. Its facilities and operations include a level II trauma center an orthopedic spinal care unit an air transport service and a home health and hospice division. Saint Alphonsus Regional Medical Center is part of Trinity Health's four-hospital Saint Alphonsus Health System which serves Boise and Nampa in Idaho and Ontario and Baker City in Oregon. The Sisters of the Holy Cross founded the hospital in 1894.

Operations

Saint Alphonsus Regional Medical Center provides outpatient services through the 70 affiliated physician practices that make up the Saint Alphonsus Medical Group. It also operates the Saint Alphonsus Health Plaza which provides urgent care and outpatient surgery laboratory rehabilitation and primary care services.

The hospital also offers rural or homebound patients telemedicine services through which remote physician visits are conducted using audio or video.

Geographic Reach

Saint Alphonsus Regional Medical Center serves a territory that includes portions of southwestern Idaho northern Nevada and eastern Oregon.

Strategy

Saint Alphonsus Regional Medical Center expands its facilities to improve medical care in its service territory. In 2014 it opened its newly expanded and renovated emergency department which included a 30% increase in square footage. Also that year it became the first hospital in the region to utilize the EndoWrist Stapler technology

---

on the da Vinci robotic system for minimally invasive surgeries.

EXECUTIVES

Cfo, Kenneth Fry
Patient Representativ, Rena Miller
Coordinator, Chris Marselle
Manager of Corporate Sales Dev, William Cafferty
Quality Assurance Director, Aline Lee
Diagnostic Radiologist, Anthony P Giauque
Doctor of Medicine, Brian C Kerr
Doctor of Medicine, David Koeplin
Chief Strategy, Janelle Reilly
Radiologist, Knochel John
Plastic Surgeon, Mark Wigod

LOCATIONS

HQ: SAINT ALPHONSUS REGIONAL MEDICAL CENTER, INC.
1055 N CURTIS RD, BOISE, ID 837061309
Phone: 208 367-2121
Web: WWW.STARSPT.ORG

COMPETITORS

Ascension Health	St. Luke's Health
Hca	System
Intermountain Health Care	

HISTORICAL FINANCIALS

Company Type: Private

Income Statement				FYE: June 30
	REVENUE ($ mil.)	NET INCOME ($ mil.)	NET PROFIT MARGIN	EMPLOYEES
06/14	572	46	8.0%	3,500
06/13	545	43	7.9%	—
06/10	449	13	3.1%	—
Annual Growth	6.2%	35.2%	—	—

2014 Year-End Financials

Return on assets: 6.4%   Cash ($ mil.): 3
Return on equity: 10.6%
Current ratio: 1.30

SAINT ELIZABETH MEDICAL CENTER, INC.

The primary teach hospital of Tufts University School of Medicine St. Elizabeth's Medical Center provides health care services to residents in Allston Boston Brighton Brookline Newton Watertown and Weston. St. Elizabeth Healthcare's programs include family medicine cardiovascular care women and infants' health cancer care neurology care and orthopedics. St. Elizabeth's Medical Center was founded in 1868 by five laywomen members of the third order of St. Francis to care for women from Boston's South End. St. Elizabeth's is a member of Steward Health Care.

EXECUTIVES

Pres, John Dubis
Evp-Coo-Cfo*, Marc Hoffman
V Pres-Coo*, Garren Colvin
Treas*, Nathan Vanlaningham
SEC*, Barbara L Krohman
Dir*, Edwin Robinson
Human Resources, Linda D
Nurse Manager, Donna Parsons

Vice President, Jack Basil
Secretary To Director, Lisa Robinson
Revenue Cycle Manager, Leslie Kremer

LOCATIONS

HQ: SAINT ELIZABETH MEDICAL CENTER, INC.
 1 MEDICAL VILLAGE DR, EDGEWOOD, KY
 410173403
Phone: 859 301-2000
Web: WWW.STELIZABETH.COM

Selected locations

St. Elizabeth Covington (Covington Kentucky)
St. Elizabeth Edgewood (Edgewood Kentucky)
St. Elizabeth Grant (Williamstown Kentucky)
St. Elizabeth Ft. Thomas (St. Thomas Kentucky)
St. Elizabeth Florence (Florence Kentucky)
St. Elizabeth Falmouth (Falmouth Kentucky)

COMPETITORS

Adventist Health System Sunbelt Healthcare
Bethesda North
Catholic Health Initiatives
Cincinnati Children's Hospital
Deaconess Associations
Hca
Kettering Health Network
Mount Carmel Health
Ohiohealth
Regency Hospital
Tenet Healthcare
The Christ Hospital Corporation
Trihealth
Uc Health
Universal Health Services

HISTORICAL FINANCIALS

Company Type: Private

Income Statement | | | | FYE: December 31

	REVENUE ($ mil.)	NET INCOME ($ mil.)	NET PROFIT MARGIN	EMPLOYEES
12/19	1,293	130	10.1%	6,227
12/14	633	45	7.1%	—
12/13	984	124	12.7%	—
12/08	623	(32)	—	—
Annual Growth	6.9%	—	—	—

2019 Year-End Financials

Return on assets: 6.0% Cash ($ mil.): 69
Return on equity: 8.6%
Current ratio: —

SAINT FRANCIS HOSPITAL, INC.

EXECUTIVES

Ceo, Jake Henry
Human Resources, Brenda Garner
Director, Karen Cochran
Vice-President, Marcus McKinney
Senior Vice-President, Pete Aran
Director, Philip Marcus
Director, Tiffani Fagan
V Chm, Peter C Boylan
Vice-President Engineering, Mike Wilson
Coordinator, April M Borg
Family and General Dentistry, Larry Lander

LOCATIONS

HQ: SAINT FRANCIS HOSPITAL, INC.
 6161 S YALE AVE, TULSA, OK 741361992
Phone: 918 502-2050
Web: WWW.SAINTFRANCIS.COM

HISTORICAL FINANCIALS

Company Type: Private

Income Statement | | | | FYE: June 30

	REVENUE ($ mil.)	NET INCOME ($ mil.)	NET PROFIT MARGIN	EMPLOYEES
06/16	913	128	14.0%	4,000
06/15	877	171	19.6%	—
06/13	910	190	21.0%	—
06/12	838	157	18.7%	—
Annual Growth	2.2%	(5.0%)	—	—

2016 Year-End Financials

Return on assets: 5.6% Cash ($ mil.): 312
Return on equity: 6.5%
Current ratio: 8.90

SAINT JOSEPH HEALTH SYSTEM, INC.

EXECUTIVES

Chm, Doug Hacker
Pres, Ruth Brinkley
Tres, Brutus Clay
SEC, Nelson Fonticiella
Cmo, Travis Sewalls
Coo, Jason M Adams
Chief of Medicine, Robert Salley
Occupational Specia, Nathan Eldreth
Regional Director, Karen King
Director, Kevin Poe
Cpe Supervisor, Kenneth McCullough
Auditors: COMMONSPIRIT HEALTH
 ENGLEWOOD

LOCATIONS

HQ: SAINT JOSEPH HEALTH SYSTEM, INC.
 1 SAINT JOSEPH DR, LEXINGTON, KY 405043742
Phone: 859 313-1000
Web: WWW.CHISAINTJOSEPHHEALTH.ORG

HISTORICAL FINANCIALS

Company Type: Private

Income Statement | | | | FYE: June 30

	REVENUE ($ mil.)	NET INCOME ($ mil.)	NET PROFIT MARGIN	EMPLOYEES
06/20	844	92	10.9%	99
06/14	745	(45)	—	—
Annual Growth	2.1%	—	—	—

2020 Year-End Financials

Return on assets: 9.5% Cash ($ mil.): 398
Return on equity: 22.1%
Current ratio: 2.60

SAINT JOSEPH HOSPITAL, INC

The goal of Saint Joseph Hospital (formerly Exempla Saint Joseph Hospital) is to give residents of the Mile High City exemplary care. The Denver acute care facility has nearly 400 licensed beds and specializes in areas including cardiovascular disease cancer orthopedics pediatrics neurology diagnostics and high-risk labor and delivery. The Catholic not-for-profit hospital sees about 50000 emergency department visits annually and employs more than 1300 physicians. The hospital also offers residency programs in family practice internal medicine obstetrics and gynecology and general surgery. Catholic-sponsored Saint Joseph is part of SCL Health - Front Range.

Operations

Saint Joseph is one of the largest hospitals in the region. The medical center is a regional provider of critical cardiac care neonatal ICU orthopedic and radiation oncology services. Its pediatric ward is a satellite facility of the Children's Hospital Colorado. The Saint Joseph campus also includes three outpatient care clinics that offer charity care and the hospital conducts outreach programs in neighboring communities.

Altogether the hospital admits some 20000 inpatients per year and handles some 150000 outpatient visits more than 6875 inpatients and 6330 outpatient surgeries. As a not-for-profit entity Saint Joseph contributes more than 10% of annual revenues to charity care and community service efforts.

Sales and Marketing

Saint Joseph maintains contracts with most Denver-area health plans and is a major admitting hospital for Kaiser Health Plan of Colorado.

Strategy

Saint Joseph has constructed a replacement facility for its aging hospital facilities. The new $623 million medical center includes 365 beds (primarily in private patient rooms) as well as improved surgery emergency and diagnostic centers. The facility provides 826143 square feet of new diagnostic treatment and patient care spaces. The new facility specializes in heart and vascular care cancer treatment labor and delivery respiratory health orthopedics and emergency care. The hospital was completed in the second half of 2014 with occupancy commencing in early 2015.

In 2013 Saint Joseph announced its intention to form a joint operating agreement with National Jewish Health. Together the entities plan to collaborate on patient-centered health care methods as well as education and research programs. The clinical operations of each organization would be jointly managed through the agreement though the organizations will retain their respective assets.

The hospital is also involved in a federal pilot program designed to decrease the amount of unnecessary testing and treatments that can occur at hospitals by bundling service fees paid by Medicare; the program is managed by the Centers for Medicare and Medicaid Services. Such measures are part of the overall goal of the US health care industry to reduce medical spending.

Company Background

Saint Joseph Hospital merged with Lutheran Medical Center and Exempla Medical Group in 1997 to form Exempla Healthcare. The health network was co-sponsored by the Catholic-based Sisters of Charity of Leavenworth Health System (SCL Health System) and the Lutheran-sponsored

Community First Foundation (CFF) until 2012 when SCL Health System acquired CFF's interest in the venture in a deal worth some $275 million. SCLHS had already gained operational oversight of all of the system's hospitals in late 2009.

Saint Joseph Hospital was founded in 1873 by SCL Health System. It was the first private hospital established in Colorado.

EXECUTIVES

Pres, Bain Farris
Pres, Bain J Farris
Chb, William Jessee
V Pres, Mary Shepler
V Pres, Barb Jahn
V Pres, Shawn Dufford
V Pres, Brad Ludford
Cmo, Travis Sewalls
Staff Pharmacist, Lesa Mc Kenzie
Dir Materials Mgmt/Purchasing, Peter Mc Guire
Staff Pharmacist, Carol De Lucia

LOCATIONS

HQ: SAINT JOSEPH HOSPITAL, INC
1375 E 19TH AVE, DENVER, CO 802181114
Phone: 303 812-2000
Web: WWW.SCLHEALTH.ORG

PRODUCTS/OPERATIONS

Selected Services
Breast Care Center
Comprehensive Cancer Center
Community Outreach
Construction updates for exempla Saint Joseph Hospital
Electronic Medical Records
Emergency Care
Exemplea's Your Safety+Satisfaction
Family Medicine/Bruner Clinic
Heart Care
Home When Ready
Imaging Center
Intensive Care Unit
Medical Residency Programs
Midwife Practice
NICU-Neonatal Intensive Care Unit
Outpatient
Pediatric Care
Plastic and Reconstructive Surgery
Saint Christropher Inn
The Blood Donor Center
Weight Loss Surgery Center
Women's and Children's Services

COMPETITORS

Catholic Health Initiatives	Porter Adventist Hospital
Centura Health	Rose Medical Center
Denver Health And Hospital Authority	University Of Colorado Hospital
Healthone	Valley View Hospital

HISTORICAL FINANCIALS

Company Type: Private

Income Statement				FYE: December 31
	REVENUE ($ mil.)	NET INCOME ($ mil.)	NET PROFIT MARGIN	EMPLOYEES
12/19	614	48	7.9%	2,300
12/14	465	25	5.5%	—
12/13	490	51	10.5%	—
Annual Growth	3.9%	(1.1%)	—	—

2019 Year-End Financials

Return on assets: 5.8%   Cash ($ mil.): —
Return on equity: 8.3%
Current ratio: 2.10

SAINT LOUIS UNIVERSITY

This university gives students a SLU of opportunities. Saint Louis University (SLU) is a Jesuit Catholic school offering nearly 90 undergraduate more than 100 graduate and a host of professional degree programs through about a dozen schools and colleges including a school of medicine and a campus in Madrid Spain. Most programs require core classes in philosophy and theology. SLU has an enrollment of nearly 12855 students. Its student-teacher ratio is 9:1. Saint Louis University was founded in 1818 by Reverend Louis William Du Bourg Catholic Bishop of Louisiana.

Operations

In addition to its extensive educational programs SLU's students and staff are involved in a number of research projects in areas including cancer infectious disease liver disease aging and brain disorders and heart/lung disease.

SLU also operates primary and specialty medical care clinics (some through its SLU Physicians organization) on its medical school campus. The university's School of Medicine is fully accredited by the Liaison Committee on Medical Education (LCME) the accrediting body for medical education in the US.

Geographic Reach

SLU's students hail from all 50 US states and more than 80 countries. In addition to its main campus in St. Louis Missouri the university operates a campus in Madrid Spain.

Mergers and Acquisitions

Company Background

Saint Louis University was founded in 1818 by Reverend Louis William Du Bourg Catholic Bishop of Louisiana.

EXECUTIVES

Pres, Fred P Pestello
Cfo, Robert Woodruff
Provost, Joseph N Weixlmann
V Pres, William R Kauffman
Associate Professor of Theatre, Thomas Malone
Assistant Professor of Law VI, Mark McKenna
Assistant Dean For Career Deve, Mary McInnis
Health Professional, Abby Mell
Health Professional, Angela Keyler
Health Professional, Angela Mulch
Health Professional, Ashley Shrum
Auditors: KPMG LLP COLUMBUS OH

LOCATIONS

HQ: SAINT LOUIS UNIVERSITY
1 N GRAND, SAINT LOUIS, MO 63103
Phone: 314 977-2500
Web: WWW.SLU.EDU

PRODUCTS/OPERATIONS

Colleges Schools and Degree Granting Centers
Advanced Dental Education Center for (CADE)
Arts and Sciences College of
Business John Cook School of
Education and Public Service College of
Engineering Aviation and Technology Parks College of
Health Care Ethics Albert Gnaegi Center for
Health Sciences Doisy College of
Law School of
Madrid Spain Campus
Medicine School of
Nursing School of
Outcomes Research Center for (SLUCOR)
Philosophy and Letters College of
Professional Studies School for
Public Health School of
Social Work School of

HISTORICAL FINANCIALS

Company Type: Private

Income Statement				FYE: June 30
	REVENUE ($ mil.)	NET INCOME ($ mil.)	NET PROFIT MARGIN	EMPLOYEES
06/10	750	28	3.8%	7,500
06/09	697	0	—	—
06/08	633	(54)	—	—
Annual Growth	8.9%	—	—	—

2010 Year-End Financials

Return on assets: 1.7%   Cash ($ mil.): 141
Return on equity: 2.3%
Current ratio: —

SAINT LUKE'S HEALTH SYSTEM, INC.

As a not-for-profit health system St. Luke's is dedicated to providing high quality care to every person who comes through its doors. From its founding in 1902 to its establishment as a health system in 2006 to today St. Luke's has long been a leader in quality care and a vital partner in addressing community health needs. St Luke's has eight medical centers more than 1000 beds in some 340 clinics and centers. It performs almost 42800 surgeries and more than 8100 births.

Operations

St. Luke's offers a heart transplant program treatment for complex brain and spinal cord diseases advanced surgical care and liver and kidney transplantation programs. Other specialized services include women's health cancer treatment rehabilitation and home care.

St. Luke's Children's Hospital is the only children's hospital in Idaho. More than 150 skilled pediatricians and pediatric specialists work with referring physicians from around the region to provide high quality care. It has a staff of over 400 nurses therapists and other dedicated pediatric caregivers.

Geographic Reach

Based in Idaho St. Luke's has operations Southern and Central Idaho Eastern Oregon and Northern Nevada.

Strategy

St. Luke's is driven by its mission to improve the health of people in the communities it serves which is grounded in its focus on population and community health. Company's strategy leads us to achieving its vision as it builds upon and enhance its reputation as the community's trusted partner in providing exceptional patient-centered care.

St. Luke's strategy follows a clearly defined path: St. Luke are meeting people where they are on their health journey?improving health and lives by delivering exceptional performance and outcomes in quality access and affordability.

Company Background

The predecessor to Saint Luke's Hospital was founded in 1882 by Episcopal priest Henry David Jardine.

EXECUTIVES

Int Ceo, Cliff A Robertson
Chb*, Robert West
Treas*, John Holland
Cfo*, Charles Robb
Chief Quality Officer*, William C Daniel
Hospitalist, Jayne Bumgarner
Orthopedic Surgeon, Lowry Jones
Registered Nurse, Marc Loner
Engineer, Mark Smith
Physician, Michael Giocondo
Obstetrics Gynecology, Richard McKain

LOCATIONS

HQ: SAINT LUKE'S HEALTH SYSTEM, INC.
901 E 104TH ST, KANSAS CITY, MO 641314517
Phone: 816 932-2000
Web: WWW.AMPLIFONUSA.COM

PRODUCTS/OPERATIONS

2015 Sales

	$ mil.	% of total
Hospital	1,501	61
Other university	962	39
Total	**2,463**	**100**

Selected facilities

Anderson County Hospital (Garnett Kansas)
Crittenton Children's Center (Kansas City Missouri)
Hedrick Medical Center (Chillicothe Missouri)
Saint Luke's Cushing Hospital (Leavenworth Kansas)
Saint Luke's East (Lee's Summit Missouri)
Saint Luke's Hospital (Kansas City Missouri)
Saint Luke's Northland Hospital (Kansas City Missouri)
Saint Luke's Northland Hospital (Smithville Missouri)
Saint Luke's South (Overland Park Kansas)
Wright Memorial Hospital (Trenton Missouri)

Selected Services

Cancer services
Heart and vascular
Home care and hospice
Neuroscience
Surgical services
Transplant services
Women's and maternity services

COMPETITORS

Ascension Health
Children's Mercy
  Hospital
Coxhealth
Heartland Regional
  Medical
Shawnee Mission
  Medical Center

Truman Medical Centers
University Of Kansas
  Medical Center
Via Christi Health
  System

HISTORICAL FINANCIALS

Company Type: Private

Income Statement				FYE: December 31
	REVENUE ($ mil.)	NET INCOME ($ mil.)	NET PROFIT MARGIN	EMPLOYEES
12/20	2,153	156	7.3%	5,111
12/19	2,100	131	6.3%	—
12/18	1,901	42	2.2%	—
12/17	1,721	88	5.2%	—
Annual Growth	7.8%	20.7%	—	—

2020 Year-End Financials

Return on assets: 4.7%   Cash ($ mil.): 699
Return on equity: 9.0%
Current ratio: 2.80

SAINT LUKE'S HOSPITAL OF BETHLEHEM, PENNSYLVANIA

EXECUTIVES

Pres, Richard A Anderson
Sr V Pres Fin*, Thomas P Lichtenwalner
Human Resources Director, Andrew Seidel
Gynecology/Obstetrics, Christopher B Gilbert
Security Staff, William Paslawsky
Senior Director, Jared King
Coordinator, Lisa Johnson
Orthopedic Surgeon, William Delong Jr
Manager, Scott Siegfried
Accounting Staff, Zoraida Zeno
Administrator, Brian Repetz
Auditors: WITHUMSMITHBROWN PC
  WHIPPANY

LOCATIONS

HQ: SAINT LUKE'S HOSPITAL OF BETHLEHEM,
  PENNSYLVANIA
  801 OSTRUM ST, BETHLEHEM, PA 180151000
Phone: 484 526-4000
Web: WWW.SLHN.ORG

HISTORICAL FINANCIALS

Company Type: Private

Income Statement				FYE: June 30
	REVENUE ($ mil.)	NET INCOME ($ mil.)	NET PROFIT MARGIN	EMPLOYEES
06/21	1,272	309	24.3%	6,174
06/20	982	40	4.2%	—
06/19	956	205	21.4%	—
06/18	890	126	14.2%	—
Annual Growth	12.6%	34.9%	—	—

2021 Year-End Financials

Return on assets: 11.0%   Cash ($ mil.): 337
Return on equity: 32.4%
Current ratio: 1.40

SAINT LUKE'S HOSPITAL OF KANSAS CITY

EXECUTIVES

Ceo, Jani L Johnson
V Pres-Cno*, Debbie Wilson
Coo*, Jane Peck
Cfo*, Amy Nachtigal
Chief of Medicine, George A Pagels
Optometrists, Terry D Anderson
Executive of Information Techn, Denise Kintigh
Doctor, Richard Hill
Internal Medicine Practitioner, Amit Sharma
Internal Medicine Practitioner, Chernet
  Teklemichael
Emergency Medicine Specialist, Christopher
  Bowser

LOCATIONS

HQ: SAINT LUKE'S HOSPITAL OF KANSAS CITY
  4401 WORNALL RD, KANSAS CITY, MO 641113241
Phone: 816 932-2000
Web: WWW.AMPLIFON.COM

HISTORICAL FINANCIALS

Company Type: Private

Income Statement				FYE: December 31
	REVENUE ($ mil.)	NET INCOME ($ mil.)	NET PROFIT MARGIN	EMPLOYEES
12/18	803	4	0.5%	5,000
12/17	699	63	9.1%	—
12/16	641	26	4.1%	—
12/15	561	0	0.0%	—
Annual Growth	12.7%	198.0%	—	—

2018 Year-End Financials

Return on assets: 0.3%   Cash ($ mil.): 33
Return on equity: 0.5%
Current ratio: 3.10

SAINT MARYS HOSPITAL

EXECUTIVES

Pres, Robert R Waller
Chief Marketing Officer, Kathy Zarling
Chief of Pediatrics, Ann Reed
Security Director, Byron Callis
Admissions Director, Cydni Smith
Pharmacy Director, Jason Christiansen
Chemical Substance Abuse Dir, Jody Boone
Food Director, Kelly Novicki
Radiology Director, Michelle Northland
Physician Director of Er, Thomas Hellmich
Respiratory Therapy Director, Todd Meyer

LOCATIONS

HQ: SAINT MARYS HOSPITAL
  1216 2ND ST SW, ROCHESTER, MN 559021970
Phone: 507 255-5123
Web: WWW.MAYOCLINIC.ORG

HISTORICAL FINANCIALS

Company Type: Private

Income Statement				FYE: December 31
	REVENUE ($ mil.)	NET INCOME ($ mil.)	NET PROFIT MARGIN	EMPLOYEES
12/16	2,091	556	26.6%	3,250
12/15	1,963	503	25.6%	—
Annual Growth	6.6%	10.6%	—	—

2016 Year-End Financials

Return on assets: 27.3%   Cash ($ mil.): —
Return on equity: 33.4%
Current ratio: 4.10

SALEM HEALTH

Salem Hospital serves the healthcare needs of residents in and around Oregon's Willamette Valley. The acute care hospital boasts about 455 beds and a medical staff of 440-plus physicians that represents some 45 specialty areas such as oncology joint replacement obstetrics diabetes weight loss and mental health among others. The not-for-profit hospital offers a range of services from emergency and critical care to rehabilitation and community wellness programs. Its Center for Outpatient Medicine provides cancer care outpatient surgery and imaging services and has a sleep disorders center. Salem Hospital is part of Salem Health which also includes West Valley Hospital and Willamette Health Partners.

Operations

The Oregon hospital also has a Family Birth Center that offers family-health education services and neonatal intensive-care services. Additionally it provides space to community support services to benefit families.

Salem Hospital operates under the guidance of a 15-member volunteer Board of Trustees.

Strategy

As with many healthcare institutions in this age of reform Salem Hospital is working hard to improve patient experience and the quality of healthcare it provides while reducing the cost of care and eliminating waste within its systems. It has been improving clinical documentation to ensure payments are received standardizing care processes improving scheduling of surgeries leaving 30 open positions unfilled and cutting another 30 positions.

Inspired by Toyota's lean production processes the hospital entered into a five-year contract with John Black and Associates in 2010 to begin what it projects to be a transformation that will be accomplished incrementally over the next 20 years. Its goal is to improve care using a holistic patient-centered approach and reduce waste in terms of waits inventory and other day-to-day processes.

Salem Hospital set a goal of becoming a Magnet hospital in 2003 and accomplished the feat in 2010. (Only 6% of hospitals in the US have achieved Magnet status.) Magnet certification is awarded to hospitals that meet a set of criteria that measures the quality and strength of their nursing staffs as set by the American Nurses' Credentialing Center an affiliate of the American Nurses Association. Criteria includes patient outcomes job satisfaction and low turnover.

In 2009 the hospital opened a new patient tower. In 2010 it sold its money-losing home care department to LHC Group as a way of cutting operating costs.

EXECUTIVES

Ceo, Cheryl Nester Wolfe
V Pres*, Laurie Barr
Cfo*, James Parr
Coo*, Bahaa Wanly
Secretary, Bruce Carter
Executive of Information Techn, Kathleen Dowling
Corporate Communications Staff, Sherryll Hoar
Staff, Michael Wynn
Internal Medicine Practitioner, Jaswinder Kaur
Scientist, Tracy Hickson
Internal Medicine Practitioner, Ahmad J Gill
Auditors: KPMG LLP PORTLAND OREGON

LOCATIONS

HQ: SALEM HEALTH
  890 OAK ST SE, SALEM, OR 973013905
Phone: 503 561-5200
Web: WWW.SALEMHEALTH.ORG

PRODUCTS/OPERATIONS

Selected Services
Bariatrics
Cancer
Diabetes
Gynecology
Heart
Joint replacement
Neurosciences
Obstetrics
Orthopedics
Pain management
Psychiatric medicine
Psychology
Rehabilitation
Spine
Sleep
Stroke
Weight-loss surgery
Wound care

COMPETITORS

Adventist Health System West
Asante Health System
Kadlec Regional Medical Center
Kaiser Foundation Hospitals
Legacy Emanuel Hospital And Health Center
Legacy Health System
Oregon Health & Science University
Peacehealth Southwest Medical Center
Providence St. Joseph Health

HISTORICAL FINANCIALS

Company Type: Private

Income Statement   FYE: June 30

	REVENUE ($ mil.)	NET INCOME ($ mil.)	NET PROFIT MARGIN	EMPLOYEES
06/21	953	241	25.3%	3,400
06/20	864	75	8.7%	—
06/19	820	86	10.5%	—
06/18	773	99	12.8%	—
Annual Growth	7.2%	34.6%	—	—

2021 Year-End Financials

Return on assets: 11.8%   Cash ($ mil.): 36
Return on equity: 17.8%
Current ratio: 1.10

SALT RIVER PROJECT AGRICULTURAL IMPROVEMENT AND POWER DISTRICT

One of the United States' largest government-owned utilities Salt River Project (SRP) provides Phoenix with two types of currents: electric and water. Electricity comes from the Salt River Project Agricultural Improvement and Power District a political subdivision of the State of Arizona. It operates the Salt River Project a federal reclamation project under contracts with the Salt River Valley Water Users' Association including its obligations to the United States of America for the care operation and maintenance of the project. The district owns and operates an electric system that generates purchases transmits and distributes electric power and energy and provides electric service to residential commercial industrial and agricultural power users in parts of Maricopa Gila and Pinal counties. The district sells excess power to wholesale customers.

Operations

Staying true to its mission of providing water and electricity to SRP customers the company owns or has stakes in about 15 major power generating plants fueled by diverse sources including nuclear fuel and steam. SPR also operates several dams along the Salt and Verde River and the canal system that produce electricity. SRP's portfolio of renewable energy sources includes solar geothermal wind and biomass.

Some 85% of sales were generated from its retail electric.

Geographic Reach

Headquartered in Arizona the company serves residential commercial industrial and agricultural power customers in a 2900-square-mile service territory spanning parts of Maricopa Gila and Pinal counties in Arizona. In addition the enterprise has mining loads in an adjacent 2400-square-mile area in Gila and Pinal counties.

The SRP electric service area includes major portions of the cities of Apache Junction Avondale Chandler Fountain Hills Gilbert Glendale Guadalupe Mesa Paradise Valley Peoria Phoenix Queen Creek Scottsdale Tempe and Tolleson.

Sales and Marketing

SRP serves more than 1 million customers in the greater Phoenix metropolitan area.

Financial Performance

Operating revenues were $3.5 billion for fiscal year 2021 and $3.1 billion for fiscal year 2020 an increase of $354.1 million or 11%. The increase in operating revenues was primarily due to increased retail electric and wholesale revenues.

In 2020 the company had a net income of $283.5 million a $266.2 million increase from the previous year's net income of $17.3 million.

Strategy

SRP delivered a successful financial performance in FY21 including positive CNR results primarily driven by above-normal temperatures strong customer growth and a focus on managing direct costs. Capital spending was 3% above budget as demand remained strong for new construction during the pandemic. Direct cost savings are 4% below the revised budget or 8% below the original FY21 budget due to initial expense reductions and continued savings throughout the fiscal year.

SRP reliably met customers' power needs during an intense summer that included an all-time system record peak demand and two major wildfires that threatened key transmission lines and other infrastructure. The entire West was dealing with these challenging conditions at the same time critically stressing energy availability. SRP's customers continued to receive power during this period and throughout the year with a level of reliability among the best in the nation.

Company Background

SRP was founded in 1903 under the Natural Reclamation Act.

EXECUTIVES

Pres, David Rousseau
V Pres, John R Hoopes
Treas, Dean R Duncan
Corp SEC, Stephanie Reed
Corp Treas, Steven Hulet
Human Resources Information MA, Karen A Krull
Project Coordinator, Christy Campbell
Manager, T V Lambson
Vice-President Information Ser, Clifford Rushton

Payroll Staff, Don Spirk
Chief Information Security Off, Ed Barela
Auditors: PRICEWATERHOUSECOOPERS LLP
PH

LOCATIONS

HQ: SALT RIVER PROJECT AGRICULTURAL
IMPROVEMENT AND POWER DISTRICT
1500 N MILL AVE, TEMPE, AZ 852811252
Phone: 602 236-5900
Web: WWW.SRPNET.COM

PRODUCTS/OPERATIONS

2016 Sales

	$ mil.	% of total
Retail electric	2,749	90
Water	15	1
Other	282	9
Total	**3,047**	**100**

Selected Subsidiaries

Salt River Project Agricultural Improvement and Power
District (electric utility)
New West Energy Corporation (energy support
services)
Papago Park Center Inc. (real estate facility
management)
SRP Captive Risk Solutions Ltd. (domestic captive
property boiler and machinery insurer)
Salt River Valley Water Users' Association

COMPETITORS

American States Water	Pacificorp
American Water	Pinnacle West
Calpine	Sempra Energy
Nv Energy	Southwest Gas
Pg&e Corporation	Uns Energy
Pnm Resources	Xcel Energy

HISTORICAL FINANCIALS

Company Type: Private

Income Statement				FYE: April 30
	REVENUE ($ mil.)	NET INCOME ($ mil.)	NET PROFIT MARGIN	EMPLOYEES
04/21	3,475	577	16.6%	4,336
04/20*	3,121	126	4.1%	—
01/10	2,217	517	23.3%	—
04/05	2,251	362	16.1%	—
Annual Growth	2.7%	2.9%	—	—

*Fiscal year change

2021 Year-End Financials

Return on assets: 4.1% Cash ($ mil.): 426
Return on equity: 9.7%
Current ratio: 1.60

SAMARITAN HEALTH SERVICES, INC.

EXECUTIVES

Ceo, Doug Boysen
Gynecology/Obstetrics, Jodell J Boyle
Administrative Assistant, Barbara Croney
Coordinator, Lisa Ely
Executive Officer, Pat Zeller
Chief of Medicine, Paul Daskalos
Director of Pharmacy, Penny Reher
Technical Manager, Dennis Ballard
Health Professional, Barry Smith
Assistant Professor, Thomas Lissman

Supervisor Recruitment, Anne Corcoran
Auditors: KPMG LLP PORTLAND OREGON

LOCATIONS

HQ: SAMARITAN HEALTH SERVICES, INC.
3600 NW SAMARITAN DR, CORVALLIS, OR
973303737
Phone: 541 757-5111
Web: WWW.SAMHEALTH.ORG

HISTORICAL FINANCIALS

Company Type: Private

Income Statement				FYE: December 31
	REVENUE ($ mil.)	NET INCOME ($ mil.)	NET PROFIT MARGIN	EMPLOYEES
12/20	1,339	65	4.9%	4,550
12/19	1,233	32	2.6%	—
12/18	1,168	9	0.8%	—
12/17	1,101	26	2.4%	—
Annual Growth	6.7%	35.8%	—	—

2020 Year-End Financials

Return on assets: 6.2% Cash ($ mil.): 275
Return on equity: 13.3%
Current ratio: 2.10

SAMARITAN'S PURSE

EXECUTIVES

Chb-Ceo, Franklin Graham
V Pres*, Phyllis Payne
South Sudan Country Direc, Phil Ewert
Web, Chris Hampton
Vice President of North Americ, Luther Harrison
Real Estate Agent, Michael Lagazo
Haiti Projects Logistics Manag, Pierre Julien
Manager Recruitment, Kevin Chalupka
Research Operations Director, Matt Cook
Executive Assistant, Alison Sawyer
Assistant Director Field, Jason Taft
Auditors: DIXON HUGHES GOODMAN LLP
CHA

LOCATIONS

HQ: SAMARITAN'S PURSE
801 BAMBOO RD, BOONE, NC 286078721
Phone: 828 262-1980
Web: WWW.SAMARITANSPURSE.ORG

HISTORICAL FINANCIALS

Company Type: Private

Income Statement				FYE: December 31
	REVENUE ($ mil.)	NET INCOME ($ mil.)	NET PROFIT MARGIN	EMPLOYEES
12/19	734	44	6.1%	525
12/18	709	22	3.1%	—
12/17	800	189	23.7%	—
12/16	634	51	8.0%	—
Annual Growth	5.0%	(4.1%)	—	—

2019 Year-End Financials

Return on assets: 5.9% Cash ($ mil.): 248
Return on equity: 6.4%
Current ratio: 7.90

SAN ANTONIO INDEPENDENT SCHOOL DISTRICT FAC

EXECUTIVES

Supt, Dr Sylvester Syl Perez
Pres*, Ed Garza
V Pres*, Olga M Hernandez
SEC*, Arthur V Valdez
Information Specialist, Mark McRae
Law Specialist, Andrea Tena
Child Nutrition Coordinator, Olga Perez
Web Administrator, Brad Wehring
Assistant Athletic Director, Brian Clancy
Technology Business, Ray Tena
Director, Tiffany Grant
Auditors: GARZA/GONZALEZ & ASSOCIATES S

LOCATIONS

HQ: SAN ANTONIO INDEPENDENT SCHOOL
DISTRICT FAC
141 LAVACA ST, SAN ANTONIO, TX 782101039
Phone: 210 554-2200
Web: WWW.SAISD.NET

HISTORICAL FINANCIALS

Company Type: Private

Income Statement				FYE: June 30
	REVENUE ($ mil.)	NET INCOME ($ mil.)	NET PROFIT MARGIN	EMPLOYEES
06/19	681	136	20.0%	7,600
06/16	659	43	6.5%	—
06/15	624	(14)	—	—
06/14	600	(110)	—	—
Annual Growth	2.6%	—	—	—

2019 Year-End Financials

Return on assets: 8.0% Cash ($ mil.): 362
Return on equity: 88.9%
Current ratio: —

SAN ANTONIO WATER SYSTEM

Wasting water is a sore point in drought-prone
South Texas and San Antonio Water System
(SAWS) seeks to husband this precious resource
the best it can. The company serves about 511300
water customers and some 457600 wastewater
customers or about 1.9 million people in the San
Antonio metropolitan area (including most of the
city of San Antonio Medina Anatascosa counties
and adjacent parts of Bexar County). In addition
to serving its own retail customers SAWS provides
wholesale water supplies to several smaller utility
systems in its service area. The utility is owned by
the City of San Antonio.

Operations

SAWS oversees more than 12880 miles of water
and sewer mains.

SAWS is the only sewage treatment agency in
this area and it charges a fee to the military bases
and suburban cities which maintain their own
wastewater collection systems. SAWS also pro-

vides collection and treatment services by contract to developments outside its defined service area to avoid unnecessary proliferation of state wastewater discharge permits.

SAWS includes all water resources properties facilities and plants owned operated and maintained by the city relating to supply storage treatment transmission and distribution of treated potable water; collection and treatment of wastewater; and distribution of recycled water. Additionally SAWS owns and operates four thermal energy facilities providing chilled water services to governmental and private entities.

Around 35% of the company's total sales were generated through its wastewater systems while water delivery and supply system both generated about 30% each. The chilled water and steam system and non-operating revenue accounts for the rest.

Geographic Reach

The company serves Texas customers in Bexar County as well as parts of Medina and Atascosa counties. Its main office is located in San Antonio Texas.

Sales and Marketing

The company serves retail customers and also provides wholesale water supplies to several smaller utility systems. The population includes more than 511300 water customers and approximately 457600 wastewater customers (around 1.9 million people). Both water and wastewater connections represent about 95% of the customers in Bexar County.

Financial Performance

In 2019 SAWS' net revenue increased by 7% to $765.8 million as operating revenues increased from $691 million in 2018 to $733.2 million in 2019. An average rate increase of 4.7% took effect in January an increase in billed water usage of 3.1% and customer growth of 1.8% contributed to the increased in operating revenue in 2019.

The company's net position (income) increased by 19% to $147.5 million mainly due to higher net revenue.

Cash and cash equivalents at the end of the year were $292.6 million. Net cash provided by operating activities was $381.9 million and cash added from investing activities was $272.1 million. Financing activities used $475.6 million for acquisitions of plant and equipment and payment of bonds.

Strategy

In mid-November SAWS started the sewer main replacement along U.S. Highway 90 and SW Military Drive near Joint Base San Antonio-Lackland that involves five miles of tunneling more than 100 feet below ground to avoid disrupting traffic and military activity.

The much-needed infrastructure project in the planning stages since 2007 will cost up to $210 million and serve more than 500000 San Antonians. SAWS officials say it's the most costly complex sewer pipeline project in the city's history. Construction is expected to be completed in 2023.

Company Background

SAWS and a neighboring water authority the Lower Colorado River Authority signed an agreement in 2002 to study the feasibility of drawing water from the lower Colorado River basin for use by San Antonio. The LCRA reported in 2009 that it had found that there was not a sufficient amount of extra water available to build a proposed reservoir. SAWS sued LCRA for $1.2 billion over the results of the study but the suit was tossed out by a state district judge.

SAWS was formed in 1992 through a merger of three entities: the City Water Board the City Wastewater Department and the Alamo Water Conservation and Reuse District.

EXECUTIVES

Ceo, Robert R Puente
Cfo*, Doug Evanson
Coo*, Steve Clouse
Chief of Staff*, Roger Arriaga
Secretary, Salvadore M Hern Ndez
Supervisor, Joe Fernandez
Scientist, Homer Emery
Information Technology Executi, Amanda Jackson
Engineer Tech, Lucy Gonzales
Planner, Richard Donat
Engineer I, Adam Eddy
Auditors: BAKER TILLY VIRCHOW KRAUSE

LOCATIONS

HQ: SAN ANTONIO WATER SYSTEM
2800 US HIGHWAY 281 N, SAN ANTONIO, TX 782123106
Phone: 210 704-7297
Web: WWW.SAWS.ORG

PRODUCTS/OPERATIONS

2014 Sales

	$ mil.	% of total
Operating revenues		
Wastewater system	210	42
Water supply system	150	30
Water delivery system	127	25
Chilled water and steam system	11	2
Non-operating revenues	5	1
Total	**505**	**100**

HISTORICAL FINANCIALS
Company Type: Private

Income Statement				FYE: December 31
	REVENUE ($ mil.)	NET INCOME ($ mil.)	NET PROFIT MARGIN	EMPLOYEES
12/17	666	240	36.1%	1,700
12/16	622	213	34.3%	—
12/12	0	0	—	—
Annual Growth	—	—	—	—

2017 Year-End Financials
Return on assets: 3.9%   Cash ($ mil.): 36
Return on equity: 8.4%
Current ratio: 3.00

SAN BERNARDINO CITY UNIFIED SCHOOL DISTRICT

EXECUTIVES

Spdt, Dale Marsden
Staff, Susie Sellas
Coordinator, Terry Comnick
Director, Adriane Robles
Teacher, Isabel Guerrero
Speech Therapist, Tina Lozano
Program Facilitator Teacher, Cheryl Togashi
Computer Specialist, Christopher Green
Teacher, Dianna Gamez
Second Grade Teacher, Jessica Serrao
Administrator of Operations, Joe Aceto
Auditors: EIDE BAILLY LLP RANCHO CUCAMO

LOCATIONS

HQ: SAN BERNARDINO CITY UNIFIED SCHOOL DISTRICT
777 N F ST, SAN BERNARDINO, CA 924103017
Phone: 909 381-1100
Web: WWW.SBCUSD.COM

HISTORICAL FINANCIALS
Company Type: Private

Income Statement				FYE: June 30
	REVENUE ($ mil.)	NET INCOME ($ mil.)	NET PROFIT MARGIN	EMPLOYEES
06/20	766	(56)	—	6,000
06/19	775	46	5.9%	—
06/18	712	27	3.8%	—
06/08	759	97	12.8%	—
Annual Growth	0.1%	—	—	—

SAN DIEGO UNIFIED SCHOOL DISTRICT

EXECUTIVES

Supt, Cindy Marten
Cfo*, Stanley Dobbs
Principal, Trace, Trace (locat, Bob Morris
Technology Coordinator, George Olguin
Technology Coordinator, Ramon Aguirre
Management, David L Stone
Administrator, Felicia Singleton
Teacher, Shelley Carter
Education Specialist, Wendy Jacob
Information Technology Team ME, Ador Eide
Teacher Deaf, Aimee Benner
Auditors: MAYER HOFFMAN MCCANN PC IRVIN

LOCATIONS

HQ: SAN DIEGO UNIFIED SCHOOL DISTRICT
4100 NORMAL ST, SAN DIEGO, CA 921032653
Phone: 619 725-8000
Web: WWW.SANDIEGOUNIFIED.ORG

HISTORICAL FINANCIALS
Company Type: Private

Income Statement				FYE: June 30
	REVENUE ($ mil.)	NET INCOME ($ mil.)	NET PROFIT MARGIN	EMPLOYEES
06/20*	1,972	(202)	—	17,000
08/19	0	0	0.9%	—
06/06	1,112	(2)	—	—
06/05	608	73	12.1%	—
Annual Growth	8.2%	—	—	—
*Fiscal year change				

SAN JUAN UNIFIED SCHOOL DISTRICT

EXECUTIVES

Supt, Pat Jaurequi
Supt*, Glynn Thompson
Information Technology/Interne, Bart Hubbard
Teacher, Carla Elkins
Teacher, Kristen Allen
Teacher, Mike Shepherd
Teacher, Markam Cruz
Financial Executive, Lynn Brown
Assistant Superintendent, Debra Calvin
Assistant Superintendent, Melissa Bassanell
Transportation Director, Tom Carrol
Auditors: CROWE HORWATH LLP
SACRAMENTO

LOCATIONS

HQ: SAN JUAN UNIFIED SCHOOL DISTRICT
3738 WALNUT AVE, CARMICHAEL, CA 956083099
Phone: 916 971-7700
Web: WWW.SANJUAN.EDU

HISTORICAL FINANCIALS
Company Type: Private

Income Statement			FYE: June 30
	REVENUE ($ mil.)	NET INCOME ($ mil.)	NET PROFIT MARGIN	EMPLOYEES
06/20	608	(142)	—	4,200
06/19	631	105	16.7%	—
06/18	620	(38)	—	—
06/17	577	104	18.2%	—
Annual Growth	1.7%	—	—	—

SANFORD

Sanford (operating as Sanford Health) is one of the largest not-for-profit integrated health care systems in the US. It primarily serves rural areas through its network of about 45 regional and community hospitals in nine states including the Dakotas Iowa Minnesota and Nebraska. The organization also operates about 300 local clinics and specialty outpatient practices. Specialist service include cancer cardiology vascular health neurology orthopedics pediatrics virology and women's health. Sanford Health added more than 200 senior care locations in 24 states by acquiring Good Samaritan Society in 2019.

Operations

In addition to its 40-plus hospitals Sanford's network includes about 200 senior living facilities (long-term care assisted-living and independent living centers) and 140 clinics. Altogether the facilities in the Sanford Health network handle some 50000 inpatient admissions and about 1.35 million outpatient visits each year. The network's 1400 physicians provide care in more than 80 specialist fields.

Along with its health care facilities Sanford Health also operates Sanford Laboratories based in Sioux Falls and Rapid City South Dakota. The system maintains Sanford Research a not-for-profit research organization that draws upon the physicians of Sanford Health and researchers at the University of South Dakota. Sanford Research conducts some $100 million in research projects each year. Finally the Sanford Health Plan is a not-for-profit health plan that serves individuals and employers across the system's region.

Geographic Reach

Sanford Health has hospital and clinic locations in communities in nine states including California Iowa Minnesota Nebraska North Dakota Oklahoma Oregon and South Dakota. The company also operates about 200 senior care facilities in 24 states. It also has clinical affiliates in locations including Ghana Africa; Karmiel Israel; and Baja Mexico.

Strategy

Growth plans for Sanford Health include the construction of hospital and clinic facilities in Minnesota and North Dakota and new health care and research facilities in South Dakota. A $700 million gift from local philanthropist T. Denny Sanford is enabling the establishment of several new facilities. That contribution is also supporting the organization's research programs in children's health and initiatives to find cures for conditions including breast cancer and type 1 diabetes.

In addition Sanford Health expands by acquiring small community medical centers. The system is also growing by striking partnerships with small regional health care providers. In 2018 and 2019 it expanded in research and senior care by acquiring the Neuropsychiatric Research Institute and senior housing operator Good Samaritan Society.

The company agreed to merge with Iowa Health System which operates as UnityPoint Health in 2019 but the deal was terminated later that year. The transaction would have created a system with more than 75 hospitals in 26 states.

Mergers and Acquisitions

In early 2019 Sanford merged with senior health services provider The Evangelical Lutheran Good Samaritan Society. The transaction combined Sanford's hospital system with Good Samaritan's senior living facilities creating an integrated health care research and insurance entity.

In 2018 Sanford Research absorbed Neuropsychiatric Research Institute which focuses on eating disorders and obesity. With that acquisition Sanford intends to establish a major research program in Fargo North Dakota.

A deal to merge with Iowa Health System which operates as UnityPoint Health was canceled in 2019. The merger would have created a health network with about 75 hospitals in 26 states.

Company Background

Sanford was created from the 2009 merger of two Dakota health care legends: South Dakota's Sanford Health and North Dakota's MeritCare Health System. Both date back to the 1890s. Following the merger the two units briefly kept their separate identities but in 2010 organized under the Sanford Health-MeritCare name. The operating name was later shortened to Sanford Health.

EXECUTIVES

Cfo, Joann Kunkel
Information, Steve Brandt
Staff, Carol Sele
Manager, Linda Bartholomay
Principal, Kristi Crawford
Internal Medicine Practitioner, Matthew Whitbeck
Coordinator, Ashley Kann
Coordinator, Barbara Risty
Coordinator, Beverly Lofgren
Coordinator, Jessie Wolf
Coordinator, Katrina White
Auditors: DELOITTE & TOUCHE LLP
MINNEAP

LOCATIONS

HQ: SANFORD
801 BROADWAY N, FARGO, ND 581023641
Phone: 701 234-6000
Web: WWW.SANFORDHEALTH.ORG

PRODUCTS/OPERATIONS

Selected Major Regional Medical Centers
Sanford Bemidji Medical Center (Bemidji Minnesota)
Sanford Medical Center Bismarck (Bismarck North Dakota)
Sanford Medical Center Fargo (Fargo North Dakota)
Sanford USD Medical Center Sioux Falls (Sioux Falls South Dakota)

COMPETITORS

Altru Health	Rapid City Regional
Avera Health	Hospital
Catholic Health	St. Alexius Medical
Initiatives	Center
Mayo Clinic	St. Mary's Healthcare
North Memorial Health	Wellmark
Care	

HISTORICAL FINANCIALS
Company Type: Private

Income Statement			FYE: June 30
	REVENUE ($ mil.)	NET INCOME ($ mil.)	NET PROFIT MARGIN	EMPLOYEES
06/18	4,639	117	2.5%	50,000
06/17	4,411	175	4.0%	—
06/16	4,231	108	2.6%	—
06/14	3	(11)	—	—
Annual Growth	486.1%	—	—	—

2018 Year-End Financials

Return on assets: 2.7%
Return on equity: 4.6%
Current ratio: 1.60
Cash ($ mil.): 185

SANFORD HEALTH

EXECUTIVES

Pres, Kelby K Krabbenhoft
Sr V Pres-Coo*, Becky Nelson
Pres-Clinic, Dan Blue
Pres-Regional Health Services*, Ed Weiland
Pres-Foundation*, Brian Mortensen
Pres-Health Plan*, Ruth Krystopolski
Ex V Pres*, Dave Link
Cfo*, Michelle Bruhn
Cno*, Erica Deboer
Pediatrician, Nancy Free
Gift Shop Manager, Sabra Shields
Auditors: DELOITTE & TOUCHE LLP
MINNEAP

LOCATIONS

HQ: SANFORD HEALTH
1305 W 18TH ST, SIOUX FALLS, SD 571050401
Phone: 605 333-1720
Web: WWW.SANFORDHEALTH.ORG

Company Type: Private

Income Statement   FYE: December 31

	REVENUE ($ mil.)	NET INCOME ($ mil.)	NET PROFIT MARGIN	EMPLOYEES
12/18*	4,819	141	2.9%	2,939
06/17	4,411	175	4.0%	—
06/16	4,231	114	2.7%	—
06/12	2,516	72	2.9%	—
Annual Growth	9.7%	10.1%	—	—

*Fiscal year change

2018 Year-End Financials
Return on assets: 3.3%   Cash ($ mil.): 109
Return on equity: 5.3%
Current ratio: 1.80

SANFORD HEALTH

Auditors: DELOITTE TAX LLP MINNEAPOLIS

LOCATIONS

HQ: SANFORD HEALTH
1305 W 18TH ST, SIOUX FALLS, SD 571050401
Phone: 605 333-1000

HISTORICAL FINANCIALS
Company Type: Private

Income Statement   FYE: June 30

	REVENUE ($ mil.)	NET INCOME ($ mil.)	NET PROFIT MARGIN	EMPLOYEES
06/17	3,741	138	3.7%	2
06/10	1,038	35	3.4%	—
Annual Growth	20.1%	21.4%	—	—

2017 Year-End Financials
Return on assets: 5.0%   Cash ($ mil.): 78
Return on equity: 11.9%
Current ratio: —

SANFORD NORTH

EXECUTIVES

Prin, Roger L Gilbertson
Cfo*, Lisa Carlson
Coordinator, Pammie Dohman
Pediatrician, Brenda Thurlow
Neurosurgeon, Abraham Sabersky

LOCATIONS

HQ: SANFORD NORTH
801 BROADWAY N, FARGO, ND 581023641
Phone: 701 234-2000
Web: WWW.SANFORDHEALTH.ORG

Company Type: Private

Income Statement   FYE: June 30

	REVENUE ($ mil.)	NET INCOME ($ mil.)	NET PROFIT MARGIN	EMPLOYEES
06/10	677	(15)	—	7,200
06/08	112	2	2.0%	—
Annual Growth	145.1%			

2010 Year-End Financials
Return on assets: (-10.8%)   Cash ($ mil.): —
Return on equity: (-24.5%)
Current ratio: 1.40

SANTA CLARA VALLEY TRANSPORTATION AUTHORITY

EXECUTIVES

Ceo, Nuria Fernandez
Prin, Carroll W Huff
Procurement Manager, George Eaton
Supervisor, Gurpreet Gill
Marketing Communications Speci, Lupe Solis
Human Resources Analyst, Bethany Cramer
Environmental Health, Tracy Casimiro
Trasnportation Project Enginee, Arshad Syed
Operations Manager, Art Douwes
Cto, Ed Callery
Human Resources, Maria Chavez
Auditors: VAVRINEK TRINE DAY & CO LL

LOCATIONS

HQ: SANTA CLARA VALLEY TRANSPORTATION AUTHORITY
3331 N 1ST ST, SAN JOSE, CA 951341906
Phone: 408 321-2300
Web: WWW.VTA.ORG

HISTORICAL FINANCIALS
Company Type: Private

Income Statement   FYE: June 30

	REVENUE ($ mil.)	NET INCOME ($ mil.)	NET PROFIT MARGIN	EMPLOYEES
06/19	1,204	830	68.9%	2,053
06/17	16	(2)	—	—
06/16	19	(0)	—	—
06/15	27	(0)	—	—
Annual Growth	156.5%		—	—

SAPP BROS., INC.

Need air in those 18 wheels? Sapp Bros Travel Centers (formerly Sapp Bros Truck Stops) has the usual air gas food but also offers human conveniences such such as laundry rooms mailbox rentals private showers and TV lounges. The company operates a chain of some 15 truck stops — readily identifiable by the giant red-and-white coffeepot logo — along interstate highways from Utah to Pennsylvania; with a concentration in Nebraska. Half of the locations also operate service centers offering oil changes new tires and safety checks. Its sister company Sapp Bros Petroleum distributes fuels and lubricants to more than 200 retailers. The firm is run by CEO Bill Sapp one of the four founding Sapp brothers.

Geographic Reach

Omaha-based Sapp Bros. has travel centers in eight states: Nebraska Iowa Utah Colorado Wyoming Kansas Illinois and Pennsylvania.

Strategy

To raise its profile and rev up its business Sapp Bros. in 2013 joined the roster of VP Racing Fuels's retail brand partners. The benefits of the affiliation include association with an attractive retail image competitive credit card rates and the ability to source unbranded fuel for its travel centers.

EXECUTIVES

Chb, William Sapp
Ceo*, Allen J Marsh
Pres*, Andy Richard
Pres*, Dan Adams
V Pres Finance*, Kevin Musil
Board of Directors, Allen Marsh
Sales Manager, Curtiss Routh
Human Resources and Safety Man, Mary Eriksen
Cashier, Amanda Long
Executive Assistant, Andrea Galvin
Vice President of Operations, Cory Dieter
Auditors: KPMG LLP OMAHA NEBRASKA

LOCATIONS

HQ: SAPP BROS., INC.
9915 S 148TH ST, OMAHA, NE 681383876
Phone: 402 895-7038
Web: WWW.SAPPBROS.NET

2012 Locations

	No.
Nebraska	8
Iowa	2
Colorado	1
Illinois	1
Kansas	1
Pennsylvania	1
Utah	1
Wyoming	1
Total	16

COMPETITORS

Exxon Mobil	Stuckey's
Love's Country Stores	Travelcenters Of
Pilot Flying J	America

HISTORICAL FINANCIALS
Company Type: Private

Income Statement   FYE: September 30

	REVENUE ($ mil.)	NET INCOME ($ mil.)	NET PROFIT MARGIN	EMPLOYEES
09/20	920	17	1.8%	1,700
09/19	1,194	4	0.4%	—
09/18	1,259	11	0.9%	—
09/17	990	11	1.2%	—
Annual Growth	(2.4%)	13.0%	—	—

2020 Year-End Financials
Return on assets: 11.2%   Cash ($ mil.): 3
Return on equity: 23.5%
Current ratio: 1.30

SARASOTA COUNTY PUBLIC HOSPITAL DISTRICT

Sarasota County Public Hospital Board which does business as the Sarasota Memorial Health Care System is a publicly owned hospital system serving residents in and around Sarasota on Florida's western coast. It operates Sarasota Memorial Hospital a not-for-profit acute-care facility with more than 800 beds (and more than 900 doctors) that provides general medical and surgical care as well as specialized care in areas such as heart disease cancer and neuroscience. The system also features a skilled nursing facility walk-in medical centers an outpatient surgical center and home health care operations. Additionally the hospital conducts clinical trials and has an educational affiliation with Florida State University.

Operations

Sarasota Memorial has the only obstetrics program and neonatal intensive care unit in the county and its Bayside Center includes one of the county's only inpatient behavioral health facilities. The health care system's Charter Health Plan program offers group health insurance to local business owners.

Sarasota Memorial receives some 32000 inpatient visits and 950000 outpatient and physician visits each year.

Geographic Reach

Sarasota Memorial serves Florida's Sarasota County.

Sales and Marketing

Medicare and Medicaid combined account for some 60% of Sarasota Memorial's net patient service revenue. Self-pay and managed care make up the remainder.

Financial Performance

Sarasota's total revenues increased by 9% in fiscal 2016 (ended September) due to a 9% increase in net patient revenue due to higher volume. The company reported $107 million in excess revenues over expenses that year a 13% decline versus the prior year. Operating expenses including salaries fringe benefits and supplies costs all increased in 2016.

Cash flow from operations increased 38% to $85.8 million thanks to an increase in cash received from patient care services.

Strategy

Sarasota Memorial seeks to improve its financial performance by pursuing profitable inpatient and outpatient growth through an aggressive focus on physician alignment and integration and capturing new patients residing in high growth areas. The system has also been opening new facilities to boost patient service revenues. In 2016 it opened its sixth urgent care center. The following year it opened a 74000-sq.-ft. Rehabilitation Pavilion the only site of its kind in Sarasota County to offer comprehensive inpatient and outpatient rehabilitation services.

The system also introduced its nurse residency program and an internal medicine residency program in 2017.

Company Background

Sarasota Memorial was founded as a community hospital in 1925.

EXECUTIVES

Ceo, David Verinder
Chb*, Gregory Carter
Coo*, Lorrie Liang
Cfo*, William Woeltjen
Treas*, Joseph J Devirgilio Jr
SEC*, Thomas H Towler
Chief Nursing Officer*, Connie Andersen
Dir of Fin*, Donald Stitt
Chief of Psychiatric, Barbara P Srur
Chief of Pathology, J Robert Spencer
Chief of Pediatric, Patricia J Blanco

LOCATIONS

HQ: SARASOTA COUNTY PUBLIC HOSPITAL DISTRICT
1700 S TAMIAMI TRL, SARASOTA, FL 342393509
Phone: 941 917-9000
Web: WWW.SMH.COM

PRODUCTS/OPERATIONS

2016 Sales

	% of total
County Public Hospital District	
Sarasota Memorial Hospital	59
Corporate Division	2
Nursing & Rehabilitation Center	1
Charter Plan	-
SMH Health Care Inc.	33
Physician Services Inc.	5
Total	**100**

COMPETITORS

All Children's Hospital	Hca
Bayfront Health	St. Joseph's-baptist Health Care
Encompass Health	Tampa General Hospital
Florida Hospital Tampa Bay Division	

HISTORICAL FINANCIALS

Company Type: Private

Income Statement				FYE: September 30
	REVENUE ($ mil.)	NET INCOME ($ mil.)	NET PROFIT MARGIN	EMPLOYEES
09/20	986	154	15.7%	7,000
09/16	12	0	4.0%	—
09/15	590	131	22.3%	—
Annual Growth	10.8%	3.3%	—	—

2020 Year-End Financials

Return on assets: 5.7%   Cash ($ mil.): 40
Return on equity: 10.3%
Current ratio: 0.60

SAVANNAH-CHATHAM COUNTY BOARD OF EDUCATION

EXECUTIVES

Pres, Jolene Byrne
Executive of Information Techn, Cathy Mc Culloch
Chief Operating Officer, Mike Young
Auditors: KRT CPAS PC SAVANNAH GEOR

LOCATIONS

HQ: SAVANNAH-CHATHAM COUNTY BOARD OF EDUCATION
208 BULL ST, SAVANNAH, GA 314013843
Phone: 912 395-5534
Web: WWW.CHATHAMCOUNTYGA.GOV

HISTORICAL FINANCIALS

Company Type: Private

Income Statement				FYE: June 30
	REVENUE ($ mil.)	NET INCOME ($ mil.)	NET PROFIT MARGIN	EMPLOYEES
06/20	587	41	7.1%	4,800
06/19	569	86	15.2%	—
06/18	525	41	7.8%	—
06/17	500	(30)	—	—
Annual Growth	5.5%	—	—	—

2020 Year-End Financials

Return on assets: 3.1%   Cash ($ mil.): 117
Return on equity: 9.0%
Current ratio: —

SAVE THE CHILDREN FEDERATION, INC.

Save the Children helps poor and malnourished children in some 15 US states and nearly 120 countries focusing on such areas as health and nutrition economic development education child protection and HIV/AIDS. The humanitarian organization also participates in international disaster relief efforts focusing on children and their families. Save the Children spends about 90% of its budget on program services with the rest allocated to administration and fundraising. The group was founded in 1932 inspired by the international children's rights movement begun in the UK in 1919 by Eglantyne Jebb founder of the British Save the Children Fund. It is a member of the International Save the Children Alliance.

Operations

Some 43% of the humanitarian organization's work is centered in Asia with 34% in Africa. Save the Children spends the rest of its time in the US Latin America and the Middle East.

In 2012 alone Save the Children helped 125 million girls and boys worldwide.

Geographic Reach

Save the Children operates programs in some 120 countries including the US. It comprises 29 member organizations worldwide.

Financial Performance

The global aid organization's revenue declined by 3.5% in 2012 versus 2011 due largely to a 12% drop in private gifts grants and contributions which account for nearly half of its total revenue. Save the Children directed 89% of its expenses to programs which benefit children and allow the humanitarian organization to keep private costs (includes fundraising and management and general) at about 10% — one of the best ratios for nonprofit organizations.

Strategy

With about 28% of its program services devoted to emergencies and 20% to education Save the Children in 2014 partnered with The Malala Fund to help vulnerable Syrian and Jordanian children return to school. As part of the partnership Save the Children is launching a pair of education projects. Another large portion of Save the Children's program services are focused on Health and Nutrition (25%) and Hunger & Livelihoods (10%).

EXECUTIVES

Ceo, Carolyn Miles
Exec V Pres*, Carlos Carrazana
V Pres*, Michael Klosson
V Pres*, Tom Krift
V Pres*, Ken Murdoch
Chief Marketing Officer*, Jennifer Roberti
Assistant Vice President Finan, Rick Trowbridge CPA
Manager, Meghan St John
Corporate Communications Staff, Barbara Lencheck
Associate Director Corporate P, Pina Jabbari
USDA Portfolio Director, Amanda Quemore
Auditors: KPMG LLP NEW YORK NY

LOCATIONS

HQ: SAVE THE CHILDREN FEDERATION, INC.
501 KINGS HWY E STE 400, FAIRFIELD, CT 068254861
Phone: 203 221-4000
Web: WWW.SAVETHECHILDREN.ORG

Selected Countries of Operation
Australia
Brazil
Canada
Denmark
Dominican Republic
Fiji
Finland
Germany
Guatemala
Honduras
Hong Kong
Iceland
India
Italy
Japan
Jordan
Korea
Lithuania
Mexico
Netherlands
New Zealand
Norway
Romania
South Africa
Spain
Swaziland
Sweden
Switzerland
United Kingdom
United States

HISTORICAL FINANCIALS
Company Type: Private

Income Statement				FYE: December 31
	REVENUE ($ mil.)	NET INCOME ($ mil.)	NET PROFIT MARGIN	EMPLOYEES
12/16	652	(7)	—	3,000
12/15	678	(10)	—	—
Annual Growth	(3.9%)	—	—	—

2016 Year-End Financials
Return on assets: (-2.8%) Cash ($ mil.): 46
Return on equity: (-4.1%)
Current ratio: 1.50

SCAI HOLDINGS, LLC

SCAI Holdings (dba SCA or Surgical Care Affiliates) can stitch 'em up and move 'em out. The company operates one of the largest networks of outpatient surgery centers in the US. (Also known as ambulatory surgical centers or ASCs these facilities charge less than hospitals to perform routine surgeries.) SCA operates more than 200 surgery centers and surgical hospitals in about 35 states. The centers offer non-emergency day surgeries in orthopedics ophthalmology gastroenterology pain management otolaryngology (ear nose and throat) urology and gynecology. The company went public in 2013 but was acquired by insurance giant UnitedHealth in 2017 for some $2.3 billion.

EXECUTIVES

Ceo, Andrew Hayek
Cfo, Cory Roberts
Evp, Joe Clark
Chief Development Officer, Brian Mathis
Evp-General Counsel, Rich Sharff
Chief Administrative Officer, Caitlin Zulla
Chief Nursing Officer, Anne Hast
Sales and Market Development, Winborne Macphail
Senior Vice President of Devel, Mark Langston
Physician Practice and Growth, Goran Dragolovic
Development, Tim Buono
Auditors: PRICEWATERHOUSECOOPERS LLP BI

LOCATIONS

HQ: SCAI HOLDINGS, LLC
510 LAKE COOK RD STE 400, DEERFIELD, IL 600155031
Phone: 847 236-0921
Web: WWW.UNITEDHEALTHGROUP.COM

PRODUCTS/OPERATIONS

2014 Sales by Payor

	% of total
Managed care & other discount plans	62
Medicare	20
Workers' compensation	10
Patients & other third-party payors	5
Medicaid	3
Total	**100**

2014 Sales

	$ mil.	% of total
Net patient revenues	788	91
Management fee revenue	58	7
Other revenues	17	2
Total	**864**	**100**

COMPETITORS

Hca	United Surgical Partners
Novamed Inc.	Partners
Symbion	Universal Health Services
Tenet Healthcare	Services

HISTORICAL FINANCIALS
Company Type: Private

Income Statement				FYE: December 31
	REVENUE ($ mil.)	NET INCOME ($ mil.)	NET PROFIT MARGIN	EMPLOYEES
12/16	1,281	226	17.7%	5,248
12/15	1,051	273	26.0%	—
12/14	864	157	18.2%	—
12/13	802	52	6.6%	—
Annual Growth	16.9%	62.5%	—	—

2016 Year-End Financials
Return on assets: 8.5% Cash ($ mil.): 131
Return on equity: 19.6%
Current ratio: 1.30

SCHAUMBOND GROUP, INC.

EXECUTIVES

Pres-Ceo, Baohua Zheng
CPA, Kevin Hsu

LOCATIONS

HQ: SCHAUMBOND GROUP, INC.
225 S LAKE AVE STE 300, PASADENA, CA 911013009
Phone: 626 215-4998

HISTORICAL FINANCIALS
Company Type: Private

Income Statement			FYE: December 31	
	ASSETS ($ mil.)	NET INCOME ($ mil.)	INCOME AS % OF ASSETS	EMPLOYEES
12/07	65	4	7.5%	550
12/06	50	4	9.6%	—
Annual Growth	28.2%	(0.0%)	—	—

2007 Year-End Financials
Return on assets: 7.5% Sales ($ mil): 2,200
Return on equity: 8.0%

SCHOOL BOARD OF BREVARD COUNTY

EXECUTIVES

Chairperson, Andy Ziegler
Chairperson*, Amy Kneessy
Budget Specialist, Joseph Strohfus
Coordinator, Jason Faulds
Coordinator, Diane McAlister
Senior Analyst, Andrea Young
Assistant, Brittany Postlethweight
Technology Repair Technician V, Bryan Rouse
Food Director, Cynthia Barrett
Technology Support, Gary Beasley
Pdcp, Lynnette Thorstensen
Auditors: MOORE STEPHENS LOVELACE PA

LOCATIONS

HQ: SCHOOL BOARD OF BREVARD COUNTY
2700 JDGE FRAN JMESON WAY, VIERA, FL 329406699
Phone: 321 633-1000
Web: WWW.BREVARDSCHOOLS.ORG

HISTORICAL FINANCIALS
Company Type: Private

Income Statement				FYE: June 30
	REVENUE ($ mil.)	NET INCOME ($ mil.)	NET PROFIT MARGIN	EMPLOYEES
06/14	626	7	1.2%	9,031
06/09	613	(19)	—	—
06/06	628	100	15.9%	—
06/05	564	43	7.8%	—
Annual Growth	1.2%	(18.0%)	—	—

2014 Year-End Financials
Return on assets: 0.7%   Cash ($ mil.): 64
Return on equity: 1.9%
Current ratio: 2.40

SCHOOL BOARD OF BROWARD COUNTY, THE (INC)

EXECUTIVES

Chair, Nora Rupert
V Chair*, Heather Brinkworth
Asst Contrl, Lauris N Hazelwood
Accounting Staff, Darla Timmons
Staff, Carol Burton
Coordinator, Bernadette Lohrer
Accounting Staff, Chanda Peoples
Coordinator, Jennifer Austin
Acting Director, Lori Canning
Coordinator, Rachael Garafola
Purchasing Agent, Debra Swain
Auditors: MSL PA CERTIFIED PUBLIC AC

LOCATIONS

HQ: SCHOOL BOARD OF BROWARD COUNTY, THE (INC)
600 SE 3RD AVE, FORT LAUDERDALE, FL 333013125
Phone: 754 321-0000
Web: WWW.BROWARDSCHOOLS.COM

HISTORICAL FINANCIALS
Company Type: Private

Income Statement				FYE: June 30
	REVENUE ($ mil.)	NET INCOME ($ mil.)	NET PROFIT MARGIN	EMPLOYEES
06/20	3,037	169	5.6%	644
06/19	2,924	167	5.7%	—
06/18	2,806	(65)	—	—
06/17	2,738	5	0.2%	—
Annual Growth	3.5%	214.6%	—	—

SCHOOL BOARD OF ORANGE COUNTY FLORIDA

EXECUTIVES

Chairperson, Bill Sublette
Supt*, Barbara M Jenkins
Cfo*, Toni Greene
Executive of Information Techn, Jim Wolf
Occupational Specia, Yesenia Rivera
Staff, Beth McCaules
Coordinator, Frenchie Porter
Athletic Director, Julie Sanford
Assistant, Mabel Rios
Assistant Director, Peter Berry
Assistant, Robert Ryner
Auditors: CHERRY BEKAERT LLP ORLANDO F

LOCATIONS

HQ: SCHOOL BOARD OF ORANGE COUNTY FLORIDA
445 W AMELIA ST LBBY, ORLANDO, FL 328011153
Phone: 407 317-3200
Web: WWW.ORANGECOUNTYFL.NET

HISTORICAL FINANCIALS
Company Type: Private

Income Statement				FYE: June 30
	REVENUE ($ mil.)	NET INCOME ($ mil.)	NET PROFIT MARGIN	EMPLOYEES
06/12	1,823	30	1.7%	25,000
06/11	1,895	24	1.3%	—
Annual Growth	(3.8%)	26.1%	—	—

2012 Year-End Financials
Return on assets: 0.6%   Cash ($ mil.): 194
Return on equity: 1.0%
Current ratio: —

SCHOOL BOARD OF PALM BEACH COUNTY

EXECUTIVES

Chmn, Chuck Shaw
Choice Program Coordinator, Brooke Brink
Government, Cindi Walker
Executive Secretary, Claudia Robbins
Manager, Donald Scantlan
Administrative Assistant To Ch, Pat Haight
Chief Operating Officer, Donald Fennoy
Fleet Executive, Angela Barbato
It Infrastructure Network, Michael Sims
Information Technology Support, Sean Ache
Management Support Technician, Ann-Marie Haddad

LOCATIONS

HQ: SCHOOL BOARD OF PALM BEACH COUNTY
3300 FOREST HILL BLVD C316, WEST PALM BEACH, FL 334065813
Phone: 561 434-8000
Web: WWW.PALMBEACHSCHOOLS.ORG

HISTORICAL FINANCIALS
Company Type: Private

Income Statement				FYE: June 30
	REVENUE ($ mil.)	NET INCOME ($ mil.)	NET PROFIT MARGIN	EMPLOYEES
06/08	2,093	(68)	—	21,000
06/07	2,010	501	24.9%	—
06/05	1,657	(121)	—	—
06/04	1,290	61	4.8%	—
Annual Growth	12.9%	—	—	—

2008 Year-End Financials
Return on assets: (-1.4%)   Cash ($ mil.): 1,290
Return on equity: (-3.4%)
Current ratio: —

SCHOOL DISTRICT 1 IN THE CITY AND COUNTY OF DENVER AND THE STATE OF COLORADO

EXECUTIVES

Spdt, Tom Boasberg
Pres*, Carrie Olson
Principal, Emillo Esquibel
Teacher Secondary Middle, Leslie Aguilar
Teacher, Carolyn Lohr
Senior Data Analyst, Curt O'Hara
2nd Grade Teacher, Diani Riopelle
Program Leader, Jenia Hooper
Hr School Partner, Kristine Lequerique
Chief of Staff, Lauren Dunn
Office of Business Diversity, Murugan Palani
Auditors: CLIFTONLARSONALLEN LLP GREENW

LOCATIONS

HQ: SCHOOL DISTRICT 1 IN THE CITY AND COUNTY OF DENVER AND THE STATE OF COLORADO
1860 N LINCOLN ST, DENVER, CO 802037301
Phone: 720 423-3200
Web: WWW.DPSK12.ORG

HISTORICAL FINANCIALS
Company Type: Private

Income Statement				FYE: June 30
	REVENUE ($ mil.)	NET INCOME ($ mil.)	NET PROFIT MARGIN	EMPLOYEES
06/12*	916	(100)	—	14,965
12/08	0	(0)	—	—
06/08	790	(38)	—	—
Annual Growth	3.8%	—	—	—
*Fiscal year change

2012 Year-End Financials
Return on assets: (-7.5%)   Cash ($ mil.): 348
Return on equity: —
Current ratio: —

SCHWAB CHARITABLE FUND

EXECUTIVES

Exec Dir, Susan Heldman
Pres, Kim Laughton
Chb*, Carrie Schwab-Pomerantz
Dir, Brooks Walker
Mgr, Margae Diamond
Offc Mgr, Michael Smithwick
Auditors: DELOITTE & TOUCHE LLP SAN FRA

LOCATIONS

HQ: SCHWAB CHARITABLE FUND
 211 MAIN ST, SAN FRANCISCO, CA 941051905
Phone: 415 667-9131
Web: WWW.SCHWABCHARITABLE.ORG

HISTORICAL FINANCIALS

Company Type: Private

Income Statement				FYE: June 30
	REVENUE ($ mil.)	NET INCOME ($ mil.)	NET PROFIT MARGIN	EMPLOYEES
06/20	4,885	1,531	31.4%	26
06/18	3,465	1,549	44.7%	—
06/17	3,147	1,551	49.3%	—
06/16	2,018	819	40.6%	—
Annual Growth	24.7%	16.9%	—	—

2020 Year-End Financials

Return on assets: 8.9%   Cash ($ mil.): 29
Return on equity: 8.9%
Current ratio: 1.60

SCL HEALTH - FRONT RANGE, INC.

Exempla aims to provide exemplary health care to residents in the Denver area. The Exempla medical network operating as Exempla Healthcare includes three hospitals: Exempla Saint Joseph Hospital (570 beds) Exempla Lutheran Medical Center (400 beds) and Good Samaritan Medical Center (more than 230 beds). It also operates the Exempla Physician Network a chain of primary care clinics. The company employs more than 2100 physicians. Among its specialties are cardiovascular services and surgeries rehabilitation cancer care orthopedics and women's and children's services. Exempla Healthcare is sponsored by the Catholic faith-based Sisters of Charity of Leavenworth Health System (SCL Health System).

Strategy

Exempla is investing in expansion of the facilities at Lutheran Medical Center. It is also constructing a new building for Saint Joseph Hospital that is set to open in 2015.

Company Background

Exempla Healthcare was formed in 1998 when Saint Joseph Hospital and Lutheran Medical Center combined.

EXECUTIVES

Pres-Ceo, Mike Slubowski
Chb*, Jo Ann Soker
Pres-Ceo*, Jeffrey Selberg
Cfo*, William Pack
Executive Officer, David Munch
Staff, Kelly Knudson
Vice-President, Robert Fries
Senior Regional Director, Jim Warner
Emergency Medicine Specialist, Daniel W Cheek
Chief of Radiology, James Hopfenbeck
PDM Project Manager, Karen Webster
Auditors: ERNST & YOUNG US LLP PHOENIX

LOCATIONS

HQ: SCL HEALTH - FRONT RANGE, INC.
 2420 W 26TH AVE, DENVER, CO 802115301
Phone: 303 813-5000
Web: WWW.SCLHEALTH.ORG

PRODUCTS/OPERATIONS

2009 Revenues

	$ mil.	% of total
Exempla Saint Joseph Hospital	377	40
Exempla Lutheran Medical Center	302	32
Exempla Good Samaritan Medical Center	217	23
Exempla Physician Network	22	2
Colorado Lutheran Home & Exempla West Pines Behavioral Health	22	2
Exempla Lutheran Collier Hospice	6	1
Total	**948**	**100**

COMPETITORS

Catholic Health Initiatives
Centura Health
Denver Health And Hospital Authority
Healthone
Porter Adventist Hospital
Presbyterian/st. Luke's Medical Center
Rose Medical Center
University Of Colorado Hospital

HISTORICAL FINANCIALS

Company Type: Private

Income Statement				FYE: December 31
	REVENUE ($ mil.)	NET INCOME ($ mil.)	NET PROFIT MARGIN	EMPLOYEES
12/09	597	7	1.3%	5,300
12/05	472	30	6.5%	—
12/04	335	37	11.2%	—
12/02	267	27	10.1%	—
Annual Growth	12.2%	(16.2%)	—	—

2009 Year-End Financials

Return on assets: 0.9%   Cash ($ mil.): 53
Return on equity: 2.2%
Current ratio: 0.40

SCOTT & WHITE MEMORIAL HOSPITAL

EXECUTIVES

Ceo, Robert Pryor
Pres*, Shahin Motakef
Coo*, Donny Sequin
Cfo*, Ken Johnson
Accounting Staff, Bud Watson

Anesthesiologist, William Culp
Senior Network Administrator, Ted Gaines
Director of Government Affairs, Dan Posey
Surgeon, Ryan Raju
Cmaf Clinical Assistant, Brian B Anderson
Internist, Maybelline Lezama

LOCATIONS

HQ: SCOTT & WHITE MEMORIAL HOSPITAL
 2401 S 31ST ST, TEMPLE, TX 765080001
Phone: 254 724-2111
Web: WWW.BSWHEALTH.COM

HISTORICAL FINANCIALS

Company Type: Private

Income Statement				FYE: June 30
	REVENUE ($ mil.)	NET INCOME ($ mil.)	NET PROFIT MARGIN	EMPLOYEES
06/14*	832	87	10.5%	8,000
08/13	881	76	8.6%	—
08/10	902	41	4.6%	—
Annual Growth	(2.0%)	20.3%	—	—

*Fiscal year change

2014 Year-End Financials

Return on assets: 7.0%   Cash ($ mil.): 47
Return on equity: 8.1%
Current ratio: 1.40

SCOTT AND WHITE HEALTH PLAN

The Scott & White Health Plan (SWHP) works to keep its members Safe & Well. The not-for-profit company provides health insurance plans and related services to more than 200000 members across some 50 counties in and around Central Texas. Owned by the Scott & White network of hospitals and clinics SWHP has employer-sponsored plans (including HMO PPO and consumer choice options) as well as several choices for individuals and families. It also offers COBRA state-administered continuation plans the Young Texan Health Plan for children Medicare and dental and vision benefits. The company began offering its services in 1982. Owner Scott & White is exploring a merger with Baylor Health Care System.

EXECUTIVES

Pres-Ceo, Jeff Ingrum
Cfo, Stephen Bush
Management Information, Heather Ueckert
Executive Officer, Kirby Hitt
Family Medicine, Sean Delue
Web Content Manager, Zachary Beggs
Physician Recruiter, Bill Troxell
Internist, Cathleen M Rivera
General Counsel, David Ellenbogen
Vice President Facilities, Scott Liles
Customer Advocate, Alice Rankin
Auditors: ERNST & YOUNG US LLP INDIANAP

LOCATIONS

HQ: SCOTT AND WHITE HEALTH PLAN
 1206 WEST CAMPUS DR, TEMPLE, TX 765027124
Phone: 254 298-3000
Web: WWW.SWHP.ORG

PRODUCTS/OPERATIONS

Selected Products
Employer plans
Individual and family plans
Medicare plans
Vital Care programs

COMPETITORS

Aetna	Humana
Blue Cross And Blue Shield Of Texas	Texas Health Resources Ushealth Group
Cigna	Unitedhealth Group
Centene	

HISTORICAL FINANCIALS

Company Type: Private

Income Statement				FYE: December 31
	REVENUE ($ mil.)	NET INCOME ($ mil.)	NET PROFIT MARGIN	EMPLOYEES
12/09	660	13	2.0%	426
12/08	621	(4)	—	—
12/07	586	8	1.4%	—
12/06	557	3	0.7%	—
Annual Growth	5.8%	54.1%	—	—

2009 Year-End Financials

Return on assets: 8.5%
Return on equity: 18.4%
Current ratio: 1.50
Cash ($ mil.): 8

SCRIPPS HEALTH

Scripps Health is a $3.5 billion not-for-profit health system that serves the San Diego area through four acute-care hospitals. Altogether the health system treats more than 700000 patients annually through more than 3000 physicians. Its hospitals along with several outpatient Scripps Clinic and Scripps Coastal Medical Center locations is a network of integrated facilities with specialists from more than 60 medical and surgical specialist at some 30 outpatient centers and clinics. Scripps offers payer products and population health services through Scripps Accountable Care Organization Scripps Health Plan and customized narrow network plans in collaboration with third-party payers. Scripps Health was founded in 1924 by philanthropist Ellen Browning Scripps.

Operations

Scripps Health offers cancer care dermatology heart care neurology OB-GYN orthopedics primary care physical rehabilitation and Scripps Health Express. Primary care full range of services prevention wellness and early detection services for diagnosis and treatment of injuries illnesses and management of chronic medical conditions. Scripps Health Express provides same-day walk-in care for minor illnesses and injuries seven days a week.

Scripps Health operates four emergency departments and three urgent care centers and is home to two of the region's five adult trauma centers: a Level I trauma center at Scripps Mercy Hospital San Diego and Level II Trauma center at Scripps Memorial Hospital La Jolla.

Scripps Whittier Diabetes Institute is Southern California's leading diabetes center of excellence committed to providing the best evidence-based diabetes screening education and patient care in San Diego including outpatient education inpatient glucose management clinical research professional education and community-based programs.

Geographic Reach

Based in San Diego California Scripps Health extends its operation from Chula Vista to Oceanside.

HISTORY

Scripps Health was founded by Ellen Browning Scripps in 1924 when the Scripps Memorial Hospital and Scripps Metabolic Clinic opened in La Jolla.

The network grew through the opening of Scripps Green Hospital in 1977 and the Scripps Memorial Hospital Encinitas campus was added through the purchase of San Dieguito Hospital the following year.

Scripps Mercy Hospital which was first established in 1890 in San Diego joined the Scripps network in 1995.

The Scripps Health system expanded once again when it acquired the Scripps Mercy Hospital Chula Vista campus in 2004.

EXECUTIVES

Pres-Ceo, Chris D Van Gorder
Cfo*, Richard K Rothberger
Sr V Pres-General Counsel*, Richard Sheridan
Chief Medical Officer, A Brent Eastman
Sr V Pres-Chief Development of*, John B Engle
Sr V Pres*, Robin B Brown Jr
Sr V Pres*, Victor V Buzachero
Corp Svp-CIO*, Shane Thielman
Cmo*, Ghazala Sharieff
Scientist, Cynthia Macintosh
Scientist, Ellen Lambert

LOCATIONS

HQ: SCRIPPS HEALTH
10140 CAMPUS POINT DR # 415, SAN DIEGO, CA 921211520
Phone: 800 727-4777
Web: WWW.SCRIPPS.ORG

Selected Facilities

Scripps Clinic (outpatient centers)
Scripps Coastal Medical Center (outpatient centers)
Scripps Green Hospital (La Jolla)
Scripps Memorial Hospital Encinitas
Scripps Memorial Hospital La Jolla
Scripps Mercy Hospital (San Diego)
Scripps Mercy Hospital Chula Vista

COMPETITORS

Adventist Health System West	Palomar Health
Cedars-sinai Medical Center	Paradise Valley Hospital
Community Health Systems	Prospect Medical
Dignity Health	Rady Children's Hospital
Grossmont Hospital	Sharp Healthcare
Hca	Tenet Healthcare

HISTORICAL FINANCIALS

Company Type: Private

Income Statement				FYE: September 30
	REVENUE ($ mil.)	NET INCOME ($ mil.)	NET PROFIT MARGIN	EMPLOYEES
09/15	2,943	371	12.6%	5,445
09/08	1,953	18	0.9%	—
09/07	1,781	223	12.6%	—
Annual Growth	6.5%	6.5%	—	—

2015 Year-End Financials

Return on assets: 8.3%
Return on equity: 12.0%
Current ratio: 0.80
Cash ($ mil.): 464

SCRIPPS NETWORKS INTERACTIVE, INC.

Lifestyle TV is a livelihood for this company. Scripps Networks Interactive operates six lifestyle cable networks including Home & Garden Television (home building and decoration) the Food Network (culinary programs) DIY - Do It Yourself Network (home repair and improvement) the Cooking Channel (culinary how-to programming) and the Travel Channel (travel and tourism). The company additionally owns music channel Great American Country and has minority interests in Asian Food Channel and regional sports network FOX Sports Net South. It also owns a 50% stake in UKTV. Trusts for the Scripps family own majority control of the company.In 2017 Discovery Communications agreed to buy Scripps Networks in a $14.6 billion deal.

Operations

Scripps Networks has two reportable segments: US networks and International Networks. Its US network segment accounts for almost 85% of total revenue.

Geographic Reach

Scripps Networks is based in Knoxville Tennessee. The company has additional offices located in Atlanta Chicago Dallas Detroit Los Angeles New York City San Francisco Miami Chevy Chase Maryland and Washington DC. Scripps Networks maintains international offices in London Milan S o Paulo Sydney the Philippines and Singapore.

The company's Cooking Channel is available in Canada. HGTV is available in the Asia-Pacific region the Middle East North Africa and New Zealand. Scripps Networks has also expanded Food Network across Latin America and Australia.

Sales and Marketing

Cable programmers such as Scripps Networks generate most of their revenue through advertising and carriage fees paid by cable system operators and satellite TV service providers. To help keep viewer loyalty and ratings high the company targets its channels toward specific interests rather than airing programming for a general audience.

The company advertises its products through broadcast television networks online and mobile outlets radio programming and print media. Scripps Networks spent $161.1 million on advertising and promotions in fiscal 2016.

Financial Performance

Scripps Networks reported about $3.4 billion in revenue for fiscal 2016. That was an increase of more than $400 million compared to the $3 billion the company reported for revenue the previous fiscal year. The increase was due to increased advertising sales and affiliate fee revenues.

Scripps Networks' net income was $673 million in fiscal 2016. That was an increase of about $67 million compared to the prior fiscal period when the company claimed a net income of $606 million primarily as a result of an increase in total revenue.

The company ended fiscal 2016 with $948 million in cash from operating activities which was an increase compared to fiscal 2015 when Scripps Networks ended the year with $814 million in cash from operations.

Strategy

Scripps Networks is focused on growing advertising revenues by increasing video plays and attracting more unique visitors to its websites through site enhancements and adding more video. Its strategy also includes trying to attract a broader audience through programming on national video streaming sites developing new sources of revenue that capitalize on traffic growth at the company's own websites and capitalizing on the movement of advertising dollars to mobile platforms.

The growth of the company's international business continues to be a strategic priority. Scripps Networks has expanded in Asia Europe and Latin America in recent years.

Mergers and Acquisitions

EXECUTIVES

Ceo-Pres, David M Zaslav
Internal Audit, Andy Broyles
Chief Information Officer, Bob Baskerville
Director, Shared Prog, Ian Ratner
Vice President, Lynn Sadofsky
Advertising Operations Manager, Jason Tedford
Operations Staff, Liza Varnes
Director, Tim McElreath
Coordinator, Annie Tipton
Social Media, Ashley Nelson
Sales Planner, Casey Ohashi
Auditors: DELOITTE & TOUCHE LLP CINCIN

LOCATIONS

HQ: SCRIPPS NETWORKS INTERACTIVE, INC.
9721 SHERRILL BLVD, KNOXVILLE, TN 379323330
Phone: 865 694-2700
Web: WWW.SCRIPPS.COM

2016

	$ mil.	% of total
United States	2,884	85
Poland	443	13
Other International	73	2
Total	**3,401**	**100**

PRODUCTS/OPERATIONS

2016 sales

	$ mil.	% of total
operating revenue		
U.S Networks	2,871	84
International Networks	557	16
Total	**3,428**	**100**

2016 sales

	$ mil.	% of total
Advertising	2,416	71
Distribution	894	26
other	90	3
Total	**3,401**	**100**

Selected Operations

Lifestyle media
  Cooking Channel
  DIY Network
  Food Network (75%)
  Fox Sports Net South (7%)
  Great American Country
  HGTV (Home & Garden Television)
  Travel Channel (65%)
  UKTV (50%)
  Asian Food Channel (100%)
Interactive Services
  CookingChanneltv.com
  DIYNetwork.com
  FoodNetwork.com
  GACTV.com
  HGTV.com
  TravelChannel.com

COMPETITORS

A&e Networks	Nbcuniversal
Abc Cable Networks	Pbs
Amc Networks	Turner Broadcasting
Mtv Networks	

HISTORICAL FINANCIALS

Company Type: Private

Income Statement   FYE: December 31

	REVENUE ($ mil.)	NET INCOME ($ mil.)	NET PROFIT MARGIN	EMPLOYEES
12/17	3,561	814	22.9%	3,500
12/16	3,401	847	24.9%	—
12/15	3,018	778	25.8%	—
12/14	2,665	726	27.3%	—
Annual Growth	10.1%	3.9%	—	—

2017 Year-End Financials

Return on assets: 12.5%   Cash ($ mil.): 130
Return on equity: 26.2%
Current ratio: 3.10

SEACOR HOLDINGS INC.

EXECUTIVES

Exec Chb-Ceo, Charles Fabrikant
V Chb*, Oivind Lorentzen
Coo*, Eric Fabrikant
Exec V Pres-Clo-Corp SEC*, William C Long
Sr V Pres-Cfo*, Bruce Weins
Director, Angie Aldrich
Cto, Ben Melancon
Manager, Clayton Breaux
Senior Manager, Infrastructure, David Phenix
Account Manager, David Ryan
Network Engineer, Dwayne Brooks
Auditors: GRANT THORNTON LLP FORT LAUDE

LOCATIONS

HQ: SEACOR HOLDINGS INC.
2200 ELLER DR, FORT LAUDERDALE, FL 333163069
Phone: 954 523-2200
Web: WWW.SEACORHOLDINGS.COM

COMPETITORS

Bue Marine	Martin Resource
Badger State Ethanol	Management
Bristow Group Inc	Phi Inc.
Chc Group	Pacific Ethanol
Crowley Maritime	Siem Offshore
Gulfmark Offshore	Stolt-nielsen
Hornbeck Offshore	Tidewater Inc.
Kirby Corporation	
Lake Area Corn Processors	

HISTORICAL FINANCIALS

Company Type: Private

Income Statement   FYE: December 31

	REVENUE ($ mil.)	NET INCOME ($ mil.)	NET PROFIT MARGIN	EMPLOYEES
12/20	753	23	3.1%	2,195
12/19	799	34	4.3%	—
12/18	835	83	10.0%	—
12/17	577	81	14.1%	—
Annual Growth	9.3%	(34.2%)	—	—

2020 Year-End Financials

Return on assets: 1.5%   Cash ($ mil.): 65
Return on equity: 2.8%
Current ratio: 2.20

SEALASKA CORPORATION

Sealaska Corporation is a native-owned investment firm active in natural resources manufacturing services and gaming. The holding company owns land in southeastern Alaska home to the Tlingit Haida and Tsimshian peoples. Sealaska core holdings include Sealaska Timber Corporation Alaska Coastal Aggregates Sealaska Constructors Sealaska Environmental Services and Colorado-based information technology services provider Managed Business Solutions. Subsidiary End-to-End Enterprises manages the company's gaming business. Sealaska's subsidiaries operate throughout North America and around the world. Its companies often win government contracts for construction environmental and engineering projects.

Operations

More than 60% of Sealaska's revenues came from its services segment during 2015 which includes subsidiary Sealaksa Environmental Services Sealaska Constructors Sealaska Government Services Sealaska Technical Services Synergy Systems and Managed Business Solutions.

Nearly 30% of Sealaska's revenues are earned by its natural resources business which oversees land management and stewardship functions for all Sealaska lands. Sealaska owns about 290000 acres of timberland as well as the minerals rights to construction-grade aggregates on more than 565000 acres. Sealaska Timber harvest timber and markets logs for the domestic and export markets.

The company's Investment Business Segment (5% of revenues) comprised the Majorie V. Young Shareholder Permanent Fund and the Investment and Growth Fund. Its Gaming segment is managed by its subsidiary End-to-End Enterprises.

Geographic Reach

Juneau-based Sealaska has offices through the US and several other countries including Canada and Mexico as well as Europe.

Financial Performance

Sealaska's annual revenues have fallen 65% since 2012 as its portfolio holdings (such as its civil construction business in Hawaii and its natural resources business) haven't all fared well. The firm has rebounded from losses in 2013 however as it's sold off its less successful businesses and reduced costs.

The firm's revenue fell 10% to $109.4 million during 2015 with volatile markets causing a nearly $7 million decline in investment gains.

Revenue declines in 2015 caused Sealaska's net income to plunge 20% to $12 million though operational improvements helped dampen the blow. The firm's services business in particular managed to grow its profits despite a small sales decline as it focused more on higher value added work. Sealaska's operating cash levels spiked nearly 80% to $18.62 million after adjusting its earnings for non-cash expenses such as investment losses.

Strategy

Sealaska continued in 2016 to target acquisitions in businesses operating in the natural foods and seafood maritime services environmental service niche construction and data analytics sectors.The company adopted a 2012-2017 plan designed to transform Sealaska into a financially sustainable and profitable company driven by its core cultural values. To that end in 2013 the company sold its interest in its Nypro K ̃naak joint venture and the Sealaska Global Logistics business and exited the security guard services business (acquired in 2010) to support future acquisitions.

Company Background

Sealaska is the largest of 13 corporations formed under the Alaska Native Claims Settlement Act (ANCSA) of 1971 which promised some 44 million acres of land to Alaska natives. The company is owned by some 21600 tribal member shareholders.

Subsidiary Haa Aan (meaning "our land") was established in 2009 as a way to promote the culture social and economic viability of Southeast Alaska. Haa Aan has assisted tribal members with their efforts to establish businesses such as a new oyster farms in southeastern Alaska. Haa Aan also promotes renewable energy initiatives such as a biomass heating system for commercial buildings. In 2012 Haa Aan launched a non-profit community development financial institution in order to provide financing and promote economic development.

EXECUTIVES

Pres-Ceo, Anthony Mallott
V Pres-General Counsel, Joleen Araujo
Cfo, Doug Morris
Coo, Terry Downes
Communications Manager, Dixie Hutchinson
Director, Sidney Edenshaw
Program Manager, Curtis Bray
Records Manager, Linda Wynne
General Manager, Mark Poplis
Sr Administrator, Deborah Lawson
Senior Accounts Receivable Spe, Jennifer Emmons
Auditors: RSM US LLP ANCHORAGE ALASKA

LOCATIONS

HQ: SEALASKA CORPORATION
1 SEALASKA PLZ STE 400, JUNEAU, AK 998011276
Phone: 907 586-1512
Web: WWW.SEALASKA.COM

PRODUCTS/OPERATIONS

2014 Sales

	$ mil.	% of total
Services	81	67
Natural Resources	33	28
Investments	6	5
Gaming	0	-
Corporate & other	0	-
Total	**121**	**100**

Selected Subsidiaries

Alaska Coastal Aggregates
End-to-End Enterprises LLC (gaming)
Haa Aaní; LLC
Managed Business Solutions (majority owned)
Sealaska Constructors LLC
Sealaska Environmental Services
Sealaska Timber Corporation

COMPETITORS

Tembec   Chugach Alaska
West Fraser Timber

HISTORICAL FINANCIALS

Company Type: Private

| Income Statement | | | FYE: December 31 |
	REVENUE ($ mil.)	NET INCOME ($ mil.)	NET PROFIT MARGIN	EMPLOYEES
12/20	697	71	10.3%	1,400
12/19	699	86	12.3%	—
12/18	429	69	16.1%	—
12/17	293	45	15.6%	—
Annual Growth	**33.5%**	**16.2%**	**—**	**—**

2020 Year-End Financials

Return on assets: 7.9%   Cash ($ mil.): 31
Return on equity: 15.2%
Current ratio: 3.00

SEATTLE SCHOOLS DISTRICT NO. 1 OF KING COUNTY WASHINGTON

EXECUTIVES

Supt, Denise Juneau
Dir*, Carol Johnson
Dir of Fin*, Sephen Nielson
Customer Staff, Alma Clark
Coordinator, Bernardo Ruiz
Facilities, Silas Potter
Reading Specialist, Anne Presecan
Planning Staff, Anita Demahy
Teacher, Hersh Mandelman
Teacher, William Butler
Assistant Superintendent, Jolyn Berge
Auditors: PAT MCCARTHY OLYMPIA WA

LOCATIONS

HQ: SEATTLE SCHOOLS DISTRICT NO. 1 OF KING COUNTY WASHINGTON
2445 3RD AVE S, SEATTLE, WA 981341923
Phone: 206 252-0000
Web: WWW.SEATTLESCHOOLS.ORG

HISTORICAL FINANCIALS

Company Type: Private

| Income Statement | | | FYE: August 31 |
	REVENUE ($ mil.)	NET INCOME ($ mil.)	NET PROFIT MARGIN	EMPLOYEES
08/18	1,042	39	3.8%	4,650
08/06	553	4	0.8%	—
08/05	429	10	2.4%	—
Annual Growth	**7.1%**	**11.0%**	**—**	**—**

2018 Year-End Financials

Return on assets: 8.2%   Cash ($ mil.): 271
Return on equity: 24.0%
Current ratio: —

SECURITY FINANCE CORPORATION OF SPARTANBURG

Folks looking for a little financial security just might turn to Security Finance Corporation of Spartanburg. Founded in 1955 the consumer loan company provides personal loans typically ranging from $100 to $600 (some states however allow loan amounts as high as $3000). Customers can also turn to Security Finance for credit reports and tax preparation services. The company operates approximately 900 offices in more than 15 states

that are marketed under the Security Finance Sunbelt Credit and PFS banner names. A subsidiary of Security Group the financial institution also has locations operating as Security Financial Services in North Carolina and Longhorn Finance in Texas.

Operations

Security Finance boasts some 900 offices nationwide that operate under the Security Finance Sunbelt Credit and PFS names. The company specializes in offering consumers loans to individuals. It also provides consumer credit reports and assistance as well as tax preparation services.

Geographic Reach

From its headquarters in South Carolina Security Finance boasts offices in more than 15 states nationwide.

Company Background

Security Finance exited Colorado in 2010 after the state's attorney general general office filed a compliant that the company had been refinancing some consumer loans more than three times a year (the limit under Colorado law). The company agreed to repay acquisition fees that it had charged the customers for refinancing the loans.

EXECUTIVES

Pres, Heidi Bolton
Chb*, Susan A Bridges
V Chb*, C H Edwards
Treas-Cfo*, A Greg Williams
SEC*, Marshall T Walsh
Asst Treas*, Beadie H Townsel
Coo*, Judy Perkins
Unix Administrator, Bob Saccamano
Cash Management, Brenda Seagle
Auditors: ELLIOTT DAVIS DECOSIMO LLC G

LOCATIONS

HQ: SECURITY FINANCE CORPORATION OF SPARTANBURG
181 SECURITY PL, SPARTANBURG, SC 293075450
Phone: 864 582-8193
Web: WWW.SECURITYFINANCE.COM

Selected Locations

Alabama
Florida
Georgia
Idaho
Illinois
Louisiana
Missouri
Nevada
New Mexico
North Carolina
Oklahoma
South Carolina
Tennessee
Texas
Utah
Wisconsin

PRODUCTS/OPERATIONS

Selected Banners

Longhorn Finance (Texas)
PFS
Security Finance
Security Financial Services (North Carolina)
Sunbelt Credit

COMPETITORS

1st Franklin Financial	Dfc Global
Ace Cash Express	Ezcorp
Advance America	Firstcash
Bank Of America	Onemain
Capital One	Onemain Financial
Cash Plus	Value Financial
Community Choice	Services
Financial	World Acceptance

HISTORICAL FINANCIALS

Company Type: Private

Income Statement | | | | FYE: December 31

	ASSETS ($ mil.)	NET INCOME ($ mil.)	INCOME AS % OF ASSETS	EMPLOYEES
12/16	625	70	11.3%	2,500
12/15	651	78	12.1%	—
12/14	648	83	12.8%	—
12/13	616	62	10.2%	—
Annual Growth	0.5%	4.1%	—	—

2016 Year-End Financials

Return on assets: 11.3% Sales ($ mil): 558
Return on equity: 20.6%

SECURITY GROUP, INC.

EXECUTIVES

Chb, Susan A Bridges
V Chb*, Clarence Edwards
Pres, Ray Biggs
V Pres-Fin, A Greg Williams
Treas, Beadie H Townsel
Software Analyst, Danh Truong
Senior Vice President, Lisa Burroughs
Payroll Specialist, Marilyn Likes
Auditors: ELLIOTT DAVIS DECOSIMO LLC G

LOCATIONS

HQ: SECURITY GROUP, INC.
181 SECURITY PL, SPARTANBURG, SC 293075450
Phone: 864 582-8193
Web: WWW.SECURITYFINANCE.COM

HISTORICAL FINANCIALS

Company Type: Private

Income Statement | | | | FYE: December 31

	ASSETS ($ mil.)	NET INCOME ($ mil.)	INCOME AS % OF ASSETS	EMPLOYEES
12/16	1,002	87	8.8%	2,500
12/15	1,020	97	9.6%	—
12/14	1,040	135	13.0%	—
12/13	1,263	107	8.5%	—
Annual Growth	(7.4%)	(6.4%)	—	—

2016 Year-End Financials

Return on assets: 8.8% Sales ($ mil): 635
Return on equity: 12.7%

SECURITY HEALTH PLAN OF WISCONSIN, INC.

Security Health Plan of Wisconsin provides health insurance coverage and related services to some 200000 members in more than 35 Wisconsin counties. Its managed network of providers includes more than 4000 physicians 40 hospitals and health care facilities as well as 55000 pharmacies across the US. Security Health Plan provides policies for groups and individuals. Its products include HMO coverage plans and supplemental Medicare plans as well as prescription drug and equipment coverage disease management programs and administration services for self-funded plans. Established in 1986 the company is the managed healthcare arm of Marshfield Clinic which operates medical practices across the state.

Operations

Since it is affiliated with a medical care provider Security Health Plan's coverage decisions are directly impacted by the practicing physician. The company's provider network consists of independent physician locations and parent Marshfield Clinic's more than 50 locations in Wisconsin.

In addition to HMO plans the firm's comprehensive medical coverage plans include POS (point of service) and high-deductable offerings. Security Health Plan offers health care reimbursement accounts through third-party provider agreements with Employee Benefits Corporation and Diversified Benefits Services. In addition the company provides community education and wellness programs.

Geographic Reach

Headquartered in the town of Marshfield Security Health Plan serves the counties of Adams Ashland Barron Bayfield Burnett Chippewa Clark Columbia Dane Douglas Dunn Eau Claire Forest Iron Jackson Juneau Langlade Lincoln Marathon Marquette Monroe Oneida Pepin Portage Price Rusk Sauk Sawyer Shawano Taylor Trempealeau Vilas Washburn Waupaca Waushara and Wood.

Sales and Marketing

Security Health Plan serves individuals families and small to large employer groups.

Strategy

Originally started in 1986 as an offshoot of the Greater Marshfield Community Health Plan Security Health Plan's service territory has grown over the years. For instance in 2012 the company extended its Advocare Medicare Advantage plan offering into several new counties. Security Health Plan also regularly adds primary care and specialty providers to its network to provide a broader range of accessible care services to its members as well as to strengthen its operations in underserved regions. The company is also looking to enhance its IT systems to allow for greater information access communication methods and collaboration among its providers and members.

EXECUTIVES

Ceo, Julie Brussow
Pres, Dr Fredrick Wesbrook
Ceo, Steve Youso
Cafo, Krista Hoglund
Director, David George A Alexander
Director, Ellen M Schumann
Coordinator, Lynneia E Miller
Sales Manager, Ginger R Wolf
Quality Assurance Analyst, Lon Wilkosz
Rn Case Manager Team Leader, Sherri Winer
Prin, Jason Bauer
Auditors: KPMG LLP MINNEAPOLIS MN

LOCATIONS

HQ: SECURITY HEALTH PLAN OF WISCONSIN, INC.
1515 N SAINT JOSEPH AVE, MARSHFIELD, WI 544491343
Phone: 715 221-9555
Web: WWW.SECURITYHEALTH.ORG

COMPETITORS

Aetna
Blue Cross Blue Shield Of Wisconsin
Cigna
Centene
Dean Health Plan
Group Health Cooperative
Gundersen Lutheran
Humana
Unitedhealth Group
Unity Health Plans Insurance
Wea Trust
Wisconsin Physicians Service Insurance Corporation

HISTORICAL FINANCIALS

Company Type: Private

Income Statement | | | | FYE: December 31

	REVENUE ($ mil.)	NET INCOME ($ mil.)	NET PROFIT MARGIN	EMPLOYEES
12/17	1,234	9	0.8%	1,006
12/09	814	27	3.4%	—
12/05	385	0	—	—
12/04	369	17	4.7%	—
Annual Growth	9.7%	(4.4%)	—	—

2017 Year-End Financials

Return on assets: 2.8% Cash ($ mil.): 159
Return on equity: 5.7%
Current ratio: 1.10

SEMCO ENERGY, INC.

Alaska and Michigan have more in common than a cold climate. SEMCO ENERGY serves approximately 423000 natural gas consumers in both states. The company's main subsidiary is utility SEMCO ENERGY Gas which distributes gas to more than 290000 customers in 24 Michigan counties. SEMCO's ENSTAR Natural Gas unit distributes gas to more than 133000 customers in and around Anchorage Alaska. The company's unregulated operations include propane distribution in Michigan and Wisconsin; pipeline and storage facility operation; and information technology outsourcing. In 2012 SEMCO ENERGY was acquired by AltaGas.

EXECUTIVES

Ceo, David M Harris
Pres*, John D O'Brien
V Pres-Cfo-Treas*, Mark Moses
Prin*, James C Larsen
Treasury Analy, Sarah Ellis
Staff, Mike Shorkey
Tax Manager, Luanne Eikhoff
Executive Assistant, Nancy Bourdeau
Billing Clerk, Abbie Brown
Vice President Employee Servic, Ann Forster
Gis Specialist, Brad Dietzel
Auditors: ERNST & YOUNG LLP DETROIT MI

LOCATIONS

HQ: SEMCO ENERGY, INC.
1411 3RD ST STE A, PORT HURON, MI 480605480
Phone: 810 987-2200
Web: WWW.SEMCOENERGY.COM

COMPETITORS

Aep	Halliburton
Arb	Southwest Gas
Chugach Electric	Tengasco
Consumers Energy	Wec Energy
Dte Electric	

HISTORICAL FINANCIALS
Company Type: Private

Income Statement				FYE: December 31
	REVENUE ($ mil.)	NET INCOME ($ mil.)	NET PROFIT MARGIN	EMPLOYEES
12/16	575	51	9.0%	500
12/14	674	51	7.6%	—
12/13	608	48	8.0%	—
12/12	582	41	7.2%	—
Annual Growth	(0.3%)	5.5%		

2016 Year-End Financials
Return on assets: 3.2% Cash ($ mil.): 4
Return on equity: 9.0%
Current ratio: 1.20

SEMINOLE ELECTRIC COOPERATIVE, INC.

This Seminole is not only a native Floridian but it has also provided electricity in the state since 1948. Seminole Electric Cooperative generates and transmits electricity for 10 member distribution cooperatives that serve 1.4 million residential and business customers in 42 Florida counties. Seminole Electric has more than 3350 MW of primarily coal-fired generating capacity. The cooperative also buys electricity from other utilities and independent power producers and it owns 350 miles of transmission lines. Some 90% of its power load uses the transmission systems of other utilities through long-term contracts.

Operations
Seminole Electric's primary resources include the 1300 MW Seminole Generating Station and the 810 MW Richard J. Midulla Generating Station. The coop's renewable energy resources include waste-to-energy facilities landfill gas-to-energy facilities and a biomass facility. It also buys power as needed on the market.

Seminole Electric has more than 350 miles of transmission line.

Geographic Reach
The company serves customers in 45 counties in northeast south central and southeast Florida.

Financial Performance
In 2013 the coop's revenues declined by 1% due to lower rates and as well as a reduction in Member energy requirements and lower volumes sold to Non-Members.

Seminole Electric's net income increased by 48% in 2013 thanks to lower operating costs as a result of the absence of asset impairment costs and a drop in interest expenses.

The company's operating cash inflow increased to $86.05 million in 2013 (from $34.81 million in 2012) primarily due to improved net income and a change in working capital.

Strategy
The coop is seeking to respond to the State of Florida's push to get more power generation from renewable sources. In 2014 the company generating about 58% of its electricity from coal 35% from natural gas and 7% from green energy sources (up from 5.5% in 2011 making Seminole Electric one of the largest green energy providers in Florida).

Company Background
In 2012 it also made major environmental improvements to its main power plant the coal-fired Seminole Generating Station. In 2011 Seminole Electric boosted its portfolio of purchased green energy to more than 140 MW (including 113 MW from waste-to-energy facilities).

Seminole Electric was formed in 1948 to aggregate the power demands of its members and is governed by a board of trustees representing the 10 member utilities. The cooperative built its first power plant in the 1970s.

EXECUTIVES
Ceo-Gen Mgr, Lisa Johnson
V Pres*, David Gerhart
V Pres*, Mark Sherman
Cfo*, Jo Fuller
Director of Information Techno, Steven W Saunders
Sr Administrator, Will Simmons
Power Operations Super, Terry French
Manager, Martha Hewitt
Information Technology/Interne, Trudy C Novak
Supervisor, Feyzi Serim
Supervisor, Paulene Smith
Auditors: PRICEWATERHOUSECOOPERS LLP TA

LOCATIONS
HQ: SEMINOLE ELECTRIC COOPERATIVE, INC.
 16313 N DALE MABRY HWY, TAMPA, FL 336181427
Phone: 813 963-0994
Web: WWW.SEMINOLE-ELECTRIC.COM

PRODUCTS/OPERATIONS

Members
Central Florida Electric Cooperative
Clay Electric Cooperative
Glades Electric Cooperative
Lee County Electric Cooperative
Peace River Electric Cooperative
Sumter Electric Cooperative
Suwannee Valley Electric Cooperative
Talquin Electric Cooperative
Tri-County Electric Cooperative
Withlacoochee River Electric Cooperative

COMPETITORS

Duke Energy	Nextera Energy
Florida Power & Light	Progress Energy
Florida Public Utilities	Southern Company
Jea	Teco Energy

HISTORICAL FINANCIALS
Company Type: Private

Income Statement				FYE: December 31
	REVENUE ($ mil.)	NET INCOME ($ mil.)	NET PROFIT MARGIN	EMPLOYEES
12/18	1,083	21	1.9%	528
12/17*	1,067	23	2.2%	—
03/17	1,052	33	3.2%	—
12/16	1,067	20	1.9%	—
Annual Growth	0.7%	2.1%	—	—

*Fiscal year change

2018 Year-End Financials
Return on assets: 1.1% Cash ($ mil.): 35
Return on equity: 5.4%
Current ratio: 1.10

SENTARA HEALTHCARE

EXECUTIVES
Ceo, Howard Kern
Pres*, David J Masterson
Pres*, Dennis Matheis
Cfo*, Robert A Broermann
Coo*, Michael Gentry
SEC*, Jeffrey King
Cdo*, Dana Beckton
Svp-Chief Administrative Offic*, Melinda Hancock
Architect, In, John Burrows
Coordinator, Robert Jones
Pres Norfolk Gen Hospital, Carolyn Carpenter
Auditors: KPMG LLP NORFOLK VA

LOCATIONS
HQ: SENTARA HEALTHCARE
 6015 PPLAR HALL DR STE 30, NORFOLK, VA 23502
Phone: 800 736-8272
Web: WWW.SENTARA.COM

HISTORICAL FINANCIALS
Company Type: Private

Income Statement				FYE: December 31
	REVENUE ($ mil.)	NET INCOME ($ mil.)	NET PROFIT MARGIN	EMPLOYEES
12/20	8,861	738	8.3%	28,000
12/19	6,753	703	10.4%	—
12/17	5,297	580	11.0%	—
12/16	5,083	329	6.5%	—
Annual Growth	14.9%	22.4%	—	—

2020 Year-End Financials
Return on assets: 6.9% Cash ($ mil.): 1,315
Return on equity: 11.4%
Current ratio: 1.60

SENTARA HOSPITALS - NORFOLK

EXECUTIVES
Ceo, David L Bernd
Pres, Liisa Ortegon
SEC, Jeffrey King
Cfo, Robert A Broermann
Cardiologist, Gary Zeevi
Nurse, Brenda Smith
Lab Safety Officer, Dan Scungio
Otolaryngologist, Joseph Han
Team Coordinator, Viswanathan Venkataraman
Manager, Barb Kelly
Rn Director of Operational Sup, Cindy Parker
Auditors: KPMG LLP NORFOLK VIRGINIA

LOCATIONS
HQ: SENTARA HOSPITALS - NORFOLK
 600 GRESHAM DR, NORFOLK, VA 235071904
Phone: 757 388-3000
Web: WWW.SENTARA.COM

Company Type: Private

Income Statement				FYE: December 31
	REVENUE ($ mil.)	NET INCOME ($ mil.)	NET PROFIT MARGIN	EMPLOYEES
12/20	1,165	113	9.7%	5,338
12/17	877	63	7.2%	—
12/16	831	100	12.1%	—
12/15	791	92	11.7%	—
Annual Growth	8.1%	4.1%		

2020 Year-End Financials
Return on assets: 15.4% Cash ($ mil.): 30
Return on equity: 21.6%
Current ratio: 2.60

SERVCO PACIFIC INC.

Servco Pacific's business flows through an ocean's worth of enterprises. The company sells passenger vehicles (including Toyota Subaru Suzuki and Chevrolet models) and commercial trucks through dealerships in Hawaii and Australia. In addition Servco Home & Appliance wholesales kitchen and bath products to building professionals throughout the South Pacific; Servco Raynor Overhead Doors installs residential and commercial garage doors; Servco Insurance Services offers insurance coverage for businesses and individuals; and Servco School & Office Furniture outfits educational institutions and government agencies with desks seating and other furnishings. Servco Pacific was founded by Peter Fukunaga in 1919.

Operations
The diversified firm sells insurance through Servco Insurance Services (SIS) in Washington state. It clients are in the fishing shipping and cargo industries in several states including Alaska. SIS also operates in Hawaii where sister chains Servco Home & Appliance Servco Forklift & Industrial Equipment and Servco Automotive also operate. Sercvo Tire Company sells tires on Maui and in Honolulu.

Geographic Reach
Honolulu-based Servco Pacific has insurance offices in Seattle and Tacoma Washington. Its other businesses operate in Hawaii (Kauai Maui Oahu and the Big Island); and Australia (New South Wales Queensland).

Financial Performance
The private company reports revenue of approximately $800 million annually.

Strategy
Servco Pacific through its Australian subsidiary has been expanding its Toyota dealer operations in recent years. During 2010 the company acquired majority stakes in Sunshine Toyota of Queensland and Dubbo City Toyota of New South Wales. It also purchased Pacific Toyota in Cairns in 2009. The deals have significantly grown Servco Pacific's business in Australia part of a bid to strengthen its international presence; altogether Servco Pacific owns five dealerships in the country. The firm started operating in Australia in late 2007 with the acquisition of a Toyota dealership in Brisbane. Closer to home Servco is acquiring dealerships in Hawaii amid a influx of off-island businesses including Lithia Motors to Hawaii.

Mergers and Acquisitions
In February 2014 Servco acquired the assets of Maui's Island Subaru dealership in Kahului. The newly-acquired dealership will operate as Servco Subaru.

EXECUTIVES
Ceo, Mark H Fukunaga
Pres, Patric D Ching
Producer, Alton Nadamoto
Vice President Human Resources, Athan Arquette
Senior Vice President, Brian Horikami
General Manager, Bryan Lee
Fleet Manager, Cameron Kuboyama
Information Technology Busines, Chris Correa
Executive Secretary, Connie Higaki
Executive Officer, Craig Mishina
Sales Consultant, Craig Murakawa
Auditors: ACUCITY LLP HONOLULU HAWAII

LOCATIONS
HQ: SERVCO PACIFIC INC.
  2850 PUKOLOA ST STE 300, HONOLULU, HI 968194475
Phone: 808 564-1300
Web: WWW.SERVCO.COM

PRODUCTS/OPERATIONS

Selected Operations

Automotive
Rex Tire and Supply
Scion Dealers of Hawaii
Subaru Dealers of Hawaii
Suzuki Dealers of Hawaii
Servco Australia
Servco Chevy
Servco Lexus
Servco Truck & Commercial
Toyota Dealers of Hawaii
Servco Home and Appliance Distribution
Servco Insurance Services
Servco Raynor Overhead Doors
Servco School and Office Furniture

COMPETITORS
Autonation	Hd Supply
Citigroup	Inchcape
Fletcher Jones	Lithia Motors

HISTORICAL FINANCIALS
Company Type: Private

Income Statement				FYE: December 31
	REVENUE ($ mil.)	NET INCOME ($ mil.)	NET PROFIT MARGIN	EMPLOYEES
12/18	1,802	66	3.7%	1,000
12/17	1,629	26	1.6%	—
12/16	1,435	29	2.1%	—
12/12	923	15	1.7%	—
Annual Growth	11.8%	27.1%		

2018 Year-End Financials
Return on assets: 8.1% Cash ($ mil.): 61
Return on equity: 24.9%
Current ratio: 1.20

SES HOLDINGS, LLC

EXECUTIVES
Pres, Kelly Stanley

V Pres*, Faye McCarrell
Cfo*, Eric Mattson
Principal, John D Schmitz
Auditors: KPMG LLP DALLAS TX

LOCATIONS
HQ: SES HOLDINGS, LLC
  1820 N INTERSTATE 35, GAINESVILLE, TX 762402179
Phone: 940 668-1818
Web: WWW.SELECTENERGY.COM

HISTORICAL FINANCIALS
Company Type: Private

Income Statement				FYE: December 31
	ASSETS ($ mil.)	NET INCOME ($ mil.)	INCOME AS % OF ASSETS	EMPLOYEES
12/12	941	2	0.3%	1,700
12/11	1,019	131	12.9%	—
12/10	617	57	9.3%	—
Annual Growth	23.5%	(78.7%)		

2012 Year-End Financials
Return on assets: 0.3% Sales ($ mil): 945
Return on equity: 0.6%

SEVENTY SEVEN ENERGY LLC

Seventy Seven Energy (formerly Chesapeake Oilfield Services) is a company that was spun off from Chesapeake Energy one of the top onshore energy companies in the US. Chesapeake Energy reorganized six of its oilfield services subsidiaries into then Chesapeake Oilfield Services to create a new publicly traded entity that offers drilling hydraulic fracturing and trucking services as well as renting tools and manufacturing natural gas compressor equipment. It operates in onshore plays in the US. The company filed for Chapter 11 bankruptcy protection in 2016. In 2017 the company was bought by Patterson-UTI in a $1.76 billion stock deal including debt.

Operations
The company conducts business through three operating segments: Hydraulic Fracturing Drilling and Oilfield Rentals.

The hydraulic fracturing segment (51% of Seventy Seven Energy's total revenues in 2015) operates through Performance Technologies and provides high-pressure hydraulic fracturing services and other well stimulation services. This unit owns 11 hydraulic fracturing fleets with an aggregate of 440000 horsepower and six of these fleets are contracted in the Anadarko Basin and the Eagle Ford and Utica Shales. The fracturing process consists of pumping a fracturing fluid into a well at sufficient pressure to fracture the formation.

The drilling segment (38%) operates through Nomac Drilling and provides land drilling services for oil and natural gas E&P activities.

The oilfield rentals segment (11%) operates through Great Plains Oilfield Rental and provides premium rental tools and specialized services for land-based oil and natural gas drilling completion and workover activities. It offers an extensive line of rental tools including a full line of tubular products specifically designed for horizontal drilling and completion with high-torque premium-connection drill pipe drill collars and tubing.

Geographic Reach

Seventy Seven Energy operates in the Anadarko and Permian Basins and the Eagle Ford Haynesville Marcellus Niobrara and Utica Shales.

Sales and Marketing

The company got 70% of its revenues from Chesapeake Energy (CHK) and its affiliates in 2015.

Financial Performance

In 2015 Seventy Seven Energy's net revenues decreased by 46%.

Drilling revenues decreased due to lower revenue days driven by a drop in demand by non-CHK customers.

Hydraulic fracturing revenues declined due to a decrease in revenue per stage driven by market pricing pressure.

Oilfield rental revenues decreased due to a decline in utilization and pricing pressure.

In 2015 Seventy Seven Energy's net loss grew by 2675% due to lower revenues loss on sale of a business loss on sales of property and equipment net and impairment of goodwill.

Cash from operating activities increased by 7% due to the changes in the timing of collection of accounts receivable and the decline in overall operational activity.

Strategy

Chesapeake Energy decided to spin off its oilfield services in order to keep that activity separate from exploration and production. With exploration production and oilfield services under one umbrella the company only had one customer - itself. By separating the oilfield services unit Chesapeake Energy reduces its risk should exploration and production slow down much as it did with natural gas drilling and the shift to natural gas liquids.

Nomac Drilling continued to upgrade its rig fleet in 2015 making 80% of its rig fleet capable of drilling on multi well pads. As one of the most active drillers in the United States Nomac also continues to diversify its customer base serving more than 20 different operators.

Seventy Seven Energy expects to spend $100 million in aggregate growth and maintenance capital expenditures in 2016. It also intends to explore opportunistic complementary acquisitions particularly within the hydraulic fracturing segment.

In 2015 the company completed the previously disclosed sale of Hodges Trucking Company L.L.C. to a wholly-owned subsidiary of Aveda Transportation and Energy Services Inc. for $42 million.

Company Background

The company was formed in October 2011 and filed to go public in April 2012 in an initial public offering seeking up to $862.5 million. It completed the spinoff in July 2014 and renamed the company Seventy Seven Energy.

HISTORY

In 2011 Chesapeake Energy and its partners (including several joint ventures) accounted for about 94% of revenues but the company's goal is to only provide about two-thirds of Chesapeake Energy's oilfield service needs.

With the 2011 reorganization Chesapeake Oilfield Services took over a half dozen subsidiaries including Compass Manufacturing Great Plains Oilfield Rental Hodges Trucking Company Nomac Drilling Oilfield Trucking Solutions and Performance Technologies. The company generates the most revenue (about two-thirds of overall sales) from its drilling operations performed under Nomac Drilling. The majority of its rigs are contracted to Chesapeake Energy for use in the Anadarko Basin and the Marcellus Shale. The company is planning for more growth in fact Nomac Drilling ordered a dozen new rigs that can perform horizontal drilling in shale formations and other unconventional resource plays. All of the new rigs are expected to be delivered by May 2013.

Chesapeake Oilfield Services' second-largest segment is equipment rental offered through Great Plains Oilfield Rental which accounted for almost 20% of sales in 2011. Great Plains Oilfield Rental offers drill pipe drill collars tubing blowout preventers frac and mud tanks and it provides air drilling services and transfers water to wells for fracking. The rental segment also generates the highest margins since there's no operational costs involved. Oilfield trucking offered through Hodges Trucking Company and Oilfield Trucking Solutions accounted for about 10% of sales in 2011. The two companies own about 225 rig relocation trucks almost 160 fluid hauling trucks and 55 cranes and forklifts. And Compass Manufacturing which can make 600 natural gas compressor units per year accounted for about 5% of sales. Chesapeake Oilfield Services plans to have the company begin to manufacture other type of equipment used by its rental segment.

Its smallest operating segment is hydraulic fracturing services offered through Performance Technologies. Of course hydraulic fracturing accounted for about 1% of sales in 2011 only because it began operations with four fleets in the fourth quarter. Chesapeake Oilfield Services plans to have eight fleets by 2013 and a dozen fleets by 2014.

Chesapeake Oilfield Services also took over the assets of Horizon Oilfield Services (bought in November 2011 for $17.5 million) Bronco Drilling (bought in June 2011 for $339 million) and Forrest Rig Company (bought in December 2010 for $84.5 million). Despite two acquisitions in 2011 the oilfield services segment topped the $1 billion mark in sales in 2011. The company also recorded a profit for the first time.

Prior to forming Chesapeake Oilfield Services Chesapeake Energy's oilfield services subsidiaries were organized under COS Holdings L.L.C. Should Chesapeake Oilfield Services successfully go public it will own an interest in COS Holdings L.L.C. Chesapeake Energy will still be the major shareholder and customer of both companies with more than 50% of the voting power. Chesapeake Oilfield Services plans to use the proceeds from its IPO to pay off the predecessor company and to pay down debt.

EXECUTIVES

Ceo, Andy Hendricks
Coo, Karl Blanchard
Cfo, Cary Baetz
Coordinator, Adam Franca
Coordinator, Jesse Ybarra
Accounting Staff, Kristen Vickrey
Procurement Staff, Lisa Callahan
Contracts Management, Jamie Smith
Facility Supervisor, Rob Fell
Information Technology Manager, Tim Archer
Legal Assistant, Angela Turner
Auditors: PRICEWATERHOUSECOOPERS LLP OK

LOCATIONS

HQ: SEVENTY SEVEN ENERGY LLC
777 NW 63RD ST, OKLAHOMA CITY, OK 731167601
Phone: 405 608-7777
Web: WWW.77NRG.COM

PRODUCTS/OPERATIONS

SERVICES
Drilling
Pumping
Rentals

Selected Subsidiaries

Compass Manufacturing L.L.C. (maufatures natural gas compression equipment)
Great Plains Oilfield Rental L.L.C. (tool and equipment rental)
Hodges Trucking Company L.L.C. (trucking services)
Nomac Drilling L.L.C. (drilling services)
Oilfield Trucking Solutions L.L.C. (trucking services)
Performance Technologies L.L.C. (hydraulic fracturing)

2015 Sales

	$ mil.	% of total
Drilling	436.4	38
Hydraulic fracturing	575.4	51
Oilfield rentals	76.5	7
Oilfield trucking	42.7	4
other operations	0.2	-
Total	**1131.2**	**100**

COMPETITORS

Baker Hughes	Parker Drilling
Basic Energy	Patterson-uti Energy
Fts International	Precision Drilling
Halliburton	Rpc
Helmerich & Payne	Schlumberger
Key Energy	Superior Energy
Nabors Industries	Trinidad Drilling
Oil States	Weatherford
International	International

HISTORICAL FINANCIALS

Company Type: Private

Income Statement   FYE: December 31

	REVENUE ($ mil.)	NET INCOME ($ mil.)	NET PROFIT MARGIN	EMPLOYEES
12/15	1,131	(221)	—	1,700
12/14	2,080	(7)	—	—
Annual Growth	(45.6%)	—	—	—

2015 Year-End Financials

Return on assets: (-11.6%)   Cash ($ mil.): 130
Return on equity: (-186.3%)
Current ratio: 2.10

SHAMROCK FOODS COMPANY

Shamrock Foods Company is one of the nation's leading foodservice distributors with a strong presence in the western US. It primarily serves restaurants healthcare facilities military installations catering companies food banks and hospitality customers by providing everyday staples such as meats produce dry goods beverages and supplies as well as ethnic foods and artisanal gourmet and other specialty foods. Proprietary brands include Gold Canyon Four Leaf Roasters Markon Jensen Foods Pier 22 Seafood and Ridegline. Through Shamrock Farms the company is also one of the largest family-owned and -operated dairies in the country. Founded in 1922 Shamrock Foods is still owned and operated by the founding McClelland family.

Operations

Shamrock Foods is now one of the top 10 largest foodservice distributors nationwide. Its products include high-quality meats dairy fruits and vegetables beverages dry goods and groceries and kitchen supplies and equipment among others.

Shamrock Foods' exclusive brands include Bountiful Harvest Brickfire Bakery Fair Meadow ProPak ProClean ProWare and Ridgeline Coffee Roasters. The company also works with national brands such as B&G Foods Ecolab Nestl © Kellogg's Kraft Heinz Perdue Schreiber and more.

The company provides its customers with quality milk beverage milk half and half heavy cream and cultures products through Shamrock Farms.

Geographic Reach

Headquartered in Phoenix Arizona Shamrock Foods has broadline distribution warehouses located in Phoenix Arizona; Boise Idaho; Denver Colorado; Albuquerque New Mexico; and Eastvale California. In addition the company also has systems distribution warehouses in Phoenix Arizona; Denver Colorado; Sacramento California; and Portland Oregon.

Sales and Marketing

Shamrock Foods serves in restaurants healthcare casinos and entertainment lodging schools and other industries.

EXECUTIVES

Pres,chm,ceo, W Kent McClelland
Sr VIP/ SEC*, F Phillips Giltner
Sr VIP & Gen Mgr*, Tim Kelly
Cfo/ Asst SEC*, Stephen G Down
Cmo*, Ann M Ocana
Chf Hro*, Vincent C Daniels
CIO*, Daniel J Saltich
Director of Strategic Sourcing, Byron Tanigawa
Inventory Control Manager, Chad Hughes
Sales Representative, David Orozco
Account Executive, Joel Ellison

LOCATIONS

HQ: SHAMROCK FOODS COMPANY
3900 E CAMELBACK RD # 300, PHOENIX, AZ
850182615
Phone: 602 477-2500
Web: WWW.SHAMROCKFOODS.COM

PRODUCTS/OPERATIONS

Selected Products

Beverages
Center of the plate (meats)
Dairy
Cleaning supplies
Dry goods and groceries
Ethnic foods
Frozen foods
Paper and disposable products
Produce
Specialty
Supplies and equipment

COMPETITORS

Blue Bell	Performance Food Group
C&s Wholesale	Services Group Of
California Dairies	America
Inc.	Stonyfield Farm
Dairy Farmers Of	Sysco
America	Us Foods
Dean Foods	United Dairymen Of
Land O'lakes	Arizona
Mclane	Wells' Dairy
Meadowbrook Meat	
Company	

HISTORICAL FINANCIALS

Company Type: Private

Income Statement   FYE: September 30

	REVENUE ($ mil.)	NET INCOME ($ mil.)	NET PROFIT MARGIN	EMPLOYEES
09/20	3,894	0	—	4,700
09/19	4,016	0	—	—
09/18	3,900	0	—	—
09/17	3,447	0	—	—
Annual Growth	4.2%	—	—	—

2020 Year-End Financials

Return on assets: —
Return on equity: —
Current ratio: 1.10

Cash ($ mil.): 13

SHANDS JACKSONVILLE HEALTHCARE, INC.

EXECUTIVES

Pres, Susan Brownie
Internal Medicine Practitioner, Robert Kim
Cardiac Physician, Theodore Bass
Internal Medicine Practitioner, Hammad Bhatti
Internal Medicine Practitioner, Myint Thway
Internal Medicine Practitioner, Mohammad Shahid
Internal Medicine Practitioner, Tifinni Romero
Director, Jessica Schacht
Research, Joan Sacerio
Cardiovascular Disease, Ambar M Patel
Emergency Medicine Specialist, Andrew Schmidt

LOCATIONS

HQ: SHANDS JACKSONVILLE HEALTHCARE, INC.
655 W 8TH ST, JACKSONVILLE, FL 322096511
Phone: 904 244-0411
Web: WWW.UFHEALTHJAX.ORG

HISTORICAL FINANCIALS

Company Type: Private

Income Statement   FYE: June 30

	REVENUE ($ mil.)	NET INCOME ($ mil.)	NET PROFIT MARGIN	EMPLOYEES
06/16	665	22	3.3%	3,000
06/13	522	(5)	—	—
06/12	515	(22)	—	—
Annual Growth	6.6%	—	—	—

2016 Year-End Financials

Return on assets: 3.8%
Return on equity: 11.6%
Current ratio: 2.40

Cash ($ mil.): 73

SHANDS JACKSONVILLE MEDICAL CENTER, INC.

Close to the shifting sands of the northern Florida coast Shands Jacksonville Medical Center (doing business as UF Health Jacksonville) offers a range of services to the 19 counties it serves in Florida and southern Georgia. The 695-bed hospital includes a cardiovascular center Level III neonatal intensive care unit and a Level I trauma center. It also operates primary and specialty clinics in the Jacksonville area. The medical center is affiliated with the University of Florida and is the largest of seven hospitals in the Shands HealthCare family.

Operations

UF Health Jacksonville operates about 40 outpatient care centers. Overall its facilities handle some 34000 inpatient visits and 600000 outpatient visits per year. The hospital's affiliation with the University of Florida (UF) includes collaborative treatment and research programs in areas including cancer cardiovascular neurology orthopedic and pediatric care.

Together with its UF colleagues and affiliates UF Health Jacksonville provides a wide range of health care services across the continuum of care on an inpatient and outpatient basis. Backed by a team of more than 400 faculty physicians it offers nearly 100 specialty services.

Geographic Reach

UF Health Jacksonville's facilities are located in Jacksonville Florida and surrounding areas of northeastern Florida and southeastern Georgia.

Financial Performance

The company's revenues increased by 3% in 2014 due to growth in net patient service revenues as a result of a growth in inpatient and outpatient volumes. Medicare accounted for 25% net patient revenues; Medicaid 31%.

UF Health Jacksonville reported net income of $3 million in 2014 over a net loss in 2013 due to higher interest and a loss on the disposal of capital assets.

Operating cash flow in 2014 decreased by 8% due to higher payments to suppliers and vendors.

Strategy

UF Health Jacksonville has plans to build a second campus on the north side of Jacksonville to meet the needs of a growing community. It's also exploring ways to increase clinical efficiencies such as implementing an electronic health record (EHR) system (with help from federal stimulus funding); it also is looking to maximize funding opportunities for its research programs.

The company is looking to develop a Health Science Center Medical Education on Jacksonville Regional Campus including undergraduate graduate and health-related professions.

It also plans to build a 92-bed hospital wing for the North Campus which will provide greater access to more health care services for the center's residents as well as those living in surrounding communities. Construction is scheduled to begin in 2015 with completion in 2017.

In 2015 UF Health North opened the six-story 210000-square-foot outpatient medical complex in North Jacksonville which includes a 28-bed emergency room advanced imaging a midwife-led birth center rehabilitation services and more than 20 specialty services.

Company Background

Founded in 1870 as the Duval Hospital and Asylum UF Health Jacksonville started the first cancer program in Florida in 1948.

EXECUTIVES

Ceo, David S Guzick
Pres*, Russell E Armistead Jr
V Pres*, Greg Miller
Cfo*, William J Ryan
Information Specialist, Jason Herff
Contact Lens Specialist, Sally Melo
Director, Margaret Hines
Clerk, Vernice McNair
Program Director, Daniel Siragusa
Emergency Medicine Specialist, Christina Caro
Diagnostic Radiologist, Christopher Klassen
Auditors: CROWE LLP FORT LAUDERDALE

LOCATIONS

HQ: SHANDS JACKSONVILLE MEDICAL CENTER, INC.
655 W 8TH ST, JACKSONVILLE, FL 322096511
Phone: 904 244-0411
Web: WWW.UFHEALTHJAX.ORG

PRODUCTS/OPERATIONS

Selected Services
Cancer services
Cardiovascular services
Neuroscience services
Orthopaedic services
Pediatrics
Poison Center
Trauma and critical care services
Women and families

COMPETITORS

Baptist Health System
Bay Medical Center
Brooks Rehabilitation
Florida Hospital Tampa
Bay Division
Mayo Clinic
Jacksonville
Nemours Foundation
North Florida Regional
Medical Center
Ocala Regional Medical
Center
Orange Park Medical
Orlando Health
Palms West Hospital
St. Vincent's Health
System

HISTORICAL FINANCIALS

Company Type: Private

Income Statement — FYE: June 30

	REVENUE ($ mil.)	NET INCOME ($ mil.)	NET PROFIT MARGIN	EMPLOYEES
06/16	663	23	3.6%	3,000
06/15	480	10	2.2%	—
06/10	592	19	3.2%	—
Annual Growth	1.9%	3.5%		—

2016 Year-End Financials

Return on assets: 4.0%   Cash ($ mil.): 68
Return on equity: 12.3%
Current ratio: 2.50

SHANDS TEACHING HOSPITAL AND CLINICS, INC.

While its full name is Shands Teaching Hospital and Clinics most people call it UF&Shands. The network affiliated with the University of Florida provides health care services to patients in north-central and northeast Florida. The UF Health network of hospitals and physician practices manages more than 3 million inpatient and outpatient visits each year and serves patients from more than 65 Florida counties from around the nation and from more than 30 countries. Specialty services include oncology pediatrics cardiovascular transplants and neurological care. It also includes primary care and specialty practices throughout North Central and Northeast Florida as well as Southeast Georgia.

EXECUTIVES

Ceo, Marvin Dewar
Ceo-Admin*, Timothy Goldfarb
Sr Acct*, Donovan Shaw
Pres*, David S Guzick
SEC*, James M Roberts
Ceo*, Russell E Armistead
Cfo*, Michael E Gleason
Pres*, David S Guzick
Sr V Pres*, Daniel R Wilson
Sr V Pres*, Greg Miller
Treas*, James J Kelly

LOCATIONS

HQ: SHANDS TEACHING HOSPITAL AND CLINICS, INC.
1600 SW ARCHER RD, GAINESVILLE, FL 326103003
Phone: 352 265-0111
Web: WWW.UFHEALTH.ORG

PRODUCTS/OPERATIONS

Selected Hospitals
UF Health Jacksonville (Jacksonville)
UF Health Physicians (Gainesville and Jacksonville)
UF Health Shands HomeCare and Shands Jacksonville
Home Health (Gainesville and Jacksonville)
UF Health Shands Hospital (Gainesville)
UF Health Shands Psychiatric Hospital (Gainesville)
UF Health Shands Rehab Centers (Gainesville)
UF Health Shands Rehab Hospital (Gainesville

COMPETITORS

Baptist Health System
Bay Medical Center
Brooks Rehabilitation
Florida Hospital Tampa
Bay Division
Florida Hospital
Waterman
Lawnwood Medical
Center
Mayo Clinic
Jacksonville
North Florida Regional
Medical Center
Orlando Health
Palms West Hospital
St. Vincent's Health
System

HISTORICAL FINANCIALS

Company Type: Private

Income Statement — FYE: June 30

	REVENUE ($ mil.)	NET INCOME ($ mil.)	NET PROFIT MARGIN	EMPLOYEES
06/20	1,660	52	3.2%	3,000
06/19	1,651	66	4.0%	—
06/14	1,243	66	5.3%	—
06/10	1,040	(67)	—	—
Annual Growth	4.8%	—		—

2020 Year-End Financials

Return on assets: 1.9%   Cash ($ mil.): 104
Return on equity: 4.2%
Current ratio: —

SHARP HEALTHCARE

Sharp HealthCare is San Diego's leading health care provider and not for profit and dedicated delivering the highest quality patient-centered care and the latest medical technology and superior service. The network includes four acute-care hospitals (Sharp Chula Vista Medical Center Sharp Coronado Hospital Sharp Grossmont Hospital and Sharp Memorial Hospital). With approximately 2700 affiliated physicians and some 19000 employees Sharp HealthCare offers cancer treatment and heart and vascular care endoscopy mental health orthopedics and pregnancy and childbirth plastic and reconstructive surgery and hospice care. Sharp HealthCare was founded in 1957.

Operations
Sharp HealthCare operates four acute-care hospitals three specialty hospitals three affiliated medical groups and a full spectrum of facilities and services such as advance care planning alcohol and drug dependency bloodless medicines cancer treatment eating disorders emergency and urgent care heart and vascular care internal medicine laboratory services plastic and reconstructive surgery rehabilitation and physical therapy senior care weight loss surgery and wound care and hyperbaric medicine among others.

Geographic Reach
Sharp HealthCare is based in San Diego California.

Sales and Marketing
Sharp HealthCare's health plan options provide coverage for employers of all sizes throughout its region and include valuable enhancements such as interactive wellness resources dental discounts and an exclusive global emergency services program.

Company Background
In 2011 the system doubled the capacity of Sharp Chula Vista Medical Center's emergency department at a cost of $12 million and in 2012 the Chula Vista hospital opened a new cancer center.

The system began as a single hospital in 1955 named for a local pilot who died in WWII.

EXECUTIVES

Mng MBR, Christopher Howard
Mng MBR*, Michael Murphy
Svp, Finance and Cfo*, Ann Pumpian
Executive Vice President Hospi*, Daniel L Gross
Senior Vice President Business*, Alison J Fleury
Mng MBR*, William A Spooner
Mng MBR*, Carlisle KY C Lewis III
Coordinator, April Ordonez
Svp Human Resources, and Gener*, Carlisle C Lewis III
Director, Melissa Major
Manager Supply Chain, Terry Charbonneau
Auditors: ERNST & YOUNG US LLP SAN DIEG

LOCATIONS

HQ: SHARP HEALTHCARE
8695 SPECTRUM CENTER BLVD, SAN DIEGO, CA 921231489
Phone: 858 499-4000
Web: WWW.SHARP.COM

PRODUCTS/OPERATIONS

2014 Sales

	$ mil.	% of total
Net patient revenue	1,806	62
Premium	1,024	35
Other	97	3
Total	**2,928**	**100**

Selected Programs and Services
Alcohol and drug dependency
Bloodless medicine
Cancer treatment
Complimentary and alternative medicine
Diabetes
Ear nose and throat
Eating disorders

Emergency and trauma
Endoscopy
Executive health
Eye care
Flu care
Health and wellness
Heart and vascular care
  Heart valve surgery
Home care
Hospice
Integrative and complementary medicine
International patient services
Laboratory services
Men's health
Mental health
Neurology
Nutrition
Occupational health
Orthopedics
Pediatrics
Pregnancy and childbirth
Primary care and family health
Radiology and diagnostic imaging
Rehabilitation and physical therapy
Robotic surgery
Safety and injury prevention
Senior care and services
Skilled nursing
Sleep disorders
Stroke and neurology
Transplant
Travel medicine
Urgent care
Weight loss
  Weight management support
  Weight-loss surgery (bariatric)
Women's care
Worksite wellness
Wound care and hyperbaric medicine

Selected Facilities

Sharp Chula Vista Medical Center (340 beds)
Sharp Coronado Hospital (180 beds)
Sharp Grossmont Hospital (540 beds La Mesa)
Sharp Mary Birch Hospital for Women & Newborns (170
  beds San Diego)
Sharp McDonald Center (20 beds San Diego)
Sharp Memorial Hospital (675 beds San Diego)
Sharp Mesa Vista Hospital (150 beds San Diego)

COMPETITORS

Adventist Health	Rady Children's
System West	Hospital
Dignity Health	Scripps Health
Hca	Sutter Health
Palomar Health	Tenet Healthcare
Paradise Valley	Tri-city Healthcare
Hospital	District

HISTORICAL FINANCIALS
Company Type: Private

Income Statement   FYE: September 30

	REVENUE ($ mil.)	NET INCOME ($ mil.)	NET PROFIT MARGIN	EMPLOYEES
09/19	1,680	(27)	—	14,000
09/14	1,234	(12)	—	
09/13	1,158	(11)	—	
09/09	897	(0)	—	
Annual Growth	6.5%	—	—	

2019 Year-End Financials
Return on assets: (-0.7%)   Cash ($ mil.): 281
Return on equity: (-29.9%)
Current ratio: 0.40

SHARP MEMORIAL HOSPITAL

The docs and the scalpels are sharp at Sharp Memorial Hospital. The flagship facility of Sharp HealthCare the not-for-profit hospital has roughly 675 beds and is a designated trauma center for San Diego County. Specialties include cardiac care women's health multi-organ transplantation and cancer treatment. It also provides skilled nursing home health and hospice services. Sharp Memorial Hospital first opened in 1955. Sharp HealthCare completed reconstruction efforts on the Sharp Memorial facility in 2009; the new hospital has improved inpatient surgery emergency trauma and intensive care facilities.

Operations

Along with a full range of inpatient services Sharp Memorial's Outpatient Pavilion provides patients with cancer care women's imaging and endoscopy services. The center also conducts outpatient surgery procedures ranging from LASIK to orthopedic surgeries. More and more hospitals are adding outpatient services to their roster because they tend to be reimbursed at higher rates. The facility also provides patient education services such as community health classes.

Sharp Memorial which provides some $199 million in community benefits (including charity care and outreach efforts) each year is affiliated with a number of other hospitals clinics and physician groups through its parent organization.

EXECUTIVES

Ceo, Tim Smith
Manager, Debbie Dickie Sr
Director, Joshua Schmidt
Scientist, Julie C Sotomayor
Case Manager I Bu, Kimberly Eichler
Cardiology Director, John Gordon
Rheumatologist, Zdenka Fronek
Senior Vice President, Ken Lawonn
Network Management Specialist, Margie Brigham
Senior Vice President of Busin, Alison J Fleury
Director, Donald Nuss

LOCATIONS

HQ: SHARP MEMORIAL HOSPITAL
  7901 FROST ST, SAN DIEGO, CA 921232701
Phone: 858 939-3636
Web: WWW.SHARP.COM

COMPETITORS

Adventist Health	Scripps Health
System West	Tenet Healthcare
Grossmont Hospital	Tri-city Healthcare
Palomar Health	District
Rady Children's	
Hospital	

HISTORICAL FINANCIALS
Company Type: Private

Income Statement   FYE: September 30

	REVENUE ($ mil.)	NET INCOME ($ mil.)	NET PROFIT MARGIN	EMPLOYEES
09/18	1,306	247	19.0%	3,500
09/17	1,158	237	20.5%	—
09/16	1,200	290	24.2%	—
09/15	1,195	240	20.1%	—
Annual Growth	3.0%	1.0%	—	—

2018 Year-End Financials
Return on assets: 8.6%   Cash ($ mil.): 1
Return on equity: 10.2%
Current ratio: 19.90

SHAWMUT WOODWORKING & SUPPLY, INC.

Shawmut Woodworking & Supply which does business as Shawmut Design and Construction provides beginning-to-end construction services from preconstruction planning to post-construction quality assurance checks. The national construction management firm that generates nearly $225 million annual revenue has experience building retail hotel gaming spa and life science facilities. It also handles corporate interiors and high-end residential construction and boasts expertise in cultural and historical preservation projects. The employee-owned company serves clients nationwide from offices in a handful of US states.

Operations

The company provides a wide range of construction management services including lean construction integrated project delivery design/build sustainable construction virtual construction services and mechanical electrical plumbing services. Other services includes BIM?building information modeling 3D MEP coordination/clash detection building technology/peer review historic preservation consulting/peer review last planner system collaborative web-based documentation management furnishings coordination 24-hour/7-day-a-week emergency services commissioning warranty services and asset management.

Geographic Reach

Shawmut Woodworking & Supply operates from offices in Boston (headquarters); New York; Los Angeles; Las Vegas; Chicago Illinois; Irvine California; Providence Rhode Island; North Haven Connecticut; Miami Florida; and West Springfield Massachusetts.

Sales and Marketing

Shawmut Woodworking & Supply serves a range of markets with varying needs with projects involving corporate interiors cultural and historic structures healthcare restaurants retail and health clubs sports venues and universities.

Its clients have included Lacoste Louis Vuitton Balmain Dyson Walgreens Waldorf Astoria Nobu McKinsey & Company One Beacon Street and Legal Sea Foods.

Strategy

Shawmut Woodworking & Supply built on its world-class safety program and developed a robust plan to minimize coronavirus exposure?rolling out safety protocols new job-site innovations and an exhaustive risk assessment and response strategy for all project sites across the country.

Through its technology partnerships pilot programs and grassroots innovation by project team members in the field Shawmut created effective safety procedures that have been rolled out to all sites throughout the region including underway projects at Pace University Parker New York Hotel The Glasshouse Tiffany & Co. and Cultural Services of the French Embassy to name a few. These sites are equipped with Shawmut technology such as Shawmut Vitals and Smartvid.io.

Shawmut also partnered with Cottonwood Group in mid-2020 to expand both their combined real estate capabilities and portfolio in the education sector in the United States. The new partnership will further strengthen and enhance Cottonwood's development capabilities with academic real estate by allowing the firm to tap into Shawmut's solid and time-proven construction platform deep regional expertise and extensive industry sector experience.

EXECUTIVES

Ceo, Lester Hiscoe
Treas*, Roger Tougas
SEC*, Douglas Lareau
Sr Tax and Licensing, Elizabeth Gjanei
Coordinator, Kathryn Kucharski
Vp and Cfo, Roger C Tougas
Manager, Elizabeth McNeill
Senior Project Manager, Michael Kearns
Facility Manager, Puja Doni
Admin, Cara A Leblanc
Managing Director, Bob Motta

LOCATIONS

HQ: SHAWMUT WOODWORKING & SUPPLY, INC.
560 HARRISON AVE STE 200, BOSTON, MA
021182632
Phone: 617 622-7000
Web: WWW.SHAWMUT.COM

PRODUCTS/OPERATIONS

Selected Markets
Academic
Commercial
Corporate interiors
Cultural and historic
Gaming
Healthcare and science
Restaurants
Retail
Spas and healthclubs
Sports venues

Selected Services

Services
Pre-Construction
Master planning services
Master project scheduling
Lease review
Value engineering
Feasibility studies
Green design services
Drawing reviews
Facilities audits and campus assessments
Collaborative approach with architect/design team
Comprehensive conceptual estimating
BIM and virtual construction
In-house M/E/P expertise
Bid packages
Constructability reviews
Due diligence and site surveys
Pre-qualification of subcontractors
Management of permitting and approvals
Development of specific phasing schedules and delivery methods
Open book subcontractor bidding
Logistics planning
National purchasing power
Construction
Master project scheduling
Weekly project team meetings
Sites monitored by a Safety Manager
Zero-tolerance safety program
BIM and virtual construction services
LEED documentation certification and green building techniques
Permitting services
Design/build services
Communication with surrounding community
Coordination of owner-supplied items and vendors
Procurement solutions
Schedule and budget controls

24-hour/7 days-a-week emergency services
Specialized services for program clients
Indoor air quality management
Construction and demolition waste recycling
Customized waterproofing details
Post-Construction
Commissioning and close-out services
O&M manuals and training
Project services division
1-year warranty walkthrough

COMPETITORS

Andrew Velez Construction	Conti Enterprises
Bbl Construction Services	E.w. Howell
	Skanska Usa Building
Barr & Barr	Structure Tone
	Turner Corporation

HISTORICAL FINANCIALS

Company Type: Private

Income Statement

FYE: November 30

	REVENUE ($ mil.)	NET INCOME ($ mil.)	NET PROFIT MARGIN	EMPLOYEES
11/14	957	7	0.7%	1,476
11/11	662	3	0.6%	
11/09*	618	(21)	—	—
12/05	440	3	0.7%	
Annual Growth	9.0%	9.9%	—	—

*Fiscal year change

2014 Year-End Financials

Return on assets: 2.4%　　　Cash ($ mil.): 74
Return on equity: 14.5%
Current ratio: 1.20

SHAWNEE MISSION MEDICAL CENTER, INC.

Shawnee Mission Medical Center (SMMC) cares for Kansas City residents primarily on the Kansas-side. The health care facility located in the city's southwest suburbs has some 500 inpatient beds. It also offers outpatient surgery and other health services in areas such as pediatrics rehabilitation oncology and radiology. The medical center's emergency department receives some 50000 visits each year. SMMC also operates satellite facilities including the Shawnee Mission Outpatient Pavilion in nearby Lenexa which offers emergency and outpatient diagnostic general practice and surgical care. SMMC is part of Adventist Health System.

Operations

SMMC handles some 20000 inpatient admissions each year as well as some 200000 outpatient visits. Its staff includes about 700 physicians who specialize in about 50 fields of medicine. Specialist care centers include a Chest Pain Emergency Center and the Center for Women's Health. The hospital also provides primary and specialty care through the Shawnee Mission Physicians Group including after-hours clinical care and cardiology and reproductive medicine services. SMMC delivers more babies per year than any other hospital in the metropolitan area.

Geographic Reach

SMMC is located on a more than 50-acre campus in Shawnee Mission (near Kansas City) in Johnson County Kansas and serves the surrounding area. The main hospital campus includes a free-standing surgery center six physician practice buildings a child-care center for associates and a community health center.

Strategy

The SMMC organization looks at community needs to determine where it should grow. In 2013 the hospital opened a $44 million new birthing center to meet the growing need for obstetric services in the Kansas City area. The expansion effort tripled the size of the medical center's labor and delivery and postpartum rooms allowing it to accommodate up to 5000 births annually and added a level III neonatal intensive care unit.

The facility is also adding to its technological abilities to better serve the community. In late 2014 it deployed the eMediTrack platform to help document and analyze data for compliance and accreditation readiness.

Company Background

SMMC is part of a network of more than 500 health care facilities sponsored by the Seventh-day Adventist Church.

EXECUTIVES

Ceo, Ken Bacon
Sr V Pres, Robin Harrold
Vice President and Cno, Sheri Hawkins
Cfo, Jack Wagnar
Exec SEC, Tami Fson
Pres, Sam Turner
Occupational Specia, Shannon Lockwood
Vice President Customer Servic, Peggy Todd
Internal Medicine Practitioner, Heather Perry
Physical Therapist, Rosie Cresswell
Physical Therapist, Susan Clark

LOCATIONS

HQ: SHAWNEE MISSION MEDICAL CENTER, INC.
9100 W 74TH ST, SHAWNEE MISSION, KS 662044004
Phone: 913 676-2000
Web: WWW.ADVENTHEALTH.COM

PRODUCTS/OPERATIONS

Selected Centers and Services
Bariatric Surgery
Behavioral Health
Britain Center (Cancer)
Center for Pain Medicine
CorporateCare
Diabetes
Emergency Services
Express Care
GI Services
Hand Specialty Center
HEALTHaware
Heart and Vascular Center
Home Health Care
Maternity
Holistic Care
Men's Health Program
Neurology
Nutrition and Weight Loss
Orthopedics
Plastic Surgery
Radiology
Rehabilitation Services
Reproductive Medicine
Robotic Surgery
Sleep Disorders Center
SM Outpatient Pavilion
SportsCare
Support Groups
Surgical Services
TherapyPlus
Transfer Center Urgent Care
Weight Loss Surgery
Women's Health
Wound Care Center

COMPETITORS

Ascension Health	Sisters Of Charity Of
Children's Mercy	Leavenworth
Hospital	Truman Medical Centers
Coxhealth	University Of Kansas
Hca	Medical Center

Heartland Health
Mercy Health
Saint Luke's Health
  System

Via Christi Health
  System

HISTORICAL FINANCIALS
Company Type: Private

Income Statement				FYE: December 31
	REVENUE ($ mil.)	NET INCOME ($ mil.)	NET PROFIT MARGIN	EMPLOYEES
12/19	546	66	12.2%	1,850
12/17	491	55	11.3%	—
12/16	454	54	12.0%	—
12/15	435	38	8.7%	—
Annual Growth	5.9%	15.1%	—	—

2019 Year-End Financials
Return on assets: 7.2%   Cash ($ mil.): 363
Return on equity: 9.7%
Current ratio: 13.70

SHEA HOMES LIMITED PARTNERSHIP, A CALIFORNIA LIMITED PARTNERSHIP

EXECUTIVES

Ptnr, Jim Shontere
Ptnr, John F Shea LP
Treasurer, Robert Odell
Chief Information Officer, Bruce Verker
Sales Director, Janet Benavidez
Customer Manager, Chip Pennington
Sales Executive, Adam Heib
Technology/Computer Coordinato, Bert Selva
Sales Executive, Eric Snider
Sales Executive, Heather Stevenson
Sales Executive, Ken Peterson
Auditors: ERNST & YOUNG LLP LOS
  ANGELES

LOCATIONS

HQ: SHEA HOMES LIMITED PARTNERSHIP, A
  CALIFORNIA LIMITED PARTNERSHIP
  655 BREA CANYON RD, WALNUT, CA 917893078
Phone: 909 594-9500
Web: WWW.JFSHEA.COM

HISTORICAL FINANCIALS
Company Type: Private

Income Statement				FYE: December 31
	REVENUE ($ mil.)	NET INCOME ($ mil.)	NET PROFIT MARGIN	EMPLOYEES
12/13	930	125	13.5%	1,200
12/12	680	29	4.3%	—
12/99	1,793	184	10.3%	—
Annual Growth	(4.6%)	(2.7%)	—	—

2013 Year-End Financials
Return on assets: 8.4%   Cash ($ mil.): 206
Return on equity: 28.3%
Current ratio: 1.30

SHELL MEDICAL PLAN

Auditors: PNCEWATERHOUSECOOPERS LLP
PIT

LOCATIONS

HQ: SHELL MEDICAL PLAN
  , PHOENIX, AZ 85072
Phone: 800 352-3705

HISTORICAL FINANCIALS
Company Type: Private

Income Statement				FYE: December 31
	REVENUE ($ mil.)	NET INCOME ($ mil.)	NET PROFIT MARGIN	EMPLOYEES
12/16	617	5	1.0%	2
12/15	571	(40)	—	—
12/13	536	6	1.2%	—
Annual Growth	4.8%	(1.6%)	—	—

2016 Year-End Financials
Return on assets: 10.1%   Cash ($ mil.): 58
Return on equity: 10.1%
Current ratio: —

SHI INTERNATIONAL CORP.

SHI International is one of the world's largest transformational technology solutions providers. The company distributes scores of computer hardware and software products from suppliers such as Adobe Cisco Microsoft VMware Symantec and Lenovo. It resells PCs networking products data storage systems printers software and keyboards among other items. SHI offers a range of professional services including software licensing asset management managed desktop services systems integration and vocational training. The company serves corporate government and health care customers from approximately 35 offices across Australia Canada France Hong Kong Ireland Singapore the US and the UK. SHI was founded in 1989 by Chairman Koguan Leo.

Operations

SHI helps companies achieve business goals through the use of technologies ranging from software licensing and end user computing devices to innovative cloud and edge solutions. The company provides foundational solutions that allow its customers to build resilient agile technology-based answers to their most pressing business needs. These solutions include Integration Centers IT Asset and Lifecycle Management SHI Mobility and Managed and Professional Services.

The company's popular product categories include laptops desktop tablets printers and monitors. Among its featured brands are Acer Citrix HP LG Nvidia McAfee and Samsung.

Geographic Reach

Based in Somerset New Jersey SHI has a global reach through approximately 35 offices worldwide including its seven international offices in Australia Canada France Hong Kong Ireland Singapore and in the UK.

Sales and Marketing

SHI has some 5000 experts from every area of IT operations from volume licensing to security

data center to mobility and collaboration supporting approximately 10 million end-users.

Strategy

In late 2021 SHI International launched SHI Complete its new fully-managed IT service that helps small-and medium-sized businesses (SMBs) accelerate and optimize their IT transformation.

SHI Complete includes endpoint cloud network management cybersecurity and IT professional services into a single managed service so that SMB business leaders can take full advantage of the latest technologies and skills without having to take their eye off business growth or invest in a large in-house team.

With SHI Complete experts at SHI can take full ownership of a customer organization's IT operations and ensure the right skills and strategies are leveraged to aid in scale and optimization efforts.

Auditors: COHN REZNICK LLP WHITE PLAINS

LOCATIONS

HQ: SHI INTERNATIONAL CORP.
  290 DAVIDSON AVE, SOMERSET, NJ 088734145
Phone: 732 764-8888
Web: WWW.SHI.COM

PRODUCTS/OPERATIONS

Selected Products

Accessories

Peripherals

Hardware

Memory

Software

Selected Services
Cloud services
Computer vocational training services
Data center services
Events
Hardware services
Networking
POLARIS Software asset management
Storage
Strategic consulting
Webinars

COMPETITORS

Asi Computer Technologies	Computacenter
Agilysys	Ingram Micro
Arrow Electronics	Insight Enterprises
Avnet	Pc Mall
Cdw	Softchoice
Compucom	Tech Data

HISTORICAL FINANCIALS
Company Type: Private

Income Statement				FYE: December 31
	REVENUE ($ mil.)	NET INCOME ($ mil.)	NET PROFIT MARGIN	EMPLOYEES
12/19	10,372	253	2.4%	5,000
12/18	9,767	245	2.5%	—
12/17	8,243	197	2.4%	—
12/16	7,268	104	1.4%	—
Annual Growth	12.6%	34.3%	—	—

2019 Year-End Financials
Return on assets: 10.4%   Cash ($ mil.): 63
Return on equity: 36.9%
Current ratio: 1.30

SHRINERS INTERNATIONAL

EXECUTIVES

Ceo, Louis A Molnar
Cdo*, Stuart P Sullivan
Senior Manager, Data Center Op, Bradford Lydon
Occupational Specia, Cheryl Hanley
Law Specialist, Jesse Jacobowitz
Human Resources Director, Kristina Hamel
Staff, Pam Yao
Corporate Project Manager of H, Diane Jenkins
Public Relations Director, Tammy Dugan
Director, Christine Harrison
Director of Outpatient, Cindy Steiner

LOCATIONS

HQ: SHRINERS INTERNATIONAL
2900 N ROCKY POINT DR, TAMPA, FL 336071460
Phone: 813 281-0300
Web: WWW.SHRINERSINTERNATIONAL.ORG

HISTORICAL FINANCIALS

Company Type: Private

Income Statement				FYE: December 31
	REVENUE ($ mil.)	NET INCOME ($ mil.)	NET PROFIT MARGIN	EMPLOYEES
12/19	815	(87)	—	6,100
12/16	584	(269)	—	
Annual Growth 11.8%		—	—	—

2019 Year-End Financials

Return on assets: (-0.9%)   Cash ($ mil.): 33
Return on equity: (-1.0%)
Current ratio: —

SIERRA NEVADA CORPORATION

Sierra Nevada Corp. (SNC) is a trusted leader in solving the world's toughest challenges through advanced engineering technologies in Space Systems Commercial Solutions and National Security and Defense. The company's Dream Chaser spacecraft is scheduled for a 2021 launch for a trip to the International Space Station. The company also delivers tailored solutions to government and commercial customers with applications in space exploration and satellites aircraft integrations navigation and guidance systems threat detection and security scientific research and infrastructure protection. SNC's subsidiaries are Straight Flight and Sierra Completions. The privately held company was founded in 1963.

Operations

SNC is a trusted leader in engineering answers to the world's toughest challenges delivering customer-focused technologies and best-of-breed integrations in aerospace and defense. It creates the Dream Chaser spacecraft a multi-mission space utility vehicle designed for transporting crew and cargo to low-Earth orbit (LEO) destinations. It is also a world leader in Command Control Computers Communications and Intelligence Surveillance and Reconnaissance (C4ISR) that provide swift flexible and comprehensive solutions for the most difficult operational challenges. Its other solutions have included aircraft design modification and support rotary-wing integration and modernization shooting star transport vehicle cybersecurity navigation guidance and landing satellite solutions and electronic warfare systems.

Geographic Reach

SNC based in Sparks Nevada operates from about 40 offices in across the US and at customer sites around the world. It has offices in England Germany and Turkey

Sales and Marketing

Its existing supplier is Exostar.
Mergers and Acquisitions

EXECUTIVES

Ceo, Fatih Ozmen
Pres*, Eren Ozmen
Procurement Staff, Pete Palleschi
Vice President Logistics Isr, Wayne Killian
Information Technology Manager, Willa Simpson
Director of Technology, Tom Bernritter
Director of Applications Suppo, Roy Dorado
Engineer, Brian Flynton
Program Manager, Deb Kopecky
Director Programs, Jack Kimberly
Vice President Special Program, Jeff Summers
Auditors: DELOITTE & TOUCHE LLP LOS ANG

LOCATIONS

HQ: SIERRA NEVADA CORPORATION
444 SALOMON CIR, SPARKS, NV 894349651
Phone: 775 331-0222
Web: WWW.SNCORP.COM

PRODUCTS/OPERATIONS

Business Units

Dream Chaser
Integrated ISR Solutions
Aircraft Design Modification and Support
Rotary-Wing Integration & Remanufacturing
Space Exploration
Cyber Security
Navigation Guidance & Landing
Spacecraft & Satellite Solutions
Electronic Warfare Systems

COMPETITORS

Argon St	L3 Technologies
Bae Systems	Lockheed Martin
Drs Technologies	Northrop Grumman
Exelis	Raytheon
General Dynamics	United Technologies
Honeywell International	

HISTORICAL FINANCIALS

Company Type: Private

Income Statement				FYE: December 31
	REVENUE ($ mil.)	NET INCOME ($ mil.)	NET PROFIT MARGIN	EMPLOYEES
12/14	1,481	0	—	3,063
12/13	1,623	0	—	
12/12	1,400	0	—	
Annual Growth 2.9%		—	—	—

2014 Year-End Financials

Return on assets: —   Cash ($ mil.): 22
Return on equity: —
Current ratio: 1.50

SIGNATURE FINANCIAL LLC

EXECUTIVES

Ceo-MBR, Joseph J Depaolo
MBR, Eric Howell
Senior Vice President, Ann Buzzo
Senior Vice President, Anne Doligale
Senior Vice President, Lisa Wente
Senior Vice President, Marietta Mullane
Vice President, Brad Kranich
Senior Vice President, Peter Olsen
Vice President, Josh Schuyler
Vice President Commercial Lend, Brian Reid
Employee, Huy Doan

LOCATIONS

HQ: SIGNATURE FINANCIAL LLC
565 5TH AVE AT46TH, NEW YORK, NY 100172413
Phone: 646 865-0767
Web: WWW.SIGNATURENY.COM

HISTORICAL FINANCIALS

Company Type: Private

Income Statement				FYE: December 31
	ASSETS ($ mil.)	NET INCOME ($ mil.)	INCOME AS % OF ASSETS	EMPLOYEES
12/18	47,364	505	1.1%	30
12/17	43,119	387	0.9%	—
12/16	39,047	396	1.0%	—
12/15	33,450	373	1.1%	—
Annual Growth 12.3%		10.6%	—	—

2018 Year-End Financials

Return on assets: 1.1%   Sales ($ mil): 1,733
Return on equity: 11.5%

SINAI HOSPITAL OF BALTIMORE, INC.

Sinai Hospital of Baltimore part of the LifeBridge Health network provides medical care in northwestern Baltimore. The 470-bed hospital is a not-for-profit medical center that includes such facilities as a heart center a children's hospital a cancer institute and a rehab center. Other specialties include orthopedics neurology and women's care. Medical students from Johns Hopkins University and the University of Maryland do some of their training at the hospital. Sinai Hospital of Baltimore was founded in 1866 as the Hebrew Hospital and Asylum and became a subsidiary of LifeBridge when it merged with other area providers in 1998.

Operations

The Sinai Hospital of Baltimore handles about 26000 inpatient admissions and some 75000 emergency room visits per year. It also conducts about 20000 inpatient and outpatient surgeries annually.

The medical center conducts a number of education and training programs including residencies and fellowships for about 400 medical students each year. It is a designated training site for the Johns Hopkins University's ambulatory and internal medicine clerkships.

Strategy

Sinai Hospital of Baltimore has completed several expansion efforts in recent years. In 2012 it opened a new dedicated inpatient hospice unit as well as a new center for geriatric surgery. In addition the 20-bed Friedman Neurological Rehabilitation Center was completed that year.

EXECUTIVES

Ceo, Neil Meltzer
Chief Medical Officer*, Daniel C Silverman
Chm*, Brian L Moffet
Treas*, Barry F Levin
SEC*, Nancy Hackerman
Staff, Roger Sheets
Occupational Specia, Amy Herman
Doctor In Physical Therapy, Maureen Abenoja
MD, Amadeo Rivera
Controller, Lauren Relf

LOCATIONS

HQ: SINAI HOSPITAL OF BALTIMORE, INC.
2401 W BELVEDERE AVE, BALTIMORE, MD 212155270
Phone: 410 601-5678
Web: WWW.LIFEBRIDGEHEALTH.ORG

PRODUCTS/OPERATIONS

Selected Centers
Alvin & Lois Lapidus Cancer Institute at LifeBridge Health
Center for Joint Preservation and Replacement
Children's Hospital at Sinai
ER-7 Emergency Center
Heart Center at Sinai
International Center for Limb Lengthening
Krieger Eye Institute
Louis and Phyllis Friedman Neurological Rehabilitation Center
Rubin Institute for Advanced Orthopedics
Sandra and Malcolm Berman Brain & Spine Institute
Sinai Rehabilitation Center
The Spine Center at Sinai

Selected Services
Allergy and Immunology
Anesthesia
Cardiology
Cancer/Medical Oncology
Dermatology
Dialysis
Emergency Medicine
Endocrinology and Metabolism
Family Medicine
Gastroenterology
General Internal Medicine
Geriatric Medicine
Infectious Diseases
Nephrology (kidneys)
Pulmonary and Critical Care Medicine
Rheumatology (joints tendons)
Neurology
Neurosurgery
Obstetrics and Gynecology
Ophthalmology (eye care)
Oral and Maxillofacial Surgery and Dentistry
Orthopedic Surgery
Otolaryngology (ear nose & throat)
Pathology
Pediatrics
Pharmacy
Physical Medicine and Rehabilitation
Psychiatry
Radiation Oncology
Radiology
Surgery
Urology

COMPETITORS

Anne Arundel Medical Center
Ascension Health
Bon Secours Health
Johns Hopkins Health System
Medstar Health
Meritus Health

Franklin Square Hospital Center Gbmc
University Of Maryland Medical System

HISTORICAL FINANCIALS
Company Type: Private

Income Statement   FYE: June 30

	REVENUE ($ mil.)	NET INCOME ($ mil.)	NET PROFIT MARGIN	EMPLOYEES
06/20	853	59	7.0%	4,497
06/19	803	41	5.1%	—
06/17	769	63	8.2%	—
06/16	690	26	3.9%	—
Annual Growth	5.4%	22.4%	—	—

2020 Year-End Financials

Return on assets: 9.4%   Cash ($ mil.): 74
Return on equity: 55.0%
Current ratio: 1.00

SKANSKA USA CIVIL INC.

Skanska USA Civil builds some of the world's largest cable-stayed bridges. Part of the US operations of Swedish engineering and construction giant Skanska Skanska USA Civil focuses on infrastructure projects throughout the country. Along with sister firm Skanska USA Building it is a market leader in the New York area where it has worked on the Brooklyn Bridge the AirTrain light-rail system and the Roosevelt Island Bridge. It builds roads tunnels and rail systems in addition to bridges and industrial and marine facilities such as power and water filtration plants gas-treatment plants and dry docks.

Operations

Parent-company Skanska USA operates Skanska USA Civil and three sister business units with different specialties such as Skanska USA Building Infrastructure Development USA and Commercial Development USA. The parent boasts a staff of nearly 11000 US employees (as of mid-2016).

Among Skanska USA Civil's divisions is Bayshore Concrete which produces precast concrete components for tunnel bridge dock and pier construction. Bayshore Concrete's plant in Virginia focuses on East Coast shipments. Skanska Koch which is based in New Jersey has built or worked on some of the country's most recognizable structures such as Yankee Stadium and the Brooklyn Bridge.

Another division Underpinning & Foundation Skanska is a heavy foundation contractor based in New York. It offers underpinning and pile-driving services for private and public projects that range from single-story buildings to skyscrapers.

Geographic Reach

While the firm's largest market is in its home state of New York it serves the US from offices in California Washington Arizona and Florida. Parent Skanska USA has 31 offices across the US and works on projects in nearly all 50 states the District of Columbia and Puerto Rico (as of mid-2016). The US is Skanska AB's largest market accounting for 37% of its global revenue during 2015.

Sales and Marketing

Skanska USA Civil provides public and private clients with construction services in the civil mechanical industrial marine foundation and environmental sectors.

Financial Performance

Parent-company Skanska USA's revenue has been growing in recent years and reached $7.1 billion in 2015.

Strategy

Parent Skanska USA ranked the third-largest building/manufacturing contractor by revenue and the third-largest heavy contractor by revenue on Engineering News-Record's rankings in 2015. The Skanska USA Civil division in particular has built a dominating presence on the East Coast since completing major projects such as the Meadowlands Football Stadium and Boston's Central Artery.

Skanska USA Civil in 2015 secured a contract with Competitive Power Ventures Holdings (CPV) to build the CPV Valley Energy Center in Wawayanda New York with an order value of SEK 2.1 billion ($250 million); a new contract with MTA New York City Transit to rebuild three rail stations in Brooklyn with an order value of SEK 670 million ($80 million); and a new joint-venture contract in California to improve State Route 58 near Hinkley with Skanska USA's share of the order value worth SEK 640 million ($76 million).

Sister division Skanska USA Building in 2015 secured a SEK 750 million ($89 million) contract from existing customer Tahoma School District to construct a new high school and learning center in Maple Valley Washington. That year the division also won a SEK 730 million ($87 million) contract to build Boeing's Commercial Airplane Decorative Paint Facility in Charleston South Carolina.

Company Background

Civil construction which is often publicly funded was less affected by the economic downturn that hindered other construction segments such as home building. However Skanska is looking to diversify its business and become less dependent on public projects. In 2011 the company acquired US-based Industrial Contractors for $135 million. Industrial Contractors (integrated into Skanska US Civil) works on power and energy commercial and light industrial and heavy industrial projects.

EXECUTIVES

Pres-Ceo, Salvatore Mancini
Project Manager, James Tweedall
Project Manager, Jessica Miller
Management, Choice Sterling
Project Engineer, Steve Revitsky
Equipment Superintendent, Chris Brown
Project Engineer, Patrick Bestebreur
Engineer, Marc Vento
Project Manager, David Sharpnack
Environmental Coordinator, Jeramy Jackson
Senior Project Manager, Jeremy Cortesio
Auditors: KPMG LLP NEW YORK NY

LOCATIONS

HQ: SKANSKA USA CIVIL INC.
7520 ASTORIA BLVD STE 200, EAST ELMHURST, NY 113701135
Phone: 718 340-0777
Web: WWW.USA.SKANSKA.COM

PRODUCTS/OPERATIONS

Selected Services
Commercial development
Construction management
Design-build
Financial services
Pharmaceutical validation
Pre-construction
Public-private validation
Self-performance
Operating Units
Bayshore Concrete Products
Industrial Construction Skanska
PCI Skanska

Skanska Koch
Underpinning & Foundation Skanska

COMPETITORS

A & L
American Civil Constructors Holdings
American Infrastructure
Balfour Beatty Infrastructure
Bechtel
Flatiron Construction
Fluor
Granite Construction
J.l. Patterson & Associates
Jones Bros.
Lane Construction
Parsons Brinckerhoff
Parsons Corporation
Peter Kiewit Sons'
Railworks
Ruscilli Construction
Tutor Perini
Vecellio Group

HISTORICAL FINANCIALS

Company Type: Private

Income Statement				FYE: December 31
	REVENUE ($ mil.)	NET INCOME ($ mil.)	NET PROFIT MARGIN	EMPLOYEES
12/08	1,753	54	3.1%	5,200
12/07	1,611	52	3.2%	—
Annual Growth	8.8%	5.2%	—	—

2008 Year-End Financials

Return on assets: 6.1%
Return on equity: 13.6%
Current ratio: 1.50
Cash ($ mil.): 172

SKANSKA USA CIVIL NORTHEAST INC.

EXECUTIVES

Ceo, Richard Cavallaro
Sr V Pres*, Ralph Russo
Chief Engineer, Alfredas Daugiala
Human Resources Executive, Frank Varisco
Project Executive, Donald Fusco
Design Build Manager, David Tullis
Chief Estimator, Fabio Liscidini

LOCATIONS

HQ: SKANSKA USA CIVIL NORTHEAST INC.
7520 ASTORIA BLVD STE 200, EAST ELMHURST, NY
113701135
Phone: 718 340-0777

HISTORICAL FINANCIALS

Company Type: Private

Income Statement				FYE: December 31
	REVENUE ($ mil.)	NET INCOME ($ mil.)	NET PROFIT MARGIN	EMPLOYEES
12/08	816	51	6.3%	1,500
12/07	622	27	4.5%	—
12/06	467	17	3.7%	—
12/05	487	12	2.6%	—
Annual Growth	18.8%	59.9%	—	—

2008 Year-End Financials

Return on assets: 12.0%
Return on equity: 25.1%
Current ratio: 1.70
Cash ($ mil.): 121

SKF USA INC.

SKF USA is a subsidiary of Swedish ball bearing giant AB SKF and a global supplier of bearings seals lubricants linear motion components and condition monitoring systems. It also specializes in related services from repair and rebuilding to consulting logistics and training. Its repair stations also provide bearing inspection repair and overhaul services. With hundreds of manufacturing sales and authorized distribution locations across the US SKF USA's offerings are geared at a wide range of industries including aerospace automotive construction machine tooling and alternative energy. Brand names include Alemite Lincoln Reelcraft and S2M.

Operations

SKF USA groups its technologies across five platforms: bearings and units seals lubrication systems mechatronics (combining mechanics and electronics into intelligent systems) and services.

For the auto industry the SKF Vehicle Service Market serves the aftermarket for cars and commercial vehicles by providing high quality products and premium services to its customers.

Geographic Reach

Based in Lansdale PA SKF USA has almost 30 manufacturing sites in the US where it provides customized application engineering services through factories in Houston and Cleveland. The company additionally operates a technical Center in Plymouth Michigan that provides a range of engineering and testing services.

Sales and Marketing

SKF USA sells thousands of products and services through a network of over 4000 US-based authorized distributors. For the auto industry it serves the aftermarket for cars and commercial vehicles.

EXECUTIVES

Pres, John Schmidt
Pres, Poul Jeppesen
V Pres, Gunilla Nilsson
Cfo, Drew Cross
Treas, Terry Papincak
Area Support Manager, Ruthe Barnes
Manager, Hector Villalobos
Engineer, Joakim Bergstrm
Engineer, Robert Stam
Business Analyst, Schaik Paul
Manager, Tim Rushton

LOCATIONS

HQ: SKF USA INC.
890 FORTY FOOT RD, LANSDALE, PA 194464303
Phone: 267 436-6000
Web: WWW.SKF.COM

PRODUCTS/OPERATIONS

PRODUCTS

Actuation systems
Bearings units & housings
Condition monitoring
Coupling systems
Linear motion
Lubrication solutions
Magnetic systems
Maintenance products

Power transmission
Seals
Test & measurement equipment
Vehicle aftermarket
SERVICES
Asset management services
Business consulting
Customer training
Engineering consultancy
Logistics
Mechanical maintenance
Remanufacturing & maintenance services
Service contracts

COMPETITORS

A. Stucki Company
Accuride International
Enpro
Fag Kugelfischer
Hoover Precision
Products
Jtekt
Kaydon
Minebeamitsumi

Nn Inc.
Nsk
Ntn Bearing Corp. Of
America
Nippon Bearing
Rbc Bearings
Schaeffler
Timken
Waukesha Bearings

HISTORICAL FINANCIALS

Company Type: Private

Income Statement				FYE: December 31
	REVENUE ($ mil.)	NET INCOME ($ mil.)	NET PROFIT MARGIN	EMPLOYEES
12/14	3,138	155	5.0%	4,000
12/13	2,554	95	3.7%	—
12/12	2,397	138	5.8%	—
Annual Growth	14.4%	6.0%	—	—

2014 Year-End Financials

Return on assets: 3.8%
Return on equity: 16.4%
Current ratio: 2.40
Cash ($ mil.): 29

SMDC MEDICAL CENTER

EXECUTIVES

Ceo, Peter Person
Ceo*, John Smylie
Gen Counsel*, James N Abelsen
Director, Donna Van Kessel
Scientist, Stephen Waring
Senior Administrator, Jeff Nast

LOCATIONS

HQ: SMDC MEDICAL CENTER
502 E 2ND ST, DULUTH, MN 558051913
Phone: 218 726-4000
Web: WWW.ESSENTIAHEALTH.ORG

HISTORICAL FINANCIALS

Company Type: Private

Income Statement				FYE: June 30
	REVENUE ($ mil.)	NET INCOME ($ mil.)	NET PROFIT MARGIN	EMPLOYEES
06/20	557	(15)	—	2,405
06/18	536	6	1.2%	—
06/17	504	0	0.0%	—
06/16	500	16	3.4%	—
Annual Growth	2.7%	—	—	—

2020 Year-End Financials

Return on assets: (-1.1%)
Return on equity: (-11.0%)
Current ratio: 0.30
Cash ($ mil.): 133

SMITHSONIAN INSTITUTION

One of the world's leading cultural institutions the Smithsonian Institution houses some 155 million objects in about 20 museums gardens zoo and galleries most of which are on the National Mall in Washington DC. Admission to all but one of the Smithsonian's facilities is free. Some of its museums are Anacostia Community Museum National Air and Space Museum National Museum of African Art National Museum of American History National Postal Museum Smithsonian American Art Museum and Smithsonian Institution Building ("Castle").

Operations

The Smithsonian Institution Traveling Exhibition Service (SITES) organizes exhibitions on art history and science and circulates them around the country. Each year SITES travels more than 40 exhibitions to hundreds of U.S. cities and towns in all 50 states and the District of Columbia where they are viewed by millions of people.

Its research facilities includes the Archives of American Art Smithsonian Conservation Biology Institute Smithsonian Astrophysical Observatory Smithsonian Environmental Research Center Museum Conservation Institute Smithsonian Libraries Smithsonian Institution Archives Smithsonian Tropical Research Institute and the Marine Station at Fort Pierce Florida.

Geographic Reach

The Smithsonian Institution is located in Washington DC.

Sales and Marketing

The Smithsonian home page www.si.edu offers a wide range of information from planning a visit to exploring the collections online. Also the Smithsonian had 178 million unique visitors to its website in 2020 and has more than 30 mobile apps digital magazines and more than 17 million images and records on the Collections Search Center site. Across its most frequently used social-media platforms Facebook Twitter Instagram and YouTube the Smithsonian had more than 18 million followers and 375 million YouTube views in 2020.

Strategy

The company has a five-year strategic plan that was launched in 2017. The strategic plan has a number of goals which Includes:

Be One Smithsonian - The company will work together as One Smithsonian to amplify the power of the stories it tells increasing reach and impact. It will also view all of its exhibitions and spaces as an Institution-wide portfolio to be deployed strategically. Additionally the company will be setting standards to create a seamless visitor experience across the Smithsonian by creating a unified customer relationship approach.

Catalyze new conversations and address complex challenges - The company will be magnifying its national and global reach through new collaborative approaches. It will also create new forums across the Smithsonian to proffer solutions to problems of national and global import.

Reach 1 billion people a year with a digital-first strategy - The company will create a digital laboratory to test and develop emerging museum-related digital technologies. The company will also be forging transformative strategic partnerships with major digital leaders and create new digital platforms for scholars and educators to better access Smithsonian collections research and education resources.

Understand and impact 21st-century audiences - The company is working on learning how demographic changes new learning styles and new technologies affect the relevance of cultural institutions. It will also tell the complete American story in person and online in all of its museums exhibits and programs?and across them?with a focus on all Americans nationally and locally.

HISTORY

English chemist James Smithson wrote a proviso to his will in 1826 that would lead to the creation of the Smithsonian Institution. When he died in 1829 he left his estate to his nephew Henry James Hungerford with the stipulation that if Hungerford died without heirs the estate would go to the US to create "an Establishment for the increase and diffusion of knowledge among men." Hungerford died in 1835 without any heirs and the US government inherited more than $500000 in gold.

Congress squandered the money after it was received in 1838 but perhaps feeling pangs of guilt covered the loss. The Smithsonian was finally created in 1846 and Princeton physicist Joseph Henry was named its first secretary. That year it established the Museum of Natural History the Museum of History and Technology and the National Gallery of Art. The Smithsonian's National Museum was developed around the collection of the US Patent Office in 1858. The Smithsonian continued to expand adding the National Zoological Park in 1889 and the Smithsonian Astrophysical Observatory in 1890.

The Freer Gallery a gift of industrialist Charles Freer opened in 1923. The National Gallery was renamed the National Collection of Fine Arts in 1937 and a new National Gallery created with Andrew Mellon's gift of his art collection and a building opened in 1941. The Air and Space Museum was established in 1946.

More museums were added in the 1960s including the National Portrait Gallery in 1962 and the Anacostia Museum (exhibits and materials on African-American history) in 1967. The Kennedy Center for the Performing Arts was opened in 1971. The Collection of Fine Arts was renamed the National Museum of American Art and the Museum of History and Technology was renamed the National Museum of American History in 1980.

The Smithsonian placed its first-ever contribution boxes in four of its museums in 1993.

A planned exhibit featuring the Enola Gay — the plane that dropped the atomic bomb on Hiroshima — created a firestorm in 1994 with critics charging that the exhibit downplayed Japanese aggression and US casualties in WWII. The original exhibit was canceled in 1995 the director of the Air and Space Museum resigned and a scaled-down version of the exhibit premiered. In 2004 the exhibit attracted more protestors prompting Smithsonian officials to evacuate and temporarily close the museum.

Large contributions from private donors continued in the 1990s; the Mashantucket Pequot tribe gave $10 million from its casino operations in 1994 for the Smithsonian's planned American Indian museum and prolific electronics inventor Jerome Lemelson donated $10.4 million in 1995. The museum celebrated its sesquicentennial in 1996 amid news that $500 million in repairs were needed over the next 10 years.

California real estate developer Kenneth Behring gave the largest cash donation ever to the museum in 1997 — $20 million for the National Museum of Natural History. Short of funds the Smithsonian had to cut back on its 150th-anniversary traveling exhibit that year. The Smithsonian announced a $26 million renovation for the National Museum

of Natural History in 1998. Two years later Behring quadrupled his record-breaking 1997 donation of $20 million by giving $80 million to the National Museum of American History. Catherine Reynolds withdrew most of her $38 million gift in 2002 after the Smithsonian Institution refused to implement her ideas for an exhibit at the National Museum of American History.

The National Museum of the American Indian opened on the National Mall in 2004.

Secretary Lawrence Small resigned under pressure in March 2007 amid criticism of his spending practices. Cristi¨n Samper director of the Smithsonian's National Museum of Natural History was named acting secretary. A report on the matter issued by the Smithsonian in June said its Board of Regents failed to provide the oversight that might have prevented Small's extravagant spending.

In July 2008 Wayne Clough became the 12th secretary of the Smithsonian.

EXECUTIVES

Ceo, Gary M Beer
Pres, Christopher Liedel
Cfo, Alice C Maroni
Cfo, Albert Horvath
Treas, Sudeep Anand
SEC, Lonnie G Bunch III
Early Childhood Director, Meredith McMahon
Director of Production, Rick Pelasara
Auditors: KPMG LLP WASHINGTON DISTRICT

LOCATIONS

HQ: SMITHSONIAN INSTITUTION
1000 JEFFERSON DR SW, WASHINGTON, DC
205600009
Phone: 202 633-1000
Web: WWW.SI.EDU

PRODUCTS/OPERATIONS

2016 Operating Revenue

	% of total
Federal appropriations	53
Contributions & private grants	18
Business activities	11
Government grants & contracts	8
Endowment	5
Other	5
Total	**100**

Selected Museums and Research Centers

Anacostia Community Museum
Arthur M. Sackler Gallery
Arts and Industries Building
Center for Folklife and Cultural Heritage
Conservation and Research Center
Cooper-Hewitt National Design Museum (New York)
Freer Gallery of Art
Hirshhorn Museum and Sculpture Garden
National Air and Space Museum
National Museum of African Art
National Museum of American History
National Museum of Natural History
National Museum of the American Indian
National Museum of the American Indian - George
  Gustav Heye Center (New York)
National Science Research Center
National Portrait Gallery
National Postal Museum
National Zoological Park
Smithsonian American Art Museum
Smithsonian Astrophysical Observatory
Smithsonian Center for Latino Initiatives
Smithsonian Center for Materials Research and
  Education
Smithsonian Environmental Research Center (SERC)
Smithsonian Institution Building (The Castle)
Smithsonian Museum Conservation Institute
Smithsonian Tropical Research Institute

HISTORICAL FINANCIALS

Company Type: Private

Income Statement				FYE: September 30
	REVENUE ($ mil.)	NET INCOME ($ mil.)	NET PROFIT MARGIN	EMPLOYEES
09/20	1,389	302	21.8%	6,100
09/19	1,375	180	13.1%	—
09/18	1,563	177	11.3%	—
09/17	1,514	153	10.1%	—
Annual Growth	(2.8%)	25.5%	—	—

2020 Year-End Financials

Return on assets: 5.0%
Return on equity: 6.5%
Current ratio: 1.20

Cash ($ mil.): 886

SMMH PRACTICE PLAN, INC.

Auditors: KPMG LLP PITTSBURGH PA

LOCATIONS

HQ: SMMH PRACTICE PLAN, INC.
7175 SALTSBURG RD, PITTSBURGH, PA 152352252
Phone: 412 795-6069

HISTORICAL FINANCIALS

Company Type: Private

Income Statement				FYE: June 30
	REVENUE ($ mil.)	NET INCOME ($ mil.)	NET PROFIT MARGIN	EMPLOYEES
06/15	2,060	27	1.3%	26
06/14	2,005	570	28.4%	—
06/13	1,985	402	20.3%	—
06/12	1,976	(90)	—	—
Annual Growth	1.4%	—	—	—

2015 Year-End Financials

Return on assets: 4.8%
Return on equity: 1.3%
Current ratio: 0.60

Cash ($ mil.): 49

SNAKE RIVER SUGAR COMPANY

EXECUTIVES

Prin, Duane Grant
Pres*, Vic Jaro
Exec Dir*, Terry L Ketterling
SEC*, John McCreedy
Cfo*, Wayne Neely
Project Engineer Controls, Larry McLeister
Auditors: EIDEBAILLY LLP BOISE IDAHO

LOCATIONS

HQ: SNAKE RIVER SUGAR COMPANY
1951 S SATURN WAY STE 100, BOISE, ID 837092924
Phone: 208 383-6500
Web: WWW.AMALGAMATEDSUGAR.COM

HISTORICAL FINANCIALS

Company Type: Private

Income Statement				FYE: August 31
	REVENUE ($ mil.)	NET INCOME ($ mil.)	NET PROFIT MARGIN	EMPLOYEES
08/11	876	13	1.5%	2,500
08/10	839	18	2.2%	—
08/09	658	22	3.4%	—
Annual Growth	15.3%	(23.8%)	—	—

2011 Year-End Financials

Return on assets: 1.9%
Return on equity: 4.8%
Current ratio: 0.80

Cash ($ mil.): 17

SNYDER'S-LANCE, INC.

If you're familiar with the Eatsmart Emerald Lance Snyder's-Lance (formerly Lance) has undoubtedly helped you satisfy a snack attack. The company produces iconic brands that satisfy snackers across the globe with its one of the largest distribution networks in the business and an advanced research & development. Its snacks are sold under the Lance Cape Cod Tom's Archway and Snyder's brands at food retailers mass merchants and convenience and club stores in the US. International brands include Kettle Chips.

Operations

Synder's-Lance manufactures pretzels sandwich crackers kettle cooked chips pretzel crackers cookies potato chips tortilla chips popcorn nuts and other salty snacks. It operates under brand names Snyder's Lance Kettle Cape Cod Pretzel Crisps Pop Secret Emerald Late July Krunchers Tom's Archway Jays Stella Doro Eatsmart and O-Ke-Doke.

Geographic Reach

Based in North Carolina Snyder's-Lance operates manufacturing facilities in the US in North Carolina Oregon Pennsylvania Indiana Georgia Arizona Massachusetts Florida Ohio and Wisconsin as well as in the UK.

HISTORY

A business deal gone awry stuck coffee dealer Philip Lance with 500 pounds of peanuts in 1913. Selling nickel bags of roasted peanuts and then peanut butter Lance began packaging peanut-butter-and-cracker sandwiches. His son-in-law Salem Van Every joined him two years later to form Lance Packing. Lance introduced Toastchee in 1938 and by 1939 the year the firm became Lance sales reached $2 million. The company began serving the institutional market in 1953 and began selling through vending machines the next year. Lance went public in 1961.

The family continued to run the company until 1973 when Van Every's grandson retired as CEO. After decades of serving mom-and-pop retailers Lance found the snack market changing. Individual stores gave way to chains; Frito-Lay gobbled up grocery shelf space; and regional rival Austin Quality Foods nabbed sales in the new warehouse/club store market. Eventually the conservative company responded with an influx of new

management restructuring and the advent of marketing.

Lance purchased Tamming Foods (sugar wafers) and Cape Cod Potato Chips (salty snacks) in 1999. Lance then signed an agreement with China Peregrine (now China Premium Food Corp) to export private-label snack foods to China. (Lance has since ceased distribution in China.)

In 2005 Lance's board of directors elected Bill Prezzano as chairman. David Singer formerly EVP and CFO of Coca-Cola Bottling Co. Consolidated was named president and CEO of the company. And in 2005 Lance purchased a Canadian sugar-wafer manufacturing plant from A&M Cookie Company Canada.

The $40 million acquisition of Tom's Foods in 2005 added four new bakery and potato chip manufacturing plants to the company's operations. Lance manufactures about 90% of its products; the remainder is purchased for resale.

While Frito-Lay dominates the snack-aisle grocery shelves Lance's stronghold has been its company-owned vending machines placed in 15000 locations such as break rooms and cafeterias. In order to concentrate on more profitable operations in 2006 Lance began phasing out its vending-machine sales and ceased vending operations altogether in 2007. In addition the company joined the ranks of munchies makers that offer healthier products in 2007 with the $2 million purchase of a minority interest in Late July Products a Massachusetts-based organic snack food maker (crackers and sandwich crackers and cookies).

EXECUTIVES

Pres, Valerie Oswalt
Cco, John T Maples
Sr V Pres, Margaret E Wicklund
Director Compensation, Kim Littlejohn
Packaging Department Manager, Kirk Steiner
Quality Assurance Supervisor, Malinda Delbridge
Key Account Manager, Manny Ardeljan
Manager, Mark Morris
Manager, Sales Strategy, Bari Kriependorf
National Direct Account Manage, Chris Jeffrey
District Sales Manager, Eric Szymczyk
Auditors: PRICEWATERHOUSECOOPERS LLP CH

LOCATIONS

HQ: SNYDER'S-LANCE, INC.
13515 BALNTYN CORP PL, CHARLOTTE, NC 282772706
Phone: 704 554-1421
Web: WWW.SNYDERSLANCEPRODUCTLOCATOR.COM

PRODUCTS/OPERATIONS

2015 Revenue

	$ mil.	% of total
Branded products	1,155	70
Private brands	335	20
Other	165	10
Total	**1,656**	**100**

Selected Brands

Archway
Brent
Bugles
Cape Cod Potato Chips
Captain's Wafers
Choc-o-Lunch
Delicious
Diamond of California
Don Pablo's
EatSmart
Emerald
Grande
Jays
Kettle brand
KETTLE

Krunchers!
Lance
Nekot
Nipchee
Pop Secret
Pretzel Crisps
Sam's
Salerno
Snyder's of Hanover
Stella D'oro
Texas Pete
Thunder
Toastchee
Toasty
Tom's
Van-o-Lunch
Vista

COMPETITORS

American Pop Corn	Kettle Foods
Beer Nuts	King Nut Companies
Bridgford Foods	Legacy Bakehouse
Campbell Soup	Mckee Foods
Chattanooga Bakery	Mondelez International
Conagra	Old Dutch Foods
Evans Food Products	Otis Spunkmeyer
Flowers Foods	Pepperidge Farm
Frito-lay	Poindexter Nut
General Mills	Pretzels Inc.
Golden Enterprises	Procter & Gamble
Inventure Foods	Snappy Popcorn
John Sanfilippo & Son	Weaver Popcorn Company
Kellogg U.s. Snacks	

HISTORICAL FINANCIALS

Company Type: Private

Income Statement				FYE: December 30
	REVENUE ($ mil.)	NET INCOME ($ mil.)	NET PROFIT MARGIN	EMPLOYEES
12/17	2,226	149	6.7%	6,100
12/16*	2,109	14	0.7%	—
01/15	1,620	192	11.9%	—
12/13	1,761	79	4.5%	—
Annual Growth	6.0%	17.2%	—	—

*Fiscal year change

2017 Year-End Financials

Return on assets: 4.1% Cash ($ mil.): 18
Return on equity: 7.4%
Current ratio: 1.60

SOCORRO INDEPENDENT SCHOOL DISTRICT

EXECUTIVES

Superintendent, Jose Espinoza
Superintendent, Charles Fighs
Cfo, Tony Reza
Staff, Philip A Acosta
Coordinator, Susie Godina
Project Coordinator, Zaide Cabezuela
Network Administrator, Oscar Dominguez
Admin Specialist I, Adriana Balandran
Nurse, Ramona Garcia
Maintenance Supervisor Mechani, Antonio Regalado
Teacher Athletic Coordinator, Mark Torres
Auditors: GIBSON RUDDOCK PATTERSON LLC

LOCATIONS

HQ: SOCORRO INDEPENDENT SCHOOL DISTRICT
12440 ROJAS DR, EL PASO, TX 799285261
Phone: 915 937-0100
Web: WWW.SISD.NET

HISTORICAL FINANCIALS

Company Type: Private

Income Statement				FYE: June 30
	REVENUE ($ mil.)	NET INCOME ($ mil.)	NET PROFIT MARGIN	EMPLOYEES
06/20	549	48	8.8%	6,000
06/19	509	120	23.7%	—
06/18	470	168	35.8%	—
06/17	453	200	44.1%	—
Annual Growth	6.6%	(37.6%)	—	—

2020 Year-End Financials

Return on assets: 3.2% Cash ($ mil.): 566
Return on equity: 45.1%
Current ratio: —

SOLSTICE HOLDINGS INC.

EXECUTIVES

Pres, Mr Doug L Devos
Chm, Stephen Van Andel
Exec V Pres-Cfo, Russ Evans
Exec V Pres-Coo, Alvin Koop
V Pres, Mr Michael Mohr
Cntrl, Mr Craig V Witcher
Senior Software Developer, Carolyn Knott

LOCATIONS

HQ: SOLSTICE HOLDINGS INC.
7575 FULTON ST E, ADA, MI 493550001
Phone: 616 787-1000
Web: WWW.AMWAY.COM

HISTORICAL FINANCIALS

Company Type: Private

Income Statement				FYE: December 31
	REVENUE ($ mil.)	NET INCOME ($ mil.)	NET PROFIT MARGIN	EMPLOYEES
12/08	8,235	0	—	14,000
12/07	7,168	0	—	—
12/06	6,387	0	—	—
Annual Growth	13.5%	—	—	—

2008 Year-End Financials

Return on assets: — Cash ($ mil.): 1,072
Return on equity: —
Current ratio: 1.10

SOUTH BROWARD HOSPITAL DISTRICT

South Broward Hospital District (dba Memorial Healthcare System) is one of the largest public healthcare systems in the nation and highly re-garded for its exceptional patient- and family-centered care. It has been a leader in providing high-quality healthcare services to South Florida residents the system's major hospitals include Memorial Regional Hospital Memorial Hospital Pembroke Memorial Hospital West and Memorial Hospital Miramar. The system operates a total of 1980 licensed hospital beds and some 120 licensed nursing home beds and provide services including diagnostic emergency surgical and rehabilitative care. Memorial also operates a pediatric hospital cardiac and vascular medicine institute a cancer treatment center and a center for women's health as well as community clinics.

Operations

The system's hospitals include Memorial Regional Memorial Regional Hospital South Joe DiMaggio Children's Memorial Hospital West Memorial Hospital Miramar Memorial Hospital Pembroke Memorial Home Health Services and the Memorial Manor nursing home.

Memorial Regional offers a cardiac and vascular institute a cancer institute and a neuroscience center. ER and Trauma Center is a Level I Trauma Center staffed by board-certified trauma surgeons and equipped to handle the most critical situations.

Memorial Regional Hospital and affiliated providers bring in about 50% of the company's revenue followed by Memorial Hospital West (more than 25%) Memorial Hospital Miramar (approximately 10%) and Memorial Hospital Pembroke (about 10%) while other non-hospital operations and eliminations account for the remaining.

In addition the system's net patient service provides more than 90% of revenue. Disproportionate share distribution accounts for less than 5% while other operating revenue represents the remainder.

Geographic Reach

Memorial Healthcare System hospitals and care centers provide patient- and family-centered care throughout South Florida.

Financial Performance

The company's revenue for fiscal 2021 increased by 8% to $2.3 billion compared from the prior year with $2.2 billion.

Cash held by the company at the end of fiscal 2021 decreased to $138.0 million. Cash provided by operations and financing activities were $81.9 million and $15.3 million respectively. Cash used for investing activities was $235.9 million mainly for payments of investments.

Mergers and Acquisitions

In mid-2020 Memorial Healthcare System acquired Broward Guardian a Medicare accountable care organization (ACO) composed of mostly primary care physicians in South Florida. This acquisition allows Memorial to support the continued development of a vibrant network of community-based primary care physicians to coordinate care for Medicare patients while providing physicians the necessary resources to become successful in the emerging value-based healthcare model.

EXECUTIVES

Ceo, Frank V Sacco
Evp and Chief Administrative O, Anthony C Krayer III
Cfo, Matthew Muhart
Svp-Cmo, Marc Napp
Evp-Coo, Leah Carpenter
Chief Staff, Larry Shulruff
Chief of Pediatric, Rosha Mc Coy
Prin, Charmaine Baker
Chief Information Security Off, Joe Barron
Evp and Coo, Aurelio M Fernandez III
Internal Medicine Practitioner, Mirna Valencia
Auditors: ERNST & YOUNG LLP MIAMI FL

LOCATIONS

HQ: SOUTH BROWARD HOSPITAL DISTRICT
3501 JOHNSON ST, HOLLYWOOD, FL 330215421
Phone: 954 987-2000
Web: WWW.MHS.NET

PRODUCTS/OPERATIONS

2015 Sales

	$ mil.	% of total
Net patient service	1,630	92
Disproportionate share distribution	83	5
Other operating revenue	49	3
Total	**1,764**	**100**

Selected Facilities

Esther L. Grossman Women's Health & Resource Center
Memorial Cancer Institute
Memorial Hospital Miramar
Memorial Hospital Pembroke
Memorial Hospital West
Memorial Manor
Memorial Outpatient Center
Memorial Primary Care Center - Dania Beach
Memorial Primary Care Center - Hollywood
Memorial Primary Care Center - Miramar
Memorial Primary Care Center - West Hollywood
Memorial Regional Hospital
  Joe DiMaggio Children's Hospital
Memorial Regional Hospital South
Memorial Regional Hospital Fitness & Rehabilitation
  Center
Memorial Same Day Surgery Center
Memorial Urgent Care Center
Same Day Surgery Center at Memorial Hospital West

COMPETITORS

Baptist Health South Florida	Florida Hospital Heartland
Boca Raton Regional Hospital	Hca
Broward Health	Jackson Health System
Continucare	Mjhha
	South Miami Hospital

HISTORICAL FINANCIALS

Company Type: Private

Income Statement				FYE: April 30
	REVENUE ($ mil.)	NET INCOME ($ mil.)	NET PROFIT MARGIN	EMPLOYEES
04/21	2,339	283	12.1%	9,200
04/20	2,159	156	7.3%	—
04/19	2,148	165	7.7%	—
04/18	2,014	64	3.2%	—
Annual Growth	5.1%	63.7%	—	—

2021 Year-End Financials

Return on assets: 6.9%   Cash ($ mil.): 137
Return on equity: 10.6%
Current ratio: 6.60

SOUTH CAROLINA PUBLIC SERVICE AUTHORITY (INC)

This company turns the lights on in South Carolina. South Carolina Public Service Authority known as Santee Cooper (after two interconnected river systems) provides wholesale electricity to 20 cooperatives and two municipalities that serve more than 2 million customers in South Carolina. It directly retails electricity to more than 174000 customers. One of the largest US state-owned utilities Santee Cooper operates in all 46 counties in South Carolina and has stakes in power plants (fossil-fueled nuclear hydro and renewable) that give it more than 5180 MW of generating capacity. Its Santee Cooper Regional Water System also distributes water to customers in its service area.

Operations

Santee Cooper operates 5029 miles of transmission lines and more than 2841 miles of distribution lines. It also operates 105 transmission stations and 54 distribution substations. The company is the leading renewable energy producer in South Carolina.

Geographic Reach

In addition to supplying power to 20 cooperatives in all 46 counties in South Carolina Santee Cooper also supplies power directly to 29 large industrial customers in 10 counties Charleston Air Force Base the town of Bamberg and the City of Georgetown.

Sales and Marketing

The company serves more than 2 million customers in South Carolina. It directly retails electricity to more than 174000 customers.

Financial Performance

In 2015 Santee Cooper's net revenues decreased by 6% to $1.9 billion compared due to lower kilowatt-hour sales (down 3%) and demand usage (down 2%).

The company's net income decreased by 73% to $34.4 million as the result of lower net revenues and higher electric maintenance expenses.

In 2015 Santee Cooper's operating cash inflow decreased by 77% to $237.6 million.

Strategy

With a eye toward getting 40% of its power from non-carbon emitting sources and conservation by 2020 the company has begun to invest heavily in nuclear solar wind and other renewable energy sources.

In 2015 the company agreed to changes in its agreement with Westinghouse Electric which acquired assets of a second partner in the V.C. Summer Nuclear Station plant construction consortium giving Westinghouse more control over the project.

In 2014 Santee Cooper in collaboration with Central Electric Power Cooperative and the state's electric cooperatives agreed to buy the total energy output of Colleton Solar Farm a utility-scale solar power farm being built by TIG Sun Energy a subsidiary of the North Charleston-based InterTech Group. The solar array consists of 10010 photovoltaic panels. Some panels are fixed while other panels follow the direction of the sun to maximize the production of solar energy.

South Carolina Resources Santee Cooper Central Electric Power Cooperative and the state's electric cooperatives agreed in 2013 to build Colleton Solar Farm the largest solar farm in the state (3000 kilowatts of electricity).

Mergers and Acquisitions

In 2014 South Carolina Electric & Gas Company (SCE&G) principal subsidiary of SCANA Corporation and Santee Cooper announced an agreement for SCE&G to acquire from Santee Cooper a 5% ownership interest in the two new nuclear units which are under construction at V.C. Summer Nuclear Station in Jenkinsville. Under the ownership agreement SCE&G owns 55%; Santee Cooper 45%. The 5% ownership interest would be acquired in three stages with 1% to be acquired at the commercial operation date of the first new nuclear unit (late 2017 or the first quarter of 2018); an additional 2% to be acquired no later than the first anniversary of such commercial operation date; and the final 2% to be acquired no later than the second anniversary date of such commercial operation date.

Company Background

Santee Cooper is a government-owned entity.

Historically the $48.2 million Santee Cooper project (55% federal loan and 45% federal grant) which connected the Santee and Cooper rivers and established hydroelectric dams and a transmission grid began to generate electricity for the first time in 1942. It was founded in 1934.

HISTORY

In 2011 Santee Cooper dedicated a 311-kilowatt solar installation in Myrtle Beach where it also has 2.4-kW wind turbine (the first utility-connected turbine on the state grid). Santee Cooper also contracted for power from biomass combustion and from anaerobic digestion on a livestock farm.

In late 2011 the US Nuclear Regulatory Commission conducted a final review of Santee Cooper's application for a license to build and operate two new nuclear units at V.C. Summer Nuclear Station.

EXECUTIVES

Chm, O L Thompson
Chief Operating Officer*, Bill McCall Jr
Cfo*, Elaine Peterson
Sr V Pres-Exec V Pres*, Jim Brogdon
SEC*, Pamela J Williams
Sr V Pres-Cfo*, Jeff Armfield
Executive of Information Techn, Samuel P Ittard
Scientist, Julie Metts
Vp, Real State, Daniel D Camp
Project Manager, Chris Wagner
Mechanical Engineer, Ryan Millwood
Auditors: CHERRY BEKAERT LLP RALEIGH N

LOCATIONS

HQ: SOUTH CAROLINA PUBLIC SERVICE AUTHORITY (INC)
1 RIVERWOOD DR, MONCKS CORNER, SC 294612998
Phone: 843 761-4121
Web: WWW.SANTEECOOPER.COM

PRODUCTS/OPERATIONS

2015 Sales

	$ mil.	% of total
Electricity	1,856	99
Water	8	-
Other	15	1
Total	**1,879**	**100**

COMPETITORS

Delmarva Power	Ps Energy
Dominion Energy	Progress Energy
Duke Energy	Scana
Florida Public Utilities	Tva
Mlgw	Utilities Inc.
North Carolina Electric Membership	

HISTORICAL FINANCIALS

Company Type: Private

Income Statement				FYE: December 31
	REVENUE ($ mil.)	NET INCOME ($ mil.)	NET PROFIT MARGIN	EMPLOYEES
12/19	1,722	(231)		1,748
12/17	1,756	90	5.2%	—
12/15	1,879	34	1.8%	—
12/13	1,816	65	3.6%	—
Annual Growth	(0.9%)	—	—	—

2019 Year-End Financials

Return on assets: (-2.0%)   Cash ($ mil.): 311
Return on equity: (-11.2%)
Current ratio: 1.70

SOUTH FLORIDA WATER MANAGEMENT DISTRICT LEASING CORP.

EXECUTIVES

Chb, Daniel O'Keefe
V Cbb*, Kevin Powers
MBR*, Lennart Lindahl
V Pres*, Mitch Hutchcraft
Scientist, Patricia Robertshaw
Coordinator, Guangliang Liu
Compliance Staff, Jay Floyd
Coordinator, Peter Harlem
Scientist Senior, Darlene Marley
Technical Support Analyst, Gary Chirillo
Director, Gary Russ

LOCATIONS

HQ: SOUTH FLORIDA WATER MANAGEMENT
DISTRICT LEASING CORP.
3301 GUN CLUB RD, WEST PALM BEACH, FL
334063007
Phone: 561 686-8800
Web: WWW.SFWMD.GOV

HISTORICAL FINANCIALS
Company Type: Private

Income Statement				FYE: September 30
	REVENUE ($ mil.)	NET INCOME ($ mil.)	NET PROFIT MARGIN	EMPLOYEES
09/10	595	(42)	—	1,200
09/08	910	(64)	—	—
09/06	947	51	5.4%	—
Annual Growth	(11.0%)	—	—	—

SOUTH MIAMI HOSPITAL, INC.

South Miami Hospital offers primary and tertiary health care services to the residents living near the University of Miami. The hospital has about 470 beds and is one of the largest members of Baptist Health South Florida a top regional health system. Specialty services include emergency care cardiovascular services oncology neurology women's health metabolic care and rehabilitation. It operates an addiction treatment residential facility provides home health care and provides child development diagnostic and early intervention services. South Miami Hospital was founded in 1960.

Operations

South Miami Hospital handles 15000 inpatient admissions each year as well as 30000 emergency room visits 5000 outpatient surgeries and 4000 births. It has about 1300 physicians on its medical staff.

As part of the broader Baptist Health South Florida system South Miami Hospital benefits from shared resources including procurement administration and technology the coordination of which helps the member facilities control costs during times of economic trouble and rising medical care expenses in the US.

Strategy

The Baptist Health system facilities including South Miami Hospital are installing electronic health record (EHR) systems to manage patient records across the system. Such EHR systems are designed to improve quality and lower expenses by facilitating communication between care providers and increasing patient involvement in condition management.

In addition South Miami Hospital has improved its services through expansion and renovation projects. It has added specialty units for robotic surgery birthing heart care and neonatal intensive care. In addition it completed an $80 million two-story construction in 2013 that enhanced the medical center's emergency surgery and imaging departments.

EXECUTIVES

Ceo, Lincoln S Mendez
Pres*, Javier Hermandev-Lichto
SEC*, Domingo C Rodriguez
Tres*, George M Corrigan
Staff Coordinator, Christine Stiltner Angulo
Chief of Ob/Gyn, Rene A Paez
Chief of Emergency, Tracey C Patricoff
Chief of Medicine, Jorge Murillo
Staff Coordinator, Maria Cabrera
Health Professional, Ghassan Haddad
Anesthesiologist, Eric Chavoustie

LOCATIONS

HQ: SOUTH MIAMI HOSPITAL, INC.
6200 SW 73RD ST, SOUTH MIAMI, FL 331434679
Phone: 786 662-4000
Web: WWW.BAPTISTHEALTH.NET

COMPETITORS

Adventist Health System Sunbelt Healthcare
Broward Health
H. Lee Moffitt Cancer Center & Research Institute
Hca
Jackson Health System
Larkin Community Hospital
Miami Children's Hospital
Mount Sinai Medical Center Of Florida
South Broward Hospital District
Uf&shands
University Of Miami Hospital

HISTORICAL FINANCIALS
Company Type: Private

Income Statement				FYE: September 30
	REVENUE ($ mil.)	NET INCOME ($ mil.)	NET PROFIT MARGIN	EMPLOYEES
09/19	674	93	13.9%	2,205
09/18	488	37	7.7%	—
09/17	484	6	1.4%	—
09/16	492	3	0.7%	—
Annual Growth	11.1%	198.7%	—	—

2019 Year-End Financials
Return on assets: 28.6%   Cash ($ mil.): —
Return on equity: 118.3%
Current ratio: 0.30

SOUTH NASSAU COMMUNITIES HOSPITAL

EXECUTIVES

Ceo, Richard J Murphy
Svp-Cfo*, John A Pohlman
Chief Officer, Daniel McAluey
Vice-President Engineering, Lori Allocca
Information Specialist, Michael Tsymbalyuk
Chief Financial Officer, Gerard Haas
Executive, Stephen Bello
Co Chief of Nephrology, Lawrence Kleinman
Manager, Suhas Kavthekar

LOCATIONS

HQ: SOUTH NASSAU COMMUNITIES HOSPITAL
1 HEALTHY WAY, OCEANSIDE, NY 115721551
Phone: 516 632-3000
Web: WWW.SOUTHNASSAU.ORG

HISTORICAL FINANCIALS
Company Type: Private

Income Statement				FYE: December 31
	REVENUE ($ mil.)	NET INCOME ($ mil.)	NET PROFIT MARGIN	EMPLOYEES
12/19	553	35	6.4%	2,800
12/18	461	(46)	—	—
12/17	451	(47)	—	—
12/16	437	(33)	—	—
Annual Growth	8.1%	—	—	—

2019 Year-End Financials
Return on assets: 4.5%   Cash ($ mil.): 31
Return on equity: 11.8%
Current ratio: 0.30

SOUTH SHORE HOSPITAL, INC.

EXECUTIVES

Ceo, Gene E Green
Pres*, Pamela Daley Whelton
Cfo-Sr V Pres*, Michael Cullen
Sr V Pres*, Margaret Holda
Sr V Pres*, Christopher J Oconnor
Coo*, Joseph Cahill
V Pres Clinical*, Edward Liao
Pres Acute Care Oprs*, Timothy Quigley
Medical Staff, Joseph Jiang
Medical Staff, A K Elamine
Vice-President Sales and Marke, Margaret M Holda

LOCATIONS

HQ: SOUTH SHORE HOSPITAL, INC.
55 FOGG RD, SOUTH WEYMOUTH, MA 021902455
Phone: 781 624-8000
Web: WWW.SOUTHSHOREHEALTH.ORG

HISTORICAL FINANCIALS
Company Type: Private

Income Statement				FYE: September 30
	REVENUE ($ mil.)	NET INCOME ($ mil.)	NET PROFIT MARGIN	EMPLOYEES
09/19	664	14	2.2%	2,375
09/18	575	10	1.9%	—
09/17	563	9	1.7%	—
09/16	558	17	3.1%	—
Annual Growth	6.0%	(5.1%)	—	—

2019 Year-End Financials
Return on assets: 2.2% Cash ($ mil.): 40
Return on equity: 4.4%
Current ratio: 0.40

SOUTHCOAST HOSPITALS GROUP, INC.

When you feel more than a little physically washed up get to one of the Southcoast Hospitals Group facilities. The not-for-profit company provides medical services in the southeastern corner of Massachusetts and in Rhode Island. Its primary facilities in Massachusetts are the Charlton Memorial Hospital (with about 330 beds) in Fall River St. Luke's Hospital (420 beds) in New Bedford and Tobey Hospital (65 beds) in Wareham which provide acute medical care and specialty services including cardiology neurology orthopedics and women's care. Southcoast Hospitals Group also operates about 20 ancillary facilities including nursing and assisted-living facilities and home health and hospice agencies.

Auditors: DELOITTE TAX LLP JERICHO NY

LOCATIONS
HQ: SOUTHCOAST HOSPITALS GROUP, INC.
363 HIGHLAND AVE, FALL RIVER, MA 027203703
Phone: 508 679-3131
Web: WWW.SOUTHCOAST.ORG

COMPETITORS

Baystate Health
Boston Medical Center
Care New England
Caregroup
Hallmark Health
Lifespan Corporation
Mclean Hospital
Memorial Hospital Of Rhode Island

Partners Healthcare
Roger Williams Medical Center
Steward Health Care
Yale New Haven Health System

HISTORICAL FINANCIALS
Company Type: Private

Income Statement				FYE: September 30
	REVENUE ($ mil.)	NET INCOME ($ mil.)	NET PROFIT MARGIN	EMPLOYEES
09/13	687	22	3.3%	3,853
09/12	704	49	7.0%	—
09/06	506	14	2.8%	—
09/04	445	13	3.1%	—
Annual Growth	4.9%	5.4%	—	—

2013 Year-End Financials
Return on assets: 6.9% Cash ($ mil.): 6
Return on equity: 3.3%
Current ratio: 0.60

SOUTHEAST PETRO DISTRIBUTORS, INC.

EXECUTIVES

Pres, Mahesh Shah
V Pres-SEC, Rashmi Shah
V Pres, Shah Summit
Operations Manager, Helen Waugh
Prin, Mahesh R Shah
Senior Director, Michael Gazzalla
Vp Operations, Summit Shah
Manager, Joe Fields
Marketing, Monica Shah
Controller, Bob McGinty
Hr Manager, Chrissy Council
Auditors: JAMES MOORE & CO PL GAINE

LOCATIONS
HQ: SOUTHEAST PETRO DISTRIBUTORS, INC.
402 HIGH POINT DR STE A, COCOA, FL 329266600
Phone: 321 631-0245
Web: WWW.SOUTHEASTPETRO.COM

HISTORICAL FINANCIALS
Company Type: Private

Income Statement				FYE: December 31
	REVENUE ($ mil.)	NET INCOME ($ mil.)	NET PROFIT MARGIN	EMPLOYEES
12/11	553	5	1.0%	12
12/10	416	5	1.3%	—
12/09	331	4	1.5%	—
12/02	57	0	0.9%	—
Annual Growth	28.6%	29.8%	—	—

2011 Year-End Financials
Return on assets: 13.1% Cash ($ mil.): 8
Return on equity: 35.4%
Current ratio: 1.20

SOUTHERN BAPTIST HOSPITAL OF FLORIDA INC.

EXECUTIVES

Pres, Hugh Greene
Oo*, Johm Wilbanks
Chmn*, M C Harden
V Pres*, Harvey Granger
Executive Vice President*, John Wilbanks
SEC-Treas*, Richard L Sisisky
Health Professional, Christopher Carroll
Coordinator, John Polisknowski
Director Education, Pamela Turner
Admin To Bob Perez, Rita Riggs
Neurologist, Jason Day
Auditors: ERNST & YOUNG LLP JACKSON F

LOCATIONS
HQ: SOUTHERN BAPTIST HOSPITAL OF FLORIDA INC.
800 PRUDENTIAL DR FL 3220, JACKSONVILLE, FL 322078202
Phone: 904 399-5620
Web: WWW.BAPTISTJAX.COM

HISTORICAL FINANCIALS
Company Type: Private

Income Statement				FYE: September 30
	REVENUE ($ mil.)	NET INCOME ($ mil.)	NET PROFIT MARGIN	EMPLOYEES
09/20	1,465	33	2.3%	4,000
09/19	1,398	186	13.3%	—
09/18	1,234	209	17.0%	—
09/17	1,151	296	25.8%	—
Annual Growth	8.4%	(51.8%)	—	—

2020 Year-End Financials
Return on assets: 0.9% Cash ($ mil.): —
Return on equity: 1.6%
Current ratio: 0.60

SOUTHERN CAL SCHOOLS VOL EMP BENEFITS ASSOC

EXECUTIVES

Prin, George McGregor
Auditors: ROSNER BROWN TOUCHSTONE & KELL

LOCATIONS
HQ: SOUTHERN CAL SCHOOLS VOL EMP BENEFITS ASSOC
8885 RIO SAN DIEGO DR # 327, SAN DIEGO, CA 921081624
Phone: 619 278-0021

HISTORICAL FINANCIALS
Company Type: Private

Income Statement				FYE: December 31
	REVENUE ($ mil.)	NET INCOME ($ mil.)	NET PROFIT MARGIN	EMPLOYEES
12/14	598	4	0.7%	9
12/13	551	5	1.0%	—
Annual Growth	8.6%	(29.1%)	—	—

2014 Year-End Financials
Return on assets: 6.6% Cash ($ mil.): 38
Return on equity: 19.6%
Current ratio: 2.30

SOUTHERN ILLINOIS HEALTHCARE ENTERPRISES, INC.

Southern Illinois Healthcare a nonprofit health care system operates the flagship 145-bed tertiary-care Memorial Hospital of Carbondale as well as Herrin Hospital (with 114 beds) and St. Joseph Memorial Hospital (with 25 beds). The hospitals serve residents of across southern Illinois. The nearly 280-bed system provides services such as birthing cardiac cancer and emergency care as well as surgery and rehabilitation. Its cardiac care is offered through an affiliation with the Prairie Heart Institute at St. John's Hospital in Springfield Illinois. The medical school at Southern Illinois University conducts its Family Practice Residency Program at Memorial Hospital of Carbondale.

Operations

Across its health system Southern Illinois Healthcare employs more than 3000 people. Physicians at its primary hospital Memorial Hospital of Carbondale represent nearly 40 medical specialties. It maintains the only dedicated pediatric unit in the region as well as the largest birthing center with Level II Plus Special Care Nursery.

St. Joseph Memorial Hospital is a full-service critical access hospital.

In addition to the patient hospitals the system includes two clinics two physician professional buildings an urgent care clinic and dedicated neurology cancer heart sleep and rehabilitation centers.

Geographic Reach

Most of Memorial Hospital of Carbondale's inpatient and outpatient visits come from residents of seven Illinois counties (Jackson Franklin Williamson Perry Johnson Union and Saline). St. Joseph Memorial Hospital serves the Murphysboro community.

Strategy

Teaming up to provide better care independent not-for-profit health care organizations BJC HealthCare of St. Louis CoxHealth of Springfield Missouri Memorial Health System of Springfield Illinois. and Saint Luke's Health System of Kansas City Missouri created The BJC Collaborative L.L.C. (in 2012). Blessing Health System of Quincy and Southern Illinois Healthcare joined the Collaborative in 2013.

Company Background

During 2012 Southern Illinois Healthcare collaborated with community partners to conduct a Community Health Needs Assessment to spotlight health and quality of life issues in the communities served by Southern Illinois Healthcare.

Southern Illinois Healthcare was first established by four doctors in 1946 as the Southern Illinois Hospital Corporation.

EXECUTIVES

Ceo, Rex Budde
Sr Vp-Treas Cfo*, Mike Kasser
Prin*, Jerry Hickam
Office Manager, Abby Robinson
Director, Family Practice, Dale Blaise
Coordinator, Amy Wright
Administrator, Billie V Huff
Associate, Jane Hudson
Coordinator, Kristin King

Administrative Director, Lynda Kuether
Coordinator, Sherry Gann
Auditors: RSM US LLP SPRINGFIELD ILLIN

LOCATIONS

HQ: SOUTHERN ILLINOIS HEALTHCARE ENTERPRISES, INC.
1239 E MAIN ST STE C, CARBONDALE, IL 629013176
Phone: 618 457-5200

PRODUCTS/OPERATIONS

Selected Facilities
Herrin Hospital
Memorial Hospital of Carbondale
St. Joseph Memorial Hospital

Selected Services
Birthing Center
Cancer
Senior Renewal
Heart
Infusion Therapy
Neurosciences
Occupational Health
Pediatrics
Rehabilitation
Robotic-assisted Surgery
Sleep Medicine
Stroke
Surgical Services
Weight Loss Surgery
Wound Healing

COMPETITORS

Community Health Systems
Heartland Health Memorial Hospital (illinois)
Saint Francis Medical Center
St. John's Hospital (illinois)

HISTORICAL FINANCIALS

Company Type: Private

Income Statement				FYE: March 31
	REVENUE ($ mil.)	NET INCOME ($ mil.)	NET PROFIT MARGIN	EMPLOYEES
03/21	707	123	17.4%	3,493
03/20	696	(45)	—	—
03/19	685	22	3.2%	—
03/18	624	30	4.9%	—
Annual Growth	4.2%	59.3%	—	—

2021 Year-End Financials

Return on assets: 9.2%
Return on equity: 17.0%
Current ratio: 1.20

Cash ($ mil.): 21

SOUTHERN ILLINOIS UNIVERSITY INC

Southern Illinois University (SIU) helps to train future doctors dentists and other other professionals. The university enrolls some 32000 students at its two institutions — Southern Illinois University at Carbondale (SIUC which includes medical and law schools) and Southern Illinois University at Edwardsville (SIUE which houses education dental and nursing schools) — as well as smaller satellite centers. SIU offers associate baccalaureate master's doctoral and professional degrees. It also boasts a number of study abroad partnerships with international universities. Tracing its roots back to 1869 SIU is known for its extensive research programs.

Operations

Students across SIU's institutions hail from all 50 states and more than 100 countries. Combined the campuses have some 2600 faculty members and an annual budget of $870 million.

The Carbondale campus was chartered in 1869 as a teachers college while the Edwardsville campus was founded in 1957. Most of the university's doctoral programs are housed at the SIUC campus which conducts residencies through the School of Medicine. A majority of the institutions master's degrees are conferred at the SIUE campus.

Undergraduate and research programs are conducted at both primary SIU campuses. Students and faculty members participate in research programs in a number of fields including biology biodiversity and molecular science. The university receives $78.5 million in research grants annually.

Geographic Reach

From its flagship campus in Carbondale Illinois SIU reaches to Edwardsville and to other parts of Southern Illinois including Springfield through satellite campus locations. Its satellite schools include SIU School of Medicine SIU School of Dental Medicine and SIU School of Nursing.

Financial Performance

SIU logged increases of 2% in fiscal 2012 as compared to 2011 pointing to a rise in student tuition and fees private grants and contracts and sales and services for the gains. Net income for the same reporting period rose 17% due to a boost in non-operating revenues attributable to increases in gifts and contributions investment income and payments on behalf of the university.

Strategy

As part of its focus SIU is working to strengthen its undergraduate graduate and professional education. It's also concentrating on streamlining its administrative process while expanding its intercampus and intra-campus collaboration through degree programs international education distributed learning fundraising and research opportunities for both students and faculty. SIU is also establishing partnerships with public and private sector groups.

EXECUTIVES

Pres, Randy J Dunn
Sr V Pres*, Duane Stucky
Staff, John Massie
Assistant Professor, William Eichfeld
Automotive Parts Manager Asa, Cynthia Gerlock
Director, Michelle Richerson
Administrative Aide, Jane Meuth
Chief Academic Adviser College, Tamora Workman
Accountant, Judy Wright
Assistant Professor, Reza Habib
Assistant Professor, Robin Warne

LOCATIONS

HQ: SOUTHERN ILLINOIS UNIVERSITY INC
1400 DOUGLAS DR, CARBONDALE, IL 629014332
Phone: 618 536-3475
Web: WWW.SIU.EDU

HISTORICAL FINANCIALS
Company Type: Private

Income Statement				FYE: June 30
	REVENUE ($ mil.)	NET INCOME ($ mil.)	NET PROFIT MARGIN	EMPLOYEES
06/20	578	25	4.4%	9,576
06/19	581	28	4.9%	—
06/18	584	139	23.9%	—
06/17	601	(59)	—	—
Annual Growth	(1.3%)			

2020 Year-End Financials
Return on assets: 2.1% Cash ($ mil.): 83
Return on equity: 4.1%
Current ratio: 2.20

SOUTHERN INDIANA GAS & ELECTRIC COMPANY

EXECUTIVES
Ceo, Carl L Chapman
Ceo*, Niel C Ellerbrook
Exec V Pres-Cfo*, Jerome A Benkert Jr
Sr V Pres*, Ronald E Christian
V Pres-Treas*, Robert Goocher
V Pres-Controller*, M Susan Hardwick
Pres*, William S Doty
V Pres*, Daniel Bugher
V Pres*, Ellis S Redd
V Pres*, Eric J Schach
Vp, Darin Carroll
Auditors: DELOITTE & TOUCHE LLP INDIANA

LOCATIONS
HQ: SOUTHERN INDIANA GAS & ELECTRIC COMPANY
1 VECTREN SQ, EVANSVILLE, IN 477081209
Phone: 812 424-6411
Web: WWW.ACCESS2ENERGY.COM

HISTORICAL FINANCIALS
Company Type: Private

Income Statement				FYE: December 31
	REVENUE ($ mil.)	NET INCOME ($ mil.)	NET PROFIT MARGIN	EMPLOYEES
12/17	661	86	13.1%	779
12/16	692	95	13.9%	—
12/03	438	48	11.1%	—
12/02	693	59	8.6%	—
Annual Growth	(0.3%)	2.6%	—	—

2017 Year-End Financials
Return on assets: 3.8% Cash ($ mil.): 2
Return on equity: 9.7%
Current ratio: 1.80

SOUTHERN METHODIST UNIVERSITY INC

What do former first lady Laura Bush actress Kathy Bates and NFL Hall-of-Famer Doak Walker have in common? They're all graduates of Southern Methodist University (SMU). Founded in 1911 by what is now The United Methodist Church SMU is a nonsectarian private institution offering undergraduate graduate and professional degrees in arts business engineering humanities law science and theology through eight schools. It's one of a handful of schools nationwide to offer an academic major in human rights. Nearly 12375 students attend the university which has a student-faculty ratio of 11:1. About 85% of full-time faculty hold the doctorate or highest degree in their fields.

Operations
The university offers more than 100 majors and 85 minors to choose from as well as double and triple major opportunities and accelerated degree programs through eight schools. Some areas to study include accounting advertising art business entrepreneurship chemistry data sciences and earth sciences.

Geographic Reach
SMU is housed of some 130 buildings on about 235 acres five miles north of downtown Dallas County. SMU's Taos campus is nearly 425 acres with about 30 buildings located within the Carson National Forest and surrounded by the Sangre de Cristo Mountains. Students came from all 50 states the District of Columbia and approximately 90 foreign countries. Students represent diverse economic ethnic and religious backgrounds.

Financial Performance
The SMU endowment ended the fiscal year in 2019 (ended May) with a market value of $1.6 billion. Substantial endowment gifts of $25.7 million were received during the year while endowment distributions of $81.0 million an all-time high provided support to the University.

EXECUTIVES
Pres, R Gerald Turner
V Pres Bus-Fin*, Chris Casey
Provost*, Paul Ludden
V Pres Developmet and External*, Brad Cheves
V Pres*, Kenechukwu Mmeje
V Pres*, Steven Currall
V Pres*, Harold Stanley
Treas*, Rakesh Dahiya
Dean, Meadows School AR, Jos A Bowen
Coordinator, Jeff Herman
Vp Legal Affairs, General Coun, Paul J Ward
Auditors: KPMG LLP DALLAS TX

LOCATIONS
HQ: SOUTHERN METHODIST UNIVERSITY INC
6425 BOAZ LN, DALLAS, TX 75205
Phone: 214 768-2000
Web: WWW.SMU.EDU

PRODUCTS/OPERATIONS

Selected Schools and Divisions
Annette Caldwell Simmons School of Education and Human Development
Bobby B. Lyle School of Engineering
Cox School of Business
Dedman College of Humanities and Sciences
Dedman School of Law
Meadows School of the Arts
Perkins School of Theology

HISTORICAL FINANCIALS
Company Type: Private

Income Statement				FYE: May 31
	REVENUE ($ mil.)	NET INCOME ($ mil.)	NET PROFIT MARGIN	EMPLOYEES
05/20	940	100	10.7%	2,200
05/18	652	96	14.7%	—
05/17	580	56	9.8%	—
05/13	563	115	20.5%	—
Annual Growth	7.6%	(2.0%)	—	—

2020 Year-End Financials
Return on assets: 2.9% Cash ($ mil.): 155
Return on equity: 3.9%
Current ratio: —

SOUTHERN NATURAL GAS COMPANY, L.L.C.

Now here's a company that pipes in the goods that keep the South fueled naturally. Southern Natural Gas operates an 7600-mile long natural gas pipeline (SNG System) which serves major markets across the southeastern US. This system transports more than 3 billion cu. ft. of natural gas per day. The SNG pipeline system has about 60 billion cu. ft. of underground working natural gas storage capacity. Major customers include Atlanta Gas Light Company Alabama Gas Southern Company and SCANA . Southern Natural Gas is a unit of El Paso Pipeline Partners.

EXECUTIVES
Pres-Ceo, Norman G Holmes
Exec V Pres-Cfo, John R Sult
V Pres-Controller-Cao, Rosa P Jackson
Gas Accountant, Mike Rockett
Senior Vice President, Larry Powell
Scheduler, Ron Hallmark

LOCATIONS
HQ: SOUTHERN NATURAL GAS COMPANY, L.L.C.
1001 LOUISIANA ST, HOUSTON, TX 770025089
Phone: 713 420-2600
Web: WWW.KINDERMORGAN.COM

COMPETITORS
Alagasco
American Midstream Partners
Bridgeline
Crestwood Midstream Partners Lp
Gulf South Pipeline
Panhandle Eastern Pipe Line
Piedmont Natural Gas
U.s. Transmission

HISTORICAL FINANCIALS
Company Type: Private

Income Statement				FYE: December 31
	REVENUE ($ mil.)	NET INCOME ($ mil.)	NET PROFIT MARGIN	EMPLOYEES
12/17	606	143	23.7%	3
12/16	609	169	27.8%	—
Annual Growth	(0.6%)	(15.2%)	—	—

2017 Year-End Financials
Return on assets: 5.2% Cash ($ mil.): 3
Return on equity: 10.8%
Current ratio: 0.90

SOUTHERN NEW HAMPSHIRE UNIVERSITY

EXECUTIVES

Pres, Paul La Blanc
SEC*, Kimon S Zachos
Pres*, James Jacobson
Accounting Staff, Nisaphan Pringle
Information Specialist, Andrew Sakach
Information Specialist, Kristopher Amar
Information Specialist, Serena McDonough
Compliance Staff, Tia Hooper
Assistant Women's Soccer Coach, Ariel Teixeira
Assistant Men's Soccer, Burke Hazard
Assistant Softball Coach, Christina Berardi
Auditors: KPMG LLP BOSTON MA

LOCATIONS

HQ: SOUTHERN NEW HAMPSHIRE UNIVERSITY
2500 N RIVER RD, MANCHESTER, NH 031061018
Phone: 603 668-2211
Web: WWW.SNHU.EDU

HISTORICAL FINANCIALS

Company Type: Private

Income Statement				FYE: June 30
	REVENUE ($ mil.)	NET INCOME ($ mil.)	NET PROFIT MARGIN	EMPLOYEES
06/20	997	124	12.5%	1,000
06/18	737	129	17.5%	—
06/16	0	0	—	—
06/15	449	60	13.5%	—
Annual Growth	17.3%	15.6%	—	—

2020 Year-End Financials

Return on assets: 11.1%
Return on equity: 16.4%
Current ratio: 1.10

Cash ($ mil.): 294

SOUTHERN NUCLEAR OPERATING COMPANY, INC.

The night the lights went out in Georgia they should have called Southern Nuclear Operating Company. The company a subsidiary of Southern Company since 1990 operates six nuclear power units at three plant locations which combined provide about 20% of the electricity used in Alabama and Georgia. Southern Nuclear's Joseph M. Farley Nuclear Plant began commercial operation in 1977. The Edwin I. Hatch Nuclear Plant and the Alvin W. Vogtle Electric Generating Plant are jointly owned by Southern Company's Georgia Power (50%) Oglethorpe Power (30%) the Municipal Electrical Authority of Georgia (18%) and the city of Dalton.

EXECUTIVES

Ceo, Thomas Fanning
Chm*, Barnie Beasley
Vp-Fleet Operations Support, Bradley J Adam
Coordinator, Malinda Jenkins
Designer, John Lockhart
Project Engineer, Denver Atwood
Security Manager, David Burford
Controller, Sheryl Brakefield
Vice President Computing, Dave Coker
Designer, Susan Dodd
Manager Engineering, Jeremy Haughaboo

LOCATIONS

HQ: SOUTHERN NUCLEAR OPERATING COMPANY, INC.
42 INVERNESS CENTER PKWY, HOOVER, AL 352424809
Phone: 205 992-5000
Web: WWW.SOUTHERNCOMPANY.COM

COMPETITORS

Duke Energy   Progress Energy
Nextera Energy

HISTORICAL FINANCIALS

Company Type: Private

Income Statement				FYE: December 31
	REVENUE ($ mil.)	NET INCOME ($ mil.)	NET PROFIT MARGIN	EMPLOYEES
12/16	922	0	0.0%	2,960
12/04	479	0	—	—
12/03	441	0	—	—
12/02	455	0	—	—
Annual Growth	5.2%	—	—	—

2016 Year-End Financials

Return on assets: —
Return on equity: 0.1%
Current ratio: 1.00

Cash ($ mil.): 14

SOUTHWEST RESEARCH INSTITUTE INC

Founded in 1947 by oilman and rancher Thomas Slick Jr. Southwest Research Institute (SwRI) is an independent not-for-profit research and development institution that contracts to explore subjects in areas including automation and data systems applied physics space science and engineering and chemistry. SwRI has about 3000 scientists engineers and support staff at laboratories and offices in the US China and the UK. Customers include the private sector and government agencies. SwRI's Signature Science subsidiary researches national security environmental management and biotechnology.

Operations

SwRI provides contract research and development services to industrial and government clients. It keeps the scope of its work confidential and assigns patent rights arising from its sponsored research to the client. SwRI generally retains rights to Institute-funded advancements and holds more than 1300 patents awarded to staff members.

The company operates through ten technical divisions including Applied Physics Applied Power; Chemistry & Chemical Engineering; Center for Nuclear Waste Regulatory Analyses; Defense & Intelligence Solutions and Intelligent Systems.

Geographic Reach

The company is based in Texas and has operations in ten US states including Colorado Georgia and Maryland as well as international locations in China and the United Kingdom.

EXECUTIVES

Pres-Ceo, Adam Hamilton
General Counsel, Monica Trollinger
V Pres-Facilities & Service, Paul Easley
V Pres-Applied Physics, Kenneth Bennett Jr
V Pres-Applied Power, Mary Massey
Exec V Pres-Coo, Walter Downing
Treas, Linda Boehme
V Pres-Intelligent Systems, Steve Dellenback
V Pres-Chemistry - Chemical En, Mike Macnaughton
V Pres-Fuels & Lubricants Rese, Steve Marty
V Pres-Mechanical & Materials, Danny Deffenbaugh
Auditors: RSM US LLP SAN ANTONIO TEXAS

LOCATIONS

HQ: SOUTHWEST RESEARCH INSTITUTE INC
6220 CULEBRA RD, SAN ANTONIO, TX 782385100
Phone: 210 684-5111
Web: WWW.SWRI.ORG

PRODUCTS/OPERATIONS

Selected Technical Divisions
Aerospace Electronics and Information Technology
Applied Physics
Applied Power
Automation and Data Systems
Chemistry and Chemical Engineering
Engine Emissions and Vehicle Research
Fuels and Lubricants Research
Geosciences and Engineering
Mechanical Engineering
Signal Exploitation and Geolocation
Space Science and Engineering
Training Simulation and Performance Improvement

COMPETITORS

Battelle Memorial   Qinetiq
Berkeley Lab   Southern Research
Brookhaven Lab   Institute
Lawrence Livermore Lab

HISTORICAL FINANCIALS

Company Type: Private

Income Statement				FYE: September 30
	REVENUE ($ mil.)	NET INCOME ($ mil.)	NET PROFIT MARGIN	EMPLOYEES
09/19	685	41	6.0%	2,820
09/18	583	38	6.6%	—
09/17	498	11	2.3%	—
09/16	559	6	1.2%	—
Annual Growth	7.0%	81.6%	—	—

2019 Year-End Financials

Return on assets: 5.4%
Return on equity: 6.9%
Current ratio: 3.80

Cash ($ mil.): 228

SOUTHWEST WASHINGTON HEALTH SYSTEM

EXECUTIVES

Pres-Ceo, Joe Kortum
Emergency Medicine Specialist, Erik Denninghoff
Internist, Joan Hunter
Assistant General Counsel, Jennifer Mair
Manager, Radiology, Dan Goldblatt
Program Director, Ryan Parker
Director Lines, Victor Garcia

LOCATIONS

HQ: SOUTHWEST WASHINGTON HEALTH SYSTEM
400 NE MOTHER JOSEPH PL, VANCOUVER, WA
986643200
Phone: 360 514-2000
Web: WWW.PEACEHEALTH.ORG

HISTORICAL FINANCIALS

Company Type: Private

Income Statement				FYE: December 31
	REVENUE ($ mil.)	NET INCOME ($ mil.)	NET PROFIT MARGIN	EMPLOYEES
12/09	601	9	1.5%	3,500
12/08*	110	(38)	—	—
09/08	10	(0)	—	—
Annual Growth	5757.2%	—	—	—

*Fiscal year change

2009 Year-End Financials

Return on assets: 1.4%   Cash ($ mil.): 13
Return on equity: 2.9%
Current ratio: 1.40

SPARROW HEALTH SYSTEM

Ailing residents of central Michigan fly to Sparrow Health System for care. The not-for-profit network's hospitals include the flagship Sparrow Hospital Sparrow Hospital St. Lawrence Sparrow Eaton Hospital Sparrow Ionia Hospital Sparrow Clinton Hospital Sparrow Specialty Hospital and Sparrow Carson Hospital. Sparrow Health performs about 23000 surgeries in a year and 300 ER patients in a day. Sparrow Health provides inpatient and outpatient services radiology pharmacies home care hospice care rehabilitation lab and pet therapy through nearly 1300 physicians in about 115 sites of care across mid-Michigan. Through its Mother Baby Center Sparrow delivers about 4000 babies annually.

Financial Performance

EXECUTIVES

Pres-Ceo, Dennis A Swan
V Pres, Mark Brett
Exec V Pres, Andrea Price
Emergency Medicine Specialist, Matthew Rauschenberger

Data Processing Representative, Tema Evans
Patient Support, Tiffany Cotton
Coordinator, Trevor Bancroft
Vp Sparrow, Peter Graham
Application Coordinator, Pat Laforest
Treasurer, Patrick Burns
Management Information, Rick Longstreet
Auditors: PLANTE & MORAN PLLC GRAND RA

LOCATIONS

HQ: SPARROW HEALTH SYSTEM
1215 E MICHIGAN AVE, LANSING, MI 489121811
Phone: 517 364-5000
Web: WWW.SPARROW.ORG

PRODUCTS/OPERATIONS

Selected Services

Emergency room/Urgent Care
Laboratory
Medical Supply
Outpatient Rehabilitation
Pharmacy
Radiology

COMPETITORS

Bronson Battle Creek	Hurley Medical Center
Covenant Healthcare	Mclaren Health Care
Crittenton Hospital	Munson Healthcare
Detroit Medical Center	Sheridan Community
Genesys Health System	Hospital
Genesys Regional	St. John Health
Medical Center	Trinity Health (novi)
Henry Ford Health System	

HISTORICAL FINANCIALS

Company Type: Private

Income Statement				FYE: December 31
	REVENUE ($ mil.)	NET INCOME ($ mil.)	NET PROFIT MARGIN	EMPLOYEES
12/20	1,402	41	3.0%	3,400
12/19	1,340	99	7.4%	—
12/18	1,281	(57)	—	—
12/17	1,259	49	3.9%	—
Annual Growth	3.7%	(5.4%)	—	—

2020 Year-End Financials

Return on assets: 2.0%   Cash ($ mil.): 221
Return on equity: 4.1%
Current ratio: 1.80

SPARTANBURG REGIONAL HEALTH SERVICES DISTRICT, INC.

Spartanburg Regional Health Services District (dba Spartanburg Regional Healthcare System or SRHS) provides a wide range of care options to northeast South Carolina. It operates Spartanburg Medical Center Cherokee Medical Center Pelham Medical Center Spartanburg Hospital for Restorative Care Ellen Sagar Nursing Center Medical Group of the Carolinas and Union Medical Center. The 745-bed Spartanburg Medical offers services including emergency surgical maternity cancer a Heart Center and inpatient rehabilitation. It houses the Gibbs Cancer Center & Research Institute as

well as centers specializing in heart vascular women's health and outpatient care. SRHS also operates clinics specialty outpatient centers and long-term care home health rehabilitation and hospice facilities. With approximately 700 physicians on staff SRHS handles some 25000 surgical procedures delivers around 4000 babies and has approximately 200000 emergency center visits.

EXECUTIVES

Ceo, Ingo Angermeier
Sr V Pres-Cfo*, Larry Barnette
Contrl, Sloan Gray Contrl
Vp Managed Care and Executive, Sara Beth Hammond
Scientist, Lynn Raines
Health Professional, Melanie Neal
Information Technology Manager, David Beaver
Vice President, Thomas Eison
Director Emergency Med, Chris Lombardozzi
Family Practitioner, Edward L Katemba
Vice President and Chief Medic, Rob Flandry

LOCATIONS

HQ: SPARTANBURG REGIONAL HEALTH SERVICES DISTRICT, INC.
101 E WOOD ST, SPARTANBURG, SC 293033040
Phone: 864 560-6000
Web: WWW.SPARTANBURGREGIONAL.COM

PRODUCTS/OPERATIONS

2014 Sales

	$ mil.	% of total
Net patient service revenue	872	89
Premium revenue	73	7
Other operating revenue	36	4
Total	**982**	**100**

Selected Facilities

AccessHealth
Ellen Sagar Nursing Center in Union
Gibbs Cancer Center & Research Institute
Hospice Home
Medical Group of the Carolinas (MGC)
Pelham Medical Center in Greer
Regional HealthPlus (RHP)
Spartanburg Medical Center (SMC)
The Sports Medicine Institute
Union Medical Center

Selected Services

Bearden-Josey Center for Breast Health
Chest Pain Center
Comprehensive Pain Center
Congregational Nursing
Corporate Health
Emergency Center (Level I Trauma Center)
Emergency Medical Services (EMS)
Gibbs Cancer Center & Research Institute
Heart Center
Heart Wellness Program
Home Health
Hospice (Hospice Home)
Imaging and Laboratory Services
Neonatal Intensive Care Unit (Level III)
Neurology
Orthopaedic Services
Palliative Care Services
Pediatrics and Pediatric Intensive Care Unit
Rehabilitation Services
Robotic Surgery
Sleep Services
Stroke Center
Surgery (including minimally invasive)
Urology
Weight Loss Services
Women's Health
Wound Healing Center

Anmed Health
Bon Secours Health
Caromont
Community Health
  Systems
Doctors Hospital Of
  Augusta

Laurens County
  Hospital
Novant Health
Palmetto Health
Upstate Affiliate

HISTORICAL FINANCIALS

Company Type: Private

Income Statement				FYE: September 30
	REVENUE ($ mil.)	NET INCOME ($ mil.)	NET PROFIT MARGIN	EMPLOYEES
09/20	1,468	18	1.3%	5,000
09/19	1,365	42	3.1%	—
09/18	1,147	28	2.5%	—
Annual Growth	13.1%	(19.1%)	—	—

2020 Year-End Financials

Return on assets: 1.2%
Return on equity: 20.3%
Current ratio: 1.80

Cash ($ mil.): 348

SPECTRA ENERGY, LLC

Spectra Energy covers the spectrum of natural gas activities — gathering processing transmission storage and distribution. The company now part of Enbridge operates more than 15400 miles of transmission pipeline and has 305 billion cu. ft. of storage capacity in the US and Canada. Units include U.S. Gas Transmission Texas Eastern Transmission Natural Gas Liquids Division and Market Hub Partners. It also has stakes in DCP Midstream Maritimes & Northeast Pipeline Gulfstream Natural Gas System Spectra Energy Income Fund and 75% of Spectra Energy Partners. Its Union Gas unit distributes gas to 1.5 million Ontario customers. In 2017 Spectra merged with Enbridge creating the largest energy infrastructure company in North America.

Operations

Spectra Energy has managed its businesses in four reportable segments: Spectra Energy Partners Distribution Western Canada Transmission & Processing and Field Services.

Spectra Energy Partners provides transmission storage and gathering of natural gas for customers in various regions of the Midwestern northeastern and southeastern US and operates a crude oil pipeline system that connects Canadian and U.S. producers to refineries in the U.S. Rocky Mountain and Midwest regions. Spectra Energy Partners has accounted for about 50% of the company's revenue.

Distribution about 30% of revenue provides retail natural gas distribution service (its Union Gas unit distributes gas to 1.5 million customers in 400 communities in Ontario). It also provides natural gas transportation and storage services to other utilities and energy market customers.

Western Canada Transmission & Processing about 20% of revenue provides its customers with transportation services to move natural gas natural gas gathering and processing services and NGL extraction fractionation transportation storage and marketing services.

Field Services gathers processes treats compresses transports and stores natural gas; it also fractionates transports gathers processes stores markets and trades NGLs. Its DCP Midstream joint venture is 50% owned by Phillips 66. DCP operates in 17 US states.

Transportation storage and processing of natural gas have accounted for about two-thirds of Spectra Energy's revenue.

Geographic Reach

Spectra Energy's Spectra Energy Partners operates in northeastern and southeastern US and operates a crude oil pipeline system that connects Canadian and US producers to refineries in the Rocky Mountains and the Midwest. The Distribution segment serves natural gas customers in Ontario Canada. Western Canada Transmission & Processing serves customers in western Canada and the northern US. Field Services gathers natural gas from the Mid-Continent Rocky Mountain East Texas-North Louisiana Barnett Shale Gulf Coast South Texas Central Texas Antrim Shale and Permian Basin.

All told Spectra Energy has more than 100 facilities across North America.

Sales and Marketing

Spectra Energy's customers (end-users) purchase gas directly from suppliers or marketers as well as through retail and wholesale outlets.

Financial Performance

Spectra Energy reported a 6% decline in revenue in 2016 to $4.9 billion from 2015. Each segment posted lower revenue for 2016. Lower energy prices were passed on to customers and warmer weather meant they used less energy. Revenue also was hurt by a weaker Canadian dollar. The Distribution segment did see some growth with additional customers and the Dawn Parkway Expansion Project.

The company's net income jump some 250% to $693 million in 2016 from 2015 mostly because of charges and costs the company had in 2015 but not 2016.

Spectra has cash flow from operations of about $2 billion in 2016 down from about $2.2 billion in 2015. The difference was driven by non-cash goodwill impairments in 2015 offset by higher earnings.

Strategy

Mergers and Acquisitions

Company Background

In 2012 Spectra Energy acquired one-third of DCP Sand Hills Pipeline and DCP Southern Hills Pipeline (NGL pipelines) from DCP Midstream for $459 million.

In 2012 Spectra Energy opened a new natural gas processing plant in Dawson Creek British Columbia part of its $1.5 billion investment strategy in infrastructure. That year it also signed a deal with BG Group to develop a pipeline from northeast British Columbia to serve BG Group's potential LNG export facility in Prince Rupert on the northwest coast of the province.

To raise cash in 2012 it sold a 38.76% interest in Maritimes & Northeast Pipeline to Spectra Energy Partners for $375 million.

In a move to boost its Gulf Coast natural gas storage position in 2010 Spectra Energy acquired the Bobcat Gas Storage asset from Haddington Energy Partners and GE Energy Financial Service for about $540 million.

The company was founded in 2006.

EXECUTIVES

Ceo-Pres, Gregory L Ebel
Cfo, John Patrick Reddy
Cao, Dorothy M Ables
Cdo, Guy G Buckley
Cco, Julie Dill
Manager, Steve Smith
Vice President of It, Mark Wyatt
Art Director, Joe Musquiz
Director, Cassell Kincaid

Vice President, Christopher Agbe-Davies
AA, Dawn Rodriguez
Auditors: DELOITTE & TOUCHE LLP HOUSTON

LOCATIONS

HQ: SPECTRA ENERGY, LLC
  5400 WESTHEIMER CT, HOUSTON, TX 770565353
Phone: 713 627-5400
Web: WWW.SPECTRAENERGY.COM

2016 Sales

	$ mil.	% of total
U.S.	2,461	50
Canada	2,455	50
Total	**4,916**	**100**

PRODUCTS/OPERATIONS

2016 Sales

	$ mil.	% of total
Spectra Energy Partners	2,533	52
Distribution	1,370	28
Western Canada Transmission & Processing	1,005	20
Others	8	-
Total	**4,916**	**100**

2016 Sales

	$ mil.	% of total
Transportation storage and processing of natural gas	3,251	66
Distribution of natural gas	1,144	23
Transportation of crude oil	359	7
Sales of natural gas liquids	68	2
Other	94	2
Total	**4,916**	**100**

Selected Mergers and Acquisitions

COMPETITORS

Entergy
Enterprise Products
Kinder Morgan
Koch Industries Inc.

Piedmont Natural Gas
Transmontaigne
Williams Companies

HISTORICAL FINANCIALS

Company Type: Private

Income Statement				FYE: December 31
	REVENUE ($ mil.)	NET INCOME ($ mil.)	NET PROFIT MARGIN	EMPLOYEES
12/16	4,916	1,020	20.7%	8,700
12/15	5,234	460	8.8%	—
Annual Growth	(6.1%)	121.7%	—	—

SPECTRUM HEALTH HOSPITALS

EXECUTIVES

Pres, Kevin R Splaine
V Pres*, Joseph J Fifer
Pres*, David M Krhovsky
V Pres, William L Bush
Physician, Peter Vasiu
Chief of Obstetrics Gynecology, Rodman Taber
Executive Assistant, Rhonda McCarthy
Director of Engineering, Duane Nelson
Telecommunications Manager, Larry Walter
Vice President of Finance, Ron Knaus
Internist, Vetriselvi Moorthy

LOCATIONS

HQ: SPECTRUM HEALTH HOSPITALS
100 MICHIGAN ST NE, GRAND RAPIDS, MI
495032560
Phone: 616 391-1774
Web: WWW.SPECTRUMHEALTH.ORG

HISTORICAL FINANCIALS

Company Type: Private

Income Statement   FYE: June 30

	REVENUE ($ mil.)	NET INCOME ($ mil.)	NET PROFIT MARGIN	EMPLOYEES
06/16	1,905	196	10.3%	11,000
06/15	1,764	196	11.1%	—
06/08	2,595	(21)	—	—
06/06	1,013	77	7.6%	—
Annual Growth	6.5%	9.8%	—	—

2016 Year-End Financials

Return on assets: 7.9%   Cash ($ mil.): 206
Return on equity: 22.0%
Current ratio: 1.90

SPECTRUM HEALTH SYSTEM

Spectrum Health is an integrated health system with award winning health plan teams of nationally recognized doctors providers and network of hospitals and care facilities serving dozen of counties in West Michigan. The not-for-profit network operates some 15 hospitals including Spectrum Health Ludington Hospital Spectrum Health Zeeland Community Hospital Spectrum Health Lakeland Medical Center Spectrum Health Hospitals Butterworth Hospital and Spectrum Health Ludington Hospital. The nation's third-largest provider-sponsored health plan Priority Health currently serving over one million members across the state of Michigan. In early 2022 Spectrum Health and Beaumont Health are moving forward to create a new health system that is For Michigan By Michigan.

Operations

Spectrum Health operates three rehabilitation and nursing centers about 120 outpatient sites and telehealth services. Spectrum Health Helen DeVos Children's Hospital provides expert care from 350-plus pediatric specialists in more than 70 specialties and programs. Spectrum Health's other hospitals include Blodgett Hospital Butterworth Hospital Kelsey Hospital Reed City Hospital and United Hospital.

Spectrum Health works with 4000 physicians and advanced practice providers including Spectrum Health Medical Group one of the largest and most comprehensive multispecialty physician groups in West Michigan.

Geographic Reach

Spectrum Health is based in Grand Rapids Michigan.

Mergers and Acquisitions

In early 2022 Spectrum Health and Beaumont Health are moving forward to create a new health system that is For Michigan By Michigan. Its focus as its launch its new health system is to continue to provide excellent health care and coverage in its communities. The new system which will be temporarily known as BHSH System will launch Feb. 1 2022. While Spectrum Health and Beaumont Health create this new health system patients and health plan members are encouraged to access care in the same ways they currently do. All patients will continue to have access to their same sites of care physicians and health providers and insurance plans.

Company Background

Spectrum Health was formed through the 1997 merger of Blodgett Hospital and Butterworth Hospital. Kent Community Hospital joined the organization in 1999 and the United Memorial Health System (Kelsey Hospital and United Hospital) became a member in 2003.

EXECUTIVES

Pres, Tina Freese Decker
Dir, Robert Roth
Dir, Michael Todman
Dir, Stephen Boshoven
Dir, Gloria Lara
Dir, Sean Welsh
Dir, Doug Devos
Dir, Melonie Ice
Dir, Angel Hernandez
Dir, Philomena Mantella
Dir, Michael Jandernoa
Auditors: ERNST & YOUNG LLP GRAND RAPID

LOCATIONS

HQ: SPECTRUM HEALTH SYSTEM
100 MICHIGAN ST NE, GRAND RAPIDS, MI
495032560
Phone: 616 391-1774
Web: WWW.SPECTRUMHEALTH.ORG

PRODUCTS/OPERATIONS

2014 Sales

	$ mil.	% of total
Health plan	2,136	52
Net patient service revenue	1,868	45
Other	102	3
Total	**4,107**	**100**

Selected Services

Cancer
Continuing care
Digestive disease
Heart & vascular
Neurosciences
Orthopedics
Outpatient
Pediatric
Rehabilitation
Transplant
Women's health

Selected Operations

Helen DeVos Children's Hospital
Priority Health
Spectrum Health Blodgett Hospital
Spectrum Health Butterworth Hospital
Spectrum Health Continuing Care
Spectrum Health Kent Community Campus
Spectrum Health Gerber Memorial Hospital
Spectrum Health Pennock Hospital
Spectrum Health Reed City Hospital
Spectrum Health Special Care Hospital
Spectrum Health United Memorial
Kelsey Hospital
United Hospital

COMPETITORS

Ascension Health	Mclaren Bay
Borgess Health	Mclaren Health Care
Bronson Battle Creek	Mercy Health Hackley
Bronson Health Care	Munson Healthcare
Caresource	Omnicare Health Plan
Covenant Healthcare	Sheridan Community
Great Lakes Health	Hospital
Plan	Total Health Care
Hayes Green Beach	Zeeland Community
Memorial Hospital	Hospital
Health Alliance Plan	
Of Michigan	

HISTORICAL FINANCIALS

Company Type: Private

Income Statement   FYE: December 31

	REVENUE ($ mil.)	NET INCOME ($ mil.)	NET PROFIT MARGIN	EMPLOYEES
12/20*	8,299	714	8.6%	16,996
06/19	6,884	332	4.8%	—
06/18	6,004	332	5.5%	—
06/17	5,681	357	6.3%	—
Annual Growth	9.9%	18.9%		

*Fiscal year change

2020 Year-End Financials

Return on assets: 7.9%   Cash ($ mil.): 1,248
Return on equity: 12.3%
Current ratio: 1.60

SPIRE MISSOURI INC.

EXECUTIVES

Director, Edward Glotzbach
Chief Financial Officer, Senior Vice President, Mark Waltermire
Director, William Nasser
Chief Governance Officer, Corporate Secretary, Mary Kullman
Chairman Of The Board, Chief Executive Officer, Suzanne Sitherwood
Vice President - Finance, Steven Rasche
President, Chief Operating Officer - Distribution Operations, Executive Vice President, Steven Lindsey
Director, John Stupp
Director, W. Stephen Maritz
Director, Mary Van Lokeren
Director, Anthony Leness
Director, Arnold Donald
Auditors: DELOITTE & TOUCHE LLP ST LOU

LOCATIONS

HQ: SPIRE MISSOURI INC.
700 MARKET ST, SAINT LOUIS, MO 631011829
Phone: 314 342-0500
Web: WWW.SPIREENERGY.COM

HISTORICAL FINANCIALS

Company Type: Private

Income Statement   FYE: September 30

	REVENUE ($ mil.)	NET INCOME ($ mil.)	NET PROFIT MARGIN	EMPLOYEES
09/18	1,285	129	10.1%	2,271
09/17	1,171	113	9.6%	—
09/16	1,087	105	9.7%	—
09/15	1,416	105	7.4%	—
Annual Growth	(3.2%)	7.1%		

2018 Year-End Financials

Return on assets: 3.5%   Cash ($ mil.): 2
Return on equity: 6.2%
Current ratio: 0.50

SPIRIT REALTY CAPITAL, INC.

EXECUTIVES

President, Chief Executive Officer, Director, Jackson Hsieh, $879,170 total compensation
Executive Vice President And General Counsel, Rochelle Thomas
Executive Vice President, Chief Administrative Officer, Chief Legal Officer, Jay Young, $365,650 total compensation
Independent Director, Nicholas Shepherd
Independent Director, Todd Dunn
Independent Director, Kevin Charlton
Independent Director, Diana Laing
Independent Director, Elizabeth Frank
Lead Independent Chairman Of The Board, Richard Gilchrist
Chief Financial Officer, Executive Vice President, Michael Hughes, $463,500 total compensation
Executive Vice President, Chief Investment Officer, Ken Heimlich, $388,722 total compensation
Auditors: ERNST & YOUNG LLP DALLAS TEX

LOCATIONS

HQ: SPIRIT REALTY CAPITAL, INC.
2727 N HARWOOD ST STE 300, DALLAS, TX 752012407
Phone: 480 606-0820
Web: WWW.SPIRITREALTY.COM

HISTORICAL FINANCIALS

Company Type: Private

Income Statement				FYE: December 31
	ASSETS ($ mil.)	NET INCOME ($ mil.)	INCOME AS % OF ASSETS	EMPLOYEES
12/17	7,263	77	1.1%	82
12/16	7,677	97	1.3%	—
12/14	8,017	(33)	—	—
12/13	7,231	1	0.0%	—
Annual Growth	0.1%	160.4%	—	—

2017 Year-End Financials

Return on assets: 1.1%   Sales ($ mil): 668
Return on equity: 2.3%

SPOHN INVESTMENT CORPORATION

EXECUTIVES

Pres, David Frum
Srvcs Exec Acct, Deanne D Kindred
General, Barney Rodriguez
General, Martha Kiel
General, Rebecca Heinsohn
General, Rebecca Woods
General, Robert Wang
General, Susan Oakley
General, Christopher Miskovsky
General, Jessie Ybarra
General, Sandra Williams
Auditors: IT ERNST & YOUNG US LLP INDI

LOCATIONS

HQ: SPOHN INVESTMENT CORPORATION
600 ELIZABETH ST, CORPUS CHRISTI, TX 784042235
Phone: 800 756-7999
Web: WWW.CHRISTUSHEALTH.ORG

HISTORICAL FINANCIALS

Company Type: Private

Income Statement				FYE: June 30
	REVENUE ($ mil.)	NET INCOME ($ mil.)	NET PROFIT MARGIN	EMPLOYEES
06/20	811	(6)	—	80
06/19	828	8	1.1%	—
Annual Growth	(2.0%)	—	—	—

2020 Year-End Financials

Return on assets: (-0.8%)   Cash ($ mil.): 9
Return on equity: (-1.0%)
Current ratio: 2.00

SPORTS, INC.

EXECUTIVES

Pres, Tony Cardinal
V Pres & Asst SEC-Treas, Nancy Wilson
Executive Officer, Frances Hines
Accounts Payable, Roxanne Gordon
Human Resources Manager, Pam Derosier
Director of Oprs, Andy Eames
Invoicing Accounts Pay, Angela Woolett
Program and Member Support Coo, Corry Arntzen
Shipping Supervisor, Craig Kriskovich
Outdoor Program Manager, Kale Schwede
Web Developer, Michael Hoerner
Auditors: JUNKERMIER CLARK CAMPANELLA

LOCATIONS

HQ: SPORTS, INC.
333 2ND AVE N, LEWISTOWN, MT 594572700
Phone: 406 538-3496
Web: WWW.SPORTSINC.US

HISTORICAL FINANCIALS

Company Type: Private

Income Statement				FYE: December 31
	REVENUE ($ mil.)	NET INCOME ($ mil.)	NET PROFIT MARGIN	EMPLOYEES
12/20	1,191	0	0.1%	38
12/19	983	0	0.0%	—
12/18	960	0	0.0%	—
12/17	913	0	0.0%	—
Annual Growth	9.3%	75.5%	—	—

2020 Year-End Financials

Return on assets: 0.3%   Cash ($ mil.): 3
Return on equity: 3.6%
Current ratio: 1.10

SPRING BRANCH INDEPENDENT SCHOOL DISTRICT (INC)

EXECUTIVES

Supt, Scott R Muri
Transportation Director, Sherri Lawson
Elementary Assistant, Sherrie Folger
Field Supervisor, Jessica Jackowski
Food Director, Chris Kamradt
Assistant Superintendent, Jennifer Blaine
Boys Head Coach Soccer, Agustin Estrada
Administrator, Alan Gray
Manager, Patricia Reyes
Team Leader, Kenneth Shorts
Dietetic Supervisor, Elizabeth Lofgren
Auditors: WHITLEY PENN LLP HOUSTON TEX

LOCATIONS

HQ: SPRING BRANCH INDEPENDENT SCHOOL DISTRICT (INC)
955 CAMPBELL RD, HOUSTON, TX 770242803
Phone: 713 464-1511
Web: WWW.SPRINGBRANCHISD.COM

HISTORICAL FINANCIALS

Company Type: Private

Income Statement				FYE: June 30
	REVENUE ($ mil.)	NET INCOME ($ mil.)	NET PROFIT MARGIN	EMPLOYEES
06/21	564	(56)	—	4,484
06/20	540	161	29.9%	—
06/19	582	22	3.9%	—
06/18	513	135	26.4%	—
Annual Growth	3.1%	—	—	—

2021 Year-End Financials

Return on assets: (-3.5%)   Cash ($ mil.): 41
Return on equity: (-31.0%)
Current ratio: —

SRCTEC, LLC

EXECUTIVES

Pres, Drew James
Treas*, Deborah Sabella
SEC*, Mary Pat Hartnett
Scientist, Laura Morlacci
Director, Stephen Winslow
Senior Quality Engineer, Bill Laveck
Manager, Operations, Kevin Germaine
Senior Program Management Spec, Brenda Arena
Director of Business Developme, David Bessey
Vice President of Operations, Gary Stevens
Senior Manufacturing Engineer, Johannus J Moolenschot

LOCATIONS

HQ: SRCTEC, LLC
5801 E TAFT RD STE 7, SYRACUSE, NY 132123382
Phone: 315 452-8700
Web: WWW.SRCINC.COM

Income Statement				FYE: September 30
	REVENUE ($ mil.)	NET INCOME ($ mil.)	NET PROFIT MARGIN	EMPLOYEES
09/10	583	42	7.3%	150
09/09	365	19	5.4%	—
Annual Growth	59.7%	115.0%	—	—

2010 Year-End Financials

Return on assets: 14.3% Cash ($ mil.): 44
Return on equity: 7.3%
Current ratio: 1.30

SSM HEALTH CARE CORPORATION

The mission of SSM Health began with five nuns who fled religious persecution in Germany in 1872 only to arrive in St. Louis in the midst of a smallpox epidemic. They formed their first hospital there in 1877. Today the Midwest-based not-for-profit system sponsored by the Franciscan Sisters of Mary owns some 25 acute care hospitals more than 290 physician offices and other outpatient and virtual care services ten post-acute facilities comprehensive home care and hospice services a pharmacy benefit company a health insurance company and an accountable care organization. SSM Health's hospital operations are located primarily in Missouri Wisconsin Oklahoma and Illinois and its related businesses provide health related services in about 50 states.

Operations

SSM Health has some 11000 physicians on its staff. The system has some 104840 inpatient admissions and some 1.3 million outpatient visits each year.

Geographic Reach

Based in St. Louis Missouri SSM Health's facilities are located in Illinois Missouri Oklahoma and Wisconsin.

Sales and Marketing

Managed care payments account for about half of SSM Health's net patient revenue while Medicare accounts for about 25% and Medicaid accounts for about 15%.

SSM Health advertising expenses were $21085 and 22851 in 2020 and 2019 respectively.

Financial Performance

Total operating revenues and other support for the year 2020 was $8.2 billion a 4% increase from the previous year's revenue of $7.9 billion.

In 2020 the company had a net income of $397.7 million a 24% increase from the previous year's net income of $319.5 million.

The company's cash at the end of 2020 was $820.9 million. Operating activities generated $1.1 billion while investing activities used $688.8 million primarily for purchase of assets limited as to use or restricted and short-term investments. Financing activities provided another $147.3 million.

Strategy

To satisfy the company's long-term rate-of-return objectives SSMH relies on a total return strategy in which investment returns are achieved through both capital appreciation (realized and unrealized) and interest and dividend income.

SSMH uses a diversified asset allocation to achieve its long-term return objectives within prudent risk constraints to preserve capital.

EXECUTIVES

President And Ceo, Laura Kaiser
Chief Financial Officer, Randy Combs
Chief Clinical Officer, Matthew Hanley
Chief Transformation Officer, Carter Dredge
Chief Community Health Officer, Alexander Garza
Auditors: DELOITTE & TOUCHE LLP ST LOU

LOCATIONS

HQ: SSM HEALTH CARE CORPORATION
10101 WOODFIELD LN # 120, SAINT LOUIS, MO 631322937
Phone: 314 994-7800
Web: WWW.SSMHEALTH.COM

PRODUCTS/OPERATIONS

Selected Facilities

Illinois
St. Mary's Good Samaritan (joint sponsorship with Felician Services two hospitals in Mt. Vernon and Centralia)
Missouri
St. Francis Hospital & Health Services (Maryville)
St. Mary's Health Center (Jefferson City)
SSM Cardinal Glennon Children's Medical Center (St. Louis)
SSM DePaul Health Center (Bridgeton)
SSM St. Clare Health Center (St. Louis)
SSM St. Joseph Health Center (St. Charles)
SSM St. Joseph Health Center (Wentzville)
SSM St. Joseph Hospital West (Lake St. Louis)
SSM St. Mary's Health Center (Richmond Heights)
Oklahoma
Bone & Joint Hospital (Oklahoma City)
Shawnee Medical Center Clinic (Shawnee)
St. Anthony Hospital (Oklahoma City)
Unity Health Center (Shawnee)
Wisconsin
Boscobel Area Health Care (managed hospital and clinics Boscobel)
Columbus Community Hospital (affiliate Columbus)
Edgerton Hospital and Health Services (Edgerton)
St. Clare Hospital (Baraboo)
St. Clare Meadows Care Center (nursing home Madison)
St. Mary's Care Center (nursing home Madison)
St. Mary's Hospital (Madison)
St. Mary's Janesville Hospital (Janesville)
Stoughton Hospital (affiliate Stoughton)
Uplands Hill Health (affiliate hospital and nursing care Dodgeville)

COMPETITORS

Adventist Health System Sunbelt Healthcare
Advocate Health Care
Allina Hospitals
Ascension Health
Bjc Healthcare
Carle Physician Group
Community Health Systems
Hca
Hospital Sisters Health System
Mayo Clinic
Mercy Health
Meriter Health Services
Metrosouth Medical
Rush System For Health
Tenet Healthcare
University Of Wisconsin Hospital And Clinics
Vitas Healthcare

Income Statement				FYE: December 31
	REVENUE ($ mil.)	NET INCOME ($ mil.)	NET PROFIT MARGIN	EMPLOYEES
12/17	6,497	245	3.8%	24,230
12/16	6,109	(30)	—	—
12/13	1,177	32	2.8%	—
Annual Growth	53.3%	65.9%	—	—

2017 Year-End Financials

Return on assets: 3.3% Cash ($ mil.): 126
Return on equity: 10.5%
Current ratio: 0.80

ST BARNABAS MEDICAL CENTER (INC)

Part of the RWJBarnabas Health system Saint Barnabas Medical Center is a 600-bed acute-care hospital that provides a full range of health services to residents of Livingston New Jersey and surrounding areas. The not-for-profit medical center provides general inpatient and outpatient care programs as well as burn and perinatal care. It also houses units specializing in organ transplant stroke care cardiac surgery and comprehensive cancer treatment. Its Institute for Reproductive Medicine and Science provides assisted reproductive technology services.

Operations

In combination with its satellite Saint Barnabas Ambulatory Care Center the medical center serves about 300000 outpatients per year. Saint Barnabas Medical Center is also a teaching affiliate of several regional schools including the University of Medicine and Dentistry of New Jersey and Drexel University College of Medicine .

Company Background

New Jersey's first hospital Saint Barnabas Medical Center was founded in 1865 in a private home.

EXECUTIVES

Ceo, Richard Davis
Pres, Ronald J Del Mauro
Cfo, Patrick Aheran
Cao, Franz Smith
Chro, Ruth Bash
Coordinator of Social Work Svs, Joanne Hall
Director of Environmental Svs, Jane Mc Gill
Director of Patient Education, Mary Beth Russell
Chief Information Officer, Michael Mc Tigue
Health Professional, Abdulmajid Y Adam
Nurse Recruiter, Terri Di Elmo
Auditors: KPMG LLP NEW YORK NY

LOCATIONS

HQ: ST BARNABAS MEDICAL CENTER (INC)
94 OLD SHORT HILLS RD # 1, LIVINGSTON, NJ 070395668
Phone: 973 322-5000
Web: WWW.RWJBH.ORG

COMPETITORS

Atlantic Health
Children's Specialized Hospital
Chilton Medical Center
East Orange General Hospital
Hackensack Meridian Health
Hackensack University Medical Center

Jfk Medical Center
Newark Beth Israel Medical Center
Raritan Bay Medical Center
Robert Wood Johnson University Hospital
Robert Wood Johnson University Hospital At Rahway
Saint Peter's University Hospital
St. Joseph's Healthcare System
Trinitas Regional Medical Center
Virtua Health

HISTORICAL FINANCIALS
Company Type: Private

Income Statement — FYE: December 31

	REVENUE ($ mil.)	NET INCOME ($ mil.)	NET PROFIT MARGIN	EMPLOYEES
12/18	818	113	13.9%	4,000
12/17	818	113	13.9%	—
12/16	760	84	11.1%	—
12/15	728	87	12.0%	—
Annual Growth	4.0%	9.0%	—	—

2018 Year-End Financials
Return on assets: 7.5%   Cash ($ mil.): —
Return on equity: 11.3%
Current ratio: 9.20

ST JOHN'S UNIVERSITY, NEW YORK

EXECUTIVES

Pres, Conrado Gempesaw
Exec V Pres For Mission*, Bernard M Tracey
V Pres For Academic Affairs*, Robert Mangione
V Pres-Cfo*, Sharon Hewitt Watkins
Vp Academic Support, Andr McKenzie
Coordinator, Crystal Diaz
Assistant Professor, Meghan Clark
Assistant Professor, Xiaojun Chen
Accounting Staff, Mian Wang
Administrative Assistant, Mary Morehart
Assistant Exec Director, Barbara Carr
Auditors: KPMG LLP GREENSBORO NC

LOCATIONS

HQ: ST JOHN'S UNIVERSITY, NEW YORK
  8000 UTOPIA PKWY, JAMAICA, NY 114399000
Phone: 718 990-6161
Web: WWW.STJOHNS.EDU

HISTORICAL FINANCIALS
Company Type: Private

Income Statement — FYE: May 31

	REVENUE ($ mil.)	NET INCOME ($ mil.)	NET PROFIT MARGIN	EMPLOYEES
05/20*	810	55	6.8%	3,310
12/16	0	(0)	—	—
Annual Growth	3132.6%	—	—	—
*Fiscal year change

2020 Year-End Financials
Return on assets: 3.7%   Cash ($ mil.): 60
Return on equity: 5.9%
Current ratio: —

ST LOUIS CHILDREN'S HOSPITAL

EXECUTIVES

Act Pres, Peggy Gordin
Sr V Pres*, Michael Dehaven
V Pres*, David Aplington
Pres*, Joan Magruder
Distribution/Shipping/Transpor, Lynne Andreski
General Manager, Ellie Glenn
Manager of Child Life, Jill Malan
Pediatric Nurse Practitioner, Michelle Nadler
Clinical Nurse Manager GI, Tammy Keeling
Lab Supervisor, David Baker
Director, Vivian Boyd

LOCATIONS

HQ: ST LOUIS CHILDREN'S HOSPITAL
  1 CHILDRENS PL FL 2, SAINT LOUIS, MO 631101081
Phone: 314 454-6000
Web: WWW.STLOUISCHILDRENS.ORG

HISTORICAL FINANCIALS
Company Type: Private

Income Statement — FYE: December 31

	REVENUE ($ mil.)	NET INCOME ($ mil.)	NET PROFIT MARGIN	EMPLOYEES
12/18	668	65	9.8%	2,959
12/17	609	62	10.2%	—
12/16	563	58	10.3%	—
12/15	527	50	9.5%	—
Annual Growth	8.2%	9.1%	—	—

2018 Year-End Financials
Return on assets: 11.1%   Cash ($ mil.): —
Return on equity: 13.1%
Current ratio: 2.20

ST LUKE'S HOSPITAL & HEALTH NETWORK INC

EXECUTIVES

Pres, Richard A Anderson
Sr V Pres, Rthomas P Lichtenwalner
Coordinator, Kathleen Hedges
Administrative Assistant, Emilia Dossantos
Network Director Real Estate, James Reyes
Patient Experience Manager, Lisa Litak
Information Technology Directo, Mike Owsinsky
Chief of Endocrinology, Bankim Bhatt
Director Surgical, Cheryl Semmel
Linear Accelerator Technician, Don Beliveau
Regional Manager, Karen Schantz

LOCATIONS

HQ: ST LUKE'S HOSPITAL & HEALTH NETWORK INC
  801 OSTRUM ST, BETHLEHEM, PA 180151000
Phone: 484 526-4000
Web: WWW.SLHN.ORG

HISTORICAL FINANCIALS
Company Type: Private

Income Statement — FYE: June 30

	REVENUE ($ mil.)	NET INCOME ($ mil.)	NET PROFIT MARGIN	EMPLOYEES
06/16	648	47	7.4%	75
06/15	602	38	6.4%	—
Annual Growth	7.6%	24.9%	—	—

2016 Year-End Financials
Return on assets: 5.1%   Cash ($ mil.): 43
Return on equity: 130.2%
Current ratio: 1.30

ST LUKE'S HOSPITAL OF KANSAS CITY

LOCATIONS

HQ: ST LUKE'S HOSPITAL OF KANSAS CITY
  4401 WORNALL RD, KANSAS CITY, MO 641113220
Phone: 816 932-2000
Web: WWW.SAINTLUKESHEALTHSYSTEM.ORG

HISTORICAL FINANCIALS
Company Type: Private

Income Statement — FYE: December 31

	REVENUE ($ mil.)	NET INCOME ($ mil.)	NET PROFIT MARGIN	EMPLOYEES
12/13	647	11	1.8%	4
12/09	479	13	2.7%	—
Annual Growth	7.8%	(2.8%)	—	—

2013 Year-End Financials
Return on assets: 1.0%   Cash ($ mil.): 34
Return on equity: 1.4%
Current ratio: 0.40

ST LUKES-ROOSEVELT INSTITUTE

EXECUTIVES

Prin, Kenneth Barritt
Auditors: ERNST & YOUNG US LLP INDIANAP

LOCATIONS

HQ: ST LUKES-ROOSEVELT INSTITUTE
  1111 AMSTERDAM AVE, NEW YORK, NY 100251716
Phone: 212 523-4000
Web: WWW.STLUKESHOSPITALNYC.ORG

HISTORICAL FINANCIALS
Company Type: Private

Income Statement — FYE: December 31

	REVENUE ($ mil.)	NET INCOME ($ mil.)	NET PROFIT MARGIN	EMPLOYEES
12/19	1,348	(22)	—	3
12/14	21	0	—	—
Annual Growth	128.7%	—	—	—

Return on assets: (-1.6%) Cash ($ mil.): 167
Return on equity: (-32.5%)
Current ratio: 0.20

ST. CHARLES HEALTH SYSTEM, INC.

EXECUTIVES

Pres-Ceo, Joe Sluka
Coordinator, Sue Takemoto
Operating Room Dir, Carla Stevens
Chief Operations Officer, Iman Simmons
Clinical Oncology Pharmacist, Alexis Barr
Licensed Clinical Social Worke, John Walkenhorst
Point of Care Coordinator, Lura Wilhelm
Education Coordinator, Debbie Cole
Project Manager, Jarred McDonald
Clinical Risk, Michele Frandsen
Applications Analyst, Arielle Ocel

LOCATIONS

HQ: ST. CHARLES HEALTH SYSTEM, INC.
2500 NE NEFF RD, BEND, OR 977016015
Phone: 541 382-4321
Web: WWW.STCHARLESHEALTHCARE.ORG

HISTORICAL FINANCIALS

Company Type: Private

Income Statement				FYE: December 31
	REVENUE ($ mil.)	NET INCOME ($ mil.)	NET PROFIT MARGIN	EMPLOYEES
12/19	1,002	168	16.8%	3,200
12/17	809	41	5.1%	—
12/13	631	40	6.4%	—
12/07	367	8	2.4%	—
Annual Growth	8.7%	27.8%	—	—

2019 Year-End Financials

Return on assets: 14.0% Cash ($ mil.): 52
Return on equity: 21.8%
Current ratio: 0.50

ST. DOMINIC HEALTH SERVICES, INC.

EXECUTIVES

Chb, Mary Dorothea
Manager, Janet McAdory
Chief of Medicine, Dan Woodliff
Coordinator, Stacey Ferguson
Scientist, Keshia Mallett
Executive, Patrick Bufkin
Senior Accountant, Sam Yeager
Executive Assistant Informatio, Shana Watkins
Family Medicine, Arturo Blanco
Counsel, Crystal Jackson
Family Practitioner, Ernesto Aguilera
Auditors: KPMG LLP BATON ROUGE LOUISIA

LOCATIONS

HQ: ST. DOMINIC HEALTH SERVICES, INC.
969 LAKELAND DR, JACKSON, MS 392164606
Phone: 601 200-2000
Web: WWW.STDOM.COM

HISTORICAL FINANCIALS

Company Type: Private

Income Statement				FYE: June 30
	REVENUE ($ mil.)	NET INCOME ($ mil.)	NET PROFIT MARGIN	EMPLOYEES
06/20*	560	397	71.0%	2,500
12/17	2	2	87.6%	—
12/13	0	0	—	—
12/12	2	(0)	—	—
Annual Growth	118.4%	—	—	—

*Fiscal year change

2020 Year-End Financials

Return on assets: 56.3% Cash ($ mil.): 138
Return on equity: 100.0%
Current ratio: 1.60

ST. FRANCIS HOSPITAL, INC.

EXECUTIVES

Ceo, Melody Trimble
Prin*, Mark Nantz
President*, Valinda Reutledge
Vice President-Finance*, Ronnie Hyatt
Chief Officer, Mary Jo Cagle
Coordinator, Shannon Bates
Director of Maintenance, James Kelly
Rn, Nicole Meredith
Chief Sponsorship, Thom Morris
Auditors: DELOITTE TAX LP ATLANTA GA

LOCATIONS

HQ: ST. FRANCIS HOSPITAL, INC.
1 SAINT FRANCIS DR, GREENVILLE, SC 296013955
Phone: 864 255-1000
Web: WWW.BONSECOURS.COM

HISTORICAL FINANCIALS

Company Type: Private

Income Statement				FYE: August 31
	REVENUE ($ mil.)	NET INCOME ($ mil.)	NET PROFIT MARGIN	EMPLOYEES
08/19	652	69	10.6%	2,105
08/14	534	60	11.3%	—
Annual Growth	4.1%	2.9%	—	—

2019 Year-End Financials

Return on assets: 11.0% Cash ($ mil.): 230
Return on equity: 22.6%
Current ratio: 8.70

ST. FRANCIS HOSPITAL, ROSLYN, NEW YORK

Sure St. Francis Hospital can handle your gall bladder and sinus difficulties but it's really on top of your heart problems. The hospital's Heart Center — New York State's only specially designated cardiac center — provides surgical diagnostic and treatment services. The 365-bed St. Francis Hospital also has centers for ENT (ear nose and throat) orthopedic vascular prostate cancer gastrointestinal and general surgery services. As part of Catholic Health Services of Long Island St. Francis opened its doors in 1954 to children and adults. It was originally established as St. Francis Hospital and Sanatorium for Cardiac Children in 1936.

Operations

St. Francis Hospital's Heart Center performs about 8000 cardiac catheterizations 3000 coronary angioplasties and about 1500 open-heart operations every year. The center's DeMatteis Center for Cardiac Research and Education works to develop improved techniques for heart disease diagnosis including conducting clinical trials through partnerships with device and equipment makers and provides patient education and fitness programs.

Geographic Reach

St. Francis Hospital is located in Roslyn New York. In addition it has satellite New York locations in Greenvale (DeMatteis Center for Cardiac Research and Education) West Islip (South Bay Cardiovascular Center) and Hicksville (Bishop McHugh Health Center) as well as administrative offices in Port Washington.

Strategy

St. Francis Hospital has expanded in recent years to keep up with growing patient demand. It opened the Bishop McHugh Health Center to provide outpatient primary care services for uninsured and underinsured patients in 2012.

The hospital completed its largest expansion project to date in 2009 with the construction of the $190 million Nancy and Frederick DeMatteis Pavilion; the project increased the hospital's clinical space by about 40% and added 85 beds.

EXECUTIVES

Pres-Ceo, Alan Guerci
Sr V Pres-Cfo*, William C Arms
Sr Vp-Coo*, Martin A Bieber
Vp-Development & Public Relati*, Linda Cavallo-Miller
R.N., Sr V Pres*, Ann Cella Rn
Vp-Human Resources*, Betty Anson
Exec V Pres*, Ruth Hennessey
Sr V Pres*, Jack Soterakis
PH 516 705-1925, Jenny Mitchell
Chief Anesthesiology, H Sinan Berkay
Director of Discharge Planning, Mary Anne Highland
Auditors: PRICEWATERHOUSECOOPERS LLP NE

LOCATIONS

HQ: ST. FRANCIS HOSPITAL, ROSLYN, NEW YORK
100 PORT WASHINGTON BLVD, ROSLYN, NY 115761347
Phone: 516 562-2000
Web: WWW.CHSLI.ORG

PRODUCTS/OPERATIONS

Selected Services
Anesthesiology
Breast Surgery
Cardiology
Cardiothoracic Surgery
Diabetes Care Center
Emergency Medicine
Gastroenterology
General Surgery
Hematology/Oncology
Nephrology
Neurology
Orthopedic Surgery
Otolaryngology
Podiatry
Psychiatry
Pulmonary Medicine
Radiology
Rehabilitation
Urology
Vascular Services
Women's Center

COMPETITORS

Bronx-lebanon Hospital
Brookhaven Memorial Hospital Medical Center
Calvary Hospital
Continuum Health Partners
Franklin Hospital
Huntington Hospital
Mather Memorial Hospital
Medisys Health Network
Memorial Sloan-kettering
New York City Health And Hospitals
Newyork-presbyterian Healthcare
Northwell Health
Nuhealth

HISTORICAL FINANCIALS

Company Type: Private

Income Statement				FYE: December 31
	REVENUE ($ mil.)	NET INCOME ($ mil.)	NET PROFIT MARGIN	EMPLOYEES
12/15	614	37	6.2%	2,184
12/08	385	28	7.4%	—
12/04	366	47	12.9%	—
12/02	828	0	—	—
Annual Growth	—	152.0%	—	—

2015 Year-End Financials
Return on assets: 3.9%   Cash ($ mil.): 34
Return on equity: 5.5%
Current ratio: —

ST. JOHN HEALTH SYSTEM, INC.

St. John Health System aims to bring health into the lives of the ill. The not-for-profit system provides health care services to residents of Tulsa and surrounding areas in northeastern Oklahoma and southern Kansas. In addition to flagship facility St. John Medical Center it owns or manages eight other community hospitals as well as urgent care and long-term care facilities. St. John Health System provides primary and specialty medical care through OMNI Medical Group and offers health insurance through CommunityCare health plan. Established in 1926 by the Sisters of the Sorrowful Mother the health system is part of Marian Health.

Operations

Facilities owned managed or sponsored by St. John Health System include hospitals Oklahoma State University Medical Center St. John Sapulpa St. John Owasso St. John Broken Arrow Pawhuska City Hospital Sedan City Hospital Nowata Hospital and Jane Phillips Medical Center. The company's senior living facilities include Franciscan Villa Frances Streitel Villa Heartsworth House and Rosewood Terrace.

Strategy

St. John Health System will periodically add services to its offerings to meet community demand. In early 2011 St. John Health opened the St. John Weight Management Institute to offer its patients weight loss options including bariatric surgery. The health system's newest hospital St. John Broken Arrow near Tulsa was constructed in 2009.

In 2012 Marian Health entered talks with another Catholic health system operator Ascension Health over the possibility of merging St. John Health System and other Marian organizations into the Ascension organization.

EXECUTIVES

Pres, Sister Mary T Gottschalk
Chb*, Robert Lafortune
SEC*, Sister Mary Ann Nuntz
Information Specialist, Connie Terrell
Internal Medicine Practitioner, Richard Doss
Administrative Assistant, Dennis Klaver
Coordinator, Lashawna Brown
Health Professional, Allison Wilcox
Customer Staff, Barbi Zimmerman
Internal Medicine Practitioner, James V Rooks
Registered Nurse, Ramona Miller

LOCATIONS

HQ: ST. JOHN HEALTH SYSTEM, INC.
1923 S UTICA AVE, TULSA, OK 741046520
Phone: 918 744-2180
Web: WWW.HEALTHCARE.ASCENSION.ORG

PRODUCTS/OPERATIONS

Selected Facilities and Operations – Oklahoma
CommunityCare (health plan)
Jane Phillips Medical Center (Bartlesville)
Nowata Hospital
Oklahoma State University Medical Center (managed facility in Tulsa)
OMNI Medical Group (physicians group)
Pawhuska City Hospital
Regional Medical Laboratory (clinical lab testing)
Sedan City Hospital
St. John Broken Arrow Hospital
St. John Medical Center (Tulsa)
St. John Owasso Hospital
St. John Physicians
St. John Sapulpa Hospital

COMPETITORS

Anthem	Integris Health
Ardent Health Services	Kindred Healthcare
Cigna	Marian Health System
Catholic Health Initiatives	Norman Regional Health
Community Health Systems	Presbyterian Healthcare Services
Deaconess Health Care	Ssm Health Care
Hca	Saint Francis Health System
Hillcrest Medical Center	Unitedhealth Group

HISTORICAL FINANCIALS

Company Type: Private

Income Statement				FYE: June 30
	REVENUE ($ mil.)	NET INCOME ($ mil.)	NET PROFIT MARGIN	EMPLOYEES
06/14*	1,056	79	7.5%	4,011
09/12	977	74	7.7%	—
09/11	895	17	2.0%	—
Annual Growth	5.7%	64.9%	—	—

*Fiscal year change

2014 Year-End Financials
Return on assets: 5.2%   Cash ($ mil.): 44
Return on equity: 9.9%
Current ratio: 1.70

ST. JOHN HOSPITAL AND MEDICAL CENTER

St. John Hospital & Medical Center is part of the larger Detroit area-based St. John Health regional health care system. Besides providing acute and trauma care the 770-bed teaching hospital operates specialized cancer and pediatric centers a hip and knee center an inpatient mental health unit and a Parkinson's Disease clinic. It also operates the only emergency trauma center on Detroit's East Side. The hospital was established in 1952 and has grown to include a 200-physician medical team that specializes in more than 50 medical and surgical fields. It boasts 34000 admissions; 14500 surgical visits; and more than 126500 emergency center visits each year.

Operations

Its emergency center is a Level II Trauma Center that boasts Chest Pain Center and Heart Failure Center accreditations. St. John Hospital also operates a large inpatient pediatric unit PICU and Level III NICU or Level II Special Care Nursery. The hospital runs the Van Elslander Cancer Center.

Strategy

St. John Hospital expanded its operations by opening the Elaine E. Blatt Endoscopy Department and a new pediatric burn treatment room both in 2012. It also expanded its mammography service capabilities with the purchase of Lakeshore Mammograph giving it more than a dozen new mammography sites across southeastern Michigan. In addition St. John Hospital opened a new cardiac catheterization lab that brought new diagnostic options to patients in the Michigan Blue Water Area.

EXECUTIVES

Ceo, Mark Taylor
Obstetrician, Nathan V Wagstaff
Internal Medicine Practitioner, Jason M Donaghue
Senior Manager, Corey Kennard
Internal Medicine Practitioner, Victoria Dufour
Information Specialist, Meghan McGinn
Coordinator, Nancy Derita
Physician Assistant, Jill Wells
Hematology Supervisor, Rana Bilbeisi
Hematology Supervisor, Allen Stawis
Information Specialist, Marcia Minard

LOCATIONS

HQ: ST. JOHN HOSPITAL AND MEDICAL CENTER
28000 DEQUINDRE RD, WARREN, MI 480922468
Phone: 313 343-4000
Web: WWW.HEALTHCARE.ASCENSION.ORG

PRODUCTS/OPERATIONS

Selected Services and Operations
Alternative Health
Breast Care
Breast Feeding (Lactation) Consultation
Cracchiolo Inpatient Rehabilitation Center
Diabetes Education and Care
Diagnostic and Imaging Services
Echocardiogram
Emergency
Heart and Vascular Care
Hip and Knee Center
Minimally Invasive Surgery
Minor Emergency
Neonatal Intensive Care Unit (NICU)
Obstetrics
Oncology (cancer)
Parkinson's Movement Disorder Clinic
Pediatrics
Physical Therapy
Spine Center
TravelCare
Urgent Care
Wound Care

COMPETITORS

Beaumont Health System
Crittenton Hospital
Detroit Medical Center
Henry Ford Health
System
Mount Clemens Regional
Medical Center
Trinity Health (novi)

HISTORICAL FINANCIALS

Company Type: Private

Income Statement | | | | FYE: June 30

	REVENUE ($ mil.)	NET INCOME ($ mil.)	NET PROFIT MARGIN	EMPLOYEES
06/15	753	36	4.8%	5,000
06/09	638	1	0.3%	—
06/05	0	0	—	—
06/03	1,642	9	0.6%	—
Annual Growth	(6.3%)	12.0%	—	—

2015 Year-End Financials
Return on assets: 3.0%
Return on equity: 6.1%
Current ratio: 2.20

Cash ($ mil.): 1

ST. JOHN PROVIDENCE PHYSICIANS-CMG

EXECUTIVES

Admin, Kim Harrell
Human Resources Manager, Brendon Weill
Auditors: DELOITTE TAX LLP DETROIT MI

LOCATIONS

HQ: ST. JOHN PROVIDENCE PHYSICIANS-CMG
8444 ENGLEMAN, CENTER LINE, MI 480151567
Phone: 586 755-2400
Web: WWW.FATHERMURRAYVHC.COM

HISTORICAL FINANCIALS

Company Type: Private

Income Statement | | | | FYE: June 30

	REVENUE ($ mil.)	NET INCOME ($ mil.)	NET PROFIT MARGIN	EMPLOYEES
06/09	1,562	(1)	—	317
06/08	15	(0)	—	
Annual Growth	9831.8%	—	—	—

2009 Year-End Financials
Return on assets: (-24.4%)
Return on equity: (-293.2%)
Current ratio: 2.10

Cash ($ mil.): —

ST. JOHN'S HOSPITAL OF THE HOSPITAL SISTERS OF THE THIRD ORDER OF ST. FRANCIS

Truck-struck Homer Simpson might use his last gasp trying to blurt out "St. John's Hospital of the Hospital Sisters of the Third Order of St. Francis-Springfield" to his ambulance driver but he might be better off using the hospital's more common name St. John's. D'oh! The 440-bed St. John's Hospital serves residents of central and southern Illinois with general and specialized health care services. The teaching hospital affiliated with Southern Illinois University's School of Medicine has centers devoted to women and children's health trauma cardiac care cancer orthopedics and neurology. It also operates area health clinics. Founded in 1875 St. John's is part of the Hospital Sisters Health System.

Operations
The facility is Hospital Sisters Health System's flagship hospital. It has grown to boast about 700 physicians podiatrists and dentists from more than 30 specialties. In addition to educating medical students through Southern Illinois University's School of Medicine St. Johns also supports those working on careers in nursing through its own nursing school St. John's College. It also offers courses in pharmacy pathology respiratory therapy and electroneurodiagnostics (brain disorder diagnostics) professions.

St. John's physicians perform more than 15000 surgical procedures each year. It also receives some 54000 emergency department visits and helps deliver about 2000 babies annually.

Financial Performance
In 2014 revenue fell 26% to $450 million; this was primarily due to an 89% decline in contributions investments and foundation assets.

Strategy
The hospital has been expanding its offerings to provide more specialized services to area residents. Recent additions include 3-D mammographies and expanded children's surgical services. St. John's is also focused on improving access to health care through technology such as telemedicine. In 2014 it partnered with Greenville Regional Hospital to provide advanced treatment to stroke patients at their home hospital through STAT Stroke TeleMedicine.

Other strategic initiatives at the hospital include increasing doctor and nurse retention rates growing nursing school enrollment rates and increasing patient satisfaction scores. Part of its efforts to reach more patients has led St. John's to open new outpatient health centers in areas near the main hospital facility. The hospital has also renovated its main buildings including the revamp of its day surgery and intermediate care departments.

EXECUTIVES

Ceo, Charles Lucore
Cfo*, Larry Ragel
Coo*, Dave Olejniczak
Doctor, Nestor A Ramirez Lopez
Telecommunications Staff, Bonnie Williams
Vice-President Legal, Amy Bulpitt
Information Technology, Denise Rice
Management, Brian Churchill
Senior Cost Accountant, Nancy Peddycoart
Anesthesiologist, Antoinette Appling
Child Passenger Seat Safety, Healthy E-Newsletter
Auditors: CROWE HORWATH LLP CHICAGO IL

LOCATIONS

HQ: ST. JOHN'S HOSPITAL OF THE HOSPITAL
SISTERS OF THE THIRD ORDER OF ST. FRANCIS
800 E CARPENTER ST, SPRINGFIELD, IL 627691000
Phone: 217 544-6464
Web: WWW.HSHS.ORG

PRODUCTS/OPERATIONS

2014 Sales

	$ mil.	% of total
Amount generated for taking care patients excluding provision	427	95
Other contributions	20	5
Other	1	-
Total	**449**	**100**

Selected Services
AthletiCare
Behavioral Health Services
Birth Center
Cancer Institute
Center for Living
Children's Hospital
Connect
Emergency/Trauma Care
Gastroenterology
Health Centers | Priority Care
Home Health
Hospice
Intensive Care Unit
Lab
Neurosciences Institute
Orthopedics
Pain Management Center
Prairie Heart Institute
Radiology
Regional Wound Care Center
Sleep Center
Stroke Treatment
Surgery | daVinci
TherapyCare | Rehab
Third Age Living
Women's Services

COMPETITORS

Advocate Health Care
Blessing Hospital
Community Health
Systems
Decatur Memorial
Hospital
Memorial Health System
Memorial Hospital
(illinois)
Southern Illinois
Healthcare

Company Type: Private

Income Statement				FYE: June 30
	REVENUE ($ mil.)	NET INCOME ($ mil.)	NET PROFIT MARGIN	EMPLOYEES
06/20	574	(11)	—	3,000
06/16	494	3	0.7%	—
06/15	501	3	0.8%	—
06/14	500	10	2.1%	—
Annual Growth	2.3%	—	—	—

2020 Year-End Financials

Return on assets: (-1.7%)   Cash ($ mil.): 28
Return on equity: (-11.1%)
Current ratio: 0.40

ST. JOSEPH HEALTH SYSTEM

St. Joseph Health System has earned a medal for decades by caring for patients on the West Coast and more recently the South Plains. The health care network includes 16 acute care hospitals home health agencies hospice care outpatient services skilled nursing facilities community clinics and physician organizations throughout California and in eastern New Mexico and West Texas. In its primary market of California the health system has some 2900 beds at 10 hospitals. Its Covenant Health System unit operates in Texas and New Mexico with about 1200 beds in its network of some 50 primary care facilities. St. Joseph is merging with fellow not-for-profit Providence Health & Services.

Operations
In 2013 the system discharged more than 142000 patients and had more than 4 million outpatient and 513000 emergency department visits.

Geographic Reach
The network operates acute care hospitals home health agencies urgent care centers and other health care delivery organizations throughout California and in eastern New Mexico and West Texas. Based in Irvine St. Joseph serves 10 communities in its operating regions.

Sales and Marketing
Government payments accounted for 44% of net patient revenue in 2013 while private payers accounted for 42%.

Financial Performance
Revenue increased 14% to $5.6 million due to an increase in patient service earnings. Net income decreased 83% though to $353 million as salary and benefits expenses increased. Operating cash flow fell 38% to $327 million that year.

Strategy
Already one of the largest health systems on the West Coast St. Joseph continues to grow thanks principally to its proficient fundraising.

The system invests regularly in network and facility expansion efforts. In 2013 it formed an affiliation with Hoag Memorial Hospital Presbyterian which operates two hospitals in Orange County. The Hoag operations are being combined with five of St. Joseph's area hospitals to form a new network called Covenant Health Network. The affiliated facilities will provide comprehensive care in the region while retaining their respective identities and religious affiliations.

In 2014 St. Joseph entered a collaborative care initiative with Cigna to improve access to health care and enhance care coordination.

In 2015 the system agreed to merge with Providence Health & Services which operates more than 30 hospitals in five western states. The combination will create a larger provider network of hospitals physician groups and outpatient centers eliminating some overhead expenses in the process. Furthermore by creating economies of scale the new organization will be better positioned to negotiate with health plans.

Company Background
St. Joseph Health System traces its roots back to 1920 when St. Joseph Hospital in Eureka California was first established. The health care system was officially organized in 1982 as it expanded and took on additional health care facilities. The system is a ministry of The Sisters of St. Joseph of Orange which itself was organized in 1912.

EXECUTIVES

Ceo-Pres, Richard Afable
Pres-Strat, Annette M Walker
Exec V Pres-Gen Counsel, Shannon Dwyer
Exec V Pres-Cfo, Jo Ann Escasa-Halgh
Reg-Exec V Pres, Kevin Klockenga
Event Coordinator and Developm, Katie Gozzarino
Manager, Vanessa De Gier
Chief Information Officer, Benjamin R Williams
Coordinator, Hala Abduljalil
Coordinator, Kimberly Reynolds
Project Manager, Albert Nguyen
Auditors: ERNST & YOUNG LLP IRVINE CA

LOCATIONS

HQ: ST. JOSEPH HEALTH SYSTEM
3345 MICHELSON DR STE 100, IRVINE, CA 926120693
Phone: 949 381-4000
Web: WWW.STJHS.ORG

Selected Operations
Northern California
  Petaluma Valley Hospital
  Queen of the Valley Medical Center (Napa)
  Redwood Memorial Hospital (Fortuna)
  St. Joseph Home Care Network (Sonoma)
  St. Joseph Hospital (Eureka)
  Santa Rosa Memorial Hospital
Southern California
  Mission Hospital (Mission Viejo)
  Mission Hospital Laguna Beach
  St. Joseph Hospital (Orange)
  St. Jude Medical Center (Fullerton)
  St. Mary Medical Center (Apple Valley)
West Texas/Eastern New Mexico
  Covenant Health System
  Artesia General Hospital (New Mexico)
  Covenant Hospital Levelland (Texas)
  Covenant Hospital Plainview (Texas)
  Covenant Medical Center (Lubbock TX)
  Nor-Lea General Hospital (Lovington NM)
  Roosevelt General Hospital (Portales NM)

PRODUCTS/OPERATIONS

2014 Sales

	$ mil.	% of total
Net patient service net of provision for doubtful accounts	4,275	76
Premium	1,130	20
Other	225	4
Total	**5,631**	**100**

Company Type: Private

Income Statement				FYE: June 30
	REVENUE ($ mil.)	NET INCOME ($ mil.)	NET PROFIT MARGIN	EMPLOYEES
06/13	4,955	2,082	42.0%	5,400
06/10	4,268	268	6.3%	—
Annual Growth	5.1%	98.1%		

2013 Year-End Financials

Return on assets: 3.6%   Cash ($ mil.): 329
Return on equity: 42.0%
Current ratio: 0.80

ST. JOSEPH HOSPITAL OF ORANGE

If you're feeling green or blue in Orange County St. Joseph Hospital of Orange is there to help get back to feeling pink and rosy. The California hospital provides general medical and surgical services as well as specialty care such as women's health mental health services oncology cardiology and physical rehabilitation. Part of the St. Joseph Health System the hospital provides primary care and specialty outpatient services through a network of affiliated physician practices. It also operates low-income and mobile clinics. The hospital has about 468 beds and a medical staff of some 1000.

Operations
In addition to physician group affiliates St. Joseph Hospital Affiliated Physicians and St. Joseph Heritage Medical Group the hospital also partners with the Childrens Hospital of Orange County to help expand pediatric care throughout the region. The hospital has more than 20100 inpatient discharges and about 290400 outpatient visits a year.

Geographic Reach
St. Joseph Hospital serves Orange County California and the greater Los Angeles metropolitan area.

Strategy
St. Joseph Hospital has been working to expand its community outreach programs related to cancer through a number of projects including offering improved access to clinical trials; providing better overall access to cancer care; and implementing measures to garner support for the implementation of cancer electronic health records. St. Joseph Hospital is using stimulus money and about a $3 million award from the National Cancer Institute Community Cancer Centers Program to help fund its various projects.

Company Background
The company was founded in 1929 by the Sisters of St. Joseph of Orange.

EXECUTIVES

Pres-Ceo, Larry K Ainsworth
Chm*, Jim Cora
V Chb*, Warren D Johnson
Cfo*, Tina Nycroft
Chief of Staff*, Martin J Feldman
Cardiology, Cindy Carter
Coordinator Specia, Shannon King
Manager, Christine Pierce

Director Physician Operations, Christopher E
Wood
Director, Karen Savage
Anesthesiologist, Bill Tsu

LOCATIONS

HQ: ST. JOSEPH HOSPITAL OF ORANGE
1100 W STEWART DR, ORANGE, CA 928683891
Phone: 714 633-9111
Web: WWW.SJO.ORG

PRODUCTS/OPERATIONS

Selected Services
Bariatric Surgery
Behavioral Health
Cancer
Nasal & Sinus Center
Heart & Vascular Center
Kidney Dialysis Center
Maternity
Orthopedic Services
Sleep Disorders Center

COMPETITORS

Anaheim Regional
 Medical Center
Children's Hospital Of
 Orange County
Citrus Valley Health
 Partners
Hoag Memorial Hospital
Memorial Health
 Services
Pasadena Hospital
 Association

Providence St. Joseph
 Health
Southwest Healthcare
Sutter Health
Tenet Healthcare
Torrance Memorial
 Medical Center
Trinity Health (novi)
Western Medical Center
 - Santa Ana

HISTORICAL FINANCIALS

Company Type: Private

Income Statement   FYE: June 30

	REVENUE ($ mil.)	NET INCOME ($ mil.)	NET PROFIT MARGIN	EMPLOYEES
06/18	627	40	6.5%	3,300
06/17	655	29	4.5%	—
06/16	599	11	2.0%	—
06/15	567	2	0.5%	—
Annual Growth	3.4%	144.6%	—	—

2018 Year-End Financials

Return on assets: 5.2%   Cash ($ mil.): 17
Return on equity: 14.4%
Current ratio: 1.20

ST. JOSEPH HOSPITAL, INC.

EXECUTIVES

Ceo, Bain J Farris
Prin*, Barb Jahn
Internal Medicine Practitioner, Thomas Perille
Cardiology, Glenn Hirsch
Nursing, Nicole Lauwers
Rn, Barbara Engers
Radiation Oncologist, Brandon Patton
Registered Nurse, Caileigh Minihan
Registered Nurse, Caroline Jones
Nursing, Celeste Bonnecarrere
Executive Assistant, Chellie Panzera

LOCATIONS

HQ: ST. JOSEPH HOSPITAL, INC.
1375 E 19TH AVE, DENVER, CO 802181114
Phone: 303 837-7111

HISTORICAL FINANCIALS

Company Type: Private

Income Statement   FYE: December 31

	REVENUE ($ mil.)	NET INCOME ($ mil.)	NET PROFIT MARGIN	EMPLOYEES
12/19	614	48	7.9%	2,400
12/16	530	(49)	—	—
12/15	498	37	7.5%	—
Annual Growth	5.4%	6.8%		

2019 Year-End Financials

Return on assets: 5.8%   Cash ($ mil.): —
Return on equity: 8.3%
Current ratio: —

ST. JOSEPH'S HEALTH PARTNERS LLC

St. Joseph's Healthcare System takes care of
northern New Jersey. The system includes St.
Joseph's Regional Medical Center a tertiary teaching hospital with about 650 beds that includes the
120-bed St. Joseph's Children's Hospital. The regional hospital boasts a state-designated trauma
center and provides such specialty services as cardiology oncology obstetrics behavioral health and
neurology. The system also operates St. Joseph's
Wayne Hospital a community medical center with
about 230 beds. Other operations include St. Vincent's Nursing Home a home health agency and a
community clinic network. St. Joseph's Healthcare
System is sponsored by the Sisters of Charity of
Saint Elizabeth.

Operations
With a total of some 1400 physicians and more
than 1000 beds the St. Joseph's Healthcare facilities serve more than 1.6 million patients each year.
The St. Joseph Regional facility handled some 1.3
million inpatient and outpatient visits as well as
123000 emergency room visits while the St.
Joseph's Wayne center saw 680000 patients including 27000 ER visitors.

Geographic Reach
St. Joseph's facilities are located in Cedar Grove
Paterson Totowa and Wayne in northern New Jer-
sey.

Financial Performance
Revenue rose by 2% in fiscal 2013 to $714 mil-
lion from $700 million in 2012. Income grew $110
million to $89 million from a net loss in 2012.
Medicare accounts for about 34% of net patient
revenues while Medicaid accounts for 8%.

Strategy
The St. Joseph's Wayne and St. Joseph's Regional centers are undergoing a multi-year facility
improvement project that boasts a total cost of
some $250 million. The first phase was completed
in 2009 and expanded St. Joseph's Regional outpatient services in areas including neurology orthopedics ophthalmology and pediatrics. And the
facility completed a new lobby and conference center in 2010. In 2012 its St. Joseph's Children's
Hospital completed expansion efforts on its emergency and MRI facilities; it also opened a new birth
defects center and launched a telemedicine suite

through a partnership with St. Jude Children's Research Hospital. At the St. Joseph's Wayne facility
a new cardiac catheterization lab was added in
2012.
In addition in 2012 the St. Joseph's Children's
Hospital added a new specialist facility to serve
residents of Paramus and nearby communities. In
2012 St. Joseph's Children's Hospital in Tampa
opened its new Steinbrenner Children's Emer-
gency/Trauma Center.

Company Background
St. Joseph's Healthcare traces its roots to the
1867 opening of the St. Joseph's Hospital by the
Sisters of Charity of Saint Elizabeth.

EXECUTIVES

Prin, Marianne Lanno
Svp-Cfo, Caswell Samms III
Cmo, Philip Falcone
Vp Affairs, James Labagnara Jr
Project Manager, Joseph De Bari
Chief Information Officer, James Cavanaugh
Information Technology, Tariq Matin
Senior Vice President Operatio, Christine Maher
Vp-Medical Affairs, Cristian Andrade
Librarian, Madeleine M Taylor
Speech Pathologist, Jo Petronchak
Auditors: ERNST & YOUNG LLP ISELIN NJ

LOCATIONS

HQ: ST. JOSEPH'S HEALTH PARTNERS LLC
703 MAIN ST, PATERSON, NJ 075032621
Phone: 973 569-6006
Web: WWW.STJOSEPHSHEALTH.ORG

PRODUCTS/OPERATIONS

Selected Facilities
St. Joseph's Regional Medical Center (Paterson)
 St. Joseph's Children's Hospital (Paterson)
St. Joseph's Wayne Hospital (Wayne)
St. Vincent's Nursing Home (Cedar Grove)
Visiting Health Services of New Jersey Inc. (Totowa)

Selected Services
Blood Bank/Donation
Care Management/Social Work
Clinical and Educational Services
Driver Rehabilitation Program
Food and Nutrition Services
Identifying Obstacles
Information Technology
Laboratory Services
Mission Services
Pain Management Services
Pain Medicine Center
Palliative Care
Pathology/Laboratory
Pharmacy Services
Radiology
Rehabilitation
Swallowing Center
Telemedicine
Telemedicine Programs at St. Joseph's
Transfer Center

COMPETITORS

Atlantic Health
Centrastate Healthcare System
Children's Specialized Hospital
Chilton Medical Center
East Orange General Hospital
Hackensack University Medical Center
Newton Medical Center
Princeton Healthcare
Raritan Bay Medical Center
Robert Wood Johnson University Hospital
Robert Wood Johnson University Hospital At Rahway
Trinitas Regional Medical Center
Virtua Health

Income Statement   FYE: December 31

	REVENUE ($ mil.)	NET INCOME ($ mil.)	NET PROFIT MARGIN	EMPLOYEES
12/19	827	(4)	—	8,864
12/18	808	(22)	—	
12/17	0	0	—	
12/16	796	(13)	—	
Annual Growth	1.3%	—	—	

2019 Year-End Financials

Return on assets: (-0.5%)   Cash ($ mil.): 60
Return on equity: (-2.3%)
Current ratio: 2.60

ST. JOSEPH'S HOSPITAL HEALTH CENTER

With about 450 inpatient beds St. Joseph's Hospital Health Center serves the residents of 16 central New York counties. The not-for-profit hospital system provides general emergency and surgical care as well as specialty services in areas such as obstetrics cardiology dialysis and wound care. In addition to its inpatient facilities the organization operates a home health agency a nursing school medical and dental residency programs and several outpatient care centers. Its Franciscan Companies affiliate offers some ancillary services including the provision of medical supplies home health equipment and senior services. St. Joseph's Hospital Health Center was founded in 1869 and became part of Trinity Health in 2015.

Operations

With a total of some 800 physicians St. Joseph's Hospital Health Center admits some 28000 inpatients each year. It also handles some 957000 emergency room visits and about 640000 outpatient visits annually. The hospital provides about $22 million in charity and community care each year as well.

Geographic Reach

St. Joseph's Hospital Health Center's service territory includes the New York counties of Broome Cayuga Chenango Cortland Delaware Herkimer Jefferson Lewis Madison Oneida Onondaga Oswego Otsego St. Lawrence Tioga and Tompkins.

Financial Performance

In 2013 revenue rose 7% to $626 million as patient and other revenue grew. Net income also improved by 33% due to better investment returns.

Strategy

St. Joseph's Hospital Health Center is conducting a massive $220 million expansion program at its main campus. The first phase opened in 2011 and includes a larger emergency room facility with chest pain and psychiatric units. The hospital broke ground on the second phase of the project in 2012. The program will add a new patient tower surgery facilities a sterilization center and an intensive care unit. In 2013 it opened a sleep center and a new surgical suite at the hospital. The following year St. Joseph's expanded its primary care center in west Syracuse and launched it electronic health record system.

Mergers and Acquisitions

In 2013 the center purchased Upstate Surgical Group creating a general surgery group in St. Joseph's ambulatory surgery group.

In late 2010 St. Joseph's Hospital Health Center boosted its physician network significantly by acquiring North Medical a physician practice organization that operates five practices: Family Physicians Urgent Care Orthopedics & Rehabilitation The Women's Place and Living Proof Longevity Centre. Its practices are home to about 80 physicians and mid-level practitioners.

EXECUTIVES

Pres-Ceo, Leslie Paul Luke
Coo-Cno*, Annemarie W Czyz
Cmo*, Joseph W Spinale
Cso*, Mark E Murphy
General Counsel*, Lowell Seifter
Asst General Counsel*, Regina McGraw
Cfo*, Meredith Price
Hrvp*, Erika Duncan
V Pres-It/Cio*, Charles Fennell
V Pres-Chief Integrity & Compl*, Jennifer Bolster
V Pres-Mission Integration*, Deborah Welch

LOCATIONS

HQ: ST. JOSEPH'S HOSPITAL HEALTH CENTER
301 PROSPECT AVE, SYRACUSE, NY 132031899
Phone: 315 448-5882
Web: WWW.SJHSYR.ORG

PRODUCTS/OPERATIONS

Selected Services
Centers of Excellence
  Cardiac Services
  The Center for Orthopedic and Spine Care
  Vascular Services
  Women and Children's Services
  Wound Care
  Home Care
  Dialysis
  Bariatric (Weight Loss) Services
Other Services and Centers
  Aesthetic Services
  Behavioral Health
  da Vinci Robotic Surgery
  Emergency Services
  Imaging
  Infusion (CPEPCNY)
  Interventional Radiology
  Medical Equipment
  Obstetric Services
  Palliative Care
  Pharmacy
  Physical Medicine & Rehabilitation
  Pulmonary Services
  Sleep Laboratory
  Social Adult Day Care
  Surgical Services
  Urology Services
Outpatient Services
  Dental Services
  Family Medicine Center
  Obstetrics and Gynecology
  Pediatric Office
  Physician Health
  Primary Care
  Westside Family Health Center

COMPETITORS

Catholic Health System
Ellis Hospital
Kaleida Health
Lifetime Health
Oneida Healthcare Center
Suny Upstate Medical University
United Health Services Hospitals
Upstate University Hospital At Community General

Income Statement   FYE: December 31

	REVENUE ($ mil.)	NET INCOME ($ mil.)	NET PROFIT MARGIN	EMPLOYEES
12/15	542	(2)	—	3,300
12/14	523	0	0.1%	
12/09	436	5	1.2%	
12/08	399	6	1.6%	
Annual Growth	4.5%	—	—	

2015 Year-End Financials

Return on assets: (-0.6%)   Cash ($ mil.): 36
Return on equity: (-3.9%)
Current ratio: 1.80

ST. JOSEPH'S HOSPITAL, INC.

EXECUTIVES

Pres, Lorraine Lutton
Pres*, Isaac Mallah
Cfo*, Cathy Yoder
V Pres-Fin*, Tommy Inzina
Pres*, Kimberly Guy
Pres*, Paula McGuiness
Cmo*, Peter Charvat
C-Level Human Resources, Craig Brethauer
Executive of Information Techn, Brenda Pingle
Manager Food 6075bc, Erica Salgado
Cardiac Cath Lab Director, Michelle Hare

LOCATIONS

HQ: ST. JOSEPH'S HOSPITAL, INC.
3001 W DR MRTN LTHER KING, TAMPA, FL 336076307
Phone: 813 554-8500
Web: WWW.BAYCARE.ORG

HISTORICAL FINANCIALS
Company Type: Private

Income Statement   FYE: December 31

	REVENUE ($ mil.)	NET INCOME ($ mil.)	NET PROFIT MARGIN	EMPLOYEES
12/14	872	141	16.2%	300
12/09	719	75	10.4%	
12/08	663	29	4.5%	
12/06	565	63	11.2%	
Annual Growth	5.6%	10.6%	—	

2014 Year-End Financials

Return on assets: 11.0%   Cash ($ mil.): —
Return on equity: 12.5%
Current ratio: 5.40

ST. JOSEPH'S UNIVERSITY MEDICAL CENTER INC

EXECUTIVES

Pres-Ceo, Kevin Slavin
Cfo*, Dennis Roemer
Chm*, Patricia Thiele
Coo*, Lisa Brady
Anesthesiologist, Pablo T Figueroa
Treasurer, Michael Cairoli
Director of Nursing, Pamela Schaefer
Vice President, Robert Budelman
Chief of Neonatology, Adel M Zauk
Administrative Assistant To Vp, Christine Strangeway
Director of Environmental Svs, John Di' Giovani

LOCATIONS

HQ: ST. JOSEPH'S UNIVERSITY MEDICAL CENTER INC
703 MAIN ST, PATERSON, NJ 075032621
Phone: 973 754-2000
Web: WWW.STJOSEPHSHEALTH.ORG

HISTORICAL FINANCIALS

Company Type: Private

Income Statement   FYE: December 31

	REVENUE ($ mil.)	NET INCOME ($ mil.)	NET PROFIT MARGIN	EMPLOYEES
12/19	821	(8)	—	6,000
12/18	798	(12)	—	—
12/16	763	(12)	—	—
12/15	752	60	8.0%	—
Annual Growth	2.2%	—	—	—

2019 Year-End Financials

Return on assets: (-1.0%)   Cash ($ mil.): 59
Return on equity: (-4.5%)
Current ratio: 2.70

ST. JUDE CHILDREN'S RESEARCH HOSPITAL, INC.

St. Jude Children's Research Hospital is leading the way world understand treats and defeats childhood cancer and other life threatening disease. The American Lebanese Syrian Associated Charities (ALSAC) exist only to raise the funds to operate St. Jude. St. Jude is dedicated to providing best care for patients and research that leads to fighting catastrophic pediatric diseases such as cancer and sickle cell. Majority of funding comes for generous donors. Families never receive a bill from St. Jude for treatment travel housing or food. St. Jude Children's Research Hospital was founded in 1962 by Danny Thomas.

Operations

St. Jude Children's Research Hospital has the following divisions such as Biostatistics Department which focuses in advancement of cures and prevention of pediatric catastrophic diseases through biostatistics and data science collaboration and research. Bone Marrow Transplant Department focuses in advance cures for pediatric catastrophic diseases through research and treatment focused on cell gene and immune therapies. Cell Molecular Biology Department the institution's commitment to basic biologic discovery. Current areas of research include elucidating the molecular mechanisms that govern RNA granule dynamics and those that regulate autophagy and mRNA translation. Developmental of Neurobiology Department investigate the fundamental processes that govern normal brain development and function and more.

Geographic Reach

St. Jude Children's Research Hospital is located in Memphis Tennessee.

Sales and Marketing

St. Jude Children's Research Hospital market its products and services through its online websites.

Strategy

St. Jude Children's Research Hospital is launching the largest strategic investment in its nearly 60-year history committing $11.5 billion during the next six years to accelerate research and treatment globally for children with catastrophic diseases.

The Six-Year St. Jude Strategic Plan approved March 25 2021 by the St. Jude Board of Governors focuses on the expansion of patient care and clinical and laboratory-based research related to pediatric catastrophic illnesses including work in cancer blood disorders neurological diseases and infectious diseases. The plan calls for an additional 1400 jobs; the expenditure of $1.9 billion in new construction renovation and capital needs; and the development of new research areas.

The new plan continues this momentum by concentrating on five areas: fundamental science childhood cancer pediatric catastrophic diseases global impact and workforce and workplace culture.

Company Background

Entertainer Danny Thomas founded St. Jude in 1962; Thomas also founded the fundraising organization for the hospital the American Lebanese Syrian Associated Charities (ALSAC).

EXECUTIVES

Pres-Ceo, James Downing
Evp Scientific Dir*, James I Morgan
Evp Clinical Dir*, Ellis J Neufeld
Evp Cao*, Mary Anna Quinn
Evp Dir CCC*, Charles W M Roberts
Evp Dir*, Carlos Rodriguez-Galindo
Svp Clo*, Robyn Diaz
Svp Cfo*, Pat Keel
Svp CIO*, Keith Perry
Exec V Pres, Dr Joseph Mirro
Customer Support Coordinator, Nancy Thompson
Auditors: DELOITTE & TOUCHE LLP MEMPHI

LOCATIONS

HQ: ST. JUDE CHILDREN'S RESEARCH HOSPITAL, INC.
262 DANNY THOMAS PL, MEMPHIS, TN 381053678
Phone: 901 595-3300
Web: WWW.STJUDE.ORG

PRODUCTS/OPERATIONS

2014 Sales

	$ mil.	% of total
Support revenue	983	62
Net investment income	390	25
Net patient service revenue	97	6
Research grants	81	5
Other	34	2
Total	**1,586**	**100**

Selected US Affiliate Clinics

Children's Hospital of Illinois (OSF Healthcare System) University of Illinois College of Medicine at Peoria
Feist-Weiller Cancer Center LSU Health Sciences Center (Shreveport Louisiana)
Huntsville Hospital (Huntsville Alabama)
Johnson City Medical Center East Tennessee State University
Our Lady of the Lake Regional Medical Center (Baton Rouge Louisiana)
St. John's Health System (Springfield Missouri)

Selected International Outreach Partner Sites

American University of Beirut/Children's Cancer Center of Lebanon (Beirut Lebanon)
Beijing Children's Hospital (Beijing)
Davao Medical Center (Philippines)
Hospital 20 Aout 1953 (Casablanca Morocco)
Hospital Benjamin Bloom (San Salvador El Salvador)
Hospital Civil de Guadalajara (Guadalajara Mexico)
Hospital de Especialidades Pediatricas (Maracaibo Venezuela)
Hospital de la Sociedad de Lucha Contra el Cancer Nucleo de Quito (Quito Ecuador)
Hospital de Ninos Baca Ortiz (Quito Ecuador)
Hospital de Ninos J.M. de los Rios (Caracas Venezuela)
Hospital d'Enfants (Rabat Morocco)
Hospital Escuela Materno Infantil (Tegucigalpa Honduras)
Hospital Luis Calvo Mackenna (Santiago Chile)
Hospital Nacional de Ninos (San Jose Costa Rica)
Hospital Pediatrico de Sinaloa (Culiacan Mexico)
King Hussein Cancer Center (Amman Jordan)
Our Lady's Hospital for Sick Children (Dublin Ireland)
Shanghai Children's Medical Center (Shanghai)
Unidad de Oncologia Pediatrica - Instituto Materno Infantil de Pernambuco; Centro de Hematologia e Oncologia Pediatrica (Recife) - Brazil
Unidad Nacional de Oncologia Pediatrica (Guatemala City Guatemala)

COMPETITORS

Ascension Health
Baptist Memorial Health Care
Children's Medical Center Of Dallas
Children's National Medical Center
Cincinnati Children's Hospital
City Of Hope
Damon Runyon Cancer Research
Dana-farber
Fox Chase Cancer Center
H. Lee Moffitt Cancer Center & Research Institute
Hca
Lifepoint Health
Md Anderson Cancer Center
Memorial Sloan-kettering
Methodist Healthcare
Nationwide Children's Hospital
Roswell Park Cancer Institute
Shelby County Health Care
Shriners Hospitals For Children
Tenet Healthcare
Ut Medical Group

HISTORICAL FINANCIALS

Company Type: Private

Income Statement   FYE: June 30

	REVENUE ($ mil.)	NET INCOME ($ mil.)	NET PROFIT MARGIN	EMPLOYEES
06/20	1,238	134	10.8%	2,500
06/15	205	195	94.9%	—
06/11	573	(26)	—	—
06/10	589	(5)	—	—
Annual Growth	7.7%	—	—	—

2020 Year-End Financials

Return on assets: 2.0%   Cash ($ mil.): 4
Return on equity: 2.0%
Current ratio: 0.60

ST. JUDE HOSPITAL

St. Jude Medical Center gets sickly Southern Californians on their feet again. The faith-based not-for-profit acute care facility with some 385 beds serves the residents of Orange County. The medical center provides an onsite cancer center (the Virginia K. Crosson Cancer Center) and a heart institute that offers cardiac surgeries and rehabilitation programs. It also provides inpatient and outpatient physical rehabilitation services and a variety of community outreach programs. Established by the Sisters of St. Joseph of Orange religious order in the 1950s St. Jude Medical Center is part of the St. Joseph Health System.

Operations

Beyond the medical center's campus St. Jude operates its Heritage Medical Group with outpatient locations throughout its region. The medical group includes specialists in plastic surgery rheumatology and gastroenterology. Altogether St. Jude employs some 700 physicians. It handles more than 17000 inpatient admissions each year as well as 13000 surgeries 2000 births and 54000 emergency room visits.

The organization spends some $47 million in community benefits including outreach and charity care. Its mobile and fixed-site community clinics offer medical dental and preventative care services for low-income residents.

Geographic Reach

St. Jude serves residents in communities in California's Orange County including Brea Buena Park Fullerton La Habra Placentia and Yorba Linda.

Strategy

St. Jude is expanding its facilities through the construction of a new $312 million patient tower schedule to open in late 2014. The Northwest Tower will feature private patient rooms as well as enhanced surgical and data management capabilities. Other improvement measures include technology upgrades such as a new neurovascular surgical system added in 2012.

In October 2011 St. Jude Medical Center closed its 12-bed pediatric unit and redirected patients younger than 16 to nearby Children's Hospital of Orange County. St. Jude's NICU (neonatal intensive care unit) remains open and the hospital continues to provide emergency and outpatient services to children.

EXECUTIVES

Ceo-Pres, Robert Fraschetti
Ceo*, Lee Penrose
Coo-Ceo*, Doreen Dann
Staff Pharmacist, Sue J Kim
Chief of Medicine, Lytton Smith
Administrative Assistant, Leslee Mc Gregor
Staff Pharmacist, Norman Q Jung
Chief Staff, James L Benoit
Chief of Pathology, Patrick L Fitzgibbons
Staff Pharmacist, Huong V Le
Radiologist, Hao Q Ngo

LOCATIONS

HQ: ST. JUDE HOSPITAL
101 E VALENCIA MESA DR, FULLERTON, CA 928353875
Phone: 714 871-3280
Web: WWW.STJUDEMEDICALCENTER.ORG

COMPETITORS

Anaheim Regional Medical Center	Memorial Health Services
Children's Hospital Of Orange County	Western Medical Center - Santa Ana
Hoag Memorial Hospital	

HISTORICAL FINANCIALS
Company Type: Private

Income Statement				FYE: June 30
	REVENUE ($ mil.)	NET INCOME ($ mil.)	NET PROFIT MARGIN	EMPLOYEES
06/18	557	50	9.1%	2,600
06/17	544	45	8.3%	—
06/16	490	4	0.9%	—
06/15	458	8	2.0%	—
Annual Growth	6.8%	77.9%	—	—

ST. LUKE'S HEALTH NETWORK, INC.

St. Luke's University Hospital (formerly St. Luke's Hospital - Bethlehem Campus) serves residents of Pennsylvania's Lehigh Valley with primary specialty and emergency care services. The not-for-profit teaching hospital has about 480 acute-care beds. Its medical specialties include trauma oncology cardiology orthopedics neurology open-heart surgery radiology and robotic surgery. The medical center also operates outpatient surgery centers and general physician care clinics and it operates home health and community wellness programs. St. Luke's University Hospital was founded in 1872 and is part of the St. Luke's University Health Network.

EXECUTIVES

Pres, Richard A Anderson
Sr V Pres*, Tom Lichpenwalner
Management Engineer, Scott Siegfried
Interim President Visiting Nur, Lisa Giovanni
Emergency Medicine Residency P, Scott Melanson
Vp Finance, Carl Alberto
Marketing and Public Relations, Andrea Hahn
Copd Care Coordinator, Maureen Cope
Infection Prevention Director, Becky Haden
Manager Cancer Care Center, Christine Figler
Educator, Jane Fisk
Auditors: WITHUMSMITHBROWN PC MORRISTOW

LOCATIONS

HQ: ST. LUKE'S HEALTH NETWORK, INC.
801 OSTRUM ST, BETHLEHEM, PA 180151000
Phone: 610 954-4000
Web: WWW.SLHN.ORG

PRODUCTS/OPERATIONS

Selected Services
Cancer Center
Children's health
Diagnostic and Treatment Centers
Emergency
Heart Center
Neuroscience
Orthopaedics
Radiology/Imaging
Regional Breast Center (Center Valley)
Urgent Care Centers
Women's Imaging & Health Centers

COMPETITORS

Ascension Health	Sacred Heart Hospital Of Allentown
Evangelical Community Hospital	Wyoming Valley Health Care System
Lvhn	
Moses Taylor Hospital	
Reading Hospital And Medical Center	

HISTORICAL FINANCIALS
Company Type: Private

Income Statement				FYE: June 30
	REVENUE ($ mil.)	NET INCOME ($ mil.)	NET PROFIT MARGIN	EMPLOYEES
06/19	2,116	59	2.8%	2,958
06/18	1,844	159	8.6%	—
06/17	1,521	121	8.0%	—
06/15	0	0	—	—
Annual Growth	—	—	—	—

2019 Year-End Financials
Return on assets: 2.5%   Cash ($ mil.): 100
Return on equity: 6.7%
Current ratio: 1.50

ST. LUKE'S HEALTH SYSTEM, LTD.

Founded in 1902 St. Luke's Health System is a not-for-profit health system and offers an emergency department advanced inpatient and outpatient surgery mother-baby services diagnostics form x-ray to MRI state of the art cancer treatment critical care a chest pain center and more. Its flagship facility is St. Luke's Boise Medical Center which also includes a full-service children's hospital and primary and specialty physician clinics.

Operations

St. Luke's hospitals has eight hospitals and about 340 clinics & centers. The network also sees about 858000 outpatients 8120 newborns 42790 surgeries more than 1000 beds and over 52000 hospital admissions.

St. Luke's Boise is the largest health care provider and the flagship hospital of St. Luke's Health System providing access to highly skilled specialists nurses and staff within a friendly campus designed for healing. In additions it is nationally recognized for quality and patient safety and proud to be designated a Magnet hospital the gold standard for nursing care.

Geographic Reach

St. Luke's has Idaho operations in Boise Caldwell Eagle Fruitland Jerome Ketchum McCall Mountain Home Nampa and Twin Falls.

Strategy

St. Luke's strategy follows a clearly defined path:

Quality ? The company will work to advance its position as the go-to provider for consumers by delivering safe effective care and an exceptional patient experience;

Access ? The company will evolve the way it delivers care to best meet the health needs of the people it serves when where and how they deserve; and

Affordability ? The company will ensure the cost of high-quality health care is reasonable in the communities it serves that it is understandable and that it creates certainty for health care.

Company Background

In 2011 St. Luke's completed a $130 million project to rebuild the St. Luke's Magic Valley Medical Center. The new hospital building had about 190 beds and expanded emergency cancer and cardiac centers. The health system was also working to expand its Boise Medical Center's heart and vascular and pediatric departments as well as its system-wide MSTI facilities.

The health system has also expanded its outpatient network to include new family practice emergency care and urgent care clinics in recent years. The network opened a St. Luke's Nampa emergency care clinic and medical complex in 2012. In addition to updating its facilities the St. Luke's Health System was working to upgrade its information technology assets.

St. Luke's added its fifth and sixth acute care hospitals in 2010 and 2011 when the 15-bed St. Luke's McCall (formerly McCall Memorial Hospital) and 25-bed St. Luke's Jerome (formerly St. Benedicts Medical Center) hospitals joined the health network through affiliation and merger agreements.

The health system was formed in 2006 when the three hospitals of the old St. Luke's Regional Medical Center network (Boise Meridian and Wood River) merged with Magic Valley Regional Medical Center a former county facility in Twin Falls Idaho.

EXECUTIVES

Ceo, Chris Roth
Coo, Pam Lindemoen
Chief Admin Officer, Dave Self
Int Chief Hr Officer, Erin Simms
Sr Acct, Robyn Morris
Compliance Staff, Cecelia Bishop
Project Manager, Pamela Bommarito
Coordinator, John Leary
Information Specialist, Jason Ewing
Information Security Analyst, Ronald Boman
Director, Jason Reynolds
Auditors: DELOITTE & TOUCHE LLP BOISE

LOCATIONS

HQ: ST. LUKE'S HEALTH SYSTEM, LTD.
190 E BANNOCK ST, BOISE, ID 837126241
Phone: 208 381-2222
Web: WWW.STLUKESONLINE.ORG

PRODUCTS/OPERATIONS

Selected Idaho Facilities

St. Luke's Boise Medical Center (Boise)
  St. Luke's Children's Hospital
St. Luke's Clinics (multiple locations)
St. Luke's Eagle Urgent Care (Eagle)
St. Luke's Jerome Medical Center (Jerome)
St. Luke's Magic Valley Medical Center (Twin Falls)
St. Luke's McCall Memorial Hospital (McCall)
St. Luke's Meridian Medical Center (Meridian)
St. Luke's Mountain States Tumor Institute (multiple locations)
St. Luke's Wood River Medical Center (Hailey/Ketchum)

COMPETITORS

Ascension Health
Benedictine Health System
Hca
Intermountain Health Care
Saint Alphonsus Regional Medical Center
Trinity Health (novi)

Company Type: Private

Income Statement				FYE: September 30
	REVENUE ($ mil.)	NET INCOME ($ mil.)	NET PROFIT MARGIN	EMPLOYEES
09/20	3,059	171	5.6%	7,891
09/19	2,894	91	3.2%	—
09/18	2,602	34	1.3%	—
09/17	2,327	10	0.4%	—
Annual Growth	9.6%	156.7%	—	—

2020 Year-End Financials

Return on assets: 5.4%   Cash ($ mil.): 123
Return on equity: 12.9%
Current ratio: 0.80

ST. LUKE'S REGIONAL MEDICAL CENTER, LTD.

EXECUTIVES

Pres, Edwin Dahlberg
V Pres*, Gary Fletcher
V Pres-Fin*, Clarence Pumeroy
Health Professional, Colleen Walker-Vamos
Emergency Medicine Specialist, Bradley Chatlin
Oncologist, Silvana Bucur
Diagnostic Radiologist, Michael Fisher
Diagnostic Radiologist, Michael Fuchs
Interventional Radiology Coord, Audrey Reynolds
Diagnostic Radiologist, Sean M Carr
Director, Pat Burton

LOCATIONS

HQ: ST. LUKE'S REGIONAL MEDICAL CENTER, LTD.
190 E BANNOCK ST, BOISE, ID 837126241
Phone: 208 381-5500
Web: WWW.STLUKESONLINE.ORG

HISTORICAL FINANCIALS

Company Type: Private

Income Statement				FYE: September 30
	REVENUE ($ mil.)	NET INCOME ($ mil.)	NET PROFIT MARGIN	EMPLOYEES
09/19	1,583	114	7.2%	4,500
09/14	1,255	31	2.5%	—
09/13	1,121	(19)	—	—
09/08	898	44	4.9%	—
Annual Growth	5.3%	9.0%	—	—

2019 Year-End Financials

Return on assets: 6.5%   Cash ($ mil.): 42
Return on equity: 15.9%
Current ratio: 0.30

ST. MARY'S HEALTH, INC.

St. Mary's Medical Center of Evansville is a 433-bed hospital serving Indiana's River City. It is the primary facility in regional St. Mary's Health System which is in turn part of Ascension Health. The Evansville hospital provides emergency trauma diagnostic surgical and rehabilitative services as well as specialized cancer cardiac orthopedic and neurological services. With a total of some 750 physicians St. Mary's Health System also includes St. Mary's Hospital for Women & Children (100 beds adjacent to the main hospital) and St. Mary's Warrick (a 25-bed hospital in Boonville Indiana) as well as specialty outpatient surgical cancer and home health units in surrounding areas of southern Indiana.

Operations

St. Mary's Medical Center of Evansville admits some 17000 inpatients annually. It also handles around 64000 emergency room visits and performs approximately 4700 inpatient and 18000 outpatient surgeries each year.

Company Background

St. Mary's Medical Center of Evansville was originally a Marine Hospital built by the US government. When the government shuttered its doors city business leaders bought the building in 1872 and partnered with the Daughters of Charity to operate a community hospital.

EXECUTIVES

Pres, Daniel Parod
Coding & Reimbursement Special, Kelly Raines
Events Coordinator, Nancy Bennett
Head of Pediatric Endocrinolog, Stephen Lafranchi
Coordinator, Mary Raley
Staff, Diane Parrish
Compliance Staff, Lee Raab
Rn, Carol Woodard
Administrative Assistant, Debbie Boyer
Manager of Patient Care Servic, Robin Wolford
Human Resources Manager, Suzanne Fant
Auditors: DELOITTE TAX LLP INDIANAPOLIS

LOCATIONS

HQ: ST. MARY'S HEALTH, INC.
3700 WASHINGTON AVE, EVANSVILLE, IN 477140541
Phone: 812 485-4000

PRODUCTS/OPERATIONS

Selected Services

Breast Center
Cancer Care Services
Children's Health Care Services and Programs
Community Outreach Services
Convenient Care Centers
Diabetic Foot Clinic
Diabetes Services
Emergency Services Department
Endoscopy Suite
Foundation
Heart Services
Home Health Services
Hospitalists
Imaging/Radiology
Infusion Center
Laboratory Services
LifeFlight
Medical Equipment
Mental Health Services
Neurosciences & Stroke Care
Occupational Medicine Services
Orthopedic Healthcare
Palliative Care
Pastoral Care
Quality and Patient Safety
Rehabilitation Services
Respiratory Care
Senior Services
Sleep Disorders Center
Surgical Services
Trauma Services
Volunteers & Auxiliary
Weight Management Center
Women's Services and Programs
Women's Wellness Center

COMPETITORS

Ball Memorial Hospital	Henry County Memorial
Community Health	Hospital
Network	Kosciusko Community
Daviess Community	Hospital
Hospital	Memorial Hospital
Deaconess Health	(logansport)
System	
Good Samaritan	
Hospital (in)	

HISTORICAL FINANCIALS

Company Type: Private

Income Statement   FYE: June 30

	REVENUE ($ mil.)	NET INCOME ($ mil.)	NET PROFIT MARGIN	EMPLOYEES
06/15	574	52	9.2%	3,500
06/13	468	48	10.4%	—
06/11	0	0	—	—
Annual Growth	—	—	—	—

2015 Year-End Financials

Return on assets: 6.4%   Cash ($ mil.): 12
Return on equity: 9.1%
Current ratio: 2.80

ST. PETER'S HEALTH CARE SERVICES

EXECUTIVES

Ceo, Ann Errichettii
Vice President For Facilities, Charles Gianfagna
Network Manager, Kyle Stark
Director, Linda Berner
Manager, Anne Martin
Scientist, Alfonzo Diblasio
Director of Surgery, Kathleen Marsch
Chief of Pathology, Russell Newkirk
Pharmacist, Carmen Mojica
Telecommunications Executive, George Seabury
Chief of Cardiology, Steve Cameron
Auditors: DELOITTE & TOUCHE LLP ROCHEST

LOCATIONS

HQ: ST. PETER'S HEALTH CARE SERVICES
  315 S MANNING BLVD, ALBANY, NY 122081707
Phone: 518 525-1550
Web: WWW.SPHP.COM

HISTORICAL FINANCIALS

Company Type: Private

Income Statement   FYE: June 30

	REVENUE ($ mil.)	NET INCOME ($ mil.)	NET PROFIT MARGIN	EMPLOYEES
06/17	1,327	37	2.9%	6,000
06/16	552	39	7.1%	—
06/15	527	44	8.5%	—
06/14	509	21	4.1%	—
Annual Growth	37.6%	21.7%	—	—

2017 Year-End Financials

Return on assets: 2.7%   Cash ($ mil.): 124
Return on equity: 4.4%
Current ratio: 2.60

ST. PETER'S HEALTH PARTNERS

EXECUTIVES

Pres-Ceo, James Reed
Cfo*, Thomas Schuhle
Administrator, Dennis Eames
Materials Manager Troy Hospita, Gloria Perry
Education Specialist Patient C, Suja Thomas
Infectious Disease Specialist, Afroza S Liton
Information Technology Manager, Dennis M Eames Jr
Neonatologist, Stephen R Pratt
Physician Neurosurgeon, Craig Goldberg
Cardiac, Dorothy Urschel
Physician Member, Gary Cohen
Auditors: DELOITTE & TOUCHE LLP ROCHEST

LOCATIONS

HQ: ST. PETER'S HEALTH PARTNERS
  315 S MANNING BLVD, ALBANY, NY 122081707
Phone: 518 525-1111
Web: WWW.SPHP.COM

HISTORICAL FINANCIALS

Company Type: Private

Income Statement   FYE: June 30

	REVENUE ($ mil.)	NET INCOME ($ mil.)	NET PROFIT MARGIN	EMPLOYEES
06/20	1,446	(10)	—	4,000
06/18	1,337	6	0.5%	—
Annual Growth	4.0%	—	—	—

2020 Year-End Financials

Return on assets: (-0.7%)   Cash ($ mil.): 13
Return on equity: (-1.2%)
Current ratio: 1.60

ST. VINCENT HOSPITAL OF THE HOSPITAL SISTERS OF THE THIRD ORDER OF ST. FRANCIS

EXECUTIVES

Chb-Pres, Mary Beth Culnan
Ceo*, Theresa Shuck
V Pres*, Joseph J Neidenbach
Director, Bobbi Giles
Program Manager, Doreen Kluth
Manager Radiology, Jill Dooley
Prin, Karl Appleton
Manager Patient Financial, Marlene Schmidt
Genetic Counselor, Sumedha Ghate
Manager, Connie Dorn
Buyer, Nancy Adams
Auditors: CROWE HORWATH LLP CHICAGO IL

LOCATIONS

HQ: ST. VINCENT HOSPITAL OF THE HOSPITAL
  SISTERS OF THE THIRD ORDER OF ST. FRANCIS
  835 S VAN BUREN ST, GREEN BAY, WI 543013526
Phone: 920 433-0111
Web: WWW.HSHS.ORG

HISTORICAL FINANCIALS

Company Type: Private

Income Statement   FYE: June 30

	REVENUE ($ mil.)	NET INCOME ($ mil.)	NET PROFIT MARGIN	EMPLOYEES
06/20	585	16	2.7%	2,360
06/19	567	29	5.1%	—
06/16	505	(35)	—	—
06/15	480	29	6.0%	—
Annual Growth	4.0%	(11.2%)	—	—

2020 Year-End Financials

Return on assets: 2.0%   Cash ($ mil.): 47
Return on equity: 2.9%
Current ratio: 1.10

STAN BOYETT & SON, INC.

EXECUTIVES

Pres, Dale Boyett
V Pres*, Scott Castle
Accounting Staff, Laverne Couch
District Manager, James Martin
Account Executive, Kristine Freitag
Marketing, Michelle Gill
Account Manager, Cesar Betancourt
Account Executive, Chris Kwietkauski
Account Executive, Carl Haney
Account Executive, Dennis Barton
Account Executive, Doug Martin

LOCATIONS

HQ: STAN BOYETT & SON, INC.
  601 MCHENRY AVE, MODESTO, CA 953505411
Phone: 209 577-6000
Web: WWW.BOYETT.NET

HISTORICAL FINANCIALS

Company Type: Private

Income Statement   FYE: December 31

	REVENUE ($ mil.)	NET INCOME ($ mil.)	NET PROFIT MARGIN	EMPLOYEES
12/08	656	0	0.1%	170
12/07	559	0	0.0%	—
12/06	475	0	0.1%	—
12/05	416	0	0.1%	—
Annual Growth	16.4%	28.4%	—	—

2008 Year-End Financials

Return on assets: 3.3%   Cash ($ mil.): 2
Return on equity: 17.6%
Current ratio: 1.00

STANFORD HEALTH CARE

Stanford Health Care (formerly Stanford Hospital and Clinics) operates a licensed acute care hospital (Stanford Hospital) and a cancer center in Palo Alto California along with numerous outpatient physician clinics in the San Francisco Bay Area. As Stanford University's primary medical teaching facility the more than 600-bed Stanford Hospital specializes in such areas as cardiac care cancer treatment neurology surgery and organ transplant. It delivers clinical innovation across its inpatient services specialty health centers physician offices virtual care offerings and health plan programs. Stanford Health Care is part of the Stanford Medicine a leading academic health system that includes the Stanford University School of Medicine and Stanford Children's Health.

Operations
Stanford Health Care handles more than 72530 adult emergency room visits about 16315 pediatric emergency visits and some 2016490 outpatient visits. The organization boasts such specialized clinics as the Byers Eye Institute the Stanford Comprehensive Cancer Center the Stanford Center for Marfan Syndrome and Aortic Disorders and the California VitreoRetinal Center. It also operates centers for orthopedic brain blood and marrow transplant and other specialist procedures.

Educational programs include medical and graduate student training as well as residency and fellowship programs. The organization also conducts research in medical and biological fields.

Additionally the system owns stakes in physician network University HealthCare Alliance radiation therapy facility Stanford Emanuel Radiation Oncology Center health care advocacy firm Care-Counsel The Hospital Committee for the Livermore-Pleasanton Areas (dba Stanford Health Care - ValleyCare) Sanford Blood Center SUMIT Holding International Professional Exchange Assurance Company and Stanford Health Care Advantage.

Together with Lucile Salter Packard Children's Hospital at Stanford it operates the clinical settings through which the SoM educates medical and graduate students trains residents and clinical fellows supports faculty and community clinicians and conducts medical and biological sciences research.

Overall Stanford Health Care generates about 90% of revenue from patient services.

Sales and Marketing
Stanford Health Care receives about 80% of its revenues from managed care (commercial insurance) providers. Another 20% of patient service income is sourced to Medicare and Med-Cal programs. It serves as a community blood center and provides blood products and testing services to hospitals clinics companies and other clients.

Financial Performance
In 2021 the company had total revenues of $6.8 billion a 22% increase from the previous year's revenue of $5.6 billion. This was mainly due to a higher volume of net patient service revenue.

The company's cash at the end of 2021 was $407 million. Operating activities generated $657.7 million while investing activities used $1.8 billion primarily for purchases of investments. Financing activities used another $48.8 million mainly for payment of long-term debt and finance lease obligations.

EXECUTIVES

Ceo, David Entwistle
Cfo*, Lynda Hoff
Cdo*, Erica Yabokla
Cmo, Norman Rizk
Coo*, Quinn McKenna
Staff Facilities and Space Pla, Ramoncito Cuenco
Director of Education, Allison Guerin
Staff Nurse IV, Amanda Degregori
Directed Individual Study, Ashley Jowell
Neuroradiology Specialist, Cynthia Chan
Clinical Nurse, Dana Benders
Auditors: PRICEWATERHOUSECOOPERS LLP SA

LOCATIONS

HQ: STANFORD HEALTH CARE
300 PASTEUR DR, STANFORD, CA 943052200
Phone: 650 723-4000
Web: WWW.STANFORDHEALTHCARE.ORG

PRODUCTS/OPERATIONS

2014 Sales

	$ mil.	% of total
Net patient service revenue	2,839	95
Premium revenue	60	2
Other revenue	98	3
Total	**2,998**	**100**

Selected Services
Heart Center
Neurosciences
Orthopaedics
Sports Medicine
Stanford Cancer Center
Surgical Services
Transplant

COMPETITORS

Dignity Health	Sutter Health
Sequoia Capital	Ucsf Medical

HISTORICAL FINANCIALS
Company Type: Private

Income Statement				FYE: August 31
	REVENUE ($ mil.)	NET INCOME ($ mil.)	NET PROFIT MARGIN	EMPLOYEES
08/20	5,567	104	1.9%	14,100
08/18	4,910	456	9.3%	—
08/17	4,454	450	10.1%	—
08/15	3,570	372	10.4%	—
Annual Growth	9.3%	(22.4%)	—	—

2020 Year-End Financials
Return on assets: 1.1%
Return on equity: 2.4%
Current ratio: 1.60
Cash ($ mil.): 1,642

STANFORD HEALTH SERVICES

Auditors: PRICEWATERHOUSECOOPERS LLP BO

LOCATIONS

HQ: STANFORD HEALTH SERVICES
300 PASTEUR DR, STANFORD, CA 943052200
Phone: 650 723-4000
Web: WWW.STANFORDCHILDRENS.ORG

HISTORICAL FINANCIALS
Company Type: Private

Income Statement				FYE: August 31
	REVENUE ($ mil.)	NET INCOME ($ mil.)	NET PROFIT MARGIN	EMPLOYEES
08/11	2,510	415	16.6%	4
08/10	2,141	186	8.7%	—
Annual Growth	17.2%	123.2%	—	—

2011 Year-End Financials
Return on assets: —
Return on equity: 16.6%
Current ratio: 0.50
Cash ($ mil.): 395

STAPLE COTTON COOPERATIVE ASSOCIATION

Referred to as Staplcotn the Staple Cotton Cooperative has been a staple of its member-producers' business lives since 1921. One of the oldest and largest cotton marketing co-ops in the US it provides domestic and export marketing cotton warehousing and agricultural financing to some 9730 members in 47 states. As of 2011 the co-op handles nearly 14000 farm accounts in 10 states. Staplcotn's inventory is consigned by member-producers and averages from 2.5 million to 3 million bales of cotton a year. The co-op operates though 15 warehouses serving the mid-south and southeastern US to supply more than 25% of the cotton consumed by the US textile industry as well as the needs of textile mills overseas.

EXECUTIVES

Pres-Ceo, Hank Reichle
Chb*, Mike P Sturdivant III
Chb*, Ben Lamensdorf
Cfo*, Mike Moffatt
Chm*, Woods E Eastland
SEC*, Kenneth E Downs
Vice President, Meredith Allen
CPA, Mack L Alford
Office Administrator, Jeff McPhail
Sales Operation Support Specia, Kassie Bailey
Executive Secretary, Debbie Fennell

LOCATIONS

HQ: STAPLE COTTON COOPERATIVE ASSOCIATION
214 W MARKET ST, GREENWOOD, MS 389304329
Phone: 662 453-6231
Web: WWW.STAPLCOTN.COM

PRODUCTS/OPERATIONS

Selected Services
Cotton services
  Loans
  Mill Sales Program
Marketing
Stapldiscount
Warehouse

COMPETITORS

Alabama Farmers Cooperative	King Ranch
Calcot	Louis Dreyfus Group
Cargill	Noble Group
	Olam

Dunavant Enterprises International Cotton Marketing J.g. Boswell Co. Jb Cotton

Plains Cotton Southern States Tennessee Farmers Co-op Weil Brothers Cotton

HISTORICAL FINANCIALS
Company Type: Private

Income Statement				FYE: August 31
	REVENUE ($ mil.)	NET INCOME ($ mil.)	NET PROFIT MARGIN	EMPLOYEES
08/13	1,138	5	0.5%	312
08/12	1,236	8	0.7%	—
08/11	963	875	90.8%	—
Annual Growth	8.7%	(91.7%)	—	—

2013 Year-End Financials
Return on assets: 2.5%   Cash ($ mil.): 33
Return on equity: 5.3%
Current ratio: 1.80

STATE OF ALABAMA

EXECUTIVES

Governor, Kay Ivey
Comptroller*, Kathleen D Baxter
Atty Gen, Troy King
Cmptlr, Robert Childree
Director and State Law Librari, Timothy Lewis
Associate Justice, Tom Parker
Chief of Staff, Jo Bonner
Program Manager, Donna Jordan
Donor Relations Coordinator, Cherie H Smith
Web Resources Librarian, Myra Sabel
Asst Bureau Chief Environmenta, Adam Anderson
Auditors: RONALD L JONES MONTGOMERY A

LOCATIONS

HQ: STATE OF ALABAMA
   300 DEXTER AVE, MONTGOMERY, AL 361043741
Phone: 334 242-7100
Web: WWW.ALABAMA.GOV

HISTORICAL FINANCIALS
Company Type: Private

Income Statement				FYE: September 30
	REVENUE ($ mil.)	NET INCOME ($ mil.)	NET PROFIT MARGIN	EMPLOYEES
09/20	26,307	836	3.2%	37,659
09/19	23,698	677	2.9%	—
09/18	22,258	(34)	—	—
09/17	21,740	1,393	6.4%	—
Annual Growth	6.6%	(15.7%)	—	—

2020 Year-End Financials
Return on assets: 1.3%   Cash ($ mil.): 8,634
Return on equity: 2.5%
Current ratio: —

STATE OF ALASKA

EXECUTIVES

Governor, Michael Dunleavy
Lt. Governor, Kevin Meyer
Accounting Staff, Nove Barril
Coordinator, Sara Chambers
Accounting Staff, Christine Spence
Accounting Staff, Amy Johnson
Accounting Staff, Caroline Byford
Coordinator, Heidi Hedberg
Coordinator, Katie Reilly
Employee, Dinah Aquino
Senior Adviser On Fish and Gam, Ephraim Froehlich
Auditors: KRIS CURTIS CPA CISA JUNEAU

LOCATIONS

HQ: STATE OF ALASKA
   120 4TH ST, JUNEAU, AK 998011162
Phone: 907 465-3500
Web: WWW.ALASKA.GOV

HISTORICAL FINANCIALS
Company Type: Private

Income Statement				FYE: June 30
	REVENUE ($ mil.)	NET INCOME ($ mil.)	NET PROFIT MARGIN	EMPLOYEES
06/19	12,421	2,275	18.3%	4,300
06/18	12,318	2,779	22.6%	—
06/17	12,693	3,224	25.4%	—
Annual Growth	(1.1%)	(16.0%)	—	—

STATE OF ARIZONA

EXECUTIVES

Governor, Doug Ducey
Attor Gen*, Terry Goddard
Treas*, David Petersen
Acctng Mgr, Jean Bell
Sergeant, Joe Kubacki
Chief Information Security Off, Mike Lettman
U.S. District Court Judge, Susan Brnovich
Member, Nancy Barto
Member, Frank Pratt
Manager, Ted Hale
Information Technology Infrast, Allan Gazza
Auditors: LINDSEY PERRY CPA CFE PHOENI

LOCATIONS

HQ: STATE OF ARIZONA
   1700 W WASHINGTON ST FL 7, PHOENIX, AZ
   850072808
Phone: 602 542-4331
Web: WWW.AZ.GOV

HISTORICAL FINANCIALS
Company Type: Private

Income Statement				FYE: June 30
	REVENUE ($ mil.)	NET INCOME ($ mil.)	NET PROFIT MARGIN	EMPLOYEES
06/20	37,221	611	1.6%	34,161
06/19	34,554	1,496	4.3%	—
06/18	32,354	539	1.7%	—
06/17	31,295	385	1.2%	—
Annual Growth	6.0%	16.7%	—	—

2020 Year-End Financials
Return on assets: 1.1%   Cash ($ mil.): 8,771
Return on equity: 1.9%
Current ratio: 1.50

STATE OF ARKANSAS

EXECUTIVES

Governor, Asa Hutchinson
Lt Gov*, Tim Griffin
Chief of Staff*, Morril Harriman
Purchasing Agent, Kara Simmons
Dhs Policy, Lech Matuszewski
General Manager, Michael Sindelar
Executive, Michelle Spoor
Community Director, Natalie Desalvo
Dhhs Division of Children, Rosalind Burgess
Purchasing Agent, Ruthie Bain
Hsse Supervisor, Saiyed Ali
Auditors: ROGER A NORMAN JD CPA CFE

LOCATIONS

HQ: STATE OF ARKANSAS
   4 CAPITOL MALL RM 403A, LITTLE ROCK, AR
   722011013
Phone: 501 682-2345
Web: WWW.PORTAL.ARKANSAS.GOV

HISTORICAL FINANCIALS
Company Type: Private

Income Statement				FYE: June 30
	REVENUE ($ mil.)	NET INCOME ($ mil.)	NET PROFIT MARGIN	EMPLOYEES
06/20	19,761	724	3.7%	28,272
06/19	13,821	997	7.2%	—
06/18	17,966	40	0.2%	—
06/17	17,915	(91)	—	—
Annual Growth	3.3%	—	—	—

2020 Year-End Financials
Return on assets: 2.2%   Cash ($ mil.): 3,561
Return on equity: 4.0%
Current ratio: 3.40

STATE OF COLORADO

EXECUTIVES

Governor, Jared Polis
Lt Gov*, Dianne Primavera
Treasurer*, Dave Young
Sergeant, Ron Watkins

Acting Communications Director, Holly
  Shrewsbury
Staff, Jessika Shipley
Press Secretary, Jacque Montgomery
Vice-President Research and Te, Gert Thygesen
Staff, Ron Kirk
Coordinator, Tammy Schneiderman
Staff, Lauren Ris
Auditors: DIANNE E RAY CPA DENVER CO

LOCATIONS

HQ: STATE OF COLORADO
  200 E COLFAX AVE STE 91, DENVER, CO 802031716
Phone: 303 866-5000
Web: WWW.COLORADO.GOV

HISTORICAL FINANCIALS
Company Type: Private

Income Statement				FYE: June 30
	REVENUE ($ mil.)	NET INCOME ($ mil.)	NET PROFIT MARGIN	EMPLOYEES
06/17	22,949	(240)	—	81,349
06/16	23,139	(295)	—	—
06/13	18,658	788	4.2%	—
06/12	17,586	472	2.7%	—
Annual Growth	5.5%	—	—	—

2017 Year-End Financials
Return on assets: (-0.5%)   Cash ($ mil.): 5,708
Return on equity: (-1.4%)
Current ratio: 2.20

STATE OF DELAWARE

EXECUTIVES

Governor, John Carney
Lt Gov*, Bethany Hall-Long
Prin*, Beau Biden
Treas*, Chip Flowers
Prin*, Thomas Wagner Jr
Comm*, Karen Weldin Stewart
Information Specialist, Tim LI
Information Technology Custome, John
  Trabaudo
Information Technology Custome, Dorothy Kope
Adjutant General, Michael Berry
Human Resources Administrator, Kim Thornton
Auditors: KPMG LLP PHILADELPHIA PENNSY

LOCATIONS

HQ: STATE OF DELAWARE
  860 SILVER LAKE BLVD # 1, DOVER, DE 199042402
Phone: 302 744-4101
Web: WWW.DELAWARE.GOV

HISTORICAL FINANCIALS
Company Type: Private

Income Statement				FYE: June 30
	REVENUE ($ mil.)	NET INCOME ($ mil.)	NET PROFIT MARGIN	EMPLOYEES
06/20	8,513	535	6.3%	25
06/19	8,124	371	4.6%	—
06/17	7,368	(351)	—	—
06/16	7,106	(347)	—	—
Annual Growth	4.6%	—	—	—

2020 Year-End Financials
Return on assets: 3.0%   Cash ($ mil.): 2,564
Return on equity: —
Current ratio: —

STATE OF GEORGIA

EXECUTIVES

Governor, Brian Kemp
Lt Governor*, Geoff Duncan
Treas*, Lynnette Riley
Microbiologist, Amanda Balish
Director, Andrew Dent
Microbiologist, Anne Whitney
Officer, Catherine McLean
Supreme Court Judge, Charlie Bethel
Information Technology Special, Cheri Gatland-
  Lightne
Court of Appeals Judge, Christian A Coomer
Public Affairs Specialist, Courtney Lenard
Auditors: GREG S GRIFFIN STATE AUDITOR

LOCATIONS

HQ: STATE OF GEORGIA
  206 WSHNGTON ST 111 STATE, ATLANTA, GA 30334
Phone: 404 656-1776
Web: WWW.GEORGIA.GOV

HISTORICAL FINANCIALS
Company Type: Private

Income Statement				FYE: June 30
	REVENUE ($ mil.)	NET INCOME ($ mil.)	NET PROFIT MARGIN	EMPLOYEES
06/19	45,109	1,235	2.7%	67,139
06/17	42,410	1,167	2.8%	—
06/16	40,422	1,513	3.7%	—
06/15	38,901	512	1.3%	—
Annual Growth	3.8%	24.6%	—	—

2019 Year-End Financials
Return on assets: 1.5%   Cash ($ mil.): 6,236
Return on equity: 3.4%
Current ratio: —

STATE OF HAWAII

EXECUTIVES

Gov, David Ige
Lt. Gov*, Josh Green
Chief Information Security Off*, Vincent Hoang
Director of Operations, Jing Xu
Supervisor, Kristine Shimogawa
Director, Hawaii Officer of Pl, Mary Alice Evans
Hawaii Attorney General, Russell Suzuki
Director, Zheng Fang
Information Specialist, Andrew Jackson
Executive Officer, Charlene Tamanaha
Information Technology Special, Daniel Santos
Auditors: ACCUITY LLP HONOLULU HAWAII

LOCATIONS

HQ: STATE OF HAWAII
  201 MERCHANT ST STE 1805, HONOLULU, HI
  968132963
Phone: 808 695-4620
Web: WWW.PORTAL.EHAWAII.GOV

HISTORICAL FINANCIALS
Company Type: Private

Income Statement				FYE: June 30
	REVENUE ($ mil.)	NET INCOME ($ mil.)	NET PROFIT MARGIN	EMPLOYEES
06/20	12,091	(244)	—	44,201
06/19	11,744	57	0.5%	—
06/18	11,316	(39)	—	—
06/17	10,516	435	4.1%	—
Annual Growth	4.8%	—	—	—

2020 Year-End Financials
Return on assets: (-0.7%)   Cash ($ mil.): 2,993
Return on equity: —
Current ratio: —

STATE OF IDAHO

EXECUTIVES

Governor, Brad Little
Lt Governor*, Janice McGeachin
Cmsnr*, Tom Katsilometes
Cmsnr*, Rich Jackson
Cmsnr*, Elliot Werk
Information Specialist, Cory Woodbury
Admin Idaho Div Veterans Serv, Marv Hagedorn
Director, Christopher Freeburne
Director, Joyce Broadsword
Executive Director, Shawn Keough
Administrator, Bill Burns
Auditors: APRIL RENFRO CPA MANAGER BO

LOCATIONS

HQ: STATE OF IDAHO
  700 W JEFFERSON ST, BOISE, ID 837200001
Phone: 208 334-2100
Web: WWW.CAPITOLCOMMISSION.IDAHO.GOV

HISTORICAL FINANCIALS
Company Type: Private

Income Statement				FYE: June 30
	REVENUE ($ mil.)	NET INCOME ($ mil.)	NET PROFIT MARGIN	EMPLOYEES
06/20	9,664	600	6.2%	18,407
06/19	8,615	157	1.8%	—
06/18	8,403	542	6.5%	—
06/17	7,788	473	6.1%	—
Annual Growth	7.5%	8.3%	—	—

2020 Year-End Financials
Return on assets: 2.6%   Cash ($ mil.): 766
Return on equity: 3.6%
Current ratio: —

STATE OF ILLINOIS

EXECUTIVES

Governor, J B Pritzker
Lt Gov*, Julianna Stratton
SEC of State*, Jesse White
Treasurer*, Michael Frerichs
Deputy Governor*, Sol Flores
General Counsel*, Roma Larson
Director, Pamela Simon
Deputy Director, Ryan Prehn
Quality Assurance Director, Scott Hughes
Executive Director, Scott McFarland
Accounting Manager, Tracy McGee
Auditors: WILLIAM G HOLLAND

LOCATIONS

HQ: STATE OF ILLINOIS
207 STATE HOUSE, SPRINGFIELD, IL 627060001
Phone: 217 782-6830

HISTORICAL FINANCIALS

Company Type: Private

Income Statement — FYE: June 30

	REVENUE ($ mil.)	NET INCOME ($ mil.)	NET PROFIT MARGIN	EMPLOYEES
06/13	62,451	1,596	2.6%	59,659
06/12	58,747	(522)	—	—
06/11	55,157	869	1.6%	—
Annual Growth	6.4%	35.5%	—	—

2013 Year-End Financials
Return on assets: 2.1%   Cash ($ mil.): 11,764
Return on equity: —
Current ratio: —

STATE OF INDIANA

EXECUTIVES

Lt Gov*, Suzanne Crouch
Director of Finance, Carl Zapfe
Public Relations Executive, Carlos Pettiford
Commissioner, Christine Klika
Manager-Geo-Spatial Is, Chuck Carufel
Mis, Ron Bolander
Marketing Director, Stephanie Genrich
SEC, Stephene Reeve
Superintendent, Suellen Reed
Accounting and Financial Contr, Nurain Yusuf
Auditors: PAUL D JOYCE CPA INDIANAPOL

LOCATIONS

HQ: STATE OF INDIANA
200 W WA ST STE 201, INDIANAPOLIS, IN 462042731
Phone: 317 232-4567
Web: WWW.STATE.IN.US

HISTORICAL FINANCIALS

Company Type: Private

Income Statement — FYE: June 30

	REVENUE ($ mil.)	NET INCOME ($ mil.)	NET PROFIT MARGIN	EMPLOYEES
06/20	38,553	375	1.0%	33,000
06/19	36,469	986	2.7%	—
06/18	33,877	408	1.2%	—
06/17	32,576	(78)	—	—
Annual Growth	5.8%	—	—	—

STATE OF IOWA

EXECUTIVES

Governor, Kim Reynolds
Lt Governor*, Adam Gregg
Consultants, Jillian Dotson
Indexing Supervisor, Kristin Wentz
Teacher Visually Impair, Michelle Tauke
Ddm Contractor, Balaji Punukula
Desktop Technician I, Kayla Bishop
Vice Chairman, Sandy Salmon
Assistant Aud 6 Auditor of STA, Donna Kruger
Assistant ATT Gn3, Bridget Chambers
Residential Treatment Supervis, David Cohen
Auditors: MARLYS K GASTON CPA DES MOI

LOCATIONS

HQ: STATE OF IOWA
1007 E GRAND AVE RM 105, DES MOINES, IA
503199003
Phone: 515 281-5211
Web: WWW.IOWA.GOV

HISTORICAL FINANCIALS

Company Type: Private

Income Statement — FYE: June 30

	REVENUE ($ mil.)	NET INCOME ($ mil.)	NET PROFIT MARGIN	EMPLOYEES
06/20	19,439	348	1.8%	24,304
06/19	18,006	471	2.6%	—
06/18	17,093	(79)	—	—
06/17	16,806	(130)	—	—
Annual Growth	5.0%	—	—	—

STATE OF KANSAS

EXECUTIVES

Governor, Laura Kelly
Lt Gov*, David Toland
Treasurer*, Jake Laturner
Chief Information Technology O*, Lee Allen
Chief Information Officer, Ashley Templin
Edi Coordinator, Carole Sadler
Administrative Officer, Chasity Uhl
Director, Rehabilitation Servi, Daniel Decker
Cheif Fiscal Officer, Dawn Palmberg
Assistant Administrator, Jamie Medaris
Employee, Kenworthy Lisa
Auditors: CLIFFTONLARSONALLEN LLP
BROOM

LOCATIONS

HQ: STATE OF KANSAS
534 S KANSAS AVE STE 1210, TOPEKA, KS
666033434
Phone: 785 354-1388
Web: WWW.PORTAL.KANSAS.GOV

HISTORICAL FINANCIALS

Company Type: Private

Income Statement — FYE: June 30

	REVENUE ($ mil.)	NET INCOME ($ mil.)	NET PROFIT MARGIN	EMPLOYEES
06/20	15,721	278	1.8%	22,375
06/19	14,988	794	5.3%	—
06/18	14,322	895	6.3%	—
06/17	12,935	(187)	—	—
Annual Growth	6.7%	—	—	—

2020 Year-End Financials
Return on assets: 0.9%   Cash ($ mil.): 3,976
Return on equity: 1.4%
Current ratio: —

STATE OF LOUISIANA

EXECUTIVES

Governor, John Bel Edwards
Lt Gov, Jay Dardenne
Director, Margaret Gehdauer
Treasurer, John Schroder
Compensation Division Administ, Brandy Malatesta
Finance, Marella Houghton
Sphr Human Resources Director, Sophia Pipsair
Vice President Management, Joseph Livingston
Information Technology Technic, Mike Cavell
Senior, Alden Clement
Specialist, Brooke Guidry
Auditors: DARYL G PURPERA CPA CFE BA

LOCATIONS

HQ: STATE OF LOUISIANA
900 N 3RD ST FL 4, BATON ROUGE, LA 708025236
Phone: 225 342-0991
Web: WWW.LOUISIANA.GOV

HISTORICAL FINANCIALS

Company Type: Private

Income Statement — FYE: June 30

	REVENUE ($ mil.)	NET INCOME ($ mil.)	NET PROFIT MARGIN	EMPLOYEES
06/20	32,178	560	1.7%	47,937
06/19	30,034	1,386	4.6%	—
06/18	28,849	829	2.9%	—
Annual Growth	5.6%	(17.7%)	—	—

2020 Year-End Financials
Return on assets: 0.9%   Cash ($ mil.): 8,550
Return on equity: 3.7%
Current ratio: —

STATE OF MAINE

EXECUTIVES

Governor, Janet Mills
Senior Health Policy Adviser, Nick Adolphsen
Senior Policy Adviser, Sean Ingram
Legislative Policy Coordinator, Andrew Bracy
Information Specialist, Dale Irish
Sergeant, Jonathan Shapiro
Accounting Staff, Laura Larrabee
Procurement Staff, Marie Malloy
Sergeant, Mark Tibbetts
Coordinator, Michael Laberge
Coordinator, Michael Mayo
Auditors: POLA A BUCKLEY CPA CISA/MAR

LOCATIONS

HQ: STATE OF MAINE
1 STATE HOUSE STA, AUGUSTA, ME 043330001
Phone: 207 287-3531
Web: WWW.MAINE.GOV

HISTORICAL FINANCIALS

Company Type: Private

Income Statement				FYE: June 30
	REVENUE ($ mil.)	NET INCOME ($ mil.)	NET PROFIT MARGIN	EMPLOYEES
06/20	9,868	44	0.4%	12,000
06/19	8,155	357	4.4%	—
06/18	7,798	110	1.4%	—
06/17	7,623	146	1.9%	—
Annual Growth	9.0%	(33.0%)	—	—

2020 Year-End Financials

Return on assets: 0.2%   Cash ($ mil.): 2,419
Return on equity: 1.0%
Current ratio: 2.00

STATE OF MARYLAND

EXECUTIVES

Governor, Lawrence J Hogan Jr
Lt Gov., Boyd K Rutherford
Chief of Staff, Matthew Clark
Human Resources Director, Mitchell Hose
Urology Basic Cell Biology Pro, Mundy Ronald
Assistant To Deputy Secretary, Paula Webber
Voting Manager, Reider White
Quality Assurance Manager, Rich Mangone
Public Member, Taneesha Deshields
Director, Security, Gregory Jones
Director, Mark A Leeds
Auditors: SB & COMPANY LLC OWINGS MILL

LOCATIONS

HQ: STATE OF MARYLAND
45 CALVERT ST STE 1, ANNAPOLIS, MD 214011994
Phone: 410 767-6356
Web: WWW.MARYLAND.GOV

STATE OF MINNESOTA

EXECUTIVES

Governor, Tim Walz
SEC of State, Mary Kiffmeyer
St Treas, Carol C Johnson
Lt Governor, Peggy Flanagan
ATT Gen, Mike Hatch
Security Staff, William Fowler

HISTORICAL FINANCIALS

Company Type: Private

Income Statement				FYE: June 30
	REVENUE ($ mil.)	NET INCOME ($ mil.)	NET PROFIT MARGIN	EMPLOYEES
06/20	40,437	381	0.9%	58,020
06/19	38	1	3.2%	—
06/18	35,653	314	0.9%	—
06/17	34,822	(687)	—	—
Annual Growth	5.1%	—	—	—

2020 Year-End Financials

Return on assets: 0.5%   Cash ($ mil.): 5,006
Return on equity: —
Current ratio: —

STATE OF MICHIGAN

EXECUTIVES

Governor, Gretchen Whitmer
Lt Governor*, Garlin Gilchrist
SEC*, Joseph Gordon
Chief Deputy Treasurer*, Jeff Guilfoyle
Member Advisor, Alyssa Vanhyfte
Accounting Staff, Anita Westry
Senior Management Analyst, Bill Bartels
Trade Developmen, Chris Bosio
Business Capital Relationship, Chris Cook
Scientist, Clarence Jones
Director, Eric Dean
Auditors: DOUG A RINGLER CPA CIA LAN

LOCATIONS

HQ: STATE OF MICHIGAN
111 S CAPITOL AVE, LANSING, MI 489331555
Phone: 517 373-7910
Web: WWW.MICHIGAN.GOV

HISTORICAL FINANCIALS

Company Type: Private

Income Statement				FYE: September 30
	REVENUE ($ mil.)	NET INCOME ($ mil.)	NET PROFIT MARGIN	EMPLOYEES
09/18	54,684	832	1.5%	55,416
09/17	52,459	702	1.3%	—
09/16	52,181	168	0.3%	—
Annual Growth	2.4%	122.5%	—	—

2018 Year-End Financials

Return on assets: 1.1%   Cash ($ mil.): 11,188
Return on equity: 3.5%
Current ratio: 2.70

Coordinator, Evie Wold
Minnesota Adjutant General, Jon A Jensen
Supreme Court Judge, Paul Thissen
Court of Appeals Judge, Randall J Slieter
Court of Appeals Judge For Six, Jeanne M Cochran
Auditors: LORI LEYSEN CPA/SCOTT TOMSLAN

LOCATIONS

HQ: STATE OF MINNESOTA
130 STATE CPTOL 75 REV DR, SAINT PAUL, MN 551550001
Phone: 651 201-3400
Web: WWW.VALIDATE.PERFDRIVE.COM

HISTORICAL FINANCIALS

Company Type: Private

Income Statement				FYE: June 30
	REVENUE ($ mil.)	NET INCOME ($ mil.)	NET PROFIT MARGIN	EMPLOYEES
06/20	41,929	126	0.3%	35,217
06/19	41,741	1,040	2.5%	—
06/17	37,751	793	2.1%	—
06/16	36,717	479	1.3%	—
Annual Growth	3.4%	(28.4%)	—	—

2020 Year-End Financials

Return on assets: 0.2%   Cash ($ mil.): 17,730
Return on equity: 0.4%
Current ratio: 2.40

STATE OF MISSISSIPPI

EXECUTIVES

Governor, Phil Bryant
Lieutenant Governor*, Tate Reeves
Executive Director*, Kevin J Upchurch
Executive Assistant, Dorthy Kuykendall
Administrator, Dana Kidd
Scientist, Kerwin Cuevas
Procurement Staff, Vicki Brown
Special Projects Officer IV, Kenneth Judie
Staff, Susanne Merchant
U.S. Marshal, Southern Distric, Mark B Shepherd
Director, Kevin Lackey
Auditors: STEPHANIE C PALMERTREE CPA

LOCATIONS

HQ: STATE OF MISSISSIPPI
501 NW ST STE 1301 WLFOL, JACKSON, MS 39201
Phone: 601 359-3100
Web: WWW.MISSISSIPPI.GOV

HISTORICAL FINANCIALS

Company Type: Private

Income Statement				FYE: June 30
	REVENUE ($ mil.)	NET INCOME ($ mil.)	NET PROFIT MARGIN	EMPLOYEES
06/20	17,717	492	2.8%	27,775
06/19	16,887	773	4.6%	—
06/18	16,518	(9)	—	—
06/17	16,436	156	0.9%	—
Annual Growth	2.5%	46.7%	—	—

2020 Year-End Financials

Return on assets: 1.3%   Cash ($ mil.): 1,780
Return on equity: 2.6%
Current ratio: 2.20

STATE OF MISSOURI

EXECUTIVES

Governor, Mike Parson
Lt Gov, Mike Kehoe
Comm, Doug Nelson
Scientist, Alica Alexander
Coordinator, Karen Cassmeyer
Scientist, Tracey Mason
Server Administrator, Billy Sarver
Actuary, David Cox
Director, Dean Linneman
Alcohol and Tobacco Enforcemen, Keith Hendrickson
Environmental Public Health SE, Melinda Laughlin
Auditors: THOMAS A SCHWEICH JEFFERSON

LOCATIONS

HQ: STATE OF MISSOURI
301 W HIGH ST RM 570, JEFFERSON CITY, MO 651011517
Phone: 573 751-4013
Web: WWW.MO.GOV

HISTORICAL FINANCIALS

Company Type: Private

Income Statement | | | | FYE: June 30

	REVENUE ($ mil.)	NET INCOME ($ mil.)	NET PROFIT MARGIN	EMPLOYEES
06/20	27,080	962	3.6%	51,488
06/19	25,748	309	1.2%	—
06/18	25,326	110	0.4%	—
06/17	24,769	(153)	—	—
Annual Growth	3.0%	—	—	—

2020 Year-End Financials

Return on assets: 1.6% Cash ($ mil.): 4,652
Return on equity: 2.7%
Current ratio: —

STATE OF MONTANA

EXECUTIVES

Governor, Greg Gianforte
Executive Assistant, Human RES, Angela Volden
Publications Designer, Ann Reber
Accounting Technician, April Kidwell
Member and Mail, Bethany Clark
R2 River Recreation Manager, Christine Oschell
Section Supervisor, Christopher Cronin
Compliance Specialist, Diana Emmons
Court Administrator, Diane Kaatz
Supervisor, James Zito
Communications Manager, Jennifer McKee
Auditors: CINDY JORGENSON CPA HELENA

LOCATIONS

HQ: STATE OF MONTANA
1301 E 6TH AVE FL 2, HELENA, MT 596013875
Phone: 406 444-3111
Web: WWW.MT.GOV

HISTORICAL FINANCIALS

Company Type: Private

Income Statement | | | | FYE: June 30

	REVENUE ($ mil.)	NET INCOME ($ mil.)	NET PROFIT MARGIN	EMPLOYEES
06/19	6,740	509	7.6%	418
06/18	6,228	95	1.5%	—
06/17	5,921	(195)	—	—
06/16	5,558	(89)	—	—
Annual Growth	6.6%	—	—	—

2019 Year-End Financials

Return on assets: 2.8% Cash ($ mil.): 2,578
Return on equity: 4.3%
Current ratio: —

STATE OF NEBRASKA

EXECUTIVES

Governor, Pete Ricketts
Lt. Gov*, Mike Foley
Staff, Traci Cooney
Acting Superintendent, Russ Stanczyk
Coordinator, John Rockenbach
Fire Marshal, Christopher Cantrell
Information Technology Infrast, Garry Kapperman
Legal Counsel, Ron Theis
Law Enforcement Officer, Scott Eveland
Government Official, Steve Burns
Budget Coordinator, Kadi Lukesh
Auditors: PHILIP J OLSEN CPA CISA LI

LOCATIONS

HQ: STATE OF NEBRASKA
521 S 14TH ST STE 400, LINCOLN, NE 685082707
Phone: 402 471-2311
Web: WWW.NEBRASKA.GOV

HISTORICAL FINANCIALS

Company Type: Private

Income Statement | | | | FYE: June 30

	REVENUE ($ mil.)	NET INCOME ($ mil.)	NET PROFIT MARGIN	EMPLOYEES
06/20	10,006	354	3.5%	18,653
06/19	9,322	401	4.3%	—
06/18	8,643	(108)	—	—
06/17	8,449	(266)	—	—
Annual Growth	5.8%	—	—	—

2020 Year-End Financials

Return on assets: 1.3% Cash ($ mil.): 2,524
Return on equity: 1.6%
Current ratio: —

STATE OF NEVADA

EXECUTIVES

Governor, Steve Sisolak
Lt Governor, Lisa Cano Burkhead
Attorney General, Catherine Cortez Masto
Chief of Staff, Gerald Gardner
State Contrl, Kim Wallin
SEC of State, Ross Miller
Dir, Jim Groth
General Counsel, Kathryn Reynolds
Purchasing Officer II, Annette Morfin
Master Information Technology, David Lahti
Bep State Director, Drazen Elez
Auditors: EIDE BAILLY LLP RENO NEVADA

LOCATIONS

HQ: STATE OF NEVADA
101 N CARSON ST STE 1, CARSON CITY, NV 897017011
Phone: 775 684-5670
Web: WWW.NV.GOV

HISTORICAL FINANCIALS

Company Type: Private

Income Statement | | | | FYE: June 30

	REVENUE ($ mil.)	NET INCOME ($ mil.)	NET PROFIT MARGIN	EMPLOYEES
06/20	11,924	73	0.6%	14,790
06/16	10,436	301	2.9%	—
06/15	9,446	(144)	—	—
06/14	8,131	161	2.0%	—
Annual Growth	6.6%	(12.3%)	—	—

STATE OF NEW HAMPSHIRE

EXECUTIVES

Governor, Chris Sununu
Commissioner, Beth Edes
Park Manager IV, Andrew Zboray
Payroll Officer I, Angela Theberge
Secretary II, Anita Terrio
Facility Supervisor, Anne Bailey
Secretary II, Annie M Laurendeau
Payroll Officer I, Bonita M Huckins
Registered Nurse I, Brian Mortimer
Sergeant, Casey Shingleton
Senior Audit Manager, Christine L Young
Auditors: KPMG LLP BOSTON MA

LOCATIONS

HQ: STATE OF NEW HAMPSHIRE
107 N MAIN ST, CONCORD, NH 033014951
Phone: 603 271-1110
Web: WWW.NH.GOV

HISTORICAL FINANCIALS

Company Type: Private

Income Statement | | | | FYE: June 30

	REVENUE ($ mil.)	NET INCOME ($ mil.)	NET PROFIT MARGIN	EMPLOYEES
06/20	6,398	(116)	—	12,280
06/19	5,955	110	1.9%	—
06/18	5,874	145	2.5%	—
06/17	5,585	8	0.1%	—
Annual Growth	4.6%	—	—	—

2020 Year-End Financials

Return on assets: (-1.0%) Cash ($ mil.): 1,126
Return on equity: (-3.5%)
Current ratio: 1.50

STATE OF NEW MEXICO

EXECUTIVES

Governor, Michelle Lujan Grisham
Lt. Governor*, Howie Morales
Dep Chief of Staff*, Scott Darnell
Auditor*, Wayne Johnson
Coordinator, Laura Dalemarre
Court of Appeals Judge, Zachary A Ives
Chief of Police, Tim Johnson
Deputy Chief, Robert O Thornton III
Deputy Chief, Nick Aragon
Deputy Chief, Carolyn N Huynh
Staff, Deborah A Armstrong
Auditors: CLIFTONLARSONALLEN LLP
ALBUQU

LOCATIONS

HQ: STATE OF NEW MEXICO
237 DON GASPAR AVE, SANTA FE, NM 875012178
Phone: 505 827-3000
Web: WWW.NEWMEXICO.GOV

HISTORICAL FINANCIALS

Company Type: Private

Income Statement				FYE: June 30
	REVENUE ($ mil.)	NET INCOME ($ mil.)	NET PROFIT MARGIN	EMPLOYEES
06/20	18,637	1,136	6.1%	22,217
06/19	18,370	3,033	16.5%	—
06/18	17,364	2,968	17.1%	—
06/17	32	1	3.6%	—
Annual Growth	726.7%	881.5%	—	—

2020 Year-End Financials

Return on assets: 2.1%   Cash ($ mil.): 2,403
Return on equity: 3.3%
Current ratio: 2.50

STATE OF NEW YORK MORTGAGE AGENCY

The State of New York Mortgage Agency (SONYMA pronounced "Sony Mae") is a public benefit corporation of the State of New York that makes homebuying more affordable for low- and moderate-income residents of the state. SONYMA has two program divisions: Its single-family programs and financing division provides low-interest rate mortgages to first-time homebuyers with low and moderate incomes through the issuance of mortgage revenue bonds while its mortgage insurance fund provides mortgage insurance and credit support for multi-family affordable residential projects and special care facilities throughout the state.

Operations

SONYMA is overseen by a board of directors comprised of the State Comptroller Director of the Budget Commissioner of Housing and Community Renewal and four appointees of the Governor Temporary President of the Senate and Speaker of the Assembly. Operations of the agency rest with the president/CEO who also serves in this capacity for the New York State Housing Finance Agency the State's other major housing finance entity. The two agencies are jointly operated out of a New York City headquarters office plus regional offices in Albany Buffalo and Long Island.

SONYMA receives no direct operating support from the State. All of its programs and operations are supported by agency funds consisting of mortgage income application fees insurance premiums and investment proceeds. The agency uses proceeds from the sale of tax-exempt and taxable bonds to finance the purchase of homes statewide through a network of lenders.

Financial Performance

SONYMA's operations — specifically its volume of mortgage originations — were impacted in fiscal 2011 by the ongoing weakness in the US real estate market and disruptions in the international capital markets. Mortgage reservations in 2011 were down 26% from 2010. This was offset partially by a low-interest rate environment which provided opportunity to refund outstanding SONYMA bonds lowering the agency's cost of borrowing and somewhat improving its financial condition.

Strategy

SONYMA is developing a program with the New York State Higher Education Services Corporation (HESC) to offer education loans to eligible students attending colleges and universities in the state.

EXECUTIVES

Cfo, Sheila Robinson
Auditor, Stephen B Chopey
Senior Vice President, Michael Friedman
Assistant Counsel, Remy Bernardo
Assistant Vice President, Robert Rosado
Associate Counsel, Barbara Roslyn
Associate Accountant, John Paluch
Senior Project Manager, James O'Hare
Secretary, Lillian Cabera
Vice President, Michael Esposito
Database Administrator, Ping Chen
Auditors: ERNST & YOUNG LLP NEW YORK N

LOCATIONS

HQ: STATE OF NEW YORK MORTGAGE AGENCY
641 LEXINGTON AVE FL 4, NEW YORK, NY 100224503
Phone: 212 688-4000
Web: WWW.HCR.NY.GOV

HISTORICAL FINANCIALS

Company Type: Private

Income Statement				FYE: October 31
	ASSETS ($ mil.)	NET INCOME ($ mil.)	INCOME AS % OF ASSETS	EMPLOYEES
10/19	5,936	392	6.6%	221
10/18	5,324	147	2.8%	—
10/17	5,228	34	0.7%	—
10/16	5,187	63	1.2%	—
Annual Growth	4.6%	83.2%	—	—

2019 Year-End Financials

Return on assets: 6.6%   Sales ($ mil): 221
Return on equity: 13.2%

STATE OF NORTH CAROLINA

EXECUTIVES

Governor, Roy Cooper
Lt Gov*, Mark Robinson
Chief of Staff*, Thomas Stith
Controller*, Linda M Combs
Vice President, Finance Chief, Adrienne Covington
Nursing Instructor, Amber Anders
Vice President, Amber Greer
Administrative Adminis, Angela Tousey
Administrative Assistant, Angela Washington
Dean, Ann McNeely
Financial Aid Advisor, Barbara Wiley
Auditors: BETH A WOOD CPA RALEIGH NO

LOCATIONS

HQ: STATE OF NORTH CAROLINA
20301 MAIL SERVICE CTR, RALEIGH, NC 276990300
Phone: 919 715-1411
Web: WWW.NC.GOV

HISTORICAL FINANCIALS

Company Type: Private

Income Statement				FYE: June 30
	REVENUE ($ mil.)	NET INCOME ($ mil.)	NET PROFIT MARGIN	EMPLOYEES
06/19	48,977	836	1.7%	69,869
06/18	46,551	208	0.4%	—
06/17	45,371	1,172	2.6%	—
06/16	44,395	1,501	3.4%	—
Annual Growth	3.3%	(17.7%)	—	—

2019 Year-End Financials

Return on assets: 0.7%   Cash ($ mil.): 16,804
Return on equity: 1.2%
Current ratio: —

STATE OF NORTH DAKOTA

EXECUTIVES

Governor, Doug Burgum
Lt Gov*, Brent Sanford
Auditor*, Bob Peterson
Coo*, Jodi Uecker
Cao*, Jodee Hanson
Chief People Officer*, Kelsey Roth
Dept of Agriculture Livestoc, Becky Gietzen
Dept of Agriculture Exec Srv, Bonnie Sunby
Instructional Special, Cheryl Thompson
Dept of Agriculture Plant In, Elaine Sayley
Dept of Agriculture Plant In, Jeff Olson
Auditors: JOSHUA C GALLION BISMARCK N

LOCATIONS

HQ: STATE OF NORTH DAKOTA
600 E BOULEVARD AVE # 101, BISMARCK, ND 585050601
Phone: 701 328-4905
Web: WWW.ND.GOV

HISTORICAL FINANCIALS
Company Type: Private

Income Statement				FYE: June 30
	REVENUE ($ mil.)	NET INCOME ($ mil.)	NET PROFIT MARGIN	EMPLOYEES
06/19	7,860	1,955	24.9%	8,800
06/17	6,408	172	2.7%	—
06/16	5,667	(1,080)	—	—
06/15	7,902	1,203	15.2%	—
Annual Growth	(0.1%)	12.9%	—	—

2019 Year-End Financials
Return on assets: 5.8%   Cash ($ mil.): 1,010
Return on equity: 7.7%
Current ratio: —

STATE OF OHIO

EXECUTIVES

Governor, Mike Dewine
Lt Govnr*, Jon Husted
Chief of Staff, AVI Zaffini
Communications Director, Joshua Eck
Dpty Communications Director, Eve Mueller
Press Secretary, Dan Tierney
Minority Affairs Liaison, Ronald C Todd
Chief of Staff, Laurel Dawson
Director, Washington DC Office, Nikki Guilford
Vice Chair, Chris Widener
Manager, Angela Albrecht
Auditors: KEITH FABER COLUMBUS OHIO

LOCATIONS

HQ: STATE OF OHIO
  30 E BROAD ST FL 40, COLUMBUS, OH 432153414
Phone: 614 466-3455
Web: WWW.OHIO.GOV

HISTORICAL FINANCIALS
Company Type: Private

Income Statement				FYE: June 30
	REVENUE ($ mil.)	NET INCOME ($ mil.)	NET PROFIT MARGIN	EMPLOYEES
06/19	60,384	1,717	2.8%	57,631
06/17	56,959	(267)	—	—
Annual Growth	3.0%	—	—	—

2019 Year-End Financials
Return on assets: 1.3%   Cash ($ mil.): 14,916
Return on equity: 4.2%
Current ratio: —

STATE OF OKLAHOMA

EXECUTIVES

Governor, Kevin Stitt
Lt Gov*, Matt Pinnell
General Counsel-Sec*, James Williamson
Sec, Science and Innovation, Kayse Shrum
Sec, Health and Mental Health, Jerome
 Loughridge
Contracting Andamp, Kathy Hallum

Coordinator Mark, Barbara Charlet
Senior Screening Consultant, Dane Libart
Editor, Donna Bruce
Board of Trustees Member, James Hixon
Director of Student Informatio, Matt Morgan
Auditors: GARY A JONES CPA CFE OKLAH

LOCATIONS

HQ: STATE OF OKLAHOMA
  421 NW 13TH ST STE 220, OKLAHOMA CITY, OK
  731033784
Phone: 405 521-2342
Web: WWW.OKLAHOMA.GOV

HISTORICAL FINANCIALS
Company Type: Private

Income Statement				FYE: June 30
	REVENUE ($ mil.)	NET INCOME ($ mil.)	NET PROFIT MARGIN	EMPLOYEES
06/20	19,511	27	0.1%	37,613
06/19	19,784	1,636	8.3%	—
06/18	17,805	602	3.4%	—
06/17	17,175	48	0.3%	—
Annual Growth	4.3%	(17.0%)	—	—

2020 Year-End Financials
Return on assets: 0.1%   Cash ($ mil.): 10,640
Return on equity: 0.1%
Current ratio: 2.60

STATE OF OREGON

EXECUTIVES

Governor, Kate Brown
State SEC*, Bev Clarno
Superintendent, Mike Riggan
Social Media Coordinator, Sarah Stone
Staff, Caroline Zavitkovski
Public Safety Policy Adviser, Constantin Severe
Human Resources Administration, Donna Minor
Deputy Health Care Policy Advi, Jackie Yerby
North Coast Regional, Jennifer Purcell
Coordinator, Jessica Guerrero
Dhs Human, Larry Nicholson
Auditors: OFFICE OF THE SECRETARY OF STA

LOCATIONS

HQ: STATE OF OREGON
  900 COURT ST NE STE 160, SALEM, OR 973014046
Phone: 503 378-3111
Web: WWW.STATE.OR.US

HISTORICAL FINANCIALS
Company Type: Private

Income Statement				FYE: June 30
	REVENUE ($ mil.)	NET INCOME ($ mil.)	NET PROFIT MARGIN	EMPLOYEES
06/20	28,755	(409)	—	36,176
06/19	28,230	2,142	7.6%	—
06/18	26,037	874	3.4%	—
06/17	24,296	1,536	6.3%	—
Annual Growth	5.8%	—	—	—

2020 Year-End Financials
Return on assets: (-0.6%)   Cash ($ mil.): 14,481
Return on equity: (-1.3%)
Current ratio: 3.20

STATE OF RHODE ISLAND AND PROVIDENCE PLANTATIONS

EXECUTIVES

Gov, Daniel J McKee
Manager, Public Health Informa, Akshar Patel
Interim Chief, Alysia Mihalakos
Manager, Andrea Creach
Commissioner, Angelica Infantegreen
Control Administrator, Arthur Sheridan
Secondary Marketing Manager, Bernadette Lynch
Chief Legal Counsel, Cecelia Pelkey
Manager, Cheryl Josephson
Chief Clerk, Cheyenne Seymour
Chief Clerk, Dena Vezina
Auditors: DENNIS E HOYLE CPA PROVIDEN

LOCATIONS

HQ: STATE OF RHODE ISLAND AND PROVIDENCE
  PLANTATIONS
  82 SMITH ST STE 102, PROVIDENCE, RI 029031121
Phone: 401 222-2080
Web: WWW.RI.GOV

HISTORICAL FINANCIALS
Company Type: Private

Income Statement				FYE: June 30
	REVENUE ($ mil.)	NET INCOME ($ mil.)	NET PROFIT MARGIN	EMPLOYEES
06/19	7,547	(49)	—	13,535
06/17	7,012	215	3.1%	—
06/16	6,860	(10)	—	—
06/15	6,787	160	2.4%	—
Annual Growth	2.7%	—	—	—

2019 Year-End Financials
Return on assets: (-0.3%)   Cash ($ mil.): 1,905
Return on equity: (-1.9%)
Current ratio: 2.10

STATE OF SOUTH CAROLINA

EXECUTIVES

Gov, Henry Dargan McMaster
Lt Gov*, Pamela S Evette
Exec Asst*, Kara Smoak
Atty Gen, Henry McMaster
Governors Aid, Susane Cooper
Director of Information Techno, Andrew Blais
Branch Manager, Robert Liming
Adjutant General, R Van McCarty
Operations Director, John Barfield
Finance, Karen Rumfelt
Governor, Nikki Haley
Auditors: GEORGE L KENNEDY III COLUMB

LOCATIONS

HQ: STATE OF SOUTH CAROLINA
1205 PENDLETON ST, COLUMBIA, SC 292013756
Phone: 803 734-2100
Web: WWW.SC.GOV

HISTORICAL FINANCIALS

Company Type: Private

Income Statement   FYE: June 30

	REVENUE ($ mil.)	NET INCOME ($ mil.)	NET PROFIT MARGIN	EMPLOYEES
06/19	24,767	1,774	7.2%	67,816
06/15	21,191	224	1.1%	—
06/14	20,459	613	3.0%	—
06/13	19,706	944	4.8%	—
Annual Growth	3.9%	11.1%	—	—

2019 Year-End Financials

Return on assets: 2.6%   Cash ($ mil.): 8,923
Return on equity: 6.6%
Current ratio: —

STATE OF SOUTH DAKOTA

EXECUTIVES

Governor, Kristi L Noem
Lt. Governor*, Larry Rhoden
SEC of State*, Chris Nelson
State Auditor*, Rich Sattgast
Attorney General*, Larry Long
Director of Finance Compliance, Ron Wire
Attorney, Michael F Shaw
Staff, Dj Hausmann
Compliance Staff, Paige Olson
Coordinator, Bell Jacobsen
Coordinator, Grace Kessler
Auditors: MARTIN L GUINDON CPA PIERRE

LOCATIONS

HQ: STATE OF SOUTH DAKOTA
500 E CAPITOL AVE, PIERRE, SD 575015007
Phone: 605 773-3378
Web: WWW.SD.GOV

HISTORICAL FINANCIALS

Company Type: Private

Income Statement   FYE: June 30

	REVENUE ($ mil.)	NET INCOME ($ mil.)	NET PROFIT MARGIN	EMPLOYEES
06/20	4,349	179	4.1%	8,256
06/19	3,945	71	1.8%	—
06/18	3,828	87	2.3%	—
06/17	3,820	153	4.0%	—
Annual Growth	4.4%	5.2%	—	—

2020 Year-End Financials

Return on assets: 1.2%   Cash ($ mil.): 3,192
Return on equity: 1.8%
Current ratio: —

STATE OF TENNESSEE

EXECUTIVES

Governor, Bill Lee
Lt Gov, Ron Ramsey
Speaker - House, James O Naifeh
Speaker - Senate, John S Wilder
East TN Field Dr, Harlow Sumerford
Staff, Amanda Carter
Assistant Chief, Glenn Moates
Coordinator, Steve Cross
Director - Communications, Jennifer Donnals
Staff Assistant To Treasur, Ashley Humphrey
Specialist, Barry Bryant
Auditors: DEBORAH V LOVELESS CPA DIRE

LOCATIONS

HQ: STATE OF TENNESSEE
312 ROSA L PARKS AVE, NASHVILLE, TN 372431102
Phone: 615 741-2001
Web: WWW.TN.GOV

HISTORICAL FINANCIALS

Company Type: Private

Income Statement   FYE: June 30

	REVENUE ($ mil.)	NET INCOME ($ mil.)	NET PROFIT MARGIN	EMPLOYEES
06/19	32,779	754	2.3%	37,737
06/18	32,194	902	2.8%	—
06/17	31,145	981	3.2%	—
06/16	30,452	1,162	3.8%	—
Annual Growth	2.5%	(13.4%)	—	—

2019 Year-End Financials

Return on assets: 1.2%   Cash ($ mil.): 12,711
Return on equity: 1.6%
Current ratio: —

STATE OF TEXAS

EXECUTIVES

Governor, Greg Abbott
Lt. Gov.*, Dan Patrick
Chief of Staff*, Luis Saenz
Deputy Chief of Staff*, David Whitley
Chief Operating Officer*, Reed Clay
Deputy Chief of Staff*, Jordan Hale
Senior Adviser For State Opera, Steven Albright
Texas District Attorney, Andria Bender
Senior Adviser, Sarah Hicks
Chief of Staff, Amy Bruno
Shift Coordinator, Darrell Taylor
Auditors: LISA R COLLIER AUSTIN TX

LOCATIONS

HQ: STATE OF TEXAS
1100 SAN JACINTO BLVD, AUSTIN, TX 787011935
Phone: 512 463-2000
Web: WWW.TEXAS.GOV

HISTORICAL FINANCIALS

Company Type: Private

Income Statement   FYE: August 31

	REVENUE ($ mil.)	NET INCOME ($ mil.)	NET PROFIT MARGIN	EMPLOYEES
08/17	115,336	1,882	1.6%	144,175
08/15	107,350	1,993	1.9%	—
08/14	109,860	8,184	7.4%	—
08/13	0	0	—	—
Annual Growth	—	—	—	—

2017 Year-End Financials

Return on assets: 0.6%   Cash ($ mil.): 29,217
Return on equity: 1.1%
Current ratio: 1.90

STATE OF UTAH

EXECUTIVES

Gov, Spencer J Cox
Lt Gov, Deidre M Henderson
Exec-Dir, Q Val Hale
General Counsel, Ron Gordon
Program Manager, Brenna Brooks
Human Resources Manager, Brent Urry
General, Brittany Huff
Deputy Director, Cade Meier
Public Information Specialist, Charla Haley
Uintah Special Distric, Chelsey Hatch
Department of Human D, Chrystal Martin
Auditors: OFFICE OF THE STATE AUDITOR

LOCATIONS

HQ: STATE OF UTAH
350 N STATE ST STE 200, SALT LAKE CITY, UT 841140002
Phone: 801 538-1000
Web: WWW.UTAH.GOV

HISTORICAL FINANCIALS

Company Type: Private

Income Statement   FYE: June 30

	REVENUE ($ mil.)	NET INCOME ($ mil.)	NET PROFIT MARGIN	EMPLOYEES
06/20	15,501	1,117	7.2%	29,821
06/19	14,316	696	4.9%	—
06/18	13,582	986	7.3%	—
06/17	12,668	199	1.6%	—
Annual Growth	7.0%	77.6%	—	—

2020 Year-End Financials

Return on assets: 2.0%   Cash ($ mil.): 5,888
Return on equity: 2.8%
Current ratio: —

STATE OF VERMONT

EXECUTIVES

Governor, Phil Scott
Lt. Gov*, Molly Gray
Chief of Staff*, Liz Miller
Coordinator, Amy Tucker

Staff, Diane Hahn
Staff, Judith Barbera
Supervisor, Sgt Prevost
Law Specialist, Nancy Williams
Acting Washington County Atty, Rory Thibault
Policy, Austin Davis
Public Safety Barracks Clerk, Hannah Neilson

LOCATIONS

HQ: STATE OF VERMONT
109 STATE ST STE 4, MONTPELIER, VT 056090003
Phone: 802 828-1452
Web: WWW.VERMONT.GOV

HISTORICAL FINANCIALS

Company Type: Private

Income Statement				FYE: June 30
	REVENUE ($ mil.)	NET INCOME ($ mil.)	NET PROFIT MARGIN	EMPLOYEES
06/20	6,091	38	0.6%	8,795
06/19	5,868	(13)	—	—
06/18	5,790	144	2.5%	—
Annual Growth	2.6%	(48.3%)	—	—

2020 Year-End Financials
Return on assets: 0.3%   Cash ($ mil.): 2,536
Return on equity: 4.3%
Current ratio: 1.60

STATE OF WASHINGTON

EXECUTIVES

Governor, Jay Inslee
Lieutenant Governor*, Denny Heck
SEC State*, Sam Reed
Treas*, Michael Murphy
Pub Inst*, Terry Bergeson
Exec SEC*, Sue Martin
Chief of Staff*, Mary Alice Heuschel
Senior Adviser, Joby Shimomura
Manager, Linda Garland
Deputy Chief Information Offic, Debbie Hoxit
Manager, Ginny Schenck
Auditors: PAT MCCARTHY OLYMPIA WA

LOCATIONS

HQ: STATE OF WASHINGTON
106 LEGISLATIVE BUILDING, OLYMPIA, WA
985040001
Phone: 360 902-4111
Web: WWW.ACCESS.WA.GOV

HISTORICAL FINANCIALS

Company Type: Private

Income Statement				FYE: June 30
	REVENUE ($ mil.)	NET INCOME ($ mil.)	NET PROFIT MARGIN	EMPLOYEES
06/19	50,993	264	0.5%	57,659
06/18	49,114	2,692	5.5%	—
06/17	46,269	1,100	2.4%	—
06/16	43,294	1,096	2.5%	—
Annual Growth	5.6%	(37.8%)	—	—

2019 Year-End Financials
Return on assets: 0.2%   Cash ($ mil.): 17,528
Return on equity: 1.0%
Current ratio: —

STATE OF WEST VIRGINIA

EXECUTIVES

Governor, Jim Justice
State Auditor*, Glen Gainer III
Chief of Staff*, Chris Stadelman
Chief of Staff*, Nick Casey
Member, L W Linger
Assistant Treasurer, Josh Stowers
Director Participant Accountin, Diane Holcomb
Supreme Court of Judge, John Hutchison
Debt Manager, Bryan Archer
Web Designer, Jeff Takarsh
Executive Director, Randall Kirk
Auditors: ERNST & YOUNG LLP CHARLESTON

LOCATIONS

HQ: STATE OF WEST VIRGINIA
1900 KANAWHA BLVD E, CHARLESTON, WV
253050009
Phone: 304 558-2000
Web: WWW.WV.GOV

HISTORICAL FINANCIALS

Company Type: Private

Income Statement				FYE: June 30
	REVENUE ($ mil.)	NET INCOME ($ mil.)	NET PROFIT MARGIN	EMPLOYEES
06/19	12,469	649	5.2%	19,357
06/17	11,650	(2)	—	—
06/16	11,147	(231)	—	—
06/15	11,175	(159)	—	—
Annual Growth	2.8%	—	—	—

2019 Year-End Financials
Return on assets: 2.2%   Cash ($ mil.): 6,813
Return on equity: 5.0%
Current ratio: 3.20

STATE OF WISCONSIN

EXECUTIVES

Governor, Tony Evers
Lt. Governor*, Mandela Barnes
Coordinator, Lisa Jorgensen
Project Coordinator, Cynthia Moore
Office Press Secretary, Amy Hasenberg
Deputy Chief of Staff, Jack Jablonski
Chief of Staff, Eric Schutt
Specialist, Erika Ryerson
Civil Engineering Supervisor, David Castleberg
Revenue Section Chief, Dawn Wenzel
Accountant, Doug Meek
Auditors: JOE CHRISMAN MADISON WI

LOCATIONS

HQ: STATE OF WISCONSIN
115 E CAPITOL, MADISON, WI 537020021
Phone: 608 266-1212
Web: WWW.WISCONSIN.GOV

HISTORICAL FINANCIALS

Company Type: Private

Income Statement				FYE: June 30
	REVENUE ($ mil.)	NET INCOME ($ mil.)	NET PROFIT MARGIN	EMPLOYEES
06/20	33,421	627	1.9%	35,522
06/19	31,683	693	2.2%	—
06/17	28,874	474	1.6%	—
06/16	28,533	357	1.3%	—
Annual Growth	4.0%	15.1%	—	—

2020 Year-End Financials
Return on assets: 0.9%   Cash ($ mil.): 13,438
Return on equity: 1.8%
Current ratio: —

STATE UNIVERSITY OF NEW YORK

SUNY days are ahead for many New Yorkers seeking higher education. With an enrollment of more than 460000 students The State University of New York (SUNY) is vying with California State University System for the title of largest university system in the US. Most students are residents of New York State. Students come from all 50 states as well as 160 countries. SUNY maintains 64 campuses around the state including four university centers about two dozen university colleges 30 community colleges and a handful of technical colleges as well as medical centers. The system has a student-teacher ratio of about 16:1.

Operations

The school offers more than 7500 undergraduate programs of study — including engineering business literature medicine agriculture performing arts and human services. SUNY also offers about 400 study abroad programs.

HISTORY

The State University of New York was organized in 1948 but it traces its roots back to several institutions founded in the 19th century. In 1844 the New York state legislature authorized the creation of the Albany Normal School which was charged with educating the state's secondary school teachers. Two years later the University of Buffalo was chartered to provide academic theological legal and medical studies. More normal schools later were founded between 1861 and 1889 in Brockport Buffalo Cortland Fredonia Geneseo New Paltz Oneonta Oswego Plattsburgh and Potsdam.

In the early 1900s the state established several agricultural colleges including schools in Canton (1907) Alfred (1908) Morrisville (1910) Farmingdale (1912) and Cobleskill (1916). New York also set up several schools as units of Cornell University including colleges of veterinary medicine (1894) agriculture (1909) home economics (1925) and industrial and labor relations (1945).

After WWII veterans began to fill US colleges and universities taking advantage of the GI Bill to secure a college education. The legislature set up SUNY in 1948 to consolidate 29 institutions under a single board of trustees charged with meeting the growing demand. The board coordinated the state colleges into a single body and established four-year liberal arts colleges professional and graduate schools and research centers. During the

1950s and 1960s new campuses were created at Binghamton Stony Brook Old Westbury Purchase and Utica/Rome and enrollment began to take off jumping from 30000 in 1955 to 63000 in 1959.

By the early 1970s SUNY had more than 320000 students at 72 institutions. But budget constraints later that decade led to higher tuition reduced enrollment goals and employment cutbacks. In 1975 eight New York City community colleges were transferred to City University. SUNY's enrollment began growing again during the 1980s reaching more than 400000 by 1990. Early in the decade the institution began implementing SUNY 2000 a plan that called for increasing access to education and diversifying undergraduate studies. Following his election in 1994 Governor George Pataki proposed more than $550 million in cuts to the SUNY system.

In 1997 John Ryan replaced Thomas Bartlett as chancellor. The following year SUNY became the exclusive sponsor of The College Channel a guide to colleges and college life aimed at high school juniors and seniors and broadcast by PRIMEDIA's Channel One. In 1999 the governor's budget director Robert King was named chancellor to replace the retiring Bartlett. King challenged SUNY administrators and the state to increase levels of funding to help keep the university competitive against other top-flight institutions. In 2000 SUNY faced rising budget shortfalls at its teaching hospitals in part because money was being siphoned off to other areas. That year King announced a set of initiatives to raise an additional $1.5 billion in federal research grants and $1 billion in private donations over five years.

King retired as the university's chancellor in June 2005. Nancy Zimpher became the university's first female chancellor in 2009. The university had been without a permanent leader since 2007 when John Ryan resigned.

EXECUTIVES

Pres, Havidan Rodriguez
Chb, Merryl H Tisch
Int Pres, Dennis Craig
Acting Pres, James Stellar
Prin, John B King Jr
Interim Chancellor, John B Clark
Cfo - V Chancellor, Kimberly R Cline
Provost - V Chancellor - Acade, Peter D Salins
V Chancellor - SEC of The Univ, John O'Connor
V Chancellor - Finance & Busin, Brian Stenson
V Chancellor - Business & Indu, R Wayne Diesel
Auditors: KPMG LLP ALBANY NY

LOCATIONS

HQ: STATE UNIVERSITY OF NEW YORK
353 BROADWAY, ALBANY, NY 122462915
Phone: 518 320-1100
Web: WWW.SUNY.EDU

HISTORICAL FINANCIALS

Company Type: Private

Income Statement				FYE: June 30
	REVENUE ($ mil.)	NET INCOME ($ mil.)	NET PROFIT MARGIN	EMPLOYEES
06/12	5,961	(374)	—	88,024
06/06*	4	(2)	—	—
10/05	0	0	—	—
Annual Growth	—	—	—	—

*Fiscal year change

2012 Year-End Financials

Return on assets: (-2.5%)   Cash ($ mil.): 1,642
Return on equity: —
Current ratio: 1.50

STATEN ISLAND UNIVERSITY HOSPITAL

Staten Island University Hospital (SIUH) ferries health care services to residents of New York City's fastest growing borough and surrounding areas at its two medical campuses. Established in 1861 SIUH maintains about 715 beds and is a teaching affiliate of the State University of New York's Brooklyn Health Science Center. Its larger north campus includes units specializing in cardiology pathology cancer blood-related diseases burn treatment trauma and women's health. The south campus site offers specialty programs such as sleep medicine geriatric psychiatry and substance abuse services. A member of Northwell Health SIUH employs approximately 1200 physicians.

Operations

SIUH's Heart Institute of Staten Island located on the north campus is a joint venture between the hospital and Richmond University Medical Center. The Heart Institute specializes in cardiac diagnostics and "beating heart" surgeries.

The hospital operates several general physician practice and specialty health clinics on Staten Island. It also provides a home visit program and hospital-based hospice services.

SIUH is an affiliate of the SUNY Health Science Center at Brooklyn; its campuses serve as clinics for the Hofstra North Shore-LIJ School of Medicine which SIUH owns in partnership with Hofstra University.

In 2013 SIUH had nearly 3000 births nearly 45000 hospital discharges about 126000 emergency department visits and more than 16000 ambulatory surgeries.

EXECUTIVES

Pres, Anthony C Ferreri
Exec V Pres*, Robin Wittenstein
V Pres-Fin-Controller*, John Steiger
Cfo*, Thomas Reca
Exec V Pres*, Nicholas Caruselle
Sr V Pres*, Margaret Dialto
V Pres*, John P Demoleas
SEC*, Arthur Fried
Exec Dir*, Donna Proske
Staff, Vincent Logatto
Sr Hr Rep, Jenie Grodowski

LOCATIONS

HQ: STATEN ISLAND UNIVERSITY HOSPITAL
475 SEAVIEW AVE, STATEN ISLAND, NY 103053436
Phone: 718 226-9000
Web: WWW.SIUH.NORTHWELL.EDU

PRODUCTS/OPERATIONS

Selected Services

Behavioral Health
Cancer Services
Cardiac Services
Cardiovascular and Thoracic Surgery
Medical Services including Endocrinology Gastroenterology Nephrology and Pulmonary
Neuroscience and Spine Services
Orthopedic Services
Pediatrics
Rehabilitation Medicine
Surgical Services including General Surgery Colorectal Head & Neck and Urology
Trauma and Burn Services
Women's Health

Selected Centers of Care

Center for Bariatric Surgery
Comprehensive Breast Center

Heart Institute
Institute of Sleep Medicine
Level III Perinatal Center
New York Head & Neck Institute at Staten Island University Hospital
Regional Burn Center
Stroke Center
The Elizabeth A. Connelly Emergency and Trauma Center
The Sanford R. Nalitt Institute for Cancer and Blood Related Diseases; Children's Cancer Center

COMPETITORS

Bronx-lebanon Hospital
Catholic Healthcare System
Centerlight Health System Inc.
Continuum Health Partners
Eger Health Care
Kingsbrook Jewish Medical Center

Maimonides Medical Center
Medisys Health Network
New York City Health And Hospitals
Newyork-presbyterian Healthcare

HISTORICAL FINANCIALS

Company Type: Private

Income Statement				FYE: December 31
	REVENUE ($ mil.)	NET INCOME ($ mil.)	NET PROFIT MARGIN	EMPLOYEES
12/18	934	(33)	—	5,700
12/17	891	69	7.8%	—
12/16	871	57	6.6%	—
12/15	850	41	4.9%	—
Annual Growth	3.2%	—	—	—

2018 Year-End Financials

Return on assets: (-3.1%)   Cash ($ mil.): 34
Return on equity: (-6.7%)
Current ratio: 3.50

STEPHEN GOULD CORPORATION

Others can worry about what's inside — Stephen Gould Corporation concentrates on the package. The company provides a full range of packaging-related design and printing services for customers worldwide. Its products include gift packaging point-of-purchase displays product merchandising and retail and industrial packaging. Stephen Gould Corporation also provides graphic design and package-engineering services as well as assembly and fulfillment. The company was originally founded in 1939 by Stephen Gould David Golden and Leonard Beckerman.

Geographic Reach

Stephen Gould Corporation operates from about 40 facilities; branches are located primarily in the US (more than 20 states) but also in China Ireland Malaysia and Mexico.

EXECUTIVES

Ceo, Michael Golden
Exec V-Pres*, John Golden
Pres*, Justin Golden
Cfo*, Anthony Lupo
Vice-President, Peter V Slyke
Internal Medicine Practitioner, Ethan Bliss
Director, Oleh Holynskyj
Director, Nanette Rosenbaum

Sales Manager, Tom Klosinski
Designer Project MA, Andrew Reddy
Account Coordinator, Gabriela Rodriguez

LOCATIONS

HQ: STEPHEN GOULD CORPORATION
35 S JEFFERSON RD, WHIPPANY, NJ 079811043
Phone: 973 428-1500
Web: WWW.STEPHENGOULD.COM

PRODUCTS/OPERATIONS

Selected Products and Services

Products
Aerospace reusable cases
Corrugated containers
Gift packaging
Industrial packaging
Point of sale packaging
Protective packaging
Services
Creative services
Logistics & facilities
Package design & engineering

COMPETITORS

Consolidated
Carqueville
Focus Packaging &
Display Group
Fort Dearborn

Metro Packaging And
Imaging
R.r. Donnelley
Ws Packaging Group

HISTORICAL FINANCIALS

Company Type: Private

Income Statement   FYE: December 31

	REVENUE ($ mil.)	NET INCOME ($ mil.)	NET PROFIT MARGIN	EMPLOYEES
12/20	782	11	1.4%	800
12/19	757	5	0.8%	—
12/16	665	11	1.8%	—
12/13	526	3	0.7%	—
Annual Growth	5.8%	16.0%	—	—

2020 Year-End Financials

Return on assets: 3.3%   Cash ($ mil.): 8
Return on equity: 12.7%
Current ratio: 2.00

STEVENS TRANSPORT, INC.

Staying cool is a must for Stevens Transport. An irregular-route refrigerated truckload carrier (or reefer) Stevens hauls temperature-controlled cargo throughout the US covering the 48 contiguous states. Through alliances Stevens also covers every province in Canada and every state in Mexico. The company operates a fleet of about 2000 Kenworth and Peterbuilt tractors and 3500 Thermo King refrigerated trailers from a network of more than a dozen service centers. Partnerships with railroads allow Stevens to arrange intermodal transport of temperature-controlled cargo. The company also provides third-party logistics services. Stevens Transport was founded in 1980.

Operations
The company owns 49% of B2B Transport which provides an array of transportation related services to large mid-sized and small companies throughout North America.

Geographic Reach
Stevens Transport maintains its operations across Canada Mexico and the US through its partnerships with BNSF Norfolk Southern CSX and Union Pacific. It has 13 logistics offices located in Canada and throughout the US.

Sales and Marketing
Stevens has provided refrigerated shipping services for such big names as General Mills Kraft Foods M&M Mars Procter & Gamble and Wal-Mart.

Strategy
Even in a US economy ripe with unpredictable fuel costs and a decline in consumer confidence one thing has always worked in Stevens' favor: people will always need their food. The company has managed to maintain a steady growth rate by keeping costs down updating the technology of its trucking equipment and maintaining an efficient operating structure. Along these lines in 2012 it implemented new mobile computing platforms across its fleet of tractors to enhance its customer services and optimize productivity.

EXECUTIVES

Chm, Steven L Aaron
Pres, Clay Aaron
V Pres, Bob H Nelson
Sr V Pres, Todd Aaron
Exec V Pres, Mike Ritchey
Vpres, Robert Solimani
Customer Representativ, Chaundray Glover
Recruiter, Jim Potter
Vice President Risk Management, William Tallent
Accounting Staff, Amanda Kennedy
Director of Mexico Operations, Alberto Ortega
Auditors: SADDOCK & CO PLLC DALLAS T

LOCATIONS

HQ: STEVENS TRANSPORT, INC.
9757 MILITARY PKWY, DALLAS, TX 752274805
Phone: 972 216-9000
Web: WWW.STEVENSTRANSPORT.COM

PRODUCTS/OPERATIONS

Selected Services

Intermodal

International

Logistics

Truckload

COMPETITORS

C.r. England
Central Refrigerated
Service
Comcar
Covenant
Transportation
Frozen Food Express
Henderson Trucking
Jim Palmer Trucking
Kllm Transport
Services

Marten Transport
Navajo Shippers
Prime Inc.
Southern Refrigerated
Transport
Transam Trucking
Watkins Associated
Industries
Willis Shaw Express

HISTORICAL FINANCIALS

Company Type: Private

Income Statement   FYE: December 31

	REVENUE ($ mil.)	NET INCOME ($ mil.)	NET PROFIT MARGIN	EMPLOYEES
12/15	668	87	13.0%	2,100
12/12	607	85	14.0%	—
12/11	566	76	13.5%	—
12/08	550	0	0.0%	—
Annual Growth	2.8%	505.7%	—	—

2015 Year-End Financials

Return on assets: 13.0%   Cash ($ mil.): 152
Return on equity: 16.3%
Current ratio: 4.60

STEWARD HEALTH CARE SYSTEM LLC

Steward Health Care System is the largest private tax-paying hospital operator in the country. With a total of more than 7900 beds Steward Health operates about 40 hospitals in nine states and the country of Malta including Holy Family Hospital Norwood Hospital St. Elizabeth's Medical Center St. Joseph's Medical Center and Jordan Valley Medical Center. Several of the hospitals are affiliated with Boston-area medical schools. The company also has managed operations in Arizona Utah and Massachusetts. Steward Health serves its patients through a closely integrated network of hospitals multispecialty medical groups urgent care centers skilled nursing facilities and behavioral health centers.

Operations
Steward Health is a community-based care organization that offers a full range of health care services. Its operations include integrated network physicians about 35 hospital campuses more than 25 affiliated urgent care providers more than 105preferred skilled nursing facilities and other services.

The system's network includes Steward Health Care Network Steward Medical Group Steward Urgent Care and Steward Insurance Plans.

With more than 12 million patient encounters per year Steward Health Care Network is comprised of physicians who provide care for approximately 2.2 million patients annually. Steward Medical Group provides more than 6 million patient encounters per year. Steward Urgent Care network includes multiple affiliated and owned urgent care centers. The network includes affiliations with Doctors Express Prima CARE Compass Medical Hawthorn Medical Health Express All Care Medical and others. The system also partners with Steward Health Choice which covers approximately 680000 lives in three states.

Geographic Reach
Headquartered in Dallas Steward Health currently operates nearly 40 hospitals across Arizona Arkansas Florida Louisiana Massachusetts Ohio Pennsylvania Texas and Utah.

Sales and Marketing
Serving over 800 communities Steward Health has more than 43000 health care professionals who care for more than 12 million patients annually.

Company Background
The company changed its name from Caritas Christi to Steward Health after being acquired by Cerberus Capital Management in 2010; it had previously been operated by the Catholic Archdiocese of Boston. The acquisition by Cerberus was worth some $895 million and provided operational funding and capital for hospital improvement projects; it also helped pay down debt obligations. As a result of the transaction Steward Health became a for-profit corporation; however a stipulation of the deal mandated that the health system's hospitals retain their pastoral and charitable care policies. The sale to Cerberus was not the first attempt by the Archdiocese of Boston to sell the ailing Caritas

Christi system which had been suffering from financial troubles for several years prior to the deal.

EXECUTIVES

MBR, Ralph De La Torre
MBR*, Robert Guyon
MBR*, Mark Girard
Coordinator, Jeanne Lewis
Rep, Yannette Alvarez
Regional Pres, Brian Dunn
Evp and General Counsel, Joseph Maher Jr
Pres Reg East Division, Trip Pilgrim
or Nurse Manager, Connie Brennan
National Director, Brad Hardy
Registered Dietitian, Alysha Gebo

LOCATIONS

HQ: STEWARD HEALTH CARE SYSTEM LLC
1900 N PEARL ST STE 2400, DALLAS, TX 752012470
Phone: 469 341-8800
Web: WWW.STEWARD.ORG

Services

Behavioral Health Services
Centers for Cancer Care
Center for Advanced Cardiac Surgery
Centers for Cardiac and Vascular Care
Centers for Weight Control
Home Care and Hospice
MAKOplasty®: Services
Maternity Services

Selected Hospitals

Arizona
Mountain Vista Medical Center (Mesa)
St. Luke's Medical Center (Phoenix)
Tempe St. Luke's Hospital
Arkansas
Wadley Regional Medical Center at Hope
Colorado
Pikes Peak Regional Hospital & Surgery Center (Woodland Park)
Florida
Rockledge Regional Medical Center
Sebastian River Medical Center
Louisiana
Glenwood Regional Medical Center (West Monroe)
Massachusetts
Carney Hospital (Dorchester)
Good Samaritan Medical Center (Brockton)
Holy Family Hospital (Methuen)
Morton Hospital (Taunton)
Nashoba Valley Medical Center (Ayer)
New England Sinai Hospital (Stoughton)
Norwood Hospital
Quincy Community Care Network
Saint Anne's Hospital (Fall River)
St. Elizabeth's Medical Center (Brighton)
Ohio
Northside Regional Medical Center (Youngstown)
Trumbull Regional Medical Center (Warren)
Pennsylvania
Easton Hospital
Sharon Regional Medical Center
Texas
Southwest General Hospital (San Antonio)
The Medical Center of Southeast Texas (Port Arthur)
The Medical Center of Southeast Texas — Victory Campus (Beaumont)
Utah
Davis Hospital and Medical Center (Layton)
Jordan Valley Medical Center (West Jordan)
Mountain Point Medical Center (Lehi)

COMPETITORS

Adventist Health System Sunbelt Healthcare
Berkshire Health Systems
Boston Medical Center
Cambridge Health Alliance
Cape Cod Healthcare
Care New England
Caregroup
Children's Hospital Boston
Emerson Hospital
Hallmark Health
John C. Lincoln Health Network

New England Alliance For Health
Northeast Health System
Partners Healthcare
Southcoast Hospitals Group
University Of Utah Hospitals & Clinics
Winchester Healthcare

HISTORICAL FINANCIALS
Company Type: Private

Income Statement | | | | FYE: September 30

	REVENUE ($ mil.)	NET INCOME ($ mil.)	NET PROFIT MARGIN	EMPLOYEES
09/07	1,240	30	2.5%	37,000
09/06	1,220	47	3.9%	—
09/05	27	2	8.0%	—
Annual Growth	572.6%	272.9%	—	—

2007 Year-End Financials

Return on assets: 3.6%   Cash ($ mil.): 73
Return on equity: 10.8%
Current ratio: 1.10

STEWART'S SHOPS CORP.

I scream you scream we all scream for Stewart's ice cream — especially if we live in upstate New York or Vermont home to some 330 Stewart's Shops. The chain of convenience stores sells more than 3000 products across 30-plus counties. They include dairy items groceries food to go (soup sandwiches hot entrees) beer coffee gasoline and of course ice cream. In addition to its retail business the company owns about 100 rental properties including banks hair salons and apartments near its stores. Stewart's Shops formerly known as Stewart's Ice Cream Company was established in 1945. The founding Dake family owns about two-thirds of the company; employee compensation plans own the rest.

Operations
The convenience store chain which spans New York and Vermont offers consumers milk ice creams coffee to-go foods beer gasoline and groceries. As part of its business Stewart's Shops also acquires and develops (preferably adjacent) properties the likes of shops banks hair salons and apartments that it then leases or sells.

Stewart's Shops makes its own dairy products including its own ice cream in more than 50 flavors that are hand-dipped and packaged. Recognized for its quality products the company relies on a group of about 45 farmers in New York to supply its milk.

The vertically-integrated company which makes about 75% of the items it sells also offers private-label goods and national brands in its stores. Its private-label brands extend far beyond dairy products to include soda chips bread and juices.

Geographic Reach
Based in New York Stewart's Shops operates a chain of convenience stores across upstate New York and in Vermont.

Sales and Marketing
Stewart's Shops serves consumers through its New York and Vermont shops; two-thirds of its stores sell gas.

Strategy
The convenience store operator regularly extends its reach. In 2014 it's focused on Syracuse New York following several store openings in 2013

in Keeseville Herkimer Rotterdam and Heuvelton New York. The latter shops boast an expanded cooler walk-in beer cave and seating.

The company is also investing in environmentally friendly facilities. In 2013 for instance it had 2400 solar panels installed at its manufacturing and distribution center. Stewart's Shops anticipates that the effort will save nearly $40000 a year in energy costs at the plant after about a 5-year period.

It enlisted the help of Paragon Software in 2014 to automate the planning of daily and seasonal deliveries. In turn Stewart's Shops aims to lower mileage reduce fuel usage and improve truckload efficiencies.

EXECUTIVES

Pres, Gary C Dake
Chm*, William P Dake
V Pres*, Nancy Trimbur
Asst Treas*, David Farr
Treas*, Michael Cocca
SEC*, Matthew Gutch
Distribution/Shipping/Transpor, Chris Burby
Project Coordinator, Mike Cannizzo
Human Resources Compliance and, Shannon Potter
Gasoline Marketing Manager, Rhonda Bouchard
Human Resources Generalist, Jacqueline Merritt
Auditors: BST & CO CPAS LLP ALBANY

LOCATIONS

HQ: STEWART'S SHOPS CORP.
2907 STATE ROUTE 9, BALLSTON SPA, NY 120204201
Phone: 518 581-1201
Web: WWW.STEWARTSSHOPS.COM

PRODUCTS/OPERATIONS

Selected Products

Beverages

Coffee
Ice Cream
Food to go
Gasoline
Groceries
Milk

COMPETITORS

7-eleven	Hannaford Bros.
Ben & Jerry's	Kroger
Carvel	Mcdonald's
Cumberland Farms	Sunoco
Exxon Mobil	Travelcenters Of
Friendly's Ice Cream	America
Golub	

HISTORICAL FINANCIALS
Company Type: Private

Income Statement | | | | FYE: January 3

	REVENUE ($ mil.)	NET INCOME ($ mil.)	NET PROFIT MARGIN	EMPLOYEES
01/21*	1,667	166	10.0%	3,800
12/19	1,699	124	7.3%	—
12/17	1,542	92	6.0%	—
12/16	1,405	80	5.7%	—
Annual Growth	4.4%	20.1%	—	—

*Fiscal year change

2021 Year-End Financials

Return on assets: 19.4%   Cash ($ mil.): 94
Return on equity: 24.9%
Current ratio: 3.30

STILLWATER MINING COMPANY

Stillwater Mining has staked a claim to one of the few significant sources of platinum and palladium outside South Africa and Russia. The company extracts processes and refines platinum group metals (PGMs) — platinum palladium and associated minerals — at mines and a smelter in Montana. PGMs are used in catalytic converters for automobiles as well as in jewelry and other applications. Stillwater Mining also owns exploratory properties of PGM and copper in Canada and copper and gold in Argentina. It produces about 404000 ounces of palladium and 120000 ounces of platinum annually. By-products include copper gold nickel and silver. In 2016 Sibanye Gold bid $2.2 billion to buy the company.

Operations

Stillwater produces palladium platinum and associated metals (PGMs) through two segments: PGM Recycling (54% of sales) and Mine Production (46%).

The company operates the Stillwater and East boulder mines in Montana as well as concentrating plants at both sites to upgrade ore to a concentrate. In addition it operates a smelter refinery and laboratory in Columbus Montana to refine the concentrate to a PGM-rich filter cake. It also recycles spent catalyst material at the smelter and refinery to recover PGMs.

In addition to its producing mines Stillwater holds the Blitz and Graham Creek development projects in Montana. It also owns a PGM-copper deposit in Ontario Canada which is in the permitting process as well as the Altar porphyry copper-gold deposit in Argentina.

Financial Performance

Increased metal prices worldwide boosted Stillwater's revenues to $1.04 billion in 2013 up 30% from the previous year. Stillwater's PGM Recycling segment revenue increased due to a spike in recycling ounces sold and an increase in combined average realization on recycling sales.

However after posting net income of $55 million in 2012 Stillwater suffered a net loss of $270 million in 2013. This was due to a large impairment charge of $461 million it paid in 2013 related to properties in Argentina and Marathon (in Ontario Canada). Stillwater saw an increase of $46 million in operating cash flow from 2012 to 2013 due to higher prices for its products.

EXECUTIVES

Pres-Ceo, Michael J McMullen
Cfo*, Christopher M Bateman
V Pres Safety Health & Hr*, Kristen K Koss
V Pres Mine Oprs*, Dee L Bray
Accounting Team Member, Luttschwager Yvonne
Senior Site Accountant, Joyce Weber
Financial Planning, Ashlee Mendive
Executive Vpres, Richard Stewart
Information Technology Manager, Cheryl Kennedy
Parks Director, Christy Waters
Processing Coordinator, Mike Gaustad
Auditors: KPMG LLP BILLINGS MONTANA

LOCATIONS

HQ: STILLWATER MINING COMPANY
536 E PIKE AVE, COLUMBUS, MT 590197616
Phone: 406 373-8700
Web: WWW.STILLWATERCOUNTYNEWS.COM

PRODUCTS/OPERATIONS

2016 Sales

	$ mil.	% of total
Mine production	405	57
PGM recycling	305	43
All others	0	
Total	**711**	**100**

2016 Sales

	$ mil.	% of total
Palladium	410	58
Platinum	247	35
Rhodium	21	3
Other minerals	32	4
Total	**711**	**100**

HISTORICAL FINANCIALS
Company Type: Private

Income Statement   FYE: December 31

	REVENUE ($ mil.)	NET INCOME ($ mil.)	NET PROFIT MARGIN	EMPLOYEES
12/16	711	9	1.3%	1,432
12/15	726	(23)	—	—
12/14	943	68	7.3%	—
12/13	1,039	(302)	—	—
Annual Growth	(11.9%)	—	—	—

2016 Year-End Financials
Return on assets: 0.7%
Return on equity: 1.0%
Current ratio: 7.00
Cash ($ mil.): 123

STOCKTON UNIFIED SCHOOL DISTRICT

EXECUTIVES

Supt, Dr Steve Lowder
Pres*, Sara L Cazares
Vice Pres*, Gloria Allen
Research/Development Director, Mong Thi Nguyen
Kindergarten Teacher, Tracey Gray
Program Technician, Cathy Holman
Communications and Marketing, Dianne Barth
Buildings, Chris Benson
Director Labor Relations, Claudia Moreno-Robago
Buildings, Leonard Whitlock
World Language Instructor, Margaret Salazar
Auditors: CROWE LLP SACRAMENTO CALIFOR

LOCATIONS

HQ: STOCKTON UNIFIED SCHOOL DISTRICT
701 N MADISON ST, STOCKTON, CA 952021634
Phone: 209 933-7000
Web: WWW.STOCKTONUSD.NET

HISTORICAL FINANCIALS
Company Type: Private

Income Statement   FYE: June 30

	REVENUE ($ mil.)	NET INCOME ($ mil.)	NET PROFIT MARGIN	EMPLOYEES
06/20	618	(22)	—	3,000
06/19	602	8	1.3%	—
06/18	536	(24)	—	—
06/17	557	36	6.6%	—
Annual Growth	3.5%	—	—	—

STORMONT-VAIL HEALTHCARE, INC.

EXECUTIVES

Ceo, Randall Peterson
Ceo*, Randy Peterson
Vice Pres*, Tracy O'Rourke
Sr V Pres-Medi Dir, Kent Palmberg
V Pres-Medi Svc Div*, Deb Yocum
V Pres-Chf Info Offc*, Janet Stanek
V Pres-Patient Care Svcs*, Carol Perry
V Pres-Fclty Mgmt*, David Cuningham
V Pres-Hr*, Bernard Becker
Cfo*, Kevin Han
Svp-Gen Counsel-Chief Complian*, Kevin Steck
Auditors: RSM US LLP DAVENPORT IOWA

LOCATIONS

HQ: STORMONT-VAIL HEALTHCARE, INC.
1500 SW 10TH AVE, TOPEKA, KS 666041301
Phone: 785 354-6000
Web: WWW.STORMONTVAIL.ORG

HISTORICAL FINANCIALS
Company Type: Private

Income Statement   FYE: September 30

	REVENUE ($ mil.)	NET INCOME ($ mil.)	NET PROFIT MARGIN	EMPLOYEES
09/20	784	56	7.2%	4,500
09/19	768	34	4.4%	—
09/18	719	88	12.4%	—
09/17	654	70	10.8%	—
Annual Growth	6.2%	(7.2%)	—	—

2020 Year-End Financials
Return on assets: 5.4%
Return on equity: 10.2%
Current ratio: 1.80
Cash ($ mil.): 241

STRACK AND VAN TIL SUPER MARKET INC.

One of Chicagoland's leading grocery chains Strack & Van Til operates more than 35 supermarkets in and around Chicago and northern Indiana. Stores operate under the banners of Strack & Van Til Town & Country Food Market and Ultra Foods. The regional grocery chain offers fresh and packaged foods and has delicatessen and bakery divisions in each of its stores. Its websites offer weekly circulars and coupons as well as feature recipes cooking videos meal planners and food-related articles. The company is owned by Chicago-based grocery distributor Central Grocers which also operates supermarkets under the Berkot's and Key Market banners.In 2017 Central Grocers filed for Chapter 11 bankruptcy protection and put Strack & Van Til up for sale as part of the filing.

Strategy

Strack & Van Til and its regional rivals are facing increased competition from national chains including Wal-Mart and Trader Joe's moving into the market while taking advantage of the woes of smaller ones. Rather than retreat the grocery chain is pursuing a growth strategy acquiring seven stores in its market area in late 2012. (With Safeway-owned Dominick's Supermarkets on the block its stores are in play.) It is also investing in its existing stores and stocking more organic foods to compete with the likes of Whole Foods. The company is revamping supermarkets in Valpariso Hobart and Chesterton was well as an Ultra Foods store in Highland Strack's supermarkets in Munster and Schereville and an Ultra in Lansing are slated for upgrades as well.

Wal-Mart which had been expanding aggressively in the Chicago suburbs has begun opening supercenters and smaller Walmart Express stores within the city limits. Its arrival has sparked fierce price competition among area grocers. Other relative newcomers to the Illinois grocery market include Roundy's and non-traditional grocery chains such as SuperTarget stores and limited-assortment ALDI. To take on nationwide retailers Strack & Van Til bands together with other independent stores as members of the Central Grocers cooperative. The combined buying power helps the stores to offer competitive pricing and product selection.

In late 2013 the grocery chain launched a new marketing campaign I'm a Strack & Van Til Shopper to appeal to a wide audience while maintaining the company's value proposition.

Mergers and Acquisitions

In December 2012 Strack & Van Til acquired seven grocery stores from Indiana-based WiseWay Supermarkets. Four of the stores were converted to the Strack & Van Til banner while three became Ultra Foods stores. Like Strack & Van Til WiseWay was also supplied by Central Grocers.

EXECUTIVES

Pres, David Wilkinson
V Pres*, Andrew Raab
V Pres*, Jeff Strack
Cfo*, Keith Bruxvoort
V Pres*, Robert Wasiuta
V Pres*, Rex Mudge
V Pres*, Joe Kolavo
SEC*, Jim Denges
Vice President Operations, Andy Raab
Vice President Operations, Jeffrey Strack
Operations Staff, Lawrence Moore
Auditors: MCGLADREY & PULLEN LLP CHICAG

LOCATIONS

HQ: STRACK AND VAN TIL SUPER MARKET INC.
2244 45TH ST, HIGHLAND, IN 463222629
Phone: 219 924-7588
Web: WWW.STRACKANDVANTIL.COM

COMPETITORS

Aldi	Target Corporation
Jewel Osco	Trader Joe's
Kmart	Wal-mart
Meijer	Whole Foods
Roundy's	

HISTORICAL FINANCIALS
Company Type: Private

Income Statement				FYE: August 1
	REVENUE ($ mil.)	NET INCOME ($ mil.)	NET PROFIT MARGIN	EMPLOYEES
08/10	961	15	1.7%	2,000
08/09	995	13	1.4%	—
Annual Growth	(3.4%)	16.1%	—	—

2010 Year-End Financials
Return on assets: 7.7%   Cash ($ mil.): 10
Return on equity: 12.9%
Current ratio: 1.40

SUASIN CANCER CARE INC.

Auditors: ERNST & YOUNG US LLP SAN DIEG

LOCATIONS

HQ: SUASIN CANCER CARE INC.
1301 PUNCHBOWL ST, HONOLULU, HI 968132402
Phone: 512 583-0205

HISTORICAL FINANCIALS
Company Type: Private

Income Statement				FYE: June 30
	REVENUE ($ mil.)	NET INCOME ($ mil.)	NET PROFIT MARGIN	EMPLOYEES
06/15	1,003	50	5.0%	4
06/14	851	31	3.7%	—
06/13	856	109	12.8%	—
Annual Growth	8.2%	(32.4%)	—	—

2015 Year-End Financials
Return on assets: 3.4%   Cash ($ mil.): 29
Return on equity: 7.9%
Current ratio: 0.30

SUFFOLK CONSTRUCTION COMPANY, INC.

Suffolk Construction Company provides construction services from top to bottom. The company kicks off the building process with pre-construction services and follows through with design/build and construction management. Suffolk Construction builds for both the public and private organizations in the science and technology health care education government and commercial sectors operating in the Northeast South and West Coast regions of the US. Founded in 1982 the privately-held firm is owned by president and CEO John Fish whose family has been in construction for four generations.

Operations

Suffolk Construction provides value throughout the entire project lifecycle by leveraging its core construction management services with vertical service lines that include real estate capital investment design self-perform construction services technology start-up investment and innovation research/development. Some projects have included 78 Haight housing development in San Francisco a ground-up construction of Agua Caliente Casino Resort & Spa luxury boutique hotel Alila Marea Beach Resort and the construction of construction of two modern hotel Aloft and Element Hotels on D Street.

Geographic Reach

The Boston-based construction firm operates nationwide across the Northeast South and West Coast regions. Its offices are located Oakland and San Jose California; Texas; Boston; Miami; Los Angeles; San Diego; San Francisco; New York; West Palm Beach and Estero Florida.

Sales and Marketing

Suffolk Construction offers its services for projects in the assisted living aviation and transportation commercial education entertainment government healthcare hospitality non-profit residential retail and science and technology sectors.

The company has also worked on projects for federal and local governments. In the past Suffolk has built for the Army Corps of Engineers the US Marine Corps and US Navy.

Strategy

Suffolk made a diversification and rebranding effort to expand services beyond construction into startup funding and academic research and development.

The diversification strategy focused on leveraging its core competency of construction and expanding into additional service lines to create a fully integrated platform.

As part of its new strategy Suffolk plans to build "The Garage" an incubator with up to 30000 sq. ft. for academic partnerships startups co-working spaces and industry-related research and experimentation adjacent to the firm's Boston headquarters. The firm says this will allow for in-house product development and industry problem solving.

Company Background

Already a successful builder in the New England area Suffolk Construction has expanded nationally in the past through acquisitions. In 2009 it bought Massachusetts-based William A. Berry & Son creating Suffolk's Berry Division which specializes in health care and biomedical projects.

Suffolk Construction also acquired The Dietze Construction Group based in Ashburn Virginia in 2010. The deal strengthened Suffolk's position in the Mid-Atlantic region and expanded its ability to serve the government health care education science/technology and commercial sectors. Giving the company a boost in the West Suffolk Construction acquired Southern California-based ROEL Construction in 2011.

EXECUTIVES

Chm-Ceo, John Fish
Cfo-Exec V Pres*, Michael Azarela
SEC*, John Tangney Jr
Treas*, Mike Lindblom
Cmo*, Lea Stendahl
Cfo*, Puneet Mahajan
Evp*, Ann Klee
President of The West Region, Andrew Ball
Executive Officer, Kevin Koehler
Vp External Affairs, Nick Dhimitri
Bim Vdc Coordinator, Aaron Waddle

LOCATIONS

HQ: SUFFOLK CONSTRUCTION COMPANY, INC.
65 ALLERTON ST, BOSTON, MA 021192923
Phone: 617 445-3500
Web: WWW.SUFFOLK.COM

PRODUCTS/OPERATIONS

Selected Services
Building information modeling
Construction management
Design/build
General contracting
Preconstruction
Sustainable building

COMPETITORS

Balfour Beatty Construction	Pepper Construction
	Swinerton
Clark Enterprises	Turner Corporation
Dooleymack	Tutor Perini
Kraus-anderson	Walsh Group
Mccarthy Building	Whiting-turner

	REVENUE ($ mil.)	NET INCOME ($ mil.)	NET PROFIT MARGIN	EMPLOYEES
				FYE: August 31
08/15	2,500	0	—	2,536
08/14	1,761	0	—	—
08/13	1,825	0	—	—
Annual Growth	17.0%	—	—	—

Income Statement

2015 Year-End Financials

Return on assets: —
Return on equity: —
Current ratio: 1.10

Cash ($ mil.): 126

SUMMA HEALTH

Summa Health is one of the largest integrated healthcare delivery systems in the state. Formed in 1989 with the merger of Akron City and St. Thomas Hospitals this nonprofit system now encompasses a network of hospitals community-based health centers a health plan a multi-specialty group practice an accountable care organization research and medical education and a foundation. Summa serves more than one million patients each year in comprehensive acute critical emergency outpatient and long-term/home care settings. Outpatient care is extended throughout Summit Portage and Medina counties in multiple community health centers.

Operations

Summa Health has more than 1300 licensed beds at at Summa Health System ? Akron Barberton and St. Thomas campuses and Summa Rehab Hospital.

Geographic Reach

Akron-based Summa Health serves customers in five counties in northeastern Ohio.

Financial Performance

Summa reported revenues of about $1.6 billion in 2012. The organization estimates that it makes a $2.8 billion business impact on the Ohio economy as well as a $99 million impact on the state government's revenue.

Strategy

Summa has conducted growth efforts in recent years to expand its presence and service offerings in the region through organic growth efforts and partnership formations. For instance the organization opened a new Summa Rehab Hospital through a partnership with Vibra; the $25 million facility consists of a 70000-sq. ft. freestanding medical building. The Summa network also invested in expanding new emergency care clinics in Green and Medina and it consolidated its home health and hospice organizations to improve profitability.

Also in 2012 Summa formed a joint management services organization with two affiliated physician organizations: Community Health Care and Pioneer Physicians Network. Together the organizations aim to streamline clinical processes.

In 2013 Summa also entered talks to form a partnership with hospital group Catholic Health Partners (CHP). The strategic partnership would give CHP a minority stake in the Summa network. Through the deal Summa hopes to expand its strategic initiatives and strengthen its finances.

Summa invests heavily in the latest technology continually seeking out the latest treatment options for some of today's most serious medical conditions.

Company Background

The company was formed in 1989 through the merger of Akron City Hospital and St. Thomas Hospital.

EXECUTIVES

Pres-Ceo, Cliff Deveny
Coo, Valerie Gibson
Cfo, Brian Derrick
Gen Counsel, Robert Gerberry
Svp-CIO, Tanya Arthur
Obstetrician Gynecologist, Meghan Mehl
Unit Manager, Melissa Sauer
Director, Nikki Hawk
Coordinator, Rebecca Dye
Director, Robert Kroupa
Unit Secretary, Rosie Saunders
Auditors: ERNST & YOUNG US LLP INDIANAP

LOCATIONS

HQ: SUMMA HEALTH
1077 GORGE BLVD, AKRON, OH 443102408
Phone: 330 375-3000
Web: WWW.SUMMAHEALTH.ORG

PRODUCTS/OPERATIONS

2012 Payers

	% of total
Medicare	47
Commercial/Managed care/Other	31
Medicaid	15
Self-pay	7
Total	**100**

Selected Ohio Facilities

Hospitals
Akron City Hospital (Akron)
Barberton Hospital (Barberton)
Cuyahoga Falls General Hospital (aka Western Reserve Hospital Cuyahoga Falls)
Robinson Memorial Hospital (affiliate Ravenna)
St. Thomas Hospital (Akron)
Wadsworth-Rittman Hospital (Wadsworth)
Other facilities
Crystal Clinic Orthopaedic Center (Akron)
Natatorium Rehabilitation and Wellness Center (Cuyahoga Falls)
Summa Health Center at Cuyahoga Falls (Cuyahoga Falls)
Summa Health Center at Green (Uniontown)
Summa Health Center at Lake Medina
Summa Health Center at Western Reserve (Hudson)
Summa Health Center at White Pond/Park West (Akron)
Summa Rehabilitation Services at White Pond (Akron)
Summa Wellness Institute at Western Reserve (Hudson)
Specialty Surgery Center (Akron)

COMPETITORS

Akron Children's Hospital	Parma Community General Hospital
Akron General Health System	Regency Hospital
Aultman Health Foundation	The Cleveland Clinic
Humana Health Plan Of Ohio	Trinity Health System
Lake Health	United Healthcare Of Ohio
Medical Mutual	University Hospitals Health System
Mercy Medical Center (oh)	

HISTORICAL FINANCIALS

Company Type: Private

Income Statement

	REVENUE ($ mil.)	NET INCOME ($ mil.)	NET PROFIT MARGIN	EMPLOYEES
				FYE: December 31
12/20	1,462	(208)	—	7,431
12/09	168	6	3.8%	—
12/08	1,264	(75)	—	—
12/07	940	71	7.6%	—
Annual Growth	3.5%	—	—	—

2020 Year-End Financials

Return on assets: (-9.1%)
Return on equity: (-22.6%)
Current ratio: 1.60

Cash ($ mil.): 171

SUMMIT COUNTY

EXECUTIVES

Prin, Russell M Pry
Exec Director*, Jim McCarthy
Deputy Dir*, Patrick Bravo
Social Worker, Jillian Palowski
Licensed Social Worker, Judie Sturgill
Information Technology Manager, Todd Schauffler
Highway Technician, Lisa King
Training Coordinator, Jodie Hembree
Auditors: DAVE YOST COLUMBUS OHIO

LOCATIONS

HQ: SUMMIT COUNTY
650 DAN ST, AKRON, OH 443103909
Phone: 330 643-2500
Web: WWW.CO.SUMMITOH.NET

HISTORICAL FINANCIALS

Company Type: Private

Income Statement

	REVENUE ($ mil.)	NET INCOME ($ mil.)	NET PROFIT MARGIN	EMPLOYEES
				FYE: December 31
12/20	546	41	7.7%	3,354
12/19	544	126	23.2%	—
12/18	421	(4)	—	—
12/17	412	(7)	—	—
Annual Growth	9.8%	—	—	—

2020 Year-End Financials

Return on assets: 3.5%
Return on equity: 9.7%
Current ratio: —

Cash ($ mil.): 5

SUN COAST RESOURCES, INC.

Breaking the glass ceiling with large containers of Texas tea woman-owned Sun Coast Resources buys refined oil and sells it to more than 10000 third-party customers such airlines and construction educational energy industrial and retail companies in about 40 states. The company has an extensive truck fleet (more than 1000 vehicles) and delivers gasoline and diesel fuels marine and aviation fuels and lubricants. It also provides oilfield transportation and services onsite and fleet fueling petroleum tanks and generator fueling services. Sun Coast was founded in 1985 by president and CEO Kathy Lehne.

Operations

Sun Coast carries a full line of Chevron oils and lubricants and is one of Chevron's largest lubricant distributors in the US. Other Sun Coast services include additive packages bulk storage and warehousing a computerized fleet tracking system and customized schedule and deliveries. The company has approximately 1 billion gallons of bulk fuel storage more than 10000 fuel and lubricant tanks including skid tanks aviation certified tanks emergency ISO tanks and others. Its truck fleet includes bobtails lowboys lube trucks pick-ups roll-backs and vacuum trucks.

Its transport trucks are capable of hauling approximately 6000 gallons of diesel fuel and approximately 8600 gallons of gasoline. Sun Coast's lubricant trucks are capable of hauling 2000 gallons of bulk lubricants as well as drums totes and other packaged products.

The company's products include aviation gasoline (avgas) gasoline jet fuel kerosene marine diesel ultra-low sulfur diesel fuel and Chevron Conoco Mystik Phillips 66 and TOTAL lubrication products. It also offers services card lock service filtration and fluid purification fleet fueling and mobile on-site fueling spill response and other services.

Geographic Reach

Sun Coast owns and operates more than 15 offices in Arkansas New Mexico Mississippi Oklahoma Texas and Louisiana. It also has of office and warehouse space in nine facilities in Texas. It markets its products in about 40 US states. Sun Coast also provides equipment and services in fast-growing shale plays including the Eagle Ford Eagle Ford Bryan Permian Haynesville Cline Woodford and Marcellus.

Sales and Marketing

Sun Coast provides fuel supply services and related equipment to communication companies delivery services firms government entities utilities and other fleet operators.

Company Background

It expanded into Louisiana in 2012 with the purchase of St. Martin Oil and Gas which operated a small fleet of fuel transportation trucks from two bulk storage facilities in St. Martinville and Denham Springs.

Further expanding its portfolio in 2012 the company acquired assets from bankrupt SMF Energy including its wholly owned affiliate H&W Petroleum Co. Properties included more than 100 fuel trucks and support vehicles previously used by SMF's mobile refueling operations outside of Texas and about 100 fuel and chemical transportation and support vehicles from H&W its Lufkin blending facility and fuel storage tanks across Texas.

That year Sun Coast further expanded its branded and unbranded fuel and lubricant distribution business by buying Houston-based ADA Resources.

In 2011 the company bought the commercial fuel and disaster response businesses of Cypress Texas-based Roy Moffitt Customized Fueling.

EXECUTIVES

Pres, Kathy E Lehne
SEC-Treas, Lisa L Smith
Tax Department Supervisor, Alison Bishop
Employee, Cady Charlie
Representative, Christine Giraldo
Salesforce Administrator, Christine Selick
Employee, Justin Burnett
Sales Representative, Krystin Kilgore
Director of Sales, Lisa Moore

General Manager, Marc Childers
Training Specialist, Rob Chapman

LOCATIONS

HQ: SUN COAST RESOURCES, INC.
6405 CAVALCADE ST BLDG 1, HOUSTON, TX 770264315
Phone: 713 844-9600
Web: WWW.SUNCOASTRESOURCES.COM

PRODUCTS/OPERATIONS

Selected Products
Petroleum Products
  Aviation gasoline
  High sulfur diesel fuel
  Jet fuel
  Kerosene
  Lubricants
  Marine fuels
  Mid-grade fuel
  Low sulfur diesel fuel
  Premium low sulfur diesel fuel
  Premium unleaded gasoline
  Unleaded gasoline
Oils and Lubricants
  Automatic transmission fluid
  Chain oils
  Food-grade oils
  Fuel Additives
  Gear oils
  Greases
  Heat transfer oils
  Hydraulic oils
  Metal-working oils
  Motor oils
  Refrigeration oils
  Solvents and chemicals

Selected Mergers and Acquisitions

COMPETITORS

George Warren	Martin Resource
Global Partners	Management
Gulf Oil	Mercury Air Group
J.a.m. Distributing	

HISTORICAL FINANCIALS

Company Type: Private

Income Statement				FYE: December 31
	REVENUE ($ mil.)	NET INCOME ($ mil.)	NET PROFIT MARGIN	EMPLOYEES
12/07	1,064	2	0.3%	1,649
12/06	864	7	0.8%	—
12/05	867	13	1.6%	—
12/04	697	3	0.4%	—
Annual Growth	15.1%	(2.7%)	—	—

2007 Year-End Financials

Return on assets: 2.3%   Cash ($ mil.): —
Return on equity: 13.4%
Current ratio: 3.30

SUN MAR MANAGEMENT SERVICES

EXECUTIVES

Ceo, Frank Johnson
Cfo, Bill Presnell
Director of Quality Assurance, Susanne Dean
Registered Nurse, Juliet Dimaandal

LOCATIONS

HQ: SUN MAR MANAGEMENT SERVICES
3050 SATURN ST STE 201, BREA, CA 928216278
Phone: 714 577-3880

HISTORICAL FINANCIALS

Company Type: Private

Income Statement				FYE: March 31
	REVENUE ($ mil.)	NET INCOME ($ mil.)	NET PROFIT MARGIN	EMPLOYEES
03/09*	742	0	0.1%	500
12/08	6	(0)		
Annual Growth	**********%	—	—	—

*Fiscal year change

SUNBELT SUPPLY L.P.

EXECUTIVES

Ceo-Pres, Scott Jackson
S Vp of Fin, Joao Vaz
Sr V Pres-Gen Counsel, Suzanne Mailes-Dineff
Senior Vice President of Busin, Dan Sisney
Area Sales Manager, Gus Vasquez
Sales Manager, Joshua Venable
Inside Sales Account Manager, Samantha Cureton
Outside Sales Account Manager, Morgan McDowell
Sales Assistant, Carolyn Kilty
Operations Manager, Chris Gault
Account Manager, Craig Kershaw

LOCATIONS

HQ: SUNBELT SUPPLY L.P.
3750 HWY 225, PASADENA, TX 77503
Phone: 713 672-2222
Web: WWW.SUNBELTSUPPLY.COM

HISTORICAL FINANCIALS

Company Type: Private

Income Statement				FYE: January 31
	REVENUE ($ mil.)	NET INCOME ($ mil.)	NET PROFIT MARGIN	EMPLOYEES
01/14	657	24	3.8%	573
01/13	668	28	4.3%	—
Annual Growth	(1.6%)	(14.5%)	—	—

SUNDT CONSTRUCTION, INC.

EXECUTIVES

Ceo-Pres, G Michael Hoover
Svp-Gen Counsel*, Ronald Stuff
Svp/Cfo/Treas*, Kevin M Burnett
Payroll Staff, Karolyn Comstock
Vice-President Business Develo, Cade Rowly
Coordinator, Kimberly Evans
Pres-Industrial Group, Richard Keil

Contractor, Dave Fleming
Project Director, Hal Hardister
Operations Manager, Jim Pullen
Talent Acquisition Specialist, Sarah Clapper
Auditors: MAYER HOFFMAN & MCCANN

LOCATIONS

HQ: SUNDT CONSTRUCTION, INC.
2620 S 55TH ST, TEMPE, AZ 852821903
Phone: 480 293-3000
Web: WWW.SUNDT.COM

HISTORICAL FINANCIALS

Company Type: Private

Income Statement   FYE: September 30

	REVENUE ($ mil.)	NET INCOME ($ mil.)	NET PROFIT MARGIN	EMPLOYEES
09/18	1,432	0	—	1,000
09/17	1,134	0	—	
09/16	813	0	—	
09/13	895	0	—	
Annual Growth	9.8%	—	—	—

2018 Year-End Financials

Return on assets: —   Cash ($ mil.): 140
Return on equity: —
Current ratio: 1.70

SUNKIST GROWERS, INC.

Sunkist Growers is one business that is least susceptible to an outbreak of scurvy among its employees. America's oldest continually operating citrus cooperative the company is owned by California and Arizona citrus growers who farm some 300000 acres of citrus trees. Sunkist offers traditional and organic fresh oranges lemons limes grapefruit and tangerines worldwide. The co-op which operates some 20 packing facilities also makes juice and cut fruit packaged in jars. Fruit that doesn't meet fresh market standards is turned into oils and peels for use in food products made by other manufacturers. Sunkist's customers include food retailers and manufacturers and foodservice providers worldwide.

Operations

The cooperative's seasonal citrus includes Meyer lemons mandarin oranges Clementine oranges blood oranges and tangelos. Sunkist is one of the most recognized brand names in the world.

Through some 40 licensing agreements the Sunkist name appears on more than 600 beverages and other products — from vitamins to candy to soda to pistachios. It offers Sunkist Fruit Gems (gummie candies) made for the company by the Jelly Belly Candy Company.

Some 45% of Sunkist's fresh fruit sales revenues come from markets outside the US as well as more than 20% of its processed products revenues. To maintain its reach abroad Sunkist works with the US government and the governments of foreign countries to open new markets that are off limits to Western citrus growers.

Geographic Reach

California-based Sunkist operates in the Americas Europe the Middle East and Asia Pacific.

Sales and Marketing

Sunkist regularly advertises worldwide to encourage use of its citrus products and build its brand. Additionally the company leverages television to get its name out such as its alliance with the NBC motivational weight loss competition The Biggest Loser .

Sunkist which has operated a centralized sales organization since 2009 sells its products primarily to food retailers and manufacturers as well as to foodservice providers worldwide. The company is the largest marketing cooperative in the global fruit and vegetable industry.

Financial Performance

Gross annual sales of Sunkist-brand products exceed $1.2 billion worldwide.

Strategy

The company has been focused on market and portfolio expansion and getting the most from its citrus juice and oils and for-profit businesses. It is working to extend its reach to new markets such as India the Middle East and Eastern Europe where its core product has not historically been traded. To reach beyond citrus and expand its products portfolio Sunkist is concentrating on table grapes. Through a pilot program with its existing citrus growers the company markets Sunkist-branded California table grapes grown by them.

It also worked in recent years to improve the productivity of its Tipton juice processing plant. To this end Sunkist in 2012 entered a 50:50 joint venture agreement with fellow juice processor Ventura Coastal. Under the name Ventura Coastal LLC the entity operates the Ventura Coastal plant in Visalia and the Sunkist plant in Tipton. Beginning in 2013 Sunkist also partnered with Greene River Marketing to sell its Florida citrus in promising domestic and export markets.

The 2011-2012 growing season got off to a late start thanks to slow maturing fruit. Its navel orange crop grew to a manageable 88 million cartons as compared to a challenging 93-million-carton crop the previous year. Lemons started slowly as well but both demand and price picked up. Protected groves fared well during the year while unprotected ones — those outside the traditional growing areas — did not. More susceptible to the cold mandarins crops have suffered.

HISTORY

Sunkist Growers was founded in the early 1890s as the Pachappa Orange Growers a group of California citrus farmers determined to control the sale of their fruit. Success attracted new members and in 1893 the Southern California Fruit Exchange was born. The name "Sunkissed" was coined by an ad copywriter in 1908 and it was soon reworked into "Sunkist" and registered as a trademark becoming the first brand name for a fresh produce item. Eventually the co-op renamed itself after its popular brand: It became Sunkist Growers in 1952. Sunkist began licensing its trademark to other companies in the early 1950s.

As early as 1916 efforts to increase citrus consumption included designing and marketing glass citrus juicers and encouraging homemakers to "Drink an Orange." The co-op also promoted the practice of putting lemon slices in tea or water and funded early research on the health benefits of vitamins (vitamin C in particular). In 1925 tissue wrappers gave way to stamping the Sunkist name directly on each piece of fruit.

Although Sunkist pioneered bottled orange juice in 1933 its juice marketing efforts were never as successful as those of its Florida competitors. Florida oranges are drippy and dowdy and thus better suited for juicing. Capitalizing on this aspect Florida growers dominated the market for fresh and frozen juice.

In 1937 Congress created a system of citrus shipment quotas and limits (known as "marketing orders") that ultimately proved most beneficial to large citrus cooperatives. By the early 1990s the marketing order system was under political attack and in 1992 the Justice Department filed civil prosecution against Sunkist alleging that the co-op had

reaped unfair extra profits by surpassing its lemon shipment limits. In 1994 after much legal wrangling the quotas were abolished and the Justice Department dropped its case against Sunkist.

Inconveniently warm weather and increasing competition from imported citrus marked the harvests of 1996. That year the co-op had trouble maintaining discipline among its members; some undercut Sunkist price levels while others flooded the market to sell their fruit at the higher early market prices creating a supply surplus. Also that year the co-op relinquished the marketing of all Sunkist juices in North America to Florida-based Lykes Bros. in a licensing agreement.

The co-op agreed in 1998 to distribute grapefruit from Florida's Tuxedo Fruit providing Sunkist with a winter grapefruit supply and increasing its year-round consumer a-peel. Also in 1998 Russell Hanlin Sunkist president and CEO since 1978 was succeeded by Vince Lupinacci. Lupinacci who had held positions with Pepsi and Six Flags became the first person from outside the citrus business to hold Sunkist's top post.

In 1998 the company sold 90 million cartons of fresh citrus — the greatest volume in its history — despite increased competition from imported Latin American South African and Spanish crops a damaging California freeze and the ill effects of El Ni ±o . The next year production was almost halved because of adverse weather.

Lupinacci resigned in 2000 citing personal and family reasons. Chairman emeritus James Mast then took the helm as acting president. Although the company grew its market through exports to China in 2000 its profits were squeezed that year by increasing foreign competition a citrus glut and lessened demand. In mid-2001 Jeff Gargiulo replaced Mast as Sunkist's president and CEO.

In 2003 Sunkist formed a joint venture with strawberry shipper Coastal Berry Co. to market strawberries under the Sunkist label year-round. (Coastal Berry's president and CEO John Gargiulo and Sunkist's former president and CEO Jeff Gargiulo are brothers.) Also that year Sunkist began offering pre-cut bagged fruit to retail customers and restaurants in order to keep up with a changing market and consumer demand.

In retrospect 2006 was an eventful year for Sunkist. The co-op's largest producer and 16-year-member Paramount Citrus Association left the organization. In addition chairman and CEO David Krause stepped down and president Jeff Gargiulo left the company. Krause was replaced as chairman by Nicholas Bozick president of produce grower/packer Richard Bagdasarian Inc. Sunkist veteran and former president of Fruit Growers Supply Company Timothy Lindgren was appointed president and CEO. And citing expense as the determining factor the co-op discontinued marketing berries (strawberries blueberries and raspberries) in 2006. Lindgren retired in 2008; he was replaced by EVP Russ Hanlin.

EXECUTIVES

Pres-Ceo, Russell Hanlin II
V Pres-Cfo, Richard G French
Sr V Pres, Michael Wootton
V Pres, John Mc Guigan
V Pres, Russell L Hanlin II
Human Resources Director, Diane P Johnson
Sales Manager, Kimberly Mangum
Director of Global Licensing, Mazen Safadi
Operations Manager, Dean Troxell
Business Analyst, Grant Tomkins
Executive Vice President, Kevin Fiori
Auditors: MOSS ADAM LLP STOCKTON CALIF

LOCATIONS

HQ: SUNKIST GROWERS, INC.
27770 ENTERTAINMENT DR, VALENCIA, CA
913551092
Phone: 661 290-8900
Web: WWW.SUNKIST.COM

PRODUCTS/OPERATIONS

Selected Products
Fresh fruit
Grapefruit
Melo Golds
Oro Blancos
Pummelos
Sweeties
Texas Rio Star
Western
Lemons
Eurkea/Lisbon
Meyer
Limes
Key
Persian
Mandarins
Clementine
Honey
Royal
Satsuma
Shasta Gold
W. Murcott
Oranges
Cara Cara
Moro
Navel
Valencia
Tangelos
Minneola
Orlando
Tangerines
Dancy
Fairchild
Pixie
Packaged fruit
Beverage concentrates
Carbonated beverages (under license)
Chilled fruit jellies (under license)
Fruit juice
Fruit juice drinks
Fruit snacks (under license)
Powdered fruit drinks
Vitamins (under license)

COMPETITORS

Alico Inc.	Lionel Hitchen
Big Heart Pet Brands	Louis Dreyfus Group
Chiquita Brands	M&b Products
Citrus World	Old Orchard
Coca-cola	Orchard House Foods
Dole Food	R & Z Ventures
Dundee Citrus Growers	Silver Springs
Edinburg Citrus	Southern Gardens
Fresh Del Monte	Citrus
Produce	Sunny Delight
Freshco	Tropicana
Great Western Juice	U.s. Sugar
King Ranch	Wonderful Company
Lake Placid Groves	

HISTORICAL FINANCIALS

Company Type: Private

Income Statement   FYE: October 31

	REVENUE ($ mil.)	NET INCOME ($ mil.)	NET PROFIT MARGIN	EMPLOYEES
10/18	1,359	2	0.2%	500
10/17	1,299	9	0.7%	—
10/16	1,207	7	0.6%	—
Annual Growth	6.1%	(37.6%)	—	—

2018 Year-End Financials

Return on assets: 1.2%   Cash ($ mil.): 31
Return on equity: 2.0%
Current ratio: 1.40

SUNOCO PIPELINE L.P.

LOCATIONS

HQ: SUNOCO PIPELINE L.P.
4041 MARKET ST, UPPER CHICHESTER, PA
190143121
Phone: 610 859-5700

HISTORICAL FINANCIALS

Company Type: Private

Income Statement   FYE: December 31

	REVENUE ($ mil.)	NET INCOME ($ mil.)	NET PROFIT MARGIN	EMPLOYEES
12/17	804	1,419	176.6%	3
12/16	1,070	796	74.4%	—
Annual Growth	(24.9%)	78.2%	—	—

SUNTORY INTERNATIONAL

Suntory USA established in the 1960s on the other side of the globe from its parent Japanese trading giant Suntory Holdings Limited imports Suntory products to the US market from its New York headquarters. Well-known offerings include wine beer and distilled spirits such as Yamazaki Single Malt Whisky and Zen Green Tea and Midori Melon liqueurs. Other operations handled by Suntory USA include a soft drink bottling business (Pepsi Bottling Ventures) a winery various restaurants and its parent's bottled water division Suntory Water Group once the second-largest bottled water producer in the US. Altogether Suntory USA comprises 17 companies contributing 4% of its parent's 2013 revenue.

EXECUTIVES

Pres, Tsuyoshi Nishizaki
Exec V Pres, Yoshihiko Kunimoto
Cfo, Tsutomu Santoki
Treas, Yoshito Shihara
SEC, Masaru Ijima
Agent, David L Hayutin
Sales Manager, Mauro Vidale
Auditors: PRICEWATERHOUSECOOPERS LLP NE

LOCATIONS

HQ: SUNTORY INTERNATIONAL
4141 PARKLAKE AVE STE 600, RALEIGH, NC
276122380
Phone: 917 756-2747
Web: WWW.SUNTORY.CO.JP

PRODUCTS/OPERATIONS

Selected Products & Brands
Beer & Happoshu
Diet Draft Happoshu
Hop's Draft Happoshu
Jokki Beer
Kinmugi Beer
Magnum Dry Happoshu
Malt's Beer
The Premium Malt's Beer
Cocktails
Calori
Cocktail Bar
Cocktail Calori
Ginza Cocktail
Super Chu-hi
Distilled Spirits
Barley Shochu Wanko
Daijuhyo Ko-rui Shochu
HAKUSHU Blended Whiskey
Hanauta Shochu Nanco
HIBIKI Blended Whiskey
KAKUGBIN Whiskey
Ko-otsu Blended Shochu
Kyogetsu GREEN
Midori Melon liqueur
Otsu-rui Sochu
Suntory Shirofuda Whiskey
Sweet Potato Shochu Wanco
YAMAZAKI Single Malt Whiskey
Zen Green Tea liqueur
Wine
Akadama Sweet Wine
Delica Maison Delicious Wine
Sankaboshizai Mutenka Wine
Tomi no oka Wine
Tomi Wine
Yukisaibai Budo no Oishii Wine

COMPETITORS

Anheuser-busch	Heineken
Aquaterra Corporation	Kirin Holdings Company
Asahi Breweries	Kokubu
Coca-cola	Kyowa Hakko Kirin
Coca-cola Bottling	Naked Juice
Consolidated	Nestl © Waters
Coca-cola Refreshments	Odwalla
Coke United	Pepsico
Danone Water	Sabmiller
Diageo	Sapporo
Dr Pepper Snapple	Takara
Group	

HISTORICAL FINANCIALS

Company Type: Private

Income Statement   FYE: December 31

	REVENUE ($ mil.)	NET INCOME ($ mil.)	NET PROFIT MARGIN	EMPLOYEES
12/10	790	60	7.7%	2,199
12/09	13	5	42.0%	—
Annual Growth	5928.4%	1002.2%	—	—

2010 Year-End Financials

Return on assets: 8.1%   Cash ($ mil.): 60
Return on equity: 13.8%
Current ratio: 1.50

SUPERIOR COMMUNICATIONS, INC.

EXECUTIVES

Chb, Solomon Chen
Ceo*, Jeffrey Banks
Sr V Pres*, Robert Chen
Cfo*, Keith Kam
Legal Counsel*, Jennifer Ju
Stckhldr*, Michael Cavanah
Coo*, Mike Cost
Accounts Receivable Payable MA*, Ava Cheung
Cmo*, Scott Shanks
Purchasing Director, Armando Jara
Procurement Coordinator, Caroline Chin
Auditors: PRICEWATERHOUSECOOPERS LLP IR

HQ: SUPERIOR COMMUNICATIONS, INC.
5027 IRWINDALE AVE # 900, IRWINDALE, CA
917062187
Phone: 877 522-4727
Web: WWW.SUPERIORCOMMUNICATIONS.COM

HISTORICAL FINANCIALS
Company Type: Private

Income Statement				FYE: December 31
	REVENUE ($ mil.)	NET INCOME ($ mil.)	NET PROFIT MARGIN	EMPLOYEES
12/14*	734	6	0.9%	273
06/13	296	2	0.7%	—
12/12	1,365	0	—	—
Annual Growth	(26.7%)	177565.4%	—	—

*Fiscal year change

2014 Year-End Financials
Return on assets: 2.2%   Cash ($ mil.): 25
Return on equity: 73.8%
Current ratio: 1.10

SUTTER BAY HOSPITALS

Sutter West Bay Hospitals (doing business as California Pacific Medical Center or CPMC) is a health care complex located in the heart of hospital-heavy San Francisco. The private not-for-profit center's four area campuses (California Davies Pacific and St. Luke's) offer acute and specialty care including obstetrics and gynecology cardiovascular services pediatrics neurosciences orthopedics and organ transplantation. With more than 1300 beds between its campuses the center also conducts professional education and biomedical clinical and behavioral research. CPMC is part of the West Bay Region division of the Sutter Health hospital system.

Operations

CPMC's Sutter Health West Bay Region also includes Novato Community Hospital Sutter Lakeside Hospital and Sutter Medical Center of Santa Rosa. In addition to acute medical services CPMC also provides outpatient services at clinics in the San Francisco area operates home health and hospice organizations and conducts health education and charity care programs.

In 2011 CPMC's Research Institute conducted more than 200 clinical trials including studies on aging cancers epilepsy diabetes cardiovascular disease osteoporosis organ transplantation and more. That year CPMC's Kidney and Pancreas Transplant Program performed the first ever single-hospital five-way kidney swap transplant in California. CPMC's Joint Replacement Center is one of the leading joint replacement centers in the Bay Area performing roughly 1200 hip knee shoulder and elbow procedures per year. It has 1859 CPMC Medical Staff (including St. Luke's) and 109 medical residents and fellows.

That year the healthcare system reported about 619400 outpatient visits and 30300 inpatient cases.

Geographic Reach

CPMC serves patients from San Francisco Marin San Mateo Oakland Berkeley Palo Alto Santa Rosa San Jose. and the Bay Area.

Strategy

In order to meet California's seismic construction standards CPMC plans to renovate or rebuild most of its hospital campuses which are among the oldest medical centers in the San Francisco

---

area. Its $2.5 billion reorganization plan includes the construction of a new 550-bed Cathedral Hill Campus that will include a full acute care hospital plus specialized women's and children's departments. CPMC also plans to rebuild and downsize the St. Luke's campus and convert the Pacific and California campuses into ambulatory care clinics. Reconstruction efforts at the Davies campus will include a new patient pavilion and a new Davies Neurosciences Institute for expanded neurological care. Major construction projects began in 2011 and will extend through 2015.

In 2010 the company sold its outpatient kidney dialysis operations to DaVita to focus on core operations.

Company Background

In 2007 parent Sutter Health merged St. Luke's Hospital into California Pacific to help keep the ailing St. Luke's afloat; St. Luke's provides care to many of San Francisco's low-income patients. CPMC had announced plans to turn St. Luke's into an outpatient facility in 2007; however the company rescinded those plans after San Franciscans objected to the proposal.

EXECUTIVES

Ceo, Jeff Gerard
Pres*, Martin Brotman
Acting Chair, Department of Pe, Kathleen Lewis
Chief of Pediatric Cardiac Sur, Michael Black
Payroll Staff, Blanche Marlowe
Coordinator, Ginny Noell
Coordinator, Kathleen Molumby
Information Specialist, Michelle Fassio
Information Specialist, Howard George
Contracts Analyst, Jeffrey Ziarno
Clinical Coordinator of Er, Bruce Deas
Auditors: ERNST & YOUNG LLP ROSEVILLE

LOCATIONS

HQ: SUTTER BAY HOSPITALS
475 BRANNAN ST STE 130, SAN FRANCISCO, CA
941075419
Phone: 415 600-6000
Web: WWW.CPMCRI.ORG

PRODUCTS/OPERATIONS

Selected Hospitals

California Campus (aka Children's Hospital of San Francisco)
Davies Campus (aka Davies Medical Center or Franklin Hospital)
Pacific Campus (aka Presbyterian Medical Center)
St. Luke's Campus (aka St. Luke's Hospital)

COMPETITORS

Children's Hospital & Research Center At Oakland
Dignity Health
Hca
John Muir Health
Stanford Health Care
Tenet Healthcare
Ucsf Medical
Valleycare Health System

HISTORICAL FINANCIALS
Company Type: Private

Income Statement				FYE: December 31
	REVENUE ($ mil.)	NET INCOME ($ mil.)	NET PROFIT MARGIN	EMPLOYEES
12/11	1,616	67	4.1%	3,597
12/09	1,245	159	12.8%	—
12/08	830	168	20.3%	—
Annual Growth	24.9%	(26.5%)	—	—

2011 Year-End Financials
Return on assets: 4.3%   Cash ($ mil.): 76
Return on equity: 6.6%
Current ratio: 1.20

SUTTER HEALTH

EXECUTIVES

President-Ceo, Patrick Fry
Chb*, Jim Gray
Sr Vice Pres-Chief Medial Offi, Gordon Hunt
Sr Vice Pres-General Counsel, Gary F Loveridge
Sr Vice Pres-Chief Financial O, Robert D Reed
Credentialing Specialist, Catrina Casarez
Family Practitioner, Ana L Pacheco-Clark
Inv Specialist, Artie Aguirre
Director, Cpmc Human Resources, Laura Van
Mha Director, Lea Bernick
Rn, Wcc, Terry Tomaro

LOCATIONS

HQ: SUTTER HEALTH
2200 RIVER PLAZA DR, SACRAMENTO, CA
958334134
Phone: 916 733-8800
Web: WWW.SUTTERMEDICALCENTER.ORG

HISTORICAL FINANCIALS
Company Type: Private

Income Statement				FYE: December 31
	REVENUE ($ mil.)	NET INCOME ($ mil.)	NET PROFIT MARGIN	EMPLOYEES
12/20	13,220	82	0.6%	48,000
12/19	13,304	189	1.4%	—
12/18	12,697	(447)	—	—
12/17	12,444	1,060	8.5%	—
Annual Growth	2.0%	(57.4%)	—	—

2020 Year-End Financials
Return on assets: 0.4%   Cash ($ mil.): 1,169
Return on equity: 0.9%
Current ratio: 2.50

SUTTER HEALTH PLAN

EXECUTIVES

Prin, Jennifer Longoria
Manager, Tom Cox
Utilization Management Program, Jessica Camilleri
Marketing, Patrice Wohl
Hospitalist, Sohail Gagan
Auditors: ERNST & YOUNG LLP ROSEVILLE

LOCATIONS

HQ: SUTTER HEALTH PLAN
2700 GATEWAY OAKS DR # 120, SACRAMENTO, CA
958334337
Phone: 916 643-1197
Web: WWW.SUTTERHEALTHPLUS.ORG

HISTORICAL FINANCIALS
Company Type: Private

Income Statement				FYE: December 31
	REVENUE ($ mil.)	NET INCOME ($ mil.)	NET PROFIT MARGIN	EMPLOYEES
12/20	573	14	2.4%	30
12/19	518	25	4.8%	—
12/18	429	(16)	—	—
Annual Growth	15.6%	—	—	—

2020 Year-End Financials
Return on assets: 9.0%
Return on equity: 25.0%
Current ratio: 1.50

Cash ($ mil.): 79

SUTTER HEALTH SACRAMENTO SIERRA REGION

EXECUTIVES

Ceo, Patrick E Fry
Sr Staff Pres, Darling Lones
Coordinator, Sue Hawley
Interventional Radiology, David Gover
Radiology, Dylan Witt
Family Medicine, Elisa Horta
Radiology, Linda Mar
Urology, Matthew Janiga
Radiology, Scott Foster
Auditors: ERNST & YOUNG US LLP SAN DIEG

LOCATIONS

HQ: SUTTER HEALTH SACRAMENTO SIERRA REGION
2200 RIVER PLAZA DR, SACRAMENTO, CA 958334134
Phone: 916 733-8800
Web: WWW.SUTTERHEALTH.ORG

HISTORICAL FINANCIALS
Company Type: Private

Income Statement				FYE: December 31
	REVENUE ($ mil.)	NET INCOME ($ mil.)	NET PROFIT MARGIN	EMPLOYEES
12/13	1,884	148	7.9%	4,000
12/11	1,752	(16)	—	—
12/09	1,453	154	10.6%	—
12/02	4,634	322	6.9%	—
Annual Growth	(7.9%)	(6.8%)	—	—

2013 Year-End Financials
Return on assets: 8.6%
Return on equity: 30.8%
Current ratio: 0.30

Cash ($ mil.): 69

SUTTER ROSEVILLE MEDICAL CENTER

EXECUTIVES

Ceo, Patrick Brady
Pharmacist, Charles Elliot
Human Resources Manager, Julie Fralick
Case Manager, Mary Nourot
Senior Officer, Rebecca Thompson
Hospitalist, Prasad Jogu
Associate Planner, Lance Lowe
Senior Financial Analyst, Marthea Johnson
Registered Nurse, Amy Beazizo
Registered Nurse, Audrey Laino
Physical Therapist Director, Diane Kraker

LOCATIONS

HQ: SUTTER ROSEVILLE MEDICAL CENTER
1 MEDICAL PLAZA DR, ROSEVILLE, CA 956613037
Phone: 916 781-1000
Web: WWW.SUTTERROSEVILLE.ORG

HISTORICAL FINANCIALS
Company Type: Private

Income Statement				FYE: December 31
	REVENUE ($ mil.)	NET INCOME ($ mil.)	NET PROFIT MARGIN	EMPLOYEES
12/17	669	126	18.9%	1,700
12/16	628	121	19.3%	—
12/15	558	74	13.3%	—
12/12	484	95	19.6%	—
Annual Growth	6.7%	5.9%	—	—

2017 Year-End Financials
Return on assets: 35.4%
Return on equity: 129.3%
Current ratio: 3.70

Cash ($ mil.): —

SUTTER VALLEY HOSPITALS

EXECUTIVES

Ceo, Anne Platt
Chief of Emergency Room, Paul R Beatty
Internal Medicine Practitioner, Prabjit Singh
Director of Business Office, Melanie Stroberg
Human Resources Manager, Beverly Revels
Pediatrics, Kathy Lewis
Mobile Solution, Kranthi Vallamreddy
Technical Analyst II, Raychiel Craven
Surgery, Ronald Rosen
Director, Gino Moio
Sales Associate, Keri Steele

LOCATIONS

HQ: SUTTER VALLEY HOSPITALS
2200 RIVER PLAZA DR, SACRAMENTO, CA 958334134
Phone: 916 733-8800
Web: WWW.SUTTERMEDICALCENTER.ORG

HISTORICAL FINANCIALS
Company Type: Private

Income Statement				FYE: December 31
	REVENUE ($ mil.)	NET INCOME ($ mil.)	NET PROFIT MARGIN	EMPLOYEES
12/20	3,735	168	4.5%	405
12/19	3,614	12	0.3%	—
12/17	80	1	2.4%	—
12/16	83	8	10.3%	—
Annual Growth	158.5%	110.4%	—	—

2020 Year-End Financials
Return on assets: 6.4%
Return on equity: 14.3%
Current ratio: 1.40

Cash ($ mil.): 120

SUTTER VALLEY MEDICAL FOUNDATION

EXECUTIVES

Ceo, Tom Blinn
Project Coordinator, Dalena Spahr
Coordinator, Rebeca Colom
Regional Director Nutrition, Jack Breezee
Project Manager III, Mark Hajny
Radiology, Hani Greiss
Network Engineering Manager, Robert Haubeck
Surgeon, Eric London
Director of Education, Ali Myers
Clinical Laboratory Technical, Christine Manley
External Affairs Associate, Thomas Trejo
Auditors: ERNST & YOUNG LLP ROSEVILLE

LOCATIONS

HQ: SUTTER VALLEY MEDICAL FOUNDATION
2700 GATEWAY OAKS DR, SACRAMENTO, CA 958334337
Phone: 916 887-7122
Web: WWW.SUTTERHEALTH.ORG

HISTORICAL FINANCIALS
Company Type: Private

Income Statement				FYE: December 31
	REVENUE ($ mil.)	NET INCOME ($ mil.)	NET PROFIT MARGIN	EMPLOYEES
12/20	1,666	242	14.5%	700
12/19	1,651	23	1.4%	—
12/18	1,556	(2)	—	—
12/09	505	(21)	—	—
Annual Growth	11.5%	—	—	—

2020 Year-End Financials
Return on assets: 26.9%
Return on equity: 54.9%
Current ratio: 2.00

Cash ($ mil.): 398

SWEDISH HEALTH SERVICES

Swedish Health Services doing business as Swedish Medical Center is the largest not-for-profit health provider in the greater Seattle area. Swedish Medical operates five acute care hospitals; it also runs two ambulatory care centers and a network of more than 100 primary and specialty care offices in the greater Puget Sound region. Swedish Medical is affiliated with Providence St. Joseph Health a Catholic not-for-profit organization with about 35 hospitals in five states. Swedish's perform procedures such as robotic-assisted surgery and personalized treatment in cardiovascular care cancer care neuroscience orthopedics high-risk obstetrics pediatric specialties organ transplantation and clinical research.

EXECUTIVES

Ceo, Guy Hudson
Cno*, Linda Gray
Cmo*, Jaya Kumar
Cdeio*, Mardia Shands
Prn, John L Verrilli
Interim Information S, Shannon Diede
Coordinator, Edna Doerksen
Coordinator, Marissa Dizon-Scott
Coordinator, Cathy Jorg
Coordinator, Cherica Carlson
Coordinator, Dwayne Biles
Auditors: ERNST & YOUNG US LLP SAN FRAN

LOCATIONS

HQ: SWEDISH HEALTH SERVICES
747 BROADWAY, SEATTLE, WA 981224379
Phone: 206 386-6000
Web: WWW.SWEDISH.ORG

PRODUCTS/OPERATIONS

Selected Washington Facilities
Ballard Campus (Seattle)
Cherry Hill Campus (Seattle)
Edmonds Campus (Edmonds)
First Hill Campus (Seattle)
Issaquah Campus (Issaquah)
Mill Creek Campus (ambulatory center in Everett)
Redmond Campus (ambulatory center in Redmond)

Selected Institutes and Services
Cancer Institute
Emergency Services
Heart and Vascular Institute
Neuroscience Institute
Orthopedic Institute
Pediatric Specialty Care
Primary Care
Pregnancy and Childbirth
Surgical Services
Transplant Program
Women's Health

COMPETITORS

Franciscan Health System	Seattle Children's Hospital
Harrison Medical Center	University Of Washington
Multicare Health System	Wenatchee Valley Medical Center
Overlake Hospital	Yakima Valley Memorial
Peacehealth	

HISTORICAL FINANCIALS

Company Type: Private

Income Statement   FYE: December 31

	REVENUE ($ mil.)	NET INCOME ($ mil.)	NET PROFIT MARGIN	EMPLOYEES
12/17	2,438	(9)	—	50
12/16	1,278	(2)	—	—
12/15	1,240	56	4.6%	—
12/14	1,127	79	7.1%	—
Annual Growth	29.3%	—	—	—

2017 Year-End Financials

Return on assets: (-0.3%)   Cash ($ mil.): 51
Return on equity: (-1.2%)
Current ratio: —

SWEETWATER UNION HIGH SCHOOL DISTRICT

EXECUTIVES

Supt, Karen Janney
School Psychologist, Rosa Ruiz
Planning Project Manager, Frank Mendoza
Senior Administrative Assistan, Erika Gonzales
Buildings, Douglas Knapp
Buildings, Isaias Arroyo
Bus Finance Purchasing Dir, Nancy Picone
School Psychologist, Nitza Romero
Credentials Specialist, Anna Hurtado
Manager, George Williams
Teacher, Aaron Sias
Auditors: CROWE LLP SACRAMENTO CALIFOR

LOCATIONS

HQ: SWEETWATER UNION HIGH SCHOOL DISTRICT
1130 FIFTH AVE, CHULA VISTA, CA 919112812
Phone: 619 691-5500
Web: WWW.SWEETWATERSCHOOLS.ORG

HISTORICAL FINANCIALS

Company Type: Private

Income Statement   FYE: June 30

	REVENUE ($ mil.)	NET INCOME ($ mil.)	NET PROFIT MARGIN	EMPLOYEES
06/20	589	38	6.5%	3,521
06/19	601	22	3.8%	—
06/18	553	(17)	—	—
06/17	546	(48)	—	—
Annual Growth	2.5%	—	—	—

SWINERTON BUILDERS, INC.

Swinerton Builders a subsidiary of Swinerton focuses on commercial and sustainable construction and renovation projects. Operating primarily in the western US its interiors group offers interior tenant finishes and remodeling working on such projects as high-tech and lab renovations hospitals retail facilities and seismic upgrades. The employee-owned company's building group focuses on new construction and retrofitting for such projects as the San Francisco Museum of Modern Art a Lockheed Martin launch vehicle assembly plant in Colorado and the Bay Bridge toll operations building in San Francisco. Swinerton Builders operates from offices in California Colorado Hawaii Texas New Mexico and Washington.

Operations

As part of its business Swinerton Builders is involved in high-tech and lab renovations hospitals retail facilities and seismic upgrades as well as new construction and retrofitting projects.

Swinerton Builders also constructs many buildings to meet environmental standards. Green projects have ranged from fire stations and retail outlets to college facilities and hotels. Swinertons' own corporate offices in California are solar powered.

Geographic Reach

The building arm of Swinerton serves the western US through offices in California Colorado Hawaii Texas Oregon and Washington. Its offices are located across California as well as in Austin Texas; Denver Colorado; Portland Oregon; Seattle Washington; and Honolulu Hawaii.

Sales and Marketing

Swinerton Builders serves a variety of sectors involving: critical facilities education government healthcare hospitality interiors multi-family residential native American and renewable energy projects. Its clients have included NASA the Federal Aviation Administration Bureau of Indian Affairs and several military and governmental entities including the US Air Force US Army US Department of Agriculture US Department of Homeland Security and the US National Park Service.

Strategy

Swinerton Builders continues to work on high-value projects around the country. In 2015 after being selected from a two-phase best value selection process the company secured a contract to lead the design-build construction project of a $46 million parking building (with some 1795 parking spaces) at the Denver International Airport (DIA) in Colorado.

The company's Swinerton Renewable Energy unit which builds and offers services to the solar utility industry expanded its capabilities in 2013 by adding comprehensive operations and maintenance (O&M) services for any solar facility across North America. The unit also launched a monitoring platform named SOLV to manage all the operational needs of customers with solar utility plants.

EXECUTIVES

Chb, Jeffrey C Hoopes
Pres-Coo, Gary J Rafferty
Exec V Pres, Frank Foellmer
Exec V Pres, Eric Foster
Sr V Pres-Cfo-Sec, Linda G Schowalter
Sr V Pres-Cao, John T Capener
Sr V Pres, Donald D Adair
V Pres, Kerry M Atkinson
V Pres, David C Callis
V Pres, Scott V Conrad
V Pres, George S Ehara
Auditors: CLIFTONLARSONALLEN LLP WALNU

LOCATIONS

HQ: SWINERTON BUILDERS, INC.
2001 CLAYTON RD STE 700, CONCORD, CA 945202792
Phone: 415 421-2980
Web: WWW.SWINERTON.COM

PRODUCTS/OPERATIONS

Selected Services

BIM/VD&C
Corporate Services
Critical Facilities
General Contracting
Government Construction
Management & Consulting
Preconstruction
Renewable Energy
Sustainable Construction/LEED

COMPETITORS

Andersen Construction	Hensel Phelps
Charles Pankow	Construction
Builders	J.f. Shea
Clark Builders Group	Jaynes Companies
Cordoba	Kitchell
Dpr Construction	Torix General
Devcon Construction	Contractors
Gilbane Building	Turner Corporation
Company	W. L. Butler
Hathaway Dinwiddie	Webcor Builders
Construction	Whiting-turner

HISTORICAL FINANCIALS

Company Type: Private

Income Statement				FYE: December 31
	REVENUE ($ mil.)	NET INCOME ($ mil.)	NET PROFIT MARGIN	EMPLOYEES
12/19	4,272	46	1.1%	900
12/18	3,541	38	1.1%	—
12/17	3,306	39	1.2%	—
12/16	3,664	53	1.5%	—
Annual Growth	5.2%	(4.8%)	—	—

2019 Year-End Financials
Return on assets: 3.3%   Cash ($ mil.): 243
Return on equity: 14.6%
Current ratio: 1.30

SWINERTON INCORPORATED

Swinerton is building up the West just as it helped rebuild San Francisco after the 1906 earthquake. One of the largest contractors in California the construction group builds commercial industrial and government facilities including resorts subsidized housing public schools soundstages hospitals and airport terminals. Through its subsidiaries (including Swinerton Builders) Swinerton offers general contracting and design/build services as well as construction and program management. The firm also provides property management for conventional subsidized and assisted living residences and is active in the renewable energy sector. The 100% employee-owned company traces its roots to 1888.

Operations

Swinerton has a special renewable energy division (Swinerton Renewable Energy) focused on solar and wind projects.

For North American solar power facilities the company also offers comprehensive operations and maintenance (O&M) services which include performance monitoring and alerting parts management service ticketing reporting preventive and corrective maintenance warranty administration and site maintenance (including vegetation mitigation and module washing).

Swinerton also has a special division to handle government construction projects delivering large-scale complex design and construction services for government agencies. Through the division Swinerton has worked on federal courthouses and administrative buildings training centers VA hospitals and military housing projects.

Geographic Reach

San Francisco-based Swinerton has more than a dozen offices throughout California Colorado Hawaii Texas Oregon and Washington.

Financial Performance

With the California construction market experiencing some of the strongest growth the industry has seen since 2008 Swinerton posted nearly $1.8 billion in revenue in 2013 about $1.4 billion of which was rung up in California.

Strategy

Swinerton's renewable energy division has been busy with a series of projects and new services coming to the fold in recent years. In 2014 Duke Energy awarded Swinerton a contract to develop a pair of 20-megawatt solar farms called the Pumpjack and Wildwood solar power projects which will power some 10000 households in central California once they're completed. In 2013 the company began offering comprehensive operations and maintenance (O&M) services for any North American solar facility.

The company also continues to work on other projects in recent years. In 2014 it started building the five-story 117000-square-foot building on behalf of the developer Breevast which secured a 12-year lease agreement on the building with file-sharing service provider Dropbox. In 2013 it started work on Telecom Real Estate Services' Block Data Center in Las Vegas with the goal of turning an existing warehouse facility into a Tier III modular data center. That year it also began construction on Chevron's 340000 square-foot office complex and campus in Midland Texas.

As one of the top waste-reducing companies in California Swinerton employs green building construction and design practices to conserve resources reduce waste and create healthier environments. The company's own headquarters building in San Francisco received Gold LEED-EB (Leadership in Energy & Environmental Design for Existing Buildings) — a top certification from the U.S. Green Building Council. Swinerton also built the LEED platinum rated NASA Ames Research Center Sustainability Base the greenest government building in history.

EXECUTIVES

Ceo, Eric Foster
Ceo, Eric M Foster
Pres-Coo, Gary J Rafferty
Exec V Pres, Frank Foellmer
Sr V Pres-Cfo-Sec, Linda G Showalter
V Pres, Wade Oberman
Sr V Pres-Cao, John T Capener
V Pres, Charles R Moore
V Pres, Brenda A Reimche
V Pres, Charlene M Atkinson
V Pres, Sue E Twitchel
Auditors: CLIFTONLARSONALLEN LLP WALNUT

LOCATIONS

HQ: SWINERTON INCORPORATED
2001 CLAYTON RD FL 7 FLR 7, SAN FRANCISCO, CA 94107
Phone: 415 421-2980
Web: WWW.SWINERTON.COM

PRODUCTS/OPERATIONS

Selected Companies and Divisions
Cameron Swinerton
Harbison-Mahony-Higgins Builders Inc. (HMH general contracting)
Swinerton Builders (general contracting)
Swinerton Government Services
Swinerton Management & Consulting (property assessment)
Swinerton Property Services (property management)
William P. Young Construction (engineering and civil construction)

Selected Projects
100 Montgomery
AECOM
Agilent Technologies
Andaz Wailea Resort & Villas
Avaya Research & Development
Bank of New York Mellon Newport Beach
Bank of New York Mellon San Francisco
Bright Horizons Colorado
Bright Horizons South Lake Union
Bruceville | 19.15 MWdc
Cache Creek Casino Resort
CalSTRS Office Headquarters
Caltech Solar Project | 1.10 MWdc
Cathedral of the Blessed Sacrament
Christopher High School
Ciné;polis Del Mar
City Center Plaza and Entry Upgrades
City Target at the Metreon
CNET Headquarters
Columbia 3 | 11.06 MWdc Columbia Sportswear
de Young Museum
Delta Airlines Sky Club
Dillard | 12.03 MWdc

COMPETITORS

A.g. Spanos	J.f. Shea
Bechtel	Jcm Partners
Beck Group	Kitchell
Charles Pankow	Mccarthy Building
Builders	Menas Realty
Clark Construction	Pcl Construction
Group	Enterprises
Cordoba	Rudolph & Sletten
Dpr Construction	Skanska Usa Building
Devcon Construction	Sundt
Gilbane	Turner Corporation
Hathaway Dinwiddie	Tutor-saliba
Construction	Webcor Builders
Hensel Phelps	Western National Group
Construction	Whiting-turner

HISTORICAL FINANCIALS

Company Type: Private

Income Statement				FYE: December 31
	REVENUE ($ mil.)	NET INCOME ($ mil.)	NET PROFIT MARGIN	EMPLOYEES
12/19	4,304	42	1.0%	900
12/18	3,631	36	1.0%	—
12/17	3,365	31	0.9%	—
12/16	0	0	—	—
Annual Growth	—	—	—	—

2019 Year-End Financials
Return on assets: 2.6%   Cash ($ mil.): 285
Return on equity: 14.0%
Current ratio: 1.30

TA CHEN INTERNATIONAL, INC.

EXECUTIVES

Ceo, Johnny Hsieh
V Pres*, James Chang
V Pres*, John Hellighausen
Cfo*, Andrew Chang
Account Manager, Billy Reeder
Specialist, Phina Castillo
Analyst, Vincent Song
Director, Raymond Ginette
Director, Aluminum, Bruce Ferguson
Vice President, Danny Tu
Assistant Director of Finance, John Lin
Auditors: CHEN & FAN ACCOUNTANCY COPR

LOCATIONS

HQ: TA CHEN INTERNATIONAL, INC.
5855 OBISPO AVE, LONG BEACH, CA 908053715
Phone: 562 808-8000
Web: WWW.TACHEN.COM

HISTORICAL FINANCIALS
Company Type: Private

Income Statement   FYE: December 31

	REVENUE ($ mil.)	NET INCOME ($ mil.)	NET PROFIT MARGIN	EMPLOYEES
12/17	1,257	32	2.6%	548
12/14	1,178	27	2.3%	—
12/13	904	8	1.0%	—
Annual Growth	8.6%	38.0%	—	—

2017 Year-End Financials

Return on assets: 3.2%   Cash ($ mil.): 3
Return on equity: 7.8%
Current ratio: 6.10

TACOMA PUBLIC SCHOOLS

EXECUTIVES

Supt, Carla Fantorno
Pres*, Debbie Winskill
V Pres*, Kurt Miller
Coo*, Christopher Williams
Coordinator, Deana Siegel
Payroll Staff, Maggie Thomas
Technology/Computer Coord, Shaun Taylor
Director of Budget, Kristin Bell
Officer, John Hines
Director of Internal Audit, Paul Walker
Student Worker Coordinator, Donald Gillis
Auditors: PAT MCCARTHY OLYMPIA WA

LOCATIONS

HQ: TACOMA PUBLIC SCHOOLS
601 S 8TH ST, TACOMA, WA 984054614
Phone: 253 571-1000
Web: WWW.TACOMASCHOOLS.ORG

HISTORICAL FINANCIALS
Company Type: Private

Income Statement   FYE: August 31

	REVENUE ($ mil.)	NET INCOME ($ mil.)	NET PROFIT MARGIN	EMPLOYEES
08/20	554	(75)	—	3,700
08/19	544	(57)	—	—
08/18	495	(50)	—	—
08/17	469	3	0.8%	—
Annual Growth	5.7%	—	—	—

2020 Year-End Financials

Return on assets: (-5.4%)   Cash ($ mil.): 6
Return on equity: (-20.1%)
Current ratio: —

TALEN ENERGY SUPPLY, LLC

EXECUTIVES

Pres-Ceo, Ralph Alexander
Cfo*, Alex Hernandez
Svp-Cno*, Brad Berryman
Auditors: PRICEWATERHOUSECOOPERS LLP HO

LOCATIONS

HQ: TALEN ENERGY SUPPLY, LLC
600 HAMILTON ST STE 600 # 600, ALLENTOWN, PA 181012130
Phone: 888 211-6011
Web: WWW.TALENENERGY.COM

HISTORICAL FINANCIALS
Company Type: Private

Income Statement   FYE: December 31

	REVENUE ($ mil.)	NET INCOME ($ mil.)	NET PROFIT MARGIN	EMPLOYEES
12/20	1,726	(664)	—	4,981
12/19	2,597	(8)	—	—
12/18	2,714	(37)	—	—
12/16	3,913	(352)	—	—
Annual Growth	(18.5%)	—	—	—

2020 Year-End Financials

Return on assets: (-7.8%)   Cash ($ mil.): 279
Return on equity: (-42.6%)
Current ratio: 1.40

TALLGRASS ENERGY, LP

Tallgrass Energy holds 22.5% of (and manages) Tallgrass Equity which itself owns (through Tallgrass MLP GP LLC) all of Tallgrass Energy Partners' (TEP) incentive distribution rights and a 1.4% general partner interest in TEP. Tallgrass Equity owns a 32.75% limited partner interest in TEP. TEP's business consists of the Tallgrass Interstate Gas Transmission (TIGT) system (in Colorado Kansas Missouri Nebraska and Wyoming); the Trailblazer Pipeline (Colorado Wyoming and Nebraska); a 66.7% membership interest in Tallgrass

Pony Express Pipeline; the Casper and Douglas natural gas processing plants; and the West Frenchie Draw natural gas treating facility. It went public in 2015.

IPO
Tallgrass Energy raised $1.2 billion in its May 2015 IPO. It used the proceeds buy a 22.5% stake in Tallgrass Equity. As a result of the offering Kelso & Co. the Energy & Minerals Group and Tallgrass Energy company executives and directors reduced their collective holdings in the company from 99% to 77%.

Strategy
The company looks to TEP's stable fee-based cash flow and strong potential for future distribution growth to directly benefit the company as a result of Tallgrass Energy's interest in Tallgrass Equity.

EXECUTIVES

Ceo, William R Moler
Pres, Matthew Sheehy
Coo, Crystal Heter
Technology Associate, Carl West
Operations Manager, Charles McCoy
Measurement Technician, Daniel Brennan
Director, David Dehaemers
Director, Doug Griffin
General Manager, Doug Johnson
Chief Financial Officer of Com, Gary Brauchle
Operations Supervisor, Gene Thim
Auditors: PRICEWATERHOUSECOOPERS LLP DE

LOCATIONS

HQ: TALLGRASS ENERGY, LP
4200 W 115TH ST STE 350, LEAWOOD, KS 662112733
Phone: 913 928-6060
Web: WWW.TALLGRASS.COM

COMPETITORS

Colorado Interstate Gas
Kinder Morgan
Merit Energy
Newfield Exploration
Stone Energy
Western Gas Partners

HISTORICAL FINANCIALS
Company Type: Private

Income Statement   FYE: December 31

	REVENUE ($ mil.)	NET INCOME ($ mil.)	NET PROFIT MARGIN	EMPLOYEES
12/18	793	467	59.0%	800
12/17	655	223	34.1%	—
12/16	605	243	40.2%	—
Annual Growth	14.5%	38.7%	—	—

2018 Year-End Financials

Return on assets: 7.9%   Cash ($ mil.): 9
Return on equity: 21.1%
Current ratio: 0.70

TARRANT COUNTY HOSPITAL DISTRICT

If Fort Worth residents are searching for health care they need look no further than Tarrant County Hospital District (dba JPS Health Network). Founded in 1906 in Fort Worth Texas the network's flagship facility John Peter Smith Hospital has approximately 540 beds and provides specialty services including orthopedics cardiology and women's health. JPS Health Network also includes behavioral health treatment center Trinity Springs Pavilion and the JPS Diagnostic & Surgery Hospital of Arlington. The company provides family medical dental and specialty care through dozens of health care centers in northern Texas.

Operations
JPS Hospital is a member of the Council of Teaching Hospitals and Health Systems (COTH).

Sales and Marketing
The health system carries a Level 1 Trauma designation across the spectrum of health care specialties meaning it is the referral hospital of choice for patients who are terribly injured.

Strategy
The health system works to improve the health of Tarrant County as a whole by training health care workers and physicians about working outside the hospital walls and within the community. The institution sponsors programs that are accredited through the Accreditation Council for Graduate Medical Education (ACGME) American Osteopathic Association (AOA) and the Council on Podiatric Medical Education (CPME).

JPS Health Network opened JPS Medical Home Southeast Tarrant a primary and specialty care facility in 2014. The following year the system relocated its Pain Management Clinic to a renovated site in Fort Worth.

EXECUTIVES

Ceo, Robert Earley
Pres*, David M Cecero
Coo*, Bill Whitman
Interim Cfo*, Randy Rogers
Compliance Staff, Charlotte Luce
Payroll Staff, Mary Brooks
Manager, Karen Van Wagner
Psychologist, Alan Frol
Senior Network Engineer, Bill Johnson
Family Practitioner, Christian Burton
Internal Medicine Practitioner, Muhammad Anwar

LOCATIONS

HQ: TARRANT COUNTY HOSPITAL DISTRICT
1500 S MAIN ST, FORT WORTH, TX 761044917
Phone: 817 921-3431
Web: WWW.JPSHEALTHNET.ORG

Primary Locations – Texas
Ambulatory Surgery Center (Fort Worth)
Cardiology Center (Fort Worth)
Enrollment & Eligibility Center (Fort Worth)
Family Medicine & Surgical Specialty Center (Fort Worth)
Healing Wings AIDS Center (Fort Worth)
John Peter for Cancer Care (Fort Worth)
JPS Urgent Care Center (Fort Worth)
Lifespan Family Medicine & Pediatrics (Fort Worth)
Patient Care Pavilion (Fort Worth)
Professional Building-Medicine Clinic (Fort Worth)
Trinity Springs Pavilion for Psychiatric Services (Fort Worth)

PRODUCTS/OPERATIONS

Selected Services
Behavioral Services
Cancer
Cardiology
Dental
Geriatrics
Healing Wings HIV/AIDS Center
Orthopedics and Sports Medicine
Robotic Surgery
School-Based Health Centers
Sexual Assault Nurse Examiner Program
Stroke / N
Surgical Services

Trauma Services
Women's Services

COMPETITORS

Baylor University Medical Center	Presbyterian Hospital Of Dallas
Christus Health	Southwestern Medical Center
Community Health Systems	Tenet Healthcare
Cook Children's Health Care System	Texas Health Resources
Hca	The Methodist Health System
Harris Methodist Fort Worth Hospital	Universal Health Services
Parkland Health & Hospital System	

HISTORICAL FINANCIALS
Company Type: Private

Income Statement				FYE: September 30
	REVENUE ($ mil.)	NET INCOME ($ mil.)	NET PROFIT MARGIN	EMPLOYEES
09/18	632	(3)	—	3,000
09/16	576	18	3.2%	—
09/15	557	48	8.7%	—
09/14	285	48	16.9%	—
Annual Growth	**22.0%**	—	—	—

2018 Year-End Financials
Return on assets: (-0.3%)   Cash ($ mil.): 161
Return on equity: (-0.4%)
Current ratio: 4.30

TARRANT COUNTY TEXAS (INC)

EXECUTIVES

Administrator, G K Manieus
Cfo*, B Glen Whitley
County Exe.sec, Judy Scott
Coordinator, Lori McEndree
Commissioner, Andy Nguyen
Supervisor of Mental Health SE, Cobi Tittle
Elections Coordinator, Germaine Woolridge
Commissioner, Roy Brooks
Supervisor Accounts Payable, Ty Dupont
Network Engineer, Vernon Leonard
Chief Information Officer, Christopher Ayafor
Auditors: DELOITTE & TOUCHE LLP DALLAS

LOCATIONS

HQ: TARRANT COUNTY TEXAS (INC)
100 E WEATHERFORD ST, FORT WORTH, TX 761960206
Phone: 817 884-1111
Web: WWW.ACCESS.TARRANTCOUNTY.COM

HISTORICAL FINANCIALS
Company Type: Private

Income Statement				FYE: September 30
	REVENUE ($ mil.)	NET INCOME ($ mil.)	NET PROFIT MARGIN	EMPLOYEES
09/19	687	19	2.9%	3,945
09/18	650	(10)	—	—
09/17	625	(20)	—	—
09/16	597	5	1.0%	—
Annual Growth	**4.8%**	**49.2%**	—	—

TAUBER OIL COMPANY

Tauber Oil is a family-owned company that markets refined petroleum products carbon black feedstocks natural gas natural gas liquids crude oil petrochemicals and refined products. The company is one of the US's leading suppliers of feedstocks for reforming and olefin cracking. It also has oil and gas exploration and production operations. Subsidiary Tauber Petrochemical was created to beef up the company's international petrochemical business. The Houston-based company serves major and independent oil companies major petrochemical producers and consumers and small- to medium-sized end-users. Tauber Oil which is owned by David and Richard Tauber maintains a fleet of more than 500 rail cars to supply its customers.

EXECUTIVES

Pres, Richard E Tauber
Exec V Pres*, David W Tauber
V Pres-Fin*, Matthew Crotts
Executive Officer, Fred Shato
Coordinator, Robby Crabtree
Vice President, Bob Mackenzie
Vice President Refined, Blake Hale
Vice President Supply, Bobby Combs
G L Accounting, Melinda Rains
Executive Assistant, Myla Wunderlich
Administrative Assistant, Saide Alvarez
Auditors: MOHLE ADAMS HOUSTON TEXAS

LOCATIONS

HQ: TAUBER OIL COMPANY
55 WAUGH DR STE 700, HOUSTON, TX 770075837
Phone: 713 869-8700
Web: WWW.TAUBEROIL.COM

PRODUCTS/OPERATIONS

Selected Products:
Natural Gas Liquids
 Butane
 Ethane
 Isobutane
 Propane
Petrochemicals
 Benzene
 Methanol
 MTBE
 Styrene monomer
 Toluene
 Xylene
Refined
 Aviation jet fuel
 Kerosene
 Low sulfur diesel
 No. 2 fuel oil

COMPETITORS

Cabot Oil & Gas	Marathon Oil
Devon Energy	Occidental Petroleum
Exxon Mobil	Tesoro
George Warren	Valero Energy
Global Partners	

HISTORICAL FINANCIALS
Company Type: Private

Income Statement				FYE: December 31
	REVENUE ($ mil.)	NET INCOME ($ mil.)	NET PROFIT MARGIN	EMPLOYEES
12/14	4,831	10	0.2%	135
12/13	4,769	16	0.3%	—
12/12	5,088	21	0.4%	—
Annual Growth	**(2.6%)**	**(29.0%)**	—	—

Return on assets: 2.7%   Cash ($ mil.): 15
Return on equity: 6.9%
Current ratio: 1.50

TECHNIP USA, INC.

EXECUTIVES

Pres, Deanna Goodwin
V Pres, Matthew Seinsheimer
Designer, Allan Salvador
Coordinator, Christopher Bennett
Procurement Staff, Sam Daik
Manager, Natalie Michulka
Senior Project Manager, James Lee
Refurbishment, Brett Folmar
Applications Engineer Ucos, Carlos Alvarez
Senior Buyer, Charlie Reynoso
Buyer, Constance Rice

LOCATIONS

HQ: TECHNIP USA, INC.
  13460 LOCKWOOD RD, HOUSTON, TX 770446444
Phone: 281 591-4000
Web: WWW.TECHNIPFMC.COM

HISTORICAL FINANCIALS
Company Type: Private

Income Statement   FYE: December 31

	REVENUE ($ mil.)	NET INCOME ($ mil.)	NET PROFIT MARGIN	EMPLOYEES
12/08	1,377	111	8.1%	4,346
12/04	609	(1)	—	—
12/97	225,116	0	0.0%	—
Annual Growth	(37.1%)	79.2%		

2008 Year-End Financials
Return on assets: 10.7%   Cash ($ mil.): 205
Return on equity: 26.5%
Current ratio: 1.20

TECUMSEH PRODUCTS COMPANY LLC

Named for the legendary Shawnee chief Tecumseh Products makes a line of hermetically sealed compressors and heat pumps for residential and commercial refrigerators and freezers water coolers air conditioners dehumidifiers and vending machines. The company's line of scroll compressor models are suited for demanding commercial refrigeration applications and consist primarily of reciprocating and rotary designs. Tecumseh sells its products to OEMs and aftermarket distributors in more than 100 countries worldwide with more than 80% of its sales generated outside of the US. In mid-2015 Tecumseh agreed to be acquired by affiliates of Mueller Industries and Atlas Holdings for $123 million.

Geographic Reach
Tecumseh's products are manufactured in about a dozen plants in the US Brazil France (five facilities) and India (two facilities); assembly plants are located in Canada Malaysia and Mexico. Some of the company's facilities are made possible through joint ventures; one such venture is Song Jiang in China.

Sales and Marketing
The company serves 1600 customers including Whirlpool and Electrolux which together generate about 12% of the company's business. In 2014 almost 45% of the sales from its Brazilian location were made to its three largest customers. The company sells its products in 97 countries primarily through its own sales staff as well as independent sales representatives and authorized wholesale distributors. It markets its products under brand names that include Celseon Tecumseh Wintsys Masterflux Silensys and Vector.

Financial Performance
Tecumseh has suffered four straight years of declining revenues and two straight years of net losses. Revenues fell 12% from $824 million in 2013 to $724 million in 2014 as the company posted a net loss of $33 million in 2014.

The decrease in revenue for 2014 was primarily due to a 8% drop in sales of compressors used in commercial refrigeration and aftermarket applications a 23% decrease in sales of compressors for air conditioning applications and a 13% drop in sales for compressors used in household refrigeration and freezer applications. Tecumseh was also negatively affected by a competitive pricing environment in Brazil and soft market conditions in North America throughout 2014.

Strategy
Focused on growing internationally Tecumseh has invested in research and development engineering laboratories in North America Europe South America and India. It also partners with R&D facilities at universities throughout the globe to provide life science research on how its products interface with the environment.

HISTORY

Master toolmakers Ray Herrick (friend and advisor to Henry Ford and Thomas Edison) and Bill Sage founded the Michigan-based company in 1930 as Hillsdale Machine & Tool. Its first products included small tools toys and car and refrigerator parts. By 1933 Herrick controlled the company. The next year the company bought a facility in Tecumseh Michigan where it began mass-producing car and refrigerator parts. The company changed its name to Tecumseh Products in 1934 and went public in 1937.

By the end of the 1930s Tecumseh was a major producer of hermetic compressors. In 1941 its focus shifted to WWII efforts and it began making anti-aircraft projectile casings and aircraft engine parts. Herrick's son Kenneth began working for Tecumseh in 1945. Two years later a company-made compressor was used in the first home window air-conditioning unit.

Tecumseh bought two Ohio companies in 1950 and 1952 and introduced an AC compressor for cars in 1953. Two years later the company bought compressor designer Tresco and hired Joseph Layton as Tecumseh's president and CEO. Tecumseh gained entry into the gasoline engine market with the purchase of Wisconsin's Lauson Engine (1956) and Power Products (1957). Acquisitions in the 1960s allowed Tecumseh to tap into the power-train market.

EXECUTIVES

Ceo, Jay Pittas
Pres, Harold M Karp
Evp-Cfo-Treas, Janice E Stipp
Cbd&ro*, Igor Popov
Evp*, Jerry L Mosingo
Pres Compressor Business Unit, Eric L
  Stolzenberg
Pres Elec Comp Business Unit, Ronald E Pratt
Global Engineering, Ryan Burns
Global Human Resources, Roger Jackson
Customer Manager, Anne Kocian Spyhalsk
Accountant, Jennifer McCurdy

LOCATIONS

HQ: TECUMSEH PRODUCTS COMPANY LLC
  5683 HINES DR, ANN ARBOR, MI 481087901
Phone: 734 585-9500
Web: WWW.TECUMSEH.COM

2014 Sales

	$ mil.	% of total
Europe	191	26
South America		
Brazil	182	25
Other countries	45	6
North America		
US	125	18
Other countries	15	2
Asia		
India	105	14
China	13	2
Other countries	5	1
Middle East & Africa	39	6
Total	724	100

PRODUCTS/OPERATIONS

2014 Sales

	% of total
Commercial refrigeration	62
Household refrigerator & freezer	19
Residential & specialty air conditioning	19
Total	100

Selected Products
Compressors (all hermetically sealed)
  Reciprocating (for air conditioning and commercial refrigeration)
  Rotary (for room and mobile air conditioning)
  Scroll (especially designed for demanding commercial refrigeration applications)
  Highlighted Products
  A Legend Reborn
  Tecumseh";K” Kits

COMPETITORS

Brasmotor	Mitsubishi Electric
Bristol Compressors	Panasonic Corp
Daikin	Sanyo
Danfoss Turbocor	Sullair
Emerson Electric	Trane Inc.
Lg Electronics	Weg Electric
Lennox	

HISTORICAL FINANCIALS
Company Type: Private

Income Statement   FYE: December 31

	REVENUE ($ mil.)	NET INCOME ($ mil.)	NET PROFIT MARGIN	EMPLOYEES
12/14	724	(32)	—	4,800
12/13	823	(37)	—	—
12/12	854	22	2.6%	—
Annual Growth	(7.9%)			

2014 Year-End Financials
Return on assets: (-8.3%)   Cash ($ mil.): 42
Return on equity: (-21.8%)
Current ratio: 1.40

TEKNOR APEX COMPANY

Teknor Apex offers a wide-ranging portfolio of chemicals and synthetic polymers. The company's six business divisions provide colorants (through its Teknor Color unit) vinyl compounds thermoplastic elastomers engineering thermoplastics chemicals for the polyvinyl chloride (PVC) plasticizer market and garden hoses. The company's compounds are used for building and construction consumer products industrial manufacturing electrical and electronic devices medical tools packaging and vehicular components. Founded in 1924 by Alfred A. Fain and his son-in-law Albert Pilavin Teknor invented the first plasticized (flexible) PVC.

Operations

Teknor Apex operates via six business segments.

The company's Teknor Color unit offers standard and custom colorants for polymers including olefins styrenics polyethylene terephthalate (PET) engineering thermoplastics and thermoplastic elastomers.

Teknor's vinyl products include flexible and rigid polyvinyl chloride (PVC) fire-resistant plenum PVC PVC elastomers PVC blends (including rigid blends) chlorinated PVC PVC film and halogen-free flame retardant.

The company's thermoplastic elastomers lineup comprises styrenic block copolymer (SBC) compounds polyolefin blends thermoplastic vulcanizates polyurethane compounds and other specialty blends.

Through its Engineering Thermoplastics business Teknor markets three nylon-based compounds that are used in outdoor power equipment hinges furniture and cars ? including chassis exterior and interior parts and engine components.

The company's Chemicals segment produces esters for the PVC plasticizer market under its TruVis brand. Its offerings include adipate low-viscosity trimellitate high-viscosity trimellitate and polyol esters. The chemicals are used as base stocks and additives for automotive and industrial applications metalworking fluid and grease.

Teknor also sells hoses under brands like ZeroG Neverkink Flexalloy and Apex for gardens professional landscaping farms and ranches RVs and marine vehicles industrial and construction applications and food and services.

Geographic Reach

Pawtucket Rhode Island-based Teknor Apex has about 10 US manufacturing plants (including one manufacturing plant and sales office) in California Kentucky Massachusetts the Carolinas Rhode Island Tennessee Texas and Vermont; one plant in each of Belgium Germany and China; one sales office in each of Germany the Netherlands and China; and a plant and sales office in Singapore.

Sales and Marketing

Teknor Apex serves a diverse client base including building and construction firms consumer goods producers electrical and electronics companies industrial manufacturers healthcare providers packaging companies and vehicle fabricators.

Strategy

Teknor Apex released a series of acrylic-based compounds for highly weatherable dark-color outer or "cap" layers in PVC exterior products. The company has given the entire range of these capstocks the new brand name Weatherguard.

The company and Covestro cooperated closely on compounding thermoplastic polyurethane (TPU) and signed a cooperation agreement to this effect. The products made from the agreement will be marketed under the name Desmoflex.

Mergers and Acquisitions

Company Background

The company was founded in 1924 as a tire distributor and retreader by Alfred Fain in 1924. Fain's grandson now leads the privately held company.

EXECUTIVES

Chb, Jonathan Fain
Pres*, Suresh Swaminathan
Cfo*, Paul Morrisroe
Coordinator, Debbie Lopes
Senior Vice President of Manuf, Bill Murray
Vice President Human Resources, Laurie Meisner
Information Technology Manager, John Wood
Senior Technical Analyst, Harvey Blanchette
Sales Representative, Jon Mello
National Sales Operations Mana, Cindy Chatell
Process Engineer, Darren Fraim
Auditors: PICCERELLI GOLSTEIN & COMPANY

LOCATIONS

HQ: TEKNOR APEX COMPANY
   505 CENTRAL AVE, PAWTUCKET, RI 028611900
Phone: 401 725-8000
Web: WWW.TEKNORAPEX.COM

PRODUCTS/OPERATIONS

Selected Products and Services
Vinyl
FLEXIBLE PVC COMPOUNDS
Apex Flexible PVC
FireGuard LS FR PVC
Flexalloy PVC Elastomers
Apex PVC Blends
RIGID PVC COMPOUNDS
Apex Rigid PVC
AquaGuard CPVC
Apex Rigid PVC Blends
CALENDERED PVC FILM
Apex Calendered PVC Film
Thermoplastic Elastomers (TPE)
TPS TPV TPO AND TPU COMPOUNDS
Medalist Medical TPEs
Monprene
Sarlink
Elexar
Engineering Thermoplastics
POLYAMIDES
Chemlon
Creamid
Polyolefins
HalGuard LS HFFR Compounds
   Colorants
Teknor Color
Color Store
Esters
TruVis Esters
Garden Hose

COMPETITORS

Gls	Rb Rubber
Natureworks	Synthomer
Pmc Global	Tekni-plex
Polyone	Vulcan International

HISTORICAL FINANCIALS
Company Type: Private

Income Statement   FYE: July 31

	REVENUE ($ mil.)	NET INCOME ($ mil.)	NET PROFIT MARGIN	EMPLOYEES
07/14	996	50	5.0%	2,808
07/05	574	0	—	—
Annual Growth	6.3%	—	—	—

2014 Year-End Financials

Return on assets: 6.8%	Cash ($ mil.): 74
Return on equity: 5.0%	
Current ratio: 2.40	

TEKSYSTEMS, INC.

TEKsystems a subsidiary of staffing giant Allegis provides IT consulting and staffing services from locations in North America Europe and Asia. Considered one of the nation's largest IT staffing firms the company places more than 80000 technical professionals each year who work in a variety of fields including telecommunications construction and engineering. TEKsystems has more than 100 locations serving about 6000 clients. Spinning off of fellow Allegis unit Aerotek TEKsystems was formed in 1994 to focus on the IT needs of clients.

Operations

TEKsystems is an industry in full-stack technology services talent services and real-world application. It offers services such as cloud enablement data analytics and insights DevOps and automation digital experience enterprise applications modern enterprise management risk and security telecom design implementation and operations.

Geographic Reach

Headquartered in Hanover Maryland the company has more than 100 locations throughout North America Europe and Asia.

Sales and Marketing

TEKsystems works to help its clients control cost mitigate risk and deliver quality product outcomes.

The company is working with over 6000 customers including 80% of the Fortune 500. It serve various industries primarily communications financial services healthcare services and government. Additional industries the company serves are aerospace and defense food and beverage agriculture automotive among others.

Strategy

TEKsystems acquired 1Strategy to leverage a mutual familiarity with the expanding portfolio of AWS cloud solutions.

Mergers and Acquisitions

In 2019 TEKsystems acquired 1Strategy a Premier Consulting partner in the AWS Partner Network. The acquisition is to leverage a mutual familiarity with the expanding portfolio of AWS cloud solutions.

EXECUTIVES

Pres, Jay Alvather
Director, Michael Pricher
Senior Recruiter, Mickey McLean
Digital, Molly Moorfoot
Business Manager, Patrick Flanagan
End User Support Recruiter, Samantha Hatcher
Account Manager, Scott Parkinson
Area Director, Shaun Franklin
Senior Business Operations, Taylor Stefanie
Recruiter Lead, Tyler Feiga
Proposal Manager, Ursula Walker
Auditors: PRICEWATERHOUSECOOPERS LLP BA

LOCATIONS

HQ: TEKSYSTEMS, INC.
   7437 RACE RD, HANOVER, MD 210761112
Phone: 410 540-7700
Web: WWW.ALLEGISGROUP.COM

PRODUCTS/OPERATIONS

SELECTED SERVICES
IT STAFFING SOLUTIONS
Communications Staffing Services
Digital Services
End User Services
IT Applications Staffing Services
IT Direct Placement Services

Network Infrastructure Staffing Services
TEKsystems Staffing Quality Process
Time and Expense
IT SERVICES
Applications Services
Education Services
Global Delivery Network
Infrastructure Services
Project Governance
IT TALENT MANAGEMENT EXPERTISE
Local Market

Selected Markets Served

Communications
Financial services
Government
Information technology
Expertise

COMPETITORS

Acro Service	Info Technologies
Adecco	Kelly Services
Cdi	Manpowergroup
Corsource Technology	Prosum
Group	Robert Half

HISTORICAL FINANCIALS

Company Type: Private

Income Statement				FYE: December 31
	REVENUE ($ mil.)	NET INCOME ($ mil.)	NET PROFIT MARGIN	EMPLOYEES
12/20	4,815	0	—	2,900
12/19	4,927	0	—	
12/18	4,677	0	—	
12/17	4,350	0	—	
Annual Growth	3.4%	—	—	—

2020 Year-End Financials

Return on assets: —
Return on equity: —
Current ratio: 2.80

Cash ($ mil.): 12

TEMPLE UNIVERSITY HEALTH SYSTEM, INC.

Temple University Health System (TUHS) is a network of academic and community hospitals associated with the Temple University School of Medicine. It provides primary secondary and tertiary care to residents in the Philadelphia County (Pennsylvania) area. The system includes 722-bed Temple University Hospital (a Level 1 trauma center) and a pair of community-based hospitals that provide acute and emergency care as well as the Jeanes Hospital and TUH-Episcopal Campus (home to a 120-bed behavioral health unit). TUHS supports programs in cardiology organ transplantation and oncology. In late 2019 the health system agreed to sell the Fox Chase Cancer Center to Philadelphia-based Thomas Jefferson University.

Operations

The $1.4-billion academic health system comprises Temple University Hospital TUH-Episcopal Campus TUH-Northern Campus Fox Chase Cancer Center Jeanes Hospital Temple Transport Team and Temple Physicians. It's affiliated with Temple University School of Medicine. Bermuda-based TUHS Insurance Company Ltd. is a captive insurance company established to reinsure the professional liability claims of TUHS subsidiaries.

It offers everything from specialized cardiac care and spinal rehabilitation to a lung care center a burn center and stroke treatments.

Medicare and Medicaid account for 65% of net patient revenues.

Geographic Reach

Temple University Health System serves the residents of Philadelphia.

Sales and Marketing

TUHS markets itself through TV commercials and print and billboard advertising.

Financial Performance

In fiscal 2012 revenue rose by 37% to $1.35 billion vs. 2011. It attributes the double-digit gains to increases in net patient service revenue research revenue and other revenue. The system logged $107 million in net income during the reporting period as compared to a net loss in 2011.

Strategy

TUHS concentrates on adding services and expanding its geographic reach. It added Fox Chase Cancer Center in 2012; opened the women's care center in Elkins Park Pennsylvania in 2012; opened a third urgent care facility in Jenkintown Pennsylvania in 2013; and expanded into new markets by opening the Temple Health Center City facility.

EXECUTIVES

Ceo, Michael Young
Pres*, Richard M Englert
Vp For Public Affairs*, William T Bergman
Administrative Coordinator, Diana Douglas
Manager, Kanchana Perera
Manager, Alison Pipkin
Senior Director, Business Deve, Joseph Rudy
Chief Operating Officer, Lisa Fino
Operations Director, Michael Dugan
MD, Robin D Rothstein
Director Planning, Steve Szybowski
Auditors: DELOITTE & TOUCHE LLP PHILADE

LOCATIONS

HQ: TEMPLE UNIVERSITY HEALTH SYSTEM, INC.
2450 W HUNTING PARK AVE, PHILADELPHIA, PA 191291302
Phone: 215 707-2000
Web: WWW.TEMPLEHEALTH.ORG

COMPETITORS

Albert Einstein Healthcare Network
Aria Health
Children's Hospital Of Philadelphia
Community Health Systems
Crozer-keystone Health System
Doylestown Hospital
Jefferson Health
Main Line Health System
Mercy Health System
North Philadelphia Health System
Northwestern Human Services
Our Lady Of Lourdes Medical Center
Pennsylvania Hospital
The Magee Memorial Hospital For Convalescents
University Of Pennsylvania Health System

HISTORICAL FINANCIALS

Company Type: Private

Income Statement				FYE: June 30
	REVENUE ($ mil.)	NET INCOME ($ mil.)	NET PROFIT MARGIN	EMPLOYEES
06/12	1,004	(48)	—	7,573
06/11	994	45	4.6%	—
06/09	0	(0)	—	—
Annual Growth	1819.9%	—	—	—

2012 Year-End Financials

Return on assets: (-5.1%)
Return on equity: (-22.0%)
Current ratio: 2.30

Cash ($ mil.): 103

TEMPLE UNIVERSITY-OF THE COMMONWEALTH SYSTEM OF HIGHER EDUCATION

Temple University provides education and training services to approximately 39000 undergraduate graduate and professional students are enrolled in its more than 500 academic programs across the Philadelphia university's over 15 schools. Its Health Sciences Center includes Temple University Hospital and schools that teach medicine and dentistry. Part of Pennsylvania's Commonwealth System of Higher Education Temple has eight different campuses in the Philadelphia area as well campuses in Tokyo and Rome and offers study abroad programs in various locations. The system has a student-teacher ratio of about 13:1. Dr. Russell Conwell founded the university in 1884; it was incorporated as Temple University in 1907.

Operations

Temple's campus in suburban Ambler Pennsylvania offers programs in ecological planning and design horticulture and landscape architecture. The university offers more than 150 majors across a wide range of challenging and in-demand fields. Students can obtain professional degrees in dentistry law medicine pharmacy and podiatric medicine among others.

Geographic Reach

Temple's main campus is located in North Philadelphia. About 125 countries represent in the university's student body.

Strategy

EXECUTIVES

Pres, Neil D Theobald
Prin*, Ann Weaver Hart
Accnt, Thomas Brauner
Assistant Professor, Chandra A Dass
Scientist, April Suriano
Coordinator, Cheryl Jackson
Assistant Professor, David Orr
Scientist, Edward Gawlinski
Scientist, Jon B Suzuki
Scientist, Monica Busuioc
Executive of Information Techn, Arthur C Papacostas
Auditors: DELOITTE & TOUCHE LLP PHILADE

LOCATIONS

HQ: TEMPLE UNIVERSITY-OF THE COMMONWEALTH SYSTEM OF HIGHER EDUCATION
1801 N BROAD ST, PHILADELPHIA, PA 191226003
Phone: 215 204-1380
Web: WWW.TEMPLE.EDU

Selected Campuses

Philadelphia
  Ambler
  Center City
  Fort Washington
  Harrisburg
  Main
  Podiatric Medicine
  Health Sciences Center
International
  Japan
  Rome Italy

HISTORICAL FINANCIALS

Company Type: Private

Income Statement				FYE: June 30
	REVENUE ($ mil.)	NET INCOME ($ mil.)	NET PROFIT MARGIN	EMPLOYEES
06/21	3,722	553	14.9%	9,061
06/20	3,628	154	4.3%	—
06/13	2,635	192	7.3%	—
06/12	2,254	(37)	—	—
Annual Growth	5.7%	—	—	—

2021 Year-End Financials

Return on assets: 9.1% Cash ($ mil.): 844
Return on equity: 15.0%
Current ratio: 3.40

TENASKA ENERGY, INC.

EXECUTIVES

Chb-Ceo, Howard L Hawks
Pres-Dir*, Jerry K Crouse
Dir*, Thomas E Hendricks
Exec V Pres*, Michael C Lebens
SEC*, Ronald N Quinn
Assistant Controller, Lisa Jones
Executive Vice President, David Schettler
Maintenance Manager, David Wilroy
Marketing, Heather Delmas
Executive Administrator, INA Schumacher
Marketing, Jeff Rohrig

LOCATIONS

HQ: TENASKA ENERGY, INC.
14302 FNB PKWY, OMAHA, NE 681544446
Phone: 402 691-9500
Web: WWW.TENASKA.COM

HISTORICAL FINANCIALS

Company Type: Private

Income Statement				FYE: December 31
	REVENUE ($ mil.)	NET INCOME ($ mil.)	NET PROFIT MARGIN	EMPLOYEES
12/07	654	0	—	300
12/05	10,020	0	—	—
Annual Growth	(74.4%)	—	—	—

2007 Year-End Financials

Return on assets: — Cash ($ mil.): 142
Return on equity: —
Current ratio: 1.70

TENERITY, INC.

Through its partners and affiliations Affinion Group aims to make fans of its customers' customers. The company operates membership and loyalty programs on behalf of corporate clients seeking to strengthen their ties to consumers. It specializes in launching a variety of media services — through direct mail and the Internet — and packaging these benefits to its clients' customers. Programs overseen include AutoVantage Buyers Advantage and Travelers Advantage. Overall the group offers its programs to some 65 million members worldwide through more than 5700 partners.

Geographic Reach

The company has offices in Europe South Africa and the US. Most recently Affinion expanded its footprint into Brazil and into Turkey. However the company gets about 80% of its revenue from US.

Sales and Marketing

Affinion provides its customer engagement and loyalty solutions through retail and wholesale arrangements with its marketing partners in addition to its direct to consumer marketing efforts. Under a retail arrangement it usually markets products to a marketing partner's customers by using that marketing partner's brand name and customer contacts. Under a wholesale arrangement the marketing partner bears the expense to market products and services to its customers collects revenue from the customer and typically pays us a monthly fee per end-customer.

Marketing partners have included Citibank JP-Morgan Chase Royal Bank of Scotland and Wells Fargo. Revenues generated from Wells Fargo accounted for 15.3% of total revenues in fiscal 2012.

Affinion also markets its products through direct efforts such direct mail online marketing point-of-sale marketing and telemarketing.

Financial Performance

In fiscal 2012 the company reported revenue of about $1.49 billion down by 2.6% compared to the $1.53 billion it reported in revenue for fiscal 2011. The decline in revenue was attributed to decreases in revenue from membership products along with declines in revenue from insurance and package products.

Strategy

The company intends to continue its growth in international markets through both organic initiatives including geographic expansion as well as the continued evaluation of strategic acquisitions that strengthen its customer engagement solutions grow its distribution capabilities or enhance its scale.

Affinion sees substantial opportunities to add new marketing partners in the retail financial travel Internet cable telecom and utilities industries in both North America and Europe.

Mergers and Acquisitions

In 2012 Affinion extended its geographic reach in Europe with the acquisition of a majority stake in Back-Up a leading concierge service. Affinion has accelerated its entry into that growing market through the formation of a partnership with Boyner Holding Company one of the most respected and successful brands currently serving Turkish consumers.

EXECUTIVES

Ceo, Greg Miller
Cfo, Kanuj Malhotra
Chief Digital Officer, Rachel Bicking
Cto, Loic Blondel
Pres Insurance, Robert J Dudacek
Senior Project Manager Infrast, Daniel Kobylanski
Infrastructure, James McDowell
Vice President, Jim Daxner
Senior Vice President, Richard Pitrolo
Director, Rick Frier
Senior Quality Assurance Analy, Autumn Sands-Caldwell

LOCATIONS

HQ: TENERITY, INC.
6 HIGH RIDGE PARK, STAMFORD, CT 069051327
Phone: 203 956-1000
Web: WWW.CXLOYALTY.COM

2012 Sales

	$ mil.	% of total
US	1,191	80
UK	117	8
Other countries	186	12
Total	**1,495**	**100**

PRODUCTS/OPERATIONS

Selected Membership Products and Services

AutoVantage
Buyers Advantage
CompleteHome
CardCops
Everyday Privileges Gold
Everyday Values
Great Fun
Great Options
HealthSaver
Hot-Line
ID Secure
IdentitySecure
Just For Me
PC SafetyPlus
Privacy Guard
Shoppers Advantage
Travelers Advantage

Selected Partners

American Express
Bank of America
Choice Hotels
HSBC
JPMorgan Chase
TransWorld Entertainment
Wells Fargo

COMPETITORS

Aegon Direct Marketing Services	Maritz Loyalty & Motivation
Aig	Provell
Access Plans Usa	Q Interactive
Assurant	Rewards Network
Hospitality Marketing Concepts	Student Advantage
Intersections Inc.	Synapse Group

HISTORICAL FINANCIALS

Company Type: Private

Income Statement				FYE: December 31
	REVENUE ($ mil.)	NET INCOME ($ mil.)	NET PROFIT MARGIN	EMPLOYEES
12/18	699	303	43.3%	3,860
12/17	953	(24)	—	—
12/16	969	16	1.7%	—
Annual Growth	(15.0%)	331.4%	—	—

2018 Year-End Financials

Return on assets: 44.5% Cash ($ mil.): 84
Return on equity: —
Current ratio: 1.00

TERRACON CONSULTANTS, INC.

Employee-owned Terracon Consultants (Terracon) provides geotechnical environmental construction material evaluation pavement engineering and construction management and facilities engineering services. One of the nation's top design firms the company serves the agriculture oil & gas telecommunications commercial development and transportation sectors as well as government clients. The company has more than 150 offices in all 50 US states. It helps its customers comply with new building codes and environmental regulations assess environmental hazards and tackle the problem of aging structures.

Operations

Terracon provides practical solutions to environmental facilities geotechnical and materials engineering challenges. Environmental services includes asbestos and lead services brownfields and site redevelopment environmental management systems regulatory compliance and solid waste planning and design among others. It also provides facility engineering including building enclosure condition assessments MEP consulting engineering diagnostics structural analysis and design geotechnical consulting construction monitoring & support and construction material evaluation.

Geographic Reach

Kansas-based Terracon has operations throughout the US.

Sales and Marketing

Terracon serves variety of industries such as agriculture aquatics commercial/retail disaster response federal financial healthcare industrial oil & gas power generation/transmission telecommunications and transportation/infrastructure.

Some of its agricultural partners includes Agriliance LLC Cenex/Harvest States Helena Chemical Company Murphy Family Farms Seaboard Farms United Agri Products Terra Industries as well as its government clients such as US Air Force US Department of Agriculture NASA Department of Commerce and Federal Highway Administration.

Strategy

Terracon continues to expand its business and geographic reach through strategic acquisitions. Among its recent acquisitions are Environmental Services Inc. and Geotechnical & Environmental Consultants Inc. Skelly and Loy and Environmental Planning Group. These acquisitions expand Terracon's business operations geographically across Georgia the Mid-Atlantic and the Southwest.

Terracon's acquisition of Environmental Services Inc. and Geotechnical & Environmental Consultants Inc. enhances the company's geographic presence and depth of services in Georgia and the Southeast. ESI and GEC's expertise and services complement its existing environmental geotechnical and materials capabilities and will allow Terracon to support its clients throughout the Southeast even more nimbly.

While Terracon's acquisition of Skelly and Loy allows it to further strengthen its service offerings and geographic resources in Pennsylvania and the Mid-Atlantic. In joining forces the companies' shared capabilities and focus on outstanding client experience allows it to bring even greater resources to clients regionally and nationally. In addition the acquisition of the Environmental Planning Group brings a tremendous wealth of experience and strong professional presence in the region further enhancing its environmental engineering and consulting services in the Southwest and Western US.

Aside from acquisitions Terracon also implemented key organizational changes in late 2019 designed to guide the company as it continues its pattern of growth.

Mergers and Acquisitions

Terracon has expanded its geotechnical environmental engineering and testing capabilities with a string of recent purchases.

In 2013 it expanded its presence in the Northeast with the acquisition of New Hampshire-based environmental consulting firm New England EnviroStrategies Inc.

In 2012 Terracon acquired California-based Earthtec Inc. a provider of geotechnical environ-

mental special inspection and other services to clients in Northern California. Also in 2012 it purchased Utah-based IHI Environmental a provider of industrial hygiene occupational safety and environmental consulting services to public and private sector clients across the western US. Previously Terracon bought Colorado firm Geotechnical Engineering Group boosting its presence in the West; and Stafford Consulting Engineers a building envelope system specialist with a presence in the Southeast. Also that year Terracon acquired Dressler Consulting Engineers a building forensics engineering firm based in Kansas and Nodarse & Associates a Florida-based environmental geotechnical and construction materials engineering firm.

Company Background

The company was founded in Iowa in 1965 as a joint venture between Shive Hall and Hattery (civil consulting) Soil Testing Services (geotechnical testing) and Gerald Olson P.E. (the company's founder and a project engineer).

Terracon is owned by its employees. The firm was ranked 51st on the Employee Ownership 100 the list of the top 100 largest majority employee-owned companies in the US in 2012.

EXECUTIVES

Ceo, Gayle Packer
Staff, Alex Goharioon
Administrative Manager, Custom, Alisha Cook
Engineer, Allen Minks
Staff Environmental Scientist, Andrew Mildenberger
Manager, Andy Ruocco
Office Manager, Arturo Barrera
Project Manager, Bachan Sinha
Senior Associate Office Manage, Benjamin Taylor
Office Manager, Bill Jacobs
Staff Engineer, Blake Morgan
Auditors: BKD LLP KANSAS CITY MISSOURI

LOCATIONS

HQ: TERRACON CONSULTANTS, INC.
10841 S RIDGEVIEW RD, OLATHE, KS 660616456
Phone: 913 599-6886
Web: WWW.TERRACON.COM

PRODUCTS/OPERATIONS

Selected Services

Materials
Special InspectionsOn-site Observation and MonitoringConstruction Quality Control and Quality Assurance ProgramsField and Laboratory Testing and AnalysisDesign and Review of Concrete Grout and Asphaltic Concrete MixesStructural Steel Nondestructive Testi
Geotechnical
Subsurface exploration and testing
Foundation analysis and design
Soil stabilization
Groundwater control
Pavement design
Environmental
Site assessment
Industrial hygiene and occupational safety
Regulatory compliance
Solid waste planning and design
Facilities
Roof/waterproofing consulting
Foundation/structural consulting
Life cycle cost analysis
Peer reviews
Seismic risk assessments
Construction administration

Selected Markets

Agriculture
Commercial/Retail
Energy
Federal
Financial

Industrial
Telecommunications
Transportation/Infrastructure

COMPETITORS

Aecom	Jacobs Engineering
Fluor	Kbr
Hntb Companies	

HISTORICAL FINANCIALS

Company Type: Private

Income Statement   FYE: December 31

	REVENUE ($ mil.)	NET INCOME ($ mil.)	NET PROFIT MARGIN	EMPLOYEES
12/20	818	23	2.9%	4,000
12/19	804	21	2.7%	—
12/18	751	22	2.9%	—
Annual Growth	4.3%	3.4%	—	—

2020 Year-End Financials

Return on assets: 7.5%   Cash ($ mil.): 18
Return on equity: 14.2%
Current ratio: 2.50

TESLA ENERGY OPERATIONS, INC.

Ready to get off the grid? SolarCity can help. The company sells installs finances and monitors turnkey solar energy systems that convert sunlight into electricity. Its systems either mounted on a building's roof or the ground are used by residential commercial and government customers such as eBay Intel Wal-Mart and Homeland Security. SolarCity doesn't manufacture its systems but uses solar panels from Trina Solar Yingli Green Energy and Kyocera Solar and inverters from Power-One SMA Solar Technology and Schneider Electric. In late 2016 SolarCity was acquired by Tesla Motors in a deal worth $2.6 billion.

Operations

SolarCity's main selling point is that it offers renewable energy for less than traditional utility companies. While customers feel good about choosing an alternative energy source they're also usually saving money. Much of the costs associated with new installation and monthly fees are offset by SolarCity's investment funds. To date the company has formed more than 20 investment funds and raised more than $1.5 billion from banks and other companies such as Credit Suisse Google PG&E Corporation and U.S. Bancorp. (Two funds however are being audited by the IRS.) SolarCity also depends on federal and state tax rebates and credits to lower costs and create incentives for fund investors. For example the federal government offers a tax credit of 30% to install solar power through 2016. (After 2016 the tax credit will fall to 10%.)

Electricity is sold under long-term contracts; generally customers agree to a 20-year term. Customers are either signed up as leases or power purchase agreements. Lease customers pay a fixed monthly rate while the rate for power purchase agreement customers depends on the amount of electricity the solar energy system produces. The vast majority of its customers (some 90%) "rent" the solar installations instead of buying them outright in order to keep SolarCity in charge of the product warranty.

Geographic Reach

California-based SolarCity serves customers in 16 states and the District of Columbia. Its offices and warehouses reside in Arizona California Colorado Connecticut Hawaii Maryland Massachusetts Nevada New Jersey New York Oregon Texas Canada and China. The company earned over 75% of its revenue collectively from California Arizona Colorado Hawaii and New York.

Sales and Marketing

The company's client list includes residential customers commercial entities such as Wal-Mart eBay Intel and Safeway and government entities such as the U.S. Military. SolarCity sells its products and services through a direct outside sales force from 64 sales offices in 16 states and Washington DC. (Most states have one sales office but its home state of California has 12.) It also has a call center.

Financial Performance

Fast-growing SolarCity is posting impressive revenue gains but no profits yet. Indeed the solar services company reported $255 million in sales in 2014 an increase of 56% versus 2013. The company credited the double-digit gain for 2014 to a major increase in the installation and operation of solar energy systems under lease and power purchase agreements in new and existing markets along with an increase in sales of solar energy systems and components. SolarCity's net loss for 2014 was fueled by an increase in sales and marketing costs and interest expenses.

Strategy

SolarCity installs about one of every four solar energy systems in the US but is still hungry for more. The company's products and services are available through home-improvement-retail-giant The Home Depot. Also in 2014 the company partnered with electronics retailer Best Buy to offer its products and services through some 60 Best Buy stores in California Arizona Hawaii New York and Oregon. SolarCity also partners with more than 100 homebuilders including Pulte and Del Webb. Other channel partners include Tesla Motors Viridian Energy Honda Acura and BMW.

While residential customers are important to the company going forward SolarCity is seeking to install larger solar energy systems for businesses and government customers. The company is also growing its business through acquisitions.

Mergers and Acquisitions

In mid-2014 SolarCity acquired Silevo a solar panel technology and manufacturing company. The acquisition helped to manage the company's supply chain and control the design and manufacturing of solar cells and photovoltaic panels that are a key component of its solar energy systems. The deal also enabled SolarCity to utilize and combine Silevo's technology with economies of scale to achieve significant cost reductions.

Company Background

SolarCity was founded in 2006 by CEO Lyndon Rive and his brother COO and CTO Peter Rive. The Rives are cousins of non-executive chairman Elon Musk a notable entrepreneur who co-founded PayPal and also heads Tesla Motors and SpaceX.

EXECUTIVES

Chb, Elon Musk
Customer Staff, Dave Parrent
Field Energy Consultant, Alex Corbett
Senior Inspection Coordinator, Ryan Romard
Senior Engineer, Albert Lou
Field Energy Consultant, Arthur Bell
Director of Ecommerce, Mark Colwell
Field Energy Consultant, Matthew Bellacicco
Field Energy Consultant, Michael Bradford
Field Energy Consultant, Enking Daniel

Senior Vice President of Produ, Jiunn Heng
Auditors: ERNST & YOUNG LLP LOS ANGELES

LOCATIONS

HQ: TESLA ENERGY OPERATIONS, INC.
3055 CLEARVIEW WAY, SAN MATEO, CA 944023709
Phone: 888 765-2489
Web: WWW.SOLARCITY.COM

PRODUCTS/OPERATIONS

2013 Sales

	$ mil.	% of total
Operating leases	82	51
Solar energy system	81	49
Total	**163**	**100**

Selected Products and Services

Products
Solar energy systems (panels inverters and mounting racks)

Services
Energy efficiency upgrades
Home energy evaluations

COMPETITORS

Aee Solar	Real Goods Solar
Ameresco	Solarcraft Services
Chevron	Sunedison
Conergy Inc.	Sunpower
First Solar	Sunvalley Solar
Rec Solar	

HISTORICAL FINANCIALS

Company Type: Private

Income Statement				FYE: December 31
	REVENUE ($ mil.)	NET INCOME ($ mil.)	NET PROFIT MARGIN	EMPLOYEES
12/16	730	(820)	—	12,000
12/15	399	(768)	—	—
12/14	255	(375)	—	—
12/13	163	(151)	—	—
Annual Growth	**64.6%**	—	—	—

2016 Year-End Financials

Return on assets: (-9.0%)   Cash ($ mil.): 290
Return on equity: (-42.5%)
Current ratio: 0.50

TEXAS AROMATICS, LP

EXECUTIVES

Pres, Melbern Glasscock
V Pres, Trenton Kelley
Vice President, Robert Cooksey
Administrative Assistant, Ann Loyo
Vice President, Edwin Echols
Distribution Coordinator, Lauren Hall
Senior Accountant, Nadine Boyle
Scheduler, Natalie Pappas
Vice President, Robert W Cooksey
Distribution Coordinator, Tiffany Thornton
Auditors: WEAVER & TIDWELL LLP HOUS

LOCATIONS

HQ: TEXAS AROMATICS, LP
3555 TIMMONS LN STE 700, HOUSTON, TX 770276450
Phone: 713 520-2900
Web: WWW.TEXASAROMATICS.COM

HISTORICAL FINANCIALS

Company Type: Private

Income Statement				FYE: December 31
	REVENUE ($ mil.)	NET INCOME ($ mil.)	NET PROFIT MARGIN	EMPLOYEES
12/18	567	5	0.9%	21
12/17	470	9	2.0%	—
12/16	449	11	2.6%	—
12/15	531	10	2.0%	—
Annual Growth	**2.2%**	**(20.4%)**	—	—

2018 Year-End Financials

Return on assets: 7.4%   Cash ($ mil.): 27
Return on equity: 13.6%
Current ratio: 2.20

TEXAS CHILDREN'S HOSPITAL

Texas Children's Hospital (TCH) is one of the nation's best largest and most comprehensive specialty pediatric hospitals with more than 4.3 million patient encounters annually. Founded in 1954 the not-for-profit hospital provides full-service medical care for children conducts extensive research and trains pediatric medical professionals. Part of the Texas Medical Center complex it has clinical facilities for every ailment ranging from psychological troubles to surgery and physical rehabilitation as well as specialized heart cancer and neurological care. TCH is the primary pediatric training facility for Baylor College of Medicine.

Operations

TCH comprises Jan and Dan Duncan Neurological Research Institute; the Feigin Tower for pediatric research; Texas Children's Pavilion for Women a comprehensive obstetrics/gynecology facility focusing on high-risk births; Texas Children's Hospital West Campus a community hospital in suburban West Houston; and Texas Children's Hospital The Woodlands the first hospital devoted to children's care for communities north of Houston. In addition the organization also created Texas Children's Health Plan the nation's first HMO for children; has the largest pediatric primary care network in the country Texas Children's Pediatrics; Texas Children's Urgent Care clinics that specialize in after-hours care tailored specifically for children; and a global health program that's channeling care to children and women all over the world.

The hospital prides itself on providing a strong and supportive culture to empower its more than 3500 nurses. It provides care in more than 40 pediatric specialties and has multiple locations across Houston. Additionally research at Texas Children's Hospital spans more than 800 active clinical trials over 800000 square feet of laboratory space and one of the largest and most diverse pediatric patient populations in the country. With funding of more than $115 million annually over 120 TCH's and Baylor College of Medicine principal investigators are conducting over 1000 clinical basic science and translational research projects at any given moment.

TCH encounters more than 4.3 million patient annually.

Geographic Reach

TCH has more than 10 locations across the greater Houston area. Its medical providers see patients at its hospitals in the Texas Medical Center Katy in West Houston and The Woodlands.

Strategy

In early 2021 Texas Children's Hospital and Texas Hearing Institute worked alongside each other to provide a one-stop-shop in Greater Houston for children with hearing loss.

The goal of the collaboration is to provide exceptional care with a comprehensive integrated streamlined approach. Texas Children's medical professionals including Ear Nose and Throat (ENT) physicians and audiologists are co-located in Texas Hearing Institute's new state-of-the-art building in the Texas Medical Center where children receive specialized medical clinical and educational services.

Texas Hearing Institute plans to continue expanding the number of children it serves throughout Texas in the coming years. It will provide additional services to families by building upon the strong foundation of education speech and audiology it has developed over its 73- year history.

EXECUTIVES

Ceo-Pres, Mark Wallace
Acct Mgr*, Tanu Ganatra
V Pres Quality and, May Joe Andre
Anesthesiology, Chris D Glover
Executive Officer, Edwina J Popek
Gastroenterology, Paula M Hertel
Physician-In-Chief, Mark W Kline
Coordinator, Debra Grote
Coordinator, Stella Speed
Assistant Vice President of Co, Lori Williams
CIO, Myra Davis
Auditors: IT CROWE LLP DALLAS TX

LOCATIONS

HQ: TEXAS CHILDREN'S HOSPITAL
6621 FANNIN ST, HOUSTON, TX 770302399
Phone: 832 824-1000
Web: WWW.TEXASCHILDRENS.ORG

PRODUCTS/OPERATIONS

2014 Sales

	$ mil.	% of total
Net patient revenue	1,530	60
Premium revenue	876	34
Medicaid & other supplemental reimbursement	59	2
Net assets released from restrictions for operations	28	1
Grants	21	1
Other income	41	2
Total	**2,558**	**100**

2014 Net Patient Revenue

	% of total
Managed care	61
Medicaid managed care	15
Medicaid	13
Self-pay	6
Commercial	5
Total	**100**

Selected Serives

Bariatric/weight control services
Certified trauma center
Chemotherapy
Dental services
Heart catheterization;diagnostic (child)
Genetic testing/counseling
HIV-AIDS services
Heart catheterization;treatment (child)
Kidney dialysis
Chemotherapy
Physical rehabilitation
Psychiatric services (Child/adolescent services Consultation and Outpatient care)
Sleep center
Sports medicine
Urgent-care center
Women's health center
Wound management services

COMPETITORS

Christus Health
Children's Hospital Of Philadelphia
Children's Medical Center Of Dallas
Cook Children's Health Care System
Dell Children's Medical Center
Mayo Clinic
Memorial Hermann Healthcare
Methodist Hospital System
Shriners Hospitals For Children
St. Jude Children's Research Hospital
St. Luke's Episcopal Hospital
Tenet Healthcare

HISTORICAL FINANCIALS

Company Type: Private

Income Statement   FYE: September 30

	REVENUE ($ mil.)	NET INCOME ($ mil.)	NET PROFIT MARGIN	EMPLOYEES
09/19	2,601	181	7.0%	6,000
09/15	1,546	96	6.3%	—
09/14	1,383	70	5.1%	—
09/13	1,229	78	6.4%	—
Annual Growth	13.3%	14.9%	—	—

2019 Year-End Financials

Return on assets: 3.2%   Cash ($ mil.): 56
Return on equity: 4.3%
Current ratio: 0.50

TEXAS CHRISTIAN UNIVERSITY INC

Home of the Horned Frogs (the school mascot) Texas Christian University (TCU) offers bachelor's master's and doctorate degrees in approximately 220 fields of study. More than 11000 undergraduate and graduate students attend the university's ten colleges and schools the cover fields of study ranging from liberal arts to engineering to business. TCU has nearly 700 full-time faculty members and a student-to-faculty ratio of 13:1. It also has one of the NCAA's top football programs. TCU is affiliated with the Disciples of Christ a Protestant denomination.

Operations

The TCU academic programs are organized under ten schools in fields including liberal arts communication education fine arts science and engineering nursing and health and business. It offers more than 115 bachelors approximately 65 masters and nearly 40 doctoral degrees.

Tuition fees room and board and books cost about $66600 per year for undergraduate and nearly $50540 for graduate/professional.

Geographic Reach

TCU's campus takes up about 295 acres about five miles from downtown Fort Worth.

Strategy

TCU's strategy includes fostering a diverse and inclusive university for all; promoting academic excellence and elevating its academic profile and reputation through focused and dynamic academic planning; providing a highly engaging and inclusive its student experience and recruiting and retaining a diverse world-class workforce; and telling compelling stories of TCU and its students faculty and staff.

Company Background

Brothers Addison and Randolph Clark established the school in 1873 as Addran Male and Fe-

male College (the school changed its name to Texas Christian University in 1902).

EXECUTIVES

Chancellor, Victor J Boschini Jr
Staff, Alvin J Allcon
Staff, Amy Freund
Staff, Annice R Ipser II
Staff, Ash Nyangani
Assistant Professor, Steffen Palko
Reporter, Rob Crabtree
Assistant Professor, Alan M Daniel
Assistant Professor, Jon Carr
Staff, Alice Hogg
Staff, Allison C Owen
Auditors: GRANT THORNTON LLP DALLAS TE

LOCATIONS

HQ: TEXAS CHRISTIAN UNIVERSITY INC
2800 S UNIVERSITY DR, FORT WORTH, TX 761290001
Phone: 817 257-7000
Web: WWW.TCU.EDU

PRODUCTS/OPERATIONS

Selected Colleges and Schools

AddRan College of Liberal Arts
College of Communication
College of Education
College of Fine Arts
College of Science and Engineering
Harris College of Nursing and Health Sciences
John V. Roach Honors College
Neeley School of Business
Relationship with Brite Divinity School

HISTORICAL FINANCIALS

Company Type: Private

Income Statement   FYE: May 31

	REVENUE ($ mil.)	NET INCOME ($ mil.)	NET PROFIT MARGIN	EMPLOYEES
05/21	545	443	81.3%	3,400
05/20	562	(47)	—	—
05/19	558	26	4.8%	—
05/18	521	185	35.6%	—
Annual Growth	1.5%	33.7%	—	—

2021 Year-End Financials

Return on assets: 11.3%   Cash ($ mil.): 32
Return on equity: 15.8%
Current ratio: —

TEXAS COUNTY AND DISTRICT RETIREMENT SYSTEM

EXECUTIVES

Exec Dir, Amy Bishop
Prin*, Casey Wolf
Prin*, Tom Harrison
Prin*, Sandra Bragg
Network Analyst, Brad Watkins
Contrl, Vincent Prendergast
Hedge Associate, Derek Bergquist
Accounting Manager, Tom Shephard
Investment Administrator, Vickie Dodson

Business Analyst, Claudia Garcia
Manager of Human Resources, David Redd
Auditors: KPMG LLP AUSTIN TX

LOCATIONS

HQ: TEXAS COUNTY AND DISTRICT RETIREMENT SYSTEM
  901 S MO PAC EXPY STE V50, AUSTIN, TX 787465776
Phone: 512 328-8889
Web: WWW.TCDRS.ORG

HISTORICAL FINANCIALS

Company Type: Private

Income Statement   FYE: December 31

	ASSETS ($ mil.)	NET INCOME ($ mil.)	INCOME AS % OF ASSETS	EMPLOYEES
12/16	26,387	1,761	6.7%	108
12/15	24,654	(182)	—	—
12/14	24,832	0	—	—
12/10	18,116	2,178	12.0%	—
Annual Growth	6.5%	(3.5%)	—	—

2016 Year-End Financials

Return on assets: 6.7%   Sales ($ mil): 3,030
Return on equity: 6.7%

TEXAS EASTERN TRANSMISSION, LP

EXECUTIVES

Pres-Ceo-Ptnr, Martha B Wyrsch
Vice President of Business Dev, David Shammo
Administrative Asst III, Deanna Cordova
Sr Analyst, Eric Munsayac
Legal Secretary, Felecia Lee
GM, Leah Moss
Administrative Assistant, Nancy Price
Manager, Wayne Thibodeaux
Manager, Doug Nelson
Sr Right of Way Specialist, Lara Bailey
Account Manager, Gina Gray
Auditors: DELOITTE & TOUCHE LLP HOUSTO

LOCATIONS

HQ: TEXAS EASTERN TRANSMISSION, LP
  5400 WESTHEIMER CT, HOUSTON, TX 770565353
Phone: 713 627-5400
Web: WWW.SPECTRAENERGY.COM

HISTORICAL FINANCIALS

Company Type: Private

Income Statement   FYE: December 31

	REVENUE ($ mil.)	NET INCOME ($ mil.)	NET PROFIT MARGIN	EMPLOYEES
12/17	1,389	347	25.0%	700
12/16	1,350	329	24.4%	—
12/12	956	406	42.5%	—
Annual Growth	7.8%	(3.1%)	—	—

TEXAS HEALTH HARRIS METHODIST HOSPITAL FORT WORTH

Harris Methodist Fort Worth Hospital is the largest and busiest hospital in Fort Worth. It is a private not-for-profit almost 730-bed tertiary care hospital serving the residents of Tarrant County and nearby communities in Texas. Harris Methodist provides both inpatient and outpatient care through its main medical center and on-site health clinics. Specialized services include emergency medicine trauma care orthopedics occupational health women's health oncology and rehabilitation. Its Harris Methodist Heart Center has about 100 beds. The hospital is the flagship facility of the Texas Health Resources hospitals system.

Operations

Harris Methodist also known as Texas Health Harris Methodist Hospital Fort Worth serves as a regional referral center. The hospital employs a medical staff of about 1000 physicians.

Sales and Marketing

To promote its services to area residents Harris Methodist uses a range of marketing avenues including print television online radio and outdoor advertising.

Strategy

To meet the growing needs of Fort Worth area residents in 2012 Harris Methodist launched a $58 million construction project to add a new emergency care center adjacent to the medical center campus. The 75000-sq. ft. center scheduled for completion in 2014 will increase the hospital's emergency room capacity from about 60 beds to 90 beds. A sky bridge will connect the new emergency care center to the main hospital.

Mergers and Acquisitions

To further expand outpatient services in 2012 Harris Methodist acquired the Clear Fork Surgery Center (now named Texas Health Outpatient Surgery Center Fort Worth). The ambulatory surgery center is located on the Harris Methodist hospital campus and was previously operated through a venture with Symbion and a group of physicians. The center performs about 10000 procedures per year.

Company Background

The organization opened its doors in 1930 the leadership of Dr. Charles Harris and the Methodist Church.

EXECUTIVES

Pres, Lillie Biggins
Cmo*, Joseph Prosser
Cno*, Elaine Nelson
Sr Asst, Elizabeth Goenn
Staff, Carla A Castaneda
Purchasing Coordinator, Chris Benson
Assistant Vice President Marke, Pam Marecki
Supervisor, Tommy Jackson
Hospitalist, Cynthia Dockins
Senior Administrative Assistan, Roshonda Helm
Emergency Management Coordinat, Susan Curfman

LOCATIONS

HQ: TEXAS HEALTH HARRIS METHODIST HOSPITAL FORT WORTH
  1301 PENNSYLVANIA AVE, FORT WORTH, TX 761042122
Phone: 817 250-2000
Web: WWW.TEXASHEALTH.ORG

PRODUCTS/OPERATIONS

Selected Centers and Services

Breast Center
Breastfeeding Resource Center
Business Health Services
Cancer
Complementary or Alternative Medicine
Diabetes
Emergency Trauma Services
Executive Health Program
Fitness Center
Heart and Vascular
Gastroenterology
Home Health
Hospitalist Program
Imaging
Infertility
Mobile Health Unit
Neurosciences
Occupational Health
Orthopedics
Outpatient Physical Therapy
Respiratory
Weight Loss
Texas Health Physician Offices Saginaw
Palliative Care
Rehabilitation
Sports Medicine
Primary Stroke Center
Surgery
Texas Health Physician Offices Keller
Vascular and Interventional Radiology
Women and Infants
Wound Care

COMPETITORS

Baylor University
  Medical Center
Cook Children's Health
  Care System
Encompass Health
Hca

Jps Health Network
Parkland Health &
  Hospital System
Tenet Healthcare
The Methodist Health
  System

HISTORICAL FINANCIALS

Company Type: Private

Income Statement   FYE: December 31

	REVENUE ($ mil.)	NET INCOME ($ mil.)	NET PROFIT MARGIN	EMPLOYEES
12/17	843	55	6.5%	3,500
12/15	770	55	7.1%	—
Annual Growth	4.6%	0.1%	—	—

TEXAS HEALTH RESOURCES

Texas Health Resources (THR) is a faith-based nonprofit health system that cares for more patients in North Texas than any other provider. THR serves North Texas through primary care and specialty physician practices hospitals outpatient facilities urgent care centers home health and preventive and fitness services. It has about 30 acute care and short-stay hospitals including owned managed and joint venture facilities. THR also operates outpatient and surgical centers and physicians' offices and it maintains affiliations with imaging diagnostic rehabilitation facilities and home health agencies. THR's network includes more than 6400 doctors and more than 4100 licensed beds.

Operations

Texas Health Medial Associates offers primary services (family care illness care disease management screening and testing) and specialist services (gastroenterology general surgery OB/GYN pediatrics rheumatology and ENT).

With about 1075 physicians and other medical professionals in 250-plus locations Texas Health Physicians Group offers extensive network of primary care including family care and internal medicine.

Geographic Reach

THR has operations in about 15 counties throughout North Texas including Collin Dallas Ellis Grayson Henderson Johnson Kaufman Parker Rockwall Somervell Tarrant and Wise.

Sales and Marketing

THR serves more than 7 million residents of North Texas.

Financial Performance

Company Background

THR was formed in 1997 by the merger of Harris Methodist Health System Presbyterian Healthcare System and Arlington Memorial Hospital Foundation. In 2008 the organization rebranded its hospitals unifying them all under the Texas Health Resources name.

THR had originally been the minority shareholder in a venture with Triad Hospitals to own Presbyterian Hospital of Denton. However THR grew dissatisfied when Triad was acquired by Community Health Systems in 2007. After a long legal tussle THR paid $100 million to acquire the hospital outright in 2009 and changed its name to Texas Health Presbyterian Hospital Denton. Texas Health Presbyterian found itself the focus of international media attention in 2014 when it treated the first case of Ebola on US soil.

EXECUTIVES

Ceo, Barclay Berdan
Pres*, Charles W Boes
Cfo*, Ronald R Long
Exec V Pres*, Harold Berenzweig
Sevp and Coo*, Jeffrey L Canose
Analy Application II, Christi Muno
Sevp and Chief Clinical Office, Daniel W Varga
Radiology Director, David Robinson
Family Practice, Kevin Kuenstler
Chief of Radiology, William Reese
Physician Remuneration Manager, Andrea G Fache
Auditors: KMPG LLP DALLAS TEXAS

LOCATIONS

HQ: TEXAS HEALTH RESOURCES
612 E LAMAR BLVD STE 400, ARLINGTON, TX 760114125
Phone: 682 236-7900
Web: WWW.TEXASHEALTH.ORG

PRODUCTS/OPERATIONS

Selected Facilities and Affiliates
Acute Care and Specialty Hospitals
Texas Health Arlington Memorial
Texas Health Harris Methodist Hospital Fort Worth
Texas Health Huguley Hospital Fort Worth South
Texas Health Presbyterian Hospital Dallas
Texas Health Presbyterian Hospital Flower Mound
Texas Health Presbyterian Hospital Rockwall
Texas Health Center for Diagnostics & Surgery Plano
Texas Heath Heart & Vascular Hospital Arlington
USMD Hospital at Arlington
USMD Hospital at Fort Worth
Affiliates
Envision Imaging of North Fort Worth
Texas Rehabilitation Partners
Two Forest Imaging Dallas
Southwest Diagnostic Imaging Center

COMPETITORS

Community Health Systems

Southwestern Medical Center

Cook Children's Health Care System
Hca
Jps Health Network
Parkland Health & Hospital System

Tenet Healthcare
The Methodist Health System

HISTORICAL FINANCIALS

Company Type: Private

Income Statement   FYE: December 31

	REVENUE ($ mil.)	NET INCOME ($ mil.)	NET PROFIT MARGIN	EMPLOYEES
12/17	4,688	869	18.6%	21,277
12/13	718	285	39.8%	—
12/09	334	2	0.9%	—
12/06	2,287	2,299	100.5%	—
Annual Growth	6.7%	(8.5%)	—	—

2017 Year-End Financials

Return on assets: 9.8%   Cash ($ mil.): 435
Return on equity: 14.2%
Current ratio: 1.60

TEXAS STATE UNIVERSITY SYSTEM

EXECUTIVES

Chancellor, Brian McCall
Vice Chancellor For Finance, Claire Jackson
Director, Scott Cupp
Abroad Coordinator Follow, Josh Andrews
Assistant Director of Admissio, Joshua Hector
Director Email, Rusti Wade
Accounting Clerk, Heather Adams
Associate Professor of Art, Martin Amorous
Administrative Associate, Suzanne Kitts
Security Coordinator, Renee Starns
Social SCI Human Resources, Brandy Pace

LOCATIONS

HQ: TEXAS STATE UNIVERSITY SYSTEM
601 COLORADO ST, AUSTIN, TX 787012904
Phone: 512 463-1808
Web: WWW.TSUS.EDU

HISTORICAL FINANCIALS

Company Type: Private

Income Statement   FYE: August 31

	REVENUE ($ mil.)	NET INCOME ($ mil.)	NET PROFIT MARGIN	EMPLOYEES
08/19	878	(61)	—	3,196
08/18	862	190	22.0%	—
08/17	854	145	17.1%	—
08/16	846	126	14.9%	—
Annual Growth	1.3%	—	—	—

2019 Year-End Financials

Return on assets: (-1.4%)   Cash ($ mil.): 410
Return on equity: (-4.6%)
Current ratio: 1.10

TEXLA ENERGY MANAGEMENT, INC.

EXECUTIVES

Pres, Lacy H Williams II
Cfo-V Pres, Randy Miller
Administrator, George Fritz
Trade Analyst, Nathan Offers
Member of Marketing, David Musgrove
Business, Andy Alarid
Director of Operations, Beverly Beaty
Auditors: MOHLE ADAMS LLP HOUSTON TEXA

LOCATIONS

HQ: TEXLA ENERGY MANAGEMENT, INC.
1100 LA ST STE 4700, HOUSTON, TX 77002
Phone: 713 655-9900
Web: WWW.TEXLAENERGY.COM

HISTORICAL FINANCIALS

Company Type: Private

Income Statement   FYE: December 31

	REVENUE ($ mil.)	NET INCOME ($ mil.)	NET PROFIT MARGIN	EMPLOYEES
12/18	1,462	2	0.2%	19
12/17	1,291	3	0.3%	—
12/04	949	2	0.3%	—
12/03	596	1	0.2%	—
Annual Growth	6.2%	4.0%	—	—

2018 Year-End Financials

Return on assets: 1.7%   Cash ($ mil.): 26
Return on equity: 11.1%
Current ratio: 1.20

THE ADMINISTRATORS OF THE TULANE EDUCATIONAL FUND

EXECUTIVES

Pres, Scott Cowen
Sr V Pres*, Yvette M Jones
Cfo*, Anthony Lorino
Prin*, Tanya O'Rourke
Assistant Professor, Raja Roy
Assistant Professor, David Spruill
Assistant Professor, Thomas G Voss
Project Coordinator, Eleanor Berault
Scientist, Nathalia Katz
Executive of Information Techn, John D Lawson
Scientist, Don Sibley
Auditors: DELOITTE & TOUCHE LLP NEW ORL

LOCATIONS

HQ: THE ADMINISTRATORS OF THE TULANE EDUCATIONAL FUND
6823 SAINT CHARLES AVE, NEW ORLEANS, LA 701185665
Phone: 504 865-5000
Web: WWW.TULANE.EDU

HISTORICAL FINANCIALS
Company Type: Private

Income Statement   FYE: June 30

	REVENUE ($ mil.)	NET INCOME ($ mil.)	NET PROFIT MARGIN	EMPLOYEES
06/16	924	(63)	—	5,500
06/15	1,054	40	3.9%	—
06/10	738	48	6.5%	—
06/09	737	0	—	—
Annual Growth	3.3%	—	—	—

2016 Year-End Financials
Return on assets: (-2.7%)   Cash ($ mil.): 22
Return on equity: (-4.5%)
Current ratio: —

THE AEROSPACE CORPORATION

A not-for-profit company the Aerospace Corporation provides space-related research development and advisory services primarily for US government programs. Its chief sponsor is the US Air Force and its main customer have included the Space and Missile Systems Center of Air Force Space Command. Other clients have included NASA and the National Oceanic and Atmospheric Administration as well as commercial enterprises universities and international organizations. Areas of expertise include launch certification process implementation systems engineering and technology application. The Aerospace Corporation was established in 1960 and operates in around two dozen locations across about 10 states.

Operations
Officially The Aerospace Corporation operates a federally funded research and development center or FFRDC for the Air Force. FFRDCs fill a unique role in service to the government and the nation. Along with commercial industry and academia FFRDCs support government science engineering and technology development. The company also focuses in the areas of launch assurance spanning all stages of the space lifecycle from concept to operations mission success. Satellite technology includes space debris and space traffic management and satellite docking tool. Space exploration such as laser for studying the solar system testing Orion's impenetrable heat shield as well as creating astronauts' space suit.

Geographic Reach
The Aerospace Corporation's headquarters with engineering and laboratory facilities is located in El Segundo California. Major regional offices are located in Chantilly Virginia and Colorado Springs Colorado. The company has testing and research center for space systems with more than 80 specialized laboratories test analyze and troubleshoot virtually every aspect of rocket and satellite systems.

Strategy
In mid-2020 Aerospace started building a second facility in Colorado Springs. This facility recently approved by the Aerospace Board of Trustees is planned to be 70 percent classified space and includes a multi-purpose high-technology center to meet the growing requirements of the US Space Command the US Space Force and a variety of other customers.

Construction started in July with ground-breaking activities planned for this fall. Completion and occupancy are scheduled for spring 2022.

Company Background
Founding of The Aerospace Corporation in 1960 the progress of the corporation's work in support of the U.S. Air Force paralleled the advances that the country witnessed in the fields of science and technology.

Auditors: DELOITTE & TOUCHE LLP LOS ANG

LOCATIONS
HQ: THE AEROSPACE CORPORATION
2310 E EL SEGUNDO BLVD, EL SEGUNDO, CA 902454609
Phone: 310 336-5000
Web: WWW.AERO.ORG

PRODUCTS/OPERATIONS

Selected Services
Civil and Commercial
CORDS
Cyber Security
Labs
Launch Support
Mission Assurance
Systems Engineering
Technical Resources

COMPETITORS
Akka Technologies   Qinetiq
Orbital Research

HISTORICAL FINANCIALS
Company Type: Private

Income Statement   FYE: September 30

	REVENUE ($ mil.)	NET INCOME ($ mil.)	NET PROFIT MARGIN	EMPLOYEES
09/19	1,111	57	5.1%	3,920
09/15	916	(15)	—	—
09/14	881	5	0.6%	—
09/13	868	0	0.0%	—
Annual Growth	4.2%	149.2%	—	—

2019 Year-End Financials
Return on assets: 8.0%   Cash ($ mil.): 82
Return on equity: —
Current ratio: 1.50

THE AMALGAMATED SUGAR COMPANY LLC

The Amalgamated Sugar Company with roots reaching back to 1915 turns beets into sweets. It's the second-largest US sugar producer processing sugar beets grown on about 180000 acres in Idaho Oregon and Washington. The company manufactures granulated coarse powdered and brown consumer sugar products marketed under the brand White Satin. It also makes products for retail grocery chains under private labels. The sugar company produces beet pulp molasses and other beet by-products for use by food and animal-feed manufacturers. Since 1997 Amalgamated Sugar has been owned by the Snake River Sugar Company a cooperative that comprises sugar beet growers in Idaho Oregon and Washington.

Operations
The Amalgamated Sugar Company processes up to 1.6 billion pounds of sugar each year. Along

with processing the cooperative's crops the company provides its owner-farmers with agronomy advice and services runs workshops and seminars operates a co-op store and sells used equipment.

The company's key management team is employed on a contract basis. A seven-member Management Committee oversees the management team. The committee comprises members of the cooperative's board of directors.

Geographic Reach
The Idaho-based company's sugar beets which are grown in Idaho Oregon and Washington are processed through the three sugar processing facilities it operates in Idaho. The Amalgamated Sugar Company's warehouses and bulk transfer stations are strategically located from the Midwest to the West Coast.

Sales and Marketing
The Amalgamated Sugar Company markets its sugar primarily in the nation's North Central Intermountain and Northwest regions. The company competes with not only cane sugar refiners but also manufacturers of other forms of sweeteners such as regular and high fructose corn syrup (HFCS) and non-nutritive high intensity sweeteners the likes of aspartame.

Financial Performance
The Amalgamated Sugar Company generates some 90% of its annual sales through the sale of refined sugar. The balance of its revenue comes from animal feed derived from beet pulp and molasses and other by-products as a result of sugar beet processing.

Strategy
The industry's return to the use of real sugar in soft drinks and other beverages has become a boon for The Amalgamated Sugar Company. To this end Pepsi Bottling Ventures has tapped the sugar beet processor to supply the bottler with granulated sugar. During the past few decades more beverage makers have moved to using lesser-expensive high fructose corn syrup (HFCS) to sweeten their beverages as a way to cut costs and boost profits but the shift spurred by consumers to return to sugar-sweetened drinks has become profitable for sugar processors the likes of The Amalgamated Sugar Company.

EXECUTIVES
Pres-Ceo, John McCreedy
V Pres-Coo, Joe Huff
V Pres, Pat Laubacher
V Pres-Fins, Craig Hanks
V Pres-SEC, Scott Blickenstaff
Purchasing Clerk, Faith Larios
Logistics Manager, Kerry Bowman
Director, Safety, Michael Shuey
Auditors: EIDE BAILLY LLP BOISE IDAHO

LOCATIONS
HQ: THE AMALGAMATED SUGAR COMPANY LLC
1951 S SATURN WAY STE 100, BOISE, ID 837092924
Phone: 208 383-6500
Web: WWW.AMALGAMATEDSUGAR.COM

PRODUCTS/OPERATIONS

Selected Products
Bakers' special sugar
Brown sugar
Dark brown sugar
Extra-fine granulated sugar
Fine granulated sugar
Gel gran granulated sugar
Industrial coarse sugar
Powdered sugar 10x and 12x
Sugar packets
Sugar standards
Type 50 medium invert sugar
Type O liquid sucrose (66.5 brix)
Type O liquid sucrose (67.5 brix)

COMPETITORS

Alico Inc.
American Crystal Sugar
Associated British Foods
C&h Sugar
Cosun
Cumberland Packing
Eurosugar
Florida Crystals
Imperial Sugar
Ingredion
M. A. Patout
Merisant
Michigan Sugar Company
Minn-dak Co-op
Nippon Beet Sugar
Nordzucker
Nutrasweet
Smbsc
Sterling Sugars
Sugar Cane Growers Cooperative Of Florida
S dzucker
U.s. Sugar
Western Sugar Cooperative

HISTORICAL FINANCIALS

Company Type: Private

Income Statement				FYE: December 31
	REVENUE ($ mil.)	NET INCOME ($ mil.)	NET PROFIT MARGIN	EMPLOYEES
12/13	953	62	6.6%	1,500
12/12	907	14	1.6%	—
12/11	886	46	5.3%	—
Annual Growth	3.7%	16.0%	—	—

2013 Year-End Financials

Return on assets: 8.0%   Cash ($ mil.): 1
Return on equity: 54.7%
Current ratio: 0.90

THE AMERICAN ENDOWMENT FOUNDATION

EXECUTIVES

Executive Vice President, John Farren
Administrator, Kristin Wilcoxson
Grant Administrator, Elyse Smith
Vp Marketing, Eric Kinaitis
Senior Grants Administrator, Michelle Cozens
Vp, William Hewitt
Vice President Investments, Jeff Scherer
Assistant, Deborah Casselman
Director, Laura Malone
Marketing Research Assistant, Cheryl Casey
Director Information Technolog, Meg Fernando
Auditors: MALONEY NOVOTNY LLC CANTON O

LOCATIONS

HQ: THE AMERICAN ENDOWMENT FOUNDATION
5700 DARROW RD STE 118, HUDSON, OH 442365026
Phone: 330 655-7552
Web: WWW.AEFONLINE.ORG

HISTORICAL FINANCIALS

Company Type: Private

Income Statement				FYE: December 31
	REVENUE ($ mil.)	NET INCOME ($ mil.)	NET PROFIT MARGIN	EMPLOYEES
12/16	848	349	41.2%	5
12/15	640	335	52.3%	—
12/12	133	86	64.7%	—
12/11	68	42	61.6%	—
Annual Growth	65.4%	52.6%	—	—

2016 Year-End Financials

Return on assets: 23.9%   Cash ($ mil.): 70
Return on equity: 24.3%
Current ratio: 21.30

THE ANDREW W MELLON FOUNDATION

Recipients of funds from The Andrew W. Mellon Foundation don't take the organization for granted. One of the leading charitable foundations in the US the organization provides about $280 million annually in grants including awards in five core areas: including higher education and scholarship performing arts and museums and art conservation. Recent grant recipients include the Detroit Symphony Orchestra Oberlin College and the Metropolitan Museum of Art. The foundation was created in 1969 when Paul Mellon and Ailsa Mellon Bruce the son and daughter of banking titan Andrew W. Mellon merged their charitable foundations (Old Dominion Foundation and Avalon Foundation).

EXECUTIVES

Pres, William G Bowen
V Pres*, Harriet Zuckerman
V Pres-Fin*, John Hull
SEC*, Michele Warman
Chief Financial Officer*, Thomas Sanders
Portfolio Manager, Karen Inal
Senior Portfolio Manager, Monica Spencer
Director Facilities, Ronald Sheppard
Information Technology, Peter Greenwood
Senior Program Officer, Donald Waters
Director of Information Techno, Doug Torre
Auditors: PRICEWATERHOUSECOOPERS LLP NE

LOCATIONS

HQ: THE ANDREW W MELLON FOUNDATION
140 E 62ND ST, NEW YORK, NY 100658124
Phone: 212 838-8400
Web: WWW.MELLON.ORG

HISTORICAL FINANCIALS

Company Type: Private

Income Statement				FYE: December 31
	REVENUE ($ mil.)	NET INCOME ($ mil.)	NET PROFIT MARGIN	EMPLOYEES
12/19	782	435	55.6%	70
12/18	54	(285)	—	—
12/17	980	655	66.9%	—
12/16	487	151	31.1%	—
Annual Growth	17.1%	42.2%	—	—

2019 Year-End Financials

Return on assets: 6.2%   Cash ($ mil.): 9
Return on equity: 6.4%
Current ratio: —

THE ASSOCIATED PRESS

The Associated Press (AP) is an independent global news organization dedicated to factual reporting. AP is the most trusted source of fast accurate unbiased news in all formats and the essential provider of the technology and services vital to the news business with news bureaus in some 250 locations. It provides some 2000 stories per day as well as 70000 videos and 1 million photos per year. It works with organizations of all sizes across a broad spectrum of industries. A group of New York newspapers founded the AP in 1846 in order to chronicle the US-Mexican War more efficiently.

Operations

The AP offers services such as live and location services branded content services production services advertising services and operates through its media solutions including news production system editorial planning and events planning.

Geographic Reach

The Associated Press is headquartered in New York City and has an office in London. The AP also operates in some 250 locations in 100 countries.

Sales and Marketing

The company works with companies across all industries to provide engaging stories that resonate with their target audiences and customers. It caters to industries such as news and media (broadcasters digital publishers newspapers production houses OTT) brands and agencies (local and global brands such as finance technology travel health pharma and creative agencies) and institutions (governments NGO's researchers universities and colleges).

HISTORY

The Associated Press traces its roots to 1846 when New York Sun publisher Moses Yale Beach agreed to share news arriving by telegraph about the Mexican-American War with four other New York newspapers. The cooperative news gathering effort was later established as the AP which began selling wire reports to other papers and started creating regional associations. Adapting to changing technologies and public interests AP began covering sports financial and public interest stories in the 1920s and was selling news reports to radio stations in the 1940s. Advancements during WWII included using transatlantic cable and radio-teletype circuits to deliver news and photos.

In the late 1960s AP and Dow Jones introduced services to improve business and financial reporting. AP improved photo delivery reception and storage in the 1970s with the advent of Laserphoto and the Electronic Darkroom. It began transmitting news by satellite and offering color photographs to newspapers in the 1980s. In 1985 Louis Boccardi took over the job as president and CEO of AP.

AP adjusted to the media-heavy culture of the 1990s by launching the APTV international news video service and the All News Radio network in 1994. It then moved onto the Internet with The WIRE in 1996 and began offering online access to its Photo Archive in 1997. It bought Worldwide Television News in 1998 combining it with APTV to form AP Television News Limited (APTN). The following year it purchased the radio news contracts of UPI after the rival organization announced it was getting out of broadcast news.

In 2000 AP created an Internet division AP Digital to focus on marketing news to online providers. The cooperative continued its Internet focus the following year launching AP Online en Espa ±ol (news for Spanish-language websites) and AP Entertainment Online (multimedia entertainment news for websites). Also that year AP bought the Newspaper Industry Communication Center from the Newspaper Association of America.

In 2002 the company launched an expanded editorial partnership with Dow Jones Newswires increasing the amount of financial news distributed on AP wires. Later that year it acquired Capitolwire a provider of state government news. Boccardi stepped down as CEO in 2003 handing the reins to former USA TODAY publisher Tom Curley.

AP relocated in 2004 from Rockefeller Plaza (its home for 65 years) to a new headquarters on the west side of Manhattan that features a 105000-sq.-ft. newsroom and serves as a central hub of digital news streams.

The organization moved to strengthen its sports information coverage in 2005 merging its AP MegaSports operation with News Corporation's STATS Inc. to form STATS LLC a 50-50 joint venture that provides sports-related information content and statistical analysis.

The following year AP launched The Online Video Network (OVN) service to provide news video to AP member and customer websites. The co-op responded to the harsh economy by cutting costs in 2008 with consolidation of its print broadcast and digital sales and marketing units. It continued its cost-cutting efforts in 2009 when it cut some 90 jobs instituted a hiring freeze and bought out about 100 employees.

EXECUTIVES

Pres-Ceo, Gary Pruitt
Sr V Pres-Cfo, Kenneth Dale
Dir of Fin, Hanna LI
Reporter, A D Gram
Reporter, Andrew Welsh-Huggins
Reporter, April Castro
Chief Administrator, Michelle Faul
Chief Administrator, Ray Lilley
Chief Administrator, Vijay Joshi
Reporter, Matthew Lee
Reporter, Mike Fitzpatrick
Auditors: ERNST & YOUNG LLP NEW YORK N

LOCATIONS

HQ: THE ASSOCIATED PRESS
200 LIBERTY ST FL 19, NEW YORK, NY 102811105
Phone: 212 621-1500
Web: WWW.AP.ORG

PRODUCTS/OPERATIONS

Selected Products and Services
AP Digital News (Internet and wireless news delivery)
AP Images (photo services)
AP Mobile (mobile applications)
APTN (AP Television News international television news service)
ENPS (electronic news production system)
Online Video Network (video content distribution)

COMPETITORS

Agence France-presse	Globenewswire
Bloomberg L.p.	Marketwire
Business Wire	New York Times
Comtex News	Pr Newswire
Corbis	Reuters
Dow Jones	Tegna
E. W. Scripps	Tribune Media
Getty Images	Upi

HISTORICAL FINANCIALS
Company Type: Private

Income Statement				FYE: December 31
	REVENUE ($ mil.)	NET INCOME ($ mil.)	NET PROFIT MARGIN	EMPLOYEES
12/16	556	1	0.3%	3,533
12/15	568	183	32.3%	—
12/14	604	140	23.3%	—
Annual Growth	(4.0%)	(89.4%)	—	—

2016 Year-End Financials
Return on assets: 0.4%   Cash ($ mil.): 24
Return on equity: —
Current ratio: 0.60

THE BIG TEN CONFERENCE INC

EXECUTIVES

Comm, Jim Delany
SEC*, Chad Hawley
Treas*, Brad Traviolia
Administrative Assistant, Mary Jo O'Donoghue
Controller, Julie Suderman
Information Technology Team ME, Mike McComiskey
Meeting Planner, Sue Immekus
Officiating Coordinator, William F Carollo
Chief Financial Officer, Brad Traviola
Associate Director, Davon Robb
Football Coordinator, Bill Carollo
Auditors: RSM US LLP CHICAGO IL

LOCATIONS

HQ: THE BIG TEN CONFERENCE INC
5440 PARK PL, ROSEMONT, IL 600183732
Phone: 847 696-1010
Web: WWW.BIGTEN.ORG

HISTORICAL FINANCIALS
Company Type: Private

Income Statement				FYE: June 30
	REVENUE ($ mil.)	NET INCOME ($ mil.)	NET PROFIT MARGIN	EMPLOYEES
06/20	768	41	5.4%	25
06/16	483	(10)		—
06/15	448	12	2.8%	—
06/14	338	2	0.6%	—
Annual Growth	14.6%	64.6%	—	—

2020 Year-End Financials
Return on assets: 12.6%   Cash ($ mil.): 62
Return on equity: 21.2%
Current ratio: —

THE BLOOMBERG FAMILY FOUNDATION INC

EXECUTIVES

Prin, Steve Fadem
Associate, Matt Lipsky
Auditors: GELLER & COMPANY LLC NEW YORK

LOCATIONS

HQ: THE BLOOMBERG FAMILY FOUNDATION INC
909 3RD AVE, NEW YORK, NY 100224731
Phone: 212 205-0100
Web: WWW.BLOOMBERG.ORG

HISTORICAL FINANCIALS
Company Type: Private

Income Statement				FYE: December 31
	REVENUE ($ mil.)	NET INCOME ($ mil.)	NET PROFIT MARGIN	EMPLOYEES
12/15	1,194	736	61.7%	2
12/14	1,328	1,048	79.0%	—
12/13	809	538	66.5%	—
12/09	452	279	61.8%	—
Annual Growth	17.6%	17.5%	—	—

2015 Year-End Financials
Return on assets: 10.3%   Cash ($ mil.): 73
Return on equity: 10.3%
Current ratio: —

THE BOARD OF EDUCATION OF FAYETTE COUNTY

EXECUTIVES

Supt, Demetrus Liggins
Cfo*, Mary Browning
Suprt*, Dr Marlene Helm
Principal*, Taquoya Shegog
Auditors: STROTHMAN AND COMPANY LOUISVI

LOCATIONS

HQ: THE BOARD OF EDUCATION OF FAYETTE COUNTY
450 PARK PL, LEXINGTON, KY 405111829
Phone: 859 381-4141

HISTORICAL FINANCIALS

Company Type: Private

Income Statement
FYE: June 30

	REVENUE ($ mil.)	NET INCOME ($ mil.)	NET PROFIT MARGIN	EMPLOYEES
06/21	631	45	7.3%	5,800
06/13	431	35	8.2%	—
06/12	422	(63)	—	—
Annual Growth	4.6%	—	—	—

2021 Year-End Financials

Return on assets: 4.7% Cash ($ mil.): 152
Return on equity: —
Current ratio: —

THE BOLDT GROUP INC

EXECUTIVES

Pres, Oscar C Boldt
V Pres*, Thomas J Boldt
SEC*, Michelle M Gawinski
Project Financial Coordinator, Maria Drezek
Project Engineer, Brian Cutler
Senior Designer, Eric Siebers
Project Coordinator III, Tammie Beitz
Director, Daren Maas
Senior Project Manager, Jeremy Moe
Senior Executive Vice Presiden, Jim Rossmeissl
Senior Administrator, Lori Reeths
Auditors: SCHENCK SC APPLETON WISCONSI

LOCATIONS

HQ: THE BOLDT GROUP INC
    2525 N ROEMER RD, APPLETON, WI 549118623
Phone: 920 739-7800
Web: WWW.THEBOLDTCOMPANY.COM

HISTORICAL FINANCIALS

Company Type: Private

Income Statement
FYE: December 31

	REVENUE ($ mil.)	NET INCOME ($ mil.)	NET PROFIT MARGIN	EMPLOYEES
12/18	1,046	(11)	—	1,500
12/17	989	0	—	—
12/16	1,022	17	1.7%	—
12/15	978	0	—	—
Annual Growth	2.2%	—	—	—

2018 Year-End Financials

Return on assets: (-3.8%) Cash ($ mil.): 39
Return on equity: (-30.9%)
Current ratio: 1.10

THE BOND FUND OF AMERICA INC

EXECUTIVES

President, Abner D Goldstine

LOCATIONS

HQ: THE BOND FUND OF AMERICA INC
    333 S HOPE ST FL 55, LOS ANGELES, CA 900713061
Phone: 213 486-9200
Web: WWW.CAPITALGROUP.COM

HISTORICAL FINANCIALS

Company Type: Private

Income Statement
FYE: December 31

	REVENUE ($ mil.)	NET INCOME ($ mil.)	NET PROFIT MARGIN	EMPLOYEES
12/19	1,320	1,099	83.2%	2
12/18	1,140	1,775	155.6%	—
12/17	866	1,056	122.0%	—
Annual Growth	23.5%	2.0%	—	—

2019 Year-End Financials

Return on assets: 2.0% Cash ($ mil.): 4
Return on equity: 2.2%
Current ratio: —

THE BRIGHAM AND WOMEN'S HOSPITAL INC

It took three of Boston's oldest and most prestigious hospitals to form the health care behemoth that is Brigham and Women's Hospital. The Harvard-affiliated facility has nearly 800 beds and includes the Dana-Farber/Brigham and Women's Cancer Center a partnership between the hospital and the Dana Farber Cancer Institute. Other specialty units focus on cardiology neurology transplants and obstetrics. In addition to being a teaching hospital for Harvard Medical School Brigham and Women's Hospital conducts research and clinical trials to help advance medical care. It's a top recipient of research grants from the National Institutes of Health and is a founding member of the Partners HealthCare System.

Operations

Brigham and Women's Hospital employs more than 3000 physicians fellows and residents and almost as many nurses. Inpatient admissions reach 46000 and ambulatory visits have grown to more than 3.5 million.

Brigham and Women's Hospital also operates the 150-bed Faulkner Hospital which is located near the main campus and offers acute care and specialty services including psychiatry and orthopedics. In addition Brigham and Women's operates satellite physician offices including primary and rehabilitation care.

The hospital is also known for performing the first full face transplant in the US. Brigham and Women's doctors performed the surgery in 2011 on a man whose face was severely burned when his head touched a high voltage line. Sponsored by the Department of Defense the surgery was part of the military's efforts to expand research on innovative medical procedures.

Strategy

The hospital system has positioned itself to do remarkable work such as a face transplant through its continued focus on research. Brigham and Women's research institute: The Biomedical Research Institute at BWH spends on average $500 million annually to conduct research in a whole host of fields including tissue engineering emergency medicine genomics and infectious disease (to name a few).

In 2014 Brigham and Women's Hospital opened the Ann Romney Center for Neurologic Diseases which will conduct medical research on five complex neurologic diseases including multiple sclerosis (MS) Alzheimer's disease Lou Gehrig's disease (ALS) Parkinson's disease and brain tumors.

Company Background

The hospital was formed through the 1980 merger of Peter Bent Brigham Hospital Robert Breck Brigham Hospital and Boston Hospital for Women.

EXECUTIVES

Pres, Elizabeth G Nabel
Immunologist, Annemieke De Jong
Chief Officer, Stanley W Ashley
Chief Officer, Susan Rapple
Coordinator, Amanda Harless
Director Cardiovascular Divisi, Raymond Kwong
Physician, Benjamin D Sommers
Inventory Manager Angio, Frantz Pierre
Pathologist, Jane E Brock
Pathologist, Kenneth Lee
Pharmacist, Kevin Anger

LOCATIONS

HQ: THE BRIGHAM AND WOMEN'S HOSPITAL INC
    75 FRANCIS ST, BOSTON, MA 021156106
Phone: 617 732-5500
Web: WWW.BRIGHAMANDWOMENS.ORG

HISTORICAL FINANCIALS

Company Type: Private

Income Statement
FYE: September 30

	REVENUE ($ mil.)	NET INCOME ($ mil.)	NET PROFIT MARGIN	EMPLOYEES
09/17	2,128	55	2.6%	8,376
09/16	1,938	94	4.9%	—
09/15	1,811	60	3.4%	—
Annual Growth	8.4%	(4.1%)	—	—

2017 Year-End Financials

Return on assets: 1.9% Cash ($ mil.): 60
Return on equity: 7.9%
Current ratio: 1.30

THE BROAD INSTITUTE INC

EXECUTIVES

Pres-Ceo-Dir, Eric Lander
Principal*, Derek Martyn
Exec V Pres-V Pres*, Alan Fein
Dir*, David Baltimore
Coo*, Samantha Singer
Cso*, Todd Golub
Cdo*, Justine Levin
Cco*, Clare Midgley
Cpo*, Andy Porter
Scientist, Ashlee M Earl
Scientist, Heng LI
Auditors: PRICEWATERHOUSECOOPERS LLP BO

HQ: THE BROAD INSTITUTE INC
415 MAIN ST, CAMBRIDGE, MA 021421027
Phone: 617 714-7000
Web: WWW.BROADINSTITUTE.ORG

HISTORICAL FINANCIALS
Company Type: Private

Income Statement				FYE: June 30
	REVENUE ($ mil.)	NET INCOME ($ mil.)	NET PROFIT MARGIN	EMPLOYEES
06/20	551	53	9.6%	800
06/19	551	53	9.6%	—
06/18	466	(18)	—	—
06/17	451	23	5.2%	—
Annual Growth	6.9%	31.4%	—	—

2020 Year-End Financials
Return on assets: 3.2%   Cash ($ mil.): 248
Return on equity: 5.0%
Current ratio: 1.70

THE CHARLES STARK DRAPER LABORATORY INC

The Charles Stark Draper Laboratory (also known as Draper Lab) guides research into space under water and across continents. The not-for-profit corporation develops guidance navigation and control technologies for aircraft missiles and spacecraft. It works with NASA to develop technologies and fabricate prototypes. The organization also solves healthcare problems with its work in biomedical engineering.

Operations
Draper Lab's innovations include a personal navigation system that allows soldiers to find their way in GPS-denied areas. The corporation boasts expertise in guidance navigation and control sytems; advanced algorithms and software; fault-tolerant computing; modeling and simulation; and microelectromechanical system (MEMS) and multichip module technology.

Geographic Reach
Headquartered in Cambridge Massachusetts Draper Lab maintains operations in Huntsville Alabama; Annapolis Junction Maryland; Cambridge and Road Pittsfield Massachusetts; Houston; Huntsville Alabama; Cape Canaveral Tampa and St. Petersburg Florida; Houston Texas; Reston Virginia; and Washington D.C.

Sales and Marketing
The company provide engineering services directly to government commercial companies and academia.

Strategy
Fueled by the brain power and expertise of its hundreds of engineers Draper Lab aims to solve problems by designing developing and deploying solutions built using advanced technologies. Its primary areas of focus include space exploration security healthcare and energy.

In late 2019 Draper Lab unveiled its LiDAR-on-a-Chip that uses patented all digital MEMS optical switches for beamsteering. Draper has successfully built a high-resolution solid-state LiDAR that images objects at 50 meters. This new offering adds to Drapers' growing portfolio of autonomous system and self-driving car capabilities. Draper's latest addition to this portfolio was in 2020 with its new PathScout system which equips drivers with a system that alerts them to nearby pedestrians when it detects GPS signals emitted by their mobile phones.

Draper also continues its collaborations with other organizations. In early 2019 Draper Lab and 3Derm collaborated to create new automated capabilities for 3Derm's high0quality skin imaging systems with the aim of improving the management of chronic inflammatory skin disease such as psoriasis and eczema. Draper also collaborated with Bristol-Myers Squibb in developing a unique liver tissue model for screening the toxicity of drugs in which Draper used its Human Organ Systems (HOS) platform.

Draper has also been selected by government institutions for various projects. NASA has selected Dynetics and Draper to develop and demonstrate a Human Landing System (HLS) to return humans to the lunar surface by 2024. The Department of Defense is also working with Draper to address challenges and improve upon UAV software to give it an autonomy architecture and software package that can enable UAVs to do more than ever before.

Company Background
The organization was founded in 1932 by MIT professor Charles Stark Draper as a teaching lab.

EXECUTIVES

Pres-Ceo, William A Laplante
V Pres*, Tara Clark
Cfo*, Christine Albertelli
V Pres*, Neil J Adams
V Pres*, Anthony S Kourepenis
V Pres*, Richard J Russell
Scientist, Donald C Bass
Real Estate Agent, Hui J Hui
Director of Information Techno, Mark Singleton
Information Specialist, Lex Dimatteo
Information Specialist, David Beckman
Auditors: GRANT THORNTON LLP BOSTON MA

LOCATIONS

HQ: THE CHARLES STARK DRAPER LABORATORY INC
555 TECHNOLOGY SQ, CAMBRIDGE, MA 021393539
Phone: 617 258-1000
Web: WWW.DRAPER.COM

PRODUCTS/OPERATIONS

Selected Research Areas
Biomedical engineering
  Tissue engineering
  Sensor development
Space systems
  Military space systems
  Planetary exploration
  Scientific spacecraft
  Space transportation
Special operations
  Robotics
  Small low-power electronics
  Surveillance systems
Strategic systems
  Inertial guidance systems
Tactical systems
  Precision engagement systems
  Manned/unmanned systems
  Missile defense

COMPETITORS

Applied Research Associates	Qinetiq
Institute For Defense Analyses	Quantum Research

HISTORICAL FINANCIALS
Company Type: Private

Income Statement				FYE: July 31
	REVENUE ($ mil.)	NET INCOME ($ mil.)	NET PROFIT MARGIN	EMPLOYEES
07/16*	676	36	5.5%	1,800
06/14	522	28	5.4%	—
06/13	542	17	3.2%	—
06/12	514	(20)	—	—
Annual Growth	7.1%	—	—	—

*Fiscal year change

2016 Year-End Financials
Return on assets: 6.0%   Cash ($ mil.): 51
Return on equity: 9.7%
Current ratio: 1.50

THE CHARLOTTE-MECKLENBURG HOSPITAL AUTHORITY

The medical facilities under the watchful eye of the Charlotte-Mecklenburg Hospital Authority care for the injured and infirmed. As the largest health care system in the Carolinas the organization operating as Carolinas HealthCare System (CHS) owns or manages more than 30 affiliated hospitals. It also operates long-term care facilities research centers rehabilitation facilities surgery centers home health agencies radiation therapy facilities and other health care operations. Collectively CHS facilities have more than 6400 beds and affiliated physician practices employ more than 1700 doctors. The network's flagship facility is the 875-bed Carolinas Medical Center in Charlotte North Carolina.

HISTORY

Carolinas HealthCare System has expanded its network through acquisitions and affiliations. In 2006 it purchased the 100-bed Lincoln Medical Center (now named Carolinas Medical Center-Lincoln) which the company had already been managing for several years. In 2007 it acquired the 460-bed NorthEast Medical Center (now Carolinas Medical Center-NorthEast). Carolinas HealthCare made improvements at both facilities including a complete reconstruction of the Lincoln campus and an eight-story patient tower addition at the NorthEast campus.

In 2008 and 2009 Carolinas HealthCare entered management services partnerships with AnMed Health (Anderson South Carolina) Cannon Memorial Hospital (Pickens South Carolina) St. Luke's Hospital (Columbus North Carolina) Stanly Regional Medical Center (Albemarle North Carolina) and Scotland Health Care System (Laurinburg North Carolina).

EXECUTIVES

Ceo, Eugene Woods
Svp-Cmo*, Michael Parkerson
Svp-Ciao*, Andy Crowder
Cfo*, Anthony Defurio
Coo*, Kenneth Haynes
Svp*, Roy Hawkins Jr
Vice President, Paula Beaver

Supervisor, Rhonda Coolidge
Patient Access Manager, Richard Shuster
Technical Project Manager, Roberta Hutsell
Residency Program Director, Sandra Craig
Auditors: KPMG LLP CHARLOTTE NORTH CAR

LOCATIONS

HQ: THE CHARLOTTE-MECKLENBURG HOSPITAL
AUTHORITY
1000 BLYTHE BLVD, CHARLOTTE, NC 282035812
Phone: 704 412-7330
Web: WWW.ATRIUMHEALTH.ORG

PRODUCTS/OPERATIONS

2010 Revenue

	% of total
Tertiary & acute care services	72
Physicians' services	16
Post-acute care services	3
Specialty services	2
Other services & non-operating activities	7
Total	**100**

Selected Hospitals and Health Care Pavilions

AnMed Health Medical Center
AnMed Health Rehabilitation Hospital
AnMed Health Women's and Children's Hospital
Anson Community Hospital
Bon Secours/St. Francis Hospital
Cannon Memorial Hospital
Carolinas Medical Center
Carolinas Medical Center - Kannapolis (health care
pavilion)
Carolinas Medical Center - Lincoln
Carolinas Medical Center - Mercy
Carolinas Medical Center - NorthEast
Carolinas Medical Center - Pineville
Carolinas Medical Center - Steele Creek (health care
pavilion)
Carolinas Medical Center - Union
Carolinas Medical Center - University
Carolinas Medical Center - Waxhaw (health care
pavilion)
Carolinas Rehabilitation
Carolinas Rehabilitation - Mount Holly
Cleveland Regional Medical Center
CMC - Randolph
Columbus Regional Healthcare System
Crawley Memorial Hospital
Grace Hospital
Kings Mountain Hospital
Levine Children's Hospital
MedWest - Harris
MedWest - Haywood
MedWest - Swain
Roper Hospital
Roper St. Francis - Mount Pleasant Hospital
Scotland Memorial Hospital
Stanly Regional Medical Center
St. Luke's Hospital
Valdese Hospital
Wallace Thomson Hospital
Wilkes Regional Medical Center

COMPETITORS

Alamance Regional	Haywood Regional
Medical Center	High Point Regional
Caromont	Health System
Community Health	Mcleod Health
Systems	Mission Hospitals
Cone Health	Morehead Memorial
Conway Medical Center	Hospital
Cumberland County	New Hanover Regional
Hospital System	Medical Center
Davis Regional Medical	Novant Health
Center	Palmetto Health
Duke University Health	Presbyterian
System	Healthcare
Firsthealth Of The	Rex Healthcare
Carolinas	Soliant Health
Georgetown Hospital	Tenet Healthcare
System	Unc Hospitals
Grand Strand Regional	Upstate Affiliate
Medical Center	Vidant Health
Hca	Wakemed

HISTORICAL FINANCIALS

Company Type: Private

Income Statement				FYE: December 31
	REVENUE ($ mil.)	NET INCOME ($ mil.)	NET PROFIT MARGIN	EMPLOYEES
12/20	7,324	616	8.4%	62,000
12/19	7,510	1,223	16.3%	—
12/18	6,228	(69)	—	—
12/17	5,991	829	13.9%	—
Annual Growth	**6.9%**	**(9.4%)**	—	—

2020 Year-End Financials

Return on assets: 4.3%
Return on equity: 7.5%
Current ratio: 0.90

Cash ($ mil.): 912

THE CHEROKEE NATION

EXECUTIVES

Chief, Chad Smith
Accounting Manager, Larry T Smith
Reporter, Jami Custer
Information Specialist, Melissa Bostwick
Education, Wade Blevins
Contracts Manager, Mike Robinson
Family Practitioner, Clinton Childs
Finance, David James
Gis Specialist, Eric Dean
Occupational Therapist, Felipe Zamarron
Chief of Parties, Guy Caughron

LOCATIONS

HQ: THE CHEROKEE NATION
17675 S MUSKOGEE AVE, TAHLEQUAH, OK
744645492
Phone: 918 453-5000

HISTORICAL FINANCIALS

Company Type: Private

Income Statement				FYE: September 30
	REVENUE ($ mil.)	NET INCOME ($ mil.)	NET PROFIT MARGIN	EMPLOYEES
09/16	541	1	0.4%	5,500
09/15	511	(15)	—	—
09/05	226	15	6.7%	—
09/04	203	14	6.9%	—
Annual Growth	**8.5%**	**(15.3%)**	—	—

2016 Year-End Financials

Return on assets: 0.1%
Return on equity: 0.1%
Current ratio: —

Cash ($ mil.): 313

THE CHILDREN'S HOSPITAL CORPORATION

The Children's Hospital Corporation dba Boston
Children's Hospital is dedicated to improving and

advancing the health and well-being of children
around the world through its life-changing work
in clinical care biomedical research medical education and community engagement. The medical
center is Harvard Medical School's main teaching
hospital for children's health care and it is the
world's largest pediatric research center. Its nursing department partners with more than 25
schools of nursing throughout Massachusetts and
New England. It maintains relationships with
Brigham and Women's Hospital Massachusetts
General Hospital and many other hospitals in caring for its patients. It has more than 1100 scientist
for its research community.

Operations

With more than 40 clinical departments and
about 260 specialized clinical programs Boston
Children's is one of the largest pediatric medical
centers in the US. It provides a complete range of
health care services for children of all ages and in
some cases it can offer fetal interventions and treatments for adults.

Dana-Farber/Boston Children's Cancer and
Blood Disorders Center an integrated pediatric
hematology and oncology program through Dana-
Farber Cancer Institute and Boston Children's Hospital provides ? in one specialized program.

Geographic Reach

Boston Children's Hospital has satellite locations
and affiliates throughout Massachusetts. In addition to its main campus in Boston it has satellites
in Lexington North Dartmouth Peabody and
Waltham; doctors' offices in Brockton Milford Norwood and Weymouth; and affiliates in Beverly Fall
River Milford New Bedford South Weymouth and
Winchester.

EXECUTIVES

Ceo, Kevin Churchwell
Ceo*, James Mandell
Pres*, Sandra Fenwick
SEC*, Dianne Hatfield
Pres*, David S Weiner
Prin*, Craig J Gerard
Svp-CIO*, Heather Nelson
Anesthesiologist, William Rhoads
Exe Asst Cfo, Leigh Degrandis
Chief of Dentistry, Man Wai Ng
Trustee, George W Phillips
Auditors: ERNST & YOUNG LLP BOSTON MA

LOCATIONS

HQ: THE CHILDREN'S HOSPITAL CORPORATION
300 LONGWOOD AVE, BOSTON, MA 021155737
Phone: 617 355-6000
Web: WWW.CHILDRENSHOSPITAL.ORG

PRODUCTS/OPERATIONS

Selected Services

Major centers
  Brain Center
  Cancer and Blood Diseases Center
  Heart Center
  Orthopedic Center
  Transplant Center
Other Services
  Airway breathing and lungs
  Allergies and asthma
  Anatomy and function
  Bone joint and muscle
  Brain and nervous system
  Cancer and blood disorders
  Common childhood health topics and conditions
  Craniofacial anomalies
  Diet and nutrition
  Digestive metabolic and renal disorders
  Ears nose and throat
  Emergency medicine and trauma
  Eyes and vision
  Genetic disorders and birth defects
  Heart blood and circulation

International patient care
Medical tests
Newborns
Psychiatric (mental) conditions
Reproductive and urinary conditions
Skin and vascular
Viruses and infections

COMPETITORS

Baystate Medical
 Center
Beth Israel Deaconess
 Medical Center
Boston Medical Center
Cambridge Health
 Alliance
Cape Cod Hospital
Children's Hospital Of
 Philadelphia

Nemours Foundation
Newton-wellesley
 Hospital
Northeast Health
 System
Partners Healthcare
Shriners Hospitals For
 Children
Steward Health Care
Sturdy Memorial

HISTORICAL FINANCIALS

Company Type: Private

Income Statement				FYE: September 30
	REVENUE ($ mil.)	NET INCOME ($ mil.)	NET PROFIT MARGIN	EMPLOYEES
09/19	2,046	136	6.7%	8,000
09/14	1,514	111	7.3%	—
09/09*	1,348	94	7.0%	—
06/05	4	0	13.0%	—
Annual Growth	54.0%	46.8%	—	—

*Fiscal year change

2019 Year-End Financials

Return on assets: 2.2%   Cash ($ mil.): 30
Return on equity: 3.2%
Current ratio: 0.30

THE CHILDREN'S HOSPITAL OF ALABAMA

EXECUTIVES

Ceo, William Michael Warren Jr
Exec V Pres-Coo*, Thomas G Shufflebarger
Exec V Pres*, Mike McDevitt
Facilities Manager, David Cantrell
Chief Engineer, Dale Williams
Msn, Ehrica Speigner
Supervisor Technical Support G, Kyle Fincher
Director of Pediatric, Lynne Hamer
Director, Christopher Guion
Chief Officer, Coke Matthews
Otolaryngologist, Heather Baty
Auditors: DELOITTE & TOUCHE LLP BIRMIN

LOCATIONS

HQ: THE CHILDREN'S HOSPITAL OF ALABAMA
 1600 7TH AVE S, BIRMINGHAM, AL 352331711
Phone: 205 939-9100
Web: WWW.CHILDRENSAL.ORG

HISTORICAL FINANCIALS

Company Type: Private

Income Statement				FYE: December 31
	REVENUE ($ mil.)	NET INCOME ($ mil.)	NET PROFIT MARGIN	EMPLOYEES
12/19	751	165	22.0%	3,329
12/18	733	17	2.4%	—
12/17	736	113	15.4%	—
12/16	713	86	12.1%	—
Annual Growth	1.8%	24.3%	—	—

2019 Year-End Financials

Return on assets: 9.9%   Cash ($ mil.): 190
Return on equity: 12.8%
Current ratio: 7.40

THE CHILDREN'S HOSPITAL OF PHILADELPHIA

The Children's Hospital of Philadelphia (CHOP) is the nation's first hospital devoted exclusively to the care of children. CHOP Primary Care practices located throughout southeastern Pennsylvania and Southern New Jersey provide convenient access to primary health and wellness services for children close to home. Children's Hospital Home Care offers a multidisciplinary team of doctors nurses pharmacists respiratory therapists social workers dieticians and delivery technicians and others who coordinate home visits infusion therapy and medical equipment for thousands of area children. CHOP had more than 25000 inpatient admissions 1.2 million outpatient visits and more than $603 million in research grants. CHOP was founded in 1855 by Francis West Lewis MD.

Operations

CHOP operates through two hospitals - in Philadelphia and in King of Prussia.

Its Philadelphia campus located in the hub of the University City section of the city includes a 546-bed Hospital devoted primarily to inpatient care with a complete range of medical and surgical services specialty intensive care units and a level-one Emergency Department and Trauma Center; The Buerger Center for Advanced Pediatric Care; The Richard D. Wood Pediatric Ambulatory Care Center which houses some outpatient clinical services and serves as a referral center for area pediatricians; Children's Seashore House a medical care and rehabilitation facility for children with chronic illnesses and severe developmental disabilities; The Leonard and Madlyn Abramson Research Center home to CHOP's Research Institute and most of the institution's research investigations; and The Ruth and Tristram Colket Jr. Translational Research Building home to clinical and lab space that fosters synergy between disciplines.

CHOP's King of Prussia Campus conveniently located near several major roadways includes a 52-bed all private-room hospital the Middleman Family Pavilion devoted to inpatient care with a range of medical and surgical services available onsite radiology imaging and testing pediatric intensive care and recovery area; Specialty Care Center for outpatient clinical visits with specialists; and Madelyn K. Abramson Emergency Department.

Children's Hospital of Philadelphia Research Institute is one of the largest pediatric research programs in the country with more than $100 million in total federal awards and an annual budget of more than $250 million. It is also affiliated with the Perelman School of Medicine at the University of Pennsylvania making CHOP the premier training ground for future pediatric leaders.

Geographic Reach

The Children's Hospital of Philadelphia has more than 50 pediatrician offices specialty care centers and surgical centers located Pennsylvania and New Jersey.

EXECUTIVES

Ceo-Pres, Steven M Altschuler
Chb*, Kim Buckley
Sr V Pres*, Philip R Johnson Jr
Chief Investment Officer and S*, Nicholas
 Procyk
Sr V Pres-Chief Nursing Office*, K Chavanu
 Gorman
General Counsel, Exec V Pres*, Jeffrey D Kahn
Sr V Pres-Chief Nursing Office*, Paula Agosto
Pres*, Madeline Bell
Exec V Pres*, Bryan Wolf
Exec V Pres*, Margaret M Jones
Evp-Cfo*, Sophia G Holder

LOCATIONS

HQ: THE CHILDREN'S HOSPITAL OF PHILADELPHIA
 3401 CIVIC CENTER BLVD, PHILADELPHIA, PA
 191044319
Phone: 215 590-1000
Web: WWW.CHOP.EDU

PRODUCTS/OPERATIONS

2014 Sales

	$ mil.	% of total
Net patient revenue	2,021	84
Research	211	9
Contributions	64	4
Other operating revenue	104	3
Total	**2,401**	**100**

Selected Specialties

Behavioral health
Blood and marrow transplantation program
Cardiac center
Center for fetal diagnosis and treatment
Center for airway disorders
Center for inflammatory bowel disease
Craniofacial reconstruction center
Diagnostic imaging center
Endocrinology
Gastroenterology
Hematology
Intensive care
Liver disease center
Neurosurgery
Orthopedic surgery
Pathology
Pediatric oncology
Pain management
Reconstructive surgery
Sickle cell center
Sports medicine and performance center
Stroke center
Surgery (general thoracic and fetal)
Transplant center
Urology

COMPETITORS

Aria Health
Children's Hospital Boston
Children's Hospital Of Pittsburgh
Fox Chase Cancer Center
Main Line Health System
Nemours Foundation
North Philadelphia Health System
Shriners Hospitals For Children
St. Jude Children's Research Hospital

St. Luke's University Health Network
Tuhs
Tenet Healthcare
Universal Health Services
University Of Pennsylvania Health System

HISTORICAL FINANCIALS
Company Type: Private

Income Statement				FYE: June 30
	REVENUE ($ mil.)	NET INCOME ($ mil.)	NET PROFIT MARGIN	EMPLOYEES
06/20	2,624	163	6.2%	13,519
06/19	3,057	469	15.4%	—
06/10	1,425	135	9.5%	—
06/09	1,439	197	13.7%	—
Annual Growth	5.6%	(1.7%)	—	—

2020 Year-End Financials
Return on assets: 3.2%　　Cash ($ mil.): 598
Return on equity: 4.7%
Current ratio: 0.70

THE CHILDRENS HOSPITAL LOS ANGELES

Childrens Hospital Los Angeles (CHLA) is dedicated to treating the youngest critical care patients in the region. The about 570-bed hospital specializes in treating seriously ill and injured children from its neonatal intensive care unit to its pediatric organ transplant center. CHLA's pediatric specialists also provide care at its ambulatory care center in Arcadia and through about 40 off-site practice sites. The hospital's pediatric specialties include cancer kidney failure and cystic fibrosis care. CHLA serves more than 107000 children every year. It is one of only 12 children's hospitals in the nation (and the only one in California) ranked in all 10 pediatric specialties by U.S. News & World Report .

Operations
The CHLA medical staff includes about 600 physicians most of which are members of the CHLA Medical Group. Its emergency department treats some 71000 patients and the hospital sees more than 343000 outpatients annually. Nearly 50% of its patients are under the age of four. CHLA is also the only freestanding level I Pediatric Trauma Center in LA County approved by the Committee on Trauma of the American College of Surgeons and among only 5% of US hospitals to be designated as a Magnet Hospital by the American Nurses Credentialing Center.

It is also a teaching hospital through its affiliation with the Keck School of Medicine of the University of Southern California and is home to the Saban Research Institute which conducts biomedical research into pediatric diseases. CHLA's training programs include 575 medical students 85 full-time residents three chief residents and 98 fellows.

Financial Performance
Revenue decreased 7% to $803 million in 2014 due to a decline in net patient service revenue. Also that year the company reported a net loss of $30 million due to the decline in revenue and higher operating expenses.

Strategy
CHLA is expanding its facilities to keep up with demand. In 2015 it opened the doors of a new outpatient center in Encino.

Company Background
Although it sometimes operates as Children's Hospital Los Angeles the absent apostrophe in the legal Childrens Hospital of Los Angeles name is no accident. The intentional spelling honors the original incorporation documents filed in 1901 when the institution was founded as Childrens Hospital Society of Los Angeles.

EXECUTIVES

Pres-Ceo, Richard Cordova
Cfo*, Lannie Tonnu
V Pres-CIO*, Steven R Garske
Svp-Cdo*, Alexandra Carter
Executive of Information Techn, John K Patterson
Coordinator, Gloria Gomez
Chief of Medicine, Jessica Scholes
Coordinator, Terry Dizon
Project Coordinator, Beatriz Ornelas
Assistant Professor, Ellen Iverson
Assistant Professor, Tishya Wren
Auditors: DELOITTE & TOUCHE LLP LOS ANG

LOCATIONS

HQ: THE CHILDRENS HOSPITAL LOS ANGELES
4650 W SUNSET BLVD, LOS ANGELES, CA 900276062
Phone: 323 660-2450
Web: WWW.CHLA.ORG

COMPETITORS

Cedars-sinai Medical Center
Children's Hopsital Of Chicago
Children's Hospital & Research Center At Oakland
Children's Hospital Boston
Children's Hospital Of Orange County
Children's Hospital Of Philadelphia
Children's National Medical Center
Cincinnati Children's Hospital
Cook Children's Health Care System
Dignity Health
Good Samaritan Hospital (los Angeles)
Hollywood Presbyterian Medical Center
Nationwide Children's Hospital
Shriners Hospitals For Children

HISTORICAL FINANCIALS
Company Type: Private

Income Statement				FYE: June 30
	REVENUE ($ mil.)	NET INCOME ($ mil.)	NET PROFIT MARGIN	EMPLOYEES
06/20	1,325	47	3.6%	3,000
06/19	1,485	216	14.6%	—
06/18	1,393	247	17.8%	—
06/17	1,035	(14)	—	—
Annual Growth	8.6%	—	—	—

2020 Year-End Financials
Return on assets: 2.0%　　Cash ($ mil.): 122
Return on equity: 2.8%
Current ratio: 2.70

THE CHRIST HOSPITAL

Perched on the hilltop of Mt. Auburn The Christ Hospital oversees the health of ailing residents throughout Greater Cincinnati. Along with the flagship 555-bed hospital the organization operates in more than 100 locations throughout the area. An extensive network of approximately 1200 physicians and 600 volunteers the Christ Hospital offers specialized care in a variety of fields including cardiac care cancer treatment kidney transplantation spine treatment and orthopedics. The not-for-profit hospital also provides an internal medicine residency program a family medicine residency program and a school of nursing. The Christ Hospital conducts research through its Lindner Research Center.

EXECUTIVES

Pres-Ceo, Deborah Hayes
ADM*, Jack Cook
Pres*, Mike Keating
V Pres*, Heather Adkins
Cfo*, Chris Bergman
V Pres*, Elizabeth Johnson
V Pres*, Peter Greis
V Pres*, Berc Gawne
V Pres*, Paul Gelter
Pres*, Dean Kereiakes
Vice-Pres of Hr, Allan Jones
Auditors: ERNST & YOUNG US LLP CINCINNA

LOCATIONS

HQ: THE CHRIST HOSPITAL
2139 AUBURN AVE, CINCINNATI, OH 452192989
Phone: 513 585-2000
Web: WWW.THECHRISTHOSPITAL.COM

PRODUCTS/OPERATIONS

Selected Services
Cancer Services
Comprehensive Medicine
Heart & Vascular
Orthopaedics & Sports Medicine
Primary Care
Spine
Women's Health

COMPETITORS

Bethesda North	Premier Health
Cincinnati Children's	Partners
Hospital	St. Elizabeth
Deaconess Associations	Healthcare
Kettering Health	Trihealth
Network	Uc Health

HISTORICAL FINANCIALS
Company Type: Private

Income Statement				FYE: June 30
	REVENUE ($ mil.)	NET INCOME ($ mil.)	NET PROFIT MARGIN	EMPLOYEES
06/20	1,050	8	0.8%	4,000
06/18	742	95	12.9%	—
06/17	929	14	1.5%	—
06/16	681	90	13.2%	—
Annual Growth	11.4%	(44.4%)	—	—

2020 Year-End Financials
Return on assets: 0.6%　　Cash ($ mil.): 202
Return on equity: 1.5%
Current ratio: 1.20

THE CITY OF SEATTLE-CITY LIGHT DEPARTMENT

City of Seattle - City Light Department (Seattle City Light) keeps guitars humming and coffee grinders running in the Seattle metropolitan area. The US's 10th largest municipally owned power company Seattle City Light transmits and distributes electricity to almost 1 million residential commercial industrial and government customers and owns hydroelectric power plants with more than 1800 MW of generation capacity. The utility also purchases power from the Bonneville Power Administration and other generators and it sells power to wholesale customers.

Operations
The company owns and operates generating transmission and distribution facilities and supplies electricity to 408000 customer meters in Seattle and certain surrounding communities. It also supplies electrical energy to other City agencies at rates prescribed by City ordinances.

Geographic Reach
The Seattle City Light service area includes all of the City of Seattle portions of the cities of Burien Tukwila SeaTac Shoreline Lake Forest Park and Renton as well as parts of unincorporated King County.

Financial Performance
Seattle City Light reported a revenue increase of 5% (to $842.2) in 2013 primarily due to increased retail power revenues stemming from a 4% rate increase and a 1.2% Bonneville Power Administration pass-through rate adjustment.

It net income increased that year due to higher retail power sales rate stabilization account unearned revenue transferred-in power related revenues and capital contributions. These were partially offset by higher expenses for generation customer service administrative and general taxes depreciation interest and lower investment earnings.

In 2013 Seattle City Light's operating cash inflow decreased to $229.7 (from $243.5 million in 2012) was due to higher tax paid and increased cash paid to a supplier.

Strategy
The company's long term objective is to continue to secure reliable low-cost and environmentally-sensitive power for its customers. To lower costs the utility is pushing its customers to conserve by taking green energy options such as installing more energy-efficient appliances and by buying renewable energy credits (allowing customers to pay for slightly higher costs of integrating renewable energy into the region's power grid).

Seattle City Light's six-year strategic plan adopted in 2012 calls for an annual rate increase of 4.7% to pay for expanding Seattle City Light's infrastructure and services including building its first electric substation for 30 years.

In 2013 the company added two new service request types to the 'Find It Fix It' smartphone app enabling Smartphone to report illegal dumping and streetlight outages in addition to its existing features for reporting abandoned vehicles graffiti potholes and parking enforcement issues.

That year Seattle City Light and the Seattle Aquarium announced the start of construction for the largest solar array at any aquarium on the West Coast as part of the utility's Community Solar and Green Up programs. The $330000 system will cover a large portion of the south side of the Seattle Aquarium's roof. Most of its 247 solar panels will produce electricity on behalf of City Light customers who want to buy solar power through the utility's Community Solar program. The rest of the panels are being installed as a demonstration project through the utility's voluntary Green Up renewable energy program with the electricity produced helping to power the Aquarium's operations.

Company Background
Evolving from several neighborhood electric companies that began serving Seattle in 1886 Seattle City Light was created in 1910 to power

the city's streetlights. In 2005 the electric utility became the first in the US to become greenhouse gas neutral in its power generation.

EXECUTIVES

Ceo, Jorge Carrasco
Interim Cfo*, Brian Brunfield
Information Specialist, James Sprinkle
Information Specialist, Steve Mulford
Information Specialist, Charlie Tacardon
Information Specialist, Gerald McCrury
Information Specialist, Patrick Minvielle
Facilities Specialist, Tasha Bassett
Information Specialist, John Giamberso
Information Specialist, Trinette Trinh
Information Technology Is Mana, Aditi Duggal
Auditors: BAKER TILLY VIRCHOW KRAUZE LLP

LOCATIONS

HQ: THE CITY OF SEATTLE-CITY LIGHT DEPARTMENT
700 5TH AVE STE 3200, SEATTLE, WA 981045065
Phone: 206 684-3200
Web: WWW.SEATTLE.GOV

PRODUCTS/OPERATIONS

2013 Sales

	% of total
Non-residential	63
Residential	37
Total	**100**

COMPETITORS

Avista	Pacificorp
Cascade Natural Gas	Portland General
Idacorp	Electric
Nv Energy	Puget Energy
Nw Natural	Xcel Energy

HISTORICAL FINANCIALS
Company Type: Private

Income Statement				FYE: December 31
	REVENUE ($ mil.)	NET INCOME ($ mil.)	NET PROFIT MARGIN	EMPLOYEES
12/18	991	162	16.4%	1,600
12/17	989	120	12.2%	—
12/16	903	85	9.4%	—
12/09	723	34	4.7%	—
Annual Growth	3.6%	18.9%	—	—

2018 Year-End Financials
Return on assets: 3.3%   Cash ($ mil.): 135
Return on equity: 10.8%
Current ratio: 1.20

THE CLEVELAND CLINIC FOUNDATION

The not-for-profit Cleveland Clinic Foundation operates about 20 hospitals in Ohio Florida Abu Dhabi Toronto and soon in London. Combined the foundation's hospitals have more than 6000 beds. Its flagship location is its namesake Cleveland Clinic an academic medical center in Cleveland Ohio. The campus specializes in cardiac care digestive disease treatment and urological and kidney care along with education and research opportunities. It has an international care center

children's hospital and an outpatient center; it also contains research and educational institutes covering clinical drug research ophthalmic studies and cancer research as well as physician and scientist training programs.

Operations
The Cleveland Clinic operates approximately 220 outpatient facilities in northern Ohio. These include outpatient family health centers ambulatory surgery centers physician offices specialized cancer centers and wellness centers.

The foundation operates the Lerner College of Medicine and the Lerner Research Institute through a partnership with Case Western Reserve University and it has continuing education nursing and residency programs. It also operates Cleveland Clinic Innovations a unit that oversees collaborative research and technology commercialization programs with partners including MedStar Health and the University of Notre Dame. Cleveland Clinic educates about 1975 residents and fellows and receives more than $305 million in research funding (from grants contracts and federal support) each year.

Altogether the medical centers known as the Cleveland Clinic Health System include more than 6000 beds and employ more than 4500 full-time physicians. The group handles almost 308770 hospital admissions and more than 9.5 million outpatient visits each year. In 2019 it had more than 255000 surgical cases.

Geographic Reach
In addition to its primary campus Cleveland Clinic operates regional hospitals and numerous family and specialty health centers in northeastern Ohio. It operates a handful of facilities in Florida and several brain clinics in Nevada.

Internationally it operates a health and wellness center in Canada and manages health centers in the United Arab Emirates.

Its corporate headquarters is located in Cleveland Ohio.

Strategy
In late 2019 Cleveland Clinic and American Well are partnering on a first-of-its-kind initiative to provide broad access to comprehensive and high-acuity care services via telehealth. Together the organizations will form a Cleveland-based joint venture company named The Clinic which will offer virtual care from Cleveland Clinic's highly specialized experts through American Well's well-established digital health technology platform.

Mergers and Acquisitions
In early 2019 Cleveland Clinic expanded its operations in the Sunshine State when it acquired Martin Health System and its three hospitals (with more than 520 beds) in Southeast Florida. It also acquired Indian River Medical Center which has more than 330 beds and is located on Florida's Treasure Coast. The system plans to invest millions in the newly added operations over the next few years.

Company Background
Cleveland Clinic Foundation traces its roots to 1921 when a group of Cleveland doctors teamed up to improve medical care and education. Its main campus has conducted breakthrough medical innovations through its history such as the first face transplant in 2008 and it is regularly named to the US News & World Report's list of America's Best Hospitals.

EXECUTIVES

Ceo, Tomislav Mihaljevic
Cfo, Steven Glass
Chief Strategy Officer, Josette Beran
Cbdo, Semih Sen
Cno, Dana Kocsis
Ccto, James Merlino

Chief Research Information Off, Lara Jehi
CIO, Matthew Kull
Director, Susan Bernat
Director, Jason Heckman
Analyst, Joe Cestat
Auditors: ERNST & YOUNG LLP CLEVELAND

LOCATIONS

HQ: THE CLEVELAND CLINIC FOUNDATION
9500 EUCLID AVE, CLEVELAND, OH 441950002
Phone: 216 636-8335
Web: WWW.MY.CLEVELANDCLINIC.ORG

Selected Facilities

Ashtabula County Medical Center (Ashtabula Ohio; management contract)
The Cleveland Clinic (Cleveland Ohio)
 Cleveland Clinic Children's Hospital
 Cleveland Clinic International Center
Cleveland Clinic Canada (Toronto)
Cleveland Clinic Children's Hospital for Rehabilitation (Shaker Campus in Cleveland Ohio)
Cleveland Clinic Family Health Centers (multiple locations in northeast Ohio)
Cleveland Clinic Florida (Weston Florida)
Cleveland Clinic Florida (West Palm Beach Florida)
Cleveland Clinic Lou Ruvo Center for Brain Health (Elko Nevada)
Cleveland Clinic Lou Ruvo Center for Brain Health (Las Vegas Nevada)
Cleveland Clinic Lou Ruvo Center for Brain Health (Reno Nevada)
Euclid Hospital (Euclid Ohio)
Fairview Hospital (Cleveland Ohio)
Hillcrest Hospital (Mayfield Heights Ohio)
Lakewood Hospital (Lakewood Ohio)
Lutheran Hospital (Cleveland Ohio)
Marymount Hospital (Garfield Heights Ohio)
Medina Hospital (Medina Ohio)
Richard E. Jacobs Health Center (Avon Ohio)
South Pointe Hospital (Warrensville Heights Ohio)

Selected Institutes

Cleveland Clinic Institutes
 Anesthesiology and Pain Management
 Bariatric and Metabolic
 Cancer Center/Taussig Cancer Institute
 Cleveland Clinic Children's and Pediatric
 Dermatology and Plastic Surgery
 Digestive Disease and Surgery
 Emergency Services
 Endocrinology and Metabolism
 Genomics
 Head and Neck
 Heart and Vascular
 Imaging
 Medicine
 Neurological
 Nursing
 Orthopaedic and Rheumatologic
 Pathology and Laboratory Medicine
 Respiratory
 Urology and Kidney
 Wellness
Special Expertise Institutes
 Arts and Medicine
 Body Donation
 Patient Experience
 Philanthropy
 Professional Staff Affairs
 Quality and Patient Safety
 Research

PRODUCTS/OPERATIONS

2018 Sales

	$ mil.	% of total
Net patient service revenue		
Self-pay	4,465	50
Managed care & commercial	2,871	32
Medicare	649	7
Medicaid	45	1
Other	895	10
Total	**8,927**	**100**

COMPETITORS

Akron Children's Hospital
Catholic Health Initiatives
Deaconess Associations
Kettering Health Network
Lake Health
Mayo Clinic
Memorial Sloan-kettering
Metrohealth System
Ohiohealth
Parma Community General Hospital
Premier Health Partners
Robinson Memorial Hospital
Shriners Hospitals For Children
Summa Health System
University Hospitals Health System

HISTORICAL FINANCIALS

Company Type: Private

Income Statement				FYE: December 31
	REVENUE ($ mil.)	NET INCOME ($ mil.)	NET PROFIT MARGIN	EMPLOYEES
12/20	10,627	1,482	14.0%	44,000
12/19	10,559	2,239	21.2%	—
12/18	8,927	176	2.0%	—
12/17	8,407	1,150	13.7%	—
Annual Growth	8.1%	8.8%	—	—

2020 Year-End Financials

Return on assets: 6.8%
Return on equity: 11.2%
Current ratio: 1.20
Cash ($ mil.): 1,045

THE CLEVELAND ELECTRIC ILLUMINATING COMPANY

The Cleveland Electric Illuminating Company (CEI) has a glowing reputation. The utility commonly referred to as The Illuminating Company distributes electricity to a base population of about 1.8 million inhabitants in a 1600 sq. ml. area of northeastern Ohio. CEI has 33210 miles of distribution lines. In 2010 the utility met 4420 MW of hourly maximum generating demand from interests in fossil-fueled and nuclear power plants (which are operated by fellow FirstEnergy subsidiaries). It also engages in wholesale energy transactions with other power companies. CEI is also a competitive retail electric service provider in Ohio alongside sister companies Ohio Edison and Toledo Edison.

EXECUTIVES

Pres, John E Skory
Exec V Pres-Cfo, Mark T Clark
V Pres-Contrl, Harvey L Wagner
Exec V Pres-Gen Cnsl, L L Vespoli
V Pres-Treas, J F Pearson
Auditors: PRICEWATERHOUSECOOPERS LLP CL

LOCATIONS

HQ: THE CLEVELAND ELECTRIC ILLUMINATING COMPANY
76 S MAIN ST, AKRON, OH 443081812
Phone: 800 589-3101
Web: WWW.FIRSTENERGYCORP.COM

COMPETITORS

Columbia Gas Of Ohio
Dpl
Dominion East Ohio
Duke Energy Ohio
Ohio Power
Vectren Energy Delivery Of Ohio

HISTORICAL FINANCIALS

Company Type: Private

Income Statement				FYE: December 31
	REVENUE ($ mil.)	NET INCOME ($ mil.)	NET PROFIT MARGIN	EMPLOYEES
12/16	928	37	4.0%	897
12/10	1,221	73	6.0%	—
12/09	1,676	(10)	—	—
12/08	1,815	284	15.7%	—
Annual Growth	(8.0%)	(22.4%)	—	—

THE COMMUNITY HOSPITAL GROUP INC

JFK Medical Center plays a central role in health care in central New Jersey. The medical center is an acute care facility with some 500 beds and 950 physicians providing emergency surgical trauma and other inpatient services. The hospital includes the JFK New Jersey Neuroscience Institute which treats stroke and other neurological conditions and the JFK Johnson Rehabilitation Institute which treats traumatic injuries. JFK Medical Center also offers diagnostic imaging cancer care senior and hospice care and family practice services. It is also a teaching hospital affiliated with several area universities. The hospital is part of the JFK Health System.

Strategy

To expand its capacity for emergency services JFK Medical Center launched construction of a new ER pavilion in 2013. The project includes the addition of a three-story structure above the existing ER facilities. To keep pace with cutting-edge medical technologies the hospital has also made recent investments in upgrades to its diagnostic imaging cardiac catheterization and wound healing equipment.

EXECUTIVES

Pres-Ceo, John P McGee
Exec V Pres*, Louis P Amato
SEC*, Peter Cappareli
Treas*, Robert J Mc Kenna
Diagnostic Radiologist, Eric Schmell
Director, Annari Griesel
Andreia Soares, Andreia Soares
Associate Dean, Sharon Ferrante
Registered Nurse, Asia Alston
Attending Physician, Christine Greiss
Network Administrator, Dan Mleczko
Auditors: BAKER TILLY

LOCATIONS

HQ: THE COMMUNITY HOSPITAL GROUP INC
98 JAMES ST STE 400, EDISON, NJ 088203902
Phone: 732 321-7000
Web: WWW.JFKHEALTHSYSTEM.ORG

PRODUCTS/OPERATIONS

Selected Centers and Affiliates
Adult Medical Day Program

Haven Hospice
JFK at Home
JFK Dental Clinic
JFK Family Medicine Center
JFK Hartwyck Nursing Convalescent and Rehabilitation
  Centers
JFK Johnson Rehabilitation Institute (JRI)
JFK Mediplex Surgery Center
JFK New Jersey Neuroscience Institute
JFK Medical Center Muhlenberg Campus/JFK-
  Muhlenberg Snyder Schools
Whispering Knoll Assisted Living

COMPETITORS

Ball Memorial Hospital	Newton Medical Center
Bergen Regional	Princeton Healthcare
Medical	Robert Wood Johnson
Capital Health System	University Hospital
Centrastate Healthcare	Saint Peter's
System	University Hospital
Henry County Memorial	St. Joseph's
Hospital	Healthcare System
Monmouth Medical	
Center	

HISTORICAL FINANCIALS

Company Type: Private

Income Statement				FYE: December 31
	REVENUE ($ mil.)	NET INCOME ($ mil.)	NET PROFIT MARGIN	EMPLOYEES
12/17	551	(13)	—	3,000
12/16	532	28	5.3%	—
12/14	467	(3)	—	—
12/10	427	(17)	—	—
Annual Growth	3.7%	—	—	—

2017 Year-End Financials

Return on assets: (-4.9%)   Cash ($ mil.): 39
Return on equity: (-46.5%)
Current ratio: 1.40

THE CONLAN COMPANY

EXECUTIVES

Ceo, Gary D Condron
Pres*, Kevin Turpin
V Pres*, Tom Lutz
V Pres*, Ryan Triesenberg
Cfo*, Bill Hayne
Exec V Pres*, David Staley
Exec V Pres*, Stuart Price
Sr V Pres*, Scott Austin
V Pres*, Charles King
V Pres*, Ronnie Cupp
Human Resources Compliance, Larry Robbins
Auditors: SMITH ADCOCK & COMPANY LLP A

LOCATIONS

HQ: THE CONLAN COMPANY
  1800 PARKWAY PL SE # 1010, MARIETTA, GA
  300678293
Phone: 770 423-8000
Web: WWW.CONLANCOMPANY.COM

HISTORICAL FINANCIALS

Company Type: Private

Income Statement				FYE: December 31
	REVENUE ($ mil.)	NET INCOME ($ mil.)	NET PROFIT MARGIN	EMPLOYEES
12/18	953	40	4.2%	391
12/17	930	40	4.3%	—
12/16	772	41	5.3%	—
12/15	589	13	2.3%	—
Annual Growth	17.3%	42.9%	—	—

2018 Year-End Financials

Return on assets: 16.3%   Cash ($ mil.): 93
Return on equity: 90.9%
Current ratio: 1.20

THE COOPER HEALTH SYSTEM

EXECUTIVES

Ceo, John P Sheridan Jr
Coo*, George J Weinroth
Chm*, George E Norcross III
Recruiter, Bernadette Collins
Vice President of Community Ou, Catherine
  Curley
Assistant Vice President Regul, Danielle Majuri
Clinical Director, Joanne Fox
Senior Executive Vice Presiden, Kevin O'Dowd
Vice President of Facilities, Pamela M Ward
Administrative Assistant, Timothy Holtz
Pathologist, William Rafferty
Auditors: ERNST & YOUNG LLP ISELIN NJ

LOCATIONS

HQ: THE COOPER HEALTH SYSTEM
  1 COOPER PLZ, CAMDEN, NJ 081031461
Phone: 856 342-2000
Web: WWW.COOPERHEALTH.ORG

HISTORICAL FINANCIALS

Company Type: Private

Income Statement				FYE: December 31
	REVENUE ($ mil.)	NET INCOME ($ mil.)	NET PROFIT MARGIN	EMPLOYEES
12/20	1,545	73	4.7%	4,900
12/19	1,439	105	7.3%	—
12/18	1,292	54	4.2%	—
12/17	1,197	33	2.8%	—
Annual Growth	8.9%	29.7%	—	—

2020 Year-End Financials

Return on assets: 3.9%   Cash ($ mil.): 582
Return on equity: 7.7%
Current ratio: 2.10

THE CORE GROUP LTD

EXECUTIVES

Pres, James K Jacobs
SEC, Dennis Barber
Dir of Fin, John Verhoff
Auditors: MAYER HOFFMAN MCCANN PC PHO

LOCATIONS

HQ: THE CORE GROUP LTD
  6320 RESEARCH RD, FRISCO, TX 750333774
Phone: 602 494-0800
Web: WWW.CORECONSTRUCTION.COM

HISTORICAL FINANCIALS

Company Type: Private

Income Statement				FYE: December 31
	REVENUE ($ mil.)	NET INCOME ($ mil.)	NET PROFIT MARGIN	EMPLOYEES
12/20	1,151	20	1.8%	451
12/19	1,004	14	1.4%	—
12/18	1,000	17	1.7%	—
Annual Growth	7.3%	7.8%	—	—

2020 Year-End Financials

Return on assets: 5.9%   Cash ($ mil.): 81
Return on equity: 42.4%
Current ratio: 1.10

THE COUNTY OF BUCKS

EXECUTIVES

Chief, David Steinbach
Chb*, Michael G Fitzpatrick
Treas*, William R Snyder
Interim Coo*, Leader Brian Hessenthaler
Coronor, Thomas J Rosko
Register of Wills, Barbara G Reilly
Human Resources, Suzanne Colonna
Coordinator, Karen Platts
Adjunct Faculty, Brenda Price
Controller, David Jerdan
Information Specialist, Diane Meyer
Auditors: ZELENKOFSKE AXELROD LLC
  JAMIS

LOCATIONS

HQ: THE COUNTY OF BUCKS
  55 E COURT ST FL 5, DOYLESTOWN, PA 189014318
Phone: 215 348-6424
Web: WWW.BUCKSCOUNTY.GOV

HISTORICAL FINANCIALS

Company Type: Private

Income Statement				FYE: December 31
	REVENUE ($ mil.)	NET INCOME ($ mil.)	NET PROFIT MARGIN	EMPLOYEES
12/19	549	(42)	—	2,500
12/18	549	16	3.0%	—
12/17	514	(28)	—	—
12/16	508	8	1.6%	—
Annual Growth	2.6%	—	—	—

2019 Year-End Financials

Return on assets: (-4.0%)   Cash ($ mil.): 172
Return on equity: (-12.1%)
Current ratio: —

THE DANBURY HOSPITAL

EXECUTIVES

Ceo, John M Murphy
Coo*, Michael Daglio
Cfo*, Steven Rosenberg
Sr V Pres*, Moreen O Donahue
Sr V Pres*, Matthew A Miller
Sr V Pres*, Phyllis F Zappala
Neurology, Victor E Ylagan
Accts Mgr, Mary Joe Pollet
Dir, Mary Branigan Lowe
Assistant Professor In Psychia, Daniel Tobin
Chief Resident In Neurological, Scott Sanderson
Auditors: ERNST & YOUNG LLP HARTFORD C

LOCATIONS

HQ: THE DANBURY HOSPITAL
24 HOSPITAL AVE, DANBURY, CT 068106077
Phone: 203 739-7000
Web: WWW.NUVANCEHEALTH.ORG

HISTORICAL FINANCIALS

Company Type: Private

Income Statement				FYE: September 30
	REVENUE ($ mil.)	NET INCOME ($ mil.)	NET PROFIT MARGIN	EMPLOYEES
09/19	741	24	3.4%	3,000
09/18	636	1	0.3%	
Annual Growth	16.5%	1280.0%	—	—

2019 Year-End Financials

Return on assets: 2.9% Cash ($ mil.): 46
Return on equity: 6.4%
Current ratio: 1.40

THE DAVID AND LUCILE PACKARD FOUNDATION

One of the wealthiest philanthropic organizations in the US The David and Lucile Packard Foundation primarily provides grants to not-for-profit entities. The foundation focuses on operating in three areas: conservation and science; children families and communities; and population. The David and Lucile Packard Foundation boasts approximately $4.6 billion in assets. In 2009 the organization committed $100 million for the expansion of the Lucile Packard Children's Hospital at Stanford. The late David Packard (co-founder of Hewlett-Packard) and his wife the late Lucile Salter Packard created the foundation in 1964. Their children run the organization.

EXECUTIVES

Pres-Ceo, Carol S Larson
Exec Dir*, Julie Packard
Prin*, Katy Lnp
Manager, Edwin Van Bronkhorst
Deputy Director, Meg Caldwell
Program Officer, Jamaica Maxwell
Director, Irene Wong
Program Officer Local Grantmak, Jessica Mancini
Director Children, Meera Mani

Compensation, Nora Prentice
Associate Director, Ben Chiquoine
Auditors: PRICEWATERHOUSECOOPERS LLP

LOCATIONS

HQ: THE DAVID AND LUCILE PACKARD FOUNDATION
300 2ND ST, LOS ALTOS, CA 940223621
Phone: 650 917-7167
Web: WWW.PACKARD.ORG

HISTORICAL FINANCIALS

Company Type: Private

Income Statement				FYE: December 31
	REVENUE ($ mil.)	NET INCOME ($ mil.)	NET PROFIT MARGIN	EMPLOYEES
12/10	701	412	58.8%	85
12/09	398	74	18.8%	—
12/06	809	587	72.6%	—
12/05	0	0	69.6%	
Annual Growth	302.5%	289.2%		

2010 Year-End Financials

Return on assets: 6.7% Cash ($ mil.): 213
Return on equity: 6.8%
Current ratio: 2.00

THE DELTA ACADEMY

EXECUTIVES

Supt, Kyle Konold
Coordinator, Monica Robles
Executive of Information Techn, Alisha Bragg
Coordinator, Ransom Terrell
Executive of Information Techn, Chris Ahrens
Executive Officer, Teresa Holden
Executive of Information Techn, Robin Thomas
Information Specialist, Jonathan Swaby
Supt, Patrick Skorkowsky
Executive Assistant, Cindy Krohn
Assistant, Constantine Christopulos
Auditors: EIDE BAILLY LLP LAS VEGAS NE

LOCATIONS

HQ: THE DELTA ACADEMY
5100 W SAHARA AVE, LAS VEGAS, NV 891463406
Phone: 702 799-5000
Web: WWW.CCSD.NET

HISTORICAL FINANCIALS

Company Type: Private

Income Statement				FYE: June 30
	REVENUE ($ mil.)	NET INCOME ($ mil.)	NET PROFIT MARGIN	EMPLOYEES
06/20	3,616	285	7.9%	37,361
06/19	3,519	274	7.8%	—
06/18	3,313	134	4.1%	—
06/17	3,178	(112)	—	—
Annual Growth	4.4%	—	—	—

THE DREES COMPANY

The Drees Company is a big homebuilder in Cincinnati and one of the nation's top private builders. Drees targets first-time and move-up buyers with homes that are priced from about $100000 to more than $1 million. Drees also builds condominiums townhomes and patio homes. Its homes portfolio ranges from its former Zaring Premier Homes luxury division to the company's more financially accessible and modest Marquis Homes division. Drees is active in Florida Indiana Kentucky Maryland North Carolina Ohio Tennessee Texas Virginia and Washington DC. The family-owned firm was founded in 1928.

Operations

In addition to home building architecture energy efficiency upgrades and design services Drees also provides new construction financing solutions through its subsidiary and mortgage lending business First Equity Mortgage which has closed more than $1 billion in loans.

Geographic Reach

Headquartered in Fort Mitchell Kentucky Drees operates across nearly 10 states in cities including Cincinnati and Cleveland Ohio; Indianapolis; Nashville; Raleigh North Carolina; Jacksonville Florida; Austin Houston and Dallas Texas; and the Greater Washington DC area.

Sales and Marketing

In recent years Drees has concentrated on the fast-growing "move up" segment market targeting home buyers looking to upgrade into larger houses.

In 2012 Drees converted its longtime Zaring Premier Homes luxury brand name to its flagship Drees Homes brand. While the move required rebranding in the greater Cincinnati area Drees is banking on its brand reputation and recognition. It also allowed the residential homebuilder to consolidate its advertising sales and marketing efforts.

Financial Performance

While full details of the private company could not be found Drees' CEO David Drees announced in July 2013 that he expected the company to reach $629 million in revenue by April 1 2014.

Looking further back Drees had revenues as high as $1.2 billion in 2006 which slid dramatically following the financial crisis to $490 million in revenue in 2010. To its benefit Texas markets — specifically Austin and Dallas — remained active throughout the recession. Drees was also helped by entering the recession with a relatively low debt load of $364 million. By March 2013 Drees had sold land to generate cash flow and reduced its debt to $125 million.

Strategy

Ranked among the top 25 largest national homebuilders by BUILDER Magazine Drees has been steadily expanding over the past few years to capitalize on an improving housing market.

In recent years Drees has concentrated on the fast-growing and lucrative "move up" segment of the homebuyer's market targeting home owners that are looking to upgrade to larger houses with higher-end amenities. In late 2014 the company landed a $100 million contract to build 237 homes in three Cincinnati-based residential communities with the average house priced between $307000 and $360000. In September 2014 the company entered its first ever foray into the Houston Texas market with plans to price its houses there for more than $300000 — prime pricing to lure these "move up" buyers.

Company Background

A family-operated enterprise since its founding by immigrant Theodore Drees in 1928 the company is run by the third generation of the Drees family.

EXECUTIVES

Chb-Ceo, Ralph Drees
Pres-Coo, David Drees

V Pres-Sec-Treas, Lawrence Herbst
Director of Communications, Jocelyn Cates
Market Manager, Carla Houdek
Architecture Specialist, Saavan Patel
Market Manager, Carolyn Jorden
Sales Vice President, Gary Feldkamp
Market Manager, Lisa Sheldon
Realtor, Mike Carey
Sales Coordinator, Nicole Wallace
Auditors: DELOITTE & TOUCHE LLP CINCINN

LOCATIONS

HQ: THE DREES COMPANY
515 S CAPTAL OF TEXAS HWY, WEST LAKE HILLS,
TX 787464314
Phone: 859 578-4200
Web: WWW.DREESHOMES.COM

Selected Locations

Florida
  Jacksonville
Indiana
  Indianapolis
Kentucky
  Fort Mitchell
Maryland
  Frederick
North Carolina
  Raleigh
Ohio
  Cincinnati
  Cleveland
  Dayton
Tennessee
  Nashville
Texas
  Austin
  Dallas
Washington DC

COMPETITORS

D.r. Horton	Lennar
Fischer Homes	M/i Homes
Kb Home	Pultegroup

HISTORICAL FINANCIALS

Company Type: Private

Income Statement   FYE: March 31

	REVENUE ($ mil.)	NET INCOME ($ mil.)	NET PROFIT MARGIN	EMPLOYEES
03/16	722	31	4.3%	549
03/15	669	36	5.4%	—
03/14	683	35	5.3%	—
03/13	584	19	3.3%	—
Annual Growth	7.3%	17.6%	—	—

2016 Year-End Financials

Return on assets: 6.5%   Cash ($ mil.): 10
Return on equity: 14.1%
Current ratio: 1.90

THE EMPIRE DISTRICT ELECTRIC COMPANY

Empire District Electric (EDE) light ups the middle of the US. The utility transmits and distributes electricity to a population base of more than 450000 (about 217000 customers in southwestern Missouri and adjacent areas of Arkansas Kansas and Oklahoma. It also supplies water to three Missouri towns and natural gas throughout most of the state. EDE's interests in fossil-fueled and hy-droelectric power plants give it a generating capacity of 1377 MW; it also wholesales power. The company also provides fiber-optic services. In early 2017 the company was bought by an Algonquin Power & Utilities unit in a C$3.2 billion (US$2.3 billion) deal.

Operations

EDE operates its businesses in three segments: electric gas and other. The electric segment serves an area of 10000 sq. ml. located principally in southwestern Missouri and also includes smaller areas in southeastern Kansas northeastern Oklahoma and northwestern Arkansas. It also provides water service to three towns in Missouri.

Coal-fired generating units 1 and 2 at the Iatan Plant are jointly-owned by KCP&L (a subsidiary of Great Plains Energy) Missouri Joint Municipal Electric Utility Commission Kansas Electric Power Cooperative and EDE with EDE's share of ownership being 12% in each plant. The Plum Point Energy Station is a 670-MW coal-fired generating facility near Osceola Arkansas of which EDE owns 50 MW of capacity.

EDE's natural gas operations distribute natural gas through The Empire District Gas Company. Its principal gas utility properties consist of about 87 miles of transmission mains and approximately 1160 miles of distribution mains.

EDE's other segment consists of its fiber optics business (which it also uses in its own utility operations).

In 2013 the company generated about 90% of its revenue from its electric segment.

Geographic Reach

The company serves customers in Arkansas Kansas Missouri and Oklahoma.

Sales and Marketing

EDE supplies retail electric service to 119 incorporated communities (and to various unincorporated areas) and wholesale service to four municipally owned distribution systems. The largest urban area it serves is the city of Joplin Missouri and its immediate vicinity with a population of 160000. Its three largest classes of customers are residential commercial and industrial which provided 43% 30% and 15% respectively of its electric operating revenues in 2013. The company derived about 90% of its retail electric revenues from Missouri.

Its gas operations serve 44000 customers in northwest north central and west central Missouri. It provides natural gas distribution to 48 communities and 377 transportation customers. The largest urban area it serves is the city of Sedalia with a population of more than 20000. Residential and commercial provided 63% and 27% respectively of its gas operating revenues in 2013.

EDE also has 118 fiber customers.

Financial Performance

The company's revenues increased by 7% in 2013 due to improved revenues across all of its segments. Electric sales increased due to higher electric rates a growth in customers and colder weather (which increased demand). However commercial sales decreased due to a net unbilled sales adjustment recorded in 2012; Industrial sales decreased due to operating reductions by several large industrial customers; and it wholesale sales decreased due to the closure of a large dairy facility in Monett Missouri.

EDE's gas retail sales and revenues increased due to the colder weather; and other revenues also increased due to a growth in Southwest Power Pool transmission revenues in 2013.

The company's net income increased by 14% in 2013 primarily due to higher revenues and as well as an increased allowance for equity funds used during construction.

EDE has seen growth in revenues since 2009 however it decreased in 2012 due to lower demand as a result of milder winter temperatures that year. The company has seen a healthy growth in cash flow from operations since 2009.

Strategy

The company has been boosting its generating capacity including through its partial ownership in the Plum Point Energy Station in Arkansas and through several wind farm contracts. Total property additions for the three years ending in 2013 totaled $398 million and retirements during the same period totaled $39 million.

Seeking to boost its revenues to cover maintenance and expansion costs in 2013 EDE filed for rate increases for its Arkansas and Missouri electric customers.

In 2013 the company filed an Integrated Resource Plan with the Missouri Public Service Commission to introduce additional demand-side management programs to help its customers use energy more efficiently.

Company Background

In May 2011 EDE's power system suffered extensive damage as as a result of the major tornado that tore through Joplin Missouri. Initial damage reports from the Joplin tornado included the loss of 130 transmission poles.

Mild weather and the global recession suppressed demand and revenues in 2009 but lower gas and power costs helped EDE post an increase in operating income for that year. Cooler-than-normal winter weather and warmer-than-usual summer weather and a rate increase helped to boost power usage and lifted the company's revenues in 2010. A shrinking gas customer base due to depressed economic conditions led to lower gas revenues that year. Lower expenses allowed EDE to report an overall improved net income position in 2010.

EXECUTIVES

Ceo-Pres, Bradley P Beecher
Vp Finance-Cfo*, Laurie A Delano
Vp-Coo Electric*, Kelly S Walters
Vp-Coo Gas*, Ronald F Gatz
SEC*, Dale W Harrington
Treas*, Mark T Timpe
Executive Officer, Myron McKinney
Information Technology Manager, Jared Wicklund
Information Specialist, Matt Hannaford
Coordinator, Karen Mullins
Vp Energy Supply and Delivery, Blake A Mertens

LOCATIONS

HQ: THE EMPIRE DISTRICT ELECTRIC COMPANY
602 S JOPLIN AVE, JOPLIN, MO 648012337
Phone: 417 625-5100
Web: WWW.LIBERTYUTILITIES.COM

PRODUCTS/OPERATIONS

Selected Subsidiaries

EDE Holdings Inc. (nonregulated operations)
  Empire District Industries Inc. (fiber-optic services)
The Empire District Gas Company

COMPETITORS

Aep	Great Plains Energy
Ameren	Oge Energy
Associated Electric	Southern Union
Berkshire Hathaway	Spire
Energy	Westar Energy
Charter Communications	Western Farmers
Entergy	Electric
Grand River Dam	Xcel Energy
Authority	

Income Statement				FYE: December 31
	REVENUE ($ mil.)	NET INCOME ($ mil.)	NET PROFIT MARGIN	EMPLOYEES
12/17	584	36	6.3%	749
12/16	568	64	11.3%	—
12/15	605	56	9.3%	—
12/14	652	67	10.3%	—
Annual Growth	(3.6%)	(18.2%)	—	—

2017 Year-End Financials

Return on assets: 1.5% Cash ($ mil.): 5
Return on equity: 4.4%
Current ratio: 1.20

THE EVANGELICAL LUTHERAN GOOD SAMARITAN SOCIETY

The Evangelical Lutheran Good Samaritan Society strives to be a good neighbor to all particularly to the elderly people in need of housing and health care. The not-for-profit organization owns or leases some 200 senior living facilities including nursing homes assisted living facilities and affordable housing projects for seniors. Through its facilities it also provides home health care services outpatient rehabilitation adult day care and a variety of other services such as specialized units for people with Alzheimer's disease and related dementias. Good Samaritan Society merged with hospital system Sanford Health in early 2019.

Operations
In 2013 the society owned or leased 177 continuum of care communities and 34 home care hospice and private duty agencies (and controlled 29 operating affordable housing and senior housing with services projects). TELGSS managed 10 facilities owned by others and held minority stakes in a handful of joint ventures.

Geographic Reach
Outside its home state of South Dakota TELGSS serves more than 27000 clients across its 240 locations nationwide. It operates in Arizona New Mexico Texas Florida Colorado Arkansas Tennessee Kentucky West Virginia Ohio Indiana Iowa Wisconsin Kansas Nebraska North Dakota Minnesota Montana Idaho Oregon Washington and Hawaii.

Financial Performance
The society's revenue has risen steadily for the past five years. Revenues increased by 2% to $972 million in 2013 from $954 million in 2012 due to higher Housing and Services and other revenues. Rehabilitation/skilled care activities contributed about 80% of total revenues.

Net income decreased by 76% to $7.7 million in 2013 due to an increase in housing and services and administrative expenses. A higher loss on disposal and impairment of property also contributed to the decline in net income.

Strategy
TELGSS' innovation strategy is to create and implement new products and services that respond to the changing needs of its clients.

In this regard TELGSS has embraced the digital age by offering home telehealth services (the re-

mote delivery of health care between a patient and his or her physician). Telehealth aims to reduce health care costs by eliminating the need to import expensive specialists to remote areas allowing patients to more actively participate in their health care and letting doctors to more accurately track patient medication compliance.

The health care society is also using a technology called WellAWARE through a partnership with Philips Lifeline and Honeywell HomMed. It uses sensor monitoring to keep tabs on the subscriber's daily routine. If there are blips in that routine (for example the patient does not get out of bed) a clinician can intervene more quickly. The system is made of small wireless sensors that use infrared light beams to detect motion; major declines in a subscriber's activity level or a fall can also trigger the detectors to call 911.

TELGSS has expanded its operations in recent years boosting its number of locations by nearly 10. The health services provider opened a new campus in Fairfield Glade Tennessee with 30 rehabilitation and skilled care beds 24 assisted living units and 42 senior living apartments and cottages. In Hastings Nebraska it also added a pair of housing locations including a 40-unit tax credit project and a tax renovation of a 51-unit facility in Omaha. It's extending its reach in South Dakota as well by breaking ground on a new Good Samaritan Society in St. Martin Village near Rapid City South Dakota.

TELGSS collaborates with the Mayo Clinic and other members of the Healthy Aging and Independent Living Consortium on OpenIDEO.com exploring how to help patients maintain well-being and thrive as they age. In this context in 2013 the company reported that it had developed three Services@Home agencies (serving more than 300 clients) during the last three years in Hot Springs Village (Arkansas) Loveland (Colorado) and Sioux Falls (South Dakota).

Company Background
Founded in 1922 TELGSS opened its first Good Samaritan center in 1923 as a home for disabled children.

EXECUTIVES

Pres, Randy Bury
V Pres-Cfo, Raye Nae Nylander
Prin, Diane M Cummins
Security Staff, Cindy Nielsen
Coordinator, Amy Smith
Coordinator, Michelle Erpenbach
Coordinator, Tanya Hickman
Corporate Compliance Officer, Blair Jackson
Business Office Manager, Tammie Bankhead
Executive Director, Jim Mertz
Administrator, Jeff Achtenberg
Auditors: CLIFTON LARSON ALLEN LLP MINN

LOCATIONS

HQ: THE EVANGELICAL LUTHERAN GOOD SAMARITAN SOCIETY
4800 W 57TH ST, SIOUX FALLS, SD 571082239
Phone: 866 928-1635
Web: WWW.GOOD-SAM.COM

COMPETITORS

Bpm Senior Living	Genesis Healthcare
Brookdale Senior Living	Golden Horizons
Enlivant	Kindred Healthcare
Extendicare	Rehabcare
Five Star Senior Living	Select Medical
	Sunrise Senior Living

HISTORICAL FINANCIALS
Company Type: Private

Income Statement				FYE: December 31
	REVENUE ($ mil.)	NET INCOME ($ mil.)	NET PROFIT MARGIN	EMPLOYEES
12/15	1,011	(33)	—	24,000
12/13	979	0	0.0%	—
12/07	841	17	2.1%	—
12/06	836	44	5.3%	—
Annual Growth	2.1%	—	—	—

2015 Year-End Financials

Return on assets: (-1.9%) Cash ($ mil.): 17
Return on equity: (-4.5%)
Current ratio: 2.30

THE FINISH LINE INC

The Finish Line sells performance and casual footwear and apparel through nearly 900 Finish Line stores and JD branded shops inside Macy's department stores across the US. Its core Finish Line stores are bigger than those of competitors and offer a wider array of clothing accessories and other merchandise including jackets backpacks sunglasses and watches. Finish Line offers big brand names (such as adidas NIKE and Timberland) and also markets its own private-label line of T-shirts socks and other basics. The company also sells athletic shoes and apparel online. It is a subsidiary of European sports retailer JD Sports.

Operations
Finish Line delivers the EPIC FINISH by providing the most desirable sneakers latest trends and exclusives from the best brands such as Jordan adidas Puma Vans and Converse among others.

Geographic Reach
Indianapolis-based Finish Line operates in more than 45 states and in Puerto Rico.

Sales and Marketing
Nearly all of Finish Line's merchandise is shipped directly from suppliers to its different retail stores where the company processes and ships the merchandise by contract and common carriers to its stores/shops or directly to customers. The company also sell products online through its official website. In addition the company employs approximately 13000 associates.

Company Background
In 1976 boyhood friends Alan Cohen (a lawyer) and David Klapper (a retailer) founded Athletic Enterprises the Indiana franchisee for The Athlete's Foot. By 1981 they had all The Athlete's Foot stores that the state's big malls could hold — about a dozen. To expand beyond those confines the pair teamed up with Dave Fagin and Larry Sablosky and formed The Finish Line.

EXECUTIVES

Ceo, Samuel M Sato
Exec V Pres-Cfo, Edward W Wilhelm
Exec V Pres-Chief Information, Albert J Sutera
Exec V Pres-Cmo, John J Hall
Project Management Office Aana, Amy Martinez
Sales Manager, Andy Campbell
General Manager, Briston Hunt
Director Customer Care Operati, Cindie Norris
Business Manager, Jason Garcia
Project Manager, Kris Jones
Business Manager, Tim Snyder
Auditors: ERNST & YOUNG LLP INDIANAPOLI

LOCATIONS

HQ: THE FINISH LINE INC
3308 N MITTHOEFER RD, INDIANAPOLIS, IN
462352332
Phone: 317 899-1022
Web: WWW.FINISHLINE.COM

PRODUCTS/OPERATIONS

Selected Brands

adidas

Asics

Brooks

Lacoste

Mizuno
New Balance
NIKE
Pastry
Puma
Reebok
Saucony
The North Face
Timberland
Under Armour

Selected Products
Accessories
  Athletic equipment
  Athletic socks
  Backpacks
  Gym bags
  Headbands and sweatbands
  Shoe care
  Shoe insoles and liners
  Shoe laces
  Sunglasses
  Watches
Fan
  High school
  MLB
  NBA
  NCAA
  NFL
  Kids
  Shoes
  Clothing
Men's
  Caps
  Hats
  Jackets
  Jerseys
  Pants
  Shoes
  Shorts
  Socks
  Sweatshirts/fleece
  Tanks
  T-shirts
  Workout clothing
Women's
  Caps
  Hats
  Jackets
  Jerseys
  Pants
  Shoes
  Shorts
  Socks
  Sweatshirts/fleece
  Tanks
  T-shirts
  Team clothing
  Workout clothing

COMPETITORS

Academy Sports	Patagonia Inc.
Dsw	Rei
Dick's Sporting Goods	Rack Room Shoes
Foot Locker	Sports Authority
Genesco	Target Corporation
Hat World	Wal-mart
Hibbett Sports	Zappos.com
Kmart	Shoebuy.com
Modell's	

HISTORICAL FINANCIALS

Company Type: Private

Income Statement — FYE: March 3

	REVENUE ($ mil.)	NET INCOME ($ mil.)	NET PROFIT MARGIN	EMPLOYEES
03/18*	1,838	14	0.8%	13,500
02/17	1,844	(18)	—	—
02/16	1,888	21	1.2%	—
02/15	1,820	79	4.4%	—
Annual Growth	0.3%	(43.5%)	—	—

*Fiscal year change

2018 Year-End Financials

Return on assets: 2.1%   Cash ($ mil.): 93
Return on equity: 3.2%
Current ratio: 2.70

THE FIRST DISTRICT ASSOCIATION

EXECUTIVES

Ceo, Clinton Fall
SEC*, Kevin Schueler
Fleet Administrator, Diane Housman

LOCATIONS

HQ: THE FIRST DISTRICT ASSOCIATION
101 S SWIFT AVE, LITCHFIELD, MN 553552800
Phone: 320 693-3236
Web: WWW.FIRSTDISTRICT.COM

HISTORICAL FINANCIALS

Company Type: Private

Income Statement — FYE: September 30

	REVENUE ($ mil.)	NET INCOME ($ mil.)	NET PROFIT MARGIN	EMPLOYEES
09/18	556	14	2.6%	150
09/17	609	19	3.2%	—
09/16	553	19	3.5%	—
09/15	615	13	2.2%	—
Annual Growth	(3.3%)	2.2%	—	—

THE FISHEL COMPANY

The Fishel Company reels in revenues by laying out lines. The company (also known as Team Fishel) provides engineering construction management and maintenance services for electric and gas utility and communications infrastructure projects. The aerial and underground utility contractor designs and builds distribution networks for telecommunications cable and broadband television gas transmission and distribution and electric utilities throughout the US. It also counts municipalities state and federal agencies universities commercial building owners financial services companies health care providers manufacturers and residential real estate developers among its clients.

Operations

The company's products and services include Structured Cabling Systems Data Center build-outs Wireless Networks and Building Security and Automation. It has installed more than 16000 communications networks for the healthcare financial education manufacturing logistics and government sectors.

Geographic Reach

The Fishel Company is licensed to do business in some two dozen states. It operates from 32 offices located in about 15 states including Arkansas Arizona California Florida Georgia Kentucky Nevada New Mexico Ohio Oklahoma Pennsylvania Tennessee Texas and Virginia.

Sales and Marketing

The company's power customers include American Electric Power Arizona Public Service Arkansas Valley Electric Dayton Power & Light Dominion Virginia Power Duke Energy Entergy and First Electric Cooperative among others.

In addition to utilities and power coops the company serves other markets including Repair and Planning Broadband Broadband Network Services Enterprise Solutions and Advanced Technology Services.

Strategy

Fishel Company is tracking its business to a Vision 2020 initiative which has a three-pronged goal of customer development operational excellence and teammate development. Its customer development focus involves natural gas distribution power transmission and distribution (T&D) construction and fiber network installation. Operational excellence goals are centered on bidding and pricing project management and being accident-free. Its teammate management focus comprises leadership development performance management workforce planning and continuous improvement.

The company has strategic business relationships with TE Connectivity Andrews Wireless Belden Commscope Corning Cable Systems Legrand Ortronics Leviton Nexans Berktek OASIS and Panduit.

Company Background

Kenneth Fishel founded the firm in 1936 as an underground contractor for telephone companies.

EXECUTIVES

Chm, Diane Keeler
Ceo, John Phillips
V Pres-Cfo, Paul Riewe
Pres, Ken Katz
Vice-Chairman, Eric Smith
Vice President, Joe Mayhew
Office Manager, Becky Blackstone
Engineer, Brian Archer
Shop Foreman, Joe Colella
Applications Engineer, Terry Sparks
Corporate Tax Manager, Kathy Blackstone
Auditors: CROWE LLP COLUMBUS OHIO

LOCATIONS

HQ: THE FISHEL COMPANY
1366 DUBLIN RD, COLUMBUS, OH 432151093
Phone: 614 274-8100
Web: WWW.TEAMFISHEL.COM
Selected Locations
Arizona
Arkansas
California
Florida
Georgia
Kentucky
Nevada
New Mexico
Ohio
Oklahoma
Pennsylvania
Tennessee
Texas
Virginia

PRODUCTS/OPERATIONS

Selected Services
Emergency restoration repair & maintenance
Fiber overbuilds
GPS survey
Network installation
Permitting
Project management
Right of way
Site Design
Utility construction

Selected Markets
Commercial industrial advanced logistics
Electric Distribution & Transmission
Financial & health care
Gas distribution & transmission pipeline
Telecom & broadband cable
Wireless backhaul

COMPETITORS

Dycom	Myr Group
Emcor	Mastec
Ies Holdings	Pike Corporation
Mdu Construction Services	Quanta Services

HISTORICAL FINANCIALS

Company Type: Private

Income Statement   FYE: December 31

	REVENUE ($ mil.)	NET INCOME ($ mil.)	NET PROFIT MARGIN	EMPLOYEES
12/19	540	36	6.8%	2,512
12/17	434	29	6.8%	—
12/16	341	8	2.6%	—
12/15	301	10	3.3%	—
Annual Growth	15.7%	38.2%	—	—

2019 Year-End Financials

Return on assets: 13.0%   Cash ($ mil.): 33
Return on equity: 43.8%
Current ratio: 1.60

THE FORD FOUNDATION

As one of the nation's largest philanthropic organizations the Ford Foundation can afford to be generous. The foundation offers grants to individuals and institutions worldwide that work to meet its goals of strengthening democratic values reducing poverty and injustice promoting international cooperation and advancing human achievement. The Ford Foundation's charitable giving has run the gamut from A (Association for Asian Studies) to Z (Zanzibar International Film Festival). The foundation has an endowment of about $10 billion. Established in 1936 by Edsel Ford whose father founded the Ford Motor Company the foundation no longer owns stock in the automaker or has ties to the founding family.

Operations
The foundation which is governed by an international board of trustees makes grants in all 50 US states and supports programs in more than 50 countries.

It boasts about 10 regional offices in Latin America Africa the Middle East and Asia.

Geographic Reach
Based in New York the Ford Foundation is a grantmaking foundation that primarily serves the US but also global programs.

Strategy
The Ford Foundation's programs address several social justice issues including democratic and accountable government freedom of expression access to education economic fairness and opportunity sexuality and reproductive rights sustainable development social justice metropolitan opportunity and human rights.

A small portion of its endowment is set aside for social investing. The foundation's funds typically finance critical projects set new business models and develop sustainable organizations. By investing $1 million or more in initiatives the Ford Foundation's investment strategy aims to make a noteworthy impact and encourage other investors to also fund projects.

HISTORY

Henry Ford and his son Edsel gave $25000 to establish the Ford Foundation in Michigan in 1936 followed the next year by 250000 shares of nonvoting stock in the Ford Motor Company. The foundation's activities were limited mainly to Michigan until the deaths of Edsel (1943) and Henry (1947) made the foundation the owner of 90% of the automaker's nonvoting stock (catapulting the endowment to $474 million the US's largest).

In 1951 under a new mandate and president (Paul Hoffman former head of the Marshall Plan) the Ford Foundation made broad commitments to the promotion of world peace the strengthening of democracy and the improvement of education. Early education program grants overseen by University of Chicago chancellor Robert Maynard Hutchins ($100 million between 1951 and 1953) helped establish major international programs (e.g. Harvard's Center for International Legal Studies) and the National Merit Scholarships.

Under McCarthyite criticism for its experimental education grants the foundation in 1951 granted $550 million to noncontroversial recipients such as liberal arts colleges and not-for-profit hospitals. Public TV support became a foundation trademark that year when the organization's money set up the Radio and Television Workshop.

The Ford family and the Ford Foundation held sole ownership of the Ford company until 1956 when the company offered shares of its stock to the public. The foundation sold some 22% of its Ford Motor Company shares that year and shed the rest over the next 20-plus years.

The 1950s saw the beginning of international work; begun in Asia and the Middle East (1950) and extended to Africa (1958) and Latin America (1959) the programs focused on education and rural development. The foundation also supported the Population Council and research in high-yield agriculture with The Rockefeller Foundation.

The Ford Foundation targeted innovative approaches to employment and race relations in the early 1960s. McGeorge Bundy (former national security adviser to President John Kennedy) named president of the foundation in 1966 increased the activist trend with grants for direct voter registration; the NAACP; public-interest law centers serving consumer environmental and minority causes; and housing for the poor.

The early 1970s saw support for black colleges and scholarships child care and job training for women but by 1974 inflation weak stock prices and overspending had eroded assets. Programs were cut but continued support for social-justice issues led the conservative Henry Ford II to quit the board in 1976.

Under lawyer Franklin Thomas (named president in 1979) The Ford Foundation established the nation's largest community development support organization Local Initiatives Support. Thomas the first African-American to lead the foundation was a catalyst in a series of meetings between white and black South Africans in the mid-1980s.

Thomas stepped down in 1996 and new president Susan Berresford formerly EVP consolidated the foundation's grant programs into three areas: Asset Building and Community Development; Peace and Social Justice; and Education Media Arts and Culture. In the late 1990s Ford was surpassed by various other foundations and it had to relinquish its 30-year title as the biggest charitable organization in the US.

In 2000 the foundation announced its largest grant ever the 10-year $330 million International Fellowship Program to support graduate students studying in 20 countries.

After the September 11 2001 terrorist attacks the foundation joined other philanthropic organizations in providing disaster relief. It made grants of $10 million in New York and more than $1 million in Washington DC.

Berresford retired in early 2008 after 12 years as president of the foundation. She was succeeded by Luis Ubi ±as formerly a director at McKinsey & Company.

EXECUTIVES

Pres, Susan V Berresford
Treas*, Nicholas Gabriel
Evp*, Hilary Pennington
Coo-Treas*, Depelsha McGruder
Vp-Sec-Gen Counsel*, Nishka Chandrasoma
Trustee, Juliet V Garc A
Vp, Asset Building and Communi, Pablo J Far As
Representative, Andean Region, Mart N Abreg
Assistant To Human Resources D, Elsie Lopez
Vice President Democracy Right, Martfn Abrega
Vice-President, Xavier D Briggs

LOCATIONS

HQ: THE FORD FOUNDATION
320 E 43RD ST FL 4, NEW YORK, NY 100174890
Phone: 212 573-5370
Web: WWW.FORDFOUNDATION.ORG

PRODUCTS/OPERATIONS

Selected Core Issues
Democratic and accountable government
Economic fairness
Education opportunity and scholarship
Freedom of expression
Human rights
Metropolitan opportunity
Sexuality and reproductive health rights
Social justice philanthropy
Sustainable development

HISTORICAL FINANCIALS

Company Type: Private

Income Statement   FYE: December 31

	ASSETS ($ mil.)	NET INCOME ($ mil.)	INCOME AS % OF ASSETS	EMPLOYEES
12/15	12,114	(270)	—	556
12/14*	12,400	(7)	—	—
09/11	10,344	(5)	—	—
09/09	10,234	0	—	—
Annual Growth	2.8%	—	—	—

*Fiscal year change

2015 Year-End Financials

Return on assets: (-2.2%)   Sales ($ mil): 486
Return on equity: (-2.3%)

THE FRESH MARKET INC

The Fresh Market is a specialty grocery retailer that operates about 160 full-service upscale specialty grocery stores in over 20 US states from Florida to New York. As the name suggests the chain specializes in perishable goods including fruits and vegetables meat and seafood. The initial 14000-square-foot store differentiated itself from conventional supermarkets with a farmer's market atmosphere. It is a destination for those looking to discover the best including convenient restaurant-quality meals hand-picked produce premium baked goods fresh-cut flowers custom-cut meats and carefully curated offerings. The company was founded by husband-and-wife team Ray and Beverly Berry who opened their first store in 1982.

Operations

The Fresh Market's departments include produce meat seafood bakery grocery and dairy deli and cheese wine and beer coffee candy bulk floral and gifts and private label.

The company sources produce from around the corner and around the world. Its fruits and veggies are carefully curated for optimal flavor and nutrition. Premium Choice beef is tender and savory due in large part to having superior marbling and includes only the top 10% of all beef in the US. Offering high quality chicken and turkey the company's meat selections also include lean pork made-in-store gourmet burgers and a range of specialty meat and superior cuts.

The Fresh Market's seafood department offers a great selection of fresh fish and shellfish including customer favorites like seasonal Alaskan salmon wild-caught sashimi-grade tuna and its succulent cocktail shrimp that are cooked in-shell with absolutely no preservatives. It provides the freshest most flavorful live shellfish offerings including mussels to clams and oysters. In addition the company also features a range of prepared seafood including marinated & stuffed fish breaded shrimp smoked salmon and its ultimate crab cakes.

The company's deli and cheese department offers delicious charcuterie deli meats and cheeses imported and specialty cheese and a tasty selection of gourmet entrees salads and sides for any occasion. Wine and beer department offers a beautiful assortment of chilled whites and ros © wines. Coffee department offers a wide variety of coffee beans from across the globe. Its custom roasts include special flavors like Molten Chocolate rich decaffeinated blends and customer favorites like Jamaican Blue Mountain Blend and the company's limited-edition seasonal coffees.

The Fresh Market's candy department offers extensive variety of candies including chocolate bars Jelly Belly jelly beans and gummi bears. Its confection perfection includes exquisite treats from Godiva and Vosges. Its bulk department is a wonderful source for nuts seeds snack mixes dried fruits and more. Floral and gifts department offers custom gift baskets.

Geographic Reach

Headquartered in Greensboro North Carolina the company currently operates nearly 160 stores in over 20 states across the US. Its stores are located in Alabama Connecticut Delaware Florida Georgia Illinois Louisiana and some other states.

Sales and Marketing

In addition to its website the company connects with its customers through social media platforms such as Facebook Twitter Pinterest YouTube and Instagram.

EXECUTIVES

Ceo, Jason Potter
Exec V Pres-Cfo, Jeffrey C Ackerman
Sr V Pres Hr, Matt Argano
Sr V Pres-General Counsel, Scott Duggan
V Pres-Contrl, Jeffrey B Short
Cfo, Brian Nicholson
Chro, Chris Himbauch
Chief Marketing Officer, Mary Kellmanson
Cmo, Dan Portnoy
Cmo, Kevin Miller
Cfo, Jim Heaney
Auditors: ERNST & YOUNG LLP CHARLOTTE

LOCATIONS

HQ: THE FRESH MARKET INC
300 N GREENE ST STE 1100, GREENSBORO, NC 274012171
Phone: 336 272-1338
Web: WWW.THEFRESHMARKET.COM

2016 Stores

	No.
Florida	45
North Carolina	22
Virginia	16
Georgia	15
Illinois	9
Tennessee	9
South Carolina	9
Alabama	6
Indiana	5
Louisiana	5
New York	5
Ohio	5
Pennsylvania	5
Maryland	4
Connecticut	3
Kentucky	3
New Jersey	3
Arkansas	2
Wisconsin	2
Delaware	1
Massachusetts	1
Mississippi	1
New Hampshire	1
Oklahoma	1
Total	**178**

COMPETITORS

Earth Fare	Trader Joe's
Food Lion	Wal-mart
Kroger	Wegmans
Publix	Weis Markets
Safeway	Whole Foods
Sprouts	Winn-dixie
Target Corporation	

HISTORICAL FINANCIALS

Company Type: Private

Income Statement				FYE: January 31
	REVENUE ($ mil.)	NET INCOME ($ mil.)	NET PROFIT MARGIN	EMPLOYEES
01/16	1,857	65	3.5%	12,600
01/15	1,753	63	3.6%	—
01/14	1,511	50	3.4%	—
01/13	1,329	64	4.8%	—
Annual Growth	11.8%	0.7%	—	—

2016 Year-End Financials

Return on assets: 11.3%   Cash ($ mil.): 60
Return on equity: 18.0%
Current ratio: 1.10

THE GEISINGER CLINIC

EXECUTIVES

Ceo, Glenn D Steele Jr
Sr V Pres-Treas, Frank J Trembulak
Vice-President Information Ser, David Macko
Emergency Room Directo, John Skiendzielewski
Vice-President, Frank Rubino
Technical Analyst, Radiology I, Sean Spangler

LOCATIONS

HQ: THE GEISINGER CLINIC
100 N ACADEMY AVE, DANVILLE, PA 178229800
Phone: 570 271-6211
Web: WWW.GEISINGER.ORG

HISTORICAL FINANCIALS

Company Type: Private

Income Statement				FYE: June 30
	REVENUE ($ mil.)	NET INCOME ($ mil.)	NET PROFIT MARGIN	EMPLOYEES
06/20	1,625	(194)	—	12,000
06/18	1,290	(163)	—	—
06/15	991	(12)	—	—
06/14	849	(3)	—	—
Annual Growth	11.4%	—	—	—

2020 Year-End Financials

Return on assets: (-40.5%)   Cash ($ mil.): 52
Return on equity: (-88.1%)
Current ratio: 0.70

THE GEORGE WASHINGTON UNIVERSITY

The George Washington University is the largest institution of higher education in the District of Columbia. The private coeducational university's approximately 12500 undergraduate and 15300 graduate students are scattered across its primary campus at Foggy Bottom as well as its campuses in Mount Vernon and Ashburn Virginia. With nearly 1225 non-medical and nearly 1270 medical faculty staff the school's student-teacher ratio is about 13:1. Its academic programs spread across some 10 schools run the gamut from business to law to medicine. Notable alumni include former First Lady Jacqueline Kennedy Onassis former SEC Chairman Mary Schapiro and former US Secretary of State Colin Powell.

Operations

George Washington University has students enrolled in a range of disciplines from forensic science and creative writing to international affairs and computer engineering as well as medicine public health the law and public policy.

It runs the Columbian College of Arts & Sciences Corcoran School of the Arts & Design School of Business Graduate School of Education & Human Development School of Engineering & Applied Science as well as the Elliott School of International Affairs GW Law School of Media & Public Affairs School of Medicine & Health Sciences School of Nursing Graduate School of Political Management College of Professional Studies

Milken Institute School of Public Health Trachtenberg School of Public Policy & Public Administration.

About 45% of its total sales come from student tuition fees nearly 20% from patient care and approximately 15% from grants and contracts including indirect cost recoveries. It also generates a small amount from endowments medical education agreements auxiliary enterprises contributions and investments.

Geographic Reach
The George Washington University's students come from all 50 US states Washington DC Guam Puerto Rico Virgin Islands and nearly 140 countries.

Financial Performance
The company's revenue for fiscal 2021 decreased to $1.57 billion compared from the prior year with $1.69 billion.

Cash held by the company at the end of fiscal 2021 decreased to $280.1 million. Operating investing and financing activities used $11.0 million $277.8 million and $127.6 million respectively. Main cash uses were unrealized gain on investments; purchases of investments; and payments of proceeds from borrowings on lines of credit.

Company Background
Chartered by the US Congress in 1821 as The Columbian College in the District of Columbia the university adopted its present name in 1904.

EXECUTIVES

Pres, Thomas Leblanc
Cfo*, Mark Diaz
Dean, School of Engineering An, David S Dolling
Interim Dean, Elliott School O, Hugh L Agnew
Dean, School of Medicine and H, Jeffrey S Akman
Dean, School of Business, Linda A Livingstone
Evp and Treasurer, Louis H Katz
Dean, Milken Institute School, Lynn R Goldman
Dean, Graduate School of Educa, Michael J Feuer
Dean, School of Nursing, Pamela R Jeffries
Assistant Director, Brandy Vause
Auditors: PRICEWATERHOUSECOOPERS LLP MC

LOCATIONS

HQ: THE GEORGE WASHINGTON UNIVERSITY
1918 F ST NW, WASHINGTON, DC 200520042
Phone: 202 994-6600
Web: WWW.GWU.EDU

PRODUCTS/OPERATIONS

Selected Schools
College of Professional Studies
Columbian College of Arts and Sciences
Elliott School of International Affairs
George Washington School of Business
George Washington University Law School
Graduate School of Education and Human Development
Graduate School of Political Management
School of Engineering and Applied Science
School of Media and Public Affairs
School of Medicine and Health Sciences
School of Public Health and Health Services

HISTORICAL FINANCIALS
Company Type: Private

Income Statement				FYE: June 30
	REVENUE ($ mil.)	NET INCOME ($ mil.)	NET PROFIT MARGIN	EMPLOYEES
06/13	1,177	59	5.0%	5,000
06/06	921	146	15.9%	—
06/05	832	115	13.8%	—
Annual Growth	4.4%	(7.9%)	—	—

2013 Year-End Financials
Return on assets: 1.7%   Cash ($ mil.): 224
Return on equity: 3.1%
Current ratio: —

THE GEORGETOWN UNIVERSITY

Georgetown University is the oldest Catholic university in the US. The institution's 17400 undergraduate and graduate students are instructed by more than 2340 faculty members (representing both full- and part-time) in nine schools ranging from the university's renowned Law Center to the Edmund A. Walsh School of Foreign Service and the Georgetown School of Medicine. The system has a student-teacher ratio of about 10:1. The university is also home to the Georgetown University Medical Center and has forged numerous ties with its neighboring institutions in the Washington DC community.

Operations
The Georgetown University Medical Center provides a variety of medical services to area residents in addition to serving as a teaching and research facility for the university. The medical center has several specialty medicine and research programs through a partnership with MedStar's Georgetown University Hospital including Huntington disease care and brain development studies. Georgetown's research institutes are working to discover new medical treatments including potential breast cancer therapies. The university receives some $179 million in research funding each year.

Geographic Reach
Georgetown University's main campus (54 buildings including the medical center) is located on about 100 acres on the banks of the Potomac in Washington DC. It also has locations in downtown Washington DC and in Arlington Virginia.

Internationally Georgetown University operates a School of Foreign Service campus in Qatar. The university also has study abroad programs in Argentina Turkey China Chile Italy and England and a nursing study program with the Australian Catholic University.

Financial Performance
Georgetown University reported about $1.12 billion in revenues in fiscal 2014 virtually flat with the previous year. Its earnings come from student tuition and fees grants and contracts auxiliary activities and other sources. In fiscal 2015 undergraduate tuition was $46200 per student (up from $44280 in fiscal 2014 and $42360 in fiscal 2013).

Strategy
Georgetown University expands and upgrades its facilities periodically to keep pace with modern technologies and appeal to a variety of students.

To expand its outreach programs Georgetown University built a new location for its School of Continuing Studies in downtown Washington DC. The new campus located near the Law Center opened in late 2013 and extends the reach of the university's presence downtown as it works to expand beyond its historical campus. It also officially launched its McCourt School of Public Policy in 2013.

It also launches new degree programs such as the MIDP (master's of international development policy) and the Master of Science in Global Health.

Company Background
In 2010 Georgetown University received its largest philanthropic gift ever when it was granted a nearly $90 million endowment to support medical research at the university's medical center from a charitable trust established by the will of the late Harry Toulmin in 1965.

Georgetown University was founded in 1789 by John Carroll the nation's first Catholic bishop. At the time of its founding Georgetown University's historic campus was located in Georgetown Maryland; the location is now part of the Washington DC metropolitan area. Among Georgetown University's alumni are President Bill Clinton basketball great Patrick Ewing and former US Surgeon General Antonia Novello.

EXECUTIVES

Pres, John J Degioia
V Pres-CIO*, H David Lambert
Sr V Pres*, Spiros Dimolitsas
Exec V Pres*, Howard Federoff
Exec V Pres*, Robert M Groves
V Pres*, Lisa Brown
V Pres*, Lisa Davis
Neurosurgeon, Kevin M McGrail
Director of Digital Media, Robert Murray
Executive Assistant, Robin Reath
Assistant Dean, Executive Care, Diana Banks
Auditors: PRICEWATERHOUSECOOPERS LLP MC

LOCATIONS

HQ: THE GEORGETOWN UNIVERSITY
37TH AND O ST NW, WASHINGTON, DC 200570001
Phone: 202 687-0100
Web: WWW.GEORGETOWN.EDU

PRODUCTS/OPERATIONS

Selected Schools
Edmund A. Walsh School of Foreign Service
Georgetown College
Graduate School of Arts and Sciences
Law Center
McCourt School of Public Policy
Robert E. McDonough School of Business
School of Medicine
School of Nursing and Health Studies
School for Summer and Continuing Education

HISTORICAL FINANCIALS
Company Type: Private

Income Statement				FYE: June 30
	REVENUE ($ mil.)	NET INCOME ($ mil.)	NET PROFIT MARGIN	EMPLOYEES
06/21	1,274	756	59.4%	9,700
06/20	1,341	(128)	—	—
06/19	1,330	(77)	—	—
06/18	1,249	130	10.4%	—
Annual Growth	0.7%	79.8%	—	—

2021 Year-End Financials
Return on assets: 16.3%   Cash ($ mil.): 218
Return on equity: 32.2%
Current ratio: —

THE GOLUB CORPORATION

Supermarket operator The Golub Corporation offers tasty come-ons such as table-ready meals gift certificates automatic discount cards and a hotline where cooks answer food-related queries.

Golub operates supermarkets under the Price Chopper Market 32 and Market Bistro banners in six states in the northeastern US (New York is its largest market). Some New York stores provide shopping and delivery service through the Instacart program. The company also provides catering foodfare pharmacy cooking school and Kosher services.

Geographic Reach

Golub's Price Chopper chain is active in six US states such as New York Connecticut Massachusetts Vermont Pennsylvania and New Hampshire.

Sales and Marketing

The company sells its products in its stores and online. It serves customers in pharmaceutical school and food service industries.

Strategy

The company partners with Instacart to offer the customer the convenience of grocery delivery and pickup service. Instacart's network of personal shoppers will grocery shop for the customers and either deliver their order directly at their doorstep or have it ready for pickup.

Company Background

Like many other retailers the company is experimenting with new formats. In May 2012 it opened its first small-format store known as Price Chopper Limited. The 19000-square-foot store (about a third of the size of a typical Price Chopper supermarket) is located in a residential neighborhood in downtown Saratoga Springs New York. The "Limited" store offers an edited selection of Price Chopper's most popular products a bakery full-service meat deli and seafood departments and a cafe with eat-in or take-out meals.

In fall 2011 Price Chopper launched a new online ordering and home delivery program called Price Chopper Shops4U . The service charges a service fee of $10 with an additional $6 fee for delivery. Customers can either pick up their orders at the store or have them delivered.

Brothers Bill and Ben Golub founded the company in 1932.

EXECUTIVES

Pres-Ceo, Scott Grimmett
Chb, Neil M Golub
Coo, Blaine R Bringhurst
Vp Distribution, Robert Doyle
Vp Public Relations and Consum, Mona J Golub
Vice Chb, Jerel T Golub
Cao, Leo Taylor
Cfo, Jim Peterson
Site Manager, Denise Taylor
Telecommunications, Mike Phlipsak
Recruitment Supervisor, Paul Riley

LOCATIONS

HQ: THE GOLUB CORPORATION
461 NOTT ST, SCHENECTADY, NY 123081812
Phone: 518 355-5000
Web: WWW.PRICECHOPPER.COM

2013 Stores

	No.
New York	81
Massachusetts	16
Vermont	15
Connecticut	8
Pennsylvania	8
New Hampshire	4
Total	**132**

COMPETITORS

7-eleven	Gerrity's
A&p	Hannaford Bros.
Aldi	Shaw's
Bj's Wholesale Club	Stewart's Shops
Big Y Foods	Stop & Shop
Cvs	Tops Markets
Costco Wholesale	Target Corporation
Cumberland Farms	Wal-mart
Demoulas Super Markets	Wegmans

HISTORICAL FINANCIALS

Company Type: Private

Income Statement   FYE: April 24

	REVENUE ($ mil.)	NET INCOME ($ mil.)	NET PROFIT MARGIN	EMPLOYEES
04/16	3,427	8	0.2%	19,500
04/15	3,476	21	0.6%	—
04/14	3,472	18	0.5%	—
Annual Growth	(0.7%)	(32.3%)	—	—

2016 Year-End Financials

Return on assets: 1.2%   Cash ($ mil.): 22
Return on equity: 13.3%
Current ratio: 0.70

THE HEALTH CARE AUTHORITY OF THE CITY OF HUNTSVILLE

Health Care Authority of the City of Huntsville ensures that residents get the medical attention they need. The volunteer board consists of nine members that governs the more than 880-bed Huntsville Hospital one of the largest medical centers in Alabama with a staff of more than 650 physicians as well as other medical facilities. Huntsville Hospital is also a teaching facility for the University of Alabama-Birmingham. The Health Care Authority of the City of Huntsville provides a list of nominees for board members to the City Council which decides who is appointed to the board.

EXECUTIVES

Eo, David Spillers
Cfo*, Kelly Towers
V Pres, Michael W Brown
Chief of Medicine, Richard Spera
Chief of Psychology/Psychiatry, Anupama Yedla
Auditors: DIXON HUGHES GOODMAN LLP BIRM

LOCATIONS

HQ: THE HEALTH CARE AUTHORITY OF THE CITY OF HUNTSVILLE
101 SIVLEY RD SW, HUNTSVILLE, AL 358014421
Phone: 256 265-1000
Web: WWW.HUNTSVILLEHOSPITAL.ORG

HISTORICAL FINANCIALS

Company Type: Private

Income Statement   FYE: June 30

	REVENUE ($ mil.)	NET INCOME ($ mil.)	NET PROFIT MARGIN	EMPLOYEES
06/19	1,700	218	12.9%	14,000
06/18	1,524	53	3.5%	—
06/17	1,407	46	3.3%	—
06/07	591	49	8.3%	—
Annual Growth	9.2%	13.3%	—	—

2019 Year-End Financials

Return on assets: 11.7%   Cash ($ mil.): 88
Return on equity: 16.4%
Current ratio: 1.40

THE HERTZ CORPORATION

EXECUTIVES

Executive Vice President; President Of Vehicle Rental And Leasing Of The Americas And Pacific, Joseph Nothwang, $565,385 total compensation
Director, Henry Wolf
Senior Vice President, Chief Information Officer, Joseph Eckroth
Executive Vice President - Supply Chain Management, John Thomas
Senior Vice President, General Counsel, Secretary, Harold Rolfe
Executive Vice President - Sales And Marketing, Brian Kennedy
Senior Vice President - Quality Assurance & Administration, Charles Shafer
Director, Carolyn Everson
Director, Barry Beracha
Senior Vice President, Chief Accounting Officer, Principal Accounting Officer, Controller, Eric Esper
Director, Michael Durham
Chief Financial Officer, Jamere Jackson
Interim Treasurer, Anthony Fiore
Independent Lead Director, Linda Levinson
Director, Debra Kelly-Ennis
Independent Director, Michael Koehler
Director, Carl Berquist
Independent Director, Philippe Laffont
President, Chief Executive Officer, Director, Paul Stone
Executive Vice President, General Counsel, Secretary, M. David Galainena
Auditors: PRICEWATERHOUSECOOPERS LLP FO

LOCATIONS

HQ: THE HERTZ CORPORATION
8501 WILLIAMS RD, ESTERO, FL 339283325
Phone: 239 301-7000
Web: WWW.HERTZ.COM

HISTORICAL FINANCIALS

Company Type: Private

Income Statement   FYE: December 31

	REVENUE ($ mil.)	NET INCOME ($ mil.)	NET PROFIT MARGIN	EMPLOYEES
12/17	8,803	332	3.8%	38,000
12/16	8,803	(488)	—	—
12/15	10,535	276	2.6%	—
Annual Growth	(8.6%)	9.7%	—	—

2017 Year-End Financials

Return on assets: 1.7%   Cash ($ mil.): 1,072
Return on equity: 21.8%
Current ratio: —

THE HOWARD UNIVERSITY

EXECUTIVES

Pres, Dwayne Frederick
Vp Communications-Chief Commun*, Crystal Brown
Chief Compliance Officer*, Robert Clark
Cntlr, Rosoloc Henderson
Staff, Claude Williams
Assistant Professor, Debra White-Coleman
Assistant Professor, Ella Carter
Coordinator, Gaelle Amazan
Health Professional, Philip Lucas
Staff, Quito Swan
Information Specialist, Raven Smith
Auditors: BDO USA LLP RALEIGH NC

LOCATIONS

HQ: THE HOWARD UNIVERSITY
2400 6TH ST NW, WASHINGTON, DC 200590002
Phone: 202 806-6100
Web: WWW.HOWARD.EDU

HISTORICAL FINANCIALS

Company Type: Private

Income Statement				FYE: June 30
	REVENUE ($ mil.)	NET INCOME ($ mil.)	NET PROFIT MARGIN	EMPLOYEES
06/21	1,041	377	36.2%	5,600
06/20	1,025	59	5.8%	—
06/18	792	46	5.9%	—
Annual Growth	9.5%	100.2%	—	—

2021 Year-End Financials

Return on assets: 18.3%   Cash ($ mil.): 204
Return on equity: 35.0%
Current ratio: 1.00

THE INCOME FUND OF AMERICA INC

EXECUTIVES

Chb, Janet McKinley
Pres, Darcy Kopcho
Treas, Dayna Yamabe
Sr V Pres, Stephen E Bepler
Sr V Pres, Abner K Goldstein
V Pres, John Smet
SEC, Patrick F Quan
Auditors: DELOITTE & TOUCHE LLP COSTA

LOCATIONS

HQ: THE INCOME FUND OF AMERICA INC
1 MARKET PLZ, SAN FRANCISCO, CA 941051101
Phone: 415 421-9360

HISTORICAL FINANCIALS

Company Type: Private

Income Statement				FYE: July 31
	REVENUE ($ mil.)	NET INCOME ($ mil.)	NET PROFIT MARGIN	EMPLOYEES
07/20	4,217	2,611	61.9%	7
07/19	4,050	160	4.0%	—
07/18	4,051	2,343	57.9%	—
07/16	3,577	6,660	186.2%	—
Annual Growth	4.2%	(20.9%)	—	—

2020 Year-End Financials

Return on assets: 2.1%   Cash ($ mil.): 11
Return on equity: 2.4%
Current ratio: —

THE INSTITUTE OF ELECTRICAL AND ELECTRONICS ENGINEERS INCORPORATED

The Institute of Electrical and Electronics Engineers (IEEE) has over 396005 members including nearly 107620 students in over 160 countries. The IEEE is the world's largest technical professional organization dedicated to advancing technology for the benefit of humanity. IEEE and its members inspire a global community through its highly cited publications conferences technology standards and professional and educational activities. It sponsors around 1610 annual conferences and publishes a variety of technical literature including journals magazines and conference proceedings. The IEEE was formed in 1963 in a combination of the American Institute of Electrical Engineers (founded in 1884) and the Institute of Radio Engineers (founded in 1912).

Operations

Periodicals and media together contribute approximately half of IEEE's total revenue. The remaining revenue comes from conferences memberships standards public imperatives and others.

The Institute offers membership for terms of one year. The Institute satisfies its performance obligation and recognizes revenue evenly over the membership term as its members simultaneously receive and consume the benefits over that timeframe. Periodicals revenues primarily include subscriptions and online products and content. Media revenue primarily includes advertising space sold in newsletters and periodicals. Conference revenues primarily include registration and sponsorships and also includes the conference proceedings and published articles related to respective conferences.

Geographic Reach

Based in New York the company has its presence in USA (around 40% of total members) India and China (about 20%) Canada Japan and Tunisia. Overall the organization is known across 160 countries.

Sales and Marketing

The company has over 396005 members as well as nearly 107620 student members.

Financial Performance

The IEEE Statement of Activities reflects total revenues for 2020 of $467.0 million a decrease of $90.6 million or 16% from 2019.

Cash held by the company at the end of fiscal 2020 increased to $20.1 million. Cash provided by operations and financing activities were $109.5 million and $1.9 million respectively. Cash used for investing activities was $113.4 million mainly for purchases of investments.

Strategy

IEEE's strategic priorities are: Drive global innovation through broad collaboration and the sharing of knowledge; Enhance public understanding of engineering and technology and pursue standards for their practical application; Be a trusted source of educational services and resources to support life-long learning; Provide opportunities for career and professional development; and Inspire a worldwide audience by building communities that advance technical interests inform public policy and expand knowledge for the benefit of humanity.

EXECUTIVES

Pres-Ceo, Karen Barleston
Pres, James A Jeffries
Exec Dir, Dr E James Prendergast
Cfo, Thomas Siegert
Staff Dir-Fin Svcs, Thomas Lynch
SEC, William P Walsh
Controller, Anthony Patane
Exec Director, Melissa Russell
Staff, Jonathan Dahl
Scientist, Wes Cobb
Marketing Director, Heather Gore
Auditors: GRANT THORNTON LLP ISELIN NE

LOCATIONS

HQ: THE INSTITUTE OF ELECTRICAL AND ELECTRONICS ENGINEERS INCORPORATED
445 HOES LN, PISCATAWAY, NJ 088544141
Phone: 212 419-7900
Web: WWW.IEEE.ORG

2013 Members

	% of total
US	47
India China & Pacific Rim	18
Canada	3
Other regions	32
Total	**100**

PRODUCTS/OPERATIONS

2013 Sales

	$ mil.	% of total
Periodicals	157	38
Conferences	153	37
Memberships & public imperatives	67	17
Standards	32	8
Other income	1	-
Total	**412**	**100**

Selected IEEE Societies

Aerospace and Electronic Systems
Antennas and Propagation
Broadcast Technology
Circuits and Systems
Communications
Computational Intelligence
Electromagnetic Compatibility
Geoscience and Remote Sensing

Income Statement   FYE: December 31

	REVENUE ($ mil.)	NET INCOME ($ mil.)	NET PROFIT MARGIN	EMPLOYEES
12/19	563	80	14.3%	1,068
12/17	494	34	6.9%	—
12/16	480	22	4.7%	—
12/09	338	18	5.5%	—
Annual Growth	5.2%	15.7%	—	—

2019 Year-End Financials

Return on assets: 9.8%   Cash ($ mil.): 117
Return on equity: 14.1%
Current ratio: —

THE JAMAICA HOSPITAL

Jamaica Hospital Medical Center has been operating in the Queens Borough of New York since before the nation of Jamaica even was born. The hospital serves Queens and eastern Brooklyn with general medical pediatric psychiatric and ambulatory care services. The facility has about 430 beds. Its specialty services include a coma recovery unit a dialysis center a psychiatric emergency department a rehabilitation center as well as a traumatic brain injury recovery unit. The hospital also operates a nursing home with more than 220 beds as well as family practice ambulance and home health services. Jamaica Hospital Medical Center is a subsidiary of MediSys Health Network.

Operations

Jamaica Hospital Medical Center treats some 130000 patients annually through its emergency department which contains a level I regional trauma center. The hospital also handles about 2000 births each year in its labor and delivery wing.

In addition to acute care services the hospital is a teaching facility associated with several educational organizations including Cornell University's Weill Medical College the Mount Sinai School of Medicine and St. George's University School of Medicine. It provides residency and training programs in areas including dentistry podiatry physician assistant and osteopathic medicine. Some of its residency programs are conducted in partnership with other regional health centers including the New York Hospital and the Montefiore Medical Center.

The Ambulatory Care Centers include a Sleep Clinic where sleep disorders in adults and children are evaluated and treated.

In 2014 the hospital had nearly 120000 patients were treated in the Emergency Department; 300000 patients were seen in the Ambulatory Care Centers (with locations at the main campus and also at the offsite centers in the community); and some 2904 deliveries were performed.

Geographic Reach

Jamaica Hospital Medical Center serves a population greater than 1.2 million in Queens and eastern Brooklyn.

Strategy

To improve care for area residents Jamaica Hospital Medical Center has expanded its sleep medicine division to include a new sleep disorder diagnosis center for adults and children. The hospital has also expanded its community care provisions through partnerships with area businesses and organizations.

Upgrading its technology in 2015 the company introduced da Vinci Robot Now at its Flushing location.

Company Background

Jamaica Hospital Medical Center was founded in 1892.

EXECUTIVES

Ceo, Neil Foster Phillips
V Pres-Finance*, Manzar Sassani
Doctor, Nilesh Patel
Executive Director, Pauline Marks
Editor, Robert Levine
Case Manager, Sanderson Oliva
Director Information, Bryan Yap
Respiratory Therapy Director, Celeste Murphy
Emergency Medicine Specialist, Chetankumar Patel
Analyst, Claudia Price
Director of Operations, John Arline
Auditors: PRICEWATERHOUSECOOPERS LLP NE

LOCATIONS

HQ: THE JAMAICA HOSPITAL
8900 VAN WYCK EXPY FL 4N, RICHMOND HILL, NY 114182897
Phone: 718 206-6290
Web: WWW.JAMAICAHOSPITAL.ORG

PRODUCTS/OPERATIONS

Selected Centers and Services
Advanced Center for Psychotherapy
Allergy and Immunology
Ambulatory Care
Anesthesia
Cardiology
Clinical Services
Corporate Health
Critical Care Medicine
Dental
Dermatology
Dialysis-Island Rehabilitation
Emergency Medicine
Family Medicine
Gastroenterology
Home Health
Infectious Disease
Lupus Center
MediSys Family Care Centers
Nephrology
Neurology
Nursing
OB-GYN
Oncology
Orthopedic Surgery
Palliative Care
Pathology
Pediatrics
Podiatry
Prehospital Care
Psychiatry
Pulmonary Medicine
Radiology
Rehabilitation
Rheumatology
Surgery
TCU
The Brady Institute
Trump Pavilion~Jamaica Hospital Nursing Home
Women's Health
Women's Health Center

COMPETITORS

Catholic Healthcare System	Montefiore Medical
Continuum Health Partners	New York City Health And Hospitals
Maimonides Medical Center	Newyork-presbyterian Healthcare
	Northwell Health

Income Statement   FYE: December 31

	REVENUE ($ mil.)	NET INCOME ($ mil.)	NET PROFIT MARGIN	EMPLOYEES
12/20	845	35	4.2%	3,251
12/19	623	11	1.8%	—
12/18	739	15	2.1%	—
12/17	436	(45)	—	—
Annual Growth	24.7%	—	—	—

2020 Year-End Financials

Return on assets: 11.3%   Cash ($ mil.): 21
Return on equity: —
Current ratio: 1.20

THE JOHNS HOPKINS HEALTH SYSTEM CORPORATION

Named after philanthropist Johns Hopkins the Johns Hopkins Health System (JHHS) gifts Baltimore residents with an array of health care services. The health system is an affiliate of world-renowned Johns Hopkins Medicine and oversees six hospitals: All Children's Hospital Johns Hopkins Hospital Bayview Medical Center Howard County General Hospital Sibley Memorial Hospital and Suburban Hospital. The not-for-profit teaching hospitals offer inpatient and outpatient health services that include general medicine emergency/trauma care pediatrics maternity care senior care and numerous specialized areas of medicine. JHHS also operates community health and satellite care facilities.

Operations

JHHS facilities handle 2.8 million patient encounters each year including 115000 inpatient admissions and 350000 emergency room visits. In addition to the six Johns Hopkins Medicine hospitals (which combined house more than 2600 beds) the JHHS organization includes four surgery centers two dozen primary care clinics associated with the Johns Hopkins Community Physicians practice organization and a home health care services agency. JHHS offers unified shared services to its members including advertising purchasing finance legal and other administrative functions.

The Johns Hopkins name is well-known for health care but is probably equally as well-known for its medical education and research initiatives. The health system's hospitals are affiliated with Johns Hopkins University offering physicians-in-training a whole host of residency options.

Geographic Reach

The JHHS inpatient and outpatient facilities are located throughout Maryland and the Washington DC-area as well as in Florida. The system operates a handful of outpatient surgery and imaging centers as well. The group's hospitals serve visitors from all over the world.

Strategy

The organization regularly expands through small to large construction efforts as well as through acquisitions. For example it has acquired two hospitals (All Children's Hospital in Florida and Sibley Memorial Hospital in Washington DC) since 2010.

EXECUTIVES

Pres, Ronald R Peterson
Chb*, C Micheal Amstrong
V Pres Fin-Cfo*, Ronald J Werthman
V Pres-Medical Affairs*, Beryl Rosenstein
Corp SEC*, Hannah Jones
Coordinator, Matthew Trojanowski
Senior Vice-President, Bertrand M Emerson
Scientist, Edina Avdic
Assistant Professor, Ming-Hsien Wang
It, Dushyant Gupta
Assistant Director Finance, George Kuehn
Auditors: PRICEWATERHOUSECOOPERS LLP
 BA

LOCATIONS

HQ: THE JOHNS HOPKINS HEALTH SYSTEM
 CORPORATION
 600 N WOLFE ST, BALTIMORE, MD 212870005
Phone: 410 955-5000
Web: WWW.HOPKINSMEDICINE.ORG

PRODUCTS/OPERATIONS

Selected Facilities

All Children's Hospital (St. Petersburg FL)
Bayview Medical Center (Baltimore MD)
Howard County General Hospital (Columbia MD)
Johns Hopkins at Cedar Lane (Columbia MD)
Johns Hopkins at Greenspring Station (Lutherville MD)
Johns Hopkins at Odenton (Odenton MD)
Johns Hopkins at White Marsh (White Marsh MD)
Johns Hopkins Hospital (Baltimore MD)
Johns Hopkins Outpatient Center (Baltimore MD)
Sibley Memorial Hospital (Washington DC)
Suburban Hospital (Bethesda MD)

COMPETITORS

Anne Arundel Medical
 Center
Ascension Health
Bon Secours Health
Carilion Clinic
Christiana Care
Dimensions Healthcare
Franklin Square
 Hospital Center
Gbmc
Good Samaritan
 Hospital Of Maryland
Harbor Hospital
Levindale Hospital

Lifebridge Health
Medstar Health
Medstar Union Memorial
 Hospital
Sinai Hospital Of
 Baltimore
St. Agnes Healthcare
St. Joseph Medical
 Center
University Of Maryland
 Medical System
Upper Chesapeake
 Health

HISTORICAL FINANCIALS

Company Type: Private

Income Statement — FYE: June 30

	REVENUE ($ mil.)	NET INCOME ($ mil.)	NET PROFIT MARGIN	EMPLOYEES
06/21	7,807	1,434	18.4%	13,000
06/20	7,110	(306)	—	—
06/19	6,826	(59)	—	—
06/18	6,558	308	4.7%	—
Annual Growth	6.0%	66.9%	—	—

2021 Year-End Financials

Return on assets: 14.2%
Return on equity: 27.4%
Current ratio: 1.50
Cash ($ mil.): 983

THE LANCASTER GENERAL HOSPITAL

Lancaster General Health is a not-for-profit health system with a comprehensive network of care including more than 300 primary-care and specialty physicians; outpatient and Urgent Care services; and four hospitals with a total of nearly 800 licensed beds: Lancaster General Hospital Women & Babies Hospital Lancaster Rehabilitation Hospital and Lancaster Behavioral Health Hospital. Its membership in Penn Medicine brings together the strengths of a world-renowned not-for-profit academic medical center and a nationally recognized not-for-profit community health care system.

EXECUTIVES

Ceo, Jan L Bergen
Evp, Chief Administrative and, Robert P Macina
Director, Kate Ritter
Ophthalmologist, John W Sharp
Ophthalmologist, Catherine T Rommel
Vice President of Customer Ser, Carolyn Carlson
Family Practice Specialist, Matthew J Beelen
Fitness Center Director, Cory Bowman
Library Director, Cynthia McClellan
Vice President, Doug Rinehart
Director Trauma, Frederick Rogers

LOCATIONS

HQ: THE LANCASTER GENERAL HOSPITAL
 555 N DUKE ST, LANCASTER, PA 176022207
Phone: 717 544-5511
Web: WWW.LANCASTERGENERALHEALTH.ORG

PRODUCTS/OPERATIONS

2014 Sales

	$ mil.	% of total
Net patient services revenue less provision for bad debts	920	95
Medical services	10	4
Other revenue	35	1
Other	2	-
Total	**969**	**100**

Selected Specialties

Cardiology
Emergency medical
Intensive care
Neurology
Oncology
Radiology
Rehabilitation
Urology

COMPETITORS

Altoona Regional
Ascension Health
Catholic Health Initiatives
Evangelical Community Hospital
Hanover Healthcare
Holy Spirit
Lewistown Hospital
Main Line Health System
Memorial Hospital (pa)
Pinnaclehealth System
Saint Vincent Health System
St. Luke's University Health Network
University Of Pennsylvania Health System
Wellspan Health

HISTORICAL FINANCIALS

Company Type: Private

Income Statement — FYE: June 30

	REVENUE ($ mil.)	NET INCOME ($ mil.)	NET PROFIT MARGIN	EMPLOYEES
06/16	958	122	12.8%	7,000
06/15	920	110	12.1%	—
06/14	867	(13)	—	—
06/13	823	(15)	—	—
Annual Growth	5.2%	—	—	—

2016 Year-End Financials

Return on assets: 14.5%
Return on equity: 28.6%
Current ratio: 2.50
Cash ($ mil.): 23

THE LANE CONSTRUCTION CORPORATION

Lane likes people to be in the fast lane. For more than a century the heavy civil contractor and its affiliates have been widening paving and constructing lanes for highways bridges runways railroads dams and mass transit systems in the eastern and southern US. The group also produces bituminous and precast concrete and mines aggregates at plants and quarries in the northeastern mid-Atlantic and southern US. Additionally it sells and leases construction equipment. Founded in 1902 Lane Construction has offices in more than 20 states and is owned by descendants of Lane and employees.

Operations

Lane Construction specializes in heavy civil construction services and products in the transportation infrastructure and energy industries. During the past decade Lane Construction has participated in more than 70 design-building projects with a combined value of more than $4 billion.

Beyond its construction projects Lane operates divisions that manufacture bituminous and precast concrete with mine aggregates at 70 plants and 12 quarries throughout the U.S.

Lane's business divisions are spread across the US and include: Civil Wall Solutions Cold River Materials Prestress of the Carolinas Senate Asphalt Virginia Paving Company and Virginia Sign & Lighting Company.

Lane affiliates include New Hampshire-based Cold River Materials Senate Asphalt of Washington D.C. and Virginia Paving and Virginia Sign & Lighting Co. among about a half a dozen others. In 2013 its Rea Contracting division in the Carolinas changed its name to Lane Construction Corp.

Geographic Reach

Lane Construction has offices in more than 20 US states including Florida Illinois Maine North Carolina Pennsylvania Texas and Virginia. While most of Lane's projects take place along the East Coast it also operates in the South/Southwest and has international operations — under the Lane Worldwide Infrastructure Inc. name — in the Middle East.

Financial Performance

While full financials of the privately-held company were not available Lane Construction has posted annual revenues of more than $1 billion since 2010.

Strategy

The company continues to work for both public and private entities on a variety of high-value projects. In early 2015 the contractor was working on a joint-venture project with Skanska and Granite Construction Company on the $2.3 billion "I-4 Ultimate project" which involves design build finance operating and maintenance work on 21 miles of Interstate 4 from Orange County to Seminole County in Florida.

Also as of early 2015 Lane reported that it recently completed its $1.5-billion construction project on the I-495 Express Lanes in Virginia in one of the largest public-private joint ventures in the US. The same team also completed a $722 million expansion and improvement project on 29 miles of the I-95 Express (high occupancy toll road) lanes in Virginia. Both of these Virgina-based projects were completed ahead of schedule.

EXECUTIVES

Ceo, Mark Schiller
Chief Operating Officer, Kirk D Junco
Exec V Pres, Donald P Dobbs
SEC, Ann M Falsey
Project Manager, John Campbell
Procurement Specialist, John-Randall Gorby
Eg Chief Estimator, Kevin Kirk
Office Manager, Patricia Monge
Director, Robert McKeever
Environmental Coordinator, Shirani Fuller
AP Accounts Payable Clerk, Stella Burton
Auditors: KPMG LLP HARTFORD CT

LOCATIONS

HQ: THE LANE CONSTRUCTION CORPORATION
90 FIELDSTONE CT, CHESHIRE, CT 064101212
Phone: 203 235-3351
Web: WWW.LANECONSTRUCT.COM

PRODUCTS/OPERATIONS

Selected Projects

Airports

Bridges

Design-Build

Federal
Heavy Civil
Highways
Public Private Partnerships
Plants & Paving
Rail
Specialty Paving

Selected Divisions
Civil Wall Solutions
Cold River Materials Prestress of the Carolinas
Senate Asphalt
Sunquip
Sunrise Materials
Virginia Paving Company
Virginia Sun & Lighting Company
Wardwell
White Bros.

COMPETITORS

Angelo Iafrate	Sargent Corp
Austin Industries	Skanska Usa Civil
Balfour Beatty Inc	The Middlesex
Bechtel	Corporation
Clark Enterprises	Turner Corporation
Granite Construction	Tutor-saliba
J.f. White Contracting	Vecellio & Grogan
Mbc Holding	Walsh Group
Peter Kiewit Sons'	

HISTORICAL FINANCIALS

Company Type: Private

Income Statement — FYE: December 31

	REVENUE ($ mil.)	NET INCOME ($ mil.)	NET PROFIT MARGIN	EMPLOYEES
12/18	847	76	9.0%	3,500
12/17	1,476	18	1.3%	—
12/16	1,196	39	3.3%	—
12/15	1,115	(16)	—	—
Annual Growth	(8.7%)	—	—	—

2018 Year-End Financials

Return on assets: 7.6%   Cash ($ mil.): 136
Return on equity: 15.2%
Current ratio: 1.80

THE MARY IMOGENE BASSETT HOSPITAL

EXECUTIVES

Pres-Ceo, Tommy Ibrahim
Chm, Douglas Hastings
Exec V Pres-Coo, Bertine McKenna
V Pres-Cfo, Sue Andrews
Cco, Steven Heneghan
Evp-Chief Operating Officer, Ronette Wiley
Svp-Coo, Jeff Joyner
Svp-Chief Stategy&transformati, Lisa Betrus
Vp-Chief of Staff, Cailin Purcell
Svp-Cpe, Reginald Knight
Svp-CNE, Denise Robinson

LOCATIONS

HQ: THE MARY IMOGENE BASSETT HOSPITAL
1 ATWELL RD, COOPERSTOWN, NY 133261394
Phone: 607 547-3456
Web: WWW.BASSETT.ORG

HISTORICAL FINANCIALS

Company Type: Private

Income Statement — FYE: December 31

	REVENUE ($ mil.)	NET INCOME ($ mil.)	NET PROFIT MARGIN	EMPLOYEES
12/19	604	0	0.0%	3,200
12/17	547	4	0.8%	—
12/16	443	5	1.3%	—
12/15	412	(2)	—	—
Annual Growth	10.0%	—	—	—

2019 Year-End Financials

Return on assets: 0.1%   Cash ($ mil.): 2
Return on equity: 0.1%
Current ratio: 0.70

THE MASSACHUSETTS GENERAL HOSPITAL

Founded in 1811 Massachusetts General Hospital (Mass General) is the original and largest teaching hospital of Harvard Medical School. Mass General provides comprehensive primary care and medical specialty services to some 200000 adult and pediatric patients in about 15 locations throughout Greater Boston. Its specialized medical departments include cancer cardiology and heart surgery; neurology and neurosurgery; and diabetes and endocrinology. As a leading research facility Mass General hosts a number of clinical drug and device trials and has an annual research budget of more than $1 billion.

Operations

Mass General Hospital for Children provides a full spectrum of care ? from primary care to a broad range of specialty and subspecialty pediatric services ? for newborns children and adolescents from New England and around the world.

The Mass General Brigham connects a full continuum of care across a system of academic medical centers community and specialty hospitals a health insurance plan physician networks community health centers home care and long-term care services.

Additionally Mass General operates as one of the largest hospital-based research networks in the nation consisting of more than 30 clinical departments and centers and conducting some 1200 clinical trials at any given time. With Harvard Medical School Mass General offers about 30 residency programs 140 fellowship programs and continuing medical education programs.

Geographic Reach

Mass General's main hospital is located in downtown Boston and includes nearly 30 buildings housing inpatient and ambulatory care services located in Andover Boston Charlestown Chelsea Danvers Everett Foxborough Revere and Waltham.

Sales and Marketing

Mass General offers high-quality coordinated care for patients and families via phone video email and mobile applications.

Financial Performance

Strategy

EXECUTIVES

Chm, Cathy E Minehan
Pres, Peter L Slavin
Cfo, Laura Wysk
Treas, Peter K Markell
Fo, Sally Mason Boemer
Esq.-SEC, John R Hingham
Prin, Edward Ryan
Vp-Ceio, Joseph Betancourt
Pres, David F M Brown
Research, Anisha Illa
Publisher, Anne Dubitzky

LOCATIONS

HQ: THE MASSACHUSETTS GENERAL HOSPITAL
55 FRUIT ST, BOSTON, MA 021142696
Phone: 617 726-2000
Web: WWW.MASSGENERAL.ORG

Selected Research Centers

AIDS

Cancer
Cardiovascular research
Computational and integrative biology
Cutaneous biology
Human genetics
Medical imaging
Neurodegenerative disorders
Photomedicine
Regenerative medicine
Reproductive biology
Systems biology
Transplantation biology

COMPETITORS

Beth Israel Deaconess
  Medical Center
Boston Medical Center
Cambridge Health
  Alliance
Cape Cod Hospital
Care New England
Caregroup
Catholic Medical
  Center
Children's Hospital
  Boston
Dana-farber

Elliot Health System
Emerson Hospital
Milford Regional
  Medical Center
New England Alliance
  For Health
Northeast Health
  System
Southcoast Hospitals
  Group
Steward Health Care
Sturdy Memorial
Winchester Healthcare

HISTORICAL FINANCIALS

Company Type: Private

Income Statement				FYE: September 30
	REVENUE ($ mil.)	NET INCOME ($ mil.)	NET PROFIT MARGIN	EMPLOYEES
09/14	2,201	186	8.5%	10,156
09/13	2,274	148	6.5%	—
09/12	2,281	267	11.7%	—
Annual Growth	(1.8%)	(16.5%)	—	—

2014 Year-End Financials

Return on assets: 7.7%   Cash ($ mil.): 38
Return on equity: 17.7%
Current ratio: 1.40

THE MEDICAL COLLEGE OF WISCONSIN INC

EXECUTIVES

Ceo-Pres, John R Raymond Sr
Prin*, T Michael Bolger
Exec V Pres*, Joseph E Kerschner
Cfo*, Marjorie Spencer
Vp-Chief Development Officer*, Mitchell R
 Beckman
Vp-Cpo*, Adrienne Mitchell
Acct Mgr, Angela M Summers
Scientist, Candice Klug
Research and Staff, Colin J Humphries
Pathologist, Elena V Roukhadze
Pathologist, Natalia V Markeloa
Auditors: LB PRICEWATERHOUSECOOPERS
 LLP

LOCATIONS

HQ: THE MEDICAL COLLEGE OF WISCONSIN INC
 8701 WATERTOWN PLANK RD, MILWAUKEE, WI
 532263548
Phone: 414 456-8296
Web: WWW.MCW.EDU

HISTORICAL FINANCIALS

Company Type: Private

Income Statement				FYE: June 30
	REVENUE ($ mil.)	NET INCOME ($ mil.)	NET PROFIT MARGIN	EMPLOYEES
06/20	1,286	68	5.3%	4,700
06/19	1,258	79	6.3%	—
06/15	1,036	107	10.4%	—
Annual Growth	4.4%	(8.8%)	—	—

2020 Year-End Financials

Return on assets: 2.7%   Cash ($ mil.): 117
Return on equity: 3.8%
Current ratio: 0.50

THE MEDICAL UNIVERSITY OF SOUTH CAROLINA

Established in 1824 the Medical University of South Carolina (MUSC) provides Charleston with a wide range of health-related services including medical care training and research. The 50-acre medical school has more than 1800 faculty members and trains approximately 3000 full- and part-time students and 800 residents each year through its six schools which cover medical pharmacy nursing dental health professional and graduate training. The MUSC Health organization includes the MUSC Medical Center in Charleston which has some 1600 beds and includes a children's hospital and a psychiatric institute as well as the University Medical Associates physician practice organization.

Operations

MUSC has extensive research facilities and programs in areas including bioengineering and translational sciences. The university also participates in drug discovery clinical trial research programs. Its technology transfer program allows small start-up companies to license or purchase research programs that are nearing commercial development stages.

MUSC's key areas of research include cancer addiction sciences drug discovery health disparities inflammation and fibrosis neuroscience oral health rehabilitation and stroke.

MUSC Health MUSC's clinical health system is dedicated to delivering the highest quality patient care available while training generations of competent compassionate health care providers to serve the people of South Carolina and beyond. It comprises some 1600 beds more than 100 outreach sites the MUSC College of Medicine and the physicians' practice plan and nearly 275 telehealth locations.

Overall grants and contracts bring in nearly 30% of sales sales and services account for about 25% state and capital appropriations provide around 15% student tuition and fees generate more than 10% transfers ring up around 10% gifts and grants investment income and other operating revenues represent the remaining.

Geographic Reach

MUSC is located in Charleston South Carolina.

Financial Performance

The university's operating revenues for 2020 was $615.2 million.

The university's cash at the end of 2021 was $447.3 million. Operating activities used $197.8 million while investing activities provided $3.9 million.

Mergers and Acquisitions

In mid-2021 Medical University of South Carolina (MUSC) finalized the acquisition of Providence Health and KershawHealth which are currently part of LifePoint Health for approximately $75 million. The acquisitionincludes three community hospitals a freestanding emergency department (FSED) and affiliated physician practice locations serving communities in the Midlands. Providence Health serves Columbia SC and the surrounding region with two full-service hospitals and a freestanding emergency room. KershawHealth is a full-service medical center located in Camden SC which has been an affiliate of MUSC Health.

Company Background

MUSC was created by an act of South Carolina's General Assembly in 1824. It is historically recognized as the first medical school in the South.

EXECUTIVES

Pres, David Cole
V Pres, Dr John Raymond Sr
V Pres, Lisa Montgomery
V Pres, Josesph G Reves
V Pres, Frank C Clark
V Pres, W Stuart Smith
V Pres, William J Fisher
Cfo, Patrick Wamsley
Dir, Joseph A Helpern
Dir, Truman R Brown
Dir, Ann-Marie Broome
Auditors: KPMG LLP GREENSBORO NC

LOCATIONS

HQ: THE MEDICAL UNIVERSITY OF SOUTH
 CAROLINA
 171 ASHLEY AVE, CHARLESTON, SC 294258908
Phone: 843 792-2123
Web: WWW.RESEARCH.MUSC.EDU

COMPETITORS

Beaufort Memorial
  Hospital
Carolinas Hospital
  System
Conway Medical Center
Duke University

Grand Strand Regional
  Medical Center
North Carolina State
  University
Roper St. Francis
  Healthcare

HISTORICAL FINANCIALS

Company Type: Private

Income Statement				FYE: June 30
	REVENUE ($ mil.)	NET INCOME ($ mil.)	NET PROFIT MARGIN	EMPLOYEES
06/18	992	4	0.4%	5,500
06/17	914	9	1.0%	—
06/13	780	26	3.3%	—
06/09	836	3	0.4%	—
Annual Growth	1.9%	1.8%	—	—

2018 Year-End Financials

Return on assets: 0.3%   Cash ($ mil.): 322
Return on equity: 3.8%
Current ratio: 3.70

THE METHODIST HOSPITAL

Houston Methodist (formerly The Methodist Hospital) owns and operates eight Houston-area medical centers including the flagship location which has roughly 985 operating beds and is known for innovations in urology and neurosurgery among other specialties. Other hospitals include Houston Methodist Baytown Houston Methodist Clear Lake Houston Methodist Sugar Land Houston Methodist The Woodlands Houston Methodist West Houston Methodist Willowbrook and Houston Methodist Continuing Care. Together the hospitals have more than 1555 beds and employ more than 5250 physicians. In addition to hospitals the organization operates emergency care imaging outpatient and rehab centers and manages a physician organization of around 775.

Operations
The health system has been recognized for high performance in several specialty areas including cancer diabetes nephrology pulmonology and geriatrics. It's also been lauded for its specialties in cardiology and heart surgery endocrinology gastroenterology and GI surgery gynecology neurology and neurosurgery orthopedics and urology.

The hospital has educational and research affiliations with Cornell University's Weil Cornell Medical College the New York-Presbyterian Hospital University of Houston Texas Annual Conference of the United Methodist Church Texas A&M and other organizations.

The 440000-square-foot Houston Methodist Research Institute Translational Research Building provides the technology and support its doctors need to effectively and efficiently bring cures through all stages of clinical trials and to all patients around the world. The Research Institute includes open laboratory space designed to house some 90 principal investigators over 20 core facilities to enhance interdisciplinary research and two Good Manufacturing Practice (GMP) facilities to prepare clinical-grade radiopharmaceuticals biological agents and small molecules.

Geographic Reach
Based in Houston Texas and operates mostly in and around Houston Texas Houston Methodist has hospitals and medical facilities in Sugar Land the Woodlands Baytown Nassau Bay Clear Lake and Katy.

Its Houston Methodist Global Health Care Services has operations in Dubai UAE; Riyadh KSA; Guadalajara Mexico City and Monterrey Mexico; Guatemala City Guatemala; Guayaquil Ecuador; Managua Nicaragua; Montevideo Uruguay; San Salvador El Salvador; and Tegucigalpa Honduras.

Sales and Marketing
Partner with more than 450 companies representing several industries population sizes and locations Houston Methodist's programs provide financial and medical assistance to more than 150000 patients every year.

EXECUTIVES
Pres, Marc L Boom
Sr V-Pres of Finance*, Edward L Tyrrell
Dir of Treasuary*, Mike V Giblin
Exec V-Pres*, Roberta Schwartz
Treas*, Carlton Baucum
Cfo*, Kevin Burns
Pres*, Ewing Werlein Jr
Chairperson*, John F Bookout
Chairperson*, David M Underwood
Cardiology, Samuel Ferris
Cardiology, Sangeeta Saikia
Auditors: DELOITTE & TOUCH LLP HOUSTON

LOCATIONS
HQ: THE METHODIST HOSPITAL
6565 FANNIN ST, HOUSTON, TX 770302892
Phone: 713 441-2340
Web: WWW.HOUSTONMETHODIST.ORG

PRODUCTS/OPERATIONS

Selected Houston-Area Hospitals
Houston Methodist Hospital - Texas Medical Center (Houston)
Houston Methodist Sugar Land Hospital
Houston Methodist Willowbrook Hospital (Houston)
Houston Methodist West Hospital (Houston)
Houston San Jacinto Methodist Hospital (Baytown)
Houston Methodist St. John Hospital (Texas)

Houston Methodist St. Catherine Hospital (Texas)

Selected Services
Cancer / Oncology
Diabetes / Endocrinology
Digestive Diseases
Ear Nose & Throat
Emergency Care
Heart & Vascular
Imaging / Radiology
Internal Medicine
Neurology
Neurosurgery
Obstetrics & Gynecology
Ophthalmology
Oral and Maxillofacial Surgery & Dentistry
Orthopedics & Sports Medicine
Otolaryngology Head & Neck Surgery
Pathology & Genomic Medicine
Plastic & Reconstructive Surgery
Psychiatry
Rehabilitation
Robotic Surgery
Transplant
Urology
Weight Management
Wellness

COMPETITORS
Christus Health
Dynacq Healthcare
Hca
Johns Hopkins Medicine
Md Anderson Cancer Center
Mayo Clinic
Memorial Hermann Healthcare
St. Luke's Episcopal Health System
Tenet Healthcare
Texas Children's Hospital
Texas Health Resources
Tomball Regional
Universal Health Services

HISTORICAL FINANCIALS
Company Type: Private

Income Statement				FYE: December 31
	REVENUE ($ mil.)	NET INCOME ($ mil.)	NET PROFIT MARGIN	EMPLOYEES
12/19	5,225	1,275	24.4%	15,000
12/18	4,496	291	6.5%	—
12/17	3,887	531	13.7%	—
Annual Growth	15.9%	54.9%	—	—

2019 Year-End Financials
Return on assets: 12.2%
Return on equity: 16.1%
Current ratio: 1.10

Cash ($ mil.): 198

THE METROHEALTH SYSTEM

Founded in 1837 MetroHealth System is redefining health care by going beyond medical treatment to improve the foundations of community health and well-being: affordable housing a cleaner environment economic opportunity and access to fresh food convenient transportation legal help and other services. MetroHealth has an academic medical center to research and for teaching and caregivers. Each active physicians holds an appointment at Case Western Reserve University Schools of Medicine. Its main campus hospital houses the Cleveland Metropolitan School District's Lincoln-West School of Science & Health the only high school in America located inside a hospital.

Operations
MetroHealth has more than 600 doctors and 1700 nurses. Services include behavioral health vascular surgery orthopedics burn care and pediatrics. The system also operates outpatient clinics a regional rehabilitation clinic a heart and vascular center two skilled nursing centers an outpatient center and a medical- and surgical subspecialties. MetroHealth is home to Cuyahoga County's most experience in Level I Adult Trauma Center and Ohio's only adult and pediatric trauma burn center.

Geographic Reach
MetroHealth operates four hospitals four emergency departments and more than 20 health centers and 40 additional sites throughout Cuyahoga County.

Sales and Marketing
The system serves more than 300 000 patients and two thirds of whom are uninsured or covered by Medicare or Medicaid.

Company Background
MetroHealth has been serving the medical needs of the Greater Cleveland community since 1837. It has been a major affiliate of Case Western Reserve University since 1914.

EXECUTIVES
Cob, Thomas McDonald
Vice Cob*, J B Silvers
Bod*, Maureen Dee
Bod*, Rev Thomas Anthony Minor
Bod*, Terry Monnolly
Bod*, John M Moss
Bod*, Mitchell Schneider
Bod*, Charles Spain Jr
Exec V Pres-Cco*, Bernard Boulanger
Sr V Pres*, Elizabeth Heller Allen
Sr V Pres*, Nabil Chehade
Auditors: RSM US LLP CLEVELAND OHIO

LOCATIONS
HQ: THE METROHEALTH SYSTEM
2500 METROHEALTH DR, CLEVELAND, OH 441091900
Phone: 216 398-6000
Web: WWW.METROHEALTH.ORG

Selected Locations
J. Glen Smith Health Center (In partnership with the City of Cleveland Cleveland)
MetroHealth Asia Town Health Center (Cleveland)
MetroHealth Beachwood Health Center (Beachwood Ohio)
MetroHealth Broadway Health Center (Cleveland)
MetroHealth Brooklyn Health Center (Cleveland)
MetroHealth Buckeye Health Center (Cleveland)
MetroHealth Center for Sleep Medicine South Campus (Independence Ohio)
MetroHealth Center for Sleep Medicine West Campus (Westlake Ohio)
MetroHealth Lakewood Health Center (Lakewood)
MetroHealth Lee-Harvard Health Center (Cleveland)
MetroHealth Medical Center Main Campus (Cleveland)
MetroHealth Old Brooklyn Campus (Cleveland)
MetroHealth Pepper Pike Health Center (Pepper Pike Ohio)
MetroHealth Premier Health Center (Westlake Ohio)
MetroHealth Rehabilitation Institute of Ohio (Cleveland)
MetroHealth Strongsville Health Center (Strongsville Ohio)
MetroHealth West 150th Health and Surgery Center (Cleveland)
MetroHealth Westlake Health Center (Westlake)
MetroHealth West Park Health Center (Cleveland)
The Elisabeth Severance Prentiss Center for Skilled Nursing Care at MetroHealth (Cleveland)
Thomas F. McCafferty Health Center (In partnership with the City of Cleveland Cleveland)

PRODUCTS/OPERATIONS

MetroHealth System Departments and Services
Aamoth Family Pediatric Wellness Center
Adolescent Clinic (Teen Health)
Advanced Gynecology (Center for Advanced Gynecology)
Advantage (MetroHealth Advantage)

Allergy & Immunology Clinic
Allergy Services (Department of Ear Nose & Throat)
Amigas Unidas Program
Anesthesiology
Art Therapy
Arthritis Center (Rheumatology)
Audiology
Bariatric Surgery (Weight Loss Surgery Program)
Behavioral Health (Child and Teen Mental Health Services)
Birth Control Procedures
Birthing Services
Bone Health and Surgery (Orthopaedics)
BREAST Program (Community Breast Cancer Outreach)
Burn Care Center
Cancer Care Center
Cardiology Cardiovascular (Heart & Vascular Center)
Center for Advanced Gynecology
Center for Behavioral Health (Child and Teen Mental Health Services)
Centers for Community Health
Center for Sleep Medicine
Cerebrovascular
Childbirth Education
Child Life and Education
Children's Health (Pediatrics)
Children's Health Specialties
Closing the Gap (MetroHealth Buckeye Health Center)
Comprehensive Care Program (Services for Children with Special Needs)
Concussion Clinic
Cosmetic Dermatology
Dentistry and Oral Health
Dermatology
Diabetes Self-Management Program
Digital Mammogram
Ear Nose and Throat (ENT/Otolaryngology)
Emergency Medicine/Emergency Department
Endocrinology
Endoscopy Suite (Gastroenterology)
ExpressCare (MetroExpressCare)
Family Medicine Clinic at MetroHealth Medical Center
Fertility Services
Freedom From Smoking
Gastroenterology and Endoscopy Suite
Genetics Clinic
Geriatrics (Senior Health & Wellness Center)
Gynecology
Gynecology Advanced (Center for Advanced Gynecology)
Gynecologic Oncology
Hand Center
Heart & Vascular Center
Hematology and Oncology (Cancer Care Center)
High-Risk Pregnancy Services
Hospital Medicine
Immunology (Allergy & Immunology Clinic)
Infectious Disease
Infertility Clinic
Infusion Therapy (Allergy & Immunology Clinic)
Internal Medicine Clinic at MetroHealth Medical Center
Internal Medicine and Pediatrics (Med-PEDS)
Kids' Health (Pediatrics
Kids' Korner Free Daycare Service at MetroHealth Medical Center
Latina Clinic: English | En espa?ol
LGBT Pride Clinic (At Thomas F. McCafferty Health Center Health Center)
Life Flight (Metro Life Flight)
Long-Term/Skilled Nursing Care
Maternal-Fetal Medicine (High-Risk Pregnancy Services)
Medicine (Department of Medicine)
Mental Health (Psychiatry)
Metro Life Flight
MetroHealth Advantage
MetroExpressCare
MetroHealth Rehabilitation Institute of Ohio
MetroHealth Select Health Plan
MetroHealth Simulation Center
Mi MetroHealth Mi Comunidad
MyChart
Neonatology Neonatal Intensive Care Unit (NICU)
Nephrology
Neurology
Neurosciences
Northeast Ohio Chapter of the National Spinal Cord Injury Association (NSCIA)
Northeast Ohio Regional Spinal Cord Injury System (NORSCIS)
Nose Ear and Throat (ENT Otolaryngology)
Nursing
Nutrition

Obstetrics
Obstetrics and Gynecology
Occupational Medicine
Oncology (Cancer Care Center)
Opthalmologic (Eye) Surgery
Oral Health (Dentistry)
Oral and Maxillofacial Surgery
Orthopaedics
Osteopathic Medicine
Otolaryngology (Ear Nose and Throat)
Pain Management
Palliative Care
Pastoral Care
Pathology
Pediatrics
Permanent Birth Control Procedures
Pharmacy
Pregnancy Resources
Pride Clinic (At Thomas F. McCafferty Health Center Health Center)
Psychiatry (Behavioral/Mental Health)
Pulmonary and Critical Care
Quality Indicators
Radiology
Rehab Rehabilitation Services (MetroHealth Rehabilitation Institute of Ohio)
Reiki
Reproductive Endocrinology and Infertility Clinic
Rheumatology (Arthritis Center)

Select Health Plan

Senior Health and Wellness Center
Simulation Center
Skeletal (Orthopaedics)
Skilled Nursing/Long-Term Care
Sleep Medicine Sleep Studies
Spanish-language Information
Special Needs Services for Children (Comprehensive Care)
Spine Center
Stroke Stroke & Cerebrovascular Center
Surgery
Throat (Otolaryngology ENT)
Teen Health
Trauma Burns and Critical Care
Travel Clinic
Urgent Care (MetroExpressCare
Urology
Vascular Health and Surgery (Heart & Vascular Center
Weight Loss Surgery Program (Bariatric Surgery)
X-ray (Radiology)

COMPETITORS

Adcare	Lake Health
Catholic Health Initiatives	Ohiohealth
Cincinnati Children's Hospital	Premier Health Partners
Community Health Systems	Robinson Memorial Hospital
Kettering Health Network	The Cleveland Clinic University Hospitals Health System

HISTORICAL FINANCIALS
Company Type: Private

Income Statement   FYE: December 31

	REVENUE ($ mil.)	NET INCOME ($ mil.)	NET PROFIT MARGIN	EMPLOYEES
12/15	888	37	4.2%	7,700
12/13	813	41	5.1%	—
12/09	673	58	8.7%	—
Annual Growth	4.7%	(7.1%)	—	—

2015 Year-End Financials
Return on assets: 3.6%   Cash ($ mil.): 4
Return on equity: 20.0%
Current ratio: 1.10

THE MICHAELS COMPANIES INC

EXECUTIVES

Ceo, Ashley Buchanan
Exec V Pres-Cfo, Michael Diamond
Exec V Pres-Coo Stores, Patrick Venezia
Exec V Pres-Chief Compliance O, Tim Cheatham
Exec V Pres Stores & Developme, J Robert Koch
Sr V Pres-Cao-Contrl, James E Sullivan
Sales Staff, Amanda Allison
Class Instructor, Amber Gold
Customer Experience Manager, Amy Klusmeyer
Associate, Ana Gonzalez
Category Manager, Angela Gordon
Auditors: ERNST & YOUNG LLP DALLAS TEX

LOCATIONS

HQ: THE MICHAELS COMPANIES INC
3939 W JOHN CARPENTER FWY, IRVING, TX 750632909
Phone: 972 409-1300
Web: WWW.INVESTORS.MICHAELS.COM

HISTORICAL FINANCIALS
Company Type: Private

Income Statement   FYE: January 30

	REVENUE ($ mil.)	NET INCOME ($ mil.)	NET PROFIT MARGIN	EMPLOYEES
01/21*	5,271	294	5.6%	45,000
02/20	5,072	272	5.4%	—
12/19	5,072	272	5.4%	—
02/19	5,271	319	6.1%	—
Annual Growth	(0.0%)	(3.9%)	—	—

*Fiscal year change

2021 Year-End Financials
Return on assets: 6.5%   Cash ($ mil.): 1,194
Return on equity: —
Current ratio: 1.30

THE MIDDLE TENNESSEE ELECTRIC MEMBERSHIP CORPORATION

Middle Tennessee Electric Membership Corporation's service territory is smack dab in the middle of Tennessee. The utility cooperative distributes electricity to 190750 residential and business customers (member/owners) in four counties (Cannon Rutherford Williamson and Wilson) via more than 10470 miles of power lines connected to 34 electric distribution substations. Middle Tennessee Electric purchases its power supply from the Tennessee Valley Authority. The corporation is Tennessee's largest electric cooperative and the sixth largest in the US.

Geographic Reach

The cooperative serves customers in Cannon Rutherford Williamson and Wilson counties. According to a US Census report three of Tennessee's five fastest growing counties (Rutherford Williamson and Wilson) are in Middle Tennessee Electric's service area which also includes three of

Tennessee's top five fastest-growing cities — LaVergne Smyrna and Franklin.

Strategy

To harness green energy as a way to limit fossil fuel power sources and reduce carbon emissions the utility cooperative is installing solar panels for customers. In 2012 the company completed a 850-panel solar field next to the City of Franklin's water plant. That year Middle Tennessee Electric had 70 solar projects operating across its service area and 30 more in the planning stages.

Company Background

Middle Tennessee Electric was formed in 1936 as part of a national rural electrification push.

EXECUTIVES

Pres, Chris Jones
V Pres-Cfo*, Bernie Steen
Chairman of Board*, Michael Woods
Exec SEC*, Debbie Fuller
Vp of Engnrng*, Keith Thomason
Vice Chair*, Tom Purkey
Secretary Treasurer*, Steve Seger
Coo*, Tom Suggs
Sr Vp*, Brad Gibson
Coordinator, Michelle Ford
Senior Analyst, Jeff Sullivan
Auditors: WINNETT ASSOCIATES PLLC SHELB

LOCATIONS

HQ: THE MIDDLE TENNESSEE ELECTRIC MEMBERSHIP CORPORATION
555 NEW SALEM HWY, MURFREESBORO, TN 371293390
Phone: 615 890-9762
Web: WWW.MTE.COM

HISTORICAL FINANCIALS

Company Type: Private

Income Statement				FYE: December 31
	REVENUE ($ mil.)	NET INCOME ($ mil.)	NET PROFIT MARGIN	EMPLOYEES
12/19*	618	0	—	410
06/16	542	10	1.9%	—
06/13	524	27	5.3%	—
06/12	510	19	3.8%	—
Annual Growth	2.4%	—	—	—

*Fiscal year change

2019 Year-End Financials

Return on assets: —
Return on equity: —
Current ratio: 1.30
Cash ($ mil.): 40

THE MITRE CORPORATION

A private not-for-profit organization MITRE Corporation provides consulting engineering and technical research services primarily for agencies of the federal government. It has primary research facilities in Massachusetts and Virginia. It also manages several federally funded research and development centers serving organizations such as the Department of Defense the Federal Aviation Administration the Internal Revenue Service and the Department of Veterans Affairs. MITRE was founded in 1958 by former MIT researchers.

Operations

MITRE also supports the Department of Homeland Security (DHS). For the DHS MITRE provides systems engineering practices and acquisition expertise.

MITRE brings innovative ideas into existence in areas as varied as artificial intelligence intuitive data science quantum information science health informatics space security policy and economic expertise trustworthy autonomy cyber threat sharing and cyber resilience.

The company operates federally funded research and development centers (FFRDCs) unique organizations that assist the United States government with scientific research and analysis; development and acquisition; and systems engineering and integration. It also has an independent research program that explores new and expanded uses of technologies to solve our sponsors' problems.

Geographic Reach

The company has primary research facilities in Bedford Massachusetts and McLean Virginia.

Sales and Marketing

MITRE works in the public interest across federal state and local governments as well as industry and academia.

Company Background

The MITRE Corporation was chartered in 1958 as a private not-for-profit company to provide engineering and technical guidance for the federal government. Since then MITRE has operated at the intersection of advanced technology and vital national concerns. The company grown to serve a variety of government agencies at the highest levels through the operation of federally funded research and development centers (FFRDCs).

EXECUTIVES

Ceo, Alfred Grasso
Chb, John Hamre
Chm, James R Schlesinger
SEC, Sol Glasner
Treas, Mark Kontos
Vp-Chief Human Resources Offic, Julie Gravallese
V Pres, Richard Byrne
V Pres, Jmaes Cook
V Pres, Greg Crawford
Coo, Peter Sherlock
Svp, Julie Bowen

LOCATIONS

HQ: THE MITRE CORPORATION
202 BURLINGTON RD, BEDFORD, MA 017301420
Phone: 781 271-2000
Web: WWW.MITRE.ORG

COMPETITORS

Altarum	Sita
Battelle Memorial	Sri International
Berkeley Lab	Sandia National
Comglobal Systems	Laboratories
Edsi	Swri
General Atomics	The Scripps Research
Institute For Defense	Institute
Analyses	Wyle Information
Leidos	Systems
Qinetiq	

HISTORICAL FINANCIALS

Company Type: Private

Income Statement				FYE: October 5
	REVENUE ($ mil.)	NET INCOME ($ mil.)	NET PROFIT MARGIN	EMPLOYEES
10/08	1,234	22	1.8%	7,000
10/07	1,113	23	2.1%	—
Annual Growth	10.9%	(4.6%)	—	—

2008 Year-End Financials

Return on assets: —
Return on equity: 1.8%
Current ratio: 0.80
Cash ($ mil.): 36

THE NATURE CONSERVANCY

The Nature Conservancy is a global conversation organization. The mission of The Conservancy is to conserve the lands and waters on which all life depends. The Conservancy conducts its activities throughout the United States Canada Latin America the Caribbean Europe Africa Asia and the Pacific. It preserves the diversity of Earth's wildlife by saving more than 125 million acres of land and 100 marine areas in every US state and over 70 countries worldwide. The organization partners with indigenous communities government corporate and business to protect and restore natural systems use nature sustainably and broaden support for conservation. The Nature Conservancy was founded in 1951.

Operations

The Nature and Conservancy gets more than 60% of its support and revenues from dues and contributions followed by the Government grants and contracts which gives around 10% land and easements for conservation with over 5% and the rest comes from investments and other income.

The Nature Conservancy is urgently taking on the dual threats of biodiversity loss and the climate crisis maximizing resilience and benefits for communities. It includes tackle climate change protects land and water provides food and water sustainably and build healthy cities.

Geographic Reach

Based in Arlington Virginia The Nature Conservancy operates in more than 70 countries worldwide and all 50 US states. The organization works in Africa the Asia-Pacific region the Caribbean Europe Canada India and the Americas.

EXECUTIVES

Chm, Teresa Beck
Pres*, Mark Trecek
Cfo and Chief Administrative O*, Stephen Howell
Treas*, Muneer Satter
SEC*, Frank E Loy
Prin*, Bernardo Suarez
Bod, Frank Schurz
Director, Cristi N Samper
US Fire Learning Network Direc, Lynn Decker
Chief External Affairs Officer, Glenn Pricket
Chief of Staff and Acting Chie, Janine M Wilkin
Auditors: PRICEWATERHOUSECOOPERS LLP MC

LOCATIONS

HQ: THE NATURE CONSERVANCY
4245 FAIRFAX DR STE 100, ARLINGTON, VA 222031650
Phone: 703 841-5300
Web: WWW.NATURE.ORG

Selected Areas of Operation

Africa
Australia
Asia & the Pacific Islands
Caribbean
Central America
Europe
North America
South America

PRODUCTS/OPERATIONS

2014 Support & Revenue

	$ mil.	% of total
Dues & contributions	560	50
Investment income	235	22
Land sales & gifts	138.5	
12		
Government grants	120	11
1Other income	59	5
Total	**1,114**	**100**

2014 Dues & Contributions

	%
Individuals	37
Foundations	28
Bequests	23
Other organizations	6
Corporations	6
Total	**100**

HISTORICAL FINANCIALS
Company Type: Private

Income Statement   FYE: June 30

	REVENUE ($ mil.)	NET INCOME ($ mil.)	NET PROFIT MARGIN	EMPLOYEES
06/19	992	118	11.9%	3,400
06/16	803	(8)	—	—
06/14	949	201	21.2%	—
06/13	859	106	12.4%	—
Annual Growth	**2.4%**	**1.7%**	—	—

2019 Year-End Financials
Return on assets: 1.5%   Cash ($ mil.): 193
Return on equity: 1.8%
Current ratio: —

THE NEBRASKA MEDICAL CENTER

Cornhuskers take note: If health care is what you seek The Nebraska Medical Center aims to please. The not-for-profit health system provides tertiary care at two campuses in Omaha University Hospital and Clarkson Hospital that collectively house about 680 licensed beds. The medical center the largest health care facility in Nebraska is the primary teaching facility of the University of Nebraska Medical Center (UNMC). It also serves as a designated trauma facility for eastern Nebraska and western Iowa and provides highly specialized care including organ transplantation. Its Clarkson West Medical Center campus houses outpatient surgery facilities an emergency room and doctors' offices.

Operations
The system has more than 1000 physicians. In 2013 it had some 51000 emergency department visits more than 24500 inpatient admissions and about 428000 outpatient visits.

In addition to University Hospital and Clarkson Hospital Nebraska Medical Center operates a network of 40 specialty and primary care clinics in and around Omaha. The health system's Centers of Excellence include its Cancer Center Heart Center Neurological Sciences Transplant Center and Women's Health.

Geographic Reach
In addition to serving the residents of Omaha the Nebraska Medical Center serves as a desig-

nated trauma facility for patients in eastern Nebraska and western Iowa.

Strategy
Like most other health care providers the Nebraska Medical Center is looking for ways to cut costs in the face of decreasing reimbursements from federal payers (such as Medicare and Medicaid) and as pressure from health care reform mounts and hospitals are required to implement expensive digital record-keeping and physician order entry systems. One way that Nebraska Medical Center has sought to reduce its expenses it by signing up with companies such as Medassets to receive sourcing and group purchasing (GPO) medical device and clinical consulting services for items used most by its physicians and for its pharmacy services.

The medical center and its sponsoring university are looking to expand its medical facilities to keep pace with a growing and aging population. UNMC is developing a new cancer center at the medical center's Omaha campus. Plans include three facilities - a multidisciplinary outpatient clinic a 98-lab research tower and a hospital tower with 108 beds dedicated to oncology patients. The project (estimated to cost $370 million) is expected to create 1200 new jobs by 2020 and pump $100 million annually into Nebraska's economy.

The system is also working with UNMC to add a new outpatient center to the university's midtown campus. The Lauritzen Outpatient Center will feature 10 operating rooms including four dedicated to opthalmic surgical procedures.

EXECUTIVES

Ceo, William S Dinsmoor
Chb, Harlan J Noddle
V Chb, Kenneth E Stinson
Treas, Bruce R Lauritsen
Treas, Bruce E Grewcock
SEC, James Milliken
Physician Assistant, J Calvin Russell
Clinical Quality Coordinator, Terrie Johansen
Assistant Professor, Curtis W Hartman
Project Coordinator, Liliana P Bronner
Coordinator, Beverly Hilburn
Auditors: KPMG LLP OMAHA NE

LOCATIONS

HQ: THE NEBRASKA MEDICAL CENTER
987400 NEBRASKA MED CTR, OMAHA, NE
681980001
Phone: 402 552-2000
Web: WWW.NEBRASKAMED.COM

PRODUCTS/OPERATIONS

Selected Services
Cancer Center
General Health Services
Heart and Vascular Services
Neurological Sciences
Transplantation

COMPETITORS

Bryanlgh Medical Center
Chi Health
Children's Hospital & Medical Center
Fremont Area Medical Center
Madonna Rehabilitation Hospital
Methodist Health System
Saint Elizabeth Regional Medical Center

HISTORICAL FINANCIALS
Company Type: Private

Income Statement   FYE: June 30

	REVENUE ($ mil.)	NET INCOME ($ mil.)	NET PROFIT MARGIN	EMPLOYEES
06/17	1,389	74	5.4%	4,100
06/16	1,119	60	5.4%	—
Annual Growth	**24.1%**	**22.1%**	—	—

2017 Year-End Financials
Return on assets: 5.2%   Cash ($ mil.): 67
Return on equity: 9.0%
Current ratio: 2.40

THE NEW JERSEY TRANSIT CORPORATION

Government-owned New Jersey Transit (NJ TRANSIT) is the nation's third largest provider of bus rail and light rail passenger transportation services. Its systems connect major points in New Jersey and provide links to the neighboring New York City and Philadelphia metropolitan areas. Overall the NJ TRANSIT service area spans about 5325 sq. miles. One of the largest transportation companies of its kind in the US NJ TRANSIT operates a fleet of around 2220 buses approximately 1230 trains and about 95 light rail vehicles. Collectively the agency's passengers make nearly 270 million trips a year. NJ TRANSIT oversees public transportation programs for the elderly people with disabilities and people in rural areas.

Operations
Aside from bus rail and light rail passenger transportation services NJ TRANSIT also offers bike abroad program where customers are permitted to carry bicycles on all NJ Transit's trains buses and light rails with some restrictions and schedules.

Geographic Reach
NJ TRANSIT is headquartered in New Jersey.

Sales and Marketing
NJ TRANSIT has an application where customers can plan and buy tickets for the company's services. The company also offers deals and discounts to its customers including students with its promotional partners.

Strategy
In 2020 NJ TRANSIT launched new features on its mobile app in a pilot program that allows rail and bus customers to see how full their ride is before they step on board making a better-informed personal decision that optimizes their comfort level as they return to the system.

In June 2020 NJ Transit launched strategic and capital plans that will guide the agency though 2030 called "NJT2030: A 10-Year Strategic Plan" and a complementary 5-Year Capital Plan. Together these plans provide the vision for the agency to build the future of transportation in New Jersey and with it drive a 21st century economy in an accountable transparent and environmentally-sustainable way.

As the first strategic plan of its kind for NJ TRANSIT NJT2030 begins with a vision to transform the agency into an innovative world-class public transportation provider that meets the travel needs of every customer. To achieve that vision NJT2030 establishes five over-arching goals: ensure the reliability and continued safety of its transit system; deliver a high-quality experience for all its customers with the customer's entire journey in mind; power a stronger and fairer economy for all communities in the region; promote a more sustainable future for its planet; build an accountable innovative and inclusive organization that delivers for New Jersey.

Company Background
NJ TRANSIT was founded in 1979 by the New Jersey legislature.

EXECUTIVES

Cfo-Treas, William Viqueira
Cco, Christine Baker
Act CIO, Christopher Montgomery
Chief Hr, Jeanne Victor
Exec Dir, Kevin S Corbett
Assistant Manager MMC Shop Ser, Anthony Decarolis
Drug and Alcohol Program Manag, Carolyn Robinson
Dirrector, Dale Sulpy
Procurement, Dave Amecangelo
Regional Director of Sales, Jeff Kovacs
Assistant Director, John McCarthy
Auditors: DELOITTE & TOUCHE LLP PARSIPP

LOCATIONS

HQ: THE NEW JERSEY TRANSIT CORPORATION
1 PENN PLZ E, NEWARK, NJ 071052245
Phone: 973 491-7000
Web: WWW.NJTRANSIT.COM

COMPETITORS

Port Imperial Ferry
Corp.

HISTORICAL FINANCIALS

Company Type: Private

Income Statement				FYE: June 30
	REVENUE ($ mil.)	NET INCOME ($ mil.)	NET PROFIT MARGIN	EMPLOYEES
06/19	1,059	22	2.1%	1,000
06/18	1,056	(67)	—	—
06/04	583	256	44.0%	—
06/03	569	482	84.7%	—
Annual Growth	4.0%	(17.5%)	—	—

2019 Year-End Financials
Return on assets: 0.3%
Return on equity: 0.6%
Current ratio: 0.90
Cash ($ mil.): 75

THE NEW SCHOOL

When James Lipton asks you what your favorite swear word is you know you've made it. The New School's drama department (formerly called The Actor's Studio) was made famous by the cable show Inside the Actors Studio which features Lipton interviewing movie and television stars. The school offers degrees in theater for playwriting directing and acting and has taught "Method" acting to grads such as Marlon Brando and Robert De Niro. It is also home to Parsons The New School for Design and has schools devoted to general studies liberal arts social research management and urban policy and music. More than 10500 traditional students and 5600 continuing education students are enrolled at The New School.

Operations
The New School offers more than 90 degree and diploma programs and majors to a population of undergraduate and graduate students who come from all 50 states and more than 100 foreign countries (about one-quarter of its students hail from international locations). It boasts small class sizes and a student-teacher ratio of about 10:1.

The New School for Public Engagement is the university's founding division and is composed of five schools: Milano School of International Affairs Management and Urban Policy; School of Language Learning and Teaching; School of Media Studies; School of Undergraduate Studies; and School of Writing. It has since added six divisions: Drama Jazz Lang Mannes Parsons and Social Research.

Financial Performance
The New School's 2011 revenue grew by more than 5% vs. 2010. Net income increased 13% over the same period.

Strategy
Parsons' new academic center in Paris is slated to open in fall 2013. The Paris site will offer students a program that addresses the global nature of contemporary art and design practice and reflects Europe's culture and philosophy.

The New School was founded in 1919 by a group of university professors and intellectuals in New York City as place for students wanting to explore their creativity and engage in deep thought while studying liberal arts. Dozens of years later The New School has gained a reputation for its unconventional teaching methods as well as for being the home of many world-renowned institutes including the think tank The World Policy Institute. It also hosts the annual National Book Awards which has helped establish the careers of some of the country's most recognized authors including Richard Powers and Jonathan Franzen.

EXECUTIVES

Pres, Dwight A McBride
Coo*, Tim Marshall-Provost
Executive of Information Techn, Maria Kutsumalis
Executive of Information Techn, Shannon Mattern
Assistant Professor, Peter Asaro
Information, Frank G Rizulo
Executive Officer, Benjamin Lee
Assistant Professor, Richard Huff
Assistant Professor, Kenneth Krushel
Assistant Professor, Mariah Fee
Assistant Professor, Christina Moon
Auditors: KPMG LLP NEW YORK NY

LOCATIONS

HQ: THE NEW SCHOOL
66 W 12TH ST, NEW YORK, NY 100118871
Phone: 212 229-5600
Web: WWW.NEWSCHOOL.EDU

PRODUCTS/OPERATIONS

Selected Schools
Eugene Lang College The New School for Liberal Arts
Mannes College The New School for Music
Milano The New School for Management and Urban Policy
The New School for Drama
The New School for General Studies
The New School for Jazz and Contemporary Music
The New School for Public Engagement
The New School for Social Research
Parsons The New School for Design

HISTORICAL FINANCIALS

Company Type: Private

Income Statement				FYE: June 30
	REVENUE ($ mil.)	NET INCOME ($ mil.)	NET PROFIT MARGIN	EMPLOYEES
06/20	559	(20)	—	855
06/19	427	20	4.8%	—
06/18	411	28	7.0%	—
06/16	370	(15)	—	—
Annual Growth	10.9%	—	—	—

2020 Year-End Financials
Return on assets: (-1.6%)
Return on equity: (-3.6%)
Current ratio: 0.10
Cash ($ mil.): 6

THE NEW YORK AND PRESBYTERIAN HOSPITAL

The New York and Presbyterian Hospital is one of the most comprehensive integrated academic health care delivery systems and affiliated with two renowned medical schools Weill Cornell Medicine and Columbia University of Vagelos college of Physician and Surgeons New Presbyterian is consistently recognized as leader of medical education groundbreaking research and innovative patient-centered clinical care. New York and Presbyterian Hospital have 2600 beds 6500 affiliated physicians and four major division such as New York and Presbyterian Hospital NewYork-Presbyterian Regional Hospital Network NewYork-Presbyterian Physician Services and NewYork-Presbyterian Community and Population Health. Founded in 1771 and was formed in 1998 by the merger of The New York Hospital and The Presbyterian Hospital.

Operations
Altogether the NewYork-Presbyterian Hospital campuses handle some 2 million patient visits each year (both on an inpatient and outpatient basis) including inpatient admissions and more than 310000 emergency room visits and about 15000 births. The facilities employ a total of more than 6500 physicians including residents and fellows.

Geographic Reach
In addition to its flagship campuses NewYork-Presbyterian/Columbia and NewYork-Presbyterian/Weill Cornell NewYork-Presbyterian Hospital operates two small community hospitals in Manhattan — the Allen Hospital and the Lower Manhattan Hospital — and an inpatient mental health facility (the Westchester Division). The broader NewYork-Presbyterian Healthcare System operates facilities in other areas of New York. The NewYork-Presbyterian Hospital/Columbia campus houses the Morgan Stanley Children's Hospital as well as other specialist units.

Sales and Marketing
New York and Presbyterian Hospital's markets its products and services through digital health services and provides patient easy access to experts doctors from Columbia University of Vagelos College of Physicians and Surgeons and Weill Cornell Medicine.

Company Background

NewYork-Presbyterian Hospital was formed through the 1998 merger of the New York Hospital (founded in 1771) and the Presbyterian Hospital (founded in 1868). New York Hospital was known for advancing care in areas including women's health and surgery while the Presbyterian Hospital was known for its pediatric division and its cancer center.

EXECUTIVES

Chb, John J Mack
Pres-Ceo, Herbert Pardes
Exex V Pres-Coo, Steven J Corwin
Exec V Pres-Cfo-Treas, Phyllis R Lantos
Sr V Pres-Chief Legal Officer-, Maxine Fass
Dir, Brian C Nelson
Svp-Cto, Peter M Fleischut
Safety Inspector, Emma C Guevarra
Clinical Nurse, Emma L Beckley
Office Manager, Erick Gesualdo
Risk Management Analyst, Ethelore C Sow
Auditors: ERNST & YOUNG LLP NEW YORK N

LOCATIONS

HQ: THE NEW YORK AND PRESBYTERIAN HOSPITAL
525 E 68TH ST, NEW YORK, NY 100654870
Phone: 212 746-5454
Web: WWW.NYP.ORG

PRODUCTS/OPERATIONS

2016 Patient Mix

	% of total
Medicare Managed	9
Medicare FFS	22
Medicaid Managed	23
Medicaid FFS	7
Managed Care and Other	37
Self-Pay	1
Workers Comp	1
Total	**100**

Selected Services

Cancer
Children's Health
Digestive
Geriatrics
Heart
Mens Health
Neuroscience
Orthopedic
Psychiatry
Rehabilitation Medicine
Transplant
Vascular
Womens Health

COMPETITORS

Ascension Health
Beth Israel Medical
  Center
Bronx-lebanon Hospital
Catholic Healthcare
  System
Continuum Health
  Partners
Lenox Hill Hospital
Lutheran Healthcare
Maimonides Medical
  Center

Medisys Health Network
Memorial
  Sloan-kettering
Montefiore Medical
New York City Health
  And Hospitals
Northwell Health
Winthrop-university
  Hospital
Yale New Haven Health
  System

HISTORICAL FINANCIALS

Company Type: Private

Income Statement — FYE: December 31

	REVENUE ($ mil.)	NET INCOME ($ mil.)	NET PROFIT MARGIN	EMPLOYEES
12/20	9,115	(382)	—	23,709
12/18	8,483	526	6.2%	—
12/17	5,616	762	13.6%	—
12/16	4,935	496	10.1%	—
Annual Growth	16.6%	—	—	—

2020 Year-End Financials

Return on assets: (-2.0%) Cash ($ mil.): 3,818
Return on equity: (-4.2%)
Current ratio: 2.00

THE NORTH CAROLINA MUTUAL WHOLESALE DRUG COMPANY

EXECUTIVES

Ceo, David S Moody
Pres*, Thomas P Davis
SEC*, Michael C Broome
V Pres*, Hal Harrison
Programmer, Brad Bigger
Administration, Jessica Watson
Contracts and Chargebacks Mana, Kevin Cross
Vice President Sales, Meredith Lauderdale
Chief Operations Officer, Clint Syvinski
Employee, Eric Arner
Sales Administrator, Josephine Cobb
Auditors: THOMAS KNIGHT TRENT KING AN

LOCATIONS

HQ: THE NORTH CAROLINA MUTUAL WHOLESALE
DRUG COMPANY
816 ELLIS RD, DURHAM, NC 277036019
Phone: 919 596-2151
Web: WWW.MUTUALDRUG.COM

HISTORICAL FINANCIALS

Company Type: Private

Income Statement — FYE: March 31

	REVENUE ($ mil.)	NET INCOME ($ mil.)	NET PROFIT MARGIN	EMPLOYEES
03/10	1,035	0	0.0%	160
03/09	1,024	0	0.1%	—
03/08	1,007	1	0.2%	—
Annual Growth	1.4%	(64.1%)	—	—

2010 Year-End Financials

Return on assets: 0.2% Cash ($ mil.): 53
Return on equity: 0.8%
Current ratio: 1.20

THE OHIO STATE UNIVERSITY WEXNER MEDICAL CENTER

EXECUTIVES

Pres, Michael V Drake
Director, Jennifer Lanter
Research Dietitian, Elizabeth Grainger
Assistant Director of Competit, Charles Anderson
Radiation Oncologist, Karl Haglund
Prin, Robert N Pompa
Radiology, Adele Lipari
Professor, Brandon Biesiadecki
Professor, Christina Arnold
Information Technology Team ME, Christopher
  Steiner
Obstetrician Gynecologist, Emily Oliver
Auditors: PRICEWATERHOUSECOOPERS LLP
  CO

LOCATIONS

HQ: THE OHIO STATE UNIVERSITY WEXNER
  MEDICAL CENTER
410 W 10TH AVE, COLUMBUS, OH 432101240
Phone: 614 293-8000
Web: WWW.WEXNERMEDICAL.OSU.EDU

HISTORICAL FINANCIALS

Company Type: Private

Income Statement — FYE: June 30

	REVENUE ($ mil.)	NET INCOME ($ mil.)	NET PROFIT MARGIN	EMPLOYEES
06/19	3,433	39	1.2%	35,000
06/18	3,106	137	4.4%	—
06/16	2,628	126	4.8%	—
Annual Growth	9.3%	(31.9%)	—	—

2019 Year-End Financials

Return on assets: 1.0% Cash ($ mil.): 987
Return on equity: 6.2%
Current ratio: 4.40

THE ORANGE COUNTY PUBLIC SCHOOL DISTRICT

EXECUTIVES

Supt, Barbara Jenkins
Executive of Information Techn, Giovanna Bravo
Coordinator, Jody Bernier
Senior Buyer, Belinda Biddle
Information Technology Sap, Charlie Boston
Teacher, Christy Malandra
Information Technology Project, Nancy Cox
Senior Business Process Specia, Basilio Reyes
Director of Bands, Bernie Hendricks
Resource Teacher, Loretta Hall
School Bookkeeper, Lori Orr
Auditors: CHERRY BEKAERT LLP ORLANDO

HISTORICAL FINANCIALS

Company Type: Private

Income Statement   FYE: June 30

	REVENUE ($ mil.)	NET INCOME ($ mil.)	NET PROFIT MARGIN	EMPLOYEES
06/20	2,661	(26)	—	24,000
06/19	2,646	95	3.6%	—
06/18	2,506	107	4.3%	—
06/17	2,341	(25)	—	—
Annual Growth	4.4%	—	—	—

2020 Year-End Financials

Return on assets: (-0.4%)   Cash ($ mil.): 377
Return on equity: (-0.6%)
Current ratio: —

THE PARSONS CORPORATION

Industrial construction giant Parsons provides engineering construction and other services for corporate institutional and government projects worldwide. The company designs and builds structures; provides environmental remediation services including hazardous materials cleanup; and adds improvements to airports rail systems bridges and highways. Parsons developed significant expertise and differentiated capabilities in key areas of cybersecurity missile intelligence defense C5ISR space geospatial and connected communities. North America accounts for more than 80% of revenues. The company was founded in 1944 by Ralph M. Parsons.

HISTORY

Ralph Parsons the son of a Long Island fisherman was born in 1896. At age 13 he started his first business venture a garage and machine shop which he operated with his brother. After a stint in the US Navy Parsons joined Bechtel as an aeronautical engineer. The company changed its name to Bechtel-McCone-Parsons Corporation in 1938. However Parsons later sold his shares in that company and left in 1944 to start his own design and engineering firm the Ralph M. Parsons Co. after splitting with partner John McCone (who later headed the CIA).

Parsons Co. expanded into the chemical and petroleum industries in the early 1950s. During that decade it oversaw the building of several natural gas and petroleum refineries overseas including the world's largest in Lacq France.

In the early 1960s the company began working in Kuwait which later proved to be one of its biggest markets. By 1969 Parsons had built oil refineries for all of the major oil companies designed launch sites for US missiles and constructed some of the largest mines in the world. In 1969 the company went public. With annual sales of about $300 million it ranked second only to Bechtel in the design and engineering field. Ralph Parsons died in 1974.

The company built oil and gas treatment and production plants in Alaska in the 1970s and reorganized itself into The Parsons Corporation and RMP International in 1978. It went private in 1984 as The Parsons Corporation taking advantage of a new tax law that favored corporations with employee stock ownership plans (ESOPs). Not all employees were happy though. Several groups sued maintaining that the plan disproportionately benefited executives and that the buyout left the ESOP with all of the debt but no decision-making power. A Labor Department investigation later exonerated Parsons executives.

Parsons had just finished work on a power plant in Kuwait when Iraq invaded in 1990. Several employees were detained by the Iraqis but were released shortly before the Persian Gulf War. Two years later the company returned to Kuwait to rebuild some of the country's demolished infrastructure.

In 1995 Parsons acquired Gilbert/Commonwealth an engineering company that specializes in designing nuclear power plants as part of an effort to bolster Parsons' ability to compete for power plant projects in industrializing countries. That year Parsons was awarded a contract to help build the Seoul International Airport one of the largest airport projects in the world.

James McNulty who had led the company's infrastructure and technology group replaced Leonard Pieroni as CEO in 1996 after Pieroni died in the Bosnia plane crash that also claimed the life of US Secretary of Commerce Ronald Brown. Later that year a Parsons-led consortium won a $164.5 million contract for infrastructure projects in Bosnia.

Parsons restructured in 1997 to focus on energy transportation and infrastructure projects. A Parsons/Inelectra joint venture won a $150 million construction contract in 1998 to develop Cerro Negro's heavy oil production facilities in Venezuela and the next year Parsons was chosen to manage construction of a $5 billion refinery in Bahrain a $1.4 billion gas plant in Saudi Arabia and a $1 billion polyethylene project in Abu Dhabi.

Parsons partnered with TRW in 2000 to create TRW Parsons Management & Operations to bid on the DOE's Yucca Mountain site in Nevada a potential repository for the US's high-level radioactive waste and spent nuclear fuel. It also was awarded a three-year contract to help rebuild the war-torn Serbian province of Kosovo and the next year was awarded a similar contract for Bosnia-Herzegovina.

In 2001 the company won a US Federal Aviation Agency contract to upgrade air traffic control towers and other equipment and systems a contract that had been held by rival Raytheon since 1988. Parsons also strengthened its 80-year-old bridge division by acquiring bridge engineering firm Finley McNary. That year the company's joint venture with construction giant Fluor was awarded a contract to design and engineering work for the first offshore oil field in Kazakhstan.

In 2002 Parsons completed construction of the Parsons Fabrication Facility as a part for the US Army's push for alternative methods of chemical weapons disposal. The facility was designed to test process systems for chemical weapon and bulk agent disposal.

Also that year Parsons won a contract from Dallas Area Rapid Transit (DART) to provide systems engineering and construction management services for the second phase of the buildout for the light-rail system the largest expansion of its kind in North America. In 2003 it also won a contract for final design and construction management of the first light-rail system in Charlotte North Carolina. In 2004 the Parsons' joint venture with Kellogg Brown & Root won a controversial defense

contract for oil field and refinery engineering construction and maintenance in Iraq.

Another project for Parsons was the design and engineering support for construction of Carquinez Bridge near San Francisco the first major suspension bridge to be built in the US in more than 35 years.

Parsons' Infrastructure & Technology Group subsidiary sold its Cultural Resources group to Versar in 2005. The following year it was selected to provide engineering management support for Russia's Chemical Weapons Destruction Complex.

The company ran into trouble in war-torn Iraq in 2007. The army cancelled the remainder of a $70 million contract to build 20 hospitals in Iraq due to performance problems with the construction. The company maintained (and an investigation supported) that the problems stemmed from mismanagement by the Army Corps of Engineers. It then lost a $99 million contract to build a prison in northern Iraq.

In 2009 the company acquired analytic services provider McMunn Associates which did work for the Department of Defense Department of Energy and other government agencies.

EXECUTIVES

Chb-Ceo, Charles L Harrington
Pres-Coo*, Carey A Smith
Exec V Pres-Cfo, George L Ball
Clo-General Counsel-Corp SEC, Michael R Kolloway
Chro, Susan Balaguer
Quality Assurance Manager, Ahmad Popal
Senior Geologist, Alexander Mussio
Project Manager Testing, Amandeep Singh
Senior Project Engineer, Ann Truong
Engineering Manager, Bashir Idilbi
Training Specialist, Becca Millard
Auditors: PRICEWATERHOUSECOOPERS LLP LO

LOCATIONS

HQ: THE PARSONS CORPORATION
5875 TRINITY PKWY STE 300, CENTREVILLE, VA 201201971
Phone: 703 988-8500
Web: WWW.PARSONS.COM

PRODUCTS/OPERATIONS

Selected Markets and Services
Parsons Commercial Technology
  Advanced manufacturing
  Commercial facilities
  Data management services
  Educational facilities
  Entertainment
  Health care
  Industrial environmental remediation
  Life sciences
  Mission critical facilities
  Telecommunications
  Vehicle inspection and compliance
  Wireless telecommunications systems
Parsons Infrastructure and Technology
  Community relations
  Construction
  Construction management
  Design
  Engineering
  Estimating
  Operations
  Operator training
  Procurement
  Program management
  Start-up and operations
Parsons Transportation
  Aviation
  Bridges
  Highways
  Railroads
  Revenue collection and management systems

Systems engineering
Transportation consumer services
Transportation planning
Tunneling
Urban Transit
Parsons Water and Infrastructure
Biosolids management
Combined sewer overflows
Construction/Construction management
Desalination and membrane technology
Design-build
Emergency response support
Environmental planning and restoration
Master planning
Ocean outfalls
Operations and maintenance
Storm water management
Utility tunneling
Wastewater collection systems
Wastewater treatment
Water resources
Water supply and pipelines

COMPETITORS

Abb	Kaiser Group
Aecom	Layne Christensen
Arcadis	Lend Lease
Bechtel	Louis Berger
Black & Veatch	M. A. Mortenson
Bouygues	Michael Baker
Day & Zimmermann	Mott Macdonald
Fluor	Paragon Project
Gilbane	Resources
Granite Construction	Pernix Group
Hochtief	Peter Kiewit Sons'
Halliburton	Rbf Consulting
Hill International	Railworks
Hyundai Engineering	Tic Holdings
And Construction	Turner Corporation
Jacobs Engineering	Tutor-saliba
Kbr	Vecellio & Grogan
Kbr Building Group	

HISTORICAL FINANCIALS
Company Type: Private

Income Statement				FYE: December 31
	REVENUE ($ mil.)	NET INCOME ($ mil.)	NET PROFIT MARGIN	EMPLOYEES
12/18	3,560	239	6.7%	15,500
12/15	846	28	3.4%	—
Annual Growth	61.4%	102.7%	—	—

2018 Year-End Financials

Return on assets: 9.2%   Cash ($ mil.): 280
Return on equity: —
Current ratio: 1.50

THE PENNSYLVANIA HOSPITAL OF THE UNIVERSITY OF PENNSYLVANIA HEALTH SYSTEM

Early to bed early to rise may have made Ben Franklin healthy wealthy and wise. But for those not so healthy he (along with Dr. Thomas Bond) found it wise to establish Pennsylvania Hospital the nation's first such medical institution. The hos-

pital is now a part of the University of Pennsylvania Health System (UPHS) and offers a comprehensive range of medical surgical and diagnostic services to the Philadelphia County area. Housing some 520 beds Pennsylvania Hospital offers specialized care in areas such as orthopedics vascular surgery neurosurgery and obstetrics; it is also a leading teaching hospital and a center for clinical research.

Operations
Pennsylvania Hospital has an average of about 29000 inpatient admissions per year including 5200 births as well as 115000 outpatient and emergency care visits. The medical center has more than 800 physicians on its medical staff. In addition to its extensive medical care services the company conducts medical training programs through its relationship with the University of Pennsylvania School of Medicine. Medical and clinical research programs are conducted with the school and with other research entities including government agencies. The hospital also collaborates with other UPHS entities including the Penn Presbyterian Medical Center and the Hospital of the University of Pennsylvania. The medical center also provides educational services across academic programs inlcuding Clinical Psychology Internship Program Medicine OB/GYN Pathology Radiology Sports Medicine Fellowship Surgery and Vascular Surgery Fellowship.

Financial Performance
For the fiscal year 2014 (ended June 30) Pennsylvania Hospital's revenues increased by 8.4% with a 9% increase in net patient service revenues 94% of total revenues); offset by a 1% decline in other revenues.

The company's net loss for the year decreased by 38% due to higher revenues and a decline in employee benefits paid.

Strategy
To improve the quality of care in the region UPHS is expanding specialist programs at its facilities.

In 2014 Pennsylvania Hospital opened its new Well Mother & Baby Unit which will represent Philadelphia's first all-private maternity suite unit. The new unit is part of Pennsylvania Hospital's $61 million long-range facility master plan and expands the company's offerings by providing private rooms to all of their maternity patients along with an array of obstetrical services from conception to discharge from the hospital following childbirth.

In 2013 UPHS expanded the orthopedic surgery program at Pennsylvania Hospital. The medical center is also enhancing services in fields including stroke care and women's health.

Company Background
The hospital was founded in 1751 by Benjamin Franklin and Dr. Thomas Bond to care for the sick-poor and insane of Philadelphia.

EXECUTIVES

Exec Asst, Teresa Laribee
Assistant Professor, Cherie Ditre
Palliative Care Consultant, Jeremy Souder
Associate Professor of Emergen, Edward T Dickinson
Do Radiology Director, Jack Hering
Assistant Professor of Medicin, Andrew B Dancis
Doctor, Carrie Burns
Obstetrician Gynecologist, Erin Kunkel
Director Clinical Studies Unit, Joel Gelfand
Pathologist, Jui-Han Huang
Neonatologist, Karen Szczepanski
Auditors: LB PRICEWATERHOUSECOOPERS LLP

LOCATIONS

HQ: THE PENNSYLVANIA HOSPITAL OF THE UNIVERSITY OF PENNSYLVANIA HEALTH SYSTEM 800 SPRUCE ST, PHILADELPHIA, PA 191076130
Phone: 215 829-3000
Web: WWW.PENNMEDICINE.ORG

PRODUCTS/OPERATIONS

Selected Centers
ALS Center
Birthing Suite
Center for Bloodless Medicine and Surgery
Crisis Response Center
CyberKnife
Diabetes Education Center
Joan Karnell Cancer Center
Pain Management Center
Parkinson's Disease and Movement Disorders Center
Penn Comprehensive Neurosciences Center
Penn Orthopaedic Institute
Penn Center for Voice
Sports Medicine and Rehabilitation Center
Sleep Disorders Center
Vascular Center
Women's Imaging Center

Selected Services
Behavioral health
Heart and vascular
Neonatology
Neurosurgery
Obstetrics (including high-risk maternal and fetal services)
Orthopedics
Otorhinolaryngology (ENT)
Urology
Vascular medicine/surgery

COMPETITORS

Abington Memorial Hospital
Albert Einstein Healthcare Network
Aria Health
Bryn Mawr Hospital
Children's Hospital Of Philadelphia
Crozer-keystone Health System
Fox Chase Cancer Center
Jefferson Health
North Philadelphia Health System
Tuhs
The Magee Memorial Hospital For Convalescents

HISTORICAL FINANCIALS
Company Type: Private

Income Statement				FYE: June 30
	REVENUE ($ mil.)	NET INCOME ($ mil.)	NET PROFIT MARGIN	EMPLOYEES
06/20	678	2	0.4%	2,200
06/15	579	21	3.7%	—
06/14	534	(2)	—	—
06/10	485	27	5.7%	—
Annual Growth	3.4%	(20.8%)	—	—

2020 Year-End Financials

Return on assets: 0.3%   Cash ($ mil.): —
Return on equity: 0.5%
Current ratio: —

THE PENNSYLVANIA STATE UNIVERSITY

The Pennsylvania State University system is one of the top of the world universities. Penn State has an enrollment of nearly 100000 students. It offers more than 275 undergraduate programs at 20 campuses. The school's oldest and largest campus with about half of the system's undergraduate students is at University Park in central Pennsylvania. Other sites include the Penn State College of Medicine in Hershey Pennsylvania and the Dickinson School of Law in Carlisle Pennsylvania.

Operations

It's more than 275 undergraduate programs include majors such as agriculture and natural resources biological science business engineer humanities and language and social science. Penn State offers more than 190 graduate major programs several stand-alone graduate minor programs and approximately 100 undergraduate certificates and 20 two-year associate degrees. Some majors include accounting aerospace engineering anatomy architectural engineering art and astrobiology.

Geographic Reach

Its two dozen campuses are located throughout Pennsylvania including in Abington Altoona Behrend Berks Carlisle Great Valley (School of Graduate Professionals) Wilkes-Barre University Park (largest Penn State campus) and York.

Company Background

Chartered in 1855 to apply scientific principles to farming Penn State has conferred almost 800000 degrees since its founding.

The university's storied football program was hit in 2012 with a four year postseason ban the significant reduction of scholarships the vacating of 112 wins and a $60 million fine all stemming from the school's handling of the child molestation scandal involving former coach Jerry Sandusky. However in 2015 the NCAA reversed its decision on the vacating of wins restoring the late head coach Joe Paterno as the winningest coach in major college football history.

EXECUTIVES

Pres, Eric J Barron
Pres*, Rodney A Erickson
Chm*, Keith Masser
Chairman*, Karen Peetz
Pres*, Neeli Bendapudi
Maintenance Worker, James Rieg
Faculty Staff, Jennifer Loveland-Curtze
Assistant Director, John Bechtel
Professor of Economics, John Riew
Analyst, Kenton Laubscher
Professor, Janet Swim
Auditors: DELOITTE & TOUCHE LLP PHILADE

LOCATIONS

HQ: THE PENNSYLVANIA STATE UNIVERSITY
201 OLD MAIN, UNIVERSITY PARK, PA 168021503
Phone: 814 865-4700
Web: WWW.PSU.EDU

PRODUCTS/OPERATIONS

Selected Colleges
College of Agricultural Sciences
College of Arts and Architecture
Smeal College of Business
College of Communications
College of Earth and Mineral Sciences
College of Education
College of Engineering
College of Health and Human Development
College of Information Sciences and Technology
School of International Affairs
School of Law
College of the Liberal Arts
College of Medicine
School of Nursing
Eberly College of Science
Graduate School
Schreyer Honors College

Selected Campuses
Penn State Abington Penn State Altoona
Penn State Beaver
Penn State Berks
Penn State Brandywine
Penn State DuBois
Penn State Erie The Behrend College
Penn State Fayette The Eberly Campus
Penn State Greater Allegheny
Penn State Harrisburg
Penn State Hazleton
Penn State Lehigh Valley
Penn State Mont Alto
Penn State New Kensington
Penn State Schuylkill
Penn State Shenango
Penn State Wilkes-Barre
Penn State Worthington Scranton
Penn State York

HISTORICAL FINANCIALS

Company Type: Private

Income Statement

FYE: June 30

	REVENUE ($ mil.)	NET INCOME ($ mil.)	NET PROFIT MARGIN	EMPLOYEES
06/20	6,795	(712)	—	44,000
06/19	6,576	583	8.9%	—
06/18	6,363	1,081	17.0%	—
06/17	6,059	635	10.5%	—
Annual Growth	3.9%	—	—	—

2020 Year-End Financials

Return on assets: (-4.1%)
Return on equity: (-7.3%)
Current ratio: 2.80
Cash ($ mil.): 2,359

THE PEPPER COMPANIES INC

EXECUTIVES

Pres-Ceo, J Stanley Pepper
SEC, Richard S Pepper
Exec V Pres-Gen Counsel, Thomas M O'Leary
Exec V Pres, Christopher R Averill
Project Engineer I, John Mueting
Marketing Coordinator, Ryan Delcourt
Vice President, Project Direct, Mick Metzger
Vice President, Accounting, Stephanie Vitner
Senior Project Manager, Steven Moore
Senior Vice President and Gene, Timothy Sullivan
Auditors: BKD LLP OAKBROOK TERRACE IL

LOCATIONS

HQ: THE PEPPER COMPANIES INC
643 N ORLEANS ST, CHICAGO, IL 606543608
Phone: 312 266-4703

HISTORICAL FINANCIALS

Company Type: Private

Income Statement

FYE: September 30

	REVENUE ($ mil.)	NET INCOME ($ mil.)	NET PROFIT MARGIN	EMPLOYEES
09/20	1,255	20	1.6%	1,100
09/17	1,119	22	2.0%	—
09/16	1,179	21	1.8%	—
09/11	1,177	10	0.9%	—
Annual Growth	0.7%	7.9%	—	—

2020 Year-End Financials

Return on assets: 4.5%
Return on equity: 15.3%
Current ratio: 1.30
Cash ($ mil.): 82

THE PRESIDENT AND FELLOWS OF HARVARD COLLEGE

Auditors: PRICEWATERHOUSECOOPERS LLP
B

LOCATIONS

HQ: THE PRESIDENT AND FELLOWS OF HARVARD COLLEGE
600 ATLANTIC AVE, BOSTON, MA 022102211
Phone: 617 495-1502
Web: WWW.WEBMEDIAUNIVERSITY.COM

HISTORICAL FINANCIALS

Company Type: Private

Income Statement

FYE: June 30

	REVENUE ($ mil.)	NET INCOME ($ mil.)	NET PROFIT MARGIN	EMPLOYEES
06/14	4,408	4,607	104.5%	11,500
06/13	4,214	1,056	25.1%	—
06/12	4,037	(1,446)	—	—
06/09	0	0	—	—
Annual Growth	—	—	—	—

2014 Year-End Financials

Return on assets: 7.2%
Return on equity: 104.5%
Current ratio: —
Cash ($ mil.): 87

THE PRIDDY FOUNDATION

EXECUTIVES

President, David Wolverton
Director, Debbie White

LOCATIONS

HQ: THE PRIDDY FOUNDATION
807 8TH ST STE 1010, WICHITA FALLS, TX 763013310
Phone: 940 723-8720
Web: WWW.PRIDDYFDN.ORG

HISTORICAL FINANCIALS

Company Type: Private

Income Statement				FYE: December 31
	REVENUE ($ mil.)	NET INCOME ($ mil.)	NET PROFIT MARGIN	EMPLOYEES
12/13	8,791	3	0.0%	4
12/12	3	(4)	—	
12/10	32	27	86.7%	—
12/09	0	0	—	—
Annual Growth	—	—	—	—

2013 Year-End Financials

Return on assets: 2.5% Cash ($ mil.): 14
Return on equity: 2.5%
Current ratio: —

THE PUBLIC HEALTH TRUST OF MIAMI-DADE COUNTY

Jackson Memorial Hospital is the flagship facility of the Jackson Health System (JHS). It has roughly 2450 beds and offers a wide variety of services including burn treatment trauma pediatrics rehabilitation obstetrics and transplants. It is also a teaching facility for the University of Miami School of Medicine. JHS also operates Holtz Children's Hospital a rehabilitation hospital a mental health hospital primary and specialty care centers two long-term care nursing facilities six corrections health clinics and two community hospitals. Jackson Memorial Hospital and JHS are overseen by The Public Health Trust of Miami-Dade County.

Operations

Jackson Memorial Hospital's Ryder Trauma Center is Miami-Dade County's only adult and pediatric Level 1 trauma center.

JHS is its region's primary provider of charity care spending some $700 million annually to administer health care to Florida's uninsured and underinsured populations. Along with Jackson Memorial Hospital JHS delivers medical care to Floridians through the Jackson South Community Hospital (226 beds) and the Jackson North Medical Center (382 beds) which also serves as a teaching hospital for the Florida International University College of Medicine. Holtz Children's Hospital is one of the largest children's hospitals in the state and one of three in the US that specializes in pediatric multi-organ transplants.

Strategy

The system has acquired a site to build a new campus (Jackson West) that will include a children's outpatient center and a free-standing emergency department. JHS is also adding a new walk-in facility on South Beach. The company has invested in bringing new lab equipment and software to its facilities.

Other initiatives have included adjusting prices to be more competitive doing business with HMOs and drawing in more affluent patients through first-class offerings.

Company Background

The Public Health Trust was created in 1973 by the Board of County Commissioners as an independent governing body to provide leadership for joint planning between Jackson Health System the University of Miami Miller School of Medicine

Miami-Dade County and other private and community organizations. Today the Public Health Trust is considered the hospital system's governing board picking its CEO and overseeing the system's operations.

EXECUTIVES

Pres, Carlos A Migoya
Chm, Michael Kosnitzky
V Chm, Arthur Hertz
SEC, Larry Handfield
Treas, Andres Murai Jr
Associate Nurse Manager, James Sinsurin
Executive Vice President Chief, Jeffrey Crudele
Director, Jenifer Betancourt
Doctor, Juan Solano
Associate Nurse Manager, Julia Fenton
Executive Assistant, Juliet Rico

LOCATIONS

HQ: THE PUBLIC HEALTH TRUST OF MIAMI-DADE COUNTY
1611 NW 12TH AVE, MIAMI, FL 331361005
Phone: 305 585-1111
Web: WWW.JACKSONHEALTH.ORG

COMPETITORS

Baptist Health South Florida
Broward Health
Continucare
Encompass Health
Hca
Larkin Community Hospital
Mjhha
Miami Children's Hospital
Mount Sinai Medical Center Of Florida
Nch Healthcare
Plantation General
South Broward Hospital District
South Miami Hospital
University Of Miami Hospital

HISTORICAL FINANCIALS

Company Type: Private

Income Statement				FYE: September 30
	REVENUE ($ mil.)	NET INCOME ($ mil.)	NET PROFIT MARGIN	EMPLOYEES
09/18	1,166	206	17.7%	12,990
09/17	1,160	184	15.9%	—
09/15*	883	200	22.7%	—
06/05	0	0	—	—
Annual Growth	—	—	—	—

*Fiscal year change

2018 Year-End Financials

Return on assets: 8.8% Cash ($ mil.): 308
Return on equity: 33.2%
Current ratio: 1.30

THE QUEEN'S HEALTH SYSTEMS

EXECUTIVES

Ceo, Arthur A Ushijima
Pres, Gary A Okamoto
Exec V Pres, Tracy Woo
Asst Treas, Kanoe Margol
Pres, William G Obana
V Pres, Mark Yamakawa
V Pres, Eric K Martinson
V Pres, Janice Kalanihuia

CIO, Harold Moscho
Coo, Jason C Chang
Director of Him, Iris Kawasaki
Auditors: KPMG LLP HONOLULU HI

LOCATIONS

HQ: THE QUEEN'S HEALTH SYSTEMS
1301 PUNCHBOWL ST, HONOLULU, HI 968132402
Phone: 808 691-5900
Web: WWW.QUEENS.ORG

HISTORICAL FINANCIALS

Company Type: Private

Income Statement				FYE: June 30
	REVENUE ($ mil.)	NET INCOME ($ mil.)	NET PROFIT MARGIN	EMPLOYEES
06/17	1,279	173	13.6%	8,000
06/15	118	7	6.0%	—
06/11	24	3	14.2%	—
06/10	25	5	22.4%	—
Annual Growth	75.2%	63.1%	—	—

2017 Year-End Financials

Return on assets: 6.9% Cash ($ mil.): 80
Return on equity: 11.3%
Current ratio: 4.90

THE REGENTS OF THE UNIVERSITY OF COLORADO

The University of Colorado System spans four campuses and some 60000 students. The Boulder campus home to about 30000 students provides more than 2500 courses in 150-plus fields through nine colleges and schools. The University of Colorado at Denver has an enrollment of more than 14000 and has 120 study programs at a dozen schools and its nearby Anschutz Medical Campus serves more than 500000 patients annually. The smallest campus University of Colorado at Colorado Springs has six colleges with about 10000 students and offers nearly 60 undergraduate graduate and doctoral degree programs. The system which began in Boulder as the University of Colorado in 1876 boasts more than 4000 faculty members.

Operations

In addition to its primary campuses in the cities of Boulder Denver and Colorado Springs The University of Colorado System operates the Anschutz Medical Campus which has an enrollment of about 3500 students.

The university system has an annual budget of more than $2.9 billion. It receives a number contracts and grants through its extensive research programs which also serve as teaching and training programs for its students. Areas of research include science technology and health care.

The University of Colorado System boasts a number of noteworthy faculty members including Nobel Laureates John Hall Eric Cornell Carl Wieman and Thomas Cech all of which earned honors in either physics or chemistry.

Geographic Reach

The University of Colorado System serves some 60000 students across several University of Colorado campuses in Boulder Denver and Colorado Springs. It's known for its leadership in higher education and research in the Rocky Mountain region.

Financial Performance

The University of Colorado System has enjoyed rising revenue in recent years due to organic growth.

EXECUTIVES

Exec Dir, Bruce Benson
Pres*, Mark Kennedy
Coo-Exec V Chancellor*, Kelly Fox
Researcher, Blake Redabaugh
Poc, Melissa Englund
Project Coordinator, Gabriele Cheatham
Information Specialist, Nik Levinsky
Coordinator, Heidi Eckhoff
Internal Medicine Practitioner, Samantha Miles
Coordinator, Angela Annan
Assistant Professor, Jung-In Kim
Auditors: BKD LLP DENVER COLORADO

LOCATIONS

HQ: THE REGENTS OF THE UNIVERSITY OF COLORADO
3100 MAR ST STE 481 572 U, BOULDER, CO 803090001
Phone: 303 735-6624
Web: WWW.COLORADO.EDU

PRODUCTS/OPERATIONS

Selected Campuses

University
University of Colorado - Colorado Springs
University
University of Colorado Anschutz Medical Campus

HISTORICAL FINANCIALS

Company Type: Private

Income Statement   FYE: June 30

	REVENUE ($ mil.)	NET INCOME ($ mil.)	NET PROFIT MARGIN	EMPLOYEES
06/20	4,239	584	13.8%	12,980
06/18	3,833	(197)	—	—
06/17	3,728	77	2.1%	—
06/16	3,451	72	2.1%	—
Annual Growth	5.3%	68.2%	—	—

2020 Year-End Financials

Return on assets: 7.4%   Cash ($ mil.): 221
Return on equity: 22.0%
Current ratio: 3.90

THE RESEARCH FOUNDATION FOR THE STATE UNIVERSITY OF NEW YORK

The Research Foundation of State University of New York (The Research Foundation) collects and administers research and education grants from state and federal governments corporations and foundations on behalf of the 24-campus State University of New York known as SUNY. The foundation has formed several affiliated divisions — including Long Island High Technology Incubator

and NanoTech Resources — to operate research facilities encourage scientific collaboration and otherwise facilitate research for the university. It facilitates research for studies such as engineering and nanotechnology; physical sciences and medicine; life sciences and medicine; social sciences; and computer and information sciences.

Operations

The foundation manages SUNY's research portfolio. Research Foundation administrators help SUNY faculty students and staff through every step of the research grant process allowing them to focus on their work and ensuring compliance with university grant sponsor and government requirements.

The Research Foundation protects SUNY's intellectual property (SUNY ranks among the nation's top faculty to commercialize their inventions for the public good).

The organization makes strategic investments to maximize the collective impact of SUNY research to drive investment and job growth. SUNY's Networks of Excellence assemble scientists and scholars from all campuses to collaborate on research projects in areas ranging from advanced manufacturing and energy to health and the humanities.

The Research Foundation is an integral partner in the execution and administration of the START-UP NY initiative to transform SUNY campuses and university communities across the state into tax-free communities for new and expanding businesses.

The organization funds its operations primarily from recoveries of indirect costs provided from grants and contracts.

Geographic Reach

The Research Foundation comprises a central office and operating units at 31 campus locations across New York State.

Financial Performance

The Research Foundation reported $1 billion in revenues in 2014 compared to $1.07 billion in 2013. The primary reason for the decline was due to decreased sales from federal grants and contracts private grants and contracts and investment income.

Investment income/loss included dividends and interest realized and unrealized gains and losses and equity adjustments from the foundation's investment in the Brookhaven Science Associates partnership.

The organization's net income decreased by $30 million in 2014 due to lower revenues and increased other program expenses.

Net cash provided by the operating activities increased by $127.7 million due to changes in interest payments on capital debts and other payments.

Strategy

In 2014 Iliad Neurosciences a company focused on the development of innovative approaches to diagnosing and treating Autism Spectrum Disorders entered into an Exclusive License Agreement with The Research Foundation for The State University of New York. Under this deal Iliad will provide a new biomarker to identify an abnormality in folate transport to the brain associated with susceptibility to Autism Spectrum Disorders. . The identification of this defect could lead to a targeted therapy that may improve the transport of folate to the brain in children and to the fetus in pregnant women who test positive for the folate receptor autoantibody.

Company Background

The Research Foundation was established in 1951 just three years after SUNY itself.

EXECUTIVES

Pres/Ceo, Jeffrey Chee
Pres/Ceo*, Jeffrey Cheek
Executive Director of Developm, Alan Greene
Customer Integration Manager, Daniel Coleman
Professor of Engineering, George Lee
Account Executive, Jerry Gretzinger
Professor of Chemistry, Kathy Olszewski
Associate Vice President For M, Kristin Haacker
Information Technology Project, Michael Mastromarino
Chief Operating, Pradeep Haldar
Networking Lan Management, Robert Williams
Auditors: KPMG LLP BOSTON MA

LOCATIONS

HQ: THE RESEARCH FOUNDATION FOR THE STATE UNIVERSITY OF NEW YORK
35 STATE ST, ALBANY, NY 122072826
Phone: 518 434-7000
Web: WWW.RFSUNY.ORG

PRODUCTS/OPERATIONS

2014 Revenues

	% of total
Federal grants & contracts	50
Private grants & contracts	23
State grants & contracts	17
Investments	2
Inventions & licenses	2
Local grants & contracts	2
Investment income	0
Gifts capital gifts & grants	0
Other	4
Total	**100**

HISTORICAL FINANCIALS

Company Type: Private

Income Statement   FYE: June 30

	REVENUE ($ mil.)	NET INCOME ($ mil.)	NET PROFIT MARGIN	EMPLOYEES
06/20	1,572	422	26.8%	15,000
06/13	1,079	42	3.9%	—
06/12	1,114	12	1.2%	—
06/09	985	(71)	—	—
Annual Growth	4.3%			

2020 Year-End Financials

Return on assets: 31.3%   Cash ($ mil.): 207
Return on equity: 93.4%
Current ratio: 0.80

THE RUDOLPH/LIBBE COMPANIES INC

The corporate model of a conglomerate composed of independent unrelated businesses is not for The Rudolph/Libbe Companies. The group of companies can build or oversee real estate projects (general contractor Rudolph/Libbe Inc.); perform mechanical electrical and structural work (GEM Industrial); and then represent those properties in the market (RLWest Properties). Operating in the Ohio/Michigan corridor the group provides site selection design/build and construction management. Its portfolio includes industrial retail municipal residential educational health care and mixed-use projects. Fritz and Phil Rudolph and their cousin Allan Libbe founded flagship subsidiary Rudolph/Libbe Inc. in 1955.

EXECUTIVES

Chm, Bill Rudolph
Pres*, Allan J Libbe
SEC*, John A Libbe
Treas-Cfo*, Robert Pruger
Pres*, Frederick W Rudolph
Pres*, Philip J Rudolph
Business Manager, Brandon Gartee
Project Manager Estimator, Jay Gillette
Business Manager, Michelle Dean
Safety Manager, Neil Smith
Business Manager, Brad Delventhal
Auditors: REHMANN ROBSON TOLEDO OH

LOCATIONS

HQ: THE RUDOLPH/LIBBE COMPANIES INC
   6494 LATCHA RD, WALBRIDGE, OH 434659788
Phone: 419 241-5000
Web: WWW.RLGBUILDS.COM

COMPETITORS

Albert M. Higley	Messer Construction
Atlas Industrial	Ruhlin
Holdings	Skanska Usa Building
Danis	

HISTORICAL FINANCIALS

Company Type: Private

Income Statement   FYE: December 31

	REVENUE ($ mil.)	NET INCOME ($ mil.)	NET PROFIT MARGIN	EMPLOYEES
12/18	573	16	2.8%	600
12/17	567	20	3.5%	—
12/16	502	23	4.8%	—
12/15	425	16	3.8%	—
Annual Growth	10.5%	(0.2%)	—	—

2018 Year-End Financials

Return on assets: 7.4%   Cash ($ mil.): 16
Return on equity: 25.9%
Current ratio: 1.30

THE SAINT CLOUD HOSPITAL

EXECUTIVES

Pres, Craig Broman
Cfo*, Greg Klugherz
Coordinator, Kevin Mentzer
Chief of Medicine, Richard Jolkovsky
Chief of Medicine, Peter Charvat
Chief of Internal Medicine, Joe Mercuri
Cardiologist, Richard Aplin
Infectious Disease, Richard Backes
Hr Administrative Assistant, Erica Ferguson
Administrative Specialist, Gwen Muehring
Internist, Madhu Suryadevara
Auditors: MCGLADREY LLP MINNEAPOLIS MN

LOCATIONS

HQ: THE SAINT CLOUD HOSPITAL
   1406 6TH AVE N, SAINT CLOUD, MN 563031901
Phone: 320 251-2700
Web: WWW.CENTRACARE.COM

HISTORICAL FINANCIALS

Company Type: Private

Income Statement   FYE: June 30

	REVENUE ($ mil.)	NET INCOME ($ mil.)	NET PROFIT MARGIN	EMPLOYEES
06/20	931	55	5.9%	4,957
06/18	864	39	4.5%	—
06/16	756	3	0.5%	—
06/15	767	170	22.2%	—
Annual Growth	4.0%	(20.2%)	—	—

2020 Year-End Financials

Return on assets: 3.7%   Cash ($ mil.): 165
Return on equity: 7.9%
Current ratio: 3.60

THE SALVATION ARMY

EXECUTIVES

Pres-Trus, William A Bamford III
President-Trustee*, William A Bamfordiii
V Pre-Trustee*, Kenneth O Johnson Jr
Chb-Trustee*, David E Jeffrey
Treasurer-Trustee*, Donald W Lance
Secretary*, Michael J Southwick
Fist Asst Treas-Trustee*, D Sue Foley
Second Asst Treas*, Thomas O Henson
Asst SEC-Legal*, Richard D Allen
Asst Sec-Property*, Jorge E Diaz
Second Asst Sec-Property*, Adolph M Orlando
Auditors: GRANT THORNTON LLP NEW YORK

LOCATIONS

HQ: THE SALVATION ARMY
   440 W NYACK RD OFC, WEST NYACK, NY 109941739
Phone: 845 620-7200
Web: WWW.SACONNECTS.ORG

HISTORICAL FINANCIALS

Company Type: Private

Income Statement   FYE: September 30

	REVENUE ($ mil.)	NET INCOME ($ mil.)	NET PROFIT MARGIN	EMPLOYEES
09/16	859	(224)	—	10,447
09/12	1,034	207	20.0%	—
09/09	782	(96)	—	—
09/08	288	(463)	—	—
Annual Growth	14.6%	—	—	—

2016 Year-End Financials

Return on assets: (-5.4%)   Cash ($ mil.): 122
Return on equity: (-9.7%)
Current ratio: 0.30

THE SALVATION ARMY

EXECUTIVES

Chb, David Jeffrey
Pres*, Donald Bell
Treas*, James Seiler
Assis Treas*, Stephen Ellis
SEC*, Ward Matthews

V Pres*, Ralph Bukiewicz
MBR*, Susan Bukiewicz
MBR*, William Mockabee
Cfo*, Alberto Flores
Senior Manager, Colonel B Bailey
Coordinator, Alvin Jones

LOCATIONS

HQ: THE SALVATION ARMY
   1424 NORTHEAST EXPY NE, BROOKHAVEN, GA
   303292088
Phone: 404 728-1300
Web: WWW.SOUTHERNUSA.SALVATIONARMY.ORG

HISTORICAL FINANCIALS

Company Type: Private

Income Statement   FYE: September 30

	REVENUE ($ mil.)	NET INCOME ($ mil.)	NET PROFIT MARGIN	EMPLOYEES
09/09	830	(220)	—	16,168
09/08	533	(336)	—	—
09/07	1,185	318	26.9%	—
Annual Growth	(16.3%)	—	—	—

2009 Year-End Financials

Return on assets: (-6.7%)   Cash ($ mil.): 89
Return on equity: (-8.6%)
Current ratio: 1.30

THE SAVANNAH COLLEGE OF ART AND DESIGN INC

With more than 12000 students Savannah College of Art and Design (SCAD) in Georgia is a private nonprofit accredited university with students from across the US and more than 100 countries. It has undergraduate degrees in arts and fine arts as well as master's degrees in a range of subjects. The institution offers courses of study in 40-plus majors including fields such as architecture interior and graphic design fashion film and television painting dance and art history. The school also offers certificates in digital publishing digital publishing management historic preservation interactive design and typeface design and more than 60 other minors.

Operations

Annual tuition runs at about $30000. The institution employs about 700 full- and part-time faculty members.

The school's most popular majors include animation fashion graphic design illustration and photography. In addition to regular coursework SCAD provides online distance education courses.

Geographic Reach

SCAD has campuses in Atlanta and Savannah Georgia as well as in Hong Kong and Lacoste France. Students at the college hail from all 50 US states and more than 100 international countries.

Company Background

The school was founded in 1978 and has taken an active role in restoring architectural landmarks in Savannah.

EXECUTIVES

Pres, Paula Wallace
Exec V Pres, Brian Murphy

THE SCHOOL BOARD OF MIAMI-DADE COUNTY

EXECUTIVES

Chb, Perla Tabares Hantman
Staff, Martin A Berkowitz
Administrative Assistant, Jerold Blumstein
Teacher, Claudine Etienne
Teacher, Dudley Parker
Teacher, Kathy Happell
Teacher, Kimberly Lewis
Auditors: MCGLADREY LLP MIAMI FLORIDA

LOCATIONS

HQ: THE SCHOOL BOARD OF MIAMI-DADE COUNTY
1450 NE 2ND AVE, MIAMI, FL 331321308
Phone: 305 995-1000

HISTORICAL FINANCIALS

Company Type: Private

Income Statement				FYE: June 30
	REVENUE ($ mil.)	NET INCOME ($ mil.)	NET PROFIT MARGIN	EMPLOYEES
06/21	4,458	141	3.2%	9
06/20	4,120	(41)	—	—
06/19	3,948	(14)	—	—
06/18	3,868	(46)	—	—
Annual Growth	4.8%	—	—	—

2021 Year-End Financials

Return on assets: 2.1%   Cash ($ mil.): 585
Return on equity: —
Current ratio: 2.10

THE SCHOOL DISTRICT OF OSCEOLA COUNTY FLORIDA

EXECUTIVES

Supt, Melba Luciano
Cbfo*, Bill Collins
Principal, George Sullivan
Coordinator, Jean Riggs
Public Information Director, Dana Lee Schafer
Management Info Dir, Robert Curran Sr
Senior Buyer, Megan Pearison
Tech Prep Coordinator, Melanie Stefanowicz
Senior Programmer, Glen Hammer
Facilities Director, Michael Clark
Language Arts Teacher, Abbreyel Jessup
Auditors: SHERRILL F NORMAN CPA TALLA

LOCATIONS

HQ: THE SCHOOL DISTRICT OF OSCEOLA COUNTY FLORIDA
817 BILL BECK BLVD, KISSIMMEE, FL 347444492
Phone: 407 870-4600
Web: WWW.OSCEOLASCHOOLS.NET

HISTORICAL FINANCIALS

Company Type: Private

Income Statement				FYE: June 30
	REVENUE ($ mil.)	NET INCOME ($ mil.)	NET PROFIT MARGIN	EMPLOYEES
06/19	787	25	3.2%	6,250
06/18	695	13	2.0%	—
06/17	638	117	18.4%	—
06/16	601	37	6.2%	—
Annual Growth	9.4%	(12.2%)	—	—

2019 Year-End Financials

Return on assets: 1.7%   Cash ($ mil.): 225
Return on equity: 3.7%
Current ratio: —

THE SCHOOL DISTRICT OF PHILADELPHIA

EXECUTIVES

Spdt, William Hite Jr
Cfo*, Matthew E Stanski
Food Director, Wayne T Grasela
Teacher, Abram Taber
Health, Julia Smith
Director, Majeedah Scott
Personnel Assistant, Michelle Stokes
Health, Brandon Coleman
Educator, Robert Tate
Special Education Teacher, Chanelle Harley
Teacher, Elaine Braun
Auditors: CHRISTY BRADY CPA PHILADELPH

LOCATIONS

HQ: THE SCHOOL DISTRICT OF PHILADELPHIA
440 N BROAD ST, PHILADELPHIA, PA 191304090
Phone: 215 400-4000
Web: WWW.PHILASD.ORG

HISTORICAL FINANCIALS

Company Type: Private

Income Statement				FYE: June 30
	REVENUE ($ mil.)	NET INCOME ($ mil.)	NET PROFIT MARGIN	EMPLOYEES
06/18	3,473	210	6.1%	21,065
06/17	3,250	220	6.8%	—
06/16	3,064	23	0.8%	—
06/11	2,930	(259)	—	—
Annual Growth	2.5%	—	—	—

2018 Year-End Financials

Return on assets: 5.7%   Cash ($ mil.): 190
Return on equity: —
Current ratio: —

THE SCHOOL DISTRICT OF WEST PALM BEACH COUNTY

EXECUTIVES

Coordinator, Elizabeth Parsley
Staff, Linda Esta
Coordinator, Noemi Moreno
Reading Teacher, Amy McGregor
Financial Applications Manager, Angela Saccareccia
School Counselor, Anne Kim
Teacher, Annie Yarensky
Mathematics Administrator, Joi Grant
Teacher, Julia Brown
Social Studies District Admini, Laurie Cotton
Senior Buyer, Leslie Millar
Auditors: RSM US LLP WEST PALM BEACH

LOCATIONS

HQ: THE SCHOOL DISTRICT OF WEST PALM BEACH COUNTY
3300 FOREST HILL BLVD, WEST PALM BEACH, FL 334065813
Phone: 561 434-8747
Web: WWW.PALMBEACHSCHOOLS.ORG

HISTORICAL FINANCIALS

Company Type: Private

Income Statement				FYE: June 30
	REVENUE ($ mil.)	NET INCOME ($ mil.)	NET PROFIT MARGIN	EMPLOYEES
06/18	2,307	136	5.9%	9,414
06/17	2,146	78	3.7%	—
06/16	1,986	64	3.2%	—
06/15	1,903	(61)	—	—
Annual Growth	6.6%	—	—	—

2018 Year-End Financials

Return on assets: 2.8%   Cash ($ mil.): 959
Return on equity: 9.2%
Current ratio: —

THE SCOULAR COMPANY

The Scoular Company buys sells stores handles processes and transports agricultural products (mainly grains) worldwide. It gets the mainstays of farming ? corn millet rye peas and lentils soybeans and wheat ? where they need to go. The company transports these products via rail truck and barge shipping partners. Scoular's other divisions offer fishmeal products for farm-animal pet and aquaculture feeds; ingredients for food manufacturers; and renewable fuels as well as a host of risk management logistics and product-related services. Scoular has more than 100 locations locally and internationally.

Operations

Scoular facilitates solutions for its customers at every step in the agricultural supply chain. It provides solutions for grains food ingredients animal feed ingredients pet food ingredients international trades and transportation.

The company has the network confidence and creativity to make connections between farmers processors manufacturers facilities shippers and carriers worldwide. When it comes to animal feed the company delivers flexible and valuable nutrition solutions whether it is for a dairy feedmill or another animal feed manufacturer. Scoular's indirect wholly owned and independently operated subsidiary Petsource provides comprehensive freeze-dried pet food manufacturing capabilities for ultimate quality control.

Scoular's grain products include barley flaxseed soybean and sunflower seeds among others. Other products include fats and oils fibers flours sweeteners and more.

Geographic Reach

In addition to the company's headquarters in Omaha Nebraska and corporate offices in Overland Park Kansas and Minneapolis Minnesota Scoular has more than 100 locations around the world.

Sales and Marketing

Scoular serves farmers grain processors animal feed manufacturers aquafeed manufacturers pet food manufacturers food beverage and supplement manufacturers distilleries and renewable energy producers.

Strategy

Scoular in mid-2021 created a new division to lead its businesses in the early stages of development and to serve as an incubator for strategic investment opportunities. Scoular Senior Vice President Ed Prosser will lead the new division called "Emerging Businesses". The Emerging Businesses Division will include business activities focusing on biofuels renewable energy carbon markets investments in agricultural technology such as Roger LLC and other future growth ventures.

Company Background

George Scoular founded the George Scoular Grain & Lumber Company in Nebraska in 1892. It was family-owned until 1967 when it was sold to a group of grain industry executives. It grew through acquisitions and partnerships over the following decades.

EXECUTIVES

Chairman Emeritus, Marshall Faith
Director, Todd McQueen
Director, John Heck
Senior Vice President And Grain Division Manager, Bob Ludington
Senior Vice President, Director And Feed Division Manager, John Messerich
Chief Executive Officer, Director, Paul Maass
Senior Vice President, General Counsel, Company Secretary, Megan Belcher
Chief Financial Officer, Senior Vice President, Andrew Kenny
Auditors: KPMG LLP OMAHA NEBRASKA

LOCATIONS

HQ: THE SCOULAR COMPANY
2027 DODGE ST, OMAHA, NE 681021240
Phone: 402 342-3500
Web: WWW.SCOULAR.COM

COMPETITORS

Adm	Excel Maritime
Andersons	Carriers
Bartlett And Company	Louis Dreyfus Group
Bunge Limited	Syntroleum
Chs	Tbs International
Cargill	Torm
Debruce Grain	

HISTORICAL FINANCIALS

Company Type: Private

Income Statement				FYE: May 31
	REVENUE ($ mil.)	NET INCOME ($ mil.)	NET PROFIT MARGIN	EMPLOYEES
05/18	4,486	22	0.5%	801
05/17	4,366	25	0.6%	—
05/16	4,667	(10)	—	—
Annual Growth	(2.0%)	—	—	—

2018 Year-End Financials

Return on assets: 2.6%
Return on equity: 7.3%
Current ratio: 1.40
Cash ($ mil.): 37

THE SIMONS FOUNDATION INC

EXECUTIVES

President, David Spergel
V Pres*, Mark Silver
Board Co-Chair*, James H Simons
Cfo*, Marlow Kee
Coo*, Euan Robertson
Board Co-Chair*, Marilyn Simons
Vice President, Marion Greenup
Director, Apoorva Mandavilli
Accounting Manager, Lawrence Bianco
Human Resources Director, Kathleen Savarese
Editor, Emily Singer

LOCATIONS

HQ: THE SIMONS FOUNDATION INC
160 5TH AVE FL 7, NEW YORK, NY 100107037
Phone: 646 654-0066
Web: WWW.SIMONSFOUNDATION.ORG

HISTORICAL FINANCIALS

Company Type: Private

Income Statement			FYE: December 31
	ASSETS ($ mil.)	NET INCOME ($ mil.)	INCOME AS % OF ASSETS	EMPLOYEES
12/20	4,324	134	3.1%	425
12/19	4,000	302	7.6%	—
12/18	3,651	283	7.8%	—
12/17	3,297	236	7.2%	—
Annual Growth	9.5%	(17.3%)	—	—

2020 Year-End Financials

Return on assets: 3.1%
Return on equity: 4.1%
Sales ($ mil): 722

THE SOUTHEASTERN CONFERENCE

EXECUTIVES

Commissioner, Greg Sankey
Commissioner*, Michael Flive
Commissioner*, Mark Womack
Associate Director, Sylvia Hagan
Director, Torie Johnson
Media Relations Assistant, Charles Dunlap
Assistant Commissioner Complia, Matt Boyer
Coordinator Impressio, Melinda Calderini
Auditors: BARFIELD MURPHY SHANK & SMITH

LOCATIONS

HQ: THE SOUTHEASTERN CONFERENCE
2201 RICHARD ARRINGTN JR, BIRMINGHAM, AL 352031103
Phone: 205 949-8960
Web: WWW.SECSPORTS.COM

HISTORICAL FINANCIALS

Company Type: Private

Income Statement				FYE: August 31
	REVENUE ($ mil.)	NET INCOME ($ mil.)	NET PROFIT MARGIN	EMPLOYEES
08/20	728	32	4.4%	30
08/19	720	23	3.3%	—
08/16	639	17	2.7%	—
08/15	527	17	3.3%	—
Annual Growth	6.7%	13.5%	—	—

2020 Year-End Financials

Return on assets: 22.9%
Return on equity: 22.9%
Current ratio: —
Cash ($ mil.): 34

THE STAMFORD HOSPITAL

EXECUTIVES

Ceo-Pres, Brian Grissler
Exec V Pres, Kathleen Silard
Cfo, Kevin Gage

Cmo, Sharon Kiely
Sr V Pres, Darryl McCormick
Dentist, David B Weinstein DDS
Vp- Ambulatory Network Dev't, Andrew Snyder
Librarian, Guillaume V Moorsel
Coordinator, Joyce Potter
Coordinator, Marcel Souza
Procurement Staff, Gloria Vallo
Auditors: ERNST & YOUNG LLP HARTFORD

LOCATIONS

HQ: THE STAMFORD HOSPITAL
1 HOSPITAL PLZ, STAMFORD, CT 069023602
Phone: 203 325-7000
Web: WWW.STAMFORDHEALTH.ORG

HISTORICAL FINANCIALS

Company Type: Private

Income Statement				FYE: September 30
	REVENUE ($ mil.)	NET INCOME ($ mil.)	NET PROFIT MARGIN	EMPLOYEES
09/20	728	4	0.6%	2,000
09/19	608	(44)	—	—
09/18	574	3	0.7%	—
Annual Growth	12.6%	9.6%	—	—

2020 Year-End Financials

Return on assets: 0.4%   Cash ($ mil.): 208
Return on equity: 1.0%
Current ratio: 1.70

THE SUNDERLAND FOUNDATION

EXECUTIVES

Prin, Lester T Sunderland

LOCATIONS

HQ: THE SUNDERLAND FOUNDATION
5700 W 112TH ST STE 320, LEAWOOD, KS
662111759
Phone: 913 319-6194
Web: WWW.SUNDERLAND.ORG

HISTORICAL FINANCIALS

Company Type: Private

Income Statement				FYE: December 31
	REVENUE ($ mil.)	NET INCOME ($ mil.)	NET PROFIT MARGIN	EMPLOYEES
12/18	1,552	1,429	92.1%	7
12/10	6	2	35.2%	—
12/09	2	(2)	—	—
Annual Growth	105.9%	—	—	—

2018 Year-End Financials

Return on assets: 95.8%   Cash ($ mil.): 542
Return on equity: 95.8%
Current ratio: —

THE SUNDT COMPANIES INC

Sundt has put its stamp on the Southwest. Through Sundt Construction and other subsidiaries The Sundt Companies offers preconstruction construction management general contracting and design/build services for commercial government and industrial clients. Projects include commercial buildings military bases light rails airports and schools. It builds mostly in Arizona Nevada California New Mexico and Texas. Sundt has overseen some notable projects including the development of the top-secret town of Los Alamos New Mexico (where the first atomic bomb was built) and the relocation of the London Bridge to Arizona. Sundt Companies was formed in 1998 as a holding company for various company interests.

Operations

The Sundt Companies performs its work through various divisions: Industrial; concrete; building; heavy civil; and federal. The building division is divided into geographic regions: California; Southwest; and Texas; as well as a Federal Division.

Strategy

Like its peers Sundt is dealing with the lingering effects of the construction downturn that greatly impacted the Southwest. (The company lost more than $750 million in government projects due to state budget constraints.) Indeed Sundt anticipates that it may be 2015 before it sees a strong economy for construction. In the meantime the firm has relied on a healthy backlog of projects and diversification efforts to sustain its business. To that end it entered new geographic markets in 2012 including New Mexico where it is building new dorms at New Mexico State University. It also recently began construction of new schools in El Paso Texas its first in the city. The firm formed a new Criminal Justice Specialization group in 2012 to win courthouse and detention facility work.

Sundt also has focused on making investments in improving technology used in the preconstruction and construction process. It also grew its self-perform work capabilities when it acquired Foley Masonry and Tile Inc. in 2010. Also that year Sundt opened a new office in San Antonio as part of the company's growth plan. The company expanded once again in 2011. It opened new offices to support projects in New Mexico North Carolina and Texas.

EXECUTIVES

Pres-Ceo, Mike Hoover
Svp/Cfo*, Kevin M Burnett
Sr V Pres-Gen Counsel*, Ronald Stuff
Vice President Engineering, Nobuyuki Kuroki
Auditors: MAYER HOFFMAN & MCCANN

LOCATIONS

HQ: THE SUNDT COMPANIES INC
2015 W RIVER RD STE 101, TUCSON, AZ 857041676
Phone: 520 750-4600
Web: WWW.SUNDT.COM

PRODUCTS/OPERATIONS

Selected Projects

Aviation
Commercial buildings
Concrete construction
Courthouses
Federal government
Hospitality

Hospitals & health care
Infrastructure & site development
Juvenile detention facilities
K-12 schools
Mining
Mission critical/Data center
Municipal buildings
Parking structures
Power plants & alternative energy
Prisons
Research & development facilities
Residential
Retail
Roads & bridges
Student housing & dormitories
Universities & community colleges
Water & wastewater treatment

Selected Services
Build-to-suit
Construction manager at risk (CMAR)
Construction/program manager
Design-bid-build/general contractor (DBB)
Preconstruction
Self-perform contracting

COMPETITORS

Austin Industries	Mccarthy Building
Core Construction	Meadow Valley
Charles Pankow Builders	O'neil Industries
	Peter Kiewit Sons'
Dpr Construction	Swinerton
Granite Construction	Tutor Perini
Hunt Construction	Weitz
Kitchell	

HISTORICAL FINANCIALS

Company Type: Private

Income Statement				FYE: September 30
	REVENUE ($ mil.)	NET INCOME ($ mil.)	NET PROFIT MARGIN	EMPLOYEES
09/18	1,432	0	—	1,800
09/17	1,134	0	—	—
09/16*	813	0	—	—
06/16	0	0	—	—
Annual Growth	—	—	—	—

*Fiscal year change

2018 Year-End Financials

Return on assets: —   Cash ($ mil.): 82
Return on equity: —
Current ratio: 1.30

THE TRUSTEES OF COLUMBIA UNIVERSITY IN THE CITY OF NEW YORK

EXECUTIVES

Pres, Lee C Bollinger
Interim Provost*, John H Coatsworth
Sr Ex V Pres*, Robert Kasdin
Gen Counsel*, Jane E Booth
Ex V Pres-Fin*, Anne Sulivan
Cntrl*, Cheryl A Ross
Psychiatry, Lourival B Neto
Pedodontist, Luz Aguirre
Psychiatry, Maura Boldrini

Professor, Richard Baer
Co Director, Andrew Dwork
Auditors: PRICEWATERHOUSECOOPERS LLP

LOCATIONS

HQ: THE TRUSTEES OF COLUMBIA UNIVERSITY IN
THE CITY OF NEW YORK
202 LOW LIB 535 W 116 ST, NEW YORK, NY 10027
Phone: 212 854-9970
Web: WWW.COLUMBIA.EDU

HISTORICAL FINANCIALS

Company Type: Private

Income Statement				FYE: June 30
	REVENUE ($ mil.)	NET INCOME ($ mil.)	NET PROFIT MARGIN	EMPLOYEES
06/21	5,195	3,332	64.1%	13,200
06/20	5,201	271	5.2%	—
06/13	3,738	1,048	28.0%	—
Annual Growth	4.2%	15.5%	—	—

2021 Year-End Financials

Return on assets: 13.5%
Return on equity: 17.0%
Current ratio: —
Cash ($ mil.): 754

THE TRUSTEES OF PRINCETON UNIVERSITY

With over 200 campus buildings Princeton University offers more than 40 doctoral departments and programs including biophysics chemistry cognitive science and many more. The university have approximately 1.3 thousand faculty with 5:1 student faculty ratio. The university was founded in 1746 and renamed to Princeton University in 1896.

Company Background

Founded in 1746 as the College of New Jersey Princeton is the fourth-oldest college in the nation. In 1756 the college was moved to Nassau Hall which served as the temporary capitol of the US in 1783 and is still part of the Princeton campus.

EXECUTIVES

Pres, Christopher L Eisgruber
Exec V Pres, Treby Williams
Vp Public Affairs, Robert K Durkee
Treas, Kenneth Molinaro
Dept Ofc Sprt Ofc Vice Preside, Randall Setlock
Vice President of Financial Ai, Reagan E
Maraghy
Editor, Sara Lerner
Asst Vp of Annual Giving, William Hardt
Communications Manager, Zia Best
Accounting Staff, Charles Schneider
Chief Audit and Compliance Off, Nilufer K Shroff
Auditors: PRICEWATERHOUSECOOPERS LLP
NE

LOCATIONS

HQ: THE TRUSTEES OF PRINCETON UNIVERSITY
1 NASSAU HALL, PRINCETON, NJ 085442001
Phone: 609 258-3000
Web: WWW.PRINCETON.EDU

PRODUCTS/OPERATIONS

Select Councils Institutes and Centers

Bendheim Center for Finance
Center for Migration and Development
Center for the Study of Religion
Council of the Humanities
Council on Science and Technology
Davis Center for Historical Studies
James Madison Program in American Ideals and
Institutions
Lewis-Sigler Institute for Integrative Genomics
Liechtenstein Institute on Self-Determination
Princeton Environmental Institute (PEI)
Princeton Institute for International and Regional
Studies (PIIRS)
Princeton Institute for the Science and Technology of
Materials (PRISM)
Princeton Writing Program
Program of Freshman Seminars in the Residential
Colleges
Program in Law and Public Affairs
Program in Neuroscience
University Center for Human Values

COMPETITORS

Brown University	Harvard University
Columbia University	Penn
Cornell University	Rutgers University
Dartmouth	Yale University

HISTORICAL FINANCIALS

Company Type: Private

Income Statement				FYE: June 30
	REVENUE ($ mil.)	NET INCOME ($ mil.)	NET PROFIT MARGIN	EMPLOYEES
06/21	2,162	10,983	507.9%	6,000
06/20	2,173	383	17.7%	—
06/19	2,146	677	31.6%	—
06/18	2,012	2,582	128.3%	—
Annual Growth	2.4%	62.0%	—	—

2021 Year-End Financials

Return on assets: 24.7%
Return on equity: 27.8%
Current ratio: —
Cash ($ mil.): 37

THE TURNER CORPORATION

The Turner Corporation a subsidiary of German construction giant HOCHTIEF is the leading general building and construction management firm in the US (as ranked by Engineering News-Record) ahead of rivals Bechtel and Fluor. The firm operates primarily through subsidiary Turner Construction and has worked on notable projects such as Madison Square Garden the UN headquarters Yankee Stadium the Taipei 101 Tower and the 68000-seat open-air stadium for the San Francisco 49ers. Known for its large projects also offers services for midsized and smaller projects and provides interior construction and renovation services.

Operations

Turner works on more than 1500 projects in a year totaling $8 billion in volume. The group has divisions dedicated to serving the aviation health care biotechnology public assembly sports education justice and industrial sectors. Its homeland security group was established in order handle a growing demand for security systems and protection. The unit installed detection equipment in some 450 airports throughout the US. Turner Cor-

poration also has an arm specializing in green building with a focus on Leadership in Energy and Environmental Design (LEED) -certified projects. Turner Green Building has more than 400 LEED projects and green projects either completed or in progress.

Turner Corporation has subsidiaries providing auxiliary operations. Turner's risk management department offers contract review project safety and claims handling. Turner Logistics handles procurement and supply chain management for projects and Turner Facilities Management Solutions offers ongoing operations services. Also the Turner School of Construction Management provides training for local subcontractors.

Geographic Reach

Dallas-based Turner Corporation boasts a network of offices across the US (with most in California and Ohio) and Canada (Vancouver and Toronto) with an global presence in 20 countries in Europe Africa East Asia India Latin America and the Caribbean.

Sales and Marketing

Turner works on variety of projects from several sectors. It's known for its work in the categories of healthcare education offices commercial properties cultural facilities sports facilities and hotels. The company is also a leader in the green building category.

Strategy

With the construction market rebounding from the economic downturn Turner is looking to high-growth markets in the US and overseas. As of early 2015 it was working on more than 1900 projects 80% of which were Education Commercial or Interior project-related. Some of these projects included the 17000 sq. ft- interior remodel for Salesforce's Vancouver office; the 325000 sq. ft-construction of the LEED-Certified RAND Corporation Headquarters in Santa Monica California; and the 25000-seat Charlotte Coliseum event arena for the City of Charlotte North Carolina.

The company has also been making moves to expand its business abroad in recent years. In 2012 for example Turner partnered with one of India's largest real estate developers Sahara Prime City Ltd. to form Sahara Turner which would lead the development and construction of multiple townships across the country with an approximate value of $2.5 billion by 2017. It also purchased a majority stake in Clark Builders Canada to capitalize on the country's growing construction market.

Turner often partners with fellow US-based HOCHTIEF subsidiary Flatiron which specializes in civil engineering. Examples of the teamwork are the expansions of airports in San Diego and Sacramento.

HISTORY

At the turn of the century an engineer and devout Quaker named Henry Chandlee Turner was convinced that a new type of steel-reinforced concrete (called the Ransome system) would change the construction industry. With this conviction and with the help of his partner D. H. Dixon Turner bought the rights to the technology for $25000 and in 1902 founded Turner Construction Company.

One of the company's early projects was building the stairways for New York's first subway stations. As the Ransome method proved to be successful Turner's reputation grew. Defense contracts during WWI raised Turner's take to $35 million in 1918.

Before the Depression Turner was building high-rises hotels and stadiums. During the economic crash that started in 1929 the company survived by building retail stores churches and public buildings a strategy it would employ successfully in later recessions.

Henry Turner retired in 1941. His brother Archer Turner managed the company during most of the war effort. As WWII raged more than 80% of the company's work was defense-related. Projects included building and managing a submarine base in Oak Ridge Tennessee during the development of the atomic bomb.

In 1947 Henry C. Turner Jr. the founder's son became president and within four years he had led the company to more than $100 million in sales. By the time he stepped down as chairman in 1970 the firm had built skyscrapers futuristic airports and such landmarks as Madison Square Garden and the United Nations Secretariat and Plaza in New York City. Turner went public in 1969.

Howard S. Turner (the final family member to head the business) led the company during the 1970s. The company extended its global presence opening offices in more countries including Iran Pakistan and the United Arab Emirates. Turner also developed construction management services.

In 1984 The Turner Corporation was formed as a holding company for the construction company and the subsidiaries created or acquired as a result of diversification. Property development was one of these activities but by 1987 Turner had begun to dispose of its real estate holdings. It did not move quickly enough however and when the real estate market crashed Turner was caught with a large portfolio.

As commercial projects slowed Turner sought work in more sectors including public works and amusement projects (aquariums arenas hospitals and universities). By 1994 these areas accounted for 70% of business. In 1993 as the building slump continued Turner began a cost-cutting plan which included laying off workers and closing offices. That year the company set up an $8.5 million restructuring reserve and as the real estate market eased into recovery Turner sold more of its real estate holdings.

In 1996 Turner won a contract to build a 10000-seat arena in Salt Lake City to be used for the 2002 Winter Olympics. In 1997 Turner contracted to renovate 811 schools and build two campuses in California's San Fernando Valley and in 1998 it was chosen to manage the construction of the Kansas City Motor Speedway.

Profits were recovering quickly. Nonetheless in 1999 the company agreed to be acquired by German construction giant HOCHTIEF in a $370 million deal that ended Turner's joint venture with Switzerland's Karl Steiner. The company also relocated its corporate headquarters to Dallas that year to take advantage of the construction boom in the US Southwest.

In 2000 Turner created three new business groups to serve the aviation pharmaceutical and sports sectors. By the next year Turner's sports group was working on 17 projects. In 2001 the company was a member of the construction team that responded to the September 11 devastation at Ground Zero in New York City.

The next year the company celebrated its 100th anniversary with an exhibit at the National Building Museum in Washington DC; the exhibit featured drawings and photos of some of Turner's notable projects during the past century. In 2003 Turner Construction acquired the assets of Tompkins Builders the third-largest construction company in the Washington DC area from former rival J.A. Jones Construction Co.

Turner Construction which celebrated its 100th anniversary in 2002 has ranked among the leading general builders in the US since WWI. For 80 of the 100 years the group had a Turner among its senior executives. Howard S. Turner was the last member of the family to serve in the company's senior ranks. The company's appointment of Peter Davoren in 2003 as president of Turner Construc-

tion reflected the rise of a new generation of leaders for the unit. Davoren was additionally appointed chairman and CEO in 2007.

Turner Construction announced in 2008 that it had signed the contract on its 15000th major project.

EXECUTIVES

Pres-Chb-Ceo, Peter J Davoren
Sr V Pres-Cfo & Treas, Karen Gould
V Pres-Finance & Asst Treas, Don Oshiro
Attrny, Richard L Smith Jr
Svp, Turner, Thomas B Gerlach Jr
Project Engineer, Bernardo Lomeli
Superintendent, Austin Armstrong
Superintendent, Michael Depoortere
Project Engineer, Sam Padovano
Information Technology Manager, Bryan Vinci
Superintendant, James Smith
Auditors: DELOITTE & TOUCHE LLP PRINCET

LOCATIONS

HQ: THE TURNER CORPORATION
375 HUDSON ST RM 700, NEW YORK, NY 100143667
Phone: 212 229-6000
Web: WWW.TURNERCONSTRUCTION.COM

PRODUCTS/OPERATIONS

Selected Related Companies
E. E. Cruz (infrastructure)
Flatiron Construction Corp. (transportation construction civil engineering)
Clark Builders (51% Canada)

Selected Markets Served
Aviation
Commercial
Cultural and entertainment
Data center
Education
Government
Green building
Health care
Infrastructure
Industrial
Interiors
Pharmaceutical
Public Assembly
Religious
Research and development
Residential/hotel
Sports

Selected Services
Building information modeling
Building maintenance
Construction management
Design-build
Design-build/finance
Facilities management
General construction
Lean construction
Logistics
Medical planning and procurement
Preconstruction consulting
Program management
Project management

COMPETITORS

Balfour Beatty Construction	Hunt Construction
Bechtel	Imperial Construction Group
Clark Construction Group	Jacobs Engineering
Fluor	Parsons Corporation
Gilbane Building Company	Peter Kiewit Sons'
	Skanska
	Structure Tone

HISTORICAL FINANCIALS
Company Type: Private

Income Statement				FYE: December 31
	REVENUE ($ mil.)	NET INCOME ($ mil.)	NET PROFIT MARGIN	EMPLOYEES
12/15	10,523	107	1.0%	5,000
12/14	10,560	95	0.9%	—
12/13	9,522	80	0.8%	—
12/12	8,575	74	0.9%	—
Annual Growth	7.1%	12.9%	—	—

2015 Year-End Financials
Return on assets: 2.9%   Cash ($ mil.): 880
Return on equity: 16.5%
Current ratio: 1.00

THE UCLA FOUNDATION

Helping to make La-La Land a little more erudite The UCLA Foundation raises manages and disperses funds to help support the tripartite education research and service mission of UCLA. With more than $1 billion in assets the organization funds the aforementioned purposes as well as campus improvements and special programs. About half of the foundation's gifts received are provided by foundations; corporations and alumni each account for some 15% of gifts. The UCLA Progress Fund predecessor of the foundation was established in 1945 by the school's alumni association.

EXECUTIVES

Chairperson, Craig Ehrlich
Ex Dir, Peter Hayashida
Vp of Fin-Treas, Neal Axelrod
EXT Dir, Jocelyn Smith
Assistant Professor, Tara Young
Director Parent, Alexandra Price
Senior Executive Director Core, Amy Carpenter
Senior Director, Amy Lassere
Senior Art Director Marketing, Anthony Stella
Regional Director, Carrie Smith
Assistant Director State Rel G, Chaitanya Komanduri
Auditors: PRICEWATERHOUSECOOPERS LLP SA

LOCATIONS

HQ: THE UCLA FOUNDATION
10889 WILSHIRE BLVD # 11, LOS ANGELES, CA 900244201
Phone: 310 794-3193
Web: WWW.UCLAFOUNDATION.ORG

HISTORICAL FINANCIALS
Company Type: Private

Income Statement				FYE: June 30
	ASSETS ($ mil.)	NET INCOME ($ mil.)	INCOME AS % OF ASSETS	EMPLOYEES
06/18	3,539	336	9.5%	317
06/17	3,050	346	11.4%	—
Annual Growth	16.0%	(3.1%)	—	—

2018 Year-End Financials
Return on assets: 9.5%   Sales ($ mil): 691
Return on equity: 10.7%

THE UNITED ILLUMINATING COMPANY

EXECUTIVES

Pres-Ceo, James P Torgerson
Chb*, Nathaniel D Woodson
Pres-Coo*, Anthony J Vallillo
V Pres-Finance-Cfo*, Richard Nicholas
Vp-Info Tech/CIO*, W Marie Zanavich
Vp-Controller*, Steven P Favuzza
Engineer, Ramone Henry
Senior Analyst, Robert Torento
Customer Care Representative, Roberta Jones
Seniore Buyer Contractor, Theresa Terry
Customer Care Representative, Therese Garcia
Auditors: KPMG LLP STAMFORD CT

LOCATIONS

HQ: THE UNITED ILLUMINATING COMPANY
180 MARSH HILL RD, ORANGE, CT 064773629
Phone: 203 499-2000
Web: WWW.UINET.COM

HISTORICAL FINANCIALS

Company Type: Private

Income Statement   FYE: December 31

	REVENUE ($ mil.)	NET INCOME ($ mil.)	NET PROFIT MARGIN	EMPLOYEES
12/17	921	105	11.4%	920
12/16*	866	84	9.7%	—
06/00	344	34	10.0%	—
Annual Growth	5.6%	6.4%	—	—

*Fiscal year change

THE UNIVERSITY OF CENTRAL FLORIDA BOARD OF TRUSTEES

The University of Central Florida (UCF whose mascot is a stylized knight) is part of the State University System of Florida. Boasting an enrollment of more than 69000 students UCF offers more than 220 degree programs through a dozen colleges. Areas of study include psychology health sciences biomedical sciences nursing computer science mechanical engineering biology integrated business finance and hospitality management. In addition to its main campus UCF operates more than a dozen locations throughout Central Florida.

Operations

The University offers about a hundred bachelor's 90 master's around 30 research doctorates three professional doctorates and three specialist degree programs. The university's research programs annually attract more than $192 million in funding.

In addition to more traditional areas of study the university also boasts the Florida Interactive Entertainment Academy where graduate students learn video-game development including art pro-

gramming and production. The academy is funded jointly by the State of Florida and UCF.

Geographic Reach

UCF is located on a 1400-acre campus in Orlando. Through its main campus and its satellite locations UCF serves around a dozen of county service areas including Brevard Citrus Flagler Indian River Lake Levy Marion Orange Osceola Polk Seminole Sumter and Volusia. Its students hail from all 50 US states and nearly 150 international countries. The university also conducts study abroad programs in about 35 countries.

Strategy

UCF leverages innovative learning discovery and partnerships fostering social mobility while developing the skilled talent needed to advance industry for its region state and beyond.

The university partnered with Adobe in late 2020. UCF specifically is working with Adobe on a digital reading project that aims to reduce information overload. The project is part of Adobe's continuing efforts toward creating products that empower people to change the world such as its recent collaboration with a UCF-spin-off the non-profit Limbitless Solutions Inc.

UCF has also added a new physical therapy program solely focused on pain. The 12-week summer course debuted in 2019 and teaches students about the physical psychological and social aspects of pain management. The course helps students apply and understand the new overall wellness model of patient care. UCF also added a new hybrid-class format called BlendFlex. The new class strategy includes some face-to-face and online components and has been added to the lineup of fully online and face-to-face classes.

Company Background

The school was founded in 1963 as Florida Technological University and held its first classes five years later. UCF changed its name to the current moniker in 1978.

EXECUTIVES

Chb, Beverly Seay
V Chm, Alex Martins
Vp Marketing, Communications,, Thomas Huddleston Jr
Coordinator, Jennifer Le
Assistant Professor, Michael Leuenberger
Coordinator, Shannon M O'Donoghue
Assistant Professor, Honghui N Chen
Scientist, Jeanette Nadeau
Assistant Professor, Libby W Cowgill
Assistant Professor, Maysoun D Masri
Associate Professor, Winston V Schoenfeld
Auditors: SHERRILL F NORMAN CPA TALLA

LOCATIONS

HQ: THE UNIVERSITY OF CENTRAL FLORIDA BOARD OF TRUSTEES
4000 CENTRAL FLORIDA BLVD, ORLANDO, FL 328168005
Phone: 407 823-2000
Web: WWW.UCF.EDU

PRODUCTS/OPERATIONS

Selected Colleges and Schools
Burnett Honors College
College of Arts and Humanities
College of Business Administration
College of Education
College of Engineering and Computer Science
College of Graduate Studies
College of Health and Public Affairs
College of Medicine
College of Nursing
College of Optics and Photonics
College of Sciences
Interdisciplinary Studies
Rosen College of Hospitality Management

HISTORICAL FINANCIALS

Company Type: Private

Income Statement   FYE: June 30

	REVENUE ($ mil.)	NET INCOME ($ mil.)	NET PROFIT MARGIN	EMPLOYEES
06/19	558	89	16.0%	6,500
06/08	374	108	28.9%	—
06/07	382	152	40.0%	—
06/06	311	61	19.6%	—
Annual Growth	4.6%	3.0%	—	—

2019 Year-End Financials

Return on assets: 4.1%   Cash ($ mil.): 6
Return on equity: 7.5%
Current ratio: 4.20

THE UNIVERSITY OF CHICAGO MEDICAL CENTER

The University of Chicago Medical Center (UCMC) is a complex of facilities located on The University of Chicago campus that include the acute care Mitchell Hospital - Hyde Park campus the Comer Children's Hospital a women's health and maternity facility and an outpatient care center. Established in 1927 (and dedicated on Halloween of that year) the complex includes the affiliated University of Chicago Pritzker School of Medicine and forms the clinical arm of The University of Chicago Division of Biological Sciences. UCMC houses about 810 beds.

Operations

Its Bernard A. Mitchell Hospital is home to a variety of specialty care including our post-natal mother-baby unit advanced imaging services physical therapy services and in-patient units. Other amenities include wireless internet a chapel an on-site restaurant and a gift shop. The more than 170-bed Comer Children's Hospital offers disease care education and research as well as expanded newborn intensive care services.

UCMC sees some 32710 hospital admissions and about 106640 emergency room visits per year. The hospital is one of the largest providers of uncompensated care in Illinois providing millions of dollars in charity care every year.

As part of the university's Biological Sciences division UCMC operates medical research centers focused on cancer immunology diabetes cardiology and neurology. The cancer center is especially intent on discovering improved treatment and prevention measures using gene and protein-based treatments. The Gwen and Jules Knapp Center for Biomedical Discovery works on discovery programs for a variety of medical conditions including diabetes cancer and pediatrics.

Overall patient service accounts for around 80% of revenue.

Geographic Reach

UCMC is located in Hyde Park on the south side of Chicago. Its main medical campus includes the Center for Care and Discovery Comer Children's Hospital Bernard A. Mitchell Hospital Chicago Lying-in Hospital and Duchossois Center for Advanced Medicine. UCMC also manages a network of area physicians and specialty clinics located in Chicago and its suburbs.

Its corporate headquarters is located in Chicago Illinois.

Financial Performance

In 2020 the company had a total operating revenue of $2.5 billion a 7% increase from the previous year. This was mainly due to a higher other operating revenues and net assets released from restrictions used for operating purposes for the year.

The company's cash at the end of 2020 was $538.7 million. Operating activities generated $586.8 million while investing activities used $125.1 million mainly for purchases of investments. Financing activities used another $97.1 million primarily for additional repayment of long-term debt.

Company Background

The University of Chicago was founded in 1890 and expanded into medicine in 1898. Under then-University President William Rainey Harper the University of Chicago temporarily became affiliated with the Rush Medical College with "the distinct purpose" of establishing a medical school when funds became available according to Harper's Decennial address in 1902.

In 1916 the University of Chicago Board of Trustees set aside $5.3 million for construction equipment and an endowment for an expansion into health care. However World War I put a halt to the development. The project resumed in 1921 eventually reaching completion in 1927. By that time costs had skyrocketed to nearly five times the original estimate.

EXECUTIVES

Ceo, James L Maderd
Pres, Thomas E Jackiewicz
Pres, David Hesner
V Pres, Susan Sher
Director, James Hamaguchi
Doctor, Jeffrey Gossett
Vice President of Supply Chain, Jonathan Stegner
Doctor, Kevin Roggin
Director, Mark Fehlberg
Professor, Nathan Tarcov
Director, Susan Huie
Auditors: KPMG LLP CHICAGO ILLINOIS

LOCATIONS

HQ: THE UNIVERSITY OF CHICAGO MEDICAL CENTER
5841 S MARYLAND AVE, CHICAGO, IL 606371443
Phone: 773 702-1000
Web: WWW.UCHICAGOMEDICINE.ORG

PRODUCTS/OPERATIONS

Selected Services

Cancer
Endocrinology
Gastroenterology
Geriatrics
Heart
Kidney disease
Neurosciences
Orthopaedics
Respiratory disease
Surgery
Transplantation
Women's services

Selected Facilities

Bernard A. Mitchell Hospital
Center for Care and Discovery
Chicago Lying-in Hospital (Maternity and Women's Hospital)
Comer Children's Hospital
Duchossois Center for Advanced Medicine (outpatient care and diagnostics)
Gwen and Jules Knapp Center for Biomedical Discovery

LaRabida Children's Hospital (affiliated facility)
Mercy Hospital (affiliated facility)
University of Chicago Pritzker School of Medicine
Weiss Memorial Hospital (affiliated facility)

COMPETITORS

Advocate Health Care
Alexian Brothers Health System
Covenant Ministries
Elmhurst Memorial Healthcare
Loyola University Health System
Mercy Hospital And Medical Center
Northshore University Healthsystem
Northwest Community Healthcare
Northwestern Memorial Healthcare
Rush System For Health
Silver Cross Hospital
Sinai Health System
St. Bernard Hospital And Health Care Center

HISTORICAL FINANCIALS

Company Type: Private

Income Statement — FYE: June 30

	REVENUE ($ mil.)	NET INCOME ($ mil.)	NET PROFIT MARGIN	EMPLOYEES
06/21	2,789	519	18.6%	9,346
06/20	2,547	(53)	—	
06/19	2,387	27	1.2%	
06/18	2,212	49	2.2%	
Annual Growth	8.0%	119.2%	—	—

2021 Year-End Financials

Return on assets: 11.5%
Return on equity: 22.4%
Current ratio: 1.30
Cash ($ mil.): 184

THE UNIVERSITY OF DAYTON

More than 11600 students make the University of Dayton one of the nation's largest Catholic universities and the largest private university in Ohio. The institution offers more than 80 undergraduate and 50 graduate and doctoral programs. Students are recruited on a national basis and from foreign countries. The student population more than 8300 undergraduate and more than 3000 graduate students. It has a student-to-faculty ratio of 14:1. Well-known alumni include the late author and columnist Erma Bombeck and Super Bowl-winning NFL coaches Jon Gruden and Chuck Noll.

Operations

The university academic units include College of Arts and Sciences School of Business Administration School of Education and Health Sciences School of Engineering and School of Law. Its program has included accounting aerospace engineering art history biochemistry biology chemistry communication economics finance and music.

Geographic Reach

The university is located in Dayton Ohio.

Strategy

Partnerships and Exchanges seeks builds and maintains relationships with institutions and organizations all over the world for the purpose of increasing direct global opportunities for UD faculty staff students and partners abroad. Partnerships and Exchanges support activities that include education abroad programs joint international research dual degree agreements faculty mobility to

teach and achieve professional development and other special enrollment programs.

Company Background

The University of Dayton was founded in 1850 by the Society of Mary (the Marianists).

EXECUTIVES

Pres-Ceo, Dr Daniel J Curran
Assistant Vice President, New, Wiggins Med
Coordinator, Morgan Wagner
Coordinator, Patrick Czupik
E-Business Point of Contact, Linda Young
Attorney, Retired, Laurence Wohl
Scientist, Wayne A Rubey
Executive Officer, Fred Pestello
Scientist, Gary Miller
Staff, Josh Haworth
Dean, School of Engineering, Tony E Saliba
Auditors: RSM US LLP DAYTON OHIO

LOCATIONS

HQ: THE UNIVERSITY OF DAYTON
300 COLLEGE PARK AVE, DAYTON, OH 454690002
Phone: 937 229-2919
Web: WWW.UDAYTON.EDU

HISTORICAL FINANCIALS

Company Type: Private

Income Statement — FYE: June 30

	REVENUE ($ mil.)	NET INCOME ($ mil.)	NET PROFIT MARGIN	EMPLOYEES
06/20	747	29	4.0%	4,500
06/19	774	30	4.0%	
06/16	521	(11)	—	
Annual Growth	9.4%	—	—	—

2020 Year-End Financials

Return on assets: 1.7%
Return on equity: 2.4%
Current ratio: 0.50
Cash ($ mil.): 69

THE UNIVERSITY OF IOWA

EXECUTIVES

V Pres, Marty Scholtz
Assistant Professor, Adam Ward
Oral and Maxillofacial Surgeon, Emma Cole
Oral and Maxillofacial Surgeon, Grace Chabal
Scientist, Youhua Tang
Assistant Professor, Megan Gilster
Project Coordinator, Nick Benson
Executive Officer, Nitin Karandikar
Assistant Professor, Phuong Nguyen
Assistant Professor, Shea Brown
Assistant Professor, Hai Fu
Auditors: MARLYS K GASTON CPA DES MOI

LOCATIONS

HQ: THE UNIVERSITY OF IOWA
2660 UCC, IOWA CITY, IA 52242
Phone: 319 335-2119
Web: WWW.UIOWA.EDU

HISTORICAL FINANCIALS
Company Type: Private

Income Statement				FYE: June 30
	REVENUE ($ mil.)	NET INCOME ($ mil.)	NET PROFIT MARGIN	EMPLOYEES
06/20	3,451	203	5.9%	29
06/18	3,176	588	18.5%	—
06/17	2,950	144	4.9%	—
Annual Growth	5.4%	12.3%	—	—

2020 Year-End Financials
Return on assets: 2.5%
Return on equity: 4.3%
Current ratio: 1.20

Cash ($ mil.): 159

THE UNIVERSITY OF IOWA

The University of Iowa is one of the state's largest university. Founded in 1847 the University of Iowa has some 31730 students (and a student-faculty ratio of approximately 15:1) at its Iowa City campus. It is home to a dozen colleges spanning more than 200 areas of study including distinguished programs in physics astronomy speech and hearing sciences nursing and creative writing. Its Writers' Workshop was the nation's first creative writing advanced degree program. It also includes programs in law engineering teaching and medicine as well as the affiliated University of Iowa Hospitals and Clinics health care organization.

Operations
University of Iowa comprises a dozen schools the largest being the undergraduate College of Liberal Arts and Sciences. Other undergraduates enroll in schools of business medicine education law engineering nursing and pharmacy while the dentistry public health and graduate schools provide graduate education programs.

It generates more than 65% of total sales from patient services and also small amount from tuition and fees grants contracts auxiliary enterprises and sales and services of educational departments.

Geographic Reach
University of Iowa is located in Iowa City Iowa.

Financial Performance
The company's revenue for 2020 totaled $3.5 million a 1% increase from the previous year's revenue of $3.4 billion. This was mainly due to the higher amount of patient services net of allowances as well as a higher volume of grants and contracts for the year.

The university's cash at the end of 2020 was $238 million. Operating activities generated $1.1 billion while financing activities used $483 million mainly for acquisition and construction of financial assets as well as debt payments. Investing activities provided another $1.0 billion.

Company Background
Among the University of Iowa's notable alumni are Al Jarreau John Irving Flannery O'Connor Gene Wilder and Tennessee Williams.

EXECUTIVES
Pres, Bruce Harreld
SEC-Dir, Susan Klatt
Evp-Provost, Kevin Kregel
Assistant Professor, Chris Cheatum
Assistant Professor, Nicole M Esposito
Assistant Professor, Sarah Kanouse
Project Coordinator, Amy Bowes
Assistant Vice President of ME, Jennifer Vermeer
Controller, Selina Martin
Coordinator, Amy Baumgartner
Coordinator, Anne Sparks
Auditors: MARLYS K GASTON CPA DES MOI

LOCATIONS
HQ: THE UNIVERSITY OF IOWA
125 N MADISON ST, IOWA CITY, IA 52242
Phone: 319 335-3500
Web: WWW.UIOWA.EDU

PRODUCTS/OPERATIONS

Selected Colleges
College of Dentistry
College of Education
College of Engineering
College of Law
College of Liberal Arts and Sciences
College of Nursing
College of Pharmacy
College of Public Health
Graduate College
Henry B. Tippie College of Business
Roy J. and Lucille A. Carver College of Medicine

HISTORICAL FINANCIALS
Company Type: Private

Income Statement				FYE: June 30
	REVENUE ($ mil.)	NET INCOME ($ mil.)	NET PROFIT MARGIN	EMPLOYEES
06/16	2,859	253	8.9%	17,000
06/11	2,067	253	12.3%	—
06/08	1,684	150	8.9%	—
Annual Growth	6.8%	6.8%	—	—

2016 Year-End Financials
Return on assets: 4.0%
Return on equity: 6.3%
Current ratio: 1.20

Cash ($ mil.): 144

THE UNIVERSITY OF KANSAS HOSPITAL AUTHORITY

EXECUTIVES
Ceo, Bob Page
Prin, Angela Cook
Pediatric Urologist, J Pat Murphy
Chief of Medicine, Bart McCann
Principal, Linsey Gregory
Internal Medicine Practitioner, Ahmad Tarakji
Neurology Specialist, Bhavana Patel
Internal Medicine Practitioner, Calvin Madrigal
Internal Medicine Practitioner, Donald Campbell Jr
Anesthesiologist, Nicholas Kaup
Anesthesiologist, Nicolas Patonai

LOCATIONS
HQ: THE UNIVERSITY OF KANSAS HOSPITAL AUTHORITY
4000 CAMBRIDGE ST, KANSAS CITY, KS 661608501
Phone: 913 588-5000
Web: WWW.KUMC.EDU

HISTORICAL FINANCIALS
Company Type: Private

Income Statement				FYE: June 30
	REVENUE ($ mil.)	NET INCOME ($ mil.)	NET PROFIT MARGIN	EMPLOYEES
06/15	1,362	156	11.5%	40
06/02	321	6	2.0%	—
Annual Growth	11.8%	28.1%	—	—

2015 Year-End Financials
Return on assets: 9.4%
Return on equity: 17.3%
Current ratio: 2.00

Cash ($ mil.): 140

THE UNIVERSITY OF NORTH CAROLINA

Tar heels can sink their feet into academia and athletics at The University of North Carolina. The system of 17 universities including the flagship University of North Carolina at Chapel Hill campus counts more than 220000 undergraduate and graduate students across its campuses. It offers degrees in more than 200 disciplines. The university system chartered in 1789 is home to medical schools a teaching hospital law schools a veterinary school at NC State a school of pharmacy nursing programs schools of education schools of engineering and a school for the arts. In addition the system also operates the NC School of Science and Mathematics a public residential high school for gifted students.

Operations
The university system comprises 17 public institutions that grant baccalaureate degrees. It also operates a public residential high school for gifted students under the name NC School of Science and Mathematics.

Each year the university graduates more than 30000 students.

Geographic Reach
The University of North Carolina system serves students worldwide. Of its enrollment the system attracts far more in-state students than out-of-state students.

Financial Performance
Revenue for fiscal 2014 was $1.9 billion.

Strategy
To extend its reach The University of North Carolina partners with half a dozen affiliates. They include UNC Center for Public Television The North Carolina Arboretum The North Carolina State Approving Agency The North Carolina Center for International Understanding The North Carolina State Education Assistance Authority and The University of North Carolina Press.

In 2013 the system adopted a five-year strategic plan entitled "Our Time Our Future." The plan's goals were designed to set priorities allocate resources plan programs and refine academic missions.

EXECUTIVES
Ceo, L Lee Isley
Pres*, Peter Hans
Cfo*, Charles Perusse
Chm*, Randy Ramsey
V-Chm*, Wendy Murphy
Sr V Pres*, Junius Gonzales

Adjunct Professor, John Staley
Ace Fellow, Linda Bennett
Federal Relations Assistant, Maggie Blunk
Purchasing Manager, Melaina Hall
Human Resources, Nancy Maltais

LOCATIONS

HQ: THE UNIVERSITY OF NORTH CAROLINA
910 RALEIGH RD, CHAPEL HILL, NC 275143916
Phone: 919 962-2211
Web: WWW.NORTHCAROLINA.EDU

PRODUCTS/OPERATIONS

Selected Institutions
Appalachian State University
East Carolina University
Elizabeth City State University
Fayetteville State University
NC A&T State University
North Carolina Central University
NC State University
UNC Asheville
UNC Chapel Hill
UNC Charlotte
UNC Greensboro
UNC Pembroke
UNC Wilmington
UNC School of the Arts
Western Carolina University
Winston-Salem State University
NC School of Science and Mathematics

HISTORICAL FINANCIALS

Company Type: Private

Income Statement				FYE: June 30
	REVENUE ($ mil.)	NET INCOME ($ mil.)	NET PROFIT MARGIN	EMPLOYEES
06/13	1,838	267	14.6%	55,000
06/12	0	(0)	—	—
06/06	30	(9)	—	—
Annual Growth 79.3%		—	—	—

2013 Year-End Financials

Return on assets: 3.3%   Cash ($ mil.): 520
Return on equity: 5.9%
Current ratio: 5.00

THE UNIVERSITY OF TEXAS HEALTH SCIENCE CENTER AT SAN ANTONIO

EXECUTIVES

Pres*, William L Henrich
Exec V Pres*, Steven A Wartman
Sr V Pres*, Michael E Black
Prin*, Mary G Delay
Endocrinology, Chris Mc Daniel
Thoracic Surgeon, Sreenath V Reddy
Assistant Professor, Jason Morrow
Project Coordinator, Sharon Bressette
Assistant Professor, Beth Thai
Assistant Professor, Sandeep Patel
Assistant Professor, Cristina Boccalandro

LOCATIONS

HQ: THE UNIVERSITY OF TEXAS HEALTH SCIENCE
CENTER AT SAN ANTONIO
7703 FLOYD CURL DR, SAN ANTONIO, TX 782293901
Phone: 210 567-7000
Web: WWW.UTHSCSA.EDU

HISTORICAL FINANCIALS

Company Type: Private

Income Statement				FYE: August 31
	REVENUE ($ mil.)	NET INCOME ($ mil.)	NET PROFIT MARGIN	EMPLOYEES
08/11	767	62	8.2%	4,000
08/05	289	56	19.6%	—
08/04	289	56	19.6%	—
Annual Growth 15.0%		1.5%	—	—

2011 Year-End Financials

Return on assets: 4.3%   Cash ($ mil.): 99
Return on equity: 4.9%
Current ratio: 1.60

THE UNIVERSITY OF TOLEDO

One of Ohio's 14 state universities The University of Toledo (UT) is the third-largest by operating budget. It enrolls more than 20200 students and offers more than 270 programs of study including master's degree and doctoral programs. The university has a student-to-faculty ratio of 19:1. Its about 15 colleges focus on subjects ranging from visual and performing arts to business and innovation as well as education engineering law medicine nursing pharmacy languages and chemistry. The school also operates the University of Toledo Medical Center.

Operations

The University of Toledo Medical Center affiliated with UT provides advanced care and healing in a patient-centered environment. It has access to the latest clinical trials and medical research and committed to teaching the next generation of health-care professionals.

The UT Medical Center features a Level I trauma center and extensive medical training programs on UT's Health Science Campus. It provides treatments for strokes and cancer that are unique within the state. Other specialties include kidney transplants and cardiology.

Geographic Reach

UT students come from more than 40 US states and about 85 international countries. The school has an extensive distance learning program. In addition to the main campus in Toledo UT operates several satellite centers in Toledo (including the Health Science Campus the Scott Park Campus and the Center for the Visual Arts facility) and the Lake Erie Research and Education Center in Oregon Ohio.

Financial Performance
Strategy

UT continues to work on its five-year strategic plan that ends in 2022 which includes promoting student success and academic excellence; improving research scholarship and creative activities; taking care of faculty staff and alumni; and improving the university's fiscal positioning and infrastructure among others.

Company Background

UT and the Medical University of Ohio merged in 2006. UT is accredited by the Higher Learning Commission of the North Central Association of Colleges and Schools.

UT was established in 1872 and became a member of the state university system in 1967.

EXECUTIVES

Pres, Gregory Postel
Cno, Norma Tomlinson
Coordinator, Debbra L Kraftchick
Director, Jim Ferris
Associate Professor, Anthony D Johnson
Dean, College of Communication, Debra A Davis
Coordinator, Tamara L Phares
Coordinator, Joseph D Drees
Assistant Vice President Enrol, Steve Schissler
Secretary 1 Nursing Advertisin, Nora Longsworth
Librarian Associate, Rodney Lambdin
Auditors: CLIFTONLARSONALLEN LLP
TOLEDO

LOCATIONS

HQ: THE UNIVERSITY OF TOLEDO
2801 W BANCROFT ST, TOLEDO, OH 436063390
Phone: 419 530-4636
Web: WWW.UTOLEDO.EDU

HISTORICAL FINANCIALS

Company Type: Private

Income Statement				FYE: June 30
	REVENUE ($ mil.)	NET INCOME ($ mil.)	NET PROFIT MARGIN	EMPLOYEES
06/18	716	55	7.8%	7,000
06/17	728	(62)	—	—
Annual Growth (1.6%)		—	—	—

2018 Year-End Financials

Return on assets: 4.7%   Cash ($ mil.): 40
Return on equity: 176.9%
Current ratio: 1.20

THE UNIVERSITY OF UTAH

The University of Utah (U of U) is the state's oldest and most comprehensive institution of higher education and is the flagship institution of the state system of higher education. Founded in 1850 as the University of Deseret the U of U has a total enrollment of more than 34000 undergraduate and graduate students with a student-to-faculty ratio of some 17:1. It offers over 100 major subjects at the undergraduate and graduate level at about 20 colleges and schools; its business science humanities and engineering departments are the university's largest. It also offers medical nursing and pharmacy programs as well as health and social science research programs. U of U confers nearly 8950 baccalaureate masters and doctoral degrees annually.

Operations

The university includes an academic health system University of Utah Health Care which includes the U of U School of Medicine and the University of Utah Hospitals and Clinics. The University of Utah School of Medicine combines teaching research and clinical expertise to train future physicians for the rapidly changing world of medicine.

With a faculty of more than 1000 physicians and researchers and more than 20 clinical and basic science departments the School of Medicine trains the majority of Utah physicians MD degrees physician assistant training residencies fellowship specialty training degrees in public health degrees in medical laboratory science and science and research. U of U also includes institutes that conduct research programs in a variety of fields ? including health math fine arts and engineering ? as well as technology commercialization projects.

Nearly 55% of total sales were generated from patient services about 25% from sales and services approximately 10% of sales from grants and contracts and the remainder came from tuition and fees and auxiliary.

Geographic Reach

The 1500 acre campus is located along the foothills of the Wasatch Mountains the westernmost branch of the Rockies overlooking Salt Lake City. U of U's international students hail from more than 130 countries which some are from Latin American Bosnian Pacific Islander and Sri Lankan communities.

Financial Performance

In 2021 the university's total operating revenue for the year was $4.1 billion. The university's net position was $851.7 million.

The university's cash at the end of 2021 was $2.1 billion. Operating activities used $59.2 million. Investing activities used another $27.3 billion.

Strategy

The University diversifies assets among several investment managers of varying investment strategies. Diversification is an effective means of maximizing return while mitigating risk. In mid-2021 the University held more than 5% of its total investments in the Federal Home Loan Bank and the Federal Agricultural Mortgage Corporation. These investments represent 5.5% and 5.2% respectively of the University's total investments.

EXECUTIVES

Pres, Taylor Randall
Cso*, Marlon Lynch
Staff Phased Retiree, Senior V, Susan Dean
Information Specialist, Todd Prins
Accounting Staff, Christine Connors
Assistant Professor, Bradley Greger
Assistant Professor, Kristen L Carroll
Assistant Professor, Michael Moats
Assistant Professor, Shay R Bess
Digital & Social Media Special, Linda Aagard
Professor, Mike S Mike
Auditors: OFFICE OF THE UTAH STATE AUDIT

LOCATIONS

HQ: THE UNIVERSITY OF UTAH
201 PRESIDENTS CIR, SALT LAKE CITY, UT
841129049
Phone: 801 581-7200
Web: WWW.UTAH.EDU

PRODUCTS/OPERATIONS

2015 Sales

	$ mil.	% of total
Patient services net	1,816	53
Sales and services	740	21
Grants and contracts	362	10
Tuition and fees net	304	9
Auxiliary and other	237	7
Total	**3,460**	**100**

Selected Colleges

College of Architecture and Planning
College of Education
College of Engineering
College of Fine Arts
College of Health
College of Humanities

College of Law
College of Mines and Earth Sciences
College of Nursing
College of Pharmacy
College of Science
College of Social and Behavioral Sciences
College of Social Work
David Eccles School of Business
Graduate School
Honors College
School of Medicine

HISTORICAL FINANCIALS
Company Type: Private

Income Statement

FYE: June 30

	REVENUE ($ mil.)	NET INCOME ($ mil.)	NET PROFIT MARGIN	EMPLOYEES
06/13*	2,907	186	6.4%	18,000
12/08	0	0	—	—
06/08	22	(10)	—	—
Annual Growth	**164.4%**	—	—	—

*Fiscal year change

2013 Year-End Financials

Return on assets: 3.7%   Cash ($ mil.): 486
Return on equity: 4.8%
Current ratio: 3.60

THE UNIVERSITY OF VERMONT MEDICAL CENTER INC

The University of Vermont Medical Center (formerly Fletcher Allen Health Care) provides medical care in the Green Mountain State. The company operates an academic medical center in alliance with the University of Vermont College of Medicine. The not-for-profit health system serves residents of Vermont and northern New York through three primary hospital campuses in Chittenden County Vermont over 65 outpatient practices and 100-plus clinics programs and services. UVM Medical Center is Vermont's only Level 1 Trauma Center with the state's sole Neonatal Intensive Care Unit.

Operations

UVM Medical Center is part of an integrated health network across Vermont and northern New York that includes its UVM Health Network partners: UVM Health Network - Central Vermont Medical Center (Berlin VT) UVM Health Network - Champlain Valley Physicians Hospital (Plattsburgh NY) UVM Health Network - Elizabethtown Community Hospital (Elizabethtown NY) UVM Health Network - Alice Hyde Medical Center (Malone NY) UVM Health Network - Porter Medical Center (Middlebury VT) the UVM Health Network Medical Group and Home Health & Hospice (formerly the Visiting Nurse Association of Chittenden and Grand Isle counties). It also maintains affiliation with Canton-Potsdam Hospital (Potsdam NY) and Inter-Lakes Health (Ticonderoga NY).

The UVM Medical Center in alliance with the University of Vermont College of Medicine is Vermont's academic medical center and one of approximately 130 centers in the country.

Geographic Reach

UVM Medical Center serves 1 million people who live in Vermont and Northern New York.

Company Background

The hospital system was created through the 1995 merger of the Fanny Allen Hospital (which opened in 1894) the Medical Center Hospital of Vermont (or Mary Fletcher Hospital founded in 1876) and the University Health Center (formed in 1971). The hospitals are now known as Fanny Allen Campus Medical Center Campus and UHC Campus.

Fletcher Allen Health Care completed the implementation of an electronic health records (EHR) system that connects patient records at all of its facilities in 2010.

EXECUTIVES

Ceo, John R Brumsted
Ceo*, John R Brumssted
Cfo*, Todd Keating
Sr V Pres*, Theresa Alberghini Dipalma
Chief Officer*, Stephen Leffler
C-Level Human Resources, Paul Macuga
Chief Information Offi, Adam P Buckley
Ophthalmologist, Robert H Millay
Optometrists, Brian Hanlon
Provost and Senior Vice Presid, David Rosowsky
Ophthalmologist, Stephen Pecsenyicki
Auditors: PRICEWATERHOUSECOOPERS LLP BO

LOCATIONS

HQ: THE UNIVERSITY OF VERMONT MEDICAL
CENTER INC
111 COLCHESTER AVE, BURLINGTON, VT 054011473
Phone: 802 847-0000
Web: WWW.UVMHEALTH.ORG

PRODUCTS/OPERATIONS

Selected Services

Cancer Care
Heart & Vascular
Orthopedics
Primary Care
Urgent Care
Women's Health

COMPETITORS

Albany Medical Center	Rutland Regional
Ellis Hospital	Medical Center
New England Alliance	Southwestern Vermont
For Health	Health Care
Newyork-presbyterian	Springfield Hospital
Healthcare	St. Peter's Health
Northwell Health	Partners

HISTORICAL FINANCIALS
Company Type: Private

Income Statement

FYE: September 30

	REVENUE ($ mil.)	NET INCOME ($ mil.)	NET PROFIT MARGIN	EMPLOYEES
09/18	1,363	68	5.1%	7,000
09/17	1,246	129	10.4%	—
09/16	1,181	85	7.2%	—
Annual Growth	**7.4%**	**(10.0%)**	—	—

2018 Year-End Financials

Return on assets: 4.1%   Cash ($ mil.): 144
Return on equity: 7.1%
Current ratio: 2.00

THE UNIVERSITY OF VIRGINIA

EXECUTIVES

Pres, Lindsay H Kidd
Cardiologist, Michael Ragosta
Assistant Professor, Brian Pusser
Director, David Bearinger
Senior Human Resources, Donna Kauffman
Doctor, Robert A Sinkin
Associate Professor, Emad Abdelrahman
Assistant Professor, Sara Dexter
Professor, Zhenqi Liu
Doctor, Brian W Behm
Doctor, Christopher C Moore

LOCATIONS

HQ: THE UNIVERSITY OF VIRGINIA
1215 LEE ST, CHARLOTTESVILLE, VA 229080816
Phone: 434 924-0000
Web: WWW.VIRGINIA.EDU

HISTORICAL FINANCIALS

Company Type: Private

Income Statement				FYE: June 30
	REVENUE ($ mil.)	NET INCOME ($ mil.)	NET PROFIT MARGIN	EMPLOYEES
06/19	2,915	350	12.0%	447
06/18	2,788	544	19.5%	—
Annual Growth	4.5%	(35.6%)	—	—

2019 Year-End Financials

Return on assets: 2.7%   Cash ($ mil.): 149
Return on equity: 3.9%
Current ratio: 1.00

THE VALLEY HOSPITAL INC

The Valley Hospital is second to none when it comes to its Same-Day Service program. More than one-third of the company's annual patients experience its longstanding continuum of one-day service; fully half the surgeries performed are same-day. The not-for-profit hospital is a 450-bed facility providing general and emergency services to residents of New Jersey's Bergen County. The hospital belongs to the Valley Health System which also includes subsidiaries Valley Home Care and Valley Health Medical Group and is an affiliate member of NewYork-Presbyterian Healthcare. The Valley Hospital New Jersey's second busiest has more than 800 physicians on its medical staff.

Operations

The Valley Hospital is well known for its cardiology cancer maternity and neonatal care programs (including its neonatal ICU). Its key services also include emergency care orthopedics and neurosciences. The hospital's emergency department treated more than 75000 patients in 2013. That year the hospital also admitted more than 49240 patients and the delivered almost 3200 babies.

The Valley Hospital's cardiac service includes a full range of diagnostic and interventional cardiac treatment services including cardiac surgery coronary angioplasty and electrophysiology studies.

The hospital is also known for its work in lung cancer diagnosis and treatment radiation oncology (including tomotherapy) chemotherapy and infusion GYN oncology prostate cancer care and other clinical and support services.

Geographic Reach

The hospital serves more than 440000 people in 32 towns in Bergen County and surrounding communities.

Strategy

The medical system is looking to improve its facilities and technology in order to keep up with demand. The Valley Hospital is the first and only hospital in northern New Jersey to offer brain and spinal surgery with a state-of-the-art O-arm® surgical imaging system purchased through a $1 million grant from The Bolger Foundation.

In 2012 The Valley Hospital Valley became the first hospital in northern New Jersey to offer the latest breast imaging technology — 3D breast tomosynthesis.

That year it also enhanced its capacity to perform minimally invasive surgery with the acquisition of the robotic da Vinci® Surgical System funded by a $1.6 million donation from The Bolger Foundation.

In 2012 the hospital opened a new Women's and Children's Resource Center to coordinate wide range of services for women and their families.

EXECUTIVES

Pres, Audrey Meyers
V Pres*, Richard Keenan
SEC*, Cathy Follten
Accountant, Junwen Pan
Director, Brad Haspel
Coordinator, Deb Rath
Radiation Oncology, Deborah Panetta
Director of Pharmacy, Ron Krych
Patient Account Manager, Joyce Parshall
Nurse Manager, Kathleen McKenna
Phamacy Manager, Carlo Lupano

LOCATIONS

HQ: THE VALLEY HOSPITAL INC
223 N VAN DIEN AVE, RIDGEWOOD, NJ 074502736
Phone: 201 447-8000
Web: WWW.VALLEYHEALTH.COM

PRODUCTS/OPERATIONS

Selected Services
Adoption Screening and Evaluation Program
Ambulatory Infusion Center
Anticoagulation Management Service
Autism Services
Auxiliary
Barrett's Esophagus Center
Bariatric Surgery
Bereavement Services
Biplane
Bladder Cancer Care
Breast Center
Cancer Care
Capsule Endoscopy
Cardiac MRI
Cardiac Rehabilitation
Cardiac Surgery
Cardiology
Center for Childbirth
Kireker Center for Child Development
Center for Metabolic and Weight Loss Surgery
Center for Family Education
Center for Women's Heart Health
Center for Youth Fitness
Clinical Trials Oncology
Clinical Trials Cardiology
Colonoscopy
Community Resources
Complementary Medicine
Concussion Management Program
Continence Services
Cosmetic Laser Treatment

Critical Care
Diabetes Support Services
Diagnostic Imaging
Doula Program
Emergency Services
Emergency Services Pediatric
Employee Recognition
Endoscopic Ultrasound
Epilepsy Monitoring Program Adult
Epilepsy Center Pediatric
ERCP
Esophagogastroduodenoscopy (EGD)
Extended Care

COMPETITORS

Bergen Regional Medical
Englewood Hospital And Medical Center
Hackensack Meridian Health
Hackensack University Medical Center
Jersey City Medical Center
Newton Medical Center
Raritan Bay Medical Center
Robert Wood Johnson University Hospital At Rahway

HISTORICAL FINANCIALS

Company Type: Private

Income Statement				FYE: December 31
	REVENUE ($ mil.)	NET INCOME ($ mil.)	NET PROFIT MARGIN	EMPLOYEES
12/19	860	113	13.2%	2,900
12/18	695	128	18.4%	—
12/17	657	80	12.2%	—
12/16	638	73	11.6%	—
Annual Growth	10.5%	15.4%	—	—

2019 Year-End Financials

Return on assets: 6.1%   Cash ($ mil.): 417
Return on equity: 9.6%
Current ratio: 1.00

THE VANDERBILT UNIVERSITY

The house that Cornelius built Vanderbilt University was founded in 1873 with a $1 million grant from industrialist Cornelius Vanderbilt. Since then the university's endowment has grown to approximately $6.9 billion making the Nashville school a haven for its more than 12300 students and nearly 4360 full-time faculty members. Boasting a 7:1 student-faculty ratio Vanderbilt offers undergraduate and graduate programs in areas such as education and human development divinity engineering and the arts and sciences. The university operates some 10 schools and colleges. Vanderbilt's Owen Graduate School of Management and its medical school regularly rank near the top in national surveys.

Operations

Top-ranked in both academics and financial aid Vanderbilt offers residential undergraduate experience with programs in the liberal arts and sciences engineering music education and human development. The university also is home to nationally and internationally recognize graduate schools of law education business medicine nursing and divinity and offers robust graduate-degree programs across a range of disciplines.

Vanderbilt is closely affiliated with the nonprofit Vanderbilt University Medical Center (VUMC) which manages more than 2 million patient visits yearly and collaborates closely with the university through education and research. Its home to an acute care hospital an adults' and children's hospital and several clinics as well as the university's medical school research facilities and nursing programs.

Geographic Reach

Its approximately 340.7 acres campus is located a mile and a half southwest of downtown Nashville Tennessee and it has about 180 buildings. Vanderbilt Dyer Observatory located about nine miles from campus also is listed on the National Register of Historic Places.

Company Background

During its first 40 years of existence Vanderbilt was under the auspices of the Methodist Episcopal Church South. The Vanderbilt Board of Trust severed its ties with the church in 1914 after a dispute with the bishops over who would appoint university trustees.

EXECUTIVES

Chancellor, Nicholas Zeppos
Cfo, Brett Sweet
Chb, Mark Dalton
Gen Counsel, Audrey Anderson
Coo, Lee Ann Liska
Dean of Academic Affairs, Bonnie Dow
Employee, Clair Brigman
Executive Director, Learning, Cory Colton
Msn, Rn, Heather Flynn
PHD, Cnm, Rn, Jeremy Neal
PHD, Rn, Mary Jessee
Auditors: PRICEWATERHOUSECOOPERS LLP N

LOCATIONS

HQ: THE VANDERBILT UNIVERSITY
2301 VANDERBILT PL, NASHVILLE, TN 372350002
Phone: 615 322-7311
Web: WWW.VANDERBILT.EDU

PRODUCTS/OPERATIONS

Selected Schools and Colleges

Blair School of Music
College of Arts and Science
Divinity School
Graduate School
Law School
Owen Graduate School of Management
Peabody College of Education and Human Development
School of Engineering
School of Medicine
School of Nursing

HISTORICAL FINANCIALS

Company Type: Private

Income Statement				FYE: June 30
	REVENUE ($ mil.)	NET INCOME ($ mil.)	NET PROFIT MARGIN	EMPLOYEES
06/17	1,311	374	28.6%	21,000
06/16	1,270	(569)	—	—
06/15	4,121	131	3.2%	—
Annual Growth	(43.6%)	68.9%	—	—

2017 Year-End Financials

Return on assets: 5.5%   Cash ($ mil.): 935
Return on equity: 6.5%
Current ratio: —

THE WALSH GROUP LTD

Operating through subsidiaries Walsh Construction Walsh Canada and Archer Western Contractors The Walsh Group provides design/build general contracting and construction services for industrial public and commercial projects. The family-owned company offers complete project management services from demolition and planning to general contracting and finance. The company is involved in the construction of highways water treatment facilities airports hotels convention centers correctional facilities and commercial industrial and residential buildings. Walsh operates out of roughly 20 offices in North America. The company was founded in 1898 by Matthew Myles Walsh.

Operations

Walsh Group offers seamlessly integrated services to plan finance build operate and maintain the full life-cycle of a project including preconstruction design-build public-private partnerships operations & maintenance logistics lean construction sustainability self-performance and building information modelling (BIM).

Geographic Reach

Walsh Group operates in about 20 regional offices across the United States and Canada each strategically located to support maximum quality and responsiveness to a growing customer base. Walsh Construction Archer Western and Walsh Canada headquarters are located in Chicago Illinois; Atlanta Georgia; and in Toronto Ontario respectively.

Sales and Marketing

Walsh Group mostly works on projects in the commercial building transportation aviation water industrial and power sectors. These include wastewater and water treatment plants rapid transit highway and bridgework educational facilities warehouse/distribution facilities athletic facilities correctional facilities and offices.

The company continued in 2016 its long history working with Travelers Casualty and Surety Company of America as its bonding company and Bank of America as its primary bank.

Financial Performance

One of America's largest private companies Walsh Group reported its annual revenue grew 12% to $4.6 billion during 2014 up from $4.1 billion in 2013. Its annual revenues are up nearly 30% since 2007 and have more than doubled since 2004 when they were at $1.95 billion.

Strategy

Walsh Group opened new offices to support maximum responsiveness to the company's growing customer base. The new location reflects the company's commitment to the region's construction market and its talented workforce.

Company Background

The company was founded in the year 1898 by Matthew Myles Walsh. In 2012 Walsh Group acquired California-based R&L Brosamer which specializes in heavy highway and other transportation projects. R&L Brosamer often works on projects for Bay Area Rapid Transit California Department of Transportation and Los Angeles World Airports. The deal helped Walsh strengthen its presence in California and bordering states including Nevada and Arizona.

In 2011 Walsh was awarded its first overseas embassy project a $200 million contract to build the New American Embassy at Oslo Norway.

EXECUTIVES

Ceo, Matthew M Walsh
Pres*, Daniel Walsh

SEC*, Pete Glimco
Financial Controller, W Jed Mundell
Software, Christopher May
Assistant To Human Resources V, Colleen Stack
Mep Coordinator, Dan Heitz
Dbia Senior Project Manager, Dan Gallagher
Operations Manager, Mike Gomez
Program Manager, Terry Gill
Executive Administrative Assis, Lisa Christy
Auditors: WOLF & COMPANY LLP OAKBROOK T

LOCATIONS

HQ: THE WALSH GROUP LTD
929 W ADAMS ST, CHICAGO, IL 606073021
Phone: 312 563-5400
Web: WWW.WALSHGROUP.COM

PRODUCTS/OPERATIONS

Projects

Airports

Athletic facilities
Bridges
Conference centers
Correctional facilities
Data centers
Educational facilities
Entertainment
Government
Health care
High rise residential
Highways and bridges
Hotels
Interiors
Laboratories
Parking garages
Renovations
Retail centers
Senior housing
Treatment plants
Warehouse and distribution

COMPETITORS

Bechtel	James Mchugh
Black & Veatch	Lane Construction
Brasfield & Gorrie	Mwh Global
C. G. Schmidt	Mccarthy Building
Flatiron Construction	Peter Kiewit Sons'
Fluor	Skanska
Granite Construction	Tic Holdings
Hunt Companies	Turner Corporation
Hunt Construction	Vecellio & Grogan
Jacobs Engineering	

HISTORICAL FINANCIALS

Company Type: Private

Income Statement				FYE: December 31
	REVENUE ($ mil.)	NET INCOME ($ mil.)	NET PROFIT MARGIN	EMPLOYEES
12/10	3,462	186	5.4%	5,000
12/09	3,316	191	5.8%	—
12/08	3,534	203	5.8%	—
Annual Growth	(1.0%)	(4.4%)	—	—

2010 Year-End Financials

Return on assets: 11.9%   Cash ($ mil.): 656
Return on equity: 27.9%
Current ratio: 1.80

THE WASHINGTON UNIVERSITY

Washington University is a national hub for important research and business development especially in the fields of biotechnology and plant science. Founded in 1853 by William Green leaf Eliot Jr. the independent university offers 300+ academic programs such as accounting biology chemistry dance economics french and more. It has about 3645 faculty members. The university has 14500 full time students and students and faculty are from more than 100 countries. More than 6000 graduate and professional students study at the university. The affiliated Washington University Medical Center is an acute-care hospital that also provides educational training and research services.

EXECUTIVES

Chancellor, Mark Wrighton
Exec Vice Chancellor*, Richard Roloff
Controller*, Michael Dunlap
Int CIO*, Stephanie Reel
Cco*, Dedric Carter
Cardiopulm Pulm Function Tech, Ann Straka
Editor Communications Coordina, Gaia Remerowski
Adjunct Instructor, Judith Griffin
Facilities Tech II, Michael Spratt
Senior Scientist, Radiology, Sergey Komarov
Adjunct Instructor, Douglas Bram
Auditors: PRICEWATERHOUSECOOPERS LLP ST

LOCATIONS

HQ: THE WASHINGTON UNIVERSITY
1 BROOKINGS DR, SAINT LOUIS, MO 631304899
Phone: 314 935-5000
Web: WWW.WUSTL.EDU

PRODUCTS/OPERATIONS

2015 Sales

	$ mil.	% of total
Patient service	985	36
Grants	368	14
Tuition & fees	356	13
Endowment spending distribution	266	10
Gifts	186	7
Educational	162	6
Others	382	14
Total	**2,707**	**100**

Selected Schools and Colleges

College of Arts & Sciences
   Graduate School of Arts & Sciences
   University College and Summer School (Arts & Sciences)
George Warren Brown School of Social Work
Sam Fox School of Design & Visual Arts
School of Engineering & Applied Science
School of Law
School of Medicine
Olin Business School

COMPETITORS

Bucknell University
Missouri State University
Saint Louis University
Southeast Missouri State University
University Of Missouri

HISTORICAL FINANCIALS

Company Type: Private

Income Statement

	REVENUE ($ mil.)	NET INCOME ($ mil.)	NET PROFIT MARGIN	EMPLOYEES
06/21	3,837	5,981	155.9%	9,600
06/20	3,749	719	19.2%	—
06/19	3,544	554	15.7%	—
06/18	3,543	1,011	28.6%	—
Annual Growth	**2.7%**	**80.8%**	—	—

FYE: June 30

2021 Year-End Financials

Return on assets: 28.2%   Cash ($ mil.): 263
Return on equity: 33.7%
Current ratio: —

THE WHITING-TURNER CONTRACTING COMPANY

Whiting-Turner Contracting provides construction management general contracting and design/build services primarily for large commercial institutional and infrastructure projects conducted across the US. A key player in retail construction the employee-owned company also undertakes such projects as biotech cleanrooms theme parks historical restorations senior living residences educational facilities stadiums and corporate headquarters. Clients past and present include the US military AT&T General Motors and Texas A&M University. Whiting-Turner Contracting operates from more than 30 offices across the US.

Geographic Reach

The Baltimore-based company has offices in Arizona California Colorado Connecticut Delaware Florida Georgia Maryland Massachusetts Missouri Nevada New Jersey New York North Carolina Ohio Pennsylvania Texas Virginia and Washington DC.

Sales and Marketing

The contractor works on projects across a wide range of industries related to arts and entertainment education federal and military healthcare industrial office retail multi-family residential sports and fitness transportation and utilities among other fields.

Strategy

Whiting-Turner prefers to grow organically instead of making acquisitions. It has been steadily expanding by opening new offices in places such as California Texas and Virginia. The company in 2016 continued to rank among the Engineering News Record (ENR) top domestic general building contractors in the nation.

Some of the firm's recently awarded projects (as of mid-2016) include the Tropicana Pedestrian Bridge the Jacksonville Lung Bio Facility the Westowne Elementary School the Lexington Market the Costco Meat Production Plant the Sentara Norfolk General Hospital and the CoolSprings Galleria among others.

Whiting-Turner Contracting's past projects include the Joseph B. Whitehead Building at Emory University Vanderbilt Hall at Yale University projects at Universal Studios theme park and a vaccine facility at Chesapeake Biological Laboratories. Projects in the firm's hometown of Baltimore have included the city's convention center and the football stadium for the Baltimore Ravens. More recent projects include the Horseshoe Casino Cleveland University of Maryland Baltimore County (UMBC) Performing Arts & Humanities Naval Facilities Engineering Command (NAVFAC) Jacksonville Sentara Princess Anne Hospital Norwalk Community College Texas A&M University at Galveston Mary Moody Northen Student Center renovation Opry Mills the College of Business & Economics Vinson Hall Parking Garage a Coastal Studies Institute facility a Blue Diamond Growers building and a USPS Call Center.

Company Background

G.W.C. Whiting and LeBaron Turner classmates at MIT founded the company in 1909 to build sewer lines.

EXECUTIVES

Pres-Ceo, Timothy J Regan
Coo, Anthony G Moag
Exec V Pres, Daniel M Bauer
Exec V Pres, Keith A Douglas
Exec V Pres, Leonard A Cannatelli Jr
Exec V Pres, Frank R Palmer IV
Exec V Pres, Michael Ernst
Coordinator, Mike Dickerson
Svp, Bethesda, Richard L Vogel Jr
Svp, Irvine, Len Cannatelli Jr
Director Human Resources, Shawna Apodaca

LOCATIONS

HQ: THE WHITING-TURNER CONTRACTING COMPANY
300 E JOPPA RD STE 800, BALTIMORE, MD 212863047
Phone: 410 821-1100
Web: WWW.WHITING-TURNER.COM

Selected Locations

Maryland - Baltimore (Headquarters)
   California
California - Los Angeles
   California
   California
California - San Diego
   Colorado -
Connecticut - New Haven
   Delaware -
District of Columbia
Florida - Ft. Lauderdale
   Florida -
   Florida -
   Georgia -
   Maryland -
   Massachuse
Missouri - Kansas City
Nevada - Las Vegas
   New Jersey
New York - White Plains
   North Caro
   North Caro
   Ohio - Cle
   Pennsylvan
   Texas - Da
   Texas - Ho
Texas - San Antonio
   Virginia -
   Virginia -
   Virginia -

PRODUCTS/OPERATIONS

Selected Services

Construction management
   Agency
   At-risk
Design/build
General contracting
Preconstruction

Selected Markets

Biotechnology and pharmaceutical
Cleanroom and high-technology
Education
Entertainment

Federal/military
Food/beverage distribution
Health care
Historical restoration
Industrial and manufacturing
Interiors
Life sciences
Lodging and hospitality
Mission critical facilities
Mixed use
Offices and headquarters
Parking garages
Restaurants
Retail
Senior living
Sports
Sustainable
Technology
  Microelectronics
  Nano
Theme parks
Utilities
Warehouse and distribution

COMPETITORS

Barton Malow	J.e. Dunn Construction
Bechtel	Group
Choate Construction	Jacobs Engineering
Clark Construction	Kitchell
Group	Mccarthy Building
Dpr Construction	Peter Kiewit Sons'
Fisher Development	Skanska
Fluor	Suffolk Construction
Gilbane	Swinerton
Hensel Phelps	Turner Corporation
Construction	Tutor Perini
Hoffman Corporation	Weitz

HISTORICAL FINANCIALS

Company Type: Private

Income Statement				FYE: December 31
	REVENUE ($ mil.)	NET INCOME ($ mil.)	NET PROFIT MARGIN	EMPLOYEES
12/16	5,522	90	1.6%	4,560
12/15	5,729	80	1.4%	—
12/14	6,347	75	1.2%	—
Annual Growth	(6.7%)	9.8%	—	—

2016 Year-End Financials

Return on assets: 3.6%   Cash ($ mil.): 26
Return on equity: 11.4%
Current ratio: 1.40

THEDACARE, INC.

ThedaCare is a community health system that provides a wide range of health services to residents of fourteen northeast Wisconsin counties. It consists of seven hospitals including Appleton Medical Center Theda Clark Medical Center New London Family Medical Center Shawano Medical Center and ThedaCare Medical Center in Waupaca; 35 physician clinics; and community health and wellness programs. The hospitals provide back and pain care neuroscience behavioral health bone muscle & joint pain and heart and vascular services. ThedaCare also operates long-term care and assisted living facilities and provides occupational health and emergency transport services.

Operations

The health system operates seven hospitals and some 35 physician locations and manages approximately 235000 patients per year.

Its offers ThedaCare's Heritage Peabody Manor and Juliette Manor Communities ? choose from independent living assisted living or skilled care

units all on the same campus. It manages 24-hour emergency response system and on-site nursing staff.

Geographic Reach

ThedaCare serves patients in about 15 counties in Northeastern Wisconsin.

Strategy

ThedaCare Neuroscience Group and Hand To Shoulder Center of Wisconsin celebrated the groundbreaking of the new Orthopedic Spine and Pain Center. This milestone marks the official start in creating the region's only comprehensive health center specializing in orthopedic spine and pain care. These groups form a team of experts at one location allowing patients to access outstanding individualized care. By enhancing that coordinated care it can live its mission of improving the health of the communities creating peace of mind for all they serve.

Together the partners will focus on creating excellence in key areas including neuro and spine upper extremity total joint foot and ankle sports medicine physical therapy and pain. Patients can be confident knowing they have access to the highest levels of fully integrated care physician talent and training. The local economy was considered as partners determined the importance of moving forward with this project. Approximately 75 healthcare jobs are expected to be created with the opening of the new Center plus the equivalent of an additional 200 construction jobs.

EXECUTIVES

Ceo-Pres, Imran Andrabi
Cfo*, Tim Olson
Chb*, John Davis
Vice Chb*, Terry Timm
Chb*, Jim Kotek
Cfo-Coo*, Mark Thompson
Chief Officer, Dean Gruner
Registered Nurse, Laura Anklam
Supervisor, Kathryn Felton
Education Assistant, Vickie Abrahamson
Practice Supervisor, Kathy Roehl
Auditors: WIPFLI LLP MILWAUKEE WISCONS

LOCATIONS

HQ: THEDACARE, INC.
  3 NEENAH CTR, NEENAH, WI 549563070
Phone: 920 454-4156
Web: WWW.THEDACARE.ORG

PRODUCTS/OPERATIONS

Selected Facilities and Programs
Appleton Medical Center
The Heritage Community (senior living)
ThedaCare Medical Center-New London
Peabody Manor (senior living)
Riverside Medical Center
Shawano Medical Center
Theda Clark Medical Center
ThedaCare at Home
ThedaCare at Work (occupational health services)
ThedaCare Behavioral Health
ThedaCare Physicians

COMPETITORS

Aspirus
Beaver Dam Community Hospitals
Beloit Health System
Benedictine Health System
Children's Hospital And Health System
Columbia St. Mary's
Dean Health Systems Inc.
Howard Young Health Care
Luther Midelfort
Marian Health System
Marshfield Clinic Health System
Sacred Heart Hospital
Tomah Memorial Hospital

Uw Medical Foundation
University Of Wisconsin Hospital And Clinics

HISTORICAL FINANCIALS

Company Type: Private

Income Statement				FYE: December 31
	REVENUE ($ mil.)	NET INCOME ($ mil.)	NET PROFIT MARGIN	EMPLOYEES
12/20	1,031	110	10.7%	7,000
12/19	1,057	126	12.0%	—
12/18	995	(1)	—	—
12/17	909	88	9.7%	—
Annual Growth	4.3%	7.8%	—	—

2020 Year-End Financials

Return on assets: 6.9%   Cash ($ mil.): 76
Return on equity: 10.2%
Current ratio: 6.60

THOMAS JEFFERSON UNIVERSITY

Thomas Jefferson University named after a founding father of diverse interests is itself diversifying the world of medical training. Its Sidney Kimmel Medical College (formerly Jefferson Medical College) boasts departments in surgery and specialized areas including obstetrics neurology and psychiatry. The Graduate Studies department offers programs in occupational therapy and engineering. The College of Health Professions has programs in nursing pharmacy biotechnology and counseling. Founded as Jefferson Medical College in 1824 it has granted more than 30000 medical degrees. The school merged with Philadelphia University a design-focused liberal arts school.

Operations

Thomas Jefferson University's schools include College of Architecture & The Built Environment College of Health Professions College of Humanities & Sciences College of Life Sciences College of Nursing College of Pharmacy College of Population Health College of Rehabilitation Sciences and Sidney Kimmel Medical College.

It also operates the Institute of Emerging Health Professions Kanbar College of Design Engineering & Commerce School of Business School of Design & Engineering and School of Continuing & Professional Studies. In addition it offers the Philadelphia University Honors Institute.

The university enrolls more than 3700 future healthcare professionals.

The university's medical school tests or treats nearly 43000 inpatients and about 1.5 million outpatients each year.

Geographic Reach

Thomas Jefferson University has campuses in the Center City and East Falls areas of Philadelphia.

Financial Performance

Company Background

Thomas Jefferson University was founded in 1824 as Jefferson Medical College. In 1877 Thomas Jefferson University Hospital was established and Jefferson Medical College became the second medical school in the country with a separate teaching hospital. In 1891 the school established the Jefferson Hospital Training College for Nurses and in 1967 the College of Allied Health Sciences.

Thomas Jefferson University was officially established in 1969. In 1991 the NCI-designated Sidney Kimmel Cancer Center was established and in 2006 the university had renamed and added the Schools of Nursing and Health Professions. Two years later the Schools of Pharmacy and Population Health were formed. In 2014 the Sidney Kimmel Foundation bestowed a $110 million gift to Jefferson ? the largest gift in its history ? and Jefferson Medical College became Sidney Kimmel Medical College at Thomas Jefferson University.

In 2015 Thomas Jefferson University merged with Abington Health a Philadelphia health care organization with two hospitals and several clinics. The merger gave Abington access to the university's educational and training facilities and expands the university's reach to the Philadelphia suburbs. In 2016 the organization's medical operations combined forces with Aria Health which now operates as Aria — Jefferson Health.

Jefferson and Philadelphia University merged in 2017 and kept the Thomas Jefferson name. (Philadelphia University was founded in 1884 as the Philadelphia Textile School.)

EXECUTIVES

Ceo, Stephen K Klasko
Pres*, Richard Webster
V Pres*, Richard J Schmid
Treas-CIO*, Alfred Salvato
Chief of Medicine, Geno J Merli
Assistant Professor, Erica Johnson
Associate Professor, Federica Sotgia
Assistant Professor of Occupat, Audrey Zapletal
Director, Clara Callahan
Assistant Professor, Dimitri Markov
Associate Professor, Ed Winter
Auditors: PRICEWATERHOUSECOOPERS LLP PH

LOCATIONS

HQ: THOMAS JEFFERSON UNIVERSITY
1020 WALNUT ST STE 1, PHILADELPHIA, PA 191075567
Phone: 215 955-6000
Web: WWW.JEFFERSON.EDU

PRODUCTS/OPERATIONS

Selected Research Centers and Institutes
Center for Translational Medicine
Daniel Baugh Institute
Delaware Health Science Alliance
Farber Institute for Neuroscience
Jefferson Coordinating Center for Clinical Research
Jefferson Vaccine Center
Kimmel Cancer Center

Selected Colleges and Schools
Sidney Kimmel Medical College
Jefferson Graduate School of Biomedical Sciences
Jefferson School of Health Professions
Jefferson School of Nursing
Jefferson School of Pharmacy
Jefferson School of Population Health

HISTORICAL FINANCIALS

Company Type: Private

Income Statement				FYE: June 30
	REVENUE ($ mil.)	NET INCOME ($ mil.)	NET PROFIT MARGIN	EMPLOYEES
06/17	3,951	700	17.7%	10,625
06/16	136	8	6.5%	—
Annual Growth	2788.6%	7723.4%	—	—

2017 Year-End Financials
Return on assets: 12.0%   Cash ($ mil.): 259
Return on equity: 23.1%
Current ratio: 3.20

THOMAS JEFFERSON UNIVERSITY HOSPITALS, INC.

Named after the "Man of the People" Thomas Jefferson University Hospitals (dba Jefferson Health) serves the people of the Keystone State with a medical staff of more than 1200 and some 1550 beds. The system provides acute tertiary and specialty medical care from a dozen hospitals nearly 20 outpatient centers and about 10 urgent care centers. The hospital also administers cardiac care at the Jefferson Heart Institute which provides everything from minimally invasive surgical procedures to heart transplants. Additionally Jefferson Health operates as the teaching hospital for Thomas Jefferson University.

Operations
As part of its operations Jefferson Health offers several premier programs to its patients as well as 35 different specialties. The system performed Delaware Valley's first liver transplant and designated a kidney transplant center for live and deceased donor transplants. In addition to transplantation it provides surgical services heart and vascular digestive diseases and bones and joints in addition to its Kimmel Cancer Center and Jefferson Hospital for Neuroscience. In 2014 the health system logged more than 470000 outpatient visits 45000 admissions and about 115000 emergency room visits.

Geographic Reach
Through a handful of locations Jefferson Health provides health care services to the residents of Philadelphia and the Delaware Valley. It shares a 13-acre campus with Thomas Jefferson University.

Strategy
In October 2017 Jefferson Health merged with New Jersey-based Kennedy Health which operated three hospitals. The transaction followed closely on the heels of Jefferson's mergers with Aria Health and Abington Health.

In 2015 Jefferson Health added a new feature to its telemedicine program JeffConnect called On-Demand Virtual Care which allows patients to connect with an emergency medicine physician via computers and mobile devices.

That year the Philadelphia 76ers partnered with the Rothman Institute and Jefferson Health. The Rothman Institute will provide the Official Orthopedics & Urgent Care of the Philadelphia 76ers as well as the Official Team Physicians; Jefferson Health became an official hospital of the Philadelphia 76ers.

In 2014 the system opened the Jefferson Angioplasty Center the outpatient practice for Jefferson's interventional cardiologists. It is co-located with the Vascular Center allowing for streamlined consultations and convenience as the two specialties often see the same patients.

That year it also introduced genomic analyses of breast cancer in-house using the Prosigna Breast Cancer Prognostic Gene Signature Assay significantly reducing turn-around time for test results and allowing patients to begin effective treatment sooner.

Company Background
Thomas Jefferson University Hospital was founded in 1825.

EXECUTIVES

Ceo, Stephen Klasko
Sr V Pres*, Neil Lubarsky
Family Practitioner, Christopher V Chambers
Hematology, Frederick M Fellin
Dentist, Brigitte V Lovell
Director, Mary Kate M Karam
Assistant Professor, Yaacov R Lawrence
Assistant Professor, Matthew S Austin
Assistant Professor, Monisha A Kumar
Information Manager, Nick Degregorio
Assistant Chief, Catherine Guaglione

LOCATIONS

HQ: THOMAS JEFFERSON UNIVERSITY HOSPITALS, INC.
111 S 11TH ST, PHILADELPHIA, PA 191074824
Phone: 215 955-6000
Web: WWW.HOSPITALS.JEFFERSON.EDU

PRODUCTS/OPERATIONS

Selected Services

Cancer
Diabetes & Endocrinology
Ear Nose & Throat
Gastroenterology
Geriatrics
Gynecology
Nephrology
Orthopedics
Pulmonology
Rehabilitation
Urology

Selected University Locations
Jefferson at the Navy Yard
Jefferson Medical College
Jefferson College of Graduate Studies
Jefferson Radiology
Jefferson School of Health Professions
Jefferson School of Nursing
Jefferson School of Pharmacy
Jefferson School of Population Health
Jefferson Voorhees

COMPETITORS

Albert Einstein Healthcare Network
Bryn Mawr Hospital
Community Health Systems
Doylestown Hospital
Mercy Health System
North Philadelphia Health System
Our Lady Of Lourdes Medical Center
Pennsylvania Hospital
Tuhs
Universal Health Services
University Of Pennsylvania Health System

HISTORICAL FINANCIALS

Company Type: Private

Income Statement				FYE: June 30
	REVENUE ($ mil.)	NET INCOME ($ mil.)	NET PROFIT MARGIN	EMPLOYEES
06/16	1,495	76	5.1%	4,701
06/15	1,456	42	2.9%	—
06/14	1,510	51	3.4%	—
06/10	1,250	49	4.0%	—
Annual Growth	3.0%	7.7%	—	—

2016 Year-End Financials
Return on assets: 4.4%   Cash ($ mil.): 57
Return on equity: 8.7%
Current ratio: 3.20

THOMPSON CREEK METALS COMPANY USA

Thompson Creek Metals has branched out from only mining molybdenum at its Thompson Creek site in Idaho to holding a diversified North American portfolio that also includes copper gold and silver assets. The company still obtains most of its sales (97%) from producing molybdenum a metal used to strengthen steel and make it corrosion-resistant. It operates the Thompson Creek mine and mill in Idaho and owns 75% of the Endako mine in British Columbia (Japan's Sojitz owns 25%). Thompson Creek has a metallurgical facility in Pennsylvania and holds exploration assets in British Columbia and in the Yukon and Nunavut territories. It controls about 449 million pounds of molybdenum proved and probable reserves.

Operations

The company splits its activities into three main segments: US Operations Molybdenum Canadian Operations Molybdenum and Copper-Gold (Development). Its US Operations segment includes mining milling roasting and sale of molybdenum products from the Thompson Creek Mine and Langeloth facility. The Canadian Operations includes these activities from its 75%-owned Endako mine. Its Copper-Gold segment includes development expenditures from the Mt. Milligan project.

Geographic Reach

Although Thompson Creek operates primarily in North America it sells to customers worldwide.

Financial Performance

In 2011 the company generated sales of $669.1 million up about 13% from the previous year due to higher sales volumes and higher average molybdenum prices. These higher volumes and prices were offset by the company's higher operating expenses for its waste stripping activities at the Thompson Creek mine in the latter half of 2011.

However on the strength of its sales the company posted a net income for 2011 of $292.1 million a jump of nearly 157% from the previous year.

Except for spike in 2008 revenues Thompson Creek reported a downward trend in revenues from 2007 to 2010 primarily due to weak prices and lower production but gained momentum in 2011. The spike in 2008 is attributable to the sales volumes in 2008 which were higher than 2007 primarily due to increased production levels.

Strategy

The company ranked as the fifth-largest producer of molybdenum in the Western world in 2011. Its flagship project the open-pit molybdenum mine at the Thompson Creek property in Idaho is its principal producing property (75% of molybdenum production). The company has produced more than 25 million pounds of molybdenum at its Thompson Creek mine annually since 1983.

Its majority-controlled Endako molybdenum mine in British Columbia is also a producing property. The company expanded its Endako property starting up a new mill in 2012. It expects production at the Endako Mine to be as much as 16 million pounds of molybdenum per year.

Thompson Creek also is developing the Mt. Milligan project an open-pit mine and copper flotation processing plant in British Columbia. The project has an estimated annual production of 81 million pounds of copper and 194000 ounces of gold over the life of the mine. Commercial production is slated to commence in late 2013.

An underground copper molybdenum and silver exploration project is underway at the Berg property in British Columbia. The company also has

two joint venture exploration projects the Howard's Pass lead and zinc project (Yukon) and the Maze Lake gold project (Nunavut).

HISTORY

Things began looking up in 2010 after Thompson Creek acquired exploration company Terrane Metals in a deal worth $625 million. The move diversified Thompson Creek's commodity exposure to copper and gold through Terrane's flagship Mt. Milligan project in central British Columbia while giving it further growth prospects through Terrane's Berg project a copper-molybdenum-silver project also in BC. By the end of 2010 the company's proved and probable reserves for it Mt. Milligan project totaled 2.1 billion pounds of contained copper and 6 million ounces of contained gold.

EXECUTIVES

Pres-Ceo, Jacques Perron
Chb*, Kevin Loughrey
V Pres*, Robert Dorfler
Cfo*, Pamela L Saxton
Accounting Staff, Jamie Patterson
Coordinator, Raymond Gelinas
Manager, Mark Piper
Director, Robert Clifford
Auditors: KPMG LLP DENVER COLORADO

LOCATIONS

HQ: THOMPSON CREEK METALS COMPANY USA
26 W DRY CREEK CIR # 225, LITTLETON, CO
801208064
Phone: 303 761-8801
Web: WWW.THOMPSONCREEKMETALS.COM

HISTORICAL FINANCIALS

Company Type: Private

Income Statement				FYE: December 31
	REVENUE ($ mil.)	NET INCOME ($ mil.)	NET PROFIT MARGIN	EMPLOYEES
12/14	806	(124)	—	1,700
12/13	434	(215)	—	—
12/12	401	(546)	—	—
Annual Growth	41.8%	—	—	—

2014 Year-End Financials

Return on assets: (-4.4%)   Cash ($ mil.): 265
Return on equity: (-14.0%)
Current ratio: 2.50

THRUWAY AUTHORITY OF NEW YORK STATE

Leaving Manhattan or Brooklyn to shuffle off to Buffalo? The New York State Thruway Authority oversees a 641-mile toll road system and a 524-mile canal system. The authority's toll road system known as the Governor Thomas E. Dewey Thruway is the largest in the US. It crosses the state from New York City to Buffalo and more than 80% of the population of New York State lives along the corridor formed by the Thruway's 426-mile main line. Other arms of the Thruway connect with toll roads and other highways in neighboring states. The New York State Canal Corporation oversees the state's canal system of five lakes and four canals which connect bodies of water such as the Hudson River with Lake Champlain.

EXECUTIVES

Xec Dir, Thomas Madison
Exec Dir*, Michael R Fleischer
Chief Operating Officer*, John Bryan
Executive Director*, Bill Finch
Information Specialist, Shawn Mancini
Secretary, Henry Collins
Chief Technology Officer, Kim McKinney
Traffic Supervisor, Heather Garrison
Information Technology Manager, James Miller
Communications Supervisor, John Mecca
Database Administrator, Terri Cordell
Auditors: TOSKI & CO CPAS PC WILLI

LOCATIONS

HQ: THRUWAY AUTHORITY OF NEW YORK STATE
200 SOUTHERN BLVD, ALBANY, NY 122092018
Phone: 518 436-2700
Web: WWW.THRUWAY.NY.GOV

HISTORICAL FINANCIALS

Company Type: Private

Income Statement				FYE: December 31
	REVENUE ($ mil.)	NET INCOME ($ mil.)	NET PROFIT MARGIN	EMPLOYEES
12/10	674	(127)	—	2,840
12/09	640	(129)	—	—
12/08	598	(129)	—	—
Annual Growth	6.1%	—	—	—

2010 Year-End Financials

Return on assets: (-2.3%)   Cash ($ mil.): 203
Return on equity: (-6.1%)
Current ratio: 0.80

TMH PHYSICIAN ORGANIZATION

EXECUTIVES

V Pres-Ceo, John Lyle
Dir-Treas, Mike Giblin
Treas, Edward L Tyrrell
SEC, Marc L Boom
Manager, Ganesh Kalambur
Coordinator, Jennifer Hamilton
Information Specialist, Thomas Daubner
Vice-President, Liisa Ortegon
Vice-President, Hackett Carole
Manager, Jill Roach
Consultant, Jose Solis

LOCATIONS

HQ: TMH PHYSICIAN ORGANIZATION
6565 FANNIN ST STE D200, HOUSTON, TX
770302703
Phone: 713 441-4182

HISTORICAL FINANCIALS

Company Type: Private

Income Statement				FYE: December 31
	REVENUE ($ mil.)	NET INCOME ($ mil.)	NET PROFIT MARGIN	EMPLOYEES
12/19	693	6	0.9%	46
12/18	600	0	0.1%	—
12/17	532	(0)	—	—
12/15	413	0	0.2%	—
Annual Growth	13.8%	71.2%	—	—

2019 Year-End Financials

Return on assets: 6.7%   Cash ($ mil.): 1
Return on equity: —
Current ratio: 0.50

TMV CORP.

EXECUTIVES

Ceo, Mark J Whitt
Chm*, Howard L Hawks
Ceo*, Fred R Hunzeker
Chief Marketing Officer*, Lori A Bruck
Evp-Cfo*, John Obermiller
Svp-Bus Devt*, Martin E Titus
Svp-Gen Counsel*, Mark A McQuade
Vice President, Corey S Kopiasz
Vice President, Todd M Litjen
Senior Vice President, Bradley K Heisey
Senior Vice President, David W Kirkwood

LOCATIONS

HQ: TMV CORP.
14302 FNB PKWY, OMAHA, NE 681545212
Phone: 402 691-9500
Web: WWW.TENASKA.COM

HISTORICAL FINANCIALS

Company Type: Private

Income Statement				FYE: December 31
	REVENUE ($ mil.)	NET INCOME ($ mil.)	NET PROFIT MARGIN	EMPLOYEES
12/07	10,309	0	—	91
12/05	9,470	0	—	—
12/04	0	0	—	—
12/03	4,940	0	—	—
Annual Growth	20.2%	—	—	—

TOLEDO PROMEDICA HOSPITAL

One of the region's largest acute-care facilities The Toledo Hospital provides medical care to the residents of northwestern Ohio and southeastern Michigan. Boasting nearly 800 beds the facility offers several specialties and services including the Jobst Vascular Center which provides cardiac and vascular services in conjunction with The University of Michigan. The Toledo Hospital which shares a medical complex with the Toledo Children's Hospital also operates trauma emergency outpatient arthritis sleep disorder and women's health centers. The Toledo Hospital is a member of Toledo-based ProMedica Health System a mission-based not-for-profit healthcare organization formed in 1986.

Operations

The health care facility has expanded its footprint in Toledo in recent years. Besides its primary hospital it operates a stroke unit the Jobst Vascular Center a medical complex with the Toledo Children's Hospital and centers devoted to trauma emergencies arthritis sleep disorders and women's health. The Toledo Hospital and the Toledo Children's Hospital operate the Renaissance a 10-story medical complex that has enabled the pair to expand capacity with private rooms intensive and intermediate care units and pediatric hematology and oncology services.

Geographic Reach

The Toledo Hospital serves the residents of a 27-county area consisting of northwest Ohio and southeast Michigan.

Strategy

To address the needs of area residents The Toledo Hospital in late 2012 rolled out a program that makes a cardiologist available 24 hours a day seven days a week. It's the only hospital in the region to provide this service. In early 2012 the hospital opened a 20-bed stroke unit and a new 15-bed neuro intensive care unit on a newly developed floor of its Renaissance tower.

EXECUTIVES

Ceo, Alan Brass
Pres*, Barbara Steele
Cfo*, Cathy Hanley
Pres*, Kevin Webb
Manager, Debbie Fritz
Case Manager, Jean Butler
Coordinator, Tom Renshaw
Human Resources, Pat Appley
Registered Nurse, Brooke Bellman
Rn, Karla Stewart
Rn, Barbara Hughes

LOCATIONS

HQ: TOLEDO PROMEDICA HOSPITAL
2142 N COVE BLVD, TOLEDO, OH 436063895
Phone: 419 291-4000
Web: WWW.PROMEDICA.ORG

PRODUCTS/OPERATIONS

Selected Services
Arthritis and Osteoporosis Center
Bariatric Surgery
Behavioral Health and Psychiatric Services
Breast Care Center
Cancer Care
Critical Care
Diabetes
Dialysis
Emergency Services
Endoscopy Services
Fertility Services
Heart Care
Hemophilia Outpatient Clinic
Hyperbaric Medicine
Laboratory Services
Lactation Services
Maternal - Fetal Medicine
Mom & Me Boutique
Neurology
Neurophysiology
OccuHealth
Orthopaedics
Outpatient Surgery
Palliative Care
Radiology / Imaging Services
Rehabilitation Services
Respiratory Care
Sleep Medicine
Surgical Services
Trauma Services
Urology /
Vascular Services
Women's Services

COMPETITORS

Firelands Regional Health System
Mercy Health Partners Toledo
Sylvania Franciscan Health
Tenet Healthcare
Trinity Health (novi)
University Of Michigan Health System

HISTORICAL FINANCIALS

Company Type: Private

Income Statement				FYE: December 31
	REVENUE ($ mil.)	NET INCOME ($ mil.)	NET PROFIT MARGIN	EMPLOYEES
12/17	854	(115)	—	5,586
12/14	745	20	2.8%	—
12/09	635	19	3.0%	—
12/08	548	33	6.1%	—
Annual Growth	5.0%	—	—	—

2017 Year-End Financials

Return on assets: (-8.1%)   Cash ($ mil.): 83
Return on equity: (-35.3%)
Current ratio: 0.30

TOM LANGE COMPANY, INC.

EXECUTIVES

Ceo, Rock Gumpert
Pres, Greg Reinauer
V-Pres, Michael Smith
Sr V Pres, Jimmy Griswold
Sr V Pres, Bruce Rubin
SEC-Treas, Hugh Seelbach
Compliance Specialist, Mary Hannon
Administrative Assistant, Nichole Webb
Account Manager Nashville, Phil Mattingly
Vice President Imports, Bill Weyland
Account Manager Atlanta, Preston McBrayer
Auditors: KERBER ECK & BRAECKEL LLP SP

LOCATIONS

HQ: TOM LANGE COMPANY, INC.
2904 GREENBRIAR DR STE A, SPRINGFIELD, IL 627047431
Phone: 217 786-3300
Web: WWW.TOMLANGE.COM

HISTORICAL FINANCIALS

Company Type: Private

Income Statement				FYE: August 31
	REVENUE ($ mil.)	NET INCOME ($ mil.)	NET PROFIT MARGIN	EMPLOYEES
08/20	578	6	1.1%	110
08/19	0	(0)	—	—
08/16	466	2	0.6%	—
08/15	441	1	0.2%	—
Annual Growth	5.6%	42.8%	—	—

2020 Year-End Financials

Return on assets: 6.3%   Cash ($ mil.): 17
Return on equity: 12.9%
Current ratio: 1.60

TORRANCE HEALTH ASSOCIATION, INC.

EXECUTIVES

Ceo, Craig Leach
Sr V Pres*, John McNamara
Cfo*, Bill Larson
Sr V Pres*, Sally Eberhard
V Pres*, Bernadette Reid
Internal Medicine Practitioner, Anhtuan Tong
Internal Medicine Practitioner, Hong Ahn
General Practitioner, Ludmila Afonicheva
General Practitioner, Maria Vollucci
General Practitioner, Marina Raikhel
Internal Medicine Practitioner, Michelle Falcon
Auditors: ERNST & YOUNG LLP LOS ANGELES

LOCATIONS

HQ: TORRANCE HEALTH ASSOCIATION, INC.
3330 LOMITA BLVD, TORRANCE, CA 905055002
Phone: 310 325-9110
Web: WWW.TORRANCEMEMORIALIPA.ORG

HISTORICAL FINANCIALS
Company Type: Private

Income Statement				FYE: June 30
	REVENUE ($ mil.)	NET INCOME ($ mil.)	NET PROFIT MARGIN	EMPLOYEES
06/21	913	132	14.6%	3,500
06/20	187	(22)	—	—
06/19	186	(3)	—	—
06/18	76	(4)	—	—
Annual Growth	129.1%	—	—	—

2021 Year-End Financials
Return on assets: 9.1%
Return on equity: 19.7%
Current ratio: 1.70
Cash ($ mil.): 32

TORRANCE MEMORIAL MEDICAL CENTER

EXECUTIVES

Pres-Ceo, Craig Leach
Occupational Specia, Jennifer C Dalziel
Anesthesiology, Mark V Ancheta
Information, Alex Morales
General Practitioner, Haruko Yawata
Pediatrics, John Lu
Laboratory Supervisor, Ed Bernardo
Internist, Edward Wilson
Pediatrics, Julie Douglass
Hris Database Administrator, Linda Telles
Pathologist, Michael Dunlap
Auditors: ERNST & YOUNG LLP LOS ANGELES

LOCATIONS

HQ: TORRANCE MEMORIAL MEDICAL CENTER
3330 LOMITA BLVD, TORRANCE, CA 905055002
Phone: 310 325-9110
Web: WWW.TORRANCEMEMORIAL.ORG

HISTORICAL FINANCIALS
Company Type: Private

Income Statement				FYE: June 30
	REVENUE ($ mil.)	NET INCOME ($ mil.)	NET PROFIT MARGIN	EMPLOYEES
06/21	724	76	10.6%	3,500
06/20*	695	23	3.4%	—
03/20	503	15	3.1%	—
06/19	681	35	5.2%	—
Annual Growth	3.1%	46.8%	—	—
*Fiscal year change				

2021 Year-End Financials
Return on assets: 5.9%
Return on equity: 11.7%
Current ratio: 1.70
Cash ($ mil.): 12

TOWN OF HEMPSTEAD

EXECUTIVES

Sup, Anthony Santino
Clerk*, Nasrin Ahmad
Council Member, Dorothy Goosby
Commissioner, Gerald Marino
Executive, Beverly Hester
Supervisor, Laura Gillen
Analyst, Mike Defilippis
Network Administrator, Richard Gogarty
Deputy Executive Director Cfo, Edie M Longo
Finance Director, Kevin Conroy
Director of Information Techno, Tara Schneider
Auditors: ALBRECHT VIGGIANO ZURECK & C

LOCATIONS

HQ: TOWN OF HEMPSTEAD
1 WASHINGTON ST, HEMPSTEAD, NY 115504921
Phone: 516 489-5000
Web: WWW.TOWNOFHEMPSTEAD.ORG

HISTORICAL FINANCIALS
Company Type: Private

Income Statement				FYE: December 31
	REVENUE ($ mil.)	NET INCOME ($ mil.)	NET PROFIT MARGIN	EMPLOYEES
12/20	710	53	7.5%	2,052
12/19	588	5	0.9%	—
12/18	549	48	8.8%	—
12/17	677	71	10.5%	—
Annual Growth	1.6%	(8.9%)	—	—

2020 Year-End Financials
Return on assets: 1.6%
Return on equity: 4.2%
Current ratio: —
Cash ($ mil.): 265

TRAMMO, INC.

Trammo Inc. is a leading global commodity merchandiser engaged in the marketing trading distribution and transportation of wide variety of commodity products including being a market leader in anhydrous ammonia sulfur sulfuric acid nitric acid and petroleum coke. Trammo was founded by Ronald P. Stanton in 1965 with the intention of specializing in the international trade of ammonia. Trammo remains privately held and manages its operations through its headquarters in New York City and offices worldwide.

Operations

Anhydrous ammonia is an alkaline compound consisting of nitrogen and hydrogen which is transported worldwide in gaseous or liquid form on board pressurized or refrigerated vessels. These vessels (gas carriers) are also used in transporting liquefied petroleum gas (LPG). Only around 18 million metric tons are available for international marketing and seaborne trade out of more than 200 million metric tons of ammonia produced annually worldwide.

Sulfur is a by-product of oil and gas production and refining with this involuntary production accounting for up to 95% of traded volume. Annual production is about 70 million metric tons of sulfur of which about 40%-45% is available for seaborne trade.

Sulfuric acid is a key element in the production of fertilizer (phosphates and ammonium sulfate) which is its primary use (approximately 65% of total consumption). Sulfuric acid is also used in the mining industry for leaching of copper nickel uranium and other elements from ores (approximately 15% of total consumption). It is also is used in various industrial processes (approximately 20% of total consumption) including the production of titanium dioxide for dyes and pigments the production of other industrial chemicals water treatment the production of cellulose paper and rubber and in the food and glass industries. Sulfuric acid is one of the most widely used chemical commodities its total worldwide annual production is approximately 265 million metric tons.

Nitric acid used predominantly as an intermediate for fertilizer production (mainly ammonium and calcium ammonium nitrate) and for the production of nitro-containing organic intermediates.Nitric acid used predominantly as an intermediate for fertilizer production (mainly ammonium and calcium ammonium nitrate) and for the production of nitro-containing organic intermediates.

Petroleum coke ("petcoke") is a by-product of crude oil refining. The coking processes produce "green coke" which is then further processed into two main products calcined petcoke and fuel grade petcoke. Annual production is around 140 million metric tons (MT). Calcined petcoke (approximately 25% of production) is used for making anodes for aluminum smelting the dioxide industry and production of steel and titanium whiles Fuel grade petcoke (approximately 75% of production) makes up most of the petcoke traded internationally.

Geographic Reach

Headquartered in New York NY Trammo has operations in Brazil Chile Switzerland France Moscow China India Singapore South Korea the UAE and some part in US. The company also owns and operates ammonia terminals in Meredosia and Niota Illinois and a nitric acid production facility in North Bend Ohio.

Strategy

In mid-2020 Trammo successfully extended its committed secured revolving credit facility through June 2021 with a syndicate of eight international banks. Co ¶perative Rabobank UA New York Branch will serve as administrative and collateral agent and along with BNP Paribas will serve as joint lead arranger and joint book runner. Other participating banks include ABN AMRO ING Belgium JPMorgan Chase Zurcher Kantonalbank HSBC Trinkaus & Burkhardt and Brown Brothers Harriman.

The $200 million secured facility with an accordion feature that can permit an increase in total commitments up to $275 million is available for working capital and general corporate purposes in support of Trammo's commodities trading and distribution businesses around the world. The over-subscribed syndication was a strong indication of the ongoing commitment and support of Trammo's bank group.

Company Background

In 2013 Transammonia changed its name to Trammo to more accurately represent the broad spectrum of products and services it provides.

In 2010 the company's bulk carriers division entered the commodity shipping business. TA Bulk Carriers operates a fleet of 15 to 20 vessels which trade worldwide but focus on the handysize market (25000-35000 metric tons deadweight) in the Atlantic basin. In 2010 it transported about 2.9 million metric tons of cargo primarily fertilizers and grains.

Ronald Stanton founded the company in 1965 as an international ammonia trader. It branched into fertilizer merchandising and trading in 1967 LPG trading in 1978 and petrochemicals trading in 1987.

EXECUTIVES

Ceo-Pres, Edward G Weiner
Sr V Pres-Cro, James H Benfield
Sr V Pres, Oliver K Stanton
Sr V Pres-General Counsel, Louis Epstein
Sr V Pres-Ciao, Robert Lovett
Sr V Pres-Cfo, William E Markstein
Sr V Pres-Cbo, Donald V Madden
Sr V Pres-Cao, Nicholas J Wilson
Sr V Pres-CIO, Benjamin A Tan
Senior Manager, Scott Chu
Controller, Leonard Dower
Auditors: RSM US LLP NEW YORK NEW YOR

LOCATIONS

HQ: TRAMMO, INC.
8 W 40TH ST FL 12, NEW YORK, NY 100182307
Phone: 212 223-3200
Web: WWW.TRAMMO.COM

PRODUCTS/OPERATIONS

Major SubsidiariesSea-3 (liquefied propane)Trammo Gas (LPG)Trammo Gas International Inc. (LPG transportation for third parties.Trammo Petroleum (crude oil and oil products)Trammochem (petrochemicals)Fertilizers and CommoditiesNitrogen BasedAnhydrous Ammo

COMPETITORS

Basf Se	Helm
Cf Industries	Koch Industries Inc.
Cargill	Magellan Midstream
Conagra	Yara

HISTORICAL FINANCIALS

Company Type: Private

Income Statement — FYE: December 31

	REVENUE ($ mil.)	NET INCOME ($ mil.)	NET PROFIT MARGIN	EMPLOYEES
12/20	1,786	21	1.2%	184
12/19	2,267	22	1.0%	—
12/18	3,212	(12)	—	—
12/16	6,453	(229)	—	—
Annual Growth (27.5%)		—	—	—

2020 Year-End Financials

Return on assets: 4.4%   Cash ($ mil.): 59
Return on equity: 12.9%
Current ratio: 1.20

TRC COMPANIES, L.L.C.

TRC Companies is a leading global consulting engineering and construction company that provides environmentally focused and digitally powered solutions. The company provides engineering construction and remediation services for power and utilities industrial transportation real estate water and government. Services include energy efficiency and solid- and hazardous-waste management consulting infrastructure improvements and landfill cleanup. TRC's services also include remediation for brownfield sites discontinued industrial operations operating assets and Superfund sites. It also offers an Exit Strategy Program in which it assumes complete responsibility for a contaminated site's closure and cleanup. In late 2021 TRC was acquired by the private equity firm Warburg Pincus from New Mountain Capital. The company was incorporated in Connecticut in 1969.

HISTORY

TRC was born as Travelers Research Center a unit set up in 1953 by Travelers Insurance to do meteorological and industrial hygiene research. In 1969 Travelers (now part of Citigroup) spun off TRC Companies which prospered as government spending on the environment and pollution control increased. It became a free-standing public entity in 1976. When the government began cutting back during the 1980s TRC started courting the commercial market.

In 1994 TRC expanded acquiring Environmental Solutions and Mariah Associates. It increased its international interests forming joint ventures in 1995 and 1996 to help with the remediation of Poland's horrendous pollution.

Sales fell in 1996 and 1997 the result of a weak market and stiff competition in the environmental services industry. TRC responded with a major cost-cutting effort. In 1997 chairman and CEO Vincent Rocco and president Bruce Cowen resigned amid an investigation into options exercised by the two executives that the company's board had not authorized. Richard Ellison head of the TRC Environmental Solutions subsidiary was named chairman president and CEO.

Also in 1997 TRC teamed up with insurer American International Group to introduce a service called the Exit Strategy Program in which TRC is paid to take full responsibility — including liability risks — for a contaminated site's closure and remediation.

In 1998 the company sold its Monitoring Instruments for the Environment subsidiary for about $2.7 million. The next year TRC embarked on a major buying spree: It purchased Alton Geoscience which specialized in installation removal and replacement of fuel tanks; A&H Engineers a transportation consulting and engineering firm in New York City; and Vectre which provided brownfield remediation services in New Jersey. The company also landed an Exit Strategy contract to clean up a Superfund site in Maine.

Continuing to grow through acquisitions in 2000 TRC acquired Texas-based Hunter Associates North Carolina-based Triange Environmental and California-based Lowney Associates. Also that year the TRC twice scored big with its Exit Strategy product: a $103 million contract with Consolidated Edison to clean up a site in New York City and a $21 million contract with Lockheed Martin to clean up sites in California Massachusetts and New Jersey.

TRC kept on snapping up companies in 2001. The company bought Engineered Automation Systems which provided electrical mechanical and en-

vironmental controls and ECON a provider of environmental services to the oil and gas companies that was to take on Exit Strategy business in the Gulf Coast region. The company also bought two infrastructure engineering companies LandCon and CSM that were to be combined with Hunter Associates.

The next year eager to expand its outsourcing operations for the power industry TRC acquired engineering firm E/PRO which had experience in the US Northeast in the licensing of hydroelectric plants as well as in designing constructing and managing other power utilities. TRC also completed its acquisition of transportation infrastructure firm SITE-Blauvelt Engineers which targeted mid-Atlantic states.

In 2002 the group expanded westward by acquiring California-based environmental planning training and compliance management firm Essex Environmental. It also enhanced its Midwestern operations by buying Novak Engineering a power transmission and distribution planning and design firm. In 2004 the group won a contract from the Department of Defense to design an "intelligent building" system to optimize energy use and detect threats within the Pentagon.

Ellison retired as president and CEO effective January 1 2006 but remained chairman. Christopher Vincze who had been COO took over as president and CEO.

But TRC began to broaden its reach nationally in all segments of its business in 2010. Since 2010 the company has been marketing its energy and infrastructure services on a national basis and its environmental services are being integrated into its national platform. Its national platform is linked to TRC's corporate sales and marketing organization.

Pursuing strategic acquisitions in 2011 TRC continued acquired Alexander Utility Engineering a San Antonio-based engineering and design firm that specializes in services to the electric utility and communications utility markets. The deal for Alexander which posted earnings of about $3 million in 2010 expands TRC's engineering presence in the Texas market and advances its growth strategy. That same year TRC acquired the environmental business of RMT Inc. a subsidiary of Alliant Energy Corp. The deal expands TRC's growth in the solar wind and geothermal energy markets. The company also picked up environmental consulting company The Payne Firm.

On the heels of acquiring RMT and Payne the company formed a strategic partnership with California-based environmental consulting group EORM to acquire its eastern region operations based in Danvers Massachusetts. The deal enhances TRC's environmental management sustainability and safety operations as well as broadens its geographic reach.

Broadening its geographic coverage in 2012 the company opened an office in London.

In 2013 TRC acquired GE Air Emissions Testing for $3.2 million.

EXECUTIVES

Ceo, Christopher Vincze
Cfo*, Thomas Bennet
Chief Strategy Officer-Svp*, Jim Stephenson
Project Coordinator, David Benson
Srcommissioning Engineer, Alemayehu Getiso
Chief Risk Officer, Marc Faecher
Environmental Scientist, Scott Birmingham
Environmental Scientist, Heather Quattlebaum
Project Director, Patrick Ford
Vice President, Jason Hostetter
Vp Chief Engineer, Kevin Bodenhamer

Auditors: DELOITTE & TOUCHE LLP HARTFOR

LOCATIONS

HQ: TRC COMPANIES, L.L.C.
21 GRIFFIN RD N, WINDSOR, CT 060951590
Phone: 860 298-9692
Web: WWW.TRCCOMPANIES.COM

PRODUCTS/OPERATIONS

2016 Sales

	% of total
Environmental	45
Energy	33
Infrastructure	12
Pipeline	10
Total	**100**

2016 Sales

	$ mil.	% of total
Net services	465	97
Insurance recoverable and others	16	3
Total	**481**	**100**

Selected Customers

AES Enterprises
ASARCO
Burlington Northern Santa Fe (BNSF)
Connecticut Resources Recovery Authority
Consolidated Edison
Duke Energy
El Paso Energy
Environmental Protection Agency
Exxon Mobil
Goodyear Tire & Rubber
Kinder Morgan
PG&E Corporation
Sempra Energy
State Departments of Transportation/Power Authorities
    California
    Louisiana
    Massachusetts
    New Hampshire
    New Jersey
    New York
    Pennsylvania
    Texas
    West Virginia

Selected Subsidiaries

Alexander Utility Engineering
Center Avenue Holdings
Cubix Corporation
Environomics Southwest
Hunter Associates
Site-Blauvelt Engineers Inc.
Site Construction Services
TRC Engineers Inc.
TRC Environmental Corporation
TRC Solutions Inc.
Vectre Corporation

COMPETITORS

3e Company	Black & Veatch
Arcadis	Clyde Bergemann Eec
Atc Associates	Fluor
Bechtel	Weston Solutions

HISTORICAL FINANCIALS

Company Type: Private

Income Statement   FYE: June 30

	REVENUE ($ mil.)	NET INCOME ($ mil.)	NET PROFIT MARGIN	EMPLOYEES
06/20	711	(58)	—	4,800
06/19	693	(30)	—	—
06/18	590	(48)	—	—
Annual Growth	9.8%	—	—	—

2020 Year-End Financials

Return on assets: (-5.3%)   Cash ($ mil.): 64
Return on equity: (-25.9%)
Current ratio: 1.30

TRI STAR ENERGY, LLC

EXECUTIVES

Mng MBR, John B Jewell III
MBR, Steve Hostetter
MBR, Rick Hamilton
MBR, Jeff Williams
MBR, Liane Taylor
Senior Vice President of Facil, Charlton Bell
Manager, Randy Alexander
R Credit Manager, Belinda Hilliard
Manager, Jack Cooper
District Manager, Keith Middleton
Database Analyst, Mark Roark
Auditors: LATTIMORE BLACK MORGAAN & CA

LOCATIONS

HQ: TRI STAR ENERGY, LLC
1740 ED TEMPLE BLVD, NASHVILLE, TN 372081850
Phone: 615 313-3600
Web: WWW.TRISTARTN.COM

HISTORICAL FINANCIALS

Company Type: Private

Income Statement   FYE: December 31

	REVENUE ($ mil.)	NET INCOME ($ mil.)	NET PROFIT MARGIN	EMPLOYEES
12/11	730	3	0.5%	500
12/10	635	4	0.7%	—
12/09	547	0	0.0%	—
Annual Growth	15.5%	399.7%	—	—

2011 Year-End Financials

Return on assets: 3.1%   Cash ($ mil.): —
Return on equity: 7.4%
Current ratio: 0.70

TRIBOROUGH BRIDGE & TUNNEL AUTHORITY

EXECUTIVES

V Pres-Pres, Michael C Ascher
Computer Specialist, Paul Kolodizner
Peace Officer, Anthony Barbato
Auditors: DELOITTE & TOUCHE LLP NEW YOR

LOCATIONS

HQ: TRIBOROUGH BRIDGE & TUNNEL AUTHORITY
ROBERT MSES BLDG RNDLLSI, NEW YORK, NY 10035
Phone: 212 360-3000
Web: WWW.NEW.MTA.INFO

HISTORICAL FINANCIALS

Company Type: Private

Income Statement   FYE: December 31

	REVENUE ($ mil.)	NET INCOME ($ mil.)	NET PROFIT MARGIN	EMPLOYEES
12/20	1,660	672	40.5%	1,500
12/19	2,094	485	23.2%	—
12/18	1,999	453	22.7%	—
12/17	1,931	282	14.6%	—
Annual Growth	(4.9%)	33.6%	—	—

2020 Year-End Financials

Return on assets: 7.0%   Cash ($ mil.): 507
Return on equity: —
Current ratio: 1.40

TRIHEALTH, INC.

EXECUTIVES

Ceo, Mark Clement
Pres*, John Prout
V Pres Fin*, Joe Kessler
Exec V Pres*, Claus Vonzychlin
Exec V Pres*, William Groneman
Sr V Pres*, Robert Halonen
Prin*, L Thomas Wilburn Jr
Cfo*, Andrew Devoe
Prin*, Myra James Bradley
Cdo*, Tashawna Otabil
Cmo*, Helen Koselka
Auditors: ERNST & YOUNG LLP CINCINNATI

LOCATIONS

HQ: TRIHEALTH, INC.
625 EDEN PARK DR, CINCINNATI, OH 452026005
Phone: 513 569-5400
Web: WWW.TRIHEALTH.COM

HISTORICAL FINANCIALS

Company Type: Private

Income Statement   FYE: June 30

	REVENUE ($ mil.)	NET INCOME ($ mil.)	NET PROFIT MARGIN	EMPLOYEES
06/21	553	(158)	—	13,000
06/20	552	(185)	—	—
Annual Growth	0.2%	—	—	—

2021 Year-End Financials

Return on assets: (-19.5%)   Cash ($ mil.): 194
Return on equity: (-32.2%)
Current ratio: 1.40

TRINITY HEALTH CORPORATION

One of the largest not-for-profit Catholic health care systems in the US Trinity Health runs roughly 90 acute care hospitals and approximately 130 continuing care facilities in more than 20 US states. Beyond traditional health services Trinity Health also provides health and wellness care including independent retail location Urgent Care Centers specialty pharmacies providing specialized medicines for chronic care or other debilitating conditions and an Outreach Lab where it able to send and receive lab work. Its home-based care offerings include companion care remote patient monitoring and hospice. The company employs approximately 6800 physicians and clinicians.

Operations

Its Trinity Health Pharmacy Services provides specialty medications for complex chronic and rare diseases. Its highly-trained pharmacists and specialized care team take great care to provide guidance on drug interactions allergies and therapy management to each patient as well as provide customized education follow-up and side effect management.

Trinity Health's Military and Veterans Health Care Program is committed to providing convenient access to high-quality health services to meet the specific needs of military service members veterans and their family members.

Net patient service brings roughly 85% of Trinity Health's total revenue while capitation and premium and other revenue accounts for the remaining revenue.

Geographic Reach

Based in Livonia Michigan Trinity Health operates in more than 20 states including in Alabama California Florida Georgia Idaho and Illinois.

Sales and Marketing

Medicare accounts for about 40% of net patient service revenues Blue Cross accounts for some 20% Medicaid for around 15% while uninsured commercial and other represents more than 20%.

Strategy

Xealth the leader in enabling digital health at scale in late 2021 announced that Trinity Health invested in the company. Trinity is one of 15 health system investors for the company bringing the total Series B funding to $25 million. This support demonstrates continued provider consensus in adopting digital health in a way that best engages both clinicians and patients.

Company Background

Trinity Health was established in 2013 from the merger of Catholic Health East and the former Trinity Health organization.

The predecessor Trinity Health organization was formed through the 2000 merger of Mercy Health Services and Holy Cross Health System. Holy Cross was founded in 1979 but traces its roots to the founding of the Congregation of the Sisters of the Holy Cross in 1841; Mercy Health was founded in 1976 but originates with the Sisters of Mercy establishing operations in Iowa and Michigan in the 1860s and 1870s.

Catholic Health East was formed through the 1998 merger of three health ministries: Franciscan Sisters of Allegany Health System (tracing its roots to 1883 in Boston) Eastern Mercy Health System (1847 Pittsburgh) and Sisters of Providence Health System (1892; Holyoke Massachusetts).

In 2015 New York-based St. Joseph's Hospital Health Center joined the Trinity hospital system.

EXECUTIVES

Pres-Ceo, Michael Slubowski
Coo*, Benjamin Carter
Pres*, Robert Casalou
Exec V Pres*, John Capasso
Cfo*, Cynthia Clemence
Exec V Pres*, Mary Ann Dillon
Exec V Pres*, Lou Fierens
Exec V Pres*, Edmund Hodge
Exec V Pres*, Linda Ross
Exec V Pres*, Daniel Roth
Strategic Sourcing Manager, John Zisler
Auditors: DELOITTE & TOUCHE LLP DETROIT

LOCATIONS

HQ: TRINITY HEALTH CORPORATION
20555 VICTOR PKWY, LIVONIA, MI 481527031
Phone: 734 343-1000
Web: WWW.TRINITY-HEALTH.ORG

Selected Facilities

California
Saint Agnes Medical Center (Fresno)
Idaho and Oregon
Saint Alphonsus Medical Center - Baker City
Saint Alph
Saint Alph

Saint Alphonsus Regional Medical Center (Boise)
Indiana
Saint Joseph Regional Medical Center (South Bend)
Saint Joseph Regional Medical Center (Plymouth)
Illinois
Loyola University Health System (Chicago)
Loyola University Medical Center
Loyola Gottlieb Memorial Hospital
Mercy Hospital & Medical Center (Chicago)
Iowa and Nebraska
Mercy Health Network (Clinton Des Moines Dubuque Dyersville Mason City New Hampton and Sioux City Iowa; Oakland Nebraska)
Maryland
Holy Cross Hospital (Silver Spring)
Michigan
Mercy Health Partners (Muskegon)
Mercy Hospital (Cadillac)
Mercy Hospital (Grayling)
Saint Joseph Mercy Health System (Ann Arbor)
Saint Mary's Health Care (Grand Rapids)
Ohio
Mount Carmel Health System (Columbus)

PRODUCTS/OPERATIONS

2014 Net Patient Revnue

	% of total
Medicare	38
Blue Cross	20
Medicaid	13
Uninsured	4
Commercial and other	25
Total	**100**

2014 Sales

	% of total
Net patient service revenuel less provision for bad debts	87
Capitation and premium revenue	5
Other revenue	8
Total	**100**

COMPETITORS

Advocate Health Care	Medstar Health
Amedisys	Memorial Hospital &
Ascension Health	Health System
Beaumont Health System	Ohiohealth
Community Health	St. Luke's Health
Systems	System
Encompass Health	Tenet Healthcare
Hca	Universal Health
Henry Ford Health	Services
System	University Of Chicago
Hospice Of Michigan	Medical Center
Johns Hopkins Medicine	Vitas Healthcare
Kindred Healthcare	Wheaton Franciscan
Mayo Clinic	Services

HISTORICAL FINANCIALS

Company Type: Private

Income Statement · FYE: June 30

	REVENUE ($ mil.)	NET INCOME ($ mil.)	NET PROFIT MARGIN	EMPLOYEES
06/20	18,833	(34)	—	51,220
06/19	2,046	38	1.9%	—
06/15	1,375	19	1.4%	—
Annual Growth	68.8%	—	—	—

2020 Year-End Financials

Return on assets: (-0.1%)　　Cash ($ mil.): 2,191
Return on equity: (-0.3%)
Current ratio: 1.70

TRINITY HEALTH-MICHIGAN

EXECUTIVES

Ceo, Rebekah Smith
Cfo*, Mike Gusho
Director of Geriatric Programs, Mary Jo West
Coordinator, Catherine Popour
Coordinator, Jan Hansen
Coordinator, Karen Dalton
Coordinator, Kim Graham
Sleep Lab Manager, Rosemary Bruno
Senior Vice President, Cynthia Fry
Payroll Specialist, Sue Hill
Physician, Don Campbell
Auditors: DELOITTE & TOUCHE LLP DETROIT

LOCATIONS

HQ: TRINITY HEALTH-MICHIGAN
20555 VICTOR PKWY, LIVONIA, MI 481527031
Phone: 810 985-1500
Web: WWW.STJOESHEALTH.ORG

HISTORICAL FINANCIALS

Company Type: Private

Income Statement · FYE: June 30

	REVENUE ($ mil.)	NET INCOME ($ mil.)	NET PROFIT MARGIN	EMPLOYEES
06/20	2,599	124	4.8%	1,500
06/18	3,595	303	8.4%	—
06/14	2,474	102	4.2%	—
06/13	2,475	138	5.6%	—
Annual Growth	0.7%	(1.5%)		

2020 Year-End Financials

Return on assets: 3.0%　　Cash ($ mil.): —
Return on equity: 4.8%
Current ratio: —

TRINITY MOTHER FRANCES HEALTH SYSTEM FOUNDATION

Trinity Mother Frances Health System Foundation (dba Trinity Mother Frances Hospitals and Clinics) has a complicated name but a simple mission: to improve patient health. Consisting of three general hospitals several specialist facilities and a large physicians' group Trinity Mother Frances serves northeastern Texas. Its largest acute-care facility is Mother Frances Hospital-Tyler with more than 400 beds offering comprehensive medical surgical trauma and cardiovascular care. Two smaller hospitals in Jacksonville and Winnsboro provide emergency diagnostic surgery and select specialty services. The Trinity Clinic is a multi-specialty physician group that includes 300 doctors in 36 community clinics.

Operations

Trinity Mother Frances Hospitals and Clinics' specialty facilities include the freestanding Trinity Mother Frances Rehabilitation Hospital in Tyler which has 75 beds and is operated through a joint venture with HealthSouth. It also operates the Tyler ContinueCARE Hospital a long-term acute care hospital located within the Mother Frances Hospital-Tyler as well as several urgent care centers.

Strategy

In 2010 the network added the 35-bed Mother Frances Hospital-Winnsboro facility when it took over control of the Texas Health Presbyterian Hospital Winnsboro from Texas Health Resources. The transfer was made to align the Winnsboro hospital with the main Tyler facility where the majority of specialized cases from Winnsboro were already being transferred.

The network also added a freestanding 72-bed cardiac facility the Louis and Peaches Owen Heart Hospital in Tyler. The first phase of the center was added to the existing Mother Frances Hospital-Tyler facilities in 2010; the second stage is a six-story freestanding tower adjacent to the Tyler hospital. Construction on the tower started in early 2011 and was completed by the end of 2012.

Additionally Trinity Mother Frances Hospitals and Clinics is investing in information technology initiatives. It began installing electronic health record (EHR) systems at its facilities during 2012 as part of the US government's health care improvement initiatives.

Company Background

Trinity Mother Frances Hospitals and Clinics was established by the 1995 merger of Mother Frances Hospital and the Trinity Clinic both founded in the 1930s.

EXECUTIVES

Pres, J Lindsey Bradley
Co-Pres*, David Teegarden
Cfo*, William Bellenfant
Exe Vp-Coo*, Steven Keuer
Exe Vp-Coo*, Ray Thompson
Pres*, Randall V Childress
Spine Program Director, Cathy Newman
Seniior Vice President of Medi, Greg Stovall
Supervisor, Linda Knox
Doctor Im, Lloyd Olsen
Clinic III Manager, Pamela Barron
Auditors: ERNST & YOUNG LLP DALLAS TX

LOCATIONS

HQ: TRINITY MOTHER FRANCES HEALTH SYSTEM FOUNDATION
800 E DAWSON ST, TYLER, TX 757012036
Phone: 903 531-5057
Web: WWW.CHRISTUSHEALTH.ORG

PRODUCTS/OPERATIONS

Selected Locations

DirectCARE (urgent care multiple sites)
Louis and Peaches Owen Heart Hospital Tyler
Mother Frances Hospital-Jacksonville
Mother Frances Hospital-Tyler
Mother Frances Hospital-Winnsboro
Trinity Clinics (physician practices multiple sites)
Trinity Mother Frances Rehabilitation Hospital-Tyler
Tyler ContinueCARE Hospital

Selected Services

Anesthesiology
Audiology
Bariatric Surgery Center
Cancer
Cardiac Services
Cardiothoracic Surgery
Critical Care Intensivists
Ear Nose & Throat
Emergency Medicine
Endocrinology
Gastroenterology Hepatology and Endoscopy
Family Medicine
General Surgeons
Genetics

Hospitalists
Imaging Radiology Mammography
Internal Medicine
Neonatology
Neuroscience Institute
Obstetrics & Gynecology
Occupational Medicine - Health At Work
Ophthalmology Optometry & Optical Services
Orthopedics
Pain Medicine
Pediatrics
Physical Medicine and Rehabilitation
Plastic Surgery
Podiatry
Psychiatry
Rehabilitation Hospital
Rheumatology
Sleep Medicine
Sports Medicine
Surgery Services
Trauma Services
Urgent Care
Urology Institute & Continence Center
Vascular Institute
Women & Children
WoundCARE

COMPETITORS

Community Health Systems
East Texas Medical Center Regional Healthcare
Good Shepherd Health System
Hca
Hunt Memorial
Memorial Health System Of East Texas
Parkland Health & Hospital System
Southwestern Medical Center
Tenet Healthcare
The Methodist Health System
United Surgical Partners
Wadley Regional Medical Center
Woodland Heights Medical Center

HISTORICAL FINANCIALS

Company Type: Private

Income Statement   FYE: June 30

	REVENUE ($ mil.)	NET INCOME ($ mil.)	NET PROFIT MARGIN	EMPLOYEES
06/13	653	21	3.3%	3,551
06/10	603	19	3.3%	—
06/09	901	0	—	—
Annual Growth	—	1364.1%	—	—

2013 Year-End Financials

Return on assets: 3.1%   Cash ($ mil.): 47
Return on equity: 7.2%
Current ratio: 1.50

TRUMAN ARNOLD COMPANIES

Truman Arnold Companies (TAC) is one of the largest independent fuel wholesalers and aviation service providers in the US. Its energy business markets and sells more than 2.7 billion gallons of fuel to customers in industries like energy retail trucking utilities mining and construction. The company supplies refined products like gasoline diesel biodiesel ethanol renewable fuels and Diesel Exhaust Fluid (a non-hazardous product). TAC also serves the aviation industry by selling aviation fuel and providing Fixed Base Operations (aircraft fueling hangar space and transport) through over 15 locations in the US. TAC was founded in 1964 by Truman Arnold.

Operations

TAC operates through TACenergy TAC Air TAC Private Hangars Keystone Aviation and TAC Investments.

TACenergy sells an annual fuel volume of more than 2.7 billion gallons through a vast terminal supply network. This segment also provides a 24/7 logistics call center a bulk trading desk and a real-time inventory intelligence service (matching inventory supply with trading prices) that helps minimize fuel costs for customers.

TAC Air is the company's aviation division which sells competitively priced aviation fuel and provides Fixed Base Operation services including ground handling aircraft fueling hangar space aircraft maintenance cargo handling and de-icing.

Through Keystone Aviation the company also provides private charter flights aircraft management and aircraft maintenance.

TAC Private Hangars is a secure protected environment operating 24/7/365. Each location provides hangar and connected office space conference room/meeting space private terminal and gate access secured parking ground services and fueling.

TAC Investments manage the company's capital by investing in a wide pool of assets.

Geographic Reach

TAC is headquartered in Dallas Texas. TAC Air has FBO in over 15 locations including Arkansas Colorado Connecticut Kentucky and Louisiana among others.

Sales and Marketing

TACenergy sells branded retail fuel to a range of customers including gasoline and diesel retailers industrial users transportation oil & gas waste disposal & recycling trucking government agencies utilities mining and construction as well as other commercial user or reseller of fuel. The company has a vast terminal supply network with outlets across the continent plus a 24/7 logistical call center.

Strategy

TAC Investments manages the capital of the TAC balance sheet. We carefully invest in a diverse pool of assets that in turn produces an above-average risk-adjusted return while expanding and supporting the TAC balance sheet by mitigating risk. This extensive and diverse pool of assets provides the foundation for TAC's purchasing power across all divisions.

In late 2020 The Arnold Companies is expanding its presence into New York with the addition of its 16th FBO location TAC Air - BUF at Buffalo Niagara International Airport. Acquiring Prior Aviation assets associated with its fixed base operations TAC Air also plans to maintain the 120 associates supporting these operations. The full range of FBO services including fuel hangar and aircraft handling as well as supporting the market's commercial airlines with into-plane fuel charter handling cargo services de-icing and airline maintenance will be offered by TAC Air.

Mergers and Acquisitions

In 2021 TAC acquired the assets of Gemini Air Group at Arizona's Scottsdale Airport (KSDL) Arizona Dallas-based The TAC has established a Keystone Aviation operation there. Additionally it created TAC Private Hangars which will manage more than 65000 sq ft of upscale private hangar and office space at KSDL.

In late 2020 TAC Air a division of TAC is expanding its presence into New York with the addition of its 16th FBO location TAC Air - BUF at Buffalo Niagara International Airport. Acquiring Prior Aviation assets associated with its fixed base operations TAC Air also plans to maintain the 120 associates supporting these operations. The full range of FBO services including fuel hangar and aircraft handling as well as supporting the market's commercial airlines with into-plane fuel charter handling cargo services de-icing and airline maintenance will be offered by TAC Air.

Company Background

Truman Arnold Companies was founded in 1964 as a Texas-based Conoco Distributor. It once operated a chain of 125 Road Runner convenience stores in eight states before selling this network to Total Petroleum in 1989. It revived the brand in 2003. The company presently focuses on fuel marketing and providing aviation services doing business under the TAC business name.

EXECUTIVES

Chm-Pres-Ceo, Greg Arnold
Senior Vice President*, James H Day
Cfo*, Steve McMillen
General Manager, Scott Field
Regional Sales Manager, Chad Hebert
Coordinator, Kyle Bender
Safety Manager, Oscar Flowers
General Manager, Daniel Mansfield
General Manager, Ed Malec
Regional Sales Manager, Ray Cozzi
Corporate Environmental Manage, Rick Shingleur
Auditors: THOMAS & THOMAS PLLC TEXARKAN

LOCATIONS

HQ: TRUMAN ARNOLD COMPANIES
701 S ROBISON RD, TEXARKANA, TX 755016747
Phone: 903 794-3835
Web: WWW.THEARNOLDCOS.COM

COMPETITORS

Atlantic Aviation	Sun Coast Resources
Million Air	
Petroleum Traders	
Corporation	

HISTORICAL FINANCIALS

Company Type: Private

Income Statement				FYE: September 30
	REVENUE ($ mil.)	NET INCOME ($ mil.)	NET PROFIT MARGIN	EMPLOYEES
09/17	2,119	18	0.9%	550
09/16	1,525	18	1.2%	—
09/15	1,595	17	1.1%	—
Annual Growth	15.2%	2.4%	—	—

2017 Year-End Financials

Return on assets: 5.6%   Cash ($ mil.): 3
Return on equity: 12.3%
Current ratio: 1.20

TRUMAN MEDICAL CENTER, INCORPORATED

Truman Medical Center (also known as Truman Medical Centers/University Health) provides primary and mental health care at two not-for-profit hospitals in the Kansas City (Missouri) area. Its Hospital Hill runs one of the busiest emergency rooms in Kansas City and is known for treatments related to asthma diabetes obstetrics ophthalmology weight management and women's health. TMC Lakewood a 110-bed hospital is a leading academic medical center providing a range of health care services to the greater Kansas City metropolitan area including uninsured patients. The Lakewood Family Birthplace delivers more than 1500 babies annually.

EXECUTIVES

Pres, John F Bluford
V Pres, Mitzi Cardenas
V Pres, Marcos Deleon
V Pres, Lynda Donegan
V Pres, Dmeter Dragovich
Emergency Medicine Specialist, Jeffrey L Hackman
Director, Stanley M Augustin
Chief Officer, Mark T Steele
Technology, Matthew King
Information Specialist, Lona M Lamar
Corporate Quality Dire, Shauna R Roberts
Auditors: BKD LLP KANSAS CITY MO

LOCATIONS

HQ: TRUMAN MEDICAL CENTER, INCORPORATED
2301 HOLMES ST, KANSAS CITY, MO 641082677
Phone: 816 404-1000
Web: WWW.TRUMED.ORG

PRODUCTS/OPERATIONS

Truman Medical Center Hospital Hill
Asthma Center
The Birthplace
Cardiovascular Center
Chiropractic Services KC CORE
Dental Maxillofacial Surgery
Diabetes Center
Emergency Care
Eye Clinic
Eye Foundation
GI Gastrointestinal
Hospital Hill Medical Pavilion
Infectious Disease Clinic
Oncology
Orthopaedics
Pulmonary Fibrosis
Radiology Services
Rehabilitation Services
Sickle Cell Disease Center
Sleep Center
Trauma Services
TruMed Clinic
Weight Management
Women's Care Breast Center
Women's Health Services
TMC Lakewood
Family Medicine Center
Lakewood Family Birthplace
Chiropractic Services
Counseling Services Lakewood
Dental Services
Dental Services Elks Mobile
GI Gastrointestinal
Emergency Medicine
Eye Care Center
Lakewood Medical Pavilion
Longterm Care Center
Medical Detox
Orthopaedic Services
Outpatient Surgery Center
Podiatry
Rehabilitation Services
Sports Medicine
Women's Health Services

COMPETITORS

Ascension Health	Shawnee Mission
Children's Mercy	Medical Center
Hospital	University Of Kansas
Coxhealth	Medical Center
Saint Luke's Health	Via Christi Health
System	System

HISTORICAL FINANCIALS

Company Type: Private

Income Statement				FYE: June 30
	REVENUE ($ mil.)	NET INCOME ($ mil.)	NET PROFIT MARGIN	EMPLOYEES
06/20	693	(21)	—	3,000
06/19	666	13	2.0%	—
06/18	562	22	4.0%	—
06/14	418	(78)	—	—
Annual Growth	8.8%			

2020 Year-End Financials

Return on assets: (-4.3%)   Cash ($ mil.): 63
Return on equity: (-23.9%)
Current ratio: 1.10

TRUSTEES OF BOSTON COLLEGE

Students at Boston College (BC) get both academic excellence and the Red Sox. Operate in the city of Boston the university enrolls some 14600 students. It has a student-teacher ratio of 11:1. BC offers degrees in more than 50 fields of study through its eights schools and colleges on four campuses. Some programs include biology chemistry economics geology philosophy and theology. The university also has more than 35 research centers including the Institute for Scientific Research and the Center for International Higher Education. BC is one of the oldest Jesuit Catholic universities in the nation and has the largest Jesuit community in the world.

Operations

BC offers a variety of graduate degree programs in the humanities social sciences and natural sciences lead to Ph.D. M.A. and M.S. degrees. It include Classical Studies Earth and Environmental Sciences Geophysics History Philosophy and Theology Physics Political Science Psychology and Sociology.

The university is home to more than 35 centers and institutes designated for research and teaching. Research opportunities including participation in faculty research projects exist for both undergraduate and graduate students. It also houses 8 libraries with nearly 3 million volumes.

The cost of tuition stood at $70143.

Geographic Reach

The university has campuses in Brighton Chestnut Hill Dover and Newton Massachusetts. It also operates a campus in Dublin Ireland.

Company Background

The university was founded by Jesuits in 1863. During its first seven decades BC was an exclusively undergraduate institution that served sons of the Irish working class. Its liberal arts emphasis was on the Greek and Latin classics English and modern languages and philosophy and religion. Development into the college it is today did not begin until the 1920s when the Graduate School of Arts and Sciences the Law School and the Evening College (known today as the James A. Woods S.J. College of Advancing Studies) were inaugurated. All classes became co-educational in the 1970s and today BC has a fairly equal split among male and female students.

EXECUTIVES

Pres, William P Leahy Sj

LOCATIONS

HQ: TRUSTEES OF BOSTON COLLEGE
140 COMMONWEALTH AVE, CHESTNUT HILL, MA 024673800
Phone: 617 552-8000
Web: WWW.BC.EDU

PRODUCTS/OPERATIONS

Selected Colleges and Schools
Carolyn A. and Peter S. Lynch School of Education
College of Arts and Sciences
Graduate School of Arts and Sciences
Graduate School of Social Work
James A. Woods S.J. College of Advancing Studies
School of Law
School of Theology and Ministry
Wallace E. Carroll School of Management
William F. Connell School of Nursing

HISTORICAL FINANCIALS

Company Type: Private

Income Statement				FYE: May 31
	REVENUE ($ mil.)	NET INCOME ($ mil.)	NET PROFIT MARGIN	EMPLOYEES
05/21	889	1,274	143.2%	2,493
05/20	865	(41)	—	—
05/18	835	169	20.2%	—
05/17	798	279	34.9%	—
Annual Growth	2.7%	46.2%	—	—

2021 Year-End Financials
Return on assets: 19.8%   Cash ($ mil.): 20
Return on equity: 26.3%
Current ratio: —

TRUSTEES OF DARTMOUTH COLLEGE

Part of the esteemed Ivy League Dartmouth College is a private four-year liberal arts college with an enrollment of more than 6000 students. The university has an undergraduate college (offering about 40 programs) and graduate schools of business engineering and medicine plus graduate programs in the arts and sciences. Its student-teacher ratio is about 6:1. It is also home to a number of centers and institutes including Children's Hospital at Dartmouth; Dartmouth Center on Addiction Recovery and Education; and Center for Digital Strategies. Notable alumni include Daniel Webster Robert Frost Theodore "Dr. Seuss" Geisel and Nelson Rockefeller.

Operations
Dartmouth is located on a 270-acre campus located in Hanover New Hampshire. It also conducts study-abroad programs in about 20 countries. Through its collective institutes and graduate schools the college conducts a number of research programs in areas including security capitalism energy and infectious disease. Altogether it has about 50 research-focused groups centers and institutes and attracts more than $200 million in sponsored research funding per year.

Financial Performance
For fiscal year 2011 Dartmouth reported revenues of some $763 million. Operating expenses for fiscal 2011 were some $738 million. Dartmouth has an endowment of some $3.5 billion.

Company Background
Dartmouth is the nation's ninth oldest college founded in 1769 by Reverend Eleazar Wheelock a Congregational minister from Connecticut. Land for its campus in Hanover New Hampshire was conveyed by a charter from King George III; it was the last institution of higher education established in the US under colonial rule.

EXECUTIVES

Pres, Philip J Hanlon
Assistant Professor, John D Trout
Assistant Director, Karl Von Dubuche
Assistant Professor, Kelsey Wheeler
Assistant Professor, Linda M Hoover
Assistant Professor, Michael E Cox
Assistant Professor, Beverly J Entwisle
Assistant Professor, Marc L Bertrand
Assistant Professor, Richard F Hobbs
Assistant Professor, William B Gunn
Assistant Professor, Ralph D Beasley
Auditors: PRICEWATERHOUSECOOPERS LLP B

LOCATIONS

HQ: TRUSTEES OF DARTMOUTH COLLEGE
6001 PARKHURST HALL # 207, HANOVER, NH 037553529
Phone: 603 646-1110
Web: WWW.HOME.DARTMOUTH.EDU

PRODUCTS/OPERATIONS

Selected Divisions
Admissions and Financial Aid
Advancement Office
Campus Planning and Facilities
Dean of the College
Faculty of the Arts & Sciences
Finance and Administration
Geisel School of Medicine
President's Office
Provost's Office
Thayer School of Engineering
The Trustees of Dartmouth College
Tuck School of Business

HISTORICAL FINANCIALS

Company Type: Private

Income Statement				FYE: June 30
	REVENUE ($ mil.)	NET INCOME ($ mil.)	NET PROFIT MARGIN	EMPLOYEES
06/21	1,028	2,858	277.9%	5,000
06/20	909	411	45.2%	—
06/17	1,369	691	50.5%	—
06/16	859	(301)	—	—
Annual Growth	3.7%	—	—	—

2021 Year-End Financials
Return on assets: 24.1%   Cash ($ mil.): 299
Return on equity: 28.5%
Current ratio: —

TRUSTEES OF INDIANA UNIVERSITY

Indiana University has been schooling Hoosiers (and others) since 1820. With a population of some 71000+ degree seeking undergraduate students 19000 students in graduate program 200 international students from 164 countries. The university's flagship institution IU-Bloomington; regional campuses in Fort Wayne Gary Kokomo New Albany Richmond and South Bend; and an urban campus in Indianapolis that is operated with Purdue University. The university has about 20000 faculty and professional and support staff. It has 200 research centers and institutes and offers 380 overseas study programs in more than 70 countries in 20 languages.

Operations
The university offers more than 200 undergraduate majors and more than 300 graduate programs; it also boasts more than 380 study-abroad programs.

Indiana University has more than 700000+ total living alumni and the university charged undergraduate tuition and fees of $11 2020 for residents and $37600 for non-residents.

Indiana University-Purdue University Indianapolis (IUPUI) is considered number #1 nonprofit management graduate program number #1 environmental policy and management graduate program ranking and campus statistics in university by U.S. News and World Report. With nearly 17 schools and degrees granted in more than 255+ academic programs and 95+purdue university academic program.

Geographic Reach
The university has major campuses in Bloomington and Indianapolis and regional campuses in Gary Kokomo New Albany Richmond and South Bend. It enrolls more than 50% of the students from the St. Joseph County area.

Sales and Marketing
The University markets its academic programs through websites.

Company Background
An 1820 statute created the Indiana Seminary the predecessor to Indiana University. In 1828 the legislature changed the name of the institution to Indiana College and in 1838 it established Indiana University.

EXECUTIVES

Chb, Michael J Mirro
V Chb, Patrick A Shoulders
Trustee, Maryellen Kiley Bishop
Trustee, W Quinn Buckner
Trustee, James T Morris
Chancellor, Iu South Bend, Una Mae Reck
Assistant Director, Charles De Witt
Accounting Staff, Tereasa West
Acting Director, Mike Jenson
Assistant Vice President Finan, Linda Hunt
Information Specialist, Andrew Korty
Auditors: PAUL D JOYCE CPA STATE EXAM

LOCATIONS

HQ: TRUSTEES OF INDIANA UNIVERSITY
107 S INDIANA AVE, BLOOMINGTON, IN 474057000
Phone: 812 855-4848
Web: WWW.TRUSTEES.IU.EDU

PRODUCTS/OPERATIONS

2015 Sales

	$ mil.	% of total
Student fees	1,118	51
Auxiliary enterprises	318	14
Federal grants & contracts	293	13
Non-governement grants & contracts	136	6
Sales and services of educational units	39	2
State & local grants & contracts	21	1
Other revenue	279	13
Total	**2,207**	**100**

HISTORICAL FINANCIALS
Company Type: Private

Income Statement				FYE: June 30
	REVENUE ($ mil.)	NET INCOME ($ mil.)	NET PROFIT MARGIN	EMPLOYEES
06/16	2,256	105	4.7%	16,000
06/15	2,207	138	6.3%	—
06/14	2,195	201	9.2%	—
06/13	2,146	189	8.8%	—
Annual Growth	1.7%	(17.7%)	—	—

2016 Year-End Financials
Return on assets: 2.0% Cash ($ mil.): 345
Return on equity: 2.8%
Current ratio: 1.60

TRUSTEES OF THE ESTATE OF BERNICE PAUAHI BISHOP

Kamehameha Schools provides an education fit for a king ... or queen. The private charitable trust was founded and endowed by Princess Bernice Pauahi Bishop great granddaughter and last royal descendant of Kamehameha the Great. One of the largest independent schools in the US Kamehameha educates more than 5000 elementary middle school and high school students many of whom board at one of its three Hawaii campuses. In addition it operates some 30 preschools with a total enrollment of about 1500. Kamehameha Schools is also the largest private property owner in the state of Hawaii and uses the proceeds from its real estate operations to support its schools.

EXECUTIVES
Ceo, Dee Jay Mailer
V Pres-Cfo, Michael Loo
Trustee-Chmn, Robert K U Kihune
Trustee, J Douglas Ing
Trustee, Diane J Plotts
Trustee-Dir, Nainoa Thompson
Asst Bkpr, Lisa Kokuri
ADM Asst, Liza Yucoco
Bkpr, Ermina Aflague
Asst Contrl, Ramona Hinck
Coordinator, Denise Ka
Auditors: ERNST & YOUNG US LLP SAN DIEG

LOCATIONS
HQ: TRUSTEES OF THE ESTATE OF BERNICE PAUAHI BISHOP
567 S KING ST STE 200, HONOLULU, HI 968133079
Phone: 808 523-6200
Web: WWW.KSBE.EDU

COMPETITORS
Edison Learning   Learning Care Group

HISTORICAL FINANCIALS
Company Type: Private

Income Statement				FYE: June 30
	REVENUE ($ mil.)	NET INCOME ($ mil.)	NET PROFIT MARGIN	EMPLOYEES
06/20	548	14	2.7%	1,500
06/15	767	333	43.5%	—
06/14	915	482	52.7%	—
06/13	519	109	21.1%	—
Annual Growth	0.8%	(24.8%)	—	—

2020 Year-End Financials
Return on assets: 0.2%   Cash ($ mil.): 36
Return on equity: 0.2%
Current ratio: 0.80

TRUSTEES OF TUFTS COLLEGE

Tufts University wants to light up the minds of New England scholars. The school offers undergraduate and graduate degrees in areas such as education engineering psychology art English music and medicine. The university enrolls some 11000 students and has 1300 faculty members and it offers classes in 70 fields at three campuses in Massachusetts (Boston Medford/Somerville and Grafton). It also has an international campus in Talloires France. Tufts University's Fletcher School of Law and Diplomacy is the oldest continuous international relations graduate program in the country. The school is also home to New England's only Veterinary School.

Operations
Tufts University has a number of research programs at all three campuses including clinical studies in medical dental veterinary and nutritional fields. It also has research programs in areas such as biology engineering and technology many of which are funded through grants and fellowship funds.

Financial Performance
Tufts University has an endowment of about $1.1 billion.

Strategy
Tufts University is working to expand the resources its School of Medicine. In 2012 it moved to add a new medical research lab to study serious infectious diseases (such as tuberculosis) within the Biomedical Research and Public Health Building. It also expanded the Cummings School of Veterinary Medicine by adding a new clinic for the care and study of pets with obesity problems. The university also expands by adding new degree programs such as a doctorate in mamalian genetics in 2011.

Company Background
Tufts was founded in 1852 through a land donation by Boston-area businessman Charles Tufts to the Universalist Church. The school adopted its motto Pax et Lux (Peace and Light) in 1857.

EXECUTIVES
Pres, Anthony Monaco
Exec V Pres*, Steven S Manos
Sr V Pres-Provost*, Sol Gittleman

Sr V Pres-Development*, Thomas W Murnane
V Pres Fin-Treas*, Thomas S Mc Gurty
V Pres-Human Relations*, Kathe Cronin
V Pres-Operations*, John Roberto
SEC*, Linda J Dixon
Chb*, Nathan Gantcher
Chairman*, James A Stern
Assistant Professor, David Paul
Auditors: PRICEWATERHOUSECOOPERS LLP BO

LOCATIONS
HQ: TRUSTEES OF TUFTS COLLEGE
169 HOLLAND ST STE 318, SOMERVILLE, MA 021442401
Phone: 617 628-5000
Web: WWW.TUFTS.EDU

PRODUCTS/OPERATIONS

Schools & Colleges
Cummings School of Veterinary Science
Graduate School of Arts & Sciences
The Fletcher School
Friedman School of Nutrition Science and Policy
Sackler School of Graduate Biomedical Sciences
School of Arts & Sciences
School of Dental Medicine
School of Engineering
School of Medicine
Tisch College of Citizenship and Public Service

HISTORICAL FINANCIALS
Company Type: Private

Income Statement				FYE: June 30
	REVENUE ($ mil.)	NET INCOME ($ mil.)	NET PROFIT MARGIN	EMPLOYEES
06/21	1,033	805	78.0%	4,100
06/20	1,118	32	2.9%	—
06/15	914	(25)	—	—
06/14	965	68	7.1%	—
Annual Growth	1.0%	42.3%	—	—

2021 Year-End Financials
Return on assets: 16.6%   Cash ($ mil.): 90
Return on equity: 23.0%
Current ratio: —

TRUVEN HOLDING CORP.

EXECUTIVES
Pres- Ceo, Mike Boswood
Exec V Pres, Phil Buckingham
Exec V Pres, Jon Newpol
Coo, Roy Martin
Gen Counsel, Andra Heller
Senior Director Information Te, Bryan Smith
Director Account Management, Roy Crowdis
Auditors: PRICEWATERHOUSECOOPERS LLP NE

LOCATIONS
HQ: TRUVEN HOLDING CORP.
100 PHOENIX DR STE 100 # 100, ANN ARBOR, MI 481082600
Phone: 734 913-3000
Web: WWW.IBM.COM

HISTORICAL FINANCIALS

Company Type: Private

Income Statement				FYE: December 31
	REVENUE ($ mil.)	NET INCOME ($ mil.)	NET PROFIT MARGIN	EMPLOYEES
12/15	610	(75)	—	2,110
12/14	544	(37)	—	—
12/13	492	(344)	—	—
12/12	241	(54)	—	—
Annual Growth	36.2%	—	—	—

2015 Year-End Financials

Return on assets: (-6.4%) Cash ($ mil.): 14
Return on equity: —
Current ratio: 0.80

TSVC, INC.

EXECUTIVES

Tax Specialist, Krista Johnson
Senior Litigation, Aaron Mann
Geologist, Abraham Knierim
Materials Coordinator, Alan Bridges
Field Technician, Alan Lacaze
Technician, Antwuan Crowder
Field Project Manager, Barry Tuttle
Administrative Staff II, Beverly Edwards
Senior Engineer, Bill Martin
Field Technician, Blake Pavioni
Project Inspection, Brandon Rose
Auditors: BKD LLP KANSAS CITY MO

LOCATIONS

HQ: TSVC, INC.
 10841 S RIDGEVIEW RD, OLATHE, KS 660616456
Phone: 913 599-6886
Web: WWW.TSVCONTRACTING.COM

HISTORICAL FINANCIALS

Company Type: Private

Income Statement				FYE: December 31
	REVENUE ($ mil.)	NET INCOME ($ mil.)	NET PROFIT MARGIN	EMPLOYEES
12/20	818	44	5.5%	4,000
12/18	751	30	4.1%	—
Annual Growth	4.3%	20.7%	—	—

2020 Year-End Financials

Return on assets: 9.6% Cash ($ mil.): 25
Return on equity: 15.9%
Current ratio: 3.20

TUCSON MEDICAL CENTER

EXECUTIVES

Pres-Ceo, Judith F Rich
V Pres*, Linda Wojtowicz
Chief Medical Offc, Palmer Evans
Internist, Jeffrey Robertson

Adminstrative Associate, Leanna Dominguez
Senior Network Engineer, Marcus Medina
Executive Assistant, Becky Hiser
Registered Nurse, Erica Kaercher
Vice President, Julia Strange
Manager Pharmacy, Claudia Koreny
Director Compensation, Igor Shegolev

LOCATIONS

HQ: TUCSON MEDICAL CENTER
 5301 E GRANT RD, TUCSON, AZ 857122874
Phone: 520 327-5461
Web: WWW.TMCAZ.COM

HISTORICAL FINANCIALS

Company Type: Private

Income Statement				FYE: December 31
	REVENUE ($ mil.)	NET INCOME ($ mil.)	NET PROFIT MARGIN	EMPLOYEES
12/19	615	22	3.7%	4,455
12/17	559	19	3.4%	—
12/14	449	12	2.8%	—
12/13	462	16	3.5%	—
Annual Growth	4.9%	6.0%	—	—

2019 Year-End Financials

Return on assets: 4.7% Cash ($ mil.): 34
Return on equity: 8.1%
Current ratio: 0.90

TUDOR INVESTMENT CORPORATION

EXECUTIVES

Chb-Ceo, Paul T Jones II
Ceo*, Mark Dalton JD
Cfo*, John Torell
Information Specialist, Emil Zahariev
Engineer, Enxiang Jiang
Information Specialist, Jonathan Schnapp
Captain, Dan Fennessy
Engineer, Waikin Wong
Vice President Software Develo, Amit Wadhwa
Research Analyst, Elie Kobrin
Director, Yuri Okane
Auditors: ERNST & YOUNG LLP NEW YORK N

LOCATIONS

HQ: TUDOR INVESTMENT CORPORATION
 200 ELM ST STE 200 # 200, STAMFORD, CT
 069023826
Phone: 203 863-6700
Web: WWW.TUDOR.COM

COMPETITORS

Actua	Menlo Ventures
Draper Fisher	Nea
Jurvetson	Us Venture Partners
Entrust Capital	Wexford Capital
Hummer Winblad	Vcap Investments
Kleiner Perkins	

HISTORICAL FINANCIALS

Company Type: Private

Income Statement				FYE: December 31
	ASSETS ($ mil.)	NET INCOME ($ mil.)	INCOME AS % OF ASSETS	EMPLOYEES
12/15	831	222	26.7%	291
12/14	819	(80)	—	—
12/13	905	486	53.7%	—
12/11	624	187	30.0%	—
Annual Growth	7.4%	4.4%	—	—

2015 Year-End Financials

Return on assets: 26.7% Sales ($ mil.): 784
Return on equity: 47.5%

TUFTS MEDICAL CENTER, INC.

EXECUTIVES

Pres-Ceo, Michael Wagner
Chb, Malcolm Sherman
Pres, Deeb Salem
Prin, Saul Weingart
Patient Access Coordinator, Stephen Giuliana
Patient Coordinator, Sue A Leong-Tsan
Staff Attending Physician, Susan Liang
Administrative Assistant, Suzanne Maxwell
Director Practice Management S, Theresa Reilly
Radiation Safety Officer, Tom McMahon
Professor of Medicine, John Wong
Auditors: DELOITTE & TOUCHE LLP BOSTON

LOCATIONS

HQ: TUFTS MEDICAL CENTER, INC.
 800 WASHINGTON ST, BOSTON, MA 021111552
Phone: 617 636-2254
Web: WWW.TUFTSMEDICALCENTER.ORG

HISTORICAL FINANCIALS

Company Type: Private

Income Statement				FYE: September 30
	REVENUE ($ mil.)	NET INCOME ($ mil.)	NET PROFIT MARGIN	EMPLOYEES
09/17	681	12	1.8%	3,800
09/16	646	14	2.3%	—
09/15	595	(18)	—	—
Annual Growth	7.0%	—	—	—

2017 Year-End Financials

Return on assets: 1.8% Cash ($ mil.): 21
Return on equity: 12.2%
Current ratio: 1.40

TURNER CONSTRUCTION COMPANY INC

Turner Construction has been the mastermind for scores of head-turning projects for more than a century. The company that built Madison Square

Garden has ranked among the leading general builders in the US since the early 1900s. Turner provides construction and project management services for commercial and multifamily buildings airports and stadiums as well as correctional educational entertainment and manufacturing facilities. The company is also a leader in sustainable or green building practices. Founded in 1902 by Henry Turner the company is the main operating unit of The Turner Corporation which is a subsidiary of German construction group HOCHTIEF.

Operations

Turner Construction works on some 1500 projects each year. For decades Turner has kept tabs on construction prices with its quarterly Building Cost Index which forecasts construction costs by considering labor rates productivity and material prices.

The index is used by federal and state governments to track building costs and pricing trends.

As part of HOCHTIEF's Americas division Turner works alongside other contractors in the US and Canada such as Flatiron its subsidiary E.E. Cruz and Clark Builders.

Geographic Reach

Headquartered in New York Turner Construction has offices across North America and with a presence in about 20 countries. It has operations in Latin America and the Caribbean India Europe Southeast Asia and the Middle East.

Sales and Marketing

Turner Construction works on projects in industries including aviation transportation commercial entertainment government green building manufacturing pharmaceutical research & development retail and sports.

Company Background

Notable projects in Turner Construction's history include the World War II Memorial in Washington DC the John F. Kennedy Memorial Library in Boston and the Rock and Roll Hall of Fame. Turner also built the new Yankee Stadium in New York. The company reached a milestone in 2008 by inking its 15000th major contract.

EXECUTIVES

Pres-Ceo, Peter J Davoren
Sr V Pres-Cfo, Karen Gould
Exec V Pres, Nicholas Billotti
Exec V Pres, Pasquale A Difilippo
Coo, John Diciurcio
Evp, Christa Andresky
Evp, Rosemarie Demonte
Engineer, Bernice Estrada
Spo Project Manager, Brad Fry
Project Engineer, Brintel Johnson
Safety Director, Charles Johnson
Auditors: DELOITTE & TOUCHE LLP PRINCET

LOCATIONS

HQ: TURNER CONSTRUCTION COMPANY INC
 375 HUDSON ST FL 6, NEW YORK, NY 100143667
Phone: 212 229-6000
Web: WWW.TURNERCONSTRUCTION.COM

PRODUCTS/OPERATIONS

Selected Services
Turner Engineering Group
Design+Build
Turner Logistics: Procurement Services
Medical Planning and Procurement
Building Information Modeling (BIM)
Lean Construction

COMPETITORS

Bechtel	Hunt Construction
C. G. Schmidt	Jacobs Engineering
Catamount Constructors	Pcl Employees Holdings
Dimeo Construction	Parsons Corporation
Dooleymack	Peter Kiewit Sons'
English Construction Company	Shook National
F.a. Wilhelm	Skanska Usa Building
Fluor	Structure Tone
Gilbane Building Company	Tully Construction
Hensel Phelps Construction	Tutor Perini
	Winter Construction

HISTORICAL FINANCIALS
Company Type: Private

Income Statement				FYE: December 31
	REVENUE ($ mil.)	NET INCOME ($ mil.)	NET PROFIT MARGIN	EMPLOYEES
12/14	10,516	96	0.9%	5,000
12/13	9,488	76	0.8%	—
12/12	8,552	70	0.8%	—
Annual Growth	10.9%	17.2%	—	—

2014 Year-End Financials

Return on assets: 2.8%
Return on equity: 14.1%
Current ratio: 1.10

Cash ($ mil.): 188

TURTLE & HUGHES, INC

Turtle & Hughes is one of the nation's largest independent electrical and industrial distributors. The company's exhaustive lineup is sold through two divisions: Electrical/Industrial Distribution which operates in about 20 branches and provides electrical services and solutions backed by a commitment to technical and product expertise and Turtle & Hughes Integrated Supply (THIS) which has proven its leadership in the industrial supply market by partnering with global companies to reduce their total cost of ownership. Its customers include industries such as electricalconstruction energy management infrastructure oil and gas utility specialty markets and materials management. Family-owned the company is led by its first non-family CEO Kathleen Shanahan.

Operations

Turtle & Hughes is organized into two divisions: the Electrical Distribution division provides electrical services and solutions backed by a commitment to technical and product expertise and Turtle & Hughes Integrated Supply (THIS) which has proven its leadership in the industrial supply market by partnering with global companies to reduce their total cost of ownership.

It offers products such as automation cable strays and struts conduit and conduit fittings electrical boxes and covers fasteners and hardware. It also offers alarms security and signaling batteries fuses blocks and holders and heat cables among others.

Geographic Reach

Turtle & Hughes headquartered in Linden New Jersey operates through about 20 branches across the US.

Sales and Marketing

The company serves industries including electrical construction energy management infrastructure oil & gas utility specialty markets and materials management.

Company Background

Turtle & Hughes was founded in 1923 as an electrical supply house.

EXECUTIVES

Ceo, Kathleen Shanahan
Pres*, Scott West
Coo*, Kevin Doyle
Cob*, Jayne Millard
Cfo*, Christopher Rausch
SEC*, Michael Matejek
Senior Vice President, Al Fernandes
Accounts Payable, Deborah Grainger
Vice President, Joseph Drummond
Inside Sales Representative, Patricia Fisher
Site Manager, Rick Bernier
Auditors: EISNERAMPER LLP ISELIN NEW J

LOCATIONS

HQ: TURTLE & HUGHES, INC
 1900 LOWER RD, LINDEN, NJ 070366586
Phone: 732 574-3600
Web: WWW.TURTLE.COM

PRODUCTS/OPERATIONS

Selected Products
Datacom categories
 Anchors and fasteners
 Burial products/innerduct
 Cabinets and enclosures
 Cable management
 Cable tray/ladder rack
 Category rated and coax cable
 Connectivity
 Fiber-optic cable
 Hand tools
 Outside plant
 Power protection
 Raceway and duct systems
 Safety
 Security fencing
 Splices connectors and lugs
 Tools testers and safety
Electrical categories
 Alarms annunciators and signals
 Anchors and plugs
 Automation products
 Ballasts and transformers
 Batteries and flashlights
 Box enclosures
 Breakers panels and switchgears
 Cable trays and struts
 Conduit fittings
 Cord connectors
 Dimming controls
 Electrical tools
 Emergency lighting
 Enclosures
 Fans
 Fluorescent lighting
 Fuse holders and terminal blocks
 Generators
 Groundings
 Heat shrink
 Heating
 High-bay lighting
 Incandescent lighting
 Lamps
 Limit temp. and proximity switch
 Lugs and terminals
 Metering equipment
 Motor control
 Motors AC and DC drivers
 Outdoor lighting
 Pole line products
 Programmable controls
 Relays
 Strut/channel
 Test equipment
 Time clocks
 Transformers
 Wire cable and cord
 Wiring accessories
 Wiring devices
Industrial categories
 Adhesives and tapes
 Brushes and brooms
 Carbide tools
 Cutting fluid/lubricant
 Cutting tools
 Fasteners
 Hand tools
 Hoist chain and accessories

Industrial abrasives
Janitorial paper supplies
Ladders
Locks
Lubricating devices
Material handling
MRO supplies
Paint/markets
Pipe hangers
Pipe valves and fittings
Pneumatics
Pneumatic tools
Power tools
Safety equipment
Saw blades
Shim/shim stock
Solenoid valves
Strut/channel
Tooling accessories

COMPETITORS

C. R. Laurence
Consolidated
 Electrical
Dillon Supply
Graybar Electric
Indoff
Interline Brands
Kennametal

Msc Industrial Direct
Prime Advantage
Rexel Inc.
Sonepar Usa
Steiner Electric
W.w. Grainger
Wesco International

HISTORICAL FINANCIALS

Company Type: Private

Income Statement   FYE: September 30

	REVENUE ($ mil.)	NET INCOME ($ mil.)	NET PROFIT MARGIN	EMPLOYEES
09/19	758	21	2.8%	900
09/18	754	20	2.7%	—
09/17	671	18	2.7%	—
09/16	628	16	2.6%	—
Annual Growth	6.4%	8.9%	—	—

2019 Year-End Financials

Return on assets: 8.1%   Cash ($ mil.): 11
Return on equity: 15.8%
Current ratio: 2.00

U.S. GENERAL SERVICES ADMINISTRATION

The U.S. General Services Administration (GSA) manages the rental of more than 370 million square feet of real estate in US government-owned properties. In addition to acting as the government's landlord in obtaining office space for over a million federal workers the GSA also manages properties and supplies equipment telecommunications and information technology products to its customer agencies. It spends some $55 billion annually for goods and services supporting about 8700 buildings and more than 205000 vehicles. The agency operates through divisions including the Federal Acquisition Service and Public Buildings Service. The GSA was established in 1949 to streamline the administrative work of the federal government.

Operations

GSA comprises the Federal Acquisition Service (FAS) the Public Buildings Service (PBS) and the Office of Government-wide Policy (OGP). In addition it operates over 10 staff offices and two independent offices.

Through a network of service providers FAS delivers information technology products and serv-

ices telecommunications services travel and transportation management motor vehicles and fleet services and issues some 5.1 million charge cards on average.

PBS operates within two divisions?workspace acquisition and property management. It acquires space for the federal government through new construction and leasing and leases almost 370 million square feet of workspace in more than 8700 buildings over 400 of which are on the National Register of Historic Places. PBS also manages the disposal of unused properties.

The OGP develops government policy and performance standards conducting data analysis and benchmarking and transparently reporting Government-wide data. It provides data analysis and transparent reporting to drive efficiency across key administrative areas including travel and transportation acquisition fleet management information technology modernization and real estate management.

Overall Acquisition Services Fund (ASF) accounts for over 55% of sales while Federal Buildings Fund (FBF) accounts for around 40%.

Geographic Reach

Headquartered in Washington DC the U.S. General Services Administration provides services and support to more than 60 Federal departments and agencies. It delivers goods and services across the country and overseas through more than 10 regional offices located in major US cities.

Sales and Marketing

The company's FBF top customers are US department of Justice and US Department of Homeland Security with over 15% each while ASF top customer is the US Department of Defense which accounts for over 65%.

Strategy

GSA believes that its people systems supplies processes and technology all work together to drive progress save money and help the Nation realize the benefits of our long-term and strategic investments. GSA leverages the collective buying power of the Federal Government to acquire more than $75 billion in goods and services in support of agency customers. At the same time GSA's acquisition teams focus on reducing contract duplication which allows customer agencies to more effectively use their resources to fulfill their missions. For example category management is a Government-wide initiative managed by the Office of Management and Budget (OMB) and supported by GSA which allows the Government to buy smarter by segmenting its spend into groups of related products or services enabling consolidation and efficiency. Since its 2014 launch the category management program has saved the Federal Government approximately $40 billion. Our Federal Marketplace Strategy (FMP) is another facet of our acquisitions strategy and is designed to create a seamless people-centric buying and selling experience. In support of FMP GSA consolidated 24 multiple award contract schedules into a single contract vehicle that provides consistent terms and conditions and simplifies the procurement process for buyers (agencies) and sellers (industry).

Company Background

The U.S. General Services Administration was established by President Harry Truman in 1949 to streamline the administrative work of the federal government. It consolidated the National Archives Establishment the Federal Works Agency the Public Buildings Administration the Bureau of Federal Supply the Office of Contract Settlement and the War Assets Administration into one federal agency delivering and managing supplies and providing workplaces for federal employees.

GSA's original mission was to dispose of war surplus goods manage and store government

records handle emergency preparedness and stockpile strategic supplies for wartime.

EXECUTIVES

Admin, Emily W Murphy
Acting Admin*, Timothy Horne
CIO*, Casey Coleman
Cfo*, Kathleen M Turco
Chief Innovation Adviser, Offi*, Rob Cook
General Counsel*, Jack St John
Commissioner*, Alan Thomas
Deputy Admin*, Allison F Brigati
Law, Dana M Blank
Law, Jennifer Beck
Law, Lisa Norgren

LOCATIONS

HQ: U.S. GENERAL SERVICES ADMINISTRATION
1800 F ST NW RM 6100, WASHINGTON, DC
204050001
Phone: 202 501-0450
Web: WWW.GSA.GOV

PRODUCTS/OPERATIONS

2018 Sales

	$ mil.	% of total
Federal Buildings Fund		
Building Operations-Leased	6,420	26
Building Operations-Government Owned	5,261	21
Acquisition Services Fund		
Assisted Acquisition Services	7,043	29
Travel Transportation and Logistics	2,060	8
Information Technology	1,786	7
General Supplies and Services	1,300	5
Professional Services and Human Capital	87	-
Other Programs	113	1
Other Funds		
Working Capital Fund	657	3
Other General	37	-
Eliminations	(921)	-
Total	**23,843**	**100**

Selected Products and ServicesFacilities & ConstructionConstruction Related MaterialsFacility Related MaterialsFacility Related ServicesHuman CapitalAdministrative ServicesHuman Capital and Training SolutionsHuman Resources SystemGeneral Support Services

HISTORICAL FINANCIALS

Company Type: Private

Income Statement   FYE: September 30

	REVENUE ($ mil.)	NET INCOME ($ mil.)	NET PROFIT MARGIN	EMPLOYEES
09/16	20,457	290	1.4%	13,000
09/15*	38,976	486	1.2%	—
12/05	0	0	—	—
Annual Growth	—	—	—	—

*Fiscal year change

U.S. VENTURE, INC.

Privately held US Venture Inc is a North American leader in the distribution of fuel and transportation products. US Oil its division transports more than 2 billion gallons of fuel annually via pipelines rail light oil-barges and trucks. The division maintains over 7.5 million BOE in storage capacity and has access to nearly 200 terminals. Through US AutoForce the company is also a top distributor of tires and car parts to independent tire retailers auto repair shops and dealerships. The company's Lubricants division maintains a competitive business as well set up to blend and market chemical products to automotive industrial and metalworking industries. Through the GAIN Clean Fuel brand US Venture also sells clean bio-fuels.

Operations

US Venture has six business divisions.

US Oil is a leading distributor of branded and unbranded refined products in the US and Canada. It transports more than 2 billion gallons of energy products annually. US Oil also engages in energy trading.

Tires car parts and lubricants are distributed through the US AutoForce division another industry leader. Its portfolio includes more than 35 tire brands beyond 15 lubricant brands and many branded car parts (mostly brakes chassis repair equipment and exhausts).

US Lubricants blends and distributes lubricants under its THRIVE brand for automotive industrial and metalworking needs. It also provides support services like mobile filtration systems oil analysis lab services and fluids storage and handling systems.

US Venture is also developing and building alternative fuel transportation networks and filling stations in the US. Headed by the US GAIN division the company supplies compressed natural gas (CNG) and renewable natural gas (RNG) to more than 50 fueling stations.

Breakthrough provides innovative transportation and supply chain strategies for the world's leading shippers. IGEN build excise tax software that meets the needs of the motor fuel industry.

Geographic Reach

Headquartered in Appleton Wisconsin US Venture operates throughout North America. US Oil handles fuel supply in the Midwest with 25 terminals and nearly 200 third-party terminal partners. The company has a concentration of fuel tires car parts and convenience store services in the Midwest. It distributes fuels car parts and lubricants in North America.

Sales and Marketing

The US Oil division distributes products from a-dozen major oil brands including BP Shell Exxon Mobil Marathon Citgo Sunoco Clark and Phillips 66. It offers flexible pricing and fixed-fuel contracts and commodity trading. Traded products include gasoline ethanol biodiesel jet fuels propane and butane. In the Midwest the company also owns the Express chain of convenience stores.

US AutoForce offers more than 35 tire brands including Michelin Bridgestone Dunlop Firestone and Goodyear. Together with US Lubricants it serve the agricultural construction forestry marine and mining industries. US Lubricants also supplies its products to automotive dealerships repair shops lube shops and tire centers and customers in commercial transportation as well as industrial and metalworking lubricants.

US Venture is a major sponsor of the USA Luge team.

Company Background

U.S. Oil was established in 1951 as Schmidt Oil by the sons of local fuel distributor Albert Schmidt. The company changed its name to U.S. Venture in 2010 to reflect the company's increasingly diverse portfolio of entrepreneurial businesses. It has remained family-owned since its inception and today it is one of the largest privately held companies in Wisconsin.

EXECUTIVES

Pres-Ceo, John A Schmidt
Exec Chm*, Thomas A Schmidt
Cfo*, Jay Walters
Staff, Brent Brigham
Marketing Manager, Victor Van Stralen

Payroll Staff, Jane Arnoldussen
Vp, Marketing and Strategy, Jeff Van Brunt
Comp, Charles Clarey
Sales Manager, Joe Bailey
Customer Representativ, Thomas Johnson
Regional Operations Manager, Ben Hermus
Auditors: DELOITTE & TOUCHE LLP MILWAU

LOCATIONS

HQ: U.S. VENTURE, INC.
425 BETTER WAY, APPLETON, WI 549156192
Phone: 920 739-6101
Web: WWW.USVENTURE.COM

PRODUCTS/OPERATIONS

Selected Operations

U.S. AutoForce (exhaust pipe manufacturing and autoparts distribution)
U.S. Lubricants (motor oil and related products)
U.S. Oil (gasoline fuel oil and natural gas)
U.S Gain (compressed natural gas)

COMPETITORS

American Tire Distributors	Petroleum Traders Corporation
Guttman Oil	

HISTORICAL FINANCIALS

Company Type: Private

Income Statement   FYE: July 31

	REVENUE ($ mil.)	NET INCOME ($ mil.)	NET PROFIT MARGIN	EMPLOYEES
07/15	8,076	173	2.1%	1,673
07/14	9,088	49	0.5%	—
07/13	7,346	47	0.6%	—
Annual Growth	4.9%	91.7%	—	—

2015 Year-End Financials

Return on assets: 16.9%   Cash ($ mil.): 13
Return on equity: 53.2%
Current ratio: 1.70

UAW RETIREE MEDICAL BENEFITS TRUST

EXECUTIVES

Head of Trustees, Robert Naftaly
Prin, Rober Naftaly
Director Communications, Matthew Wood
Senior Managing Director, Benjamin Cotton
Manager Strategic Opportunitie, Adrian Ohmer
Vice President, Cindy Estrada
Chief Officer, Gina Buccalo
Chief Investment Officer, Hershel Harper
Council, Horace Sheffield
General Counsel, Linda Denomme
Consultant, Nils Larson
Auditors: DELOITTE TAX LLP DETROIT MI

LOCATIONS

HQ: UAW RETIREE MEDICAL BENEFITS TRUST
200 WALKER ST STE 400, DETROIT, MI 482074229
Phone: 313 324-5900
Web: WWW.RHAC.COM

HISTORICAL FINANCIALS

Company Type: Private

Income Statement   FYE: December 31

	ASSETS ($ mil.)	NET INCOME ($ mil.)	INCOME AS % OF ASSETS	EMPLOYEES
12/18	60,352	1,176	1.9%	94
12/17	63,225	88	0.1%	—
12/16	58,966	(1,839)	—	—
Annual Growth	1.2%	—	—	—

2018 Year-End Financials

Return on assets: 1.9%   Sales ($ mil): 5,050
Return on equity: 2.1%

UC HEALTH, LLC.

From its flagship University of Cincinnati Medical Center to its state-of-the-art West Chester Hospital UC Health provides cancer care dental care surgery transplant trauma care and women's health. UC Health includes University of Cincinnati Medical Center West Chester Hospital Daniel Drake Center for Post-Acute Care UC Gardner Neuroscience Institute Lindner Center of HOPE Bridgeway Pointe and University of Cincinnati Physicians. The not-for-profit UC Health was formed in 2010 as collaboration between University of Cincinnati Physicians University of Cincinnati Medical Center and West Chester Hospital.

Geographic Reach

UC Health has more than 40 locations across Ohio Kentucky and Indiana.

Company Background

Formerly known as The Health Alliance of Greater Cincinnati the company changed its name to UC Health in 2010 after a number of its hospital members left the system and the University of Cincinnati took control of the remaining operations. Rumors of dissolution had swirled around the organization since its members began jumping ship starting in 2007.

Four of the organization's founding hospitals ultimately left the system: The 175-bed Fort Hamilton Hospital (now part of Kettering Health Network) and the 210-bed Jewish Hospital (now part of Catholic Healthcare Partners) departed in 2010. Two other hospitals (St. Luke's and Christ Hospital) broke off from the alliance after a long legal struggle in 2007.

EXECUTIVES

Ceo, James Kingsbury
Svp-Chief Legal Officer*, Katrina M English
Vp-Cdao*, Michael Legg
Evp-Cmo-Int Coo*, Evaline Alessandrini
Telecommunications Staff, Larry Ziegler
Senior Vice President, Jay Brown
Graphic Designer, Kristin Hauck
Registered Nurse, Shawn Kise
Doctor, Cynthia Miller
Doctor, Emmett Oneal
Assistant Director Pharmacy, Nancy Lobas
Auditors: DELOITTE TAX LLP CINCINNATI

LOCATIONS

HQ: UC HEALTH, LLC.
3200 BURNET AVE, CINCINNATI, OH 452293019
Phone: 513 585-6000
Web: WWW.UCHEALTH.COM

PRODUCTS/OPERATIONS

Selected Ohio Facilities
Drake Center (Cincinnati)
Linder Center of HOPE (Mason)
UC Health Surgical Hospital (West Chester)
University of Cincinnati Physicians (Cincinnati)
University of Cincinnati Medical Center (Cincinnati)
West Chester Hospital (West Chester)

COMPETITORS

Catholic Health Initiatives	Premier Health Partners
Cincinnati Children's Hospital	St. Elizabeth Healthcare
Kettering Health Network	The Christ Hospital Corporation
Mercy Hospital Springfield	Trihealth

HISTORICAL FINANCIALS

Company Type: Private

Income Statement   FYE: June 30

	REVENUE ($ mil.)	NET INCOME ($ mil.)	NET PROFIT MARGIN	EMPLOYEES
06/18	1,661	40	2.5%	10,000
06/17	1,586	73	4.7%	—
06/10	138	(81)	—	—
06/09	102	0	—	—
Annual Growth	36.3%	—	—	—

2018 Year-End Financials

Return on assets: 2.5%   Cash ($ mil.): 76
Return on equity: 4.9%
Current ratio: 4.70

UFCW & EMPLOYERS TRUST LLC

EXECUTIVES

Administrator, Jody Osterweil
Information Technology, Ken Foulke
Payroll Manager, Norma Villa
Risk Management Consultant, Darren McClain
Senior Director of Human Resou, Carrie White
Member Representative, Danny Alves
Manager, Human Resources, Karen Dyer
Claims Supervisor, Lisa Colorado
Accounting Manager, Ontiveros Claudia
Chief Information Officer, Timothy May
Auditors: VAVRINEK TRINE DAY & CO LLP S

LOCATIONS

HQ: UFCW & EMPLOYERS TRUST LLC
  1000 BURNETT AVE STE 110, CONCORD, CA
  945202000
Phone: 800 552-2400
Web: WWW.UFCWTRUST.COM

HISTORICAL FINANCIALS

Company Type: Private

Income Statement   FYE: December 31

	ASSETS ($ mil.)	NET INCOME ($ mil.)	INCOME AS % OF ASSETS	EMPLOYEES
12/18	460	10	2.3%	200
12/17	455	18	4.1%	—
Annual Growth	1.0%	(44.2%)	—	—

2018 Year-End Financials

Return on assets: 2.3%   Sales ($ mil): 555
Return on equity: 3.0%

UFCW & EMPLOYERS TRUST LLC

Auditors: HEMMING MORSE CPA'S AND CONSUL

LOCATIONS

HQ: UFCW & EMPLOYERS TRUST LLC
  1000 BURNETT AVE STE 200, CONCORD, CA
  945202058
Phone: 925 609-9068
Web: WWW.UFCWTRUST.COM

HISTORICAL FINANCIALS

Company Type: Private

Income Statement   FYE: December 31

	REVENUE ($ mil.)	NET INCOME ($ mil.)	NET PROFIT MARGIN	EMPLOYEES
12/14	553	33	6.0%	4
12/13	544	16	3.0%	—
Annual Growth	1.7%	107.2%	—	—

2014 Year-End Financials

Return on assets: 14.2%   Cash ($ mil.): 81
Return on equity: 26.2%
Current ratio: 40.60

UGI UTILITIES, INC.

EXECUTIVES

Ceo, Robert F Beard
Chb*, Lon R Greenberg
V Chb*, John L Walsh
V Pres Fin Strategy-Cfo, Kirk R Oliver
Controller-Cao, Ann P Kelly
Pres, Hans G Bell
Svp-Customer & Government Rela, Vicki O Ebner
Specialist, Christine Kramlich
Customer Experience Lead, Kathy Iglar
Vp Rates & Supply, Christopher R Brown
Vp Env, Health & Safety, Joseph R Kopalek

LOCATIONS

HQ: UGI UTILITIES, INC.
  1 UGI DR, DENVER, PA 175179039
Phone: 800 276-2722
Web: WWW.UGI.COM

HISTORICAL FINANCIALS

Company Type: Private

Income Statement   FYE: September 30

	REVENUE ($ mil.)	NET INCOME ($ mil.)	NET PROFIT MARGIN	EMPLOYEES
09/18	1,092	148	13.6%	1,520
09/17	887	116	13.1%	—
Annual Growth	23.1%	28.3%	—	—

2018 Year-End Financials

Return on assets: 4.6%   Cash ($ mil.): 10
Return on equity: 13.6%
Current ratio: 0.50

UMASS MEMORIAL HEALTH CARE INC AND AFFILIATES GROUP RETURN

Auditors: FEELEY & DRISCOLL PC BOSTON

LOCATIONS

HQ: UMASS MEMORIAL HEALTH CARE INC AND
  AFFILIATES GROUP RETURN
  306 BELMONT ST 120, WORCESTER, MA 016041004
Phone: 508 334-5106
Web: WWW.UMMHC.ORG

HISTORICAL FINANCIALS

Company Type: Private

Income Statement   FYE: September 30

	REVENUE ($ mil.)	NET INCOME ($ mil.)	NET PROFIT MARGIN	EMPLOYEES
09/13	2,613	51	2.0%	500
09/10	2,594	65	2.5%	—
Annual Growth	0.2%	(7.7%)	—	—

2013 Year-End Financials

Return on assets: 2.4%   Cash ($ mil.): 156
Return on equity: 5.8%
Current ratio: 0.80

UMASS MEMORIAL HEALTH CARE, INC.

EXECUTIVES

Pres, Peter H Levine
V Pres-Cfo*, Todd Keating
Business Analyst, Paul Anderson
Director Marketing, Peggy Thrappas
Doctor, Rebecca Kasenge
Senior Analyst, Reggie Laffond
Database Assistant Eicu, Sarah Strozina
Assistant Professor of Surgery, Theodore Patsos

Senior Administrator, Tom Harris
Vice President, William Corbett
Psychiatrist, Amy L Prince
Auditors: PRICEWATERHOUSECOOPERS LLP
  B

LOCATIONS

HQ: UMASS MEMORIAL HEALTH CARE, INC.
  365 PLANTATION ST STE 300, WORCESTER, MA
  016052397
Phone: 508 334-1000
Web: WWW.UMMHEALTH.ORG

HISTORICAL FINANCIALS

Company Type: Private

Income Statement				FYE: September 30
	REVENUE ($ mil.)	NET INCOME ($ mil.)	NET PROFIT MARGIN	EMPLOYEES
09/21	3,168	382	12.1%	11,103
09/20	2,852	(26)	—	—
09/19	2,642	60	2.3%	—
09/18	2,496	25	1.0%	—
Annual Growth	8.3%	147.9%	—	—

2021 Year-End Financials

Return on assets: 10.7%   Cash ($ mil.): 643
Return on equity: 26.2%
Current ratio: 1.40

UMASS MEMORIAL MEDICAL CENTER, INC.

EXECUTIVES

Ceo, John Obrien
Exec V Pres, Wendy Waring
Sr V Pres, Gary Lapidas
Treas, Todd Keating
Pres, Eric Dickson M D
Chief of Medicine, Robert Finberg
Vice-President Business Develo, Willis Chandler
Executive of Information Techn, Denise Skrocki
Doctor, William Corbett
Employee, Judith Siegel
Doctor of Medicine, Manisha Desai
Auditors: PRICEWATERHOUSECOOPERS LLP
  B

LOCATIONS

HQ: UMASS MEMORIAL MEDICAL CENTER, INC.
  365 PLANTATION ST STE 185, WORCESTER, MA
  016052379
Phone: 508 334-1000
Web: WWW.UMMHEALTH.ORG

HISTORICAL FINANCIALS

Company Type: Private

Income Statement				FYE: September 30
	REVENUE ($ mil.)	NET INCOME ($ mil.)	NET PROFIT MARGIN	EMPLOYEES
09/21	2,176	38	1.7%	50
09/20	2,005	237	11.8%	—
09/19	1,856	16	0.9%	—
09/18	1,712	87	5.1%	—
Annual Growth	8.3%	(24.2%)	—	—

2021 Year-End Financials

Return on assets: 2.6%   Cash ($ mil.): 190
Return on equity: 7.9%
Current ratio: 1.10

UMASS MEMORIAL MEDICAL CENTER, INC.

EXECUTIVES

Internal Medicine Practitioner, Timothy P Fitzgibbons
Manager of Payment, Barry McGrath
Coordinator, Lorie Gull
Director Ambulatory Applicatio, Dana Locke
Program Administrator, Tamara Cullen
Pediatrician, Alexander Procaskey
Prin, Caryn Sullivan
Pathologist, Ian Mukand-Cerro
Diagnostic Radiologist, Jade Watkins
Chief of General Surgery, John Kelly
Supervisor, Justine Lapierre
Auditors: PRICEWATERHOUSECOOPERS LLP
  BO

LOCATIONS

HQ: UMASS MEMORIAL MEDICAL CENTER, INC.
  55 LAKE AVE N, WORCESTER, MA 016550002
Phone: 508 334-1000

HISTORICAL FINANCIALS

Company Type: Private

Income Statement				FYE: September 30
	REVENUE ($ mil.)	NET INCOME ($ mil.)	NET PROFIT MARGIN	EMPLOYEES
09/16	1,621	(130)	—	29
09/15	1,332	60	4.5%	—
09/14	1,258	19	1.6%	—
09/13	1,183	68	5.8%	—
Annual Growth	11.1%	—	—	—

2016 Year-End Financials

Return on assets: (-10.4%)   Cash ($ mil.): 124
Return on equity: (-83.3%)
Current ratio: 1.20

UNIFIED SCHOOL DISTRICT 259

EXECUTIVES

Supt, John Allison
Treas-Dir*, Linda Jones
Cfo*, Jim Freeman
Facilities, Debbie Kandt
Office Technician, Mary Halley
Educator, Michele Steinbacher
Classroom Teacher, Annetta Albright
Teacher, Arvilla Bennett
Teacher, Kelley Schafers
Payroll Supervisor, Sharon Hoyme

Secretary, June Crockett
Auditors: ALLEN GIBBS & HOULIK LC W

LOCATIONS

HQ: UNIFIED SCHOOL DISTRICT 259
  903 S EDGEMOOR ST, WICHITA, KS 672183337
Phone: 316 973-4000
Web: WWW.USD259.ORG

HISTORICAL FINANCIALS

Company Type: Private

Income Statement				FYE: June 30
	REVENUE ($ mil.)	NET INCOME ($ mil.)	NET PROFIT MARGIN	EMPLOYEES
06/20	730	42	5.8%	5,406
06/19	688	13	1.9%	—
06/18	668	119	17.8%	—
06/17	632	15	2.4%	—
Annual Growth	4.9%	40.8%	—	—

UNIPRO FOODSERVICE, INC

UniPro Foodservice knows there's strength in numbers. As the largest US food service cooperative its members include more than 650 independent member companies that provide food and food-related products to more than 800000 food service customers including health care and educational institutions military installations and restaurants. UniPro provides training collective purchasing and marketing materials to all distributors. Its products — which include dry groceries and frozen and refrigerated foods — are sold under the brand names CODE ComSource Nifda and Nugget. Suppliers include Kraft Foods Reynolds Food Packaging Solo Cup Tyson Foods and Unilever Foodsolutions.

Operations

The cooperative's Multi-Unit Group (MUG) formed in 1985 to service multi-unit food service operators include some of the largest member distributors in the UniPro network. MUG members are like a one-stop shop for multi-unit operators offering fresh produce paper products and small wares from a single source in an effort to improve efficiency.

Geographic Reach

The Atlanta-based cooperative operates through more than 900 distribution centers across the US. Beyond the US it has distribution operations in Canada Mexico the Bahamas Australia Costa Rica Guam and Japan.

Sales and Marketing

Progressive Group Alliance a business unit distributes and supplies partners with sales marketing and advice to customers. Brands include Alliance Pro (non-food) Coral Princess (seafood) Gour-Mates (condiments) Harvest Gold (cheese butter and dairy-related products) and Premium Recipe (prepared entrees salsas and sauces).

Financial Performance

While privately-owned Unipro Foodservice doesn't report its financial results collectively the cooperatives ring up an estimated $64 billion in sales annually.

Strategy

To enhance its members' competitiveness at home and abroad in 2013 UniPro formed a strategic alliance with Technomic a leading research and consulting firm to the food service industry. As part of the partnership UnPro joined the steering committee of Technomic's Foodservice Category Management Institute.

EXECUTIVES

Reporting Coordinator, Janice Hulsey
Administrative Assistant Pro, Lisa Silva
Board / Executive Committee ME, Martin Whelan
Accounts Payable Representativ, Verla Nash
Director, Scott Ganser
Departmental Vice President FI, Sharon Nesset
Engineer, Fred Chapek
Executive Sales Assistant, Andrea Hollis
CIO, Louie Newton
Administrator, Susan McClure
Auditors: HA&W LLP ATLANTA GEORGIA

LOCATIONS

HQ: UNIPRO FOODSERVICE, INC
2500 CUMBERLAND PKWY SE, ATLANTA, GA 303393942
Phone: 770 952-0871
Web: WWW.UNIPROFOODSERVICE.COM

PRODUCTS/OPERATIONS

Selected Suppliers
Cargill Foodservice
Durable Packaging International
Handgards Inc.
Kraft Foods
Reynolds Foodservice Packaging
Solo Cup Company
Unilever Foodsolutions

COMPETITORS

Ben E. Keith
Foodbuy
Golden State Foods
Keystone Foods
Maines
Martin-brower
Mclane Foodservice

Meadowbrook Meat Company
Services Group Of America
Sysco
Us Foods

HISTORICAL FINANCIALS
Company Type: Private

Income Statement				FYE: December 31
	REVENUE ($ mil.)	NET INCOME ($ mil.)	NET PROFIT MARGIN	EMPLOYEES
12/12	987	(0)	—	140
12/11	881	0	—	—
12/10	657	0	—	—
Annual Growth	22.5%	—	—	—

2012 Year-End Financials
Return on assets: (-0.2%) Cash ($ mil.): 6
Return on equity: (-3.5%)
Current ratio: 1.00

UNITED CONCORDIA LIFE AND HEALTH INSURANCE COMPANY

EXECUTIVES

Ceo, Frederick Merkel

Fo, Daniel Wright
EC, Edward Bittner
Account Representative, Alma Rivera

LOCATIONS

HQ: UNITED CONCORDIA LIFE AND HEALTH INSURANCE COMPANY
4401 DEER PATH RD, HARRISBURG, PA 171103983
Phone: 717 260-7081
Web: WWW.UNITEDCONCORDIA.COM

HISTORICAL FINANCIALS
Company Type: Private

Income Statement				FYE: December 31
	REVENUE ($ mil.)	NET INCOME ($ mil.)	NET PROFIT MARGIN	EMPLOYEES
12/15	680	34	5.1%	1
12/14	731	57	7.9%	—
Annual Growth	(6.9%)	(39.8%)		

2015 Year-End Financials
Return on assets: 10.3% Cash ($ mil.): 54
Return on equity: 14.3%
Current ratio: 1.10

UNITED COOPERATIVE

EXECUTIVES

Ceo, David Cramer
Cfo*, Damian Girten
Chm*, Howard Bohl
SEC*, Robin Craker
Vice President Grain Operation, Alan Jentz
Human Resource Recruiter, Jamie Haas

LOCATIONS

HQ: UNITED COOPERATIVE
N7160 RACEWAY RD, BEAVER DAM, WI 539169315
Phone: 920 887-1756
Web: WWW.UNITEDCOOPERATIVE.COM

HISTORICAL FINANCIALS
Company Type: Private

Income Statement				FYE: December 31
	REVENUE ($ mil.)	NET INCOME ($ mil.)	NET PROFIT MARGIN	EMPLOYEES
12/17	644	49	7.7%	358
12/16	630	41	6.6%	—
12/15	579	41	7.1%	—
12/14	577	57	10.0%	—
Annual Growth	3.7%	(4.7%)		

2017 Year-End Financials
Return on assets: 8.0% Cash ($ mil.): 22
Return on equity: 12.1%
Current ratio: 2.20

UNITED DAIRYMEN OF ARIZONA

Its name says it all: United Dairymen of Arizona (UDA) is a group of Arizona-based dairy farmers

united together to stabilize and strengthen the market for milk products. Supplied by some 90-member producers the cooperative's plant has the capacity to process 10 million pounds of milk per day about 90% of the milk in the state. Products include sweet cream and butter fluid and condensed skim milk and non-fat dry milk among others. Customers include onsite cheese maker Schreiber Foods fluid milk processors and supermarket chains throughout The Grand Canyon State. UDA also makes dried lactose powder for food manufacturers. Started in 1960 the co-op was formed through a merger of two dairy associations.

Operations
UDA's Arizona-based manufacturing plant operates around the clock often serving as a balancing plant for other area processors. Its capacity handles a broad line of milk products shifting milk production according to dairy supply and market demand. The plant is the nation's largest supervised kosher milk facility with a weekly production capacity of more than 500 metric tons of kosher powder. UDA also produces blended dry products as part of a joint venture.

UDA's operations include providing emergency repair preventative maintenance installation and transportation services and related supplies to members. Since 2007 the co-op's service and supply division share a facility in Texas too.

Geographic Reach
Based in Arizona United Dairymen of Arizona serves other companies in the state as well as the US kosher niche. It exports products overseas.

Sales and Marketing
To its benefit UDA enjoys long-term relationships with fluid milk processors which enables it to rely on a steady market for about 30% of its fluid milk. Schreiber Foods based in Tempe Arizona buys another 30% of its products.

Strategy
While UDA's business is concentrated in Arizona its member interests cross both eastern California and Texas. Beyond the US UDA has benefited from export assistance to sell cheese to customers in Asia North Africa and the Middle East. As a member of DairyAmerica (which is controlled by California Dairies) UDA further extends its international reach by selling non-fat dry milk skim milk powder and other products on the auction block known as GlobalDairyTrade developed by Fonterra.

The only milk marketing co-op in Arizona UDA is focused on improving production processing and marketing opportunities for member-producers. To that end it strategically joins with other daily cooperatives to expand global trade of dairy products and promote legislation that addresses issues such as surplus of milk low prices and volatile markets.

EXECUTIVES

Pres, Paul Rovey
SEC, Ben Gingg
V Pres, Craig Caballero
Warehouse Manager, Bill Jansen
Plant Manager, Ron V Weide
Safe Quality Foods Team Leader, Tim Alexander
TX Network, Jeremy Penrod
Office Coordinator, Lisa Garland
Other Mis Is Information Techn, Bernie Trujillo
Office Coordinator For Supply, Alicia Newton
Vice President of Government R, Mike Billotte
Auditors: HERBEIN & COMPANY INC READI

LOCATIONS

HQ: UNITED DAIRYMEN OF ARIZONA
2008 S HARDY DR, TEMPE, AZ 852821211
Phone: 480 966-7211
Web: WWW.UDA.COOP

PRODUCTS/OPERATIONS

Selected Products and Services

Products
Dried
Dry milk blends
Kosher powder
Lactose powder
Milk protein concentrate
Nonfat dry milk
Fluid
Butter
Cream
Condensed skim milk
Skim milk
Services
Emergency repair
Installation
Preventative maintenance
Transportation
Supplies
Chemical
Equipment
Pharmaceutical

COMPETITORS

Associated Milk
  Producers
Dairy Farmers Of
  America
Dairy Manufacturers
Dean Foods
Goya
Land O'lakes

Main Street
  Ingredients
Nestl ©
Shamrock Foods
Smucker
Tate & Lyle
  Ingredients

HISTORICAL FINANCIALS

Company Type: Private

Income Statement				FYE: September 30
	REVENUE ($ mil.)	NET INCOME ($ mil.)	NET PROFIT MARGIN	EMPLOYEES
09/11	825	21	2.6%	190
09/10	612	12	2.0%	—
09/09	812	2	0.3%	—
Annual Growth	0.8%	203.7%	—	—

2011 Year-End Financials

Return on assets: 16.2%   Cash ($ mil.): 30
Return on equity: 32.4%
Current ratio: 1.40

UNITED FOOD AND COMMERCIAL WORKERS UNIONS AND FOOD EMPLOYERS BEN FUND

EXECUTIVES

Prin, Richard Klontz
Auditors: HEMMING MORSE CPA'S AND
  CONSUL

LOCATIONS

HQ: UNITED FOOD AND COMMERCIAL WORKERS
UNIONS AND FOOD EMPLOYERS BEN FUND
6425 KATELLA AVE, CYPRESS, CA 906305246
Phone: 714 220-2297
Web: WWW.SCUFCWFUNDS.COM

HISTORICAL FINANCIALS

Company Type: Private

Income Statement				FYE: March 31
	REVENUE ($ mil.)	NET INCOME ($ mil.)	NET PROFIT MARGIN	EMPLOYEES
03/18	581	(13)	—	16
03/17	593	3	0.5%	—
03/12	512	(34)	—	—
03/11	460	(74)	—	—
Annual Growth	3.4%	—	—	—

2018 Year-End Financials

Return on assets: (-4.2%)   Cash ($ mil.): 45
Return on equity: (-7.0%)
Current ratio: 161.40

UNITED HEALTH SERVICES HOSPITALS, INC.

United Health Services Hospitals (UHS Hospitals) can service injuries from a slip in the snow or a slipped disc to health that's just plain slipping. The organization operates Binghamton General Hospital (about 200 beds) Wilson Medical Center (some 280 beds) and a group of primary and specialty care clinics in upstate New York. Specialty services include cardiology dialysis neurology rehabilitation neonatal and psychiatry. The Wilson Medical Center serves as a teaching hospital offering residency and fellowship programs. UHS Hospitals is a subsidiary of United Health Services which operates a network of affiliated hospitals clinics long-term care centers and home health agencies in the region.

Geographic Reach

Binghamton General is located in Binghamton New York while Wilson Medical Center is located in Johnson City New York both within the boundaries of Broome County. UHS Hospitals also operates primary and specialty care clinics in Broome Chenango Delaware and Tioga counties in upstate New York.

Strategy

United Health Services Hospitals is investing in equipment upgrades and facility improvements at Binghamton General to help the facility remain at the forefront of medical technology and services. Wilson Medical Center which acts as a regional referral center in areas including emergency medicine newborn care neurology and heart surgery has also been the subject of enhancement measures. The hospital recently completed construction of the new Decker Center for Advanced Medical Treatment which offers high-tech diagnostic and acute care services.

EXECUTIVES

Pres, Atthew J Salanger
Sr V Pres, Robert Gomulka
Exec V Pres, Rajesh Dave

Dir, Halsey Bagg
Exe SEC, Brandi Phelan
Director, Gail Thalacker
Qa Qc Manager, Kathleen Wold
Neurology, Khalid Sethi
Psychiatrist, Inna K Factourovich
Dir of Psychiatric Srvs, Leslie Major
Data Coordinator, Michelle Kettle
Auditors: FUST CHARLES CHAMBERS LLP
  SYR

LOCATIONS

HQ: UNITED HEALTH SERVICES HOSPITALS, INC.
10-42 MITCHELL AVE, BINGHAMTON, NY 139031617
Phone: 607 762-2200
Web: WWW.STMRI.COM

COMPETITORS

Albany Medical Center
Guthrie Healthcare
Kaleida Health
Lifetime Health
Oneida Healthcare Center
Suny Upstate Medical University
St. Joseph's Hospital Health Center
Upstate University Hospital At Community General

HISTORICAL FINANCIALS

Company Type: Private

Income Statement				FYE: December 31
	REVENUE ($ mil.)	NET INCOME ($ mil.)	NET PROFIT MARGIN	EMPLOYEES
12/20	753	(1)	—	5,000
12/19	732	32	4.5%	—
12/18	685	(0)	—	—
12/16	611	21	3.4%	—
Annual Growth	5.4%	—	—	—

2020 Year-End Financials

Return on assets: (-0.2%)   Cash ($ mil.): 46
Return on equity: (-0.6%)
Current ratio: 1.70

UNITED SPACE ALLIANCE, LLC

United Space Alliance (USA) is a space-race heavyweight; the Houston-based prime contractor has run NASA's 173000 pound Shuttles — Discovery Atlantis and Endeavour. USA a joint venture between Lockheed Martin and Boeing was formed in response to NASA's move to consolidate multiple Space Shuttle contracts under a single entity. It is now wrapping up those contracts. USA has supported mission operations astronaut and flight controller training flight software development Shuttle payload integration and vehicle processing launch and recovery. It also has led training and planning for the International Space Station. USA served the Johnson and Kennedy Space Centers and Marshall Space Flight Center.

Operations

The company has consolidated more than 30 heritage contracts which supported the Space Shuttle Program (including the Space Flight Operations contract the Space Program Operations Contract and the Integrated Mission Operations Contract).

Geographic Reach

Based in Houston the company has another location in Titusville Florida.

Strategy

The company served as NASA's primary partner in human space operations for the management of the Space Shuttle fleet and worked together for 55 Space Shuttle missions and more than 35 International Space Station increments.

In 2014 the company had no active contracts and will not pursue future contracts. The company is currently operating in an administrative capacity to close-out its managed government contracts (a process that will take a further about 5-7 years).

Company Background

In 2012 NASA awarded a one-year extension of the Integrated Mission Operations Contract to USA to continue providing mission and flight crew operations support for the International Space Station and Exploration Programs. The deal includes a further option for 2014. Throughout 2012 and 2013 however USA laid off waves of workers that resided in its former Space Shuttle program.

The launch of space shuttle Atlantis in July 2011 marked the end of NASA's 30-year Space Shuttle program. The shuttles have transported astronauts launched recovered and repaired satellites as well as driven new research and built and stocked the International Space Station with parts and provisions.

The joint venture was formed in 1996.

Auditors: PRICEWATERHOUSECOOPERS LLP
HO

LOCATIONS

HQ: UNITED SPACE ALLIANCE, LLC
3700 BAY AREA BLVD # 100, HOUSTON, TX 770582783
Phone: 281 282-2592
Web: WWW.UNITEDSPACEALLIANCE.COM

PRODUCTS/OPERATIONS

Selected Capabilities
Flight software
Ground operations and processing
GSA (General Services Administration) services
Integrated logistics
Integration and program management
Mission operations
Safety

COMPETITORS

Airbus Group	Meggitt-usa
Arianespace	Northrop Grumman
Astrotech	Raytheon
Bae Systems	Sgt
Honeywell Aerospace	Thales Aerospace

HISTORICAL FINANCIALS

Company Type: Private

Income Statement   FYE: December 31

	REVENUE ($ mil.)	NET INCOME ($ mil.)	NET PROFIT MARGIN	EMPLOYEES
12/07	1,859	168	9.0%	8,000
12/06	1,920	146	7.6%	—
Annual Growth	(3.2%)	14.8%	—	—

2007 Year-End Financials
Return on assets: 60.5% Cash ($ mil.): 57
Return on equity: —
Current ratio: 1.00

UNIVERSITY COMMUNITY HOSPITAL, INC.

University Community Health (doing business as Florida Hospital Tampa Bay Division) is a 1000-bed regional health care system with four locations spanning the Hillsborough Pinellas and Pasco counties of Florida. It oversees a network of eight hospitals in Florida's Tampa Bay area. Its four general hospitals — three located in Tampa and one in nearby Tarpon Springs — collectively house some 860 beds and provide emergency surgical and acute medical care as well as provide outpatient services. The system also includes a specialty heart hospital a women's hospital and a long-term acute care hospital. Florida Hospital Tampa Bay Division is part of the Adventist Health System.

Strategy

As part of the Adventist Health System's network the system has access to a broader statewide network of physicians and specialists as well as enhanced administrative and technological services organization.

In 2012 Florida Hospital Tampa Bay Division opened Florida Hospital Wesley Chapel and began work on three major construction projects including a new full-service Emergency Department (ED) expanding The Women's Center and exterior and interior upgrades to the main hospital which should add a total of 54000 sq. ft. to the scope of Florida Hospital Tampa.

Company Background

Its original name of University Community Health (UCH) reflected its proximity to the University of South Florida. UCH teamed up with Adventist Health in 2007 to build Wesley Chapel Medical Center. Buoyed by the success of the venture in 2010 UCH and Adventist Health reached an accord and UCH became a member of Adventist Health.

EXECUTIVES

V Pres, Michael Schultz
Acct*, Lynn Addiscott
Acct*, Ariel De Prada
Coo*, Jack Chubb
Cno*, Theresa Trivette
Internal Medicine Practitioner, Ashley Robaina
Nurse, Amy Thatavakorn
Pediatrician, Alison Simpson
Emergency Medicine Specialist, Andrew Spencer
Internist, Barbara Sanford
Obstetrician Gynecologist, Beverly Belle

LOCATIONS

HQ: UNIVERSITY COMMUNITY HOSPITAL, INC.
3100 E FLETCHER AVE, TAMPA, FL 336134613
Phone: 813 971-6000
Web: WWW.UNIVERSITYCOMMUNITYHOSPITAL.COM

PRODUCTS/OPERATIONS

Selected Centers
Diabetes and Endocrinology Institute
Don Lau Family Center for Cancer Care
Florida Hospital Pepin Heart Institute
Occupational Health Service
Orthopedic Care Center
Pediatric Care Center
Sleep Center
The Women's Center
Wound Healing Institute

Selected Hospitals
Florida Hospital at Connerton
Florida Hospital Carrollwood
Florida Hospital North Pinellas
Florida Hospital Pepin Heart Institute
Florida Hospital Tampa
Florida Hospital Wesley Chapel
Florida Hospital Zephyrhills
Long Term Acute Care

COMPETITORS

All Children's Hospital	Lakeland Regional Medical Center
Baycare Health System	Northside Hospital And Heart Institute
Bayfront Health	
Hca	Tampa General Hospital

HISTORICAL FINANCIALS

Company Type: Private

Income Statement   FYE: December 31

	REVENUE ($ mil.)	NET INCOME ($ mil.)	NET PROFIT MARGIN	EMPLOYEES
12/19	761	62	8.2%	8,000
12/17	688	66	9.6%	—
12/16	483	39	8.2%	—
12/15	460	38	8.4%	—
Annual Growth	13.4%	12.5%	—	—

2019 Year-End Financials
Return on assets: 5.5% Cash ($ mil.): 209
Return on equity: 9.2%
Current ratio: 4.90

UNIVERSITY HEALTH CARE INC

University Health Care wants to give patients a passport to good health. The company which does business as Passport Health Plan provides managed Medicaid insurance services to about 150000 members throughout 16 counties in Kentucky. Offerings include HMO Medicare Advantage and children's health plans. University Health Care was founded in 1997 by a group of affiliated providers including the University of Louisville Medical Center Jewish Hospital and St. Mary's HealthCare and the Louisville/Jefferson County Primary Care Association. The health plan has an administration partnership with the AmeriHealth Mercy organization a Medicaid managed care joint venture between AmeriHealth and Mercy Health System.

EXECUTIVES

Exec Dir, Joyce Schifano
Chm-Pres, Larry N Cook
Cmo, Jackie Simmons
Prin, John L Kiesel
V Pres*, James Taylor
Chm*, William B Wagner
SEC*, Mark B Carter
Treas*, Allan Tasman
Coordinator, Melissa Dickey
Coordinator, Teran Ransom
Coordinator, Sandy Roland
Auditors: MOUNTJOY CHILTON MEDLEY LLP
L

HQ: UNIVERSITY HEALTH CARE INC
5100 CMMERCE CROSSINGS DR, LOUISVILLE, KY
402292128
Phone: 502 585-7900

COMPETITORS

Amerigroup	Health Net
Aetna	Healthspring
Anthem Health Plans Of	Humana
Kentucky	Kaiser Foundation
Bluegrass Family	Health Plan
Health	Unitedhealth Group
Cigna	

HISTORICAL FINANCIALS

Company Type: Private

Income Statement				FYE: December 31
	REVENUE ($ mil.)	NET INCOME ($ mil.)	NET PROFIT MARGIN	EMPLOYEES
12/14	1,299	114	8.8%	165
12/00	330	3	1.2%	—
12/99	284	5	2.0%	—
12/98	809	0	—	—
Annual Growth	3.0%	—	—	—

2014 Year-End Financials

Return on assets: 31.8%   Cash ($ mil.): 140
Return on equity: 52.2%
Current ratio: —

UNIVERSITY HEALTH SYSTEM SERVICES OF TEXAS, INC.

As the hospital system of the Bexar County Hospital District University Health System serves residents of San Antonio and the surrounding region. Its flagship facility University Hospital boasts about 720 beds and is the primary teaching facility for The University of Texas Health Science Center at San Antonio. In addition to general medical and surgical care the hospital is a designated Level I trauma center and a Level II pediatric trauma and burn center. The system provides health care for families near its clinic locations including the Robert B. Green Campus Texas Diabetes Institute more than a dozen neighborhood clinics five ExpressMed urgent-care clinics and four outpatient renal dialysis centers.

Operations

The system which has about 800 physicians also operates preventive care centers including the Texas Diabetes Institute which provides treatment research and education for diabetes patients and health care professionals. The University Transplant Center performs a range of procedures such as kidney liver and lung transplants. The Harlandale Independent School District school-based Health Center is a collaboration with Harlandale ISD that helps keep students healthy and learning.

University Health System's emergency department is the busiest in the area taking in nearly 70000 visits annually. In 2013 it had about 22000 inpatient discharges 3000 births and 139000 outpatient visits.

As part of its operations University Health System is joint owner of San Antonio AirLIFE which provides emergency air medical transport services aboard its fleet of Bell 430 helicopters.

University Health System provides health insurance through its Community First Health Plans a not-for-profit HMO with thousands of members in Bexar and surrounding counties.

Geographic Reach

The system's University Hospital is the lead trauma hospital for a 22-county area of Texas serving patients from Bexar County to South Texas and beyond.

Financial Performance

University Health System's revenue rose 11% to $564 million in 2013 thanks to net patient revenue growth. Net income decreased 24% to $75 million that year as operating expenses including salaries and benefits purchased services and supplies rose.

Strategy

To its benefit University Hospital is the only pediatric trauma center that serves San Antonio and the greater South Texas area. Its emergency center remains the busiest in the region averaging nearly 70000 visits annually.

The organization is in the midst of a system-wide capital improvement program aimed at "rightsizing" its facilities to meet growing demand. To this end the system in 2014 completed construction on a $778 million 10-story Sky Tower at University Hospital that features an expanded emergency department 35 new surgical suites and 420 new private patient rooms. It also opened a six-story Clinical Pavilion at its Robert B. Green Campus in 2013. In 2015 the system was granted approval to renovate and expand its emergency department which will convert most semi-private rooms to fully private rooms and provide additional observance and recovery space. The new facilities are part of University Health System's $900 million Capital Improvement Program to expand and renovate facilities at University Hospital and its downtown Robert B. Green Campus.

Additionally University Health System's downtown health center has added services that include acute and crisis care diagnostic imaging and pharmacy.

In 2014 the system launched its healthyUexpress2 mobile health vehicle which extends its new school-based health care initiative throughout Bexar County.

Company Background

University Health System was founded in 1968.

EXECUTIVES

Pres-Ceo, George B Hernndez Jr
Exec V Pres-Cfo, Peggy Demming
Exec V Pres, Christann Vasquez
Exec V Pres, Bryan Alsip
Ceo, Tim Brierty
It Field Engineer II, John Strader
Specialist, Lisa Alcoser
Employee, Lizbeth Thompson
Pain Management Specialist, Naumit Bhandari
Diagnostic Radiologist, Rachel Darling
Reproductive Endocrinology, Randal Robinson
Auditors: BKD LLP DALLAS TEXAS

LOCATIONS

HQ: UNIVERSITY HEALTH SYSTEM SERVICES OF TEXAS, INC.
4502 MEDICAL DR STOP 85-1, SAN ANTONIO, TX 782294402
Phone: 210 358-4000
Web: WWW.UNIVERSITYHEALTHSYSTEM.COM

PRODUCTS/OPERATIONS

2013 Sales

	$ mil.	% of total
Net patient services revenue	462	60
Premium revenue	261	34
Other revenue	49	6
Total	**773**	**100**

2013 Net Patient Revenue

	% of total
Medicare	22
Medicaid	21
Self-Pay including CareLink	37
Commercial insurance	19
Other	1
Total	**100**

Selected Locations

University Hospital
University Health Care
Texas Diabetes Institute
University Family Health Centers

Selected Medical Services

Audiology
Blood Bank
Breast Health
Cancer
Cardiology
Craniosynostosis
Diabetes
ExpressMed
Emergency Center
Endoscopy
Epilepsy
Gynecology
Health Education
Hepatology
HIV/AIDS
Mammography
Maternal-fetal Medicine
Men's Health
Neurosciences
Newborn Services
NICU
Obstetrics
Outpatient Surgery
Pharmacy Services
Pediatrics
Primary Care
Rehabilitation
Respiratory Care
Robot Assisted Surgery
Stroke
Texas Diabetes Institute
Transcatheter Aortic Valve Replacement
Transplant Center
Trauma Center
Vascular
Women's Health

COMPETITORS

Christus Health	Tenet Healthcare
Methodist Healthcare	Valley Baptist Health
System	System (texas)

HISTORICAL FINANCIALS

Company Type: Private

Income Statement				FYE: December 31
	REVENUE ($ mil.)	NET INCOME ($ mil.)	NET PROFIT MARGIN	EMPLOYEES
12/20	1,780	249	14.0%	3,998
12/19	1,610	150	9.3%	—
12/18	1,488	95	6.4%	—
12/17	1,349	54	4.1%	—
Annual Growth	9.7%	65.5%	—	—

2020 Year-End Financials

Return on assets: 6.7%   Cash ($ mil.): 319
Return on equity: 15.6%
Current ratio: 3.10

UNIVERSITY HOSPITALS HEALTH SYSTEM, INC.

University Hospitals Health System (UHHS) is on a mission to teach research and administer good health throughout northeastern Ohio. Its flagship facility University Hospitals of Cleveland (UHC) which operates as University Hospitals Case Medical Center (UHCMC) is a more than 1000-bed tertiary care center serving Cleveland and other parts of northeastern Ohio. The teaching hospital which is affiliated with Case Western Reserve University is also home to Rainbow Babies & Children's Hospital Seidman Cancer Center and MacDonald Women's Hospital. the not-for-profit UHHS is also home to community hospitals outpatient health and surgery centers mental health facilities and senior care centers.

Operations

UHHS' eight community hospitals some of which are operated through affiliation agreements provide a full range of specialty and general acute care from anesthesia to vascular surgery. Along with those the system operates urgent care and neighborhood medical centers throughout the region. The UH Extended Care Campus includes a specialty hospital outpatient rehabilitation and extended care facility. UHHS also operates home health occupational health wellness and managed care (health plan) divisions. The UHHS facilities have a total of some 1800 beds.

Altogether the network's facilities handle some 65000 inpatient visits per year as well as 5.8 million outpatient procedures and 206000 emergency room visits. It delivered more than 5200 babies and conducted more than 60000 surgeries in 2013.

In addition to conducting education and training programs for Case Western Reserve University School of Medicine students UHHS partners with the university to operate the Center for Clinical Research and Technology. The center is the largest biomedical research facility in Ohio and focuses on translational research which connects laboratory research to clinical bedside care.

UHHS' physician network consists of 1700 physicians and 3000 affiliated members. The system provided $270 million for community benefit and provided $253 million for research in 2013.

The hospital system is affiliated with three Cleveland-area health care providers: St. John Medical Center UH Rehabilitation Hospital (a joint venture with Center Healthcare) and Southwest General.

Geographic Reach

UHHS operates about 30 health centers and outpatient office buildings as well as more than 100 physician practice locations across the northeastern Ohio region. It serves 16 counties.

Financial Performance

UHHS' revenues increased by 4% to $2.3 billion in 2013 due to higher patient service revenues.

Operating income increased by 21% $78.6 million that year due to a change in fair value of derivative instruments and a growth in investment income partially offset by higher operating expenses.

UHHS' operating cash flow decreased by $143 million in 2013 due a change in beneficial interest in foundation and perpetual trusts pension liability adjustments and a change in operating assets and liabilities.

Strategy

The medical system is expanding by installing smaller regional and community hospitals and additional specialty care units within its larger facilities including a neonatal intensive care unit emergency care center and a cancer care center within UH Case Medical.

To strengthen its clinical capabilities it also expanded its established areas of excellence and developed new areas to improve access it has forged new hospital partnerships. To enhance care in the communities served by its new partners UHHS has opened satellites of some of its centers of excellence initially for cancer care cardiac care pediatrics and women's health. Pursuant to the growth strategy it has added two community hospitals that are now UHHS' largest: 387-bed UH Elyria Medical Center (formerly EMH Healthcare) and 332-bed UH Parma Medical Center (formerly The Parma Community General Hospital).

The company also plans to break ground on a $28 million state-of-the-art outpatient health center and freestanding emergency department in Broadview Heights with a projected completion date in late 2016. In 2013 University Hospitals Seidman Cancer Center expanded to Parma Community General Hospital providing integrated cancer care to residents in Parma and surrounding communities.

To expand in another neighboring community the system launched renovation of an office building that became the UH Solon Health Center in 2013. It also opened a new outpatient center the UH Aurora Health Center in 2012.

UHHS is also in the process of implementing an electronic health records (EHR) system across its facilities. The EHR system could make the network eligible for certain government incentives if they meet government guidelines for "meaningful use."

On the research front in 2014 UHHS Case Medical Center conducted a Phase 3 clinical trial to evaluate the safety and effectiveness of an investigational medicine called LMTX in people with a type of dementia known as behavioral-variant Frontotemporal Dementia (previously known as Pick's Disease).

Company Background

UHHS completed construction of the UH Ahuja Medical Center a new community hospital in 2011.

The company was founded in 1866.

EXECUTIVES

Ceo, Thomas S Zenty
Sr V Pres Gen Counsel*, Janet L Miller
V Pres-Treas*, Bradley Bond
Cfo*, Michael Szubski
Cno*, Kim Monaco
Coo*, Eric Beck
Executive Secretary, Maria Jefferson
Clinical Application Analyst, Tara Ennis
Clinical Data Analyst, Anuja Sarode
Senior Information Technology, Bill Ziss
Allergist, Dawn Zacharias
Auditors: DELOITTE TAX LLP CINCINNATI

LOCATIONS

HQ: UNIVERSITY HOSPITALS HEALTH SYSTEM, INC.
3605 WARRENSVILLE CTR RD, SHAKER HEIGHTS, OH 441229100
Phone: 216 767-8900
Web: WWW.UHHOSPITALS.ORG

PRODUCTS/OPERATIONS

Selected Facilities
Main Campuses
  Case Medical Center
  MacDonald Women's Hospital
  Rainbow Babies & Children's Hospital
  Seidman Cancer Center
Community Hospitals
  Ahuja Medical Center
  Bedford Medical Center (UH Regional Hospitals)
  Conneaut Medical Center
  Elyria Medical Center
  Geauga Medical Center
  Geneva Medical Center
  Parma Medical Center
  Richmond Medical Center (UH Regional Hospitals)

COMPETITORS

Akron Children's Hospital	Parma Community General Hospital
Akron General Health System	Robinson Memorial Hospital
Lake Health	Summa Health System
Mercy Medical Center (oh)	The Cleveland Clinic
Metrohealth System	Trinity Health System

HISTORICAL FINANCIALS
Company Type: Private

Income Statement — FYE: December 31

	REVENUE ($ mil.)	NET INCOME ($ mil.)	NET PROFIT MARGIN	EMPLOYEES
12/17	580	33	5.7%	30,099
12/12	2,266	54	2.4%	—
12/09	1,938	110	5.7%	—
12/08	1,800	(153)	—	—
Annual Growth	(11.8%)	—	—	—

2017 Year-End Financials

Return on assets: 0.8%   Cash ($ mil.): 184
Return on equity: 1.6%
Current ratio: 0.20

UNIVERSITY MEDICAL CENTER INC

EXECUTIVES

Ceo, James Taylor
Pres*, Ken Marshall
Sr V Pres*, Mark Pfeifer
Cfo-Sr V Pres*, Robert P Barbier
SEC*, Amber Denham
Prin*, Mary Jane Adams
Assistant Professor of Radiolo, Peter Hentzen
Assistant Professor of Radiolo, Richard Goldwin
Assistant Professor of Radiolo, Barbara Pawley
Director of Oncology, Den Ellen Coldiron
Director, Hiram C Polk

LOCATIONS

HQ: UNIVERSITY MEDICAL CENTER INC
530 S JACKSON ST, LOUISVILLE, KY 402021675
Phone: 502 562-3000
Web: WWW.UOFLHOSPITAL.ORG

HISTORICAL FINANCIALS
Company Type: Private

Income Statement — FYE: June 30

	REVENUE ($ mil.)	NET INCOME ($ mil.)	NET PROFIT MARGIN	EMPLOYEES
06/21	713	13	1.9%	2,000
06/20	435	45	10.4%	—
06/19	607	23	3.8%	—
06/18	487	(72)	—	—
Annual Growth	13.5%	—	—	—

Return on assets: 1.9%   Cash ($ mil.): 156
Return on equity: 4.7%
Current ratio: 2.00

UNIVERSITY MEDICAL CENTER MANAGEMENT CORPORATION

EXECUTIVES

Ceo, Danny Hardman
Buyer*, Todd Scurto
General Practitioner, Joseph Kanter
Assistant Professor, Yingnan Zhao
Assistant Professor, Zhe Wang
Admissions Director, Allenda Hendry
Operating Room Dir, Anne Ertel
Pharmacy Director, Anthony Laurent
Radiology Director, Anthony Mosley
Food Director, Candice Gallagher
Utilization Review Director, Connie Brider
Auditors: LAPORTE APAC METAIRIE LA

LOCATIONS

HQ: UNIVERSITY MEDICAL CENTER MANAGEMENT CORPORATION
2000 CANAL ST, NEW ORLEANS, LA 701123018
Phone: 504 903-3000
Web: WWW.UMCNO.ORG

HISTORICAL FINANCIALS

Company Type: Private

Income Statement				FYE: December 31
	REVENUE ($ mil.)	NET INCOME ($ mil.)	NET PROFIT MARGIN	EMPLOYEES
12/19	731	5	0.7%	2,000
12/18	675	1	0.2%	—
12/16	448	(65)	—	—
Annual Growth	17.7%	—	—	—

2019 Year-End Financials

Return on assets: 1.1%   Cash ($ mil.): 86
Return on equity: —
Current ratio: 2.80

UNIVERSITY OF ALABAMA

EXECUTIVES

Exec Dir, Kevin Stevens
Accounting Staff, Lisa H McKinney
Accounting Staff, Tina Dorroh
Assistant Professor, Jane Rasco
Assistant To President, Charles Hilburn
Staff, June Vance
Staff, Paul A Leblanc
Staff, Sunee Lavender
Staff, Michael Steinberg

Staff, Paula House
Staff, Natalie Champion
Auditors: PRICEWATERHOUSECOOPERS LLP BI

LOCATIONS

HQ: UNIVERSITY OF ALABAMA
301 ROSE ADMIN BLDG, TUSCALOOSA, AL 354870001
Phone: 205 348-7840
Web: WWW.OVPRED.UA.EDU

HISTORICAL FINANCIALS

Company Type: Private

Income Statement				FYE: September 30
	REVENUE ($ mil.)	NET INCOME ($ mil.)	NET PROFIT MARGIN	EMPLOYEES
09/20	870	166	19.2%	3,950
09/19	906	55	6.1%	—
09/18	875	188	21.6%	—
09/17	833	224	26.9%	—
Annual Growth	1.5%	(9.4%)	—	—

2020 Year-End Financials

Return on assets: 3.3%   Cash ($ mil.): 156
Return on equity: 7.2%
Current ratio: 1.30

UNIVERSITY OF ALABAMA HEALTH SERVICES FOUNDATION, P.C.

EXECUTIVES

Ceo, Will Ferniany
Pres*, Anton Bueschen
V Pres*, Reed F Jones
Cfo*, Michael Heckman
Pres*, Dr Jim Bonner
Exec V Pres*, Patricia Pritchett
Exec Admin, Melanie Brewer
Project Coordinator, Niki Woodall
Director, Chuck Patrick
Executive Administrator, Mark Schmidt
Office Associate 1, Shirley Glenn
Auditors: PRICEWATERHOUSECOOPERS LLP BI

LOCATIONS

HQ: UNIVERSITY OF ALABAMA HEALTH SERVICES FOUNDATION, P.C.
500 22ND ST S STE 100, BIRMINGHAM, AL 352333110
Phone: 205 731-9600

HISTORICAL FINANCIALS

Company Type: Private

Income Statement				FYE: September 30
	REVENUE ($ mil.)	NET INCOME ($ mil.)	NET PROFIT MARGIN	EMPLOYEES
09/20	779	12	1.6%	3,205
09/19	705	(19)	—	—
09/18	668	12	1.9%	—
09/15	561	1	0.2%	—
Annual Growth	6.8%	62.8%	—	—

2020 Year-End Financials

Return on assets: 1.3%   Cash ($ mil.): 49
Return on equity: 3.1%
Current ratio: 1.10

UNIVERSITY OF ARKANSAS SYSTEM

Calling "Wooo Pig Sooie" at anyone in The University of Arkansas System (UA) is not an insult. The system encompasses more than a dozen schools institutes and campuses throughout the state including five universities a college of medicine a math and science high school and the Clinton School of Public Service started in 2004 by former president Bill Clinton and offering the only Master of Public Service degree in the country. UA which has an enrollment of more than 60000 hails the razorback or hog as its mascot. "Wooo Pig Sooie" or "hog calling" is the school's cheer at sporting events. Its student-teacher ratio is 19:1; it has about 17000 employees.

Operations

The flagship University of Arkansas campus in Fayetteville offers students undergraduate graduate and law degrees through about nine schools. Areas of study include architecture agriculture food and life sciences arts and sciences business education and health engineering and law. UA's Global Campus provides long-distance education online and via video streaming. Along with undergraduate training the Global Campus offers professional degrees and career training.

Other system facilities include five community colleges two law schools and divisions of architecture archeology and criminal justice.

Financial Performance

Revenue increased about 1% in 2013 from $1.8 billion to $1.82 billion due to record enrollment and increases in other revenue.

Strategy

In order to keep students coming to UA year after year the system regularly improves it classroom offerings as well as it facilities. To that end the university is building a $60 million performing arts center and a $20 million admissions building on the site of its former Bryce Hospital in Tuscaloosa.

Company Background

The Arkansas General Assembly established UA in Fayetteville in 1871 as the Arkansas Industrial University and under the the Morrill Act of 1862 it became the state land-grant institution and first state-assisted college in Arkansas. On opening day January 22 1873 there were four teachers and eight students.

EXECUTIVES

Pres, Donald R Bobbitt
Pres*, B Alan Sugg
V Pres-Fin & Admin*, Ann Kemp
V Pres-Agriculture*, Milo Shult
Cdo*, W Cody Decker
Int Cfo*, Chaundra Hall
Assistant Professor, Shane Gadberry
Coordinator, Brent Talley
Chancellor, G David Gearhart
Manager, Chris Walker
Director, Kathy Van Laningham
Auditors: ROGER A NORMAN JD CPA CFE

LOCATIONS

HQ: UNIVERSITY OF ARKANSAS SYSTEM
2404 N UNIVERSITY AVE, LITTLE ROCK, AR
722073608
Phone: 501 686-2500
Web: WWW.UASYS.EDU

PRODUCTS/OPERATIONS

Selected Campuses
Arkansas Archeological Survey
Arkansas School for Mathematics Sciences and the Arts
(high school)
Clinton School of Public Service
Cossatot Community College of the University of
Arkansas
Criminal Justice Institute
Division of Agriculture
Phillips Community College of the University of
Arkansas
University of Arkansas Community College at Morrilton
University of Arkansas Fayetteville
University of Arkansas at Fort Smith
University of Arkansas at Little Rock
University of Arkansas for Medical Sciences
University of Arkansas at Monticello
University of Arkansas at Pine Bluff
Winthrop Rockefeller Institute

HISTORICAL FINANCIALS

Company Type: Private

Income Statement   FYE: June 30

	REVENUE ($ mil.)	NET INCOME ($ mil.)	NET PROFIT MARGIN	EMPLOYEES
06/20	2,449	85	3.5%	14,025
06/19	2,515	153	6.1%	—
06/18	2,402	139	5.8%	—
06/17	2,297	88	3.9%	—
Annual Growth	2.1%	(1.3%)	—	—

2020 Year-End Financials
Return on assets: 1.7%   Cash ($ mil.): 596
Return on equity: 3.1%
Current ratio: 3.40

UNIVERSITY OF CALIFORNIA, DAVIS

University of California Davis (UC Davis) is one of the leading universities around the world. The school one of 10 University of California campuses offers a wide variety of agricultural programs; its Viticulture and Enology department provides professional education for aspiring winemakers. Located between Sacramento and San Francisco UC Davis also has colleges and professional schools in biology engineering education law business medicine and veterinary medicine and it is recognized for its research programs. Offering about 105 academic majors and nearly 100 graduate degrees throughout its six schools UC Davis enrolls approximately 38440 undergraduate graduate and professional students and it has a student-faculty ratio of 20:1.

Operations
UC Davis comprises four colleges: Agricultural and Environmental Sciences; Biological Sciences; Engineering; and Letters and Science. The university also operates six professional schools: Education; Law; Management; Medicine; Veterinary Medicine; and the Betty Irene Moore School of Nursing. It also includes a 646-bed acute care teaching hospital in Sacramento (UC Davis Health) and the UC Davis Veterinary Medicine Teaching Research Center in Tulare.

It also has access to more than 10 million items in the university's library including books journals music and maps in print and digital formats.

Geographic Reach
Spanning approximately 5300 acres campus borders the city of Davis the state capital is 20 minutes away and destinations such as the San Francisco Bay Area Lake Tahoe and the Napa Valley are within a two-hour drive. UC Davis has satellite campuses in San Ramon and Sacramento as well as related educational facilities elsewhere in California and in Nevada.

Company Background
The school was originally known as the University Farm School and accepted its first students at its new campus in the town of Davisville (later changed to Davis) in 1909. The California Legislature in 1905 authorized the establishment of a state agricultural college; the school that became UC Davis was administratively tied to UC Berkeley for decades before gaining its status as an independent university in 1959.

EXECUTIVES

Chancellor, Gary S May
Accounting Staff, Christine McIntire
Accounting Staff, Deanna Park
Accounting Staff, Joann Fisher
Accounting Staff, Mana Aynechi
Accounting Staff, Mary Chan
Assistant Professor, Christopher Haas
Assistant Professor, Jeffrey Moehlis
Assistant Professor, Katherine Pollard
Assistant Professor, Kimberly Hardin
Assistant Professor, Nancy Aranda

LOCATIONS

HQ: UNIVERSITY OF CALIFORNIA, DAVIS
1 SHIELDS AVE, DAVIS, CA 956168500
Phone: 530 752-1011
Web: WWW.UCDAVIS.EDU

HISTORICAL FINANCIALS

Company Type: Private

Income Statement   FYE: June 30

	REVENUE ($ mil.)	NET INCOME ($ mil.)	NET PROFIT MARGIN	EMPLOYEES
06/11*	2,697	360	13.4%	17,741
12/08	0	0	9.6%	—
06/08	14	0	6.1%	—
Annual Growth	474.6%	644.1%	—	—

*Fiscal year change

2011 Year-End Financials
Return on assets: 6.5%   Cash ($ mil.): 1,114
Return on equity: 10.4%
Current ratio: 2.50

UNIVERSITY OF CALIFORNIA, SAN FRANCISCO FOUNDATION

EXECUTIVES

Pres, Michael Bishop
Dir, Jim Asp
Vice Chair For Diversity and H, Christina Mangurian
Assistant Director, David Fung
Dean, Graduate Division, Elizabeth Watkins
Licensing Officer, Gemma Rooney
Licensing Officer, Kathleen Wilson-Edell
Executive Vice Chair, Lowell Tong
Associate Chair For Operations, Michael Walker
Vice Chair For Research, Andrew Krystal
Rn Is Director, Barbara Koenig

LOCATIONS

HQ: UNIVERSITY OF CALIFORNIA, SAN FRANCISCO FOUNDATION
220 MONTGOMERY ST STE 500, SAN FRANCISCO, CA 941043412
Phone: 415 476-6922
Web: WWW.GIVING.UCSF.EDU

HISTORICAL FINANCIALS

Company Type: Private

Income Statement   FYE: June 30

	REVENUE ($ mil.)	NET INCOME ($ mil.)	NET PROFIT MARGIN	EMPLOYEES
06/18	628	332	53.0%	73
06/99	33	39	117.7%	—
Annual Growth	16.6%	11.8%	—	—

2018 Year-End Financials
Return on assets: 15.2%   Cash ($ mil.): 395
Return on equity: 18.0%
Current ratio: —

UNIVERSITY OF CHICAGO

LOCATIONS

HQ: UNIVERSITY OF CHICAGO
1414 E 59TH ST, CHICAGO, IL 606372916
Phone: 773 753-2270
Web: WWW.UCHICAGO.EDU

HISTORICAL FINANCIALS

Company Type: Private

Income Statement   FYE: June 30

	REVENUE ($ mil.)	NET INCOME ($ mil.)	NET PROFIT MARGIN	EMPLOYEES
06/13	3,091	182	5.9%	2
06/11	3,056	1,052	34.4%	—
Annual Growth	0.6%	(58.4%)	—	—

UNIVERSITY OF CINCINNATI

The University of Cincinnati (UC) is a research institution offering undergraduate graduate and professional education from its campuses in Ohio including UC Blue Ash College and UC Clermont College. The university enrolls approximately 46710 students and has about 15 colleges. Academic offerings include business law medicine engineering and applied science pharmacy and music. The institution offers about 85 doctoral programs about 415 other degree programs and more than 260 minors and certificates. UC was founded in 1819 and became a state university in 1977; the school has an endowment of approximately $1.6 billion. Notable alumni include former US president William Howard Taft and architect Michael Graves.

Operations

The university has a combined faculty and staff of more than 10510 and a student teacher ratio of approximately 16.1. It consists of nine research and campus locations in the Greater Cincinnati region with an impact and reach that extends from the local to the global. This includes strategic partnerships in subject areas like engineering economics humanities and business administration with the University of Bordeaux France; Ludwig Maximilian University Germany; Chongqing University China; Hong Kong Polytechnic University; Future University Egypt and many more including institutional partnerships with about 45 colleges and universities in Europe alone. The largest employer in the region UC has an annual economic impact of approximately $4.2 billion.

Geographic Reach

The university has nearly 120 facilities on about 475 acres land located in Cincinnati Ohio. It attracts students from all 50 states and to nearly 115 countries.

Company Background

UC traces its history all the way back to 1819 when Cincinnati College and the Medical College of Ohio were chartered. In 1870 the city established the University of Cincinnati which later absorbed Cincinnati College and the Medical College of Ohio. In 1906 UC created the first cooperative education program in the world. In 1977 UC joined the University System of Ohio. Today UC is classified as a research university (meaning it has "Very High Research Activity") by the Carnegie Commission and is ranked as one of America's top 25 public research universities by the National Science Foundation.

EXECUTIVES

Pres, Gregory H Williams
Provost Head, Jane E Henney
Provost, Anthony Perzigin
Research and Staff, Sheryl E Koch
Accounting Staff, Augusto Gomez
Accounting Staff, Cynthia Lasonczyk
Accounting Staff, Gary Friedhoff
Accounting Staff, Ilse Hawkins
Accounting Staff, Jean Kaesemeyer
Accounting Staff, Kathleen Weber
Accounting Staff, Kim Petrie
Auditors: BKD LLP CINCINNATI OHIO

LOCATIONS

HQ: UNIVERSITY OF CINCINNATI
2600 CLIFTON AVE, CINCINNATI, OH 452202872
Phone: 513 556-6000
Web: WWW.UC.EDU

PRODUCTS/OPERATIONS

Selected Colleges & Schools
Clermont College (regional campus)
College-Conservatory of Music
College of Allied Health Sciences
College of Applied Science
College of Business
College of Design Architecture Art & Planning
College of Education Criminal Justice and Human Services
College of Engineering
College of Law
College of Medicine
College of Nursing
James L. Winkle College of Pharmacy
McMicken College of Arts & Sciences
Raymond Walters College (regional campus)
School of Social Work

HISTORICAL FINANCIALS

Company Type: Private

Income Statement				FYE: June 30
	REVENUE ($ mil.)	NET INCOME ($ mil.)	NET PROFIT MARGIN	EMPLOYEES
06/11	1,198	48	4.1%	14,600
06/07	594	112	18.9%	—
06/06	557	20	3.6%	—
Annual Growth	16.6%	19.2%	—	—

UNIVERSITY OF COLORADO

EXECUTIVES

Exec Dir, Hollie Stevenson
Senior Research Associate, Robin Corley
Director of Special Events, Suzanne Balog
Teaching Assistant History, Elizabeth Ernst
Senior Director of Gift Planni, Lori Goldstein
Physical Therapy, Thomas Colver
Senior Messaging, Tim Crean
Language Technology Specialist, Edwige Simon
Associate Professor, Elizabeth Dunn
Director of Real Estate, Jeff Lipton
Assistant Professor, Joel Kaar
Auditors: CLIFTON LARSON ALLEN LLP GRE

LOCATIONS

HQ: UNIVERSITY OF COLORADO
1800 N GRANT ST STE 800, DENVER, CO 802031187
Phone: 303 831-6192
Web: WWW.COLORADO.EDU

HISTORICAL FINANCIALS

Company Type: Private

Income Statement				FYE: June 30
	REVENUE ($ mil.)	NET INCOME ($ mil.)	NET PROFIT MARGIN	EMPLOYEES
06/19	4,097	427	10.4%	8,921
06/13	2,774	308	11.1%	—
06/12	2,641	141	5.4%	—
Annual Growth	6.5%	17.1%	—	—

UNIVERSITY OF COLORADO HEALTH

EXECUTIVES

General Counsel, Emily Weber
Internal Medicine Practitioner, Darlene B Tad-Y
Coordinator, Carrie Macdonald
Coordinator, Jessica Berry
Coordinator, Meredith Snyder
Social Worker Clinical Lcsw CM, Allyson Drago
Nurse Navigator, Christine Frodella
Ems, Joy Schmitter
Case Manager Rn CM, Nicole Allsman
Vp Patient Line, Gary Henry
Clinical Documentation Special, Susan Krage

LOCATIONS

HQ: UNIVERSITY OF COLORADO HEALTH
12401 E 17TH AVE, AURORA, CO 800452548
Phone: 720 848-1031
Web: WWW.UCHEALTH.ORG

HISTORICAL FINANCIALS

Company Type: Private

Income Statement				FYE: June 30
	REVENUE ($ mil.)	NET INCOME ($ mil.)	NET PROFIT MARGIN	EMPLOYEES
06/20	5,055	485	9.6%	7,593
06/19	4,952	773	15.6%	—
06/18	4,341	747	17.2%	—
Annual Growth	7.9%	(19.4%)	—	—

UNIVERSITY OF COLORADO HOSPITAL AUTHORITY

University of Colorado Hospital Authority doing business as UCHealth operates the University of Colorado Hospital (UCH) in Aurora Colorado. The facility is a teaching institution for — you guessed it — the University of Colorado. UCH is a 400-bed community hospital that includes a number of specialty care facilities including centers specializing in oncology respiratory care and endocrinology. The facility also conducts medical training and research programs in partnership with the University of Colorado's Denver School of Medicine. In addition UCHealth operates 10 primary care clinics in the Denver metropolitan area.

Operations

UCH is located on the University of Colorado's Anschutz Medical Campus along with other health care providers and the University of Colorado's primary medical school campus in Aurora Colorado. Its Anschutz Inpatient Pavilion includes ICU operating imaging pharmacy and other care facilities. It also includes the Anschutz Cancer Pavilion which not only offers cancer treatment but also conducts research; Rocky Mountain Lions Eye Institute for ophthalmic care; and a rehabilitation department offering addiction treatment services.

While UCH's operations are closely tied to the University of Colorado UCH is governed by the UCH Authority a separate legal entity.

Strategy

UCHealth has upgraded its facilities in recent years to provide state-of-the art medical care and educational and research resources. Among its recent projects has been a $20 million renovation and expansion of the Anschutz Cancer Pavilion the addition of a brain tumor treatment lab to the Anschutz Outpatient Pavilion and the construction of a new 12-story emergency department tower.

In 2015 the authority broke ground on another project — the construction of a new $12.3 million emergency center at its Harmony Campus in Fort Collins Colorado. It also acquired a majority stake in a dozen freestanding emergency rooms in Colorado that are operated by Adeptus Health. The facilities (plus two more under construction) operated under the First Choice banner but were rebranded as UCHealth ER.

EXECUTIVES

Pres-Ceo, Bruce Chroffel
Prin*, Mary Schumer
Coo*, John Harney
Cfo*, Anthony Desurio
Staff Coordinator, Carolyn Boston
Occupational Specia, Katherine T Barnum
Staff Coordinator, Liya Taylor
Vp Clinical Affairs, Gregory V Stiegmann
Internal Medicine Practitioner, Heidi Wald
Executive Director, Martha Van Gelder
Chief of Medicine, Jean Kutner

LOCATIONS

HQ: UNIVERSITY OF COLORADO HOSPITAL AUTHORITY
4200 E 9TH AVE, DENVER, CO 802203706
Phone: 720 848-0000
Web: WWW.UCHEALTH.ORG

COMPETITORS

Banner Health	Memorial Health System
Catholic Health	(colorado)
Initiatives	Poudre Valley Health
Centura Health	System
Denver Health And	Sisters Of Charity Of
Hospital Authority	Leavenworth
Exempla Healthcare	Valley View Hospital
Healthone	

HISTORICAL FINANCIALS
Company Type: Private

Income Statement				FYE: June 30
	REVENUE ($ mil.)	NET INCOME ($ mil.)	NET PROFIT MARGIN	EMPLOYEES
06/10	795	151	19.1%	4,200
06/09	1	0	—	—
06/05	464	1	0.2%	—
Annual Growth	11.4%	169.7%	—	—

2010 Year-End Financials

Return on assets: 12.0% Cash ($ mil.): 22
Return on equity: 24.3%
Current ratio: 1.30

UNIVERSITY OF DELAWARE

Delaware brings up images of many things our first president that famous river and now the private University of Delaware (UD). The school's flagship campus in Newark has an enrollment of roughly 17000 undergraduate and close to 4000 graduate students. The school also has four auxiliary campuses around the state. UD offers almost 150 undergraduate degrees about 120 master's programs and more than 50 doctoral programs as well as associate's and dual graduate programs through seven academic schools. Among its instructors are well-known authors scientists artists and Nobel Laureates.

Operations

UD is a Land Grant Sea Grant and Space Grant institution meaning the school is eligible for government grants in each of these areas. The Carnegie Foundation for the Advancement of Teaching also classifies UD as a research university with very high research activity — a designation given to less than 3% of US colleges and universities. UD ranks among the nation's top 100 universities in federal research and development support for science and engineering. The university even has its own 146-foot research vessel (named the Hugh R. Sharp) for undersea exploration.

The school has a student-teacher ratio of about 15:1. It has roughly 1130 faculty members nearly 80% of which are tenured. Almost 90% have doctorate or terminal professional degrees in their field. (A terminal degree is also referred to as a Ph.D and refers to the fact that no higher degree can be obtained on that track.)

UD's 2012-13 tuition and fees were $11682 (in-state) and $28772 (out-of-state).

Geographic Reach

The university has campuses in Dover Georgetown Lewes Newark and Wilmington.

Financial Performance

The school reported a 5% increase in revenues in 2012 as the result of an increase in tuition and fees contributions and sales and services of auxiliary enterprises.

However UD's net income dropped by 118% in 2012 over 2011 due to higher expenses and a larger net realized and unrealized loss and an increase in a post-retirement benefit obligation.

In 2012 the university was supported by $1.21 billion endowment.

Company Background

UD got its start in 1743 as a private academy and was chartered by the state of Delaware in 1833. In athletics the school began NCAA Division I competition for men in 1973 and for women in 1982. US Vice President Joe Biden and his wife Jill are both UD graduates.

EXECUTIVES

Pres, Patrick T Harker
Exec V Pres-Treas*, Scott R Douglass
V Pres-SEC*, Pierre Hayward
V Pres-Fin-Admn*, Jennifer Davis
Int Chief Diversity Officer*, Fatimah Conley
Vice Provost Academic Affairs, Havid N Rodr Guez
Information Technology Manager, Dave Heckman
Coordinator, Karen Peterson
Coordinator, Linda Robinson
Coordinator, Deborah Fields
Assistant Professor, Dan Freeman
Auditors: KPMG LLP PHILADELPHIA PA

LOCATIONS

HQ: UNIVERSITY OF DELAWARE
210 S COLLEGE AVE, NEWARK, DE 197165200
Phone: 302 831-2107
Web: WWW.UDEL.EDU

PRODUCTS/OPERATIONS

Selected Schools and Colleges
Agriculture and Natural Resources
Arts and Sciences
Business and Economics
Earth Ocean and Environment
Education and Human Development
Engineering
Health Sciences
25 Most Popular Majors (2011)
Biological Sciences
Nursing
Finance
Psychology
Elementary Teacher Education
Exercise Science
Mechanical Engineering
Accounting
English
Chemical Engineering
Criminal Justice
Political Science
Civil Engineering
Marketing
Hotel Restaurant & Institutional Management
History
Human Services
Communication Interest
International Relations
Fashion Merchandising
Business Administration
Dietetics
Communication
Management
Pre-Veterinary Medicine & Animal Biosciences

HISTORICAL FINANCIALS
Company Type: Private

Income Statement   FYE: June 30

	REVENUE ($ mil.)	NET INCOME ($ mil.)	NET PROFIT MARGIN	EMPLOYEES
06/20	1,312	(19)	—	3,600
06/19	1,069	60	5.7%	—
06/18	1,023	139	13.7%	—
06/17	992	159	16.1%	—
Annual Growth	9.8%	—	—	—

2020 Year-End Financials
Return on assets: (-0.5%)
Return on equity: (-0.8%)
Current ratio: 0.40
Cash ($ mil.): 211

UNIVERSITY OF DENVER

Want a mile-high education? Colorado Seminary which does business as University of Denver (DU) offers graduate and undergraduate degrees in more than 300 fields of study including law political science humanities education engineering and psychology. About 12000 undergraduate and graduate students from across the US and more than 80 countries are enrolled at the school. Founded in 1864 the university has a student-to-faculty ratio of 11:1. DU is located on a 125-acre campus. Former Secretary of State Condoleezza Rice former Interior Secretary Gale Norton and former Coors Brewing CEO Peter Coors attended DU.

Operations
The university offers over 100 undergraduate degree programs in schools from Daniels College of Business Daniel Felix Ritchie School of Engineering and Computer Science Josef Korbel School of International Studies Morgridge College of Education and Sturm College of Law. It also offers over 120 programs across more than 10 schools and colleges ranging from business entrepreneurship and international politics to the natural and social sciences.

Geographic Reach
Based in Denver the university's students study international economics in Prague work on sustainable development in Thailand and use their spring breaks to provide medical relief in Central America.

Strategy
Despite campus growth between 2006 and 2015 the University shrank its carbon footprint by 27% due to the use of carbon offsets and vehicles fueled by compressed natural gas (CNG). It operates the only CNG fueling station on a Colorado university campus.

Company Background
Founded in 1864 as the Colorado Seminary only six years after the founding of Denver City in what was then the Colorado Territory.

EXECUTIVES

Chancellor, Dr Jeremy Haefner
Vice Chancellor*, Craig Woody
Chief Information Officer*, Kenneth R Stafford
Provost*, Gregg Kvistadt
Chairman*, Joy Burns
Dean, Sturm College of Law, Jos Roberto Ju Rez Jr
Supervising Attorney, Lupe Orozco
Chief Information Security Off, Arlen M Fletcher

Director Administrative Inform, Susan L Lutz
Executive Director, Judith S White
Director, Career Center, Mary Michael Hawkins
Auditors: CLIFTONLARSONALLEN LLP DENVER

LOCATIONS
HQ: UNIVERSITY OF DENVER
2199 S UNIVERSITY BLVD, DENVER, CO 802104700
Phone: 303 871-3014
Web: WWW.DU.EDU

PRODUCTS/OPERATIONS

Selected Schools and Programs
Undergraduate Schools and Colleges
  Daniels College of Business
  Division of Natural Sciences & Mathematics
  Division of Arts Humanities and Social Sciences
  Josef Korbel School of International Studies
  Morgridge College of Education
  School of Engineering and Computer Science
  University College
  Women's College
Graduate and Professional Programs
  Daniels College of Business
  Divisions of Arts Humanities and Social Sciences
  Divisions of Natural Sciences and Mathematics
  Graduate School of Professional Psychology (GSPP)
  Graduate School of Social Work (GSSW)
  Graduate Tax Program
  Interdisciplinary Degree Programs
  Josef Korbel School of International Studies
  Morgridge College of Education (MCE)
  School of Engineering and Computer Science
  The Sturm College of Law
  University College

HISTORICAL FINANCIALS
Company Type: Private

Income Statement   FYE: June 30

	REVENUE ($ mil.)	NET INCOME ($ mil.)	NET PROFIT MARGIN	EMPLOYEES
06/20	716	(11)	—	1,400
06/19	521	43	8.4%	—
06/17	467	86	18.6%	—
06/16	458	9	2.2%	—
Annual Growth	11.8%	—	—	—

2020 Year-End Financials
Return on assets: (-0.6%)
Return on equity: (-0.8%)
Current ratio: 0.50
Cash ($ mil.): 87

UNIVERSITY OF FLORIDA

Founded in 1853 the University of Florida (UF) is the state's oldest university and one of the largest in the country with more than 56000 students and nearly 6000 faculty and library staff members. UF is a major land-grant research university encompassing 2000 acres in Gainesville Florida. The university's 15 colleges offer almost 100 undergraduate majors and over 200 graduate programs including education law medicine psychology and philosophy. It is also a member of the Association of American Universities comprised of approximately 65 leading research universities in the US and Canada. The university has a large international enrollment with more than 4600 international students representing over 130 countries.

Operations
UF is active in research and operates more than 200 research institutes and centers including the Nanoscale Research Facility the Pathogens Research Facility and the Biomedical Sciences Building. It has helped launch more than 190 startups based on researchers' technologies. The university received a record $838 million in research awards.

UF also has extensive health education programs including nursing and pharmacy colleges. Its medical school conducts teaching and residency programs at several Shands hospitals.

Overall grants and contracts account for about 70% of the university's revenue student tuition and fees net of scholarship allowances bring in approximately 20% sales and services of auxiliary enterprises contribute around 5% and sales and services of educational departments represent less than 5%.

Geographic Reach
The campus consists of approximately 2000 acres and more than 900 buildings including the first Leadership in Energy and Environmental Design (LEED) Platinum-certified building in the state of Florida. The university's programs and facilities span more than 180 locations throughout the state and the globe.

Financial Performance
Total operating revenues totaled $2 billion which has remained consistent with the prior year. The increase in net student tuition and fees of $24.6 million is primarily due to additional enrollment from out-of-state graduate students. Due to the University's response to the COVID-19 pandemic operations noticeably subsided to ensure the safety of students faculty and staff. Sales and Services of Auxiliary Enterprises experienced the greatest impact of this with a decrease of $16.7 million.

In 2020 the company had a net loss of $76.1 million a 229% decrease from the previous year's net income of $59 million.

The company's cash at the end of 2020 was $6.9 million. Investing activities provided $1.2 billion while operating activities used $1.1 billion. Financing activities used another $150.2 million primarily for purchase or construction of capital assets.

Strategy
The University of Florida's student population of over 56000 makes it an integral part of Gainesville a town of approximately 134000 residents and the university's host city. The University of Florida has adopted a strategic development plan based on an exploration of key issues within the university community and the City of Gainesville which seeks to shape the University and the surrounding community's future over the next 40 to 50 years. This future is based on sustainable growth - with a 2000-acre campus and more than 900 buildings including the first Leadership in Energy and Environmental Design (LEED) Platinum-certified building in the state of Florida the University now has more LEED-certified buildings than any other American university.

Mergers and Acquisitions
In late 2021 University of Florida to pay $100 to acquire California-based Scripps Florida assets including three buildings in Jupiter 70 acres of vacant land and other assets and liabilities upon the integration of the nonprofit's biomedical operation with the state university's academic health center's research operation next month.

Company Background
UF's alumni include Robert Cade the inventor of Gatorade; best-selling mystery novelist Michael Connelly; actress Faye Dunaway; and former US Senator and Florida Governor Bob Graham. Other UF alumni include two Nobel Prize winners and three NASA astronauts.

EXECUTIVES
Pres, Kent Fuchs
V Pres of Fin & ADM*, John E Poppell

Dir*, Brian Prindle
Exec SEC*, Suzanne Corilo
Professor, Miklos Bona
Professor English Language, Nathaniel Bloemke
Information Technology Staff, Rayneil Robinson
Information Technology Expert, Sullivan Beck
Professor Teaching Ctr General, Tamra Byrd
Professor Medicine At Jax, Tracy Ashby
Assistant Professor, Xin Zhao
Auditors: SHERRILL F NORMAN CPA TALLA

LOCATIONS

HQ: UNIVERSITY OF FLORIDA
   300 SW 13TH ST, GAINESVILLE, FL 326110001
Phone: 352 392-3261
Web: WWW.UFL.EDU

PRODUCTS/OPERATIONS

Selected Colleges
College of Agricultural and Life Sciences
College of Dentistry
College of Design Construction and Planning
College of Education
College of Engineering
College of Health and Human Performance
College of Journalism and Communications
College of Liberal Arts and Sciences
College of Medicine
College of Nursing
College of Pharmacy
College of Public Health and Health Professions
College of the Arts
College of Veterinary Medicine
Levin College of Law
Warrington College of Business Administration

HISTORICAL FINANCIALS
Company Type: Private

Income Statement				FYE: June 30
	REVENUE ($ mil.)	NET INCOME ($ mil.)	NET PROFIT MARGIN	EMPLOYEES
06/20	2,019	(15)	—	5,106
06/15	1,735	261	15.1%	—
06/12	3,939	64	1.6%	—
Annual Growth	(8.0%)	—	—	—

2020 Year-End Financials
Return on assets: (-0.3%)
Return on equity: (-0.8%)
Current ratio: 4.50
Cash ($ mil.): —

UNIVERSITY OF GEORGIA

Located in the quintessential college town of Athens The University of Georgia (UGA) offers a wide range of degree programs to nearly 35000 students. Forest resources veterinary medicine and law are a few of the school's academic programs. UGA which also runs 170-plus study-abroad and exchange programs administers the prestigious Peabody Awards which honors media achievements and boasts one of the nation's largest map collections. Famous alumni include former US Senator Phil Gramm TV journalist Deborah Norville and former PBS president Pat Mitchell. The University of Georgia was chartered by the State of Georgia in 1785 and graduated its first class in 1804.

Operations
As part of its business UGA offers nearly two dozen bachelor's degrees in about 140 fields and roughly 35 master's degrees in nearly 140 fields. Its doctorate or professional degrees cover a broad spectrum of disciplines such as law pharmacy veterinary medicine and 90 other areas. The university has a student-teacher ratio of about 12:1.

Sales and Marketing
The university sources 80% of its students from the Peach State. Since 1851 25 Georgia governors have graduated from UGA. The institution also boasts nine Pulitzer Prize recipients 17 presidents or provosts of US colleges and universities and four members of the National Academy of Sciences.

Strategy
Despite its annual endowment of more than $50 million UGA has logged decreases in state appropriations in recent years due to overall declines in Georgia's budget. The result spurred UGA to cut its budget increase undergraduate tuition fees institute a "Special Institutional" mandatory fee of $200 per semester reduce employer health insurance contributions and increase energy conservation measures. Going forward UGA has also not ruled out the possibility of hiking tuition further citing that an increase of up to 30% would help to replace all of the state funding the university has lost due to the recession.

EXECUTIVES

Pres, Jere Morehead
Assistant, Taylor Burge
Assistant Professor, Alfie Vick
Assistant Professor, Amy Ross
Administrator, Audrey Greeson
Assistant Professor, Betina Kaplan
Associate Director, Chris Hocking
Information Technology Manager, Chris Peters
Graphic Designer, Dianne Johnson
Assistant Professor, Doug Menke
Professor, James Cobb
Auditors: GREG S GRIFFIN ATLANTA GEOR

LOCATIONS

HQ: UNIVERSITY OF GEORGIA
   424 E BROAD ST, ATHENS, GA 306021535
Phone: 706 542-2786
Web: WWW.UGA.EDU

PRODUCTS/OPERATIONS

Selected Schools and Colleges
Agricultural and Environmental Sciences
Arts and Sciences Business
Ecology
Education
Environment and Design
Family and Consumer Sciences
Forest Resources
Graduate School
Journalism and Mass Communication
Law
Pharmacy
Public Health
Public and International Affairs
Social Work
Veterinary Medicine
The GHSU/UGA Medical Partnership
Engineering

HISTORICAL FINANCIALS
Company Type: Private

Income Statement				FYE: June 30
	REVENUE ($ mil.)	NET INCOME ($ mil.)	NET PROFIT MARGIN	EMPLOYEES
06/21	1,548	489	31.6%	17,800
06/20	1,067	(22)	—	—
06/19	1,094	72	6.7%	—
06/18	997	111	11.2%	—
Annual Growth	15.8%	63.7%	—	—

2021 Year-End Financials
Return on assets: 8.2%
Return on equity: 17.4%
Current ratio: 3.10
Cash ($ mil.): 306

UNIVERSITY OF HAWAI'I OF MANOA

EXECUTIVES

Dir, Terence Wesley-Smith
Chm, David Hanlon
Assistant Professor, Matthew Cain
Graduate Assistant, Daniel Dores
Research Assistant, Julio Rivera
Assistant Researcher, Andre Seale
Auxiliary, Beth Lehman
Maui County Administrator, Cynthia Reeves
Assistant Specialist, Robyn Chun
Admin Officer, Chris T Kaukali
Associate Specialist, Mark R Chun

LOCATIONS

HQ: UNIVERSITY OF HAWAI'I OF MANOA
   2500 CAMPUS RD, HONOLULU, HI 968222217
Phone: 808 956-7700
Web: WWW.HAWAII.EDU

HISTORICAL FINANCIALS
Company Type: Private

Income Statement				FYE: June 30
	REVENUE ($ mil.)	NET INCOME ($ mil.)	NET PROFIT MARGIN	EMPLOYEES
06/18	772	51	6.7%	8
06/11	871	139	16.0%	—
Annual Growth	(1.7%)	(13.2%)	—	—

2018 Year-End Financials
Return on assets: 1.2%
Return on equity: —
Current ratio: 2.10
Cash ($ mil.): 122

UNIVERSITY OF HAWAII SYSTEM

With a reach that extends across half a dozen islands the University of Hawai'i System consists of three university campuses seven community college campuses and several job training and research centers. The public higher education system has an enrollment of more than 60000 students about 85% of which are Hawaii residents. It offers more than 600 different doctorate graduate undergraduate and associate degrees as well as professional certificates in more than 200 fields of study. The University of Hawai'i was founded in 1907 as the College of Agriculture and Mechanic Arts in Honolulu incidentally while Hawaii was still a US territory.

Operations

Among its university campuses and community college campuses the University of Hawai'i boasts locations in Manoa Hilo West O'ahu Hawai'i Honolulu Kapi'olani Kaua'i Leeward Maui and Windward.

Strategy

The university has invested time and money in its information technology efforts. In 2012 the University of Hawai'i broke ground on a new Information Technology Center a six-story building on the Manoa campus. The center offers the university a centralized facility for its system-wide Information Technology Services (ITS) division and serves as the new home of the university's enterprise information and communications technology systems.

The University of Hawai'i tackled a multipronged strategy in 2012 and exceeded its goals. It increased degree attainment for native Hawaiians at the university degrees and certificates of achievement earned disbursement of Pell Grants going rates of public and private high schools to its campus extramural fund support degrees in STEM Fields and non-state revenue streams.

To this end a physicist at the University of Hawai'i at Manoa's John A. Burns School of Medicine partnered with colleagues from the US and Germany to provide the necessary research to provide a foundation for KinetiCor Inc. KenetiCor in 2013 received $700000 in its first round of venture financing that helped the company launch formally. It's initially focused on commercializing the motion correction technology for Magnetic Resonance Imaging that was invented by Thomas Ernst the university's Manoa physicist.

EXECUTIVES

Ceo, David McClain
Pres*, David Lassner
Cfo*, Kalbert Young
Corporate Communications Staff, Mavis Ann O Hernandez
Project Coordinator, Lynette Matsumoto
Instructor, Carleton Moore
Assistant Professor Program Di, Kathryn Yamamoto
Assistant Specialist, Noelle Kahanu
Office Administrator, Tara Humphreys
Graduate Assistant, Vimlin Auetumrongsawat
Associate Professor Area Healt, Wonneberger Raul
Auditors: ACCUITY LLP HONOLULU HAWII

LOCATIONS

HQ: UNIVERSITY OF HAWAII SYSTEM
2444 DOLE ST, HONOLULU, HI 968222399
Phone: 808 956-8111
Web: WWW.HAWAII.EDU

Selected Campuses

Manoa

Hilo
West O'ahu
Hawai'i
Honolulu
Kapi'olani
Kaua'i
Leeward
Maui
Windward

HISTORICAL FINANCIALS

Company Type: Private

Income Statement — FYE: June 30

	REVENUE ($ mil.)	NET INCOME ($ mil.)	NET PROFIT MARGIN	EMPLOYEES
06/18	772	51	6.7%	12,000
06/17	771	33	4.3%	—
Annual Growth	0.1%	57.1%	—	—

2018 Year-End Financials

Return on assets: 1.2% Cash ($ mil.): 122
Return on equity: —
Current ratio: 2.10

UNIVERSITY OF HOUSTON SYSTEM

The University of Houston System is the region's largest provider of comprehensive university services from the baccalaureate to the doctorate. The university system serves more than 72000 students at four Houston-area universities. Flagship institution the University of Houston was founded in 1927 and offers approximately 250 undergrad majors and minors about 110 master's degrees and some 50 doctoral and professional degrees; it also conducts a number of research programs. Also under the system's umbrella are the University of Houston-Clear Lake the University of Houston-Downtown the University of Houston-Victoria as well as a handful of learning centers in the area.

Operations

Its University of Houston-Clear Lake nestled on about 525-acre wildlife and nature preserve near the NASA Johnson Space Center. The Hispanic Serving Institution offers more than 90 degree programs across four colleges The University of Houston-Downtown is the second largest university in Houston and the most ethnically diverse university in the state UHD is a four-year institution located in the central business district providing valuable opportunities for student internships at major corporations. University of Houston-Victoria (UHV) offers more than 80 bachelor's and master's degree programs with concentrations in the arts and sciences business administration education and human development along with one of the most dynamic online educational programs in the state.

Through the University of Houston System Student Pathways program undergraduate students in any of the four UH System universities are able to take up to six hours of courses toward their degree at any of the universities. The system's online program (University of Houston System Online Program) offers accredited degree and certificate programs with the flexibility to help students complete an undergraduate degree seek a master's degree or earn a certification for career development.

The UH system also has Houston Public Media home to KUHT-TV8 Houston's PBS station and the nation's first educational television station; KUHF-88.7 Houston's National Public Radio station; and KUHF 88.7 HD-2 Houston's digital classical music stream.

Geographic Reach

The UH System is headquartered in Calhoun Houston Texas it has instructional sites in Katy Northwest Houston Pearland and Sugar Land.

LOCATIONS

HQ: UNIVERSITY OF HOUSTON SYSTEM
4302 UNIVERSITY DR, HOUSTON, TX 772042011
Phone: 713 743-0945
Web: WWW.UHSYSTEM.EDU

PRODUCTS/OPERATIONS

Selected Colleges and Schools
University of Houston
  C.T. Bauer College of Business
  College of Education
  College of Liberal Arts and Social Sciences
  College of Natural Sciences and Mathematics
  College of Optometry
  College of Pharmacy
  College of Technology
  Conrad N. Hilton College of Hotel and Restaurant Management
  Cullen College of Engineering
  Gerald D. Hines College of Architecture
  Graduate College of Social Work
  Honors College
  Law Center
University of Houston-Clear Lake
  School of Business
  School of Education
  School of Human Sciences and Humanities
  School of Science and Computer Engineering
University of Houston-Downtown
  College of Business
  College of Humanities and Social Sciences
  College of Public Service
  College of Sciences and Technology
University of Houston-Victoria
  School of Arts and Sciences
  School of Business Administration
  School of Education and Human Development
  School of Nursing

HISTORICAL FINANCIALS

Company Type: Private

Income Statement — FYE: August 31

	REVENUE ($ mil.)	NET INCOME ($ mil.)	NET PROFIT MARGIN	EMPLOYEES
08/15	605	41	6.9%	12,608
08/14	742	46	6.2%	—
08/13	1	81	6095.0%	—
08/12	688	132	19.3%	—
Annual Growth	(4.2%)	(31.9%)	—	—

UNIVERSITY OF IOWA HOSPITALS AND CLINICS

EXECUTIVES

Ceo, Kenneth P Kates
Ceo, Gordon Williams
Pres, Sally Mason
V Pres, Jean Robillard
Prin, Ann Williamson
Chief Nursing Officer, Kimberly Hunter
Int Coo, John N Kastanis
Int Cfo, Mark Henrichs
Coordinator, Kathy Moser

Pediatrician, Catherina Pinnaro
Diagnostic Radiologist, John D Newell
Auditors: KPMG LLP DES MOINES IOWA

LOCATIONS

HQ: UNIVERSITY OF IOWA HOSPITALS AND CLINICS
200 HAWKINS DR, IOWA CITY, IA 522421009
Phone: 319 356-1616
Web: WWW.UICHILDRENS.ORG

HISTORICAL FINANCIALS
Company Type: Private

Income Statement				FYE: June 30
	REVENUE ($ mil.)	NET INCOME ($ mil.)	NET PROFIT MARGIN	EMPLOYEES
06/20	1,939	99	5.1%	7,638
06/19	1,834	111	6.1%	—
06/18	1,666	296	17.8%	—
06/17	1,502	47	3.2%	—
Annual Growth	8.9%	27.8%	—	—

2020 Year-End Financials
Return on assets: 3.9%   Cash ($ mil.): 11
Return on equity: 5.7%
Current ratio: 1.50

UNIVERSITY OF LOUISIANA SYSTEM FOUNDATION

EXECUTIVES

Acct, Kecia Neal
Exec Dir, Caprice Leyoub
Pres, John Crain
Auditors: DARYL G PURPERA CPA CFE BA

LOCATIONS

HQ: UNIVERSITY OF LOUISIANA SYSTEM
FOUNDATION
1201 N 3RD ST STE 7300, BATON ROUGE, LA
708025243
Phone: 225 342-6950
Web: WWW.ULSYSTEM.EDU

HISTORICAL FINANCIALS
Company Type: Private

Income Statement				FYE: June 30
	REVENUE ($ mil.)	NET INCOME ($ mil.)	NET PROFIT MARGIN	EMPLOYEES
06/20	927	43	4.7%	4,500
06/19	942	28	3.0%	—
06/18	930	101	10.9%	—
06/17	906	23	2.6%	—
Annual Growth	0.8%	22.0%	—	—

2020 Year-End Financials
Return on assets: 1.5%   Cash ($ mil.): 218
Return on equity: —
Current ratio: 2.20

UNIVERSITY OF LOUISVILLE

Living up to its mandate to be a leading metropolitan research university the University of Louisville (U of L) has hit a few out of the park. The U of L completed the first self-contained artificial heart implant and the first successful hand transplant at its University of Louisville Hospital. The health care focused university offers associate baccalaureate master's professional and doctorate degrees in some 170 fields of study including medicine dentistry nursing and public health as well as arts and sciences education business law music social work and engineering. It has more than 22000 students enrolled in about a dozen colleges and schools on three campuses.

Geographic Reach
U of L's main campus the 290-acre Belknap Campus houses seven of the university's 12 colleges and schools and is located three miles from downtown Louisville. The U of L Health Sciences Center (housing the health-related schools) is located in downtown Louisville while the Shelby Campus is in eastern Jefferson County.

Strategy
Despite its focus on health care pressures on the health care industry (including the high cost of running a full-service hospital) prompted the school to explore a possible merger of the U of L Hospital with two other state health care providers Saint Joseph Health Care and Jewish Hospital & St. Mary's HealthCare (JHSMH) in 2010. However U of L was ultimately left out of the deal (completed in 2012) after Kentucky's governor voiced concerns over the potential loss of control over the U of L Hospital which operates as a regional safety net medical care provider.

Company Background
The origins of the University of Louisville date back to 1798 with a meeting to establish Jefferson Seminary which didn't open its doors until 1813 and closed 16 years later. Subsequent incarnations eventually led to the creation of the University of Louisville in 1846.

Notable alumni include author Sue Grafton US Senator Christopher Dodd and William Akers inventor of the SPF sun protection rating system.

EXECUTIVES

Chb, Mary Nixon
Pres*, Neeli Bendapudi
Pres*, Lori Stewart Gonzalez
Faculty, Frederick Parkins
Director, Gary Mans
Professor, Hornung Carlton
Assistant Professor Term, Imad Elhaj
Manager, James Simrall
Professor Term, James Snyder
Library Assistant, Janissa Moore
Training Specialist, Jennifer Potochnic
Auditors: CLIFTON LARSON ALLEN LLP ST

LOCATIONS

HQ: UNIVERSITY OF LOUISVILLE
2301 S 3RD ST, LOUISVILLE, KY 402922001
Phone: 502 852-5555
Web: WWW.LOUISVILLE.EDU

PRODUCTS/OPERATIONS

Selected Colleges and Schools
Arts & Sciences
Brandeis School of Law
Business

Dentistry
Education & Human Development
Kent School of Social Work
Medicine
Music
Nursing
Public Health & Information Sciences
School of Interdisciplinary and Graduate Studies
Speed School of Engineering

HISTORICAL FINANCIALS
Company Type: Private

Income Statement				FYE: June 30
	REVENUE ($ mil.)	NET INCOME ($ mil.)	NET PROFIT MARGIN	EMPLOYEES
06/18	717	3	0.4%	6,275
06/12	559	(36)	—	—
06/11	591	32	5.4%	—
Annual Growth	2.8%	(28.5%)	—	—

2018 Year-End Financials
Return on assets: 0.2%   Cash ($ mil.): 80
Return on equity: 0.4%
Current ratio: 1.10

UNIVERSITY OF MARYLAND MEDICAL SYSTEM CORPORATION

The thirteen academic specialty and community hospitals of the University of Maryland Medical System (UMMS) dot the map of the state's eastern half on both sides of Chesapeake Bay. UMMS one of the largest employers in the Baltimore area has more than 2485 acute care beds and attends to such specialties as trauma care cancer cardiac women's vascular and neuroscience services orthopedic rehabilitation and pediatric care. University of Maryland Medical Center the system's teaching hub is one of the oldest academic hospitals in the US. In addition to its hospitals UMMS also includes community clinics to address mental health rehabilitation and primary care. The system was established in 1984.

Operations
UMMC's members hospitals include the University of Maryland Medical Center Baltimore Washington Medical Center Chester River Home Care ChoiceOne Urgent Care UM Rehabilitation & Orthopedic Institute UM Capital Region Health Mt. Washington Pediatric Hospital UM Shore Health System University of Maryland St. Joseph Medical Center and Upper Chesapeake Health.

University of Maryland Medical Center which houses about 805 beds is staffed entirely by physicians who double as faculty members at the University of Maryland School of Medicine (SOM) the system's longtime partner. The hospital contains additional specialty facilities dedicated to such areas as pediatrics cancer treatment cardiac disease diabetes organ transplants Parkinson's disease and shock trauma.

Aside from its integral partnership with SOM UMMS has in recent years been bolstering its network of member hospitals to reach new markets in Maryland. Its affiliate University of Maryland Upper Chesapeake Health owns a pair of hospitals in northeastern Maryland (UM Upper Chesapeake

Medical Center and UM Harford Memorial Hospital).

Geographic Reach

Based in Maryland UMMS provides primary and specialty care at more than 150 locations across the state.

Strategy

The University of Maryland Medical System and CareFirst BlueCross BlueShield (CareFirst) the region's largest not-for-profit healthcare company announced a new five-year partnership to address access and quality of care for the state's most vulnerable populations. The transformative work from this initiative will focus on population health which is an approach to care aiming to improve the health outcomes for entire patient populations while also improving the healthcare experience and effectively managing costs. This includes enhanced support and focused care for the highest-risk patients to help them maintain a high quality of life through more efficient and effective management of their health. As part of this effort Care-First BlueChoice Inc. will acquire University of Maryland Health Advantage Inc. (UM Health Advantage) a Medicare Dual Eligible Special Needs health plan and University of Maryland Health Partners Inc. a Medicaid Managed Care Organization. Combined UMMS' Health Plans serve 55000 Maryland residents each year.

At the core of this partnership is the development of a jointly operated population health management team which will allow UMMS and CareFirst to collaborate on innovative care models and related resources better enabling both organizations to focus on what they do best. Specifically the work will bring new approaches to using shared data that drive improved population health outcomes by supporting the identification and delivery of the most effective care and support for vulnerable populations. This joint effort allows CareFirst and UMMS to take coordinated action focused on investing in healthier communities and improving health equity in Maryland. This collaboration also marks a shared commitment to expanding partnerships designed to transform care delivery and improve health outcomes.

Company Background

The system's flagship hospital began on its present site in 1823 as Baltimore Infirmary. It later was known for many years as University Hospital until Maryland's legislature changed it from a state-run single-building facility to a private not-for-profit medical system in 1984. In short order UMMS began expanding mainly by adding existing hospitals.

EXECUTIVES

Ceo, Robert A Chrencik
Chb*, James Dipaula Jr
Sr Vice Pres-Chief Med Officer, Tim Babino
Evp and Cfo*, Henry J Franey
Svp-Coo*, Ron Cummins Jr
Director, Robert L Pevenstein
Director, Amy Myers
Diagnostic Radiologist, Aletta Frazier
Diagnostic Radiologist, Alexis Boscak
Psychiatrist, Anson Liu
Doctor, Bonnie Kerr

LOCATIONS

HQ: UNIVERSITY OF MARYLAND MEDICAL SYSTEM CORPORATION
250 W PRATT ST, BALTIMORE, MD 212012423
Phone: 410 328-8667
Web: WWW.UMMS.ORG

PRODUCTS/OPERATIONS

Selected Facilities and Affiliates

Baltimore Washington Medical Center
Chester River Health System
Civista Medical Center
Kernan Orthopaedics and Rehabilitation
Maryland General Hospital
Mt. Washington Pediatric Hospital
Shore Health System
　Dorchester General Hospital
　The Memorial Hospital at Easton
University of Maryland Medical Center
　Marlene and Stewart Greenebaum Cancer Center
　R Adams Cowley Shock Trauma Center
　University of Maryland Hospital for Children
University of Maryland St. Joseph Medical Center
University of Maryland Specialty Hospital
Upper Chesapeake Health
　Harford Memorial Hospital
　Upper Chesapeake Medical Center

COMPETITORS

Adventist Healthcare	Franklin Square
Anne Arundel Medical	Hospital Center
Center	Gbmc
Ascension Health	Johns Hopkins Health
Bon Secours Health	System
Catholic Health	Lifebridge Health
Initiatives	Medstar Health
Dimensions Healthcare	

HISTORICAL FINANCIALS

Company Type: Private

Income Statement   FYE: June 30

	REVENUE ($ mil.)	NET INCOME ($ mil.)	NET PROFIT MARGIN	EMPLOYEES
06/21	4,769	428	9.0%	12,000
06/20	4,364	70	1.6%	—
06/19	4,235	36	0.9%	—
06/16	1,358	(29)	—	—
Annual Growth	28.6%	—	—	—

2021 Year-End Financials

Return on assets: 5.5%　　　　Cash ($ mil.): 858
Return on equity: 12.8%
Current ratio: 1.00

UNIVERSITY OF MARYLAND, COLLEGE PARK

EXECUTIVES

Pres, Darryll Pines
Acting Chief Diversity Officer, Cynthia Edmunds
Administrative Assistant, Dee Allen
Dean, Gregory Bullock
Accounting Staff, Janet Dudley-Eshbach
Manager, Jennifer Shannon
Coordinator, Sheila Goebel
Coordinator, Omar Siddique
Law Specialist, Rebecca Hunsaker
Coordinator, Patrick Kangas
Dir of The Office For Civil RI, Grace Karmiol

LOCATIONS

HQ: UNIVERSITY OF MARYLAND, COLLEGE PARK
PATUXENT BLDG 010, COLLEGE PARK, MD
207420001
Phone: 301 405-1000
Web: WWW.UMCPF.UMD.EDU

HISTORICAL FINANCIALS

Company Type: Private

Income Statement   FYE: June 30

	REVENUE ($ mil.)	NET INCOME ($ mil.)	NET PROFIT MARGIN	EMPLOYEES
06/18	1,369	100	7.3%	8,871
06/17	15	1	12.6%	—
Annual Growth	8577.7%	4931.4%	—	—

2018 Year-End Financials

Return on assets: 3.2%　　　　Cash ($ mil.): 663
Return on equity: 5.0%
Current ratio: 2.90

UNIVERSITY OF MASSACHUSETTS

The University of Massachusetts (UMass) has been expanding across the commonwealth since its founding in 1863. About 75000 students are enrolled each year. The university's flagship campus is in Amherst with 28000 students and over 200 distinct academic programs including highly ranked programs in business computer science health care and social science and largest public research university in New England. Its University of Massachusetts Medical School in Boston offers rigorous health sciences programs in three graduate school of medicine the Morningside Graduate School of Bio Medical Sciences and the Tan Chingfen Graduate School of Nursing. Other UMass campuses can be found in Boston Dartmouth and Lowell.

Operations

UMass Amherst is part of the Five Colleges consortium a partnership with other area universities including Amherst Hampshire Mount Holyoke and Smith colleges. The tuition and fees accounts for about 40% of the revenue grant and contract is about 25% other operating revenue is about 20% and followed by auxiliary with about 15% of the revenue.

The system's Boston and Dartmouth campuses are renowned for their academic programs. UMass Boston is nationally recognized as a model of excellence for urban public research universities. Boston's distinguished intellectual contributions span the social sciences education health and wellness. UMass Dartmouth distinguishes itself as a variant university dedicated to engaged learning and innovative research and offers students high-quality academic programs through undergraduate majors and professional and doctorial programs including the state state's only public law school.

Geographic Reach

University of Massachusetts is a world class public research university system with four comprehensive undergraduate and graduate campuses located in rural urban suburban and urban areas. The University of Massachusetts has more than 90 core research facilities across the state that are available to researchers from government academia and industry on a fee-for-service basis.

Sales and Marketing

University of Massachusetts offers about hundred degree programs at four undergraduate/graduate degree program on its website.

Financial Performance

Total operating revenues for the year was $2.4 billion a 1% decrease from the previous year's total operating revenue. This was mainly due to a lower sales volume in the company's auxiliary enterprises.

Net position at the end of the year was $2.4 billion a 2% decrease from the previous year.

The company's cash at the end of 2020 was $462.6 million. Investing activities generated $45.3 million while operating activities used $627 million mainly for payments to employees. Cash flows from noncapital financing activities provided $977.4 million.

Strategy

In March 2020 the World Health Organization declared a pandemic as a result of the novel coronavirus (COVID-19). As cases began to increase in the country and in Massachusetts in March 2020 the University suspended in-person education and other campus-based activities and provided refunds to students for a portion of their residence and dining fees. The University took significant budget actions across all campuses to address the resulting loss of revenue. These actions included salary freezes furloughs and targeted operating and personnel reductions. The University was awarded $46.0 million of funding under the Coronavirus Aid Relief and Economic Security Act (CARES Act) half of which was required to be used to provide emergency financial aid to students. The University distributed $14.7 million in emergency aid to students.

Mergers and Acquisitions

In 2021 University of Massachusetts has taken control of Brandman University a California-based network of schools for adults learners and rebranded it as UMass Global and plans to expand its online education offerings. The acquisition came after the end of a yearlong partnership between UMass and Brandman's former parent Chapman University. Brandman serves about 22000 students spreads across 25 locations and online as part of Chapman University.

Company Background

Notable UMass alumni include entertainer Bill Cosby singer Natalie Cole and former General Electric CEO Jack Welch.

EXECUTIVES

Pres, Martin Meehan
V Chm*, Peter Levine
Pres*, Jack M Wilson
V Pres-Eco Development*, Thomas Chumura
V Pres-Treas*, Stephen W Lenhardt
Ex V Pres*, James Julian
Exec V Pres-Coo*, Michael J Green
Prin*, Mohammad Ranjbar
Director Oit Business Office, Gloria Chang-Wade
Project Manager, Iris Lyons
Senior Applications Developer, Jim Muchata
Auditors: KPMG LLP BOSTON MA

LOCATIONS

HQ: UNIVERSITY OF MASSACHUSETTS
1 BEACON ST, BOSTON, MA 021083107
Phone: 617 287-7000
Web: WWW.MASSACHUSETTS.EDU

PRODUCTS/OPERATIONS

Selected Colleges and Schools

College of Engineering
College of Humanities and Fine Arts
College of Natural Sciences and Mathematics
College of Social and Behavioral Sciences
Commonwealth College
Graduate School
School of Education
School of Management
School of Nursing
School of Public Health and Health Sciences

HISTORICAL FINANCIALS

Company Type: Private

Income Statement — FYE: June 30

	REVENUE ($ mil.)	NET INCOME ($ mil.)	NET PROFIT MARGIN	EMPLOYEES
06/20	2,426	(39)	—	13,196
06/18	2,468	77	3.1%	—
06/17	2,442	325	13.3%	—
06/16	2,403	129	5.4%	—
Annual Growth	0.2%	—	—	—

2020 Year-End Financials

Return on assets: (-0.5%)   Cash ($ mil.): 86
Return on equity: (-1.6%)
Current ratio: 1.70

UNIVERSITY OF MINNESOTA PHYSICIANS

EXECUTIVES

Ceo, Bobbi Daniels
Coo*, Mary Johnson
V Pres*, Barbara Gold
Cao*, Rachel Croson
Assistant Professor, Ila Harris
Health Professional, Alison Williams
Coordinator, Anne Jedlicki
Director, Susan Holt
Senior Information Technology, Kelly Savage
Manager Corporate Office Servi, Renee Pagano
Project Manager, Eric Bergerson
Auditors: KPMG LLP MINNEAPOLIS MN

LOCATIONS

HQ: UNIVERSITY OF MINNESOTA PHYSICIANS
720 WASHINGTON AVE SE # 200, MINNEAPOLIS, MN 554142924
Phone: 612 884-0600
Web: WWW.MPHYSICIANS.ORG

HISTORICAL FINANCIALS

Company Type: Private

Income Statement — FYE: June 30

	REVENUE ($ mil.)	NET INCOME ($ mil.)	NET PROFIT MARGIN	EMPLOYEES
06/20	702	27	3.9%	200
06/15	482	10	2.2%	—
06/14	490	23	4.8%	—
06/13	452	12	2.8%	—
Annual Growth	6.5%	12.0%	—	—

2020 Year-End Financials

Return on assets: 10.6%   Cash ($ mil.): 147
Return on equity: 23.2%
Current ratio: 1.10

UNIVERSITY OF MISSISSIPPI MEDICAL CENTER

EXECUTIVES

Ceo, Louann Woodward
Assistant Professor, Benjamin Stronach
Assistant Professor, Rebecca Sugg
Human Resources Business Partn, Constance Suber
Lab Reg Med Tech, Robin Galey
Associate Professor Clinical, Bo Huang
Program Administrator, Briana Thompson
Assistant Professor, Claude Harbarger
Nurse Practitioner, Courtney Sanders
Director of Radiology, Cristy Seibel
Assistant Professor of Medicin, Decynthia Haynes

LOCATIONS

HQ: UNIVERSITY OF MISSISSIPPI MEDICAL CENTER
2500 N STATE ST, JACKSON, MS 392164500
Phone: 601 984-2150
Web: WWW.UMC.EDU

HISTORICAL FINANCIALS

Company Type: Private

Income Statement — FYE: June 30

	REVENUE ($ mil.)	NET INCOME ($ mil.)	NET PROFIT MARGIN	EMPLOYEES
06/20	1,375	(72)	—	9,000
06/18	1,252	(87)	—	—
06/17	1,204	(78)	—	—
Annual Growth	4.5%	—	—	—

2020 Year-End Financials

Return on assets: (-3.7%)   Cash ($ mil.): 385
Return on equity: —
Current ratio: 1.90

UNIVERSITY OF MISSISSIPPI MEDICAL CENTER

EXECUTIVES

Dir, Daniel W Jones
Administrative Assistant III, Linda Buckley

LOCATIONS

HQ: UNIVERSITY OF MISSISSIPPI MEDICAL CENTER
2500 N STATE ST, JACKSON, MS 392164500
Phone: 601 984-5670
Web: WWW.UMC.EDU

HISTORICAL FINANCIALS
Company Type: Private

Income Statement   FYE: June 30

	REVENUE ($ mil.)	NET INCOME ($ mil.)	NET PROFIT MARGIN	EMPLOYEES
06/14	1,042	30	2.9%	20
06/13	940	23	2.5%	—
Annual Growth	10.9%	29.9%	—	—

2014 Year-End Financials
Return on assets: 8.9%   Cash ($ mil.): 176
Return on equity: 2.9%
Current ratio: 2.20

UNIVERSITY OF MISSOURI HEALTH CARE

EXECUTIVES

Ceo-Pres, Mitch Wasden
Dir of Treas, Ann Toellner
Cfo, Kevin Necas
Clinic Coordinator, Andrea Beneke
Rheumatologist, Chokkalingam Siva
Staff, Rhonda Cuddy
Project Manager, Cecilia Molina-Clark
Internal Medicine Practitioner, Harihoran Regunath
Internal Medicine Practitioner, Hraleen Chela
Programmer Analyst, Abigail Hartsfield
Programmer Analyst, Phyllis Lin
Auditors: KPMG LLP

LOCATIONS

HQ: UNIVERSITY OF MISSOURI HEALTH CARE
1 HOSPITAL DR, COLUMBIA, MO 652015276
Phone: 573 882-4141
Web: WWW.MUHEALTH.ORG

HISTORICAL FINANCIALS
Company Type: Private

Income Statement   FYE: June 30

	REVENUE ($ mil.)	NET INCOME ($ mil.)	NET PROFIT MARGIN	EMPLOYEES
06/16	749	62	8.4%	5,000
06/15	696	64	9.3%	—
06/08	0	0	1.0%	—
Annual Growth	140.0%	212.1%	—	—

2016 Year-End Financials
Return on assets: 5.9%   Cash ($ mil.): 27
Return on equity: 10.0%
Current ratio: 1.40

UNIVERSITY OF MISSOURI SYSTEM

The University of Missouri (UM) is one of the nation's largest higher education institutions. Founded in 1839 UM educates more than 70000 students at four campuses and through a statewide extension program with activities in every county of the state. Serving nearly 115 counties the university's campuses include flagship UM-Columbia UM-Kansas City UM-St. Louis and the Missouri University of Science and Technology. It has an endowment and similar funds of approximately $1.27 billion. Nicknamed "Mizzou" the University of Missouri System has close to 5120 faculty members and a student?teacher ratio of about 13:1.

Operations
In addition to its university campuses the University of Missouri System operates the University of Missouri HealthCare which encompasses University Hospital and Clinics Women's and Children's Hospital Ellis Fischel Cancer Center Rusk Rehabilitation Center Missouri Psychiatric Institute Missouri Orthopaedic Institute and University Physicians. Its hospitals and clinics provide high-risk obstetrics orthopaedic surgery neurosciences and cardiovascular care among other services. It also has the region's only Level I Trauma Center.

In addition patient medical services account for approximately 45% tuition and fees generate about 20% other auxiliary enterprises provide more than 10% state appropriations and grants and contracts bring in about 10% each and others represent the remaining less than 5%.

Geographic Reach
The University of Missouri's four campuses are located in Columbia Kansas City Rolla and St. Louis. The system has an exchange program with South Africa through which UM students study at the University of the Western Cape in Bellville (Cape Town) South Africa and vice versa.

EXECUTIVES

Pres, Mun Y Choi
V Pres-Fin-Admin*, Natalie Krawitz
Treas*, Tom Richards
Gen Counsel*, Steve Owens
Int CIO-Vp Info Tech*, Beth Chancellor
Assistant Professor, Daniel E Hassett
Scientist, Steven R Van Doren
Information Specialist, Meridith Berry
Staff, Donald S Piland
Account Executive Komu TV, Andrea Kaiser
Vice President, Gary Allen
Auditors: BKD LLP KANSAS CITY MISSOUR

LOCATIONS

HQ: UNIVERSITY OF MISSOURI SYSTEM
321 UNIVERSITY HALL, COLUMBIA, MO 652113020
Phone: 573 882-2712
Web: WWW.UMSYSTEM.EDU

PRODUCTS/OPERATIONS

Selected Campuses
University of Missouri-Columbia
University of Missouri Health System (Columbia)
UM-Kansas City
UM-St. Louis
Missouri University of Science and Technology (Rolla)

Selected Colleges and Schools
College of Agriculture Food and Natural Resources
  School of Natural Resources
College of Arts and Sciences
  School of Music
College of Education
  School of Information Science and Learning Technologies
College of Engineering
College of Human Environmental Sciences
  School of Social Work
College of Veterinary Medicine
Graduate School
  Harry S Truman School of Public Affairs
School of Health Professions
School of Journalism
School of Law

School of Medicine
Sinclair College of Nursing
Trulaske College of Business
  School of Accountancy

HISTORICAL FINANCIALS
Company Type: Private

Income Statement   FYE: June 30

	REVENUE ($ mil.)	NET INCOME ($ mil.)	NET PROFIT MARGIN	EMPLOYEES
06/18	2,851	267	9.4%	30,282
06/16	2,702	108	4.0%	—
06/13	2,404	221	9.2%	—
Annual Growth	3.5%	3.8%	—	—

2018 Year-End Financials
Return on assets: 3.1%   Cash ($ mil.): 360
Return on equity: 5.5%
Current ratio: 1.30

UNIVERSITY OF NEW MEXICO

The University of New Mexico (UNM) based in Albuquerque is most renowned for its schools of medicine law and education. Students also attend one of the school's four branches located around the northern part of the state at Gallup Los Alamos Rio Rancho Taos and Valencia. Through its schools and colleges the university offers about 95 bachelor's degrees around 70 master's degrees more than 35 doctorate degrees as well as professional practice programs in law medicine and pharmacy.

Geographic Reach
UNM's main campus is located in Albuquerque. Satellite campuses are in Gallup Los Alamos Rio Rancho Taos and Valencia.

Company Background
UNM was founded in 1889.

EXECUTIVES

Pres, Robert Frank
Exec V Pres, David Harris
Exec V Pres, Chaouki Abdallah
V Pres, Carlos Romero
Chancellor, Paul Roth
Director of Finance, Paula Williams
Director, Brian Despain
Administrative Assistant II, Jeanene Sisk
General Manager, Joseph Cruz
Assistant Professor, Jason Smith
Assistant Professor, John C Barnes
Auditors: MOSS ADAMS LLP ALBUQUERQUE N

LOCATIONS

HQ: UNIVERSITY OF NEW MEXICO
1800 ROMA BLVD NE, ALBUQUERQUE, NM 871310001
Phone: 505 277-0111
Web: WWW.GALLUP.UNM.EDU

PRODUCTS/OPERATIONS

2013 Sales

% of sales	
Clinical operations	42
Grants & contracts	21
Sales & services	16
Tuition & fees	10
Patients services	8

Other		3
Total	**0**	**100**

Schools and Colleges

Schools and Colleges
Anderson School of Management
College of Arts & Sciences
College of Education
College of Fine Arts
College of University Libraries & Learning Sciences
Honors College
School of Architecture & Planning
School of Engineering
School of Law
School of Public Administration
University College

HISTORICAL FINANCIALS

Company Type: Private

Income Statement — FYE: June 30

	REVENUE ($ mil.)	NET INCOME ($ mil.)	NET PROFIT MARGIN	EMPLOYEES
06/20	2,050	629	30.7%	18,362
06/19	1,913	(137)	—	—
06/18	1,826	(181)	—	—
06/17	1,807	11	0.6%	—
Annual Growth	**4.3%**	**284.6%**	**—**	**—**

2020 Year-End Financials

Return on assets: 18.2%   Cash ($ mil.): 541
Return on equity: 71.9%
Current ratio: 2.80

UNIVERSITY OF NORTH CAROLINA AT CHAPEL HILL

The University of North Carolina at Chapel Hill (UNC-Chapel Hill) has the education market cornered. One of the three original points making up North Carolina's Research Triangle (along with Duke University and North Carolina State University) Carolina is the flagship campus of the University of North Carolina (UNC) system. The institution is consistently among the top-ranked research schools in the US. It enrolls some 29000 students and offers more than 250 undergraduate graduate and professional programs including law and medicine. It has 3200 full-time faculty members.

Operations

The university includes 15 schools and colleges as well as an adult learning center for continuing education programs. Its degree offerings include more than 100 master's degrees and about 70 doctorate programs.

UNC-Chapel Hill conducts extensive research programs in a variety of fields at its five health science schools (medicine dentistry pharmacy nursing and public health) its patient care facilities (operated through the University of North Carolina Hospitals affiliate) and its scientific teaching divisions (at the College of Arts and Sciences). The university attracted some $770 million in research grants and contracts during 2012. Funding sources include the National Institutes of Health. Research funding at UNC-Chapel Hill makes up more than half of awards for the entire UNC system.

Geographic Reach

UNC-Chapel Hill is located on a 730-acre campus that holds about 300 buildings. The university

attracts students from all 50 US states and more than 145 international countries. It also has study abroad opportunities.

Financial Performance

UNC-Chapel Hill reported $2.5 billion in total revenues in 2012. Operating revenues make up the majority of earnings ($1.7 billion) from activities including student tuition fees federal grants and contracts and patient services. Non-operating revenues include state appropriations non-capital grants and gifts and investment income. Operating expenses ran at about $2.4 billion for 2012 and the university had a budget for fiscal 2013 of some $2.5 billion.

Strategy

To expand its international education opportunities in 2013 UNC-Chapel Hill formed a dual-degree partnership with Tsinghua University in China. The partnership offers business administration executive master's degrees.

Company Background

Chartered in 1789 Carolina is the oldest public university in the US. Notable alumni include author Thomas Wolfe and President James K. Polk as well as athlete Michael Jordan and journalist Charles Kuralt.

EXECUTIVES

Pres, Thomas W Ross
Chancellor*, Holden Thorp
Vice Chancellor Finance*, Richard L Mann
Associate Vice Chancellor/Fina*, Roger Patterson
Controller*, Dennis Press
Chb*, Michael A Steinback
Prin*, Avery B Hall Sr
SEC*, Bradley T Adcock
Prin*, James M Barnes
Nurse, Jason Clark
Assistant Professor of Anesthe, Jay Schoenherr
Auditors: BETH A WOOD CPA RALEIGH NO

LOCATIONS

HQ: UNIVERSITY OF NORTH CAROLINA AT CHAPEL HILL
    104 AIRPORT DR, CHAPEL HILL, NC 275995023
Phone: 919 962-1370
Web: WWW.UNC.EDU

PRODUCTS/OPERATIONS

Selected Schools Colleges and Centers

College of Arts and Sciences
Eshelman School of Pharmacy
Friday Center for Continuing Education
General College
Gillings School of Global Public Health
Graduate School
Kenan-Flagler Business School
School of Dentistry
School of Education
School of Government
School of Information and Library Science
School of Journalism and Mass Communication
School of Law
School of Medicine
School of Nursing
School of Social Work

Selected Academic Departments

African and AfroAmerican Studies
Air Force ROTC
Anthropology
Army ROTC
Art
Biology
Chemistry
Classics
Communication Studies
Dramatic Art
Economics
English and Comparative Literature
Exercise and Sport Science
Geography

History
Marine Sciences
Music
Nutrition
Pharmacology
Philosophy
Political Science
Psychology
Religious Studies
Sociology
Surgery

HISTORICAL FINANCIALS

Company Type: Private

Income Statement — FYE: June 30

	REVENUE ($ mil.)	NET INCOME ($ mil.)	NET PROFIT MARGIN	EMPLOYEES
06/19	2,073	229	11.0%	12,204
06/17	1,773	95	5.4%	—
06/11	1,704	391	23.0%	—
06/08	281	149	53.1%	—
Annual Growth	**19.9%**	**3.9%**	**—**	**—**

2019 Year-End Financials

Return on assets: 8.0%   Cash ($ mil.): 240
Return on equity: 378.1%
Current ratio: 2.10

UNIVERSITY OF NORTH CAROLINA HOSPITALS

University of North Carolina Hospitals (UNCH) is at the heart of the UNC Health Care System (UNC HCS). The medical center provides acute care to the Tar Heel State through North Carolina Memorial Hospital North Carolina Children's Hospital North Carolina Neurosciences Hospital and North Carolina Women's Hospital. Combined the facilities have more than 800 beds. Specialties include cancer treatment at the North Carolina Cancer Hospital organ transplantation cardiac care orthopedics wound management and rehabilitation. Not-for-profit UNC HCS is owned by the state of North Carolina and is affiliated with the UNC-Chapel Hill School of Medicine.

Operations

UNCH operates under the umbrella of UNC HCS.

UNC HCS already extends beyond Chapel Hill and into the greater Triangle area through its network of primary care and specialty physician practices located in Orange Wake Durham Chatham and Lee counties. The system treats some 800000 people at UNC HCS practices and clinics annually.

UNCH handles more than 37000 patients each year and delivers 3500 babies annually.

North Carolina Children's offers 150 inpatient beds and a comprehensive children's outpatient center. Every year provides specialty care to more than 70000 children from all 100 North Carolina counties. The North Carolina Cancer Hospital is the clinical home of the UNC Lineberger Comprehensive Cancer Center. The state's only public cancer hospital the North Carolina Cancer Hospital treats patients from every county in North Carolina with more than 135000 patient visits a year.

Geographic Reach

UNCH not only serves patients from all North Carolina counties with about a third coming from the Research Triangle area it also serves patients from neighboring states.

Strategy

Being one of the primary health care providers in the area UNC HCS is nearly always expanding its services and service areas either through acquisitions or new construction.

In 2015 UNCH filed a petition with state regulators seeking the ability to add 42 acute-care beds at its Chapel Hill campus. If approved UNC estimates it will cost the hospital $17 million and would be completed by mid-2018.

UNC HCS planned to open a new 86-bed acute-care hospital in Hillsborough in 2015 as part of an effort to reduce pressure on its Chapel Hill campus. The construction of the hospital will cost about $200 million. The new facility will offer an emergency department outpatient surgery and a range of inpatient services to our patients in Alamance and Western Orange counties.

Dedicated cancer care and cancer research is another area in which UNC HCS is expanding. It opened a North Carolina Cancer Hospital at Rex Hospital in 2014.

The system is also building an Imaging Research Building expected to open in 2013 to house the Biomedical Research Imaging Center and serve as a state resource for handling the acquisition processing analysis storage and retrieval of scientific images.

In 2013 UNC HCS established the first stage of its Hillsborough campus with the opening of a 60000-square-foot medical office building. The building includes hospital services such as imaging laboratory pharmacy and medical and surgical oncology.

Company Background

In 2011 the hospital opened a new wing of the Newborn Critical Care Unit in the North Carolina Children's Hospital that houses 10 new patient beds bringing the number of beds in the unit to 58.

UNCH was founded in 1952 under the name North Carolina Memorial Hospital. In 1989 the North Carolina General Assembly created UNCH.

EXECUTIVES

Pres, Gary Park
Exec V Pres, Brian P Goldstein
Svp and Cfo, Chris Ellington
Sr V Pres, Mary Beck
V Pres, Amy Bragg
Otolaryngology, Jill A Alexander Ritch
Accounting Staff, Mike Sumner
Coordinator, Samara Robinson
Staff, David Reed
Staff, Douglas Robinson
Coordinator, Margaret Brooks
Auditors: BETH A WOOD CPA RALEIGH NC

LOCATIONS

HQ: UNIVERSITY OF NORTH CAROLINA HOSPITALS
101 MANNING DR BLDG 2, CHAPEL HILL, NC
275144423
Phone: 919 966-5111
Web: WWW.UNCHEALTHCARE.ORG

PRODUCTS/OPERATIONS

Selected Facilities

North Carolina Cancer Hospital (Chapel Hill)
  UNC Lineberger Comprehensive Cancer Center
North Carolina Children's Hospital (Chapel Hill)
North Carolina Memorial Hospital (Chapel Hill)
North Carolina Neurosciences Hospital (Chapel Hill)
North Carolina Women's Hospital (Chapel Hill)

COMPETITORS

Alamance Regional Medical Center	Grady Health System
Carolinas Healthcare System	High Point Regional Health System
	Morehead Memorial
Cone Health	Hospital
Cumberland County Hospital System	New Hanover Regional Medical Center
Danville Regional Medical Center	Rowan Regional Medical Center
Duke University Health System	Vidant Health
Emory Healthcare	Wakemed

HISTORICAL FINANCIALS

Company Type: Private

Income Statement   FYE: June 30

	REVENUE ($ mil.)	NET INCOME ($ mil.)	NET PROFIT MARGIN	EMPLOYEES
06/21	2,397	516	21.5%	6,000
06/16	1,551	87	5.6%	—
06/15	1,385	110	8.0%	—
Annual Growth	9.6%	29.2%	—	—

2021 Year-End Financials

Return on assets: 12.8%   Cash ($ mil.): 107
Return on equity: 53.5%
Current ratio: 1.00

UNIVERSITY OF NORTH TEXAS SYSTEM

EXECUTIVES

Mgr, Cynthia Doll
Chief Human Capital Officer, Barbara Abercrombie
Interim Assistant Director, Renee McBride
Vice Chancellor, Gary Rahlfs
Senior Director, AP, Bharath Prabhakaran
Associate Controller, Brittany Wisdom
Recruiting Assistant, Cristella Rodriguez
Associate General Counsel, Dolly Garcia
Manager, Payroll Processing, Effie Foster
Programmer Analyst Information, Franklin Danja
Senior Director, Jim Gross
Auditors: BKD LLP FORT WORTH TEXAS

LOCATIONS

HQ: UNIVERSITY OF NORTH TEXAS SYSTEM
1302 TEASLEY LN, DENTON, TX 762057946
Phone: 940 565-2281
Web: WWW.UNTSYSTEM.EDU

HISTORICAL FINANCIALS

Company Type: Private

Income Statement   FYE: August 31

	REVENUE ($ mil.)	NET INCOME ($ mil.)	NET PROFIT MARGIN	EMPLOYEES
08/20	668	(20)	—	814
08/19	657	(83)	—	—
08/18	654	79	12.2%	—
08/17	619	82	13.4%	—
Annual Growth	2.5%	—	—	—

2020 Year-End Financials

Return on assets: (-0.7%)   Cash ($ mil.): 219
Return on equity: (-2.9%)
Current ratio: 1.10

UNIVERSITY OF OREGON

This school's got all its ducks in a row. As one of the largest schools in the state the University of Oregon (UO) has an enrollment of about 22760 students and some 2095 faculty members. It offers its students eight different schools and colleges plus a graduate college with fields of study range from the arts and journalism to business and law. Part of the Oregon University System UO also offers development services an honors program research institutes and continuing education courses. The school's athletic department organizes around 15 sports activities including lacrosse and football; the teams are called The Ducks.

Operations

UO has a student-to-teacher ratio of 16:1 and an average class size of 20. Course offerings range across lecture discussion seminar activity laboratory independent study and independent research formats and UO has a total of more than 300 undergraduate programs more than 80 graduate subject areas and more than 30 research centers and institutes. The university's most popular majors for undergraduates include accounting architecture art biology business administration chemistry education economics english environmental science human physiology journalism political science public relations and sociology. Its freshman retention success rate is nearly 90%.

Geographic Reach

UO is located at some 295-acre campus in Eugene Oregon that includes about 80 buildings. It also has a satellite campus in Portland. Students come to UO from all 50 US states (plus Washington DC and two US territories) as well as about 100 foreign countries. More than half of students are Oregon residents. A number of students also participate in more than 300 study abroad and internship programs in approximately 90 international locations.

Company Background

The Oregon State Legislature created the university in 1872 and students first enrolled in 1876.

EXECUTIVES

Int Pres, Scott Coltrane
Customer Staff, Robin H Olmes
Assistant Professor, Bob Madrigal
Project Coordinator, Chad Bush
Scientist, Daniel Ruscitto
Scientist, Emily Sweeney
Assistant Professor, Joel Sneed
Coordinator, Judith Blair
Reporter, Patrick Malee
Scientist, Eric Carlson
Reporter, Lucas Clark
Auditors: MOSS ADAMS LLP PORTLAND ORE

LOCATIONS

HQ: UNIVERSITY OF OREGON
1585 E 13TH AVE, EUGENE, OR 974031657
Phone: 541 346-1000
Web: WWW.UOREGON.EDU

PRODUCTS/OPERATIONS

Colleges and Schools

Charles H. Lundquist College of Business
College of Arts and Sciences
College of Education
Graduate School
Robert D. Clark Honors College
School of Architecture and Allied Arts
School of Journalism and Communication
School of Law
School of Music and Dance

HISTORICAL FINANCIALS
Company Type: Private

Income Statement				FYE: June 30
	REVENUE ($ mil.)	NET INCOME ($ mil.)	NET PROFIT MARGIN	EMPLOYEES
06/21	692	(16)	—	7,971
06/20	741	329	44.4%	—
06/18	740	(8)	—	—
06/17	713	31	4.5%	—
Annual Growth	(0.7%)	—	—	—

2021 Year-End Financials
Return on assets: (-0.6%)   Cash ($ mil.): 197
Return on equity: (-1.3%)
Current ratio: 1.40

UNIVERSITY OF PITTSBURGH

The University of Pittsburgh (Pitt for short) operates its flagship campus in the Oakland neighborhood of Pittsburgh. More than 35000 graduate and undergraduate students attend the main campus as well as four regional campuses. Pitt Panthers pursue degrees in about 400 disciplines including arts and sciences business law medicine and engineering. The school has a student-teacher ratio of 14:1. Pitt is also affiliated with the UPMC health system which operates about 20 hospitals numerous clinics and an insurance company. Pitt was founded in 1787 making it one of the oldest universities in the US.

Operations
Pitt is considered a leading US public research university and as such spends more than $700 million annually on research projects. Pitt is recognized for its work in about a dozen disciplines including computer modeling philosophy the humanities international studies aging neuroscience bioengineering commercial innovation education national preparedness drug discovery translational medicine and nanoscience. It was at Pitt that Jonas Salk developed the polio vaccine at what is now known as Salk Hall.

Notable Pitt alumni include Academy Award winner Gene Kelly Nobel Peace Prize winner Wangari Maathai Pulitzer Prize winner Michael Chabon and US Senator Orrin Hatch.

Geographic Reach
In addition to the main campus in Pittsburgh which houses 17 schools colleges and a center for social and urban research Pitt has regional campus locations in Bradford Greensburg Johnstown and Titusville.

Financial Performance
Pitt reported revenues of some $2 billion in 2014. Most of the university's revenues come from grants and contracts followed by student tuition and feescommonwealth appropriation endowment distributions and other sources of income.

Strategy
In addition to providing high quality education programs for its students Pitt works to engage in research scholarly and artistic projects that advance global learning. It also works to collaborate with government agencies and businesses to advance science medicine and technology seeking active partners as well as funding provider to further its programs.

EXECUTIVES
Chancellor, William Dietrich
Ceo*, Mark Nordenberg
Fo*, Arthur Ramicone
SEC*, Gene B Ferketish
Treas*, Amy K Marsh
Asst Treas*, Susan Gilbert
Asst Treas*, Paul Lawrence
Womens Basketball Video Coordi, Brianne O'Rourke
Account Executive Petersen Eve, Christina Zedreck
Predoctoral Fellow, Evan Gretok
Senior Advisor, Frey Gugsa
Auditors: KPMG LLP PITTSBURGH PA

LOCATIONS
HQ: UNIVERSITY OF PITTSBURGH
4200 5TH AVE, PITTSBURGH, PA 152600001
Phone: 412 624-4141
Web: WWW.PITT.EDU

PRODUCTS/OPERATIONS

Selected Schools and Colleges
The John A. Swanson School of Engineering
The Joseph M. Katz Graduate School of Business
  College of Business Administration
Kenneth P. Dietrich School of Arts and Sciences
  College of General Studies
School of Dental Medicine
School of Education
School of Health and Rehabilitation Sciences
School of Information Sciences
School of Law
School of Medicine
School of Nursing
School of Pharmacy
School of Public and International Affairs
School of Public Health
School of Social Work
University Center for International Studies
University Honors College

HISTORICAL FINANCIALS
Company Type: Private

Income Statement				FYE: June 30
	REVENUE ($ mil.)	NET INCOME ($ mil.)	NET PROFIT MARGIN	EMPLOYEES
06/21	2,502	1,548	61.9%	9,607
06/20	2,352	(168)	—	—
06/19	2,352	111	4.8%	—
06/18	2,276	381	16.8%	—
Annual Growth	3.2%	59.5%	—	—

2021 Year-End Financials
Return on assets: 16.0%   Cash ($ mil.): 76
Return on equity: 23.6%
Current ratio: —

UNIVERSITY OF SAN FRANCISCO INC

EXECUTIVES
Ceo, Stephen A Privett
V Pres-Fin-Cntrl*, Charles E Cross
V Pres*, Carmen Jordan-Cox
Head of Collection, Reference,, Locke J Morrisey
Director Recreation Sports, Charlies B White Jr
Associate Dean Student Develop, Linda L Thomas
Assistant Dean Multicultural S, Mary G Almandrez
Assistant Professor, Alessandra Cassar
Coordinator, Alev Efendioglu
Vice President, Aaron Moser
Executive Director, Donal Godfrey
Auditors: PRICEWATERHOUSECOOPERS LLP BO

LOCATIONS
HQ: UNIVERSITY OF SAN FRANCISCO INC
2130 FULTON ST, SAN FRANCISCO, CA 941171050
Phone: 415 422-5555
Web: WWW.USFCA.EDU

HISTORICAL FINANCIALS
Company Type: Private

Income Statement				FYE: May 31
	REVENUE ($ mil.)	NET INCOME ($ mil.)	NET PROFIT MARGIN	EMPLOYEES
05/20	554	34	6.2%	1,200
05/17	417	50	12.1%	—
Annual Growth	9.9%	(11.8%)	—	—

2020 Year-End Financials
Return on assets: 2.7%   Cash ($ mil.): 80
Return on equity: 4.1%
Current ratio: 0.50

UNIVERSITY OF SOUTH ALABAMA

When you go by the moniker USA and the campus beauty queen wins the Miss USA title year after year (the Pi Kappa Phi Miss USA pageant that is) you're standing on hallowed ground. In this case it's the ground of the University of South Alabama situated on the upper Gulf Coast. The school's crown jewel is its College of Medicine and other facilities including USA Medical Center USA Knollwood Hospital and USA Children's and Women's Hospital. USA also offers degrees in Health Arts and Sciences Business Education Engineering Nursing Computer and Information Sciences Continuing Education and Special Programs and the Graduate School. More than 14880 students call the USA home.

Operations
USA offers 41 different bachelor programs 31 masters programs and 10 doctoral programs.

Financial Performance
The school reported an 8% increase in revenues in 2012 thanks to higher tuition and fee rates and an increase in student enrollment and credit hours taken and a rise in net patient service revenues (29% of total 2012 revenues). Other operating revenues also increased in 2012 thanks to higher revenues from the Electronic Health Records Incentive Program.

USA reported net income in 2012 of $38 million (versus a net loss in 2011) due to decline in operating loss and an increase in non-operating revenues (primarily from higher investment returns and state appropriations).

The university saw an increase in revenues between 2010 and 2012 largely due to organic growth.

Strategy

USA is pushing to expand and strengthen its development program and increase student enrollment. In 2013 the school received a gift of $250000 from alumni Dr. and Mrs. Steven H. Stokes to start a new Center for Environmental Resiliency.

Company Background

Founded in 1963 USA has graduated more than 75000 students including 18200 teachers and school administrators (including 85% of Mobile's public school teachers).

EXECUTIVES

Pres, Tony G Waldrop
V Pres-Fin, Wayne Davis
Assistant Vice President For R, Michael Chambers
Assistant Professor, Gwendolyn Pennywell
Assistant Professor, Treena Gillespie
Assistant Professor, David Benko
Accounting Team Member, Angie Logan
Assistant Professor, Christy W West
Assistant Professor, Corina Schulze
Associate Professor of Spanish, Federico Perez-Pineda
Professor, Joseph Glover
Auditors: KPMG LLP JACKSON MS

LOCATIONS

HQ: UNIVERSITY OF SOUTH ALABAMA
307 N UNIVERSITY BLVD, MOBILE, AL 366883053
Phone: 251 460-6101
Web: WWW.SOUTHALABAMA.EDU

PRODUCTS/OPERATIONS

USA Colleges and Schools
Arts and Sciences
Auburn University School of Pharmacy at USA
Computing
Continuing Education and Special Programs
Education
Engineering
Mitchell College of Business
Medicine
Nursing
Pat Capps Covey College of Allied Health Professions

HISTORICAL FINANCIALS

Company Type: Private

Income Statement   FYE: September 30

	REVENUE ($ mil.)	NET INCOME ($ mil.)	NET PROFIT MARGIN	EMPLOYEES
09/20	782	124	15.9%	5,403
09/18	653	(0)	—	—
09/17	662	47	7.2%	—
09/16	624	25	4.1%	—
Annual Growth	5.8%	48.0%	—	—

2020 Year-End Financials

Return on assets: 7.7%   Cash ($ mil.): 237
Return on equity: 57.4%
Current ratio: 1.40

UNIVERSITY OF SOUTH FLORIDA

The University of South Florida (USF) is a high-impact global research university serving more than 50000 students at three campuses in Tampa St. Petersburg and Sarasota-Manatee. It offers about 245 undergraduate graduate specialty and doctoral degree programs through some 15 colleges including arts and sciences business education engineering marine science pharmacy and public health. USF also offers graduate certificates continuing education courses and teacher certifications and it is a major research institution among US universities. With student-faculty ratio of 21:1 the university has approximately 16310 faculty and staff members. USF was founded in 1956; its mascot is the bull.

Operations

The university has about 2145 teaching faculty members and maintains a 21:1 student-to-faculty ratio. USF's core offerings include an extensive health sciences program including medical nursing pharmacy and public health colleges grouped under the USF Health banner. The health organization also includes patient care facilities such as family care practices emergency clinics and Alzheimer's centers.

USF Health also hosts medical research programs in areas such as neurological conditions cardiovascular care pediatrics infectious disease and biotechnology. The university also has research programs in a range of science engineering and arts fields such as veteran reintegration. Altogether USF's research programs were granted approximately $535.4 million in awards and contracts.

Geographic Reach

USF's international students (nearly 10% of the total student population) come from nearly 45 US states and about 145 countries. USF also supports study abroad programs. The university's campuses in Florida encompass some 1645 acres. The main Tampa campus includes the USF Health facilities and health-related schools.

EXECUTIVES

Pres, Rhea Law
Sr V Pres*, Charles Lockwood
Government and, Kiki Caruson
English, Rita L Ciresi
Facilities Planning, Roy A Clark
Asst Contrl, Samantha Merrera
SA Assistant Vice President Fo, Jennifer Larson
Vice President Research, Judith Lowry
Coordinator, Julie Schneider
Assistant Vice President For R, Valerie McDevitt
Assistant Vice President and C, Jennifer Condon
Auditors: SHERRILL F NORMAN CPA TALLA

LOCATIONS

HQ: UNIVERSITY OF SOUTH FLORIDA
4202 E FOWLER AVE, TAMPA, FL 336208000
Phone: 813 974-2011
Web: WWW.USF.EDU

PRODUCTS/OPERATIONS

2013 Revenue

	% of total
Contracts & grants	26
Student financial aid	26
Tuition	16
General revenue	14
Auxiliary enterprises	11
Intercollegiate athletics	3
Lottery	2
Concessions & fees	2
Total	**100**

Selected Colleges
The Arts
Arts & Sciences
Behavioral & Community Sciences
Business
Education
Engineering

Global Sustainability
Honors College
Marine Science
Medicine
Nursing
Pharmacy
Public Health
University College (graduate school)

HISTORICAL FINANCIALS

Company Type: Private

Income Statement   FYE: June 30

	REVENUE ($ mil.)	NET INCOME ($ mil.)	NET PROFIT MARGIN	EMPLOYEES
06/20	821	(95)	—	16,165
06/19	849	4	0.5%	—
06/18	871	36	4.1%	—
06/09	892	42	4.7%	—
Annual Growth	(0.7%)	—	—	—

2020 Year-End Financials

Return on assets: (-3.9%)   Cash ($ mil.): 66
Return on equity: (-11.6%)
Current ratio: 6.30

UNIVERSITY OF TENNESSEE

Whether you want to learn the art of aviation or get ready for a career in public service the University of Tennessee System (UT) is here to help. The 200-year-old school provides undergraduate graduate and professional academic programs to about 50000 students; programs include business engineering law pharmacy medicine and veterinary medicine. It has a student-teacher ratio of about 16:1. Campuses include the flagship Knoxville location as well as the Health Science Center at Memphis the Space Institute at Tullahoma the statewide Institute for Public Service and the Institute of Agriculture. Other UT System campuses are located in Chattanooga and Martin. UT was founded in 1794 as Blount College.

Financial Performance

UT's funding comes from gifts grants and contracts (about 30%) state appropriations (roughly 28%) tuition and fees (20%) and a handful of auxiliary enterprises and independent operations (the remainder).

Company Background

Notable alumni include former Senate Majority Leader Howard Baker Nobel Prize-winning economist James Buchanan and author Cormac McCarthy.

EXECUTIVES

Chm, Governor Phil Bredesen
Exec V Pres, David Millhorn
Pres, Joseph A Dipietro
V Pres, Emerson H Fly
V Pres, Anthony Haynes
V Pres, Mary Jinks
V Pres, Linda Hendricks
Prin, John Petersen
Prin, Jan Simek
Treas, Charles M Peccolo
Pres, Randy Boyd

LOCATIONS

HQ: UNIVERSITY OF TENNESSEE
  1331 CIRCLE PARK DR, KNOXVILLE, TN 379163801
Phone: 865 974-2303
Web: WWW.UTK.EDU

PRODUCTS/OPERATIONS

Selected Colleges Schools and Institutes

College of Agricultural Sciences and Natural Resources
College of Allied Health Sciences
College of Architecture and Design
College of Arts and Sciences
College of Business Administration
College of Communication and Information
College of Dentistry
College of Education Health and Human Sciences
College of Engineering
College of Graduate Health Sciences
College of Health Science Engineering
College of Law
College of Medicine
College of Nursing
College of Pharmacy
College of Social Work
College of Veterinary Medicine
Graduate School of Medicine
School of Art
School of Music
Space Institute

HISTORICAL FINANCIALS

Company Type: Private

Income Statement				FYE: June 30
	REVENUE ($ mil.)	NET INCOME ($ mil.)	NET PROFIT MARGIN	EMPLOYEES
06/12	1,092	60	5.5%	12,000
06/11*	1,034	296	28.7%	—
12/08	1	0	—	—
Annual Growth 847.7%	—	—	—	—

*Fiscal year change

2012 Year-End Financials

Return on assets: 1.6%   Cash ($ mil.): 357
Return on equity: 2.3%
Current ratio: 1.50

UNIVERSITY OF TEXAS SYSTEM

EXECUTIVES

Ceo, Mark A Houser
Chb*, Paul L Foster
V Chb*, R Steven Hicks
V Chb*, Jeffery D Hildebrand
Gen Coun*, Francie A Frederick
Regent*, James Huffines
Coordinator Head Coach, Audralee Scofield
Support Specialist, Barry Grove
Administrative, Carrie Mills
Local Area Network Administrat, Corey Means
Human Resources Business Analy, Crystal Anderson
Auditors: DELOITTE & TOUCHE LLP AUSTIN

LOCATIONS

HQ: UNIVERSITY OF TEXAS SYSTEM
  210 W 7TH ST, AUSTIN, TX 787012903
Phone: 512 499-4587
Web: WWW.UTSYSTEM.EDU

HISTORICAL FINANCIALS

Company Type: Private

Income Statement				FYE: August 31
	REVENUE ($ mil.)	NET INCOME ($ mil.)	NET PROFIT MARGIN	EMPLOYEES
08/20	16,359	2	0.0%	104,000
08/19	16	0	2.9%	—
08/18	14,884	6,189	41.6%	—
Annual Growth	4.8%	(97.9%)		

2020 Year-End Financials

Return on assets: —   Cash ($ mil.): 3,089
Return on equity: —
Current ratio: 0.90

UNIVERSITY OF UTAH HEALTH HOSPITALS AND CLINICS

University of Utah Health is the only academic medical center in the state of Utah and the Mountain West and provides patient care for the people of Utah Idaho Wyoming Montana western Colorado and much of Nevada. It also serves as the training ground for the majority of the state's physicians nurses pharmacists therapists and other health care professionals. Its system is comprised of five hospitals and twelve community health care centers as well six schools and colleges including the colleges of Health Nursing and Pharmacy the Eccles Health Sciences Library and the schools of Dentistry and Medicine. The University Hospital provides care in areas including surgery emergency care cardiology radiology and organ transplant services; it also houses centers for medical education training and research. It is headquartered in Salt Lake City Utah.

EXECUTIVES

Ceo, Dan Lundergan
Principal, Richard A Fullmer
Coordinator, Barbara Glanville
Accounts Receivable, Michael Kemp
Program Coordinator, Abby Elieson
Nursing, Andrew Black
Assistant Professor Clinical, Kalena Tao
Director, Martin Caravati
Grants Contracts Officer, Paul Frankel
Research Director, Scott Youngquist
Assistant Dean, Shari Lindsey

LOCATIONS

HQ: UNIVERSITY OF UTAH HEALTH HOSPITALS AND CLINICS
  50 N MEDICAL DR, SALT LAKE CITY, UT 841320001
Phone: 801 581-2121
Web: WWW.EMPLOYMENT.UTAH.EDU

COMPETITORS

Christus Health
Intermountain Health Care
Lifepoint Health

Ogden Regional Medical Center
St. Mark's

HISTORICAL FINANCIALS

Company Type: Private

Income Statement				FYE: June 30
	REVENUE ($ mil.)	NET INCOME ($ mil.)	NET PROFIT MARGIN	EMPLOYEES
06/14	1,282	20	1.6%	4,200
06/06	0	(0)	—	—
06/05	0	(0)	—	—
Annual Growth 126.0%		—	—	—

2014 Year-End Financials

Return on assets: 2.0%   Cash ($ mil.): 179
Return on equity: 4.5%
Current ratio: 2.30

UNIVERSITY OF VERMONT & STATE AGRICULTURAL COLLEGE

The University of Vermont (UVM) boasts scenic views and comprehensive secondary education. the university offers more than 100 majors through its seven undergraduate colleges as well 46 master's programs and 21 doctoral programs at its Graduate College and College of Medicine. UVM has an enrollment of more than 12820 students including undergraduate graduate medical and continuing education program participants. The university also conducts research programs in areas including translational science cancer care and transportation. UVM a public land grant university has more than 1360 faculty members.

Operations

UVM comes from Universitas Veridis Montis which is Latin for "University of the Green Mountains." Its campus consists of more than a dozen dining facilities — including a pair of convenience stores and Cyber Cafe — and nearly 40 residence halls for on-campus students. Off-campus UVM offers a research park four research farms nine natural areas (including the summit of Mount Mansfield) and the Rubenstein Ecosystem Science Laboratory in the Leahy ECHO Center for Lake Champlain.

Geographic Reach

The UVM campus which spans 460 acres in Burlington Vermont enrolls students from nearly all US states. The university also provides education to some 350 international students from more than 50 countries.

Financial Performance

As a public land grant university UVM draws a portion of its budget from the state of Vermont. Other sources of income include student tuition and fees charitable gifts and returns on investment funds. The university's office of technology commercialization brings in some income by licensing out research discoveries to spinoff entities.

Strategy

To attract and retain a quality student population UVM regularly conducts construction and renovation efforts on its campus facilities in areas ranging from academics and recreation to research and athletics.

Furthermore UVM seeks to provide more flexible education options for students including expanding its onlinep rograms.

Company Background

UVM is the fifth oldest university in the New England area after Harvard Yale Dartmouth and Brown. It's the first institution of higher education to declare public support for the freedom of religion and the first university to admit women and African-Americans into Phi Beta Kappa honor society.

Notable alumni include education philosopher John Dewey and film producer Jon Kilik.

Ira Allen founded the university in 1791 the same year that Vermont became the 14th state. Located in between the Adirondack and Green mountain ranges UVM's motto is the Latin phrase Universitas Viridis Montis or University of the Green Mountains.

EXECUTIVES

Pres, E Thomas Sullivan
V Pres*, Jane Knodell
SEC*, Donna Sweaney
Vp of Fin and Treas*, Richard H Cate
Sr Vp*, David Rosowsky
Dean, Joseph H Gavin
Assistant, Joseph W Gingras
Associate, Josie H Davis
Coordinator, Kay B Fay
Director, Linda Seavey
Senior Associate Counsel Vice, Lucy Singer
Auditors: KPMG LLP COLCHESTER VERMONT

LOCATIONS

HQ: UNIVERSITY OF VERMONT & STATE AGRICULTURAL COLLEGE
85 S PRSPECT ST WTRMAN BL, BURLINGTON, VT 054050001
Phone: 802 656-3131
Web: WWW.MED.UVM.EDU

PRODUCTS/OPERATIONS

Selected Colleges and Schools
College of Agriculture and Life Sciences
College of Arts and Sciences
College of Education and Social Services
College of Engineering and Mathematical Sciences
College of Medicine
College of Nursing and Health Sciences
Continuing Education
Graduate College
Honors College
Rubenstein School of Environment and Natural Resources
School of Business Administration

HISTORICAL FINANCIALS
Company Type: Private

Income Statement				FYE: June 30
	REVENUE ($ mil.)	NET INCOME ($ mil.)	NET PROFIT MARGIN	EMPLOYEES
06/21	647	188	29.2%	3,710
06/20	661	23	3.6%	—
06/19	650	39	6.1%	—
06/17	613	34	5.6%	—
Annual Growth	1.3%	52.8%	—	—

2021 Year-End Financials
Return on assets: 10.0%   Cash ($ mil.): 218
Return on equity: 31.3%
Current ratio: 3.90

UNIVERSITY OF WASHINGTON INC

The University of Washington (UW) is one of the world's preeminent public universities. Founded in 1861 as the Territorial University of Washington UW has smaller branches in Tacoma and Bothell in addition to its main campus in downtown Seattle. The university whose mascot is a Husky offers 1800 undergraduate courses each quarter. It also operates four hospitals: University of Washington Medical Center Harborview Medical Center Northwest Hospital and Valley Medical Center.

Operations
University of Washington confers some 18200 bachelor's master's doctoral and professional degrees each year. Around 20 of its undergraduate and graduate received Fulbright Student awards. The school's some bachelor degree fields include biology psychology political science economics and communications.

The school's annual sponsored grant and contract research funding exceeds $1.63 billion.

Geographic Reach
The UW is a multi-campus university in Seattle Tacoma and Bothell Washington.

Financial Performance
Operating revenues increased $339 million or 6% in 2021. Revenue from patient services increased $115 million as fewer non-emergent and elective procedures were cancelled during the year due to the COVID pandemic compared to 2020 resulting in higher volumes and revenue.

Profit for fiscal 2021 increased to $7.9 billion compared from the prior year with $5.9 billion.

Cash held by the company at the end of fiscal 2021 decreased to $137.4 million. Cash used for operations and investing activities were $307.0 million and $368.7 million respectively. Cash provided by financing activities was $668.9 million.

Strategy
The ability to increase profitability will depend in part on successfully executing UW Medicine strategies. In general these strategies are intended to improve financial performance through the reduction of costs and streamlining how clinical care is provided as well as mitigating the negative reimbursement trends experienced within the market. With a continued focus on patient volumes shifting from inpatient to outpatient settings due to technological advancements and demand for care that is more convenient affordable and accessible as well as the industry-wide migration to value-based payment models as government and private payers shift risk to providers UW Medicine's focus is on successfully managing costs and care.

EXECUTIVES

Pres, Mark Emmerc
Treas*, V'Ella Warren
Vice Provost Academic Personne, Cheryl A Cameron
Vice Provost Information Manag, Sara Gomez
Manager, Mary Jo Hershly
Compliance Staff, Rick Hudson
Assistant Professor, Brian Hawkins
Assistant Professor, Amie McNeel
Assistant Professor, Arturo Centurion-Lara
Assistant Professor, Helen Anderson
Accounting Staff, Leedia Keriacous
Auditors: KPMG LLP SEATTLE WASHINGTON

LOCATIONS

HQ: UNIVERSITY OF WASHINGTON INC
4300 ROOSEVELT WAY NE, SEATTLE, WA 981054718
Phone: 206 543-4444
Web: WWW.WASHINGTON.EDU

PRODUCTS/OPERATIONS

Selected Colleges and Schools
College of Arts and Sciences
College of Built Environments
College of Education
College of Engineering
College of the Environment
Evans School of Public Affairs
The Graduate School
Information School
Michael G. Foster School of Business
School of Dentistry
School of Law
School of Medicine
School of Nursing
School of Pharmacy
School of Public Health
School of Social Work

HISTORICAL FINANCIALS
Company Type: Private

Income Statement				FYE: June 30
	REVENUE ($ mil.)	NET INCOME ($ mil.)	NET PROFIT MARGIN	EMPLOYEES
06/21	5,841	2,001	34.3%	27,228
06/20	5,511	343	6.2%	—
06/19	5,485	481	8.8%	—
06/18	5,171	490	9.5%	—
Annual Growth	4.1%	59.8%		

2021 Year-End Financials
Return on assets: 12.7%   Cash ($ mil.): 137
Return on equity: 25.3%
Current ratio: 1.70

UNIVERSITY OF WISCONSIN HOSPITALS AND CLINICS AUTHORITY

The University of Wisconsin Hospitals and Clinics Authority (UW Hospitals and Clinics) has the last word when it comes to the health of Badger Staters. The centerpiece of the authority is the UW Hospitals and Clinics medical campus which is home to a nearly 1490-bed hospital the American Family Children's Hospital a cancer clinic and a small inpatient psychiatric ward as well as Level I adult and pediatric trauma centers. Serving more than 600000 patients each year with approximately 1750 physicians at seven hospitals and more than 80 outpatient sites the hospital administers cancer treatment heart and stroke care organ transplantation and a host of other medical services. The UW Hospitals and Clinics organization also operates area health clinics that provide general and specialty outpatient care and emergency room services.

Financial Performance
In fiscal 2014 revenue increased 8% to $1.3 billion on an increase of net patient service revenues

(which grew 7.7% that year). Net income rose 24% to $108 million due to an increase of non-operating revenue (grants gifts and donations for example). Cash flow from operations fell 20% to $141 million as more was paid out to suppliers and employees.

UW Hospitals and Clinics is an independent not-for-profit organization and receives no state funding with the exception of reimbursement for care of Medicaid patients.

EXECUTIVES

Ceo, Alan Kaplan
Ceo*, Donna Katen Bahensky
V Pres*, Jeri Murphy
Fin Dir*, Renee M Rizzo
SEC*, Ellen Schwenn
Cfo*, Gary Eiler
Coordinator, Jonathon Ferguson
Assistant Professor, Alberto Del Pia
Assistant Professor, King Robinson
Project Coordinator, Kristin Cooper
Assistant Professor, Nam Kim
Auditors: RSM US LLP MINNEAPOLIS MINNE

LOCATIONS

HQ: UNIVERSITY OF WISCONSIN HOSPITALS AND CLINICS AUTHORITY
600 HIGHLAND AVE, MADISON, WI 537920001
Phone: 608 263-6400
Web: WWW.UWHEALTH.ORG

PRODUCTS/OPERATIONS

Selected Services
Adult Primary CareFamily MedicineGeriatricsInternal MedicinePrimary CareWomen's Health and WellnessAdult Specialty CareAllergy Asthma and ImmunologyAudiologyBehavioral Health Services (Addiction)Blood and Bone Marrow TransplantBreast Care ServicesBurn Ce

COMPETITORS

Beaver Dam Community Hospitals	Meriter Health Services
Beloit Health System	Prohealth Care
Dean Health Systems Inc.	Ssm Health Care Stoughton Hospital
Hospital Sisters Health System	Thedacare Inc. Tomah Memorial
Marian Health System	Hospital

HISTORICAL FINANCIALS
Company Type: Private

Income Statement				FYE: June 30
	REVENUE ($ mil.)	NET INCOME ($ mil.)	NET PROFIT MARGIN	EMPLOYEES
06/21	2,337	435	18.6%	1,350
06/20	2,075	202	9.8%	—
06/19	3,396	231	6.8%	—
06/18	3,213	170	5.3%	—
Annual Growth	(10.1%)	36.5%	—	—

2021 Year-End Financials
Return on assets: 10.2%   Cash ($ mil.): 531
Return on equity: 19.5%
Current ratio: 2.30

UNIVERSITY OF WISCONSIN MEDICAL FOUNDATION, INC.

UW Medical Foundation provides administrative services to faculty physicians at the University of Wisconsin School of Medicine and Public Health. The foundation a not-for-profit entity is a physician practice organization that works in cooperation with the UW Hospital and Clinics and other medical offices and clinics throughout the Badger State. The foundation coordinates clinical sites and provides technical and professional staffing services as well as administrative support for legal marketing information technology and logistics functions.

Operations
UW Medical Foundation provides support services for more than 1200 member doctors located at about 45 physician practices and 60 clinical outreach locations. It also helps clinical practices with quality initiatives. The foundation provides some $200 million in charity care each year. Its community activities include sponsoring health outreach events and donating safety products to low-income families.

Physicians in the organization provide services across a number of medical specialties including oncology gastroenterology women's health kidney care orthopedics respiratory therapy and urology.

Company Background
The organization has expanded over time: UW Medical Foundation merged with Physicians Plus Medical Group in 1998 and with the University Community Clinics in 2003.

EXECUTIVES

Ceo, Alan Kaplan
Chb, Robert Golden
Coo*, Robert Flannery
Sam Poc, Sarah Meyer
Information Specialist, Debra Hopke
Information Specialist, Jamie Buchanan
Hipaa Privacy Officer, Amanda Reese
Clinical Assistant Professiona, Deborah Raehl
Cardiologist, Anwer Dhala
Is Customer Director, Elaine Gerke
Cardiac Physician, Kathleen Maginot
Auditors: MCGLADREY LLP PALOS HILLS IL

LOCATIONS

HQ: UNIVERSITY OF WISCONSIN MEDICAL FOUNDATION, INC.
7974 UW HEALTH CT, MIDDLETON, WI 535625531
Phone: 608 821-4223
Web: WWW.UWHEALTH.ORG

COMPETITORS

Ascension Health	Marian Health System
Beaver Dam Community Hospitals	Meriter Health Services
Beloit Health System	Prohealth Care
Catholic Health Initiatives	Ssm Health Care Stoughton Hospital
Dean Health Systems Inc.	Thedacare Inc. Tomah Memorial
Hospital Sisters Health System	Hospital

HISTORICAL FINANCIALS
Company Type: Private

Income Statement				FYE: June 30
	REVENUE ($ mil.)	NET INCOME ($ mil.)	NET PROFIT MARGIN	EMPLOYEES
06/21	824	34	4.2%	3,200
06/20	785	7	1.0%	—
06/19	796	2	0.3%	—
06/18	784	40	5.2%	—
Annual Growth	1.7%	(5.1%)	—	—

2021 Year-End Financials
Return on assets: 4.1%   Cash ($ mil.): 353
Return on equity: 9.0%
Current ratio: 1.20

UNIVERSITY OF WISCONSIN SYSTEM

The University of Wisconsin System (UW System) is one of the largest public university systems in the US. Across its vast operations there are almost 13 four-year universities about 26 branch campuses and a statewide extension program that reaches every Wisconsin county. The UW System has more than 165000 students and approximately 40000 faculty and staff members. Its two main campuses are UW at Madison and UW at Milwaukee which offer hundreds of undergraduate and graduate programs including doctoral and professional degrees. The university was founded in 1848 by the state of constitution.

Operations
The UW Systems operating revenue comes from: Tuition and fees generating about 40% of revenue; Federal grants and contract (nearly 20%); State local & private grants and contracts (accounts for more than 10%); Sales and services of educational activities (accounts for some 10%); Sales and service of auxiliaries account for more than 10% and all other operating revenues account for about 15%. The UW Systems is the largest systems of public higher education in the country with 13 universities across 26 campuses and statewide extension network with offices in every country.

Geographic Reach
One of the nation's largest public universities the UW System boasts offices and campuses in every county in Wisconsin.

Financial Performance
Total operating revenue for 2020 was $3.7 billion a 2% dip from the previous year's total operating revenue.

In 2020 the company had a net income of $5.4 billion a 1% increase from the previous year's net income.

The company's cash at the end of 2020 was $1.9 billion. Investing activities provided $41.5 million while operating activities used $1.2 billion. Net cash provided by noncapital financing activities generated $1.6 billion.

Strategy
In early 2021 The University of Wisconsin System launched a new precollege pipeline initiative to help guide high school students in preparing for applying to and enrolling in one of its 13 universities. The initiative involves placing student coaches and recruiters in a select number of regional high schools.

The initial investment of $1 million will be equally divided among five universities ? UW Oshkosh UW-Parkside UW-Platteville UW-Stout and UW-Whitewater.

In addition to raising the profile of UW institutions across the state this effort is intended to create a more robust pipeline to the UW System by engaging students earlier in the college-going process and providing additional hands-on support including for students who may be the first in their families to pursue a university education. Strong partnerships between UW universities and local high schools their high school counselors and community organizations that serve young people will be a hallmark of this important effort.

Each of the universities that receives funding will use it to develop and implement precollege activities and programs that best serve the needs of the students in their respective areas.

Company Background

The University of Wisconsin System was created in 1971 through the merger of the University of Wisconsin (established 1848) and Wisconsin State Universities (originating in 1857 as the Normal Schools).

HISTORY

When Wisconsin became a state in 1848 its constitution called for the establishment of a state university. A board of regents was named and it first established a preparatory school because regents felt Wisconsin's secondary schools were not advanced enough to prepare students for university studies. The school began classes in 1849 with 20 students in the Madison Female Academy Building. The University of Wisconsin's first official freshman class began studies in the fall of 1850. A campus was established a mile west of the state capitol in Madison. By 1854 when it held its first commencement (with two graduates) the school had 41 students.

Enrollment dipped during the Civil War (all but one of the school's senior class joined the army) but soon rebounded and by 1870 the university had almost 500 students. Meanwhile it established a school of agriculture (1866) and a school of law (1868). The state established normal schools (teachers' colleges) in Platteville (1866) Whitewater (1868) Oshkosh (1871) and River Falls (1874).

There was also a teachers' course for women at the university in Madison. However when John Bascom became president in 1874 he transformed the university into a truly coeducational institution putting women "in all respects on precisely the same footing" with the men.

While the university at Madison remained Wisconsin's primary seat of learning the state continued to establish normal schools. It opened institutions in Milwaukee (1885) Superior (1893) Stevens Point (1894) La Crosse (1909) and Eau Claire (1916). The nine normal schools eventually became a system of state colleges called Wisconsin State Universities.

The university at Madison also continued to grow and by the late 1920s it had almost 9000 students. WWII brought a drop in enrollment but afterward it took off jumping from about 7000 in 1945 to over 22000 by the late 1950s. The University of Wisconsin-Milwaukee branch was founded in 1956. Other branch campuses were established in Green Bay (1965) and Kenosha (1968).

The Madison campus became a focal point for student protests during the Vietnam War. Events came to a head in 1970 when President Fred Harrington resigned during a four-day standoff between students and the National Guard. War protesters also placed a bomb outside Sterling Hall which housed the Army Math Research Center;

the explosion killed one student and injured three others.

The state legislature merged the University of Wisconsin and the Wisconsin State Universities in 1971 to create The University of Wisconsin System.

EXECUTIVES

Gov, Tony Evers
Pres*, Raymond Cross
V Pres-Fin*, Sean Nelson
Finance Executive, Benjamin Davis
Senior Library Consultant, Lorie Docken
Operations Executive, Ruth Olson
Manager, Stanley Novotny
Risk Management Specialist Sen, Stephanie Kutz
Accountant, Conni Christianson
Physician Recruitment Program, Randy Munson
Admin Program Specialist, Tracy Ohrt
Auditors: PLANTE & MORAN PORTAGE MI

LOCATIONS

HQ: UNIVERSITY OF WISCONSIN SYSTEM
1220 LINDEN DR, MADISON, WI 537061525
Phone: 608 262-2321
Web: WWW.WISCONSIN.EDU

PRODUCTS/OPERATIONS

Selected Four-Year Campuses
UW-Eau Claire
UW-Green Bay
UW-La Crosse
UW-Madison
UW-Milwaukee
UW-Oshkosh
UW-Parkside
UW-Platteville
UW-River Falls
UW-Stevens Point
UW-Stout
UW-Superior
UW-Whitewater

Selected Two-Year Colleges
UW-Baraboo/Sauk County
UW-Barron County
UW-Fond du Lac
UW-Fox Valley
UW-Manitowoc
UW-Marathon County
UW-Marinette
UW-Marshfield/Wood County
UW-Richland
UW-Rock County
UW-Sheboygan
UW-Washington County
UW-Waukesha

HISTORICAL FINANCIALS
Company Type: Private

Income Statement				FYE: June 30
	REVENUE ($ mil.)	NET INCOME ($ mil.)	NET PROFIT MARGIN	EMPLOYEES
06/18	3,613	203	5.6%	3,190
06/17	3,702	(20)	—	—
Annual Growth	(2.4%)	—	—	—

2018 Year-End Financials
Return on assets: 2.2%
Return on equity: 3.7%
Current ratio: 4.00
Cash ($ mil.): 1,868

UNIVERSITY SYSTEM OF NEW HAMPSHIRE

The University of New Hampshire (UNH) is a liberal arts college that serves about 12600 undergraduate and more than 2200 graduate students. The institution offers more than 100 majors and academic programs of study at nine colleges and schools. The student-faculty ratio is 20:1. UNH is the flagship institution of the University System of New Hampshire. In 2007 the university graduated its first international class in Seoul under a program run by its Whittemore School of Business and Economics. Founded in 1866 as the New Hampshire College of Agriculture and the Mechanic Arts UNH is a designated land-grant sea-grant and space-grant chartered school.

Operations

UNH's most popular bachelor's programs include business administration undeclared liberal arts psychology English and communication followed by mechanical engineering biology biomedical science civil engineering and political science.

The University System of New Hampshire includes Keene State College Plymouth State University and Granite State College in addition to UNH.

Geographic Reach

In addition to its main campus in Durham UNH has a campus in Manchester and its School of Law is in Concord. Almost 60% of the school's student body comes from within state with a concentration of others coming from the northeastern region of the US. UNH is developing new academic programs expanding its online courses and opportunities and creating new international initiatives for faculty and students in Costa Rica Chile Ghana India South Korea and China.

Strategy

UNH is engaged in a strategic plan to support its growth through 2020. Its plan for creating a learning-centered environment includes such initiatives as establishing a New Venture Fund to promote collaborative research and teaching opportunities; developing new programs to support independent research and scholarship; commercializing UNH's intellectual capital; and promoting diversity and inclusiveness as well as international opportunities. It also includes making major capital investments in technology to build a high-capacity cyber-infrastructure and a learning portal to promote interdisciplinary collaboration; renovating restoring and adding on to facilities; and constructing a new center for the arts.

EXECUTIVES

Pres, James W Dean Jr
Vice Chancellor*, Catherine Provencher
Assistant Professor, Lin Guo
Coordinator, Steve Wright
Assistant Professor, Weiwei MO
Assistant To President, Cheri O'Neil
Coordinator, Cynthia Nizzari-Mcclain
Assistant Professor, Shawna Hollen
Assistant Coach, Kasey Croce
Administrative Assistant I, Michelle Horn
Faculty, Wendy Ferrucci
Auditors: CLIFTONLARSONALLEN LLP QUINCY

LOCATIONS

HQ: UNIVERSITY SYSTEM OF NEW HAMPSHIRE
5 CHENELL DR STE 301, CONCORD, NH 033018522
Phone: 603 862-1800
Web: WWW.USNH.EDU

PRODUCTS/OPERATIONS

Selected Colleges and Schools
College of Engineering and Physical Sciences
College of Health and Human Services
College of Liberal Arts
College of Life Sciences and Agriculture
The Graduate School
Thompson School of Applied Science
University of New Hampshire at Manchester
University of New Hampshire School of Law
Whittemore School of Business and Economics
Special Academic Opportunities
Graduate Research Conference
Hamel Center for Undergraduate Reasearch
Honors program
International research opportunities program
Student internships
Study abroad
Undergraduate research opportunities program

HISTORICAL FINANCIALS

Company Type: Private

Income Statement   FYE: June 30

	REVENUE ($ mil.)	NET INCOME ($ mil.)	NET PROFIT MARGIN	EMPLOYEES
06/21	633	161	25.5%	16,000
06/20	642	(1)	—	—
06/19	700	52	7.5%	—
06/16	692	(9)	—	—
Annual Growth	(1.7%)	—	—	—

2021 Year-End Financials

Return on assets: 6.7%   Cash ($ mil.): 85
Return on equity: 9.7%
Current ratio: 1.20

UOFL HEALTH, INC.

EXECUTIVES

Ceo, Thomas Miller
Cfo, Michael Bouzuk
Injury Prevention Manager, Annabelle Pike
Svp Human Resources, Terry Johnson
Director, Risk Management, Sandra Pugh

LOCATIONS

HQ: UOFL HEALTH, INC.
530 S JACKSON ST, LOUISVILLE, KY 402021675
Phone: 502 562-3000
Web: WWW.UOFLBROWNCANCERCENTER.ORG

HISTORICAL FINANCIALS

Company Type: Private

Income Statement   FYE: June 30

	REVENUE ($ mil.)	NET INCOME ($ mil.)	NET PROFIT MARGIN	EMPLOYEES
06/21	1,935	87	4.5%	10,000
06/20	1,109	212	19.1%	—
Annual Growth	74.5%	(59.0%)	—	—

2021 Year-End Financials

Return on assets: 7.6%   Cash ($ mil.): 163
Return on equity: 15.3%
Current ratio: 1.80

UPMC

For University of Pittsburgh students and area residents medical care is spelled UPMC. University of Pittsburgh Medical Center (UPMC) is a leading not-for-profit health care delivery system in western Pennsylvania. UPMC operates 40 academic community and specialty hospitals 800 doctors' offices and outpatient sites employs 4900 physicians and offers an array of rehabilitation retirement and long-term care facilities.

Geographic Reach
UPMC's primary operating territory is the Pittsburgh area and western and central Pennsylvania Maryland and New York. Outside the US UPMC operates health care facilities in Ireland Italy Kazakhstan and China.

Its headquarters is in Pittsburgh Pennsylvania.

Strategy
UPMC maintained financial stability during the pandemic through a diversified Integrated Delivery and Financing System (IDFS) business model that includes both insurance and provider segments. Despite disruption to the nationwide health care system including a government-mandated halt on elective care in Pennsylvania its flexible payer-provider structure enabled the company to quickly adapt and grow.

Company Background
UPMC traces its roots to 1893 when Louise Lyle the wife of a Presbyterian minister founded its predecessor. The hospital was incorporated as Presbyterian Hospital of Pittsburgh two years later. In 1930 the hospital joined forces with the University of Pittsburgh and broke ground on a new location which opened its doors in 1938.

EXECUTIVES

Ceo, Leslie Davis
Pres, Jeffrey A Romoff
Cco, Janilee Johnson
Cfo, Robert Be Michiei
Coo, Gregory Peaslee
V Pres, Eileen Simmons
Evp-Chief Innovation Officer, Derek Angus
Evp-Chief Scientific Officer, Tim Billiar
Svp-Pres Physician Services, Joon Lee
Svp-Cmo Health Services, Donald Yealy
Administrator Help, Lori Spahr
Auditors: ERNST & YOUNG LLP

LOCATIONS

HQ: UPMC
200 LOTHROP ST, PITTSBURGH, PA 152132536
Phone: 412 647-8762
Web: WWW.UPMC.COM

Selected Pennsylvania Facilities
Children's Hospital of Pittsburgh of UPMC
Magee-Womens Hospital of UPMC (Pittsburgh)
UPMC Bedford Memorial (Everett)
UPMC East (Pittsburgh)
UPMC Hamlot (Erie)
UPMC Horizon (Greenville and Shenango Valley)
UPMC McKeesport (McKeesport)
UPMC Mercy (Pittsburgh)
UPMC Montefiore (Pittsburgh)
UPMC Northwest (Seneca and Oil City)
UPMC Passavant (McCandless and Cranberry)
UPMC Presbyterian (Pittsburgh)
UPMC Shadyside (Pittsburgh)
UPMC St. Margaret (Pittsburgh)
UPMC Western Psychiatric Institute and Clinic
(Pittsburgh)

PRODUCTS/OPERATIONS

2018 Sales

	$ mil.	% of total
Net patient services	8,823	47
Insurance enrollment	8,492	45
Other	1,462	8
Total	18,777	100

2018 Sales by Segment

	$ mil.	% of total
Health Services	11,881	57
Insurance Services	9,005	43
Adjustments	(2109)	-
Total	18,777	100

Selected Services
Behavioral and Mental Health Services
Cancer
COPD and Emphysema Center
Dermatology
Diabetes and Endocrinology
Ear Nose and Throat
Emergency Medicine
Family/Primary Care Medicine
Gastroenterology
Geriatrics
Heart and Vascular
Imaging Services
Kidney Disease
Liver
Neurology
Ophthalmology
Pain Medicine
Pathology
Pediatrics
Pulmonology and Respiratory
Rehabilitation
Rheumatology
Sports Medicine
Stroke Care
Thyroid
Urology
Women's Health
Wound Healing Services

COMPETITORS

Amerihealth Mercy Health Plan
Butler Health System
Capital Bluecross
Conemaugh Health System
Excela Health
Geisinger Health System
Healthamerica
Heritage Valley Health
Highmark
Independence Blue Cross
Jefferson Regional Medical Center Of Pennsylvania
Ohio Valley General
St. Clair Health
Universal Health Services
West Penn Allegheny Health System

HISTORICAL FINANCIALS

Company Type: Private

Income Statement   FYE: December 31

	REVENUE ($ mil.)	NET INCOME ($ mil.)	NET PROFIT MARGIN	EMPLOYEES
12/20	23,093	1,113	4.8%	80,000
12/19*	20,609	462	2.2%	—
06/15	614	326	53.1%	—
06/13	10,188	441	4.3%	—
Annual Growth	10.8%	12.3%	—	—

*Fiscal year change

2020 Year-End Financials

Return on assets: 5.2%   Cash ($ mil.): 1,541
Return on equity: 11.8%
Current ratio: 1.10

UPMC MAGEE-WOMENS HOSPITAL

EXECUTIVES

Pres, Leslie C Davis
SEC*, Claire Williams
Treas*, Peter Eisenbrandt
Oncology, Margaret V Ragni
Director, Dan Pototo
Genetic Counselor, Maureen May
Urogynecologist, Halina Zyczynski
Neonatal Nurse Practitioner, Mary Kish
Speech Pathologist, Urvashi Surti
Physician, Katie Bunge
Surgery Director, Jill Hague

LOCATIONS

HQ: UPMC MAGEE-WOMENS HOSPITAL
300 HALKET ST, PITTSBURGH, PA 152133108
Phone: 412 641-1000
Web: WWW.UPMC.COM

HISTORICAL FINANCIALS

Company Type: Private

Income Statement — FYE: June 30

	REVENUE ($ mil.)	NET INCOME ($ mil.)	NET PROFIT MARGIN	EMPLOYEES
06/16	838	92	11.1%	2,300
06/15	823	62	7.6%	—
06/00	7	7	98.8%	—
Annual Growth	33.9%	16.8%	—	—

2016 Year-End Financials

Return on assets: 17.7%
Return on equity: 19.0%
Current ratio: 9.40
Cash ($ mil.): 1

UPMC PINNACLE HOSPITALS

EXECUTIVES

Pres, Michael Young
Analyst, Sherry Stoner
Pres Cumberland Region, Louis Baverso
Auditors: PARENTEBEARD LLC YORK PA

LOCATIONS

HQ: UPMC PINNACLE HOSPITALS
409 S 2ND ST STE 1C, HARRISBURG, PA 171041612
Phone: 717 782-5678
Web: WWW.PINNACLEHEALTH.ORG

HISTORICAL FINANCIALS

Company Type: Private

Income Statement — FYE: June 30

	REVENUE ($ mil.)	NET INCOME ($ mil.)	NET PROFIT MARGIN	EMPLOYEES
06/20	1,130	61	5.4%	4,500
06/10	559	14	2.5%	—
06/09	538	0	—	—
06/08	513	(14)	—	—
Annual Growth	6.8%	—	—	—

2020 Year-End Financials

Return on assets: 5.1%
Return on equity: 6.3%
Current ratio: —
Cash ($ mil.): 313

UPMC PRESBYTERIAN SHADYSIDE

EXECUTIVES

Pres, John Innocenti
Cfo, Eileen Simmons
Nurse Practitioner, Kristen Baileys
Nurse Practitioner, Kristin Ermine-Baer
Director of Operations, Melanie Houston
Nurse Practitioner, Patti Gigliotti
Nurse Practitioner, Timothy Coleman
Manager, Vicki Bedel
Member, William S Dietrich II
Managing Partner, William Pietragallo II
Member, John Pelusi Jr
Auditors: ERNST & YOUNG LLP PITTSBURGH

LOCATIONS

HQ: UPMC PRESBYTERIAN SHADYSIDE
200 LOTHROP ST MH-N739, PITTSBURGH, PA 152132536
Phone: 412 647-2345
Web: WWW.UPMC.COM

HISTORICAL FINANCIALS

Company Type: Private

Income Statement — FYE: June 30

	REVENUE ($ mil.)	NET INCOME ($ mil.)	NET PROFIT MARGIN	EMPLOYEES
06/10	8,046	276	3.4%	8,200
06/09	1,723	83	4.8%	—
06/06	1,627	0	—	—
Annual Growth	49.1%	—	—	—

2010 Year-End Financials

Return on assets: 3.5%
Return on equity: 9.1%
Current ratio: 0.80
Cash ($ mil.): 158

URM STORES, INC.

URM Stores is a leading wholesale food distribution cooperative serving more than 160 grocery stores in the Northwest. Its member-owner stores operate under a variety of banners including Family Foods Harvest Foods Super 1 Foods Trading Co. Stores and Yoke's Fresh Market. It also owns the Rosauers Supermarkets chain. In addition to grocery stores URM supplies 1500-plus restaurants hotels and convenience stores; it also offers such services as merchandising store development consulting and technology purchasing. The cooperative was founded in 1921 as United Retail Merchants. The business is privately owned by its members.

Operations

The company's Spokane Washington-based Peirone Produce distribution subsidiary supplies fresh produce including organic produce as well as specialty items source from Arizona California Florida Mexico and Texas. In addition to groceries and produce URM Stores sells insurance to its members and food service customers through URM Insurance Agency. Insurance products include business insurance for stores and personal lines of coverage for owns and their employees.

Geographic Reach

Regional wholesaler URM Stores supplies stores and other customers in much of eastern Washington northern Idaho Oregon and Montana.

Financial Performance

URM Stores rings up sales of about $775 million employs more than 2700 people and has assets exceeding $100 million.

Strategy

In 2010 the company moved its Spokane Washington-based Peirone Produce distribution subsidiary into a larger facility boasting 70000 sq. ft. of warehouse space and 7000 sq. ft. of office space. It is equipped with about 15 docks for loading outgoing trucks and another dozen docks for unloading incoming trucks. The facility is more than twice the size of Peirone's previous building which had nearly 10 docks total. Because of the larger space and greater number of docks Peirone Produce said it has been able to improve its productivity.

EXECUTIVES

Ceo, Ray Sprinkle
Dir*, Ron B McIntire
Dir*, Paul Matejovsky
Dir*, Philip Juckeland
Sec-Treas-Cfo*, Laurie Bigej
SEC*, Joyce Mann
Treas*, Brian Eldred
Internal Medicine Practitioner, Zach Nybo
Associate, Kevin MAI
Accounts Receivable Manager, Randi Harrison
Vice President of Human Resour, Linda Wilson
Auditors: BDO USA LLP SPOKANE WA

LOCATIONS

HQ: URM STORES, INC.
7511 N FREYA ST, SPOKANE, WA 992178043
Phone: 509 467-2620
Web: WWW.URMSTORES.COM

PRODUCTS/OPERATIONS

Selected Banners

CenterPlace Market
Family Foods
Harvest Foods
Trading Co. Stores
Rosauers Supermarkets
Super 1 Foods
Yoke's Fresh Market

COMPETITORS

Amcon Distributing	Mclane
Albertsons	Supervalu
Associated Food	Safeway
C&s Wholesale	Sysco
Core-mark	Us Foods
Farner-bocken	Wal-mart
Fred Meyer Stores	

HISTORICAL FINANCIALS

Company Type: Private

Income Statement — FYE: August 2

	REVENUE ($ mil.)	NET INCOME ($ mil.)	NET PROFIT MARGIN	EMPLOYEES
08/08*	932	8	0.9%	2,100
07/07	859	7	0.8%	—
07/06	799	4	0.6%	—
Annual Growth	8.0%	41.0%		—

*Fiscal year change

Return on assets: 3.8%   Cash ($ mil.): 2
Return on equity: 11.0%
Current ratio: 1.20

US HEALTHCARE SYSTEM

EXECUTIVES

Prin, Ajitesh Kakade
Director, Peter Kotcher

LOCATIONS

HQ: US HEALTHCARE SYSTEM
   3200 BURNET AVE, CINCINNATI, OH 452293019
Phone: 513 585-1821

HISTORICAL FINANCIALS

Company Type: Private

Income Statement				FYE: June 30
	REVENUE ($ mil.)	NET INCOME ($ mil.)	NET PROFIT MARGIN	EMPLOYEES
06/18	1,695	52	3.1%	7
06/17	1,583	25	1.6%	—
06/15	1,482	80	5.5%	—
06/13	4	(0)	—	—
Annual Growth	224.3%	—	—	—

2018 Year-End Financials

Return on assets: 3.2%   Cash ($ mil.): 48
Return on equity: 6.4%
Current ratio: 0.60

USG CORPORATION

USG Corporation is a leading manufacturer of building products in the US serving the residential nonresidential and repair & remodel end markets. It is a top seller of wallboard gypsum fiberboard and construction plaster products that are used for finishing interior walls ceilings and floors. The company is also a major North American supplier of building-related performance materials (water fire and mold retardants) ceiling grid and acoustic tiles. Recognized brands include Sheetrock Durock Fiberock and Securock. Thanks to a tie-up with Boral Limited USG also distribute products across Asia and Australia. A merger deal with the Knauf Group (with USG becoming a wholly owned subsidiary) is currently pending (expected 2019).

Operations

USG Corporation reports five segments: US Wallboard and Surfaces US Performance Materials US Ceilings Canada and the USG Boral Building Products joint-venture (UBBP).

More than half of its revenue comes from gypsum products that help put the finishing touches on the walls of residential and commercial buildings. This whole business is managed under the US Wallboard and Surfaces segment. Some 15% more sales comes from tiles and grids meant to complete the ceilings of nonresidential buildings reported under US Ceilings. The third big product line of USG beyond wall and ceiling products is its roof-related products like reinforced concrete planes and mold-resistant boards. Housed under Performance Materials these products bring in some 10% of total sales mostly from commercial projects. The rest of its revenue some 15% comes from the company's Canadian segment that sells products from its three other producing segments.

The joint-venture UBBP manufactures and sells plasterboard and non-board lines for metal products in Asia Australia and the Middle East. Its revenue is reported separately.

Geographic Reach

Headquartered in Chicago Illinois USG Corporation operates plants mines and quarries in the US and some parts of Canada (Alberta British Columbia Ontario and Quebec). USG also owns three gypsum mines outside of North America through its UBBP joint venture.

The US accounts for more than 80% of its sales followed by Canada (nearly 15%).

Sales and Marketing

USG Corporation's products are sold through a network of distributors installation contractors and home improvement centers. The company makes most of its revenue through residential and non-residential repair and remodel activity. A quarter of its sales come from The Home Depot with another 15% coming from L&W Supply Corp.

USG's well-known brands include Sheetrock Securock Red Top Imperial Diamond and Supremo (gypsum business line); Durock Fiberock and Levelrock (performance materials); and Radar Eclipse Donn Curvatura and Ensemble (ceiling systems).

USG's advertising expenses was $15 million in 2018.

Financial Performance

USG Corporation has enjoyed a modestly upward trajectory in annual sales for the last five years. Revenue grew from $2.9 billion in 2014 to $3.3 billion by the end of 2018. In 2018 the company grew 3% coming mostly from higher selling prices in Sheetrock branded gypsum products Durock branded cement products and Securock branded roof boards and ceiling tiles.

Net income rose to $196 million in 2018 from $88 million the year before. A year-over-year $204 million reduction in income tax expenses improved company profits. Gross profit declined by $50 million as unit cost of producing its products climbed along with a hike in transportation costs.

The company's cash and cash equivalents fell by $61 million ending 2018 with $328 million on hand. Cash from operations generated $284 million while cash from investing used $195 million ($219 million on CAPEX). Financing activities further used $150 million.

Strategy

USG Corporation is facing two major challenges: anemic growth in the gypsum segment as well as a steep competition from substitute products in its ceiling materials business.

Gypsum market outlook is bleak for 2019 as residential and non-residential activity in the US is expected to remain well below historical averages. Demand in the Australian and South Korean markets are also expected to slow due to a slowing housing market. USG's volume growth of its gypsum board market share in the US shrank by 5%.

Furthermore there is excess wallboard production capacity in the US market and unless housing starts and repair activity pick up in 2019 the conditions won't improve for USG. This means that the company will not be able to charge higher prices for its materials (unlike 2018) going forward.

The Ceilings segment is experiencing an even bigger crisis: the market preference for the construction material of choice has rapidly shifted to open plenum and specialty ceilings products that directly compete with the company's own materials. USG has tried to catch up with this trend by acquiring Ceilings Plus in 2017 but its command over the market has taken a hit in recent years.

Mergers and Acquisitions

In late 2017 the company acquired US-based Ceilings Plus a leading manufacturer of specialty ceiling products for $52 million. The addition of Ceilings Plus made USG a leader in the specialty ceiling market especially in ceiling grid and acoustic ceiling tile products.

Company Background

In 1901 a group of 35 companies joined to form U.S.G. the largest gypsum producing and processing business in the industry. In 1915 the company began producing lime followed by paint manufacturing in 1924.

By 1931 it was producing insulating board and metal lath fields. When the company bought Masonite in 1984 its changed its name to USG the next year.

In 2019 the company is expected to bt acquired by Germany-based company Knauf.

HISTORY

In 1901 a group of 35 companies joined to form U.S.G. the largest gypsum producing and processing business in the industry. Sewell Avery became CEO in 1905 (he led U.S.G. until 1951). U.S.G. began producing lime in 1915. It became United States Gypsum (U.S. Gypsum) in 1920 and began making paint in 1924. By 1931 it was producing insulating board and metal lath fields. It also added two lime businesses and two gypsum concerns.

The company bought Masonite in 1984 and changed its name to USG the next year. It acquired Donn (remodeling materials) in 1986 and DAP (caulk and sealants) in 1987.

EXECUTIVES

Pres-Ceo, Christopher R Griffin
Plant Manager, Matthew Huss
Operations Manager, Kyle Hightower
Plant Manager, Matthew Craig
Plant Manager, Dan Coyner
Plant Manager, David Bunch
Senior Designer and In, Eric Best
Reliability Technician, Joe Scaff
Plant Manager, Lonnie Dyck
Manager Corporate Accounting, Mona Carroll
Licensing Manager, Patrick Desmond
Auditors: DELOITTED & TOUCHE LLP
   CHICAG

LOCATIONS

HQ: USG CORPORATION
   550 W ADAMS ST, CHICAGO, IL 606613665
Phone: 312 436-4000
Web: WWW.USG.COM

2018 Sales

	$ mil.	% of total
US	2,871	81
Canada	448	13
Other Foreign	211	6
Geographic transfers	(194)	-
Total	**3,336**	**100**

Subsidiaries

Subsidiaries
United States Gypsum Company
USG Interiors LLC
USG Foreign Investments Ltd.
USG Netherlands Global Holdings B.V.
CGC Inc.
USG Latin America LLC.
USG Holding de Mexico S.A. de C.V.
USG Mexico S.A. de C.V.

Selected schools

School of Dentistry
School of Medicine

School of Nursing
School of Pharmacy (with Oregon State University)
School of Science & Engineering

PRODUCTS/OPERATIONS

2018 Sales (by Segment)

	$ mil.	% of total
US Wallboard and Surfaces	1,927	54
US Performance Materials	392	11
US Ceilings	541	15
Canada	448	13
Other	252	7
Eliminations	(224)	-
Total	**3,336**	**100**

COMPETITORS

Allied Building Products	James Hardie Industries
American Gypsum	Laticrete
Armstrong World Industries	New Ngc
Certainteed	Pacific Coast Building Products
Continental Bp	Worthington Industries
Georgia-pacific	

HISTORICAL FINANCIALS

Company Type: Private

Income Statement				FYE: December 31
	REVENUE ($ mil.)	NET INCOME ($ mil.)	NET PROFIT MARGIN	EMPLOYEES
12/17	3,204	88	2.7%	7,300
12/16	3,017	510	16.9%	—
Annual Growth	6.2%	(82.7%)	—	—

2017 Year-End Financials

Return on assets: 2.3%   Cash ($ mil.): 394
Return on equity: 4.8%
Current ratio: 2.40

USS-UPI, LLC

US and Korean steel manufacturing interests come together in the form of USS-POSCO Industries (UPI) a 50/50 joint venture between United States Steel (US Steel) and POSCO. The company operates a steel plant (formerly owned by US Steel) in Pittsburg Northern California. It manufactures flat-rolled steel sheets in various forms: cold-rolled steel galvanized steel and tinplate. In addition USS-POSCO churns out iron oxide which is used to make hard and soft ferrites. UPI sells its products to more than 150 customers in more than dozen states throughout the western US. End products include office furniture computer cabinets metal studs cans culverts and metal building materials.

Operations

UPI's main product lines include cold rolled sheet galvanized sheet hot rolled pickled and oiled sheet and tin plate. It has the capacity to produce about 1.5 million tons of product per year.

Geographic Reach

The company markets its products primarily in the western US.

Sales and Marketing

UPI ships steel products to more than 150 customers across North America. The company sells its products to a wide range of manufacturers whose end products include automotive parts computer cabinets culverts food packaging metal buildings metal studs and office furniture. About 1/3 of UPI's product line is tinplate for the canning industry.

Strategy

Its Korean co-owner supplied high quality raw materials for use at the plant. In order to stay competitive in the face of cheaper steel imports UPI jettisoned non-core product lines to focus on steel sheet and tin. However strong competition and poor market prices forced the company in 2011 to introduce furloughs at the plant and enforce temporary shutdowns of the facility.

Company Background

The company rebounded from a major fire in 2001. In 2010 UPI invested heavily in remediation measures to clean up soil and groundwater impacted by its plant activities.

US Steel teamed up with POSCO (then Pohang Iron & Steel Company) in 1986 as part of a major reorganization of the aging Pittsburg plant which first opened in 1910.

EXECUTIVES

Pres, Michael Piekut
V Pres of Finance, Sungwon Shin
Staff, Jennifer Manto
Staff, David Martin
Law Specialist, Brandy Evans
Customer Manager, Maecy Jelly
Technology Coordinator, Young Sohn
Process Manager, Pat Martucci
Editor, Angela Marin
Quality Engineer, Katherine Valencia
Developer, Randy Sanders
Auditors: KPMG LLP SACRAMENTO CALIFOR

LOCATIONS

HQ: USS-UPI, LLC
  900 LOVERIDGE RD, PITTSBURG, CA 945652808
Phone: 800 877-7672
Web: WWW.USS-POSCO.COM

PRODUCTS/OPERATIONS

Selected Steel Products
Cold Rolled Annealed
Hot Dipped Galvanized
Hot Rolled Pickled and Oiled
Tinplate

COMPETITORS

Ak Steel Holding Corporation	Gerdau Ameristeel
Arcelormittal Usa	Nucor
Bluescope Steel	Steel Dynamics

HISTORICAL FINANCIALS

Company Type: Private

Income Statement				FYE: December 31
	REVENUE ($ mil.)	NET INCOME ($ mil.)	NET PROFIT MARGIN	EMPLOYEES
12/15	648	(4)	—	1,326
12/08	1,198	11	1.0%	—
12/07	998	(40)	—	—
12/06	1,034	14	1.4%	—
Annual Growth	(5.1%)	—	—	—

2015 Year-End Financials

Return on assets: (-1.5%)   Cash ($ mil.): —
Return on equity: —
Current ratio: 0.90

UTAH STATE UNIVERSITY

Utah State University (USU) has more than 40 academic departments at colleges of agriculture arts business education and human services engineering science natural resources and humanities and social sciences. It offers about 170 bachelor's degree programs and more than 140 graduate degree programs. Biology elementary education mechanical and aerospace engineering and business administration are among the university's most popular majors. About 29000 students attend its main campus in northern Utah its three branch campuses or extension facilities located across the state. USU was established in 1888 as an agricultural college.

Operations

USU has a student-to-faculty ratio of 18:1. Alumni of the university include Greg Carr founder of the Greg C. Carr Foundation and Charlie Denson former president of NIKE.

Geographic Reach

USU students hail from all 50 US states and some 80 international countries. The university's students have the opportunity to study abroad through partnerships with 140 other institutions located around the world. USU's main campuses or branch offices in Utah are located in Brigham City Logan San Juan Tooele and Uintah Basin.

Financial Performance

Revenues increased at USU by 4% to some $340 million due to increased income from tuition and fees higher enrollment and increased state appropriations. The gain was offset by decreases in gifts grants and contracts. Net income fell 41% to $68 million due to higher operating expenses from salary benefit and other costs.

Strategy

To expand its facilities and meet growing student needs USU is adding a new school of business building and a new athletics center to its main campus. The university recently completed construction of a new $47 million agricultural building on the main campus as well as a new administration building on the USU Eastern campus. In addition USU is building a new distance education building on its Logan campus.

To further expand resources for students USU began offering a Master of Business Administration (MBA) program at the Brigham Young University's Idaho campus in 2013.

EXECUTIVES

Pres, Stan L Albrecht
V Pres Bus-Fin, Ronald S Godfrey
Aamft Approved Supervisor, Scot Allgood
Assistant Professor, Lauri Nelson
Rsvp Coordinator, Rodney Pack
Assistant Professor, Jiming Jin
Assistant Professor, Lillian Duran
Staff, Shauna Meikle
Scientist, Hyrum Gillespie
Executive Officer, Vicki Read
Staff, Kami McNeil
Auditors: OFFICE OF THE STATE AUDITOR S

LOCATIONS

HQ: UTAH STATE UNIVERSITY
  1000 OLD MAIN HL, LOGAN, UT 843221000
Phone: 435 797-1000
Web: WWW.UTAHSTATEAGGIES.COM

HISTORICAL FINANCIALS
Company Type: Private

Income Statement				FYE: June 30
	REVENUE ($ mil.)	NET INCOME ($ mil.)	NET PROFIT MARGIN	EMPLOYEES
06/20	559	77	13.9%	700
06/19	537	94	17.5%	—
06/18	461	39	8.7%	—
06/17	435	59	13.7%	—
Annual Growth	8.7%	9.1%		

2020 Year-End Financials
Return on assets: 3.9% Cash ($ mil.): 110
Return on equity: 5.4%
Current ratio: 1.90

UTI, (U.S.) HOLDINGS, INC.

EXECUTIVES

Pres-Ceo, Christopher Dale
Treas*, Clinton Smith
Vice Pres*, Mary Anne Henry
Asst Treas*, Matthew Tachouet
Asst SEC*, Kristen Galbreath
Acct, Lorraine Disarlo
Acct Mgr, Patrick Billera
Cash Mgr, Mark Burrow
Director of Information Techno, Craig Jarrett
Vice-President, Tom Riester
Manager, Jay Newey
Auditors: DELOITTE & TOUCHE LLP LOS AN

LOCATIONS
HQ: UTI, (U.S.) HOLDINGS, INC.
400 SW 6TH AVE STE 906, PORTLAND, OR
972041634
Phone: 503 953-1300

HISTORICAL FINANCIALS
Company Type: Private

Income Statement				FYE: January 31
	REVENUE ($ mil.)	NET INCOME ($ mil.)	NET PROFIT MARGIN	EMPLOYEES
01/10	3,567	45	1.3%	5,981
01/08	534	12	2.3%	—
Annual Growth	158.3%	91.3%	—	—

2010 Year-End Financials
Return on assets: 20.5% Cash ($ mil.): 350
Return on equity: 1.3%
Current ratio: 1.20

VALLEY CHILDREN'S HEALTHCARE FOUNDATION

EXECUTIVES

Ceo, Todd Suntrapak
V Pres*, William Chaltraw
Director of Strategic Planning, Brian Sabbatini
Director of Information Securi, Joe Egan
Director, Rod Benedict
Director, Tim Curley
Director, Michelle Brunetti
Director Recruitment, Suzan Parsons
Director of Patient SA, Samuel Lehman
Clinical Laboratory Scientist, Ashley Owens
Payroll Analyst, Tami Evers

LOCATIONS
HQ: VALLEY CHILDREN'S HEALTHCARE
FOUNDATION
9300 VALLEY CHILDRENS PL, MADERA, CA
936368761
Phone: 559 353-3000
Web: WWW.VALLEYCHILDRENS.ORG

HISTORICAL FINANCIALS
Company Type: Private

Income Statement				FYE: September 30
	REVENUE ($ mil.)	NET INCOME ($ mil.)	NET PROFIT MARGIN	EMPLOYEES
09/19	793	159	20.0%	2,800
09/18	698	122	17.6%	—
09/17	604	121	20.1%	—
09/16	601	83	13.9%	—
Annual Growth	9.7%	23.9%	—	—

2019 Year-End Financials
Return on assets: 9.0% Cash ($ mil.): 31
Return on equity: 12.1%
Current ratio: 1.30

VALLEY CHILDREN'S HOSPITAL

EXECUTIVES

Pres- Ceo, Todd Sunterapak
Cfo*, Michele Waldrin
Coo*, Jessie Hudgins
Exec SEC*, Stephanie Scott
Prin*, Gordon Alexander
Human Resources, Heather San Julian
Manager of Gift Shop, Peggy Ellithorpe
Doctor, Randall D Morton
Hematologist Oncologist, Ruetima Titapiwatanakun
Clinical Quality Coordinator, Diana Johnson
Secretary To Human Resources, Jodi Koop
Auditors: MOSS ADAMS LLP STOCKTON CA

LOCATIONS
HQ: VALLEY CHILDREN'S HOSPITAL
9300 VALLEY CHILDRENS PL, MADERA, CA
936368762
Phone: 559 353-3000
Web: WWW.VALLEYCHILDRENS.ORG

HISTORICAL FINANCIALS
Company Type: Private

Income Statement				FYE: September 30
	REVENUE ($ mil.)	NET INCOME ($ mil.)	NET PROFIT MARGIN	EMPLOYEES
09/19	771	41	5.4%	1,800
09/15	575	24	4.3%	—
09/13*	542	103	19.0%	—
06/05	457	(24)	—	—
Annual Growth	3.8%	—	—	—

*Fiscal year change

2019 Year-End Financials
Return on assets: 2.5% Cash ($ mil.): 412
Return on equity: 3.5%
Current ratio: 3.80

VALLEY HEALTH SYSTEM GROUP RETURN

EXECUTIVES

Ex Dir, Kevin Callanan
Urology Specialist, John Warner
Auditors: VALLEY HEALTH SYSTEM WINCHEST

LOCATIONS
HQ: VALLEY HEALTH SYSTEM GROUP RETURN
220 CAMPUS BLVD STE 310, WINCHESTER, VA
226012889
Phone: 540 536-4302

HISTORICAL FINANCIALS
Company Type: Private

Income Statement				FYE: December 31
	REVENUE ($ mil.)	NET INCOME ($ mil.)	NET PROFIT MARGIN	EMPLOYEES
12/17	904	32	3.6%	7
12/13	625	22	3.7%	—
12/12	628	46	7.4%	—
12/09	538	45	8.5%	—
Annual Growth	6.7%	(4.2%)	—	—

2017 Year-End Financials
Return on assets: 2.3% Cash ($ mil.): 65
Return on equity: 3.9%
Current ratio: 0.40

VALUE DRUG COMPANY

Value Drug Company (Value Drug) sees a great deal of value in keeping independent pharmacies competitive. The company is a purchasing cooperative of hundreds of independent drugstores that provides wholesale pharmaceutical distribution services to its members primarily in the central Pennsylvania area. Its products include pharmaceuticals and non-prescription medications medical equipment health and beauty aids nutritional supplies and other health care-related products. The company works with some of the world's largest pharmaceutical makers. Value Drug was founded in 1934 and incorporated in 1936. The company is led by president Greg Drew a former Rite-Aid executive.

Operations

The company is not just a pharmaceutical wholesaler but it also provides retail and specialty pharmacy services long-term care pharmacy support and immunization service offerings. Value Drug offers more than 25000 products including brand generic injectable and specialty pharmaceuticals over-the-counter products home health care long-term care supplies health beauty and wellness as well as seasonal and everyday gifts. Value Drug also participates in such retail initiatives as the federal 340B Drug Discount Program an adult immunization tracking program and competitive generic sourcing program OptiSource.

Geographic Reach

Value Drug is located in Duncansville Pennsylvania.

Sales and Marketing

Value Drug customers include pharmacists and business owners. It offers a variety of marketing tools for its customers such as store signage and consumer email communications to physician marketing support for CP specialty pharmacy services. Value Drug provides valuable resources that help generate traffic and its customer's increase sales.

Strategy

Value Drug is committed to providing transparency in its pricing and optimizing manufacturer relationships and purchasing power to improve buying conditions for its members. Value Drug also takes note of the changing consumer and independent pharmacy owners' needs. The company has assembled a diverse portfolio of programs and services that satisfy both the customer's need for convenience and low-cost healthcare and the pharmacist's need to increase growth efficiency and profitability.

Value Drug strives to keep independent pharmacies independent. Its Value Buy/Sell Program was established to assist those seeking to sell their business as well as those looking for new ownership or expansion opportunities. Through its partnership with PRS members have access to industry-leading buying selling and transferring services while its partnership with Sykes & Co. provides members with access to accounting tax and advisory services.

Value Drug also provides resources that help generate traffic and increase sales in pharmacies. It offers a variety of marketing tools to help its members stay top-of-mind with patients and customers in their communities. Through Value Drug's partnerships with leading suppliers clients can purchase high-quality apparel and promotional products featuring the clients' pharmacy's logo and brand designs.

Company Background

Value Drug Company was founded in 1934. Value Drug Company was then incorporated in 1936. The first warehouse occupied was located at 5th Avenue and 24th Street. In 1970 Drenning Trucking Co. was the first delivery service. In 2015 Value Drug introduces the ValueDrugHub mobile app the first pharmaceutical wholesaler to provide a mobile app for order receiving and discrepancies.

EXECUTIVES

Pres, Greg Drew

Chb*, Rowland Tibbott
Pres*, John L Letizia
V Pres-Cfo*, Robert E Tyler
SEC*, Richard T Moran
SEC*, Robert L Maher
Treas*, William D Thompson Jr
Cntrl, Michael Remillard
Regional Sales Manager, Steve Shryock
Controller, Mike Remillard
Graphic Designer, Terry McCaulsky
Auditors: HILL BARTH & KING LLC WEXFOR

LOCATIONS

HQ: VALUE DRUG COMPANY
195 THEATER DR, DUNCANSVILLE, PA 166357144
Phone: 814 944-9316
Web: WWW.VALUEDRUGCO.COM

COMPETITORS

Amerisourcebergen	Kinray
Cardinal Health	Mckesson
H. D. Smith Wholesale Drug	Quality King

HISTORICAL FINANCIALS
Company Type: Private

Income Statement				FYE: March 31
	REVENUE ($ mil.)	NET INCOME ($ mil.)	NET PROFIT MARGIN	EMPLOYEES
03/21	1,010	1	0.2%	200
03/20*	1,156	0	0.1%	—
12/18	1,034	(0)	—	—
12/17	842	0	0.1%	—
Annual Growth	6.2%	23.9%	—	—

*Fiscal year change

2021 Year-End Financials

Return on assets: 0.9%   Cash ($ mil.): 12
Return on equity: 7.3%
Current ratio: 1.40

VAN ATLAS LINES INC

The main subsidiary of Atlas World Group moving company Atlas Van Lines provides transportation of household goods throughout the US and between the US and Canada. The company is one of the largest movers in the US. Atlas Van Lines also offers specialized transportation services for such cargo as trade show materials fine art electronics pianos store fixtures and even individual cars and motorcycles. It operates through a network of some 500 agents in the US and about 150 in Canada — independent companies that use the Atlas brand in assigned geographic territories and cooperate on interstate moves. Atlas Van Lines was formed in 1948 by a group of 33 small moving companies.

EXECUTIVES

Ceo, John P Griffin
Cfo*, Donald R Breivogel Jr
Sr Vp*, James K McMurray
Vp*, Joab Schultheis
Vp*, Stacie L Banks
Vp*, Steve Hermann
Vp*, Ryan McConnell
Vp*, Mary Beth Johnson
Vp*, Nancy L Priebe
Vp*, Jeffery L Schimmel
Asst SEC*, Todd A Suter

LOCATIONS

HQ: VAN ATLAS LINES INC
1212 SAINT GEORGE RD, EVANSVILLE, IN 477112364
Phone: 812 424-4326
Web: WWW.ATLASVANLINES.COM

COMPETITORS

Amerco	Penske Truck Leasing
Bekins	Sirva
Graebel	United Van Lines

HISTORICAL FINANCIALS
Company Type: Private

Income Statement				FYE: December 31
	REVENUE ($ mil.)	NET INCOME ($ mil.)	NET PROFIT MARGIN	EMPLOYEES
12/08	696	19	2.8%	606
12/06	58	2	4.3%	—
12/05	59	3	6.5%	—
Annual Growth	127.4%	71.0%	—	—

VANDERBILT UNIVERSITY MEDICAL CENTER

The Vanderbilt University Medical Center (VUMC) is one of the largest academic medical centers in the Southeast and primary specialty is and primary care in hundreds of adult and pediatric specialties. The VUMC school of medicine's biomedical research program is among the top 10 in terms of National Institutes of Health peer review funding and receiving more than $500 million in public and private awards in 2016. In 2021 Vanderbilt University Medical Center-acquired of Tennova Healthcare-Shellbyville and Tennova Healthcare-Harton hospitals and their related businesses including physician clinic operations and outpatient services from subsidiaries of Community Health Systems Inc. (CHS) and the Vanderbilt-Ingram Cancer Center a National Cancer Institute-designated facility.

Operations

Vanderbilt University Medical Center is working with over 60 hospitals and 5000 clinicians across Tennessee and five neighboring estates.

Geographic Reach

VUMC's was based in Tennessee.

Sales and Marketing

Vanderbilt University Medical Center markets its products and services by working in 60 hospitals and 5000 clinicians across Tennessee and five neighboring estates and share best practices and bring value-driven and cost-effective health care to the Mid-South.

Mergers and Acquisitions

In 2021 Vanderbilt University Medical Center-acquired of Tennova Healthcare-Shellbyville and Tennova Healthcare-Harton hospitals and their related businesses including physician clinic operations and outpatient services from subsidiaries of Community Health Systems Inc. (CHS). Terms of the transactions will remain confidential. With the acquisition of the hospitals in Shelbyville and Tullahoma and the partnership with Tennova Healthcare-Clarksville VUMC is expanding its ability to serve the communities of Middle Tennessee. Vanderbilt Bedford Hospital is a 60-bed Joint Commission-accredited facility that employs approximately 275 physicians nurses and staff and offers a range of inpatient and outpatient medical and surgical services along with urgent care services. Vanderbilt Tullahoma-Harton Hospital employs approximately 450 physicians nurses and staff and is a 135-bed Joint Commission-accredited facility offering a full range of inpatient and outpatient surgical and specialty services including a sleep center cardiac and physical rehabilitation.

EXECUTIVES

Ceo, Jeff Balser
Treas, Alaine Zachary
Dir, John Bingham
Coo, Lee Ann Liska
Neurologist, David Phillip Charles
Coordinator, Cheryl Markin
Assistant Professor, Megha Talati
Assistant Professor, Hendrik Weitkamp
Physical Therapist, Adam Meidinger
Registered Nurse, Alana Britt
Pastoral Care Director, Andy Peterson
Auditors: ERNST & YOUNG LLP NASHVILLE

LOCATIONS

HQ: VANDERBILT UNIVERSITY MEDICAL CENTER
1211 MEDICAL CENTER DR, NASHVILLE, TN 372320004
Phone: 615 322-5000
Web: WWW.VANDERBILTHEALTH.COM

PRODUCTS/OPERATIONS

Selected Facilities
Annette and Irwin Eskind Biomedical Library
Bill Wilkerson Center for Otolaryngology and Communication Sciences
Comprehensive Spine Center
Dayani Center for Health and Wellness
Monroe Carell Jr. Children's Hospital at Vanderbilt
Orthopaedic Institute
School of Medicine
School of Nursing
Sports Medicine Center
Stallworth Rehabilitation Hospital
Transplant Center
Vanderbilt Center for Better Health
The Vanderbilt Clinic
Vanderbilt Heart and Vascular Institute
Vanderbilt Psychiatric Hospital
Vanderbilt University Hospital
Vanderbilt-Ingram Cancer Center

COMPETITORS

American Healthchoice
Ascension Health
Blount Memorial Hospital
Catholic Health Initiatives
Community Health Systems
Covenant Health
Duke University Health System
Emory Healthcare
Erlanger Health System
Hca
Lifepoint Health
Mountain States Health
Tennova Healthcare

HISTORICAL FINANCIALS
Company Type: Private

Income Statement				FYE: June 30
	REVENUE ($ mil.)	NET INCOME ($ mil.)	NET PROFIT MARGIN	EMPLOYEES
06/20	4,930	182	3.7%	19,000
06/18	4,086	98	2.4%	—
06/17	3,894	264	6.8%	—
Annual Growth	8.2%	(11.5%)	—	—

2020 Year-End Financials
Return on assets: 3.5%   Cash ($ mil.): 1,182
Return on equity: 13.0%
Current ratio: 1.20

VANGUARD CHARITABLE ENDOWMENT PROGRAM

EXECUTIVES

Pres, Benjamin Pierce
Chief Dev't Officer, David Ryder
Cfo, Kevin Cavanaugh
Cfo, Mark Froehlich
Marketing Manager, James R Barnes
Senior Philanthropic, Jodi Rosen
Sr Business Execut, Cindy Vanamburgh
Manager, Karen Levandoski
Marketing Coordinator, Kevin Cella
Project Manager, Sean Gordon
Trustee, Vikra Mdewan
Auditors: PRICEWATERHOUSECOOPERS LLP PH

LOCATIONS

HQ: VANGUARD CHARITABLE ENDOWMENT PROGRAM
2670 WARWICK AVE, WARWICK, RI 028894269
Phone: 888 383-4483

HISTORICAL FINANCIALS
Company Type: Private

Income Statement				FYE: June 30
	REVENUE ($ mil.)	NET INCOME ($ mil.)	NET PROFIT MARGIN	EMPLOYEES
06/13	1,117	608	54.4%	22
06/12	908	424	46.7%	—
06/11	890	402	45.2%	—
06/10	490	15	3.2%	—
Annual Growth	31.6%	239.7%	—	—

2013 Year-End Financials
Return on assets: 16.8%   Cash ($ mil.): 14
Return on equity: 16.9%
Current ratio: —

VCC, LLC

EXECUTIVES

Member, Derek Alley
Superintendent, Iulian Trofin
Superintendent, Dennis Haynes
Superintendent, James McClain
Senior Project Manager, Hayden Herring
Graphic Designer, Brent Murray
Accountant, Jordys Barr
Project Engineer, Chase Barnes
Sr Accountant, Jeff Dillman
Project Manager, James Connet
Vice President Operations, Dale Laster
Auditors: HOGAN TAYLOR LLP LITTLE ROCK

LOCATIONS

HQ: VCC, LLC
1 INFORMATION WAY STE 300, LITTLE ROCK, AR 722022197
Phone: 214 574-4500
Web: WWW.VCCUSA.COM

HISTORICAL FINANCIALS
Company Type: Private

Income Statement				FYE: December 31
	REVENUE ($ mil.)	NET INCOME ($ mil.)	NET PROFIT MARGIN	EMPLOYEES
12/19	746	0	—	350
12/18	779	0	—	—
12/17	682	0	—	—
Annual Growth	4.6%	—	—	—

2019 Year-End Financials
Return on assets: —   Cash ($ mil.): 51
Return on equity: —
Current ratio: 1.10

VCU HEALTH SYSTEM AUTHORITY

EXECUTIVES

Ceo, John Duval
Pres, Michael RAO
Cfo-Evp, Dominic J Puleo
Coo, Deborah Davis
Rn, Carol Clark
Physician Assistant, Katherine Vita
Assistant Professor of Urology, Aaron Krill
Registered Nurse, Adrienne Harris
Editor In Chief, Ann Ritter
Clinical Nurse II, Caroline Clark
Safe Kids Virginia, Corri Miller-Hobbs
Auditors: ERNST & YOUNG LLP RICHMOND V

LOCATIONS

HQ: VCU HEALTH SYSTEM AUTHORITY
1250 E MARSHALL ST, RICHMOND, VA 232985023
Phone: 804 828-9000
Web: WWW.VCUHEALTH.ORG

HISTORICAL FINANCIALS
Company Type: Private

Income Statement				FYE: June 30
	REVENUE ($ mil.)	NET INCOME ($ mil.)	NET PROFIT MARGIN	EMPLOYEES
06/19	3,895	140	3.6%	7,399
06/18	3,399	162	4.8%	—
06/17	3,014	309	10.3%	—
06/05	899	47	5.3%	—
Annual Growth	11.0%	8.0%	—	—

2019 Year-End Financials
Return on assets: 3.6%   Cash ($ mil.): 408
Return on equity: 5.5%
Current ratio: 2.20

VICTORY INTERNATIONAL GROUP, LLC

EXECUTIVES

Ceo, Dawson Fan
V Pres*, Amanda Meng
Managing Director, Marc Itow
National Accounts Director, Cory Knuteson
Product Development Manager, Kelly Lu

LOCATIONS

HQ: VICTORY INTERNATIONAL GROUP, LLC
  14748 PIPELINE AVE STE B, CHINO HILLS, CA
  917096024
Phone: 949 407-5888
Web: WWW.VICTORYINTLGROUP.COM

HISTORICAL FINANCIALS
Company Type: Private

Income Statement				FYE: December 31
	REVENUE ($ mil.)	NET INCOME ($ mil.)	NET PROFIT MARGIN	EMPLOYEES
12/20	896	62	6.9%	230
12/07	87	1	1.4%	—
Annual Growth	19.5%	35.2%	—	—

2020 Year-End Financials
Return on assets: 7.3%   Cash ($ mil.): 260
Return on equity: 10.8%
Current ratio: 2.90

VIRGINIA COMMONWEALTH UNIVERSITY

Virginia Commonwealth University (VCU) serves the common interests of its more than 30000 enrolled students. The university offers more than 200 certificate undergraduate graduate and doctoral programs through its 15 schools. Spread across two campuses in Richmond: Monroe Park and Medical College of Virginia (MCV) which includes the Schools of Allied Health Dentistry Medicine Nursing Pharmacy and Public Health. Specialty facilities include the VCU Medical Center and a branch campus of the School of the Arts in Qatar. Founded in 1917 as the Richmond School of Social Work and Public Health in 1968 the school merged with the Medical College of Virginia to form VCU.

EXECUTIVES

Pres, Eugene P Trani
Chief Communications Officer*, Grant J Heston
Principal, Vanessa Y Byrd
Accounting Staff, Dvora B Courtland
Accounting Staff, Jong E Lee
Accounting Staff, Rasoul H Tondkar
Accounting Staff, Robert L Freed
Accounting Staff, Alfreda Cheatham
Accounting Staff, Andrea S Smith
Accounting Staff, Barbara C Jackson
Accounting Staff, Cordellia S Braxton
Auditors: MARTHA S MAVREDES RICHMOND

LOCATIONS

HQ: VIRGINIA COMMONWEALTH UNIVERSITY
  912 W FRANKLIN ST, RICHMOND, VA 232849040
Phone: 804 828-0100
Web: WWW.VCU.EDU

HISTORICAL FINANCIALS
Company Type: Private

Income Statement				FYE: June 30
	REVENUE ($ mil.)	NET INCOME ($ mil.)	NET PROFIT MARGIN	EMPLOYEES
06/20	784	49	6.3%	11,000
06/18	763	12	1.7%	—
06/17	760	84	11.1%	—
06/16	737	37	5.1%	—
Annual Growth	1.5%	6.7%	—	—

2020 Year-End Financials
Return on assets: 2.4%   Cash ($ mil.): 124
Return on equity: 6.2%
Current ratio: 2.00

VIRGINIA DEPARTMENT OF TRANSPORTATION

EXECUTIVES

Commissioner, C Kilpatrick
Commissioner*, Charles A Kilpatrick
Assistant Secretary*, Amy Wight
Acting Deputy SEC*, John W Lawson
Payroll Staff, Carol Clatterbaugh
Accounting Staff, Lu Lutero
Business Analyst, Liliya Fedzhora
Safety Manager, Billie Miller
Engineering Manager, Jeff Wyatt
Quality Assurance Manager, Robert Liberatore
Environmental Policy Analyst, Angel Aymond

LOCATIONS

HQ: VIRGINIA DEPARTMENT OF TRANSPORTATION
  1401 E BROAD ST, RICHMOND, VA 232192052
Phone: 804 786-2701
Web: WWW.VIRGINIADOT.ORG

HISTORICAL FINANCIALS
Company Type: Private

Income Statement				FYE: June 30
	REVENUE ($ mil.)	NET INCOME ($ mil.)	NET PROFIT MARGIN	EMPLOYEES
06/10	3,240	473	14.6%	10,737
06/06	3,047	410	13.5%	—
06/05	0	0	—	—
06/04	2,857	56	2.0%	—
Annual Growth	2.1%	42.7%	—	—

2010 Year-End Financials
Return on assets: 2.3%   Cash ($ mil.): 2,013
Return on equity: 2.7%
Current ratio: —

VIRGINIA HOUSING DEVELOPMENT AUTHORITY

Though Virginia is famous for its Civil War-era plantations these historic estates represent a lifestyle out of reach for most. For Virginians seeking a more modest homestead there's the Virginia Housing Development Authority (VHDA). The not-for-profit quasi-government agency founded by the Virginia General Assembly in 1972 provides developers of rental properties and low- to moderate-income borrowers with low interest rate loans to renovate or purchase houses and apartments across the state. Its loan products are offered by more than 140 authorized lenders throughout Virginia. The VHDA is self-supporting issuing bonds to raise capital.

EXECUTIVES

Exec Dir, Susan F Dewey
Gen Cousel, Judsen McKellar
Officer, Cindy Holsapple
Finance Manager, Janet Little
Consultant, Renee Lacy
Managing Director Finance and, Arthur N Bowen
Developer Manager, Juan Acosta
Manager, Sherry Long
Accounting Manager Single Fami, Elsie Handy
Creative Team Leader, Suzie Bird
Business Officer, Shelia Doplemore
Auditors: KPMG LLP RICHMOND VIRGINIA

LOCATIONS

HQ: VIRGINIA HOUSING DEVELOPMENT AUTHORITY
  601 S BELVIDERE ST, RICHMOND, VA 232206504
Phone: 804 780-0789
Web: WWW.VHDA.COM

HISTORICAL FINANCIALS
Company Type: Private

Income Statement				FYE: June 30
	ASSETS ($ mil.)	NET INCOME ($ mil.)	INCOME AS % OF ASSETS	EMPLOYEES
06/16	8,024	171	2.1%	300
06/15	8,070	176	2.2%	—
06/14	8,014	132	1.7%	—
Annual Growth	0.1%	13.7%	—	—

2016 Year-End Financials
Return on assets: 2.1%   Sales ($ mil): 554
Return on equity: 5.7%

VIRGINIA INTERNATIONAL TERMINALS, LLC

Virginia International Terminals (VIT) operates marine terminals and an inland port on behalf of the Virginia Port Authority (VPA) a state agency. Established in 1982 VIT's marine terminals handle containerships and other vessels in Newport News Norfolk and Portsmouth. The terminals are linked by rail to the Virginia Inland Port in Front Royal which serves as an intermodal container transfer facility conveying cargo from ships to trucks and vice versa. CenterPoint Properties investment firm The Carlyle Group and terminal operator Carrix Inc. bid to create a public-private partnership with VIT. The Transportation Secretary dismissed the bids in late 2010 after cargo activity started improving.

EXECUTIVES

Ceo, Joseph P Ruddy
Pres, Joseph Dorto
Dir, Regina P Brayboy
V Pres, Wilson S Goode
Dir, Franklin P Earley
SEC-Treas, William M Grace
Coo, Shawn Tiddettes
Corporate Counsel, John M Ryan
Customer Representativ, Becky Coore
Customer Representativ, Patty Marlow
Coordinator, Shirby Dunton
Auditors: PB MARES LLP HARRISONBURG V

LOCATIONS

HQ: VIRGINIA INTERNATIONAL TERMINALS, LLC
601 WORLD TRADE CTR, NORFOLK, VA 23510
Phone: 757 440-7120
Web: WWW.VIT.ORG

COMPETITORS

Georgia Ports Authority
North Carolina State Ports Authority
Port Authority Of New York And New Jersey
South Carolina Ports

HISTORICAL FINANCIALS

Company Type: Private

Income Statement				FYE: June 30
	REVENUE ($ mil.)	NET INCOME ($ mil.)	NET PROFIT MARGIN	EMPLOYEES
06/20	619	(27)	—	400
06/19	551	(1)	—	—
06/18	521	16	3.1%	—
06/17	478	(7)	—	—
Annual Growth	9.0%	—	—	—

2020 Year-End Financials

Return on assets: (-14.1%) Cash ($ mil.): 54
Return on equity: (-26.7%)
Current ratio: 1.60

VIRGINIA MASON MEDICAL CENTER

EXECUTIVES

Pres, James Young
V Pres*, James Orlikoff
Treas*, Robert Lemon
SEC*, Dorothy Mann
Chb-Ceo*, Gary S Kaplan
Sr V Pres-Cio-Cfo*, Suzanne Anderson
Pres*, Carolyn Corvi
Physician, Anthony Gerbino
Managing Director, Bruce Nitsche
Supervisor, Carolyn Smalley

Vascular Surgeon, Damon Pierce
Auditors: KPMG LLP SEATTLE WA

LOCATIONS

HQ: VIRGINIA MASON MEDICAL CENTER
1100 9TH AVE, SEATTLE, WA 981012756
Phone: 206 223-6600
Web: WWW.VIRGINIAMASON.ORG

HISTORICAL FINANCIALS

Company Type: Private

Income Statement				FYE: December 31
	REVENUE ($ mil.)	NET INCOME ($ mil.)	NET PROFIT MARGIN	EMPLOYEES
12/20	1,118	47	4.3%	5,000
12/19*	1,156	29	2.5%	—
03/19	274	10	4.0%	—
12/18	1,101	(16)	—	—
Annual Growth	0.8%			

*Fiscal year change

2020 Year-End Financials

Return on assets: 3.3% Cash ($ mil.): 205
Return on equity: 8.5%
Current ratio: 1.60

VIRGINIA POLYTECHNIC INSTITUTE & STATE UNIVERSITY

Virginia Polytechnic Institute and State University more commonly known as Virginia Tech is the state's largest university enrolling more than 37000 students. The university offers more than 280 undergraduate graduate and professional degree programs through nine academic colleges and graduate school. It has a student-teacher ratio of 14 to 1. In addition to the university's approximately 2070 full-time and part-time faculty members Virginia Tech has approximately $1.33 billion endowment. The school's most popular majors include agriculture architecture business journalism and computer and information sciences. Virginia Tech which was formed in 1872 serves the surrounding community through outreach and education programs.

Operations

Virginia Tech offers more than 110 bachelor's degree programs over 170 master's and doctoral degree programs and eight undergraduate academic colleges. Major offerings include Aerospace Engineering Biological Sciences Computational Modeling and Data Analytics Dairy Science English Language Arts Education and Food Science and Technology among others.

The university manages a research portfolio of more than $556 million. It has Graduate School Virginia-Maryland College of Veterinary Medicine Virginia Tech Carilion School of Medicine and Honors College.

Geographic Reach

Virginia Tech has approximately 235 campus buildings a 2600-acre main campus in Blacksburg off-campus educational facilities in Alexandria Arlington Fairfax Falls Church Leesburg Manassas and Middleburg and a study-abroad site in Switzerland.

Company Background

Virginia Tech was founded as a land-grant college in 1872.

EXECUTIVES

Pres, Tim Sands
Exec V Pres & Provost*, Cyril Clarke
V Pres For Oprs*, Sherwood G Wilson
V Pres For Advancement*, Charles D Phlegar
V Pres of Fin & Cfo*, M Dwight Shelton Jr
Vp-Student Affairs, Edward F D Spence
Assistant Professor, Yong Cao
Assistant Professor, Markus Breitschmid
Accounting Staff, Tammy Harris
Assoc Vp Dev't For Colleges, Michael Moyer
Coordinator, David Travis Jr
Auditors: COMMONWEALTH OF VIRGINIA AUDIT

LOCATIONS

HQ: VIRGINIA POLYTECHNIC INSTITUTE & STATE UNIVERSITY
300 TURNER ST NW STE 4200, BLACKSBURG, VA 240616100
Phone: 540 231-6000
Web: WWW.VT.EDU

PRODUCTS/OPERATIONS

Selected Colleges

College of Agriculture and Life Sciences
College Architecture and Urban Studies
College of Engineering
College of Liberal Arts and Human Sciences
College of Natural Resources and Environment
College of Science
Pamplin College of Business
Virginia-Maryland Regional College of Veterinary Medicine

HISTORICAL FINANCIALS

Company Type: Private

Income Statement				FYE: June 30
	REVENUE ($ mil.)	NET INCOME ($ mil.)	NET PROFIT MARGIN	EMPLOYEES
06/20	1,188	120	10.2%	6,866
06/19	1,160	130	11.2%	—
06/18	1,279	181	14.2%	—
06/17	1,031	64	6.2%	—
Annual Growth	4.8%	23.6%	—	—

2020 Year-End Financials

Return on assets: 4.0% Cash ($ mil.): 187
Return on equity: 8.0%
Current ratio: 0.90

VIRGINIA PREMIER HEALTH PLAN, INC.

EXECUTIVES

Ceo, Linda Hines
Talent Acquisition Specialist, Jasmine Lewis
Director, Kenneth Hepler
Supervisor, Amy Feathers
Business Analyst II, Courtney Eliot
Compliance Analyst I, Dustin Harrel
Vice President, Elizabeth Veliz
Case Manager, Katrinka Pauley
Analyst, Sushma Chowdary

Social Worker, Tia Weaver
Business Analyst I, Tyler Workman
Auditors: KPMG LLP MC LEAN VA

LOCATIONS

HQ: VIRGINIA PREMIER HEALTH PLAN, INC.
 600 E BROAD ST STE 400, RICHMOND, VA
 232191800
Phone: 804 819-5164
Web: WWW.VIRGINIAPREMIER.COM

HISTORICAL FINANCIALS

Company Type: Private

Income Statement   FYE: December 31

	REVENUE ($ mil.)	NET INCOME ($ mil.)	NET PROFIT MARGIN	EMPLOYEES
12/20*	1,650	71	4.3%	165
06/19	1,730	(51)	—	—
06/18	1,372	(14)	—	—
06/15	969	(0)	—	—
Annual Growth	9.3%	—	—	—

*Fiscal year change

2020 Year-End Financials

Return on assets: 9.6%   Cash ($ mil.): 32
Return on equity: 18.3%
Current ratio: 0.80

VIRTU FINANCIAL LLC

EXECUTIVES

Chm, Vincent Viola
Ceo, Douglas Cifu
Pres-Coo, Chris Concannon
Exec V Pres-Cfo, Joseph Molluso
Cao, Anthony Manganiello
Managing Director, Matthew Levine
Complaince Registration Analys, Renee
 Richardson
Oracle Developer, Huang Eric
Manager I, Electronic Trade Su, Alex Goldstein
Software Engineer, Alexandre Kolomentsev
Hr Coordinator, Celia Denson
Auditors: DELOITTE & TOUCHE LLP NEW
 YOR

LOCATIONS

HQ: VIRTU FINANCIAL LLC
 165 BROADWAY, NEW YORK, NY 100061404
Phone: 212 418-0100
Web: WWW.VIRTU.COM

HISTORICAL FINANCIALS

Company Type: Private

Income Statement   FYE: December 31

	ASSETS ($ mil.)	NET INCOME ($ mil.)	INCOME AS % OF ASSETS	EMPLOYEES
12/14	3,324	190	5.7%	18
12/13	3,963	182	4.6%	—
Annual Growth	(16.1%)	4.3%	—	—

2014 Year-End Financials

Return on assets: 5.7%   Sales ($ mil): 723
Return on equity: 89.5%

VIRTUA-WEST JERSEY HEALTH SYSTEM, INC.

EXECUTIVES

Pres-Ceo, Richard Miller
Chm*, Dennis Flanagan
Cfo*, Robert Segin
Treas*, David Kindlick
SEC*, Edward Cloues
Coordinator, Monica Fiorini
Staff, Beverly Crawford
Coordinator, Leha Anderson
Coordinator, Joanne Sebastiano
Accounting Manager, Sharyn McConnell
Vice President Finance, Jennifer L Romond

LOCATIONS

HQ: VIRTUA-WEST JERSEY HEALTH SYSTEM, INC.
 1000 ATLANTIC AVE, CAMDEN, NJ 081041132
Phone: 856 246-3000
Web: WWW.VIRTUA.ORG

HISTORICAL FINANCIALS

Company Type: Private

Income Statement   FYE: December 31

	REVENUE ($ mil.)	NET INCOME ($ mil.)	NET PROFIT MARGIN	EMPLOYEES
12/19	843	117	13.9%	4,100
12/17	919	207	22.6%	—
12/04	399	29	7.4%	—
12/03	354	6	1.8%	—
Annual Growth	5.6%	20.0%	—	—

2019 Year-End Financials

Return on assets: 5.0%   Cash ($ mil.): 62
Return on equity: 8.2%
Current ratio: 0.20

VIZIO, INC.

VIZIO offers HDTVs and sound bars on its web-store online across dozens of retailers and in thousands of brick and mortar stores throughout the US. The company also offers a portfolio of innovative sound bars that deliver consumers an elevated audio experience as well as Universal Smart-Cast TV remotes and sound bar display remotes. VIZIO sells many of its low-priced electronics through top discount chains including Amazon Best Buy Costco Wholesale Sam's Club Target and Walmart. Thanks to its low prices VIZIO ranked as the #1 American-based sound bar brand.

Operations

The company designs a collection of televisions sound bars and the SmartCast smart TV platform with the consumer's desires in mind and has been rated America's Fastest Growing TV Brand with Quantum Dot and America's Fastest Growing Sound Bar Brand with Dolby Atmos. In addition it offers remote controls and built-in bluetooth for streaming music wirelessly.

The company partners with Inscape and generates more comprehensive TV viewing data and helps companies gain a deeper and more accurate understanding of their audience.

Geographic Reach

Irvine California-based VIZIO sells its products across North America.

Sales and Marketing

VIZIO offers other businesses to showcase contents or applications in Vizio platform. The company markets its products through retailers such as Nebraska Furniture Dell.com Fred Meijer B&H Photo and Meijer among others.

Strategy

The company continuously participates in partnerships to expand its offerings.

In late 2020 VIZIO Inc. announced that customers in the US and Canada can now access the Apple TV app on SmartCast TVs to enjoy Apple TV+ Apple TV channels new and popular movies and personalized and curated recommendations. Earlier that year the company announced that Disney+ has been made available directly on SmartCast expanding entertainment options accessible through the platform.

In January the company teamed up with FOX Deportes as an official sponsor of NFLeros as the network makes the most-watched game in football available to Spanish-speaking audiences.

Company Background

The company was founded by William Wang in 2002 and initially sold its TVs at membership retailers such as Costco Wholesale BJ's Wholesale Club and Sam's Club. It then extended its reach to discount retailers Wal-Mart and Sears.

The TV maker entered the market for smart TVs which are integrated with i nternet functionality when it shipped its first model during the second half of 2011.

VIZIO entered the PC market in mid-2012 with a new line of laptops and desktops starting at about $890. By combining its entertainment know-how with the power of the latest Intel Core processors VIZIO hopes to set a new standard for the Windows experience. The line consists of the VIZIO Thin + Light Notebook and All-in-One PC.

EXECUTIVES

Ceo, William Wang
Cfo, Adam Townsend
Vice-President Engineering, Ken Lowe
Customer Staff, Glenda Evans
Coordinator, Drew Goodell
Director Marketing, Robynne Curry
Director of Information Techno, Trevor Jones
Vice President, Jodie McAfee
Chief Marketing Officer, Lisa Johnstone
Manager, Mitch LI
Director, Victor Shu

LOCATIONS

HQ: VIZIO, INC.
 39 TESLA, IRVINE, CA 926184603
Phone: 855 833-3221
Web: WWW.VIZIO.COM

PRODUCTS/OPERATIONS

Selected Products

Cables and other accessories
Blue-ray disc players
HDTVs
HD home theater systems
Headphones
Internet routers
Personal computers
Tablet computers
Smartphones
Speakers

COMPETITORS

Acer	Lg Electronics
Bose	Lenovo
Dell	Panasonic Corp

Funai Electric
Harman International
Hewlett-packard
 Limited
Koss

Philips Electronics
Pioneer Corporation
Samsung Electronics
Sony
Westinghouse

HISTORICAL FINANCIALS
Company Type: Private

Income Statement				FYE: December 31
	REVENUE ($ mil.)	NET INCOME ($ mil.)	NET PROFIT MARGIN	EMPLOYEES
12/08	2,006	10	0.5%	398
12/07	1,929	7	0.4%	—
12/06	671	1	0.2%	—
12/04	46	0	1.0%	—
Annual Growth	155.8%	115.7%	—	—

2008 Year-End Financials
Return on assets: 3.2%   Cash ($ mil.): 42
Return on equity: 0.5%
Current ratio: 0.90

VNS CHOICE

EXECUTIVES

Prin, Mark Flannery
Clinical Field Manager, Alicia Gagne-Giuffo
Manager, Chantal Louisma
Manager, Christine Wynter
Manager, James Balchunas
Clinical Director Queens, Maryam Gaibi
Manager, Qin Wang
Regional Director, Susan Northover
Medicare Part D Manager, Ramya Devineni
Organizational Man, Anastacio Alaniz
Chief Compliance and Privacy O, Annie Miyazaki
Auditors: KPMG LLP HARTFORD CT

LOCATIONS

HQ: VNS CHOICE
 220 E 42ND ST FL 3, NEW YORK, NY 100175806
Phone: 212 609-7235
Web: WWW.VNSNYCHOICE.ORG

HISTORICAL FINANCIALS
Company Type: Private

Income Statement				FYE: December 31
	REVENUE ($ mil.)	NET INCOME ($ mil.)	NET PROFIT MARGIN	EMPLOYEES
12/19	1,863	55	3.0%	651
12/14	1,388	(72)	—	—
12/13	1,299	(90)	—	—
12/09	419	4	1.0%	—
Annual Growth	16.1%	29.1%	—	—

2019 Year-End Financials
Return on assets: 11.7%   Cash ($ mil.): 124
Return on equity: 165.6%
Current ratio: 7.90

W.S. BADCOCK CORPORATION

EXECUTIVES

Pres, Rob Burnette
Chm, William K Pou Jr
V Pres, Stephen N Bargamin
Evp-Strategic Planning, Henry C Badcock
Evp-Marketing, William Daughtrey
Exec V Pres, Ben M Badcock
Cfo, Magda Farren
Vp-Dealer Retail Oper, Mitchell P Stiles
Manager Information Technology, David
 McClellan
Accounting Staff, Beverly Hicks
Coordinator, Donya-Faye Wix
Auditors: KPMG LLP TAMPA FL

LOCATIONS

HQ: W.S. BADCOCK CORPORATION
 190 NW PHOSPHATE BLVD, MULBERRY, FL
 338602327
Phone: 863 425-4921
Web: WWW.BADCOCK.COM

HISTORICAL FINANCIALS
Company Type: Private

Income Statement				FYE: June 30
	REVENUE ($ mil.)	NET INCOME ($ mil.)	NET PROFIT MARGIN	EMPLOYEES
06/21	901	86	9.6%	1,689
06/19	874	38	4.4%	—
Annual Growth	1.6%	50.8%	—	—

2021 Year-End Financials
Return on assets: 10.7%   Cash ($ mil.): 108
Return on equity: 18.6%
Current ratio: 5.00

WAKE COUNTY PUBLIC SCHOOL SYSTEM

LOCATIONS

HQ: WAKE COUNTY PUBLIC SCHOOL SYSTEM
 5625 DILLARD DR, CARY, NC 275189226
Phone: 919 431-7343
Web: WWW.WCPSS.NET

HISTORICAL FINANCIALS
Company Type: Private

Income Statement				FYE: June 30
	REVENUE ($ mil.)	NET INCOME ($ mil.)	NET PROFIT MARGIN	EMPLOYEES
06/10	1,224	13	1.1%	17,000
06/09	1,425	(7)	—	—
06/08	1,374	(1)	—	—
Annual Growth	(5.6%)	—	—	—

2010 Year-End Financials
Return on assets: 0.5%   Cash ($ mil.): 91
Return on equity: 0.5%
Current ratio: 1.40

WAKE FOREST UNIVERSITY HEALTH SCIENCES

EXECUTIVES

Pres, William B James
Coordinator, Lynda Doomy
Assistant Professor, Jeffrey Willey
Project Coordinator, Caresse Hightower
Professor of Surgery, Alan Farney
Oncologist, George Yacoub
Certified Registered Nurse Ane, Kathryn Phares
Laboratory Compliance Officer, Melanie Haire
Neurologist, Aarti Sarwal
Alumni Events Coordinator, Andrea Garton
Certified Physician Assistant, Daniel Bryan
Auditors: KPMG LLP GREENSBORO NC

LOCATIONS

HQ: WAKE FOREST UNIVERSITY HEALTH SCIENCES
 250 HOSPITAL DR, LEXINGTON, NC 272926792
Phone: 336 248-5161
Web: WWW.WAKEHEALTH.EDU

HISTORICAL FINANCIALS
Company Type: Private

Income Statement				FYE: June 30
	REVENUE ($ mil.)	NET INCOME ($ mil.)	NET PROFIT MARGIN	EMPLOYEES
06/21	1,283	396	30.9%	136
06/18	1,002	43	4.4%	—
Annual Growth	8.6%	108.6%	—	—

2021 Year-End Financials
Return on assets: 19.1%   Cash ($ mil.): 177
Return on equity: 32.6%
Current ratio: 0.70

WAKE, COUNTY OF NORTH CAROLINA

EXECUTIVES

County Mgr, David Ellis
Commissioner*, Betty Lou Ward
Accountant*, William Phillips
Chairman*, Joe Bryan
Vice Chair*, Phil Matthews
Commissioner*, Tony Gurley
Commissioner*, Caroline Sullivan
Commissioner*, James West
Commissioner*, Paul Coble
Attorney, Stephen Sizemore
Customer Staff, Mike Bass
Auditors: ELLIOT DAVIS PLLC RALEIGH N

LOCATIONS

HQ: WAKE, COUNTY OF NORTH CAROLINA
 300 S SALISBURY ST # 1700, RALEIGH, NC
 276011751
Phone: 919 856-6160
Web: WWW.WAKEGOV.COM

Company Type: Private

Income Statement				FYE: June 30
	REVENUE ($ mil.)	NET INCOME ($ mil.)	NET PROFIT MARGIN	EMPLOYEES
06/19	1,537	(93)	—	3,700
06/18	1,377	67	4.9%	—
06/16	1,291	(297)	—	—
06/15	0	0	—	—
Annual Growth	—	—	—	—

2019 Year-End Financials

Return on assets: (-4.8%)   Cash ($ mil.): 654
Return on equity: —
Current ratio: —

WAKEFERN FOOD CORP.

Wakefern Food is the largest retailer-owned co-operative in the nation with approximately 50 member companies who independently own and operate more than 360 supermarkets across the northeastern US. The cooperative offers more than $10 billion in purchasing power and provides unmatched support services including private label brand development advertising support category management engineering services store quality assurance and inspections health and wellness services marketing retail store development pharmacy support services and media and public relations. The members' stores operate under the Fairway Market ShopRite The Fresh Grocer Price Rite Marketplace Gourmet Garage and Dearborn Market banners. Wakefern was founded by eight independent grocers in 1946.

Operations

From supplying virtually everything in center store from general merchandise to beauty aids along with produce frozen foods meats and dairy Wakefern provides outstanding service that enables its wholesale customers to deliver constant value to consumers. In addition to a milk processing and distribution facility and a seafood processing plant wholesale customers can benefit from a wide range of capabilities offered through Wakefern including transportation quality assurance category management merchandising support services technical support and store development.

Readington Farms Wakefern's wholly-owned subsidiary is a high volume multi-product line producer of Bowl & Basket milk and spring water orange juice iced teas and drinks for Wakefern banner brands ShopRite and Price Rite Marketplace. The cooperative's unique brand offerings include Wholesome Pantry Bowl & Basket and Paperbird.

Geographic Reach

Based in Keasbey New Jersey Wakefern's member retailers own and operate more than 360 retail supermarkets in Connecticut Delaware Maryland Massachusetts New Jersey New York Pennsylvania Rhode Island and New Hampshire.

Sales and Marketing

Wakefern has a network of more than 70000 associates. The company markets its brand through its website.

Company Background

In 1946 in an effort to assist struggling independent grocers a sales representative from Del Monte Foods introduced cooperative buying to eight independent grocers from Newark New Jersey. By the end of that year each grocer having invested $1000 Wakefern Food Corp. was officially founded.

HISTORY

Wakefern Food was founded in 1946 by seven New York- and New Jersey-based grocers: Louis Weiss Sam and Al Aidekman Abe Kesselman Dave Fern Sam Garb and Albert Goldberg. The company got its name by taking the first letters of the last names of five of the original founders (Weiss Sam and Al Aidekman Kesselman and Fern). Like many cooperatives the association sought to lower costs by increasing its buying power as a group.

They each put in $1000 and began operating a 5000-sq.-ft. warehouse often putting in double time to keep both their stores and the warehouse running. The shopkeepers' collective buying power proved valuable enabling the grocers to stock many items at the same prices as their larger competitors.

In 1951 Wakefern members began pooling their resources to buy advertising space. A common store name — ShopRite — was chosen and each week co-op members met to decide which items would be sale priced. Within a year membership had grown to over 50. Expansion became a priority and in the mid-1950s co-op members united in small groups to take over failed supermarkets. One such group called the Supermarkets Operating Co. (SOC) was formed in 1956. Within 10 years it had acquired a number of failed stores remodeled them and given them the ShopRite name.

During the late 1950s sales at ShopRite stores slumped after Wakefern decided to buck the supermarket trend of offering trading stamps (which could then be exchanged for gifts) figuring that offering the stamps would ultimately lead to higher food prices. The move initially drove away customers but Wakefern cut grocery prices across the board and sales returned. The company did embrace another supermarket trend: stocking stores with nonfood items.

The co-op was severely shaken in 1966 when SOC merged with General Supermarkets a similar small group within Wakefern becoming Supermarkets General Corp. (SGC). SGC was a powerful entity with 71 supermarkets 10 drugstores six gas stations a wholesale bakery and a discount department store. Many Wakefern members opposed the merger and attempted to block the action with a court order. By 1968 SGC had beefed up its operations to include department store chains as well as its grocery stores. In a move that threatened to break Wakefern SGC broke away from the co-op and its stores were renamed Pathmark.

Wakefern not only weathered the storm it grew under the direction of chairman and CEO Thomas Infusino elected shortly after the split. The co-op focused on asserting its position as a seller of low-priced products. Wakefern developed private-label brands including the ShopRite brand. In the 1980s members began operating larger stores and adding more nonfood items to the ShopRite product mix. With its number of superstores on the rise and facing increased competition from club stores in 1992 Wakefern opened a centralized nonfood distribution center in New Jersey.

In 1995 30-year Wakefern veteran Dean Janeway was elected president of the co-op. The company debuted its ShopRite MasterCard co-branded with New Jersey's Valley National Bank in 1996. The following year the co-op purchased two of its customers' stores in Pennsylvania then threatened to close them when contract talks with the local union deteriorated. In 1998 Wakefern settled the dispute then sold the stores.

The company partnered with Internet bidding site Priceline in 1999 offering customers an opportunity to bid on groceries and then pick them up at ShopRite stores. Big V Wakefern's biggest customer filed for Chapter 11 bankruptcy protection in 2000 and said it was ending its distribution agreement with the co-op. In July 2002 however Wakefern's ShopRite Supermarkets subsidiary acquired all of Big V's assets for approximately $185 million in cash and assumed liabilities.

Infusino retired in May 2005 after 35 years with Wakefern Food. He was succeeded by former vice chairman Joseph Colalillo. The cooperative added to its footprint in 2007 when it acquired about 10 underperforming retail locations from Stop & Shop. The stores located mostly in South Jersey were rebranded under the ShopRite banner.

EXECUTIVES

Ceo-Chm, Joseph Colalillo
Pres, Joseph Sheridan
Cfo, Douglas Wille
Sr V Pres, Chris Lane
Sr V Pres, Bill Mayo
V Pres, James J Sumas
V Pres, Larri Wolfson
Treas, Lawrence Inserra Jr
Asst Treas, Richard Saker
SEC, Irving Glass
Asst SEC, Joel Perlmutter
Auditors: KPMG LLP SHORT HILLS NJ

LOCATIONS

HQ: WAKEFERN FOOD CORP.
5000 RIVERSIDE DR, KEASBEY, NJ 088321209
Phone: 908 527-3300
Web: WWW.WAKEFERN.COM

COMPETITORS

A&p	Iga
Acme Markets	Krasdale Foods
Bozzuto's	Supervalu
C&s Wholesale	Stop & Shop
Cvs	Wal-mart
Hannaford Bros.	Wawa Inc.

HISTORICAL FINANCIALS

Company Type: Private

Income Statement				FYE: September 27
	REVENUE ($ mil.)	NET INCOME ($ mil.)	NET PROFIT MARGIN	EMPLOYEES
09/14	11,871	5	0.0%	3,500
09/13	11,455	0	0.0%	—
09/12	11,010	5	0.0%	—
Annual Growth	3.8%	(0.0%)	—	—

2014 Year-End Financials

Return on assets: 0.3%   Cash ($ mil.): 128
Return on equity: 2.7%
Current ratio: 0.80

WALSH CONSTRUCTION COMPANY

EXECUTIVES

Chb-Ceo, Matthew M Walsh
Pres*, Daniel J Walsh
Manager, Brian R Walsh
Project Administrator, Diane Mitchell
Senior Project Manager, Steve Schneider
Auditors: WOLF & COMPANY LLP OAKBROOK

LOCATIONS

HQ: WALSH CONSTRUCTION COMPANY
929 W ADAMS ST, CHICAGO, IL 606073021
Phone: 312 563-5400
Web: WWW.WALSHCONSTRUCTION.COM

HISTORICAL FINANCIALS

Company Type: Private

Income Statement				FYE: December 31
	REVENUE ($ mil.)	NET INCOME ($ mil.)	NET PROFIT MARGIN	EMPLOYEES
12/10	1,627	35	2.2%	3,000
12/09	1,711	56	3.3%	—
12/08	1,847	68	3.7%	—
Annual Growth	(6.2%)	(27.7%)	—	—

2010 Year-End Financials

Return on assets: 4.7%   Cash ($ mil.): 281
Return on equity: 14.1%
Current ratio: 1.50

WALTON CONSTRUCTION - A CORE COMPANY, LLC

EXECUTIVES

Mng MBR, James K Jacobs
Executive Vice President, Brad Roberts
Chief Administrative Officer, Tom Budde

LOCATIONS

HQ: WALTON CONSTRUCTION - A CORE COMPANY, LLC
2 COMMERCE CT, NEW ORLEANS, LA 701233225
Phone: 504 733-2212
Web: WWW.CORECONSTRUCTION.COM

HISTORICAL FINANCIALS

Company Type: Private

Income Statement				FYE: December 31
	REVENUE ($ mil.)	NET INCOME ($ mil.)	NET PROFIT MARGIN	EMPLOYEES
12/08	695	0	—	700
12/07	626	0	—	—
12/06	0	0	—	—
12/05	0	0	—	—
Annual Growth	—	—	—	—

2008 Year-End Financials

Return on assets: 15.8%   Cash ($ mil.): 4
Return on equity: —
Current ratio: 1.20

WALTON FAMILY FOUNDATION INC

EXECUTIVES

Exec Dir, Buddy Philpot
Coordinator, Karis Butler
Computer Support Technician, Josh Senty

Senior Program Officer, Cathy N Lund
Training Manager, Janet Post
Human Resources Coordinator, Leigh Oliver
Program Officer, Yoo Cheong
Senior Program Officer, Sandy Nickerson
Director, Barry Gold
Program Officer, Delvon Worthy
Communications Officer, Jessica Young

LOCATIONS

HQ: WALTON FAMILY FOUNDATION INC
125 W CENTRAL AVE RM 218, BENTONVILLE, AR 727125248
Phone: 479 273-5605
Web: WWW.WALTONFAMILYFOUNDATION.ORG

HISTORICAL FINANCIALS

Company Type: Private

Income Statement				FYE: December 31
	REVENUE ($ mil.)	NET INCOME ($ mil.)	NET PROFIT MARGIN	EMPLOYEES
12/09	740	368	49.8%	7
12/08	421	244	58.0%	—
12/00	244	190	78.0%	—
Annual Growth	13.1%	7.6%	—	—

2009 Year-End Financials

Return on assets: 20.2%   Cash ($ mil.): 24
Return on equity: 20.2%
Current ratio: —

WASHINGTON HEALTHCARE PHYSICIANS, MARY

EXECUTIVES

Ceo, Fred M Ryan III
Chief Financial Officer*, Sean T Barden
Chief Operating Officer*, Walter J Kiwall
Health Professional, April Dillow
Senior Vice President of Prope, Marie Fredrick
Evice President Community Affa, Xavier Richardson
Compliance Specialist, Amy McClain
Social Worker, Margaret Kenerly
Supervisor, Donna Saunders
Director, Care Center, Leaanne Wilkinson
Rn Specialty Coordinator, Tricia Boring
Auditors: ARNETT CARBIS TOOTHMAN NEW CA

LOCATIONS

HQ: WASHINGTON HEALTHCARE PHYSICIANS, MARY
2300 FALL HILL AVE # 101, FREDERICKSBURG, VA 224013342
Phone: 540 741-1100
Web: WWW.MARYWASHINGTONHEALTHCARE.COM

HISTORICAL FINANCIALS

Company Type: Private

Income Statement				FYE: December 31
	REVENUE ($ mil.)	NET INCOME ($ mil.)	NET PROFIT MARGIN	EMPLOYEES
12/19*	734	28	3.9%	883
06/18	328	1	0.4%	—
12/16	610	30	5.0%	—
12/15	584	17	3.1%	—
Annual Growth	5.9%	12.6%	—	—
*Fiscal year change

2019 Year-End Financials

Return on assets: 6.1%   Cash ($ mil.): —
Return on equity: 17.7%
Current ratio: 0.50

WASHINGTON HOSPITAL CENTER CORPORATION

Washington Hospital Center (doing business as MedStar Washington Hospital Center) may be the official hospital of the Washington Redskins but you don't have to be a professional football player to make use of the facility's services. The hospital at the heart of the MedStar Health system serves some 500000 patients living in and around the nation's capital each year. Washington Hospital Center has 912 beds and includes specialized care centers for cancer cardiovascular conditions and stroke. Other offerings include organ transplantation a regional burn treatment center and emergency air transportation. MedStar Washington also conducts clinical research and offers educational residency and fellowship programs.

Operations

MedStar Washington has about 1350 doctors and dentists on staff; many of whom are involved in Washington Hospital Center's 520 clinical research studies. The hospital is affiliated with the medical schools of The George Washington University Georgetown University Johns Hopkins and several other regional educational institutions. Its Cardiac Ventricular Assist Device program is accredited by The Joint Commission.

The hospital is also home to MedSTAR one of the country's top shock-trauma and medevac programs and also operates the region's only adult burn center.

MedStar Washington has some 390000 outpatient and 37000 inpatient visits each year. It also provides care for some 3500 births and some 87000 emergency department visits.

Strategy

Company Background

Washington Hospital Center was created through the merger of three regional hospitals: Emergency Garfield and Episcopal Eye Ear and Throat. The actual idea of the Hospital Center was conceived in 1943 but it took nearly 15 years for funding planning and construction to be completed.

EXECUTIVES

Ceo, Kent Samet
Infectious Diseases, Maria Elena Ruiz
Cardiovascular Specialist, Edward V Platia
Internal Medicine Practitioner, Shannon D Sullivan

Health Professional, Raymond K Smith Jr
Internal Medicine Practitioner, Deborah A Topol
Facilities Specialist, Mike Gangi
Doctor, Stephanie Bruce
Obstetrics, Lauren F Damle
Radiation Oncologist, Marc E Boisvert
Chief of Orthopedic Surgery, James Tozzi

LOCATIONS

HQ: WASHINGTON HOSPITAL CENTER
CORPORATION
110 IRVING ST NW, WASHINGTON, DC 200103017
Phone: 855 546-1686
Web: WWW.MEDSTARWASHINGTON.ORG

COMPETITORS

Adventist Healthcare	Hsc Pediatric Center
Bon Secours Health	Inova
Children's National	Mary Washington
Medical Center	Healthcare
Dimensions Healthcare	Sibley Memorial
Doctors Community	Hospital
Hospital	Suburban Hospital

HISTORICAL FINANCIALS

Company Type: Private

Income Statement   FYE: June 30

	REVENUE ($ mil.)	NET INCOME ($ mil.)	NET PROFIT MARGIN	EMPLOYEES
06/16	1,166	36	3.1%	5,637
06/15	1,121	23	2.1%	—
06/14	1,107	22	2.1%	—
06/08	1,028	14	1.4%	—
Annual Growth	1.6%	12.3%	—	—

2016 Year-End Financials

Return on assets: 6.6%   Cash ($ mil.): —
Return on equity: 10.6%
Current ratio: 1.20

WASHINGTON SUBURBAN SANITARY COMMISSION (INC)

Washington Suburban Sanitary Commission (WSSC) provides water and wastewater services in Maryland's Montgomery and Prince George's counties just outside the nation's capital. WSSC serves around 474000 customers representing 2 million residents in an area of about 1000 square miles. The agency draws water from the Potomac and Patuxent rivers and maintains three reservoirs. The commission also operates two water filtration plants six wastewater treatment plants and some 11000 miles of sewer and water main lines including a network of nearly 5600 miles of fresh water pipeline and over 5400 miles of sewer pipeline. WSSC was established in 1918.

EXECUTIVES

Coo, Michael Crean
Chief Administrative Officer*, Wayne Fallin
Treasurer*, Mary J Kirby
Internal Auditing Manager*, Mel Schwartz
General Counsel*, Nathan Greenbaum
Gen Mgr*, Jerry N Johnson
Chief Technology Officer, Dervel Reed
Engineer, Gary Grey

Engineer, Hala Flores
Chief of Staff, Jackie Vincent
Watershed Environmental Superv, Jasper Sirk
Auditors: BCA WATSON RICE LLP
WASHINGTO

LOCATIONS

HQ: WASHINGTON SUBURBAN SANITARY
COMMISSION (INC)
14501 SWEITZER LN, LAUREL, MD 207075901
Phone: 301 206-8000
Web: WWW.WSSCWATER.COM

HISTORICAL FINANCIALS

Company Type: Private

Income Statement   FYE: June 30

	REVENUE ($ mil.)	NET INCOME ($ mil.)	NET PROFIT MARGIN	EMPLOYEES
06/21	749	49	6.6%	2,000
06/20	749	23	3.2%	—
06/19	742	139	18.8%	—
06/18	725	119	16.5%	—
Annual Growth	1.1%	(25.7%)	—	—

2021 Year-End Financials

Return on assets: 0.5%   Cash ($ mil.): 83
Return on equity: 1.0%
Current ratio: 0.60

WASHOE COUNTY SCHOOL DISTRICT

EXECUTIVES

Spdt, Traci Davis
Payroll Staff, Barbara Hawkins
Coordinator, Diana Cox
Coordinator, Josephine J Johnson
Coordinator, Lynette Larson
Coordinator, Marianne Campbell
Coordinator, Mary Green
Information Specialist, Kelli Pennington
Staff, Mariah Evans
Coordinator, Trudy Nunn
School Nurse, Erin Dehahn

LOCATIONS

HQ: WASHOE COUNTY SCHOOL DISTRICT
425 E 9TH ST, RENO, NV 895122800
Phone: 775 348-0200
Web: WWW.WASHOESCHOOLS.NET

HISTORICAL FINANCIALS

Company Type: Private

Income Statement   FYE: June 30

	REVENUE ($ mil.)	NET INCOME ($ mil.)	NET PROFIT MARGIN	EMPLOYEES
06/19	713	(95)	—	7,000
06/18	683	190	27.8%	—
06/17	640	57	8.9%	—
06/08	578	38	6.7%	—
Annual Growth	1.9%	—	—	—

WAUKESHA MEMORIAL HOSPITAL, INC.

Waukesha Memorial Hospital is a 300-bed teaching hospital that provides health care services for Wisconsin's Milwaukee Waukesha and Dane counties. With about 670 physicians representing several specialties and 2700 employees the hospital operates centers for excellence focused on cardiology oncology neurology women's health and orthopedics as well as emergency neonatal and family practice services. Additionally Waukesha Memorial Hospital conducts a physician residency program. Established in 1914 the medical facility is a subsidiary of not-for-profit ProHealth Care a medical network that serves southeastern Wisconsin with acute care and specialty health services.

Operations

ProHealth Care runs Waukesha Memorial Hospital alongside its other critical-care hospital Oconomowoc Memorial Hospital. As part of its operations the hospital boasts a neuroscience center orthopedic center regional cancer center regional heart and vascular center and a women's center. Its newborn intensive care unit and its emergency department which averages more than 39000 visits are both Level III.

Geographic Reach

Despite its name Waukesha Memorial Hospital serves the residents of Milwaukee and Dane counties along with Waukesha County.

EXECUTIVES

Pres, John Robertstad
Cfo*, Robert W Mlynarek
Executive of Information Techn, Bill Miller
Executive of Information Techn, Kasey Valkoun
Coordinator, Renee McHale
Pathologist, Steven Dubner
Internal Medicine Practitioner, Brad Malehorn
Osteopathic Physician, Nancy L Ryburn
Manager Emergency Department, Alan Johnson
Vice President of Revenue Cycl, Curtis Glaunert
Director, Gary Beyer
Auditors: PLANTE & MORAN PLLC GRAND RA

LOCATIONS

HQ: WAUKESHA MEMORIAL HOSPITAL, INC.
725 AMERICAN AVE, WAUKESHA, WI 531885099
Phone: 262 928-1000
Web: WWW.PROHEALTHCARE.ORG

PRODUCTS/OPERATIONS

Selected Services

Birthing

                             Blood / Ly

Bones Joints & Muscles
Brain & Nerves
Cancer
Cancer Second Opinion
Children's Health
CyberKnife
Diabetes
Diagnostic Services
Digestive
Ear Nose & Throat
Emergency Services/Urgent Care
Eyes & Vision
General Surgery
Genetics
Heart & Vascular
Infections
Integrative Medicine
Kidneys & Urinary System

Lungs / Br

Men's Health
Mental Health
Nutrition
Orthopedic
Pain
Rehabilitation Services
Senior's Health
Sleep
Stroke
Wellness & Lifestyle
Women's Health

COMPETITORS

Children's Hospital And Health System
Columbia St. Mary's
Froedtert Hospital
Hospital Sisters Health System
Ministry Health Care
Swedishamerican Health System
University Of Wisconsin Hospital And Clinics

HISTORICAL FINANCIALS

Company Type: Private

Income Statement   FYE: September 30

	REVENUE ($ mil.)	NET INCOME ($ mil.)	NET PROFIT MARGIN	EMPLOYEES
09/19	543	13	2.5%	2,071
09/18	520	27	5.3%	—
09/17	470	59	12.6%	—
09/16	457	37	8.3%	—
Annual Growth	5.9%	(29.2%)	—	—

2019 Year-End Financials

Return on assets: 2.5%   Cash ($ mil.): 6
Return on equity: 8.2%
Current ratio: 1.50

WAYNE STATE UNIVERSITY

Wayne State University is a public university with an annual enrollment of nearly 27000 students and a student-to-teacher ratio of 16:1. It offers more than 350 bachelor's master's and doctoral degree programs as well as certificate specialist and professional programs through about a dozen colleges and schools. Located in midtown Detroit WSU traces its heritage back to 1868 with the founding of the Detroit Medical College now part of its School of Medicine. Prominent alumni include US Congressman John Conyers radio DJ Casey Kasem and actor Tom Sizemore.

Operations

WSU's areas of study include accountancy finance management education engineering arts as well as nursing pharmacy and social work. It also offers online studies for theatre and dance and information management.

A notable indicator of the research program's success is its classification as a doctoral university highest research activity by the Carnegie Classification of Higher Education. WSU also ranks among the top public institutions for annual research expenditures by the National Science Foundation.

Geographic Reach

WSU's 200-acre campus includes more than 95 academic research and residential buildings. The university also has five satellite campuses around Detroit (and one in Jackson) and six extension centers offering educational programs across southeastern Michigan.

It has affiliations with more than 100 institutions globally and offers study abroad programs in about 15 countries on five continents.

The school hosts students from every US state and 75 countries.

EXECUTIVES

Pres, Roy Wilson
Int Chm*, Samuel Johnson
Exec-SEC*, Laurie Scarborough
Avp-Chro*, Debra F Williams
Exec Dean*, Karen Mourtzikos
Provost, Nancy Barrett
Wsu Foundation, Susan Burns
Assoc V Pres-Dev't & Alum Aff, David W Ripple
Sam Poc, Lashonda Cooley
Information Specialist, Kashmira Mehta
Assistant Professor, Eva Waineo
Auditors: PLANTE & MORAN PLLC EAST LANS

LOCATIONS

HQ: WAYNE STATE UNIVERSITY
6135 WOODWARD AVE, DETROIT, MI 482023502
Phone: 313 577-1771
Web: WWW.WAYNE.EDU

PRODUCTS/OPERATIONS

Selected Colleges and Schools
College of Education
College of Engineering
College of Fine Performing and Communication Arts
College of Liberal Arts and Sciences
College of Nursing
Eugene Applebaum College of Pharmacy and Health Sciences
Irvin D. Reid Honors College
Law School
School of Business Administration
School of Library and Information Science
School of Medicine
School of Social Work
The Graduate School

HISTORICAL FINANCIALS

Company Type: Private

Income Statement   FYE: September 30

	REVENUE ($ mil.)	NET INCOME ($ mil.)	NET PROFIT MARGIN	EMPLOYEES
09/17	640	46	7.2%	8,500
09/11	520	(15)	—	—
09/05	445	37	8.4%	—
09/04	418	(3)	—	—
Annual Growth	3.3%	—	—	—

2017 Year-End Financials

Return on assets: 3.2%   Cash ($ mil.): 355
Return on equity: 7.0%
Current ratio: 1.90

WELCH FOODS INC., A COOPERATIVE

Welch is a co-op owned by farming families across the country who bring their best to every harvest. A company owned by more than 700 farmer families Welch produces the Welch's brand grape and white grape juices. Its beverage line includes sparkling juices and cocktails. Welch supplies fresh grapes and snacks as well as preserved offerings (jellies jams and spreads). The company was founded in 1849 by Ephraim Bull when he grows the first Concord grape on his farm in Massachusetts.

Operations

Welch Foods offers juices jams jellies spreads and cocktails primarily made from grapes It also offers snacks from fresh fruit slushies to gummy snacks to frozen mixed fruit.

Geographic Reach

Massachusetts-based Welch Foods has vineyards in Cincinnati Ohio; Grandview Washington; Lawton Michigan; North East Pennsylvania; Rogers Arizona; and Westfield New York.

Financial Performance

National Grape Cooperative and Welch Foods's sales grew to $608.5 million in 2014. Volume grew 4% during the year with its Bottled 100% Juice product leading the way with 11% growth though all core product categories showed market share and volume growth. Spread sales grew by 7% during the year while refrigerated juices grew by 8%.

The cooperative's net proceeds jumped significantly to $84 million in FY2014 the second highest level in its history according to the company.

Company Background

In 1869 Dr. Thomas Bramwell Welch pasteurized Concord grape juice to create a non-alcoholic alternative to wine for his church. The beverage was a hit at the World's Fair in Chicago in 1893 and by 1923 Concord grape jelly was introduced.

The farmers who grew grapes for Welch's took ownership of the company and began operating it as a co-op in 1952.

EXECUTIVES

Pres-Ceo, Trevor Bynum
V Pres, Delisle Flynn
V Pres, Vivian Tseng
V Pres Hr, Lisa Flynn
V Pres International, Wayne D Lutomski
V Pres - Cfo, Michael Perda
Gen Counsel-Vp Legal, Matt Aufman
Cfo, Tom Dixon
MO, David Eisen
V Pres, Randy C Papdellis
Information Specialist, Chris Camelio

LOCATIONS

HQ: WELCH FOODS INC., A COOPERATIVE
575 VIRGINIA RD, CONCORD, MA 017422761
Phone: 978 371-1000
Web: WWW.WELCHS.COM

PRODUCTS/OPERATIONS

Selected Brands and Products

BAMA
Jams jellies and preserves
Peanut butter
Welch
Bottled and canned juices
Dried fruit
Fresh table grapes
Frozen juices
Fruit juice bars
Jams jellies and preserves
Pourable concentrated juices
Refrigerated juices
Single-serve juices

COMPETITORS

Chiquita Brands   Old Orchard
Citrus World   Silver Springs
Coca-cola   Smucker
Coloma Frozen Foods   Snapple
Dole Food   South Beach Beverage
Fresh Del Monte   Stapleton-spence
  Produce   Packing
Great Western Juice   Sun-maid

Lion Raisins
Monster Beverage
Mott's
Naked Juice
National Raisin
Ocean Spray
Odwalla

Sunny Delight
Sunview Vineyards
Tree Top
Tropicana
Unilever Nv
Wet Planet Beverages

HISTORICAL FINANCIALS

Company Type: Private

Income Statement				FYE: August 31
	REVENUE ($ mil.)	NET INCOME ($ mil.)	NET PROFIT MARGIN	EMPLOYEES
08/16	600	83	14.0%	1,000
08/15	609	81	13.3%	—
08/14	609	76	12.6%	—
08/13	608	65	10.7%	—
Annual Growth	(0.5%)	8.8%	—	—

2016 Year-End Financials

Return on assets: 20.6%   Cash ($ mil.): 7
Return on equity: 233.2%
Current ratio: 1.40

WELLMONT HEALTH SYSTEM

At Wellmont Health System wellness is paramount. Wellmont Health System provides general and advanced medical-surgical care to residents of northeastern Tennessee and southwestern Virginia. The health system consists of about a dozen owned and affiliated hospitals that collectively have more than 1000 licensed beds. One of its facilities is a rehabilitation hospital operated in partnership with HealthSouth. The system's Holston Valley Medical Center features a level I trauma center and a level III neonatal intensive care unit (NICU). Wellmont also operates numerous ancillary facilities including an assisted living center a mental health clinic home health care and hospice agencies and outpatient centers.

Operations

Today Wellmont is one of the region's largest employers with a staff of more than 6500 medical professionals. Nearly 600 physicians deliver care at Wellmont's facilities that include eight hospitals in Tennessee and Virginia. Other facilities include an outpatient surgery center a child development center a cancer center urgent care centers and a health network of physicians that include occupational health providers. The hospital also offers urgent care transportation with its Wellmont One Air Transport.

Wellmont is the only health system in Tennessee to offer two major trauma centers (at Holston Valley Medical Center in Kingsport and Bristol Regional Medical Center in Bristol).

Sales and Marketing

Medicare payments accounted for nearly 85% of Wellmont's net patient revenue in fiscal 2013 (ended June); Medicaid and TennCare (Tennessee's state Medicaid program) each accounted for nearly 10%.

Financial Performance

Revenue increased 1% to $798 million in fiscal 2013 (ended June) on higher net patient revenue. However patient volumes were mixed: Some categories declined while others increased. For example emergency department visits dropped 7%

as more patients chose to visit the system's more affordable urgent care centers.

Net income rose significantly that year increasing 79% to $47 million. This was due to a change in net unrealized gains on investments and a change in the funded status of benefit plans. Cash flow from operations fell 5% to $74 million.

Strategy

Wellmont has expanded by opening new outpatient facilities including a new physical therapy clinic in 2013 and by acquiring existing medical facilities. For example in 2015 it agreed to buy out Adventist Health in their partnership owning Takoma Regional Hospital in Tennessee. The system also expands its service territory by partnering with other area care providers.

In 2014 the company migrated to a new electronic medical records (EMR) system replacing its four existing EHR platforms.

Mergers and Acquisitions

In 2015 Wellmont announced plans to merge with a neighboring health system Mountain States Health Alliance. By combining operations the two systems hope to better provide care for communities in northeast Tennessee as well as Virginia Kentucky and North Carolina. The states of Tennessee and Virginia have to approve the transaction.

Company Background

Founded in 1996 Wellmont has grown over the years primarily through acquisitions including Lee Regional Medical Center Mountain View Regional Medical Center and Takoma Regional Hospital (through a partnership with Adventist Health).

EXECUTIVES

Pres-Ceo, Denny Denarvaez
Chb*, Roger K Mowen Jr
Cfo*, Beth Ward
Cmo*, Dale Sargent
Prin*, Richard Salluzzo
Cfo*, Alice Pope
Coo*, Tracey Moffatt
President*, Bart Hove
Pres Holston Valley Med Ctr, Blaine Douglas
Pres Mtn View Reg Med, David Brash
Pres Takoma Reg Hosp, Daniel Wolcott
Auditors: KPMG LLP NASHVILLE TENNESSEE

LOCATIONS

HQ: WELLMONT HEALTH SYSTEM
1905 AMERICAN WAY, KINGSPORT, TN 376605882
Phone: 423 230-8200
Web: WWW.BALLADHEALTH.ORG

PRODUCTS/OPERATIONS

Selected Facilities

Bristol Regional Medical Center (Bristol Tennessee)
Hancock County Hospital (Sneedville Tennessee)
Hawkins County Memorial Hospital (Rogersville Tennessee)
HealthSouth Rehabilitation Hospital of Kingsport (HealthSouth partnership; Kingsport Tennessee)
Holston Valley Medical Center (Kingsport Tennessee)
Lee Regional Medical Center (Pennington Gap Virginia)
Lonesome Pine Hospital (Big Stone Gap Virginia)
Mountain View Regional Medical Center (Norton Virginia)
Takoma Regional Hospital (Greeneville Tennessee)

Selected Services

Cancer Care
Children
Diabetes
Emergency and Trauma
Family Medicine
Hearing Services
Heart Care
Home Care
Hospice
Hospitalists

Marsh Regional Blood Center
Neurology
Occupational Medicine
Orthopedics
Palliative Care
Psychiatry
Radiology
Rehabilitation and Therapy
Sleep Medicine
Stroke Care
Surgical Services
Weight Loss
Women's Health

COMPETITORS

Ascension Health
Baptist Memorial Health Care
Community Health Systems
Cookeville Regional Medical Center

Kindred Healthcare
Lifepoint Health
Mountain States Health
Tenet Healthcare

HISTORICAL FINANCIALS

Company Type: Private

Income Statement				FYE: June 30
	REVENUE ($ mil.)	NET INCOME ($ mil.)	NET PROFIT MARGIN	EMPLOYEES
06/17	908	53	5.9%	6,114
06/10	622	33	5.5%	—
06/09	2	0	—	—
Annual Growth	104.4%	—	—	—

2017 Year-End Financials

Return on assets: 4.5%   Cash ($ mil.): 60
Return on equity: 8.8%
Current ratio: 1.60

WELLS REAL ESTATE INVESTMENT TRUST II

Auditors: DELOITTE & TOUCHE LLP ATLANT

LOCATIONS

HQ: WELLS REAL ESTATE INVESTMENT TRUST II
1 GLENLAKE PKWY STE 1200, ATLANTA, GA 303287267
Phone: 404 465-2200
Web: WWW.WELLSREITII.COM

HISTORICAL FINANCIALS

Company Type: Private

Income Statement				FYE: December 31
	REVENUE ($ mil.)	NET INCOME ($ mil.)	NET PROFIT MARGIN	EMPLOYEES
12/12	576	48	8.3%	9
12/11	613	56	9.2%	—
Annual Growth	(5.9%)	(15.2%)	—	—

2012 Year-End Financials

Return on assets: —   Cash ($ mil.): —
Return on equity: 8.3%
Current ratio: 0.10

WELLSPAN MEDICAL GROUP (INC)

EXECUTIVES

Ceo, Tom McGann
Controller, Steffney Calp
Administrator, Laurie Brown
Auditors: ERNEST & YOUNG LLP BALTIMORE

LOCATIONS

HQ: WELLSPAN MEDICAL GROUP (INC)
140 N DUKE ST, YORK, PA 174011170
Phone: 717 851-6515
Web: WWW.WELLSPAN.ORG

HISTORICAL FINANCIALS

Company Type: Private

Income Statement   FYE: June 30

	REVENUE ($ mil.)	NET INCOME ($ mil.)	NET PROFIT MARGIN	EMPLOYEES
06/20	567	(13)	—	709
06/16	375	(43)	—	—
06/15	336	(36)	—	—
06/14	251	(25)	—	—
Annual Growth	14.5%	—	—	—

2020 Year-End Financials

Return on assets: (-10.3%)   Cash ($ mil.): —
Return on equity: (-53.3%)
Current ratio: 0.70

WESCO AIRCRAFT HOLDINGS, INC.

Incora formerly Wesco Aircraft and Pattonair is a leading provider of comprehensive supply chain management services to the global aerospace and other industries. Beginning with a strong foundation in aerospace and defense Incora also utilizes its supply chain expertise to serve industrial manufacturing marine pharmaceuticals and beyond. Incora incorporates itself into customers' businesses managing all aspects of supply chain from procurement and inventory management to logistics and on-site customer services. In 2020 Wesco Aircraft was acquired by an affiliate of private equity firm Platinum Equity Advisors LLC and at closing combined with Pattonair an existing portfolio company of Platinum Equity Advisors LLC.

Operations

Incora divides its operations across five main product lines: hardware chemicals electronic components tooling other machined & fabricated parts and other products. The company sources its inventory from over 7000 suppliers.

Geographic Reach

The company is headquartered in Valencia California with a global footprint that includes some 70 locations in more than 15 countries.

Sales and Marketing

Incora markets its products and services to a diverse range of industries such as aerospace automotive pharmaceuticals deference and more. The company also sales its products through online ecommerce store.

Mergers and Acquisitions

In 2020 Wesco Aircraft and Pattonair announced the new merged company's official brand name Incora and unveiled its logo. The company is one of the world's leading providers of comprehensive supply chain management services to the aerospace defense and other industries. Incora reflects the company's commitment to its customers' mission-critical work ? both in choice of name and brand identity. With a solid foundation in the aerospace and defense market Incora now serves industrial manufacturing marine pharmaceuticals and beyond. Incora manages all aspects of supply chain from procurement and inventory management to logistics and on-site customer services.

EXECUTIVES

Ceo, David Coleal
Cco*, Declan Grant
Pres-Coo*, Wayne Hollinshead
Cfo*, Ray Carney
Chief People & Diversity Offic*, Kevin Erickson
Cco*, Dave Fawcett
CIO*, Ryan Worobel
Chief Legal Officer*, Dawn Landry
Sales Team Member, Yanelys Varona
Senior Information Technology, Yen Liu
Director of Master Data Admini, Ada Sepulveda
Auditors: PRICEWATERHOUSECOOPERS LLP LO

LOCATIONS

HQ: WESCO AIRCRAFT HOLDINGS, INC.
2601 MEACHAM BLVD STE 400, FORT WORTH, TX 761374213
Phone: 817 284-4449
Web: WWW.INCORA.COM

2016 Sales

	$ mil.	% of total
North America	1,185	80
Rest of World	292	20
Total	1,477	100

2016 Sales

	$ mil.	% of total
United States of America	1,087	74
United Kingdom	195	13
Other foreign counties	194	13
Total	1,477	100

PRODUCTS/OPERATIONS

2016 Sales

	$ mil.	% of total
Hardware	711	48
Chemicals	600	41
Electronic components	105	7
Bearings	34	2
Machined parts and other	26	2
Total	1,477	100

PRODUCTS

HARDWARE
Blind fasteners
Bolts and screws
Clamps
Hi lok pins and collars
Hydraulic fittings
Inserts
Lockbolts and collars
Nuts
Panel fasteners
Rivets
Springs
Valves
Washers
CHEMICALS
Adhesives
Cleaners and cleaning solvents
Coolants and metalworking fluids
Industrial gases
Lubricants
Oil and grease

Paints and coatings
Sealants and tapes
ELECTRONIC COMPONENTS
Circuit breakers
Connectors
Interconnect accessories
Lighted products
Relays
Switches
Wire and cable
BEARINGS
Airframe control bearings
Ball bearing
Bushings
Needle roller bearings
Precision bearings
Rod ends
Spherical bearings
OTHER PRODUCTS
Brackets
Installation tooling
Milled parts
Shims
Stampings
Turned parts
Welded assemblies

COMPETITORS

Aar Corp.
Align Aerospace
Aviall Services
First Aviation
Gecas Asset Management Services
Kellstrom Industries

HISTORICAL FINANCIALS

Company Type: Private

Income Statement   FYE: September 30

	REVENUE ($ mil.)	NET INCOME ($ mil.)	NET PROFIT MARGIN	EMPLOYEES
09/19	1,696	21	1.3%	3,527
09/18	1,570	32	2.1%	—
09/17	1,429	(237)	—	—
09/16	1,477	91	6.2%	—
Annual Growth	4.7%	(38.4%)	—	—

2019 Year-End Financials

Return on assets: 1.2%   Cash ($ mil.): 38
Return on equity: 3.0%
Current ratio: 3.60

WESLEY MEDICAL CENTER, LLC

EXECUTIVES

Ceo, Bill Voloch
Prin*, Carl Fitch
Cfo*, Matt Leary
Coordinator, Diana Lippoldt
Director, David Miller
Coordinator, Stacey Wright
Internal Medicine Practitioner, Bob Ragan
Director of Risk Management, Joey Dean
Consultant, Kent Potter
Coordinator, Teena Johnston
Pediatrician, Stephanie Binder

LOCATIONS

HQ: WESLEY MEDICAL CENTER, LLC
550 N HILLSIDE ST, WICHITA, KS 672144976
Phone: 316 962-2000
Web: WWW.WESLEYMC.COM

HISTORICAL FINANCIALS

Company Type: Private

Income Statement   FYE: December 31

	REVENUE ($ mil.)	NET INCOME ($ mil.)	NET PROFIT MARGIN	EMPLOYEES
12/17	608	80	13.3%	40
12/16	555	56	10.3%	—
12/15	545	60	11.1%	—
12/14	520	88	17.0%	—
Annual Growth	5.3%	(3.0%)		

WEST PENN POWER COMPANY

EXECUTIVES

Distribution Senior Engineer, Randy Cochenour

LOCATIONS

HQ: WEST PENN POWER COMPANY
76 S MAIN ST BSMT, AKRON, OH 443081817
Phone: 800 686-0021
Web: WWW.FIRSTENERGYCORP.COM

HISTORICAL FINANCIALS

Company Type: Private

Income Statement   FYE: December 31

	REVENUE ($ mil.)	NET INCOME ($ mil.)	NET PROFIT MARGIN	EMPLOYEES
12/17	1,009	110	11.0%	11
12/16	1,020	116	11.4%	—
Annual Growth	(1.1%)	(5.0%)	—	—

WEST VIRGINA UNIVERSITY HOSPITALS, INC.

West Virginia University Hospitals (WVUH) has West Virginians covered. The health care system's 530-bed main campus includes the Ruby Memorial Hospital the WVU Children's Hospital and the behavioral health Chestnut Ridge Center as well as outpatient care centers. Other services include centers for eye and dental care cancer treatment and family medicine. WVUH's facilities serve as the primary teaching locations for the West Virginia University's health professions schools. Cheat Lake Physicians is the physicians group associated with the health system. WVUH is a member of the West Virginia United Health System.

Strategy

To increase its capacity for patient services WVUH launched a $230 million project to build a new tower addition at its main Ruby Memorial Hospital facility in 2012. The project will add about 115 general inpatient beds.

WVUH is also working to expand its community outreach capabilities and lower the cost of inpatient care through technology initiatives. The health system is adding a number of tele-health services including psychiatry and stroke programs that allow patients to communicate with doctors via video conferencing systems. These services especially help residents living in rural settings.

EXECUTIVES

Pres-Ceo, Albert L Wright Jr
SEC, Marguerite Cianfrocca
Chief Information Security Off, Mark Combs
Coordinator, Joshua Austin
Assistant Director, Frank Ali
Secretary, Star Hammond
Assistant Students, Trevor Wolfe
Coordinator, Brian Rehwinkel
Director of Mis Information Te, Dave Smallwood
Analyst, Debbie Carter
Nurse Manager, Dan Bazzoli
Auditors: DIXON HUGHES GOODMAN LLP CHAR

LOCATIONS

HQ: WEST VIRGINA UNIVERSITY HOSPITALS, INC.
1 MEDICAL CENTER DR, MORGANTOWN, WV
265061200
Phone: 304 598-4000
Web: WWW.WVUCANCER.ORG

COMPETITORS

Camc Health	West Penn Allegheny
Hca	Health System

HISTORICAL FINANCIALS

Company Type: Private

Income Statement   FYE: December 31

	REVENUE ($ mil.)	NET INCOME ($ mil.)	NET PROFIT MARGIN	EMPLOYEES
12/20	1,452	57	3.9%	6,267
12/18	1,193	(39)	—	—
12/12	1,386	96	6.9%	—
12/06	0	0	—	—
Annual Growth	—	—	—	—

2020 Year-End Financials

Return on assets: 2.9%   Cash ($ mil.): 229
Return on equity: 6.5%
Current ratio: 2.10

WEST VIRGINIA UNITED HEALTH SYSTEM, INC.

West Virginia United Health System (WVUHS) helps residents in the Mountain State stay on top of their health. The system operates United Hospital Center (in Clarksburg) as well as hospitals in the West Virginia University Hospitals (WVUH) system including City Hospital (Martinsburg) Jefferson Memorial Hospital (Ranson) and WVUH's home hospital in Morgantown. In addition WVUHS operates WVUH's Cheat Lake physicians ambulatory center as well as a network of about a dozen primary care clinics located throughout central and northern West Virginia. Combined the system's hospitals and clinics have more than 1000 beds and treat approximately 1.4 million patients annually.

EXECUTIVES

Ceo, Christopher Colenda
Dir*, David C Hardesty Jr
Pres*, J Thomas Jones
Treas*, Robert D'Alessandri
V Pres*, Jeff Gibson
Staff, Amy Rogers
Computer Technician, Aaron Leatherman
Assistant Director of Donor RE, Brett Nuckles
Staff, Geraldine Jacobson
Gift Operationsreal Estate Man, Holly Loar
Network Engineer, Jeff Slavensky
Auditors: DIXON HUGHES GOODMAN LLP CHAR

LOCATIONS

HQ: WEST VIRGINIA UNITED HEALTH SYSTEM, INC.
1 MEDICAL CENTER DR, MORGANTOWN, WV
265061200
Phone: 304 598-4000
Web: WWW.WVUMEDICINE.ORG

PRODUCTS/OPERATIONS

Selected facilities

Barbour Country Family Medicine
Bridgeport Physicians Care
Chestnut Ridge Center
City Hospital
Doddridge Family Medicine
Elk Memorial Clinic
Harrisville Medical Center
Jefferson Memorial Hospital
Lumberport Family Medicine
Oakland Family Medicine Center
Pennsboro Medical Center
Pinewood Medical Center
Shinnston Healthcare Clinic
United Hospital Center
United Summit Center
WVU Hospitals

COMPETITORS

Camc Health	West Penn Allegheny
Hca	Health System

HISTORICAL FINANCIALS

Company Type: Private

Income Statement   FYE: December 31

	REVENUE ($ mil.)	NET INCOME ($ mil.)	NET PROFIT MARGIN	EMPLOYEES
12/20	3,122	213	6.8%	7,000
12/19	2,770	238	8.6%	—
12/17	2,172	132	6.1%	—
12/16	1,877	103	5.5%	—
Annual Growth	13.6%	20.0%	—	—

2020 Year-End Financials

Return on assets: 5.2%   Cash ($ mil.): 729
Return on equity: 11.8%
Current ratio: 2.00

WEST VIRGINIA UNIVERSITY

West Virginia University (WVU) is the intellectual home of more than 29000 Mountaineers (the school's mascot) and the state's preeminent institution of higher learning. WVU offers more than 180 bachelor's master's doctoral and professional degree programs through some 15 colleges and schools. The university's clinical psychology and forestry programs have been recognized nationally and it boasts 100% post-graduate job placement for its nursing pharmacy and mining engineering majors. WVU also runs a two-year residential school Potomac State College in Keyser West Virginia.

Operations
Its 1099 acres campus university offers a joint petroleum and natural gas engineering major. It also operates eight experimental farms and four forests throughout the state in addition to WVU Jackson's Mill State 4-H Camp and Lifelong Learning Center near Weston. Some 93% of its full-time faculty have earned doctorates or first-professional degrees in their disciplines. More than 800 students traveled to another country for study abroad courses in the 2011-12 academic year. Undergraduate tuition and fees for the 2012-13 year was reported as $9808.

WVU is an independent operating unit of the West Virginia Higher Education Fund.

Geographic Reach
The university's main campus is in Morgantown. It also has divisional campuses in Charleston Keyser Martinsburg and Montgomery.

Financial Performance
The university reported a 4% increase in revenues in 2012 due to a growth in capital grants and gifts revenue tuition and fees as well as revenues from auxiliary enterprise gifts and other sources. Capital grants and gifts increased by $55.9 million thanks to a donation of a master license agreement from Siemens PLM for educational software. Tuition and fees increased by $19.9 million in 2012 thanks to a fee rate hike and an increase in non-resident student enrollment. Auxiliary revenues grew by $12.2 million due to an increase in revenues from room and dining services auxiliary fees and athletics revenues. Organic growth has lifted the company's revenues since 2009.

Net income increased by 51% in 2012 due to a growth in other net non-operating revenues of $3.2 million as a result of a settlement agreement in the amount of $7.2 million partially offset by operating revenues.

Strategy
In addition to WVU's campus-based activities the university is focusing on expanding its online and distance learning options to increase educational access and research activities.

Company Background
WVU was founded in 1867 as a public land-grant institution. It one of only 11 schools in the US that are land-grant doctoral research universities with a comprehensive medical school.

EXECUTIVES
Pres, E Gordon Gee
Chief of Staff, Jay Cole
Exec Offcr For Policy Dev't, Jennifer Fisher
Interim Parent Rel'ns Dir, Lisa Hanselman
Chief Grievance Admin, Sue Keller
Accountant, Tara McMillen
Doctor, Valeriya Gritsenko
Biologist, William Peterjohn
Research Associate Professor, Alan Barnes
Secretary, John Lucas
Professor, Kenneth Showa Showalter
Auditors: CLIFTONLARSONALLEN LLP PLYMOU

LOCATIONS
HQ: WEST VIRGINIA UNIVERSITY
1500 UNIVERSITY AVE, MORGANTOWN, WV 26506
Phone: 304 293-2545
Web: WWW.WVUPRESSONLINE.COM

PRODUCTS/OPERATIONS

Selected Colleges and Schools
Benjamin M. Statler College of Engineering and Mineral Resources
College of Business and Economics
College of Creative Arts
College of Education and Human Services
College of Law
College of Physical Activity and Sport Sciences
Davis College of Agriculture Natural Resources and Design
Eberly College of Arts and Sciences
Perley Isaac Reed School of Journalism
Potomac State College of WVU
School of Dentistry
School of Medicine
School of Nursing
School of Pharmacy
School of Public Health
WVU Institute of Technology

HISTORICAL FINANCIALS
Company Type: Private

Income Statement				FYE: June 30
	REVENUE ($ mil.)	NET INCOME ($ mil.)	NET PROFIT MARGIN	EMPLOYEES
06/18	808	41	5.1%	6,245
06/17	783	8	1.1%	—
Annual Growth	3.2%	390.3%		

2018 Year-End Financials
Return on assets: 1.8%   Cash ($ mil.): 85
Return on equity: 3.9%
Current ratio: 1.40

WEST VIRGINIA UNIVERSITY

EXECUTIVES
Pres, E Gordon Gee
Assistant Professor, David W Graham
Assistant Professor, Kristen Matak
Assistant Professor, Sergei Urazhdin
Project Coordinator, Linda McMillen
Assistant Professor, Shelda Martin
Assistant Professor, Deborah A Boone
Assistant Professor, Janet Tou
Assistant Professor, Richard Vaglienti
Assistant Professor, Abhishek Srivastava
Director, Jim Jolly

LOCATIONS
HQ: WEST VIRGINIA UNIVERSITY
1501 UNIVERSITY AVE, MORGANTOWN, WV 265055523
Phone: 304 293-0111
Web: WWW.WVU.EDU

HISTORICAL FINANCIALS
Company Type: Private

Income Statement				FYE: June 30
	REVENUE ($ mil.)	NET INCOME ($ mil.)	NET PROFIT MARGIN	EMPLOYEES
06/21	775	127	16.5%	723
06/20	797	45	5.8%	—
Annual Growth	(2.8%)	178.0%	—	—

2021 Year-End Financials
Return on assets: 5.0%   Cash ($ mil.): 107
Return on equity: 10.3%
Current ratio: 1.50

WESTCHESTER COUNTY HEALTH CARE CORPORATION

EXECUTIVES
Ceo-Pres, Michael D Israel
Sr V Pres*, Anthony Mahler
Cfo*, Gary Brudnicki
Gen Counsel*, Julie Switzer
Sr V Pres*, John Morgan
Information Specialist, Michelle Weinraub
Information Specialist, Omar Ziyadeh
Information Specialist, Ann Addison
Information Specialist, Donna Dozor
Information Specialist, Lindsey McPhillips
Information Specialist, Madeline Lynett
Auditors: GRANT THORNTON LLP NEW YORK

LOCATIONS
HQ: WESTCHESTER COUNTY HEALTH CARE CORPORATION
100 WOODS RD, VALHALLA, NY 105951530
Phone: 914 493-7000
Web: WWW.WESTCHESTERMEDICALCENTER.ORG

HISTORICAL FINANCIALS
Company Type: Private

Income Statement				FYE: December 31
	REVENUE ($ mil.)	NET INCOME ($ mil.)	NET PROFIT MARGIN	EMPLOYEES
12/20	1,536	(65)	—	12,000
12/19	1,718	12	0.7%	—
12/18	1,641	(10)	—	—
12/16	2,008	45	2.3%	—
Annual Growth	(6.5%)	—	—	—

2020 Year-End Financials
Return on assets: (-3.1%)   Cash ($ mil.): 387
Return on equity: —
Current ratio: 1.40

WESTERN FARMERS ELECTRIC COOPERATIVE

Power also comes sweeping down the plain in Oklahoma thanks to the Western Farmers Electric Cooperative. Led by its coal- and natural gas-fueled generating plants — three in Anadarko one in Mooreland and one in Hugo (all in Oklahoma) — the generation and transmission co-op produces more than 1845 MW of capacity. It pipes power over 3700 miles of transmission lines to two-thirds of rural Oklahoma and parts of New Mexico. It also operates 264 substations and 59 switch stations. Western Farmers Electric Cooperative which is owned by its member distribution cooperatives supplies 22 distribution co-ops and Altus Air Force base which serve a total of a half million members.

Operations

The company maintains a well-balanced and diversified portfolio of generation resources reflecting a mix of technologies and fuel types. In 2013 coal represented 33% of Western Farmers Electric Cooperative's energy production with natural gas at 12 percent. Power generated from wind resources represents about 14% of the coop's energy mix hydro 7%. Economy purchases energy imbalance purchases and contract power (primarily natural gas) made up the balance.

Geographic Reach

Western Farmers Electric Cooperative's members consist of 22 distribution cooperatives (serving customers in Kansas Oklahoma New Mexico and Texas) and the Altus Air Force Base in Oklahoma.

Financial Performance

In 2013 the company's revenues increased by 15% to $525.3 million due to a 7.7% energy sales increase. (Its average MWh sales growth rate of 5.5% over the past three year is above the national average). Western Farmers Electric Cooperative also gets a small amount of off-system sales from three of its four New Mexico members. Power sales increased $64 million in 2013 due to higher MWh sales a slight increase in wholesale power rates and a 40% rise in natural gas prices.

Western Farmers Electric Cooperative's net income increased by 61% in 2013 due to higher sales and an increase in noninterest income.

That year the company's operating cash inflow increased to $53.3 million (compared to $21.2 million in 2012) primarily due to higher net income and increased coal and oil inventory.

Strategy

Western Farmers Electric Cooperative has diversified its fuel mix to meet green energy regulations and boasts one of the state's largest renewable energy portfolios. The diversity in generation mix helps reduce exposure to changing market conditions helping to keep rates competitive.

In 2013 the company signed a purchase with Apex Clean Energy through its subsidiary Balko Wind LLC for 100 MW of wind energy from the Balko Wind Project. With this agreement Apex has sold all the capacity of 300 MW project which will produce enough electricity to power over 110000 U.S. homes. This new site represents the fifth Oklahoma wind farm development that is a part of an ongoing commitment to diversify Western Farmers Electric Cooperative's portfolio of generation sources.

That year it also entered into a purchase and sale agreement with community-wind developer National Renewable Solutions to acquire the development assets for the Broadview Wind Projects in New Mexico. The two projects with a combined 19.8 MW capacity will each sell power over the next 20 years to Western Farmers Electric Cooperative. This wind farm site is in the service territory of Western Farmers Electric Cooperative member Farmers' Electric Cooperative.

In 2012 the company teamed up with Enel Green Power which that year began operating the 150-MW Rocky Ridge Wind Project in Kiowa and Washita counties Oklahoma. The energy generated by the wind farm will be bought by Western Farmers Electric Cooperative.

In 2012 Calpine Corporation agreed to supply Western Farmers Electric Cooperative with electric generation capacity and power (up to 280 MW) from Calpine's gas-fired Oneta Energy Center from June 2014 through 2035.

Company Background

Growing its geographic coverage in late 2010 Western Farmers Electric Cooperative added four New Mexico-based cooperatives (Farmers' Central Valley Lea County and Roosevelt County with a total of 400 MW of load) to its membership.

Responding to a growing demand for power in 2009 the power co-op completed an expansion project at its gas-fueled Anadarko plant adding some 145 MW of power generating capacity.

Western Farmers Electric Cooperative was organized in 1941 by western Oklahoma rural electric distribution cooperatives in order to secure power generation and distribution at an affordable rate. The co-op began generating power in 1950.

EXECUTIVES

Executive Vice President - Power Delivery And Technology, Ron Cunningham
Chief Executive Officer, Gary Roulet
Chief Financial Officer, Vice President, Jane Lafferty
Vice President - Generation, Gary Gilleland
Auditors: KPMG LLP OKLAHOMA CITY OK

LOCATIONS

HQ: WESTERN FARMERS ELECTRIC COOPERATIVE
701 NE 7TH ST, ANADARKO, OK 730052297
Phone: 405 247-3351
Web: WWW.WFEC.COM

COMPETITORS

Empire District Electric	Oge Energy
Entergy	Oneok
Grand River Dam Authority	Pg&e Corporation

HISTORICAL FINANCIALS
Company Type: Private

Income Statement				FYE: December 31
	REVENUE ($ mil.)	NET INCOME ($ mil.)	NET PROFIT MARGIN	EMPLOYEES
12/18	715	14	2.0%	378
12/17	686	13	2.0%	—
12/16	655	24	3.7%	—
12/15	671	31	4.6%	—
Annual Growth	2.2%	(22.8%)	—	—

2018 Year-End Financials
Return on assets: 1.0%   Cash ($ mil.): 14
Return on equity: 3.9%
Current ratio: 1.10

WESTERN GOVERNORS UNIVERSITY

EXECUTIVES

Pres, Scott Pulsipher
Chief Information Officer-Svp, David Morales
Cfo, Nadeem Syed
Mgr, David R Grow
Pres-Academic Advancement, Sally Johnstone
Coordinator, Juan Maestas
Information Technology/Interne, Travis Hitz
Information Specialist, Erik Jorgensen
Coordinator, Kami Hobson
Academic Vp-College of It, Elke Leeds
Information Technology Team ME, Donald J Cook
Auditors: TANNER LLC SALT LAKE CITY UT

LOCATIONS

HQ: WESTERN GOVERNORS UNIVERSITY
4001 S 700 E STE 700, SALT LAKE CITY, UT 841072533
Phone: 801 274-3280
Web: WWW.WGU.EDU

HISTORICAL FINANCIALS
Company Type: Private

Income Statement				FYE: June 30
	REVENUE ($ mil.)	NET INCOME ($ mil.)	NET PROFIT MARGIN	EMPLOYEES
06/20	922	40	4.3%	208
06/19	855	62	7.3%	—
06/15	381	25	6.8%	—
06/14	297	24	8.3%	—
Annual Growth	20.8%	8.4%	—	—

2020 Year-End Financials
Return on assets: 7.7%   Cash ($ mil.): 48
Return on equity: 16.0%
Current ratio: 0.40

WESTERN OREGON UNIVERSITY

EXECUTIVES

Pres, Mark D Weiss
Project Coordinator, Angela Christensen
Staff, Heitho Reuter
Assistant Professor, Lauren Roscoe
Coordinator, Emily Lafon
Associate Professor of Compute, Becka Morgan
Assistant Professor, Erin Barnes
Project Coordinator, Gina Herrera
Project Coordinator, Ruth McDonald
Assistant, Elizabeth Balding
Marketing, Erin McDonough

LOCATIONS

HQ: WESTERN OREGON UNIVERSITY
345 MONMOUTH AVE N, MONMOUTH, OR 973611329
Phone: 503 838-8000
Web: WWW.WOU.EDU

HISTORICAL FINANCIALS
Company Type: Private

Income Statement				FYE: June 30
	REVENUE ($ mil.)	NET INCOME ($ mil.)	NET PROFIT MARGIN	EMPLOYEES
06/08	1,251	80	6.4%	706
06/06*	0	(0)	—	—
12/05	1	0	30.1%	—
06/04	1	0	22.9%	—
Annual Growth	483.6%	324.8%	—	—

*Fiscal year change

2008 Year-End Financials
Return on assets: —   Cash ($ mil.): 355
Return on equity: 6.4%
Current ratio: 0.70

WGL HOLDINGS, INC.

WGL Holdings owners of the regulated Washington Gas Light Company sells natural gas to more than 1 million customers in the District of Columbia Maryland and Virginia. Whether the company is distributing clean natural gas safely to a customer's home providing electric power through renewable wind energy or installing energy-efficient systems for the federal government its vision is consistent and clear throughout its business: to be the preferred source of clean and efficient energy solutions.

Operations

WGL Holdings is the parent company of Washington Gas WGL Energy WGL Midstream and Hampshire Gas. Washington Gas its leading subsidiary has provided safe reliable natural gas service to customers in the D.C. area and serves more than one million customers in the District of Columbia Maryland and Virginia. Its unregulated subsidiaries provide energy-related services to residential and commercial customers including government organizations.

Geographic Reach

Headquartered in Pittsburgh Pennsylvania WGL Holdings primarily operates in Washington DC Maryland and Virginia.

Sales and Marketing

WGL sells and delivers natural gas and/or electricity directly to residential and commercial customers. Washington Gas has some 1 million customers in the District of Columbia Maryland and Virginia.

Strategy

Company Background

WGL was established in the year 2000 as a Virginia corporation. On January 25 2017 WGL entered into an Agreement and Plan of Merger (Merger Agreement) to combine with AltaGas Ltd. a Canadian Corporation (AltaGas). On July 6 2018 the merger was consummated between AltaGas WGL and Wrangler Inc. (Merger Sub) a newly formed indirect wholly owned subsidiary of AltaGas.

EXECUTIVES

Pres-Ceo, Adrian P Chapman
Exec V Pres-Cfo*, Vincent L Ammann Jr
Exec V Pres-Chief ADM Officer, Luanne S Gutermuth
Sr V Pres-Gen Counsel-Corp SEC, Leslie T Thornton
V Pres-Cao-Contrl, William R Ford
V Pres-Treas, Douglas I Bonawitz
V Pres-Cro, Louis J Hutchinson III
Vp Business Svcs, Marcellous P Frye Jr
Vp Gas Supply & Engineering, Mark A Lowe
Vp Corp Dev't, Richard H Moore
Vp Strategy Business Dev't, Anthony M Nee

LOCATIONS

HQ: WGL HOLDINGS, INC.
1000 MAINE AVE SW, WASHINGTON, DC 200243494
Phone: 202 624-6011
Web: WWW.WGLHOLDINGS.COM

PRODUCTS/OPERATIONS

2018 Sales

	$ mil.	% of total
Retail energy marketing	1,009	42
Utility	1,248	53
Commercial energy services	79	3
Midstream energy services	40	2
Eliminations	(36.4)	-
Total	**2,341**	**100**

2018 Sales

	$ mil.	% of total
Non-utility	1,112	47
Utility	1,229	53
Total	**2,341**	**100**

Selected Subsidiaries

Hampshire Gas Company (underground natural gas storage)
Wrangler SPE LLC
Washington Gas Light Company (natural gas utility)
Washington Gas Resources Corp. (nonregulated business holding company)
Washington Gas Energy Services Inc. (retail energy services)
Washington Gas Energy Systems Inc. (commercial energy systems and HVAC services)

COMPETITORS

Appalachian Power	Northern Virginia
Comfort Systems Usa	Electric Cooperative
Commerce Energy Group	Pepco Holdings
Constellation Energy	Rgc Resources
Group	Rappahannock Electric
Dominion Energy	Cooperative
Firstenergy	

HISTORICAL FINANCIALS

Company Type: Private

Income Statement				FYE: September 30
	REVENUE ($ mil.)	NET INCOME ($ mil.)	NET PROFIT MARGIN	EMPLOYEES
09/18	2,341	21	0.9%	1,586
09/17	2,354	177	7.6%	—
09/16	2,349	168	7.2%	—
09/15	2,659	132	5.0%	—
Annual Growth	(4.2%)	(45.8%)	—	—

2018 Year-End Financials

Return on assets: 0.3%   Cash ($ mil.): 57
Return on equity: 1.2%
Current ratio: 0.60

WHEATON FRANCISCAN SERVICES, INC.

Wheaton Franciscan Services Inc. (WFSI) is the not-for-profit parent company for more than 100 health care housing and social service organizations in Colorado Illinois Iowa and Wisconsin. Also known as Wheaton Franciscan Healthcare WFSI operates about 15 hospitals including Affinity Health System Rush Oak Park Hospital and United Hospital System with more than 1600 beds total. WFSI also includes long-term care centers home health agencies and physician offices. Its Franciscan Ministries division provides affordable housing units including assisted-living facilities and low-income dwellings. The health system is sponsored by The Franciscan Sisters Daughters of the Sacred Hearts of Jesus and Mary.

Operations

Many of WFSI's hospitals are operated in partnership with other area providers. For instance the Affinity Health System in Wisconsin is jointly sponsored by Wheaton Franciscan Sisters and Ministry Health Care while the Rush Oak Park Hospital in Illinois is operated through a partnership between WFSI and the Rush System for Health.

The health system partners with the YMCA of Milwaukee to try to address chronic health concerns of area residents. The two organizations converted a local YMCA campus into the YMCA Healthy Lifestyle Village. The center offers health screenings health education outpatient therapy and fitness services. WFSI and the YMCA have more Healthy Lifestyle Village campuses planned for other locations within their service areas.

The organization had a total of 1656 beds and 2620 housing units at the end of 2014.

In fiscal 2013 WSFI delivered more than 8000 babies and had more than 330000 emergency department visits. It reported more than 1580000 outpatient visits and some 64000 hospital admissions. It employs more than 500 physicians and has some 2000 affiliated physicians.

Geographic Reach

WFSI operates in Wisconsin Iowa Colorado and Illinois.

Financial Performance

The not-for-profit system's revenues were flat in fiscal 2014 at $1.8 billion. Net income totaled $184 million.

Strategy

To increase the scope of specialty health care services it can provide to the community WFSI recruits new physicians and specialists to the Wheaton Franciscan Medical Group. The system also works to improve communication among its physicians and facilities by adding electronic health record (EHR) systems.

In 2013 the system opened a new 80000-sq.-ft. outpatient center specializing in neurology services.

Company Background

The Franciscan Sisters Daughters of the Sacred Hearts of Jesus and Mary (also known as the Wheaton Franciscan Sisters) founded WSFI in 1983 as a holding company for their ministry operations. The health system traces its roots back to the founding of the St. Mary's Hospital in Racine Wisconsin in 1882.

EXECUTIVES

Pres-Ceo, John D Oliverio
Chm, Joseph Lewis
V Chm, Michael Mack
SEC, Michael Murry
Treas, Robert Walker
Manager, Denise Nitsch
Director Retirement Plans, Karen Hanley
Senior Accountant, Michael Koser
Director, Carol Hess
Technical Application Analyst, Aaron Roemer
Endocrinology, Ivica Boban
Auditors: KPMG LLP CHICAGO IL

LOCATIONS

HQ: WHEATON FRANCISCAN SERVICES, INC.
400 W RIVER WOODS PKWY, GLENDALE, WI 532121060
Phone: 414 465-3000
Web: WWW.HEALTHCARE.ASCENSION.ORG

PRODUCTS/OPERATIONS

Selected Operations

Franciscan Ministries Inc. (housing in Colorado Illinois Iowa and Wisconsin)
Illinois
    Marianjoy Rehabilitation Hospital (Wheaton)
    Rush Oak Park Hospital (affiliate Oak Park)
Iowa (Wheaton Franciscan Healthcare of Iowa)
    Covenant Medical Center (Waterloo)
    Mercy Hospital (Oelwein)
    Sartori Memorial Hospital (Cedar Falls)
Wisconsin
    Affinity Health System (partnership with Minstry Health Care)
    Calumet Medical Center (Chilton)
    Mercy Medical Center (Oshkosh)
    St. Elizabeth Hospital (Appleton)

Wheaton Franciscan Healthcare of Southeast
Wisconsin
All Saints Hospital (two campuses in Racine)
Elmbrook Memorial Hospital (Brookfield)
Franklin Hospital (Franklin)
St. Francis Hospital (Milwaukee)
St. Joseph Hospital (Milwaukee)
Wisconsin Heart Hospital (Wauwatosa)
United Hospital System Inc. (affiliated system)
Kenosha Medical Center (Kenosha)
St. Catherine's Medical Center (Pleasant Prairie)

COMPETITORS

Advocate Health Care	Kishhealth
Alden Management	Loyola University
Services	Health System
Children's Hospital	Ministry Health Care
And Health System	Morris Hospital
Columbia St. Mary's	Northshore University
Elmhurst Memorial	Healthsystem
Healthcare	Osf Healthcare System
Fhn	Prohealth Care
Froedtert Hospital	Rockford Health System
Hospital Sisters	Swedishamerican Health
Health System	System

HISTORICAL FINANCIALS

Company Type: Private

Income Statement   FYE: June 30

	REVENUE ($ mil.)	NET INCOME ($ mil.)	NET PROFIT MARGIN	EMPLOYEES
06/14	1,754	128	7.3%	18,000
06/13	1,763	177	10.1%	—
06/12	1,723	(112)	—	—
Annual Growth	0.9%	—	—	—

2014 Year-End Financials

Return on assets: 5.5%   Cash ($ mil.): 58
Return on equity: 11.4%
Current ratio: 1.30

WHITE PLAINS HOSPITAL MEDICAL CENTER

EXECUTIVES

Pres-Ceo, Jon B Schandler
Chb*, Paul Weissman
Pres*, Susan Fox
Exec V Pres-Coo*, Edward F Leonard
V Pres-Fin-Cfo*, John Schiurba
Information Specialist, Allison Schurko
Information Specialist, Anna Perselis
Information Specialist, Carmita Pacheco
Information Specialist, Celia Caceres
Information Specialist, Christin Barnett
Information Specialist, Danielle Vespertino

LOCATIONS

HQ: WHITE PLAINS HOSPITAL MEDICAL CENTER
41 E POST RD, WHITE PLAINS, NY 106014607
Phone: 914 681-0600
Web: WWW.WPHOSPITAL.ORG

HISTORICAL FINANCIALS

Company Type: Private

Income Statement   FYE: December 31

	REVENUE ($ mil.)	NET INCOME ($ mil.)	NET PROFIT MARGIN	EMPLOYEES
12/17	620	40	6.5%	2,000
12/16	460	23	5.1%	—
12/15	389	23	6.1%	—
12/14	353	8	2.3%	—
Annual Growth	20.7%	70.9%	—	—

2017 Year-End Financials

Return on assets: 5.9%   Cash ($ mil.): 45
Return on equity: 10.1%
Current ratio: 1.00

WHOLE FOODS MARKET, INC.

Whole Foods Market is the world's largest natural foods grocery chain. Founded in 1980 it pioneered the supermarket concept in natural and organic foods retailing. The company operates more than 500 stores throughout the US Canada and the UK. It sells private-label items through its 365 Organic Everyday Value and Allegro Coffee lines among others and offers a variety of non-GMO vegan and gluten-free foods.

HISTORY

With a $10000 loan from his father John Mackey started SaferWay Natural Foods in Austin Texas in 1978. Despite struggling Mackey dreamed of opening a larger supermarket-sized natural foods store. Two years later SaferWay merged with Clarksville Natural Grocery and Whole Foods Market was born. Led by Mackey that year it opened an 11000-sq.-ft. supermarket in the counterculture hotbed of Austin. The store was an instant success and a second store was added 18 months later in suburban Austin.

The company slowly expanded in Texas opening or buying stores in Houston in 1984 and Dallas in 1986. Whole Foods expanded into Louisiana in 1988 with the purchase of like-named Whole Food Co. a single New Orleans store owned by Peter Roy (who served as the company's president from 1993 to 1998). Sticking to university towns Whole Foods added another store in California the next year and acquired Wellspring Grocery (two stores North Carolina) in 1991. In 1992 it debuted its first private-label products under the Whole Foods name. Seeking capital to expand even more the company raised $23 million by going public in early 1992 with 12 stores.

Every competitor in the fragmented health foods industry became a potential acquisition and the chain began growing rapidly. In 1992 Whole Foods bought the six-store Bread & Circus chain in New England. The next year it added Mrs. Gooch's Natural Foods Markets (seven stores in the Los Angeles area). Its biggest acquisition came in 1996 when it bought Fresh Fields the second-largest US natural foods chain (22 stores on the East Coast and in Chicago). Although the purchase hurt profits in 1996 sales surpassed $1 billion for the first time in fiscal 1997 as Whole Foods neared 70 stores. In 1997 it introduced the less-expensive 365 private label and acquired the Granary Market

(Monterey California) and Bread of Life (two stores South Florida) natural foods supermarkets.

Capitalizing on the growing popularity of nutraceuticals (natural supplements with benefits similar to pharmaceuticals) the company paid $146 million in 1997 for Amrion a maker of nutraceuticals and other nutritional supplements (merged with subsidiary WholePeople.com in 2000). It capped the year by buying coffee roaster Allegro Coffee. (Both companies are based in Boulder Colorado home of its former main rival the smaller Wild Oats.) Also in 1997 Whole Foods acquired the six-store Merchant of Vino natural foods and wine shop chain to foster the development of its wine departments.

In 1998 Whole Foods opened its first store in Boulder — a 39000-sq.-ft. superstore with amenities such as a juice bar and a prepared foods section. At year's end Roy resigned as president and was replaced by Chris Hitt. In 1999 Whole Foods bought four-store Boston-area chain Nature's Heartland.

In 2000 Whole Foods merged its online operations (wholefoods.com) with its direct marketing and nutritional supplement unit (Amrion) to form Wholepeople.com. Later that year the company merged Wholepeople.com with lifestyle marketing firm Gaiam; Whole Foods received a minority stake in Gaiam and started selling food online through Gaiam.com.

Hitt resigned in mid-2001 and Mackey took over his duties. Later that year Whole Foods acquired the three upscale Harry's Farmers Market stores in Atlanta; the sale did not include the Harry's In A Hurry stores which later shut down.

In 2002 Whole Foods crossed the border into Canada. Its first foreign store opened in downtown Toronto that May.

Mackey was named Entrepreneur of the Year in 2003 by consulting firm Ernst & Young. That year Whole Foods acquired Select Fish a Seattle-based seafood processor and distributor and opened a seafood distribution facility in Atlanta.

In 2004 Whole Foods opened a 59000-sq.-ft. store in the new Time Warner Center in Manhattan. The new store which includes a 248-seat cafe sushi bar wine shop and gourmet bakery is the largest supermarket in New York City. That year the company acquired the UK organic-food retailer Fresh & Wild for $38 million.

To support its rapid growth in 2004 Whole Foods Market expanded its number of operating regions from eight to 10 by separating the Southwest region into the Southwest and Rocky Mountain regions and the Northern Pacific region into the Northern California and Pacific Northwest region. The company announced the opening of its first Gluten-Free Bakehouse a dedicated gluten-free baking facility located outside Raleigh North Carolina. Overall the company opened 12 new stores in 2004.

In January 2005 Whole Foods launched the Animal Compassion Foundation an independent nonprofit organization dedicated to the compassionate treatment of livestock. The company moved that month to its new corporate headquarters across the street from its old location in downtown Austin. Its new flagship store opened its doors in March at the same location. In October Whole Foods increased its number of operating regions from 10 to 11 by separating the North Atlantic region into the North Atlantic and Tri-State regions. Overall in fiscal 2005 the company opened a dozen new stores including its first in Nebraska and Ohio. In 2006 the company acquired a store in Portland Maine and converted it to the Whole Foods Market banner.

In August 2007 Whole Foods acquired its main competitor — Boulder Colorado-based Wild Oats Markets — in a deal valued at about $565 million (plus $106 million in debt). In early October the company sold 35 Henry's Farmers Market and Sun Harvest stores to a subsidiary of Los Angeles-based Smart & Final for about $166 million. The stores in California and Texas were acquired with Wild Oats.

The company launched a bi-monthly magazine called Whole Foods Market Magazine at its midwestern stores in 2008. On the heels of its disappointing third-quarter results in August 2008 shares of the company's stock fell to a six-year low and Whole Foods suspended its dividend. Blaming the poor economy the company announced the layoffs of some 50 employees at its Austin headquarters in August 2008. Overall in fiscal 2008 the company introduced about 300 new private-label items.

For the first time in its 29-year history Whole Foods reported negative same-store sales in the quarter ended December 2008 as traffic in its stores fell.

In March 2009 the company reached a settlement in its long-running dispute with the FTC over its acquisition of Wild Oats in 2007. Whole Foods agreed to sell 32 stores including 19 Wild Oats locations that had already been closed. In exchange the FTC dropped its crusade to undo the merger. In December 2009 John Elstrott was named chairman of Whole Foods Market after Mackey voluntarily relinquished the chairmanship which he had held since 1980. In May 2010 Walter Robb formerly co-president of the company was promoted to co-CEO of Whole Foods a title he now shares with Mackey.

EXECUTIVES

Ceo, John Mackey
Pres*, Anthony Gallo
Exec V Pres-Cfo*, Keith Manbeck
Associate, Omar Tejada
Customer Supervisor, Oswaldo Cortes
Chef, Rodney Chenoweth
Associate Store Team Leader, Bill Balderson
Manager, Cheryl James
Whole Body Team Leader, Colleen Rogers
Body Care, Corinne Schultz
Bakery Team Leader, Daniel Dasilva
Auditors: ERNST & YOUNG LLP AUSTIN TEX

LOCATIONS

HQ: WHOLE FOODS MARKET, INC.
550 BOWIE ST, AUSTIN, TX 787034644
Phone: 512 477-4455
Web: WWW.WHOLEFOODSMARKET.COM

PRODUCTS/OPERATIONS

Selected Product Categories

Bakery
Body care
Educational products
Floral
Grocery
Household products
Meat and poultry
Nutritional supplements
Pet products
Prepared foods
Produce
Seafood
Specialty (beer wine cheese)
Textiles

COMPETITORS

Aldi	Natural Grocers By
Albertsons	Vitamin Cottage
Costco Wholesale	Publix
Fiesta Mart	Safeway
Gnc	Sprouts
H-e-b	Tesco

Kroger	Trader Joe's
Loblaw	Wal-mart

HISTORICAL FINANCIALS

Company Type: Private

Income Statement   FYE: September 24

	REVENUE ($ mil.)	NET INCOME ($ mil.)	NET PROFIT MARGIN	EMPLOYEES
09/17	16,030	245	1.5%	95,000
09/16	15,724	507	3.2%	—
09/15	15,389	536	3.5%	—
09/14	14,194	579	4.1%	—
Annual Growth	4.1%	(24.9%)	—	—

2017 Year-End Financials

Return on assets: 3.7%   Cash ($ mil.): 322
Return on equity: 7.1%
Current ratio: 1.60

WILBUR-ELLIS HOLDINGS II, INC.

Seed 'em weed 'em and feed 'em could be the motto of San Francisco's Wilbur-Ellis Co. (aka WECO). Through its agribusiness division WECO sells fertilizer herbicides insecticides seed and farm machinery in North America. The Connell Bros. unit exports and distributes food ingredients and specialty chemicals throughout the Pacific Rim. Its feed division serves international customers in the livestock pet food and aquaculture industries. Additionally WECO provides consulting pesticide application and other agriculture-related services. Beyond North America WECO has operations in about 15 countries in the Asia/Pacific Region. WECO was founded in 1921 by Brayton Wilbur Sr. and Floyd Ellis.

Operations

WECO's Agribusiness division is one of the top marketers and distributors of agricultural products in the US with sales of $2 billion. Connell Bros. is the largest marketer and distributor of specialty chemicals and ingredients with about three dozen offices across the Asia/Pacific region and annual sales of about $815 million. The $500-million-in-sales Feed division supplies value-added feed ingredients and markets for customers' by-products.

Geographic Reach

The San Francisco-based company has agribusiness operations in the West Southwest and Midwest regions on the US. Connell Bros. has offices in 17 countries across the Asia/Pacific Region including Australia China and Vietnam. The Feed unit has operations in North America and in Australia and New Zealand.

Sales and Marketing

WECO's ProMarket business serves such markets as nurseries greenhouses forests and golf courses and sporting facilities. The Connel Bros. division sells ingredients and specialty chemicals to the coatings food personal care plastics paper construction and other industries.

Financial Performance

WECO's annual sales continue to exceed $3 billion.

Strategy

WECO employs a strategy of acquiring successful businesses and integrating them into its existing operations. Geography is no barrier when it comes to buying companies: The group has acquired operations in such faraway places as Malaysia Taiwan

the Philippines China Australia and New Zealand. WECO continues to expand both through acquisitions and organically across its three divisions.

Mergers and Acquisitions

The company continued its acquisitive streak in 2014 and 2015. In early 2014 it acquired one of its alliance partners New Horizons Ag Service an agricultural retail business in Elgin North Dakota. New Horizons became part of Wilbur-Ellis Midwest. The company also acquired Accu-Rate Services a full-service agricultural retailer in Sedgwick Kansas and Advanced Ag located in Creston Iowa. Other agribusinesses added in 2014 included retail facility Poynter's Ag Supply (North Dakota) and feed provider Allied Premium Protein.

Also that year WECO's Connell Brothers unit purchased Enzyme Solutions of Melbourne Australia extending its capabilities in enzymes. Furthering its Asia/Pacific business it acquired Bioworld Fine Chemical (Shanghai) which distributes upscale botanical oils and plant extracts.

Agribusiness purchases in 2015 include The Seed House a Nebraska-based professional seed company; Lacey's Farmacy a South Dakota-based agriculture retail outfit and Aero Spray Services an aerial spraying and fire-fighting firm also based in South Dakota.

EXECUTIVES

Pres, John L Buckley
Exec Chm, John P Thacher
V Pres, Anne E Cleary
V Pres, David P Granoff
V Pres, Troy M Hackett
Cfo, Michael J Hunter
V Pres, Michael D Wilbur
Controller, Roger Y Tanaka
Treas, Alison J Amonette
Asst SEC, Timothy J Nestler
Engineer, Mike Shea
Auditors: PRICEWATERHOUSECOOPERS LLP SA

LOCATIONS

HQ: WILBUR-ELLIS HOLDINGS II, INC.
345 CALIFORNIA ST FL 27, SAN FRANCISCO, CA 941042644
Phone: 415 772-4000
Web: WWW.WILBURELLIS.COM

PRODUCTS/OPERATIONS

Selected Products and Services
Agribusiness Division
  Agricultural chemicals
  Fertilizers
  Fungicides
  Herbicides
  Insecticides
  Machinery
  Pesticides
  Seed protectants
  Seed treatments
  Sprayers
  Supply-chain management
Connell Bros. Division
  Industrial chemicals
Feed Division
  Aquaculture products
  Feed ingredients
  Food oils
  Forage products
  Pet food
Professional Products
  Forestry
  Fungicides
  Herbicides
  Golf
  Fungicides
  Landscape
  Fungicides
  Nursery/Greenhouse
  Fungicides

Vegetation Management
Selective and nonselective growth regulators

COMPETITORS

Adm	Dupont Agriculture
Agri Industries	Frontier Agriculture
Ag Processing Inc.	Growmark
Andersons	Goulding Chemicals
Basf Se	Ingredion
Bayer Cropscience	Jr Simplot
Cf Industries	Land O'lakes Purina
Chs	Feed
Cargill	Southern States
Dow Agrosciences	

HISTORICAL FINANCIALS

Company Type: Private

Income Statement				FYE: December 31
	REVENUE ($ mil.)	NET INCOME ($ mil.)	NET PROFIT MARGIN	EMPLOYEES
12/11	2,812	0	—	4,600
12/10	2,342	0	—	—
12/09	0	0	—	—
12/00	1,100	0	—	—
Annual Growth	8.9%	—	—	—

WILLIAM BEAUMONT HOSPITAL

Beaumont Health System is an eight-hospital regional health system with more than 3337 beds and more than 5000 physicians along with numerous community-based medical centers throughout suburban Detroit (in Oakland Macomb and Wayne counties). Additional facilities include nursing homes a home health care agency a research institute and primary and specialty care clinics as well as rehabilitation cardiology and cancer centers. Beaumont is the exclusive clinical teaching site for the Oakland University William Beaumont School of Medicine; it also has affiliations with Michigan State University College of Osteopathic Medicine and Wayne State University School of Medicine.

Operations

The system draws on a rich history of pioneering medical research to serve the health needs of southeastern Michigan and advance healing techniques nationwide.

Beaumont holds a Level I trauma designation in Oakland and Macomb counties. The system's Children's Hospital has more than 80 pediatric subspecialists. Its research institute has more than 1000 active clinical studies including interventional clinical research trials.

A teaching hospital Beaumont has 40 residency and fellowship programs with more than 450 participants. The system is also the exclusive clinical partner of William Beaumont School of Medicine providing more than 1500 physicians to the school's faculty.

In fiscal 2014 the system had more than 103000 admissions some 9700 infant births more than 250000 emergency department visits and more than 2.3 million outpatient visits.

Financial Performance

In 2014 Beaumont's annual revenues totaled $2.5 billion.

Strategy

The system expands its care offerings by partnering with other service providers (such as insurance groups) adding new facilities to its network and by taking advantage of government initiatives to modernize its systems. For example in 2015 Beaumont opened a breast care and imaging services center in Trenton Michigan.

In 2014 Beaumont merged with hospital operators Oakwood Healthcare and Botsford Hospital creating a $3.8 billion not-for-profit organization that can provide improved care services across their communities. For example patients will benefit from having a single electronic health record across all of the system's sites.

Company Background

The health system traces its roots to Dr. William Beaumont an army doctor who conducted groundbreaking research on the human digestive system on Mackinac Island Michigan in the 1820s. The first Beaumont Hospital was opened in Royal Oak in 1955; the Troy facility was opened in 1977; and its third hospital in Grosse Pointe was acquired in 2007 from Bon Secours Health System.

EXECUTIVES

Ceo-Pres, Gene Michalski
Pres, Brian Connolly
SEC, Gale R Colwell
Treas, Barbara Mahone
Chief Med, Ananias Diokno
Chm, Stephen R Howard
V Chm, Mark Shaevsky
Sr V Pres, Margaret Casey
Fo/Exe V Pres, John Keuten
Director, Hadley Mack French
Director, Martha James Quay

LOCATIONS

HQ: WILLIAM BEAUMONT HOSPITAL
36555 26 MILE RD, LENOX, MI 480483102
Phone: 947 522-1177
Web: WWW.BEAUMONT.ORG

HISTORICAL FINANCIALS

Company Type: Private

Income Statement				FYE: December 31
	REVENUE ($ mil.)	NET INCOME ($ mil.)	NET PROFIT MARGIN	EMPLOYEES
12/17	1,473	71	4.9%	18,050
12/16	1,396	118	8.5%	—
12/15	1,300	142	10.9%	—
Annual Growth	6.5%	(29.1%)	—	—

2017 Year-End Financials

Return on assets: 3.8%
Return on equity: 3.9%
Current ratio: 12.30
Cash ($ mil.): 175

WILMINGTON TRUST COMPANY

EXECUTIVES

Pres, Robert V A Harra Jr
Ceo*, Donald Foley
Exec V-Pres*, William J Farrell
Exec V-Pres*, Mark A Graham
V-Pres, SEC*, Marie James

Senior V-Pres-Controller*, Michael Spychall
Stockbroker, Andrea Feeley
Assistant Vice President and E, Frank Rundatz
Assistant Vice President Wealt, Clay Weisenberg
Assistant Vice President Loan, Jennifer Anderson
Assistant Vice President of Le, Mary Fisher

LOCATIONS

HQ: WILMINGTON TRUST COMPANY
1100 N MARKET ST, WILMINGTON, DE 198900001
Phone: 302 651-1000
Web: WWW.WILMINGTONTRUST.COM

HISTORICAL FINANCIALS

Company Type: Private

Income Statement				FYE: December 31
	ASSETS ($ mil.)	NET INCOME ($ mil.)	INCOME AS % OF ASSETS	EMPLOYEES
12/17	4,960	30	0.6%	1,818
12/16	3,685	17	0.5%	—
12/15	1,928	36	1.9%	—
Annual Growth	60.4%	(9.0%)	—	—

2017 Year-End Financials

Return on assets: 0.6%
Return on equity: 5.7%
Sales ($ mil): 234

WINCO HOLDINGS, INC.

EXECUTIVES

Pres-Ceo, Steven Goddard
Vp-Cfo-Sec-treas*, David Butler
Vp-Coo*, Richard Charrier
Chb*, Gary R Piva
Vice-President Engineering, Dick Vanderlinden
Business Analyst, Dustin Earl
Vice-President Engineering, David V Etten
Director Private Brands, Susan Barry
Buyer Deli, Stephan Bosch
Vice President Deli, Mary Pierce
Store Manager, Raul Garcia
Auditors: KPMG LLP BOISE ID

LOCATIONS

HQ: WINCO HOLDINGS, INC.
650 N ARMSTRONG PL, BOISE, ID 837040825
Phone: 208 377-0110
Web: WWW.MONEYGRAM.COM

HISTORICAL FINANCIALS

Company Type: Private

Income Statement				FYE: March 28
	REVENUE ($ mil.)	NET INCOME ($ mil.)	NET PROFIT MARGIN	EMPLOYEES
03/09	4,104	225	5.5%	14,000
03/08	3,515	132	3.8%	—
03/07	2,976	106	3.6%	—
Annual Growth	17.4%	45.5%	—	—

2009 Year-End Financials

Return on assets: 15.2%
Return on equity: 24.4%
Current ratio: 1.30
Cash ($ mil.): 146

WINDSTREAM EAGLE HOLDINGS, LLC

EXECUTIVES

Ceo-Pres, Tony Thomas
Cfo, Bob Gunderman
Ezec V Pres-CHR, John Fletcher
Cmo, Joe Harding
Exec V Pres-Enterprises Sales, Jeff Howe
Pres-Consumer, Sarah Day
Pres-Wholesale, Mike Shippey
Exec V Pres-Access, John Dobbins
Exec V Pres, Engr, Jeff Small
Auditors: ERNST & YOUNG LLP ATLANTA GE

LOCATIONS

HQ: WINDSTREAM EAGLE HOLDINGS, LLC
4001 N RODNEY PARHAM RD, LITTLE ROCK, AR
722122459
Phone: 501 748-5839
Web: WWW.WINDSTREAM.COM

HISTORICAL FINANCIALS

Company Type: Private

Income Statement				FYE: December 31
	REVENUE ($ mil.)	NET INCOME ($ mil.)	NET PROFIT MARGIN	EMPLOYEES
12/16	959	7	0.8%	60
12/15	1,097	(43)	—	—
12/14	1,176	(72)	—	—
Annual Growth	(9.7%)	—	—	—

2016 Year-End Financials
Return on assets: 1.2%   Cash ($ mil.): 51
Return on equity: 38.0%
Current ratio: 1.00

WIPRO, LLC

Auditors: DELOITTE HASKINS & SELLS LLP

LOCATIONS

HQ: WIPRO, LLC
2 TOWER CENTER BLVD # 2200, EAST BRUNSWICK,
NJ 088161100
Phone: 732 509-1664
Web: WWW.WIPRO.COM

HISTORICAL FINANCIALS

Company Type: Private

Income Statement				FYE: March 31
	REVENUE ($ mil.)	NET INCOME ($ mil.)	NET PROFIT MARGIN	EMPLOYEES
03/18	585	(45)	—	800
03/13	120	(17)	—	—
Annual Growth	37.1%	—	—	—

2018 Year-End Financials
Return on assets: (-4.8%)   Cash ($ mil.): 22
Return on equity: (-20.4%)
Current ratio: 0.70

WISCONSIN MILWAUKEE COUNTY

EXECUTIVES

Ceo, Chris Abele
County Clerk*, Joseph Czarnezki
District Attorney*, John Chisholm
Clerk of Courts*, John Barrett
Register of Deeds*, John La Fave
County Exec*, Scott Walker
Chairman of Board*, Marina Dimitrijevic
Treasurer*, David Cullen
Managing Director*, Teig Whaley-Smith
Controller*, Scott Manske
Certification Analyst, Ruby Brooks
Auditors: BAKER TILLY VIRCHOW KRAUSE

LOCATIONS

HQ: WISCONSIN MILWAUKEE COUNTY
901 N 9TH ST STE 306, MILWAUKEE, WI 532331425
Phone: 414 278-4211
Web: WWW.LASMILWAUKEE.COM

HISTORICAL FINANCIALS

Company Type: Private

Income Statement				FYE: December 31
	REVENUE ($ mil.)	NET INCOME ($ mil.)	NET PROFIT MARGIN	EMPLOYEES
12/20	941	45	4.9%	4,400
12/19	877	16	1.9%	—
12/18	851	2	0.3%	—
12/17	852	5	0.7%	—
Annual Growth	3.4%	100.3%	—	—

WORKFORCE COMMISSION, TEXAS

The Texas Workforce Commission (TWC) supports economic development in the Lone Star State by developing its workforce. The state government agency with 28 regional workforce boards offers a number of services benefiting employers (recruiting retention and outplacement services) and workers (training and job-search resources). The agency also provides support services such as child care for targeted groups employment and training services for veterans publishes labor law and labor market information and administers the state's unemployment insurance program. Texans receive most of TWC's services for free; the agency is funded primarily by the federal government.

Strategy

TWC has received over $2.8 million in a DOL grant award to fund the Apprenticeship Texas State Expansion Grant project which has realigned agency services to support the expansion and implement Registered Apprenticeship as a leading talent development strategy. Target industries include Information Technology Advanced Manufacturing Aerospace and Defense STEM Finance and Energy. The project will serve 634 apprentices with a focus on women in apprenticeship youth and individuals with disabilities veterans Native Americans and persons of color among others.

EXECUTIVES

Interim Exec Dir, Ed Serna
Cfo*, Randy Townsend
Executive Director Texa, Larry Temple
Program Manager, Matthew Sniadecki
Deputy Executive Director, Edward Serna
Supervisor, John Meyer
Braille Specialist, BJ Cepeda
Employment Consultant and Recr, Danette
Vincent
Program Supervisor, Elida Arriaga
Security Officer Manager, Elizabeth Peirce
Consultant, Janice Tinsley

LOCATIONS

HQ: WORKFORCE COMMISSION, TEXAS
101 E 15TH ST, AUSTIN, TX 787781442
Phone: 512 463-9729
Web: WWW.TWC.TEXAS.GOV

PRODUCTS/OPERATIONS

Program / Service
Adult Education & Literacy
Appeals
Apprenticeship
Career Schools & Colleges
Child Care Services
Choices
Civil Rights
Employment Services
Foreign Labor Certification
Labor Law
Labor Market & Career Information
Noncustodial Parent Choices
Rapid Reemployment Services
Self Sufficiency
Senior Community Service Employment Program
Skills Development
Skills for Small Businesses
Skills for Veterans
Supplemental Nutrition Assistance Program
    Employment & Training
Trade Adjustment Assistance
Unemployment Benefits
Unemployment Tax
Veterans' Services
Workforce Investment Act

HISTORICAL FINANCIALS

Company Type: Private

Income Statement				FYE: August 31
	REVENUE ($ mil.)	NET INCOME ($ mil.)	NET PROFIT MARGIN	EMPLOYEES
08/20	2,276	495	21.8%	4,600
08/19	1,898	46	2.5%	—
08/18	1,822	134	7.4%	—
08/11	1,466	3	0.2%	—
Annual Growth	5.0%	74.0%	—	—

2020 Year-End Financials
Return on assets: 77.4%   Cash ($ mil.): 438
Return on equity: 97.4%
Current ratio: 4.80

WORLD WIDE TECHNOLOGY HOLDING CO., LLC

EXECUTIVES

Ceo, James P Kavanaugh
Chb*, David Steward
Cfo*, Tom Strunk
Project Coordinator, Jennifer Barrett
Business Manager, Nicole Reichert
Human Resources Business Partn, Abby Baker
Regional Manager, Doug Warner
Lead Analyst, Barry Brandt
Administrator, Bryan Peroutka
Client Executive, Chris Rogers
Supply Chain Coordinator, Erica Cox
Auditors: ERNST & YOUNG LLP ST LOUIS

LOCATIONS

HQ: WORLD WIDE TECHNOLOGY HOLDING CO., LLC
1 WORLD WIDE WAY, SAINT LOUIS, MO 631463002
Phone: 314 919-1400
Web: WWW.WWT.COM

HISTORICAL FINANCIALS

Company Type: Private

Income Statement FYE: December 31

	REVENUE ($ mil.)	NET INCOME ($ mil.)	NET PROFIT MARGIN	EMPLOYEES
12/14	6,702	88	1.3%	1,052
12/13	6,392	77	1.2%	—
12/12	5,041	68	1.3%	—
Annual Growth	15.3%	14.2%	—	—

2014 Year-End Financials

Return on assets: 6.4%   Cash ($ mil.): 109
Return on equity: 38.0%
Current ratio: 1.20

WORLEY & OBETZ, INC.

Auditors: HOROVITZ RUDOY & ROTEMAN LLC

LOCATIONS

HQ: WORLEY & OBETZ, INC.
85 WHITE OAK RD, MANHEIM, PA 175458550
Phone: 717 665-6891
Web: WWW.WORLEYOBETZ.COM

HISTORICAL FINANCIALS

Company Type: Private

Income Statement FYE: August 31

	REVENUE ($ mil.)	NET INCOME ($ mil.)	NET PROFIT MARGIN	EMPLOYEES
08/17	677	2	0.4%	68
08/16	584	1	0.3%	—
08/15	520	2	0.4%	—
08/14	466	1	0.4%	—
Annual Growth	13.2%	14.0%	—	—

2017 Year-End Financials

Return on assets: 3.0%   Cash ($ mil.): —
Return on equity: 16.3%
Current ratio: 1.50

WTG GAS PROCESSING, L.P.

EXECUTIVES

Gen Ptnr, Ealmoor GP
Gen Ptnr, James L Davis
Vice President Business Develo, Dave Freeman
Producer Accounting Manager, Joey Farquhar
Safety Manager, Kendall McCasland
Director of Gas Supply, Rick Watkins
Supervisor Right of Way, Tom Segulja

LOCATIONS

HQ: WTG GAS PROCESSING, L.P.
211 N COLORADO ST, MIDLAND, TX 797014607
Phone: 432 682-4349
Web: WWW.WTGGASPROCESSING.COM

HISTORICAL FINANCIALS

Company Type: Private

Income Statement FYE: December 31

	REVENUE ($ mil.)	NET INCOME ($ mil.)	NET PROFIT MARGIN	EMPLOYEES
12/07	588	85	14.5%	25
12/06	498	64	13.0%	—
12/05	484	69	14.4%	—
12/04	342	39	11.5%	—
Annual Growth	19.7%	29.2%	—	—

2007 Year-End Financials

Return on assets: 29.8%   Cash ($ mil.): 45
Return on equity: 37.2%
Current ratio: 2.90

XMED OXYGEN & MEDICAL EQUIPMENT, LP

EXECUTIVES

Ptnr-Pres, Russel Scott Phillips
Pntr-V Pres, Ali Mutlu
Ptnr-Ceo, John Skono
Store Manager, Kendall Moore

LOCATIONS

HQ: XMED OXYGEN & MEDICAL EQUIPMENT, LP
15230 SURVEYOR BLVD, ADDISON, TX 750014338
Phone: 972 416-5502
Web: WWW.XMED4U.COM

HISTORICAL FINANCIALS

Company Type: Private

Income Statement FYE: December 31

	REVENUE ($ mil.)	NET INCOME ($ mil.)	NET PROFIT MARGIN	EMPLOYEES
12/18	4,060	227	5.6%	24
12/08	3	0	7.2%	—
12/06	0	0	—	—
12/05	4	0	11.7%	—
Annual Growth	68.6%	59.3%	—	—

2018 Year-End Financials

Return on assets: 19.1%   Cash ($ mil.): 13
Return on equity: —
Current ratio: 1.00

YALE NEW HAVEN HEALTH SERVICES CORPORATION

Yale New Haven Health System is a health care haven for residents of Southern Connecticut Southwestern Rhode Island and parts of New York's Westchester County. The company operates Yale-New Haven Hospital Greenwich Hospital Bridgeport Hospital and Lawrence & Memorial Hospital and has a contract relationship with The Westerly Hospital in Rhode Island (Northeast Medical Group) as well as children's cancer psychiatric care hospitals. In addition Yale New Haven Health Services operates outpatient facilities and provides such managed care services as network contracting as well as disease management programs. The system is affiliated with Yale University's medical school and has a grand total of about 2680 beds.

Operations

Through its Yale-New Haven Bridgeport Greenwich Lawrence & Memorial and Northeast Medical Group delivery networks the company provides comprehensive cost effective advanced patient care. The system's clinical services include primary and preventive care specialty acute care rehabilitation skilled nursing and coordination of home care.

Yale New Haven Health System in affiliation with the Yale School of Medicine and other universities and colleges educates health professionals and advances clinical care.

The 500-bed Bridgeport Hospital serves more than 23000 inpatients and nearly 350000outpatients a year.

The 206-bed Greenwich Hospital is a community teaching hospital. Lawrence & Memorial Hospital is a 280-bed general and acute care hospital serving parts of Connecticut New York and Rhode Island.

Northeast Medical Group is a not-for-profit multispecialty medical foundation. Its Westerly Hospital (served by the Yale New Haven Health System) is a 125-bed not-for-profit acute care community hospital serving southern Rhode Island and southeastern Connecticut.

Geographic Reach

Yale New Haven Health System serves patients in Southern Connecticut Southwestern Rhode Island and parts of New York's Westchester County.

Strategy

Yale New Haven Health's Northeast Medical Group (NEMG) opened a new multispecialty center at 1152 Kings Highway Cutoff in Fairfield CT in September. The new 25000-square-foot facility will house 45 exam rooms and three procedure rooms for some 30 providers in a number of specialties including family medicine internal medicine cardiology obstetrics-gynecology endocrinology gastroenterology pulmonary and sleep medicine urology ear nose and throat surgery and colorectal surgery.

In November 2020 two of the state's largest employers are partnering together for the betterment of healthcare in southeastern Connecticut. The Mohegan Tribe headquartered on their reservation in Uncasville and Yale New Haven Health (YNHHS) the state's largest healthcare system has been working in collaboration for nearly two years. Most recently that partnership has expanded greatly to ensure the safety and health of not just team members of Mohegan Sun but for the larger surrounding community. The intent of the collaboration is to holistically manage the health of those with chronic disease in collaboration with all members of the health care team with the goal of providing safe compassionate patient-centered care that is high quality and achieves cost effective outcomes.

This unique partnership brings Yale New Haven Health's care signature to the employees of Mohegan Sun and members of the Tribe as well as the opportunity to expand its reach into the surrounding communities. Creating access to its YNHHS physician colleagues across the region as well as to its local centers of excellence will help to improve care and reduce costs.

Company Background

Yale New Haven Health System was formed in 1996.

EXECUTIVES

Pres, Marna P Borgstrom
Exec V Pres*, Frank A Corvino
Evp and Coo, Yale-New Haven Ho*, Richard D'Aquila
Sr V Pres*, William S Gedge
Coordinator, Peggy Simonette
Coordinator, Nancy Martin
Information Security, Christopher Parchinski
Information Technology Securit, Edward Wright
Help Desk Analyst, Ismail Campbell
Desktop Support Technician, Nigel Hill
Senior Analyst, Devon Bushey
Auditors: LB KPMG LLP HARTFORD CT

LOCATIONS

HQ: YALE NEW HAVEN HEALTH SERVICES CORPORATION
789 HOWARD AVE, NEW HAVEN, CT 065191300
Phone: 888 461-0106
Web: WWW.YNHH.ORG

PRODUCTS/OPERATIONS

Selected Facilities

Bridgeport Hospital (Bridgeport Connecticut)
Greenwich Hospital (Greenwich Connecticut)
Yale-New Haven Hospital (New Haven Connecticut)
   Yale-New Haven Children's Hospital
   Yale-New Haven Psychiatric Hospital
   Smilow Cancer Hospital at Yale-New Haven

COMPETITORS

Bristol Hospital
Griffin Hospital
Hartford Health Care
Hospital Of Central Connecticut
Kent Hospital
Memorial Sloan-kettering

Midstate Medical Center
New Milford Hospital
Newyork-presbyterian Hospital
Saint Francis Hospital And Medical Center
Stamford Health
University Of Connecticut Health Center
Waterbury Hospital
Westchester Medical Center
Western Connecticut Health Network
Yale-new Haven Hospital Saint Raphael Campus

HISTORICAL FINANCIALS

Company Type: Private

Income Statement   FYE: September 30

	REVENUE ($ mil.)	NET INCOME ($ mil.)	NET PROFIT MARGIN	EMPLOYEES
09/19	657	0	0.0%	22,490
09/15	449	19	4.4%	—
09/13	427	35	8.2%	—
Annual Growth	7.5%	(56.3%)	—	—

2019 Year-End Financials

Return on assets: —
Return on equity: 0.1%
Current ratio: 1.00
Cash ($ mil.): 89

YALE NEW HAVEN HOSPITAL, INC.

Yale-New Haven Hospital (YNHH) is the flagship member of the Yale New Haven Health System. It provides tertiary care in more than 100 medical specialties to residents of southwestern Connecticut. The not-for-profit hospital has around 1540 beds on two campuses. Its main location includes the Yale-New Haven Children's Hospital and the Yale-New Haven Psychiatric Hospital. Its Smilow Cancer Hospital provides the very best cancer care available. YNHH provides cardiac and cancer care performs organ transplants and offers a variety of outpatient clinics. Yale New Haven Hospital was founded as the General Hospital Society of Connecticut in 1826.

Operations

YNHH offers heart and vascular services cancer (oncology) transplantation pediatrics neurosciences obstetrics and digestive health to name a few.

A key component of the main hospital facility is the Smilow Cancer Hospital which conducts cancer care and research in partnership with Yale University's Cancer Center. In addition to Smilow it also operates the Yale New Haven Children's Hospital and Yale New Haven Psychiatric Hospital.

Geographic Reach

The company is headquartered in New Haven Connecticut.

EXECUTIVES

Ceo-Pres, Marna P Borgstrom
Pres, Richard D Aquila
SEC, Vincent A Calarco
Executive of Information Techn, Jean Pawlich
Corporate Counsel/Legal, Stuart Warner
Chief Information Security Off, Null N Nizami
Svp Patient and Chief, Patricia Sue Fitzsimons
Pathologist, Kisha Mitchell
Certified Pharmacy Technician, Garfield Stewart
Program Inspector, Harold Russo
Manager, Jessica Nuzzo

LOCATIONS

HQ: YALE NEW HAVEN HOSPITAL, INC.
20 YORK ST, NEW HAVEN, CT 065103220
Phone: 203 688-4242
Web: WWW.YNHH.ORG

PRODUCTS/OPERATIONS

Selected Services

Ambulatory (outpatient) services
Bariatric surgery
Blood draw stations
Dental center
Diabetes and endocrinology
Diagnostic radiology
Ear nose and throat
Emergency services
Endocrine surgery
Gastroenterology
Geriatrics
Kidney disease
Maternity
Psychiatry
Pulmonology
Urology

COMPETITORS

Bristol Hospital
Connecticut Children's Medical Center
Griffin Hospital
Hartford Health Care
New Milford Hospital
St. Vincent's Health Services
Waterbury Hospital
Western Connecticut Health Network

HISTORICAL FINANCIALS

Company Type: Private

Income Statement   FYE: September 30

	REVENUE ($ mil.)	NET INCOME ($ mil.)	NET PROFIT MARGIN	EMPLOYEES
09/19	3,266	258	7.9%	22,000
09/15	2,388	107	4.5%	—
09/14	2,360	120	5.1%	—
09/13	2,360	120	5.1%	—
Annual Growth	5.6%	13.5%	—	—

2019 Year-End Financials

Return on assets: 6.2%
Return on equity: 12.2%
Current ratio: 1.40
Cash ($ mil.): 252

YALE UNIVERSITY

What do former President George W. Bush and actress Meryl Streep have in common? They are Yalies. Yale University is one of the nation's most prestigious private liberal arts institutions as well as one of its oldest (founded in 1701). Yale comprises an undergraduate college a graduate school and more than a dozen professional schools. Programs of study include architecture law medicine and drama. Its 12 residential colleges (a system borrowed from Oxford) serve as dormitory dining hall and social center. The school has around 12000 students and nearly 4000 faculty members.

Operations

Yale's graduate students of which there are more than 6500 outnumber its more than 5300 undergrads. Undergraduate tuition runs at around $42000 per year plus $13000 in room and board. Graduate tuition is about $35000 per year. The university has some 4000 faculty members.

The university has extensive research programs affiliated with its graduate school and its graduate-level professional schools which cover architecture art divinity drama engineering and applied science forestry and environmental studies law management medicine music nursing and public health.

Yale also operates the Yale University Press which publishes works of academics and professionals including e-books and traditional books. It published 475 titles during 2012 and has produced about 9000 titles in total.

Geographic Reach

Yale's facilities cover a total of 1100 acres including a 340-acre central campus with 260 buildings in New Haven Connecticut; a 140-acre West Campus on the edge of New Haven; and 600 acres of athletic fields and natural preserve areas outside of town. Yale's students come from all 50 US states and about 110 foreign countries.

Financial Performance

Sales for Yale have grown over the last five years and the university showed a 1% increase in revenues to more than $2.8 billion in 2012 due to higher student income grants and contracts (for research and training programs) medical service revenues and other income sources. Endowment income and grants and contracts are the largest source of revenue.

Yale's annual operating budget is about $2.7 billion.

Yale's roughly $19 billion endowment ranks as one of the largest in the US. Yale's Endowment grew about 9% in 2010 producing a gain of $1.4 billion.

Company Background

Yale was founded in 1701 through the vision of a group of colonial clergymen who began planning for a university in the 1640s. It was named Yale College in 1718 after a Welsh merchant Elihu Yale who made a sizable donation to the institution.

EXECUTIVES

Pres, Richard C Levin
Vice Pres-General Counsel*, Dorothy Robinson
Vice Pres-SEC*, Linda Koch Lorimer
Vice Pres-Finance-Admin*, John E Pepper Jr
Provost*, Andrew D Hamilton
Principal*, Peter Salovey
Coordinator, Holly G Nardini
Chief of Neurovascular Surgery, Murat Gunel
Program Coordinator Project Di, Barb Nangle
Associate Professor of Medicin, Joseph Akar
Doctor Neurology, Bryan Desouza
Auditors: PRICEWATERHOUSECOOPERS LLP

LOCATIONS

HQ: YALE UNIVERSITY
105 WALL ST, NEW HAVEN, CT 065118917
Phone: 203 432-2550
Web: WWW.YALE.EDU

PRODUCTS/OPERATIONS

Colleges and Schools
Graduate School of Arts and Sciences
Professional schools
  School of Architecture
  School of Art
  Divinity School
  School of Drama
  School of Engineering & Applied Science
  School of Forestry & Environmental Studies
  Law School
  School of Management
  School of Medicine
  School of Music
  School of Nursing
  School of Public Health
  Institute of Sacred Music
Yale College (undergraduate studies)
Residential Colleges
  Berkeley College
  Branford College
  Calhoun College

Davenport College
Ezra Stiles College
Jonathan Edwards College
Morse College
Pierson College
Saybrook College
Silliman College
Timothy Dwight College
Trumbull College

HISTORICAL FINANCIALS
Company Type: Private

Income Statement
FYE: June 30

	REVENUE ($ mil.)	NET INCOME ($ mil.)	NET PROFIT MARGIN	EMPLOYEES
06/20	4,246	(509)	—	11,000
06/19	4,105	(15)	—	—
06/18	3,848	3,270	85.0%	—
06/17	3,647	2,447	67.1%	—
Annual Growth	5.2%	—	—	—

2020 Year-End Financials
Return on assets: (-1.1%)   Cash ($ mil.): 1,011
Return on equity: (-1.6%)
Current ratio: —

YATES GROUP, INC.

E-Z Mart Stores aims to make filling gas tanks and stomachs EZR for small-town America. The regional convenience store chain operates about 295 stores across four neighboring states including Arkansas Louisiana Oklahoma and Texas. Rather than build its own stores the company usually expands through acquisitions. In addition to the standard hot dogs sodas coffee and cigarettes most E-Z Mart locations also offer Shell Conoco Phillips 66 or CITGO gasoline. E-Z Mart was founded in 1970 by Jim Yates in Nashville Arkansas. Yates died in 1998 when the plane he was piloting crashed leaving his daughter Sonja Hubbard at the company's helm as CEO.

Geographic Reach

Ranked #35 on Convenience Store News ' "Top 100 Convenience Stores Report" E-Z Mart is a regional c-store chain that primarily serves Texas and Arkansas as well as Oklahoma and Louisiana.

Sales and Marketing

Aiming to offer the chain's customers access to updated fuel prices a list of locations and in-store promotions among other items E-Z Mart partnered with OpenStore by GasBuddy to roll out a new E-Z Mart website and mobile app. The fully integrated mobile app enables consumers to send feedback from their mobile phones and receive time-sensitive electronic mobile coupons.

Strategy

While E-Z Mart has trimmed its store count during the past decade or so including exiting markets such as Missouri it continues to make strategic acquisitions. Like other convenience store operators seeking to boost in-store sales E-Z Mart is expanding its food and beverage offering adding fresh-brewed iced tea to all of its stores and installing freezers. Outside the company has a deal with Redbox to place its movie rental kiosks outside of E-Z Mart stores.

EXECUTIVES

Ceo, Sonja Hubbard
Cfo*, Stacy Yates
Cash Management, Dena Parsons
Database Administrator, Jack Williams

Helpdesk Supervisor, Courtney Mitchell
Administrator, Ryther John
Office Manager, Debbie Flowers
Director, Human Resources and, Amy Smith
Executive Officer, Bob Ivey
Vice President, Lifford Luthringer
Division Manager, Marketing, Mike West
Auditors: BKD LLP FORT SMITH ARKANSAS

LOCATIONS

HQ: YATES GROUP, INC.
2015 GALLERIA OAKS DR, TEXARKANA, TX 755034618
Phone: 903 336-6246
Web: WWW.CONOCOPHILLIPS.COM

2014 Stores

	No.
Texas	96
Arkansas	95
Oklahoma	80
Louisiana	18
Total	**289**

COMPETITORS

7-eleven	Love's Country Stores
Allsup's	Quiktrip
Brookshire Grocery	Racetrac Petroleum
Chevron	Susser Holdings
Exxon Mobil	Valero Energy
Krause Gentle	

HISTORICAL FINANCIALS
Company Type: Private

Income Statement
FYE: December 31

	REVENUE ($ mil.)	NET INCOME ($ mil.)	NET PROFIT MARGIN	EMPLOYEES
12/16	786	16	2.1%	2,100
12/15	827	16	2.0%	—
12/14	1,026	19	1.9%	—
12/13	1,003	15	1.5%	—
Annual Growth	(7.8%)	3.2%	—	—

2016 Year-End Financials
Return on assets: 7.9%   Cash ($ mil.): 7
Return on equity: 12.6%
Current ratio: 1.30

YORK HOSPITAL

York Hospital operating as WellSpan York Hospital takes its name from the community whose health it seeks to preserve. Part of WellSpan Health the medical center has about 570 beds and serves residents of York and surrounding area of south-central Pennsylvania. It is a regional leader in cardiovascular and orthopedic care and has programs in other specialty areas including oncology behavioral health and geriatrics. Additionally WellSpan York Hospital operates a Level 1 trauma center offers outpatient surgery emergency home health and diagnostic imaging services. It is also has teaching and research programs. The hospital was founded in 1880.

Operations

WellSpan York Hospital has been recognized as a top 100 US hospital by US News for more than five years in a row. It is also recognized for its cardiovascular and orthopedic programs. The center employs about 700 doctors.

The hospital's education programs include five allied health schools and seven residency programs. Affiliated organizations include the medical schools of Drexel University Pennsylvania State University and University of Maryland.

Strategy

WellSpan York Hospital is working to improve its specialist programs to meet the growing medical needs of area residents. In 2011 for instance it collaborated with technology firm Cerner and pharmaceuticals firm Hospira to form an infusion management program for its intensive care unit; the program aims to reduce infusion-related errors. In addition it launched a urinary catheter removal protocol to reduce infection rates and it implemented an aortic valve replacement program (making it one of three facilities in Pennsylvania to offer the open-heart surgery alternative).

EXECUTIVES

Ceo, Donald B Dellinger
Ceo*, Kevin H Mosser
Pres*, Richard L Seim
Sr V Pres, R Hal Baker
V Pres*, Richard H Brown
Cfo*, Michael F O'Connor
V Pres*, Raymond Rosen
SEC*, Jan Herrold
Staff, Jeri Pickle
Internal Medicine Practitioner, Ese Uwadia
Internal Medicine Practitioner, Faiza Rahim

LOCATIONS

HQ: YORK HOSPITAL
1001 S GEORGE ST, YORK, PA 174033645
Phone: 717 851-2345
Web: WWW.WELLSPAN.ORG

COMPETITORS

Ascension Health	Hanover Healthcare
Catholic Health	Hershey Medical Center
Initiatives	Holy Spirit
Geisinger Health	Lancaster General
System	Memorial Hospital (pa)
Guthrie Healthcare	Pinnaclehealth System

HISTORICAL FINANCIALS

Company Type: Private

Income Statement				FYE: June 30
	REVENUE ($ mil.)	NET INCOME ($ mil.)	NET PROFIT MARGIN	EMPLOYEES
06/20	1,163	15	1.4%	6,200
06/18	1,063	181	17.0%	—
06/16	990	17	1.8%	—
06/15	925	82	9.0%	—
Annual Growth	4.7%	(28.3%)	—	—

2020 Year-End Financials

Return on assets: 0.7%   Cash ($ mil.): 249
Return on equity: 1.2%
Current ratio: 1.20

YUMA REGIONAL MEDICAL CENTER INC

Yuma Regional Medical Center (YRMC) is an acute care hospital that provides medical services for Yuma Arizona and its surrounding communities. The not-for-profit hospital which has more than 400 beds and 400 doctors provides general medical surgical and emergency services. YRMC also operates about 40 additional facilities around Yuma including a rehabilitation hospital laboratories a wound care clinic primary care clinics and diagnostic imaging centers.

Sales and Marketing
Financial Performance

EXECUTIVES

Ceo, Pat T Walz
Cfo, Tony Struck
SEC, Phillip Richemont
Purchasing Coordinator, Lisa Anaya
Coordinator, Patti Mixon
Scientist, Annette Fletcher
Information Specialist, Linda Corrie
Information Specialist, Rhonda Bennett
Information Specialist, Hector Delatorre
Trustee, Khidir Osman
Information Specialist, Marilyn Lara

LOCATIONS

HQ: YUMA REGIONAL MEDICAL CENTER INC
2400 S AVENUE A, YUMA, AZ 853647170
Phone: 928 344-2000
Web: WWW.YUMAREGIONAL.ORG

PRODUCTS/OPERATIONS

Selected Services

Children
Cancer Care
Children's Rehabilitative Services
Critical Care
Diabetes Education
Diagnostic Imaging
Emergency Department
First Health Medical Supply
Gastroenterology
Heart
Hospitalist Program
Lab
Medical Staff Services
Nursing Units
Outpatient Surgical Center
Pharmacy
Spiritual Care and Patient Advocacy
Surgical Services
Weight Loss
Women's Services
Wound Care Center

COMPETITORS

Banner Health	Northern Arizona
Community Health	Healthcare
Systems	Phoenix Children's
Dignity Health	Hospital
Hca	Providence St. Joseph
John C. Lincoln Health	Health
Network	Scottsdale Healthcare

HISTORICAL FINANCIALS

Company Type: Private

Income Statement				FYE: September 30
	REVENUE ($ mil.)	NET INCOME ($ mil.)	NET PROFIT MARGIN	EMPLOYEES
09/19	543	28	5.2%	2,400
09/18	483	66	13.7%	—
09/17	442	50	11.5%	—
09/16	410	37	9.2%	—
Annual Growth	9.9%	(9.1%)	—	—

2019 Year-End Financials

Return on assets: 3.3%   Cash ($ mil.): 111
Return on equity: 5.4%
Current ratio: 0.90

ZEN-NOH GRAIN CORPORATION

EXECUTIVES

Ceo, Charles Colbert
Ceo, John D Williams
Exec V Pres, Shin Inoue
Sr. V Pres, Charles E Colbert
Ctlr, Robin Gerarve
Dir, Hiroyuki Kawasaki
Dir, Yoshihiro Sugiyama
Dir, Yoshinori Ohara
Executive Vice-President, Osamu Yako
Feed Ingredients Manager, Jeigh Hymel
Sales Manager, Akira Hayashi
Auditors: KPMG LLP NEW ORLEANS LOUISIA

LOCATIONS

HQ: ZEN-NOH GRAIN CORPORATION
1127 HWY 190 E SERVICE RD, COVINGTON, LA
704334929
Phone: 985 867-3500
Web: WWW.CGB.COM

HISTORICAL FINANCIALS

Company Type: Private

Income Statement				FYE: May 31
	REVENUE ($ mil.)	NET INCOME ($ mil.)	NET PROFIT MARGIN	EMPLOYEES
05/21*	9,771	211	2.2%	250
03/21	9,771	211	2.2%	—
05/20	5,930	44	0.7%	—
05/19	5,983	53	0.9%	—
Annual Growth	27.8%	98.9%	—	—

*Fiscal year change

2021 Year-End Financials

Return on assets: 8.2%   Cash ($ mil.): 41
Return on equity: 27.3%
Current ratio: 1.20

Hoover's Handbook of

Private Companies

Index of Executives

Index of Executives

A

A, Juliet V Garc 558
Aagard, Linda 588
Aamodt, Patsy 41
Aanenson, Gary 103
Aaroe, David 218
Aaron, Steven L 520
Aaron, Clay 520
Aaron, Todd 520
Abalos, Glenda C 434
Abando, Napoleon P 335
Abatti, Mike 261
Abbas, Fouad 300
Abbas, Syed 352
Abbott, Jordan 158
Abbott, Mary J 271
Abbott, Amber 427
Abbott, Greg 517
Abdalla, Amy 428
Abdallah, Chaouki 228
Abdallah, Chaouki 625
Abdel-Kerim, Ahmed 39
Abdelhafiz, Gada M 243
Abdelrahman, Emad 589
Abdou, Nicklaus 218
Abduljalil, Hala 502
Abdullah, Butool 102
Abel, Gregory E 386
Abele, Lawrence 216
Abele, Chris 658
Abelsen, James N 483
Abelson, David 406
Abenoja, Maureen 482
Abercrombie, Les 222
Abercrombie, Barbara 627
Abeyta, Mary 154
Ables, Dorothy M 494
Aboitiz, Jon R 427
Aboularage, Anthony 222
Abraham, Karen 78
Abraham, Shema 290
Abrahamson, Vickie 592
Abramowitz, Bernard H 373
Abrams, Mandy 135
Abrams, Robin 244
Abreg, Mart N 558
Abrega, Martfn 558
Abruzzo, Pat 283
Abutineh, Mike 60
Aceto, Joe 462
Acevedo, Dana-Lise 67
Acevedo, Elizabeth 371
Acevedo, Elizabeth 377
Acevedo, Debby 451
Aceves, Abraham 214
Ach, Heidi 159
Achat, Catherine 161
Ache, Sean 467
Acheson, Eleanor D 364
Achtenberg, Jeff 556
Ackerman, Eileen 335
Ackerman, Melissa Melshenker 429
Ackerman, Jeffrey C 559
Ackroyd, Jim 4
Acord, Elizabeth L 96
Acosta, Philip A 486
Acosta, Juan 641
Acosta-Trant, Ivette 59
Acres, Harold R 174
Adachi, Hiroshi 94
Adair, Donald D 530
Adam, Mark 422
Adam, Bradley J 492
Adam, Abdulmajid Y 497
Adams, J Phillip 9
Adams, Jacob 41
Adams, Alecia 80
Adams, Kevin D 110
Adams, Korey 120
Adams, Lancing 122
Adams, Cathy 140
Adams, Kevin D 151

Adams, Susan 163
Adams, Alan 251
Adams, Patricia 271
Adams, Leah 275
Adams, Gregory A 279
Adams, Janice 279
Adams, Joe M 282
Adams, H E 285
Adams, H E 285
Adams, Martin 303
Adams, Martin L 303
Adams, Connie 315
Adams, Megan 347
Adams, Mary 449
Adams, Kerry 452
Adams, Jason M 457
Adams, Dan 464
Adams, Nancy 508
Adams, Heather 542
Adams, Neil J 547
Adams, Mary Jane 614
Adcock, David B 196
Adcock, Bradley T 626
Addiscott, Lynn 612
Addison, Lewis C 107
Addison, Ann 652
Adebo, Olo 184
Adkins, Chuck 259
Adkins, Heather 550
Adler, Steve 123
Adolphsen, Nick 513
Adzick, Susan 322
Afable, Richard 502
Afienko, Abbey 332
Aflague, Ermina 603
Afonicheva, Ludmila 596
Agamanolis, Stefan 118
Agbamu, Omoyefe 261
Agbe-Davies, Christopher 494
Agee, Nancy Howell 99
Agee, Shannon 579
Aggarwal, Nidhi 70
Aggarwal, Prateek 244
Aggus, Gary 251
Aglialoro, Cilia 122
Agnew, Hugh L 560
Agoro, Kamaldeen 307
Agosto, Paula 549
Aguero, Rocio 384
Aguila, Adrian 126
Aguilar, Jose 303
Aguilar, Gayla 381
Aguilar, Leslie 467
Aguilera, Ernesto 499
Aguirre, Ramon 462
Aguirre, Artie 528
Aguirre, Luz 581
Agustin, Virgil 61
Aheran, Patrick 497
Ahern, Theresa M 97
Ahern, Paula 208
Aherrera, David 270
Ahlgrimm, Marijo 32
Ahmad, Nasrin 596
Ahmedfiqi, Osman 330
Ahn, Hong 596
Ahrens, Jere M 206
Ahrens, Chris 554
Ahtone, Caylen 113
Ahuja, Kishore 379
Aichele, Stephen 146
Aikens, Jason 258
Aing, Melissa 326
Ainsworth, Larry K 502
Aisd, Aaron 43
Aish, Bassil 253
Aitcheson, Latoya 126
Aitken, Stuart 309
Aivano, Joseph 209
Ajmani, Deep 390
Akamatsu, Yayoi 378
Akar, Joseph 661
Akash, Dave 89
Akeman, Jeff 379

Aken, Mary 160
Aker, Mark 131
Akers, Jeffery 394
Akhavan, Chris 230
Akin, Richard L 454
Akins, Nicholas K 30
Akiyoshi, Shiro 185
Akman, Jeffrey S 560
Akom, Francis 451
Akpakli, George 112
Akram, Adil 53
Al-Ghanoudi, Ashirf 231
Alaniz, Anastacio 644
Alarid, Andy 542
Alba, Adriana 245
Alba, Botero 286
Albam, Amy 154
Alban, Pamela K 156
Albanese, Dominic 182
Albanese, Craig 372
Albataineh, Rania 59
Alberici, John S 16
Alberici, John S 16
Alberici, John S 17
Albert, Frances 15
Albert, Andrew 370
Albert, Hans 376
Albertelli, Christine 547
Alberti, Pat 53
Alberto, Carl 506
Alberts, Jim 209
Albrecht, Raymond P 342
Albrecht, Angela 516
Albrecht, Stan L 637
Albrectsen, Anne-Birgitte 420
Albright, Matt 55
Albright, Steven 517
Albright, Annetta 609
Alcoser, Lisa 613
Aldred, John 251
Aldrich, David 431
Aldrich, Angie 470
Aldridge, Bill 93
Ales, Donna 290
Alessandrini, Evaline 607
Alexander, Jackie 25
Alexander, Paul G 61
Alexander, Pamela 124
Alexander, Kenneth Cooper 130
Alexander, Kelvin 158
Alexander, Craig 179
Alexander, Allen 185
Alexander, Barbara J 228
Alexander, Barbara 228
Alexander, David 252
Alexander, Wendy 290
Alexander, Keith 327
Alexander, Sherrie 336
Alexander, Kevin 348
Alexander, Joel 387
Alexander, Jim 410
Alexander, David George A 472
Alexander, Alica 514
Alexander, Ralph 532
Alexander, Randy 598
Alexander, Tim 610
Alexander, Gordon 638
Alfonso, David 198
Alfonso, Daniel 390
Alford, Mack L 509
Alfred, Ben 283
Algate, Scott 388
Alger, Robert 292
Ali, Mr Mushtaq 126
Ali, Saiyed 510
Ali, Frank 651
Alicandri, John 257
Alkire, Michael 426
Allaire, Bella Loykhter 436
Allam, Anthony 63
Allard, Tania 15
Allard, John 167
Allard, Francis 351
Allcon, Alvin J 540

Alldian, David P 79
Alleckson, Will 13
Allen, Mike 12
Allen, Sharon 18
Allen, Darrell 45
Allen, Les 73
Allen, Diane 101
Allen, Betsy 124
Allen, Jeff 147
Allen, Brenda 168
Allen, Joseph A 175
Allen, David 182
Allen, Charles 216
Allen, Herbert 216
Allen, Diane 220
Allen, Robert W 264
Allen, Daniel P 266
Allen, Stephen P 285
Allen, Thomas 291
Allen, Ellon 314
Allen, Jon 331
Allen, Erin 388
Allen, Mark 420
Allen, Karen 422
Allen, Jerold W 446
Allen, Teresa 453
Allen, Kristen 463
Allen, Meredith 509
Allen, Lee 512
Allen, Gloria 522
Allen, Elizabeth Heller 567
Allen, Richard D 578
Allen, Dee 623
Allen, Gary 625
Alley, Derek 640
Allgood, Jeri 163
Allgood, Scot 637
Allison, Les 238
Allison, Amanda 568
Allison, John 609
Allocca, Lori 488
Alloway, Jay 281
Allred, Mark 76
Allsman, Nicole 617
Allsup, Lonnie 9
Almandrez, Mary G 628
Almaraz, Jose 51
Almaraz, Frank 136
Almon, Robert C 403
Almquist, Andrew 19
Almquist, Jeff 169
Aloma, Angel 217
Alonzo, Leonicio 55
Alpay, John M 97
Alsip, Bryan 613
Alsobrooks, Angela 228
Alstead, Troy 297
Alston, Littleton 175
Alston, Asia 552
Alstrom, Eric 181
Altamirano, Heidi 441
Altemose, Cheryl 69
Altman, Theresa 298
Altman, Jeffrey 335
Altman, Richard 417
Altomare, Ronald 61
Alton, Gregg 427
Altschuler, Steven M 549
Aluotto, Jeff 160
Alvarado, Lily 193
Alvarado, Rodrigo S 202
Alvarado, Paulina 352
Alvarado, Douglas 404
Alvarado, Janice 411
Alvarez, Jordan 109
Alvarez, Vanessa 441
Alvarez, Yannette 521
Alvarez, Saide 533
Alvarez, Carlos 534
Alvather, Jay 535
Alves, David 67
Alves, Danny 608
Alzamora, Esteban 404
Amadi, Mariette Y 252

Index of Executives

Amador, Fernando 71
Amar, Kristopher 492
Amaro, Denise 255
Amato, Louis P 552
Amazan, Gaelle 562
Ambrose, Annemarie 165
Ambrozie, Tony 57
Ambush, Justin 316
Amecangelo, Dave 571
Ameismeier, Donna 453
Amerson, Tim 11
Ames, Raymond G 36
Ames, Craig 91
Ames, Richard 207
Amezcua, Rhonda 163
Amonette, Alison J 656
Amorous, Martin 542
Amos, Sister Helen 334
Amruthur, Iyer 284
Amsell, David 453
Amster, Laura F 29
Amstrong, C Micheal 564
Amundsen, Ashley 25
Amundson, Laura 47
An, Weizhe 338
Analdo, Stephen F 410
Anand, Manish 244
Anand, Sudeep 484
Anaya, Lisa 662
Ancheta, Mark V 596
Anchoori, Ravi 276
Andel, Steve Van 3
Andel, Steve Van 27
Andel, Stephen Van 486
Anderman, Steven 89
Anders, Amber 515
Andersen, Paul 257
Andersen, Michelle 268
Andersen, Lynn 327
Andersen, Connie 465
Anderson, Lesley 44
Anderson, Erik 45
Anderson, Candice 67
Anderson, Joyce 88
Anderson, Liz 91
Anderson, Matthew 96
Anderson, Jeffery 101
Anderson, Markham J J 108
Anderson, Ikaika 121
Anderson, Sharon 143
Anderson, Charles 148
Anderson, David 155
Anderson, Richard 159
Anderson, Doana 164
Anderson, Troy 170
Anderson, Jonnie 209
Anderson, Anjanette 233
Anderson, Paul 235
Anderson, Billie 236
Anderson, Derrick 240
Anderson, Derek 240
Anderson, Michael R 242
Anderson, Jason 247
Anderson, Lcpl 255
Anderson, Don 261
Anderson, Scott 264
Anderson, Kenneth W 266
Anderson, Suzanne 274
Anderson, Ronnie K 286
Anderson, Carl A 287
Anderson, Steven 292
Anderson, Teresa 310
Anderson, Gregory A 314
Anderson, Carol 349
Anderson, Richard H 364
Anderson, Darin 367
Anderson, Jill C 371
Anderson, Terry Sam 384
Anderson, Jeannette 404
Anderson, Joe Dean 417
Anderson, Carole 431
Anderson, Anita 441
Anderson, Richard A 459
Anderson, Terry D 459

Anderson, Brian B 468
Anderson, Richard A 498
Anderson, Richard A 506
Anderson, Adam 510
Anderson, Charles 572
Anderson, Audrey 590
Anderson, Paul 608
Anderson, Crystal 630
Anderson, Helen 631
Anderson, Suzanne 642
Anderson, Leha 643
Anderson, Jennifer 657
Andes, Lee 146
Andrabi, Imran 592
Andrade, Cristian 503
Andre, May Joe 540
Andreski, Lynne 498
Andresky, Christa 605
Andrew, Briggs 100
Andrews, Claudia 83
Andrews, Abigail 98
Andrews, Briggs 99
Andrews, Bob 165
Andrews, R D 224
Andrews, Stephanie 262
Andrews, Amanda 291
Andrews, Jarrett 360
Andrews, Victoria 387
Andrews, Sara 423
Andrews, Susan Mc 446
Andrews, Josh 542
Andrews, Sue 565
Andreyka, Timothy 15
Andrizzi, Flynn A 253
Andrulis, Erik D 102
Andruscavage, Thomas 260
Andy, Teuber 14
Anelli, Stephanie 60
Angel, Brent 125
Angel, David 169
Angelle, Bryant 139
Angelo, Philip 391
Angeloro, Vincent 230
Anger, Kevin 546
Angermeier, Ingo 493
Angley, James 373
Angulo, Christine Stiltner 488
Angus, Jeff 198
Angus, Jeff 405
Angus, Derek 634
Anhalt, Jackie 227
Anklam, Laura 592
Annan, Angela 577
Annesser, Sue 221
Anschutz, J Barron 103
Anschutz, Barron 104
Anson, Betty 499
Antes, John 346
Anthony, Chelsea 5
Anthony, Don 85
Anthony, Douglas 90
Anthony, Tim 365
Antonovich, Michael D 162
Antonsen, Erling 278
Anwar, Mariam 249
Anwar, Muhammad 533
Anwer, Muhammad 266
Aoun, Joseph 385
Apanius, Nicholas 336
Aplin, Teresa Broyles 203
Aplin, Richard 578
Aplington, David 498
Apodaca, Shawna 591
Apollony, Andrew 162
Aponte, Angel 452
Apostol, Lyndon 222
Apperson, Kevin 320
Applbaum, Hilda L 29
Appleton, Karl 508
Appley, Pat 595
Appling, Antoinette 501
Appold, Stacy R 160
Aquila, Richard D 660
Aquino, Dinah 510

Arad, Lana 231
Aragon, Nick 515
Arakawa, David Z 121
Arakawa, Alan 163
Aran, Pete 457
Aranda, Nancy 616
Araujo, Joleen 471
Arbeloff, Jill D 24
Arbuckle, Barry 326
Arbulu, Amalia 263
Arcand, Alfred 99
Arceneaux, Randy 9
Arceo, Paul 160
Archer, Donna 282
Archer, Tim 475
Archer, Bryan 518
Archer, Brian 557
Ardary, Kevin 437
Ardeljan, Manny 485
Arden-Ornt, Jeanine 102
Arena, Brenda 496
Arens, Arne 82
Argano, Matt 559
Argust, Annette 201
Arhebamen, Ebinehita 305
Arias, Eric 161
Arii, Carrie 434
Arkin, Eva 387
Arline, John 563
Arlt, Tim 367
Armater, Ann 246
Armato, Carl 390
Armato, Carl 426
Arment, Dan 86
Armfield, Jeff 487
Armini, Michael 385
Armistead, Russell E 477
Armour, Tim 98
Armour, Meri 337
Arms, William C 499
Armstrong, Leronne 130
Armstrong, David B 235
Armstrong, Christina 403
Armstrong, Greg L 420
Armstrong, Deborah A 515
Armstrong, Austin 583
Armtrong, Karen 246
Arndt, Gerald 238
Arndt, Diane 375
Arner, Steve 99
Arner, Eric 572
Arneson, Georgene 427
Arnita, Issa 310
Arnn, Roger 210
Arnold, Jennifer 14
Arnold, Sharon 135
Arnold, Judy 163
Arnold, Craig 200
Arnold, Kay K 206
Arnold, Bill 449
Arnold, Christina 572
Arnold, Greg 601
Arnoldussen, Jane 607
Arntzen, Corry 496
Aron, Adam 28
Aronne, Brian 257
Arquette, Athan 474
Arreola, Fernando 424
Arriaga, Michael 133
Arriaga, Roger 462
Arriaga, Elida 658
Arrison, Charles 48
Arroliga, Alejandro 64
Arroyo, David 171
Arroyo, Quemuel 338
Arroyo, Isaias 530
Arsenault, Matthew 57
Arthur, Lavone 64
Arthur, Donald C 308
Arthur, Tanya 524
Arwood, Steven 255
As, Norberto Due 133
As, Pablo J Far 558
Asaad, Emad 370

Asaro, Peter 571
Asbury, Alan 131
Ascher, Michael C 598
Aschoff, Timothy 175
Ash, Daniel 114
Ash, David P 156
Ashburn, Tom 261
Ashby, Tracy 620
Asher, Kelly 159
Ashford, Stephanie 125
Ashley, Marion 167
Ashley, Orozco 286
Ashley, Stanley W 546
Ashloc, Mark 6
Ashmore, Terry 444
Ashtary, Mishel 32
Ashuri, Roni 325
Ashwood, George 139
Aske, Jennings 372
Askie, Bill Van 311
Askins, Benjamin 298
Aslett, Bonnie 443
Asp, Jim 616
Aspillaga, Marea 57
Asquith, Marcia 214
Asquith, Pamella 260
Assa, Lior 54
Assaf, Michal 243
Astle, Angela 120
Astor, Frank 362
Astrup, Thomas 30
Atanasov, Atanas 288
Atandeyi, Kolawole 385
Atcherman, S Jeffrey 336
Athorn, Max 345
Atkins, Alegna 236
Atkinson, Mark 88
Atkinson, Kerry M 530
Atkinson, Charlene M 531
Attaway, David 47
Attrill, Ed 188
Attwood, James 378
Atwood, Denver 492
Aubert, Brenda 422
Aucoin, Renee N 50
Audiffred, J Douglas 321
Audiffred, J Douglas 321
Auetumrongsawat, Vimlin 621
Aufman, Matt 648
Auger, Stephen 215
Augsburger, Tod 298
Augsburger, Tod 298
August, Gerald 210
Augustin, Stanley M 601
Augustine, Cherri 316
Auman, Stan 368
Ausere, Michael J 209
Austen, Karla 360
Austin, Mike 25
Austin, Pam 55
Austin, Tara 392
Austin, Jennifer 467
Austin, Scott 553
Austin, Matthew S 593
Austin, Joshua 651
Auzenne, Byron 327
Avdic, Edina 564
Averette, Joseph W 452
Averill, Chris 411
Averill, Chris 411
Averill, Christopher R 575
Avery, Sonja 306
Avery, Christy 367
Avery, Phyllis 452
Avila, Manuel O 171
Avila, Andres S 261
Aviles, Bernadette 305
Avilez, Bernice 119
Avraham, Hava K 71
Axelrod, Neal 583
Axtell, Todd 167
Ayafor, Christopher 533
Ayers, Don 128
Aylouche, Mounzer M 318

Index of Executives

Aymond, Ariel 150
Aymond, Angel 641
Aynechi, Mana 616
Ayscue, Charles F 346
Azam, Asif 293
Azar, Mario 76
Azar, Amir Rahnamay- 100
Azar, Robert B 390
Azarela, Michael 523
Azeez, Sulaiman 300
Azevedo, Neil 160

B

Baameur, Ahmed 161
Babaeva, Inna 237
Babb, Ivy 81
Babcock, Calvin 59
Babcock, Linda 100
Babiarz, Greg 22
Babikian, Shant 18
Babino, Tim 623
Babowal, Jill 189
Bachand, Kelly 210
Bachelor, Alex 178
Bacher, Lars 208
Bachman, Howard 175
Bachman, Robert J 205
Baciarelli, Renato 119
Bacigal, Eric 249
Bacigalupo, Richard J 441
Backberg, Benjamin A 77
Backes, Richard 578
Bacon, Ken 479
Badcock, Henry C 644
Badcock, Ben M 644
Badger, Lauren 265
Badlani, Sameer 210
Badu, Kofi 286
Baer, Mark 175
Baer, Richard 582
Baerst, Peggy 97
Baetz, Cary 475
Bagg, Halsey 611
Baggett, Nancy 160
Baghdadi, Zeinab 192
Bagley, Annemarie 135
Bagshaw, Seth 376
Bahadur, John 356
Bahensky, Donna Katen 632
Bahtka, Tara 404
Baier, Bill 168
Bail, Jennifer 242
Bailey, John 47
Bailey, Teresa 145
Bailey, Jacqueline 164
Bailey, Andrew 177
Bailey, Emily J 177
Bailey, Troy 213
Bailey, David 243
Bailey, Gregory 356
Bailey, Colin 381
Bailey, Jeff 420
Bailey, Kassie 509
Bailey, Anne 514
Bailey, Lara 541
Bailey, Colonel B 578
Bailey, Joe 607
Bailey-Kanelos, Courtney 168
Baileys, Kristen 635
Bain, Ruthie 510
Baisch, Beth 132
Baker, James A 9
Baker, J Craig 30
Baker, Kathryn 78
Baker, Bill John 112
Baker, Emily A 122
Baker, James 125
Baker, Donna 139
Baker, Charlie 146
Baker, Debbie 164
Baker, Michele 166

Baker, Thomas 175
Baker, Pam 203
Baker, Angie 212
Baker, Paula 221
Baker, Joselyn Butler 233
Baker, Gary 254
Baker, Ron 270
Baker, Rick 281
Baker, Caleb 292
Baker, Brenda 447
Baker, Charmaine 486
Baker, David 498
Baker, Christine 571
Baker, Abby 659
Baker, R Hal 662
Baklarz, Ron 324
Balaguer, Susan 573
Balandran, Adriana 486
Balbosa, Suzanne 59
Balchunas, James 644
Balderrama, Melissa 114
Balderson, Bill 656
Balduzzi, Michael A 206
Baldwin, Dennis 95
Baldwin, Polly 169
Baldwin, Todd 238
Baldwin, Lawanda 345
Baliles, Jon 132
Balish, Amanda 511
Ball, Vanessa 35
Ball, Florence 172
Ball, Calvin 256
Ball, Parke D 285
Ball, James 380
Ball, George L 407
Ball, Andrew 523
Ball, George L 573
Ballance, Tom 311
Ballard, Brent 145
Ballard, Gary 212
Ballard, Dennis 461
Ballesteros, Walter 160
Ballinas, Carlos 332
Ballock, Steven 69
Ballowe, Rob 251
Balog, Suzanne 617
Balogh, Cadd 162
Balser, Jeff 640
Baltimore, David 546
Bamford, William A 578
Bamfordiii, William A 578
Bamisile, Ajoke 377
Bancroft, Trevor 493
Banda, Jose 455
Bandoma, Danna 169
Bandy, Cecli M 304
Banister, Sandi 362
Bankhead, Tammie 556
Banks, Stacie L 49
Banks, Gary 103
Banks, Jeffrey 527
Banks, Diana 560
Banks, Stacie L 639
Bao, Chengdi 207
Bar-Adon, Eshel 54
Baran, James 131
Baratian, Jacqueline 320
Barba, James J 15
Barba, James J 16
Barbao, Christina 167
Barbato, Angela 467
Barbato, Anthony 598
Barbeau-Leonard, Geraldine 242
Barber, Dennis 103
Barber, Cindy 134
Barber, Adena 393
Barber, Dennis 553
Barbera, Charles 438
Barbera, Judith 518
Barbier, Robert P 614
Barbieri, Eric 334
Barbour, Catherine 32
Barboza, Shawn 186

Barchi, Daniel 372
Barden, Sean T 646
Barela, Ed 461
Barfield, Kelle J 206
Barfield, John 516
Bargamin, Stephen N 644
Barges, Demetri 96
Bari, Joseph De 503
Baribeau, Nathan B 22
Barkela, Lori 333
Barker, James P 160
Barker, Fred 323
Barkhurst, Linda 355
Barkley, Pete 2
Barklow, Megan 151
Barlak, Paul M 203
Barlak, Paul M 375
Barleston, Karen 562
Barlows, Ted 251
Barnard, Keith 216
Barnes, Christine 133
Barnes, C Linda 157
Barnes, Andrea 281
Barnes, David G 361
Barnes, Earl 395
Barnes, Janet 431
Barnes, Ruthe 483
Barnes, Mandela 518
Barnes, John C 625
Barnes, James M 626
Barnes, James R 640
Barnes, Chase 640
Barnes, Alan 652
Barnes, Erin 653
Barnett, Kimberly 113
Barnett, Tony 125
Barnett, Tonya 125
Barnett, David 127
Barnett, Joseph 151
Barnett, Blake 240
Barnett, Phillip 436
Barnett, Carlton 655
Barnett-Sarpalius, Jenny 304
Barnette, Kimberly 112
Barnette, Larry 493
Barnhill, Kris 454
Barnum, Enid 238
Barnum, Katherine T 618
Barone, Frank 188
Barr, Bill 304
Barr, Kenneth 384
Barr, Laurie 460
Barr, Alexis 499
Barr, Jordys 640
Barreda, Victor 202
Barrera, Arturo 538
Barreta, Anthony 279
Barrett, Kayla 81
Barrett, Michael 139
Barrett, Clarissa 170
Barrett, Karin A 188
Barrett, Kevin 257
Barrett, Robert 267
Barrett, David 290
Barrett, Mark 292
Barrett, Katy 436
Barrett, Cynthia 466
Barrett, Nancy 648
Barrett, John 658
Barrett, Jennifer 659
Barrick, Robert L 62
Barriere, Charles 209
Barril, Nove 510
Barrinson, Tom 455
Barritt, Kenneth 498
Barron, Eric 216
Barron, Christi 335
Barron, Joe 486
Barron, Eric J 575
Barron, Pamela 600
Barrow-Klien, Vickie J 153
Barrows, Karen 450
Barry, John M 65
Barry, Susan 657

Barsic, Mike 579
Barsky, Carol 183
Barsky, Adam 371
Barstow, Karen 172
Barta, Michelle 114
Bartels, Bill 513
Barth, Zach 261
Barth, Dianne 522
Barthelemy, Joseph 220
Bartholomay, Linda 463
Bartholomew, Mindy 288
Bartholomew, Justine 392
Bartlett, Beth 339
Barto, Nick 102
Barto, Nancy 510
Bartolone, Jason 169
Barton, Dennis 508
Bartos, Bob 13
Bartschat, Michael 278
Barwise, Sara 200
Barwood, Marlene A 272
Basden, Daniel 112
Basehore, John 201
Bash, Ruth 497
Basil, Jack 457
Baskerville, Bob 470
Baskovic, Victoria 158
Basler, Pamela 36
Basner, Kelly 385
Bass, Alexander 157
Bass, Justin 175
Bass, Adam 180
Bass, Theodore 476
Bass, Donald C 547
Bass, Mike 644
Bassanell, Melissa 463
Bassett, Tasha 551
Bassham, Terry D 209
Bateman, Christopher M 522
Bates, Tamara 90
Bates, Melanie 130
Bates, Cathy 145
Bates, David 155
Bates, Gigi 169
Bates, Martin W 233
Bates, Jennifer 249
Bates, Ruth 334
Bates, Cera 383
Bates, Shannon 499
Batista, Alex 349
Batres, Francisco 149
Batt, Douglas A 406
Battenfield, Keith 106
Battese, Betty 311
Battles, Julie 273
Baty, Darren 258
Baty, Heather 549
Bauck, Bryan 107
Baucum, Carlton E 256
Baucum, Carlton 567
Baudhuin, Robert 23
Bauer, Mark 185
Bauer, Rebeka 332
Bauer, Jason 472
Bauer, Daniel M 591
Bauman, Larry 151
Baumgarten, Alan S 346
Baumgartner, Kim 101
Baumgartner, Mike 109
Baumgartner, Amy 586
Bautista, Javier Velez 237
Bautista, Jeremy 445
Bauwel, Chantal Van 84
Bavazls, Marcelo 43
Baverso, Louis 635
Bawa, Neena 392
Baxter, Tom 42
Baxter, Amanda 281
Baxter, Kathleen D 510
Bayarena, Marco 160
Bayer, Andrea 165
Bayless, George 225
Baylor, Jnai 29
Baytos, David 337

Index of Executives

Index of Executives

Biles, Dwayne 530
Bill, Jim 161
Billera, Patrick 638
Billiar, Tim 634
Billings, Tom 42
Billingsley, Mary 428
Billman, Brock 293
Billotte, Mike 610
Billotti, Nicholas 605
Bills, Paul 243
Bilodeau, Marc 261
Bindelglass, David 87
Binder, Stephanie 650
Binerer, David 212
Binger, Benjamen M 136
Binger, James M 136
Bingham, John 640
Binkowski, Chuck 63
Bintz, John 247
Biodrowski, Mark 130
Biondic, Katarina 8
Birchmeier, Cindy 235
Bird, Suzie 641
Birkenstock, Timothy L 116
Birkenstock, Tim 340
Birkett, Sharon E 357
Birmingham, Scott 597
Birney, Kathleen 396
Biscardi, Joseph 1
Bischoff, Lou 44
Biscoglia, Dianna 353
Bisgaard, Chris 4
Bisher, Jon 33
Bishop, Deena 36
Bishop, Karen 172
Bishop, Alan 207
Bishop, John 301
Bishop, Lisa 340
Bishop, Adrianna 424
Bishop, Jake 440
Bishop, Cecelia 507
Bishop, Kayla 512
Bishop, Alison 525
Bishop, Amy 540
Bishop, Maryellen Kiley 602
Bishop, Michael 616
Bitter, Stephen 46
Bittner, Edward 610
Bizzell, Sandra 158
Bjorck, Meredith W 252
Bjur, Jared 213
Black, Eddie 287
Black, Douglas 346
Black, Michael 528
Black, Michael E 587
Black, Andrew 630
Blackmon, Tanya 390
Blackmore, Steven 426
Blackstone, Gail 167
Blackstone, Becky 557
Blackstone, Kathy 557
Blackwelder, Megan 389
Blackwell, Donald K 361
Blagg, Tandy 253
Blain, Keith 379
Blaine, Jennifer 496
Blair, Judith 627
Blais, Andrew 516
Blaisdell, Andrew 104
Blaise, Dale 490
Blake, Vanessa 36
Blake, Joe 143
Blake, Randy 262
Blake, Joseph J 428
Blakeborough, Lawrence B 36
Blakeslee, Christopher 87
Blakey, Rachel 384
Blaku, Sherif 265
Blanc, Paul La 492
Blancas, Monica 202
Blanchard, William 165
Blanchard, Saundra 332
Blanchard, Karl 475
Blanchette, Bob 204

Blanchette, Harvey 535
Blanco, Monica 133
Blanco, Patricia J 465
Blanco, Arturo 499
Blangiardi, Rick 121
Blank, Dr Josef 184
Blank, Dana M 606
Blankenship, Jeffrey 270
Blanton, Caron 81
Blasio, Bill De 129
Blasquez, Tricia 430
Blaszyk, Michael 189
Blatnik, Balinda 271
Blatter, Sandy 437
Blaufuss, Mark 336
Blaut, Brandon 211
Blaylock, Steven 383
Blessington, Malisa 200
Blevins, Robert 176
Blevins, Wade 548
Blickenstaff, Scott 543
Blinn, Tom 529
Bliss, Lilly 443
Bliss, Ethan 519
Block, Joanna 204
Block, Lauren D 301
Blodgett, Rick 163
Bloemke, Nathaniel 620
Blom, David 395
Blondel, Loic 537
Blondin, Leon E 55
Bloom, Rick 239
Bloom, Adam 379
Bloomfield, Steven F 122
Bloomquist, Cathy 261
Blose, Dennis R 355
Bloshtein, Eli 152
Blouin, Pedrina 402
Blount, Melba 159
Blue, Dan 463
Bluford, John F 601
Blum, Audrey 120
Blum, Fred 163
Blum, John 450
Blumstein, Shelia 90
Blumstein, Jerold 579
Blunk, Maggie 587
Blunt, Ricky 161
Blythe, Douglas 161
Boasberg, Tom 467
Boban, Ivica 654
Bobbitt, Donald R 616
Bobst, Wendell J 5
Boccalandro, Cristina 587
Bock, Sharon R 166
Bockius, Tom 158
Bodenhamer, Kevin 597
Bodgs, Lynn 426
Boe, Casey 36
Boeckmann, Alan 80
Boedecker, George B 323
Boehme, Linda 492
Boemer, Sally Mason 565
Boening, Jon Van 54
Boes, Charles W 542
Bogardus, James W 228
Bogdanoff, Debra 173
Boggess, Carrie 99
Bogle, Jill 68
Bohbot, Dominic 279
Bohl, Howard 610
Bohm, Lori 177
Bohman, Mark 236
Bohn, Jeremiah 345
Bohorquez, Carlos 201
Boid, Jonathan 121
Boise, April 200
Boisvert, Gerald 242
Boisvert, Gerry J 243
Boisvert, Marc E 647
Boland, Sylvia 124
Bolander, Ron 512
Boldrini, Maura 581
Boldt, Oscar C 546

Boldt, Thomas J 546
Bolduc, Guy 309
Boley, Marygen 25
Bolger, Thomas 118
Bolger, T Michael 566
Bolin, Jonathan 254
Bolin, Mike 287
Boll, Jared 255
Bollin, Stacey 351
Bollinger, Kathy 56
Bollinger, Lee C 581
Bolster, Jennifer 504
Bolton, Heidi 471
Boltz, Jim 413
Boly, Sarah 68
Boman, Ronald 507
Bommarito, Pamela 507
Bona, Miklos 620
Bonacich, Jane 90
Bonavita, Salvatore 284
Bonawitz, Douglas I 654
Boncariewski, Susan 186
Bond, James 103
Bond, Harrison 151
Bond, Elizabeth 420
Bond, Bradley 614
Bondank, Cheryl 382
Bonds, Doug 87
Bondurant, Robert D 314
Bondurant, Bob 315
Bondy, Joel 369
Bonewell, Fred 136
Boney, John 45
Bonfiglio, Joanne 55
Bonfiglio, Gregory 87
Bongiovanni, Clarice 293
Boniface, William 160
Bonilla, Emily 166
Bonilla, Pilar 392
Bonin, Deb 24
Bonnecarrere, Celeste 503
Bonner, Allison 84
Bonner, Daniel 124
Bonner, Bill 157
Bonner, Sharon 221
Bonner, Yvonne 275
Bonner, Jo 510
Bonner, Dr Jim 615
Bonnevier, Yvonne 275
Bontrager, Jeffrey A 116
Book, Julia 73
Booker, Jessica 214
Booker-Westerfi, Judy 72
Bookman, Dominique 336
Bookout, John F 567
Boom, Marc L 256
Boom, Marc L 567
Boom, Marc L 594
Boone, Jerry E 233
Boone, Jody 459
Boone, Deborah A 652
Booth, Kerri 155
Booth, Chris 314
Booth, Steve 448
Booth, Jane E 581
Booze, Randy 128
Boozer, Angela 131
Boozer, Leslie 217
Bopp, Aric H 128
Boran, Patrick 382
Boranian, Denise 95
Bordelon, Herbie 347
Borders, Lisa 123
Borders, Charlie 286
Bordovsky, Khaki 86
Borg, April M 457
Borgard, Lawrence 35
Borger, Janet 333
Borges, Sandra Kee 126
Borges, Gary 132
Borglund, Patricia 22
Borgstrom, Marna P 660
Borgstrom, Marna P 660
Borin, Mark 323

Boring, Tricia 646
Borkoski, Virginia 338
Borlee, Grace 142
Borodkin, Theresa 118
Borowy, Don 144
Borres, Anna 168
Borroum, Leon 232
Borschuk, Richard 225
Boscak, Alexis 623
Bosch, Scott 242
Bosch, Stephan 657
Boscov, Albert 84
Boshoven, Stephen 495
Bosio, Chris 513
Boskey, Richard S 180
Bosley, Marvenia 144
Boss, Jane 97
Boster, Gina 154
Boston, Larris 239
Boston, Charlie 572
Boston, Carolyn 618
Bostrom, Matt 167
Bostrom, Brent 237
Bostwick, Melissa 548
Boswood, Mike 603
Bosworth, Jim 101
Bosworth, Jim 142
Botelho, Marcelo 94
Botelho, Lee 160
Botello, Yvette 171
Bottenhofer, Alison 299
Botticelli, Anne 92
Bottom, Angela 421
Bottoms, Keisha Lance 123
Bottorff, Jim 259
Bouchard, Rhonda 521
Bouchillon, Dennis 150
Boudreau, Helen 391
Boudreaux, Kathryn 67
Boudreaux, Mike 171
Bouet, Vivan 136
Boughner, Bob 311
Bouillon, Allison 135
Boujoulian, Tara 172
Boulanger, Normand A 196
Boulanger, Bernard 567
Boulay, Joseph 64
Bounds, Hank 81
Bourdeau, Nancy 472
Bourdon, Thomas 413
Bourey, James M 129
Bourgeois, Meagan L 348
Bourne, Anedra 132
Bouzuk, Michael 634
Bove, V 318
Bowan, Matt 253
Bowden, Randy 55
Bowen, Jos A 491
Bowen, William G 544
Bowen, Julie 569
Bowen, Arthur N 641
Bowen-Biggs, Tara 164
Bowens, Samuel 135
Bower, Charles M 42
Bower, John 261
Bowers, Alyssa 146
Bowers, Kirby M 162
Bowers, Alisa 417
Bowes, Amy 586
Bowie, Paul J 8
Bowie, Patrick C 358
Bowles, W Bryan 184
Bowles, Connie 293
Bowling, Kathy 40
Bowman, Maureen 68
Bowman, Jerry 98
Bowman, Azuree 122
Bowman, Jeff 153
Bowman, Jeffrey 417
Bowman, Kerry 543
Bowman, Cory 564
Bowser, Brad 140
Bowser, Muriel 232
Bowser, Christopher 459

Index of Executives

Index of Executives

Brown, Shea 585
Brown, Jay 607
Brown, Christopher R 608
Brown, Laurie 650
Brown, Richard H 662
Brownie, Susan 476
Browning, Mary 545
Brownlow, Ben 436
Broyles, Christine 150
Broyles, Rob 216
Broyles, Andy 470
Brubaker, Connie 151
Bruce, Donna 516
Bruce, Stephanie 647
Bruck, Lori A 595
Bruckner, Brian M 91
Bruckner, Chris B 91
Brudnicki, Gary 652
Bruff, Edward 174
Bruhl, Elise 131
Bruhn, Michelle 463
Bruland, Peter 170
Brumbaugh, Nicole 367
Brumfield, Chris N 212
Brumley, Jessica 390
Brummett, Paul 197
Brumssted, John R 588
Brumsted, John R 588
Brunell, Gregory 319
Brunell, Greg 319
Brunett, Sharon 94
Brunetti, Michelle 638
Brunfield, Brian 551
Brunk, Debbie 196
Bruno, Amy 517
Bruno, Rosemary 599
Brunson, Don 351
Brunt, Jeff Van 607
Brussow, Julie 472
Bruxvoort, Keith 523
Bryan, Alex 6
Bryan, Amanda 135
Bryan, Douglas 335
Bryan, John 594
Bryan, Daniel 644
Bryan, Joe 644
Bryant, Joan 96
Bryant, Kevin E 209
Bryant, Carissa 218
Bryant, Jonnie 242
Bryant, Phil 270
Bryant, Gordon 287
Bryant, Colin 315
Bryant, Jay 315
Bryant, Richard 322
Bryant, Shea 342
Bryant, Dawn 382
Bryant, Andrea 446
Bryant, Phil 513
Bryant, Barry 517
Bryson, Gary 74
Bsh, Julian 134
Buccalo, Gina 607
Bucciarelli, Brant 447
Buchanan, Amber 147
Buchanan, Mark 171
Buchanan, Maxine 184
Buchanan, Christina 228
Buchanan, Lindsey 449
Buchanan, Ashley 568
Buchanan, Jamie 632
Buchbinder, David K 116
Buchenau, Blaine 218
Bucher, Susan 166
Buchwald, Emily 71
Buck, Cody 40
Buck, John 163
Buck, Brian 291
Buckingham, David C 145
Buckingham, Phil 603
Buckley, Francis 21
Buckley, Morgan 151
Buckley, Neil 317
Buckley, John L 421

Buckley, Guy G 494
Buckley, Kim 549
Buckley, Adam P 588
Buckley, Linda 624
Buckley, John L 656
Buckman, David I 23
Buckner, W Quinn 602
Buckwalter, Marion 295
Bucur, Silvana 507
Buczek, Joey 436
Budde, Rex 490
Budde, Tom 646
Budelman, Robert 505
Buehler, Ralf 203
Buehrens, Eric 71
Buellesbach, Rick 188
Buen, Maureen 157
Buencamino, Alex 169
Bueschen, Anton 615
Buescher, John 321
Buettner-Schmid, Kelly 381
Buffamoyer, Ashley 47
Bufferd, Allan 71
Buffington, Ronda 64
Bufkin, Patrick 499
Bugarin, Tom 168
Bugher, Daniel 491
Buhrow, Jason 258
Buhrow, Jack A 415
Bui, Tam T 170
Bukiewicz, Ralph 578
Bukiewicz, Susan 578
Bulawa, Bryan F 342
Bulla, Stacey 249
Bullard, Ketisha 132
Bullard, Linda 166
Bullard, David 416
Bullion, Diana 429
Bullock, Diana 203
Bullock, Timothy 306
Bullock, Gregory 623
Bulpitt, Amy 501
Bumgarner, Jayne 459
Bumpus, Bill 112
Bunch, Lonnie G 484
Bunch, David 636
Bunders, Olivia 63
Bunge, Katie 635
Bunker, Mike 99
Bunn, Sheila 232
Bunnell, Ron 56
Buongiorno, Michael J 308
Buono, Tim 466
Burbach, Nicole 261
Burby, Chris 521
Burch, Robert 165
Burchett, Ronald 417
Burden, Amanda 452
Burdick, Ginny R 148
Burdiek, Ed 281
Buretta, Sheri 120
Burfitt, Gregory 20
Burfitt, Gregory H 102
Burford, David 492
Burge, Taylor 620
Burgener, Jean 45
Burgess, Kathy 81
Burgess, Michael 288
Burgess, Rosalind 510
Burgum, Doug 515
Burke, Courtney 15
Burke, Michael W 17
Burke, William 63
Burke, Carolyn 113
Burke, Janet 134
Burke, Yvonne Brathwaite 162
Burke, Mike 164
Burke, Edmund F 186
Burke, Wayne 200
Burke, Dan 237
Burke, James F 254
Burke, Richard 313
Burke, Cody 368
Burke, Kathleen 376

Burke, John D 602
Burkett, Lynn 437
Burkhead, Lisa Cano 514
Burklund, Brent 92
Burks, Lindsey 178
Burkscoats, Thurgood 284
Burlage, David P 140
Burleigh, Mary 83
Burnell, Jody 402
Burnett, Danielle 18
Burnett, Bonnie 19
Burnett, Joshua 88
Burnett, Don 157
Burnett, Walter 184
Burnett, Keisha 187
Burnett, Justin 525
Burnett, Kevin M 525
Burnett, Kevin M 581
Burnette, Kayla 100
Burnette, Don 157
Burnette, Katie 422
Burnette, Rob 644
Burns, Dwight 51
Burns, Glenn 55
Burns, Glenn 55
Burns, Ben 96
Burns, Joey 225
Burns, Patrick 493
Burns, Bill 511
Burns, Steve 514
Burns, Ryan 534
Burns, Kevin 567
Burns, Carrie 574
Burns, Joy 619
Burns, Susan 648
Burnside, Antoinette 279
Burr, Noman 9
Burr, Charles 158
Burr, Angel 392
Burrell, Carol 385
Burrell, Eric 440
Burroughs, Victor 447
Burroughs, Lisa 472
Burrow, Mark 638
Burrows, Lori 43
Burrows, John 473
Burson, Michael L 121
Burton, Lisa 134
Burton, J H 142
Burton, Carol 467
Burton, Pat 507
Burton, Christian 533
Burton, Stella 565
Bury, Randy 556
Busacca, Brian 271
Bush, Tim 176
Bush, Greg 227
Bush, Stephen 468
Bush, William L 494
Bush, Chad 627
Bushey, Devon 660
Bushong, Todd 11
Bussells, Walter 270
Bussy, Jean-Franois 149
Bustany, Kelly 154
Buster, Bob 167
Busuioc, Monica 536
Butcher, Jeremy 418
Butler, Paula 9
Butler, Charl 11
Butler, Paul Edd 73
Butler, Lucretia 147
Butler, Sgt 160
Butler, Gregory B 209
Butler, Sara L 340
Butler, Mike 429
Butler, Michael 430
Butler, William 471
Butler, Jean 595
Butler, Karis 646
Butler, David 657
Buttar, Harinder 190
Butte, Grease 271
Butter, Kathleen 131

Butterfield, Virginia 169
Butterfield, Stacy M 421
Buttino, Mario 396
Button, Gigie 125
Butz, William 320
Butz, John 353
Buzachero, Victor V 469
Buzzard, Chuck 166
Buzzetta, Alan 392
Buzzo, Ann 481
Byers, Eric 73
Byford, Caroline 510
Byington, Mike 289
Bynum, Cherlyn 255
Bynum, Jen 414
Bynum, Trevor 648
Byrd, Sandra 43
Byrd, William D 272
Byrd, Jacqueline 421
Byrd, Gary 424
Byrd, Tamra 620
Byrd, Vanessa Y 641
Byrne, David 3
Byrne, Barbara 52
Byrne, Jolene 80
Byrne, Barbara 201
Byrne, Bobbie 201
Byrne, Bobbie 201
Byrne, Mike 353
Byrne, Jolene 465
Byrne, Richard 569

C

C, Victoria 220
Caamano, Deirdre 198
Caballero, Craig 610
Cabellon, Angela L 256
Cabera, Lillian 515
Cabezuela, Zaide 486
Cabral, Heidi 186
Cabral, Cathie 420
Cabrales, Steven X 148
Cabrera, Kayla 120
Cabrera, Juan 202
Cabrera, Alfredo 352
Cabrera, Maria 488
Caceci, Laura 451
Caceres, Celia 655
Caddell, Kari 396
Cadet-Dantes, Pascale 228
Cadieux, Melissa 200
Cadman, George E 57
Cadwallader, Brian 278
Cafarella, Erika 53
Cafferty, William 456
Cafm, Francisco C 431
Cagle, Mary Jo 499
Cagler, Donna 366
Cahill, Sr Helen 220
Cahill, Eileen 253
Cahill, Joseph 488
Cahoj, Nicholas 44
Cain, Kelli 102
Cain, Kathleen 115
Cain, Pamela 266
Cain, Pam 266
Cain, Matthew 620
Caiola, Vincent 292
Cairoli, Michael 505
Cairy, Rita 131
Calabrese, Gary 29
Calaman, Diane 179
Calarco, Vincent A 660
Calcaterra, Ronald J 107
Caldera, Leo 156
Calderini, Melinda 580
Calderon, Maria 451
Caldwell, Phil 122
Caldwell, Brian 154
Caldwell, Lance 233
Caldwell, Pete 255

Index of Executives

Index of Executives

Chadaga, Smitha 293
Chadbourne, Elizabeth 315
Chaffin, Patrick 454
Chafins, Tim 118
Chagla, Dilshad F 300
Chaisson, Avis 126
Chalk, Jared 130
Chalkley, Janice 209
Chaltraw, William 638
Chalupka, Kevin 461
Chamberlin, Michael 161
Chambers, H D 19
Chambers, Matthew 64
Chambers, Phil 142
Chambers, Melissa 343
Chambers, Richard 398
Chambers, Michael J 415
Chambers, Sara 510
Chambers, Bridget 512
Chambers, Christopher V 593
Chambers, Michael 629
Chambolle, Thomas 82
Champion, Timothy 12
Champion, Bret A 286
Champion, Natalie 615
Chamroeun, Nancy 242
Chan, Edward 118
Chan, Howard 132
Chan, Simson 285
Chan, Jimmy 373
Chan, Cynthia 509
Chan, Mary 616
Chance, Leonard 177
Chancellor, James 270
Chancellor, Beth 625
Chandarana, Himanshu V 64
Chandler, H Jody 78
Chandler, Nicole 177
Chandler, Ken 323
Chandler, Suzanne 353
Chandler, Willis 609
Chandra, Subodh 125
Chandraraj, Girisha 87
Chandrasekaran, Suja 145
Chandrasoma, Nishka 558
Chanen, Daniel 345
Chaney, Curtis 339
Chaney, Cindy 362
Chang, Anthony 29
Chang, Christopher 89
Chang, Helen 237
Chang, Florence 357
Chang, James 532
Chang, Andrew 532
Chang, Jason C 576
Chang-Wade, Gloria 624
Chao, Jennie 451
Chapados, Gregory F 225
Chapados, Greg 225
Chapados, Gregory 225
Chapados, Douglas L 413
Chapek, Fred 610
Chaplain, Wayne 356
Chapman, Robert H 62
Chapman, Rachel 114
Chapman, Jeffrey 309
Chapman, Archie J 323
Chapman, Carl L 491
Chapman, Rob 525
Chapman, Adrian P 654
Chappell, Colin 363
Chapple, Helen 175
Chappuis, Cameron 290
Charbonneau, Brett 265
Charbonneau, Terry 477
Charde, Seth 190
Charette, Gary C 38
Charles, Jamina 69
Charles, Alexandra 103
Charles, Robert M 289
Charles, David Phillip 640
Charlet, Barbara 516
Charlie, Cady 525
Charlson, Paul 26

Charlson, Jay 437
Charlton, Kevin 496
Charman, Max 420
Charman, Nikki 422
Charoglu, Constantine 218
Charrier, Richard 657
Charvat, Peter 504
Charvat, Peter 578
Chase, Sarah 67
Chatell, Cindy 535
Chatlin, Bradley 507
Chattopadhyay, Lily 114
Chaturbedi, Ritesh 191
Chauvin, Robert 277
Chavarria, Carla 28
Chavez, Cara 18
Chavez, Mary 169
Chavez, Jennifer 188
Chavez, Maria 464
Chavira, Ron 429
Chavoustie, Eric 488
Cheatham, Tim 568
Cheatham, Gabriele 577
Cheatham, Alfreda 641
Cheatman, Lora C 209
Cheatum, Chris 586
Chee, Jeffrey 577
Cheek, Daniel W 468
Cheek, Jeffrey 577
Chehade, Nabil 567
Chela, Hraleen 625
Chen, Dan 73
Chen, Xiaojun 498
Chen, Ping 515
Chen, Solomon 527
Chen, Robert 527
Chen, Honghui N 584
Chenoweth, Rodney 656
Cheong, Yoo 646
Cherenek, Tc 341
Chernow, Barbara 90
Chernyavskaya, Anna 379
Cherry, Jean 145
Cherry, Jessica 215
Chersky, Susan 80
Cheryl, Pietz 233
Chessare, John B 225
Chetty, Indrin 249
Cheung, Teresa 29
Cheung, Steven 171
Cheung, Andy 278
Cheung, Chris 371
Cheung, Ava 527
Cheves, Brad 491
Chew, Roy 283
Chiaetta, Stephen V 443
Chickering, Mark 45
Chidekel, Aaron 19
Chidress, Andrea L 81
Chien, Teddy 279
Chien, Alexander 301
Chigateri, Pavi 288
Chik, Ivan 183
Child, William H 433
Child, Jeffrey 433
Child, Curtis K 433
Child, Curtis 433
Childers, Marc 525
Childree, Robert 510
Childress, Randall V 600
Childs, Rick L 175
Childs, Craig 339
Childs, Clinton 548
Chin, Rodney 164
Chin, Mary 165
Chin, Kenneth 441
Chin, Caroline 527
China, Bonita 157
Chindemi, Craig 314
Ching, Bob 244
Ching, Patric D 474
Chinn, Carol 216
Chiou, Erin 42

Chiquoine, Ben 554
Chirico, James 52
Chirillo, Sarah 271
Chirillo, Gary 488
Chirinos, Astor 153
Chisholm, John 658
Chism, James 212
Chithran, Payyanadan V 206
Chiu, Desiree 164
Chiu, Elisa 211
Choate, David 91
Choate, Mark 411
Choi, John 167
Choi, Eunsu 258
Choi, Jimmy 370
Choi, Mun Y 625
Chojnowski, Daniel 315
Chong, Steven 118
Chopey, Stephen B 515
Chopra, Arvind 244
Chou, Henry 215
Chou, Anita 416
Chowdary, Sushma 642
Choy, David 370
Chrencik, Robert A 623
Chris, Carmello 258
Christensen, Mylia 99
Christensen, Cindy 116
Christensen, Leslie 120
Christensen, Jesper V 181
Christensen, Larry 278
Christensen, Angela 653
Christian, Dan 2
Christian, Ronald E 491
Christiansen, Jason 459
Christianson, Cole 416
Christianson, Conni 633
Christie, Brenda 166
Christie, Alease 291
Christophe, Pierrot 227
Christopher, Joyce 129
Christopher, Basil 399
Christopulos, Constantine 554
Christy, Lisa 590
Chroffel, Bruce 618
Chronister, Steven 173
Chrysler, Sue 233
Chu, Scott 597
Chubb, Jack 612
Chui, Herman 376
Chumura, Thomas 624
Chun, Semin 258
Chun, Edward 402
Chun, Robyn 620
Chun, Mark R 620
Chung, Alexander N 69
Chung, David 243
Chung, Mark M 326
Church, Tracy 242
Churchill, Arthur L 247
Churchill, Brian 409
Churchill, Sally J 440
Churchill, Brian 501
Churchwell, Kevin 548
Chvez, Dr Jess H 451
Chythlook, Joseph 413
Cianfrocca, Marguerite 651
Cicarella, Tom 222
Cicerone, Keith 272
Ciello, Ronald Del 333
Ciesla, Frank 350
Cieslewicz, Richard M 228
Cifu, Douglas 643
Cimino, Amy 420
Ciorra, Anthony 302
Cipollini, Auggie 311
Ciresi, Rita L 629
Claiborne, Jess 9
Clair, Jo St 125
Clancy, Kevin 246
Clancy, James 340
Clancy, Brian 461
Clapper, Sarah 526
Claps, Francis X 177

Clardy, Donna 214
Clardy, David 256
Clare, Timothy 81
Clarey, Charles 607
Clark, Kim 9
Clark, David 11
Clark, Matthew 53
Clark, Cynthia 70
Clark, Frank 80
Clark, Buster 101
Clark, Haley 119
Clark, Vonelle 150
Clark, Talisa R 158
Clark, Donald 174
Clark, Moira 183
Clark, Steve 203
Clark, Diana 269
Clark, Jeffrey 278
Clark, Crystal 282
Clark, Karri 286
Clark, Keith 311
Clark, Stuart 322
Clark, Mark T 337
Clark, Mark T 410
Clark, Edward Stuart 426
Clark, Joe 466
Clark, Alma 471
Clark, Susan 479
Clark, Meghan 498
Clark, Matthew 513
Clark, Bethany 514
Clark, John B 519
Clark, Tara 547
Clark, Mark T 552
Clark, Robert 562
Clark, Frank C 566
Clark, Michael 579
Clark, Jason 626
Clark, Lucas 627
Clark, Roy A 629
Clark, Carol 640
Clark, Caroline 640
Clark-Sellers, Lee 421
Clarke, Jeanette A 40
Clarke, Pete 166
Clarke, Christopher 252
Clarke, Stephen L 306
Clarke, David 452
Clarke, Cyril 642
Clarkin, Cheryl E 308
Clarkson, Daniel J 47
Clarkson, Dan 47
Clarkson, David 210
Clarno, Bev 516
Clatterbaugh, Carol 641
Claudia, Ontiveros 608
Claus, Brad 137
Claus, Mary Beth 372
Clausen, Jorgen M 181
Clavel, Daniel 127
Clawson, Dan 212
Clay, Brutus 457
Clay, Reed 517
Claybrooks, John 176
Cleaf, Damian Van 311
Cleary, John 154
Cleary, James J 202
Cleary, James 207
Cleary, Timothy J 285
Cleary, Mary Elizabeth 305
Cleary, Anne E 656
Cleaver, Chuck 314
Cleeland, David W 57
Clegg, Travis 244
Cleland, Richard C 208
Clemence, Cynthia 599
Clemensen, Hal 11
Clement, Scott 99
Clement, Mark 231
Clement, Alden 512
Clement, Mark 588
Clements, Charles 14
Clements, Hal 54
Clements, Mandy 203

Index of Executives

Clements, David 422
Clemeson, Marry 28
Clemmenson, Larry 31
Clendon, Susan Mc 199
Clesceri, Shannon 99
Cleveland, Debra 166
Cleveland, Sue 253
Clevenger, Megan 287
Clifford, Reny 98
Clifford, Teresa 174
Clifford, Robert 594
Clift, Ruth 401
Clinard, Nolan 95
Cline, Kimberly R 519
Cloonan, Donna 175
Cloues, Edward 643
Clough, Jaime 56
Clough, G Wayne 228
Clougher, John 240
Clouse, Steve 462
Clutter, Robert 147
Cnor, Paul 7
Cns, Marcie 201
Coakley, John 147
Coates, Spencer 217
Coatsworth, John H 581
Cobb, Wes 562
Cobb, Josephine 572
Cobb, James 620
Coble, Tina 380
Coble, Paul 644
Coborn, Christopher 142
Coborn, Emily 142
Cocca, Michael 521
Coccagno, James A 93
Cochenour, David 222
Cochenour, Randy 651
Cochran, Mike 307
Cochran, Karen 457
Cochran, Jeanne M 513
Cochrell, Patty 242
Cockerham, Bernard 212
Cockerham, Mary 439
Cockrell, Benny 423
Coco, Debbie 52
Coco, Denae 121
Cocorullo, L Mark 314
Coder, Derrick 213
Codner, Eugene 128
Cody, Kevin 178
Coe, Scott 83
Coen, Bill 339
Coffman, Chris 155
Cogen, Jeff 164
Coggins, Jeff 76
Cohan, Sean 378
Cohen, Charles F 69
Cohen, Richard S 69
Cohen, Bernard 276
Cohen, Rebecca 294
Cohen, Matthew 302
Cohen, Shai 325
Cohen, Evan 362
Cohen, Mark 416
Cohen, Nisan 440
Cohen, Andrew 444
Cohen, Gary 508
Cohen, David 512
Cohn, Leslie 55
Coin, Nick S 349
Coker, Dave 492
Colacchio, Thomas 182
Colalillo, Joseph 645
Colanero, Stephen 28
Colangelo, Marianne 124
Colar, Patricia 251
Colbert, Michael 164
Colbert, Charles 662
Colbert, Charles E 662
Colburn, James D 314
Coldiron, Jenny 225
Coldiron, Den Ellen 614
Cole, Darin 151
Cole, Paris 184

Cole, Deborah 190
Cole, Cheryl 203
Cole, Kim Braxl 379
Cole, Bennie L 387
Cole, Debbie 499
Cole, David 566
Cole, Emma 585
Cole, Jay 652
Coleal, David 650
Colella, Carmine 353
Colella, Joe 557
Coleman, Al 60
Coleman, Leigh 64
Coleman, Edward 158
Coleman, Candace 330
Coleman, Jeff 361
Coleman, Kia 365
Coleman, Mary 440
Coleman, Daniel 577
Coleman, Brandon 579
Coleman, Casey 606
Coleman, Timothy 635
Colenda, Christopher 651
Coley, Aaron 326
Colf, Richard W 285
Colf, Richard W 412
Collard, C David 114
College, Eugene 211
Colletti, Lisa 440
Collier, Joe 429
Collingsworth, J M 342
Collins, Joshua L 76
Collins, Wendy 163
Collins, Kim 165
Collins, Mark 186
Collins, Peg 193
Collins, Tim 275
Collins, Barbara 398
Collins, Gregory 403
Collins, Mindy 434
Collins, Bernadette 553
Collins, Bill 579
Collins, Henry 594
Collver, Ronan 87
Colman, Gerard 58
Colom, Rebeca 529
Colon, Lina 228
Colon, Tairis 408
Colones, Robert L 322
Colonna, Jerome 68
Colonna, Suzanne 553
Colorado, Lisa 608
Colpack, Michael J 284
Colsch, Mike 260
Colton, Sabine 353
Colton, Cory 590
Coltrane, Scott 627
Colucci, Anthony J 208
Colucciello, Michael 427
Colver, Thomas 617
Colvin, Garren 456
Colwell, Mark 539
Colwell, Gale R 657
Colyar, Michelle 251
Combs, Robert J 414
Combs, Randy 497
Combs, Linda M 515
Combs, Bobby 533
Combs, Mark 651
Comeau, Carol 36
Comer, Diane 279
Comfort, Dan 128
Comfort, Cydney 149
Commins-Tzoumakas, Kimberly 1
Comnick, Terry 462
Compton, James M 153
Compton, Greg 167
Comstock, G 281
Comstock, Karolyn 525
Conaway, Michael 84
Concannon, Chris 643
Concino, Abby 146
Condon, Jennifer 629
Condra, Robert 173

Condren, Bert 85
Condron, Robert 339
Condron, Gary D 553
Cone, Barbara 392
Coneway, Mary 52
Congdon, Chris 455
Congress, Elaine 217
Conine, Bill 43
Conley, Eric 222
Conley, Tammy 286
Conley, Melinda 288
Conley, Amber 335
Conley, Sophie 388
Conley, Karen 422
Conley, Fatimah 618
Conlin, Chris 132
Connelly, James M 249
Connely, Patrick 253
Conner, Thomas O 338
Connet, James 640
Connoley, Stacy 197
Connolly, Bridget 183
Connolly, Melinda 408
Connolly, Brian 657
Connon, Cheryl 97
Connor, Kevin 28
Connor, Jared 372
Connors, Michael 96
Connors, Michael L 97
Connors, Dan 124
Connors, Christine 588
Conrad, Mary Jo 92
Conrad, Karen 143
Conrad, Angela D 257
Conrad, Scott V 530
Conroy, Kevin 596
Considine, William 118
Consigli, Anthony 151
Consigli, Anne M 151
Consigli, Matthew D 151
Constantine, Tom 54
Constantine, Dow 161
Conti, Richard 94
Conti, Jeanne Di 127
Contreras, Juan 207
Contreras, Sharon L 238
Contreras, Sharon 238
Contrl, Sloan Gray 493
Conway, Mike 4
Conway, Meagan 51
Conzelman, Bonnie 75
Cook, Laura 17
Cook, Marcia 20
Cook, Laura 72
Cook, Matthew 115
Cook, Chad 158
Cook, Deborah 190
Cook, Dave 212
Cook, Robert 214
Cook, Bill 217
Cook, Carter 218
Cook, Paul 262
Cook, Kayla 278
Cook, Michelle L 313
Cook, Troy D 392
Cook, Jerry 435
Cook, Matt 461
Cook, Chris 513
Cook, Alisha 538
Cook, Jack 550
Cook, Jmaes 569
Cook, Angela 586
Cook, Rob 606
Cook, Larry N 612
Cook, Donald J 653
Cooke, Renee S 301
Cooksey, Robert 539
Cooksey, Robert W 539
Cooley, Kem 379
Cooley, Lashonda 648
Coolidge, Rhonda 548
Coombs, Dan 113
Coomer, Christian A 511
Cooney, Traci 514

Coonrod, Gregory L 62
Cooper, Justin 32
Cooper, Jay 68
Cooper, Mark 106
Cooper, Gary 112
Cooper, Dorothy 174
Cooper, Elizabeth C 252
Cooper, Troye 316
Cooper, John 337
Cooper, Roy 515
Cooper, Susane 516
Cooper, Jack 598
Cooper, Kristin 632
Cooper-Boone, Deborah 218
Coore, Becky 642
Coorigan, Micheal 193
Cope, Cherie 124
Cope, Maureen 506
Copeland, Bonnie S 56
Copeland, Lynn R 114
Copeland, Lynn 114
Copeland, Paul 330
Coppa, A M 90
Coppedge, J Kenneth 274
Cora, Michael 162
Cora, Jim 502
Cora-Bramble, Denice 114
Coranet, Mike 257
Corbett, Larry 86
Corbett, Chloe 126
Corbett, Ross 207
Corbett, Brian T 308
Corbett, Alex 539
Corbett, Kevin S 571
Corbett, William 609
Corbett, William 609
Corbin, Lee Anne 240
Corbino, Ralph 230
Corcoran, Anne 461
Cordell, Terri 594
Cordero, Daniel 67
Cordero, Glendy 392
Cordes, Laura 446
Cordier, Emile De 84
Cordier, Donna 145
Cordova, Deanna 541
Cordova, Richard 550
Corielli, Emanuela 374
Corilo, Suzanne 620
Corkle, Kristy 323
Corley, Sarah T 78
Corley, Maryann 307
Corley, Robin 617
Corn, Ron 113
Corn, Ron 113
Cornell, Theodore 379
Cornett, Mick 130
Cornett, Maggie 262
Cornils, Rhnea 45
Cornuelle, Valerie 95
Coronado, Edison 259
Corr, Edwin G 311
Correa, Chris 474
Correll, Craig 337
Corrie, Linda 662
Corrigan, Joanna 236
Corrigan, George M 488
Corry, David M 299
Corse, Brian 405
Cortes, Oswaldo 656
Cortes-Vazquez, Lorraine A 129
Cortesio, Jeremy 482
Cortez, Veronica 155
Corvi, Carolyn 642
Corvino, Frank A 660
Corwin, Steven 372
Corwin, Steven J 572
Corzine, Chris 141
Cosenzo, Donna 240
Cosner, Kelley 172
Cost, Mike 527
Costello, Mary 130
Costello, Larry 277

Index of Executives

Costello, Don 316
Costello, Joseph G 441
Cotarelo, Brandon 396
Cote, Joe 186
Cote, Mike 292
Cotran, Paul R 290
Cotten, Eugene 73
Cottington, Eric 328
Cottle, Rebecca 161
Cotton, Diana 357
Cotton, Tiffany 493
Cotton, Laurie 579
Cotton, Benjamin 607
Couch, James D 130
Couch, Laverne 508
Couchman, Glen 64
Coughran, Steve 205
Coulombe, Stephen 82
Council, Alicia 322
Council, Chrissy 489
Countryman, Gary L 180
Counts, Adriane 175
Counts, Kenny 217
Couris, John 215
Courrege, Chad 304
Coursey, Leigh 8
Courtland, Dvora B 641
Courtney, Kappes 164
Cousins, Erica 332
Covacevich, Teri 179
Covey, Bill 237
Covington, David 107
Covington, Adrienne 515
Cowden, George 67
Cowen, Scott 542
Cowgill, Libby W 584
Cowin, Mark 93
Cox, Chris 28
Cox, Joseph 45
Cox, Michelle 159
Cox, Carol 161
Cox, Greg 168
Cox, Colby 205
Cox, Laura J 215
Cox, Terence C 244
Cox, Terry 244
Cox, Karen 330
Cox, George 362
Cox, Russell F 390
Cox, Susan 428
Cox, David 514
Cox, Spencer J 517
Cox, Tom 528
Cox, Nancy 572
Cox, Michael E 602
Cox, Diana 647
Cox, Erica 659
Coy, Thomas 221
Coy, Rosha Mc 486
Coyner, Dan 636
Cozart, Kevin 336
Cozens, Michelle 544
Cozzi, Ray 601
CPA, Tony M Astorga 78
CPA, Rick Trowbridge 466
Crabb, William 357
Crabiel, David B 343
Crabtree, Robby 533
Crabtree, Rob 540
Cracolici, Frank 356
Crafton, Keith 302
Craig, Julie 60
Craig, Lonnie E 125
Craig, David 160
Craig, Angie 163
Craig, C C 212
Craig, Alex 257
Craig, Deborah 421
Craig, Dennis 519
Craig, Sandra 548
Craig, Matthew 636
Crain, John 622
Craker, Robin 610
Cramer, Todd 360

Cramer, Bethany 464
Cramer, David 610
Crane, Jim 31
Cranley, John 125
Cranor, Tim 222
Craven, Raquel 244
Craven, Katherine 319
Craven, James E 402
Craven, Raychiel 529
Crawford, Terry 28
Crawford, Gordon 28
Crawford, John 432
Crawford, Kristi 463
Crawford, Greg 569
Crawford, Beverly 643
Creach, Andrea 516
Creamer, Eunice 48
Crean, Tim 617
Crean, Michael 647
Creary, Mike Mc 331
Creech, Dale 323
Creek, Dan 339
Creighton, Alecia 228
Cremin, Mary C 31
Crenshaw, Carol 114
Crenshaw, Efrem 157
Cress, David W 382
Cresswell, Rosie 479
Crew, Debra A 271
Crews, Kim 380
Criner, Elizabeth 456
Cripe, Kimberly 116
Cristina, Steven 446
Croce, Angela 141
Croce, Kasey 633
Crockett, Gary 398
Crockett, June 609
Croken, Kenneth 227
Croley, Matthew 334
Cromie, William 98
Croney, Barbara 461
Cronin, Annmarie 89
Cronin, Brian 392
Cronin, Christopher 514
Cronin, Kathe 603
Cropper, Doug 227
Crosby, Nikki 5
Croson, Rachel 624
Cross, Jeffrey D 30
Cross, Linda 156
Cross, Mary Lou 169
Cross, Coleen 224
Cross, Stephen 228
Cross, Tamela 245
Cross, Drew 483
Cross, Steve 517
Cross, Kevin 572
Cross, Charles E 628
Cross, Raymond 633
Crossett, Jonathan 182
Crossland, Millie 347
Crotts, Matthew 533
Crotty, Glenn 111
Crouch, Suzanne 512
Crouse, Jerry K 537
Crouser, Mark 55
Crow, Michael M 42
Crow, Penny 69
Crow, Scott 211
Crowder, Andy 547
Crowder, Antwuan 604
Crowdis, Roy 603
Crowe, Ronald 428
Crowe, Terri 439
Crowell, Eric 108
Crowley, David J 228
Crowther, Chip 72
Croxen, Edith 418
Croy, Jack 91
Croyle, Mike 355
Crozier, Barry 55
Crudele, Jeffrey 576
Crutcher, Allison 139
Cruz, Casey 21

Cruz, Marcella 167
Cruz, Chris 168
Cruz, Dimitri J 206
Cruz, Mike De 236
Cruz, Jose 449
Cruz, Markam 463
Cruz, Joseph 625
Crye, Stephen 202
Cryer, Angela 129
Csabon, Robin 310
Csapo, Peter 12
Csaplo-Adrian, Elizabeth 118
CU, Jennipher 173
Cubbage, Lora 160
Cuddy, Rhonda 625
Cuenco, Ramoncito 509
Cuevas, Alex 267
Cuevas, Kerwin 513
Cuffee, Clarence V 125
Cuffee-Glenn, Selena 132
Cull, Shawn 211
Cullen, Michael R 70
Cullen, Debbie 312
Cullen, Michael 488
Cullen, Tamara 609
Cullen, David 658
Culloch, Cathy Mc 465
Culnan, Mary Beth 508
Culp, William 468
Culpepper, Karen 216
Cumbie, Stephen 263
Cummings, Emily 243
Cummings, Ricardo 285
Cummings, Heather 286
Cummins, Robert 11
Cummins, Tim 91
Cummins, Richard 165
Cummins, Diane M 556
Cunha, Daniel 393
Cuningham, David 522
Cunitz, Dave 247
Cunningham, Shirley 119
Cunningham, Carla 275
Cunningham, Kim 398
Cunningham, Ron 653
Cuomo, Andrew M 206
Cupp, Mary 256
Cupp, Scott 542
Cupp, Ronnie 553
Cureton, Samantha 525
Curfman, Susan 541
Curley, John 163
Curley, Catherine 553
Curley, Tim 638
Curlin, Teresa 163
Curnow, Randy 332
Currall, Steven 491
Curran, William 132
Curran, John 155
Curran, Laura 160
Curran, Brooke 309
Curran, Michael J 324
Curran, Dr Daniel J 585
Currie, Tina 32
Currie, Pat 64
Currie, Scott 343
Currier, Rand 234
Curry, Lenny 127
Curry, Mike Mc 331
Curry, Ken 367
Curry, Krista 396
Curry, Wayne 451
Curry, Robynne 643
Curtan, Grant 103
Curti, Joseph Tate 204
Curtis, Jason 84
Curtis, Dan 98
Curtis, John M 188
Curtis, Edgar J 327
Curtis, Caroline 402
Curtis, Dana 416
Cury, Jason 310
Cushman, Audrey 319
Custer, Jami 548

Custo, Maria G 356
Cutchin, Marco 121
Cutchins, Alexis G 205
Cutijar, Anna Marie 163
Cutler, Brian 546
Cutter, Brian 152
Cvetich, Irene 313
Czajkowski, Andrew 252
Czarnezki, Joseph 658
Czebotar, Jerry A 363
Czupik, Patrick 585
Czuprynski, Vicky 260
Czyz, Annemarie W 504

D

D, Jeffrey N Joyce PH 311
D, Linda 456
D, Eric Dickson M 609
Da, Eugene 153
Dabbs, Jeremy 96
Daddario, Don 246
Daddona, Michael 210
Dadlani, Sunil 48
Dafonseca, Augusto 449
Daft, Brendon 396
Daghe, Noelle 140
Daglio, Michael 554
Daher, Amyra 202
Dahiya, Rakesh 491
Dahl, David 249
Dahl, Jonathan 562
Dahlberg, Edwin 507
Dahlen, Dennis 56
Dahlheimer, Tim 38
Dahlin, Jonathan 74
Dai, Nat 263
Daici, Silvia 206
Daigle, Art 135
Daigle, Sandra 309
Daik, Sam 534
Dajany, Adam 25
Dake, Gary C 521
Dake, William P 521
Dalal, Aruna 370
Dalbey, Christopher 169
Dale, Michael W 340
Dale, Kenneth 545
Dale, Christopher 638
Dalemarre, Laura 515
Dalena, Taylor 347
Dalessandro, Joseph 99
Dalina, Stephen J 343
Dallas, Andrew 444
Dalton, John 200
Dalton, Willam S 240
Dalton, William 240
Dalton, Mark 590
Dalton, Karen 599
Daly, Patricia 333
Dalziel, Jennifer C 596
Dam, Bill 209
Dameron, Jeffrey C 111
Damewood, Tracey 73
Damiani, Al 156
Damle, Lauren F 647
Damore, Joseph 346
Dampier, Charlette 115
Dancis, Andrew B 574
Dandeneau, Ben 422
Daniel, Patricia 196
Daniel, William C 459
Daniel, Enking 539
Daniel, Alan M 540
Daniel, Chris Mc 587
Daniels, Ronald J 276
Daniels, Vincent C 476
Daniels, Bobbi 624
Danja, Franklin 627
Dann, Doreen 506
Danner, Cynthia 444
Dantdler, Todd 421

Index of Executives

Dantuono, Louis 69
Danza, Franck 299
Dao, Anthony 12
Daprile, Joseph R 203
Daprile, Joseph R 375
Darby, Ashley 172
Dardenne, Jay 512
Dargan, David 418
Darling, Rachel 613
Darnell, Aaron 142
Darnell, Scott 515
Dasgupta, Satarupa 374
Dasilva, Daniel 656
Daskalos, Paul 461
Dasossa, Mag 186
Dass, Chandra A 536
Daubner, Thomas 594
Daughtrey, William 644
Daughtry, Kevin 26
Daugiala, Alfredas 483
Daul, Richard 156
Daunt, James 61
Dauphinee, Aimee 393
Dauterive, Eddie 409
Dave, Rajesh 611
Davenport, Fesia 162
Davenport, Clark 400
Davey, Bryan 4
David, Danielle 92
David, Yaron 100
David, Mark 114
David, Jon 230
David, Steven 374
Davidowski, Ron J 194
Davidson, Patricia 102
Davidson, Michael 114
Davidson, Julie 193
Davidson, Hollister 303
Davidson, Jack 320
Davidson, Robert G 334
Davies, Daniel 57
Davies, Neil 203
Davila, Diana 256
Davila, Rosa 347
Davis, Tim 5
Davis, Steve 7
Davis, Steven 18
Davis, Andrew 27
Davis, Elizabeth 65
Davis, Tommye Lou 65
Davis, Mary 69
Davis, Kenneth L 71
Davis, Reed 83
Davis, Alden B 90
Davis, Harold 115
Davis, Scott 120
Davis, Clinton 120
Davis, Frances 124
Davis, Robin 125
Davis, George 129
Davis, Leanne 131
Davis, Lisa S 132
Davis, Charisse 141
Davis, Laronda 145
Davis, Jacqueline 159
Davis, Dennis 165
Davis, Robert 172
Davis, Bob 172
Davis, Sonya 187
Davis, Eric 196
Davis, Pamela 201
Davis, Brian 201
Davis, Sarah 210
Davis, Janet 215
Davis, Becky 220
Davis, Greg 222
Davis, Steven 260
Davis, Shirley 261
Davis, Auston 306
Davis, Jennifer 327
Davis, Martina 370
Davis, Sondra 383
Davis, Joshua 384
Davis, Mark 395

Davis, Alphonse G 400
Davis, Steven 401
Davis, Debbie 446
Davis, William A 448
Davis, Richard 497
Davis, Austin 518
Davis, Myra 540
Davis, Lisa 560
Davis, Thomas P 572
Davis, Debra A 587
Davis, John 592
Davis, Jennifer 618
Davis, Wayne 629
Davis, Josie H 631
Davis, Benjamin 633
Davis, Leslie 634
Davis, Leslie C 635
Davis, Deborah 640
Davis, Traci 647
Davis, James L 659
Davoren, Peter J 583
Davoren, Peter J 605
Dawes, Christopher 306
Dawson, Haley 267
Dawson, Laurel 516
Dawydiak, Walter 171
Daxner, Jim 537
Day, Edwin 167
Day, Terri 283
Day, Kim 334
Day, Lynn Carmen 447
Day, Jason 489
Day, James H 601
Day, Sarah 658
DC, Sister Bernice Coreil 43
DC, Sister Maureen McGuire 43
DDS, Will Daniels 69
DDS, L Kenneth Heuler 116
DDS, Edwin Zechman 117
DDS, Rocco R Addante 182
DDS, Diane Day 351
DDS, David B Weinstein 581
De, Hector 160
Deaderick, Billy 203
Dealyn, Allen 80
Dean, DOT 25
Dean, Jennifer 119
Dean, Lloyd 145
Dean, Lloyd 189
Dean, Doug 204
Dean, Douglas 204
Dean, Melanie 286
Dean, Lesley 396
Dean, Anthony 427
Dean, Eric 513
Dean, Susanne 525
Dean, Eric 548
Dean, Michelle 578
Dean, Susan 588
Dean, Joey 650
Dearth, Jim 117
Deas, Bruce 528
Deasy, Dr John 303
Deaupre, Paul 231
Debbane, Raymond 77
Debeauvoir, Dana 171
Debertin, Jay 119
Deboer, Steven 378
Deboer, Erica 463
Debs, Jody 245
Decarolis, Anthony 571
Decker, Tina Freese 495
Decker, Daniel 512
Decker, Lynn 569
Decker, W Cody 616
Decolli, Debbie 131
Decubellis, Jennifer 249
Dee, Thomas 368
Dee, Maureen 567
Deel, Chris 100
Deeming, Fran 414
Deering, Michael 302
Deeter, Chris 33
Defenbaugh, Raymond E 73

Deffenbaugh, Danny 492
Defilippis, Mike 596
Defillo, Vicente Jose Liz 89
Defreitas, Alicia 103
Defurio, Anthony 547
Degioia, John J 560
Degrand, Robert 222
Degrandis, Leigh 548
Degregori, Amanda 509
Degregorio, Nick 593
Dehaemers, David 532
Dehahn, Erin 647
Dehaven, Michael 498
Dehring, Timothy A 386
Deines, Wyatt 31
Deiser, Peter 353
Dejaco, Lynn 241
Dejoseph, Elizabeth 134
Dekay, Donald F 265
Deken, Paul 207
Dekle, Christopher 210
Delaney, Martin 12
Delaney, Kristen 141
Delano, Laurie A 555
Delanois, Gary 1
Delany, Jim 545
Delasotta, Fernando 48
Delatorre, Hector 662
Delauder, Brad 160
Delay, Mary G 587
Delbridge, Malinda 485
Delcourt, Ryan 575
Delellis, Ronald A 444
Deleon, Melissa 304
Deleon, Marcos 601
Delgadillo, Rocky 127
Delgadillo, Joe 387
Delgado, Mercedes 206
Delgrosso, Nicole 451
Dellenback, Steve 492
Dellinger, Donald B 662
Delmas, Heather 537
Delong, Abbie 291
Delorenzo, Carl 256
Deluca, Frederick A 192
Deluca, Oneida 418
Delue, Sean 468
Delventhal, Brad 578
Demahy, Anita 471
Demarco, Nick 131
Demarco, Edward 316
Demarets, Pascal 23
Demarino, Shannon 118
Demarsh, Steven 169
Dembner, Alan 60
Demio, Doug 24
Demme, Kendra 90
Demming, Peggy 613
Demoleas, John P 519
Demond, Sharon 256
Demonte, Rosemarie 605
Dempich, Joe 109
Denarvaez, Denny 649
Denault, Leo P 206
Deneweth, Connie 358
Denges, Jim 523
Denham, Amber 614
Deninger, Matthew 319
Denizard-Thomps, Nancy 380
Dennard, Tamaya 125
Denning, Shannon 330
Denninghoff, Erik 493
Dennis, Rae 309
Dennis, David 424
Dennison, Shawn 159
Dennison, Mary 286
Denny, Betty 238
Denomme, Linda 607
Densmore, Marianne 182
Denson, Celia 643
Dent, Andrew 511
Dentler, Jane 173
Deo, Rajat 255
Deol, Jaspal 455

Depaolo, Joseph J 481
Depies, Lori 159
Depietro, Diane 415
Depoortere, Michael 583
Depta, Lisa 60
Derickson, Pat 175
Derita, Nancy 500
Dermott, Frank X Mc 368
Derosa, Rebecca 65
Derosier, Pam 496
Derouche, James 309
Deroy, Sara 131
Derrick, Brian 17
Derrick, Brian 524
Derylo, Maria 305
Desai, Nicholas 256
Desai, Manisha 609
Desalvo, Natalie 510
Descamps, Bill 11
Deshields, Taneesha 513
Deshong, Leanne 103
Desjardins, Jacques 159
Desjarlais, Roger 162
Deskins, Juanita 417
Desmond, Kenneth V 146
Desmond, Patrick 636
Desormeaux, Joseph 227
Desouza, Bryan 661
Despain, Brian 625
Despeaux, Kimberly H 206
Destefano, Alexa 311
Desurio, Anthony 618
Detherage, Mark 286
Detwiler, Jim 118
Deuschle, James 445
Deutsch, Donough 87
Devanney, George W 171
Devaraj, Tanuja 352
Deveny, Cliff 524
Devine, David 364
Devine, Scott 389
Devineni, Ramya 644
Devino, Terrence 602
Devita, Maria V 299
Devoe, Michael 48
Devoe, Andrew 598
Devoney, William 201
Devooght, Shawn 247
Devore, Susan 426
Devos, Doug 27
Devos, Mr Doug L 486
Devos, Doug 495
Dew, Stephen 160
Dewald, Steven 437
Dewar, Marvin 477
Dewer, Craig 107
Dewey, Chris 166
Dewey, Susan F 641
Dewine, Mike 516
Dewitt, Rob 294
Dexter, Sara 589
Dhala, Anwer 632
Dhanda, Anuj 18
Dhillon, Peter P 393
Dhimitri, Nick 523
Dholakia, Indira 162
Dialto, Margaret 519
Diamanti, Theodhor 427
Diamond, Robert 280
Diamond, Margae 468
Diamond, Michael 568
Diana, Edward A 166
Diaz, Aurora 18
Diaz, Joseph 188
Diaz, Diana 303
Diaz, Ulises E 368
Diaz, Crystal 498
Diaz, Robyn 505
Diaz, Mark 560
Diaz, Jorge E 578
Diaz-Macha, Maria 19
Diaz-Zablah, Alexandra 341
Diblasio, Alfonzo 508
Dibona, Laina 135

Index of Executives

Dibrell, Henry 282
Dicesare, Thor 106
Diciurcio, John 214
Diciurcio, John 605
Dickenson, James 270
Dickerson, Mike 591
Dickey, Hal 203
Dickey, Melissa 612
Dickinson, Edward T 574
Dickman, Susan F 272
Dickson, Rebecca T 157
Dickson, Mark 451
Diddee, Anu 290
Dieckmann, Anita 248
Diede, Shannon 530
Diederich, Kirsten 381
Diehl, Valerie 102
Diehl, Walter 346
Diehm, Russell C 84
Diesel, R Wayne 519
Dieter, Cory 464
Dietrich, William 628
Dietrich, William S 635
Dietz, Megan 173
Dietz, David W 191
Dietzel, Brad 472
Diewald, Wayne 227
Difilippo, Pasquale A 605
Difuntorum, Elizabeth 120
Diganci, Todd 214
Digiacomo, Sam 200
Diliberto, Matthew J 438
Dilisi, Jeffrey 451
Dill, Julie 494
Dilland, John 342
Dillard, Ashley 53
Dilley, Margarita K 108
Dillman, Jeff 640
Dillon, Bobbi 125
Dillon, Tim 257
Dillon, Danel 321
Dillon, Mary Ann 599
Dillow, April 646
Dilocker, Laurie 175
Diloreto, Andy 166
Dimaandal, Juliet 525
Dimatteo, Lex 547
Dimauro, Vincent A 159
Dimitrijevic, Marina 658
Dimmick, Ruth 18
Dimmick, Scott W 291
Dimolitsas, Spiros 560
Dinan, Susan 403
Dindin, Kevin 67
Dineen, James 172
Dingle, Phillip S 215
Dingus, John 216
Dinkler, Ayame 304
Dinsel, Doug 196
Dinsmoor, William S 570
Diokno, Ananias 657
Diorio, Dena 163
Dipalma, Theresa Alberghini 588
Dipaolo, Joseph A 11
Dipietro, Dominick 98
Dipietro, Joseph A 629
Dipofi, Phil 388
Dirocco, Melissa 456
Dirrane, Michael J 317
Dirscherl, Dan 257
Disalvatore, Tony 71
Disantis, Linda 123
Disarlo, Lorraine 638
Discello, Allison 188
Diseroad, Mark 414
Dishaw, Michael F 63
Dishman, Roy 353
Disney, Keri 179
Disney, Kathy 268
Dispensa, James V 80
Disser, Pete 386
Distel, Arlene 579
Ditre, Cherie 574
Dittemore, Karen 354

Dittus, Gina 2
Divincenzo, Joseph N 159
Divito, Robert 324
Dixon, Anastasia 198
Dixon, April 238
Dixon, Michael 333
Dixon, Linda J 603
Dixon, Tom 648
Dizenzo, Lisa 259
Dizon, Terry 550
Dizon-Scott, Marissa 530
Doan, Huy 481
Dobbins, John 658
Dobbs, Stanley 462
Dobbs, Donald P 565
Docken, Lorie 633
Dockins, Cynthia 541
Dodd, Elyssa 347
Dodd, Susan 492
Dodds, David 381
Dodge, Judy 164
Dodson, Vickie 540
Dodson-Reed, Candace 256
Doeckel, Laura 99
Doehrman, Verna 191
Doerfler, Steve 22
Doerksen, Edna 530
Doerr, David M 12
Dohany, Patrick M 165
Doherty, Tom 29
Doherty, Chris 212
Dohman, Pammie 464
Dolan, Amanda 16
Dolan, Patrick 62
Dolan, Jane 157
Dole, Rodney 170
Dolen, James 194
Dolgin, Eliot 63
Doligale, Anne 481
Doll, John 61
Doll, Cynthia 627
Dollaghan, Jim 193
Dollery, Megan 165
Dolling, David S 560
Dolman, Shael 23
Dominguez, Oscar 486
Dominguez, Leanna 604
Domnisch, Michaele 284
Domont, Lawrence 7
Donaghue, Jason M 500
Donahue, Leslie Les A 416
Donahue, Moreen O 554
Donald, James 18
Donald, Bruce Mc 87
Donald, Margie Mc 449
Donald, Arnold 495
Donaldson, Amy 257
Donat, Richard 462
Donavan, James 344
Donder, Daniel J 345
Donegan, Mark 426
Donegan, Lynda 601
Donelan, David 44
Donheiser, Gail 230
Doni, Puja 479
Donis, EMI 426
Donley, Jeffrey 101
Donnals, Jennifer 517
Donnell, Cathy Mc 116
Donnellan, Barbara 156
Donohue, Carolyn 451
Donough, Robert Mc 439
Dookiesingh, Kamanie 265
Dooley, Meta 102
Dooley, Charles 170
Dooley, Susan 428
Dooley, Kevin 450
Dooley, Jill 508
Dooling, Carrie 165
Doomy, Lynda 644
Doordan, Martin L 306
Dop, Kyle 247
Doplemore, Shelia 641
Dorado, Roy 481

Dorchester, Wendy 301
Doren, Steven R Van 625
Dores, Daniel 620
Dorfler, Robert 594
Dorn, Connie 508
Dorothea, Mary 499
Dorph, Martin 374
Dorroh, Tina 615
Dorsey, Tracey 8
Dorsey, Denicca 220
Dorto, Joseph 642
Doser, Lynn M 81
Doss, Richard 500
Dossantos, Emilia 498
Dotson, Tony 55
Dotson, Jillian 512
Dott, Edward 155
Doty, Jeff 112
Doty, Angela 160
Doty, Larry 419
Doty, William S 491
Doucette, Elmer 200
Doucette, Mer 200
Doucette, Jami 426
Doucette, Mike J 446
Dougan, Thomas 406
Doughty, Tracy 257
Douglas, Marlis 142
Douglas, Dan 386
Douglas, Diana 536
Douglas, Keith A 591
Douglas, Blaine 649
Douglass, Stephen B 96
Douglass, Julie 596
Douglass, Scott R 618
Douvris, Angelo 24
Douwes, Art 464
Dove, Reid 1
Dow, Susan 200
Dow, Robert 204
Dow, Bonnie 590
Dower, Leonard 597
Dowlin, John 160
Dowling, Michael J 301
Dowling, Michael J 384
Dowling, Kathleen 460
Down, Stephen G 476
Downard, Gary 135
Downer, Michael J 31
Downes, Terry 471
Downey, William B 446
Downey, William B 446
Downing, Walter 492
Downing, James 505
Downs, Kenneth E 509
Downs, Christina 579
Dowse, Stacey 251
Doyle, Kelli 26
Doyle, John D 43
Doyle, Jim 139
Doyle, John 200
Doyle, Robert 561
Doyle, Kevin 605
Dozono, Elisa 399
Dozor, Donna 652
Drago, Allyson 617
Dragolovic, Goran 466
Dragovich, Dmeter 601
Drain, Adolphus 141
Drake, Denny 266
Drake, Brittany 420
Drake, Matt 451
Drake, Michael V 572
Draper, Elizabeth 422
Drass, M 324
Drass, Joy 325
Drechsel, Cathy 384
Dredge, Carter 497
Drees, Ralph 554
Drees, David 554
Drees, Joseph D 587
Dresher, Carl 135
Dressen, Rich 411
Dressler, Raymond 156

Drew, Joel 97
Drew, Alton 210
Drew, Greg 639
Drezek, Maria 546
Drillings, Robert M 373
Driscoll, Barb 7
Driscoll, Paul 214
Driscoll, Justin E 371
Driver, Darienne 345
Drone, Nicole 240
Druckenmiller, Robert 233
Drum, Don 430
Drumd, Don 430
Drumm, Eric 274
Drummond, Danielle 291
Drummond, David C 427
Drummond, Joseph 605
Drury, James 166
Dua, Naveen 185
Dube, Greta 200
Dubin, James M 237
Dubis, John 456
Dubitzky, Anne 565
Dubner, Steven 647
Dubois, Joseph 93
Dubuche, Karl Von 602
Duce, Ronald C 285
Ducey, Mark 408
Ducey, Doug 510
Dudacek, Robert J 537
Dudek, Tim 162
Dudley-Eshbach, Janet 623
Dueck, Rodney R 406
Duenas, Juan 128
Duff, Brian T 46
Duff, Molli M 304
Duff, Eugenia 321
Duffaut, Edvard 317
Duffield, Jeff 125
Dufford, Shawn 458
Duffy, Brendan 152
Duffy, Janet 190
Duffy, Mary 309
Duffy, Patrick 375
Dufour, Victoria 500
Dufresne, Maryse 356
Dugan, Tammy 481
Dugan, Michael 536
Duggal, Aditi 551
Duggan, Scott 559
Dugger, John 10
Duhaney, Patrick 125
Duke, Andrew 210
Duke, Janice 340
Dulak, Catherine 92
Dulmaine, Jean 285
Dumanian, Gregory 389
Dumas, Ryan 216
Dumont, Stephanie 214
Dunavant, David 351
Dunaway, Mike 320
Dunbar, Kent 152
Duncan, Wayne 139
Duncan, Gary 217
Duncan, Ronald 225
Duncan, Dean R 460
Duncan, Erika 504
Duncan, Geoff 511
Dungan, Richard W 20
Dungee, Dorothy 48
Dunham, Kara 108
Dunkle, Jason 193
Dunlap, Edward B 106
Dunlap, Timothy M 106
Dunlap, Charles 580
Dunlap, Michael 591
Dunlap, Michael 596
Dunlay, Patrick 333
Dunleavy, Michael 510
Dunn, Dean 29
Dunn, John 47
Dunn, Cindy 233
Dunn, Stephen D 268
Dunn, Robert P 268

Index of Executives

Dunn, Terrence P 268
Dunn, Stephen D 268
Dunn, Robert P 268
Dunn, Michelle 356
Dunn, Andrew 409
Dunn, Lauren 467
Dunn, Randy J 490
Dunn, Todd 496
Dunn, Brian 521
Dunn, Elizabeth 617
Dunnahoe, Mike 454
Dunne, Gwynneth 441
Dunnie, Tookie 14
Dunton, James K 33
Dunton, Robert 164
Dunton, Shirby 642
Duplisea, Doug 412
Dupont, Michael R 368
Dupont, Ty 533
Duppong, Gerald 137
Dupre, David 78
Dupre, Lisa 172
Dupuis, Eleanor 68
Duran, Angelita 130
Duran, Lillian 637
Duren, Deborah 112
Durham, Michael 561
Durkee, Robert K 582
Durkin, Chris 58
Durst, Linda S 344
Dusel, Martin C 121
Dusenberry, Matthew 236
Dutcher, Phillip C 361
Dutton, Chuck 423
Duva, Judith 401
Duval, John 640
Dwinell, Lauren 345
Dwork, Andrew 582
Dwyer, Jay 68
Dwyer, Hugh 265
Dwyer, Shannon 430
Dwyer, Shannon 502
Dyck, Lonnie 636
Dye, Rebecca 524
Dyer, Robert M 135
Dyer, Gary 285
Dyer, Emily 367
Dyer, Karen 608
Dyhrkopp, Erik 448
Dyk, Lisa 308
Dyke, Candy V 5
Dyke, David V 228
Dykes, Melissa 270
Dykstra, Michele 230
Dymoke, Lea 399
Dzau, Victor 197
Dzierzbinski, Danusia 265
Dziobek, Judy 133
Dziuk, David A 247
D'Agosta, Jeffrey 361
D'Agostino, Teresa 133
D'Agostino, Marcelo 404
D'Alessandri, Robert 651
D'Antilio, Derek 376
D'Aquila, Richard 660
D'Arienzo, Annette Marino 79

E

E, Thomas Kevin 361
E-Newsletter, Healthy 501
Eade-Viele, Carol 19
Eads, Courtney 452
Eagle, Dustin 91
Eames, Frederick 16
Eames, Andy 496
Eames, Dennis 508
Earl, Nick 230
Earl, Ashlee M 546
Earl, Dustin 657
Earley, Robert 533
Earley, Franklin P 642

Early, Charles 365
Easley, Matthew 47
Easley, Jeanette 121
Easley, Stephen T 209
Easley, Paul 492
Easter, Wh 326
Eastland, Woods E 509
Eastman, A Brent 469
Eastwood, Stephanie 63
Eaton, Deborah R 167
Eaton, George 464
Eatough, Chris 256
Eaves, Greg 203
Ebel, Gregory L 494
Eberhard, Sally 596
Eberhardt, Karie 366
Eberling, Edward 338
Ebersole, Amy 149
Ebner, Vicki O 608
Echelard, Paul 379
Echelberger, Penny 322
Echevarria, Emmanuel 132
Echevarria, Sean 240
Echiverri, Henry C 201
Echols, Edwin 539
Eck, Michael 77
Eck, Joshua 516
Ecker, John 327
Eckert, Inger 177
Eckert, Matthew 278
Eckert, Robert 297
Eckhoff, Heidi 577
Eckroth, Joseph 561
Eddinger, Ronnie 84
Eddy, Adam 462
Edeker, Randy 258
Edelstein, Sam 134
Edelstein, Gara 230
Edenshaw, Sidney 471
Eder, Paul 324
Edes, Beth 514
Edgar, Gregory 41
Edgar, Andrew 126
Edgar, Robin 333
Edgerly, Deborah 130
Edgerton, Ivis 363
Edmondson, David 420
Edmunds, Beth 399
Edmunds, Cynthia 623
Edson, Pam 394
Edwards, Joey 3
Edwards, Steven L 76
Edwards, Steve 76
Edwards, Steve L 92
Edwards, Thomas K 120
Edwards, Leslie 146
Edwards, Darnell 160
Edwards, Laurie 175
Edwards, Joe 190
Edwards, Judy 224
Edwards, Carladenise 249
Edwards, Carolyn 253
Edwards, Susan 287
Edwards, Steven D 296
Edwards, Greg 451
Edwards, C H 471
Edwards, Clarence 472
Edwards, John Bel 512
Edwards, Beverly 604
Efendioglu, Alev 628
Effinger, Scott 136
Egan, Thomas A 360
Egan, Joe 638
Egidi, Kenneth 411
Ehara, George S 530
Ehinniah, Nim 389
Ehlers, Marc 212
Ehlinger, Jon D 195
Ehlinger, Forrest G 242
Ehrlich, Randall V 89
Ehrlich, Robert 316
Ehrlich, Craig 583
Eichelberger, Mitch 113
Eichfeld, William 490

Eichler, Kimberly 478
Eichorn, Marvin 55
Eid, Samir 370
Eide, Ador 462
Eikhoff, Luanne 472
Eiler, Gary 632
Eilerman, Chris 125
Eiselstein, Shana 143
Eisen, David 648
Eisenbrandt, Peter 635
Eisenstaedt, Richard 3
Eisgruber, Christopher L 582
Eison, Thomas 493
Eitel, Dotti 118
Eitel, William 125
Ekberg, Hugh 176
Ekey, Jennifer 143
Ekpo, Idongesit 323
Elamine, A K 488
Elder, Larry 73
Eldred, Brian 635
Eldreth, Nathan 457
Elez, Drazen 514
Elhaj, Imad 622
Eli, Robert 304
Elia, Maryellen 251
Elias, Lindsey 343
Elias, Richard 418
Eliassi-Rad, Babak 84
Elieson, Abby 630
Eliot, Courtney 642
Elizalde, Stephanie S 52
Elkins, Lorelei 160
Elkins, Carla 463
Ellefsen, Jacob 238
Ellehuus, Christoffer 103
Ellen, Jonathan 274
Ellenbogen, David 468
Ellenburg, Christina 321
Eller, Jay 206
Ellerbrook, Niel C 491
Ellert, Lisa 191
Ellington, Christopher 40
Ellington, Chris 627
Elliot, Cynthia 450
Elliot, Charles 529
Elliott, Wayne 73
Elliott, Carla 262
Elliott, William R 313
Elliott, Brandy 418
Ellis, Brian 96
Ellis, Beverly 96
Ellis, Stephanie 97
Ellis, Marianne 169
Ellis, Elmer G 199
Ellis, Mark 203
Ellis, Debbie 217
Ellis, John W 225
Ellis, Ellen 248
Ellis, Suzanne 271
Ellis, Sarah 472
Ellis, Stephen 578
Ellis, David 644
Ellison, Richard 83
Ellison, Janet 296
Ellison, Seth 297
Ellison, Joel 476
Ellithorpe, Peggy 638
Elmer, Katherine 192
Elmo, Terri Di 497
Elmore, Bill 287
Elmore, Karen 342
Elmquist, Jay 455
Elorza, Jorge O 132
Elrich, Marc 352
Elswick, Steve 157
Elwell, Richard 204
Ely, Lisa 461
Emde, Alyson 244
Emeka, Farah 158
Emerson, Christy 107
Emerson, Bertrand M 564
Emery, Karen 41
Emery, Douglas 242

Emery, Homer 462
Emmerc, Mark 631
Emmerling, John 13
Emmert, Mark A 363
Emmons, Jennifer 471
Emmons, Diana 514
Emo, Tantri 126
Emory, Frank 390
Emrich, Richard 87
Ende, Jack 427
Endres, Todd 112
Engel, Christa 91
Engel, Robert B 140
Engelbrecht, Scott 138
Engels, Bob 165
Enger, Douglas 133
Engers, Barbara 503
England, Daniel E 92
England, Dean 92
England, Chad 92
England, Josh 92
England, Todd 92
England, Corey 92
England, Tj 92
England, Zach 92
England, Chad D 207
England, Jimmy 287
Engle, John B 469
Englehart, Michael 355
Englert, Richard M 536
Engles, Gregg L 182
English, Lori 55
English, Bob 421
English, Katrina M 607
Englund, Melissa 577
Engstrand, Benjamin 436
Engstrom, Mike 74
Ennerfelt, P Goeran 298
Ennis, Tara 614
Enomoto, Hideto 378
Enos, Deborah 24
Enos, Cassandra 93
Enrique, Castro 162
Entwisle, Beverly J 602
Entwistle, David 509
Epps, Stacey 83
Epstein, Louis 597
Erbe, Cathi 170
Ercoline, Luke 166
Eric, Huang 643
Erickson, Brian 30
Erickson, Rodney A 575
Erickson, Kevin 650
Ericson, Brent 237
Erik, John 3
Eriksen, Mary 464
Ermine-Baer, Kristin 635
Ernst, Michael 591
Ernst, Elizabeth 617
Erpenbach, Michelle 556
Errichettii, Ann 508
Erschen, Leslie 162
Ersteniuk, Peter 333
Ertel, Anne 615
Ervin, Greggory 179
Ervin, Reginald 389
Erwin, Duane 45
Erwin, Michael A 186
Escarrer, Gabriel 187
Escasa-Haigh, Jo Ann 430
Escasa-Halgh, Jo Ann 502
Escobar, David 261
Escue, Dick 60
Escuyer, Vincent 247
Eshelman, Erica 410
Esparza, Ryan 269
Espel, Thomas K 437
Esper, Eric 561
Espinoza, Carina 303
Espinoza, Jose 486
Esposito, Michael 515
Esposito, Nicole M 586
Espy, Kevan 141
Esquibel, Emillo 467

Index of Executives

Essenberg, Janice 68
Essman, Shon 136
Esta, Linda 579
Estby, Rebecca 142
Esteban, A Gabriel 185
Estelle, Lameisha 81
Esterman, Michelle 27
Estes, Joel 155
Estes, Amy 249
Estes, Christopher 334
Estrada, Angel G 171
Estrada, Agustin 496
Estrada, Bernice 605
Estrada, Cindy 607
Estrict, Ronnie 408
Etheridge, Felicia 136
Etheridge, Don 362
Etienne, Claudine 579
Etten, David V 657
Ettl, Robert A 243
Eugster, Dr Cris 136
Evans, Greg 3
Evans, Doug 112
Evans, Jeremy 184
Evans, Kelley 190
Evans, Robert E 199
Evans, Crystal 205
Evans, Richard T 209
Evans, Dave 226
Evans, Gemma 256
Evans, Linda 275
Evans, Dave 283
Evans, Jeremy S 287
Evans, Joshua D 305
Evans, Kari 339
Evans, Anita 353
Evans, Donnie W 408
Evans, Patricia 419
Evans, Malik 449
Evans, Russ 486
Evans, Tema 493
Evans, Mary Alice 511
Evans, Kimberly 525
Evans, Palmer 604
Evans, Brandy 637
Evans, Glenda 643
Evans, Mariah 647
Evans-Hands, Chris 161
Evanson, Paul J 351
Evanson, Doug 462
Eveland, Scott 514
Everett, Austin 321
Everette, James 64
Evers, Tony 518
Evers, Tony 633
Evers, Tami 638
Everson, Carolyn 561
Evette, Pamela S 516
Evitts, Aaron 113
Evrard, Sharon 220
Ewert, Brian H 314
Ewert, Phil 461
Ewing, Justin 18
Ewing, Marilyn E 262
Ewing, Diane 323
Ewing, Jason 507
Exposito, Alina 341
EZ, Dino R Camu 415
Ezeigwe, Chizoba 319
Ezer, Dorit Ben 116
Ezra, Einav 325

F

Faas, Jim 418
Faber, Bob 27
Faber, Lori 327
Fabrikant, Charles 470
Fabrikant, Eric 470
Fache, Jameson Smith 102
Fache, Adrienne Palmer 321
Fache, Andrea G 542

Factourovich, Inna K 611
Fadem, Steve 545
Faecher, Marc 597
Faella, Alfred 171
Faerber, Craig 27
Fagan, Briana 166
Fagan, Cathlyn 384
Fagan, Chuck 430
Fagan, Tiffani 457
Fagello, Juanita 89
Fagen, Catherine 301
Fahey, Walter 307
Fahim, Shafei 51
Fahy, Michael 48
Faidley, Jeffrey 294
Fain, Jonathan 535
Fair, Laura J 342
Fairbanks, Donald 347
Fairbanks, Donald W 348
Fairfax, Justin E 146
Fairfield, Irene 204
Faith, Marshall 580
Fajardo, Jose 261
Falati, Stacie 393
Falb, Derek J 120
Falcon, Ray 133
Falcon, Tiji 174
Falcon, Michelle 596
Falcone, Joseph C 363
Falcone, Philip 503
Falero, Xavier O 129
Falk, Kathleen 158
Falk, David A 375
Fall, Clinton 557
Falleri, Frank 207
Fallin, Wayne 647
Fallon, Jeanne M 96
Fallon, Jeanne 97
Falsey, Ann M 565
Falvey, James 392
Falwell, Trey 299
Falzone, Lori 451
Famuyiwa, Oluyemisi O 254
Fan, Dawson 641
Fanale, James 99
Fanelli, Denise 262
Fang, Joseph 392
Fang, Zheng 511
Fanning, Thomas 492
Fansler, Janet 291
Fant, Suzanne 507
Fantorno, Carla 532
Farabell, Jacqueline 132
Fardman, Emilya 350
Farhan, Faisal 6
Farinsky, Jason 455
Farkas, Chris 251
Farland, Kenn Mc 345
Farley, Joseph M 97
Farley, James 409
Farmer, Kathryn 80
Farmer, Maelynn 99
Farmer, Jenifer 141
Farmer, Paul J 177
Farmer, Michael 319
Farney, Cheryl 335
Farney, Alan 644
Farnham, Linda 178
Farnham, Cathrine 330
Farnsworth, Diane 451
Farnum, Michelle 124
Farnum, Allan 262
Farquhar, Joey 659
Farr, Richard 173
Farr, David 521
Farrell, Julie 7
Farrell, Lori Ann 127
Farrell, Steven 218
Farrell, Benny 339
Farrell, William J 657
Farren, John 544
Farren, Magda 644
Farrimond, Katherine 381
Farrington, Shannon 426

Farris, Judy 283
Farris, Bain 458
Farris, Bain J 458
Farris, Bain J 503
Faser, Christine 332
Fasino, Jeffrey 144
Fass, Maxine 572
Fassio, Michelle 528
Fath, Noella 38
Faul, Michelle 545
Faulds, Jason 466
Faulkner, David V 259
Faulkner, Jennifer 371
Faust, Bonnie Hartley 300
Faux, Marsha 421
Fave, John La 658
Favuzza, Steven P 584
Fawcett, Tiffany 444
Fawcett, Dave 650
Fay, Kay B 631
Fc, Brett 212
Fearon, Richard 200
Feathers, Amy 642
Federoff, Howard 560
Fedzhora, Liliya 641
Fee, Mariah 571
Feeley, Andrea 657
Feeney, Jim 342
Feeney, Joe 349
Fegan, Jeff P 180
Fehlberg, Mark 585
Fehnel, Stephen H 437
Feiccabrino, Joseph 130
Feickert, Beth 261
Feidner, Susan 116
Feiga, Tyler 535
Fein, Alan 546
Feinberg, Sarah 370
Feldgreber, Rob 429
Feldkamp, Gary 555
Feldman, Greg 24
Feldman, Martin J 502
Feldman-Wiencek, Holly 362
Feldotte, Jonathon 63
Feliciano, Lynette 169
Fell, Rob 475
Fellenz, Sherry 63
Fellin, Frederick M 593
Felton, Danielle 127
Felton, Kathryn 592
Felzien, Aidan 408
Fennebresque, Kim 18
Fennell, Charles 504
Fennell, Debbie 509
Fenner, Arvie 218
Fenner, Simon 306
Fennessy, Dan 604
Fennewald, Denise 347
Fennoy, Donald 467
Fenton, Julia 592
Fenwick, Sandra 548
Fenza, Daniel 120
Feola, Tony 132
Feragne, Mark A 22
Feransi, Toni 164
Ferderber, Fred 93
Ferencz, Steve M 106
Ferguson, Alexis 291
Ferguson, Joel I 342
Ferguson, Troy 424
Ferguson, Stacey 499
Ferguson, Bruce 532
Ferguson, Erica 578
Ferguson, Jonathon 632
Ferketish, Gene B 628
Ferlin, Gregg 146
Fernandes, Al 605
Fernandez, Mario 193
Fernandez, Luz 204
Fernandez, Maria 443
Fernandez, Joe 462
Fernandez, Nuria 464
Fernandez, Aurelio M 486
Fernando, Meg 544

Ferniany, Will 615
Feroce, Anthony 164
Ferrante, Sharon 552
Ferranti, Richard 445
Ferrari, Mauro 336
Ferreira, Melissa 41
Ferreira, Deborah 434
Ferrell, Tyler 91
Ferrell, Ronnie 212
Ferrer, Fernando 338
Ferrer, Fernando 370
Ferreri, Anthony C 519
Ferris, Richard J 414
Ferris, Samuel 567
Ferris, Jim 587
Ferrucci, Wendy 633
Ferrufino, Jimena 112
Ferry, Thomas 19
Fesko, Frankie 146
Fesko, Frankie L 359
Feteira, Kelly 60
Fetterman, John 146
Fetterman, Jean 226
Feuer, Bradley A 61
Feuer, Michael J 560
Fick, Daniel 258
Fiddler, Lori 437
Fidler, Deborah 143
Fiedler, Michael 175
Field, Aaron 22
Field, Lorne 157
Field, Scott 601
Fielder, Penny 438
Fields, Karin 211
Fields, Dana 426
Fields, Joe 489
Fields, Deborah 618
Fierens, Lou 599
Fife, Jordan 75
Fife, Heather 319
Fifer, Joseph J 494
Fighs, Charles 486
Figler, Christine 506
Figora, Luke 389
Figueroa, Regina 332
Figueroa, Alex 429
Figueroa, Pablo T 505
Fijol, Emily 394
Fike, Andrea M 39
Filingeri, Stephen 251
Filizetti, Gary 188
Filotei, Ashley 419
Finale, James 99
Finberg, Robert 609
Finch, Bill 594
Finchem, Timothy W 414
Fincher, Kyle 549
Fine, Peter S 56
Fine, David J 114
Fine, Patrick C 211
Fine, Janis 305
Fine, Michael H 447
Finger, April 112
Finkel, Steven I 438
Finley, Wayne 161
Finley, Lowell 247
Finn, Brenda 196
Finnorn, Peter 262
Fino, Lisa 536
Finol, Ana 341
Fiol, Maribel 356
Fioranelli, Marcelo 13
Fioravanti, Mark 454
Fiore, Anthony 561
Fiori, Kevin 526
Fiorini, Monica 643
Fiorito, Brittany 158
Fireman, Cassie 311
Firestone, Fred 162
Firestone, Brooks 169
Fischer, Steve 71
Fischer, Danny 72
Fischer, Russell E 246
Fischer, Greg 304

Index of Executives

Index of Executives

Index of Executives

Index of Executives

Index of Executives

H

H, Hubert 2
Haacker, Kristin 577
Haak, Andrew 149
Haas, John J 191
Haas, Nancy 365
Haas, Gerard 488
Haas, Jamie 610
Haas, Christopher 616
Haase, Charlie 171
Haase, Bruce 210
Haber, Emily 124
Habib, Reza 490
Hachey, Barbara G 268
Hachey, Barbara 268
Hackel, Mark 162
Hackenberg, Kim 226
Hacker, Doug 457
Hackerman, Nancy 482
Hackett, Steven G 426
Hackett, Troy M 656
Hackman, Jeffrey L 601
Hackney, James R 385
Haddad, Ann-Marie 467
Haddad, Ghassan 488
Haddock, Diane 283
Hadduck, Katy 172
Haden, Catherine 305
Haden, Dr Kent 339
Haden, Becky 506
Hadenfeldt, Cynthia 175
Haderlein, Jane 407
Hadjiliadis, Dennis 255
Hadley, David 264
Hadley, Lester 361
Haefner, Dr Jeremy 619
Haering, Paul E 108
Haertjens, Barb 349
Hafeez, Kudsia 391
Hafer, Greg 454
Haffajee, Charles I 97
Hafner, Michelle 83
Hagan, Nicole 48
Hagan, Timothy F 158
Hagan, Michael J 392
Hagan, Sylvia 580
Hagedorn, Marv 511
Hagel, Shawn R 426
Hagen, Colby 409
Hager, Laurel 122
Hagey, Michelle 417
Haggard, Herbert C 254
Haggen, Donald 240
Haggen, Richard 240
Haggerty, Scott 155
Hagler, Tony 140
Hagler, Mendel 369
Haglund, Karl 572
Hagman, Karen 31
Hague, Jill 635
Hagy, Michelle 417
Hahn, Paul 157
Hahn, Paul J 157
Hahn, Tim 165
Hahn, Andrea 506
Hahn, Diane 518
Hahne, Christopher 333
Haidar, Wael 83
Haight, Pat 467
Haigis, Kevin 180
Haigwood, Nancy L 399
Haile, Rick 86
Hailey, Robert 152
Haines, Dennis 171
Haines, Steve 193
Haire, Gary 216
Haire, Melanie 644
Hairston, John 83
Haizel, Samantha 101
Hajny, Mark 529
Hake, James 382
Hakim, Veronique 338

Hakim, Veronique 368
Hakim, Jamal 400
Hakimzada, Ahmad 377
Haldar, Pradeep 577
Hale, Jeff 118
Hale, Kenneston 207
Hale, Daniel G 332
Hale, Ted 510
Hale, Jordan 517
Hale, Q Val 517
Hale, Blake 533
Haley, Nikki 516
Haley, Charla 517
Hall, Mary C 28
Hall, Mary C 33
Hall, Mary 33
Hall, R Alan 54
Hall, Lanny 67
Hall, Jim 73
Hall, Nicole 82
Hall, Stacyee 113
Hall, Ulysha R 126
Hall, Sheila 126
Hall, Tony 158
Hall, Juree 159
Hall, Tyrell 166
Hall, Ryan 173
Hall, Dolan 206
Hall, Alex 215
Hall, Tonia 286
Hall, Kristen 319
Hall, Jodi 384
Hall, Roger 413
Hall, Charlie 416
Hall, Pj 438
Hall, Jonna 441
Hall, Joanne 497
Hall, Lauren 539
Hall, John J 556
Hall, Loretta 572
Hall, Melaina 587
Hall, Chaundra 616
Hall-Long, Bethany 511
Hallberg, Andrea 233
Halleck, Hope 156
Halley, Mary 609
Hallian, Terence 122
Halliday, Mike 166
Halligan, Donald A 316
Halliwill, Donald 99
Hallman, Gary 26
Hallman, Ronald S 125
Hallmark, Jeff 151
Hallmark, Dustin 151
Hallmark, Ron 491
Halloran, Thomas 372
Hallquist, Raymond D 285
Hallum, Kathy 516
Halonen, Robert 598
Halperin, Lexi 55
Halsey, Drew 205
Halsey, Casey S 268
Halsey, Casey S 268
Halstead, Tammy 130
Halverson, John 51
Halverson, Pete 81
Halverson, Steve 286
Halvorson, Bob 345
Hamaguchi, James 585
Hamaty-Bird, Gail 217
Hamby, Leigh S 416
Hamel, Cathy 225
Hamel, Kristina 481
Hamer, Lynne 549
Hamilton, Evan 26
Hamilton, Kris 168
Hamilton, Stephanie 233
Hamilton, Fredrick 254
Hamilton, Andrew D 374
Hamilton, Corey 395
Hamilton, Tiffany 403
Hamilton, John R 416
Hamilton, Adam 492
Hamilton, Jennifer 594

Hamilton, Rick 598
Hamilton, Andrew D 661
Hamlin, David 139
Hamlin, Terry 427
Hamm, Michele 162
Hammer, Douglas J 264
Hammer, Glen 579
Hammers, Aaron 358
Hammes, Chris 263
Hammes, Chris 264
Hammond, John 156
Hammond, Douglas 377
Hammond, Chris 428
Hammond, Sara Beth 493
Hammond, Star 651
Hamon, David E 194
Hamon, David 194
Hamory, Bruce H 225
Hampson, Chad 272
Hampton, Jenean 145
Hampton, Monica 187
Hampton, Kelly 411
Hampton, Chris 461
Hamre, John 569
Hamrock, Dave 156
Han, Joseph 473
Han, Kevin 522
Hance, Tom 120
Hancock, Sharon 72
Hancock, Maryjean 201
Hancock, Jim 267
Hancock, Melinda 473
Handfield, Larry 576
Handley, Jack 286
Handline, Amra 146
Handy, Elsie 641
Hanerkson, David 140
Haney, Carl 508
Hanick, Mel 17
Hankins, Joyce 101
Hanks, Craig 543
Hankton, Furnell 347
Hanley, Kathleen 167
Hanley, Richard J 174
Hanley, Cheryl 481
Hanley, Matthew 497
Hanley, Cathy 595
Hanley, Karen 654
Hanlin, Russell 526
Hanlin, Russell L 526
Hanlon, Randy 13
Hanlon, Brian 588
Hanlon, Philip J 602
Hanlon, David 620
Hanly, Donna 395
Hann, Susan 7
Hanna, Gia 361
Hannaford, Matt 555
Hannah, Sara 62
Hannah, Anthony 108
Hannah, Steve 176
Hannah, Brian 333
Hannan, John 207
Hannan, Renee 247
Hannigan, Elizabeth 78
Hannon, Richard M 78
Hannon, Rita 319
Hannon, Mary 595
Hans, Peter 586
Hansberry, Kristin 333
Hanselman, Lisa 652
Hansen, Mark 38
Hansen, Rick 103
Hansen, David L 135
Hansen, Bradley 165
Hansen, Marshall 212
Hansen, Larry 247
Hansen, Steven 285
Hansen, Becky 349
Hansen, Don 398
Hansen, Douglas 433
Hansen, Dr David 447
Hansen, Jan 599
Hansman, Steve 195

Hanson, Elizabeth 102
Hanson, Dena 152
Hanson, Michael 222
Hanson, Jodee 515
Hantman, Perla Tabares 579
Happell, Kathy 579
Harasick, Richard F 303
Harbarger, Claude 624
Harbert, Joe 49
Harbert, Billy 54
Harbes, Jason 191
Harbison, Ella 132
Harcum, Rick 159
Hardage, Ryan 140
Harden, Billy 153
Harden, M C 489
Hardesty, Dean 31
Hardin, Scott 51
Hardin, Beverly 320
Hardin, Kimberly 616
Harding, Jonathan 4
Harding, Joe 658
Hardister, Hal 526
Hardman, Elizabeth 185
Hardman, Danny 615
Hardt, William 582
Hardtke, Brian 166
Hardwick, M Susan 491
Hardy, Cody 112
Hardy, Brent 260
Hardy, Leah 432
Hardy, Brad 521
Hare, Michelle 504
Haren, Lexie Van 131
Harford, Simon 406
Hargett, Fred 390
Hargis, Burns 396
Haring, Dawn 92
Harker, Patrick T 618
Harkness, Shanan 242
Harlan, Clifford C 393
Harlem, Peter 488
Harless, Amanda 546
Harley, Chanelle 579
Harman, Terry 169
Harmon, Nicole 90
Harmon, Tom 143
Harmon, Eric 150
Harms, Debra 26
Harness, Carl 161
Harney, John 618
Harold, Gennie 196
Harp, Richard 163
Harper, Keith 167
Harper, Reid 170
Harper, Sarah 221
Harper, Bethany 257
Harper, Carol 452
Harper, Hershel 607
Harr, Jenifer 32
Harr, Nathan 320
Harrel, Dustin 642
Harreld, Bruce 586
Harrell, Karen 123
Harrell, Jennie 339
Harrell, Kim 501
Harriman, Morril 510
Harrington, Russ 57
Harrington, Rich 60
Harrington, Wade 129
Harrington, Judy B 246
Harrington, Dale W 555
Harrington, Charles L 573
Harris, Anita 19
Harris, Joyce 20
Harris, Danny 40
Harris, Barbara 43
Harris, Patty 69
Harris, Gene T 144
Harris, Jennifer 177
Harris, Stephen 204
Harris, Emily 238
Harris, Rachel 241
Harris, Carolyn 249

Index of Executives

Index of Executives

Index of Executives

Index of Executives

Kaplan, Paul 195
Kaplan, Josh 208
Kaplan, Tamra 301
Kaplan, Betina 620
Kaplan, Alan 632
Kaplan, Alan 632
Kaplan, Gary S 642
Kaplon, Sari 350
Kapp, Brian 149
Kapperman, Garry 514
Karam, Mary Kate M 593
Karandikar, Nitin 585
Karaskova, Jana 233
Karels, Gordon V 81
Karl, Patricia 174
Karmiol, Grace 623
Karnei, Clifton D 86
Karnik, Amogh 182
Karo, Rachel 426
Karp, Harold M 534
Karr, Michael 404
Karran, Tony 299
Karrer, Joy 390
Kasdin, Robert 581
Kasenge, Rebecca 608
Kasey, Jay 355
Kasmin, Franklin 71
Kaspar, Kristen 158
Kasper, Curt 137
Kass, Bonnie 407
Kassel, Matt 451
Kassem, Rona 334
Kassen, Tim 307
Kasser, Mike 490
Kassim, Aj 283
Kastanis, John N 621
Kastriner, Jared 65
Katemba, Edward L 493
Kates, Kenneth P 621
Katsilometes, Tom 511
Katsoyannis, George 453
Katterheinrich, Lean 144
Katz, Ellen 72
Katz, Paul 356
Katz, Naomi L 439
Katz, Nathalia 542
Katz, Ken 557
Katz, Louis H 560
Katzman, Richard 105
Kauffman, Richard 206
Kauffman, Richard 373
Kauffman, William R 458
Kaufman, Donna 589
Kaufman, Brett 290
Kaufman, Irvin A 434
Kaufman, Irvin A 434
Kaufmann, Marli 420
Kaukali, Chris T 620
Kaul, Will 235
Kaup, Nicholas 586
Kaur, Jaswinder 460
Kavanaugh, James P 659
Kavthekar, Suhas 488
Kawanishi, David T 345
Kawasaki, Iris 576
Kawasaki, Hiroyuki 662
Kawata, Hiro 231
Kealey, Katie 308
Kealy, Mary V 303
Kean, Steve 364
Keane, John B 30
Keane, Andrea 152
Keany, James 345
Kearney, Craig 152
Kearney, Janis 317
Kearney, Jason 345
Kearns, James 26
Kearns, Michael 159
Kearns, Leslie 304
Kearns, Donald B 434
Kearns, Donald 434
Kearns, Michael 479
Keathley, Wayne E 453
Keating, Mike 550

Keating, Todd 588
Keating, Todd 608
Keating, Todd 609
Keaton, Kevin 287
Keaton, Matthew 337
Keck, Sharon J 12
Keck, Sharon 12
Keck, Kim A 78
Kee, Marlow 580
Keefer, Katrina 51
Keefer, Brian 149
Keel, Pat 505
Keeler, Thomas 165
Keeler, Tracy 256
Keeler, Brian 352
Keeler, Diane 557
Keeley, Brian E 57
Keeling, Tammy 498
Keen, Eric L 244
Keen, Eric 245
Keenan, Claudia 332
Keenan, Richard 589
Keene, Brian 60
Keene, Kristi 388
Keenum, Mark E 346
Kehaly, Pam 78
Kehl, Roxanne 261
Kehoe, Michael J 408
Kehoe, Mike 514
Kehrer, Bob 277
Keightley, Elizabeth 111
Keil, Richard 525
Keirns, Marylou 4
Keiser, Vicki 147
Keith, Greg 269
Kell, James 205
Kelleher, Margaret Ann 353
Kellen, Michael J 36
Keller, Jonell 19
Keller, San 32
Keller, Timothy M 122
Keller. Philip 124
Keller, Glenn 155
Keller, Anne 395
Keller, Sue 652
Kelley, Michael 101
Kelley, Jennifer 249
Kelley, Mark A 249
Kelley, Jim 383
Kelley, Laurie 429
Kelley, Trenton 539
Kelleyfield, Alicia 98
Kellmanson, Mary 559
Kelly, Leo 7
Kelly, Thomas B 8
Kelly, Patrick 15
Kelly, Sam 35
Kelly, Nancy 52
Kelly, William M 79
Kelly, Jhon 85
Kelly, Linda 146
Kelly, Marlena 156
Kelly, Patrick 158
Kelly, Thomas C 172
Kelly, Jack W 235
Kelly, Alan B 254
Kelly, Keven 261
Kelly, Patty 261
Kelly, Tony 304
Kelly, Stefanie 374
Kelly, Frank 388
Kelly, Angela 423
Kelly, Chere 439
Kelly, Barb 473
Kelly, Tim 476
Kelly, James J 477
Kelly, James 499
Kelly, Laura 512
Kelly, Ann P 608
Kelly, John 609
Kelly-Ennis, Debra 561
Kelsch, Kevin 282
Kelso, John 162
Kelso, Aimee 401

Kelton, Justin 321
Kelvinton, William C 410
Kemp, Matthew 337
Kemp, Ronald 426
Kemp, Brian 511
Kemp, Ann 616
Kemp, Michael 630
Kemper, Chris 36
Kemper, Charnele 363
Kempf, Jason 49
Kendall, Sean 96
Kendall, Andrew C 303
Kenerly, Margaret 646
Keninger, Jon 262
Kenna, Robert J Mc 552
Kennah, Branden 430
Kennard, Corey 500
Kennedy, Jimmie 28
Kennedy, Patrick 168
Kennedy, Murrell 330
Kennedy, Bruce 336
Kennedy, Bridget 343
Kennedy, Pamela 360
Kennedy, Daniel 444
Kennedy, Amanda 520
Kennedy, Cheryl 522
Kennedy, Brian 561
Kennedy, Mark 577
Kennel, Kaylan 342
Kenney, Jim 131
Kenny, David 378
Kenny, Michael 405
Kenny, Andrew 580
Kenoi, William P 160
Kent, Angela 4
Kent, Cherry 37
Kent, John 165
Kent, Angel 168
Kent, Rodney D 265
Kent, Geoff 265
Kent, James L 322
Kent, Thomas 367
Kenyon, Robert 48
Kenzie, Lesa Mc 458
Keo, Chamreoun 123
Keough, Shawn 541
Keough, Joseph 602
Kepler, Jody 349
Keppel, Mary Ann 246
Kepple, Yann 246
Kereiakes, Dean 550
Keriacous, Leedia 631
Kern, Howard 473
Kerner, Dave 166
Kerner, Gwen 271
Kernodle, Rex 245
Kerouani, Farida 404
Kerr, Howard J 151
Kerr, Robert W 151
Kerr, Reiko A 303
Kerr, Brian C 456
Kerr, Bonnie 623
Kerschner, Joseph E 566
Kersey, Frances 130
Kershaw, Craig 525
Kessel, Donna Van 483
Kessinger, Steve 292
Kessler, George 56
Kessler, Aaron 436
Kessler, Grace 517
Kessler, Joe 598
Ketterling, Terry L 485
Kettle, Michelle 611
Keuer, Steve 119
Keuer, Steven 600
Keuten, John 68
Keuten, John 657
Kevorkian, Sarah 393
Keyler, Angela 458
Khait-Palant, Olga V 431
Khakbaznejad, Alireza 382
Khamseh, Ladan 398
Khatua, Sanjeeb 266
Khehra, Raman 20

Khosla, Suresh 1
Khosla, Ashok K 1
Khosla, Leena 1
Khouri, Frederick 217
Khouri, Mark 217
Khoury, Raymond 147
Khullar, Puneet 89
Ki, Irena 366
Kidd, Judi 317
Kidd, Dana 513
Kidd, Lindsay H 589
Kidder, Troy 34
Kidder, Amanda 135
Kidwell, April 514
Kieffer, Adam 48
Kiel, Martha 496
Kiely, Charles 190
Kiely, Sharon 581
Kiesel, John L 612
Kiffmeyer, Mary 513
Kihune, Robert K U 603
Kilby, Jerry 145
Kileman, Joel 166
Kilgore, Krystin 525
Killian, Margaret 170
Killian, Wayne 481
Killmer, Jonathon 252
Kilmer, Steven 409
Kilpatrick, Dona 32
Kilpatrick, James T 218
Kilpatrick, C 641
Kilpatrick, Charles A 641
Kilty, Carolyn 525
Kim, Yup 15
Kim, Desir E 129
Kim, Jong Min 137
Kim, Jangyul R 142
Kim, Frank 165
Kim, Taeeuk 258
Kim, Changyoung 258
Kim, Chung 300
Kim, Jenny 389
Kim, Judy 392
Kim, Robert 476
Kim, Sue J 506
Kim, Jung-In 577
Kim, Anne 579
Kim, Nam 632
Kimball, Brian 191
Kimball, Chip 291
Kimbell, Jimmy 37
Kimberly, Jack 481
Kimmerle, David 193
Kimmerle, Sandra Sue 193
Kinaitis, Eric 544
Kinard, Olaf 124
Kincaid, Lisa 249
Kincaid, Cassell 494
Kindblad, Lisa 441
Kinder, Richard D 364
Kindle, John 171
Kindlick, David 643
Kindred, Troy 160
Kindred, Deanne D 496
King, Susan 7
King, Rick 40
King, Bob 46
King, Chuck 95
King, Chad 130
King, Randy 139
King, Jeff 139
King, Timothy 144
King, Yolanda 157
King, Fred 160
King, David F 162
King, Darlene 167
King, Andrea 169
King, Kevin 199
King, Terry 212
King, Jerry 227
King, Mark 232
King, Michael 260
King, Kelly 291
King, Michelle 303

Index of Executives

King, M W 336
King, Ron 358
King, Brigitte 374
King, Norma 412
King, Jenna 447
King, Timothy 450
King, Karen 457
King, Jared 459
King, Jeffrey 473
King, Jeffrey 473
King, Kristin 490
King, Shannon 502
King, Troy 510
King, Lisa 524
King, Charles 553
King, Matthew 601
Kingbury, Mike 222
Kingsbury, James 607
Kinnear, Katey 164
Kinneer, Mike 144
Kinsey, Armond 11
Kinsey, Armond 48
Kinsey, Stephen 163
Kintigh, Denise 459
Kinyo, Doug 337
Kirby, Sarah 205
Kirby, Mary J 647
Kirchendorfer, Diane 158
Kircher, Debra 246
Kirchoff, Mary 29
Kirchoff, Bob 154
Kirk, Rich Van 188
Kirk, Warren J 193
Kirk, Bruce M 299
Kirk, Patrick T 332
Kirk, Ron 511
Kirk, Randall 518
Kirk, Kevin 565
Kirkish, Mark S 445
Kirkwood, David W 595
Kirrish, Abed 303
Kirsch, Sandra 114
Kise, Shawn 607
Kiser, Dean 172
Kiser, Jennifer 187
Kiser, Terry 346
Kish, Mary 635
Kiss, Morgan 53
Kistner, Tim 207
Kitchen, Carol 237
Kittelson, Roger 118
Kitts, Suzanne 542
Kiwall, Walter J 646
Kizer, Kim 188
Kjos, Michael 128
Kjos, Ann 128
Kladis, Donna 108
Klaff, Hersch 18
Klaich, Daniel 367
Klaschus, Irv 96
Klasko, Stephen K 593
Klasko, Stephen 593
Klass, Cheryl 280
Klassen, Christopher 477
Klatt, Susan 586
Klausner, Rob 98
Klaver, Dennis 500
Klee, Ann 523
Kleeman, Steven 73
Klees, Dee 134
Kleiman, Joel 166
Kleiman, Dr Michael 272
Klein, Luella V 211
Klein, Jane Marie 219
Klein, Robin 283
Klein, Cathy 345
Klein, Andrew 406
Kleinhenz, Eric 207
Kleinman, Lawrence 488
Kleinschmidt, Julie 167
Klemm, Brad 187
Kleyla, John 290
Klibanski, Anne 317
Klika, Kevin A 360

Klika, Christine 512
Klimonek, Barbara 14
Klimoski, Daniel 186
Kline, Cynthia 171
Kline, Juliann 256
Kline, Douglas B 269
Kline, Mark W 540
Kling, Jonathan 362
Klinger, James M 444
Kloberdanz, Mark 411
Klocke, Kelly 40
Klocke, Deb 45
Klockenga, Kevin 502
Klontz, Richard 611
Klos, Mary Jo 238
Klosinski, Tom 520
Klossner, Rebecca 134
Klosson, Michael 466
Klosterman, Cole 42
Klosterman, Ronald 266
Klubert, Laura 19
Klueg, Steven P 311
Klug, Candice 566
Klugherz, Greg 442
Klugherz, Greg 578
Klusmeyer, Amy 568
Kluth, Doreen 508
Knabe, Don 162
Knack, Monica 442
Knapp, Jerry 10
Knapp, Peter 324
Knapp, Douglas 530
Knarr, Donald 119
Knaus, Ron 494
Knecht, Michael 61
Kneessy, Amy 466
Knelly, Shirley J 306
Knepper, Chris 149
Knesek, Michael J 342
Knierim, Abraham 604
Knight, Justin G 40
Knight, Glade M 40
Knight, Nelson G 40
Knight, Lyle R 75
Knight, Calvin 274
Knight, Reginald 565
Knighton, Nash 212
Kniskern, Matthew 177
Knisley, Melinda 257
Knoble, Jody 51
Knobloch, George 284
Knodell, Jane 631
Knoll, Thomas 222
Knoll, Allan F 437
Knoll, Josh 441
Knoop, Lindsay 258
Knopf, William D 416
Knopf, Keith 435
Knott, Carolyn 486
Knowlbauch, Andy 142
Knowles, Richard 340
Knox, Linda 600
Knudson, Dallas 21
Knudson, Kelly 468
Knuteson, Cory 641
Knutson, Curtis 30
Knutson, Paul 107
Kobashigawa, Wendy 163
Kobrin, Elie 604
Kobylanski, Daniel 537
Koch, Robert 91
Koch, Billy 256
Koch, Cheryl 275
Koch, Kevin J 322
Koch, J Robert 568
Koch, Sheryl E 617
Kochem, Gary 15
Kochem, Gary J 16
Kocher, Marisa 311
Kocsis, Dana 551
Kodachi, Cynthia 172
Kodish, Joel 54
Koedam, James J 3
Koehler, Kevin 523

Koehler, Michael 561
Koele, Chad 8
Koenen, Kirk 225
Koenig, Dawn 128
Koenig, Kristy 276
Koenig, Carolyn L 334
Koenig, Barbara 616
Koeplin, David 456
Koeppel, Holly 30
Kogan, Barry 16
Kohler, Steven A 96
Kokes, Marvin 212
Kokinda, John 201
Kokuri, Lisa 603
Kolanz, Ryan 422
Kolavo, Joe 523
Kolb, Kenneth 119
Kolb, Jeanne L 340
Kolb-Nelson, Annie 161
Kolendrander, Kirk 318
Koller, Darwin 241
Kolloway, Michael R 573
Kolodizner, Paul 598
Kolomentsev, Alexandre 643
Kolosky, Jack 240
Komanduri, Chaitanya 583
Komar, Michael 226
Komarov, Sergey 591
Komin, Ed 161
Konold, Kyle 554
Kontos, Mark 569
Konzelman, Sharon 284
Koonce, Treva 362
Koop, Alvin 486
Koop, Jodi 638
Kooyman, Brittany 401
Kopalek, Joseph R 608
Kopcho, Darcy 562
Kope, Dorothy 511
Kopecky, Deb 481
Kopiasz, Corey S 595
Koplon, Norman 123
Korbelak, Stacy 38
Kordelski, Michael 350
Koreny, Claudia 604
Korte, Scot 176
Kortum, Joe 493
Korty, Andrew 602
Koschmeder, Mark 232
Koselka, Helen 598
Koser, Michael 654
Kosidowski, Ellen 445
Kosko, Andrew 193
Kosla, Kristen 198
Kosnitzky, Michael 576
Koss, Kristen K 522
Kost, Kerry 379
Koster, John 170
Koster, John 429
Kotcher, Peter 636
Kotek, Jim 592
Kotil, Drew 91
Kott, Alison 123
Kottas, Jim 259
Kottman, Bill 201
Koukouvitakis, Sophia 177
Kourepenis, Anthony S 547
Koutny, Lance 318
Kovach, Andrew L 11
Kovacs, Jeff 571
Koval, Erin 381
Kowal, Spencer A 118
Kowalski, Suzanne 343
Koyle, Cade 433
Kozicz, Gregory J 16
Kozicz, Gregory J 16
Kozicz, Gregory J 17
Kozik, Elizabeth 243
Koziol, Michael 309
Kozlowski, Eric 67
Kozoman, Robert 185
Kozsan, Eileen 173
Krabbenhoft, Kelby K 463
Kraft, Phil 162

Kraftchick, Debbra L 587
Krage, Susan 617
Kragt, Jeff 154
Krajewski, David 300
Krake, Cynthia 288
Krake, John 288
Kraker, Diane 529
Krakos, Greg 37
Kramaric, Chuck 156
Kramer, Jessica 84
Kramer, David A 92
Kramer, Frances 100
Kramlich, Christine 608
Kramm, Jeffrey 288
Krammer, Lisa 389
Kran, Bob 342
Kranich, Brad 481
Krasnoff, Alan P 125
Kratky, Aron 357
Kratze, Alexa 434
Kratzert, Niki 287
Krause, Brian 72
Krause, Matt 97
Krause, Melissa 119
Krause, Alan J 361
Krausman, Tim 262
Krausz, Keira 392
Kravet, Steven J 275
Krawiec, Ronald 208
Krawitz, Natalie 625
Krayer, Anthony C 486
Krebsbach, David 381
Kregel, Kevin 586
Kreidler, John 445
Kremens, Robert 450
Kremer, Leslie 457
Krenk, Chris 99
Krenke, Brian 289
Kress, Lynn 451
Kretzinger, Cut 354
Krewson, Lyda 134
Krhovsky, David M 494
Kriependorf, Bari 485
Kriesberg, Barry 243
Krift, Tom 466
Krill, Aaron 640
Krings, David 160
Kriskovich, Craig 496
Krissinger, Debby 87
Krivo, George 198
Krohman, Barbara L 456
Krohn, Cindy 554
Kroloff, Mark 41
Kropiunik, Frank C 16
Kroupa, Matt 4
Kroupa, Robert 524
Krow, Reggie 363
Krpan, Marko 335
Krueger, Shari 415
Krug, Dave 124
Kruger, Donna 512
Kruk, Nadine 437
Krull, Karen A 460
Kruse, Lowell 354
Kruse, Rose 396
Krusemark, Cortni 175
Krushel, Kenneth 571
Krutak, Lynn 55
Kruzner, Melinda P 298
Kruzner, Melinda 298
Krych, Ron 589
Krylova, Alexandra 306
Krystal, Andrew 616
Krystopolski, Ruth 463
Kubacki, Joe 510
Kubik, Joellen 266
Kubota, Nina 370
Kuboyama, Cameron 474
Kuch, Logan 10
Kucharski, Kathryn 479
Kucyk, Laura 379
Kuczmanski, John D 323
Kudla, Keith 211
Kudo, Lance 31

Index of Executives

Kudumovic, Adisa 266
Kuechenmeister, Kevin 351
Kuehn, George 564
Kuenstler, Fred 424
Kuenstler, Kevin 542
Kuether, Lynda 490
Kugel, Kevin 132
Kuhn, Rebecca 56
Kuhn, William 62
Kuhn, Tiffany 271
Kuhn, Sandi 335
Kuhn, James D 375
Kuida, Elliot 409
Kuklenz, Dustin 382
Kukosky, Richard 414
Kula, Tom 384
Kulikowski, Lina 157
Kull, Matthew 552
Kullman, Betsy 145
Kullman, Mary 495
Kulper, Michael 1
Kulseth, Paul 281
Kumar, Ashok 1
Kumar, Jaya 530
Kumar, Monisha A 593
Kunimoto, Yoshihiko 527
Kunkel, Joann 463
Kunkel, Erin 574
Kunkle, Caitlin 5
Kunnary, Clifford F 136
Kunstling, Ted 196
Kuper, Susan 48
Kurdle, Florence B 306
Kurkowski, Arthur 422
Kuroki, Nobuyuki 581
Kurrle, Gunter 283
Kurtenbach, Anne 131
Kurth, Lauren 166
Kurtz, Cassidy 142
Kurtz, Leslie 269
Kurtz, William 427
Kusch, Alton 211
Kutner, Jean 618
Kutsumalis, Maria 571
Kutz, Stephanie 633
Kuykendall, Dorthy 513
Kuzma, Nathaniel 92
Kvidt, Scott 437
Kvistadt, Gregg 619
Kwak, Jin 258
Kwan, George 125
Kwietkauski, Chris 508
Kwilinski, Kevin 357
Kwock, Danny 82
Kwok, Amy 149
Kwon, Kenneth 345
Kwong, Raymond 546
Kyle, Rick 423
Kyles, David J 424
Kyles, Mable 453
Kyunghee, Lee D Ed 342

L

L, Cynthia 2
La, Paul De 404
Labarge, Kenny 259
Labeau, Tina 165
Labelle, Tom 161
Laberge, Michael 513
Labin, Karen 362
Labosky, Laura 134
Labrecque, Andre G 22
Labrecque, Rachel S 40
Labrie, John 176
Lacaze, Alan 604
Lacek, Ryan 23
Lacey, Sheila 49
Lackey, Kevin 513
Lacroix, Laurent 259
Lacroix, Marc 444
Lacy, Renee 641

Ladao, Victor 452
Ladd, Kevin 217
Ladd, Steven 236
Ladewig, Mary 416
Ladley, Herb 55
Lady, Shirley S 78
Lafferty, Jane 653
Laffond, Reggie 608
Laffont, Philippe 561
Lafon, Emily 653
Laforest, Pat 493
Lafortune, Robert 500
Lafranchi, Stephen 507
Lagazo, Michael 461
Lager, Jeffrey T 29
Lagerstrom, Timothy 242
Lagnese, Sheila 324
Lagree, Peggy A 159
Lague, Richard C 332
Laguzza, Toni 175
Lahti, David 514
Lai-Bitker, Ellis 155
Laing, Diana 496
Laino, Audrey 529
Laird, Diane 326
Lake, Robert 188
Lakey, Aaron 80
Lakner, Stephen 6
Lalas, Jose W 154
Lalchandani, Ajit 166
Lallathin, Larry 394
Lalley, Peter 450
Lally, Kevin 411
Lalor, William 54
Lam, Christina 118
Lam, Lisa 157
Lamancusa, Alicia 118
Lamar, Jim 231
Lamar, Lona M 601
Lamas, Ed 162
Lamas, Felipe Rubio 237
Lamb, Jim 107
Lamb, Michael 156
Lamb, Eric 194
Lamb, John C 313
Lambdin, Rodney 587
Lambert, Megan 84
Lambert, Patrick 438
Lambert, Ellen 469
Lambert, H David 560
Lamberton, Karin T 164
Lamble, Mark 257
Lambros, Cindy 109
Lambrugo, Lauren M 164
Lambson, T V 460
Lamensdorf, Ben 509
Lamoreaux, Brent 260
Lamoureux, Chad 277
Lampkin, Andy 301
Lampkin, Patricia M 439
Lan, Sheryl 156
Lancaster, Rick 235
Lancaster, Kathy 279
Lance, Jay 268
Lance, Donald W 578
Landahl, Mark 159
Lander, Larry 457
Lander, Eric 546
Landers, Lisa 25
Landrieu, Mitchell J 129
Landry, Sherri 104
Landry, Renee 401
Landry, Malcom 452
Landry, Dawn 650
Landsford, Gordon E 268
Landsiedel, David 137
Lane, Claudio 155
Lane, Conan 247
Lane, Chuck 337
Lane, Debbie 396
Lane, Linda 419
Lane, Chris 645
Lane-Davies, Aaron 88
Laney, Mark 248

Laney, Mark 354
Langan, John 146
Lange, Frank 21
Lange, Donald H 120
Langford, Barbara 25
Langford, Stephen 68
Langford, Mark D 285
Langley, W John 320
Langrehr, Kristina 44
Langston, Mark 466
Lanham, Amy 156
Lanier, Gina 278
Laningham, Kathy Van 616
Lankford, Damon 422
Lankswert, Bill 151
Lanni, J Terrence 427
Lanno, Marianne 503
Lannon, Timothy R 175
Lanoha, Richard A 285
Lansford, Gordon 268
Lansford, Gordon E 268
Lanter, Jennifer 572
Lantos, Phyllis R 572
Lapidas, Gary 609
Lapier, Russ 177
Lapierre, Justine 609
Laplante, William A 547
Laporte, Todd 254
Laprade, Patricia 55
Lara, Gloria 495
Lara, Marilyn 662
Larbury, Dr George 390
Lareau, Douglas 479
Laribee, Teresa 574
Larios, Faith 543
Larman, Chad 333
Laroche, Jason 165
Larose, Robert C 98
Larrabee, Laura 513
Larrick, Kurt 156
Larsen, Burke 184
Larsen, Ed 282
Larsen, James C 472
Larson, Brian 113
Larson, Gaylyn 168
Larson, Jenna 266
Larson, Jody 266
Larson, Roma 512
Larson, Carol S 554
Larson, Bill 596
Larson, Nils 607
Larson, Jennifer 629
Larson, Lynette 647
Lasaga, Manuel 59
Lashier, Mark 113
Lashier, Mark 113
Lashier, Mark E 113
Lashore, Adeola 157
Laskey, Fred 319
Lasky, Lawrence 362
Lasonczyk, Cynthia 617
Lassere, Amy 583
Lassiter, Wright 249
Lassner, David 621
Last, Corita 219
Laster, Dale 640
Lateef, Omar 453
Laten, Steve 25
Lathan, Christopher 180
Lathan, Grenita 256
Latimer, Maggie 168
Latney, Cynthia 395
Lattimore, Ocea 134
Laturner, Jake 512
Latwin, Anthony 172
Laubacher, Pat 543
Laubscher, Kenton 575
Lauderback, Bill 304
Lauderdale, Meredith 572
Lauf, Michael K 96
Lauf, Michael K 97
Laughlin, Jeannie 134
Laughlin, Joseph 402
Laughlin, Melinda 514

Laughton, Kim 468
Laura, Russell 291
Lauraine, Allen 422
Laurence, Jodi B 340
Laurendeau, Annie M 514
Laurent, Anthony 615
Laurenzi, Cynthia 132
Laures, Karen 321
Laurito, James 108
Lauritsen, Bruce R 570
Lauwers, Nicole 503
Laveck, Bill 496
Lavender, Sunee 615
Law, David 38
Law, John C 105
Law, Rhea 629
Lawhorn, Wesley L 91
Lawing, Marty 160
Lawler, Noelle S 50
Lawler, Nelda 208
Lawler, Michael A 247
Lawless, Stephen T 19
Lawonn, Ken 478
Lawrence, Bruce 264
Lawrence, Sandra Aj 330
Lawrence, Melody 363
Lawrence, Joseph 426
Lawrence, Yaacov R 593
Lawrence, Paul 628
Lawrie, J Michael 150
Lawson, Ralph E 57
Lawson, Ralph 59
Lawson, T Douglas 65
Lawson, Stephen 198
Lawson, Stacey 231
Lawson, Matthew 321
Lawson, Matthew 321
Lawson, Kale 337
Lawson, Deborah 471
Lawson, Sherri 496
Lawson, John D 542
Lawson, John W 641
Laxton, Ron 179
Layden, Kelly 261
Layher, John 440
Layman, Mark 55
Layne, Christopher 359
Laytart, David 332
Layton, Mary Jo 272
Lazarus, Anne 131
Lcsw, Marynne 172
Le, Christian 148
Le, Luyen 168
Le, Brian 437
Le, Huong V 506
Le, Jennifer 584
Lea, Jenny 287
Lea, Amy 296
Leach, Su 49
Leach, Mary Anne 116
Leach, Craig 596
Leach, Craig 596
Leahy, Kevin D 219
Leahy, Kathleen 308
Leal, Santiago 12
Leal, Susan 122
Leal, Diego 131
Leale, Erin 186
Leary, Jen 138
Leary, John 507
Leary, Matt 650
Leatherberry, Kristine W 351
Leatherman, Jacob 48
Leatherman, Aaron 651
Leavell, Jeff 62
Leavey, Meghan 163
Lebel, Steven 206
Lebens, Michael C 537
Leblanc, Stephen 183
Leblanc, Cara A 479
Leblanc, Thomas 560
Leblanc, Paul A 615
Lechler, Lillian 163
Lechner, David 81

Index of Executives

Index of Executives

Lobas, Nancy 607
Locher, Eric 406
Locke, Gary 28
Locke, Jace D 207
Locke, Dana 609
Locken, Dale 11
Lockhart, John 492
Lockwood, Shannon 479
Lockwood, Charles 629
Loeak, Wojwa 120
Loeb, David M 276
Loeb, Joanne 374
Loebs, Caren 137
Loeffler, Mike 386
Loehr, Donna 157
Loehr, Steve 289
Lofgren, Zoe 427
Lofgren, Beverly 463
Lofgren, Elizabeth 496
Loft, Chris 85
Loftin-Gainer, Keisha 67
Lofton, Kevin E 189
Loftspring, Peter D 76
Logan, Dwayne 339
Logan, Cheryl 396
Logan, Angie 629
Loganathan, Raghunandan S 89
Logatto, Vincent 519
Logeman, David 107
Logsdon, Jordan 25
Logsdon, Justin 255
Logue, Anna 26
Lohr, Carolyn 467
Lohrer, Bernadette 467
Loiacono, Joseph 230
Lokeren, Mary Van 495
Lomack, Damien 283
Lombardo, Gerald A 191
Lombardo, Anthony 196
Lombardozzi, Chris 493
Lomeli, Bernardo 583
Lomeo, Jody L 208
Lomeo, Jody L 280
Lommen, Wendy 238
London, Eric 529
Londres, Eduardo 167
Loner, Marc 459
Lonergan, Stephen 133
Lonergan, Mike 166
Lones, Darling 529
Loney, Andrew 15
Long, Tina 203
Long, Jennifer 243
Long, Amanda 464
Long, William C 470
Long, Larry 517
Long, Ronald R 542
Long, Sherry 641
Longenderfer, Roger 418
Longhi, William G 397
Longo, Edie M 596
Longoria, Jennifer 528
Longstaff, Tom 100
Longstreet, Kym 323
Longstreet, Rick 493
Longsworth, Nora 587
Longwell, Char 327
Loo, Michael 603
Lopera, Adriana 84
Lopes, Debbie 535
Lopez, Robert 95
Lopez, Amy 119
Lopez, Jeannette 145
Lopez, Zoe 159
Lopez, Anna 224
Lopez, Barbara 255
Lopez, Natalia 265
Lopez, Anthony 283
Lopez, Beatriz 303
Lopez, Kevin 317
Lopez, Jorge 328
Lopez, Archie 409
Lopez, Nestor A Ramirez 501
Lopez, Elsie 558

Lopiccolo, Charles 418
Loranger, Joe 135
Lordan, John J 217
Lorentson, John C 359
Lorentz, Theresa 345
Lorentzen, Oivind 470
Lorenzo, Marcos F 215
Lorenzo, Jennifer Di 303
Loreto, Michael J Di 44
Lorimer, Linda Koch 661
Lorino, Anthony 542
Lorne, Eric 349
Lorton, Donald E 99
Lortz, Andre 9
Lortz, Andre 110
Losito, Bernadette 156
Losntos, Juan De 381
Lostaglia-Hosko, Andrea 396
Lotz, Jeremiah 430
Lou, Albert 539
Louder, Daryl 210
Louge, Michael W 395
Loughrey, Kevin 594
Loughridge, Jerome 516
Louisma, Chantal 644
Louton, Alysa 18
Louzado, Andre 135
Love, Dan 67
Love, Ron 119
Love, Karen 147
Love, Rod A 166
Love, Dianne 171
Love, Robert 207
Love, Horace 311
Love, Karen 317
Lovelace, Rob 98
Loveland, Jennifer 430
Loveland-Curtze, Jennifer 575
Lovell, Brigitte V 593
Loveridge, Gary F 528
Lovett, Laurie 378
Lovett, Robert 597
Lovingood, Preston 284
Low, Robert 368
Lowber, John M 225
Lowder, Dr Steve 522
Lowe, Roger 9
Lowe, Terrill 148
Lowe, Patricia 243
Lowe, Jennifer 283
Lowe, Heather Amick 316
Lowe, Terril 351
Lowe, Lance 529
Lowe, Mary Branigan 554
Lowe, Ken 643
Lowe, Mark A 654
Lowenberg, John 314
Lowman, Tim 432
Lowndes, Dusti 184
Lowry, Katie 91
Lowry, Fred 172
Lowry, Judith 629
Lowther, Aaron 112
Loy, Frank E 569
Loyo, Ann 539
Loyola, Connie 303
Lozada, Waleska 274
Lozano, Rocio 38
Lozano, Tina 462
Lozen, Jeff 357
LP, John F Shea 480
Lu, Qun 155
Lu, Kimberly 403
Lu, John 596
Lu, Kelly 641
Lubarsky, Neil 593
Lubbers, Ally 89
Lubeski, Damien 308
Lubin, Richard K 180
Luca, Michele 53
Luca, Guerrino De 378
Lucas, Robert 292
Lucas, Bruce 355
Lucas, Philip 562

Lucas, John 652
Luce, Charlotte 533
Lucey, Bob 172
Luchini, David 159
Lucia, William C 252
Lucia, Donna M 325
Lucia, Carol De 458
Luciano, Melba 579
Lucido, Elizabeth Ann 162
Lucier, Jake 13
Luckas, Nancy 146
Luckenbill, Patti 437
Luckenbill, Patti 438
Luckett, Artra 52
Lucore, Charles 501
Ludden, Paul 491
Ludford, Brad 458
Ludington, Bob 580
Ludwig, Eric R 230
Ludwig, Logan 287
Ludwig, James 304
Ludwig-Beymer, Patti 201
Luedeman, Lars 63
Luedeman, Lars 63
Luegering, Mark S 336
Luger, Nancy 249
Lujan, Audrey 123
Lukas, Brad 68
Lukaszeski, Marie 290
Lukaszewski, Michael 58
Luke, Jacquelyn R 361
Luke, Richard 362
Luke, Leslie Paul 504
Lukes, Konstantina 135
Lukesh, Kadi 514
Lukish, Jeffrey 276
Lum, Anthony 169
Luna, Wuaca 431
Lund, D Allen 22
Lund, David F 22
Lund, Kathleen M 22
Lund, Edward V 22
Lund, Victor 26
Lund, Per 223
Lund, Cathy N 646
Lundberg, Marissa 236
Lundequam, Michael 429
Lundergan, Dan 630
Lung-Close, Heather 130
Lunn, Eric 28
Lupano, Carlo 589
Lupo, Hope 255
Lupo, Anthony 519
Lupo-Adams, Linda 99
Lurker, Nancy 391
Lusher, Jill 100
Lusignan, Sara 28
Lustgarten, Joyce 193
Lutero, Lu 641
Luthringer, Lifford 661
Lutomski, Wayne D 648
Lutton, Lorraine 504
Lutu, Alvina 121
Lutz, Timothy P 357
Lutz, Tom 553
Lutz, Susan L 619
Luz, Maribel La 126
Ly, Davis 146
Lyash, Jeff 64
Lydon, Thomas A 39
Lydon, Bradford 481
Lyle, John 594
Lyles, Vanessa 34
Lyles, VI 124
Lyman, Keith 411
Lynch, James 68
Lynch, Brian P 184
Lynch, Brian 184
Lynch, Linda 217
Lynch, Jim 251
Lynch, Donald M 272
Lynch, Jack 308
Lynch, Jack 308
Lynch, Kimberly 363

Lynch, Katie 368
Lynch, Mark S 450
Lynch, Bernadette 516
Lynch, Thomas 562
Lynch, Marlon 588
Lynett, Madeline 652
Lynn, Mary 233
Lynn, Scott 454
Lyon, Mark 240
Lyons, Stephanie 95
Lyons, Alison 194
Lyons, Addison 222
Lyons, Amy 293
Lyons, Jason 311
Lyons, Mitch 342
Lyons, Iris 624
Lytle, Valentina 306
L'Esperance, Thomas 23

M

M, Maeona 2
M, Anna 112
Maas, Daren 546
Maass, Paul 580
Mabel, Richard I 438
Macaluso, Diane 22
MacDiarmid, J. Hugh 23
Macdonald, Walt 201
Macdonald, Alan G 317
Macdonald, Jamie 406
Macdonald, Carrie 617
Macdougall, Betty 32
Macfie, Helen 326
Macgillivray, Diane 385
Machen, Robert 32
Macina, Robert P 564
Macinnes, Dennis 353
Macinnes, Christina 358
Macintosh, Cynthia 469
Mack, Renee 203
Mack, Jill 204
Mack, Clifford 427
Mack, John J 572
Mack, Michael 654
Mack-Brooks, Pamela 255
Mackenzie, Bob 533
Mackey, Robin 172
Mackey, John 656
Macko, David 559
Mackzum, Errol J 168
Maclennon, John 429
Macmullen, Bill 129
Macnaughton, Mike 492
Macphail, Winborne 466
Macrino, Joseph 316
Macuga, Paul 588
Macyk, Irene 384
Madalena, Ralph J 373
Madamba, Charisma 243
Madani, Mohammad 51
Madden, Ursula 128
Madden, Christy 172
Madden, Kurt 222
Madden, Rachel 319
Madden, Donald V 597
Maddox, Mark 101
Maddox, Amy 127
Maddox, Mark 142
Maddox, Max 320
Maderd, James L 585
Madero, Ana-Maria 303
Madill, Justin 69
Madison, Thomas 594
Madnick, Vicki 246
Madonna, Elena 166
Madore, Marc 287
Madrigal, Calvin 586
Madrigal, Bob 627
Madsen, Charles 11
Madsen, Alexandra 157
Madyun, Adimu 392

Index of Executives

Maestas, Juan 653
Maffei, Fay 414
Mafi, Gabriela 224
Magenheimer, Richard C 262
Maggelet, Crystal Call 110
Maggio, Michael 261
Maggs, Everett 316
Maggy, Brad 159
Magiera, Ann Kathleen 219
Magill, Clint 188
Maginot, Kathleen 632
Magness, Sue 125
Magno, Benjamin D 254
Magno, Mary 292
Magowan, Bob 25
Magruder, Joan 498
Maguin, Stephen 173
Maguire, Vivian 24
Maguire, James J 414
Mahaffie, Alan 277
Mahajan, Puneet 523
Mahaney, Sheryl 286
Maher, Christine 503
Maher, Robert L 639
Mahil, Amandip 193
Mahjoub, Ali 377
Mahler, Anthony 652
Mahmood, Dawood 277
Mahone, Barbara 657
Mahoney, Joanne M 165
Mahoney, P Michael 223
MAI, Kevin 635
Maibach, Ryan 63
Maibach, Ben C 63
Maibach, Benjamin C 63
Maibach, Douglas L 63
Maibach, Sheryl B 63
Maidlow, Spencer T 174
Maier, Andrew W 427
Mail, Ingrid M 311
Mailand, William 299
Mailer, Dee Jay 603
Mailes-Dineff, Suzanne 216
Mailes-Dineff, Suzanne 525
Main, Joel 63
Mair, Jennifer 493
Majchrowski, Don 120
Majni, J Christopher 323
Major, Cathy 253
Major, Melissa 477
Major, Leslie 611
Majuri, Danielle 553
Makaroff, Jason 6
Maki, Mark A 343
Maksimow, Andre 83
Malachowski, Jeffery 146
Malan, Jill 498
Malana, Barbara 236
Malandra, Christy 572
Malaney, Darlene 166
Malapkowski, Bob 152
Malatesta, Brandy 512
Malav, Andr S 390
Maldonado, Anjelina 96
Malec, Ed 601
Malee, Patrick 627
Malehorn, Brad 647
Malempati, Ihari 417
Malhotra, Kanuj 537
Malik, Ajaymalik 173
Malin, John 212
Mallah, Isaac 504
Mallen, Ben 259
Mallett, Keshia 499
Mallick, Imtiaz 246
Mallon, Thomas E 3
Mallott, Anthony 471
Mallow, Betsy 373
Malloy, Gary 454
Malloy, Marie 513
Malmskog, David 30
Malone, Steve 217
Malone, Richard 272
Malone, Mike 456

Malone, Thomas 458
Malone, Laura 544
Maloy, Lisa 30
Maltais, Nancy 587
Maltbie, John L 169
Malte, Bob 286
Manbeck, Keith 656
Mancari, Mayly 118
Manchester, Jim 99
Manchur, Fred 283
Mancini, Salvatore 482
Mancini, Jessica 554
Mancini, Shawn 594
Mancuso, Anthony 214
Mandavilli, Apoorva 580
Mandel, Mark 168
Mandel, Lawrence 284
Mandell, James 548
Mandelman, Hersh 471
Maneker, Amy 118
Maneri, Phil 206
Manganiello, Anthony 643
Mangano, Rob 295
Mangione, Robert 498
Mangla, Dipty 48
Mangone, Rich 513
Mangoni, John 407
Mangum, Kimberly 526
Mangurian, Christina 616
Mani, Meera 554
Manias, William G 207
Manieus, G K 533
Manifold, Stephen 64
Manigan, Mark 61
Maniglia, Richard J 427
Manion, Gary 117
Manley, Joe 145
Manley, Christine 529
Mann, Chris 177
Mann, Brady 254
Mann, Lindsay K 282
Mann, Edward 283
Mann, Will 414
Mann, Aaron 604
Mann, Richard L 626
Mann, Joyce 635
Mann, Dorothy 642
Manning, Miriam 145
Manning, Christina 308
Mannis, Raymond 91
Manocha, Pooja 244
Manoharan, Arun 193
Manory, Joseph P 579
Manos, Steven S 603
Mans, Gary 622
Mansfield, Candy 220
Mansfield, Daniel 601
Manske, Scott 658
Mansuetti, Mike 448
Mantella, Philomena 385
Mantella, Philomena 495
Manthey, Cheryl 382
Manto, Jennifer 637
Mantovani, John 334
Mantz, Constantine A 1
Manucy, Carter 216
Manwani, Harish 378
Manwill, Lisa 122
Manzo, Rose 3
Mapes, Michelle 211
Maple, Shada 26
Maples, John T 485
Mar, Brett 222
Mar, Linda 529
Maraghy, Reagan E 582
Marallo, Andrew 198
Marangi, Leonard M 407
Marano, Thomas F 191
Marbin, Jyothi N 115
Marcella, Joseph 53
Marcelo, Jeff 168
March, Jeff 430
Marchak, Margaret 242
Marchetti, Stephen 276

Marchewka, Amber 80
Marchin, George 281
Marchiniak, Jenny 311
Marchio, Debbie 428
Marchioni, Joseph 146
Marchozzi, Tom 243
Marcos, Luis R 415
Marcoux, Christa 174
Marcus, Philip 457
Mardan, Ali 333
Marecki, Pam 541
Margalit, David L 206
Margalit-Ilovich, Ayelet 325
Margol, Kanoe 576
Marianacci, Alison 51
Marin, Angela 637
Marinelli, Grngory 69
Marinho, Fatima W 404
Marino, Gerald 596
Marisa, Howard 165
Maritz, Steve 312
Maritz, W. Stephen 495
Mark, Chris 129
Mark, Christensen 168
Markell, Peter K 317
Markell, Peter K 565
Markeloa, Natalia V 566
Markey, Nancy 48
Markezin, Elaine 246
Markin, Cheryl 640
Markley, Steve 191
Markov, Dimitri 593
Markovitch, Steve 395
Marks, Elena 147
Marks, Timothy 438
Marks, Pauline 563
Markstein, William E 597
Marley, Darlene 488
Marlow, Patty 642
Marlowe, Joseph 440
Marlowe, Blanche 528
Maroney, Edgar 129
Maroni, Kathy 335
Maroni, Alice C 484
Marquardt, Jane 310
Marquardt, Dan 310
Marquez, Carl 133
Marquez, Rose 259
Marquez, Eduardo 353
Marraffa, John 288
Marrella, John 287
Marriott, Robert 236
Marro, Peter 309
Marron, Brian 448
Marsch, Kathleen 508
Marsden, Dale 462
Marselle, Chris 456
Marsh, Andrew 206
Marsh, David 337
Marsh, Allen J 464
Marsh, Allen 464
Marsh, Amy K 628
Marshall, David R 105
Marshall, Colin 139
Marshall, Craig 163
Marshall, Jay 258
Marshall, Ken 614
Marshall-Provost, Tim 571
Marsolais, John 155
Marten, Cindy 462
Marthaler, Camille 187
Martin, Julia 5
Martin, Julian 8
Martin, Michael 19
Martin, Michael 43
Martin, Carole N 50
Martin, Sherry 58
Martin, Keith 91
Martin, David 134
Martin, Carl 135
Martin, Cary W 139
Martin, Michael 143
Martin, Stephen J 152
Martin, Ashton 179

Martin, Kathleen 182
Martin, Isabella 183
Martin, DEA 186
Martin, Cherie 199
Martin, Doug 205
Martin, David 211
Martin, Jennie 279
Martin, Jody 304
Martin, Ruben S 314
Martin, Ruben S 315
Martin, Katherine 328
Martin, Antonio 369
Martin, Robert 379
Martin, Christopher 384
Martin, Ralph 385
Martin, Anne 508
Martin, James 508
Martin, Doug 508
Martin, Chrystal 517
Martin, Sue 518
Martin, Selina 586
Martin, Roy 603
Martin, Bill 604
Martin, David 637
Martin, Shelda 652
Martin, Nancy 660
Martineau, Emily 132
Martinelli, David 349
Martinez, Jason 18
Martinez, Benita 41
Martinez, Mike 123
Martinez, Oscar 139
Martinez, Kelly 172
Martinez, Angelica 218
Martinez, Marigold 374
Martinez, Stacy 393
Martinez, Amy 556
Martinez-Mccart, Sandra 135
Martino, Chris 167
Martins, Alex 584
Martinson, Eric K 576
Martucci, Pat 637
Marty, Steve 492
Martyn, Derek 546
Martz, Kurt 7
Martz, Sheila 114
Maryasis, Elysa 87
Marzilli, Shanna 420
Mascia, Jonathan 243
Masi, Niccolo De 230
Maslowski, Clem 445
Mason, Steve 64
Mason, James 95
Mason, Mary 101
Mason, Jo 150
Mason, Ensen 168
Mason, Claudia 217
Mason, April 281
Mason, Debby D 337
Mason, Cheryl 378
Mason, Tracey 514
Mason, Sally 621
Masri, Maysoun D 584
Massa, Tod 146
Massaro, Michelle 308
Massarweh, Lisa 16
Masser, Keith 575
Massey, Jerry L 199
Massey, W Kenneth 349
Massey, Mary 492
Massie, Easton Riley 19
Massie, John 490
Masters, Mary 450
Masterson, David J 473
Mastioni, Marcello 27
Masto, Catherine Cortez 514
Mastro, Lou 201
Mastromarino, Michael 577
Masuda, Ken 169
Mata, Angelica 133
Matak, Kristen 652
Matejek, Michael 605
Matejovsky, Paul 635
Mateo, Carmen 370

Index of Executives

Index of Executives

McMillen, James 248
McMillen, Steve 601
McMillen, Tara 652
McMillen, Linda 652
McMillin, Nicole 247
McMinimee, Dan 271
McMorris, Heath 413
McMullen, Marshall 111
McMullen, Michael J 522
McMurray, James K 49
McMurray, James K 639
McNab, Sarah 286
McNabb, Forrest 74
McNair, Debora 177
McNair, Vernice 477
McNamara, Patrick 151
McNamara, Meaghan 308
McNamara, Ed 426
McNamara, John 596
McNaney, Michael 439
McNaughton, Jarrod 283
McNeel, Amie 631
McNeely, Bob 47
McNeely, Ann 515
McNeil, Kami 637
McNeill, Scott 203
McNeill, Elizabeth 479
McNichols, Robin 266
McNulty, Mary Ann 293
McPeak, Katie 220
McPhail, Jeff 509
McPheely, Brian 424
McPherson, Cora 346
McPherson, Joe 392
McPhillips, Lindsey 652
McQuade, Mark A 595
McQueen, Al 3
McQueen, Todd 580
McQuirk, Chris 96
McRae, Dave 418
McRae, Mark 461
McSain, Suzanne 132
McShane, Ryan 413
McTeir, Robert H 19
McTier, Michelle 162
McVaugh, Meg 72
McVay, Ashley 339
McWay, Jake 296
McWhorter, John 65
McWhorter, Dennis 86
McWhorter, John 395
McWhorter, Haden 426
McWilliams, Judith 169
Mdevivo, Michelle 353
Mdewan, Vikra 640
Mead, Judy 172
Mead, Charles 172
Mead, Arthur 176
Meade, Edward 321
Meador, Gary 170
Meadows, Cheryl G 141
Meaney, Martin 165
Means, Corey 630
Meany, Kathleen 338
Mecca, Ray 286
Mecca, John 594
Med, Wiggins 585
Medaris, Jamie 512
Meddings, Kathy J 64
Medeiros, Karen 229
Medina, Carlos 23
Medina, Erlinda 335
Medina, Marcus 604
Medlock, Jay 158
Meehan, Ken 274
Meehan, Martin 624
Meek, Melinda 169
Meek, Julie 278
Meek, Doug 518
Meeker, Chris 422
Meekins, Deanna 150
Meeks, Richard 161
Meffert, Walt 349
Mefford, Amy 145

Megally, Michael 377
Mehl, Meghan 524
Mehler, Phillip S 187
Mehrkens, Lee 167
Mehta, Apurva 152
Mehta, Shreeketa M 431
Mehta, Kashmira 648
Meidinger, Adam 640
Meier, Margaret 4
Meier, Phillip 33
Meier, Charlie 254
Meier, Niklaus 325
Meier, Cade 517
Meikle, Shauna 637
Meisner, Laurie 535
Meitz, Mary 88
Mejia, Rosa 126
Mejia, Alberto N 131
Melancon, Ben 470
Melanson, Scott 506
Melchior, Eric L 225
Melia, Mark 103
Melillo, Nick 5
Melito, Jillian 317
Melius, Jeff 70
Mell, Abby 458
Mellado, Santiago 149
Mellinger, Kristin 41
Mello, Jon 535
Melo, Sally 477
Melshenker, George 429
Melton, Danielle 11
Melton, Jasper 124
Meltzer, Neil M 300
Meltzer, Neil 482
Melville, Jim 25
Melzer, Lynn 125
Mena, David 248
Menchel, Marc 214
Mendez, James 37
Mendez, Alex 356
Mendez, Lincoln S 488
Mendicino, Thomas 308
Mendillo, Jane L 243
Mendive, Ashlee 522
Mendoza, Leticia 190
Mendoza, Stella 261
Mendoza, Candace 447
Mendoza, Frank 530
Meng, Amanda 641
Menke, Doug 620
Mensler, Patricia 198
Mento, Quince 160
Mentzer, Kevin 578
Menuau, Karl 198
Meoon, Alim 192
Mercado, Jhowel 302
Merchant, Art 162
Merchant, Susanne 513
Mercuri, Joe 578
Meredith, Michael 48
Meredith, Cliff 93
Meredith, Nicole 499
Meriano, Frank V 114
Merka, Carla 408
Merkel, Michael T 110
Merkel, Harold 206
Merkel, Frederick 610
Merkowitz, Justin 140
Merli, Geno J 593
Merline, John 223
Merlino, James 551
Merlis, Laurence M 3
Merrera, Samantha 629
Merrill, Mike 161
Merriman, David 334
Merritt, Sheila 325
Merritt, Jacqueline 521
Mertens, Blake A 555
Mertz, Valerie 14
Mertz, Paul 374
Mertz, Suzy 424
Mertz, Jim 556
Mescan, Steve 131

Messer, Cindy 93
Messerich, John 580
Messing, Fred M 57
Metcalf, Eric 177
Metcalf, Peter 227
Metre, Chris Van 5
Mettler, William 233
Metts, Julie 487
Metz, Holly L 45
Metz, John 216
Metzger, David 418
Metzger, Mick 575
Metzing, Mike 64
Meunier, John 185
Meuth, Jane 490
Mewhinney, Len 322
Meyer, Calvin 10
Meyer, Mike 10
Meyer, Joshua 22
Meyer, Lynn 73
Meyer, David 142
Meyer, Joy 172
Meyer, Kevin S 210
Meyer, Carrie 249
Meyer, Sandy 295
Meyer, Julie A 314
Meyer, Robert 415
Meyer, Paula 416
Meyer, Cindy 421
Meyer, Todd 459
Meyer, Kevin 510
Meyer, Diane 553
Meyer, Sarah 632
Meyer, John 658
Meyer-Davis, Pamela 201
Meyers, Tony W 36
Meyers, Carole 182
Meyers, Philip A 440
Meyers, Audrey 589
Meysenburg, Galen 245
Miano, Steve 259
Miastkowski, Alicia 271
Michael, Rubell 11
Michael, Mendez 85
Michael, Sam 383
Michaels, Shaylene 366
Michalek, Kevin 31
Michalski, Gene 657
Michalsky, Bryan 282
Michaux, Charles 124
Michel, John 433
Michel, John W H 433
Michel, Robert P 433
Michele, Marilyn De 602
Micheletti, Andrew 54
Michiei, Robert Be 634
Michulka, Natalie 534
Mickey, Hollis 36
Miclat, Aileen 299
Middleton, Keith 598
Midgley, Clare 546
Mielak, Gary 201
Mielak, Gary 201
Miele, Charles 63
Miers, Charles 126
Migliorino, Robin 330
Migoya, Carlos A 576
Miguel, Sergio San 341
Mihalakos, Alysia 516
Mihaljevic, Tomislav 551
Mijango, Manuel A 404
Mike, Mike S 588
Mikulak, Stephen 392
Milasich, Julie 220
Milauskas, Grace 100
Milazzo, Joe 107
Mildenberger, Andrew 538
Mildice, Joe 411
Mildvan, Donna 71
Miles, Steven 22
Miles, Mark W 70
Miles, Elizabeth 214
Miles, David J 285
Miles, David J 285

Miles, David J 285
Miles, Steven 316
Miles, Carolyn 466
Miles, Samantha 577
Miley, Nate 155
Miley, Jennifer 332
Miliband, David 265
Milkie, Chris 89
Mill, Georgia 451
Millan, Sheila Mc 406
Millar, Leslie 579
Millard, Devin 261
Millard, Allison 304
Millard, Becca 573
Millard, Jayne 605
Millay, Robert H 588
Millen, Robert P 395
Miller, Brian 16
Miller, Carl 16
Miller, Larry 77
Miller, Debra 87
Miller, Keith 91
Miller, Catheryn 109
Miller, Tamara 133
Miller, Bruce 142
Miller, Jenifer 186
Miller, Tim 191
Miller, Darlene 206
Miller, Dean 218
Miller, Lynn 226
Miller, Dale 248
Miller, William F 252
Miller, Jennifer 254
Miller, Brad 261
Miller, Wentz J 263
Miller, Catherine 263
Miller, Gail 264
Miller, Cynthia 274
Miller, Greg 276
Miller, Neal 279
Miller, Brian 320
Miller, Allison 335
Miller, Paul 343
Miller, Stacey 344
Miller, Jonathan 378
Miller, Eddie 380
Miller, Kevin 386
Miller, Christina 392
Miller, Julie 393
Miller, Ronald D 433
Miller, Jane 451
Miller, Rena 456
Miller, Lynneia E 472
Miller, Greg 477
Miller, Greg 477
Miller, Jessica 482
Miller, Ramona 500
Miller, Ross 514
Miller, Liz 517
Miller, Kurt 532
Miller, Greg 537
Miller, Randy 542
Miller, Matthew A 554
Miller, Kevin 559
Miller, Christine Z 579
Miller, Gary 585
Miller, James 594
Miller, Cynthia 607
Miller, Janet L 614
Miller, Thomas 634
Miller, Billie 641
Miller, Richard 643
Miller, Bill 647
Miller, David 650
Miller-Hobbs, Corri 640
Millhorn, David 629
Milligan, Michael D 53
Milligan, Mason 107
Millikan, J Scott 75
Milliken, James B 81
Milliken, James 570
Mills, Kevin 29
Mills, Mike 95
Mills, Charlie 135

Index of Executives

Mills, Bryan 147
Mills, Amy 164
Mills, Stephen S 377
Mills, Michael 388
Mills, Janet 513
Mills, Carrie 630
Millunchick, Carol 37
Millwood, Ryan 487
Milner, Karen K 440
Milot, Marie-Claude 388
Milowski, Nicholas B 217
Milvo, Leslie 123
Mims, Rod 47
Min, Kyaw 291
Minard, Marcia 500
Minato, Alan 169
Mineart, Beth 142
Minehan, Cathy E 565
Miner, Stephanie 134
Mines, Linda Moss 241
Ming, Jenny 297
Minges, Sarah 147
Minich, Kent 337
Minich, Cassandra 414
Minihan, Caileigh 503
Minks, Allen 538
Minor, Richard 198
Minor, Donna 516
Minor, Rev Thomas Anthony 567
Minter, Brian 432
Mintz, Mary Theresa 3
Mintz, Susan 124
Minus-Vincent, Deanna 61
Minvielle, Patrick 551
Miquel, Chris 307
Mirabella, Mary 166
Mirabella, Alexander 171
Miranda, Raymond 160
Mirdita, Anthony 415
Miro, Mary Ann 309
Mirro, Dr Joseph 505
Mirro, Michael J 602
Misawa, Naoshi 379
Misciasci, Katelynn 178
Mishina, Craig 474
Miskinis, Judith 319
Miskovsky, Christopher 496
Mislan, Tim 346
Missenheim, Susan 188
Mistick, Kelly 131
Misulis, Karl 270
Mitcham, Debra 180
Mitchel, Larry 6
Mitchell, Pleas 55
Mitchell, Laura 121
Mitchell, C Laura 121
Mitchell, Heather 130
Mitchell, Cliff 171
Mitchell, Susan 201
Mitchell, Susan 201
Mitchell, Sheila 211
Mitchell, Rose E Kleyweg 258
Mitchell, Sara 258
Mitchell, Jay D 269
Mitchell, Michael R 299
Mitchell, Trish 368
Mitchell, Sydney L 397
Mitchell, Jay D 416
Mitchell, Pamella 440
Mitchell, Jenny 499
Mitchell, Adrienne 566
Mitchell, Diane 645
Mitchell, Kisha 660
Mitchell, Courtney 661
Mitola, John 260
Mitra, Subhro 381
Mittal, Vijay 44
Mittelstadt, Wade 237
Mitterway, Kathleen 302
Mixon, Gina 269
Mixon, Jane 269
Mixon, Patti 662
Miyares, Takisha 419
Miyazaki, Kyoichi 120

Miyazaki, Annie 644
Mize, Shawn 264
Mleczko, Dan 552
Mlynarek, Robert W 647
Mmeje, Kenechukwu 491
MO, Weiwei 633
Moag, Anthony G 591
Moates, Glenn 517
Moats, Michael 588
Moazemi, Kourosh 100
Mockabee, William 578
Modde, Margaret Mary 174
Modelski, Maureen 261
Modica, Jeffrey 351
Moe, Jeremy 546
Moebius, Scott 238
Moehlis, Jeffrey 616
Moel, Howard 89
Moff, Beth 162
Moffa, Dominic 225
Moffatt, Mike 509
Moffatt, Tracey 649
Moffet, Brian L 482
Moffett, James 215
Mohammad, Ishrat 129
Mohammad, Shirin 264
Moheed, Ameen 154
Mohon, Bill 327
Mohr, Todd M 8
Mohr, Michael A 27
Mohr, Steven L 407
Mohr, Mr Michael 486
Mohrman, Michael P 452
Moio, Gino 529
Mojica, Carmen 508
Moldafsky, Jamie 378
Molden, Craig 170
Molden, Jim 170
Moler, William R 532
Molesevich, Patrice 226
Molina, Gloria 162
Molina, Luis 187
Molina, Sergio 310
Molina-Clark, Cecilia 625
Molinaro, Marcus J 198
Molinaro, Kenneth 582
Molinini, Michael 13
Mollak, Leonard 244
Mollet, Chris 201
Mollet, Chris 201
Molluso, Joseph 643
Molmen, Dave 27
Molnar, Louis A 481
Molskness, Daryl 11
Molumby, Kathleen 528
Mombourquette, Arthur 97
Monaco, Donna 308
Monaco, Anthony 603
Monaco, Kim 614
Monahan, Thomas L 103
Monahan, Elizabeth F 191
Monahan, Michael P 392
Monarch, Jason 333
Moncayo, Erick 372
Monday, Rachel 45
Monday, Jeff 414
Mondragon, Fred 122
Mone, Brenda 167
Mones, Ann 134
Mong, Marla 150
Mongar, Shane 440
Monge, Patricia 565
Monger, Andrew 56
Mongiello, Simone 172
Monica, Esparza 303
Monk, David 438
Monnolly, Terry 567
Monroe, Sharon 347
Monson, Uri Z 164
Montague, Jennifer 386
Montalvo, Maria 168
Montalvo, Dhinora 452
Monte, John 330
Monteleone, Joseph 415

Montero, Alejandro 441
Montes, Bryan 240
Montgomery, Richard 216
Montgomery, Nate 429
Montgomery, Jacque 511
Montgomery, Lisa 566
Montgomery, Christopher 571
Montgomry, Andretta 138
Montilla, Carolyn 145
Montoya, Jessica 54
Montoya, Lorraine 187
Montplaisir, Kelly 267
Montross, Dennis 172
Mood, Shawn 103
Moody, Dionta 24
Moody, Terry 84
Moody, Barry 304
Moody, David S 572
Moolenschot, Johannus J 496
Moon, Lori 52
Moon, J Virgil 140
Moon, Kimberly 195
Moon, Don 299
Moon, Jacqueline 398
Moon, Christina 571
Moonen, Glenn 414
Mooney, John 167
Moore, Nancy 6
Moore, Candice 18
Moore, Antonette 25
Moore, Lena 57
Moore, Bud 68
Moore, Rob 74
Moore, Robert 74
Moore, Cory 74
Moore, Sarah 145
Moore, Gregory 168
Moore, Shirley 169
Moore, Margaret 171
Moore, John 179
Moore, Will 183
Moore, Cynthia 228
Moore, Brandon 254
Moore, Jeanette 274
Moore, William L 282
Moore, Betty 303
Moore, Robert 315
Moore, Debra L 325
Moore, David 339
Moore, T 343
Moore, Timothy 355
Moore, Joe 388
Moore, Theresaterri 415
Moore, Dana 418
Moore, Shaina 446
Moore, Cynthia 518
Moore, Lawrence 523
Moore, Lisa 525
Moore, Charles R 531
Moore, Steven 575
Moore, Christopher C 589
Moore, Carleton 621
Moore, Janissa 622
Moore, Richard H 654
Moore, Kendall 659
Moorfoot, Molly 535
Moorhouse, Edward L 414
Moorleghem, Jenny Van 366
Moorsel, Guillaume V 581
Moorthy, Vetriselvi 494
Moose, Selina 361
Moots, Stephanie 53
Mora, Francisco 165
Morais, Diane E 24
Morales, Adan C 19
Morales, Ron L 84
Morales, Pablo 332
Morales, Howie 515
Morales, Alex 596
Morales, David 653
Moran, Thomas 200
Moran, Linda 279
Moran, Amanda 316
Moran, Richard T 639

Moranishi, Susan 155
Morant, Felicia 11
Morawski, Chris 124
Morcom, George 107
Morde, Vishal 60
More, Ed 112
Morea, Ingrid 70
Morehart, Mary 498
Morehead, Jere 620
Moreland, Jeffrey 80
Morello, Angela 81
Morelock, Ruth 55
Moreno, Joseph 177
Moreno, Juan A Gonzalez 237
Moreno, Homero Huerta 237
Moreno, Brian 349
Moreno, Jason 455
Moreno, Noemi 579
Moreno-Robago, Claudia 522
Moretti, Marty 247
Morey, Carrie-Ann 154
Morfin, Annette 514
Morgado, Mario 340
Morgan, John 43
Morgan, Molly 52
Morgan, Chantel 116
Morgan, Kenneth 149
Morgan, Ash 157
Morgan, Cheree 157
Morgan, Diane 164
Morgan, John 188
Morgan, Christi 216
Morgan, Mark 271
Morgan, Ashley 278
Morgan, Emily 370
Morgan, Lori J 407
Morgan, Vickie 408
Morgan, Damon 423
Morgan, Henry 429
Morgan, Sandra 444
Morgan, James I 505
Morgan, Matt 516
Morgan, Blake 538
Morgan, John 652
Morgan, Becka 653
Morgante, Elizabeth 235
Morgenstern, H Richard 332
Moriarty, Bettyann 161
Morissette, Dan 145
Morlacci, Laura 496
Morley, Carol 25
Morrelli, Laura 253
Morris, Brad 1
Morris, Susan 18
Morris, Gerald J 77
Morris, Victor 87
Morris, Herman 128
Morris, Kenneth 152
Morris, Elizabeth S 156
Morris, Joseph M 163
Morris, Betty 175
Morris, Kenneth 196
Morris, David 225
Morris, Pamela 228
Morris, Damen 261
Morris, Sherrill 433
Morris, Bob 462
Morris, Doug 471
Morris, Mark 485
Morris, Thom 499
Morris, Robyn 507
Morris, James T 602
Morrisey, Locke J 628
Morrison, Julia 19
Morrison, Bethany 160
Morrison, Richard J 209
Morrison, David 238
Morrison, Bobbi 304
Morrison, Connie 333
Morrison, Tom 353
Morrison, Jeffrey 446
Morrisroe, Paul 535
Morrissey, Cassandra 327
Morrissey, Joseph 444

Index of Executives

Morrow, Sherry 16
Morrow, Terry K 88
Morrow, Diane 170
Morrow, Shawn 325
Morrow, Joseph 359
Morrow, Jason 587
Morse, Martha 67
Morse, Kristine 170
Morse, Alan R 237
Morse, Edward 353
Morshed, Bobby 278
Mortensen, Brian 463
Mortimer, Brian 514
Morton, Amy 133
Morton, Tina 171
Morton, Schapiro 389
Morton, Colleen 441
Morton, Randall D 638
Morway, Joseph 282
Mosca, Andrew 261
Moscho, Harold 576
Moseley, Stephen 15
Mosemann, Richard 316
Moser, Phillip G 14
Moser, Joseph D 306
Moser, Davis 337
Moser, Kathy 621
Moser, Aaron 628
Moses, Nancy E 135
Moses, Roxanne 144
Moses, Mark 472
Mosingo, Jerry L 534
Mosko, Todd E 410
Moskowitz, Samuel E 220
Moskowitz, Amy 352
Mosley, Anthony 262
Mosley, Anthony 615
Mosquera, Juan-Miguel 453
Moss, Erin S 194
Moss, Leah 541
Moss, John M 567
Mosser, Kevin H 662
Motakef, Shahin 468
Moto, Lila 413
Motta, Edgar 187
Motta, Bob 479
Moua, Cindy 445
Mound, Roger 62
Mount, Karen 350
Mountford, Maria 180
Mourtzikos, Karen 648
Mower, David 25
Mowreader, Jack 413
Mowrey, Mike 409
Moyer, Don 149
Moyer, Nancy 276
Moyer, Susan 373
Moyer, Michael 642
Mozumdar, Subrato 356
Mozzicato, Diane 347
Mrochinski, Mary Czech - 313
Muchata, Jim 624
Mudge, Rex 523
Mudler, Gordon A 332
Muehl, Mary 391
Muehring, Gwen 578
Mueller, Andrew 107
Mueller, Andrew T 309
Mueller, Andrea 368
Mueller, Ken 435
Mueller, Eve 516
Mueting, John 575
Muhammad, Aadam 146
Muhart, Matthew 486
Mukand-Cerro, Ian 609
Mukherjee, Rupa 71
Mukherjee, Preetika 356
Mul, James J 240
Mulch, Angela 458
Mulder, Jeff 162
Mulford, Steve 551
Mulhern, Candia 166
Mulhern, Anabel 167
Mulhern, Ben 345

Mullane, Marietta 481
Mullen, David 112
Mullen, Renee 177
Mullen, Thomas 332
Mullen, Thomas R 334
Mullen, Charles V 428
Muller, Betty 25
Mulligan, Suzan 91
Mullins, Ed 424
Mullins, Karen 555
Mullis, Michael 44
Mullokandov, Izabella R 377
Mulvey, Kevin 259
Mulvey, Amy 384
Mumford, Samantha 19
Munch, David 468
Mundell, W Jed 590
Munn, Brenda 101
Munn, Rico 278
Muno, Christi 542
Munoz, Alex 336
Munsayac, Eric 541
Munsch, Michael 127
Munson, Randy 633
Murakawa, Craig 474
Murchison, Sibyl 380
Murchy, Jodie 73
Murdoch, Ken 466
Murdock, Trish 64
Muren, Gary 232
Murgado, Mario 340
Muri, Scott R 496
Murillo, Jorge 488
Murino, John 17
Murnane, Thomas W 603
Murphey, Mike 235
Murphy, John 53
Murphy, Terry 64
Murphy, David 86
Murphy, Mark 90
Murphy, Brian 91
Murphy, Edward 99
Murphy, Michael 120
Murphy, Rita 132
Murphy, Connie 144
Murphy, Karen 226
Murphy, Chris 305
Murphy, Erin 306
Murphy, Jaren 321
Murphy, Leo 335
Murphy, Michael 346
Murphy, John 444
Murphy, Michael 477
Murphy, Richard J 488
Murphy, Mark E 504
Murphy, Michael 518
Murphy, John M 554
Murphy, Celeste 563
Murphy, Brian 578
Murphy, J Pat 586
Murphy, Wendy 586
Murphy, Emily W 606
Murphy, Jeri 632
Murray, Debbie 10
Murray, Douglas 387
Murray, Paul 433
Murray, Bill 535
Murray, Robert 560
Murray, Brent 640
Murry, Michael 654
Murthy, Ganesh 356
Musa, Sam 432
Musayev, Igor 272
Muse, David 24
Muse, Michael 228
Musgrove, David 542
Musil, Kevin 464
Musk, Elon 539
Musquiz, Joe 494
Mussio, Alexander 573
Musson, Samantha 103
Musto, Tammy 406
Mutlu, Ali 659
Muttaqi, Khaalid 132

Mvula, Mosanda 129
Myers, A Ross 20
Myers, David 32
Myers, Adam 78
Myers, Katrina 138
Myers, Rod 170
Myers, Ben 182
Myers, Jenna 191
Myers, Andrew 240
Myers, Douglas 274
Myers, Richard B 281
Myers, Dwayne 315
Myers, Michael 321
Myers, Greg 357
Myers, Jack 421
Myers, Ali 529
Myers, Amy 623
Myerson, Gary 387

N

N, Debra N Strohmaier 388
Nabel, Elizabeth G 546
Nachman, Kalfus 135
Nachtigal, Amy 459
Nadamoto, Alton 474
Nadar, Shiv 244
Nadeau, Kim 193
Nadeau, Jeanette 584
Nader, Tony 262
Nader, Anthony 263
Nadler, Michelle 498
Naftaly, Robert 607
Naftaly, Rober 607
Nagamine, Aileen 121
Naifeh, James O 517
Nail, Steve 212
Nair, Sarita 122
Nair, A Sivaram 356
Naish, Rob 31
Naito, Hiroshi 32
Najera, Luis 165
Nakagawa, Roger T 90
Nakamoto, David 127
Nakis, Dominic 52
Naldi, Robert 307
Nance, Jim 157
Nangle, Barb 661
Nantz, Mark 499
Naparstek, Scot 364
Napier, Joanna 40
Napier, Adam 422
Napolitano, John 159
Napp, Marc 486
Nardini, Holly G 661
Narowski, Janice 151
Narvaez, William 159
Nash, Verla 610
Nasser, William 495
Nast, Jeff 483
Natale-Ryan, Angela 48
Nathan, James A 105
Nathan, David G 180
Nathan, James R 292
Nathan, Jim 293
Nathenson, Mike 77
Nauertz, Cinda 301
Navarro, Eddie 223
Navarro, Ana 392
Navedo, Lorena 202
Navitskas, Ted 360
Nayak, Jay 37
Nchez, Jos R S 369
Ndez, Rom N Hern 399
Ndez, Salvadore M Hern 462
Ndoye, Fatou K 323
Neal, Jeff 155
Neal, Shelly 337
Neal, Melanie 493
Neal, Jeremy 590
Neal, Kecia 622
Neall, Robert 275

Nealy-Carter, Betty 228
Neatrour, Amanda 131
Neault, Gloria 309
Necas, Kevin 625
Nedell, Thomas 385
Nee, Anthony M 654
Needham, Sabine 16
Needham, Priscilla 75
Needham, Judy 218
Neeley, Paige 303
Neely, Tonya 81
Neely, Wayne 485
Neff, Alexanne 35
Nefkens, Mike 150
Nehasil, Craig 289
Neidenbach, Joseph J 508
Neil, Carl 213
Neilson, Hannah 518
Neiman, Samantha 32
Nelson, Mary 100
Nelson, Andy 119
Nelson, Robyn 121
Nelson, Karen 139
Nelson, W T Chip 141
Nelson, David 144
Nelson, Gary 170
Nelson, Mike 172
Nelson, Glenn 201
Nelson, Carla 203
Nelson, Deana L 215
Nelson, Bob 222
Nelson, Gregory V 256
Nelson, William 260
Nelson, Donnita 281
Nelson, Deana 291
Nelson, Vickie 296
Nelson, Patricia 384
Nelson, Tim 418
Nelson, Brock 442
Nelson, Kyle 445
Nelson, Becky 463
Nelson, Ashley 470
Nelson, Duane 494
Nelson, Doug 514
Nelson, Chris 517
Nelson, Bob H 520
Nelson, Doug 541
Nelson, Elaine 541
Nelson, Heather 548
Nelson, Brian C 572
Nelson, Sean 633
Nelson, Lauri 637
Nemerson, Steven 456
Nemeth, Karla 93
Nemeth, Joseph 333
Nemeth, Stephen 396
Nenzel, Andrea 409
Neri, Leticia 147
Nerino, Alfred 337
Ness, Jon 287
Ness, Ed 358
Nesselbush, Robert 280
Nesselbush, Robert J 280
Nesselbush, Robert 280
Nesset, Sharon 610
Nestler, Timothy J 656
Nethaway, Carry 455
Neto, Lourival B 581
Neubaur, D Ick 210
Neuenschwander, Darrel 231
Neuenschwander, Darryl 231
Neufeld, Ellis J 505
Neuhaus, Joan 19
Neuhaus, Steven M 166
Neve, Jo 289
Nevin, Zoe Mc 189
New, Wayne 161
Newallis, David 31
Newberry, Amanda 5
Newcomb, Daniel 451
Newcomer, Rex E 177
Newcomer, N Nelson 177
Newell, John D 622
Newey, Jay 638

Index of Executives

Newhouse, Marie 113
Newkirk, Russell 508
Newman, Diane 51
Newman, Kurt 114
Newman, Kurt 117
Newman, David 381
Newman, Cathy 600
Newmyer, Joyce 6
Newpol, Jon 603
Newsom, Terri 196
Newsome, Kathy 111
Newsome, Jana 380
Newsome, Paul 395
Newton, Bradford 382
Newton, Louie 610
Newton, Alicia 610
Ney, Joe 167
Neyer, Tom 160
Neyland, Stephen J 343
Nezat, David 348
Ng, Man Wai 548
Ngo, Hanna 116
Ngo, Hao Q 506
Nguyen, Johnny 12
Nguyen, Lan Quoc 224
Nguyen, Daphne 230
Nguyen, Chao 247
Nguyen, Tuan 429
Nguyen, Albert 502
Nguyen, Mong Thi 522
Nguyen, Andy 533
Nguyen, Phuong 585
Niaz, Faiza 325
Nicholas, Jack 112
Nicholas, Richard 584
Nichols, Frank 166
Nichols, Kenneth J 301
Nichols, Dave 347
Nicholson, Brenda 423
Nicholson, Larry 516
Nicholson, Brian 559
Nickel, Douglas R 90
Nickel, Ellie 137
Nickerson, Adam 26
Nickerson, Sandy 646
Nickol, Thomas 287
Nicol, Kellen 218
Nicolet, Yaira 400
Nicolino, Lynda 302
Nicosia, Santo V 240
Nielsen, Steve 452
Nielsen, Cindy 556
Nielson, Sephen 471
Niemetscheck, Amy 109
Niemi, Eric 278
Nienen, Marge 116
Nieves, Antonio De Jesus 71
Nieves, Gloribel 294
Niewinski, Erin 360
Nigrin, Daniel 309
Nill, Andrew 187
Nilles, Tracy 32
Nilon, John 161
Nilsson, Gunilla 483
Nimbley, Thomas J 110
Nino, Monica 168
Ninomiya, James 223
Nirenberg, Ron 133
Nishball, David 230
Nishioka, Marcia 63
Nishizaki, Tsuyoshi 527
Nissen, James A 411
Nitsch, Denise 654
Nitsche, Bruce 642
Niven, Christine 335
Nix, D Mark 262
Nix, Josh 269
Nixon, Andrea 135
Nixon, George 322
Nixon, Mary 622
Nizami, Null N 660
Nizzari-Mcclain, Cynthia 633
Nobis, Kenneth 342
Noble, Paula 37

Noble, David 233
Noble, Walt 358
Noble, Janice 402
Noble, Jim 407
Nobles, Sharon 383
Noblitt, Mark 13
Noddle, Harlan J 570
Noell, Ginny 528
Noem, Kristi L 517
Nolan, Bill 24
Nolan, Timothy S 164
Nolan, Christopher 165
Noland, Sherry 118
Noland, William M 212
Noonan, David L 375
Noonan-Harnsber, Helen 429
Norcross, George E 553
Nordby, Ella 291
Nordby, Roger 345
Nordenberg, Mark 628
Norgren, Lisa 606
Norkunas, Kathy 149
Norling, Richard A 426
Norman, Jim 25
Norman, Chris 31
Norman, Nina 292
Normington, Ann 271
Norrick, Matt 155
Norris, Cindie 556
North, Shannan 82
North, Dennis 217
Northam, Ralph 146
Northland, Michelle 459
Northover, Susan 644
Norton, Gale 35
Norton, Janet 58
Norton, Michael F 285
Norton, Margareta E 434
Norwick, Monica 406
Nosach, Jill 420
Noseworthy, John H 321
Nostrand, Chris Van 389
Notaro, Julie 243
Nothwang, Joseph 561
Nottoli, Don 168
Nourot, Mary 529
Novak, Andrew 366
Novak, Ernest 394
Novak, Trudy C 473
Noverati, Carol 439
Noviasky, Diana 165
Novick, Steve 131
Novicki, Kelly 459
Novokhatski, Sasha 295
Novotny, Stanley 633
Nowakowski, Rhonda 116
Nowicki, Joseph 148
Noyes, Brian 308
Noyola, Ana 172
Nuby, Angelo 318
Nuckles, Brett 651
Nugent, Frances 232
Nugyen, Diane 20
Nunez, Diana 132
Nunez, Marisa 156
Nunez, Frank 193
Nunez, Michael 202
Nunez, Edwin 216
Nunez, Milton 300
Nunez, Eduardo 307
Nunn, Chalmers M 107
Nunn, Michelle 153
Nunn, Trudy 647
Nuntz, Sister Mary Ann 500
Nusbaum, Mary Ellen 356
Nuss, Donald 478
Nutting, Kelli 85
Nutting, Ron 437
Nuzzo, Jessica 660
Nvule, Daniel 319
Nwagbo, Chike 122
Nyangani, Ash 540
Nybo, Zach 635
Nycroft, Tina 502

Nyenhuis, Michael J 311
Nygaard, Christine 403
Nylander, Raye Nae 556
Nylen, Tim 148
Nylen, Tim 351

O

O, Steven Herwig D 266
Oakes, John 212
Oakland, Pamela Witty 121
Oakley, Dennis B 91
Oakley, Susan 496
Oaks, Kenneth 284
Obana, William G 576
Obeid, Sam 284
Oberman, Wade 531
Obermiller, John 595
Oblinger, Phillip F 73
Obrand, Alexandra 263
Obrien, Lisa 124
Obrien, Julie 156
Obrien, John 609
Obryan, Megan 138
Ocana, Ann M 476
Ocel, Arielle 499
Ochi, Howard 168
Ochs, Rudy 332
Ockers, Thomas 230
Oconnor, Kathy 16
Oconnor, Cristina 96
Oconnor, Scott 103
Oconnor, Christopher J 488
Odderson, IB 403
Odean, Gerald 349
Odegaard, Richard 236
Odell, Robert 480
Oditt, Alex 262
Odom, Burt 205
Oechsner, Susan 261
Oehling, James P 410
of, Baltimore City 123
Offerman, Angela 393
Offers, Nathan 542
Offutt, Ronald D 437
Offutt, Christi 437
Oftedal, Brian 130
Ogania, Milagros 247
Ogborn, Eric 198
Ogle, Matt 173
Oglesby, Stephen R 58
Ogren, Dan 302
Ohara, Yoshinori 662
Ohashi, Casey 470
Ohemeng-Dapaah, Michael 299
Ohmer, Brandi 135
Ohmer, Adrian 607
Ohrn, Daniel 399
Ohrt, Tracy 633
Ohtake, Takashi 379
Okabe, David 244
Okamoto, Gary A 576
Okane, Yuri 604
Okes, Gary D 209
Okolie, Patricia 254
Okoro, Julie 116
Okun, Robert B 237
Olague, Jessica 7
Olague, Jesse 114
Olejniczak, Dave 501
Oleson, Cory 429
Olguin, George 462
Oliker, David 360
Oliphant, Jennifer 164
Oliphant, Gerald 231
Oliva, Sanderson 563
Olivares, Daniel 163
Oliveira, Claudia 67
Oliveira, Flavia 182
Oliver, Anne 274
Oliver, George R 277
Oliver, George 278

Oliver, Bill 316
Oliver, Emily 572
Oliver, Kirk R 608
Oliver, Leigh 646
Oliverio, John D 654
Olmes, Robin H 627
Olsen, Dorothy 38
Olsen, Neil 211
Olsen, Eric 235
Olsen, Kandance 235
Olsen, Kristin 318
Olsen, Peter 481
Olsen, Lloyd 600
Olson, Dean 157
Olson, Jeffery 220
Olson, Greg 289
Olson, Kristin 321
Olson, Don 345
Olson, Jerry 381
Olson, Toni 431
Olson, Carrie 467
Olson, Jeff 515
Olson, Paige 517
Olson, Tim 592
Olson, Ruth 633
Olszewski, Kathy 577
Oltman, Chad 396
Omar, Moanis 102
Ondik, David 209
Oneal, Emmett 607
Oneill, Jill 261
Onell, Lia 333
Onge, Jenifer 4
Ongseng, Fukiat 71
Onna, Thomas 33
Ono, Caitlin 230
Onomura, Brad 262
Ontiveros, Gregg 236
Ontiveros, Chris 236
Ontiveros, Robert 236
Opembe, Patrick 103
Opoka, James 164
Oporto, Joseph 302
Orchard, Arlen 455
Orcutt, S Renee 333
Ordonez, April 477
Orender, Donna G 414
Orgain, John B 19
Orgeron, Jerome 236
Orlandi, Marcia 133
Orlando, Anthony T 206
Orlando, Adolph M 578
Orlikoff, James 642
Orlowski, Lee 448
Ormanzhy, Natalya 12
Orndorf, Karen 14
Ornelas, Grace 222
Ornelas, Beatriz 550
Oropeza, Anthony 161
Oross, Mike 355
Orourke, Terry 102
Orozco, David 476
Orozco, Lupe 619
Orr, Stefahn 163
Orr, Mark 237
Orr, James 314
Orr, David 536
Orr, Lori 572
Orris, Donna 410
Orscheln, Art 113
Orson, Marshall D 186
Ortega, Alberto 520
Ortega-Carter, Dolores 171
Ortegon, Liisa 473
Ortegon, Liisa 594
Orth, Bradley 138
Ortiz, Veronica 193
Ortiz, Marnique 284
Ortiz, Linda 327
Ortiz, Claudia 404
Ortizlugo, Lydia 371
Ortolano, Carrie 135
Ortolano, Frank 163
Osborn-Perez, Roseann 162

Index of Executives

Osborne, Burt 128
Osborne, Tom 131
Oschell, Christine 514
Oseguera, Karen 406
Osgood, Wendy E 309
Oshiro, Don 583
Oskouie, Ali 339
Osman, Khidir 662
Ostdiek, Scott 415
Ostergard, Tonn 175
Osterweil, Jody 608
Ostrandr, Sue E 81
Ostrowsky, Barry 60
Ostrowsky, Barry 61
Oswald, Kathy 249
Oswald, Chris 303
Oswalt, Valerie 485
Otabil, Tashawna 598
Otaki, Yoshio 380
Otis, Bud 159
Otsubo, Ryan 163
Ott, Dusty 74
Ott, Joy 75
Ott, Michael 133
Ott, Ryan 266
Oubre, Joi 127
Ouchida, Michael 260
Outar, Gerald 365
Ouyang, Hongwu 217
Ouyang, Paul 407
Overstreet, Linda 75
Overton, John 206
Owen, Harry 130
Owen, Debora 386
Owen, Allison C 540
Owens, Janet 156
Owens, Russell 174
Owens, Thomas A 197
Owens, Heather 309
Owens, Steve 625
Owens, Ashley 638
Owsinsky, Mike 498
Oxenreiter, Laura 56
Oyler, Clinton 353
Ozmen, Fatih 481
Ozmen, Eren 481
Ozuah, Philip O 352
O'Brien, Lindsay 35
O'Brien, Charles 208
O'Brien, Charles T 208
O'Brien, Tom 317
O'Brien, Beth 409
O'Brien, John D 472
O'Brien-Rice, Caitlin 32
O'Brien-Wood, Brigitte 92
O'Connell, Tim 134
O'Connell, Cynthia 214
O'Connor, Kevin 76
O'Connor, Cristina 96
O'Connor, Matt 98
O'Connor, Jack 159
O'Connor, Teri 163
O'Connor, John 519
O'Connor, Michael F 662
O'Donnell, Robert G 29
O'Donnell, Robert G 33
O'Donnell, James 146
O'Donnell, Randall L 330
O'Donoghue, Mary Jo 545
O'Donoghue, Shannon M 584
O'Dowd, Kevin 553
O'Gara, Marisa 132
O'Grady, Sean 387
O'Halloran, Henry 434
O'Hara, Curt 467
O'Hare, James 515
O'Hearn, Patricia 133
O'Holleran, Jennie 146
O'Keefe, Daniel 488
O'Kusky, Steve 309
O'Leary, Neil M 135
O'Leary, Robert D 414
O'Leary, Thomas M 575
O'Mahony, Stephen 61

O'Malley, Patrick M 298
O'Malley, Edward 377
O'Moore, Paul V 3
O'Nan, Stephen B 110
O'Neal, Susan 312
O'Neil, Claire 37
O'Neil, Patricia Steeves 453
O'Neil, Cheri 633
O'Neill, Elizabeth 297
O'Quinn, Marvin 145
O'Quinn, Marvin 189
O'Reilly, Charles 245
O'Reilly, Brian 414
O'Rourke, Robert L 94
O'Rourke, Tracy 522
O'Rourke, Tanya 542
O'Rourke, Brianne 628
O'Toole, Mary 168
O'Toole, Nick 175
O'Toole, Brian 331

P

Pabst, Mary 418
Pace, Leigh 269
Pace, Gerald 345
Pace, Brandy 542
Pacheco, Fernando 271
Pacheco, Carmita 655
Pacheco-Clark, Ana L 528
Pachman, Louis J 244
Pachman, Louis 245
Pack, Barry 399
Pack, William 468
Pack, Rodney 637
Packard, Julie 554
Packer, Steven J 148
Packer, Steven 351
Packer, Gayle 538
Padgett, Francine 343
Padilla, Jos D 185
Padovano, Sam 583
Padwa, Jeffrey 132
Paez, Tina 126
Paez, Rene A 488
Pagano, Renee 624
Page, Crystal 99
Page, Katie 128
Page, Bob 168
Page, Lawrence 282
Page, Kiera 379
Page, Bob 586
Pagels, George A 459
Pagenkopf, Julie 180
Painter, Craig 288
Pak, Toni 305
Pala, Amie 211
Palacherla, Neelima 169
Palacios, Eliecer 306
Paladini, David 171
Palani, Murugan 467
Palathra, Brigit 377
Paliota, Armand 401
Palis, Adar 242
Palko, Steffen 540
Pallares, Jan 321
Pallatta, Donna 156
Pallekonda, Vinod 147
Palleschi, Pete 481
Pallin, Angel 356
Palmberg, Dawn 512
Palmberg, Kent 522
Palmer, Steve 53
Palmer, Denitrea 60
Palmer, Matthew 90
Palmer, Thomas S 177
Palmer, Matt 291
Palmer, Douglas 443
Palmer, Kelly 445
Palmieri, Christopher D 145
Palmore, Kysten 220
Palomino, Jessica 228

Palowski, Jillian 524
Paluch, John 515
Pan, Jeffrey C 3
Pan, Junwen 589
Pana, Camelia 446
Pandit, Sumesh 6
Paneak, Raymond 41
Panetta, Deborah 589
Panettieri, Christopher 246
Panizari, Robert 232
Panozaqi, Alketa 125
Pantano, Dan 87
Pantoya, Christine 454
Panzarella, Angela 38
Panzera, Chellie 503
Papacostas, Arthur C 536
Papdellis, Randy C 648
Pape, Kathy 410
Paperie, Fat C 165
Papincak, Terry 483
Pappas, Natalie 539
Paratore, Joseph 155
Paratore, Dena 450
Parchinski, Kathleen 208
Parchinski, Christopher 660
Parchment, Nadia 293
Parda, David 20
Pardes, Herbert 572
Pardo, Holly 25
Parija, Soubhagya 371
Paris, Tom Van 254
Paris, John 447
Parisi, Patricia 159
Parisi, Janet 372
Parivash, James 163
Park, Gary 14
Park, William 253
Park, Julie 288
Park, Hyun 351
Park, Jihye 367
Park, Gary 443
Park, Deanna 616
Park, Gary 627
Parker, Garrett 24
Parker, Erin 42
Parker, Dalton 82
Parker, Andy 188
Parker, Russell E 207
Parker, Keith 335
Parker, Terra 362
Parker, Scott 364
Parker, Mary 384
Parker, Cindy A 389
Parker, Mike 433
Parker, Cindy 473
Parker, Ryan 493
Parker, Tom 510
Parker, Dudley 579
Parkerson, Michael 547
Parkins, Frederick 622
Parkinson, Scott 535
Parkos, Michael 43
Parks, Richard 173
Parks, Amy 384
Parod, Daniel 507
Parolisi, John 55
Parolisi, John 55
Parquette, Kacey 315
Parr, James 460
Parra, Christian 191
Parrent, Dave 539
Parrillo, Joseph E 252
Parrish, Sheriff Lori 157
Parrish, Harvey 212
Parrish, Amy 254
Parrish, Diane 507
Parshall, Joyce 589
Parsley, David 362
Parsley, Elizabeth 579
Parson, Mike 514
Parsons, Jillian 145
Parsons, Michael 200
Parsons, Donna 456
Parsons, Suzan 638

Parsons, Dena 661
Parthemer, Shannon 291
Partington, Marshall 403
Partipilo, Mari 7
Partridge, Jack 143
Partridge, Scott 173
Pasard, Gail 6
Pascale, John 53
Pascale, John 298
Pascuzzi, Steve 177
Pasicznyk, John G 193
Paskal, Steven 50
Paskuski, Brian 408
Paslawsky, William 459
Pasquale, James F 371
Pastore, Martin J 208
Patane, Anthony 562
Patchett, Noni 301
Patchett, Richard B 314
Patel, Dipen 143
Patel, Ayut 244
Patel, Ketul J 252
Patel, Sudhir 259
Patel, Mahendrabhai 322
Patel, Jaibala 338
Patel, Samir 370
Patel, Chintan 452
Patel, Ambar M 476
Patel, Akshar 516
Patel, Saavan 555
Patel, Nilesh 563
Patel, Chetankumar 563
Patel, Bhavana 586
Patel, Sandeep 587
Pathak, Sumit 325
Patin, Al 290
Patkotak, Crawford 41
Patonai, Nicolas 586
Patoux, Fiona 446
Patrick, Gregory 130
Patrick, Tammany 298
Patrick, Chad 346
Patrick, Morris 452
Patrick, Dan 517
Patrick, Chuck 615
Patricoff, Tracey C 488
Patry, Dean 38
Patsos, Theodore 608
Patterson, George 28
Patterson, Emma 134
Patterson, Diane 163
Patterson, L Brooks 165
Patterson, Douglas E 285
Patterson, Douglas E 285
Patterson, Bill 370
Patterson, Douglas E 412
Patterson, Jason 433
Patterson, John K 550
Patterson, Jamie 594
Patterson, Roger 626
Patton, Robin Van 148
Patton, Aaron 253
Patton, Alex 272
Patton, Brandon 503
Patzke, Guy 289
Pau, Melissa 51
Paul, Brenda 130
Paul, Wanda 256
Paul, Schaik 483
Paul, David 603
Paula, Allison 162
Pauley, Katrinka 642
Paulk, Jenny 103
Paulson, Chad 76
Paulus, Ronald A 36
Paulus, Ronald A 225
Paulus, Ronald A 346
Pavioni, Blake 604
Pawelski, Len 379
Pawley, Patrick 324
Pawley, Barbara 614
Pawlich, Jean 660
Pawlus, Kathleen 28
Paxson, Christina 90

Index of Executives

Paxson, Kara 283
Paxton, Ken 51
Paxton, Stuart 294
Payne, Robert 73
Payne, Leslie 80
Payne, Demietre 107
Payne, John 139
Payne, Matthew 139
Payne, Phyllis 461
Payson, Martin D 307
Peacock, Christy 320
Peacor, Melissa S 167
Peacor, Melissa 167
Pealer, Carla 399
Pearce, Elizabeth 84
Pearce, Zach 151
Pearce, Jim 232
Pearce, Jennifer 399
Pearison, Megan 579
Pearlman, Michael 85
Pearson, Jeffrey T 32
Pearson, Amy 322
Pearson, Beth 332
Pearson, James F 337
Pearson, James F 394
Pearson, James F 410
Pearson, Ronald 411
Pearson, J F 552
Peaslee, Gregory 634
Peat, William 360
PEC, Mike 200
Peccolo, Charles M 629
Pecente, Anthony 165
Peck, Cynthia 148
Peck, Kimberly 335
Peck, Cynthia 351
Peck, Jane 459
Pecsenyicki, Stephen 588
Peddy, Amy 271
Peddycoart, Nancy 501
Pedersen, John 310
Pedonti, Patrick J 196
Pedraza, Cori 141
Peduto, William 131
Peebles, Joel 401
Peel, Matthew 195
Peeters, Clare 53
Peetz, Karen 575
Peev, Millen 7
Pefanis, Harry N 420
Pehl, Vicky 199
Peigen, Seth 345
Peinado, Fat 26
Peirce, Elizabeth 658
Pekelis, Zhanna 319
Pelasara, Rick 484
Pelavin, Sol H 32
Pelgen, Brittany 357
Pelizzari, John 358
Pelkey, Cecelia 516
Pellegrini, Frank 366
Pelletiere, Christopher V 7
Pelowski, Alton 287
Pelt, Laurie Van 165
Pelt, Russell Van 448
Pemberton, Richard S 110
Pemberton, Rick 152
Pena, Arthur 133
Pena, Dena 327
Penar, Eva 114
Pencil, Patricia 123
Pendery, Lud 152
Penlesky, Sherry 190
Penn, Kevin 336
Penn, George H 351
Pennekamp, Kim 160
Pennella, William 176
Penner, Don 159
Pennes, Victor 108
Pennetti, Frank 157
Penney, Robert 106
Penning, David 38
Pennington, Chip 480
Pennington, Hilary 558

Pennington, Kelli 647
Pennywell, Gwendolyn 629
Penrod, Jeremy 610
Penrose, Lee 506
Peoples, Rasheda 427
Peoples, Chanda 467
Peper, Catherine 78
Pepper, J David 411
Pepper, Dave 411
Pepper, J Stanley 575
Pepper, Richard S 575
Peppiatt-Combes, James 332
Peram, Roja 10
Perazzo, Glory 306
Perch, Jeanmarie 427
Perda, Michael 648
Perdue, Sandra 433
Pereira, Justine 188
Pereira, Lesley 247
Perera, Kanchana 536
Perez, Jorge 59
Perez, Cesar 167
Perez, Nicolas F 228
Perez, Dr Sylvester Syl 461
Perez, Olga 461
Perez-Pineda, Federico 629
Pergine, William 164
Perhach, Andy 81
Periago, Mirta 404
Perille, Thomas 503
Perin, Mitchell 127
Perkash, Om 1
Perkins, Elizabeth S 40
Perkins, Mike 57
Perkins, Catherine 185
Perkins, Paul 209
Perkins, James 377
Perkins, Robert 450
Perkins, Judy 471
Perkovich, Brian 338
Perlewitz, Kathy 222
Perlman, Joel A 352
Perlmutter, Joel 645
Permet, Robert 354
Pernas, Rick 160
Pero, Joseph 370
Peroutka, Bryan 659
Perrelli, Kathryn 287
Perrin, Maria 252
Perrin, Mary 304
Perrins, Alexander 422
Perron, Jacques 594
Perry, Karl E 56
Perry, Mike 60
Perry, James 188
Perry, Lee 290
Perry, Cheryl 375
Perry, Heather 479
Perry, Keith 505
Perry, Gloria 508
Perry, Carol 522
Perselis, Anna 655
Persico, Asid 272
Person, Amanda 153
Person, Peter 483
Perusse, Charles 586
Perzigin, Anthony 617
Pestello, Fred P 458
Pestello, Fred 585
Petasnick, William 223
Peter, David 14
Peterfreund, Robert A 317
Peterjohn, William 652
Peters, Michael 35
Peters, Susan 168
Peters, Loree 357
Peters, Len 374
Peters, Robert 427
Peters, Chris 620
Petersen, Jeffrey P 285
Petersen, Jeffrey P 285
Petersen, Richard W 308
Petersen, Jill 366
Petersen, David 510

Petersen, John 629
Peterson, Richard D 9
Peterson, Tiffani 28
Peterson, Jeannette 73
Peterson, Roger 83
Peterson, Richard D 110
Peterson, Nan 124
Peterson, Mary D 194
Peterson, Tim 252
Peterson, Ronald 276
Peterson, Michael 345
Peterson, Robin 442
Peterson, Ken 480
Peterson, Elaine 487
Peterson, Bob 515
Peterson, Randall 522
Peterson, Randy 522
Peterson, Jim 561
Peterson, Ronald R 564
Peterson, Karen 618
Peterson, Andy 640
Petrasso, Richard 318
Petri, Mark 445
Petrie, Kim 617
Petrilla, Cheryl 394
Petrime, Matt 40
Petrof, Constantin 370
Petrogeorge, Michael 310
Petronchak, Jo 503
Petrosino, John 147
Petrosino, Thomas 306
Petrusky, Chuck 257
Petti, Filippo 384
Pettiford, Kathy 197
Pettiford, Carlos 512
Pettus, Janice 346
Petty, Joseph M 135
Petty, Joseph 135
Petty, Lora 331
Petz, Carl 92
Pevenstein, Robert L 623
Peverly, Francis 397
Pfannenstein, Mike 142
Pfautsch, Rose Agnes 219
Pfeffer, George 194
Pfefferle, Dennis 393
Pfeifer, Kyle 332
Pfeifer, Mark 614
Pflanz, Robert 322
Phalan, Brendan 327
Phalen, Daniel 177
Phangaraj, Immanuel 311
Phares, Tamara L 587
Phares, Kathryn 644
Pharmd, Geoffrey Lawton 102
PHD, Robert Sloan 65
PHD, Barry Arbuckle 301
PHD, Charles L Beaty 447
Phelan, Paula 99
Phelan, Brandi 611
Phelps, David E 70
Phenix, David 470
Philippin, Charles 23
Phillips, J David 34
Phillips, Brent 65
Phillips, Robyn 97
Phillips, Betty 101
Phillips, David 120
Phillips, Betty 142
Phillips, Dorris 145
Phillips, Erick 165
Phillips, Roya 173
Phillips, Issac 175
Phillips, Twila 211
Phillips, Jason 265
Phillips, John 267
Phillips, Dax J 313
Phillips, Brenda 316
Phillips, Jim 343
Phillips, Dave 344
Phillips, Sheila 362
Phillips, Todd 374
Phillips, Wayne 423
Phillips, Robin 441

Phillips, George W 548
Phillips, John 557
Phillips, Neil Foster 563
Phillips, William 644
Phillips, Russel Scott 659
Philpot, Buddy 646
Phipps, Laura 109
Phipps, Tom 130
Phipps, David 267
Phlegar, Charles D 642
Phlipsak, Mike 561
Phocus, Rob 124
Phr, Catherine B 123
Pia, Alberto Del 632
Pianka, Stephanie 374
Piat, Anita 228
Piatkowski, John 99
Picarelli, Carmine 316
Piccirilli, Ed 405
Pickle, Jeri 662
Pickup, Julie 287
Picone, Nancy 530
Piechoski, Michael J 285
Piechoski, Michael J 285
Piechoski, Michael J 412
Piekut, Michael 637
Pierce, Phil 53
Pierce, Tera 131
Pierce, Gen 157
Pierce, Mike 209
Pierce, Karen 218
Pierce, Roger 223
Pierce, Mark 242
Pierce, Stonish 254
Pierce, Christine 502
Pierce, Benjamin 640
Pierce, Damon 642
Pierce, Mary 657
Pierce-Jones, Carolyn 220
Pierpoint, Janice 394
Pierre, Sharon St 352
Pierre, Bryan 427
Pierre, Frantz 546
Pietragallo, William 635
Pietruniak, Lori 165
Piggott, Julie A 80
Pike, Drew 136
Pike, Annabelle 634
Piland, Donald S 625
Pilarz, Rev Scott 313
Pileggi, Elisa 414
Pilgreen, Brian 19
Pilgrim, Tony 452
Pilgrim, Trip 521
Pilong, Al 358
Pilz, Christine 252
Pinckney, E 65
Pineault, Ray 349
Pineda, Patricia 297
Pineda, Brenda 441
Pines, Darryll 623
Ping, David 246
Ping, Andrew C 335
Pingle, Brenda 504
Pingolt, Cindy 314
Pinnaro, Catherina 622
Pinnell, Matt 516
Pino, Lisette Del 130
Pinto, Jennifer 134
Piper, Audrey 16
Piper, Mark 594
Pipkin, Alison 536
Pippen, Alycia 156
Pippin, William C 257
Pipsair, Sophia 512
Pirie, Ellen 169
Piros, Ryan 163
Pirro, Nicholas J 165
Pishko, Bernard A 130
Pistorius, Clayton 393
Pitchford, Jim 394
Pitcock, Laurie 239
Pitkin, Jeff 206
Pitrolo, Richard 537

Index of Executives

Pittas, Jay 534
Pittman, Steuart 156
Pittsford, Judy 171
Piva, Gary R 657
Pizzo, Kristine 371
Placek, Mark 151
Placencia, Eric 27
Placido, Lorraine 308
Plaines, Stephanie 378
Plam, Kathleen 126
Plamondon, William N 195
Planas, Ramon 133
Plascencia, Gustavo 127
Platia, Edward V 646
Platt, Lawrence B 105
Platt, Anne 529
Platts, Karen 553
Plenk, Bruce 135
Plewa, Jennifer 4
Plewniak, Linda 7
Ploszek, Judith M 215
Plotner, Chuck 100
Plotts, Diane J 603
Plourde, Donna 309
Plummer, Laura 73
Plummer, Shayvonne 133
Plummer, Suzy 282
Plummer, Beth 381
Pocino, Raymond M 368
Podolsky, Howard 107
Poe, Caitlin 411
Poe, Shawn K 421
Poe, Kevin 457
Poenitske, Jason P 392
Pogge, Franklyn 347
Pogrebinsky, Lena 138
Pohl, Jeffery 193
Pohlman, John A 488
Pohlner, Roger E 444
Poisson, Keith 225
Polansky, Robert B 77
Polensek, Michael D 125
Polep, Jeff 152
Polep, Eric 152
Polis, Cindy 80
Polis, Jared 510
Polisknowski, John 489
Polito, Karyn 146
Politte, Kevin 334
Poljak, Matt 93
Polk, Hiram C 614
Poll, Max 254
Pollack, Martha E 154
Pollack, Stephanie 317
Pollard, Dennis 222
Pollard, Katherine 616
Pollet, Mary Joe 554
Pollitt, Erin 334
Pollock, Allen 209
Poloncarz, Mark 159
Poludniak, Lee 222
Pomaville, David 159
Pompa, Robert N 572
Ponce, Sue 416
Pool, Dr Dennis 396
Poole, Dawn 150
Poole, Kami 178
Poole, Claude 198
Poole, Thomas 301
Poole, James 436
Popal, Ahmad 573
Pope, Audrey 19
Pope, Brian 155
Pope, Mariana 256
Pope, Alice H 263
Pope, Linda 282
Pope, Alice 649
Popek, Edwina J 540
Poplis, Mark 471
Popour, Catherine 599
Popov, Igor 534
Poppell, Jim 214
Poppell, John E 619
Popper, Charles 265

Porcari, John 316
Porcile, Renee 70
Poremba, Steve 320
Porte, Susan 167
Porter, Robert 11
Porter, Tom 63
Porter, Virginia 158
Porter, Lawana 179
Porter, Jody 225
Porter, Frenchie 467
Porter, Andy 546
Porterfield, Clark 405
Portillo, Janice 18
Portnoy, Dan 559
Posecai, Scott 393
Posey, Dan 468
Posson, Denise M 442
Post, Bill 78
Post, Shelley 148
Post, Heather 172
Post, Janet 646
Postel, Gregory 587
Postlethweight, Brittany 466
Postma, Nate 266
Postma, Sidney W 431
Potochnic, Jennifer 622
Pototo, Dan 635
Potter, Ruth 98
Potter, Roshanda 127
Potter, William 163
Potter, Silas 471
Potter, Jim 520
Potter, Shannon 521
Potter, Jason 559
Potter, Joyce 581
Potter, Kent 650
Pottle, Aj 135
Pottorff, Gary W 386
Poulsen, Richard 168
Pound, Pam 353
Pounds, Don 60
Povlitz, David 156
Powell, Charlie 1
Powell, Brittney 160
Powell, Terri 347
Powell, Willa 450
Powell, Larry 491
Powers, Roxanne 76
Powers, Kevin G 109
Powers, Glen 170
Powers, Michael 172
Powers, Donald S 359
Powers, Kevin 488
Powes, Hammond R 161
Powrie, Raymond 99
Pozen, Robert 378
Pozzo, Joseph E 172
Prabhakaran, Bharath 627
Prada, Ariel De 612
Prairie, Gregory 238
Pranckevicius, John 319
Prasad, Vinay 294
Prater, Robert 404
Prather, Patrise 6
Pratt, Marcel S 131
Pratt, Charles 134
Pratt, John 193
Pratt, Brenda 382
Pratt, Dan 382
Pratt, Ramona 416
Pratt, Stephen R 508
Pratt, Frank 510
Pratt, Ronald E 534
Prehn, Ryan 512
Preisler, Donna 201
Prendergast, Ed 55
Prendergast, Michael 167
Prendergast, Mark 234
Prendergast, Thomas F 370
Prendergast, Vincent 540
Prendergast, Dr E James 562
Prentace, Charles 130
Prentice, Nora 554
Pres, Thomas J La 256

Prescod, Elizabeth 164
Presecan, Anne 471
Presnell, Bill 525
Press, Michael B 161
Press, Dennis 626
Presto, Toni 87
Preston, Marty 369
Preston, James L 410
Pretorius, Sy 406
Pretty, Nigel 140
Prevost, Sgt 518
Price, Jody 10
Price, Heather 37
Price, Aaron 39
Price, Bill 46
Price, Cell 126
Price, McKinley 129
Price, John Wiley 158
Price, Lasundra 170
Price, Robert R 211
Price, Harold 215
Price, Jamie 290
Price, Todd M 326
Price, Ronald E 414
Price, Andrea 493
Price, Meredith 504
Price, Nancy 541
Price, Stuart 553
Price, Brenda 553
Price, Claudia 563
Price, Alexandra 583
Price-Eastburn, Dianna 399
Pricher, Michael 535
Pricket, Glenn 569
Prickett, Charlie 1
Priebe, Nancy L 49
Priebe, Nancy L 639
Priest, Harold De 203
Priester, Joann 162
Prieto, Esther 141
Prigg, Becky 147
Primavera, Dianne 510
Prime, Joshua 297
Prince, Amy L 609
Principato, Giuseppe 434
Prindeze, Nick 325
Prindle, Brian 620
Pringle, Germaine 170
Pringle, Al 433
Pringle, Nisaphan 492
Prinner, John 234
Prins, Todd 588
Priselac, Thomas M 105
Pritchett, Patricia 615
Pritzker, J B 512
Privett, Stephen A 628
Privot, John 316
Procaskey, Alexander 609
Procopio, Karen 335
Proctor, Jason 119
Procyk, Nicholas 549
Progar, Michael 226
Prohaska, Ron 109
Proksel, Jenel 366
Pronchunas, Edward M 105
Pronger, Derk 359
Proske, Donna 519
Prosper, Charles 409
Prosser, Joseph 541
Proto, Christine 215
Prout, John 72
Prout, John S 231
Prout, John 598
Provencher, Catherine 633
Pruger, Robert 578
Pruitt, Andy 113
Pruitt, Keri 172
Pruitt, Gary 545
Pruneda, Augustin 156
Pruner, Lauren 418
Prust, Robert 359
Pry, Russell M 524
Prybycien, Bonnie 217
Pryor, Juliette 18

Pryor, David B 43
Pryor, Vince 201
Pryor, Vince 201
Pryor, Robert 468
Prysock, Carrie 126
Puckett, Walter 209
Puckett, Debbie 417
Pucky, Alicia 222
Puente, Gabriel 259
Puente, Robert R 462
Puetz, Belinda 155
Puffinburger, Darren 394
Pugh, Aaron 42
Pugh, Catherine E 123
Pugh, Randall 269
Pugh, William 418
Pugh, Sandra 634
Puhy, Dorothy E 180
Puleo, Dominic J 640
Pullen, Jim 526
Pulmonologist, A Lynchburg 107
Pulomena, John 343
Pulsipher, Scott 653
Pum, Michael J 289
Pumeroy, Clarence 507
Pumpian, Ann 477
Pundrich, Shari 114
Puntel, Diane 13
Punukula, Balaji 512
Purcell, Alfred L 248
Purcell, Alfred L 354
Purcell, Paul E 448
Purcell, Jennifer 516
Purcell, Cailin 565
Purkey, Tom 569
Purrier, Paul 90
Purtee, Pamela 355
Purves, Steve 311
Pusser, Brian 589
Putney, April 161
Pyatt, Ken 341
Pyle, Richard 23

Q

Qin, Jeff 141
Quaid, Maureen A 7
Qualls, Roxanne 125
Quan, Patrick F 29
Quan, Patrick F 562
Quattlebaum, Heather 597
Quattrocchi, Robert T 387
Quay, Martha James 657
Queen, Elizabeth 395
Quemore, Amanda 466
Quenneville, Cathy L 24
Quenon, Loretta 127
Querubin, Linne 257
Quesada-Kunkel, Ginnette 377
Quick-Wasik, Cindy 323
Quien, Austine 169
Quigg, Diana 100
Quigley, Timothy 488
Quijano-Lerma, Mariselle 408
Quin, Debra 40
Quiniones, Gil C 371
Quinn, Bill 135
Quinn, Madison 165
Quinn, Joseph 175
Quinn, Brian 342
Quinn, Mary Anna 505
Quinn, Ronald N 537
Quinn-Davidson, Austin 36
Quinones, Bill 179
Quinonez, Tanya 210
Quirk, Kathleen 317
Quiroz, David 96
Qureshi, Furhan 293

Index of Executives

R

R, Shereen 2
R, Bethany 136
R, Cynthia 167
R, Marek Doll 340
Raab, Lee 507
Raab, Andrew 523
Raab, Andy 523
Raassina, Leevi 259
Rachev, Sharyn 371
Rachman, Sherry 173
Rackers, Eileen 347
Radano, Amy 421
Rademacher, Dennis 10
Radloff, Diane 44
Radtke, Alex 292
Radulesk, Jenny 164
Raehl, Deborah 632
Raetz, Jeff 339
Rafferty, James 70
Rafferty, Gary J 530
Rafferty, Gary J 531
Rafferty, William 553
Raftery, Mary 156
Ragan, Bob 650
Ragel, Larry 501
Ragni, Margaret V 635
Ragosta, Michael 589
Ragsdale, Chris 141
Rahe, Micaela 212
Rahim, Faiza 662
Rahlfs, Gary 627
Rahman, Habib 345
Rahming, Carmen M 345
Rahn, Pete K 316
Rahn, Douglas 327
Rai, Kiran 47
Raigoza, Juan 169
Raikhel, Marina 596
Raine, Ed 217
Raines, Diane S 58
Raines, Lynn 493
Raines, Kelly 507
Rains, Cherie 14
Rains, Melinda 533
Rainwater, Meghan 51
Raj, Atul 411
Raja, Andaleeb H 300
Rajan, Resmi 200
Raju, Shubha 200
Raju, Ramanathan 369
Raju, Ryan 468
Raley, Mary 507
Ralph, Stephen A 407
Ramachandran, Ramesh 325
Ramanna, Mayura 126
Rambousek, Jasmine 137
Ramicone, Arthur 628
Ramirez, Fabiola 114
Ramirez, Aimee 114
Ramirez, Shanna 136
Ramirez, Eduardo 168
Ramirez, Amie 261
Ramirez, Luis M 317
Ramos, Cruz 168
Ramos, Harold 205
Ramos, Delia 217
Ramos, Rick 312
Ramos, Annette 450
Ramsay, Michael 65
Ramsden, Peter 169
Ramsden, Deanna 318
Ramsey, Craig 28
Ramsey, David L 111
Ramsey, Brenda 337
Ramsey, Ron 517
Ramsey, Randy 586
Ramsey-Burns, Debbie 134
Ramstad, Jennifer 172
Ranck, Angela 157
Randall, Taylor 588
Rando, Anthony 177

Rangan, Kasturi 102
Rangel, Felicia 405
Ranjbar, Mohammad 624
Rankin, Jay 200
Rankin, Robert S 418
Rankin, Ralph 435
Rankin, Alice 468
Ranney, Timothy 346
Ransom, Teran 612
Ranum, Laura 261
Rao, Karthik 378
RAO, Michael 640
Rapple, Susan 546
Raquel, Thompson 132
Rardin, Laurie 182
Rasak, Jon 105
Rasche, Steven 495
Rasco, Craig 123
Rasco, Jane 615
Rash, Matthew P 40
Raskin, David 336
Rasmussen, Tiffany 233
Rath, Deb 589
Raths, Kathy 267
Ratkin, Gary 347
Ratliff, Beth 426
Ratner, Ian 470
Ratzlaff, James W 33
Raul, Wonneberger 621
Rausch, Christopher 605
Rauschenberger, Matthew 493
Rauschl, Christopher A 77
Rawlings, Hunter R 154
Rawlings, Karen 308
Rawot, Billie 200
Ray, James 112
Ray, Anish 152
Ray, David 153
Ray, Cindy 157
Ray, David 193
Ray, Monica 354
Raybon, Erine 385
Rayner, Thomas 282
Raynor, Linda 306
Raza, Adnan 377
Razo, Jennifer 267
Read, Vicki 637
Ream, Deborah 4
Reardon, Aaron 170
Reath, Robin 560
Reber, Ann 514
Rebsamen, C B 292
Rebsch, Gary 352
Rebstock, Russell 393
Reca, Thomas 519
Recchi, Giuseppe 227
Reck, Una Mae 602
Redabaugh, Blake 577
Redae, Getachew 168
Redd, Mike 401
Redd, Ellis S 491
Redd, David 541
Reddy, John Patrick 494
Reddy, Andrew 520
Reddy, Sreenath V 587
Reding, Douglas 314
Redlich, Rachel 272
Redman, Cynthia J H 305
Redmond, Katrina R 200
Redmond, Velma A 410
Redner, Ryan 439
Redner, Richard E 439
Redner, Gary W 439
Redwine, William A 114
Reece, Ronald 189
Reed, Susan 156
Reed, Betty 209
Reed, Glenn 256
Reed, Daniel C 311
Reed, Connie 311
Reed, Tyrone 318
Reed, David 318
Reed, Katie N 387
Reed, Jane 421

Reed, Colin 454
Reed, Ann 459
Reed, Stephanie 460
Reed, James 508
Reed, Suellen 512
Reed, Sam 518
Reed, Robert D 528
Reed, David 627
Reed, Dervel 647
Reeder, Billy 532
Reedy, Raquel Martinez 18
Reel, Stephanie 591
Reel-Davis, Tammi 352
Rees, Gary 179
Reese, Steven 25
Reese, Bruce 264
Reese, Cody 287
Reese, Cathy 359
Reese, Roger 400
Reese, Vincent 428
Reese, William 542
Reese, Amanda 632
Reeths, Lori 546
Reeve, Shawn 394
Reeve, Derek 432
Reeve, Stephene 512
Reeves, Denise 141
Reeves, Tate 513
Reeves, Cynthia 620
Regalado, Tomas 128
Regalado, Antonio 486
Regan, Timothy J 291
Regan, Marla 449
Regan, Timothy J 591
Regele, Michael B 267
Regunath, Harihoran 625
Reher, Penny 461
Rehmel, Tina 127
Rehwinkel, Brian 651
Reich, Jan 450
Reichert, John A 406
Reichert, James 447
Reichert, Nicole 659
Reichle, Hank 509
Reick, Angela 396
Reid, George 37
Reid, Bob 158
Reid, Monica Nino 170
Reid, John 311
Reid, David 417
Reid, Brian 481
Reid, Bernadette 596
Reif, L Rafael 318
Reifsteck, John 237
Reilly, Annemarie 103
Reilly, Christorpher B 173
Reilly, Bill 232
Reilly, Bob 306
Reilly, Paul 436
Reilly, Janelle 456
Reilly, Katie 510
Reilly, Barbara G 553
Reilly, Theresa 604
Reimche, Brenda A 531
Reimer, Elizebeth 426
Reimer, Ronaldo 448
Reinauer, Greg 595
Reiner, Carol 257
Reinhart, Thomas 289
Reinhart, Tom 289
Reinhart, Leslie 449
Reinsvold, Suize 301
Reis, Peter 12
Reis, Amy L 363
Reis, Cathleen 384
Reischlein, Greg 376
Reisig, Cliff 141
Reith, Ian 222
Reitmajer, Stephanie 172
Reitz, Pamela 170
Relf, Lauren 482
Relly, J B 294
Remark, Megan 441
Rembisz, Adam 204

Remerowski, Gaia 591
Remillard, Michael 639
Remillard, Mike 639
Remolde, Cheryl 308
Ren, Bing 182
Renaud, Dennis 405
Rench, Daniel 147
Renee, Hagen 112
Renne, Louise 122
Renner, Katy 161
Renner, Rob 214
Rense, John 413
Renshaw, Tom 595
Rensing, Willy 152
Rentfrow, Steve A 358
Rentz, Ann 421
Renuart, Gene 323
Renwick, Edward 422
Repetz, Brian 459
Reppert, Joe 383
Resamen, C B 292
Resch, Richard J 289
Reshetar, Joseph 156
Resnick, Alan 38
Resnick, Joseph D 215
Retzer, Ingrid 51
Reuland, Charles 275
Reuss, Herb J 285
Reuter, Heitho 653
Reutledge, Valinda 499
Revels, Beverly 529
Reves, Josesph G 566
Revitsky, Steve 482
Rewolinski, Andrew 413
Rex, Rock 413
Rexinger, Elwyn 345
Reyes, Tomas 129
Reyes, Norman 133
Reyes, Marlena 154
Reyes, Emilia 159
Reyes, Isabel 190
Reyes, Marcelo 233
Reyes, Patricia 496
Reyes, James 498
Reyes, Basilio 572
Reyngoudt, Mark 437
Reynolds, Kinh 99
Reynolds, Karen 266
Reynolds, Sheila 267
Reynolds, Ronald 302
Reynolds, Walt 323
Reynolds, Julie 365
Reynolds, Dale 416
Reynolds, Yoke San L 439
Reynolds, Kimberly 502
Reynolds, Jason 507
Reynolds, Audrey 507
Reynolds, Kim 512
Reynolds, Kathryn 514
Reynoso, Charlie 534
Rez, Marta P 6
Reza, Tony 486
Rezet, Penny 17
Rheinheimer, Jon 286
Rhine, Richard 233
Rhoads, Ann D 426
Rhoads, William 548
Rhoden, Larry 517
Rhodes, Chris 153
Rhodes, John B 206
Rhodes, Mike 259
Rhodes, Brad 384
Rhodes, Anne 395
Rhymer, Ernie 432
Rhyne, Anissa 163
Riach, Lorna 117
Riano, Jewell 345
Riaz, Salma 275
Riazi, Atefeh 328
Rice, David 46
Rice, April 46
Rice, David 57
Rice, Charles 129
Rice, Diane 141

Index of Executives

Rice, Katie 163
Rice, Denise 501
Rice, Constance 534
Rich, Richard 133
Rich, Melinda 445
Rich, Robert 445
Rich, Judith F 604
Richard, Michelle 70
Richard, Coco 75
Richard, Glenn 413
Richard, Andy 464
Richards, James J 146
Richards, Leslie 164
Richards, Catherine 220
Richards, Jeanne 315
Richards, James J 359
Richards, Tom 625
Richardson, Chris 36
Richardson, Don 101
Richardson, Lily 126
Richardson, Ursula 135
Richardson, Leslee 139
Richardson, Don 142
Richardson, Gary 360
Richardson, Renee 643
Richardson, Xavier 646
Richcreek, M Jean 121
Richemont, Phillip 662
Richerson, Michelle 490
Richmond, Estelle 146
Richmond, Olga 197
Richmond, Lynn 352
Richoux, Donna 406
Richter, Jeff 112
Richter, John 138
Richter, Dawn 375
Rick, Van M 120
Rickard, Matthew 98
Rickard, Deborah 333
Ricketts, Pete 514
Rickhoff, Gerry 156
Rico, Juliet 576
Ridderbusch, Greg 235
Riddle, Ashley 22
Rider, Stephanie 94
Ridley, Brad 84
Ridley, Marcus A 447
Riedman, Karol 381
Riedo, Francis X 286
Rieg, James 575
Riego, Henry Del 390
Rieke, Thomas 432
Riemer, Julie 45
Riemer, Hans 352
Riester, Tom 638
Riew, John 575
Riewe, Paul 557
Rigby, Alan 71
Rigg, Mark Knapp 121
Riggan, Mike 516
Riggins, Gregory 276
Riggs, Rita 489
Riggs, Jean 579
Riley, Debbie 4
Riley, Donna 38
Riley, Blair 73
Riley, Tammy 261
Riley, Mike 362
Riley, Trent 426
Riley, Lynnette 511
Riley, Paul 561
Rimar, Stephen 377
Rineer, Tom 410
Rinehart, Doug 564
Riner, Donna 160
Riney, Robert 249
Ring, Tricia 163
Ringeisen, Berthold 217
Ringgold, Sadie 91
Riopelle, Diani 467
Riordan, Michael C 428
Rios, Holly 87
Rios, Mabel 467
Rippe, Michelle 357

Ripple, David W 648
Ris, Lauren 511
Risberg, John F 312
Riseberg, David 332
Risen, Stan 170
Risio, Gary De 54
Rispoli, Michael J 375
Ristuben, Steve 128
Risty, Barbara 463
Ritch, Jill A Alexander 627
Ritchey, Dean 400
Ritchey, Mike 520
Ritchotte, Alan 152
Ritner, Carli 357
Ritter, Kate 564
Ritter, Ann 640
Ritts, Gregory J 27
Rivanis, Chris 116
Rivas, Isadore 248
Rivas, Manual 384
Rivas, Jesenia 415
Rivenes, Gary 139
Rivera, Joseph 48
Rivera, Brandi 53
Rivera, Julie 127
Rivera, Fabian 132
Rivera, Karen 210
Rivera, Maria 377
Rivera, Paul 406
Rivera, Yesenia 467
Rivera, Cathleen M 468
Rivera, Amadeo 482
Rivera, Alma 610
Rivera, Julio 620
Rivero, Joan 253
Rives, John 54
Rizk, Norman 509
Rizulo, Frank G 571
Rizvi, Gowher 439
Rizzo, Bre 455
Rizzo, Renee M 632
Rizzuti, Chris 157
Rizzuti, Sergeant R 170
Rn, Laurie B 220
Rn, Carol Bradley 294
Rn, Laura Espinosa PHD 336
Rn, Ann Cella 499
Roach, Sharon V 2
Roach, Dave 278
Roach, Mintha 287
Roach, Jill 594
Roan, Tiffany 12
Roark, Mark 598
Robaina, Ashley 612
Robb, Charles 459
Robb, Davon 545
Robbertz, Paul 182
Robbins, Kenneth B 244
Robbins, Clifton S 328
Robbins, Claudia 467
Robbins, Larry 553
Robbins-Meyer, H 168
Robert, Lucas 167
Robert, Gompf 170
Roberti, Isabel 60
Roberti, Jennifer 466
Roberto, Ann 444
Roberto, John 603
Roberts, Jeff 43
Roberts, Ryan 85
Roberts, Nolan 95
Roberts, Michael 98
Roberts, Anthony 141
Roberts, Alan 167
Roberts, Ron 168
Roberts, Michael 176
Roberts, Phyllis 220
Roberts, Kevin V 226
Roberts, Ben 315
Roberts, William R 324
Roberts, Charles C 330
Roberts, Jean 404
Roberts, Fred 408
Roberts, Ryan 422

Roberts, David 424
Roberts, Cory 466
Roberts, James M 477
Roberts, Charles W M 505
Roberts, Shauna R 601
Roberts, Brad 646
Robertshaw, Patricia 488
Robertson, Cliff 19
Robertson, Jake 225
Robertson, Jessica 226
Robertson, Steve 244
Robertson, William G 357
Robertson, James V 416
Robertson, Cliff A 459
Robertson, Euan 580
Robertson, Jeffrey 604
Robertson-Keck, Karen 220
Robertstad, John 647
Robillard, Jean 621
Robinette, Gary E 421
Robins, Linda 174
Robinson, Jeff 9
Robinson, Ronnie 86
Robinson, Arthur 128
Robinson, Darryl 145
Robinson, Alva 146
Robinson, Chase 152
Robinson, Jim 155
Robinson, Cedric 160
Robinson, John 184
Robinson, Veronica 201
Robinson, Patricia 209
Robinson, Vicki 215
Robinson, John R 231
Robinson, Edmondo 240
Robinson, Mark 319
Robinson, Edward 359
Robinson, Ben 379
Robinson, Melissa 384
Robinson, John 389
Robinson, Dan 419
Robinson, Daniel 419
Robinson, Daniel 419
Robinson, Allison 433
Robinson, Edwin 456
Robinson, Lisa 457
Robinson, Abby 490
Robinson, Sheila 515
Robinson, Mark 515
Robinson, David 542
Robinson, Mike 548
Robinson, Denise 565
Robinson, Carolyn 571
Robinson, Randal 613
Robinson, Linda 618
Robinson, Rayneil 620
Robinson, Samara 627
Robinson, Douglas 627
Robinson, King 632
Robinson, Dorothy 661
Robison, Mary 60
Robison, Randy 207
Robitaille, Mark 314
Robitaille, Carroll 356
Robles, Ted 123
Robles, Norberto 369
Robles, Adriane 462
Robles, Monica 554
Rocap, Nisha 211
Rocha, Zeb 404
Roche, Kevin 56
Roche, Brian 270
Rochelle, Anne La 101
Rock, Luke 424
Rocke, Javon 176
Rockenbach, John 514
Rockett, Mike 491
Rocourt, Brittney 420
Rodak, Lory 161
Roddy, Sonya 263
Rodell, Angela 178
Rodewald, Renee 38
Rodgers, Susan 176
Rodgers, Elliott 297

Rodis, Hallie 396
Rodrigue, Kathi 309
Rodrigues, Barry 60
Rodrigues, Nicholas 145
Rodriguez, Rudy 104
Rodriguez, Lara 156
Rodriguez, Martha 158
Rodriguez, Eliza 169
Rodriguez, Jessica 210
Rodriguez, Camille 218
Rodriguez, Yolanda 256
Rodriguez, Manuel 256
Rodriguez, Mayra 408
Rodriguez, Domingo C 488
Rodriguez, Dawn 494
Rodriguez, Barney 496
Rodriguez, Havidan 519
Rodriguez, Gabriela 520
Rodriguez, Cristella 627
Rodriguez-Galindo, Carlos 505
Roebuck, Rick 161
Roeck, Seppe De 84
Roehl, Kathy 592
Roemer, Dennis 505
Roemer, Aaron 654
Roest, Stan Vander 3
Rogers, Carolyn 113
Rogers, Grant 122
Rogers, Jeffrey L 132
Rogers, Dennis 132
Rogers, James 140
Rogers, Harlan 153
Rogers, Mark 227
Rogers, Woody 251
Rogers, Gilbert L 298
Rogers, Greg 343
Rogers, Cleveland 365
Rogers, Rich 428
Rogers, Randy 533
Rogers, Frederick 564
Rogers, Amy 651
Rogers, Colleen 656
Rogers, Chris 659
Rogge, James D 219
Roggero, Dinorah 404
Roggie, Brent 363
Roggin, Kevin 585
Rogier, Amy 362
Rohling, Daniel 207
Rohm, Estella 330
Rohmiller, Chelsee 381
Rohrer, Jennifer 388
Rohrig, Jeff 537
Rojas, Manuel F 71
Rojek, Kenneth J 379
Roland, Sandy 412
Rolando, Fredric V 362
Roldan, Isaac 103
Rolen, Templin 176
Rolfe, Harold 561
Rollerson, Monica 17
Rollison, Marvin L 209
Roloff, Richard 591
Rolston, Richard 175
Roman, Guadalupe 180
Roman, Jose 602
Romancyk, Janet 162
Romano, Jenna 109
Romano, Joseph 162
Romard, Ryan 539
Romero, Jose 129
Romero, Bethsabe 154
Romero, Ken 392
Romero, Tifinni 476
Romero, Nitza 530
Romero, Carlos 625
Romine, Michael 138
Romm, Sylvia 48
Rommel, Catherine T 564
Romo, Karen 134
Romoff, Jeffrey A 634
Romond, Jennifer L 643
Ron, Prill 409
Ronald, Mundy 513

Index of Executives

Index of Executives

Samper, Cristi N 569
Samples, Dustin 19
Sampson, Heath 349
Sampson, Luke 361
Sams, Jeffrey 355
Samsonov, Anastasia 402
Samuelson, Bonnie M 45
Samz, Jeff 257
Sanchez, Esther 71
Sanchez, Anna V 122
Sanchez, Ronda 159
Sanchez, Dana 171
Sanchez, Terry 202
Sanchez, Charlie 242
Sanchez, Alejandra 257
Sanchez, Anthony 261
Sand, Jamie 212
Sander, Ed 418
Sanders, Lezlie 46
Sanders, John 103
Sanders, Preston 132
Sanders, Michael 221
Sanders, Jeff 296
Sanders, Jeffrey D 308
Sanders, Morgan 363
Sanders, Stephanie 406
Sanders, Thomas 544
Sanders, Courtney 624
Sanders, Randy 637
Sanderson, La Verne 193
Sanderson, Scott 554
Sandlin, Scott 226
Sando, Gabriel 307
Sandoval, Johnny 218
Sandoz, Jonathan H 110
Sands, Jeff 128
Sands, Lester 270
Sands, Rob 403
Sands, Tim 642
Sands-Caldwell, Autumn 537
Sandstrom, Alexander 40
Sandt, Susan V 245
Sandvik, Helvi 361
Sanford, Robin 123
Sanford, Julie 467
Sanford, Brent 515
Sanford, Barbara 612
Sankey, Greg 580
Sanman, Randall P 285
Sanodo, Raquel 256
Santelises, Sonja B 56
Santillan, Alfredo A 240
Santilli, Ann M 303
Santino, Anthony 596
Santoki, Tsutomu 527
Santos, Janet 7
Santos, Rebecca 236
Santos, Antelmo 393
Santos, Daniel 511
Sapp, Jennifer 248
Sapp, William 464
Sappington, Jonathan 37
Saraei, Armin 367
Sardo, Michele 165
Sargent, Annie 408
Sargent, Dale 649
Sarno, Domenic J 133
Sarnoff, Mark 128
Sarode, Anuja 614
Sarsfield, Sally 53
Sarsfield, Sally 298
Sartain, Meg 54
Sartain, Paul 323
Sarver, Billy 514
Sarwal, Aarti 644
Sash, Nick 259
Sasich, Keith N 285
Sass, Steven 602
Sassani, Manzar 563
Sassano, Joseph 173
Sasser, Gary 52
Sasser, Gary D 53
Sasser, Robert 58
Sasso, Louis 343

Satchwell, Jennifer 359
Sathvik, Bhushan 356
Sato, Lisa 402
Sato, Brandon 408
Sato, Samuel M 556
Satter, Muneer 569
Satterlee, Maleia 353
Sattgast, Rich 517
Saucier, Grady 348
Sauer, Melissa 524
Saunders, Jim 364
Saunders, Jeff 366
Saunders, Steven W 473
Saunders, Rosie 524
Saunders, Donna 646
Sauvie, Jeff 102
Savage, Troy P 129
Savage, Brianne 163
Savage, Karen 503
Savage, Kelly 624
Savard, Matt 172
Savarese, Kathleen 580
Savickas, Diana 400
Savitch, Lane 278
Savoff, Mark T 206
Sawicki, Robert 401
Sawyer, Joy 139
Sawyer, Daryl 140
Sawyer, Alison 461
Sax, Jeff 170
Saxon, Laura 419
Saxton, Sean 123
Saxton, Pamela L 594
Sayavedra, Laura 343
Sayles, Andy 432
Sayley, Elaine 515
Saylor, Collin 284
Scaff, Joe 636
Scalzo, Bernie 172
Scamihorn, Randy 140
Scanlan, John 138
Scanlon, Donald 71
Scanlon, John 106
Scanlon, Deborah P 171
Scantlan, Donald 467
Scarantino, Charles 443
Scarborough, Leslie 253
Scarborough, Laurie 648
Scarlett, Stacy 147
Schaad, Jeff 378
Schaaf, Libby 130
Schach, Eric J 491
Schacht, Jessica 476
Schaefer, Francine 7
Schaefer, Pamela 505
Schaeffer, Aaron 284
Schaeffer, Damon 361
Schaer, Michael 75
Schafer, Kevin 47
Schafer, Amanda 116
Schafer, Curtin 120
Schafer, Dana Lee 579
Schafers, Kelley 609
Schaffer, Stewart 64
Schale, David 54
Schalow, Monica 447
Schamach, Barry 157
Schandler, Jon B 655
Schantz, Karen 498
Schapiro, Morton 389
Scharbach, Shelby 162
Scharding, Donna 156
Scharman, Raegan 168
Scharmann, Steve 190
Schaub, Bryan 167
Schauffler, Todd 524
Scheel, Phillip 136
Schek, Judy 214
Schenck, Ginny 518
Schenk, John 272
Scheppke, James B 399
Scher, Colin 434
Scherer, Nancy 42
Scherer, Jeff 544

Scherman, Carol 82
Scherzer, Irene 138
Schettler, David 537
Schick, Mike 144
Schieler, Keith 140
Schifanella, Betsy 58
Schifano, Joyce 612
Schiller, Mark 292
Schiller, Matthew 447
Schiller, Mark 565
Schiltz, Christine 55
Schimmel, Jeffery L 639
Schindler, Tina 349
Schipani, Barbara 387
Schissler, Steve 587
Schiurba, John 655
Schlapia, Jennifer 396
Schlater, Stephen 284
Schledwitz, Karl 351
Schleper, Denny 138
Schlesener, Neil 447
Schlesinger, James R 569
Schloss, Howard 214
Schmalz, Shannon 114
Schmandt, Cheryl 342
Schmarder, Eric 124
Schmell, Eric 552
Schmid, Larry 235
Schmid, Richard J 593
Schmidl, Kurt 445
Schmidt, David 25
Schmidt, Barry 237
Schmidt, Marie 261
Schmidt, Rachael 366
Schmidt, Peggy 399
Schmidt, Leigh 449
Schmidt, Andrew 476
Schmidt, Joshua 478
Schmidt, John 483
Schmidt, Marlene 508
Schmidt, John A 607
Schmidt, Thomas A 607
Schmidt, Mark 615
Schmitt, Betty 185
Schmitt, Erin 238
Schmitt, Peggy 382
Schmitter, Joy 617
Schmitz, Doan 266
Schmitz, Vince 357
Schmitz, John D 474
Schmoll, David N 421
Schmollinger, Dean 363
Schnapp, Jonathan 604
Schneden, Jim 135
Schneider, Karen 146
Schneider, Robert 283
Schneider, John 330
Schneider, Brett 377
Schneider, Ruth 418
Schneider, Mitchell 567
Schneider, Charles 582
Schneider, Tara 596
Schneider, Julie 629
Schneider, Steve 646
Schneiderman, Tammy 511
Schneidewind, Mike 235
Schnelz, Steve 345
Schnirman, Jack 165
Schnure, William 121
Schodde, Joseph 256
Schoderbek, Robert 451
Schoeb, Michael 23
Schoemer, Richard 7
Schoen, Lawrence 247
Schoenfeld, Winston V 584
Schoenherr, Jay 626
Schofield, Tom 110
Scholes, Jessica 550
Scholl, Stephan 52
Scholten, Danielle E 299
Scholtz, Marty 585
Schomburg, Jennifer 220
Schooler, Rick 292
Schott, Stevan R 93

Schottenstein, Jay 18
Schowalter, Joseph 382
Schowalter, Linda G 530
Schrader, Michael 398
Schrage, Jon M 175
Schreiber, Bill 179
Schriber, Alan 35
Schrieffer, Kerry 406
Schroder, Heather 448
Schroder, John 512
Schroeder, Mark J F 124
Schroeder, Glenn 201
Schroeder, Lisa L 330
Schropp, Tobin A 285
Schropp, Tobin A 412
Schrum, Anita 87
Schubert, Christopher 433
Schuchard, Jeff 333
Schueler, Kevin 557
Schuerman, Janice 339
Schuette, Stuart 34
Schuhle, Thomas 508
Schuler, Doug 372
Schulke, Sean 217
Schull, Claudine 164
Schulte, Christie 142
Schultheis, Joab 639
Schultz, John 20
Schultz, Tim 174
Schultz, Elena 248
Schultz, David 403
Schultz, Paul L 448
Schultz, Michael 612
Schultz, Corinne 656
Schulze, Corina 629
Schumacher, Alan 18
Schumacher, Stephen 114
Schumacher, Linda 118
Schumacher, INA 537
Schumann, Ellen M 472
Schumer, Mary 618
Schurko, Allison 655
Schurz, Frank 569
Schuster, Michael 19
Schutt, Eric 518
Schutter, George 232
Schuyler, Josh 481
Schwab, Les N 50
Schwab-Pomerantz, Carrie 468
Schwager, Charles 364
Schwalm, Laura 224
Schwarctz, Laurie 190
Schwarts, Kin 422
Schwartz, Raphe 116
Schwartz, James 156
Schwartz, Robert 277
Schwartz, James K 392
Schwartz, Roberta 567
Schwartz, Mel 647
Schwarzkopf, Paul C 379
Schwebke, Kay 249
Schwede, Kale 496
Schwenn, Ellen 632
Schwing, Amanda 197
Schwoeble, Walt 118
Scialdone, Mike 327
Scimeca, John V 3
Sciortino, Cathy L 154
Sciortino, John E 377
Sciuto, Joe 429
Sclama, Anthony 220
Scofield, Audralee 630
Scollan, Joey 204
Sconzo, Guy M 257
Scott, Jill 40
Scott, Emily Allinder 64
Scott, Keith 73
Scott, Sharon 81
Scott, Brandon 123
Scott, Edward 126
Scott, Randy 134
Scott, Mychelle 147
Scott, Deb 217
Scott, Donald 259

Index of Executives

Index of Executives

Index of Executives

Sobczak, Tiffany 335
Sobkowicz, Diane 351
Sobson, Carol L 388
Sock, Shannon 331
Sock, Shannon 334
Sockwell, Darryl 348
Sohn, Jim 330
Sohn, Young 637
Soika, Kimberly 208
Soito, Lois 456
Sojos, Sarah 421
Sok, Chantha 249
Soker, Jo Ann 468
Sola, Lester 341
Solanki, Kishore 87
Solano, Juan 576
Solanski, David 354
Solimani, Robert 520
Solis, Grace 133
Solis, Lupe 464
Solis, Jose 594
Solloway, Steven 200
Soloman, Debbie 102
Solomon, Lesley 180
Soma, Siva K 20
Somerset, Gary 432
Sommers, Benjamin D 546
Sondys, Bruce 63
Sonenreich, Steven 356
Sones, Randy 8
Sones, Randall D 21
Song, Karen 300
Song, Vincent 532
Sonkur, Matrika 12
Soofe, Abdikhayr 125
Sorenes, Steffan 208
Sorensen, Christopher M 281
Sorenson, Charles 260
Soreta, Tattika 105
Sori, Alfredo E 285
Sormella, Nancy 182
Sorrentino, Joseph 210
Sorto, Rafael 24
Sortwell, Christopher T 366
Sosnowski, Scott 360
Sotelo, Dan 307
Soterakis, Jack 499
Sotgia, Federica 593
Sotir, Paula 320
Soto, Sabrina 311
Sotomayor, Julie C 478
Souder, Jeremy 574
Soukup, Beth A 268
Soukup, Beth 268
South, John R 248
South, Tracy A 252
Southwick, Michael J 578
Souza, Marcel 581
Sow, Ethelore C 572
Sowell, Ron 145
Sowinski, Janice 126
Spackler, John Keith 10
Spafford, Mark 36
Spage, Catherine 210
Spahr, Dalena 529
Spahr, Lori 634
Spalding, William R 1
Spalding, Susan 179
Spalding, Drew 432
Spang, Jack 602
Spangler, Sean 559
Sparks, Terry 557
Sparks, Anne 586
Spatholt, David 160
Spaulding, Wynn 291
Spaziano, Greg 99
Spears, Stephen 52
Speed, Stella 540
Speer, Kevin P 248
Spees, Shane 383
Speigner, Ehrica 549
Spence, Christine 510
Spence, Edward F D 642
Spencer, John 25

Spencer, Rhonda 62
Spencer, Kipp 70
Spencer, Denise 87
Spencer, Lorraine 205
Spencer, Octavia 259
Spencer, Thomas 322
Spencer, Barbara 370
Spencer, Floyd 384
Spencer, Terry K 397
Spencer, J Robert 465
Spencer, Monica 544
Spencer, Marjorie 566
Spencer, Andrew 612
Spera, Richard 561
Sperazza, Laura 237
Spergel, David 580
Sperry, Diane 402
Sphr, Terry K 315
Sphuler, Erica 388
Spielman, Amanda 326
Spier, Scott 332
Spier, Dr Scott 334
Spiker, Brenda 174
Spiller, Scott 23
Spillers, David 257
Spillers, David 561
Spina, Lori 230
Spina, Suzana 420
Spinale, Joseph W 504
Spindle, Barbara 115
Spinelli, Ann 452
Spinnato, Joseph E 371
Spinner, Debbie 128
Spinner, Janice 354
Spirk, Don 461
Spitulnik, Aric 300
Splaine, Kevin R 494
Spoelman, Roger 305
Spoelman, Roger 330
Spong, Bernadette 400
Spong, Bernadette 443
Spooner, William A 477
Spoor, Michelle 510
Spradlin, Jim 237
Spratt, Michael 591
Sprau, Jon 27
Spraus, Joyan 224
Spreher, Michael 29
Spring, Kelly 158
Sprinkle, James 551
Sprinkle, Ray 635
Sprouse, David 67
Spruill, David 542
Sprunk, Bob 358
Spychall, Michael 657
Spyhalsk, Anne Kocian 534
Spyrow, Flo 227
Squibb, Brian 374
Squillace, Delores 439
Squires, Christine 35
Sr, Richard M Devos 27
Sr, Rex A Rock 41
Sr, George Kaleak 41
Sr, Raymond Clunie 158
Sr, Margaret Hadley 254
Sr, Linda Reedy 261
Sr, Albert R Zimmerli 264
Sr, William H Dunn 268
Sr, William H Dunn 268
Sr, Jesse T Williams 272
Sr, James A Miner 345
Sr, Anthony J Rouse 452
Sr, Debbie Dickie 478
Sr, John R Raymond 566
Sr, Dr John Raymond 566
Sr, Robert Curran 579
Sr, Avery B Hall 626
Sreenan, Meghan 332
Srivastava, Abhishek 652
Sroda, Rachael 375
Srur, Barbara P 465
Stacey, Rulon F 210
Stacey, Rulon 422
Stack, Colleen 590

Stacker, Mary 45
Stacy, Leland J 50
Stadelman, Chris 518
Stadelmann, Douglas H 222
Stadelmann, Douglas 222
Stadtler, Dj 364
Stafford, Kenneth R 619
Staheli, Ben 14
Staley, Tabitha 315
Staley, Jeanette 429
Staley, David 553
Staley, John 587
Stam, Robert 483
Stancer, Lori 126
Stancl, Craig Robert 321
Stanczyk, Russ 514
Standeven, David 21
Standing, Shannon 92
Standish, Dr Liz 396
Stanek, Sharen 155
Stanek, Janet 522
Stanford, Beth 80
Stanford, Douglas 185
Stanford, Jessica 440
Stanley, Stephen E 40
Stanley, Anthony 123
Stanley, Alicia 146
Stanley, Roger 196
Stanley, Kelly 474
Stanley, Harold 491
Stanski, Matthew E 579
Stanton, Oliver K 597
Stanwood, Michael 216
Stanzione, Laurie 21
Stanzione, Dominque 307
Stapleton, Chuck 155
Stark, Doug 211
Stark, Kyle 508
Starling, Curtis 112
Starnes, Pam 58
Starns, Renee 542
Starr, Ken 65
Starr, Dan 191
Starsiak, Michael 353
Staten, Jennifer 144
Stauder, Mark 263
Stauffer, Charlotte 81
Stauffer, Craig 351
Stawis, Allen 500
Steadman, Bevan 199
Stearns, Leo 223
Steck, Kevin 522
Steed, Connie C 428
Steel, Julie 417
Steele, Amber 113
Steele, Robert 141
Steele, Gail 155
Steele, Sara 194
Steele, Robert 390
Steele, Keri 529
Steele, Barbara 595
Steele, Mark T 601
Steelman, Tracy 413
Steen, Bernie 569
Steere, F William 14
Stefanie, Taylor 535
Stefano, Ken De 6
Stefanowicz, Melanie 579
Steffe, Ganine 316
Steffen, Mark A 103
Steffes, Cathy 31
Stegmaier, James J L 157
Stegner, Jonathan 585
Stegwell, Mary Jo 40
Stehlik, Christine 230
Steichen, Jennifer L 204
Steiger, John 519
Steigerwald, Tim 336
Steil, Jim 81
Steiman, Gerald S 355
Stein, Sue 107
Stein, Paul 309
Steinbach, David 553
Steinbacher, Michele 609

Steinback, Michael A 626
Steinberg, Darrell 132
Steinberg, Alan 159
Steinberg, Sarah 441
Steinberg, Michael 615
Steiner, Robert 26
Steiner, Kevin 26
Steiner, Cindy 481
Steiner, Kirk 485
Steiner, Christopher 572
Steinhafel, Arthur W 421
Steinmetz, Joann 92
Steinmetz, David 133
Stella, Mitsopoulos 184
Stella, Anthony 583
Stellar, James 519
Stenberg, Melissa 203
Stendahl, Lea 523
Stenman, Eric 55
Stenman, Eric 55
Stensland, Kelly 178
Stenson, Brian 519
Stenzel, Mary 366
Stephens, Michael 362
Stephens, Linda 414
Stephenson, David 25
Stephenson, Craig 101
Stephenson, Don 101
Stephenson, Rick 101
Stephenson, Harry D 142
Stephenson, Don 142
Stephenson, Craig 142
Stephenson, Jim 597
Sterett, William J 194
Sterling, Choice 482
Stern, Walter 28
Stern, Sadye 371
Stern, Rita 423
Stern, James A 603
Sternberg, Christina 28
Sterner, Kurtis 173
Sternhell, Rebecca K 129
Stevener, Donna I 303
Stevens, David 32
Stevens, Jon I 80
Stevens, Chris 185
Stevens, David 202
Stevens, Ron 240
Stevens, Clement 240
Stevens, Gary 258
Stevens, Mary Jane 269
Stevens, Sandra 309
Stevens, Ashley 375
Stevens, Matthew 437
Stevens, Gary 496
Stevens, Carla 499
Stevens, Kevin 615
Stevenson, Cindy 271
Stevenson, Jim 321
Stevenson, Heather 480
Stevenson, Hollie 617
Steward, David 659
Stewart, Leanne M 1
Stewart, William 24
Stewart, James 54
Stewart, James 60
Stewart, Jordan 98
Stewart, David 113
Stewart, Louis 132
Stewart, Denise 249
Stewart, John 256
Stewart, C Todd 314
Stewart, Brian 433
Stewart, Karen Weldin 511
Stewart, Richard 522
Stewart, Karla 595
Stewart, Garfield 660
Stiber, Barri 293
Stief, Brian 278
Stiegmann, Gregory V 618
Stieritz, Brian 214
Stiffler, Don 145
Stiles, Gaylene 333
Stiles, Dick 439

Index of Executives

Index of Executives

Index of Executives

Index of Executives

Vella, John A 27
Vellinga, David 102
Velver, Ron 212
Venable, Jerry 280
Venable, Joshua 525
Vendemo, Shelly 102
Venditto, Eileen 165
Venezia, Patrick 568
Venhuizen, John 4
Venkataraman, Viswanathan 473
Vennero, Thomas 131
Venrick, Kathy 323
Vento, Marc 482
Ventoza, Luis S 408
Ventre, Elizabeth 121
Venugopal, Dinesh 356
Vera-Vazquez, Ernest 330
Veras, Harry 371
Verdaglio, Anthony 323
Verdetti, Gina 294
Verduzco, Jorge 441
Vereb, Joseph 277
Verhoff, John 103
Verhoff, John 553
Verinder, David 465
Verker, Bruce 480
Vermeer, Jennifer 586
Vermilya, Dan 417
Verna, Tara 380
Verrette, Paula 407
Verrilli, John L 530
Verslues, Ernie 339
Verst, Robert 336
Vervalin, Paul 385
Vesely, Liv 294
Vespertino, Danielle 655
Vespoli, Leila L 337
Vespoli, Leila L 410
Vespoli, L L 552
Vessey, Beth 256
Vetter, J D 285
Vetter, J D 286
Vetterli, Kristie 115
Veurink, Jon D 386
Vezina, Dena 516
Vicari, Roberta 402
Vick, Alfie 620
Vickers, George M 444
Vickery, Peggy 255
Vickrey, Garrett 67
Vickrey, Kristen 475
Victor, Jeanne 571
Vidale, Mauro 527
Vidhani, Anand 244
Vieira, Elaine 124
Vig, Ravi 22
Vijayakumar, C 244
Vike, Jean 355
Villa, Paula 190
Villa, Antonio 237
Villa, Norma 608
Villalobos, Hilda 109
Villalobos, Hector 483
Villanueva, Hazel 116
Villanueva, David 168
Villanueva, Enrique 311
Villanueva, Eleana 404
Villarreal, Dominick 139
Villarruel, Bonnie 58
Villasenor, David 311
Villicana, Vicky 203
Villoch, Alexandra 57
Vimolrat, M 65
Vincent, Mark 127
Vincent, Suzanne M 278
Vincent, Daniel L 404
Vincent, Jackie 647
Vincent, Danette 658
Vinci, Claudio 53
Vinci, Bryan 583
Vincze, Christopher 597
Vines, Tim 78
Vingerhoets, Cindy 193
Vinson, Ashley 52

Vinson, Julienne 56
Vinson, Sara 347
Vinyard, Justin 24
Viola, Vincent 643
Vipperman, Robert 19
Viqueira, William 571
Virani, Shailesh 333
Virella, Jose 272
Vish, Nancy 65
Vita, Katherine 640
Vitas, Heather 316
Viterbo, Edgar 420
Vithoulkas, John A 161
Vitner, Stephanie 411
Vitner, Stephanie 575
Vitter, Meg 304
Viveiros, Filomena 169
Vivek, Deepak 400
Viverito, Melissa Mark 129
Viviani, Tanios 27
Vlachakis, Alexandra 198
Vleck, Kathryn Van 198
Vliet, Gretchen Van 443
Vogel, Scott 52
Vogel, Anita 154
Vogel, Colleen 413
Vogler, Jane 396
Vogt, Ed 92
Voigt, Diana G 415
Volden, Angela 514
Volk, Becky 43
Volk, Bea 333
Volkmann, Irene 368
Volle, Darren 315
Voller, Chris J 14
Vollmer, Sonya 112
Vollrath, Thomas 289
Vollrath, Dj 339
Vollucci, Maria 596
Voloch, Bill 650
Volpe, Lorraine V 206
Volpe, Michele 427
Volz, Kim 185
Vonderfecht, Dennis 426
Vonzychlin, Claus 598
Vora, Sanjeev 112
Voran, Nicholas 216
Voss, Paula 312
Voss, Zeb 338
Voss, Thomas G 542
Voyadzis, Jean-Marc 325
Voyles, Janie 453
Vozos, Frank 350
Vrancken, Jennifer Van 406
Vranken, Rita Van 354
Vreman, Hendrik J 295
Vries, Loek De 452
Vu, Kenny 64
Vuletich, Christine 172

W

Wacha, Kim 175
Waddle, Aaron 523
Wade, Sharon 134
Wade, Scott 185
Wade, David 203
Wade, Joanne E 225
Wade, Joanne E 226
Wade, Cynthia 344
Wade, Elizabeth 398
Wade, Rusti 542
Wadhwa, Amit 604
Wadsworth, Jeffrey 63
Wagnar, Jack 479
Wagner, Christian 100
Wagner, Frederick 127
Wagner, Jody 146
Wagner, Amy 233
Wagner, Eugene D Van 286
Wagner, Harvey L 337
Wagner, Harvey L 394

Wagner, Harvey L 410
Wagner, Rebecca 411
Wagner, L D 443
Wagner, Chris 487
Wagner, Karen Van 533
Wagner, Harvey L 552
Wagner, Morgan 585
Wagner, Michael 604
Wagner, William B 612
Wagstaff, Nathan V 500
Waguespack, Robert L 54
Wahlin, Rob 206
Waineo, Eva 648
Wake, Scott 414
Wakefiel, Peter D 160
Walb, Terry 102
Walcher, Michael 207
Walcott, Dennis 129
Wald, Heidi 618
Waldbillig, Cathy 330
Walde, Van Der 30
Walders, William 246
Waldman, Eyal 325
Waldman, Adam 573
Waldrin, Michele 638
Waldrip, Meagan 383
Waldron, Blain 144
Waldrop, Tony G 629
Walk, Belinda 92
Walkenhorst, John 499
Walker, Lisa 42
Walker, Gordon 68
Walker, David 76
Walker, Algernon 125
Walker, William 155
Walker, William 157
Walker, Larry 168
Walker, Johnnie 184
Walker, Stacy 213
Walker, Tom 217
Walker, Robert L 231
Walker, Brett 233
Walker, Crestina 242
Walker, Terry 267
Walker, Mark 287
Walker, Sarah 298
Walker, Kristen 314
Walker, Steve 333
Walker, Marsha 362
Walker, Jeanne 395
Walker, Angela 408
Walker, Gail 444
Walker, Cindi 467
Walker, Brooks 468
Walker, Annette M 502
Walker, Paul 532
Walker, Ursula 535
Walker, Chris 616
Walker, Michael 616
Walker, Robert 654
Walker, Scott 658
Walker-Vamos, Colleen 507
Wall, David J 96
Wall, Aicp 170
Wall, Aileen 271
Wall, Heather 409
Wallace, Jason 47
Wallace, Monique 121
Wallace, Eugene 145
Wallace, Delores 159
Wallace, Micah 165
Wallace, Deja 166
Wallace, Carol 168
Wallace, Phillip O 292
Wallace, Paul 292
Wallace, Chris 401
Wallace, Mark 540
Wallace, Nicole 555
Wallace, Paula 578
Waller, Robert R 459
Walley, Pete 81
Walliani, Hussain 263
Wallin, Kim 514
Wallis, Barbara 76

Wallis, Jackie 291
Walls, Todd 208
Walls, Ron 317
Walsh, Kate 84
Walsh, Greg 170
Walsh, Matthew 225
Walsh, Kate H 238
Walsh, Andrea 247
Walsh, Marshall T 471
Walsh, William P 562
Walsh, Matthew M 590
Walsh, Daniel 590
Walsh, John L 608
Walsh, Matthew M 645
Walsh, Daniel J 645
Walsh, Brian R 645
Walter, Stephen 222
Walter, Kevin 333
Walter, Trisha 417
Walter, Larry 494
Waltermire, Mark 495
Walters, Mark 115
Walters, Deborah D 127
Walters, H Patrick 262
Walters, Mary 449
Walters, Kelly S 555
Walters, Jay 607
Walton, David 4
Walton, Jim 296
Walts, Steven 428
Waltz, Gwen 344
Walz, Tim 513
Walz, Pat T 662
Wampler, Dan 411
Wamsley, Patrick 566
Wamuo, Ngozi 249
Wan, David 243
Wang, Peter 29
Wang, Christina 133
Wang, Huilu 180
Wang, Richard 181
Wang, WEI 182
Wang, Kedong 183
Wang, Tao 276
Wang, April 338
Wang, Joy 452
Wang, Robert 496
Wang, Mian 498
Wang, Ming-Hsien 564
Wang, Zhe 615
Wang, William 643
Wang, Qin 644
Wanly, Bahaa 460
Ward, Beth 11
Ward, David 25
Ward, Kathy 112
Ward, Doris M 122
Ward, Wendy 150
Ward, Daniel 208
Ward, Caroline 232
Ward, Ronnie 322
Ward, Matthew 349
Ward, Peter 371
Ward, Kevin 377
Ward, Kevin J 377
Ward, Alice 380
Ward, Stephen 424
Ward, Nicholas 444
Ward, Paul J 491
Ward, Pamela M 553
Ward, Adam 585
Ward, Betty Lou 644
Ward, Beth 649
Warden, Gail L 249
Wargowsky, Robert 378
Waring, Stephen 483
Waring, Wendy 609
Warkomski, Denise 212
Warman, Michele 544
Warne, Teresa 30
Warne, Robin 490
Warner, Ardis 53
Warner, Daniel 176
Warner, Dan 176

Index of Executives

Index of Executives

Index of Executives

Woolridge, Diane 345
Woolridge, Germaine 533
Woolsey, Michael 68
Wootton, Michael 526
Worf, Heather 18
Workman, Tamora 490
Workman, Tyler 643
Worley, Jay 13
Worley, Jack 428
Wormoudt, Mardi 169
Worobel, Ryan 650
Woros, Agnes 61
Worthington, Heather 167
Worthington, Julie 418
Worthy, Delvon 646
Wortman, Rand 278
Woster, Casey M 441
Wozniak, Kevin 228
Wratten, Carol 58
Wren, Tishya 550
Wright, Rodney L 12
Wright, Stephen 24
Wright, Maria 53
Wright, Eric 69
Wright, Sharon 71
Wright, David 161
Wright, Nancy 186
Wright, Lori A 209
Wright, Roxanne 262
Wright, David H 303
Wright, Lori 404
Wright, Douglas 428
Wright, Amy 490
Wright, Judy 490
Wright, Daniel 610
Wright, Steve 633
Wright, Stacey 650
Wright, Edward 660
Wrighton, Mark 591
Wrobel, Kurt 226
Wrobleski, Tammy 124
Wrobleski, Sarah 408
Wroten, Paul 144
Wskeland, Oddgeir 208
Wtulich, Peter C 404
Wu, Sherman Z 71
Wu, Michelle 124
Wu, Jun 126
Wu, Corinna 198
Wu, Jiang 231
Wu, Dolly 263
Wu, Debbie 356
Wu, Xiaoni 441
Wunderlich, Myla 533
Wurman, Richard 234
Wurster, Rosemary 437
Wurtz, David 165
Wyant, Chuck 162
Wyatt, Mark 494
Wyatt, Jeff 641
Wyckoff, Virginia 396
Wye, John Van 346
Wye, Gretchen Van 369
Wyles, Rick 361
Wylie, Warren 215
Wyman, Dan 125
Wyman, Eric 136
Wynn, Michael 460
Wynne, Linda 471
Wynter, Christine 644
Wyrsch, Martha B 541
Wysk, Laura 565
Wyss, Andre 391

X

Xiong, Bao 159
Xolocotzi, Rafael 87
Xu, Zi 64
Xu, Jing 511

Y

Yabokla, Erica 509
Yacoub, George 644
Yaeger, Erin 16
Yako, Osamu 662
Yaldo, Zaid 44
Yamabe, Dayna 562
Yamadi, Asghar 196
Yamaguchi, Tadaaki 94
Yamakawa, Mark 576
Yamamoto, Glenn 31
Yamamoto, Kathryn 621
Yancey, Shaun P 408
Yang, Null Y Null 50
Yang, Andrea 125
Yang, Nha 163
Yang, Deyun 301
Yang, Teresa 434
Yanisch, Stephen 35
Yano, Yoshifumi 133
Yao, Pam 481
Yap, Bryan 563
Yarashus, Valerie A 146
Yarensky, Annie 579
Yarobough, Martin 218
Yaroslavsky, Zev 162
Yaschik, Jeff 153
Yates, Michael 232
Yates, Stacy 661
Yaudes, Jason 34
Yaudes, Jason T 34
Yawata, Haruko 596
Ybarbo, Sylvia 160
Ybarra, Crystal 159
Ybarra, Jesse 475
Ybarra, Jessie 496
Yeager, Bill 222
Yeager, Sam 499
Yealy, Donald 634
Yeaney, Jacqueline 52
Yearta, William J 358
Yeatts, Susan 156
Yedla, Anupama 561
Yee, Brenda 118
Yee, Gim 156
Yee, John K 326
Yee, Sheryl 455
Yeh, Jason 45
Yellig, Laura 413
Yelmanchili, Oadnaha 234
Yenni, Michael 406
Yeoman, Justin 361
Yerby, Jackie 516
Ylagan, Victor E 554
Yocham, William 422
Yocum, Deb 522
Yoder, Ashlee 168
Yoder, Cathy 504
Yogi, Stacy 97
Yommer, Dale 91
Yoo, Chung-Mok 204
Yorgova, Petya 19
York, Chris 65
York, Johnny 86
Yorke, Beth 63
Young, James N 24
Young, Brent 24
Young, Carl 34
Young, Gary 105
Young, Wendell 125
Young, Christopher 149
Young, Rhiannon 164
Young, Anthony 164
Young, Edward 216
Young, Terrance 238
Young, Rebecca 240
Young, Barbara 253
Young, Charles 276
Young, Jeff 302
Young, Sandra 346
Young, Bill 392
Young, Svetlana 402

Young, Marty 449
Young, Mike 465
Young, Andrea 466
Young, Jay 496
Young, Dave 510
Young, Christine L 514
Young, Michael 536
Young, Tara 583
Young, Linda 585
Young, Kalbert 621
Young, Michael 635
Young, James 642
Young, Jessica 646
Youngblood, Mike 322
Youngquist, Gene 73
Youngquist, Scott 630
Youso, Steve 472
Yowell, Adam 332
Ysais, Dotti 302
Yucoco, Liza 603
Yuen, Shelten G 240
Yultyev, Aleksandr 231
Yusuf, Nurain 512
Yvonne, Luttschwager 522

Z

Zaas, David 196
Zabaneh, Samir 247
Zabetakis, Paul 299
Zacarias, Fernando 42
Zacariassen, Christian 364
Zachariah, Zachariah P 390
Zacharias, Dawn 614
Zachary, Alaine 640
Zachos, Kimon S 492
Zaffini, AVI 516
Zagajeski, Thomas 171
Zahariev, Emil 604
Zaharis, Chris 205
Zaied, Khalil 123
Zalaznick, Lauren 378
Zalesak, Emil J 293
Zamarron, Felipe 548
Zampini, Maria 202
Zanavich, W Marie 584
Zander, Scott 304
Zank, Dennis W 436
Zankowski, Nancy 2
Zapfe, Carl 512
Zapletal, Audrey 593
Zappala, Phyllis F 554
Zappala, Elizabeth 602
Zardetto-Smith, Andrea 175
Zarling, Angela 439
Zarling, Kathy 459
Zaslav, David M 470
Zastrow, Audra 107
Zatina, Tom 322
Zauk, Adel M 505
Zavitkovski, Caroline 516
Zbaraschuk, Amy 215
Zboray, Andrew 514
Zedreck, Christina 628
Zeevi, Gary 473
Zehm, Laura 148
Zehm, Laura 351
Zeine, Elias 44
Zell, Lisa 119
Zeller, Fred 134
Zeller, Joshua 422
Zeller, Pat 461
Zeltsman, Brian 128
Zeng, Maojun 28
Zeno, Zoraida 459
Zenty, Thomas S 614
Zepeda, Carl 119
Zeppos, Nicholas 590
Zerilli-Marim, Mariuccia 374
Zettel, John 53
Zhang, Qin 20
Zhang, Cherry 81

Zhang, Wenqin 185
Zhang, Tong 442
Zhao, Kevin 29
Zhao, Alice 45
Zhao, Dezheng 71
Zhao, Yingnan 615
Zhao, Xin 620
Zheng, Ziliang Leon 263
Zheng, Baohua 466
Zhu, Yaping 208
Zhu, Meng 263
Ziadie, Bambi 217
Ziarno, Jeffrey 528
Zichner, Veronica 374
Zickefoose, John Z 154
Ziecheck, Hal 353
Ziegelmeier, Lori 142
Ziegler, Richard A 35
Ziegler, Dawn 217
Ziegler, Andy 466
Ziegler, Larry 607
Zielinski, Trudy 143
Ziemianski, Karen 208
Zientara, David B 73
Zier, Dawn M 392
Zies, Ray 123
Zietlow, Don 289
Zietlow, Steve 289
Ziffer, Jack A 57
Zike, Madilyn 399
Zimmer, Anthony 24
Zimmer, Steve 303
Zimmerli, Bert 260
Zimmerman, Jeffrey 396
Zimmerman, Barbi 500
Zimmermann, Deirdre 435
Zink, Charles L 414
Zinkin, Peter 55
Zinn, Judy 90
Zinni, Nicholas J 378
Zins, AMI 130
Zisler, John 599
Ziss, Bill 614
Zito, James 514
Ziyadeh, Omar 652
Zmich, Kenneth 106
Zohn, Patrick 138
Zoll, Coral 88
Zoncki, Stephanie 172
Zordo, Marc De 189
Zortman, Barbara 173
Zucchero, Rocco 260
Zuckerman, Lisa 189
Zuckerman, Harriet 544
Zuhlke, Daniel L 264
Zukauckas, Linda 378
Zulla, Caitlin 466
Zumwalt, Debra 295
Zuniga, Daisy 303
Zuraitis, Nancy 52
Zweben, Lloyd 135
Zwergel, Ken 72
Zwonitzer, Michael 28
Zyczynski, Halina 635
Zyl, Adriaan Van 54

This Page left intentionally blank